Make ordering the Social Services Year Book easy!
Why not set up a standing order?

To ensure you receive your copy of the Social Services Year Book on publication, why not set up a standing order? Our fast and efficient distribution service will guarantee that you receive your copy as soon as the year book is published so you do not have to remember to reorder each year.

Setting up a standing order takes the hassle out of ordering each year and you can be sure you have access to the most up-to-date information on the day of publication.

Simply complete the form below and leave the rest to us!

ORDER FORM

☐ Please set me up a standing order for the Social Services Year Book
(*I understand that copies of the 2005 edition and subsequent editions will be dispatched on the day of publication with an invoice*)

Do you need extra copies of the 2004 edition of the Social Services Year Book?

☐ Please invoice me £ _____ for _____ extra copies of the Social Services Year Book 2004 at £130.00 each (please include £3 p&p) 0 273 68825 1

--- | **Fold here, then staple** | ---

Your details

Title _____ Initial(s) _____ Surname _____

Job Title _____

Organisation _____

Address _____

_____

_____ Postcode _____

Tel _____ Fax _____

E-mail _____

Signed _____ Date _____

If you have any queries, please contact Customer Services on 0870 607 3777

Customer Services
Pearson Education
FREEPOST LON8663
Harlow
Essex
CM20 2YH

Social Services Year Book 2004

FT Prentice Hall
FINANCIAL TIMES

An imprint of **Pearson Education**

London • New York • Toronto • Sydney • Tokyo • Singapore
Hong Kong • Cape Town • Madrid • Paris • Amsterdam • Munich • Milan

Editorial Team	James Tierney
	Johan Gregory
Advertisement Sales	Please call 01279 623623 and ask for Directories Advertising
Marketing	Omair Makhdumi

Pearson Education Limited
Edinburgh Gate
Harlow CM20 2JE
Tel: +44 (0)1279 623623
Fax: +44 (0)1279 431059

In an increasingly competitive world, it is quality of thinking that gives an edge.
An idea that opens new doors, a technique that solves a problem, or an insight that
simply helps make sense of it all.
We work with leading authors in the fields of management and finance to bring cutting-
edge thinking and best learning practice to a global market.
Under a range of leading imprints, including *Financial Times Prentice Hall*, we create
world-class print publications and electronic products giving readers knowledge and
understanding which can then be applied, whether studying or at work.
To find out more about our business and professional products, you can visit us at
www.pearson-books.com

To view sample pages from Pearson Education yearbook products,
please visit www.pearson-books.com/yearbook

For other Pearson Education publications, visit www.pearsoned.co.uk

A catalogue record for this book is available from the British Library

ISBN 0 273 68825 1

Typeset by Land & Unwin (Data Sciences) Ltd, Bugbrooke
Printed and Bound in Great Britain by Biddles Ltd, King's Lynn

The Publishers' policy is to use paper manufactured from sustainable forests

Contents

Enabling people with special needs to achieve their full potential

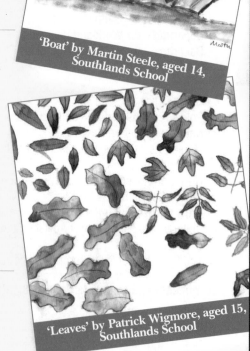

'Boat' by Martin Steele, aged 14, Southlands School

South Yorkshire - residential establishments
complex & severe learning difficulties and/or autism
Fullerton House School (8-19)
Wilsic Hall School (11-19)
Hesley Village & College (young adults)
Community Solutions
(adult homes in the community)

Lincolnshire - residential college
complex & severe learning difficulties and/or autism
Broughton House College (16-25)

Hampshire - termly schools and Post-16
Asperger Syndrome and similar disorders
Southlands School (boys, 9-16)
Grateley House School (11-16)
The Wing Centre (young men, 16-19)

Hampshire - 52 week a year
Autism
Hill House School (11-19)

Dorset - termly schools
Autism or Asperger Syndrome
The Forum School (7-16)
Purbeck View School (11-19)

'Leaves' by Patrick Wigmore, aged 15, Southlands School

For further information please contact Lesley Durston or Andrea Wooldridge
Tel: 01590 624484 Fax: 01590 622687
Email: enquiries@hesleygroup.co.uk Website: www.hesleygroup.co.uk

 The Hesley Group

INVESTOR IN PEOPLE

CERTIFICATION INTERNATIONAL
ISO 9001:2000
Cert No CI/2881

UKAS
QUALITY MANAGEMENT
063

PART TWO VOLUNTARY, PRIVATE AND NON-STATUTORY SERVICES

After a career move, more reward or more recognition?

Personnel & Care Bank are market leaders in recruiting Social Work, Social Care and Housing professionals - temporary & permanent.

Our extensive experience and large client portfolio guarantees you selection from only the best opportunities.

Our close knit teams will work hard to find the temporary/permanent job that matches your skills, aspirations and reward package. Or find you a contract which guarantees excellent pay rates, substantial benefits, continuity of work and gives you our unrivalled, supportive service 24/7.

From our consultants you can expect to feel highly valued, recognised for good performance and rewarded for commitment.

Call our team today at:

Barnet	020 8441 7038
Birmingham	0121 643 8818
Coventry	02476 237 940
Kingston	020 8549 9220
Nottingham	01158 533 888
Stratford	020 8221 3840
Wembley	020 8900 2877

Personnel & Care Bank
Recruitment Consultants

For more jobs and services register online at:

www.personnelcarebank.co.uk

 Recruitment & Employment Confederation

 INVESTOR IN PEOPLE

 POSITIVE ABOUT DISABLED PEOPLE

 ISO 9001 REGISTERED FIRM

An Equal Opportunities Recruitment Consultancy.

fifteen years
at the forefront of
fostering

Preface

The Social Services Year Book is a comprehensive guide to social services provision in the United Kingdom. This, the 32nd edition of the directory, continues to reflect the changing functions of the organisations involved in providing social and health care in the statutory, private and voluntary sectors.

For ease of use, the Year Book is split into two parts. The first part details central and local government social services, education and health throughout the UK. The second part covers non-statutory social welfare provision including a wide range of voluntary, charitable and private organisations, ranging from advice and counselling to caring, from education, training and research to the media.

This year, in consultation with Nick Johnson, Deputy Chief Executive of the Social Care Association, the team has made a number of changes in order to better present the information for the user. The Health Councils have been incorporated into Chapter 12 (now NHS Trusts, Care and Health Authorities and Health Councils), to reflect the ongoing structural changes to the NHS; please see the Department of Health website (www.doh.gov.uk) for the latest information. The Family has merged with Children and Young People's Organisations to become Chapter 13: Children, Young People and Families, as many organisations were seen to be relevant to both areas. Racial Equality has been incorporated into a new chapter – Organisations Working With Diversity – to better reflect matters of equality and discrimination relating to other issues such as age, gender, sexuality and disability, as well as race. The presentation of Local Government departments has been revised for improved clarity, and each council now lists a prominent web address.

The editorial team has made every effort to update all the information included and always welcomes constructive comments on the compilation of information. The team would like to thank the departments and organisations who have helped to produce this new edition.

If users know of any relevant organisations which are not currently listed, we would be grateful if they could fill in and return the form provided. Any other suggestions for material to be included in the directory will be received with interest.

Editorial Team

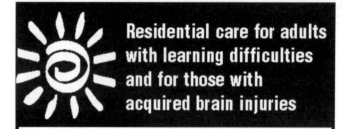

New Entry Suggestion Page

In order to ensure that our coverage is complete for the next edition of the *Social Services Year Book 2005*, your help would be much appreciated. The form below is for users to complete if they feel an organisation should be included. Please photocopy this page and return it to:

The Directories Editor (Higher and Professional Education)
Social Services Year Book
Pearson Education Limited
Edinburgh Gate
Harlow
CM20 2JE   Tel 01279 623623   E-mail directories@pearson.com

The following organisation should be included in the directory

Information to be published:

Name of organisation: ....

Address: ....

Postcode: ....

Tel No: ....

Fax No: ....

E-mail Address: ....

Website: ....

Contact name(s) of key personnel and position(s): ....

Type of organisation: ....

Most suited chapter: ....

This information will not be published but will be used as a contact name and address for correspondence only:

Information supplied by: ....

Name and position: ....

Address: ....

Tel No: ....

E-mail Address: ....

Whilst every effort will be made to include suggestions in the next edition, Pearson Education retain the right to decide on all editorial content of the year book.

Terminology and Abbreviations

Terminology

Accident Line (0500 192939)

A free telephone number set up to enable people to locate a solicitor who offers a free first consultation. All referral solicitors specialise in personal injury claims.

After Care

Services provided for people discharged from hospitals, prisons or other institutions. After care should assist with resettlement back into the community. The range and quality of after care varies between locality and institution type. Typical services may include help with housing, benefit claims and finding employment. People who generally receive this help include those with learning disablilities, discharged prisoners, young offenders and former psychiatric patients.

All Work Test

An assessment used to establish sickness and incapacity benefits. It tests "the extent of a person's incapacity by reason of some specific disease or bodily or mental disablement to perform such activities as may be prescribed." This assesses key functional activities such as standing, sitting, walking, kneeling, lifting and bending. It takes the form of a long self-completion questionnaire and most people also have to attend a medical arranged with a Benefits Agency Medical Service doctor. People with mental health disabilities have to pass a different all work test assessed via medical alone. This requires demonstration, through answers to often oblique questions, that they cannot interact socially or function in a work environment. Everyone, unless they are exempt, who claims a benefit because they are incapable of working must pass this test in order to receive benefit. Most people are assessed after 28 weeks of incapacity.

Almshouses

Housing services provided by charitable trusts for the older residents. Conditions of admission are determined by the individual trust. Resident's contributions may be covered by housing benefit. See www.almshouses.org for further information.

Asylum Seeker

Someone in the process of applying for refugee status. Asylum seekers were removed from the welfare benefits system by the Immigration and Asylum Act 1999. NASS, the Home Office National Asylum Support Service, looks after their welfare. Asylum seekers are entitled to vouchers worth 70% of basic income support, providing they can prove that they have no other means of support. These vouchers can only be used in designated shops and only £10 of this allowance can be exchanged for cash.

Attendance Allowance

A weekly allowance paid to people over 65 who need supervision or help with personal care. There is a higher and a lower rate depending on whether you need care during the day, during the night, or both. Eligibility is based on having needed care for at least six months except for cases of terminal illness. Attendance Allowance can be paid even if no one is available to provide the care and is not affected by other money coming in.

Boarding Out

Fostering with a family, usually a child in care. Boarding out allowances are paid on a regular basis and are intended to reflect the true cost of keeping a young person. It includes such things as accommodation costs, electricity and heating and elements for food, and travel, etc. Other allowances are also available for birthdays, holidays etc. See www.fostering.org.uk for further information. Some local authorities operate similar schemes for older people or those with learning disabilities to be temporarily placed.

Budgeting Loans

An interest-free loan from the Social Fund intended to help those who have been in receipt of Income Support for some time to meet one-off expenses for certain specified purposes. These loans are not for a standard amount.

Casework

A term used by social workers and others to describe work undertaken for, with or on behalf of clients. It may involve interviews, representation, advocacy or arranging and supporting with the provision of other services.

Child Benefit

This is currently a universal benefit not affected by income or savings. It is paid to everyone responsible for a child under 16; a young adult under 19 who is studying full-time up to A level, Advanced Vocational Certificate of Education (AVCE) or the equivalent; a young adult under 18 who has registered for work or training with the Careers Service or Connexion Service if one exists locally, and is actively seeking a job or a training place.

Child Support Assessment

The Child Support Agency was introduced in April 1993, with the aim to assess, collect and force absent parents to pay maintenance for their children. Parents caring for children who claim any of the means-tested

benefits are now required to provide information about the absent parent and authorise the collection of maintenance. The absent parent's income is then assessed using a complex formula which determines how much maintenance they can afford to pay. Either party is entitled to request a review by a different Child Support Officer.

Childminder

A person (not a relative) who looks after another person's child and receives payment. They are governed by strict regulations and must be registered with the local authority. Some childminders are still eleigible for Income Support providing they meet qualifying conditions e.g. they are a single parent. Please consult the National Childminding Association at www.ncma.org.uk for details.

Citizens Advice Bureau

A network of free, independent and unbiased advice providers that are serviced and supported by a central body called Citizens Advice (formerly NACAB). Workers are often trained volunteers supported by paid staff. Services vary but many provide free advocacy and/or representation in court. Most assist with benefit claims, charitable trust applications, debt advice and negotiating with creditors as well housing or immigration advice. When unable to assist, they can often refer to other agencies. For further information, please see www.nacab.org.uk.

Cohabitation

Defined as a co-resident man and woman, living together within a sexual union, without that union having been formalised by a legally recognised marriage. As a general rule, cohabiting partners are not entitled to the same treatment in law as married couples.

Cold Weather Payment

Entitlement is triggered automatically following a period of seven days where the daily mean temperature was at or below 0°C, without a need to claim, by the local benefits agency. Those eligible include people receiving Income Support or income-based Job Seekers Allowance with at least one child under five; who are disabled or long-term sick; who are over 60.

Community Care

Used to describe the range of services available in the community which enable people to live away from institutions and covering services for the elderly or disabled which allow them to live independently. Includes resident care workers, meals on wheels, supply of specialised equipment etc.

Community Care Grants

A grant from the Social Fund for people on Income Support or Income-based Job Seekers Allowance, or who are likely to get one of these benefits when moving out of residential or institutional accommodation. It is a discretionary award based on need assessment and does not need to be repaid.

Community Service Order

An alternative to imprisonment for certain classes of offender and controlled by the probation service who oversee and organise local schemes. Offenders work unpaid on tasks beneficial to the community e.g. gardening for the elderly, decorating etc.

Community Worker

Social worker or employee of a voluntary organisation who works for the welfare of a neighbourhood rather than for that of an individual or family.

Contributory Benefits

These include Contributory Jobseekers Allowance, Incapacity Benefit, Widows Benefits, Maternity Benefits and Retirement Benefits, and are only paid to those who satisfy the contribution conditions. Each benefit has its own conditions that describe the amount, type and duration of National Insurance contributions needed to qualify. Failure to meet conditions can result in a loss of entitlement or reduction in the amount paid.

Council Tax

The Council Tax was introduced in April 1993 as a replacement for Community Charge – commonly known as "Poll Tax". This is a daily local charge for residents over 18 in a local authority who do not live in exempt accommodation. Payments fund local services such as education, refuse collection etc. It is calculated based on the property value and the number of people occupying the property. Discounts are available for those living alone, students and for people with severe mental impairment, or disabilities that require specialised accommodation. The level of council tax a person has to pay less any discount is known as the council tax liability.

Council Tax Benefit

A daily benefit paid weekly for people who have low enough income to pass the means test. Successful claimants receive all or part of their council tax liability. People on Income Support receive full council tax benefit less deductions for any co-residing adults classed as non-dependents.

Council Tenant

A tenant of a property owned by a Local Authority. Since 1988, much of this housing stock in many areas has been transferred to housing associations or private ownership.

Councils for Voluntary Service

These are voluntary organisations affiliated to the National Council for Voluntary Services (www.nacvs.org.uk). They are governed by a management committee or council made up of local representatives from local charities, trade unions etc. They offer wide range of support services to voluntary organisations e.g. training, information, research etc. These resources vary depending on locality.

Criminal Injuries Compensation

A payment to compensate for a personal injury arising directly as a result of violent crime. This must have occurred within Britain or a locality where Britain exercises control. Includes child abuse, personal injury including shock, or sexually transmitted diseases through rape. Compensation also awarded to someone injured trying to prevent a crime. Awards are determined by the Criminal Injuries Compensation Authority (www.cica.gov.uk).

Criminal Law and Civil Law

The law is split into criminal and civil law. Civil law matters are dealt with by civil courts, that is the County Court (first level), the High Court (second level), and an Appeal Court and the Court of Appeal Civil Division. Criminal matters are dealt with by the Magistrates' Courts (first level), Crown Court (second level) and the Court of Appeal Criminal Division.

Crisis Loans

A loan from the Social Fund awarded following a disaster or in an emergency. It has to be the only means of preventing serious damage to health and safety.

Direct Payment

A cash payment from Social Services to help disabled people pay for the care services that they need. Claimants must be over 18 years old and in need of over 10 hours a week of Community Care services. The money cannot be used to purchase permanent residential care.

Disability Living Allowance

This benefit replaces Attendance Allowance and Mobility Allowance, and has two components, one for those with mobility needs and another for those with care or supervision needs. Only available to those who claim before their 65th birthday. Two rates are payable for those requiring the same level of care as Attendance Allowance claimants, with a third lower rate for those who only require care for part of the day. The mobility component is paid at two rates for those who have difficulties walking or a lower component for those who need guidance out of doors.

Disabled Persons Tax Credit

A means-tested benefit for people who are restricted in the hours they can work because of illness or disability. It is intended to top up low income earned from working 16 hours or more. It can be claimed by single people or those with families.

Emergency Duty Team

Emergency Duty Teams manage Social Services Departments out of office hours (4.30p.m. to 9.00a.m.) and at weekends.

Emergency Protection Order

A court order granted under section 44 of the Children Act 1989 on the grounds that a child will suffer significant harm if either: not removed to local authority accommodation; or: if the child is moved from the place where they are currently accommodated.

Eviction

The legal removal of tenants from a house or building. There are precise procedures to make an eviction legal. These processes are determined according to the type of tenancy or occupancy status a resident has.

Free Prescriptions

Certain groups are entitled to free prescriptions. These include people in receipt of Disability Working Allowance or who are: on low income, under 16 or under 19 if in full time education, aged over 60, pregnant, have given birth within the last 12 months or those who have a prescribed condition.

Foster Carers

Someone who looks after another person's child in their home on a temporary basis ranging from days to much longer, and who receives payment for it. It can be a private arrangement or one arranged by the Local Authority for a child in care. Foster Carers acquire rights after a period of caring for five years.

Funeral Payments

A payment from the Social Fund for those people in receipt of Council Tax Benefit or another qualifying benefit. To be entitled to a payment, the person must fulfil strict rules about responsibility for paying the funeral costs.

Guardians Allowance

A weekly benefit paid to someone who is looking after a child as part of their family because both the child's parents are dead. Guardians Allowance may also be paid if one of the parents is dead, and at the date of death the other is missing, or in some cases where the marriage had ended in divorce, or the parents were never married. It can also be paid if one parent is dead and the other is serving a prison sentence of five years or more.

Habitual Residence Test

The test applies to Income Support, income-based Jobseeker's Allowance, Housing Benefit and Council Tax Benefit. A claimant for these benefits has to show that she or he is habitually resident in the 'common travel area' (essentially, the British Isles), in addition to satisfying the other conditions of entitlement.

Health Authority

Assesses the health needs of the local people and draws up plans for meeting those needs. From April 2002 Strategic Health Authorities replaced both Health Authorities and Regional Health Authorities.

Health Benefits

A number of benefit areas to help people pay for eye tests, spectacles, dental treatment, prescriptions, wigs and fabric supports. Some people will automatically receive full costs and others a contribution towards the total cost. Entitlement depends on benefit entitlement, low income or other prescribed conditions.

Home-from-Hospital Scheme

Often run by voluntary organisations, these schemes aim to ease the transition back into the home by providing a limited amount of support for patients returning from hospital.

House Renovation Grants

Grants to make a house fit for human habitation. They pay for the installation of bathroom facilities, damp removal and other works to make a property suitable for occupation. They are means-tested and people often have to make a contribution to the cost of the works.

Housing Benefit

A benefit administered by the local authority to pay accomodation charges for people to occupy their home. It may include rent for tenants or fees for licensees, boat moorings or caravan pitches. It does not include help with mortgage interests for people buying their own homes. Mortgage interest and some loan interest payments can be paid as part of an Income Support or Jobseeker's Allowance award.

Incapacity Benefit

A benefit for those people who are deemed incapable of work and satisfy the contribution conditions. It is paid if Statutory Sick Pay (SSP) has ended or you cannot get SSP, and have been sick for at least four days in a row including weekends and public holidays. It is paid at three rates, one for the first 28 weeks, a slightly higher rate for the rest of the first year, and a higher payment after 52 weeks. Incapacity must be proved by claimant having a listed condition, receiving the highest rate of Disability Living Allowance, being terminally or passing the test of incapacity.

Income Support

A weekly benefit paid to people who do not have to be available for and actively seeking work. This includes disabled people, people who are incapable of work and lone parents. Young people under 18 have to fulfil certain very stringent criteria to qualify. Certain housing costs which are not met through Housing Benefit can be paid as part of Income Support.

Industrial Injuries Benefits

A benefits scheme consisting of different types and levels of payment. Rights to payment are established following an accident at work where permanent injury is sustained or where certain recognised diseases are contracted.

Industrial Injury Compensation

A lump sum paid by an employer to an employee injured at work due to an employers negligence. Employees who wish to pursue such a claim must do within three years of the accident or onset of the disease and will need legal advice from their union, a solicitor or through Accident Line. If the accident is fatal, dependents may claim.

Invalid Care Allowance

An allowance paid to someone who cares for a person for at least 35 hours per week. The person requiring care must be in receipt of Disability Living Allowance, Attendance Allowance, Constant Attendance Allowance, War Pensions Constant Attendance Allowance or Industrial Injuries Benefit at the qualifying rates. The carer does not need to reside with the person they care for and they do not have to be a relative. The carer should not earn too much money from other work.

Jobseekers Allowance

Replaced Income Support and Unemployment Benefit for those claimants who are actively seeking and available for workl and are working less than 16 hours per week. All claimants must sign a Jobseekers Agreement and demonstrate that they are complying with the very stringent rules about their role in attempting to find work. Contributory Jobseekers Allowance is paid for 182 days to those claimants who fulfil the contribution conditions. Income-based Jobseekers Allowance is paid for those who do not fulfil the contribution conditions for Contributory Jobseekers Allowance and can pass the means test. Those receiving Contributory Jobseekers Allowance can have their allowance topped up by Income-based Jobseekers Allowance if they pass the means test.

Law Centres

Law centres provide free legal advice and representation. They employ staff including trained solicitors and some use volunteers. Centres are often over-subscribed and so operate on a strict referral criteria.

Magistrates

There are over 30 000 magistrates in England and Wales. The majority of these are lay magistrates who are not qualified lawyers. They only sit part-time and do not get paid for their services other than reimbursement for expenses.

Magistrates Courts

Magistrates' Courts are only found in England and Wales and deal with virtually all criminal matters which come before the courts. A very small proportion are passed on to the Crown Court to be dealt with by a judge and jury but even in these circumstances the magistrates will have to make some initial decisions.

Maternity Allowance

A weekly payment for those women who fulfil the National Insurance contributions but who are self-employed or who have not worked continuously for the same employer. These women do not qualify for statutory maternity pay. It is paid for up to 18 weeks, starting in the 11th week before the baby is due or from the week after the baby is born.

Maternity Grant

A single one-off grant paid to those people who are in receipt of Income Support, Working Families' Tax Credit or Disable Persons Tax Credit and who do not have too much capital. It is paid to people who are within 11 weeks of giving birth or have just given birth or adopted a child. It is a payment to help with the general cost of having a baby.

Means-tested Benefit

Entitlement is determined according to a formula which compares resources (income from wages or benefits and any capital) to a pre-determined figure. Maximum entitlement is reduced according to how much extra resources a person has compared to their assessed need. The main means-tested benefits are Income Support, Working Families' Tax Credit, Disabled Person's Tax Credit, Council Tax Benefit, Housing Benefit and Jobseekers' Allowance.

Minimum Income Guarantee

Income support for people over 60 years of age. Claimants must have savings below a certain level to qualify and cannot be signing on at a job centre.

Money Advice

Advice on dealing with debts and income maximisation. Advice centres typically carry out negotiations with creditors after apportioning income to debts in priority order. Money advisers can represent at repossession hearings and can often prevent people from losing their homes or being sent to prison. Many local authorities have money advice centres and many Citizens Advice Bureaux have specialist advisers on site.

Motability Scheme

A scheme run by Motability (www.motability.co.uk) for disabled people. By converting their weekly benefits to loan repayments, this scheme enables people to purchase or lease cars or wheelchairs. The charitable arm of Motability can provide grants to cover the purchase of adaptations or specialist equipment.

Multi-agency Transition Policy

This is a strategy for handling the care of disabled children and managing their transition into adulthood whilst minimising change. Involvement with the child begins at 16 or 17 and continues for a year after they are officially deemed adults. Representatives involved include social services and health officals as well as care managers.

National Insurance Benefits

Benefits include Contributory Jobseekers' Allowance, Incapacity Benefit, Retirement Pension and Maternity Benefits which are only available to those people who fulfil the contribution conditions in terms of the number and type of national insurance contributions paid and over what period these payments should have been made.

National Insurance Contributions

These are weekly deductions from earnings over a lower limit paid to the National Insurance Fund. There are several classes of contribution payable depending on income level and whether a person is an employee or self-employed. The type of contribution paid and the period over which it is paid are important in determining entitlement to any contributory benefits.

National Insurance Credits

People who are signing on as actively seeking work or are in receipt of certain benefits receive a National Insurance credit. Carers or those who have childcare responsibilities also receive National Insurance credits. If a credit is of the right type and in the right years, they may help people protect their National Insurance record and protect entitlement to certain contributory benefits.

NHS Executive

The managing body within the Department of Health with regional offices throughout England.

NHS Plan

This was published in July 2000 listing radical changes to the NHS. The NHS Plan in the Government's 10-year plan for the modernisation of the health service in England. It aims to provide a wider range of choice, introduce new services, reduce the time patients wait for appointments and move health care closer to people's homes.

Non-Contributory Benefits

These include Child Benefit, which is available to all those who fulfil the qualifying criteria. They are not subject to means testing or to claimants satisfying any contribution conditions.

Paid Maternity Leave

Every woman who is working whilst pregnant is entitled to maternity leave. The duration and whether she receives payment is determined according to the length of service with her current employer and her weekly salary. For all leave entitlements, there are strict rules about how and when employers should be notified.

Prescription Season Tickets

For those who do not get free prescriptions, a prepayment season ticket is the only way of reducing the cost of regular prescriptions. These are available as four or 12 month certificates. If a person needs over five items in a four month period or over 14 in a 12 month period, season tickets save money.

Primary Care Trust

A NHS trust that provides all local GP, community and primary care serves and commission hospital services from other NHS trusts. They are managed by a Board elected from local GPs, community nurses, lay members, the Health Authority and Social Services.

Probation Officers

Social workers attached to the courts who supervise and assist offenders on probation. Probation orders are non-custodial methods of dealing with adult offenders.

Rapid Response Team

These respond to medical problems within the home of the patient in order to reduce the need for hospitalisation.

Reduced Earnings Allowance

A loss of earnings compensation benefit for those who are unable to return to their previous occupation and are unable to achieve the same level of earnings following an industrial accident or contracting a recognised industrial disease. The accident or onset of the disease must have occurred prior to October 1990.

Resettlement Units

Hostel or dormitory type accommodation for homeless people and in some cases for people who are supervised by the probation service. People cannot be compelled to occupy a resettlement unit to receive benefit.

Residential Care

Care of people away from the home in an institution, home or hostel. It is usually arranged, provided or owned by the Local Authority. Examples include children's homes, nursing or residential care homes for the elderly and for disabled people. Residential care packages can be arranged and funded as part of a community care assessment.

Retirement Pension

A range of benefits paid, at present, to men over 65 and women over 60 providing they fulfil the contribution conditions. Married women who opted to pay reduced contributions, and/or who do not qualify in their own right, may be able to claim a pension once her husband has retired based upon his contributions.

Severe Disablement Allowance

A non-contributory benefit for those people under 65 who are incapable of work.

Sheltered Housing

Groups of self-contained flats with a warden on site offering support. Most sheltered housing units are intended for the use of older residents. There are a few designed and intended for the use of younger disabled people. Some schemes offer communal dining or recreational facilities.

Social Fund

Various grants, loans and lump sum payments are available from this fund. They are not for standard amounts and may be affected by savings. Help provided includes Funeral Payments, Winter Fuel Payments and Crisis Loans.

Statutory Maternity Pay

This is the amount of money an employer must pay to an employee who fulfils the qualifying criteria. To become entitled a woman must have worked at least one day in the 15th week before the baby was due and have been working for the same employer for at least 26 weeks paying the right level of national insurance contribution. It is important that employers are given the appropriate notice.

Statutory Sick Pay

Subject to certain conditions, this is paid by an employer for up to 28 weeks to an employee who is off sick.

Supported Discharge

This is when a patient continues recovery at home, following discharge from hospital, with on-going support from specialists such as therapists or nurses. This may be provided by a 'community rehabilitation team', which will assess the patient's needs and arrange services accordingly.

Take-Up Rate

The proportion of people eligible for a benefit who actually claim it.

Tenant

A person occupying a property in return for payment of rent. A paying guest is not a tenant.

Tied Accommodation

Accommodation let in connection with work, e.g. school caretakers or farm workers. A person's right to occupy generally ceases with the termination of employment.

Trading Standards Officer

Located at the local Trading Standards office. They help to enforce legislation which protects consumers including weights and measures, trade descriptions, quality and standard of goods and services and consumer credit.

War Disablement Pension

A pension paid to those injured or disabled as a result of serving in Her Majesty's Service. A war pensioner's widow may be entitled to a War Widow's Pension after his death if it is judged that the death was connected in some way to his time in service. War widowers may also be entitled to a pension if they were dependent on their late wife.

Winter Fuel Payment

This is a single payment towards the winter fuel bill of citizens over 60 years of age in the week of 17–23 September in that year. Some groups do not qualify for the payment e.g. those in nursing homes. Those who have not previously qualified must put in a claim if they feel they are eligible.

Working Families' Tax Credit

A benefit for low or middle income families with less than 8000 in savings. The family can consist of one or two parents, working on average 16 hours a week or more and bringing up a child under 16, or under 19 and in full time education.

Special Needs Abbreviations

ADD
Attention Deficit Disorder

ADHD
Attention Deficit Hyperactivity Disorder

ASD
Autism Spectrum Disorder

EBD
Emotional and Behavioural Difficulties

LD
Learning Difficulties

LI
Language Impairments

MH
Mentally Handicapped

MLD
Moderate Learning Difficulties

PH
Physically Handicapped

PHAB
Physically Handicapped and Able-Bodied

PMLD
Profound and Multiple Learning Disorder

PS
Partially Sighted

PtHg
Partially Hearing

SEN
Special Educational Needs

SLD
Severe Learning Difficulties

SLDD
Students with Learning Difficulties and Disabilities

SMH
Severely Mentally Handicapped

SpLD
Specific Learning Difficulties

Bibliography

General Books: Children

Baginsky, Mary (2001) Counselling and Support Services for Young People aged 12–16 who experienced Sexual Abuse: A Study of the Provision in Italy, the Netherlands and the UK, NSPCC, £10 1842280201

Bannon, Michael; et al (2002) Protecting Children from Abuse and Neglect in Primary Care, Oxford University Press, £29.50 0192632760

Barbell, Kathy; Wright, Lois (2001) Family Foster Care in the Next Century, Transaction Publishers, £20.50 0765807122

Berg, Insoo Kim; Kelly, Susan (2000) Building Solutions in Child Protection Services, W.W. Norton, £19.09 039370310X

Biggs, Sarah (2001) Considering Adoption (Overcoming Common Problems) Sheldon Press, £6.99 0859697916

Bridge, Caroline; Swindells QC, Heather (March 2003) Adoption: The Modern Law, Family Law, £29.50 0853087628

Dubowitz, Howard; DePanfilis, Diane (2000) Handbook for Child Protection Practice Sage Publications Ltd, £39 0761913718

Dwivedi, Kedar N. (2002) Meeting the Needs of Ethnic Minority Children – Including Refugee, Black and Mixed Parentage: A Handbook for Professionals, Jessica Kingsley Publishers, £15.95 1853029599

Green, Anne; et al (2001) Keeping Track: Mapping and Tracking Vulnerable Young People, The Policy Press, £13.95 1861343248

Hamilton, Carolyn (2002) Working with Young People: Legal Responsibility and Liability, Children's Legal Centre, £14.95 0946109354

Hetherington, Rachael; et al (2002) The Welfare of Children with Mentally Ill Parents: Learning from Inter-country Comparisons, John Wiley and Sons Ltd, £65 047149724X

The Stationery Office Books (1995) Looking after Children, The Stationery Office Books, £7.50 0113218516

Kearney, Timothy R. (2001) Caring for Sexually Abused Children, Inter-Varsity Press, £5.89 0830822461

Lundrigan, Paul Stephen (2001) Treating Youth Who Sexually Abuse: An Integrated Multi-Component Approach, Haworth Press, £15.87 0789009374

Monahon, Cynthia (1997) Children and Trauma: A Guide for Parents and Professionals, Jossey Bass Wiley, £12.95 0787910716

Morris, Ann (1998) The Adoption Experience: Families Who Give Children a Second Chance, Jessica Kingsley Publishers, £11.95 1853027839

National Foster Care Association (1994) Safe Caring, National Foster Care Association, £16, 1897869010

Rowling, Louise; et al (2001) Mental Health Problems and Young People: Concepts and Practice, McGraw-Hill Education, £16.99 0074710486

Sharry, John; et al (2001) When Parents Separate: Helping Your Children Cope, Veritas Publications, £5.95 185390533X

Shore, Kenneth (2001) Keeping Kids Safe: A Guide for Parents of Toddlers and Teens-And All the Years in Between, Prentice Hall Press, £6.87 0735202141

Strand, Virginia C. (2000) Treating Secondary Victims, Sage Publications (USA), £52 0803952864

Teyber, Edward (2001) Helping Children Cope with Divorce, Jossey Bass Wiley, £11.95 078795554X

Tobin, Pnina; Kessner, Sue Levinson (2002) Keeping Kids Safe: A Child Sexual Abuse Prevention Manual, Hunter House Inc., £14.29 089793332X

Trozzi, Maria (1999) Talking with Children about Loss: Words, Strategies, and Wisdom to Help Children Cope with Death, Divorce, and Other Difficult Times Perigee Books, £7.95 0399525432

Turnell, Andrew; Edwards, Steve (1999) Signs of Safety: A Solution and Safety Oriented Approach to Child Protection Casework, W.W. Norton, £22 0393703002

Whetsall-Mitchell, Juliann (1997) Rape of the Innocent: Understanding and Preventing Child Sexual Abuse, Accelerated Development, £21.95 1560323949

General Books: Death and Bereavement

Albery, Nicholas (2000) The New Natural Death Handbook, Rider, £10.99 0712605762

Barbato, Michael (2002) Caring for the Dying, McGraw-Hill Education, £12.99 0074712144

Barnard, Paul; et al (1999) Children, Bereavement and Trauma: Nurturing Resilience, Jessica Kingsley Publishers, £13.95 1853027855

Battison, Toni (2000) Understanding Bereavement Training Pack: A Guide for Carers Working with Older People, Age Concern Books, £35 086242304X

Charlton, Rodger (2002) Primary Palliative Care: Dying, Death and Bereavement in the Community, Radcliffe Medical Press, £27.95 1857755731

Currer, Caroline (2000) Responding to Grief: Dying, Bereavement and Social Care, Palgrave, £15.99 0333736397

Dickenson, Donna; et al (2000) Death, Dying and Bereavement, Sage Publications Ltd, £18.99 0761968571

Donnellan, Craig (1999) Bereavement, Independence Educational Publishers, £6.95 186168083X

Harris, Paul (2002) What to Do When Someone Dies: How to Deal with the Practical Arrangements That Have to Be Made After a Death, Which? Books, £9.99 0852028997

Hughes, Theodore E.; Klein, David (2001) A Family Guide to Wills, Funerals, and Probate, Facts on File, £10.28 0816045518

Huntley, Elliot J. (2002) Helping Children Grieve (Revised Ed.), Augsburg Fortress Publishers, £7.65 0806642653

Parkes, Colin Murray (1996) Death and Bereavement Across Cultures, Routledge, £17.99 0415131375

Sainsbury, Anne; et al (2001) Financial Implications of the Death of a Child, Family Policy Studies Centre, £10.95 1901455416

General Books: Disability

Beckman, Paula (1999) Strategies for Working with Families of Young Children with Disabilities, Brookes Publishing Co, £24.50 1557662576

Chamba, Rampaul; et al (1999) On the Edge: Minority Ethnic Families Caring for a Severely Disabled Child, The Policy Press, £12.95 1861341342

Cuskelly, Monica; et al (2002) Down Syndrome Across the Life-span; Whurr Publishers, £37.51 1861562306

Janicki, Matthew P.; Ansello, Edward F. (2000) Community Support for Aging Adults with Lifelong Disabilities, Brookes Publishing Co, £46.95 1557664625

Leach, Steve (2002) A Supported Employment Workbook: Using Individual Profiling and Job Matching, Jessica Kingsley Publishers, £19.95 1843100525

Newton, Richard (April 2004) The Down's Syndrome Handbook, Vermilion, £7.99 0091884306

Pengra, Lilah Morton (2000) Your Values, My Values: Multicultural Services in Developmental Disabilities, Brookes Publishing Co, £22.95 155766448X

Read, Janet (2000) Disability, the Family and Society: Listening to Mothers, Open University Press, £21.99 0335203108

General Books: Drugs

Advisory Council on the Misuse of Drugs (2000) Reducing Drug Related Deaths: A Report by the Advisory Council on the Misuse of Drugs, The Stationery Office Agencies, £11.50 0113412398

Cohen, Julian (2001) Managing Drug Incidents and Supporting Young Drug Users, Healthwise, £4.99 1873460341

Emmett, David; Nice, Graeme (1996) Understanding Drugs: A Handbook for Parents, Teachers, and Other Professionals, Jessica Kingsley Publishers, £16.95 1853024007

Fisher, Gary L.; Harrison, Thomas C. (1999) Substance Abuse: Information for School Counselors, Social Workers, Therapists, and Counselors: Information for School Counselors, Social Workers, Therapists, and Counselors, Allyn & Bacon, £44.99 0205306225

Hardiman, Michael (1998) Addiction: the Common Sense Approach, Gill & Macmillan, £5.99 0717127079

International Labour Office (ILO) (1996) Management of Alcohol- and Drug-related Issues in the Workplace: An ILO Code of Practice, ILO, £8.10 9221094553

Jackson, Tricia (1999) Drugs and Alcohol Policies Chartered Institute of Personnel and Development (CIPD), £13.99 0852928114

Kroll, Brynna; Taylor, Andy (2002) Parental Substance Misuse and Child Welfare, Jessica Kingsley Publishers, £17.95 185302791X

Marlow, Alan; Pearson, Geoff (1999) Young People, Drugs and Community Safety, Russell House Publishing Ltd, £14.95 1898924384

McBride, Andrew (2002) Working with Substance Misusers: A Guide to Theory and Practice, Routledge, £65 0415235677

Miller, William R.; Weisner, Constance M. (2002) Changing Substance Abuse Through Health and Social Systems, Plenum Publishers, £40 0306472562

Muscat, Richard (2001) Drug Use in Prison: Drugs and Addiction, The Stationery Office Agencies, £10 9287145210

O'Connor, Louise; et al (1998) Drugs: Partnerships for Policy, Prevention and Education Continuum International Publishing Group, £25 0304339466

Petersen, M.; et al (2002) Working with Substance Misusers: A Guide to Theory and Practice, Routledge, £18.99 0415235685

Rasmussen, Sandra (2000) Addiction Treatment Theory and Practice, Sage Publications Ltd, £30 0761908439

Stark, Cameron; et al (1999) Illegal Drug Use in the United Kingdom: Prevention Treatment and Enforcement, Arena, £47.50 185742431X

Van der Meer, Ron (2001) Understanding Drugs: An Interactive Guide for Parents and Young People, Van der Meer, £14.99 1902413350

General Books: The Elderly

Beales, David (1997) Community Care of Older People, Radcliffe Medical Press, £19.95 1857750322

Bennett, Gerry; et al (1997) The Dimensions of Elder Abuse: Perspectives for Practitioners, Palgrave, £18.99 0333625684

Brechin, Ann; et al (1998) Care Matters: Concepts, Practice and Research in Health and Social Care, Sage Publications Ltd, £18.99 0761955666

Chiva, Anthony; Stears, David (2001) Promoting the Health of Older People: The Next Step in Health Generation, Open University Press, £17.99 0335204384

Darby, Stuart; et al (1998) Older People, Nursing and Mental Health, Butterworth Heinemann, £39.95 075062440X

Decalmer, Peter; Glendenning, Frank (1997) The Mistreatment of Elderly People, Sage Publications Ltd, £60 0761952624

Easterbrook, Lorna (2003) Moving on from Community Care: Changes to the Treatment, Care and Support of Older People in England, Age Concern Books, £14.99 0862423481

Gibson, Diane (1998) Aged Care: Old Policies, New Problems, Cambridge University Press, £17.95 052155957X

Gilchrist, Caroline (1999) Turning Your Back on Us: Older People and the NHS, Age Concern Reports, £5 1903629004

Harding, Tessa (1997) Life Worth Living: Independence and Inclusion of Older People, Help the Aged, £5 0905852001

Hartnell, Caroline (2000) The Retirement Handbook, Age Concern Books, £7.99 0862423082

Holstein, Martha B.; Mitzen, Phyllis (2001) Ethics in Community-based Elder Care: Ethics, Aging and Caring Practice, Springer Publishing Company, £47.95 0826122973

Humber, James M. (Feb 2003) Care for the Aged, Humana Press, £38.50 1588292401

Moriarty, Jo; Webb, Sarah (2000) Part of Their Lives: Community Care for Older People with Dementia, The Policy Press, £14.99 1861342179

Mosher-Ashley, Pearl M.; Barrett, Phyllis W. (1997) A Life Worth Living: A Health Professional's Guide to Reducing Depression in Older Adults, Health Professions Press, £24.50 1878812033

Raynes, Norma; et al (2001) Quality at Home for Older People: Involving Service Users in Defining Home Care Specifications, The Policy Press, £13.95 1861343523

Roberts, Emily; et al (2002) Old Habits Die Hard: Tackling Age Discrimination in Health and Social Care, King's Fund, £6.99 1857174623

Roberts, Emilie (2000) Improving the Services for Older People, King's Fund, £5.99 1857174216

Rummery, Kirstein; Glendinning, Caroline (2000) Primary Care and Social Services: Developing New Partnerships for Older People, Radcliffe Medical Press, £17.95 1857754662

Russell, Louise B.; Bookbinder, David (2000) Housing Options for Older People, Age Concern Books, £6.99 0862422876

Thompson, Keith (1997) Caring for an Elderly Relative: A Practical Guide to Managing Care at Home, Vermilion, £7.99 0091815223

Victor, Christina (1997) Community Care and Older People, Nelson Thornes, £18 0748732926

Ward, Sue (200) Pensions Handbook 2003: Planning Ahead to Boost Retirement Income, Age Concern Books, £3 0862423546

Warnes, Tony; et al (2001) Care Services for Later Life, Jessica Kingsley Publishers, £18.95 1853028525

General Books: Health Care

Brownsell, Andrew; et al (March 2003) Assistive Technology and Telecare: Forging Solutions for Independent Living, The Policy Press, £14.99 1861344627

Davies, Celia; et al (2000) Changing Practice in Health and Social Care, Sage Publications Ltd, £55 0761964967

Etherington, Kim (2001) Counsellors in Health Settings, Jessica Kingsley Publishers, £17.95 1853029386

Komaromy, Carol (2002) Dilemmas in UK Health Care, Open University Press, £18.99 033520841X

Martin, Vivian; Henderson, Euan (2001) Managing in Health and Social Care, Routledge, £17.99 0415251907

Montgomery, Jonathan (2002) Health Care Law, Oxford University Press, £24.99 0198765746

General Books: Law and Order

Drakeford, Mark; et al (2001) Pre-trial Services and the Future of Probation, University of Wales Press, £14.99 0708316433

Ireland, Jane L. (2002) Bullying Among Prisoners, Brunner, £16.99 1583911871

Johnson, Robert (2001) Hard Time: Understanding and Reforming the Prison, Wadsworth, £19.99 0534507174

Liebling, Alison; Bottoms, Tony (2001) Prisons in the UK: Theory, Policy and Practice, Longman Higher Education, £17.99 0582299675

McDermott, Paul Anthony (2000) Prison Law, Round Hall Ltd, £85 185800182X

Towl, Graham; et al (2000) Suicide in Prisons, Pavilion Publishing Ltd, £11.95 1900600935

Wortley, Richard (2002) Situational Prison Control: Crime Prevention in Correctional Institutions, Cambridge University Press, £15.95 0521009405

General Books: Mental Health

Aggleton, Peter (2000) Young People and Mental Health, John Wiley and Sons Ltd, £19.99 0471976784

Backlar, Patricia; Cutler, David L. (2002) Ethics in Community Mental Health Care: Commonplace Concerns, Plenum Publishers, £34 0306467046

Bartlett, Peter; Sandland, Ralph (2003) Mental Health Law: Policy and Practice, Oxford University Press, £31.99 0199258791

Bhargavi, Davar (2002) Mental Health from a Gender Perspective, Sage Publications Ltd, £38.14 0761994777

Caplan, Gerald (2001) An Approach to Community Mental Health, Routledge, £75 0415264596

Clark, Hewitt B.; Davis, Maryann (2000) Transition to Adulthood: A Resource for Assisting Young People with Emotional or Behavioral Difficulties, Brookes Publishing Co, £22.99 1557664544

Donnellan, Craig (2000) Dealing with Mental Illness (Issues), Independence Educational Publishers, £6.95 1861681410

Dunn, Sarah (1999) Creating Accepting Communities: Report of the Mind Inquiry into Social Exclusion, MIND, £9.99 1874690871

Foster, Angela; Roberts, Vega Zagier (1999) Managing Mental Health in the Community: Chaos and Containment, Routledge, £50 0415167965

Jones, Richard (2002) Mental Health Act Manual, Sweet & Maxwell, £52 0421798807

Howe, Gwen (1998) Mental Health Assessments, Jessica Kingsley Publishers, £12.95 1853024589

Kitwood, Tom (1997) Dementia Reconsidered: The Person Comes First, Open University Press, £17.99 0335198554

Kohen, Dora (2000) Women and Mental Health, Routledge, £18.99 0415188857

MIND (2000) Understanding Mental Illness, MIND, £1 1874690782

Regal, Steven; Roberts, Dave (2001) Mental Health Liaison: A Handbook for Health Care Professionals, Bailliere Tindall, £25.99 0702025259

Rowling, Louise (2001) Mental Health Problems and Young People: Concepts and Practice, McGraw-Hill Education, £16.99 0074710486

Slater, Lauren; et al (September 2003) The Complete Guide to Mental Health for Women, Beacon Press, £21 0807029254

Tibbs, Margaret Anne (2001) Social Work and Dementia: Good Practice and Care Management Jessica Kingsley Publishers, £14.95 1853029041

Williams, F.G.; Doessel, D.P. (2001) The Economics of Mental Health Care: Industry, Government and Community Issues, Ashgate Publishing Limited, £49.95 0754617149

Walsh, Mark; Millar, Elaine (2000) Mental Health Matters in Primary Care, Nelson Thornes, £22.50 0748745289

Wilson, Melba (1996) A–Z of Race Issues in Mental Health, MIND; £3 187469057X

General Books: Race and Immigration

Brown, Matthew; Hanna, Judith Lynne (1997) Exclusion from School and Racial Equality: A Good Practice Guide, Commission For Racial Equality (CRE), £3 1854421956

Commission for Racial Equality (1995) Racial Harassment at Work: What Employers Can Do About It, Commission for Racial Equality, £5 1854421697

Commission for Racial Equality (1998) Stereotyping and Racism, Commission For Racial Equality, £3.50 1854422146

Commission for Racial Equality (1995) Action on Racial Harassment: a Guide to Multi-agency Panels, Commission For Racial Equality (CRE), £3.50 1854421670

Commission for Racial Equality (1995) Large Companies and Racial Equality, Commission For Racial Equality (CRE), £5 185442162X

Dhooper, Surjit Singh; Moore, Sharon E. (2000) Social Work Practice with Culturally Diverse People, Sage Publications Ltd, £23 0761912975

Hanna, Judith Lynne (1997) Race, Culture and Community Care, Commission For Racial Equality (CRE), £12 1854421999

Rees, Bethan (2002) Promoting Racial Equality, Pearson Publishing, £26 1857497899

Simon, Rita J.; Altstein, Howard (2002) Adoption, Race, and Identity: From Infancy to Young Adulthood, Transaction Publishers, £15.87 0765809036

Department for Work and Pensions: Benefits Agency Information Leaflets

Bereavement

D49   What to do after a death in England and Wales.

D49S   What to do after a death in Scotland: Social Security supplement.

GL14   Widowed?

NP45   A guide to widows' benefits.

Families

BC1   Babies and children.

BC2   Expecting a baby.

BC3   Bringing up children.

N117A   A guide to maternity benefits.

Retirement

RM1   Retirement – a guide to benefits for people who are retiring or have retired.

PG1   Pensioners' guide – England and Wales.

PG2   Pensioners' guide – Scotland.

Sick or disabled

GL12   Going into hospital?

SD1   Sick or disabled.

SD2   Sick and unable to work?

SD3   Long-term ill or disabled?

SD4   Caring for someone?

SD6   Ill or disabled because of a disease or deafness caused by work?

SD7   Disabled because of an accident at work.

Working or looking for work

WFL5   Help to move to work and independence.

WK1   Financial help if you work or are looking for work.

WK2   Financial help if you are looking for work.

WK3   Need help starting work or getting back to work?

WK4   Financial help if you are working or doing voluntary work.

Other information

GL13   Separated or divorced?

GL15   Help if you live in a residential care or nursing home.

GL16   Help with your rent.

GL17   Help with your council tax.

GL18   Help from the social fund.

GL19   School leavers and students.

GL21   A helping hand for benefits?

GL22   Tell us your comments and complaints.

GL23   Social security benefit rates.

GL24   If you think our decision is wrong.

GL25   How to prove your identity for social security.

GL26   Service families abroad.

GL27   Compensation and social security benefits.

GL28   Coming from abroad and social security benefits.

GL29   Going abroad and social security benefits.

GL31   Applying for a National Insurance (NI) Number.

GL32   Prisoners and their families.

HB5   A guide to non-contributory benefits for disabled people.

IS20   A guide to income support.

MG1   A guide to benefits.

RR2   A guide to housing benefit and council tax benefit.

IB1   A guide to incapacity benefit.

Web Resources

These websites can provide useful, further information for personnel involved in the Social Services industry. The inclusion of these URLs does not imply endorsement of the contents of these sites by Pearson Education.

Age Concern	www.ace.org.uk
Barnardos	www.barnardos.org.uk
BBC Watchdog	www.bbc.co.uk/watchdog
Citizens Advice	www.nacab.org.uk
Commission for Racial Equality	www.cre.gov.uk
Community Care Magazine	www.community-care.co.uk
Consumer information site run by the DTI	www.consumer.gov.uk
The Department for Education and Skills	www.dfes.gov.uk
The Department of Health	www.doh.gov.uk
The Department for Work and Pensions	www.dwp.gov.uk
The Fostering Network	www.thefostering.net
Her Majesty's Stationery Office	www.hmso.gov.uk
MIND, the mental health charity	www.mind.org.uk
The National Assembly for Wales	www.wales.gov.uk
The NHS Direct On-Line website	www.nhsdirect.nhs.uk
The Northern Ireland Executive Department of Health, Social Services and Public Safety	www.dhsspsni.gov.uk
The Northern Ireland Office	www.nio.gov.uk
The Scottish Executive	www.scotland.gov.uk
The Scottish Parliament	www.scottish.parliament.uk
Shelter	www.shelter.org.uk
The Stationery Office Business and Professional Bookshop	www.tso.co.uk/bookshop
Westminster Parliament	www.parliament.uk
Which	www.which.net
World Health Organisation	www.who.int

Legislation and Statutory Acts

Below are some of the key Acts and Statutory Instruments which affect Social Services provision in the United Kingdom. It is not intended as a comprehensive guide but as a foundation for further research and resources. All of the following are available from The Stationery Office and are subject to Crown Copyright protection.

Relevant Acts 2003

Health (Wales) Act 2003

Chapter 4

An Act to make provision about Community Health Councils in Wales; to establish and make provision about the Wales Centre for Health; and to make provision for the establishment of, and otherwise about, Health Professions Wales.

Community Care (Delayed Discharges etc.) Act 2003

Chapter 5

An Act to make provision requiring social services authorities to make payments in cases where the discharge of patients is delayed for reasons relating to the provision of community care services or services for carers; and to enable the Secretary of State and the National Assembly for Wales to require certain community care services and services for carers provided by social services authorities to be free of charge to persons receiving those services.

National Minimum Wage (Enforcement Notices) Act 2003

Chapter 8

An Act to make provision enabling an enforcement notice under section 19 of the National Minimum Wage Act 1998 to impose a requirement under subsection (2) of that section in relation to a person, whether or not a requirement under subsection (1) of that section is, or may be, imposed in relation to that or any other person; and to limit the pay reference periods in respect of which a requirement under subsection (2) of that section may be imposed.

Human Fertilisation and Embryology (Deceased Fathers) Act 2003

Chapter 24

An Act to make provision about the circumstances in which, and the extent to which, a man is to be treated in law as the father of a child where the child has resulted from certain fertility treatment undertaken after the man's death; and for connected purposes.

Anti-social Behaviour Act 2003

Chapter 38

An Act to make provision in connection with anti-social behaviour.

Courts Act 2003

Chapter 39

An Act to make provision about the courts and their procedure and practice; about judges and magistrates; about fines and the enforcement processes of the courts; about periodical payments of damages; and for connected purposes.

Sexual Offences Act 2003

Chapter 42

An Act to make new provision about sexual offences, their prevention and the protection of children from harm from other sexual acts, and for connected purposes.

Relevant Acts 2002

State Pension Credit Act 2002

Chapter 16

An Act to make provision for and in connection with a new social security benefit called state pension credit; and to amend section 47(1) of the Pension Schemes Act 1993.

National Health Service Reform and Health Care Professions Act 2002

Chapter 17

An Act to amend the law about the national health service; to establish and make provision in connection with a Commission for Patient and Public Involvement in Health; to make provision in relation to arrangements for joint working between NHS bodies and the prison service, and between NHS bodies and local authorities in Wales; to make provision in connection with the regulation of health care professions; and for connected purposes.

Divorce (Religious Marriages) Act 2002

Chapter 27

An Act to make provision enabling a court to require the dissolution of a religious marriage before granting a civil divorce.

Adoption and Children Act 2002

Chapter 38

An Act to restate and amend the law relating to adoption; to make further amendments of the law relating to children; to amend section 93 of the Local Government Act 2000; and for connected purposes.

Nationality, Immigration and Asylum Act 2002

Chapter 41

An Act to make provision about nationality, immigration and asylum; to create offences in connection with international traffic in prostitution; to make provision about international projects connected with migration; and for connected purposes.

Relevant Acts 2001

Children's Commissioner for Wales Act 2001

Chapter 18

An Act to make further provision about the Children's Commissioner for Wales.

Health and Social Care Act 2001

Chapter 15

An Act to amend the law about the national health service; to provide for the exercise of functions by Care Trusts under partnership arrangements under the Health Act 1999 and to make further provision in relation to such arrangements; to make further provision in relation to social care services; to make provision in relation to the supply or other processing of patient information; to extend the categories of appropriate practitioners in relation to prescription-only medicinal products; and for connected purposes.

Social Security Contributions (Share Options) Act 2001

Chapter 20

An Act to make provision about the payment of National Insurance Contributions in respect of share options and similar rights obtained by persons as directors or employees during the period beginning with 6th April 1999 and ending with 19th May 2000.

Social Security Fraud Act 2001

Chapter 11

An Act to make provision, for the purposes of the law relating to social security, about the obtaining and disclosure of information; and to make provision for restricting the payment of social security benefits and war pensions in the case of persons convicted of offences relating to such benefits or pensions and about the institution of proceedings for such offences; and for connected purposes.

Special Educational Needs and Disability Act 2001

Chapter 10

An Act to amend Part 4 of the Education Act 1996; to make further provision against discrimination, on grounds of disability, in schools and other educational establishments; and for connected purposes.

Relevant Acts 2000

Carers and Disabled Children Act 2000

Chapter 16

An Act to make provision about the assessment of carers' needs; to provide for services to help carers; to provide for the making of payments to carers and disabled children aged 16 or 17 in lieu of the provision of services to them; and for connected purposes

Care Standards Act 2000

Chapter 14

An Act to establish a National Care Standards Commission; to make provision for the registration and regulation of children's homes, independent hospitals, independent clinics, care homes, residential family centres, independent medical agencies, domiciliary care agencies, fostering agencies, nurses agencies and voluntary adoption agencies; to make provision for the regulation and inspection of local authority fostering and adoption services; to establish a General Social Care Council and a Care Council for Wales and make provision for the registration, regulation and training of social care workers; to establish a Children's Commissioner for Wales; to make provision for the registration, regulation and training of those providing child minding or day care; to make provision for the protection of children and vulnerable adults; to amend the law about children looked after in schools and colleges; to repeal the Nurses Agencies Act 1957; to amend Schedule 1 to the Local Authority Social Services Act 1970; and for connected purposes.

Children (Leaving Care) Act 2000

Chapter 35

An Act to make provision about children and young persons who are being, or have been, looked after by a local authority; to replace section 24 of the Children Act 1989; and for connected purposes.

Child Support, Pensions and Social Security Act 2000

Chapter 19

An Act to amend the law relating to child support; to amend the law relating to occupational and personal pensions and war pensions; to amend the law relating to social security benefits and social security administration; to amend the law relating to national insurance contributions; to amend Part III of the Family Law Reform Act 1969 and Part III of the Family Law Act 1986; and for connected purposes.

Health Service Commissioners (Amendment) Act 2000

Chapter 28

An Act to amend the Health Service Commissioners Act 1993.

Race Relations (Amendment) Act 2000

Chapter 34

An Act to extend further the application of the Race Relations Act 1976 to the police and other public authorities; to amend the exemption under that Act for acts done for the purpose of safeguarding national security; and for connected purposes.

Relevant Acts 1999

Disability Rights Commission Act 1999

Chapter 17

An Act to establish a Disability Rights Commission and make provision as to its functions; and for connected purposes.

Health Act 1999

Chapter 8

An Act to amend the law about the national health service; make provision in relation to arrangements and payments between health service bodies and local authorities with respect to health and health-related functions; confer power to regulate any professions concerned (wholly or partly) with the physical or mental health of individuals; and for connected purposes.

Protection of Children Act 1999

Chapter 14

An Act to require a list to be kept of persons considered unsuitable to work with children; to extend the power to make regulations under section 218(6) of the Education Reform Act 1988; to make further provision with respect to that list and the list kept for the purposes of such regulations; to enable the protection afforded to children to be afforded to persons suffering from mental impairment; and for connected purposes.

Social Security Contributions (Transfer of Functions, etc.) Act 1999

Chapter 2

An Act to transfer from the Secretary of State to the Commissioners of Inland Revenue or the Treasury certain functions relating to national insurance contributions, the National Insurance Fund, statutory sick pay, statutory maternity pay or pension schemes and certain associated functions relating to benefits; to enable functions relating to any of those matters in respect of Northern Ireland to be transferred to the Secretary of State, the Commissioners of Inland Revenue or the Treasury; to make further provision, in connection with the functions transferred, as to the powers of the Commissioners of Inland Revenue, the making of decisions and appeals; to provide that rebates payable in respect of members of money purchase contracted-out pension schemes are to be payable out of the National Insurance Fund; and for connected purposes.

Youth Justice and Criminal Evidence Act 1999

Chapter 23

An Act to provide for the referral of offenders under 18 to youth offender panels; to make provision in connection with the giving of evidence or information for the purposes of criminal proceedings; to amend section 51 of the Criminal Justice and Public Order Act 1994; to make pre-consolidation amendments relating to youth justice; and for connected purposes.

Relevant Acts 1998

Community Care (Residential Accommodation) Act 1998

Chapter 19

An Act to restrict the amount of a person's capital which may be taken into account by a local authority in determining whether he should be provided with residential accommodation that would be, or would be treated as, provided under Part III of the National Assistance Act 1948.

Social Security Act 1998

Chapter 14

An Act to make provision as to the making of decisions and the determination of appeals under enactments relating to social security, child support, vaccine damage payments and war pensions; to make further provision with respect to social security; and for connected purposes.

Human Rights Act (1998)

(Effective from 2nd October 2000)
This Act introduces legislation from the European Convention on Human rights in to United Kingdom law. This means that cases can now be tried in UK courts, in addition to the European Court at Strasbourg.

The Impact on Social Services Work

All public authorities are now legally obliged to act in accordance with the convention rights, which includes the provision of Social Services. It is vital, therefore, for all those involved in Social Services work to be fully aware of the meanings and implications of these rights. The legislation is broadly intended to support the rights and freedoms of the individual, whilst reducing discrimination. As such, complying with the regulations should not pose a problem to those who endeavour to achieve best practice. However, all areas of work should be scrutinised to ensure that there are no areas of conflict. If there is any uncertainty, legal advice should always be sought.

The articles

The following is an outline of the main articles followed by suggested areas of concern in the field of social services. Please note that all articles are subject to exemptions in accordance with the law.

Article 2) Right to Life

Protecting the individual from loss of life and creating the obligation to protect life in some circumstances.
Areas of concern: deaths in care, inequality of medical treatment across the country, failure to clean up environmental hazards, deaths in police custody, abortion, euthanasia, putting clients at risk in any way.

Article 3) Prohibition of torture

Protecting the individual from treatment or punishment of an inhuman or degrading nature, whether physical or mental.
Areas of concern: Treatment and conditions of those in care, use of corporal punishment.

Article 4) Prohibition of slavery and forced labour

Slavery, servitude and compulsory labour are forbidden under this article.

Article 5) Right to liberty and security

This article gives rights to the individual in the event of unlawful arrest or detention.
Areas of concern: Locking doors of elderly residents' rooms, detention under the Mental Health Act.

Article 6) Right to a fair trial

All those charged with a criminal offence are entitled to a public trial within a reasonable period of time. They are also afforded a number of rights under this article including the presumption of innocence until proven guilty and enough time and facilities to prepare a defence.
Areas of concern: withholding of evidence by prosecution teams, rights of defendants with learning difficulties, effect on mentally ill patients of time taken to convene tribunals.

Article 7) No punishment without law

Crimes can only be punished by laws and penalties in existence at the time that they were committed.

Article 8) Right to privacy and family life

The right of the individual to respect for their private and family life, home and correspondence.
Areas of concern: Police surveillance, stop and search techniques, nursing home closures.

Article 9) Right to freedom of thought, conscience and religion

Everyone shall be allowed to hold their chosen beliefs and act upon these or change them at any time.
Areas of concern: Maintaining the religion of children in care, forcing blood transfusions against religious beliefs.

Article 10) Freedom of expression

The right to hold opinions and speak or otherwise express these opinions freely.

Article 11) Freedom of assembly

The right to hold peaceful demonstrations and associate freely with others.
Areas of concern: the right to form or join a Trade Union.

Article 12) The right to marry and found a family

The right of men and women of marriageable age to marry and to raise children.
Areas of concern: Those refused the right to become adoptive/foster parents, marriage and parenting rights of mentally handicapped persons.

Article 14) Prohibition of discrimination (can only be used in conjunction with one of the other articles)

Discrimination of any kind is not acceptable in the implementation of these articles.
Areas of concern: withholding of treatment from older patients.

Protocol 1, article 1) Protection of Property

The right to retain possessions and enjoy them peacefully. May include shares, licences and the right to engage in a profession.
Areas of concern: Council not dealing with nuisance neighbours, property belonging to Trade Unions, revocation of or refusal to renew licences.

Protocol 1, article 2) Right to education

The right of access to education for all.
Areas of concern: challenge to school expulsions, rights of special needs pupils.

Protocol 1, article 3) Right to free elections

Elections must be held by secret ballot at reasonable intervals.
Areas of concern: access to polling for ill or disabled voters.

Protocol 6, articles 1 and 2) right not to be subjected to the death penalty

The abolition of the death penalty, except in times of war.

For further information on the Human Rights Act try the following web pages:

• www.homeoffice.gov.uk	The home office
• www.echr.co.int	The European Court of Human Rights
• www.humanrights.coe.int	The Council of Europe, Human Rights
• www.hmso.gov.uk	Her Majesty's Stationery Office

Useful publications:

- Local Authorities and the Human Rights Act 1998, *Michael Supperstone; James Goudie; Jason Coppel,* Butterworths Law, 1999 £25 0406926743
- Blackstone's Guide to the Human Rights Act, *John Wadham; Helen Mountfield*, Blackstone, 2000 £24.95 1841741736
- Children and the Human Rights Act, *Sandhya Drew; Rt Hon Lord Justice Sedley*, Save the Children, 2000. £10 1841870374
- Immigration, Asylum and the Human Rights Act 1998, *Nicholas Blake QC; Razia Hussain*, Blackstone Press, 2002 £30 184174140X
- Mental Health Law and the Human Rights Act 1998, *Richard Gordon; Paul Bowen*, Blackstone Press, 2002 £25 1841741418.

Part One

Public and Statutory Services Central and Local Government

Health, Education and Employment

1

- **Department of Health**
  Including Social Services Inspectorate
- **Department for Work and Pensions**
  The Pension Service
  Jobcentre Plus
- **Department for Education and Skills**

Health, Education and Employment

DEPARTMENT OF HEALTH

Richmond Hse, 79 Whitehall, London SW1A 2NL;
URL www.doh.gov.uk; Tel 020 7210 3000
Secretary of State and Chair of the NHS Policy Board
The Rt Hon John Reid, MP
Minister of State (Health) The Rt Hon John Hutton, MP
Minister of State Rosie Winterton, MP
Parliamentary Under Secretary (Performance and Quality)
Lord Warner
Parliamentary Under Secretary of State (Community)
Dr Stephen Ladyman, MP
Parliamentary Under Secretary of State (Public Health)
Melanie Johnson, MP
Permanent Secretary and NHS Chief Executive Nigel Crisp,
KCB
Group Director (Delivery) John Bacon
Group Director (Strategy and Business Development)
Hugh Taylor, CB
*Group Director (Standards and Quality) and Chief Medical
Officer* Sir Liam Donaldson
Deputy Chief Medical Officer Vacancy
Deputy Chief Medical Officer Prof Aidan Halligan
Chief Inspector (Social Services Inspectorate) Averil Nottage
(Acting)
*Chief Nursing Officer and Director (User Experience and
Involvement)* Sarah Mullally
Director (National Cancer Services) Prof Michael Richards,
MA, MD, FRCP
Director (Corporate Affairs) Hugh Taylor, CB
Director (Strategy) Chris Ham
Director (Human Resources) Andrew Foster
Director (Finance) Richard Douglas
Director (Research and Development)
Prof Sir John Pattison
Director (Finance and Investment) Richard Douglas
Director (Communications) Sian Jarvis
Director (Policy) Andy McKeon
Director (Change) Ruth Carnall

Communications Directorate

Richmond House, Quarry House and Skipton
Director Sian Jarvis

Strategic Communications Group

Head John Worne; Tel 020 7210 5893; Fax 020 7210 5134

Customer Service Centre

Head Linda Percival; Tel 020 7210 5975; Fax 020 7210
5454

Corporate Development Team

Branch Head Peter Allanson; Tel 020 7210 5356; Fax 020
7210 5409

Marketing Communications Group

Branch Head Wyn Roberts; Tel 020 7210 5635; Fax 020 7210
5134

Media Centre

Assistant Director (News) Jon Hibbs; Tel 020 7210 5478;
Fax 020 7210 5433

Directorate of Children, Older People and Social Care Services (including Social Services Inspectorate)

Director Averil Nottage (Acting)
Deputy Director and Head (Social Care Policy)
Giles Denham; Tel 020 7972 4045; Fax 020 7972 4555
Director (Change Agent Team) Richard Humphries
(Secondee); Tel 020 7210 5005; Fax 020 7210 5023

Corporate Development Team

Head Anthea Smith; Tel 020 7972 4296; Fax 020 7972 4197

Health and Social Care Joint Unit

Head Anne McDonald; Tel 020 7972 4098; Fax 020 7972
4487

SOCIAL SERVICES INSPECTORATE

Richmond Hse, 79 Whitehall, London SW1A 2NS
Chief Inspector Averil Nottage (Acting); Tel 020 7210 5730;
Fax 020 7210 5937
Consultant (Joint Review Group) John Bolton; Tel 020 7630
0105; Fax 020 7630 0182
Head (SSI Policy) Vacancy
The Social Services Inspectorate (SSI) operates from nine
regional offices, coterminous with the Government Offices
for the Regions (see Chapter 4 for list of Government
Offices for the Regions). Its four main functions are: to
provide advice to Ministers and Central Government
departments on all matters concerning personal social care;
to assist local government, voluntary organisations and
private agencies in their delivery of efficient social care
services; to run a national programme of inspection,
evaluating services used by both users and carers and to
monitor the implementation of Government policy for the
personal social services.

East Midlands

Director   Glen Mason
2nd Fl, St. James' Place Hse, Castle Quay, Castle Blvd,
   Nottingham NG7 1FW; Tel 0115 959 7518; Fax 0115 959
   7501
Areas of Responsibility
Derby, Derbyshire, Leicester, Leicestershire, Lincolnshire,
Northamptonshire, Nottinghamshire, Rutland.

North East

Director   John Fraser
Tyne Bridge Tower, Church St, Gateshead, Tyne and Wear
   NE8 2DU; Tel 0191 490 3410; Fax 0191 490 3401
Areas of Responsibility
Darlington, Durham, Gateshead, Hartlepool,
Middlesbrough, Newcastle upon Tyne, North Tyneside,
Northumberland, Redcar and Cleveland, South Tyneside,
Stockton-on-Tees, Sunderland.

North West

Director   Vacancy
11th Fl, West Point, 501 Chester Rd, Old Trafford,
   Manchester M16 9HU; Tel 0161 876 2415; Fax 0161 876
   2429
Areas of Responsibility
Blackburn, Blackpool, Bolton, Bury, Cheshire, Cumbria,
Halton, Knowsley, Lancashire, Liverpool, Manchester,
Oldham, Rochdale, Salford, Sefton, St. Helens, Stockport,
Tameside, Trafford, Warrington, Wigan, Wirral.

South East

Director   Lynda Hoare
5th Fl, Eileen Hse, 80–94 Newington Causeway, London
   SE1 6EF; Tel 020 7972 2970; Fax 020 7972 2900
Areas of Responsibility
Bracknell Forest, Brighton and Hove, Buckinghamshire,
East Sussex, Hampshire, Isle of Wight, Kent, Medway
Towns, Milton Keynes, Oxfordshire, Portsmouth, Reading,
Slough, Southampton, Surrey, West Berkshire, West Sussex,
Windsor and Maidenhead, Wokingham.

Yorkshire and Humber

Director   Jonathan Phillips
8th Fl, 8 EO4 Quarry Hse, Quarry Hill, Leeds, West
   Yorkshire LS2 7UE; Tel 0113 245 6470; Fax 0161 245
   6463
Areas of Responsibility
Bradford, Calderdale, East Riding, Kingston upon Hull,
Kirklees, Leeds, North East Lincolnshire, North
Lincolnshire, North Yorkshire, Wakefield, York.

London

Director   Mike Rourke
6th Fl, Eileen Hse, 80–94 Newington Causeway, London
   SE1 6EF; Tel 020 7972 2994; Fax 020 7972 2921
Areas of Responsibility
Barking and Dagenham, Barnet, Bexley, Brent, Bromley,
Camden, City of London, Croydon, Ealing, Enfield,
Greenwich, Hackney, Hammersmith and Fulham,
Haringey, Harrow, Havering, Hillingdon, Hounslow,
Islington, Kensington and Chelsea, Lambeth, Lewisham,
Merton, Newham, Redbridge, Richmond, Southwark,
Sutton, Tower Hamlets, Waltham Forest, Wandsworth,
Westminster.

West Midlands

Director   John Cypher
6th Fl, Ladywood Hse, 45–46 Stephenson St, Birmingham,
   West Midlands B2 4DH; Tel 0121 606 4361; Fax 0121 606
   4388

Areas of Responsibility
Birmingham, Coventry, Dudley, Herefordshire, Sandwell,
Shropshire, Solihull, Staffordshire, Stoke-on-Trent, Telford
and Wrekin, Walsall, Warwickshire, Wolverhampton,
Worcestershire.

East of England

Director   Jenny Owen
Capital Pk, Fulbourn, Cambridge, Cambridgeshire
   CB1 5XB; Tel 01223 597523; Fax 01223 597601
Areas of Responsibility
Bedfordshire, Cambridge, Essex, Hertfordshire, Luton,
Norfolk, Peterborough, Suffolk, Southend-on-Sea,
Thurrock.

South West

Director   Gerald O'Hagan (Acting)
40 Berkeley Sq, Clifton, Bristol BS8 1HP; Tel 0117 941 6530;
   Fax 0117 941 6501
Areas of Responsibility
Bath and North East Somerset, Bournemouth, Bristol,
Cornwall, Devon, Dorset, Gloucestershire, Isles of Scilly,
North Somerset, Plymouth, Poole, Somerset, South
Gloucestershire, Swindon, Torbay, Wiltshire.

Social Care Policy – Placement, Permanence and Children's Trusts

Head   David Holmes; Tel 020 7972 4629; Fax 020 7972 4179

Children – Child Health and Maternity

Head   Jonathan Stopes-Roe; Tel 020 7972 4336; Fax 020 7972
   4983

Social Care Policy – Children in Need 1

Head   Vacancy

Social Care Policy – Children in Need 2

Head   Janet Grauberg; Tel 020 7972 4355; Fax 020 7972
   4695

Clinical Director's Office – Children

National Clinical Director (Children)   Prof Albert Aynsley-
   Green; Tel 020 7972 4203; Fax 020 7972 4430

COS – Children

Head   Janice Shersby; Tel 020 7972 4067; Fax 020 7972
   4430

Children's National Service Framework

Project Manager   Claire Phillips; Tel 020 7972 4908; Fax 020
   7972 4430

Social Care Policy – National Care Standards Commission

Team Leader   Rob Dickman; Tel 020 7972 4048; Fax 020 7972
   4181
From April 2002, the Commission was made responsible
for regulating social care services and private and
voluntary healthcare. Please see Chapter 4 – Other
Government and Public Offices England.

Social Care Policy – Older People – Community Care

Head   Richard Campbell; Tel 020 7972 4027; Fax 020 7972
   4520

1

Social Care Policy – Older People (Quality and Standards)

Head   Helen Robinson; Tel 020 7972 4020; Fax 020 7972 4863
National Director for Older People's Services   Prof Ian Philp (Secondee); Tel 020 7972 3902; Fax 020 7972 4863

Social Care Modernisation

Head   Jonathan Stopes-Roe; Tel 020 7972 4336; Fax 020 7972 4983

Directorate of Corporate Affairs

Director (Corporate Affairs)   Hugh Taylor, CB; Tel 020 7210 5449
Head (Equality Strategy Group)   Elisabeth Al-Khalifa; Tel 020 7972 4488; Fax 020 7972 4739
Head (Information Services Group)   Dr Andrew Holt; Tel 020 7972 6557; Fax 020 7972 6534
Head (Medicines, Pharmacy and Industry Group)   Dr Felicity Harvey; Tel 020 7210 5522; Fax 020 7210 5660
Head (Career Management Group)   John Middleton; Tel 020 7972 5657; Fax 020 7972 5945
Deputy Head (Corporate Change Group)   Maggie King; Tel 020 7972 5841; Fax 020 7972 5945
Chief Pharmaceutical Officer   Dr Jim Smith; Tel 020 7210 5761; Fax 020 7210 5660
Deputy Chief Pharmacist   Jeanette Howe; Tel 020 7210 5048; Fax 020 7210 5086

Corporate Development Team

Head (Corporate Development and Private Office)   Olga Senior; Tel 020 7210 5164
Head (Finance and Business Planning)   Paul Stocks

Central Support Unit – Policy on Arm's Length Bodies

Branch Head   Peter Lemmey; Tel 020 7972 3776; Fax 020 7972 1097

Change Management and Development

Branch Head   Mark Collyer; Tel 020 7972 5812; Fax 020 7972 5891

Equality Strategy Group

Branch Head   Melanie Field
Branch Head   Barry Mussenden
Branch Head   Lydia Yee

Information Management

Branch Head   Linda Wishart; Tel 020 7972 5925; Fax 020 7972 5994

Clinical and Cost Effectiveness – MPI Group

Branch Head   Alan Angilley
Senior Medical Officer   Dr Peter Clappison
Special Projects Adviser   Charles Dobson

Pharmaceutical and Health Industries Sponsorship

Branch Head   Shaun Gallagher; Tel 020 7210 5659; Fax 020 7210 5471

Pharmacy and Prescriptions

Branch Head   Kevin Guiness; Tel 020 7210 4944; Fax 020 7210 5086

Pricing and Supply

Branch Head   Mike Brownlee; Tel 020 7210 5400; Fax 020 7210 5535

Legislation

Branch Head   Richard Carter; Tel 020 7210 5845; Fax 020 7210 5453

PCTs, Systems and Partnerships

Branch Head   Chris Dowse; Tel 0113 254 6572; Fax 0113 254 6599

Chief Nursing Officer's Directorate (Public Involvement, Nursing, Mental Health, Disability and Allied Health Professions)

Richmond House, 79 Whitehall, London SW1A 2NS
Quarry Hse, Quarry Hill, Leeds, West Yorkshire LS2 7UE
Chief Nursing Officer and Director (Nursing)   Sarah Mullally
Wellington Hse, 135–155 Waterloo Rd, London SE1 8UG; Tel 020 7210 5598; Fax 0113 254 6069
Assistant Chief Nursing Officer   Kate Billingham; Tel 020 7210 4946; Fax 0113 254 6075
Assistant Chief Nursing Officer   David Moore; Tel 0113 254 5206; Fax 0113 254 6075

Directorates of Health and Social Care

The four Directorates replace the previous eight Regional NHS Offices and provide the link between the Department of Health and the frontline NHS and Social Services. Their key responsibilities are performance managing the new Strategic Health Authorities, overseeing the development of the NHS and social care, improving public health and providing support to ministers.

At the time of publication, addresses for the Directorates were not confirmed and those addresses listed below are subject to change. Please check the Department of Health's website www.doh.gov.uk for up-to-date details.

North

Quarry Hse, Quarry Hill, Leeds, West Yorkshire LS2 7UE; URL www.doh.gov.uk/about/directorates; Tel 0191 301 1333; Fax 0191 301 1403
Director   Peter Garland
Geographical Responsibilities
Cumbria, Durham, Yorkshire, Lancashire, North Lincolnshire, Cheshire, Tyne and Wear, Teeside, Merseyside, Greater Manchester.

Midlands and the East

Quarry Hse, Quarry Hill, Leeds, West Yorkshire LS2 7UE; URL www.doh.gov.uk/about/directorates; Tel 0113 254 6200; Fax 0113 254 5530
Director   Richard Stockford (Acting)
Geographical Responsibilities
Derbyshire, Nottinghamshire, Lincolnshire (except far North), Leicestershire, Staffordshire, Shropshire, Worcestershire, Herefordshire, West Midlands, Warwickshire, Northamptonshire, Cambridgeshire, Norfolk, Suffolk, Bedfordshire, Hertfordshire, Essex.

South

Richmond Hse, 79 Whitehall, London SW1A 2NS; URL www.doh.gov.uk/about/directorates; Tel 020 7725 2547; Fax 020 7258 3908
Director   Ruth Carnall

Geographical Responsibilities
Cornwall, Devon, Somerset, Dorset, Wiltshire, Avon, Gloucestershire, Oxfordshire, Berkshire, Buckinghamshire, Hampshire, Surrey, Sussex, Kent.

London

Richmond Hse, 79 Whitehall, London SW1A 2NS;
URL www.doh.gov.uk/about/directorates; Tel 020 7725 2686; Fax 020 7258 0530
Director   John Bacon
Geographical Responsibilities
Metropolitan Boroughs of Greater London.

Directorate of Access and Choice

Quarry Hse and Richmond Hse
Director   Margaret Edwards; Tel 0113 254 6177; Fax 0113 254 5173
Divisional Head (Capacity and Choice)   Bob Ricketts; Tel 020 7210 5455; Fax 020 7210 5447
Branch Head (Programme Office)   Amanda Phillips; Tel 020 7210 5068
Branch Head (Access Delivery)   Mark Stevenson; Tel 0113 254 5214; Fax 0113 254 5188
Branch Head (Diagnostic Services)   Keith Smith; Tel 0113 254 6508
Branch Head (Primary Care Services)   Rob Webster; Tel 0113 254 5288; Fax 0113 254 6341
Branch Head (Emergency Care Strategy)   Mark Davies; Tel 0113 254 5930; Fax 0113 254 5405
Branch Head (NHS Direct National Programme)   Paul Jenkins; Tel 0113 254 5021; Fax 0113 254 6349
Branch Head (Elective Care and Booking)   Liz Fleck; Tel 0113 254 5199

Finance and Investment Directorate

Director (Finance)   Richard Douglas
Commercial Director   Ken Anderson; Tel 020 7972 2024
Gateway Review Team   Rob Smith; Tel 0113 254 5313
Internal Audit   Bill Burleigh; Tel 020 7972 2732
Branch Head (Accounting)   Jeff Tomlinson
Branch Head (Cash, Administration Costs and Financial Effectiveness)   Peter Kendall
Branch Head (Financial Management)   Alastair MacLellan
Branch Head (Capital Investment)   Peter Coates
Branch Head (NHS Resource Allocation)   Carl Vincent
Branch Head (Resource Planning and Acquisition)   Martin Campbell

Modernisation Agency

Richmond Hse, 79 Whitehall, London SW1A 2NS;
URL www.modernnhs.nhs.uk; Tel 0845 600 0700; Fax 020 7210 4904
Director   David Fillingham
Director (NHS Leadership Centre)   Penny Humphris
Director (Changing Workforce Programme)   Judy Hargadon
Associate Director (NHS Collaboratives)   Sarbjit Purewal
Head (Clinical Governance Support Team)   Prof Aidan Halligan
Head (National Primary Care Development Team)   Dr John Oldham
An Executive Agency. Its two main roles are: to modernise services, ensuring they meet the needs and convenience of patients as outlined in the NHS plan; to develop current and future NHS leaders and managers at all levels in the NHS, and all health professions.

National Patients Access Team

Division Head   Michael Scott; Tel 020 7210 5986; Fax 020 7210 4904

Analyst Team

Branch Head   Mike Davidge; Tel 0116 222 5100

Critical Care Team

Branch Head   Dr Valerie Day

Clinical Team

Branch Head   Vacancy

Demand Management Team

Branch Head   Vacancy

Idea Project

Branch Head   Ben Gowland, Consultant; Tel 020 7061 6778; Fax 020 7061 6788

Redesign Team

Branch Head   Dr Helen Bevan (Secondee); Tel 0116 222 5150; Fax 0116 222 5101

Visit Team

Branch Head   Nik Patten, Consultant; Tel 0116 222 5135; Fax 0116 222 5101

National Primary Care Development Team

Medical Director   Dr Ian Rutter; Tel 0161 237 2084; Fax 0161 237 2016

NHS Human Resources Directorate

Director (Human Resources)   Andrew Foster; Tel 020 7210 5907; Fax 020 7210 5854
Deputy Director (Human Resources)   Martin Staniforth; Tel 0113 254 6365; Fax 0113 254 5173
Deputy Director (Human Resources)   David Amos; Tel 0113 254 6169; Fax 0113 254 5173
Deputy Director (Human Resources) and Head (Learning and Personnel Development)   Prof Maggie Pearson; Tel 0113 254 6722; Fax 0113 254 5959

Corporate Development Team

Branch Head   Richard Mundon; Tel 0113 254 5730; Fax 0113 254 6356

Access to Learning and Initial Qualifications

Branch Head   Adrian Fields; Tel 0113 254 5687; Fax 0113 254 5670

Health Regulatory Bodies

Branch Head   Martin Sturges; Tel 0113 254 5673; Fax 0113 254 5795

Post Qualifications and Professional Development

Branch Head   Paul Loveland; Tel 0113 254 5856; Fax 0113 254 5958

Employment Policy

Branch Head   Debbie Mellor (OBE), (Acting); Tel 0113 254 6126; Fax 0113 254 5027

NHS Pay

Branch Head Ben Dyson; Tel 0113 254 5771; Fax 0113 254 5785

Strategic Medical Workforce

Senior Medical Officer Dr Julia Moore (Secondee); Tel 020 7210 5056; Fax 020 7210 5884

Workforce Development

Branch Head Tim Sands; Tel 0113 254 5829; Fax 0113 254 6350

Public Health and Clinical Quality Directorate

Director Prof Liam Donaldson
Director (NHS Plus/Healthy Workplace Team) Dr Kit Harling
Deputy Chief Medical Officer (Public Health) Vacancy
Head (Clinical Quality, Ethics and Genetics) Ann Stephenson
Head (Public Health Division) Prof Donald Nutbeam
Branch Head (Clinical Ethics and Human Tissue) Nick Dean
Branch Head (Genetics, Embryology and Assisted Conception) Liz Woodeson
Branch Head (Enquiries and Distinction Awards) Janet Walden
Branch Head (Clinical Quality) Patience Wilson
Branch Head (International Branch) Nick Boyd
Branch Head (Communicable Disease) Dr Graham Bickler
Branch Head (Sexual Health and Substance Misuse) Cathy Hamlyn
Branch Head (Inequalities and Public Health Strategy) Dr Deidre Cunningham
Branch Head (Cardiovascular Disease and Cancer Prevention) Imogen Sharp
Chief Scientist (Environment and Health) Dr David Harper

Research Analysis and Information Directorate

Director and Head (Research and Development Division) Sir John Pattison
Director (Statistics) Dr John Fox
Assistant Director (Research and Development) Dr Peter Greenaway
Under Secretary and Chief Economic Adviser Barry McCormick
Head (Information Policy Unit) Dr Peter Drury
Branch Head (Corporate Development Team) Anne Kauder
Branch Head (Economics – Leeds) Nick York
Branch Head (Operational Research – Leeds) Dr Geoff Royston
Branch Head (Economics – London) Richard Murray
Branch Head (Operational Research – London) Andre Hare
Branch Head (Information Governance) Phil Walker
Branch Head (Information Policy Unit – Programme Management) Mike Walker
Branch Head (Information Policy Unit – Social Care) Roger Staton
Branch Head (Information Policy Unit – Management Information) Dr Pam Westley
Branch Head (Information Policy Unit – Service Improvement) Lesley Hannam
Branch Head (Strategy and Corporate Affairs) Anne Kauder
Branch Head (Health Service Policy Research and Development) Gillian Parker
Branch Head (National Health Service Research Policy) Marc Taylor
Branch Head (Policy and Dissemination – Population and Lifestyles) Patsy Bailey
Branch Head (NHS Workforce and General Practice) Andy Sutherland

Branch Head (Statistics – Social Care – Population Groups and Surveys) Ann Custance
Statistician (Dental, Optical, Pharmacy and Prescriptions) Jim Stokoe
Statistician (Public Health – Diseases – Hospital Care and Quality) Richard Willmer

Specialist Health Services Directorate

Director and Deputy Chief Medical Officer Prof Aidan Halligan
Head (Primary Care) Vacancy
Head (Prison Health) John Boyington
Head (Specialist Services) David Hewlett
Branch Head (NHS Cancer Services) Stephen Waring
Branch Head (Cardiac Services) Gavin Larner (Acting)
Branch Head (Evidence) Dr Jennie Carpenter
Branch Head (Diabetes, Renal and Transplants NSF Co-ordination) Dr Gillian Chapman
Taskforce Manager (Coronary Heart Disease and Cancer) Heather Gwynn
Chief Dental Officer Prof Raman Bedi
Senior Dental Officer Chris Audrey

Prison Health

Branch Head (Public Health) Dr Mary Piper; Tel 020 7972 4952; Fax 020 7972 4881
Branch Head (Mental Health Development – Prison Health Taskforce) Sheila Foley; Tel 020 7972 4568; Fax 020 7972 4881
Branch Head (Nursing) Richard Bradshaw; Tel 020 7972 4767; Fax 020 7972 4881

Medical and Pharmaceutical Development Project

Branch Head Dr Cliff Howells (Secondee); Tel 020 7972 4568; Fax 020 7972 4882

Dental and Optical

Branch Head Almas Mithani; Tel 020 7972 3978; Fax 020 7972 3999

Solicitor's Office

Solicitor Marilynne Morgan, CB
Director (Legal Services) Greer Kerrigan

Executive Agencies

Health Protection Agency

11th Fl, The Adelphi, 1–11 John Adam St, London WC2N 6HT; URL www.hpa.org.uk; Tel 020 7339 1300
The Health Protection Agency is a new national organisation for England and Wales established on 1st April 2003. It is dedicated to protecting people□s health and reducing the impact of infectious diseases, chemical hazards, poisons and radiation hazards. It brings together the expertise of health and scientific professionals working in public health, communicable disease, emergency planning, infection control, laboratories, poisons, chemical, and radiation hazards.

Medicines and Healthcare Products Regulatory Agency (MHRA)

Market Towers, 1 Nine Elms La, London SW8 5NQ; URL www.mhra.gov.uk; Tel (Central Enquiry Point, weekdays 0900–1700) 020 7273 0000; (Other times) 020 7210 3000; Fax 020 7273 0353
Executive Chairman Prof Breckeridge

The role of The Medicines and Healthcare Products Regulatory Agency (MHRA) is to protect and promote public health and patient safety by ensuring that medicines, healthcare products and medical equipment meet appropriate standards of safety, quality, performance and effectiveness, and are used safely.
The MHRA was formed from a merger of the Medicines Control Agency (MCA) and the Medical Devices Agency (MDA) on 1 April 2003.

NHS Estates (NHSE)

1 Trevelyan Sq, Boar La, Leeds, West Yorkshire LS1 6AE; URL www.nhsestates.gov.uk; Tel 0113 254 7070
Chief Executive Peter Wearmouth

NHS Pensions Agency (NHSPA)

Hesketh Hse, 200–220 Broadway, Fleetwood, Lancashire FY7 8LG; URL www.nhspa.gov.uk; Tel (Enquiries) 01253 774890
Chief Executive Pat Corless
Administration and provision of pensions and benefits for NHS employees in England and Wales

NHS Purchasing and Supply Agency (NHSPASA)

Premier Hse, 60 Caversham Rd, Reading RG1 7EB; URL www.pasa.doh.gov.uk; Tel 0118 980 8600
Chief Executive D. Eaton

DEPARTMENT FOR WORK AND PENSIONS

Richmond Hse, 79 Whitehall, London SW1A 2NS; URL www.dwp.gov.uk;
E-mail ministers@ms41.dwp.gov.uk; Tel 020 7238 0800; (Parliamentary Branch for all Ministers) 020 7238 0715; Fax 020 7238 0831
Secretary of State (Department for Work and Pensions) The Rt Hon Andrew Smith, MP
Minister of State for Work Des Browne, MP
Parliamentary Under Secretary for Work Chris Pond, MP
Minister for Pensions Malcolm Wicks, MP
Parliamentary Under Secretary of State, Minister (Children and the Family) The Rt Hon Baroness Hollis of Heigham

Office of Chief Medical Adviser, Medical Policy and Corporate Medical Group

The Adelphi, 1–11 John Adam St, London WC2N 6HT; Tel 020 7962 8000
Chief Medical Adviser and Medical Director Dr Mansel Aylward

Law and Special Policy Group

The Adelphi, 1–11 John Adam St, London WC2N 6HT; Tel 020 7962 8000
Solicitor Marilynne Morgan, CB;
E-mail mmorgan@nct001.dss.gov.uk

Human Resources Directorate

Director K. White

Information and Analysis Directorate

Director (SCS) David Stanton
Director Information Centre (SCS) N. Dyson

Chief Statistician (SCS) F. Johnson
Senior Economic Adviser (SCS) G. Harris
Senior Economic Adviser (SCS) T. Huddleston

Finance Directorate

Director (SCS) J. Codling

Communications Directorate

Director (Communications) (SCS) Simon MacDowall
Deputy Director (SCS) (Grade 6) Ms A. Hall
Head (Media Relations) (SCS) Ms S. Dodd
Head (Corporate Communications) (SCS) K. Young
Head (Marketing Communications) (SCS) S. O'Neil

Pensions and Disability Directorate

Group Director Paul Gray

Working Age Group

Director (SCS) Ursula Brennan
Director (Change) (SCS) S. Hewitt
Director (Strategy) (SCS) R. Devereux
Director (Employment) (SCS) M. Richardson

EXECUTIVE AGENCIES

Appeals Service

Whittington Hse, 19–30 Alfred Pl, London WC1E 7LW
Chief Executive Norman Egon (Acting)

Child Support Agency

Longbenton, Newcastle upon Tyne, Northumberland NE99 1YX
Chief Executive Doug Smith
Policy on child support and liable relatives.

Jobcentre Plus

Chief Executive David Anderson

The Pension Service

Chief Executive Alexis Cleveland

BUSINESS UNITS

Disability and Carers' Service

Warbreck Hse, Warbreck Hill, Blackpool, Lancashire FY2 0YE;
E-mail dbu-customer-service@ms24.dss.gov.uk;
Tel 01253 337 793; Fax 01253 337 794
Director John Sumner
Manager (Customer Service Group) Graham Heard;
E-mail grahamheard1@dwp.gsi.gov.uk

Benefit Enquiry Line

Victoria Hse, Ormskirk Rd, Preston, Lancashire PR1 2QP;
Tel 0800 88 22 00
Manager Martin Moore

Carer's Allowance

Palatine Hse, Lancaster Rd, Preston, Lancashire PR1 1HB;
Tel 01253 856123; Fax 01772 899354
Director Kathy Goodwin

Disability Benefits Centres (DBC)

Bootle DBC

St. Martins Hse, Stanley Precinct, Bootle, Merseyside L69
9BN; Tel 0151 934 6000; 0151 934 6185; Fax 0151 934 6294
Manager   Joy Dunne

Bristol DBC

Government Bldgs, Flowers Hill, Brislington, Bristol,
Gloucestershire BS4 5LA; Tel 0117 971 8311; Fax 0117 971
8301
Manager   John Puplett

Edinburgh DBC

Argyle Hse, 3 Lady Lawson St, Edinburgh, Midlothian
EH3 9SH; Tel 0131 222 5075; Fax 0131 222 5472
Manager   Ian Rodger

Glasgow DBC

Corunna Hse, 29 Cadogan St, Glasgow G2 7AB; Tel 0141
249 3500; Fax 0141 249 3575
Manager   Stan Shearer

Leeds DBC

Government Bldgs, Otley Rd, Leeds, West Yorkshire
LS16 5PU; Tel 0113 230 9000; Fax 0113 230 9000 ext 3231
Manager   Fiona Murie

Manchester DBC

Albert Bridge Hse East, Bridge St, Manchester M60 9DA;
E-mail customerservices@dwp.gsi.gov.uk; Tel 0161 831
2000; Fax 0161 831 2001
Manager   Mike Hulley

Midlands (Birmingham) DBC

Five Ways Complex, Islington Row, Middleway,
Birmingham, West Midlands B15 1SL; Tel 0121 626 3330;
Fax 0121 626 3093
Manager (Operations)   Mike Andrews
Manager (Business Development)   Sheila Latchford

Newcastle DBC

Arden Hse, Regent Centre, Newcastle upon Tyne, Tyne and
Wear NE3 3JN; Tel 0191 223 3000; Fax 0191 223 3000
ext 3076/3099
Manager   Tim Mazzuchi

Sutton DBC

Sutherland Hse, 29–37 Brighton Rd, Sutton, Surrey
SM2 5AN; Tel 020 8652 6000; Fax 020 8652 6166
Manager   Jane Tatum

Wales DBC

Block 3, Government Bldgs, St. Agnes' Rd, Gabalfa, Cardiff
CF14 4YJ; E-mail customerservices@dwp.gsi.gov.uk;
Tel 029 2058 6002; Fax 029 2058 6899
Manager   Adrian Moore

Wembley DBC

Olympic Hse, Olympic Way, Wembley, Greater London
HA9 0DL; Tel 020 8795 8400; Fax 020 8795 8764
Manager   Alexandra Hassani

Child Benefit Centre

Waterview Pk, Manadarin Way, Washington, Tyne and
Wear NE38 8QA; E-mail child-benefit@dwp.gsi.gov.uk
Director   Jennifer Ritchie, OBE

The Pension Service

1

Tyneview Pk, Whitley Rd, Newcastle upon Tyne, Tyne and
Wear NE98 1BA; URL www.thepensionservice.gov.uk
Chief Executive   Alexis Cleveland
Room 123 Richmond Hse, 79 Whitehall, London
SW1A 2NS; Tel 020 7238 0890
Director (Human Resources and Customer Service)
Indi Seehra
Room 333, Adelphi, 1–11 John Adam St, London
WC2N 6HT; Tel 020 7712 2835
Director (Pensions Finance Team)   Paul Greening
GW43 Quarry Hse, Quarry Hill, Leeds, West Yorkshire
LS2 7UA; Tel 0113 232 4338
Director (Performance)   Phil Bartlett
4C18 Quarry Hse, Quarry Hill, Leeds, West Yorkshire
LS2 7UA; Tel 0113 232 4346
Director (Change Programme)   George McCorkell
60A Peel Pk, Brunel Way, Blackpool, Lancashire FY4 5ES;
Tel 01253 688 850
Chief Operating Officer   Charlie McKinnon
Ground Fl, Corunna Hse, 39 Cadogan St, Glasgow, North
Lanarkshire G2 7FS; Tel 0141 249 3826
In April 2002, The Pension Service was created as a new
public service agency to replace those parts of the previous
Benefits Agency (now disbanded) which dealt specifically
with pensions. Regional offices have been set up to
incorporate the old Benefit Agency's pension-related
services.

North West

Aldine Hse, New Bailey St, Salford, Lancashire M60 9HP;
Tel 01925 401887
Director   Lee Brown

South West

Courtney Hse, Rydon La, Exeter, Devon EX2 5AZ;
Tel 01392 606300
Director   Graham Carter

Wales

Government Bldgs, St. Agnes Rd, Gabalfa, Cardiff
CF14 4YF; Tel 02920 586158
Director   Vivien Hopkins

East and East Midlands

Crown Bldg, 40 Chapel Street South, Colchester, Essex
CO2 7AZ; Tel 01206 288147
Director   Bernie Keay

North East Yorkshire and Humberside

Jubilee Hse, 33–41 Park Pl, Leeds, West Yorkshire LS1 2R;
Tel 0113 285 8709
Director   John Myers

West Midlands

St. Stephens Hse, Prospect Hill, Redditch, Worcestershire
B97 4DL; Tel 01527 590170
Director   Jenni Ord

London

236 Grays Inn Rd, London WC1X 8HL; Tel 020 7211 4361
Director   Susan Park

South East

73 London Rd, Redhill, Surrey RH1 1LP; Tel 01737 774024
Director   Barry Cox

Scotland

Corunna Hse, 39 Cadogan St, Glasgow, North Lanarkshire
G2 7SS

Jobcentre Plus

Caxton Hse, Tothill St, London SW1H 9NA;
URL www.jobcentreplus.gov.uk; Tel 020 7273 3000
Chief Executive David Anderson
Chief Operating Officer Lesley Strathie
Director (Performance and Product Management)
Mark Fisher
Director (Jobcentre Plus Implementation Project)
Jeremy Groombridge
Director (Human Resources) Jane Saint
Director (Business Design) Stephen Hewitt
Director (Modernisation and Strategy) Vacancy
Director (Employer Services) Mark Grimshaw
Director (Finance) Peter Ward
In April 2002, Jobcentre Plus was created as part of the
Department for Work and Pensions as a new public service
agency, replacing the previous Employment Service and
part of the Benefits Agency. All Jobcentres and Social
Security offices (previously run by the Employment Service
and Benefits Agency) are being integrated into Jobcentre
Plus offices. Integration of all offices is to be completed
over the next four years. Listed below are details of the
regional office structure. Details of individual sites will be
announced during the integration process by the
Department for Work and Pensions. Please visit its website
www.dwp.go.uk for further details.

REGIONAL OFFICES

East of England

Beaufort Hse, Crown Gate, Harlow, Essex CM20 1NA;
Tel 01279 693083
Director Nicola Bastin

London

236 Grays Inn Rd, London WC1X 8HL; Tel 020 7211 3000
Director Alan R. Brown, CBE

North East

Broadacre Hse, Market Street East, Newcastle upon Tyne,
Northumberland NE1 6HQ; Tel 0191 211 4200
Director Val Curran

North West

Ontario Hse, 2 Furness Quay, Salford, Greater Manchester
M5 2XZ; Tel 0161 873 1000
Director Terry Moran

East Midlands

Newton Hse, 46 Maid Marian Way, Nottingham NG1 6GG;
Tel 0115 989 5700
Director Mel Groves

Scotland

Argyle Hse, 2 Lady Lawson St, Edinburgh, Midlothian
EH3 9SD; Tel 0131 229 9191
Director Vacancy

South East

236 Grays Inn Rd, London WC1X 8HL; Tel 020 7211 3000
Director Neil Couling

South West

The Pithay, Bristol BS1 2NQ; Tel 0117 945 6000
Director Diana Ross

Wales

Companies Hse, Crown Hse, Maindy, Cardiff CF14 3UW;
Tel 029 2038 8588
Director Sheelagh Keyse

West Midlands

Duchess Pl, 2 Hagley Rd, Birmingham, Warwickshire
B16 8NS; Tel 0121 452 5200
Director Rosemary Thew

Yorkshire and the Humber

Jubilee Hse, 33–41 Park Pl, Leeds, West Yorkshire LS1 2RE;
Tel 0113 285 8500
Director Vince Robinson

DEPARTMENT FOR EDUCATION AND SKILLS

Sanctuary Bldgs, Gt Smith St, London SW1P 3BT;
URL www.dfes.gov.uk; E-mail info@dfes.gsi.gov.uk;
Tel (Public Enquiries) 0870 000 2288; (Switchboard) 0870
001 2345
Secretary of State (Education and Skills) The Rt Hon Charles
Clarke, MP; E-mail sec-of-state.ps@dfes.gsi.gov.uk;
Tel 020 7925 5829; Fax 020 7925 6995
Minister of State (School Standards) David Miliband, MP;
E-mail miliband.ps@dfes.gsi.gov.uk; Tel 020 7925 6254;
Fax 020 7925 6996
Minister of State (Children) Margaret Hodge, MP, MBE;
E-mail hodge.ps@dfes.gsi.gov.uk; Tel 020 7925 6951;
Fax 020 7925 5011
*Minister of State (Lifelong Learning, Further and Higher
Education)* Alan Johnson, MP
Parliamentary Under Secretary of State (Sure Start)
Baroness Cathy Ashton of Upholland, MP;
E-mail ashton.ps@dfes.gsi.gov.uk; Tel 020 7925 6389;
Fax 020 7925 6688
*Parliamentary Under Secretary of State (Young People and
Adult Skills)* Ivan Lewis, MP;
E-mail lewis.ps@dfes.gsi.gov.uk; Tel 020 7925 6340;
Fax 020 7925 5151
Parliamentary Under Secretary of State (Schools)
Stephen Twigg, MP; E-mail twigg.ps@dfes.gsi.gov.uk;
Tel 020 7925 6343; Fax 020 7925 6994
General email format: <firstname>.<lastname>@dfes.gov.uk
The Department for Education and Skills aims to help build
a competitive economy and inclusive society by: creating
opportunities for everyone to develop their learning;
releasing potential in people to make the most of
themselves; achieving excellence in standards of education
and levels of skills. The Department's objectives are: to give
children an excellent start in education so that they have a
better foundation for future learning; enable all young
people to develop and equip themselves with the skills,
knowledge and personal qualities needed for life and work;
to encourage and enable adults to learn, improve their
skills and enrich their lives.

Strategy and Communications Directorate

Tel (General Enquiry Number) 020 7925 5855; Fax 020 7925
6599
Director Michael Stevenson

1

Head (Press Office)   Trevor Cook
Head (News)   D.J. Collins
Divisional Manager (Corporate Communications)
   Yasmin Diamond
Divisional Manager (Publicity)   John Ross
Divisional Manager (Regional Policy)   Mohammad Haroon
Divisional Manager (e-learning Strategy Unit)
   Diana Laurillard
To ensure that strategic thinking and excellent
communications are at the heart of the Department's policy
development and delivery.

Schools Directorate (SD)

Director General   Peter Housden
Divisional Manager (Strategy and Performance)
   Christina Bienkowska
Head (School Communications Unit)   Richard Graham

Secondary Education Group

Director   Peter Wanless
Divisional Manager (School Diversity)   Susanna Todd
Divisional Manager (Academies Division)   Neil Flint
Divisional Manager (School Improvement and Excellence)
   Barnaby Shaw
Divisional Manager (London Challenge Programme)
   Jon Coles

Standards and Effectiveness Unit

Director   David Hopkins
Director (Innovation Unit)   Mike Gibbons
Divisional Manager (Pupil Standards)   Andrew McCully
Divisional Manager (Leadership and Teacher Development)
   Richard Harrison
Divisional Manager (Transforming Standards Advisers)
   David Woods
Divisional Manager (School Performance and Accountability)
   Nick Baxter

Resources, Infrastructure and Governance Group

Director   Stephen Crowne
*Divisional Manager (School Admissions, Organisation and
   Governance)*   Caroline Macready
Divisional Manager (School and LEA Funding)
   Andrew Wye
Divisional Manager (Schools Capital and Buildings)
   Sally Brooks
Divisional Manger (Schools Building and Design Unit)
   Mukund Patel

School Workforce Unit

Director   Stephen Kershaw
Local Implementation   Richard Blows
Local Standards Policy   Robert Woods

Primary Education and eLearning Group

Links with both Schools Directorate and Youth Directorate.
Director   Helen Williams
Divisional Manager (Curriculum)   Mela Watts
Divisional Manager (ICT in Schools)   Doug Brown
*Divisional Manager (PE and School Sport and Club Links
   Project)*   Matthew Conway (Joint Department for
   Education and Skills and Department for Culture, Media
   and Sport)

Children and Families

Director   Peter Makeham (Acting)
Divisional Manager (Children's Bill)   Anne Jackson
Manager (Transition Team)   Jeanette Pugh

Sure Start Unit (Cross Government Unit)

Links also with Department for Work and Pensions.
Level 2, Caxton Hse, Tothill St, London SW1H 9NA;
   URL www.surestart.gov.uk; Tel 020 7273 4830; Fax 020
   7273 5182
Director   Naomi Eisenstadt
Divisional Manager (Strategy)   Tamara Finkelstein
Divisional Manager (Quality and Standards)
   Alan Cranston
Divisional Manager (Programme Delivery Central)
   Jackie Doughty
Divisional Manager (Infrastructure)   Nick Tooze
Contact the unit directly for Sure Start programmes in your
area.

Connexions Service National Unit

Chief Executive   Anne Weinstock
Divisional Manager (Strategy and Communications)
   Jeanette Pugh
Divisional Manager (Operational Policy)
   Gordon McKenzie
Divisional Manager (Delivery and Quality)   Steve Jackson
*Divisional Manager (Activities for Young People and
   Volunteering)*   Jane Haywood

Children and Families Group

Director   Sheila Scales (Acting)
Divisional Manager (Schools Plus)   Michael Phipps
Divisional Manager (Ethnic Minority Achievement Project)
   Annabel Burns
Divisional Manager (Special Educational Needs)   Ann Gross
Divisional Manager (Improving Behaviour and Attendance)
   Alex Sevier
Divisional Manager (Improving Behaviour and Attendance)
   Ian Whitehouse
Divisional Manager (Pupil Support and Independent Schools)
   Penny Jones

Children's Group

Head   Janice Shersby
Divisional Manager (Children in Need 1)   Vacancy
Divisional Manager (Children in Need 2)   Janet Grauberg
*Divisional Manager (Placement, Permanence and Children's
   Trust)*   David Holmes

Public and Private Rights

Director   Amanda Finlay
Divisional Manager (Children and Families)   Bruce Clark
Divisional Manager (Public Law)   Sally Field

Teenage Pregnancy Unit

Head   Cathy Hamlyn

Family and Policy Unit

Divisional Manager   Ruth Kennedy

Strategy and Policy

Director   Tom Jeffery (Acting)
Divisional Manager (Green Paper)   Ravi Gurumurthy
Team Manager (Change and Bill)   Vacancy

Children and Young People's Unit

Director   Althea Efunshile
Deputy Director (National Policy)   Sue Lewis
Divisional Manager (Local Partnerships)   Kathy Bundred
Divisional Manager (Resource and Planning)
   Janette Sinclair

The Children's Fund
The Children's Fund is the largest programme being delivered by the Children and Young People's Unit. It is targeted at 5–13 year olds and is a key part of the Government's strategy to tackle disadvantages and inequalities, which derive from child poverty and social exclusion. The Fund works closely with the Government Offices for the Regions. Contact the Unit directly for local services in your area.

Lifelong Learning Directorate

Director General Janice Shiner
Divisional Manager (Strategy and Funding) John Temple
(Also supports the Youth Directorate)
Divisional Manager (Prisoners' Learning and Skills Unit)
Alan Clarke

Adult Basic Skills Strategy Unit

Director Susan Pember
Deputy Director (Planning and Delivery) Mark Dawe
Deputy Director (Standards and Achievement)
Barry Brooks

Adult Learning Group

Director Stephen Marston
Divisional Manager (Access to Learning for Adults)
Tim Down
Divisional Manager (Lifelong Learning and Technologies)
Margaret Bennett
Divisional Manager (Skills for Employment)
Simon Perryman
Divisional Manager (Workplace Learning) Hugh Tollyfield
Divisional Manager (ILA Project) Vacancy
Divisional Manager (Review of Funding of Adult Learning)
Madeleine Durie
Divisional Manager (ITB Review) Jane Mark-Lawson

Student Finance Group

Director Nick Saunders (Acting)
Divisional Manager (Student Finance Policy) Peter Swift
Divisional Manager (Student Finance Delivery) Ian Morrison
(Acting)
Divisional Manager (Student Finance Modernisation)
Noreen Graham
Divisional Manager (HE Bill Team) Lesley Longstone
HE Programme Manager (Delivery and Strategy Overview)
Chris Barnham
Adviser (HE) Nick Sanders

Higher Education Strategy and Implementation Group

Director Michael Hipkins (Acting)
Divisional Manager (Foundation Degrees, Employability and Progression Division) Steve Geary
Divisional Manager (Quality and Participation)
Paul Cohen
Divisional Manager (Funding and Research) Rachel Green
Divisional Manager (Access and Modernisation)
Martin Williams

Learning Delivery and Standards Group

Director Peter Lauener
Divisional Manager (FE Strategy) Peter Mucklow
Divisional Manager (Learning and Skills Partnerships Unit)
James Turner
Divisional Manager (Provider Plus) Eric Galvin
Divisional Manager (Financial and Management Systems Review of the LSC) Linda Dale

Standards Unit

Director (Teaching and Learning) Jane Williams
Divisional Manager (Workforce Development)
Heidi Adcock
Divisional Manager (Teaching and Learning and Success for All Programme Management) David Taylor

Qualifications and Young People

Director Rob Hull
Divisional Manager (Qualifications for Work) Sara Marshall
Divisional Manager (School and College Qualifications)
Celia Johnson
Divisional Manager (Young People Learner Support)
Trevor Fellowes
Divisional Manager (Young People's Policy) Alan Davies
Divisional Manager (Youth Co-ordination) Carol Hunter
Divisional Manager (Examinations System) Jane Benham
Divisional Manager (Review of Post-qualifications Admissions to Higher Education) Linda Dale

Joint International Unit (Links with Department for Work and Pensions)

This Unit links with both the Department for Work and Pensions and the Department for Education and Skills.
Director Clive Tucker
Divisional Manager (European Union) Vacancy
Divisional Manager (European Social Fund) Jane Evans
Divisional Manager (International Relations) Marie Niven

Legal Adviser's Office

Legal Adviser Jonathan Jones
Divisional Manager (Lifelong Learning and School Workforce)
Dudley Aries
Divisional Manager (Effectiveness and Admissions)
Francis Clarke
Divisional Manager (Governance and Finance)
Patrick Kilgarriff
Divisional Manager (Special Needs and Curriculum)
Nic Ash
Divisional Manager (Equality, Establishment and EC)
Carol Davies
Divisional Manager (Higher Education and Student Support)
Carola Geist-Divver
To provide legal advice to the Department.

Corporate Services and Development Directorate

Director General Susan Thomas
Divisional Manager (Leadership and Personnel)
Graham Archer
Divisional Manager (Change) Anne-Marie Lawlor
Divisional Manager (Learning Academy) Mike Daly
Divisional Manager (Information Services) Colin Moore
Divisional Manager (Commercial Services) Paul Neill
Divisional Manager (Equality and Diversity Unit)
Jan Stockwell
Divisional Manager (e-Delivery) Katie Driver

Finance and Analytical Services Directorate (FASD)

Director General Ruth Thompson (Acting)
Divisional Manager (Internal Audit) Suzanne Orr
Divisional Manager (Programme and Project Management Unit)
Ray Hincliffe

Finance

Director   Ruth Thompson
Divisional Manager (Finance Strategy)   Peter Houten
Divisional Manager (Corporate Planning and Performance)
   Marion Maddox
Divisional Manager (Financial Accounting)   Peter Connor,
   CBE

Analytical Services

Director   Paul Johnson

Divisional Manager (Schools 1)   Audrey Brown
Divisional Manager (Schools 2)
   Richard Bartholomew
Divisional Manager (Higher Education)
   Karen Hancock
Divisional Manager (Adults)   Bob Butcher
Divisional Manager (Central Economics and International)
   John Elliott
*Divisional Manager (Qualifications, Pupil Assessment and
   Information Technology)*   Malcolm Britton
Divisional Manager (Central Economics and International)
   Steve Leman

1

The Law

- **Home Office**
- **Police, Prisons and Remand Centres**
  Police Forces
  HM Prisons
  HM Young Offender Institutions
  Remand Centres
- **National Probation Service**
  Approved Premises
- **Magistrates' Courts and Justices' Clerks**
- **County Courts**
- **Northern Ireland Magistrates' and County Courts**
- **Sheriff Courts Scotland**
- **Crown Prosecution Service**
- **Children and Family Court Advisory and Support Service**
- **Children's Panels – Scotland**
- **Scottish Children's Reporter Administration**

The Law

HOME OFFICE

50 Queen Anne's Gate, London SW1H 9AT;
  URL www.homeoffice.gov.uk;
  E-mail public.enquiries@homeoffice.gsi.gov.uk; Tel 0870
  000 1585; Fax 020 7273 2065
Secretary of State (Home Office)   Rt. Hon. David Blunkett,
  MP
*Minister of State (Crime Reduction, Policing and
  Community Safety, Young People)*   Rt. Hon. Hazel Blears,
  MP
*Parliamentary Under Secretary of State (Organised and
  International crime, Anti-Drugs Co-ordination and
  International and European Issues)*   Caroline Flint,
  MP
Minister of State (Criminal Justice and Law Reform)
  Baroness Scotland, QC
*Parliamentary Under Secretary of State (Correctional
  Services and Reducing Re-offending)*   Paul Goggins,
  MP
*Minister of State (Citizenship, Immigration and
  Counter-Terrorism)*   Rt. Hon. Beverley Hughes,
  MP
*Parliamentary Under Secretary of State (Race Equality,
  Community Policy, and Civil Renewal)*
  Fiona MacTaggart, MP

Community Policy Directorate

Contact   C.E.C. Sinclair

Animals, Procedures and Coroners' Unit

Contact   T. Cobley; Tel (Enquiries) 020 7273 2198
Functions
Coroners; local legislation; animal procedures; animal
welfare, coroners; removal of human remains; cremation
policy; cremation certificates; burial matters; local acts;
private bills.

Race Equality Unit

Director   Mike Boyle, SCS; Tel (Enquiries) 020 7273 3047
Functions
Co-ordination of policies affecting ethnic minorities;
Section II grants to local authorities; legislation against
racial discrimination; liaison with the Commission for
Racial Equality; national and local community relations
issues, reduction of racial disadvantages, promotion of
ethnic minority enterprise; inner cities policy and
co-ordination.

Crime Reduction and Community Safety Group

Director General   John Lyon; Tel 020 7273 3194
Director (Crime)   Jim Daniell; Tel 020 7273 3676
Director (Policing Policy)   Stephen Rimmer
Director (Police Standards)   Kevin Bond
Inspectorate of Constabulary (Chief Inspector)
  Sir Keith Povey, QPM

Criminal Policy Group

Director (SCS)   D. Cooke
Director (SCS)   S. Street

HM Inspectorate of Probation

Chief Probation Inspector   G.W. Smith, CBE
Assistant Chief Probation Inspector   J. Kuipers;
  Tel (Enquiries) 020 7273 3955
Deputy Chief Probation Inspector   J. Furniss
Assistant Chief Probation Officer (Manchester)
  Frances Flaxington

London Office

50 Queen Anne's Gate, London SW1H 9AT; Tel 020 7273
  3906

Juvenile Offenders Unit

Director   Simon Hickson (SCS); Tel 020 7273 2685
Functions
Development and provision of secure training centres
(STCs) and attendance centres (ACs); secure training
orders. Juvenile policy, particularly sentencing.
Responsibility for youth court procedures, youth offending
teams and the National Youth Justice Board.

Mental Health Unit

Contact   Fiona Spencer; Tel (Enquiries) 020 273 2662
Contact   Elizabeth Moody
Functions
Mental health section: casework on restricted patients;
policy on mentally disordered offenders; legislation –
Mental Health Act 1983 and Criminal Procedure (Insanity
and Unfitness to Plead) Act 1991; mental health review
tribunals; prison transfers to hospital; remission of patients
to prison; life sentence prisoners in hospital; liaison with
regional health authorities; prison transfer statistics; leave
for and recall of restricted patients; victims; advisory board
on restricted patients.

National Probation Service

Director Eithne Wallis; Tel (Enquiries) 020 7217 0651
Functions
The unit exercises on behalf of the Home Secretary his responsibilities for the probation service in England and Wales; policy on orders of the courts for supervision by the probation service (probation orders, supervision orders, community service orders etc) and for social enquiry and welfare reports; statutory powers and organisation; pay and other conditions of service; finance and manpower recruitment and training; day centres, hostels and other facilities for offenders and ex-offenders in the community; probation officers in prison service establishments; after-care of offenders; grants to voluntary bodies for the rehabilitation of offenders and marriage guidance.

Justice and Victims Unit

Contact Jane Furniss; Tel (Enquiries) 020 7273 3063
Functions
Among others, review and overseeing of the Criminal Injuries Compensation Scheme (CICS); support for victims of crime; compensation orders. Prosecution policy (including policy issues relating to the relationship between the police, Crown Prosecution Service and the courts); cautioning; bail; custody time limits; plea bargaining; magistrates' courts procedure.

Sentencing and Offences Unit

Contact Debbie Grice; Tel 020 7273 2448
Functions
Among others sentencing; monitoring courts' sentencing practice; maximum penalties for specific offences; capital and corporal punishment; policy on mandatory life sentence for murder. Scrutiny of proposals to create new offences; decriminalisation; blasphemy; extra-territoriality; general questions about the formation of offences; offences of entering and remaining on property; treason and related offences; conspiracies relating to morals and public decency.

Organised Crime, Drugs and International Group

Director General Stephen Boys-Smith
Director (Organised Crime) Kate Collins
Director (International) Peter Storr
Director (Drugs Strategy) Sue Killen
European and International Unit (EIU) Lesley Pallett
Finance and Planning Unit (FPU) Jim Bradley

Judicial Co-operation Unit

Clive Welsh; Tel (Enquiries) 020 7273 3481
Functions
The extradition of fugitives from justice; confiscation of the proceeds of crime; operation of the UK Central Authority; and European Union, Council of Europe, Commonwealth and United Nations matters related to international judicial co-operation.

Immigration and Nationality Directorate

Apollo Hse, 36 Wellesley Rd, Croydon, Surrey CR9 3RR;
Tel 020 8760 3426
Director General Bill Jeffery
Deputy Director General (Operations) Dr Chris Mace, SCS
Deputy Director General (Policy) Peter Wrench, SCS
Deputy Director General (Operations) Robin Halward

Immigration and Nationality Policy

11th Fl, Apollo Hse, Croydon, Surrey CR9 3RR
Director (Asylum and Appeals Policy Directorate)
Felicity Clarkson; Tel (Enquiries) 020 8760 3423
Director (Nationality, Immigration and Asylum Bill Team)
Bob Eagle; Tel (Enquiries) 020 8760 8601
Director (Integrated Casework Directorate) Chris Hudson;
Tel (Enquiries) 020 8760 8149
Director (Immigration and Nationality Policy Directorate)
Brian Caffarey,
Director (International Policy Directorate) Jenny Rumble
Director (New Policy Directorate) Colin Allars
Director (National Asylum Support Services)
Freda Chaloner
Functions
Immigration and control of foreign nationals; UK passport holders and Commonwealth citizens; immigration rules and appeals. Nationality matters including the acquisition of citizenship by registration and naturalisation.

Prison Service

Headquarters, Cleland Hse, Page St, London SW1P 4LN;
URL www.hmprisonservice.gov.uk;
E-mail phil.wheatley@hmps.gsi.gov.uk; Tel 020 7217 6777; Fax 020 7217 6961
Director-General (Prison Service) Phil Wheatley
Aims
Effective execution of the sentences of the courts so as to reduce reoffending and protect the public.
Objectives
Protect the public by holding in custody those committed by the courts in a safe, decent, and healthy environment; reduce crime by providing constructive regimes which address offending behaviour, improve educational and work skills; promote law-abiding behaviour in custody and after release.

Director General Support Unit

Tel (Enquiries) 020 7217 6591
Head of Group Ken Everett
Secretariat to Prison Service Strategy and Management Boards; co-ordination of legal services; co-ordination of Ministerial briefing; parliamentary work and Director General's correspondence.

Media Relations

Tel 020 7273 4543; 020 7273 8176; Fax 020 7273 0485
Head of Group Hannah Gardiner
Deputy Director-General Peter Atherton; Tel 020 7217 6397

Area Managers' Offices

Eastern Area

Responsible for the following prisons: Bedford, Blundeston, Chelmsford, Highpoint (male), Hollesley Bay, Littlehey, The Mount, Norwich, Wayland.
Area Manager Danny McAllistar
c/o HMP Norwich, Knox Rd, Norwich, Norfolk NR1 4LU;
Tel 01603 708828; Fax 01603 708602

East Midlands (North) Area

Responsible for the following prisons: Lincoln, North Sea Camp, Nottingham, Ranby, Sudbury, Whatton.
Area Manager Steve Wagstaffe
c/o HMP Ranby, Training Unit, Retford, Nottinghamshire DN22 8FD; Tel 01777 862118;
Fax 01777 862108

2

East Midlands (South) Area

Responsible for the following prisons: Ashwell, Gartree, Glen Parva, Leicester, Onley, Stocken, Wellingborough.
Area Manager   Bob Perry
2 St. John St, Leicester LE1 3BE; Tel 0116 242 1030; Fax 0116 242 1040

Women's Prison Estate

Responsible for the following prison establishments: Askham Grange, Brockhill, Bullwood Hall, Cookham Wood, Drake Hall, East Sutton Pk, Eastwood Pk, Foston Hall, Holloway, Low Newton, New Hall, Send, Styal, Downview, Highpoint (F), Morton Hall, Buckley Hall.
Manager (Operations)   Niall Clifford
Unit 1 and 2, Faraday Crt, First Ave, Centrum 100, Burton-on-Trent, Staffordshire DE14 2WX; Tel 01283 524525

High Security Prisons

Responsible for the following prisons: Belmarsh, Durham, Frankland, Full Sutton, Long Lartin, Manchester, Wakefield, Whitemoor, Woodhill.
Director   Peter Atherton
Cleland Hse, Page St, London SW1P 4LN; Tel 020 7217 2888; Fax 020 7217 6664

Juvenile Operational Management Group

Responsible for the following prisons: Huntercombe, Warren Hill, Werrington, Wetherby.
Manager   David Waplington
Abell Hse, John Islip, London SW1P 4LH; Tel 020 7217 5298; Fax 020 7217 5227

London Area

Responsible for the following prisons: Brixton, Feltham, Latchmere House, Pentonville, Wandsworth, Wormwood Scrubs.
Area Manager   Bill Duff
Cleland Hse, Page St, London SW1P 4LN; Tel 020 7217 6180; Fax 020 7217 2893

North East Area

Responsible for the following prisons: Acklington, Castington, Deerbolt, Holme House, Kirklevington Grange.
Area Manager   Mitch Egan
3rd Fl, Eagle Star Hse, Regent Centre, Gosforth, Newcastle upon Tyne, Tyne and Wear; Tel 0191 233 6050; Fax 0191 233 6051

North West Area

Responsible for the following prisons: Garth Haverigg, Hindley, Kirkham, Lancaster Castle, Lancaster Farms, Liverpool, Preston, Risley, Thorn Cross, Wymott.
Area Manager   Ian Lockwood
Stirling Hse, Ackhurst Bus Pk, Foxhole Rd, Chorley, Lancashire PR7 1NY; Tel 01257 244140; Fax 01257 244156

South East Area

Responsible for the following prison establishments: Albany, Aylesbury, Bullingdon, Camp Hill, Grendon/Springhill, Haslar, Kingston, Parkhurst, Reading, Winchester.
Area Manager   Sarah Payne
The Old Warden's Hse, 21 Bierton Rd, Aylesbury, Buckinghamshire HP20 1EN; Tel (Enquiries) 01296 390667

South East – Kent, Surrey and Sussex

Responsible for the following prison establishments: Blantyre Hse, Canterbury, Coldingley, Dover, Elmley, Ford, High Down, Lewes, Maidstone, Rochester, Standford Hill, Swaleside.
Area Manager   Adrian Smith
80 Sir Evelyn Rd, Rochester, Kent ME1 3LU; Tel 01634 673001

South West Area

Responsible for the following prison establishments: Bristol, Channings Wood, Dartmoor, Dorchester, Erlstoke, Exeter, Gloucester, Guys Marsh, Leyhill, Portland, Shepton Mallet, The Verne, Weare.
Area Manager   Jerry Petherick
1 Tortworth Rd, Leyhill, Wotton-under-Edge, Gloucestershire GL12 8BQ; Tel 01454 264057

Wales Area

Responsible for the following prison establishments: Cardiff, Swansea, Usk and Prescoed.
Area Manager   John May
102 Maryport St, Usk, Monmouthshire NP15 1AH; Tel 01291 674850

West Midlands Area

Responsible for the following prison establishments: Birmingham, Blakenhurst, Brinsford, Featherstone, Hewell Grange, Shrewsbury, Stafford, Stoke Heath, Swinfen Hall.
Area Manager   Bryan Payling
c/o HMP Shrewsbury, PO Box 458, The Dana, Shrewsbury, Shropshire SY1 2WB; Tel 01743 280043

Yorkshire and Humberside Area

Responsible for the following prison establishments: Everthorpe, Hull, Leeds, Lindholme, Moorland Open, Moorland Closed, Northallerton, Wealstun.
Area Manager   Peter Earnshaw
c/o HMP Wetherby, York Rd, Near Wetherby, West Yorkshire LS22 5NG; Tel 01937 544217

Directorate of Operations

Director   Michael Spurr; Tel 020 7217 6756; Fax 020 7217 2890

Directorate of Healthcare

Director   John Boyington; Tel (Enquiries) 020 7972 3925; Fax 020 7972 4881

Directorate of Resettlement

Abell Hse, John Islip St, London SW1P 4LH
Director   Peter Wrench; Tel (Enquiries) 020 7217 6203; Fax 020 7217 2926

Directorate of Personnel

Director   Gareth Hadley; Tel (Enquiries) 020 7217 2944; Fax 020 7217 6584

Directorate of Finance

Director   Ann Beasley; Tel 020 7217 2681; Fax 020 7217 6746

Directorate of Corporate Affairs

Director   Derek Howard; Tel 020 7217 6779; Fax 020 7217 6247

POLICE, PRISONS AND REMAND CENTRES

Police Forces

England

Metropolitan Police Service

Property Services, Cobalt Sq, 1 South Lambeth Rd, London
SW8 1SU; Tel 020 7230 8370
Director (Property Services) A.M. Croney, FRICS
Divisional Director (Development and Asset Management)
Vacancy
Assistant Director (Design) Dick Fedorcio
Private Secretary to the Commissioner Jocelyn Hull

Youth and Community Sections

The Metropolitan Police Authority polices the 32 London
Boroughs and below is a list of the Borough Operational
Command Unit Headquarters.

Barking and Dagenham Youth and Community Section

Dagenham Police Station, 561 Rainham Rd South,
Dagenham, Essex RM10 7TU; Tel 020 8217 1212
Borough Commander Robin Hope

Barnet Youth and Community Section

Colindale Police Station, Grahame Pk Way, Colindale,
London NW9 5TW; Tel 020 8200 1212
Borough Commander Sue Akers

Bexley Youth and Community Section

Bexleyheath Police Station, 2 Arnberg Way, Bexleyheath,
Kent DA7 4QS; Tel 020 8301 1212
Borough Commander Chris Cerroni

Brent Youth and Community Section

Wembley Police Station, 603 Harrow Rd, Wembley, Greater
London HA0 2HH; Tel 020 8652 1212
Borough Commander Ian Carter

Bromley Youth and Community Section

Bromley Police Station, 48 Widmore Rd, Bromley, Kent
BR1 3BG; Tel 020 8313 1212
Borough Commander Gerry Howlett

Camden Youth and Community Section

Albany Street Police Station, 60 Albany St, London
NW1 4EE; Tel 020 7380 1212
Borough Commander Anthony Brooks

City of Westminster Youth and Community Section

Belgravia Police Station, 202–206 Buckingham Palace Rd,
London SW1V 6SX; Tel 020 7730 1212
Borough Commander Andrew Trotter

Croydon Youth and Community Section

Croydon Police Station, 71 Park La, Croydon, Surrey
CR9 1BP; Tel 020 8768 1212
Borough Commander Paul Minton

Ealing Youth and Community Section

Ealing Police Station, 67–69 Uxbridge Rd, London W5 5SJ;
Tel 020 8810 1212
Borough Commander Peter Goulding

Enfield Youth and Community Section

Edmonton Police Station, 462 Fore St, Edmonton, London
N9 0PW; Tel 020 8807 1212
Borough Commander Janet Williams

Greenwich Youth and Community Section

Greenwich Police Station, 31 Royal Hill, London SE10 8RR;
Tel 020 8855 1212
Borough Commander Sharon Kerr

Hackney Youth and Community Section

Shoreditch Police Station, 4–6 Shepherdess Wlk, London
N1 7LF; Tel 020 7253 1212
Borough Commander Derek Benson

Hammersmith and Fulham Youth and Community Section

Hammersmith Police Station, 226 Shepherds Bush Rd,
London W6 7NX; Tel 020 8563 1212
Borough Commander Anthony Wills

Haringey Youth and Community Section

Tottenham Police Station, 398 High Rd, Tottenham, London
N17 9JA; Tel 020 8808 1212
Borough Commander Stephen James

Harrow Youth and Community Section

Harrow Police Station, 74 Northolt Rd, , Harrow, Greater
London HA2 0DN; Tel 020 8423 1212
Borough Commander Alexander Fish

Havering Youth and Community Section

Romford Police Station, 19 Main Rd, Romford, Essex
RM1 3BJ; Tel 01708 751212
Borough Commander Les Owen

Heathrow Airport Youth and Community Section

Note: Not a Borough policed by the Metropolitan Police for
BAA.
Heathrow Airport Police Station, East Ramp, Hounslow,
Greater London TW6 2DJ; Tel 020 8897 1212
Borough Commander James Douglass

Hillingdon Youth and Community Section

Uxbridge Police Station, 1 Warwick Pl, Uxbridge, Greater
London UB8 1PG; Tel 01895 251212
Borough Commander Andy Bamber

Hounslow Youth and Community Section

Hounslow Police Station, 5 Montague Rd, Hounslow,
Greater London TW3 1LB; Tel 020 8577 1212
Borough Commander Michael O'Brien

Islington Youth and Community Section

Islington Police Station, 2 Tolpuddle St, London N1 0YY;
Tel 020 7704 1212
Borough Commander Ronald Hope

Kensington and Chelsea Youth and Community Section

Kensington Police Station, 72–74 Earls Court Rd, London
W8 6EQ; Tel 020 7376 1212
Borough Commander Steven Otter

2

Kingston upon Thames Youth and Community Section

Kingston Police Station, 5–7 High St, Kingston upon
  Thames, Surrey KT1 1LB; Tel 020 8541 1212
Borough Commander   Jeffrey Braithwaite

Lambeth Youth and Community Section

Kennington Police Station, 49–51 Kennington Rd, London
  SE1 7QA; Tel 020 7326 1212
Borough Commander   Robert Broadhurst

Lewisham Youth and Community Section

Catford Police Station, Bromley Rd, Southend Village,
  London SE6 2RJ; Tel 020 8695 1212
Borough Commander   Michael Humphrey

Merton Youth and Community Section

Wimbledon Police Station, 15 Queens Rd, London
  SW19 8NN; Tel 020 8947 2312
Borough Commander   Stephen Thomas

Newham Youth and Community Section

Forest Gate Police Station, 370 Romford Rd, London
  E7 8BS; Tel 020 8534 1212
Borough Commander   John Boylin

Redbridge Youth and Community Section

Ilford Police Station, 270–294 High Rd, Ilford, Essex
  IG1 1GT; Tel 020 8478 1123
Borough Commander   Robert Kynnersley

Richmond upon Thames Youth and Community Section

Twickenham Police Station, 41 London Rd, Twickenham,
  Greater London TW1 3SY; Tel 020 8607 9199
Borough Commander   Derek Cook

Southwark Youth and Community Section

Southwark Police Station, 323 Borough High St, London
  SE1 1JL; Tel 020 7378 1212
Borough Commander   Rod Jarman

Sutton Youth and Community Section

Sutton Police Station, 6 Carshalton Rd West, Sutton, Surrey
  SM1 4RF; Tel 020 8643 1212
Borough Commander   Stephen Macdonald

Tower Hamlets Youth and Community Section

Bethnal Green Police Station, 12 Victoria Park Sq, London
  E2 9NZ; Tel 020 8983 1212
Borough Commander   Rose Fitzpatrick

Waltham Forest Youth and Community Section

Chingford Police Station, King's Head Hill, London
  E4 7EA; Tel 020 8556 8855
Borough Commander   Colin Poulter

Wandsworth Youth and Community Section

Battersea Police Station, 112–118 Battersea Bridge Rd,
  London SW11 3AF; Tel 020 7350 1122
Borough Commander   Martin Jauch

Avon and Somerset Constabulary

Police Headquarters, PO Box 37, Bristol BS20 8QJ; Tel 01275
  818181
Chief Constable   S. Pilkington, QPM

YOUTH JUSTICE

Youth Justice Section, Bristol AJU, New Bridewell,
  Bridewell St, Bristol BS12 2QH; Tel 01275 818181
Officer-in-Charge   J. Roberts; Tel 01275 818181

Bedfordshire Police

Community Action Department, Police Headquarters,
  Bedford, Bedfordshire MK43 9AX;
  URL www.bedfordshire.police.uk; Tel 01234 842800;
  01234 842801

COMMUNITY INVOLVEMENT OFFICES

Ampthill Police Station Woburn Rd, Ampthill,
Bedfordshire MK45 2HX; Tel 01525 404422; Fax 01234
842605

Bedford Police Station Greyfriars, Bedford, Bedfordshire
MK40 1HR; Tel 01234 271212; Fax 01234 275005

Biggleswade Police Station Station Rd, Biggleswade,
Bedfordshire SG18 8AL; Tel 01767 312222; Fax 01234
842505

Dunstable Police Station West St, Dunstable, Bedfordshire
LU6 1SJ; Tel 01582 471212; Fax 01582 473005

Leighton Buzzard Police Station Hockliffe Rd, Leighton
Buzzard, Bedfordshire LU7 8JL; Tel 01525 372222; Fax 01525
473405

Luton Police Station Buxton Rd, Luton LU1 1SD; Tel 01582
401212; Fax 01582 394006

Cambridgeshire Constabulary

Police Headquarters, Hinchingbrooke Pk, Huntingdon,
  Cambridgeshire PE29 6NP; Tel 01480 456111
Chief Constable   B. Gunn, QPM, MA(Cantab)

DIVISIONAL FAMILY UNITS

Huntingdon Police Station Ferrars Rd, Huntingdon,
Cambridgeshire; Tel 01480 456111

Parkside Police Station Parkside, Cambridge,
Cambridgeshire CB1 1JG; Tel 01223 358966

Thorpe Wood Police Station Longthorpe, Peterborough,
Cambridgeshire PE3 6SD; Tel 01733 63232

Cheshire Constabulary

Police Headquarters, Castle Esplanade, Chester, Cheshire
  CH1 2PP; Tel 01244 350000; Fax 01244 612187
Chief Constable   N.K. Burgess, QPM

Cleveland Police

Police Headquarters, PO Box 70, Middlesbrough; Tel 01642
  326326; Fax 01642 301462
Chief Constable   S. Price, BSc(Hons), Mst(Cantab)

COMMUNITY SAFETY

Juvenile liaison work is carried out in the community
safety sections of districts.

Hartlepool Divisional Police Headquarters Avenue Rd,
Hartlepool; Tel 01429 221151

Langbaurgh Divisional Police Headquarters Dawson Hse,
11 Ridley St, Redcar, Redcar and Cleveland; Tel 01287
633531

Middlesbrough Divisional Police Headquarters Dunning
Rd, Middlesbrough; Tel 01642 248184

Stockton Divisional Police Headquarters Thistle Gdn,
Stockton-on-Tees; Tel 01642 607114

Cumbria Constabulary

Police Headquarters, Carleton Hall, Penrith, Cumbria
CA10 2AU; Tel 01768 891999; Fax 01768 217199
Chief Constable   M. Baxter

Derbyshire Constabulary

Constabulary Headquarters, Butterley Hall, Ripley,
Derbyshire DE5 3RS; URL www.derbyshire.police.uk;
E-mail pressofficer@derbyshire.pnn.police.uk; Tel 01773
570100
Chief Constable   D.F. Coleman, BA(Hons)
Officer in Charge of Juvenile Liaison: County Partnership
Inspector; Tel 01773 572806

DIVISIONAL JUVENILE LIAISON OFFICERS

A Divisional Headquarters Wyatt's Way, Ripley, Derbyshire
DE5 3SU; Tel 01773 570100
Community Safety Unit

B Divisional Headquarters Silverlands, Buxton, Derbyshire
SK17 6QJ; Tel 01298 72100
Community Safety Unit

C Divisional Headquarters Beetwell St, Chesterfield,
Derbyshire S40 1QP; Tel 01246 220100
Community Safety Unit

D Divisional Headquarters St. Mary's Wharf, Prime
Parkway, Chester Grn, Derby DE1 3AB; Tel 01332 290100
Community Safety Unit

Devon and Cornwall Constabulary

Constabulary Headquarters, Middlemoor, Exeter, Devon
EX2 7HQ; Tel 0990 777444; Fax 01392 452033
Chief Constable   J.S. Evans, QPM, LLB, FBIM

CRIME AND COMMUNITY AFFAIRS

Youth Affairs and Crime Prevention Reduction in the
community is undertaken by nominated police personnel
within each district of the force.

Dorset Police

Police Headquarters, Winfrith, Dorchester, Dorset
DT2 8DZ; URL www.dorset.police.uk;
E-mail ivor.graham@dorset.police.uk; Tel 01929
462727
Chief Constable   J. Stichbury, QPM, BA, MA

CHILD PROTECTION UNIT

Detective Chief Inspector   Ivor Graham
There are divisional child protection offices at
Bournemouth, Poole and Weymouth.

Durham Constabulary

Police Headquarters, Aykley Heads, Durham, County
Durham DH1 5TT; Tel 0191 386 4929; Fax 0191 375 2160;
0191 375 2190
Chief Constable   P.T. Garvin

JUVENILE LIAISON SCHEMES

Child and Family Protection Unit.

Essex Police

Police Headquarters, PO Box 2, Springfield, Chelmsford,
Essex CM2 6DA; Tel 01245 491491; Fax 01245 452259
Chief Constable   David F. Stevens

CHILD PROTECTION UNIT

Detective Chief Inspector   Roy Fenning

BRANCH OFFICES

Brentwood Child Protection Unit Brentwood, Essex;
Tel 01277 262412 (Harlow and Thurrock Divisions)
Detective Inspector   Vacancy

Chelmsford Child Protection Unit Chelmsford, Essex;
Tel 01245 491491
Detective Inspector   G. Glassfield

Harlow Child Protection Unit The High, Harlow, Essex
CM20 1HG; Tel 01279 641211 (Harlow Division)
Detective Inspector   Vacancy

Rayleigh Child Protection Unit 119 High St, Rayleigh, Essex
SS6 7QB; Tel (Southend, Basildon and Rayleigh Division)
01268 771919
Detective Inspector   Vacancy

Shrub End Child Protection Unit 54–56 John Kent Ave,
Colchester, Essex CO2 9EX; Tel (Colchester Division) 01206
762412
Detective Inspector   G. Glassfield

Gloucestershire Constabulary

County Police Headquarters, Holland Hse, Lansdowne Rd,
Cheltenham, Gloucestershire GL51 6QH; Tel 0845 090
1234
Chief Constable   Dr T. Brain, QPM, BA, PhD

Greater Manchester Police

Police Headquarters, PO Box 22, Manchester M16 0RE;
URL www.gmp.police.uk;
E-mail infodesk@gmp.police.uk; Tel 0161 872 5050
Chief Constable   M. Todd, QPM, BA(Hons), MPhil

PUBLIC PROTECTION SECTION – FAMILY SUPPORT UNIT

Bradford Pk, 3 Bank St, Manchester M11 4AA; Tel 0161 856
6571; Fax 0161 856 6579
Head of Department   Detective Chief Inspector Carol
Ashworth; Tel 0161 856 6571
Detective Inspector (Child Protection)   Stephen Harlow;
Tel 0161 856 6572
Detective Inspector (Domestic Violence)   Jayne Shackleton;
Tel 0161 856 6573

Hampshire Constabulary

Police Headquarters, West Hill, Winchester, Hampshire
SO22 5DB; Tel 0845 045 4545; Fax 01962 871204
Chief Constable   Paul R. Kernaghan, QPM, LLB, MA, DPM,
MCIPD
Community Youth Relations   Inspector Martin Laux

JUVENILE LIAISON SCHEMES

There are divisional youth case officers at the main police
stations throughout Hampshire and the Isle of Wight.

Hertfordshire Constabulary

Police Headquarters, Stanborough Rd, Welwyn Garden
City, Hertfordshire AL8 6XF; Tel 01707 354000; Fax 01707
354609
Chief Constable   Paul Acres

YOUTH OFFENDING TEAMS

East Hertfordshire Youth Offending Team Downs Farm, 29
McDonald Crt, Highview, Hatfield, Hertfordshire
AL10 8HR; Tel 01707 897440; Fax 01707 897441
Contact   PC Samantha Brooker
Contact   PC Rachel Loveday
Areas covered:
Hertford and Ware, Buntingford, Welwyn Garden City,
Hatfield, Bishop's Stortford, Sawbridgeworth, Hoddesdon
and Cheshunt.

North Hertfordshire Youth Offending Team Dane Cottage, London Rd, Stevenage, Hertfordshire SG1 1XW; Tel 01438 723113; Fax 01438 361083
The Valley School, Valley Way, Stevenage, Hertfordshire SG2 9AB
Contact   PC Steve Gibbs
Contact   PC Mandy Pervis
Areas covered:
Stevenage, Hitchin, Letchworth, Baldock and Royston.

South West Hertfordshire Youth Offending Team 36 Clarendon Rd, Watford, Hertfordshire WD1 1JP; Tel 01923 229012; Fax 01923 219928
Contact   PC Paul Allen
Contact   PC Kim Halifax
Areas covered:
Watford, Garston, Oxhey, Rickmansworth, Bushey, Potters Bar, Borehamwood, Radlett and Shenley.

North West Hertfordshire Youth Offending Team DARC, Greenhills, Tenzing Rd, Hemel Hempstead, Hertfordshire HP1 1HQ; Tel 01442 388755; Fax 01442 258564
Contact   PC Dave Cavanagh
Contact   PC Kevin Grigg
Areas covered:
Hemel Hempsted, Berkhamstead, Tring, St. Albans, Harpenden and London Colney.

Humberside Police

Headquarters, Priory Rd, Kingston upon Hull HU5 5SF; URL www.humberside.police.uk; Tel 01482 578200
Chief Constable   D. Westwood, MA(Oxon), PhD

DIVISIONAL JUVENILE LIAISON OFFICERS

Juvenile Liaison Officer – A Division Grimsby, Lincolnshire; Tel 01472 359171

Juvenile Liaison Officer – B Division Scunthorpe, Lincolnshire; Tel 01724 282888

Juvenile Liaison Officer – C Division Beverley, East Riding of Yorkshire; Tel 01482 881111

Juvenile Liaison Officer – D Division Bransholme, Hull, Kingston upon Hull HU7 4EE; Tel 01482 326111

Kent County Constabulary

Police Headquarters, Sutton Rd, Maidstone, Kent ME15 9BZ; Tel 01622 690690
Chief Constable   Sir David Phillips, QPM, BA(Econ)

JUVENILE LIAISON SCHEMES – POLICY

Chief Inspector   N. Thomas; Tel 01622 690690
Police Station (Canterbury) Old Dover Rd, Canterbury, Kent CT1 3JG; Tel 01227 762055
Police Station (North Kent) Windmill St, Gravesend, Kent DA12 1DB; Tel 01474 331055
Police Station (Maidstone) Palace Ave, Maidstone, Kent ME15 7SG; Tel 01622 690055
Police Station (Margate) Fort Hill, Margate, Kent CT9 1HL; Tel 01843 231055
Police Station (Medway) Cazeneuve St, Rochester, Kent ME1 1XT; Tel 01634 827055
Police Station (South East Kent) Bouverie Hse, Bouverie Rd West, Folkestone, Kent CT20 2RW; Tel 01303 850055
Police Station (Swale) Central Ave, Sittingbourne, Kent ME10 4NR; Tel 01795 477055
Police Station (The Weald) Tufton St, Ashford, Kent TN23 1BT; Tel 01233 611055
Police Station (West Kent) Pembury Rd, Tonbridge, Kent TN9 2HS; Tel 01732 771055
Traffic Headquarters London Rd, Coldharbour, Maidstone, Kent ME20 7SL; Tel 01622 882055

Lancashire Constabulary

Police Headquarters, PO Box 77, Hutton, Preston, Lancashire PR4 5SB; Tel 01772 614444
Chief Constable   P. Stephenson, QPM

Leicestershire Constabulary

St. John's, Enderby, Leicester LE19 2BX; URL www.leics.police.uk; Tel 0116 222 2222
Chief Constable   Matthew Baggott, BA(Hons)

COMMUNITY AFFAIRS

Chief Superintendent   Paul Gibson; Tel 0116 222 2222 ext 2710

Lincolnshire Police

Headquarters, PO Box 999, Lincoln, Lincolnshire LN5 7PH; URL www.lincs.police.uk; Tel 01522 532222
Chief Constable   R.J.N. Childs, QPM, BSc

COMMUNITY SAFETY

Detective Superintendent J.D. Tapley; Tel 01522 558113
Detective Sergeant (Community Safety)   Andrew Lockyer; Tel 01522 558059
Inspector (Crime and Disorder Reduction)   K. Meanwell; Tel 01522 558115
Community Safety – East Division Park Ave, Skegness, Lincolnshire PE25 1BL; URL www.lincs.police.uk; Tel 01754 762222
Crime Reduction Officer   Detective Sergeant R. Burge
Crime Reduction Officer   PC J. Marshall
Crime Reduction Officer   PC R. Cram
Community Safety – South Division Stonebridge Hse, St. Catherine's Rd, Grantham, Lincolnshire NG31 9DD; URL www.lincs.police.uk; Tel 01476 402222
Crime Reduction Officer   K. Weightman
Crime Reduction Officer   PC T. McGibbon
Crime Reduction Officer   PC D. Richardson
Community Safety – West Division West Pde, Lincoln, Lincolnshire LN1 1YP; URL www.lincs.police.uk; Tel 01522 882222
Crime Reduction Officer   Detective Sergeant P. Shaw
Crime Reduction Officer   PC R. Anker
Crime Prevention Officer   PC P. Gravells

Merseyside Police

Police Headquarters, PO Box 59, Liverpool, Merseyside L69 1JD; URL www.merseyside.police.uk; Tel 0151 709 6010; Fax 0151 777 8999
Chief Constable   Norman Bettison

COMMUNITY RELATIONS

Superintendent   Peter Kinloch

Norfolk Constabulary

Police Headquarters, Jubilee Hse, Falconers Chase, Wymondham, Norfolk URL www.norfolk.police.uk; Tel 01953 424242
Chief Constable   A. Hayman, MA, FCMI
Head (Crime Reduction Dept)   Chief Superintendent C. Grant

JUVENILE LIAISON SCHEMES

Great Yarmouth Admin Support Unit Howard St North, Great Yarmouth, Norfolk NR30 1PH; Tel 01493 842222
Contact   M. Goffin

King's Lynn Admin Support Unit St. James' St, King's Lynn, Norfolk PE30 5DE; Tel 01553 691211
Contact   P. Harrison

Norwich Admin Support Unit Dencora Hse, Norwich, Norfolk NR2 1RG
Chief Inspector P. Hurren

North Yorkshire Police

Newby Wiske Hall, Newby Wiske, Northallerton, North Yorkshire DL7 9HA;
URL www.northyorkshire.police.yk; Tel 01609 789000; Fax 01609 789025
Chief Constable D.M. Cawnings

Northamptonshire Police

Police Headquarters, Wootton Hall, Northampton, Northamptonshire NN4 0JQ; Tel 01604 700700; Fax 01604 703096
Chief Constable Peter Maddison

JUVENILE LIAISON SCHEMES

Eastern Area Juvenile Liaison Scheme Area Commander, Wellingborough Police Station, Wellingborough, Northamptonshire NN8 1HF; Tel 01933 440333

Northampton Area Juvenile Liaison Scheme Area Commander, Campbell Sq Police Station, Northampton, Northamptonshire NN1 3EL; Tel 01604 700700

Northern Area (Kettering and Corby) Juvenile Liaison Scheme Area Commander, Kettering Police Station, Kettering, Northamptonshire NN15 7QP; Tel 01536 411411

Western Area Juvenile Liaison Scheme Area Commander, Daventry Police Station, Daventry, Northamptonshire NN11 4BS; Tel 01327 300300

Northumbria Police

Police Headquarters, North Rd, Newcastle upon Tyne, Tyne and Wear NE20 0BL;
URL www.northumbria.police.uk; Tel 01661 872555
Chief Constable J.C. Strachan, QPM, MA, MIMgt

CRIME MANAGEMENT

Chief Superintendent C. Machell; Tel 01661 872555 ext 68201

South Yorkshire Police

Snig Hill, Sheffield, South Yorkshire S3 8LY; Tel 0114 220 2020
Chief Constable M.I.I. Hedges

JUVENILE LIAISON

Officer Responsible for Local Authority Liaison (Barnsley) Chief Superintendent R. Dyson
Officer Responsible for Local Authority Liaison (Doncaster) Superintendent A. Humphries
Officer Responsible for Local Authority Liaison (Rotherham) Chief Superintendent C. Burbeary
Officer Responsible for Local Authority Liaison (Sheffield South) Chief Superintendent S. Chapman
Chief Officer Responsible for Local Authority Liaison (Sheffield Central) Superintendent G. Cassidy
Officer Responsible for Local Authority Liaison (Sheffield North) Chief Superintendent J. Donnelly
Officer Responsible for Local Authority Liaison (Sheffield Attercliffe) Chief Superintendent G. Gassidy

Staffordshire Police

Chief Constable's Office, Cannock Rd, Stafford, Staffordshire ST17 0QG; Tel 01785 257717; Fax 01785 232313
Chief Constable J.W. Giffard, QPM, BA(Hons)

JUVENILE LIAISON SCHEME

The Juvenile Liaison Officer Bureau is part of the Court Support Services Department, based at Force Headquarters, and is responsible for all youth justice matters.

Suffolk Constabulary

County Constabulary Headquarters, Martlesham Heath, Ipswich, Suffolk IP5 3QS; URL www.suffolk.police.uk; E-mail headquarters@suffolk.police.uk; Tel 01473 613500
Chief Constable A. McWhirter, QPM
Community Relations Officer Inspector P. Haystead; Tel 01473 613990

Surrey Police

Police Headquarters, Mount Browne, Guildford, Surrey GU3 1HG; URL www.surrey.police.uk;
E-mail chief.constable@surrey.police.uk; Tel 01438 571212; Fax 01438 300279
Chief Constable Ian Blair, MA(Oxon)

DIVISIONAL JUVENILE LIAISON SCHEMES

Eastern Area Juvenile Liaison Scheme Reigate, Surrey; Tel 01737 765040
Chief Inspector

Northern Area Juvenile Liaison Scheme Woking, Surrey; Tel 01483 761991
Chief Inspector

Western Area Juvenile Liaison Scheme Guildford, Surrey; Tel 01483 531111
Chief Inspector

Sussex Police

Police Headquarters, Malling Hse, Church La, Lewes, East Sussex BN7 2DZ; URL www.sussex.police.uk;
E-mail chief.constable@sussex.police.uk; Tel 0845 6070 999
Chief Constable Ken Jones, QPM

JUVENILE LIAISON SCHEMES

Child protection teams and schools liaison officers are based at each divisional police station. Policy regarding the former is the responsibility of CID at headquarters; SLO policy is the responsibility of the Community Safety Department.

Thames Valley Police

Police Headquarters, Kidlington, Oxford, Oxfordshire OX5 2NX; Tel 01865 846000
Chief Constable C. Pollard, QPM, LLB

JUVENILE LIAISON SCHEMES, BERKSHIRE, BUCKINGHAMSHIRE AND OXFORDSHIRE

Juvenile Bureau schemes operate as part of the Community Liaison Department throughout the area on an area basis. Headquarters Community Safety Department.

AREA COMMANDERS

Aylesbury Area Commander
Superintendent D. McBirney

Chiltern Vale Area Commander
Superintendent J. Donlon

Milton Keynes Area Commander
Chief Superintendent M. Page

Northern Oxfordshire Area Commander
Superintendent J. Reeve

Oxford Area Commander
Superintendent   D. McWhirter

Reading Area Commander
Superintendent   D. Murray

Slough Area Commander
Superintendent   A. Setchell

Southern Oxfordshire Area Commander
Superintendent   P. Gormley

Thames Forest Area Commander
Superintendent   A. Becks

West Berkshire Area Commander
Superintendent   F. Sullivan

Warwickshire Police

Chief Constable's Office, PO Box 4, Leek Wootton,
  Warwick, Warwickshire CV35 7QB; Tel 01926 415000;
  Fax 01926 415022
Chief Constable   J. Burbeck, QPM, BSc, FIMgT

WARWICKSHIRE JUVENILE BUREAUX

Nuneaton Juvenile Bureau Hollybush Hse, Bond Gate,
Nuneaton, Warwickshire CV11 4AR
Rugby Juvenile Bureau 54 Regent St, Rugby, Warwickshire
CV21 2PS
Warwick Juvenile Bureau 1 Northgate St, Warwick,
Warwickshire CV34 4SP; Tel 01926 401542

West Mercia Constabulary

Police Headquarters, Hindlip Hall, Worcester,
  Worcestershire WR3 8SP;
  URL www.westmercia.police.uk; Tel 01905 723000
Chief Constable   Paul West, MA(Oxon), MSc, MA

YOUTH OFFENDING TEAMS

The Community Relations Department on each division
listed below has responsibility for liaison on matters
relating to juveniles.
Herefordshire Youth Offending Team 1–3 Dawes Rd,
Hereford, Herefordshire HR1 2JJ; Tel 01432 383300;
Fax 01432 383302
North Worcestershire Youth Offending Team Smallwood
Heath Centre, Church Grn West, Redditch,
Worcestershire B97 4DJ; Tel 01527 593645; Fax 01527
593631
South Worcestershire Youth Offending Team Tolladine Rd,
Worcester, Worcestershire WR4 9NS; Tel 01905 732200;
Fax 01905 732220
Wrekin and Shropshire Youth Offending Team 24 Victoria
Rd, Wellington, Shropshire TF1 1LG; Tel 01952 257477;
Fax 01952 242926

West Midlands Police

Headquarters, Lloyd Hse, Birmingham, West Midlands
  B4 6NQ; URL www.west-midlands.police.uk;
  E-mail mailmaster@west-midlands.police.uk; Tel 0845
  113 5000
Chief Constable   P.J. Scott-Lee, QPM

FAMILY PROTECTION UNITS

Each local authority area is served by family protection
units that comprise child protection and domestic violence
liaison officers. Child abuse cases are investigated in
accordance with ACPO procedures. Help and support are
provided to victims of domestic violence. Enquiries – HQ
FPU 0121 609 6909.

YOUNG OFFENDERS

Each policing area has a youth liaison officer who consults
with other agencies over cases involving juvenile offenders.
Wolverhampton currently piloting a youth justice team
(Crime and Disorder Act). Enquiries – Youth Issues to HQ
Community Services 0845 113 5000.

West Yorkshire Police

Headquarters, PO Box 9, Wakefield, West Yorkshire
  WF1 3QP; Tel 01924 375222
Chief Constable   Colin R. Cramphorn, LLB, AKC, MSc,
  FRSA
Superintendent (Community Safety)   Chief Superintendent
  Bullock

YOUTH LIAISON SCHEMES

Officers operating in divisions.

Wiltshire Constabulary

Police Headquarters, London Rd, Devizes, Wiltshire
  SN10 2DN; URL www.wiltshire.police.uk; Tel 01380
  722341
Chief Constable   E. Neville, QPM, MA, PhD

Wales

Dyfed-Powys Police

Police Headquarters, PO Box 99, Llangunnor, Carmarthen,
  Carmarthenshire SA31 2PF;
  URL www.dyfed-powys.police.uk;
  E-mail contact.centre@dyfed-powys.pnn.police.uk;
  Tel 01267 222020
Chief Constable   Terence Grange, MSc

Gwent Police

Police Headquarters, Croesyceiliog, Torfaen NP44 2XJ;
  Tel 01633 838111
Chief Constable   K. Turner

North Wales Police

Police Headquarters, Glan-y-Don, Colwyn Bay, Conwy
  LL29 8AW; URL www.north-wales.police.uk; Tel 01492
  517171
Chief Constable   R. Brunstrom, BSc(Hons), MSc

COMMUNITY PROTECTION DEPARTMENT

Co-ordinator (Public Protection)   Roz Dickinson; Tel 01492
  511193

COMMUNITY SAFETY OFFICERS

Force Community Safety Officer   Inspector M. Pendleton;
  Tel 01492 511266
Based at Headquarters, Anglesey, Gwynedd, Conwy,
Denbighshire, Flintshire, Wrexham.

FORCE CHILD PROTECTION CO-ORDINATOR

Detective Sergeant   G. Thomas; Tel 01492 511109
Family Protection Units based at Anglesey, Gwynedd,
Conwy, Denbighshire, Flintshire, Wrexham.

FORCE DOMESTIC VIOLENCE AND VULNERABLE GROUPS LIAISON OFFICER

Force Community Safety Officer   Inspector M. Pendleton;
  Tel 01492 511266
Domestic Violence Officers based at Anglesey, Gwynedd,
Conwy, Denbighshire, Flintshire, Wrexham.

South Wales Police

Police Headquarters, Bridgend CF31 3SU; Tel 01656 655555;
Fax 01656 869399
Chief Constable A.T. Burden

Scotland

Dumfries and Galloway Constabulary

Police Headquarters, Cornwall Mount, Dumfries, Dumfries
and Galloway DG1 1PZ;
URL www.dumfriesandgalloway.police.uk; Tel 01387
252112; Fax 01387 260501
Chief Constable William Rae, QPM
Community Services Sergeant Aileen Graham; Tel 01387
252112 ext 64539
Local Authority Liaison Officer Sergeant Brian Thomson;
Tel 01387 260000 ext 65931

Fife Constabulary

Police Headquarters, Detroit Rd, Glenrothes, Fife KY6 2RJ;
URL www.fife.police.uk;
E-mail policehq@fife.pnn.police.uk; Tel 01592 418888;
Fax 01592 418444
Chief Constable Peter M. Wilson, QPM, LLB
Officer-in-Charge (Community Safety/Crime Reduction)
Chief Inspector A. Fitzpatrick

Grampian Police

Police Headquarters, Queen St, Aberdeen AB10 1ZA;
E-mail mailbox@grampian.police.uk; Tel 01224 386000;
Fax 01224 643366
Chief Constable Andrew Brown

COMMUNITY DEVELOPMENT DEPARTMENT

Chief Inspector Henry C. Thorburn

Lothian and Borders Police

Police Headquarters, Fettes Ave, Edinburgh EH4 1RB;
URL www.lbp.police.uk;
E-mail hq.community.safety@lbp.police.uk; Tel 0131 311
3131; Fax 0131 311 3038
Chief Constable Paddy Tomkins, BA(Hons), RCDS

COMMUNITY SAFETY BRANCH

Superintendent Paul Gilroy

Northern Constabulary

Police Headquarters, Perth Rd, Inverness, Highland
IV2 3SY; E-mail training@north.police.uk; Tel 01463
715555
Chief Constable I.J. Latimer, MA

COMMUNITY INVOLVEMENT BRANCH

Inspector A. Polson

Strathclyde Police

Police Headquarters, 173 Pitt St, Glasgow G2 4JS;
URL www.strathclyde.police.uk;
E-mail contactus@strathclyde.police.uk; Tel 0141 532
2000; Fax 0141 532 2475
Chief Constable William Rae, QPM

FINANCE

Head (Finance and Physical Resources) A. Macleod,
BA(Hons), MBA, CPFA

Tayside Police

PO Box 59, West Bell St, Dundee DD1 9JU;
URL www.taysidepolice.gov.uk; Tel 01382 223200
Chief Constable John Vine, QPM, BA, MCITD

COMMUNITY AFFAIRS

Provides liaison with the elderly; schools and youth
groups, church and special groups; social strategy areas;
and community relations.

FAMILY PROTECTION UNIT

Specialist officers dealing in matters relating to women and
children and the investigation of both child abuse and
domestic abuse. Both are operated by officers at:

Central Division Headquarters PO Box 59, West Bell St,
Dundee DD2 9JU; Tel 01382 223200

Eastern Division Headquarters Forfar, Angus DD8 1BP;
Tel 01307 302200

Western Division Headquarters Barrack St, Perth, Perth and
Kinross PH15 6SF; Tel 01738 472256

HM Prisons

England

Bedfordshire

HMP Bedford St. Loyes St, Bedford, Bedfordshire
MK40 1HG; Tel 01234 373000; Fax 01234 373001
Governor E. Willets
Senior Probation Officer M. Rivers

Bristol

HMP/YOI Ashfield Shortwood Rd, Pucklechurch, Bristol
BS16 9QJ; Tel 0117 303 8000; Fax 0117 303 8001
Privately operated.

HMP Bristol HMP Bristol, 19 Cambridge Rd, Bristol
BS7 8PS; Tel 0117 980 8100; Fax 0117 980 8153
Governor R.D. Dixon
Senior Probation Officer S. James

Buckinghamshire

HMP Grendon Spring Hill, Grendon Underwood,
Aylesbury, Buckinghamshire HP18 0TL; Tel 01296 443000;
Fax 01296 443001
Governor T.C. Newell
Senior Probation Officer J. Cordery

HMP Spring Hill Grendon Underwood, Aylesbury,
Buckinghamshire HP18 0TH; Tel 01296 443000; Fax 01296
443001

HMP Woodhill Tattenhoe St, Milton Keynes MK4 4DA;
Tel 01908 722000; Fax 01908 722001
Governor M. Boon

Cambridgeshire

HMP Littlehey Perry, Huntingdon, Cambridgeshire
PE18 0SR; Tel 01480 333000; Fax 01480 333001
Governor M.L. Knight
Senior Probation Officer D.W.F. Wallace

HMP Peterborough Opens March 2005.

HMP Whitemoor Longhill Rd, March, Cambridgeshire
PE15 0PR; Tel 01354 602350; Fax 01354 602351
Governor R.B. Clark

Cheshire

HMP Risley Risley, Warrington, Cheshire WA3 6BP;
Tel 01925 733000; Fax 01925 733001
Governor J. Harrison
Senior Probation Officer S. Paul

HMP/YOI Styal HMP YOI Styal, Styal, Wilmslow, Cheshire
SK9 4HR; Tel 01625 553000; Fax 01354 553001
Governor M. Moulden
Senior Probation Officer M. Denton

Cleveland

HMP Holme House Holme House Rd, Stockton-on-Tees
TS18 2QU; Tel 01642 744000; Fax 01642 744001
Governor D. Roberts
Senior Probation Officer M. Waddington

HMP Kirklevington Grange Yarm, Cleveland, TS15 9PA;
Tel 01642 792600; Fax 01642 792601
Governor P. Midgeley
Senior Probation Officer J. Whitfield

County Durham

HMP Durham Old Elvet, Durham, County Durham
DH1 3HU; Tel 0191 332 3400; Fax 0191 332 3401
Governor N. Clifford
Senior Probation Officer M. Cope

HMP Frankland PO Box 40, Brasside, Durham, County
Durham DH1 5YD; Tel 0191 332 3000; Fax 0191 332 3001
Governor P.J. Leonard
Senior Probation Officer N. Thomas

Cumbria

HMP Haverigg HMP Haverigg, Haverigg Camp, Cumbria
LA18 4NA; Tel 01229 713000; Fax 01229 713001
Governor G. Brunskill
Senior Probation Officer S. Hamilton

Derbyshire

HMP Foston Hall Foston, Derby, Derbyshire DE65 5DN;
Tel 01283 584300; Fax 01283 584301
Governor P. Scriven

HMP Sudbury HMP Sudbury, Ashbourne, Derbyshire
DE6 5HW; Tel 01283 584000; Fax 01283 584001
Governor P.E. Salter
Senior Probation Officer E. Coe

Devon

HMP Channings Wood Denbury, Newton Abbot, Devon
TQ12 6DW; Tel 01803 814600; Fax 01803 814601
Governor J.K. Petherick
Senior Probation Officer G. Addison

HMP Dartmoor Princetown, Yelverton, Devon PL20 6RR;
Tel 01822 892000; Fax 01822 892001
Governor J. Lawrence
Senior Probation Officer P. Lockett

HMP/YOI RC Exeter New North Rd, Exeter, Devon
EX4 4EX; Tel 01392 415650; Fax 01392 415651
Governor N.J. Evans
Senior Probation Officer A. DaCosta

Dorset

HMP Dorchester 7 North Sq, Dorchester, Dorset DT1 1JD;
Tel 01305 214500; Fax 01305 214501
Governor D.A. Calvert
Senior Probation Officer I. Gaubert

HMP/YOI Guys Marsh Shaftesbury, Dorset SP7 0AH;
Tel 01747 856400; Fax 01747 856401
Governor R. Gaines
Senior Liaison Probation Officer M. Thomas

HMP The Verne Portland, Dorset DT5 1EQ; Tel 01305
825000; Fax 01305 825001
Governor T.M. Turner
Senior Probation Officer S. Leadley

HMP Weare Portland Port Ltd, Portland Port Business
Centre, Castledown, Portland, Dorset DT5 1PP; Tel 01305
825400; Fax 01305 825401
Governor P. O'Sullivan

Essex

HMP/YOI Bullwood Hall High Rd, Hockley, Essex SS5 4TE;
Tel 01702 562800; Fax 01702 562801
Governor C. Cawley

HMP/YOI Chelmsford Springfield Rd, Chelmsford, Essex
CM2 6LQ; Tel 01245 272000; Fax 01245 272001
Governor A.J. Gomme
Senior Probation Officer M. Werry

Gloucestershire

HMP/YOI Eastwood Park Falfield, Wotton-under-Edge,
Gloucestershire GL12 8DB; Tel 01454 382100; Fax 01454
382101
Governor P. Winkley

HMP/YOI Gloucester Barrack Sq, Gloucester,
Gloucestershire GL1 2JN; Tel 01452 453000; Fax 01452
453001
Governor R. Dempsey
Senior Probation Officer G. Gidley

HMP Leyhill Wotton-under-Edge, Gloucestershire
GL12 8HL; Tel 01454 264000; Fax 01454 264001
Governor D.T. Williams
Senior Probation Officer K. Lane

Greater Manchester

HMP/YOI Forest Bank Agecroft Rd, Pendlebury,
Manchester, M27 8FB; Tel 0161 925 7000; Fax 0161 927
7001

HMP Manchester Southall St, Manchester M60 9AH;
Tel 0161 817 5600; Fax 0161 817 5601
Governor P. Earnshaw
Senior Probation Officer S. Johnson

Hampshire

HMP Haslar 2 Dolphin Way, Gosport, Hampshire
PO12 2AW; Tel 023 9260 4000; Fax 023 9260 4001
Governor I. Truffet

HMP Kingston Milton Rd, Portsmouth PO3 6AS; Tel 023
9289 1100; Fax 023 9289 1181
Governor S. McLean
Senior Probation Officer C. Skinner

HMP Winchester Romsey Rd, Winchester, Hampshire
SO22 5DF; Tel 01962 723000; Fax 01962 723001
Governor M.K. Pascoe
Senior Probation Officer V. Young

Hertfordshire

HMP The Mount Molyneaux Ave, Bovingdon, Hemel
Hempstead, Hertfordshire HP3 0NZ; Tel 01442 836300;
Fax 01442 836301
Governor P. Wailen

2

Isle of Wight

HMP Albany Newport, Isle of Wight O30 5RS; Tel 01983 556300; Fax 01983 556301
Governor S.P. Moore
Senior Probation Officer J. MacDonald

HMP Camp Hill Newport, Isle of Wight O30 5PB; Tel 01983 554600; Fax 01983 554761
Governor W.E. Preston
Senior Probation Officer A. Bush

HMP Parkhurst Newport, Isle of Wight O30 5NX; Tel 01983 554000; Fax 01983 554001
Governor D.M. Morrison
Senior Probation Officer Vacancy

Kent

HMP Ashford
Privately operated prison to open June 2004.

HMP Blantyre House Goudhurst, Cranbrook, Kent TN17 2NH; Tel 01580 211367; Fax 01580 211060
Governor E. McLennan-Murray
Probation Officer C. Kelsey

HMP Canterbury Longport, Canterbury, Kent CT1 1PJ; Tel 01227 862800; Fax 01227 862801
Governor G. Davies
Probation Officer C. Eyre
Probation Officer S. Bourne
Probation Officer S. Swallow

HMP Cookham Wood Rochester, Kent ME1 3LU; Tel 01634 202500; Fax 01634 202501
Governor I. Smout
Probation Officer M. Bolingbroke
Probation Officer H. West

HMP/YOI East Sutton Park Sutton Valence, Maidstone, Kent ME17 3DF; Tel 01622 845000; Fax 01622 845001
Governor C.J. Galbally

HMP Elmley Church Rd, Eastchurch, Sheerness, Kent ME12 4AY; Tel 01795 882100; Fax 01795 882101
Governor A. Smith
Senior Probation Officer N. James

HMP Maidstone County Rd, Maidstone, Kent ME14 1UZ; Tel 01622 775300; Fax 01622 775301
Governor S. O'Neill
Senior Probation Officer J. McCarthy

HMP Rochester Rochester, Kent ME1 3QS; Tel 01634 838100; Fax 01634 838101
Governor R.A. Chapman
Senior Probation Officer M. Revis

HMP Standford Hill Church Rd, Eastchurch, Sheerness, Kent ME12 4AA; Tel 01795 884500; Fax 01795 884638
Governor D.M. Twiner
Senior Probation Officer I. Taylor

HMP Swaleside Barbazon Rd, Eastchurch, Sheerness, Kent ME12 4AX; Tel 01795 884100; Fax 01795 884200
Governor J. Podmore
Senior Probation Officer S. Penny

Kingston upon Hull

HMP Hull Hedon Rd, Hull, Kingston upon Hull HU9 5LS; Tel 01482 282200; Fax 01482 282400
Governor M. Newell
Senior Probation Officer V. Scargill

Lancashire

HMP Buckley Hall Buckley Rd, Rochdale, Lancashire OL12 9DP; Tel 01706 514300; Fax 01706 514399
Controller V. Bird

HMP Garth Ulnes Walton La, Preston, Lancashire PR5 3NE; Tel 01772 443300; Fax 01772 443301
Governor W. Rose-Quirie
Senior Probation Officer M. Sunderland

HMP Hindley Wigan, Greater Manchester WN2 5TH; Tel 01942 855000; Fax 01942 855001
Governor C. Sheffield
Senior Probation Officer K. Cassidy

HMP Kirkham Freckleton Rd, Kirkham, Preston, Lancashire PR4 2RA; Tel 01772 675400; Fax 01772 675401
Governor A.F. Jennings
Senior Probation Officer D. Warburton

HMP Lancaster The Castle, Lancaster, Lancashire LA1 1YJ; Tel 01524 385100; Fax 01524 385101
Governor D.G. McNaughton
Senior Probation Officer J. Noble

HMP/YOI Lancaster Farms Far Moor La, Stone Row Head, off Quernmore Rd, Lancaster, Lancashire LA1 3QZ; Tel 01524 563450; Fax 01524 563451
Governor D. Thomas
Senior Probation Officer K. Brown

HMP Preston 2 Ribbleton La, Preston, Lancashire PR1 5AB; Tel 01772 444550; Fax 01772 444551
Governor R.J. Crouch
Senior Probation Officer L. Thompson

HMP Wymott Ulnes Walton La, Preston, Lancashire PR26 8LW; Tel 01772 444000; Fax 01772 444001
Governor R. Doughty
Senior Probation Officer L. Barron

Leicestershire

HMP Ashwell Oakham, Leicestershire LE15 7LF; Tel 01572 774100; Fax 01572 774101
Governor C.P.A. Bushell
Senior Probation Officer T.J. Scotson

HMP Gartree Leicester Rd, Market Harborough, Leicestershire LE16 7RP; Tel 01858 436600; Fax 01858 436601
Governor R.J. Perry
Senior Probation Officer D. Piper

HMP Leicester Welford Rd, Leicester LE2 7AJ; Tel 0116 228 3000; Fax 0116 228 3001
Governor M. Egan
Senior Probation Officer E. Sheasby

HMP Stocken Stocken Hall Rd, Stretton, Oakham, Leicestershire LE15 7RD; Tel 01780 485100; Fax 01780 410767
Governor R. Curtis
Senior Probation Officer T.J. Scotson

Lincolnshire

HMP Lincoln Greetwell Rd, Lincoln, Lincolnshire LN2 4BD; Tel 01522 663000; Fax 01522 663001
Governor B. McCourt
Senior Probation Officer M. Stringer

HMP Morton Hall Swinderby, Lincoln, Lincolnshire LN6 9PT; Tel 01522 866700; Fax 01522 866750
Governor M.D. Murphy
Probation Officer A. Price

HMP North Sea Camp Freiston, Boston, Lincolnshire PE22 0QX; Tel 01205 769300; Fax 01205 769301
Governor M.A. Lewis
Senior Probation Officer A. Price

London

HMP Belmarsh Western Way, Thamesmead, London SE28 0EB; Tel 020 8331 4400; Fax 020 8331 4401
Governor W. Duff

HMP Brixton PO Box 369, Jebb Ave, London SW2 5XF;
Tel 020 8588 6000; Fax 020 8588 6283
Governor Dr A. Coyle
Senior Probation Officer S. Churchyard

HMP/YOI Feltham Bedfont Rd, Feltham, Middlesex,
TW13 4ND; Tel 020 8844 5000; Fax 020 8844 5001
Governor C. Welsh
Senior Probation Officer S. Watts

HMP/YOI Holloway Parkhurst Rd, London N7 0NU; Tel 020
7979 4400; Fax 020 7979 4401
Governor M. Sheldrick
Senior Probation Officer L. Hogarth

HMP Pentonville Caledonian Rd, London N7 8TT; Tel 020
7023 7000; Fax 020 7023 7001
Governor R. Duncan
Senior Probation Officer B. Ball
Senior Probation Officer J. Owens

HMP Wandsworth PO Box 757, Heathfield Rd, London
SW18 3HS; Tel 020 8588 4000; Fax 020 8588 4001
Governor C.G. Clark
Senior Probation Officer K. Biggar
Senior Probation Officer B. Elmes

HMP Wormwood Scrubs PO Box 757, Du Cane Rd, London
W12 0AE; Tel 020 8588 3200; Fax 020 8588 3201
Governor J. Mullens
Senior Probation Officer F. Ablitt
Senior Probation Officer M. Connolly

Merseyside

HMP Altcourse Higher La, Fazakerley, Liverpool,
Merseyside L9 7LH; Tel 0151 522 2000; Fax 0151 522 2121
Director W. MacGowan
Senior Probation Officer M. Redman
Privately operated.

HMP Liverpool 68 Hornby Rd, Liverpool, Merseyside
L9 3DF; Tel 0151 530 4000; Fax 0151 530 4001
Governor W. Abbott
Senior Probation Officer M. Evans

Norfolk

HMP Norwich Mousehold, Knox Rd, Norwich, Norfolk
NR1 4LU; Tel 01603 708600; Fax 01603 708601
Governor N. Wall
Senior Probation Officer M. Ashton

HMP Wayland Griston, Thetford, Norfolk IP25 6RL;
Tel 01953 858100; Fax 01953 858220
Governor M. Spurr
Senior Probation Officer J. Faulconbridge

Northamptonshire

HMP Wellingborough Millers Pk, Doddington Rd,
Wellingborough, Northamptonshire NN8 2NH; Tel 01933
232700; Fax 01933 232701
Governor J. Whetton
Senior Probation Officer S. Rawden

Northumberland

HMP Acklington Morpeth, Northumberland NE65 9XF;
Tel 01670 762300; Fax 01670 762301
Governor I. Woods
Senior Probation Officer P.J. Fox

HMP/YOI Castington Morpeth, Northumberland
NE65 9XG; Tel 01670 762100; Fax 01670 762101

Nottinghamshire

HMP Lowdham Grange Lowdham, Nottinghamshire
NG14 7TA; Tel 0115 966 9200; Fax 0115 966 9220
Privately operated.

HMP Nottingham Perry Rd, Sherwood, Nottingham
NG5 3AG; Tel 0115 872 3000; Fax 0115 872 3001
Governor P.J. Bennett
Senior Probation Officer H. Jasper

HMP Ranby Retford, Nottinghamshire DN22 8EU;
Tel 01777 862000; Fax 01777 862001
Governor J. Slater
Probation Officer S. Johnson
Probation Officer S. Storer
Probation Officer T. Wells

HMP Whatton 14 Cromwell Rd, Nottingham NG13 9FQ;
Tel 01949 859200; Fax 01949 859201
Governor D. Walmsley
Senior Probation Officer H. Jasper

Oxfordshire

HMP Bullingdon PO Box 50, Bicester, Oxfordshire
OX25 1WD; Tel 01869 353100; Fax 01869 353101
Governor P.J. Cann
Senior Probation Officer M. Myatt

Shropshire

HMP Shrewsbury The Dana, Shrewsbury, Shropshire
SY1 2HR; Tel 01743 273000; Fax 01743 273001
Governor K. Beaumont
Senior Probation Officer J. Warren

Somerset

HMP Shepton Mallet Cornhill, Shepton Mallet, Somerset
BA4 5LU; Tel 01749 823300; Fax 01749 823301
Governor J.R.S. Shergold
Senior Probation Officer L. Philpott

Staffordshire

HMP Dovegate Uttoxeter, Staffordshire ST14 8XR; Tel 01283
820000; Fax 01283 820066
Privately operated.

HMP Drake Hall Eccleshall, Stafford, Staffordshire
ST21 6LQ; Tel 01785 858100; Fax 01785 858010
Governor G. Hughes
Senior Probation Officer D. Pritchett-Farrell

HMP Stafford 54 Gaol Rd, Stafford, Staffordshire
ST16 3AW; Tel 01785 773000; Fax 01785 773001
Governor R. Feeney
Senior Probation Officer B. Brown

Suffolk

HMP Blundeston Lowestoft, Suffolk NR32 5BG; Tel 01502
734500; Fax 01502 734501
Governor S.R. Robinson
Senior Probation Officer J. Doyland

HMP/YOI Highpoint Stradishall, Newmarket, Suffolk
CB8 9YG; Tel 01440 823100; Fax 01440 823099
Governor D. Sherwood
Senior Probation Officer R. Dennis

HMP Hollesley Bay/HMYOI Warren Hill Hollesley,
Woodbridge, Suffolk IP12 3JW; Tel 01394 412400; Fax 01394
410115
Governor J.D. Forster

Surrey

HMP Coldingley Bisley, Woking, Surrey GU24 9EX;
Tel 01483 804300; Fax 01483 804427
Governor J.B. Smith
Senior Probation Officer R. Sanders

2

HMP Downview Sutton La, Sutton, Surrey SM2 5PD; Tel 020 8929 3300; Fax 020 8929 3301
Governor C. Lambert
Senior Probation Officer M. Whibley

HMP High Down (DOC) Sutton La, Sutton, Surrey SM2 5PJ; Tel 020 8722 6300; Fax 020 8722 6301
Governor D. Wilson
Senior Probation Officer P.M. Sturge

HMP Latchmere House Church Rd, Ham Common, Richmond, Surrey TW10 5HH; Tel 020 8588 6650; Fax 020 8588 6698
Governor E.R. Bott

HMP Send Ripley Rd, Send, Woking, Surrey GU23 7LJ; Tel 01483 471000; Fax 01483 471001
Governor S. Guy-Gibbons
Senior Probation Officer C. Fry

Sussex

HMP Ford Arundel, West Sussex BN18 0BX; Tel 01903 663000; Fax 01903 663001
Governor R.S. Brandon
Senior Probation Officer A. Jolley

HMP/YOI Lewes Brighton Rd, Lewes, East Sussex BN7 1EA; Tel 01273 405100; Fax 01273 405101
Governor J.F. Dixon
Senior Probation Officer Vacancy

West Midlands

HMP Birmingham Winson Green Rd, Birmingham, West Midlands B18 4AS; Tel 0121 345 2500; Fax 0121 345 2501
Governor G. Gregory-Smith
Senior Probation Officer P. Russell

HMP Featherstone New Rd, Featherstone, Wolverhampton, West Midlands WV10 7PU; Tel 01902 703000; Fax 01902 703001
Governor C. Scott
Senior Probation Officer J. Atkins

Wiltshire

HMP Erlestoke Devizes, Wiltshire SN10 5TU; Tel 01380 814250; Fax 01380 814273
Governor M.A. Cook
Senior Probation Officer S. Rubringer

Worcestershire

HMP Long Lartin South Littleton, Evesham, Worcestershire WR11 5TZ; Tel 01386 835100; Fax 01386 835101
Governor J.W. Mullen
Senior Probation Officer P. Pimpernell

HMP Blakenhurst Hewell La, Redditch, Worcestershire B97 6QS; Tel 01527 400500; Fax 01527 400501
Controller P. Hanglin

HMP Brockhill Redditch, Worcestershire B97 6RD; Tel 01527 552650; Fax 01527 552651
Governor N.M. Croft

HMP Hewell Grange Redditch, Worcestershire B97 6QQ; Tel 01527 552000; Fax 01527 552001
Governor D.W. Bamber

Yorkshire

HMP Askham Grange Askham Richard, York YO2 3FT; Tel 01904 772000; Fax 01904 772001
Governor H.E. Crew
Senior Probation Officer S.R. Wardley

HMP/YOI Doncaster off North Bridge, Marshgate, Doncaster, South Yorkshire DN5 8UX; Tel 01302 760870; Fax 01302 760851
Controller H. Jones
Privately operated.

HMP Everthorpe Brough, East Riding of Yorkshire HU15 1RB; Tel 01430 426500; Fax 01430 426501
Governor R. Smith

HMP Full Sutton Moor La, Full Sutton, York YO4 1PS; Tel 01759 375100; Fax 01759 371206
Governor R. Tasker
Senior Probation Officer K. Swallow

HMP Leeds Armley, Leeds, West Yorkshire LS12 2TJ; Tel 0113 203 2600; Fax 0113 203 2601
Governor A.J. Fitzpatrick
Senior Probation Officer A. Hutchinson
Senior Probation Officer P. Marsh

HMP Lindholme Bawtry Rd, Hatfield Woodhouse, Doncaster, South Yorkshire DN7 6EE; Tel 01302 848700; Fax 01302 848750
Governor D. Hall
Senior Probation Officer S. Daley

HMP/YOI Moorland Closed Hatfield Woodhouse, Bawtry Rd, Doncaster, South Yorkshire DN7 6BW; Tel 01302 523000; Fax 01302 523001
Governer D. Waplington

HMP/YOI Moorland Open Thorne Rd, Hatfield, Doncaster, South Yorkshire DN7 6EL; Tel 01405 746500; Fax 01405 746501
formerly HMP/YOI Hatfield

HMP New Hall Dial Wood, Flockton, Wakefield, West Yorkshire WF4 4AX; Tel 01924 844200; Fax 01924 844201
Governor M. Goodwin
Senior Probation Officer R. Heal

HMP Wakefield Love La, Wakefield, West Yorkshire WF2 9AG; Tel 01924 246000; Fax 01924 246001
Governor D. Shaw
Senior Probation Officer M. Austwick

HMP Wealstun Thorp Arch, Boston Spa, Wetherby, West Yorkshire LS23 7AZ; Tel 01937 848500; Fax 01937 848501
Governor S. Tasker
Senior Probation Officer P. Mate

HMP Wolds Everthorpe, Brough, HU15 2JZ; Tel 01430 421588; Fax 01430 421589
Privately operated.

Warwickshire

HMP Rye Hill Willoughby, Rugby, Warwickshire CV23 8AM; Tel 01788 523300; Fax 01788 523311
Privately operated.

Wales

HMP Cardiff Knox Rd, Cardiff CF24 0UG; Tel 029 2043 3100; Fax 029 2043 3318
Governor R. Walker
Senior Probation Officer L. Barker

HMP/YOI Parc Heol Hopeyn John, Bridgend CF35 6AP; Tel 01656 300200; Fax 01656 300201
Governor R. Dixon
Probation Manager E. Pritchard
Privately operated.

HMP/YOI Prescoed Coed-y-Paen, Pontypool, Gwent, NP14 0TD; Tel 01291 672231; Fax 01291 672197

HMP Swansea 200 Oystermouth Rd, Swansea SA1 2SR; Tel 01792 485300; Fax 01792 485301
Governor Vacancy
Senior Probation Officer G. King

HMP/YOI Usk and Prescoed 47 Maryport St, Usk, Monmouthshire NP15 1XP; Tel 01291 671600; Fax 01291 671752
Governor   P.J. Morgan

Scotland

Aberdeen

HMP Craiginches Aberdeen AB11 8FN; Tel (Social Work Unit) 01224 238321; Fax 01224 896209
Governor   A. Mooney
Deputy Governor   M. Hebden
Senior Social Worker   S. Williamson

Aberdeenshire

HMP Peterhead Peterhead, North Aberdeen, AB42 6YY; Tel 01779 473315 (Social Work Unit); Fax 01779 471269
Governor   Ian Gunn
Deputy Governor   G. Gordon
Team Manager   A. Shirran

Angus

HMP Noranside Fern, Forfar, Angus DD8 3QY; Tel 01356 650217; Fax 01356 650245
Governor   K. Rennie

Dumfries and Galloway

HMP Penninghame Newton Stewart, Dumfries and Galloway DG8 6RG; Tel 01387 261218
Governor   S. Swan
HMP Dumfries Terregles St, Dumfries, Dumfries and Galloway DG2 9AX; Tel 01387 261218; Fax 01387 264144
Governor   Mrs C. McGeever

East Dunbartonshire

HMP Low Moss Crosshill Rd, Bishopbriggs, Glasgow G64 2QB; Tel 0141 762 4848
Governor   Eric Fairbairn
Social Work Unit
Social Worker   Ian Ure

Edinburgh

HMP Edinburgh, 33 Stenhouse Rd, Edinburgh EH11 3LN;
   Tel (Social Work Unit) 0131 444 3080; Fax 0131 444 3036
Governor   R. McCowan
Manager (Social Work)   G. Youngson

Glasgow

HMP Barlinnie Glasgow G33 2QX; Tel 0141 770 2000; Fax 0141 770 9448
Governor   Roger Houchin
Social Work Unit HMP Barlinnie, Glasgow G33 2QX; Tel 0141 770 2123; Fax 0141 770 9808
Social Work Manager   John Owens

Highlands

HMP Inverness Porterfield, Inverness, Highland IV2 3HH; Tel 01463 229000; (Prison Social Worker) 01463 223489; Fax 01463 224010
Governor   A. MacDonald

Inverclyde

HMP Greenock Gateside, Greenock, Inverclyde PA16 9AH; Tel 01475 787801; Fax 01475 783154
Governor   Stephen Swan

Stirling

WOMEN

HMI Cornton Vale Cornton Rd, Stirling FK9 5NU; Tel 01786 832591; Fax 01786 833597
Governor   Kate Danegan
Social Work Manager   Ian McFadyen

Tayside

HMP Friarton 81 Edinburgh Rd, Perth, Perth and Kinross PH2 8DW; Tel 01738 625885; Fax 01738 630544
Governor   E.A. Gordon
HMP Perth 3 Edinburgh Rd, Perth, Perth and Kinross PH1 8AS; Tel 01738 626883
Senior Social Worker   Paul Connell

HM Young Offender Institutions

England

Buckinghamshire

HMYOI Aylesbury Bierton Rd, Aylesbury, Buckinghamshire HP20 1EH; Tel 01296 24435; Fax 01296 434169
Governor   N. Pascoe

HMYOI Grendon Grendon Underwood, Aylesbury, Buckinghamshire HP18 0TL; Tel 01296 770301; Fax 01296 770756
Governor   T.C. Newell
Senior Probation Officer   J. Cordery

Cheshire

HMP/YOI Styal
see HM Prisons
HMYOI Thorn Cross Arley Rd, Appleton Thorn, Warrington, Cheshire WA4 4RL; Tel 01925 605100; Fax 01925 605101
Governor   I. Windebank
Senior Probation Officer   G. Carr

County Durham

HMYOI Deerbolt Bowes Rd, Barnard Castle, County Durham DL12 9BG; Tel 01833 637561; Fax 01833 631736
Governor   P.J. Atkinson
Senior Probation Officer   B. Carey
HMYOI Low Newton Brasside, Durham, County Durham DH1 3YA; Tel 0191 376 4000; Fax 0191 376 4001

Devon

HMP/YOI RC Exeter
see HM Prisons

Dorset

HMP/YOI Guys Marsh
see HM Prisons

HMYOI Portland Easton, Portland, Dorset DT5 1DL;
Tel 01305 820301; Fax 01305 860794
Governor S. McCormick
Senior Liaison Probation Officer C. Kermani

Essex

HMP/YOI Bullwood Hall
see HM Prisons

HMP/YOI Chelmsford
see HM Prisons

Gloucestershire

HMP/YOI Eastwood Park
see HM Prisons

HMP/YOI Gloucester
see HM Prisons

Greater London

HMP/YOI Feltham
see HM Prisons

HMP/YOI Holloway
see HM Prisons

Greater Manchester

HMP/YOI Forest Bank
see HM Prisons

Kent

HMYOI Dover The Citadel, Western Heights, Dover, Kent
CT17 9DR; Tel 01304 203848; Fax 01304 215165
Governor B.J. Pollett

HMP/YOI East Sutton Park
see HM Prisons

Lancashire

HMP/YOI Lancaster Farms
see HM Prisons

Leicestershire

HMYOI Glen Parva
Saffron Rd, Wigston, Leicestershire LE8 2TN; Tel 0116 277
2022; Fax 0116 247 7679
Governor C. Williams
Senior Probation Officer E. Sheasby

Northumberland

HMP/YOI Castington
see HM Prisons

Oxfordshire

HMYOI Huntercombe and Finnamore Wood Camp
Huntercombe Pl, Nuffield, Henley-on-Thames, Oxfordshire
RG9 5SB; Tel 01491 641711; 01491 641715; Fax 01491 641902
Governor P. Manwaring
Senior Probation Officer C. Clarke

Shropshire

HMYOI Stoke Heath Stoke Heath, Market Drayton,
Shropshire TF9 2JL; Tel 01630 654231; Fax 01630 639581
Governor J. Alldridge
Senior Probation Officer T. Law

Staffordshire

HMYOI Brinsford New Rd, Featherstone, Wolverhampton,
West Midlands WV10 7PY; Tel 01902 791118; Fax 01902
790889
Governor B. Payling
Probation Officer N. Byford

HMYOI Drake Hall Eccleshall, Stafford, Staffordshire
ST21 6LQ; Tel 01785 858100; Fax 01785 858010
Governor G. Hughes
Senior Probation Officer D. Pritchett-Farrell

HMYOI Swinfen Hall Lichfield, Staffordshire WS14 9QS;
Tel 01543 481229; Fax 01543 480138
Governor J.P. Francis
Senior Probation Officer D. Male

HMYOI Werrington Werrington, Stoke-on-Trent ST9 0DX;
Tel 01782 303514; Fax 01782 302504
Governor B. Stanhope
Senior Probation Officer G. Oxborrow

Suffolk

HMYOI Hollesley Bay Colony Hollesley, Woodbridge,
Suffolk IP12 3JS; Tel 01394 411741; Fax 01394 411071
Governor J.D. Forster
Senior Probation Officer I. Fullelove

HMP/YOI Highpoint
see HM Prisons

Sussex

HMP/YOI Lewes
see HM Prisons

Warwickshire

HMYOI Onley Willoughby, Rugby, Warwickshire CV23 8AP;
Tel 01788 522022; Fax 01788 522160
Governor J.N. Brooke
Senior Probation Officer A.J. Webster

Yorkshire

HMP/YOI Doncaster
see HM Prisons

HMYOI Hatfield Doncaster, South Yorkshire DN7 6EL;
Tel 01405 812336; Fax 01405 811325
Governor C.L. Davies
Senior Probation Officer A. Furness

HMP/YOI Moorland Closed
see HM Prisons

HMP/YOI Moorland Open
see HM Prisons

HMYOI New Hall Dial Wood, Flockton, Wakefield, West
Yorkshire WF4 4AX; Tel 01924 848307; Fax 01924 840692
Governor M. England
Senior Probation Officer J. Bryan

HMYOI Northallerton East Rd, Northallerton, North
Yorkshire DL6 1NW; Tel 01609 780078; Fax 01609 779664
Governor D.P.G. Appleton
Senior Probation Officer E. Knowles

HMYOI Wetherby York Rd, Wetherby, West Yorkshire
LS22 4NW; Tel 01937 585141; Fax 01937 586488
Governor S. Mitson
Senior Probation Officer P. Mate

Bristol

HMP/YOI Ashfield
see HM Prisons

Wales

HMP/YOI Parc
see HM Prisons

HMP/YOI Prescoed
see HM Prisons

HMP/YOI Usk and Prescoed
see HM Prisons

Scotland

Clackmannanshire

HM Prison and Young Offenders' Institution Glenochil, King O'Muirs Rd, Tullibody, Clackmannanshire FK10 3AD; Tel 01259 760471; (Social Work Unit) 01259 760258
Governor Kate Dovegan
Deputy Governor Derek McGill
Head (Custody and Order) Angus MacVicar

Falkirk

HMYOI Polmont Falkirk FK2 0AB; Tel (Social Work Unit) 01324 711708
Governor D. Gunn
Social Work Team Leader Diane Dobbie

Perthshire and Kinross

HMP Castle Huntly Longforgan, Dundee DD2 5HL; Tel 01382 360265; Fax 01382 360510
Governor K. Rennie
Social Worker D. Spicker

Stirling

HMI Cornton Vale Cornton Rd, Stirling FK9 5NU; Tel 01786 832591; Fax 01786 833597
Governor Sue Brookes
Senior Social Worker Elaine Corvi

Remand Centres

England

County Durham

HMRC Low Newton Brasside, Durham, County Durham DH1 5SD; Tel 0191 386 1141; Fax 0191 386 2620
Governor M. Kirby
Senior Probation Officer H. Robson

Devon

HMRC Exeter New North Rd, Exeter, Devon EX4 4EX; Tel 01392 278321; Fax 01392 422647
Governor N.J. Evans
Senior Probation Officer A. DaCosta

Greater London

HMRC Feltham Bedfont Rd, Feltham, Greater London TW13 4ND; Tel 020 8890 0061; Fax 020 8893 2809
Governor C. Welsh
Senior Probation Officer S. Watts

Leicestershire

HMRC Glen Parva Tigers Rd, Wigston, Leicestershire LE8 2TN; Tel 0116 264 3100; Fax 0116 264 3116
Governor C. Williams
Senior Probation Officer D. Kemp

Reading

HMRC Reading Forbury Rd, Reading, Berkshire RG1 3HY; Tel 0118 958 7031; Fax 0118 959 1058
Governor W. Payne
Senior Probation Officer A. Palk

Staffordshire

HMRC Brinsford New Rd, Featherstone, Wolverhampton, West Midlands WV10 7PY; Tel 01902 791118; Fax 01902 790889
Governor B. Payling
Senior Probation Officer N. Byford

Wales

Cardiff

HMP Cardiff Knox Rd, Cardiff CF24 0UG; Tel 029 2043 3100; Fax 029 2043 3318
Governor P.W. Tidball
Senior Probation Officer L. Barker

NATIONAL PROBATION SERVICE

The following list does not include the Prison Probation Officers who are listed under establishments in Chapter 2.

England and Wales

Avon and Somerset

Headquarters, Brunel Hse, 83 Newfoundland Rd, Bristol BS2 9LU; Tel 0117 915 1300; Fax 0117 983 0052
Chief Probation Officer Jeanette T. Whitford
Liaison Officer: Crown Courts David Miners, SPO

Offices

Bath Probation Office The Old Convent, 35 Pulteney Rd, Bath, Bath and North East Somerset BA2 4JE; Tel 01225 460673; Fax 01225 480404

Bridgwater Probation Office The Lonsdale Centre, 3 Blake St, Bridgwater, Somerset Ta6 3NB; Tel 01278 423977; Fax 01278 453941
Senior Probation Officer T. Foy

Bristol Crown Court The Law Courts, Small St, Bristol BS1 1DA; Tel 0117 976 3071; Fax 0117 976 3073

Central/Bridewell Probation Office Bridewell St, Bristol BS1 2JX; Tel 0117 930 3700

Frome Probation Office Northover Hse, North Pde, Frome, Somerset BA11 1AU; Tel 01373 462385; 01373 463606; Fax 01373 452535
Senior Probation Officer S. Mason

Knowle Office 70 Crossways Rd, Knowle Pk, Bristol BS4 2SP; Tel 0117 983 0050

Minehead Probation Centre The Old Stables, Alexandra Rd, Minehead, Somerset TA24 5DP; Tel 01643 706564; Fax 01643 705251

North Bristol Probation Office Greystoke Ave, Westbury on Trym, Bristol BS10 6AD; Tel 0117 950 9105

Taunton Probation Office 11 Canon St, Taunton, Somerset TA1 1SN; Tel 01823 251351; Fax 01823 251354; 01823 321724
Senior Probation Officer N. Whiley

Taunton Crown Court Shire Hall, Taunton, Somerset TA1 1EU; Tel 01823 338599; Fax 01823 338946

Upper York Street Probation Office Decourcey Hse, Upper York St, Bristol BS2 8QN; Tel 0117 944 7200; Fax 0117 944 7230

Wells Probation Office St. Lawrence Lodge, 37 Chamberlain St, Wells, Somerset BA5 2PG; Tel 01749 677779; Fax 01749 670149
Senior Probation Officer S. Mason

Weston-Super-Mare Probation Office 50 The Blvd, Weston-Super-Mare, Somerset BS23 1NF; Tel 01943 623526; Fax 01934 621111

Yeovil Probation Office Court Ash Hse, Court Ash, Yeovil, Somerset BA20 1HG; Tel 01935 476461; Fax 01935 475290
Senior Probation Officer P. Stopard

Bedfordshire

3 St. Peter's St, Bedford, Bedfordshire MK40 2PN; Tel 01234 213541; Fax 01234 327497
Chief Probation Officer J.R.M. Scott
Assistant Chief Probation Officer J.B.A. Williams
Assistant Chief Probation Officer E.A. Pace
Assistant Chief Probation Officer Martin Scott
Teasurer Julie Robertson

Offices

Bedford Office 41 Harpur St, Bedford, Bedfordshire MK40 1LY; Tel 01234 350401; Fax 01234 328658

Luton Office Frank Lord Hse, 72 Chapel St, Luton LU1 5DA; Tel 01582 413172; Fax 01582 418279

Magistrates' Court Liaison Office Shire Hall, 3 St. Paul's Sq, Bedford, Bedfordshire MK40 1SQ; Tel 01234 358402; Fax 01234 358070

Crown Court Liaison Office

Luton Crown Court, 7–9 George St, Luton LU1 2AA; Tel 01582 452846; Fax 01582 485529

Magistrates' Court Liaison Office

Luton Magistrates' Courts, The Court Hse, Stuart St, Luton LU1 5DL; Tel 01582 482710; Fax 01582 457261

Programmes and Training Unit

23–27 Napier Rd, Luton LU1 1RF; Tel 01582 735153; Fax 01582 451536

Blackburn

Offices

13 Wellington Street St. John's, Blackburn BB1 8AF; Tel 01254 265221
Senior Probation Officer H. Ward
Senior Probation Officer I. Phillips

Area Office Jubilee St, Blackburn; Tel 01254 680003
Assistant Chief Officer M.C. Whyham

Training Office 19 Winckley Sq, Preston, PR1 3JJ; Tel 01772 254292
Senior Probation Officer A. Hennessy

Blackpool

Office

Blackpool Community Service 384 Talbot Rd, Blackpool FY3 7AT; Tel 01253 394031; Fax 01253 391881
Senior Probation Officer Fax 01253 305039

Bracknell Forest

Office

James Glaisher House Grenville Pl, Bracknell, Bracknell Forest RG12 1BP; Tel 01344 420446
Senior Probation Officer J.A. Cleary

Cambridgeshire

1 Brooklands Ave, Cambridge, Cambridgeshire CB2 2BB; Tel 01223 717004
Secretary to the Probation Board John Atkinson
Chief Officer John Hughes
Assistant Chief Probation Officer D. Clarke
Assistant Chief Probation Officer A. Powell

Offices

Castle Lodge 1 Museum Sq, Wisbech, Cambridgeshire PE13 1ES; Tel 01945 461451

Old County Buildings Grammar School Walk, Huntingdon, Cambridgeshire PE29 3LQ; Tel 01480 376100

Probation Office Magistrates' Court, Bridge St, Peterborough PE1 1ED; Tel 01733 564367

Probation Office Gloucester Hse, 23a London Rd, Peterborough PE2 8AP; Tel 01733 348828

Sessions House Lynn Rd, Ely, Cambridge, Cambridgeshire CB6 1DA; Tel 01353 663523

Warkworth Lodge Warkworth Terr, Cambridge, Cambridgeshire CB1 1EG; Tel 01223 712271

Cheshire

County Hall, Chester, Cheshire CH1 1SF; Tel 01244 602289; Fax 01244 602270
Secretary of the Probation Board G.L. Budd
Chief Officer S. Collett
Assistant Chief Officer S. Link

County Durham

County Durham Probation Service, Forest Hse, Durham, County Durham DH1 5TS; Tel 0191 383 9083; Fax 0191 374 6958
Secretary of the Probation Board B. Holdhusen
Chief Probation Officer P. McPhee
Treasurer P. McLoughlin
Assistant Chief Probation Officer Sue Hine

Offices

Corporation House 9 Corporation Rd, Darlington DL3 6TH; Tel 01325 486231; Fax 01325 382760
Senior Probation Officer Martyn Strike
Senior Probation Officer Anna Capstick
Senior Probation Officer Maria Albquerque-Neale

Beechburn House Kensington, Cockton Hill Rd, Bishop Auckland, County Durham; Tel 01388 602182; Fax 01388 458403
Senior Probation Officer Marc Ghosh

Claypath Office 84 Claypath, Durham, County Durham; Tel 0191 386 1265; Fax 0191 386 4668
Senior Probation Officer Nikki Disouza

Market House Office 13 Market Hse, Harlow, Essex CM20 1BL; Tel 01279 410692
Senior Probation Officer Min Stiles

Ryegate House 23 St. Peter's St, Colchester, Essex CO1 1HL; Tel 01206 768342
Group Manager Alex Bamber
Senior Probation Officer D. Mead

Gloucestershire

Bewick Hse, 1 Denmark Rd, Gloucester, Gloucestershire GL1 3HW; URL www.glosprobation.org.uk / probation; Tel 01452 426250
Secretary to the Probation Board G.D. Limbrick

Offices

Head Office Bewick Hse, 1 Denmark Rd, Gloucester, Gloucestershire GL1 3HW; Tel 01452 426250
Chief Officer John Carter
Assistant Chief Officer Peter Blomley
Assistant Chief Officer Naomi Cryer
Assistant Chief Officer Julia Oulton
Manager (Finance) D. Maloney
Manager (Business Systems and Information) T.J. Fogarty
Co-ordinator (Multi-Agency Public Protection) Kate Reynolds

Barbican House 31 Barbican Rd, Gloucester, Gloucestershire GL1 2JF; Tel 01452 426300
Senior Probation Officer (Public Protection) J. Bensted
Senior Probation Officer U. Sharma

Cainscross Road Office 118 Cainscross Rd, Stroud, Gloucestershire GL5 4HN; Tel 01453 760100
Senior Probation Officer G. Mead

County Offices St. George's Rd, Cheltenham, Gloucestershire GL50 3EW; Tel 01242 532425
Senior Probation Officer A. Foden
Senior Probation Officer (Intensive Supervision) G. Mead

Dyer Street Office 40a Dyer St, Cirencester, Gloucestershire GL7 2PF; Tel 01285 652981
Senior Probation Officer A. Foden

Community Service Unit Unit 26, Morlands Trading Est, Gloucester, Gloucestershire GL1 5PL; Tel 01452 426330
Senior Probation Officer Vacancy

Criminal Justice Drugs Team Oakes Hse, 55–57 London Rd, Gloucester, Gloucestershire GL1 3HF; Tel 01452 551200
Senior Probation Officer T. Yates; Tel 01452 551200
Intensive Supervision – Senior Probation Officer Vacancy

Coleford Office Coleford Magistrates Court, Gloucester Rd, Coleford, Gloucestershire GL16 8BL; Tel 01594 837090
Senior Probation Officer John Bensted

Greater Manchester

Head Office, 6th Fl, Oakland Hse, Talbot Rd, Manchester M16 0PQ; Tel 0161 872 4802
Secretary to the Probation Committee G.W.A. Jackson, LLB, Solicitor
Treasurer J.K. Millington, IPFA
Chief Probation Officer C. Knott
Assistant Chief Officer (Diversity/Dangerousness/Community Punishment) Mike Davies
Assistant Chief Probation Officer (Courts/CEM/Enforcement) Manjit Seale
Deputy Chief Probation Officer (Policy Support Unit) Robert Mathers
Assistant Chief Probation Officer (ETE, Partnership/Drugs, Youth Justice) Chris Noah
Assistant Chief Probation Officer (Community Supervision) Roz Hamilton
Assistant Chief Probation Officer (Prison/Victims Resettlement) D. White

District Offices

City of Manchester Management Unit, Victoria Pk, London Rd, Longsight, Manchester M14 5YJ; Tel 0161 226 3515
District Manager J. Thomas
District Manager P. Gillbard
Staff Development Unit Kearsley Town Hall, Bolton Rd, Bolton, Greater Manchester; Tel 01204 792015
Assistant Chief Officer (Training and Race Relations) M. Davies
6th Fl, Oakland Hse, Talbot Rd, Manchester M16 0PQ
Manager (Training) E. Clark

Bolton District

Bolton Probation Office St. Helena Mill, Lorne St, Bolton, Greater Manchester BL1 2DY; Tel 01204 387699
District Manager B. Bate
Senior Probation Officer S. Berry
Senior Probation Officer I. Metcalfe
Senior Probation Officer K. Riley

Bury/Rochdale District

St. Michael's Hse, Oldham Rd, Middleton, Greater Manchester M24 2LH; Tel 0161 643 0826
Argyle Hse, Castlecroft Crt, Castlecroft Rd, Bury, Greater Manchester; Tel 0161 764 9514
District Manager Diana Johnson
Senior Probation Officer C. Ramos
Senior Probation Officer A.P. Hulse

Rochdale Probation Office 193–195 Drake St, Rochdale, Greater Manchester OL11 1ER; Tel 01706 653411
Middleton Office, St. Michael's Hse, Oldham Rd, Middleton, Greater Manchester M24 2LH; Tel 0161 543 0826
Senior Probation Officer M. Boulter
Senior Probation Officer C. Robinson
Senior Probation Officer P. Culkin

Oldham District

128 Rochdale Rd, Oldham, Greater Manchester OL1 2JG; Tel 0161 620 4421
District Manager D. Brierley
Senior Probation Officer E. Ross
Senior Probation Officer M. O'Donnell
Senior Probation Officer S. Johnson

Salford District

Salford Office, 2 Redwood St, Salford, Greater Manchester M6 6PF; Tel 0161 736 6441
District Manager John Davidson
Senior Probation Officer R. Homewood
Senior Probation Officer D. Rowlands
Little Hulton Office Haysbrook Ave, Little Hulton, Manchester M28 6AY; Tel 0161 703 8813
Senior Probation Officer A. Hanley

Stockport District

19–37 High St, Stockport, Greater Manchester SK1 1EG; Tel 0161 429 0010
District Manager Joe Tumetty
Senior Probation Officer J. Ross
Senior Probation Officer S.R. Nicholls
Senior Probation Officer M. Meakin
Moss Side Office 87 Moss La West, Moss Side, Manchester M15 5PE; Tel 0161 226 3515
Senior Probation Officer J. Mitchell
Senior Probation Officer A. Shah

2

Trafford District

Newton Street Stretford, Manchester M32 8LG; Tel 0161 865 3255
District Manager Joe Tumetty
Senior Probation Officer L. Kierc

Tameside District

Frances Thompson Dr, off Water St, Ashton-under-Lyne, Greater Manchester OL6 7AJ; Tel 0161 330 3695
District Manager Penny Jones
Senior Probation Officer I. Metcalfe
Senior Probation Officer N. Elliot

Hampshire

Headquarters, Friary Hse, Winchester, Hampshire SO23 8DQ; URL www.probation.hants.gov.uk; E-mail cxlpkg@hants.gov.uk; Tel 01962 842202; Fax 01962 865278
Secretary to the Probation Board K. Gardner
Chief Officer D.M. Scott
Assistant Chief Officer B. Swyer
Head (Human Resources) Nicky Cornelius
Assistant Chief Officer R.K. Pearce

Offices

Aldershot Probation Office Imperial Hse, 2 Grosvenor Rd, Aldershot, Hampshire GU11 1DP;
E-mail ian.caren@hampshire.probation.gsx.gov.uk;
Tel 01252 324288; 01252 324289
Senior Probation Officer Ian Caren
Alton Probation Office 25 Normandy St, Alton, Hampshire GU34 1DQ; Tel 01420 84155
Senior Probation Officer Ian Caren Based at Aldershot.
Basingstoke Probation Office The Court Hse, London Rd, Basingstoke, Hampshire RG21 4AA;
E-mail laura.walker@hampshire.probation.gsx.gov.uk;
Tel 01256 324824; 01256 464272
Senior Probation Officer Laura Walker
The Court House (Andover) West St, Andover, Hampshire SP10 1QP; Tel 01264 364411
Senior Probation Officer Caroline Gray Based at Winchester;
E-mail caroline.gray@hampshire.probation.gsx.gov.uk
The Court House (Eastleigh) Leigh Rd, Eastleigh, Hampshire SO50 9ZP;
E-mail chris.jackson@hampshire.probation.gsx.gov.uk;
Tel 023 8061 2163
Senior Probation Officer Chris Jackson
Fareham Probation Office 20 High St, Fareham, Hampshire PO16 7AF;
E-mail dave.bridden@hampshire.probation.gsx.gov.uk;
Tel 01329 235888
Senior Probation Officer Dave Bridden
Havant Probation Office Elmleigh Rd, Havant, Hampshire PO9 2AS;
E-mail tom.dixon@hampshire.probation.gsx.gov.uk; Tel 023 9247 3011
Senior Probation Officer Tom Dixon
Lymington Probation Office Island Hse, Priestlands Pl, Lymington, Hampshire SO41 9GA;
E-mail chris.jackson@hampshire.probation.gsx.gov.uk;
Tel 01590 673107; 01590 677462
Senior Probation Officer Chris Jackson
Newport Probation Office 8 Sea St, Newport, Hampshire PO30 5BN;
E-mail jo.inge.svendsen@hampshire.probation.gsx.gov.uk;
Tel 01983 523265
Senior Probation Officer Jo Inge Svendsen
Portsmouth Probation Office 52 Isambard Brunel Rd, Portsmouth PO1 2BD; Tel 023 9282 9044

Senior Probation Officer Andrea King;
E-mail andrea.king@hampshire.probation.gsx.gov.uk
Senior Probation Officer Dennis Gough;
E-mail dennis.gough@hampshire.probation.gsx.gov.uk
Southampton Probation Office 70 London Rd, Southampton SO15 2AJ; Tel 023 8063 5011
Senior Probation Officer Paul Caswell;
E-mail paul.caswell@hampshire.probation.gsx.gov.uk
Senior Probation Officer Pete Morris;
E-mail pete.morris@hampshire.probation.gsx.gov.uk
Senior Probation Officer Paul O'Driscoll;
E-mail paul.odriscoll@hampshire.probation.gsx.gov.uk
Totton Probation Office 9 Testwood La, Totton, Hampshire SO40 3BT;
E-mail chris.jackson@hampshire.probation.gsx.gov.uk;
Tel 023 8086 2287
Senior Probation Officer Chris Jackson Based at Lymington.
Winchester Probation Office 3rd Fl, Cromwell Hse, Andover Rd, Winchester, Hampshire SO23 7EZ; Tel 01962 842662
Senior Probation Officer Caroline Gray;
E-mail caroline.gray@hampshire.probation.gsx.gov.uk
Senior Probation Officer Catherine Morgan; E-mail catherine.morgan@hampshire.probation.gsx.gov.uk

Community Service Units

Community Service Unit – South East Spring Gdns, Portsmouth PO1 2BT;
E-mail alan.skinner@hampshire.probation.gsx.gov.uk;
Tel 023 9287 1441 (six lines)
Unit Manager Alan Skinner
Community Service Unit – South West Old Bank Hse, 66–68 London Rd, Southampton SO15 2AJ;
E-mail brian.leigh@hampshire.probation.gsx.gov.uk;
Tel 023 8033 9992
Unit Manager Brian Leigh
Community Service Unit – North Cromwell Hse, 3rd Fl, Winchester, Hampshire SO23 7EZ;
E-mail ray.glen@hampshire.probation.gsx.gov.uk; Tel 01962 853699; 01962 861323
Unit Manager Ray Glen
Community Service Unit – Solent Old Bank Hse, 66–68 London Rd, Southampton SO15 2AJ;
E-mail nigel.james@hampshire.probation.gsx.gov.uk;
Tel 023 8033 9992
Unit Manager Nigel James

Probation Centre

The Baring Centre 35 Sarum Hill, Basingstoke, Hampshire RG21 1SS;
E-mail laura.walker@hampshire.probation.gsx.gov.uk;
Tel 01256 816004; 01256 816006
Senior Probation Officer Laura Walker

Hartlepool Probation Office

Avenue Rd, Hartlepool, TS24 8BL; Tel 01429 265101; Fax 01429 231854
Senior Probation Officer Janet Bolton

Hertfordshire

(excluding London Borough of Barnet which is in the Middlesex area)
Graham Hse, Yeomans Crt, Ware Rd, Hertford, Hertford-shire SG13 7HJ; Tel 01992 504444; Fax 01992 504544
Chair of the Probation Board Nicholas Moss
Chief Probation Officer R. Baldwin
Director (Operations) L. Mathews
Director (Operations) M. Archer
Director (Resources and Administration) D. O'Brien
Director (Operations) C. McDougall

Offices

Hertford Probation Office Graham Hse, Yeomans Crt, Ware Rd, Hertford, Hertfordshire SG13 7HJ; Tel 01992 504444; Fax 01992 516900
Chief Officer R. Baldwin
Senior Probation Officer Dave Clarke
Senior Probation Officer Jon Frayne

Mid Herts Probation Centre Victoria St, St. Albans, Hertfordshire AL1 3XH; Tel 01727 847787; Fax 01727 792700
Senior Probation Officer Vacancy
Senior Probation Officer C. Mulvie

Stevenage Probation Office Swingate Hse, Danestrete, Stevenage, Hertfordshire SG1 1XB; Tel 01438 747074; Fax 01438 765206
Senior Probation Officer Mike Napier
Senior Probation Officer Marilyn Moore

Watford Probation Office 16 King St, Watford, Hertfordshire WD1 8BP; Tel 01923 240144; Fax 01923 699195
Senior Probation Officer J. Gallagher
Senior Probation Officer F. Mulhair

Community Service Headquarters

2nd Fl, Swingate Hse, Danestrete, Stevenage, Hertfordshire SG1 1XB; Tel 01438 747074
Senior Probation Officer H. Ross

Inner London and City

71–73 Great Peter St, London SW1P 2BN; Tel 020 7222 5656; Fax 020 7960 1188
Secretary of the Probation Committee Jan Galloway
Chief Probation Officer J. Harding
Deputy Chief Probation Officer (Community Orders) A.E. Leach
Deputy Chief Probation Officer David Sleightholm
Chief Administrative Officer D.M. Whelan
Assistant Chief Probation Officer (Research/Intelligence Officer and Public Relations) S.J. Stanley

Offices

Alfred Street Probation Office 1a Alfred St, London E3 2BA; Tel 020 8980 4678; Fax 020 8980 1260
Senior Probation Officer R. Raeside
Senior Probation Officer F. Morton

Askew Road Probation Office 191a Askew Rd, London W12 9AX; Tel 020 8746 0999; Fax 020 8740 5238
Senior Probation Officer H. Miller
Senior Probation Officer T. Hearne
Senior Probation Officer B. Crossick
Senior Probation Officer Susan Taylor

Camden House Hostel Camden Hse, 199 Arlington Rd, London NW1 7HA; Tel 020 7267 9231; Fax 020 7267 5037
Contact Charles Dodd
Contact Karen Herson
Contact Andrew Hillas

Cambridge Heath Road Probation Office 377 Cambridge Heath Rd, London E2 9RD; Tel 020 7739 7931; Fax 020 7613 4909

East Hill Probation Office 79 East Hill, London SW18 2QE; Tel 020 8871 2711; Fax 020 8877 3342
Senior Probation Officer P. Northmore
Senior Probation Officer S. Rance
Senior Probation Officer P. Johnson

Englefield Road Probation Office 34 Englefield Rd, London N1 4EZ; Tel 020 7254 8772; Fax 020 7275 7627
Senior Probation Officer D. Bartram
Senior Probation Officer K. Ferguson

Great Dover Street Probation Office 2 Great Dover St, London SE1 4XW; Tel 020 7357 6373; Fax 020 7357 0864
Senior Probation Officer M. Forbes

Senior Probation Officer J. Gulley
Senior Probation Officer L. Hubbard

Great Peter Street Probation Office After Care Service, 71–73 Great Peter St, London SW1P 2BN; Tel 020 8767 5905; Fax 020 8682 3093
Assistant Chief Probation Officer (Prisons) D. Reaich

Greenwich High Road Probation Office 39 Greenwich High Rd, London SE10 8JL; Tel 020 8692 6364; Fax 020 8694 2173
Senior Probation Officer P. Coupe

Harpenden House Field Office Harpenden Hse, 248–250 Norwood Rd, London SE27 9AJ; Tel 020 8766 5700; Fax 020 8766 5746
Senior Probation Officer A. Jappy
Senior Probation Officer P. Grealish

Holloway Road Probation Office 53 Holloway Rd, London N7 8JD; Tel 020 7609 8909; Fax 020 7700 2553
Islington and Camden A. Brown (ACPO); Tel 020 7609 8909
Senior Probation Officer M. Lloyd

Kimpton Road Probation Office 2 Kimpton Rd, London SE5 7UW; Tel 020 7703 0822; Fax 020 7703 8319
Senior Probation Officer R. Haines
Senior Probation Officer S. Reilly
Senior Probation Officer S. Allman

Latchmere Road Probation Office 124 Latchmere Rd, London SW11 2JT; Tel 020 7223 2991; Fax 020 7924 4775
Senior Probation Officer M. Whibley

Lewisham High Street Probation Office 208 Lewisham High St, London SE13; Tel 020 8297 2766; Fax 020 8297 2826
Senior Probation Officer R. Brennan
Senior Probation Officer W. Henderson
Senior Probation Officer J. Wilson

Mornington Grove Probation Office 50 Mornington Gr, London E3 4NS; Tel 020 8980 1818; Fax 020 8983 0020
Senior Probation Officer V. Francis

Notting Hill Gate Probation Office 143 Notting Hill Gate, London W11 3LE; Tel 020 7727 9491; Fax 020 7221 4954
Senior Probation Officer Steve Niechcial

Powis Street Probation Office 130 Powis St, London SE18 6NN; Tel 020 8855 0266; Fax 020 8316 5502
Senior Probation Officer J. Brown
Senior Probation Officer A. Reid
Senior Probation Officer J. Slaven

Probation Office Mitre Hse, Blackfriars Crown Court, Units 4–5, 223–237 Borough High St, London SE1 1JD; Tel 020 7740 8500; Fax 020 7740 8588
Senior Probation Officer M. Connolly

Probation Office 1–5 Dorset Cl, London NW1 5AN; Tel 020 7724 1531
Senior Probation Officer Neil Turner-Nash
Senior Probation Officer L. Whiteley
Senior Probation Officer L. Robertson

Probation Office City of London, 65 Basinghall St, London EC2V 5DA; Tel 020 7332 1190; 020 7332 1192; Fax 020 7600 0433
Senior Probation Officer V. McNaughton

Probation Office Woolwich Crown Crt, 2 Belmarsh Rd, London SE28 0EY; Tel 020 8312 7000; Fax 020 8317 1605
Senior Probation Officer M. Dancer

Reed House Probation Office Reed Hse, 2–4 Rectory Rd, London N16 7QS; Tel 020 7923 4656; Fax 020 7923 4084
Senior Probation Officer L. Ward
Senior Probation Officer H. Elliott
Senior Probation Officer J. Joels

Riverside House Probation Office Riverside Hse, Beresford St, London SE18 6DH; Tel 020 8855 5691; Fax 020 8855 6147
Senior Probation Officer S. Grealish

Stockwell Road Probation Office 117 Stockwell Rd, London SW9 9TN; Tel 020 7274 7854; Fax 020 7738 4562
Senior Probation Officer M. Matas
Senior Probation Officer L. Cox
Senior Probation Officer I. Jones

West End Unit 10 Rathbone Pl, London W1P 1DE; Tel 020 7631 0535; Fax 020 7323 3567
Senior Probation Officer B. Ball
Senior Probation Officer J. Maloney

Crown Courts and Civil Work

Family Courts Office 7 Percy Rd, Shepherds Bush, London W12 9PX; Tel 020 8746 1416; Fax 020 8740 5238
Senior Probation Officer S. Hunt

Family Courts Service 2nd Fl, 217a Balham High Rd, London SW17 7BP; Tel 020 8672 2682; Fax 020 8682 3093
Senior Probation Officer C. Crawley

Family Courts Service and Civil Work Unit 195 New Kent Rd, London SE1 4AG; Tel 020 7403 0115; Fax 020 7403 6384
Senior Probation Officer S. Hunt

Great Peter Street Office 71–73 Great Peter St, London SW1P 2BN; Tel 020 7222 5656; Fax 020 7960 1112
HOHR Heather Barton

Probation Office Central Criminal Court, Old Bailey, London EC4M 7EH; Tel 020 7248 3277; Fax 020 7236 6692
Senior Probation Officer M. Morris

Probation Office Court of Appeal (Criminal Division), Room E303, London WC2A 2LL; Tel 020 7936 6066; 020 7936 6092; Fax 020 7430 1232
Senior Probation Officer (Central Criminal Court)
  M. Morris

Probation Office Inner London Crown Court, 21 Harper Rd, London SE1 6AW; Tel 020 7407 7333; Fax 020 7403 8637
Senior Probation Officer Peter Mavunga

Probation Office The Crown Court at Middlesex Guildhall, Broad Sanctuary, London SW1P 3BB; Tel 020 7799 2131 ext 2172; Fax 020 7233 2215
Senior Probation Officer L. Day

Probation Office Southwark Crown Court, 1 English Grounds, London SE1 2HY; Tel 020 7403 1045; Fax 020 7403 8602
Senior Probation Officer Rory Worthington

Royal Courts of Justice Divorce Court (Welfare), Room 917, London WC2A 2LL; Tel 020 7936 6054; Fax 020 7430 1232
Senior Probation Officer J. Mellor

Community Services and Probation Centres

Camberwell Probation Centre 123 Grove Pk, London SE5 8LB; Tel 020 7733 0972; Fax 020 7737 7857
Senior Probation Officer A. Norman

Community Service Office 210 Chiswick High Rd, London W4 1PD; Tel 020 8994 9393; Fax 020 8994 0961
Senior Probation Officer L. Dixon

Community Service Office 32–34 Greenwich High Rd, London SE10 8LF; Tel 020 8692 7123; Fax 020 8694 1957

Community Service Office Harpenden Hse, 248–250 Norwood Rd, London SE27 9AJ; Tel 020 8766 5700; Fax 020 8766 5772
Senior Probation Officer S. Wells

Community Service Office 3a Alexander Rd, London N19 3PG; Tel 020 7272 5727; Fax 020 7263 9985
Senior Probation Officer P. Cooke

Sherborne House Probation Centre 34 Decima St, London SE1 4QQ; Tel 020 7403 5027; 020 7407 2264; Fax 020 7378 6701
Senior Probation Officer J. Papworth

Special Services

Computer Systems Team Mitre Hse, 223–237 Borough High St, London SE1 1JD
Computer Systems Manager (Field Systems) S. Mortimer

The Partnership Support Unit 289 Borough High St, London SE1 1JG; Tel 020 7407 4611; Fax 020 7378 8696
Senior Probation Officer A. Cameron
Senior Probation Officer Kate Gilbert

Training

Ralph Centre, 24 Maynard Rd, Wincheap Industrial Estate, Canterbury, Kent CT1 3RH; Tel 01227 459564

Kent

Head Office, Chaucer Hse, 25 Knightrider St, Maidstone, Kent ME15 6ND; Tel 01622 350820
Secretary Solicitor of the Kent Probation Board S. Wilson
Chief Officer C. Lawrie
Deputy Chief Officer H. James
Assistant Chief Officer C. Carter
Research and Information Officer M. Oldfield

Court Services Division (Crown and Magistrates Court)

The Law Courts, Barker Rd, Maidstone, Kent ME16 8EQ; Tel 01622 202121
Manager (Court Services) N. James

Public Protection/Sex Offender Resource Team 58 College Rd, Maidstone, Kent ME15 6SJ; Tel 01622 687521

Victim Liaison Service The Law Courts, Barker Rd, Maidstone, Kent ME16 8EQ; Tel 01622 202120

Information Systems Unit 58 College Rd, Maidstone, Kent ME15 6SJ; Tel 01622 687521

Community Service County Management Team 118a West St, Faversham, Kent ME13 7UE; Tel 01795 532587

Resource Development Unit PO Box 212, Ashford, Kent TN27 0ZT; Tel 01233 840931

Metor Unit 58 College Rd, Maidstone, Kent ME15 6SJ; Tel 01622 687521

Volunteer Unit 58 College Rd, Maidstone, Kent ME15 6SJ; Tel 01622 687521

Training Unit Chaucer Hse, 25 Knightrider St, Maidstone, Kent ME15 6ND; Tel 01622 350820
Manager (Training) S. Doherty

Fleming House Probation and Bail Hostel 32 Tonbridge Rd, Maidstone, Kent ME16 8SH; Tel 01622 755918

Groupwork Programmes Unit Ralphs Centre, 24 Maynard Rd, Wincheap Ind Est, Canterbury, Kent CT1 3RH; Tel 01227 769345; 01227 785946
Senior Probation Officer Vacancy

Case Management Division

56 College Rd, Maidstone, Kent ME15 6SJ; Tel 01622 687521
Elwick Rd, Ashford, Kent TN23 1RN; Tel 01233 656500
Joynes Hse, New Rd, Gravesend, Kent DA11 0AT; Tel 01474 569546
48 High St, Sheerness, Kent ME12 1RH; Tel 01795 423321; 01795 423322
24 Maynard Rd, Wincheap Ind Est, Canterbury, Kent CT1 3RH; Tel 01227 769345
Maybrook Hse, Ground Fl, Queens Gdns, Dover, Kent CT17 9AO; Tel 01303 851140
Olwen Hse, Quarry Hill Rd, Tonbridge, Kent TN9 2RH; Tel 01732 351244
Probation Offices, The Law Courts, Castle Hill Ave, Folkestone, Kent CT20 2DH; Tel 01303 851140
Thames Hse, Roman Sq, Sittingbourne, Kent ME10 4BJ; Tel 01795 423321; 01795 423322
118a West St, Faversham, Kent ME13 7UE; Tel 01795 423321; 01795 423322
27–35 New Rd, Chatham, Kent ME4 4QQ; Tel 01634 849284
38–40 Grosvenor Pl, Margate, Kent CT9 1UW; Tel 01843 228727

Lancashire

99–191 Garstang Rd, Preston, Lancashire PR1 1LD;
Tel 01772 201209; Fax 01772 884399
Chief Probation Officer John Crawforth
Deputy Chief Probation Officer Colin Dearden
Training Development Officer Sue Hall
Manager (Information Unit) Dr David Ridpath
Information Office/Library Vacancy
Communications Officer Anne Matthews

Lancashire Probation/NSPCC Partnership Project

Meadow Hse, 127 Oxford St, Preston, Lancashire PR1 3QY;
Tel 01772 200765; Fax 01772 200768
Manager Paul Clark

Court Services

The Crown Court The Law Crts, Ring Way, Preston,
Lancashire PR1 2LL; Tel 01772 832404; 01772 832405;
Fax 01772 832413
Senior Probation Officer Mick Kenny; Tel 01772 832402
The Crown Court Hamerton St, Burnley, Lancashire
BB11 1XD; Tel 01282 457443; Fax 01282 455211
Enquiries to Preston Crown Court Tel 01772 832404.

Offices

Avenham Street Probation Office 50 Avenham St,
Preston, Lancashire PR1 3BN; Tel 01772 552700; Fax 01772
552701
Senior Probation Officer (Community Supervision)
Graham Bailey
Senior Probation Officer (Throughcare) Dave Warburton
Senior Probation Officer Andrea Bennett
Senior Probation Officer (Programmes) Mark Miller
Manager (Community Service Unit) David Troughton

Burnley Road Probation Office 84 Burnley Rd, Accrington,
Lancashire BB5 1AF; Tel 01254 232516; Fax 01254 396160
Contact Sue Baydel-Cupit
The Callum Centre 11–13 Cookson St, Blackpool,
Lancashire FY1 3ED; Tel 01253 752030; Fax 01253 752103
Contact (Preston Office) Mark Miller; Tel 01772 552700
Community Service Office Unit 8, Metropolitan Business
Pk, Blackpool, Lancashire FY3 9LT; Tel 01253 798725;
Fax 01253 839151
Manager Bill Ingram
The Esplanade Office 9 The Esplanade, Fleetwood,
Lancashire FY7 6UW; Tel 01253 879500; Fax 01253 776581
Contact Susan Poole
High Street Office Skelmersdale, Lancashire WN8 8AP;
Tel 01695 720248; Fax 01695 556579
Senior Probation Officer Roland Kid
Kensington Road Probation Office 2 Kensington Rd,
Morecambe, Lancashire LA4 5LX; Tel 01524 416171;
Fax 01524 832154
Senior Probation Officer Allan Jolly
Leigh Street Probation Office Chorley, Lancashire PR7 3DJ;
Tel 01257 260493; Fax 01257 233177
Senior Probation Officer Sue Fiddler
Manchester Road Probation Office Nelson, Lancashire
BB9 9YB; Tel 01282 615155; 01282 618429; Fax 01282
619693
Contact via Burnley Probation Office.
North Street Probation Office 1 North St, Rawtenstall,
Rossendale, Lancashire BB4 7LX; Tel 01706 217577;
Fax 01706 221973
Contact via Burnley Probation Office.
Probation Centre 55 Preston New Rd, Blackburn,
Lancashire BB2 6AY; Tel 01254 265221
Contact Andrea Bennett
50 Avenham St, Preston, Lancashire; Tel 01772 552700

Senior Probation Officer Louise Smith
Senior Probation Officer/Senior Probation Officer
Mark Miller
Stephen House Probation Office 1st Fl, Bethesda St,
Burnley, Lancashire BB11 1QW; Tel 01282 425854; Fax 01282
838947
Senior Probation Officer Linda Lock

Talbot Road Probation Office 384 Talbot Rd, Blackpool,
Lancashire FY3 7AT; Tel 01253 394031; Fax 01253 305039
Senior Probation Officer David Beddon
Senior Probation Officer Jed Graham

Towngate Probation Office 107 Towngate, Leyland, Preston,
Lancashire PR5 1LQ; Tel 01772 621043; Fax 01772 435090
Contact via Chorley or Skelmersdale Office.
Wellington Street Probation Office 13–15 Wellington St, St.
Johns, Blackburn BB1 8AF; Tel 01254 265221; Fax 01254
697852
Senior Probation Officer Mike Lock
Senior Probation Officer Helen Ward

West Road Probation Office 41 West Rd, Lancaster,
Lancashire LA1 5NU; Tel 01524 63537; Fax 01524 848519
Contact Allen Jolly

Leicestershire and Rutland

2 St. John St, Leicester LE1 3BE; Tel 0116 251 6008; Fax 0116
242 3250
Secretary of the Probation Board E. McCalla
Chief Officer Linda Jones
Training/Senior Probation Officer Wendy Poynton

Offices

County Council Area Office Leicester Rd, Melton Mowbray,
Leicestershire LE13 0DA; Tel 01664 410410; Fax 01664
480042
Senior Probation Officer Vacancy

Probation Centre 7 Haramead Rd, Leicester LE1 2LH;
Tel 0116 262 0400; Fax 0116 253 0819
Senior Probation Officer T. Worsfold

Friar Lane Office 38 Friar La, Leicester LE1 5RA; Tel 0116
253 6331; Fax 0116 242 4511
Senior Probation Officer C. Naylor

HMP Ashwell Oakham, Leicester LE15 7LS; Tel 01572
774100; Fax 01572 774101
Senior Probation Officer Vacancy

HMP Gartree Leicester Rd, Market Harborough, Leicester
LE16 7RP; Tel 01858 410234; Fax 01858 410808
Senior Probation Officer Ghislaine Marriage

HMYOI Glen Parva Saffron Rd, Wigston, Leicestershire
LE8 2TN; Tel 0116 277 2022; Fax 0116 247 7679
Senior Probation Officer S. Reynolds

HMP Leicester Welford Rd, Leicester LE2 7AJ; Tel 0116 254
6911; Fax 0116 247 1753
Senior Probation Officer S. Doran

HMP Stocken Stocken Hall Rd, Stretton, Oakham, Leicester
LE15 7RD; Tel 01780 485100; Fax 01780 410767
Senior Probation Officer Vacancy

Coalville Office 27 London Rd, Coalville, Leicestershire
LE67 3JB; Tel 01530 836688; Fax 01530 834136
Senior Probation Officer T. Scotson

Hinckley Office 35 Station Rd, Hinckley, Leicestershire
LE10 1AP; Tel 01455 615645; Fax 01455 891147
Senior Probation Officer T. Scotson

Leicester South 28 Station Rd, Wigston, Leicestershire
LE18 2DH; Tel 0116 257 3800; Fax 0116 257 0240
Senior Probation Officer B. Sisodia

Loughborough Office 12 Southfield Rd, Loughborough,
Leicestershire LE11 2UZ; Tel 01509 212904; Fax 01509
218954
Senior Probation Officer Vacancy

Community Service Unit

City Resettlement Team 38 Friar La, Leicester LE1 5RA; Tel 0116 253 6331; Fax 0116 242 4511
Senior Probation Officer M. Curran

Community Punishment 7 Haramead Rd, Leicester LE1 2LH; Tel 0116 262 0400; Fax 0116 253 0819
Senior Probation Officer Megan Jones

Lincolnshire

Probation Service, 7 Lindum Terr, Lincoln, Lincolnshire LN2 5RP; Tel 01522 520776; Fax 01522 527685
Secretary of the Probation Board M. Gregory
Chief Officer Graham Nicholls (Acting)
Assistant Chief Officer S. Higson
Assistant Chief Officer S. Lewis
Assistant Chief Officer (Human Resources) M. Gregory
Assistant Chief Officer (Finance and Information) P. Rushby

Offices

The Annexe County Hall, Boston, Lincolnshire PE21 6LX; Tel 01205 310010; Fax 01205 354051
Senior Probation Officer M. Gilbert
Senior Probation Officer A. Cooke

Broadgate House Office Broadgate Hse, Westlode St, Spalding, Lincolnshire PE11 2AF; Tel 01775 722078; Fax 01775 713936
Senior Probation Officer N. Norton
Senior Probation Officer J. Oliver

Burbury House Office Burbury Hse, 2 Morton Terr, Gainsborough, Lincolnshire DN21 2RF; Tel 01427 612260; 01427 613867; Fax 01427 612975
Senior Probation Officer S. Pollard

Corporation Street Office 8 Corporation St, Lincoln, Lincolnshire LN2 1HN; Tel 01522 510011; Fax 01522 514369
Senior Probation Officer C. Dilley
Senior Probation Officer C. Bull
Senior Probation Officer S. Reed

Grange House Office Grange Hse, 46 Union St, Grantham, Lincolnshire NG31 6NZ; Tel 01476 561061; Fax 01476 579654
Senior Probation Officer J. Oliver
Senior Probation Officer N. Norton

HM Prison, Lincoln Greetwell Rd, Lincoln, Lincolnshire LN2 4BD; Tel 01522 533633; Fax 01522 787196
Senior Probation Officer I. Miller

HM Prison Morton Hall Swinderby, Lincoln, Lincolnshire LN6 9PS; Tel 01522 866730; Fax 01522 866730
Senior Probation Officer J. Oliver

HM Prison, North Sea Camp Freiston, Boston, Lincolnshire PE22 0QX; Tel 01205 769300; Fax 01205 760098
Senior Probation Officer A. Cooke

Lindum Terrace Office Lindum Terr, Lincoln, Lincolnshire LN2 5RP; Tel 01522 520776; Fax 01522 527685
Chief Officer Graham Nicholls (Acting)

Probation Office Town Hall, North Pde, Skegness, Lincolnshire PE25 1DA; Tel 01754 763906; Fax 01754 760202
Senior Probation Officer M. Gilbert
Senior Probation Officer M. Cooke

London Probation Area, North East Region

(London Boroughs of Barking and Dagenham, Havering, Newham, Redbridge and Waltham Forest)
4th Fl, Olympic Hse, Ilford, Essex IG1 1BA; Tel 020 8514 5353; Fax 020 8478 4450
Treasurer J. Akerman
Deputy Chief Officer P. Baker
Assistant Chief Officer L. Cheston
Assistant Chief Officer (Human Resources) S. Appleby
Senior Probation Officer (Partnership) A. Weston
Senior Probation Officer (Research and Information) K. Giles

Offices

Housing and Welfare Unit 277 High Rd, Ilford, Essex IG1 1QQ; Tel 020 8478 8500; Fax 020 8478 8518
Manager (Housing and Welfare) L. Keever

WF Resource Centre Burghley Hall, 809–813 High Rd, London E11 1HQ; Tel 020 8558 2112; Fax 020 8558 5861
Senior Probation Officer C. Green

Ilford Probation Centre, Court Assessment Allocation, Public Protection and Resource Centre Teams Redbridge Team, 277 High Rd, Ilford, Essex IG1 1QQ; Tel 020 8478 8500; Fax 020 8478 8518
Senior Probation Officer C. Morris

WF Court Assessment Allocation and Public Protection Teams 1b Farnan Ave, Walthamstow, London E17 4TT; Tel 020 8531 3311; Fax 020 8531 1319
Senior Probation Officer J. Browne
Senior Probation Officer (Victims and Domestic Violence) B. Riley

Havering Court Assessment Allocation and Public Protection Team 1 Regarth Ave, South St, Romford, Essex RM1 1TP; Tel 01708 742453; Fax 01708 755353
Senior Probation Officer M. Hawthorne

Snaresbrook Crown Court Probation Suite, Hollybush Hill, London E11 1QW; Tel 020 8530 7561; Fax 020 8530 1399
Senior Probation Officer S. Osborne

Newham Court Assessment Allocation, Public Protection and Resource Centre Teams 1st and 2nd Fl, 20 Romford Rd, London E15 4BZ; Tel 020 8534 5656; Fax 020 8534 8285
Senior Probation Officer B. Thomas
Senior Probation Officer R. Austin
Senior Probation Officer K. Turley

Sex Offenders Project and Groupwork Team Probation Centre, 277 High Rd, Ilford, Essex IG1 1QQ; Tel 020 8478 8500; Fax 020 8553 1972
Senior Probation Officer Mike Head
Senior Probation Officer Shirley Kennerson

Staff Development Unit 4th Fl, Olympic Hse, Ilford, Essex IG1 1BA; Tel 020 8514 5353; Fax 020 8478 4450
Senior Probation Officer M. McVey

Community Service Units

West Community Service Unit 15 Belton Rd, Forest Gate, London E7 9PF; Tel 020 8472 5412; Fax 020 8471 6673
Senior Probation Officer G. Atherton

East Community Service Unit 29–33 Victoria Rd, Romford, Essex RM1 2JT; Tel 01708 753555; Fax 01708 752096
Senior Probation Officer N. Howell-Ives

London Probation Area, South East Region

9–13 Elmfield Rd, Bromley, Kent BR1 1LT; Tel 020 8464 3433; Fax 020 8466 1571
Secretary to London Probation Board S. Hodges; Tel 020 8464 3433
Director (Operations) D. McDonald; Tel 020 8464 3437
Manager (Personnel) Beverley Miller; Tel 020 8464 3436
Manager (Crown Court) A. Glaister; Tel 020 8681 5039

Offices

Headquarters Crosby Hse, 9–13 Elmfield Rd, Bromley, Kent BR1 1LT; Tel 020 8464 3430; Fax 020 8466 1571
Director (Operations) D. McDonald

Beckenham Road Office 6 Beckenham Rd, Beckenham, Kent BR3 4LR; Tel 020 8658 3511
Divisional Manager Peter Costello
Senior Practitioner P. Tomlin

Church Hill Office 6 Church Hill, Orpington, Kent BR6 0HE; Tel 01689 831616
Senior Practitioner Selene Grandison
Senior Probation Officer I. Anderson

Church House Office Church Hse, Old Palace Rd, Croydon, Surrey CR0 1AX; Tel 020 8686 6551
Divisional Manager Alison Dale
Senior Practitioner Barry Dickinson
Senior Practitioner Marie Heerah
Senior Probation Officer R. Gorf
Senior Probation Officer L. Felix

Crown Court The Law Courts, Altyre Rd, Croydon, Surrey CR9 5AB; Tel 020 8681 5039
Senior Probation Officer A. Glaister

Community Service Offices

Headquarters 111 Chertsey Cres, New Addington, Surrey CR0 0DH; Tel 01689 844735
Senior Probation Officer Ann Stainton

Beckenham Road Community Service Office 6 Beckenham Rd, Beckenham, Kent BR3 4LR; Tel 020 8658 3511

St. Martin's Hall Community Service Office 47c Dartnell Rd, Croydon, Surrey CR0 6JB; Tel 020 8656 8561

Norwich Place Community Service Office Bexleyheath, Kent DA6 7ND; Tel 020 8301 3067
Divisional Manager L. Bransby
Senior Practitioner Claire Thornton
Senior Practitioner Ian Forsyth

Partnerships/Community Development Team

Crosby House 1st Fl, 9–13 Elmfield Rd, Bromley, Kent BR1 1LT; Tel 020 8464 3436
Divisional Manager G. Pasquale
Manager (Community Development) D. Horne
Manager (Community Development) Nigel Austen
Manager (Community Development) G. Taylor

Offender Programme Team

Beckenham Road Offender Programme Team 6 Beckenham Rd, Beckenham, Kent BR3 4LR; Tel 020 8658 3511
Senior Probation Officer N. Porter

Probation Hostel 4 Beckenham Rd, Beckenham, Kent BR3 4LR; Tel 020 8658 3515
Hostel Manager Trevor Marshall

Public Protection Team Bromley Magistrates Court, 1 London Rd, Bromley, Kent BR1 1RA; Tel 020 8290 6255
Senior Probation Officer A. Lusk

London Probation Area, South West Region

45 High St, Kingston upon Thames, Surrey KT1 1LQ; Tel 020 8546 0018; Fax 020 8549 8990
Secretary to the Probation Committee A.G. Moore
2nd Fl, Glen Hse, London W1P 9LA
Chief Probation Officer D. Chantler
Director (Policy and Resources) A.P. Long
Director (Operations) C. Hayward

Offices

Headquarters 45 High St, Kingston upon Thames, Surrey KT1 1LQ; Tel 020 8546 0018
Contact D. Chantler (CPO)

Family Courts Unit 125 Richmond Rd, Kingston upon Thames, Surrey KT2 5BX; Tel 020 8541 0233
R. Thomas (SFCWO)

Kingston Crown Court Liaison Probation Office Canbury Park Rd, Kingston upon Thames, Surrey KT2 6JU; Tel 020 8549 5241
Manager (Courts Services) Mr A. Nelson

Hampton Wick Community Supervision Team 16 High St, Hampton Wick, Kingston upon Thames, Surrey KT1 4DB; Tel 020 8977 0133; 020 8977 0134 020 8977 0135
Borough Manager L. Pace

Merton Probation Office Newton Hse, 1 Commonside West, Mitcham, Surrey CR4 4HA; Tel 020 8685 0075
Borough Manager J. Martin

Area Resource Centre (Intensive Probation Programme etc.) and Community Service Unit Wimbledon, Greater London SW19 1EQ; Tel 020 8543 3441; 020 8543 3442; 020 8543 3443
Borough Manager C. Giles
Development Officer H. Weijman

Sutton Probation Office 103 Westmead Rd, Sutton, Surrey SM1 4JD; Tel 020 8643 7211
Borough Manager E. Walpole

Community Service Unit

Kingston and Richmond Magistrates Court Team

45 High St, Kingston upon Thames, Surrey KT1 1LQ; Tel 020 8939 4130
Contact R. Coltofeanu

Sutton Court Team

103 Westmead Rd, Sutton, Surrey SM1 4JD; Tel 020 8643 7211
Manager (Courts Services) A. Austen

Merseyside

Burlington Hse, Crosby Rd, Liverpool, Merseyside L22 0PJ; Tel 0151 920 9201; Fax 0151 949 0528
Chief Probation Officer J.W. Stafford
Deputy Chief Probation Officer D.A. Bradbury
Assistant Chief Officer P.J. Murray
Treasurer I.M. Hall
Personnel Officer J.M. Hill
Solicitor K. Moss
Property Service Officer T. Gray
NPSISS Project Leader R.I. Steele
Secretary/Administrator K. Sproul-Cran
Committee Clerk/Administrative Officer L. Atherton

Offices

Staff Development Rainford Hall, Crank Rd, St. Helens, Merseyside WA11 7RP; Tel 01744 755181; Fax 01744 454671
Staff Development/Senior Probation Officer P.J. Kelly; Tel 01744 755181
Assistant Chief Probation Officer (Staff Development) D.W. Murray (ACPO)

ACPO Management Unit Curtis Hse, 1 Derby La, Liverpool, Merseyside L13 6QA; Tel 0151 281 0832; Fax 0151 281 0866
Assistant Chief Probation Officer (Pre-and Post-Release) T.H. Eastham
Assistant Chief Probation Officer (Community Service) D.C. Metherell

ACPO Management Unit St. Mary's Hse, 50 Church St, St. Helens, Merseyside WA10 1AP; Tel 01744 606226; Fax 01744 606224
Assistant Chief Probation Officer (Community Supervision) S. Chambers

ACPO Management Unit 40 Europa Blvd, Birkenhead, Merseyside CH41 4PE; Tel 0151 666 0400; Fax 0151 666 0401
Assistant Chief Probation Officer (Community Supervision) A. Pakula

ACPO Management Unit Suite 405 Cotton, Exchange Bldg, Old Hall St, Liverpool, Merseyside L3 9LQ; Tel 0151 476 7166; Fax 0151 476 7170
Assistant Chief Probation Officer (Court Services) A.E. Stelman

Family Court Welfare Service

Knowsley and St. Helens 9–31 Barrow St, St. Helens, Merseyside WA10 1RX; Tel 01744 630245; Fax 01744 630246
Senior Court Welfare Officer/Senior Probation Officer G.H. White

Liverpool and Sefton 3rd Fl, State Hse, Liverpool, Merseyside L2 4TR; Tel 0151 286 6464; Fax 0151 286 6466
Senior Court Welfare Officer and Senior Probation Officer
  M.A. Ravey

Community Supervision Division

Knowsley Community Supervision South Knowsley Probation Centre, 597 Princess Dr, Liverpool, Merseyside L14 9NE; Tel 0151 480 4544; Fax 0151 480 3618
Senior Probation Officer A.V. Aubrey

Liverpool South Central Community Supervision Liverpool Community Probation Centre, 180 Falkner St, Liverpool, Merseyside L8 7SX; Tel 0151 706 6688; Fax 0151 708 9687
Senior Probation Officer J. Edwards

Liverpool Community Supervision 142–148 Stanley Rd, Kirkdale, Liverpool, Merseyside L5 7QQ; Tel 0151 286 6159; Fax 0151 284 7847
Senior Probation Officer S. Tonks

Liverpool Community Supervision East Liverpool Probation Centre, 1b Derby La, Liverpool, Merseyside L13 69A; Tel 0151 281 8655; Fax 0151 281 8688
Senior Probation Officer J. Kuyateh

St. Helens Community Supervision St. Helens Probation Centre, St. Mary's Hse, St. Helens, Merseyside WA10 1AP; Tel 01744 630229; Fax 01744 606224
Senior Probation Officer J. Cunliffe

Sefton Community Supervision 4 Trinity Rd, Bootle, Merseyside L20 7BE; Tel 0151 286 5667; Fax 0151 286 6900
Senior Probation Officer C.M. Barron

Sefton Community Supervision 188 Lord St, Southport, Merseyside PR9 0QQ; Tel 01704 534634; Fax 01704 501845
Senior Probation Officer C.M. Barron

Wirral Community Supervision 40 Europa Blvd, Birkenhead, Merseyside CH41 4PE; Tel 0151 666 0400; Fax 0151 666 0401
Senior Probation Officer R. Hamilton

Court Services Division

Crown Court PO Box 69, Queen Elizabeth II Law Courts, Liverpool, Merseyside L69 2NE; Tel 0151 236 5302; Fax 0151 255 0682
Senior Probation Officer J. Crawley

Liverpool Court Services Unit 6–8 Temple Crt, Liverpool, Merseyside L2 6PY; Tel 0151 286 6226; Fax 0151 286 6227
Senior Probation Officer J.F. England

Liverpool Magistrates' Court 1st Fl, State Hse, Liverpool, Merseyside L2 4TR; Tel 0151 236 0603; Fax 0151 476 7151
Senior Probation Officer J.F. England

188 Lord Street Southport, Merseyside PR9 0QQ; Tel 01704 534634; Fax 01704 501845
Senior Probation Officer R.W. Sloman

North Sefton Magistrates' Court The Law Courts, Albert Rd, Southport, Merseyside PR9 0LJ; Tel 01704 544277; Fax 01704 545840

South Knowsley Probation Centre 597 Princess Dr, Liverpool, Merseyside L14 9NE; Tel 0151 480 4544; Fax 0151 480 3618
Senior Probation Officer C.D. Rutherford

South Sefton Magistrates' Court The Court Bldg, 29 Merton Rd, Bootle, Merseyside L20 3BJ; Tel 0151 933 6999 ext 236; Fax 0151 933 8602

Wirral Court Services 40 Europa Blvd, Birkenhead, Merseyside CH41 4PE; Tel 0151 666 0400; Fax 0151 666 0401
Senior Probation Officer R. Goodwin

Pre- and Post-Release Division

Kirkby Probation Centre Oatlands Rd, Kirkby, Liverpool, Merseyside L32 4UH; Tel 0151 547 3160; Fax 0151 547 2244
Senior Probation Officer A.T. Dickinson

Liverpool North Pre- and Post-Release 137–139 Breckfield Rd North, Anfield, Liverpool, Merseyside L5 4QY; Tel 0151 284 4487; Fax 0151 284 8683
Senior Probation Officer J.L. Harrison

Liverpool South Pre- and Post-Release Liverpool Community Probation Centre, 180 Falkner St, Liverpool, Merseyside L8 7SX; Tel 0151 706 6666; Fax 0151 706 6694
Senior Probation Officer G. Hirst

Probation Department HM Prison – Liverpool, Hornby Rd, Liverpool, Merseyside L9 3DF; Tel 0151 525 5971; Fax 0151 524 1941
Senior Probation Officer P.L. Fumiss

Probation Department HM Prison – Altcourse, Higher La, Liverpool, Merseyside L9 7LH; Tel 0151 522 2000; Fax 0151 522 2121
Senior Probation Officer M. Redman

Sefton Pre- and Post- Release 25 Crosby Rd South, Waterloo, Liverpool, Merseyside L22 1RG; Tel 0151 920 4444; Fax 0151 928 9143
Senior Probation Officer D. Rimmer

Wirral Pre- and Post- Release 40 Europa Blvd, Birkenhead, Merseyside CH41 4PE; Tel 0151 666 0400; Fax 0151 666 0401
Senior Probation Officer V.G.J. Sherlock

Specialist Services Division

Merseyside Development Unit 5 Derby La, Old Swan, Liverpool, Merseyside L13 6QA; Tel 0151 252 0123; Fax 0151 252 1117
Senior Probation Officer J.R. Nottage

Merseyside Programmes Unit Liverpool Community Probation Centre, 180 Falkner St, Liverpool, Merseyside L8 7SX; Tel 0151 706 6622; Fax 0151 708 5044
Senior Probation Officer J. Best

Edge Hill Specialist Unit 13 North View, Edge Hill, Liverpool, Merseyside L7 8TS; Tel 0151 281 1245; Fax 0151 281 1246
Officer (Housing) P.J. Garner

Substance Misuse Liverpool Community Probation Centre, 180 Falkner St, Liverpool, Merseyside L8 7SX; Tel 0151 706 6611; Fax 0151 708 9687
Senior Probation Officer G.L. Crawley

Community Service Division

Community Service Unit (Knowsley and St. Helens) Belle Vale District Centre, Childwall Valley Rd, Liverpool, Merseyside L25 2RJ; Tel 0151 487 0123; Fax 0151 487 0101
Senior Probation Officer R.J. Roach

Community Service Unit (Liverpool North) 16 Derby La, Old Swan, Liverpool, Merseyside L13 6QA; Tel 0151 281 8655; Fax 0151 281 8688
Senior Probation Officer S.F. Brown

Community Service Unit (Liverpool South) Liverpool Community Probation Centre, 180 Falkner St, Liverpool, Merseyside L8 7SX; Tel 0151 706 6644; Fax 0151 708 5044
Senior Probation Officer S.F. Brown

Community Service Unit (Sefton) Sefton Hse, 1 Molyneux Way, Liverpool, Merseyside L10 2JA; Tel 0151 531 6737; Fax 0151 527 2534
Senior Probation Officer R.J. Roach

Community Service Unit (Wirral) 40 Europa Blvd, Birkenhead, Merseyside CH41 4PE; Tel 0151 666 0400; Fax 0151 666 0401
Senior Probation Officer J. Farnin

Middlesbrough

Headquarters, Probation Hse, 2 Longlands Rd, Middlesbrough TS4 2JL; URL www.teesside-probation.org.uk; Tel 01642 230533; Fax 01642 220083

Secretary of the Probation Board and Assistant Chief Officer (Human Resources) Barbara Holdhusen
Assistant Chief Officer Alistair Morrison
Assistant Chief Officer Brian Thomas
Assistant Chief Officer Peter Hadfield
Treasurer/Manager (Finance) Phil Craig

Offices

Albert Road Probation Office (Court Liaison) 160 Albert Rd, Middlesbrough TS1 2PZ; Tel 01642 247438; Fax 01642 244651
Senior Probation Officer Vacancy

Avenue Road Probation Office Avenue Rd, Hartlepool TS24 8BL; Tel 01429 265101; Fax 01429 231854
Senior Probation Officer (Community Reintegration) Peter Burnett

Community Reintegration 154 Borough Rd, Middlesbrough TS1 2EP; Tel 01642 210717; Fax 01642 230621
Senior Probation Officer Trevor Jones
Senior Probation Officer Rosana Roy

Crown Court Russell St, Middlesbrough TS1 2AE; Tel 01642 250469; Fax 01642 230541
Senior Probation Officer Doug West

Drug Resource Team 18 Woodlands Rd, Middlesbrough TS1 3BE; Tel 01642 225021; Fax 01642 252215
Senior Probation Officer Janet Bolton

Mowlam House Office Mowlam Hse, 1 Oxford St, South Bank, Middlesbrough TS6 9DF; Tel 01642 452346; Fax 01462 466021
Senior Probation Officer Elizabeth Kendall

Practitioner Training Unit Cowley Hse, 156 Borough Rd, Middlesbrough TS1 2EJ; Tel 01642 247476; Fax 01642 248486
Senior Probation Officer Mike Waddington

Public Protection Unit 160 Albert Rd, Middlesbrough TS1 2PZ; Tel 01642 247438; Fax 01642 244651
Senior Probation Officer Elaine Hynneysett

Station Road Office 38 Station Rd, Redcar, Redcar and Cleveland S10 1AG; Tel 01642 480611; Fax 01642 489424
Senior Probation Officer Sandra Sam-Drysdale

Stockton Office Advance Hse, St. Mark's Crt, Teasdale, Thornby, Stockton-on-Tees TS17 6QX; Tel 01642 606111; Fax 01642 607764
Senior Probation Officer Sarah Megan
Senior Probation Officer Isobel Townsend

What Works Advance Hse, St. Marks Crt, Teasdale, Thornaby, Stockton-on-Tees TS17 6QX; Tel 01642 606111; Fax 01642 607764
Senior Probation Officer Tina Beckett

Woodlands Probation Centre – What Works 18 Woodlands Rd, Middlesbrough TS1 3BE; Tel 01642 225021; Fax 01642 252215
Senior Probation Officer Liz Colman

Enhanced Community Punishment

Milbank House 1 Milbank St, Middlesbrough TS6 6DD; Tel 01642 515315; 01642 515316; Fax 01642 290677
Operations Manager Russell Portues

Middlesex

4th Fl, Glen Hse, 200 Tottenham Crt Rd, London W1P 9LA; Tel 020 7436 7121; Fax 020 7436 9827; (CPO/DCPO/COs only) 020 7436 9879; (Personnel Department) 020 7637 5492
Chief Probation Officer J. Walters
Deputy Chief Probation Officer C. McCulloch
Chief Officer (Finance) C. Reid
Principal Finance Officer A.R. Mastris
Chief Officer (Human Resources) U. Steiger
Chief Officer (Quality Assurance) M. Frost
Manager (Training) S. Tarrant

Manager (Human Resources) T. Webb
Manager (Information and Research) W. Brazier
Manager (Facilities) J. McKay
Senior Administrative Officer (Health and Safety) J. Cutt
Communications Officer E. George

Outstationed Divisional Managers

BARNET AND SPECIAL PROGRAMMES UNIT

Divisional Manager's Office 1st Fl, Allied Hse, 3 Burnt Oak Broadway, Edgware, Greater London HA8 5LT; Tel 020 8205 1885; Fax 020 8205 5462
Divisional Manager M. Bland

BRENT

Divisional Manager's Office 440 High Rd, Willesden, London NW10 2DW; Tel 020 8830 4393; Fax 020 8830 2502
Divisional Manager W. Jones (DM)

EALING

Divisional Manager's Office Leeland Hse, Leeland Rd, London W13 9HH; Tel 020 8840 6918; Fax 020 8579 7835
Divisional Manager M. Jenkin

ENFIELD

Divisional Manager's Office Probation Office, The Old Court Hse, Windmill Hill, Enfield, Greater London EN2 6SA; Tel 020 8363 2261; Fax 020 8367 1624
Divisional Manager R. Cerfontyne

HARINGEY

Divisional Manager's Office Marlborough Hall, 96 Landsdowne Rd, Tottenham, London N17 9XX; Tel 020 8801 6373; Fax 020 8885 4233
Divisional Manager I. Davies

HARROW

Divisional Manager's Office Probation Office, Rosslyn Cres, Harrow, Greater London HA1 2SR; Tel 020 8427 2323; Fax 020 8424 2602
Divisional Manager (Harrow and Hostels) C. Bernard

HOUNSLOW

Divisional Manager's Office Banklabs Hse, 41b Cross Lances Rd, Hounslow, Greater London TW3 2AD; Tel 020 8577 7615; Fax 020 8570 6127
Divisional Manager C. Renau

Hillingdon and Family Court Welfare Units Divisional Manager's Office, 74–75 High St, Uxbridge, Greater London UB8 1JR; Tel 01895 230035; Fax 01895 271966
Divisional Manager D. Rooney

Local Offices

Acton Probation Office 4 Birkbeck Rd, Acton, London W3 6BE; Tel 020 8992 5863; Fax 020 8993 5942
Senior Probation Officer J. Gallagher

Ealing Probation Office Leeland Hse, Leeland Rd, London W13 9HH; Tel 020 8840 6464; Fax 020 8579 8165
Contact B. Stevenson

Enfield Probation Office The Old Court Hse, Windmill Hill, Enfield, Greater London EN2 6SA; Tel 020 8366 6376; Fax 020 8367 1624
Senior Probation Officer H. Harwood

Feltham Remand Centre/YOI Probation Dept, HM Remand Centre, Bentfont Rd, Feltham, Greater London TW13 4ND; Tel 020 8890 0061 ext 299; Fax 020 8893 2809
Senior Probation Officer J. Dalkin

Contingency Team Allied Hse, 1st Fl, 3 Burnt Oak Broadway, Edgware, Greater London HA8 5LT; Tel 020 8205 2561; 020 8205 3003; Fax 020 8205 5462
Senior Probation Officer J. Cohen

Finchley Probation Office 6–8 Alexandra Gr, Finchley, London N12 8NU; Tel 020 8445 1623; Fax 020 8445 1618
Senior Probation Officer H. Ford

The Groupwork Unit Lordship La Probation Office, 71 Lordship La, Tottenham, London N17 6RS; Tel 020 8808 4522; Fax 020 8885 5946
Senior Probation Officer M. McGeown

Harrow Crown Court Hailsham Dr, Harrow, Greater London HA1 4TU; Tel 020 8424 2294; Fax 020 8424 9346
Senior Probation Officer G. James

Harrow Probation Office Rosslyn Cres, Harrow, Greater London HA1 2SR; Tel 020 8427 7246; Fax 020 8424 2101
Senior Probation Officer D. Upcott
Senior Probation Officer G. Johnson

Hendon Probation Office Allied Hse, 1st Fl, 3 Burnt Oak Broadway, Edgware, Greater London HA8 5LT; Tel 020 8205 2561; 020 8205 3003; Fax 020 8205 5462
Senior Probation Officer P. Abernethy

Highgate Probation Office Telfer Hse, Church Rd, Highgate, London N6 4QJ; Tel 020 8341 9060; Fax 020 8341 4260
Senior Probation Officer M. Bland

Hounslow Probation Office Banklabs Hse, 41a Cross Lances Rd, Hounslow, Greater London TW3 2AD; Tel 020 8570 0626; Fax (Community sentences) 020 8814 1238; (Pre- and post-release) 020 8570 1190
Senior Probation Officer G. Cross
Senior Probation Officer S. Palmer
Senior Probation Officer J. Shaw

Isleworth Crown Court Probation Office, 36 Ridgeway Rd, Isleworth, Greater London TW7 5LP; Tel 020 8568 8811; Fax 020 8758 9650
Senior Probation Officer B. Collins

Lansdowne Rd Probation Office 90 Lansdowne Rd, Tottenham, London N17 9XX; Tel 020 8808 4849; Fax 020 8365 0981
Senior Probation Officer R. Parr

Lordship Lane Probation Office 71 Lordship La, Tottenham, London N17 6RS; Tel 020 8808 4522; Fax 020 8885 5946
Senior Probation Officer C. Ferguson

Partnership Unit 4 Birkbeck Rd, Acton, London W3 6BE; Tel 020 8993 8613; Fax 020 8993 5942
Partnerships Manager C. Chater

Sex Offenders Unit 4 Birkbeck Rd, Acton, London W3 6BE; Tel 020 8992 5863; Fax 020 8993 5942
Senior Probation Officer M. Roberts

Southall Probation Office 2nd Fl, King's Hse, The Green, Southall, Greater London UB2 4QQ; Tel 020 8574 1071; Fax 020 8813 9124
Senior Probation Officer D.R. Griffiths

Special Programme Unit 1st Fl, Allied Hse, 3 Burnt Oak Broadway, Edgware, Greater London HA8 5LT; Tel 020 8205 2561; 020 8205 3003; Fax 020 8205 5462
Senior Probation Officer M. Bailey

Uxbridge Probation Office The Court Hse, Harefield Rd, Uxbridge, Greater London UB8 1PQ; Tel 01895 231972; 01895 231976; Fax 01895 257972
Senior Probation Officer I. Brooks
Senior Probation Officer D. Walls

Wembley Probation Office 402–408 High Rd, Wembley, Greater London HA9 6AL; Tel 020 8903 4921; Fax 020 8795 0472
Senior Probation Officer M. Whyte

Willesden Probation Office 440 High Rd, Willesden, London NW10 2DW; Tel 020 8451 6212; Fax 020 8451 3467
Senior Probation Officer J. Rambarath
Senior Probation Officer C. Green
Senior Probation Officer M. Leckey (Acting)

Wood Green Crown Court Probation Office, Woodall Hse, Lordship La, Wood Green, London N22 5LF; Tel 020 8881 1400; Fax 020 8881 2665
Senior Probation Officer A. Hughes

Community Service Centres

Enfield CS The Old Court Hse, Windmill Hill, Enfield, Greater London EN2 6SA; Tel 020 8366 6376; Fax 020 8367 1624
Senior Probation Officer J. Davis

Harrow CS Harrow Probation Service, Rosslyn Cres, Harrow, Greater London HA1 2SR; Tel 020 8427 7246; Fax 020 8424 2101
Senior Probation Officer M. Flynn

Southall CS 2nd Fl, King's Hse, Southall, Greater London UB2 4QQ; Tel 020 8843 1828; Fax 020 8813 9124
Senior Probation Officer M. Wells

Uxbridge CS Uxbridge Promotion Office, The Court Hse, Uxbridge, Greater London UB8 1PQ; Tel 01895 231972; 01895 231976; Fax 01895 257972
Senior Probation Officer M. Flynn

Wembley CS 402–408 High Rd, Wembley, Greater London HA9 6AL; Tel 020 8903 8551; Fax 020 8795 0472
Senior Probation Officer B. Lewis

Family Court Welfare

Ealing FCWU Lancaster Hse, Leeland Rd, Ealing, London W13 9HH; Tel 020 8840 8077; Fax 020 8840 8070

Finchley FCWU Probation Office, 6–8 Alexandra Gr, Finchley, London N12 8NU; Tel 020 8445 1637; Fax 020 8445 1041
Contact S. Walsh (SCWO)

Uxbridge FCWU 75 High St, Uxbridge, Greater London UB8 1JR; Tel 01895 251398; Fax 01895 236299
Contact J. Baddeley (SCWO)

Norfolk

4th Fl, St. James' Yarn Mill, Whitefriars, Norwich, Norfolk NR3 1SU; Tel 01603 220100; Fax 01603 664019
Chair (Norfolk Probation Board) C. Winstanley
Secretary to the Norfolk Probation Board K. Rayner
Chief Probation Officer M. Graham
Manager (Human Resources) A. Burrage

Offices

Cromer 1–3 Hamilton Rd, Cromer, Norfolk NR27 9HL; Tel 01263 512593; Fax 01263 513348
Senior Probation Officer A. Hartland
Senior Probation Officer J. Westmacott
Senior Probation Officer S. Hargrave
Senior Probation Officers can be contacted at Whitefriars, Norwich, Norfolk; Tel 01603 724000.

Great Yarmouth Rampart Rd, Great Yarmouth, Norfolk NR30 1QZ; Tel 01493 855525; Fax 01493 332769
Senior Probation Officer P. Rainton

HMP Wayland HM Prison, Wayland, Thetford, Norfolk IP25 6RL; Tel 01953 858071; Fax 01953 882248
Senior Probation Officer B. Cranna

King's Lynn Purfleet Quay, King's Lynn, Norfolk PE30 1HP; Tel 01553 669000; Fax 01553 776544
Senior Probation Officer B. Moulton

Norwich Whitefriars Probation Office, Whitefriars, Norwich, Norfolk NR3 1TN; Tel 01603 724000; Fax 01603 768270
Senior Probation Officer A. Hartland
Senior Probation Officer J. Westmacott
Senior Probation Officer S. Hargrave

Sentence Planning and Resettlement Team 68 Bishopgate, Norwich, Norfolk NR1 4AA; Tel 01603 221600
Senior Probation Officer H. Fitzsimons
Senior Probation Officer E. Butterworth

HMP Norwich HM Prison, Mousehold, Norwich, Norfolk NR1 4LU; Tel 01603 708600; Fax 01603 708619
Senior Probation Officer J. McNelly

Community Service Units 68 Bishopgate, Norwich, Norfolk NR1 4AA; Tel 01603 221600
Senior Probation Officer J. O'Byrne

Thetford 12–14 Raymond St, Thetford, Norfolk IP24 2EA; Tel 01842 754071; Fax 01842 751089
Senior Probation Officer L. Hough

Sentence Planning and Resettlement Team – Great Yarmouth

Rampart Rd, Great Yarmouth, Norfolk NR30 1QZ; Tel 01493 855525; Fax 01493 332769
Senior Probation Officer H. Fitzsimons
Senior Probation Officer E. Butterworth
68 Bishopgate, , Norwich, Norfolk NR1 4AA; Tel 01603 221600

Sentence Planning and Resettlement Team – Kings Lynn and Thetford

Purfleet Quay, King's Lynn, Norfolk PE30 1HP; Tel 01553 669000; Fax 01553 776544
Senior Probation Officer H. Fitzsimons
Senior Probation Officer E. Butterworth
68 Bishopgate, Norwich, Norfolk NR1 4AA; Tel 01603 221600

Drug Treatment and Testing Orders Unit

22–24 Colegate, Norwich, Norfolk NR3 1BQ; Tel 01603 877140; Fax 01603 877145
Senior Probation Officer C. Attfield

John Boag House Probation and Bail Hostel

John Boag Hse, Drayton Rd, Norwich, Norfolk NR3 2DF; Tel 01603 429488; Fax 01603 485903
Senior Probation Officer J. Rymer

North Wales Probation Area

Alexander Hse, Abergele Rd, Colwyn Bay, Conwy LL32 8DU; Tel 01492 513413

North Yorkshire

North Yorkshire Probation Service, Thurstan Hse, Northallerton, North Yorkshire DL6 2XQ; Tel 01609 778644; Fax 01609 778321
Essex Lodge, 15 South Pde, Northallerton, North Yorkshire DL7 8SG
Secretary of the Probation Committee Stephen Knight, BA(Hons) (Acting)
North Yorkshire County Council, County Hall, Northallerton, North Yorkshire DL7 8AD
Chief Probation Officer R. Brown
Assistant Chief Officer (Operational Support) A. Cullen
Assistant Chief Probation Officer S. Lester
Assistant Chief Probation Officer M. Murphy
Essex Lodge, 16 South Pde, Northallerton, North Yorkshire DL7 8SG; Tel 01609 772271; Fax 01609 772931

Offices

The Court House Bunker's Hill, Skipton, North Yorkshire BD23 1HU; Tel 01756 794797
Senior Probation Officer S. Wardley

Essex Lodge 16 South Pde, Northallerton, North Yorkshire DL7 8SG; Tel 01609 772271
Senior Probation Officer S. Wardley

Falsgrave Road Office 12 Falsgrave Rd, Scarborough, North Yorkshire YO12 5AT; Tel 01723 366341
Senior Probation Officer A. Radley

Haywra Crescent Office 5–7 Haywra Cres, Harrogate, North Yorkshire HG1 5BG; Tel 01423 566764
Senior Probation Officer E. Watkins

Lowther Street Office 108 Lowther St, York YO3 7ND; Tel 01904 526000
Senior Probation Officer S. Wardley

Union Lane Office Union La, Selby, North Yorkshire YO8 0AU; Tel 01757 707241
Senior Probation Officer S. Wardley

Northamptonshire

PO Box 136, County Hall, Northampton, Northamptonshire NN1 1AT; E-mail northantsprobation@yahoo.co.uk; Tel 01604 236814; Fax 01604 236223
Secretary of the Probation Board David Ryan
Chief Officer Carol Bernard
43–47 Bridge St, Northampton, Northamptonshire NN1 1NS; Tel 01604 658000; Fax 01604 658004
Assistant Chief Officer A.R. Ghumra
Assistant Chief Officer Vacancy
Assistant Chief Officer E.R. Pearse
Crown Court Liaison Officer C. Shorley
Development Training S. Rawden

Offices

Bridge Street Office 43–47 Bridge St, Northampton, Northamptonshire NN1 1NS; Tel 01604 658000; Fax 01604 658004
Chief Officer Ellie Roy
Assistant Chief Officer A.R. Ghumra
Assistant Chief Officer E.R. Pearse
Senior Probation Officer R. Bromwich
Senior Probation Officer C. Hamson

Edinburgh House 7 Corporation St, Corby, Northamptonshire NN17 1NG; Tel 01536 463920; Fax 01536 406607
Senior Probation Officer M. Doel

Oxford Street Office 20 Oxford St, Wellingborough, Northamptonshire NN8 4HY; Tel 01933 303680; Fax 01933 441547
Senior Probation Officer C. Langford
Senior Probation Ofifcer E. Chapman

Northumbria

Lifton Hse, Eslington Rd, Jesmond, Newcastle upon Tyne, Tyne and Wear NE2 4SP; Tel 0191 281 5721; Fax 0191 281 3548
Chief Executive and Chief Probation Officer S.C. Murphy
Director (Risk, Policy and Planning) D. Gardiner
Director (Programmes and Human Resources) P. Williamson
Director (Finance, IT and Performance) J. Fenwick
Assistant Director (Business Services) C. Mackie
Divisional Director (Community Punishment) J.F. North

Offices

NEWCASTLE DIVISION

Divisional Director Unit – Newcastle 6 Lansdowne Terr, Gosforth, Newcastle upon Tyne, Tyne and Wear NE3 1HW; Tel 0191 213 0611; Fax 0191 213 1361
Divisional Director W. Dale

Community Programme Division 70–78 St. James' Blvd, Newcastle upon Tyne, Tyne and Wear NE1 4BN; Tel 0191 261 9091; Fax 0191 233 0758
Manager   G. Coulthard

Glendale Terrace Byker, Newcastle upon Tyne, Tyne and Wear NE6 1PB; Tel 0191 276 6666; Fax 0191 224 2878
Team Manager   M. Ord

Lansdowne Terrace 5 Lansdowne Terr, Gosforth, Newcastle upon Tyne, Tyne and Wear NE3 1HW; Tel 0191 213 1888; Fax 0191 213 1393
Team Manager   J. Fiddes

Law Courts Quayside, Newcastle upon Tyne, Tyne and Wear NE1 3LA; Tel 0191 230 1737; Fax 0191 233 0759
Team Manager   L. Clarkin

West Road Office 717 West Rd, Newcastle upon Tyne, Tyne and Wear NE15 7PS; Tel 0191 274 1153; Fax 0191 275 0963
Team Manager   O. Nesbit

Collingwood House Office 6th Fl, Collingwood Hse, 3 Collingwood St, Newcastle upon Tyne, Tyne and Wear NE1 1JW; Tel 0191 232 3368; Fax 0191 233 0760
Team Manager   L. Clarkin

St. James' Boulevard Offices 70–78 St. Jame's Blvd, Newcastle upon Tyne, Tyne and Wear NE1 4BN; Tel 0191 261 9091; Fax 0191 233 0758
Team Manager   J. Mills

NORTHUMBERLAND AND NORTH TYNESIDE

Divisional Director Unit – Northumberland and North Tyneside Division 39 Esplanade, Whitley Bay, Tyne and Wear NE26 2AE; Tel 0191 253 3236; Fax 0191 252 7713
Divisional Director   J. McCartney

Beaconsfield Street Office 38 Beaconsfield St, Blyth, Northumberland NE24 2DR; Tel 01670 352441; Fax 01670 352921
Team Manager   J. Pooley

Bondgate Without Office 27 Bondgate Without, Alnwick, Northumberland NE66 1PR; Tel 01665 602242; Fax 01665 605184
Team Manager   L. Hill
Team Manager   C. McLaren

Former Employment Exchange South View, Ashington, Northumberland NE63 0RY; Tel 01670 813053; Fax 01670 814858
Team Manager   L. Hill
Team Manager   C. McLaren

Lovaine House 9 Lovaine Terr, North Shields, Tyne and Wear NE29 0HJ; Tel 0191 296 2335; Fax 0191 257 6170
Team Manager   P.E. Lloyd

Warwick Road Office 13 Warwick Rd, Wallsend, Tyne and Wear NE28 6SE; Tel 0191 262 9211; Fax 0191 295 4824
Team Manager   D. Downing

Wentworth Place Office 4 Wentworth Pl, Hexham, Northumberland NE46 1XB; Tel 01434 602499; Fax 01434 606195
Team Manager   G. Pooley

SOUTH TYNESIDE AND GATESHEAD DIVISION

Divisional Director Unit – South Tyneside and Gateshead Division 5–8 Cornwallis St, South Shields, Tyne and Wear NE33 1BB; Tel 0191 456 1000; Fax 0191 427 6922
Divisional Director   C. Fiddes
Manager (Partnerships)   R. Taylor

Secretan Way Office Mill Bank, South Shields, Tyne and Wear NE33 1HG; Tel 0191 455 2294; Fax 0191 427 6919
Team Manager   R. Booth

Homer Villa Office St. John's Terr, Jarrow, Tyne and Wear NE32 3BT; Tel 0191 489 7767; Fax 0191 483 3961
Team Manager   A. Love
Team Manager   I. Graves

Community Programme Division 5–8 Cornwallis St, South Shields, Tyne and Wear NE33 1BB; Tel 0191 456 1000; Fax 0191 427 6922
Manager   M. Gavin

Warwick Street Office Warwick St, Gateshead, Tyne and Wear NE8 1PZ; Tel 0191 478 2451; Fax 0191 478 1197
Team Manager   J. Kelly

Wesley Court Office Wesley Crt, Blaydon, Tyne and Wear NE21 5BT; Tel 0191 414 5626; Fax 0191 414 7809
Team Manager   M. Lamb

WEARSIDE DIVISION

Divisional Director Unit – Wearside Division 45 John St, Sunderland, Tyne and Wear SR1 1QU; Tel 0191 510 1859; Fax 0191 565 7596
Divisional Director   H. Knotek

Community Programme Division 45 John St, Sunderland, Tyne and Wear SR1 1QU; Tel 0191 510 1859; Fax 0191 565 7596
Manager   M. Gavin

Hylton Road Office Hylton Rd, Pennywell, Sunderland, Tyne and Wear SR4 8DS; Tel 0191 534 5545; Fax 0191 534 2380
Team Manager   K. Harper

Kings Road Office Kings Rd, Southwick, Sunderland, Tyne and Wear SR5 2LS; Tel 0191 548 8844; Fax 0191 548 6834
Team Manager   M. McGovern

Mainsforth Terrace West Office Hendon, Sunderland, Tyne and Wear SR2 8JX; Tel 0191 514 3093; Fax 0191 565 1625
Team Manager   L. Ferguson

Newbottle Street Office 10 Newbottle St, Houghton-Le-Spring, Tyne and Wear DH4 4AL; Tel 0191 584 3109; Fax 0191 584 4919
Team Manager   D. Rees

Old Police Buildings Spout La, Washington, Tyne and Wear NE37 2AB; Tel 0191 416 8574; Fax 0191 415 7943
Team Manager   D. Rees

Practice Development

Practice Development Lipton Hse, Eshington Rd, Jesmond, Newcastle upon Tyne, Tyne and Wear NE2 4SP; Tel 0191 281 5721; Fax 0191 281 3548
Manager/Divisional Director   J. Mackintosh

Sex Offenders Team 14 Pitt St, Newcastle upon Tyne, Tyne and Wear NE4 5SU; Tel 0191 261 9515; Fax 0191 261 1548
Manager (Risk Management)   M.A. Dodds

Training Centre

Dene House Training Centre Durham Rd, Low Fell, Gateshead, Tyne and Wear NE9 5AE; Tel 0191 491 1693; Fax 0191 491 3726
Manager (Training)   A. McIntosh

Nottinghamshire

Headquarters, Marina Rd, Nottingham NG7 1TP;
   URL www.nottinghamshire-probation.co.uk; E-mail
   general.enquiries@nottinghamshire.probation.gsx.gov.uk;
   Tel 0115 840 6500
Chair of the Probation Board   Wendy Start
Secretary to the Probation Board   D. Owen
Chief Officer   D.N. Hancock; Tel 0115 840 6492
Communications and Press and PR Officer   Jude Warrior;
   Tel 0115 840 6492

Offices

Community Supervision Teams 106 Derby Rd, Nottingham NG7 1NQ; Tel 0115 845 5101
Senior Probation Officer (Drug Abstinence)   Colin Burnage;
   Tel 0115 845 5100

Senior Probation Officer   Abirjan Khan
Senior Probation Officer   Marion Saddington
Senior Probation Officer   Linda Goode

County Substance Misuse Team Titchfield Hse, 96 Nottingham Rd, Mansfield, Nottingham NG18 1BP; Tel 01623 488470; Fax 01623 488471
Senior Probation Officer   Ed Taylor
Senior Probation Officer   June Wright

Employment, Training and Education (ACCESS) 106 Derby Rd, Nottingham NG7 1NQ; Tel 0115 845 5100; Fax 0115 845 5101
Manager   Steve Cooke

Intensive Control and Change Programme (ICCP) Traffic St, Nottingham NG2 1NU; Tel 0115 956 0956; Fax 0115 956 0900
Senior Probation Officer   Jen Meade

Mansfield Community Supervision 46 Nottingham Rd, Mansfield, Nottinghamshire NG18 1BL; Tel 01623 460800; Fax 01623 460801
Senior Probation Officer   Julie Burton
Senior Probation Officer   Jean Crookall
Senior Probation Officer   Tony Downey

Multi-Agency Public Protection Team Holmes Hse, Ratcliffe Gate, Mansfield, Nottingham NG18 2JW; Tel 01623 483052; Fax 01623 483056
Manager and Co-ordinator   Victoria Hodgett

Newark Team 11 Appleton Gate, Newark, Nottinghamshire NG24 1JR; Tel 01623 652650; Fax 01623 652651
Senior Probation Officer   Carol Steele

Nottingham Community Punishment Team Traffic St, Nottingham NG2 1NU; Tel 0115 956 0956; Fax 0115 956 0900
Senior Probation Officer   David Pratt

Nottingham Crown Court Probation Liaison Office, Canal St, Nottingham NG1 7EL; Tel 0115 910 3540; Fax 0115 958 6135
Senior Probation Officer   Ann Snowden

Nottingham Pre-Sentence Unit 2nd Fl, Albion Hse, Canal St, Nottingham NG1 7EG; Tel 0115 859 9400; Fax 0115 849 9401
Senior Probation Officer   Ann Snowden

Nottingham Substance Misuse Team 6 The Ropewalk, Nottingham, Nottinghamshire NG1 5DT; Tel 0115 910 5400; Fax 0115 910 5404
Senior Probation Officer   Ed Taylor
Senior Probation Officer   June Wright

Publication Protection Team 106 Derby Rd, Nottingham, Nottinghamshire NG7 1NQ; Tel 0115 845 5100; Fax 0115 845 5207
Senior Probation Officer   Nigel Hill

Retford Team 42 Grove St, Retford, Nottinghamshire DN22 6LD; Tel 01777 707238; Fax 01777 710201
Senior Probation Officer   Chris Kelly

Victim Contact Team 2nd Fl, Albion Hse, Canal St, Nottingham NG1 7EG; Tel 0115 859 9423; Fax 0115 859 9429
Senior Probation Officer   Hardyal Dhindsa

Worksop Team 11 Newcastle St, Worksop, Nottinghamshire S80 2AS; Tel 01909 473424; Fax 01909 530082
Senior Probation Officer   Chris Kelly

Oxfordshire and Buckinghamshire

Kingsclere Rd, Bicester, Oxfordshire OX6 8QD; Tel 01869 255300; Fax 01869 255355
Secretary of the Probation Committee   G. Mackenzie
Chief Probation Officer   R. Fishbourne (Acting)
Director (Service Delivery)   M. Myatt (Acting)
Director (Service Delivery)   G. Marshall
Director (Service Delivery)   Bruce Davison
Director (Facilities and Personnel)   G. Mackenzie
Director (Community Service)   L. Hudson
Director (Finance)   J. Wilson

Offices

Abingdon Probation Office 1–3 Ock St, Abingdon, Oxfordshire OX14 5AL; Tel 01235 535619
Senior Probation Officer   C. Dilley

Banbury Probation Office Ivy Hse, 23 South Bar, Banbury, Oxfordshire OX16 9AF; Tel 01295 268436
Senior Probation Officer   P. Jameson

Bridge House Office Bridge St, High Wycombe, Buckinghamshire HP11 2EL; Tel 01494 436622
Senior Probation Officer   J. Swan

Buckinghamshire Community Service 20 Market Sq, Stony Stratford, Milton Keynes MK11 1BE; Tel 01908 564812
Senior Probation Officer   J. Power

Cowley Probation Office 164 Oxford Rd, Cowley, Oxford, Oxfordshire OX4 2LA; Tel 01865 775482
Senior Probation Officer   G. McCartney

Easton Court Office 23a Easton St, High Wycombe, Buckinghamshire; Tel 01494 436421
Senior Probation Officer   G. Smith

Family Court Service (Oxfordshire) 1st Fl,, 2 Cambridge Terr, Oxford, Oxfordshire OX1 1TP; Tel 01865 728421
Senior Probation Officer   H. Bretherton

Kingsclere Road (Head Office) Bicester, Oxfordshire OX6 8QD; Tel 01869 255300

Magistrates' Court 301 Silbury Blvd, Witan Gate East, Milton Keynes MK9 2YH; Tel 01908 679734
Senior Probation Officer   S. Chantler
Senior Probation Officer   P. Cook
Senior Probation Officer   M. Chalmers

Oxford City Office 1st Fl, 2 Cambridge Terr, Oxford, Oxfordshire OX1 1TP; Tel 01865 240750
Senior Probation Officer   M. Toner

Oxfordshire Community Service Unit 8 Kings Meadow, Ferry Hinksey Rd, Oxford, Oxfordshire OX2 0DP; Tel 01865 247088
Senior Probation Officer   S. McIntyre
Senior Probation Officer   J. Hedge

Wynne-Jones Centre 2a Wynne-Jones Centre, Aylesbury, Buckinghamshire; Tel 01296 83174
Senior Probation Officer   A. Mulvihill
Senior Probation Officer   D. Butt

Gwent Probation Area

Cwmbran Hse, Manhilad Park Est, Pontypool, Torfaen NP4 0XD; Tel 01495 762462

Reading

Headquarters, 145 Friar St, Reading RG1 1EX; Tel 0118 957 4091
Secretary of the Berkshire Probation Committee   D.K.H. Over, LLB
Chief Probation Officer   A.M. Bridges
Assistant Chief Officer (West Berkshire)   S. Brooks
Assistant Chief Officer (East Berkshire)   P. Coker
Assistant Chief Officer (Support Services and Family Courts Welfare)   A.J. Rolley
Crown Court Liaison and Senior Probation Officer   G. Evans
The Old Shire Hall, The Forbury, Reading RG1 3EH; Tel 0118 967 4420

Offices

Crown House Office Crown St, Reading RG1 2SE; Tel 0118 956 0466
Reading Young Offender (Restorative Justice Development) and Senior Probation Officer   J. Chilvers
Reading Case Management/Senior Probation Officer   W. Sceeny

Glasson Centre 319 Oxford Rd, Reading RG30 1AU;
Tel 0118 956 6322; Fax 0118 950 2618
Family Courts Welfare Service/Senior Probation Officer
A. Jones

Community Services

Probation Office 18a Castle St, Reading RG1 7SD; Tel 0118
958 6141
Senior Probation Officer (Community Service)   J. Cleary

Development Office

Friar Street Office 145 Friar St, Reading RG1 1EX; Tel 0118
957 4091
Senior Probation Officer   M. Reynolds

Redcar

Office

Station Road Office 38 Station Rd, Redcar, Redcar and
Cleveland TS10 1AN; Tel 01642 480611; Fax 01642 489424
Senior Probation Officer   P.M. Burnett

Slough

Office

Revelstoke House Office Chalvey Pk, Slough SL1 2HF;
Tel 01753 537516
Senior Probation Officer   J. Rymer

South Yorkshire

Probation Service Headquarters, 11a Arundel Gate,
Sheffield, South Yorkshire S1 2PQ; Tel 0114 276 6911;
Fax 0114 275 2868
Secretary of the Probation Committee   J. Fox
Chief Probation Officer   J. Hicks
Deputy Chief Probation Officer   H. Harker

Offices

Barnsley Probation Centre 32 Park St, Wombwell, Barnsley,
South Yorkshire S73 0HF; Tel 01226 754646; Fax 01226
751297
Senior Probation Officer   S. McKenzie

Court House Churchfields, Barnsley, South Yorkshire
S70 2HW; Tel 01226 243331; Fax 01226 294908
Senior Probation Officer   P. Barker

CSO Unit Yarborough Terr, Bentley, Doncaster, South
Yorkshire DN5 9TH; Tel 01302 787758; Fax 01302 390865
Senior Probation Officer   P. Coddington

CSO Unit and Motor Project Masborough St, Rotherham,
South Yorkshire S60 1HW; Tel 01709 564424; Fax 01709
550952
Senior Probation Officer   S. Nothhelfer-Batten

Doncaster Probation Centre 34 Bennetthorpe, Doncaster,
South Yorkshire DN2 6AD; Tel 01302 730099; Fax 01302
730220
Contact   G. Brunt (DCO)
Senior Probation Officer   K. Dickinson
Senior Probation Officer   D. Pidwell
Senior Probation Officer   G. Jones

Family Court Welfare Team Unit 3, Dragoon Crt, Sheffield,
South Yorkshire S6 2GZ; Tel 0114 231 6119; Fax 0114 231
6120
Senior Probation Officer   A. Gamble

The Law Courts College Rd, Doncaster, South Yorkshire
DN1 3HU; Tel 01302 366585; Fax 01302 320853
Senior Probation Officer   S. Shaw

Main Street Office 12 Main St, Rotherham, South Yorkshire
S60 1AJ; Tel 01709 376761; Fax 01709 838715
Senior Probation Officer   M. Dyson
Senior Probation Officer   M. Turvey
Senior Probation Officer   G. Whitehead

Orsborn House Office 1–2 Highfields, Rotherham, South
Yorkshire S65 1EA; Tel 01709 364774; Fax 01709 829172
Contact   P. Lloyd (DCO)
Senior Probation Officer   S. Woodgate
Senior Probation Officer   J. Gooch

Pitsmoor Road Office 269 Pitsmoor Rd, Sheffield, South
Yorkshire S3 9AS; Tel 0114 272 5058; Fax 0114 275 4997
Senior Probation Officer   R. Holmes

Sheffield Probation Centre 45 Division St, Sheffield, South
Yorkshire S1 4GE; Tel 0114 281 0055; Fax 0114 281 2190
Senior Probation Officer   L. Daly

South Parade Office 25 South Pde, Doncaster, South
Yorkshire DN1 2EA; Tel 01302 327202; Fax 01302 349641
Senior Probation Officer   D. Brooks

Victoria Road Office 6 Victoria Rd, Barnsley, South
Yorkshire S70 2BB; Tel 01226 283411; Fax 01226 287441
Senior Probation Officer   P. Forbes
Senior Probation Officer   P. McNerney

West Bar Office 3 West Bar, Sheffield, South Yorkshire
S3 8PJ; Tel 0114 272 6477; Fax 0114 278 1892
DCPO   P. Proctor
Senior Probation Officer   P. Adey
Senior Probation Officer   K. Mitchell
Senior Probation Officer   S. Wright
Senior Probation Officer   J. Smith

South Wales Probation Area

33 Westgate St, Cardiff CF10 1JE; Tel 029 2023 2999; Fax 029
2034 0821
Secretary of the Probation Board   P.R. Egan
Chief Officer   Peter K. Sampson

Staffordshire

University Crt, Staffordshire Technology Pk, Beaconside,
Stafford, Staffordshire ST18 0GE; Tel 01785 223416
Secretary to the Probation Board   J.R. Gregory
Chief Officer   David Walton
*Crown Court Liaison Officer (Stafford) and Senior Probation
Officer*   Mick Gough; Tel 01785 223433
Senior Probation Officer Crown Court (Hanley)   Mick Gough;
Tel 01782 286831 (Crown Court Team)
Community Service Organiser and Senior Probation Officer
John Cartlidge

Offices

Broom Street Office Broom St, Hanley, Staffordshire
ST1 2EN; Tel 01782 286836
Senior Probation Officer   Angela Staplehurst

Bryans Lane Office Bryans La, Rugeley, Staffordshire
WS15 2JN; Tel 01889 574730
Senior Probation Officer   J. Atkins

Cross Street Office Cross St, Leek, Staffordshire ST13 6BT;
Tel 01538 399355
Senior Probation Officer   Andrew Bailey (Acting)

The Crown and County Court Bethesda St, Hanley,
Staffordshire ST1 3BP
Crown Court Team and Senior Probation Officer   Mick Gough;
Tel 01782 286831

Crown Court Liaison Office The Crown and County Court,
Victoria Sq, Stafford, Staffordshire ST16 2QQ; Tel 01785
223433
Senior Probation Officer   Mick Gough

District Council Office Leek Rd, Cheadle, Staffordshire
ST10 1JB; Tel 01538 754484
Senior Probation Officer   Andrew Bailey (Acting)

Horninglow Street Burton-upon-Trent, Staffordshire
DE14 1PH; Tel 01283 564988
Senior Probation Officer Sam Williams

Kidsgrove Town Hall Liverpool Rd, Kidsgrove,
Staffordshire ST7 4EH; Tel 01782 776181
Senior Probation Officer Geoff Woolgar

Marlborough Road Longton, Stoke-on-Trent ST3 1EJ;
Tel 01782 599690
Senior Probation Officer Trevor Hartley

PSR Writing Team Eaves La, Bucknall, Stoke-on-Trent
ST2 8JY; Tel 01782 261961
Senior Probation Officer Mick Gough

Ryecroft Office Newcastle-under-Lyme, Staffordshire
ST5 2DT; Tel 01782 717074
Senior Probation Officer (Magistrates and Courts Team)
Mick Gough
Senior Probation Officer Geoff Woolgar
Senior Probation Officer (Risk and Victim Liaison)
Mike Kosh

South Walls Office Stafford, Staffordshire ST16 3BL;
Tel 01785 223415
Senior Probation Officer Chris Boult

Spinning School Lane Office Spinning School La,
Tamworth, Staffordshire B79 7AP; Tel 01827 66906
Senior Probation Officer Lynne Corcoran

Stowe Court Office Stowe St, Lichfield, Staffordshire
WS13 6AQ; Tel 01543 251423
Senior Probation Officer Lynne Corcoran

Town Hall High St, Biddulph, Staffordshire ST8 6AR;
Tel 01782 518070
Senior Probation Officer Andrew Williams (Acting)

University Court Staffordshire Technology Pk, Beaconside,
Stafford, Staffordshire ST18 0GE; Tel 01785 223416
Chief Officer David Walton

Wolverhampton Road Office 200a Wolverhampton Rd,
Cannock, Staffordshire WS11 1AT; Tel 01543 506112; 01543
506113; 01543 506114
Senior Probation Officer Jim Atkins

DRUG TREATMENT AND TESTING ORDER DEVELOPMENT

Horninglow St, Burton, Staffordshire DE14 1PH; Tel 01283
564988
26 Sandon Rd, Meir, Stoke-on-Trent ST3 7DL; Tel 01782
330595
South Walls, Stafford, Staffordshire ST16 3BL; Tel 01785
242464

Community Service Offices

Broom Street Community Service Office Broom St, Hanley,
Stoke-on-Trent ST1 2EN; Tel 01782 213324
Senior Project Officer Neil Keeling

Dorrington Drive Community Service Office Dorrington Ind
Pk, Common Rd, Stafford, Staffordshire ST16 3DG;
Tel 01785 228608
Senior Project Officer Peter Roberts

Unit 1 Community Service Office Crossfields Ind Est,
Lichfield, Staffordshire WS13 6RJ; Tel 01543 263299
Senior Project Officer Peter Roberts (based at Stafford)

Wolverhampton Road Community Service Office 200a
Wolverhampton Rd, Cannock, Staffordshire WS11 1BH;
Tel 01543 578111/2
Senior Projects Officer Peter Roberts (based at Stafford)

Suffolk

Foundation Hse, 34 Foundation St, Ipswich, Suffolk
IP4 1SP; Tel 01473 408130; Fax 01473 408136
Secretary to the Probation Board D. White
Chief Probation Officer J. Budd
Training and Staff Development Kelly Parker

Offices

The Cottage Probation Hostel 795 Old Norwich Rd,
Ipswich, Suffolk IP1 6LH; Tel 01473 408266; Fax 01473
408268
Senior Probation Officer R. Heath

Crowland House Withersfield Rd, Haverhill, Suffolk
CB9 9LA; Tel 01440 702375; Fax 01440 712877
Senior Probation Officer D. Joscelyne
Senior Probation Officer R. Dennis

Court Liaison Office The Marland Centre, 64–70
Foundation St, Ipswich, Suffolk IP4 1BN; Tel 01473 408160;
Fax 01473 408169
Senior Probation Officer B. Burlinson
Senior Probation Officer S. Pestell

Lowestoft Office 203 Whapload Rd, Lowestoft, Suffolk
NR32 1UL; Tel 01502 501800; Fax 01502 525779
Senior Probation Officer D. Comyn
Senior Probation Officer J. Doylend

The Marland Centre 64–70 Foundation St, Ipswich, Suffolk
IP4 1BN; Tel 01473 408160; Fax 01473 408169
Senior Probation Officer B. Burlinson
Senior Probation Officer S. Pestell

Old Market Place Office 6a Old Market Pl, Sudbury, Suffolk
CO10 1SZ; Tel 01787 372003; Fax 01787 883080
Senior Probation Officer D. Joscelyne
Senior Probation Officer R. Dennis

West Suffolk Probation Centre Dettingen Way, Bury St.
Edmunds, Suffolk IP33 3TU; Tel 01284 716600; Fax 01284
716606
Senior Probation Officer D. Joscelyne
Senior Probation Officer R. Dennis

Surrey

Bridge Hse, Flambard Way, Godalming, Surrey GU7 1JB;
URL www.surreyprobation.org.uk; Tel 01483 860191;
Fax 01483 860295
Secretary of the Probation Board B. Davis
Chief Officer M. Varah
Co-Director (Operations) L. Ball
Co-Director (Operations) Y. Ball
Director (Support Services) P. Jolly

Probation Centre North West

White Rose Crt, Oriental Rd, Woking, Surrey GU22 7PJ;
Tel 01483 776262; Fax 01483 727244

Court and Community Supervision Team
Manager J. Guven

Community Punishment
Manager Kim Collins

Probation Centre South West

College Hse, Woodbridge Rd, Guildford, Surrey GU1 4RS;
Tel 01483 534701; Fax 01483 453702

Court and Community Supervision Team
Manager Ray Little

Probation Centre South East

Allonby Hse, Hatchlands Rd, Redhill, Surrey RH1 6BN;
Tel 01737 763241; Fax 01737 765688

Court and Community Supervision Team
Manager M. McLean (Acting)

Community Punishment
Deputy Manager J. Whittle

Probation Centre North East

Swan Hse, Knowle Grn, Staines, Greater London
TW18 1XR; Tel 01784 459341; Fax 01784 449932

Court and Community Supervision Team
Manager H. Turner-Samuel
Guildford Crown Court
Manager R. Little; Tel 01483 568561; Fax 01483 306724

Other Units

Youth Justice Team Churchill Hse, Mayford Grn, Woking, Surrey GU22 0PW; Tel 01483 723922; Fax 01438 771786
Manager G. Hibbert
Personnel/Staff Development Unit Bridge Hse, Flambard Way, Godalming, Surrey GU7 1JB; Tel 01483 860191; Fax 01483 860295
Manager P. Jolly

Sussex

East and West Sussex Probation Areas amalgamated in April 2001 to form Sussex Probation Area. Information on the new area offices and key contacts were unavailable at the time of publishing but please contact the Head Office for new information.
Sussex Probation Head Office, 185 Dyke Rd, Hove, BN3 1TL; Tel 01273 227979; Fax 01273 227972

Warrington

Offices

Howard House 10a Friarsgate, Warrington; Tel 01925 650613
Senior Probation Officer D. Meade
Senior Probation Officer M. Denton

Warwickshire

2 Swan St, Warwick, Warwickshire CV34 4BJ; URLwarwickshire.admin@warwickshire.probation.gsx. gov.uk; Tel 01926 405800; Fax 01926 403183
Secretary of the Probation Committee I.G. Caulfield
Shire Hall, Warwick, Warwickshire CV34 4RR; Tel 01926 412000
Chief Officer L. Stafford
Assistant Chief Officer A. Wade
Assistant Chief Officer W.J. Lacey
Area Manager (Community Services) L. Frampton

Offices

Atherstone Probation Office 1 Market St, Atherstone, Warwickshire CV9 1ET; Tel 01827 722792; Fax 01827 722970
Leamington Spa Probation Office 1 Euston Sq, Leamington Spa, Warwickshire CV32 4NB; Tel 01926 331860; Fax 01926 887808
Area Manager C. Thompson
Nuneaton Probation Office Warwick Hse, Bondgate, Nuneaton, Warwickshire CV11 4DU; Tel 024 7635 1234; Fax 01926 413098
Area Manager S. Britton
Rugby Probation Office The Courthouse, Newbold Rd, Rugby, Warwickshire CV21 2LH; Tel 01788 534900; Fax 01788 547576
Area Manager S. Chappell
Stratford-upon-Avon Probation Office Grove Rd, Stratford-upon-Avon, Warwickshire CV37 6QR; Tel 01789 299520; Fax 01789 298264

West Mercia

Head Office, Stourbank Hse, 90 Mill St, Kidderminster, Worcestershire DY11 6XA;
URL www.westmerciaprobation.org.uk;
E-mail head.office@west-mercia.probation.gsx.gov.uk;
Tel 01562 748375; Fax 01562 748407
Chair P. Bradbury
Chief Officer D. Chantler

Offices

Hereford Office Shirehall Annexe, Hereford, Herefordshire HR1 2HX; Tel 01432 272521
Leominster Office 37 Etnam St, Leominster, Herefordshire HR6 8AE; Tel 01568 611482
Market Drayton Office 10 Wilkinson Wlk, Cheshire St, Market Drayton, Shropshire TF9 1PW; Tel 01630 653879
Oswestry Office 22a Bailey St, Oswestry, Shropshire SY11 1PX; Tel 01691 656343
Redditch Office 1–4 Windsor Crt, Clive Rd, Redditch, Worcestershire B97 4BT; Tel 01527 585152
Shrewsbury Office 1 Quarry Pl, Shrewsbury, Shropshire SY1 1JU; Tel 01743 231525
Telford Office Telford Sq, Malinsgate, Telford, Shropshire TF3 4HX; Tel 01952 214100
Whitchurch Office 12a St. Mary's St, Whitchurch, Shropshire SY13 1QY; Tel 01948 667111
Worcester Office 3–4 Shaw St, Worcester, Worcestershire WR1 3QQ; Tel 01905 723591

West Midlands

1 Victoria Sq, Birmingham, West Midlands B1 1BD; Tel 0121 248 6666
Chief Officer H.A. Thompson
Secretary of the Probation Board R.A. Steer
Director (Finance and Facilities) A. Nelson
Director (Operations) R.J.V. Marsh

Offices

Programmes Division 326–328 Hamstead Rd, Handsworth, Birmingham, West Midlands B20 2RA; Tel 0121 248 6540
Assistant Chief Officer R. Green
Birmingham Office 8th Fl, 1 Victoria Sq, Birmingham, West Midlands B1 1BD; Tel 0121 616 0200
Assistant Chief Officer (Support and Liaison) D. Skidmore
Assistant Chief Officer J. Fenby
Assistant Chief Officer (Community Partnership) Ann Habens
Assistant Chief Officer (Community Punishment) Stephen Gill
Coventry Office 70 Little Park St, Coventry, West Midlands CV1 2UR; Tel 024 7663 0555
Assistant Chief Officer P. Royal
Equalities and Diversity 1 Victoria Sq, Birmingham, West Midlands B1 1BD; Tel 0121 248 6666
Assistant Chief Officer S. Hanley
Residential Services (Area Responsibility) 11–15 Lower Essex St, Birmingham, West Midlands B6 6SN; Tel 0121 248 2828
Assistant Chief Officer M. Tennant
Sandwell and Dudley Office Laurel Hse, Halesowen, West Midlands B63 3DA; Tel 0121 550 1496
Assistant Chief Officer Nigel Byford
Walsall and Wolverhampton Office 2nd Fl, Prue Earle Hse, Union St, Wolverhampton, West Midlands WV1 3JS; Tel 01902 576000
Assistant Chief Officer N. Sahota

West Yorkshire

Cliff Hill Hse, Sandy Wlk, Wakefield, West Yorkshire WF1 2DJ; Tel 01924 885300; Fax 01924 885395; Tel ext 209; Tel ext 201; Tel ext 203; Tel ext 244
Secretary of the Probation Committee c/o N.J. Thorpe
Treasurer S. Pamment
Chief Probation Officer P. Wilson
Deputy Chief Probation Officer S. Hall
Assistant Chief Probation Officer (Head Office) P. Thurston
Assistant Chief Probation Officer (Head Office) H. Mills

Assistant Chief Probation Officer (Bradford)   R. Barrows
Fraternal Hse, Cheapside, Bradford, West Yorkshire
 BD1 4HP; Tel 01274 703760; Fax 01274 703761
Assistant Chief Probation Officer (Leeds)   R. Voakes
Waterloo Hse, 58 Wellington St, Leeds, West Midlands
 LS1 2EE; Tel 0113 243 0601; Fax 0113 234 1951
Assistant Chief Probation Officer (Calderdale)   J. Bagley
Spring Hall La, Halifax, HX1 4JG; Tel 01422 340211;
 Fax 01422 320998
Manager (Policy and Performance)   M. Wilkin

Offices

Broadway House Office   Crackenedge La, Dewsbury, West
Yorkshire WF13 1PU; Tel 01924 464171; 01924 464173;
Fax 01924 453279
Senior Probation Officer   D. Thomas
Senior Probation Officer   D. Quarmby

Cavendish Street Offices   11–19 Cavendish St, Keighley,
West Yorkshire D21 3RB; Tel 01535 662771; 01535 662772;
Fax 01535 611346

The City Courts   PO Box 6, Bradford, West Yorkshire
BD1 1LB; Tel 01274 733165; Fax 01274 721010
Senior Probation Officer   V. Minogue
Senior Probation Officer   M. Austwick
Senior Probation Officer   T. Myers

1st Floor Offices   1046–1060 Manchester Rd, Bankfoot,
Bradford, West Yorkshire BD5 8NN; Tel 01274 370281;
Fax 01274 395519
Senior Probation Officer   S. Donkersley

Harropwell Lane Office   Harropwell La, Pontefract, West
Yorkshire WF8 1QY; Tel 01977 791359; 01977 794029;
Fax 01977 602041
Senior Probation Officer   A. Chandler
Senior Probation Officer   D. Haddrick

Kirklees Probation Centre   5 Albion St, Dewsbury, West
Yorkshire WF13 2AJ; Tel 01924 457744; Fax 01924 458564
Senior Probation Officer   J. Scott

Lawefield Lane Offices   20–30 Lawefield La, Wakefield,
West Yorkshire WF2 8SP; Tel 01924 361156; Fax 01924
291178
Senior Probation Officer   G. Parsisson
Senior Probation Officer   J. Brearton

Oxford Row Office   1 Oxford Row, Leeds, West Yorkshire
LS1 3BE; Tel 0113 243 1107; Fax 0113 234 1952
Senior Probation Officer   C. Stadward

Fraternal House   45 Cheapside, Bradford, West Yorkshire
BD1 4HP; Tel 01274 703760; Fax 01274 703761
Senior Probation Officer   S. MacPherson
Senior Probation Officer   L. Cameron

St. John's Road Office   21 St. John's Rd, Huddersfield,
West Yorkshire HD1 5BW; Tel 01484 427272/3; Fax 01484
422218
Senior Probation Officer   M. Smallridge
Senior Probation Officer   J. Ashton

Spring Hall Lane Office   Spring Hall La, Halifax, West
Yorkshire HX1 4JG; Tel 01422 340211; Fax 01422 320998
Senior Probation Officer   C. Branton
Senior Probation Officer   S. Charlesworth
Senior Probation Officer   D. Hillas

Waterloo House Office   58 Wellington St, Leeds, West
Yorkshire LS1 2EE; Tel 0113 243 0601; Fax 0113 234 1951
Senior Probation Officer   R. Pictan
Senior Probation Officer   D. Clark
Senior Probation Officer   P. James
Senior Probation Officer   S. Carless

West House Office   Hanover St, Batley, West Yorkshire
WF17 5DZ; Tel 01924 479006; Fax 01924 442403
Senior Probation Officer   A. Taylor

Westgate Office   28 Westgate, Leeds, West Yorkshire
LS1 3AP; Tel 0113 245 0123; Fax 0113 245 0967
Senior Probation Officer   R. Minogue

York Road Office   379 York Rd, Leeds, West Yorkshire
LS9 6TA; Tel 0113 285 0301; Fax 0113 240 0779
B. Melville (ACO)
Senior Probation Officer   C. Wright
Senior Probation Officer   R. Ellis
Senior Probation Officer   E. Neal

Community Service Offices

York Road Community Service Office   379 York Rd, Leeds,
West Yorkshire LS9 6TA; Tel 0113 285 0302

Lawefield Lane Community Service Office   20–30 Lawefield
La, Wakefield, West Yorkshire WF2 8SP; Tel 01924 361156;
Fax 01924 291178
Contact   L. Baxter (DCSO)

St. John's Road Community Service Office   21 St. John's Rd,
Huddersfield, West Yorkshire HD1 5BW; Tel 01484 427272;
01484 427273; Fax 01484 422218
Contact   R. Appleby (DSCO)

Spring Hall Lane Community Service Office   Spring Hall La,
Halifax, West Yorkshire HX1 4JG; Tel 01422 340211;
Fax 01422 320998

Wiltshire

Wiltshire Probation Headquarters, Rothermere, Bythesea
 Rd, Trowbridge, Wiltshire BA14 8JQ; Tel 01225 781950;
 Fax 01225 781969
Secretary of the Probation Board   J. Patience; Tel 01225 781961
Chief Probation Officer   D. Fulbrook

Offices

The Boulter Centre   Avon Approach, Salisbury, Wiltshire
SP1 3SL; Tel 01722 327716; Fax 01722 339557
Senior Probation Officer   Vacancy

Court Supervision Team   Mary Floyd Hse, 15 Milton Rd,
Swindon SN1 5JE; Tel 01793 536612; Fax 01793 541110
Area Manager   A. Hemming

Programmes Team   1–2 Commercial Rd, Swindon
SN1 5NE; Tel 01793 534259; Fax 01793 496468
Area Manager   K. Crallan

Parkfields Offices   51–52 Parkfields, Chippenham, Wiltshire
SN15 1NX; Tel 01249 656836; Fax 01249 445497
Area Manager   M. Wilcox

Prospect Place Office   2 Prospect Pl, Trowbridge, Wiltshire
BA14 8QA; Tel 01225 763041; Fax 01225 775667
Area Manager   M. Wilcox

Community Service Units

The Boulter Centre   Avon Approach, Salisbury, Wiltshire
SP1 3SL; Tel 01722 320897; Fax 01722 339557
Area Manager   K. Bristow

Commercial Road Community Service Office   1–2
Commercial Rd, Swindon SN1 5NF; Tel 01793 496662;
01793 534259; Fax 01793 436171
Area Manager   K. Bristow

HM Prison Erlestoke Team   Devizes, Wiltshire SN10 5TU;
Tel 01380 813475; Fax 01380 818663
Senior Probation Officer   A. Minch

Youth Justice Team   The Limes, 21 Green Rd, Swindon
SN2 6JA; Tel 01793 823153; Fax 01793 820578
Youth Justice Officer   J. Harrop
Youth Justice Officer   Vacancy

Windsor and Maidenhead

Offices

Probation Office   Bridge Rd, Maidenhead, Windsor and
Maidenhead SL6 8PB; Tel 01628 770858
Senior Probation Officer   C. Morgan

Approved Premises

England

Bedfordshire

Napier Road Approved Premises 36–40 Napier Rd, Luton LU1 1RG; Tel 01582 418200; Fax 01582 737391
Manager and Senior Probation Officer Mike Hazeltine
17+ Accommodation (20)

Bedford Approved Premises 80 Chaucer Rd, Bedford, Bedfordshire MK40 2AP; Tel 01234 340501; Fax 01234 351715

Bristol

Ashley House Approved Premises 14 Somerset St, Kingsdown, Bristol BS2 8NB; Tel 0117 924 9697; Fax 0117 944 4290
Accommodation (Male 16, Female 6).

Bridge House Approved Premises 78 Filton Rd, Horfield, Bristol BS7 0PD; Tel 0117 969 3123; Fax 0117 931 2167
17+ Accommodation (18)

St. Paul's Approved Premises 4–12 Brigstocke Rd, St.Paul's, Bristol BS2 8UB; Tel 0117 942 5851; Fax 0117 944 5945
17+ Accommodation (28)

Buckinghamshire

Great Holm Approved Premises 1 Haddon, Great Holm, Milton Keynes MK8 9AL; Tel 01908 569511; Fax 01908 265949
Senior Probation Officer/Hostel Manager Kilvinder Shahi
18+ Accommodation (16)

Cambridgeshire

Peterborough Approved Premises 5 Wesleyan Rd, Peterborough; Tel 01733 551678; Fax 01733 345161
Male 17+ Accommodation (32)

Cheshire

Ellesmere Approved Premises Banbury Hse, Alnwick Dr, Ellesmere Port, Wirral LL65 9HE; Tel 0151 357 3551; Fax 0151 356 2102
Senior Probation Officer Vacancy

Cleveland

Nelson House Approved Premises Middlesbrough Rd, South Bank, Middlesbrough TS6 6LZ; Tel 01642 456811; Fax 01642 468671
18+ Accommodation (20)

Linthorpe Approved Premises 13 The Cres, Linthorpe, Middlesbrough TS5 6SG; Tel 01642 826606; Fax 01642 829782
17+ Accommodation (20)

Cornwall

Meneghy House Approved Premises East Hill, Tuckingmill, Camborne, Cornwall TR14 8NQ; Tel 01209 715050
17+ Accommodation for Offenders (18)

Cumbria

Bowling Green Approved Premises 90 Lowther St, Carlisle, Cumbria; Tel 01228 522360; Fax 01228 590967
18+ Accommodation (24)

Derbyshire

Burdett Lodge Approved Premises 6 Bass St, Derby DE22 3BR; Tel 01332 341324; 01332 343906; Fax 01332 202089
18+ Accommodation (26)

Devon

Lawson House Approved Premises 14 Paradise Pl, Stoke, Plymouth PL1 5QU; Tel 01752 568791; Fax 01752 606815
Senior Probation Officer and Manager A. Cookson
Male (17), Female (2) Accommodation (19)

Dorset

Bournemouth Approved Premises The Pines, 11 Cecil Rd, Boscombe, Bournemouth BH5 1DU; Tel 01202 391757; Fax 01202 391867
18+ Accommodation (18)

Weston Approved Premises 2 Westway Rd, Weymouth, Dorset DTH 8SU;
E-mail p.harknett@dorset.probation.gsx.gov.uk; Tel 01305 775742; Fax 01305 766510
18+ Accommodation (25) (Male 21, Female 4)

East Riding of Yorkshire

Queen's Road Approved Premises 41 Queens Rd, Hull, Kingston upon Hull HU5 2QW; Tel 01482 446284; Fax 01482 470704

Victoria House Approved Premises 31 Normanby Rd, Scunthorpe, East Riding of Yorkshire DN15 6AS; Tel 01724 289124; Fax 01724 289126

East Sussex

Brighton Approved Premises 162 Marine Pde, Brighton, Brighton and Hove BN2 1EJ; Tel 01273 622300; Fax 01273 623486
Manager and Senior Probation Officer A. Wade

Gloucestershire

Ryecroft Approved Premises 78 Ryecroft St, Gloucester, Gloucestershire GL1 4LY; Tel 01452 380268
Senior Probation Officer Stephanie McBride

Essex

Basildon Approved Premises 1 Felmores, Basildon, Essex SS13 1RN; Tel 01268 557550; Fax 01268 558661
17+ Accommodation (26) (Male 22, Female 4)

Greater Manchester

Bradshaw House Approved Premises 147–151 Walmersley Rd, Bury, Greater Manchester BL9 5DE; Tel 0161 761 6419; Fax 0161 763 4353
17+ Accommodation (26)

St. Joseph's Approved Premises Millers St, Patricroft, Manchester M30 8PF; Tel 0161 789 5337; Fax 0161 707 9085
Male Accommodation (29)

Withington Road Approved Premises Withington Road Approved Premises, 172–174 Withington Rd, Whalley Range, Manchester M16 8JN; Tel 0161 226 1179; Fax 0161 227 9052
Male Accommodation (32 Core) Home Office Approved. Bail, parole and conditional release residents.

Hampshire

Dickson House Approved Premises 77 Trinity St, Fareham, Hampshire PO16 7SL; E-mail prob91po@hants.gov.uk
Manager   Corinne Skinner
    18

The Grange Approved Premises 145 Stakes Rd, Purbrook, Portsmouth PO7 5PL; Tel 023 9236 3474; Fax 023 9236 3481
    Accommodation (22) Male 22 (disabled 1)

Languard Road Approved Premises 32 Landguard Rd, Shirley, Southampton SO15 5DJ; Tel 023 8033 6287; Fax 023 8033 6290
    Accommodation (22) (Male 19, Female 3)

Kent

Beckenham Road Approved Premises 4 Beckenham Rd, Beckenham, Kent BR3 4LR; Tel 020 8658 3515; Fax 020 8663 6244
    18+ Accommodation (20)

Fleming House Approved Premises 32 Tonbridge Rd, Maidstone, Kent ME16 8SH; Tel 01622 755918; Fax 01622 674809
    Mixed 18+ Accommodation (25)

Lancashire

Haworth House Approved Premises Haworth Hse, St. Peter's St, Blackburn BB2 2HL; Tel 01254 59060; Fax 01254 672062
    18+ Accommodation (26)

Highfield House Approved Premises Lydia St, Wood Nook, Accrington, Lancashire BB5 0PX; Tel 01254 395997; Fax 01254 398536
    Accommodation (22) Male 18, Female 4

Stephen House Approved Premises Accommodation Unit, 1st Fl, Stephen Hse, Bethesda St, Burnley, Lancashire BB11 1QW; Tel 01282 832299; Fax 01282 838616
Senior Probation Officer   Ian Galbraith

Leicestershire

Howard House Approved Premises 71 Regent Rd, Leicester LE1 6YA; Tel 0116 254 9059; Fax 0116 254 0303
    Male 17+ Accommodation (18)

Kirk Lodge Approved Premises 322 London Rd, Leicester LE2 2PJ; Tel 0116 270 8327; Fax 0116 244 8696
    18+ Accommodation (32)

Lincolnshire

Wordsworth House Approved Premises 205 Yarborough Rd, Lincoln, Lincolnshire LN1 3NQ; Tel 01522 528520; Fax 01522 526077
Manager   K. Laughton
Programmes for adult males subject to conditions of bail, community sentence or licence (18).

London

Tulse Hill Approved Premises 147 Tulse Hill, London SW2 2QD; Tel 020 8671 4086
SPO/Manager   Lloyd LaRose Jones
    17+ Accommodation (23) Subject to bail condition of residence.

Camden House Approved Premises 199 Arlington Rd, London NW1 7HA; Tel 020 7482 4288; Fax 020 7284 3391
Andrew Hillas
    Accommodation (26) Probation order, prison licences, bail

Ellison House Approved Premises Aylesbury Est, 370 Albany Rd, London SE5 0AJ; Tel 020 7703 3332; (Referrals only) 020 7407 7273; Fax 020 7252 6327
    Male 18+ Accommodation (25)

Great Peter Street Approved Premises 71–73 Great Peter St, London SW1P 2BN; Tel 020 7222 5656; Fax 020 7960 1188

Katherine Price Hughes House Approved Premises 28 Highbury Gr, London N5 2EA; Tel 020 7226 2190; Fax 020 7354 3221
Counselling Service. All staff are qualified counsellors. Free to those on benefits, request donation from others.
Application through Central Probation Referral Service.

St. Edmund's Approved Premises 298 Leigham Court Rd, Streatham, London SW16 2QP; Tel 020 8769 8096; Fax 020 8677 1230
    17+ Accommodation (25)

Hestia Approved Premises 9 Cologne Rd, Battersea, London SW11 2AH; Tel 020 7223 3006; Fax 020 7924 2156
    17+ Accommodation (25)

Shenley Road and Bedford Hill Approved Premises 147 Tulse Hill, London SW2 2QD; Tel 020 8671 4086; Fax 020 8671 8546
Senior Probation Officer and Manager   L. Larose Jones
    21+ probation / ACR Accommodation (25)

Westbourne House Approved Premises 199 Romford Rd, London E7 9HL; Tel 020 8534 0673; Fax 020 8534 8286
    18+ Accommodation (41)

Merseyside

Adelaide House Home Office Approved Premises 115 Edge La, Liverpool, Merseyside L7 2PF; Tel 0151 260 1291 (Residents); 0151 263 1290 (Warden)
Manager   C. Earlam
    17+ Accommodation (20)

Canning House Approved Premises 55 Canning St, Liverpool, Merseyside L8 7NN; Tel 0151 709 4959; Fax 0151 707 0813
Manager   D. Baderin
    25+ Accommodation (17) 'Cluster' beds (8)

Merseybank Approved Premises 26 Great Howard St, Liverpool, Merseyside L3 7HS; Tel 0151 255 1183; Fax 0151 236 4464
Manager   Peter Needham

Southwood Approved Premises 24 Southwood Rd, Aigburth, Liverpool, Merseyside L17 7BQ; Tel 0151 280 1833; Fax 0151 280 3027
Manager   Mark McPaul
    17+ Accommodation (29)

Middlesex

Ealing Approved Premises 2 Corfton Rd, Ealing, London W5 2HS; Tel 020 8997 7127; Fax 020 8810 6213
Manager and Senior Probation Officer   A. Holland
    18+ Accommodation (19)

Seafield Lodge Approved Premises 71–73 Shoot-Up-Hill, London NW2 3PS; Tel 020 8452 4200; 020 8452 4209
Senior Probation Officer and Manager   J. Dalkin
    Accommodation (19) Male 20, Female 3

Norfolk

John Boag House Approved Premises 1 Drayton Rd, Norwich, Norfolk NR3 2DF; Tel 01603 429488; Fax 01603 485903
    17+ Accommodation (25)

Northamptonshire

Bridgwood Approved Premises 45–48 Lower Meadow Ct, Northampton, Northamptonshire NN3 8AX; Tel 01604 648704; Fax 01604 645722
　18+ Accommodation (23)

Northumbria

Cuthbert House Approved Premises Derwentwater Rd, Gateshead, Tyne and Wear NE8 2SH; Tel 0191 478 5355; Fax 0191 490 0674
Hostel Manager　Amanda Seddon

Ozanam House Approved Premises 79 Dunholm Rd, Newcastle upon Tyne, Tyne and Wear NE4 6XD; Tel 0191 273 5738; Fax 0191 272 2729
Manager　C. Gelder
　18+ Accommodation (25)

Pennywell House Approved Premises Hylton Rd, Pennywell, Sunderland, Tyne and Wear SR4 8DS; Tel 0191 534 1544; Fax 0191 534 1049
Hostel Manager　J. McElderry

St. Christopher House Approved Premises 222 Westmorland Rd, Newcastle upon Tyne, Tyne and Wear NE4 6QX; Tel 0191 273 2381
　17+ Accommodation (19)

Oxfordshire

Abingdon Road Approved Premises 112 Abingdon Rd, Oxford, Oxfordshire OX1 4PY; Tel 01865 248842; Fax 01865 794680
　18+ Accommodation (18)

Clarks House Approved Premises Clarks Row, Oxford, Oxfordshire OX1 1RE; Tel 01865 248841
　17+ Accommodation (18)

Reading

Elizabeth Fry Approved Premises 6 Coley Ave, Reading, Berkshire RG1 6LQ; Tel 0118 957 2385; Fax 0118 951 0340
　18+ Accommodation (21)

St. Leonard's Approved Premises 2 Southcote Rd, Reading RG30 2AA; Tel 0118 957 3171; Fax 0118 956 0677
Senior Probation Officer and Manager　Sally Kitson
　17+ Accommodation (22)

Somerset

Glogan House Approved Premises 59 Taunton Rd, Bridgwater, Somerset TA6 3LP; Tel 01278 424165; Fax 01278 446054
Senior Probation Officer/Manager　P. Brandt
　17+ Accommodation (18)

South Yorkshire

Norfolk Park Approved Premises 100–108 Norfolk Pk Rd, Sheffield, South Yorkshire S2 2RU; Tel 0114 272 1950; Fax 0114 278 0075

Rookwood Approved Premises Doncaster Rd, Rotherham, South Yorkshire S65 1NN; Tel 01709 361001; Fax 01709 835496
Senior Probation Officer　Philip McNerney
　18+ Accommodation (39)

Town Moor Approved Premises 38–42 Christchurch Rd, Doncaster, South Yorkshire DN1 2QL; Tel 01302 739127; Fax 01302 761920
Senior Probation Officer　Glyn Vernon
　17+ Accommodation (39)

Staffordshire

Staitheford House Approved Premises 14 Lichfield Rd, Stafford, Staffordshire ST17 4JX; Tel 01785 223417
Hostel Manager　Clive Allerton
　18+ Accommodation (20)

Wenger House Approved Premises 21a Albert St, Newcastle-under-Lyme, Staffordshire ST5 1HJ; Tel 01782 717423; Fax 01782 714332
Warden and Senior Probation Officer　C.J. Butler
　17+ Accommodation (26)

Suffolk

The Cottage Approved Premises 795 Old Norwich Rd, Ipswich, Suffolk IP1 6HL; Tel 01473 408266; Fax 01473 408268
　17+ Accommodation (14)

Lightfoot House Approved Premises 37 Fuchsia La, Ipswich, Suffolk IP4 5AA; Tel 01473 408280; Fax 01473 713559
Senior Probation Officer　R. Heath
　Accommodation (19) Male 19, Female 3

Surrey

Kew Approved Premises 96 North Rd, Kew, Richmond, Surrey TW9 4HQ; Tel 020 8876 6303; Fax 020 8876 7402
Manager　Hans Weijman
Deputy Manager　Jean Hill
　17+ Accommodation (22) Bail, bail assessment, probation and licence

St. Catherine's Priory Approved Premises Ferry La, Portsmouth Rd, Guildford, Surrey GU2 4EE; Tel 01483 571635; Fax 01483 454130
Self-catering, shared rooms. For bail, bail assessment and statutory orders. Participative regime includes groupwork programme, individual keywork, lifeskills and activities.
　Accommodation (18)

Warwickshire

Kenilworth Road Approved Premises 33 Kenilworth Rd, Leamington Spa, Warwickshire CV32 6JG; Tel 01926 339331; Fax 01926 312518
Area Probation Manager　Patricia Johnson
　18+ Accommodation (19)

McIntyre House Approved Premises 125 Edward St, Nuneaton, Warwickshire; Tel 024 7638 2889; Fax 024 7635 3982
Manager and Senior Probation Officer　Vacancy
　18+ Accommodation (18)

West Midlands

Bilston Approved Premises 23 Wellington Rd, Bilston, Wolverhampton, West Midlands WV14 6AH; Tel 01902 497688; Fax 01902 498150
　17+ Accommodation (15)

Carpenter House Approved Premises 33 Portland Rd, Edgbaston, Birmingham, West Midlands B16 9HS; Tel 0121 454 0394; Fax 0121 454 7379
　17+ Accommodation (20) Offenders on probation, bail assessment, bail, licence of parole.

Crowley House Approved Premises 31 Weoley Park Rd, Selly Oak, Birmingham, West Midlands B29 6RA; Tel 0121 472 7111
　16+ Accommodation (18) Children

Elliott House Approved Premises 96 Edgbaston Rd, Birmingham, West Midlands B12 9QA; Tel 0121 440 2657; Fax 0121 446 6818
Approved premises for mentally disordered offenders (bail, community rehabilitation orders and licence).
　18+ Accommodation (20)

Welford House Approved Premises 31 Trinity Rd, Aston, Birmingham, West Midlands B6 6AJ; Tel 0121 523 4401; Fax 0121 515 1355

    17+ Accommodation (19)

West Yorkshire

Cardigan House Approved Premises 84 Cardigan Rd, Headingley, Leeds, West Yorkshire LS6 3BJ; Tel 0113 275 2860

    Accommodation (25) (Disabled 1) Bail, community sentence and licence.

Elm Bank Approved Premises 59 Bradford Rd, Cleckheaton, West Yorkshire BD19 3LW; Tel 01274 851551; Fax 01274 851079

    Male 17+ Accommodation (22)

Holbeck House Approved Premises Springwell View, Springwell Rd, Leeds, West Yorkshire LS12 1BS; Tel 0113 245 4220; Fax 0113 245 4910

    17+ Accommodation (24)

Ripon House Approved Premises 63 Clarendon Rd, Leeds, West Yorkshire LS2 9NZ; Tel 0113 245 5488; Fax 0113 242 8053

    17+ Accommodation (24) Parole, probation and bail only.

St. John's Approved Premises 259–263 Hyde Park Rd, Leeds, West Yorkshire LS6 1AG; Tel 0113 275 5702; Fax 0113 230 5230

    17+ Offender treatment Accommodation (28)

Windsor and Maidenhead

Manor Lodge Approved Premises 8 Straight Rd, Old Windsor, Windsor and Maidenhead SL4 2RL; Tel 01753 868807; Fax 01753 620466

    17+ Accommodation (22) Court bail, prison licence, probation orders.

Worcestershire

Braley House Approved Premises 89 Ombersley Rd, Worcester, Worcestershire WR3 7BT; Tel 01905 723975; Fax 01905 617687

Case Manager   Liz Smith
Hostel Administrator   R. Kelland
    17+ Accommodation (19)

Wales

Cardiff

Mandeville House Approved Premises 9 Lewis St, Cardiff CF11 6JY; Tel 029 2039 4592; Fax 029 2023 3857

    18+ Accommodation (26)

Ty Newydd Bail Approved Premises Llandegai, Bangor, Gwynedd LL57 4LG; Tel 01248 370529; Fax 01248 371204

Senior Probation Officer   R. Murphy

Neath Port Talbot

Port Talbot Approved Premises Emroch Hse, 46 Talbot Rd, Port Talbot, Neath Port Talbot SA13 1HU; Tel 01639 883407; 01639 883551; Fax 01639 890549

Senior Probation Officer and Manager   O. Elliott

Wrexham

Plas-y-Wern Approved Premises Ruabon, Wrexham, Gwynedd LL14 6RN; Tel 01978 821202; Fax 01978 810435

Senior Probation Officer   Chris Higgins
    17+ Accommodation (12)

MAGISTRATES' COURTS AND JUSTICES' CLERKS

2

Magistrates' Courts in England and Wales are governed by a Magistrates' Courts Committee (MCC). Listed below are Magistrates' Courts in England and Wales, grouped underneath their governing MCC. During the recent amalgamations of courts, one Magistrates' Court may be attached to a number of locations.

Justices' Clerks are responsible for providing legal advice to Magistrates. The Justices' Clerks responsible for each location are also listed below.

England

Avon and Somerset MCC

Justices' Chief Executive's Office The Courthouse, Northgate, Bridgwater, Avon, Somerset TA6 3YL; Tel 01278 452182; Fax 01278 446712

Justices' Chief Executive   Brian Buckhurst, Barrister, BA

Bath and Wandsdyke (1022), Mendip (2715)

Magistrates' Court North Parade Rd, Bath, Somerset BA1 5AF; Tel 01225 463281; Fax 01225 420255

Justices' Clerk   Elaine Laken, Barrister;
    E-mail elaine.laken@avonsom.mcs.gov.uk

Bristol (1013)

Magistrates' Court PO Box 107, Nelson St, Bristol BS99 7JB; Tel 0117 943 5100; Fax 0117 925 0443

Justices' Clerk   David Speed, Barrister, MA(Oxon);
    E-mail david.speed@avonsom.mcs.gov.uk

North Avon (1021)

Magistrates' Court Kennedy Way, Yate, South Gloucestershire BS37 4PY; Tel 01454 310505; Fax 01454 319404

Justices' Clerk   Elaine Laken, Barrister;
    E-mail elaine.laken@avonsom.mcs.gov.uk

South Somerset (2714)

The Law Courts Petters Way, Yeovil, BA20 1SW; Tel 01935 426281; Fax 01935 431022

Justices' Clerk   Terry Moore, Solicitor, BA, LLM(Hons), MInstAM, InstFM

Taunton Deane (2709), Sedgemoor (2705), West Somerset (2711)

Magistrates' Court St. John's Rd, Taunton, Somerset TA1 4AX; Tel 01823 257084 248; Fax 01823 335195

Justices' Clerk   Terry Moore, Solicitor, BA, LLM(Hons), M.Inst AM, M.Inst FM

Woodspring (1023)

The Court House Walliscote Rd, Weston super Mare, BS23 1UX; Tel 01934 621503; Fax 01934 625766

Justices' Clerk   Terry Moore, Solicitor, BA, LLM (Hons), M.Inst AM, M.InstFM

Bedfordshire MCC

Justices' Chief Executive's Office Shire Hall, St. Paul's Sq, Bedford, Bedfordshire MK40 1SQ; Tel 01234 319004; (Direct Line) 01234 319000; Fax 01234 319102

Justices' Chief Executive   Dr Marilyn Dyason, PhD, MBA, FRSS, MIQA; E-mail dyason.marilyn@beds-mcc.gov.uk

Bedford and Mid Bedfordshire (1051), Luton and South Bedfordshire (1055)

Magistrates' Court Stuart St, Luton, Bedfordshire LU1 5BL; Tel 01582 524236; Fax 01582 524304
Justices' Clerk Andy Wesson, Solicitor;
E-mail wesson.andrew@beds-mcc.gov.uk

Cambridgeshire MCC

Justices' Chief Executive's Office 1st Fl, The Town Hall, Market Hill, Huntingdon, Cambridgeshire PE29 3PJ; Tel 01480 414455; Fax 01480 414499
Justices' Chief Executive Philip Peaston, Barrister, MA, MBA

Cambridge (1165), East Cambridgeshire (1166), Fenland (1167), Huntingdon (1168), Peterborough (1162)

Magistrates' Court Bridge St, Peterborough PE1 1ED; Tel 01223 314311; Fax 01733 313749
Justices' Clerk Timothy Daber, Barrister, LLB, MIMgt;
E-mail tim.daber@cambs-mcs.gov.uk

Cheshire MCC

Justices' Chief Executive's Office PWB House, Middlewich Rd, Sandbach, Cheshire CW11 1HY; Tel 01270 757950; Fax 01270 760594
Justices' Chief Executive Julia Eeles, Solicitor, LLB;
E-mail julia.eeles@cheshiremcc.mcs.gov.uk

Chester (1173), Halton (1177), South Cheshire (1187), Macclesfield (1178), Vale Royal (1179), Warrington (1180)

Magistrates' Court PWB House, Middlewich Rd, Sandbach, Cheshire CW11 1HY; Tel 01270 760344; Fax 01270 760594
Justices' Clerk Steven Walsh, Solicitor, LLB;
E-mail steven.walsh@cheshiremcc.mcs.gov.uk

Cleveland MCC

Justices' Chief Executive's Office PO Box 275, Middlesborough, TS1 2XE;
URL www.clevelandmagistrates.org.uk; Tel 01642 261601; Fax 01642 211962
Justices' Chief Executive Colin Monson

Hartlepool (1247)

Magistrates' Court Victoria Rd, Hartlepool TS24 8AG; E-mail clerktothejustices@cleveland.mcs.gov.uk; Tel 01429 230604; (Direct line) 01429 230612; Fax 01429 866696
Justices' Clerk Keith Thompson, Solicitor

Langbaurgh-East (1248), Teeside (1249)

Magistrates' Court Victoria Sq, Middlesbrough TS1 2AS; E-mail clerktothejustices@cleveland.mcs.gov.uk; Tel 01642 240301; (Direct line) 01642 261611; Fax 01642 224010
Justices' Clerk Keith Thompson, Solicitor

Cumbria MCC

Justices' Chief Executive's Office Lime Hse, The Gdn, Wetheral, Carlisle, Cumbria CA4 8EW; Tel 01228 562795; Fax 01228 562796
Justices' Chief Executive and Joint Justices' Clerk Simon Evans, LLB, DMS, MCIPD;
E-mail simon.evans@cumbria.mcs.gov.uk

Carlisle and District (1322), Eden (1324), Furness and District (1398), South Lakeland (1323), Whitehaven (1375), West Allerdale and Keswick (1325)

Lime House The Green, Wetheral, Carlisle, Cumbria CA4 8EW; Tel 01228 562795; Fax 01228 562796
Justices' Clerk Chris Armstrong, Solicitor, BA, Cert. Mgmt, MIPD;
E-mail chris.armstrong@cumbria.mcs.gov.uk

Derbyshire MCC

Justices' Chief Executive's Office West Bank Hse, Albion Rd, Chesterfield, Derby S40 1UQ; Tel 01246 220008; Fax 01246 231196
Justices' Chief Executive Alan Fowler, Barrister, LLB

Derby and South Derbyshire (1431)

Magistrates' Court Derwent St, Derby, Derbyshire DE1 2EP; Tel 01332 292100; Fax 01332 293459
Justices' Clerk Nigel E. Hallam, Barrister, DMS, MIMgt, Assoc.IPD

East Derbyshire (1429)

Magistrates' Court Pimlico, Ilkeston, Derbyshire DE7 5HZ; Tel 01159 308812; Fax 01159 444562
Justices' Clerk Nigel E. Hallam, Barrister, DMS, MIMgt, Assoc.IPD

High Peak (1430)

Magistrates' Court Peak Bldgs, Terrace Rd, Buxton, Derby SK17 6DY; Tel 01298 23951; Fax 01298 72109
Justices' Clerk Dawn Windsor Bush

North East Derbyshire and Dales (1432)

Magistrates' Court PO Box 11, West Bars, Chesterfield, Derby S40 1AE; Tel 01246 278171; Fax 01246 276344
Justices' Clerk Dawn Windsor Bush

Devon and Cornwall MCC

Justices' Chief Executive's Office First Floor, Magistrates' Court, Trevecca, Culverland Rd, Liskeard, Cornwall PL14 6RF; E-mail jce.dcmcc@dcmcc.mcs.gov.uk; Tel 01579 325325; Fax 01579 325300
Justices' Chief Executive Robert N. Hutley, Barrister, LLB

East Cornwall (1289)

Magistrates' Court PO Box 2, Launceston Rd, Bodmin, Cornwall PL31 1XQ; Tel 01208 262700; Fax 01208 77198
Justices' Clerk Tim Smith, Solicitor, BA(Law);
E-mail tim.smith@dcmcc.mcs.gov.uk

West Cornwall (1288)

Magistrates' Court PO Box 60, Truro, Cornwall TR1 2HQ; E-mail westcornwallmc@eurobell.co.uk; Tel 01872 321900; Fax 01872 276227
Justices' Clerk Nicholas Lord, Barrister

Plymouth District (1290)

Magistrates' Court St. Andrew St, Plymouth, Devon PL1 2DP; Tel 01752 206200; Fax 01752 206194
Justices' Clerk Diane Baker, Solicitor

Central Devon (1292)

Magistrates' Court 1st Fl, Blackboy Rd, Exeter, EX4 6TZ I ; E-mail centraldevonmc@eurobell.co.uk; Tel 01392 814814; Fax 01392 814830
Justices' Clerk Andrew Mimmack, Barrister, LLB, MSc

South Devon (1293)

Justices' Clerks Office 2nd Fl, Riviera Hse, Nicholson Rd, Torquay, TQ2 7TT; Tel 01803 612211; Fax 01803 618618
Justices' Clerk Stephen Peckham, Barrister, LLB

North Devon (1291)

Magistrates' Court Civic Centre, Barnstaple, Devon EX31 1DX; Tel 01271 340419; Fax 01271 340415
Justices' Clerk Andrew Mimmack, Barrister, LLB, MSc

Dorset MCC

Justices' Chief Executive's Office The Law Courts, Park Rd, Poole, Dorset BH15 2RH; Tel 01202 745309; Fax 01202 711999
Justices' Chief Executive K. Brummitt

East Dorset (1522)

The Law Courts PO Box 22, Pk Road, Poole BH15 2RH; Tel 01202 745309; Fax 01202 711996
Justices' Clerk R. Davies

West Dorset (1523)

The Law Courts Westwey Rd, Weymouth, Dorset DT4 8BS; Tel 01305 783891; Fax 01305 761418
Justices' Clerk Rachel Davies

Durham MCC

Justices' Chief Executive's Office PO Box 168, Old Elvet, Durham, County Durham DH1 3FE; URL www.ourworld.compuserve.com; E-mail jce_durham@compuserve.com; Tel 0191 384 4455; Fax 0191 375 1833
Justices' Chief Executive Robert Whitehouse, Solicitor, BA, FI Mgt, FIPD

Chester-le-Street (1576), Darlington (1577), Derwentside (1578), Durham (1579), Easington (1580), Teesdale and Wear Valley (1582), Sedgefield (1581)

Magistrates' Court Central Ave, Newton Aycliffe, County Durham DL5 5RT; Tel 01325 318114; Fax 01325 301755
Justices' Clerk Linda Brenkley, Solicitor; E-mail leb.durham-mcc@tiscali.co.uk

Essex MCC

Justices' Chief Executive's Office Greenwood Hse, PO Box 3010, 91–99 New London Rd, Chelmsford, Essex CM2 0SN; Tel 01245 543701; Fax 01245 543797
Justices' Chief Executive Peter McGuirk, Barrister, MA (Oxon), IPFA

Mid North (1612), Mid South (1610), North East (1613), North West (1619), South East (1629), South West (1626)

Magistrates' Court Greenwood Hse, PO Box 3010, 91–99 New London Road, Chelmsford, Essex CM2 OSN; Tel 01245 543703; Fax 01245 543797
Director of Legal Services and Justices' Clerk Paul Carr, Barrister, MA (cantab)

Gloucester MCC

Justices' Chief Executive's Office The Court Hse, Gander La, Tewkesbury, Gloucestershire GL20 5TR; E-mail claire.horne@glos.mcs.gov.uk; Tel 01684 294632; Fax 01684 274596
Justices' Chief Executive Alan Davies

Cirencester, Fairford and Tetbury (1689), North Gloucestershire (1696)

Magistrates' Court St. Georges Rd, Cheltenham, Gloucestershire GL50 3PF; Tel 01242 532323; Fax 01242 532376
Justices' Clerk Matthew Pink, Solicitor; E-mail matthew.pink@glos.mcs.gov.uk

Forest of Dean (1695), Gloucester (1692), South Gloucestershire (1693)

Magistrates' Court Barbican Way, Bearland, Gloucester, Gloucestershire GL1 2JH; Tel 01452 426152; Fax 01452 426158
Justices' Clerk Matthew Pink, Solicitor; E-mail matthew.pink@glos.mcs.gov.uk

Greater Manchester MCC

Justices' Chief Executive's Office 3rd Floor, Mancester City Magistrates' Court, PO Box 13, Crown Square, Manchester M60 1PR; E-mail sally-anne.rogers@gmmcc.mcs.gov.uk; Tel 0161 832 7272; Fax 0161 834 2198
Justices' Chief Executive Glenys Stacey, Solicitor

Bolton (1731)

Magistrates' Court Civic Centre, Le Mans Cres, Bolton, Greater Manchester BL1 1QX; Tel 01204 558200; Fax 01204 493669
Head (Legal Services) Robert E.S. Walker; E-mail robert.walker@gmmcc.mcs.gov.uk

Bury (1732)

Magistrates' Court Tenters Street, Bury, Greater Manchester BL9 OHX; Tel 0161 764 3358; Fax 0161 763 1190
Justices' Clerk Vacancy

Leigh (1743), Wigan (1746)

Magistrates' Court Darlington St, Wigan, Greater Manchester WN1 1DW; Tel 01942 405405; Fax 01942 405444
Head (Legal Services) Karen Mitchell, Barrister, DMS, LLB; E-mail karen.mitchell@gmmcc.mcs.gov.uk

Manchester (1733)

City Magistrates' Court Crown Sq, Manchester M60 1PR; Tel 0161 832 7272; Fax 0161 834 5421
Head (Legal Services) Jacqueline Todd, Solicitor

Oldham (1734)

Magistrates' Court St. Domingo Pl, West St, Oldham, Greater Manchester OL1 1QE; E-mail magold@globalnet.co.uk; Tel 0161 620 2331; Fax 0161 652 0172
Head (Legal Services) Richard Cooper, Solicitor; E-mail richard.cooper@gmmcc.mcs.gov.uk

2

Rochdale, Middleton and Heywood (1750)

Magistrates' Court PO Box 8, Town Meadows, Rochdale, Greater Manchester OL16 1AR; Tel 01706 514800; Fax 01706 514811
Head (Legal Services) Frederick Wood, Solicitor;
E-mail fred.wood@gmmcc.mcs.gov.uk

Stockport (1739)

Magistrates' Court PO Box 155, Edward St, Stockport, SK1 3NF; URL www.stockport.u-net.com;
E-mail jfoley@stockportmag.u-net.com; Tel 0161 477 2020; Fax 0161 474 1115
Head (Legal Services) Simon Dodgshon;
E-mail simon.dodgsnon@gmmcc.mcs.gov.uk

Tameside (1748)

Magistrates' Court Henry Sq, Ashton-under-Lyne, Lancashire OL6 7TP; Tel 0161 330 2023; Fax 0161 343 1498
Head (Legal Services) Judith Burrows;
E-mail judith.burrows@gmmcc.mcs.gov.uk

Trafford (1742)

Magistrates' Court PO Box 13, Ashton La, Sale, Cheshire M33 1UP; Tel 0161 976 3333; Fax 0161 975 4673
Head (Legal Services) David Owen;
E-mail david.owen@gmmcc.mcs.gov.uk

Hampshire and Isle of Wight MCC

Justices' Chief Executive's Office The Crt Hse, Elmleigh Rd, Havant, Hampshire PO9 2AL; Tel 02392 492024; Fax 02392 475356
Justices' Chief Executive Mike West, MBA, DML, MIMgt

Isle of Wight, New Forest (1779), North East Hampshire (1780), North West Hampshire (1781), Southampton (1775), South East Hampshire (1782), South Hampshire (1783)

The Courthouse Elmleigh Rd, Havant, Hampshire PO9 2AL; Tel 02392 492024; Fax 02392 475356
Justices' Clerk Jonathan Black, Solicitor, LLM, FCIPD;
E-mail jonathan.black@ald.mcc.hants.gov.uk

Hertfordshire MCC

Justices' Chief Executive's Office The Register Office Block, County Hall, Hertford, Hertfordshire SG13 8DF;
E-mail jce.office@herts.mcs.gov.uk; Tel 01992 556544; Fax 01992 556535
Justices' Chief Executive Jonathan Radway, Barrister, LLB, MIMgt

Central Hertfordshire (1892)

Magistrates' Court The Court House, Civic Centre, St. Peters St, St. Albans, Hertfordshire AL1 3JB; Tel 01727 816821; Fax 01727 816829
Justices' Clerk David Gibbs, Barrister;
E-mail david.gibbs@herts.mcs.gov.uk

East Hertfordshire (1888), North Hertfordshire (1889)

Magistrates' Court Bayley Hse, Sish La, Stevenage, Hertfordshire SG1 3SS; Tel 01438 730431; Fax 01438 730413
Justices' Clerk Paul Fellingham, Barrister, DML

Hemel Hempstead (1878)

Magistrates' Court Dacorum Way, Hemel Hempstead, Hertfordshire HP1 1HF
Justices' Clerk Claire Beaver, Solicitor, BA(Hons)

West Hertfordshire (1893)

Magistrates' Court Clarendon Rd, Watford, Hertfordshire WD1 1ST; Tel 01923 297516; Fax 01923 297528
Justices' Clerk Claire Beaver, Solicitor, BA (Hons)

Humberside MCC

Justices' Chief Executive's Office Magistrates' Court, PO Box 254, Market Place, Hull, HU1 1US;
E-mail jce@hmcc.mcs.gov.uk; Tel 01482 618861; Fax 01482 618867
Justices' Chief Executive Malcolm John Astbury, Barrister, DML

Bainton, Wilton and Holme Beacon (1905), Beverley (1925), Dickering and North Holderness (1904), Goole and Howdenshire (1928), South Hunsley Beacon (1901)

East Yorkshire Magistrates' Courts Champney Rd, Beverley, East Riding of Yorkshire HU17 9EJ; Tel 01482 861607; Fax 01482 882004
Justices' Clerk Ian Shepherd, Solicitor;
E-mail ian.shepherd@hmcc.mcs.gov.uk

Grimsby and Cleethorpes (1940)

Magistrates' Court Victoria St, Grimsby, DN31 1PD; Tel 01472 320444; Fax 01472 320440
Justices' Clerk Phillip Houlden, Solicitor, MIMgt;
E-mail philip.houlden@hmcc-grimsby.org.uk

Kingston upon Hull (1933), South and Middle Holderness (1902)

Magistrates' Court Alfred Gelder St, PO Box 2, Hull, Kingston upon Hull HU1 2AD; E-mail erict@indirect.co.uk; Tel 01482 228914; Fax 01482 219790
Justices' Clerk Dyfed Foulkes, Barrister, LLB;
E-mail dyfed.foulkes@hmcc.mcs.gov.uk

North Lincolnshire (1903)

Justices' Clerk's Office Corporation Rd, Scunthorpe, East Riding of Yorkshire DN15 6QB;
E-mail northlincs.magistrates@virgin.net; Tel 01724 281100; Fax 01724 281890
Justices' Clerk Philip Houden, Solicitor, MIMgt;
E-mail phil.houldon@hmcc.mcs.gov.uk

Kent MCC

Justices' Chief Executive's Office Kent Magistrates' Court Service, 25 Police Station Rd, West Malling, Kent ME19 6PP; Tel 01732 221800; Fax 01732 844985
Justices' Chief Executive Stephen Savage, Barrister, LLB, MBA; E-mail srs@kentmcs.gov.uk

Ashford, Dover, Folkstone, Canterbury and Thanet (1957)

The Law Court PO Box 432, Castle Hill Ave, Folkestone, Kent CT20 2GS; Tel 01303 221762; Fax 01303 330512
Justices' Clerk Anton Walden;
E-mail amw@kentmcs.gov.uk

Dartford and Gravesham (1969), Medway (1961)

The Court House PO Box CH4, The Brook, Chatham, Kent ME4 4JZ; Tel 01634 830232; Fax 01634 847400
Justices' Clerk Malcolm Dodds;
E-mail mdd@kentmcs.gov.uk

Faversham and Sittingbourne (1967), West Kent (1963)

Magistrates' Court Palace Ave, Maidstone, Kent ME15 6LL; Tel 01662 671041; Fax 01662 691800
Justices' Clerk Quentin Morton;
E-mail qm@kentmcs.gov.uk

Lancashire MCC

Justices' Chief Executive's Office PO Box 717, Weind Hse, Preston, Lancashire PR3 1EY; Tel 01995 601596; Fax 01995 601776
Justices' Chief Executive Idris Moorby, Barrister, BA(Law), MBA; E-mail ijmoorby@lmcs.org.uk

Blackburn, Darwen and Ribble Valley (2012); Hyndburn (2010)

Magistrates' Court Northgate, Blackburn BB2 1AF; Tel 01254 687500; Fax 01254 687524
Justices' Clerk John Robinson, Solicitor, BA, MIMgt; E-mail jrobinson@lmcs.org.uk

Blackpool (1996), Fylde (2001), Wyre (2009)

Magistrates' Court Civic Centre, PO Box 27, Chapel St, Blackpool, Lancashire FY1 5RH; Tel 01253 757021; Fax 01253 757024
Justices' Clerk John Robinson, Solicitor, BA, MIMgt; E-mail jrobinson@lmcs.org.uk

Burnley and Pendle (2011), Rossendale (2006)

Magistrates' Court PO Box 64, Colne Rd, Burnley, Lancashire BB10 2NQ; Tel 01282 610000; Fax 01282 610034
Justices' Clerk John Robinson, Solicitor, BA, MIMgt; E-mail jrobinson@lmcs.org.uk

Chorley (1998), South Ribble (2007), Ormskirk (2003)

Magistrates' Court St. Thomas's Sq, Chorley, Lancashire PR7 1DS; Tel 01257 225021; Fax 01257 261948
Justices' Clerk John Robinson, Solicitor, BA, MIMgt; E-mail jrobinson@lmcs.org.uk

Lancaster (2002)

Magistrates' Court George St, Lancaster, Lancashire LA1 1XZ; Tel 01524 597000; Fax 01524 597024
Justices' Clerk John Robinson, Solicitor, BA, MIMgt; E-mail jrobinson@lmcs.org.uk

Preston (2005)

Magistrates' Court PO Box 52, Lawson St, Preston, Lancashire PR1 2RD; Tel 01772 208000; Fax 01772 208026
Justices' Clerk John Robinson, Solicitor, BA, MIMgt; E-mail jrobinson@lmcs.org.uk

Leicestershire MCC

Justices' Chief Executive's Office Magistrates' Court Committee Secretariat Unit, Upper Bond St, Hinkley, Leicestershire LE10 1NZ; Tel 01455 623030; Fax 01455 623040
Justices' Chief Executive Mike Tildesley

Ashby de La Zouch (2047), Market Bosworth (2050)

Magistrates' Court Upper Bond St, Hinkley, Leicestershire LE10 1NZ; Tel 01455 628000; Fax 01455 623020
Director (Legal Services) Nick Watson, Barrister, LLM, MBA; E-mail nick.watson@leics.mcs.gov.uk

Leicester (2048), Market Harborough and Lutterworth (2051)

Magistrates' Court PO Box 1, Pocklingtons Walk, Leicester, Leicestershire LE1 9BE; Tel 01162 553666; Fax 01162 545851
Director (Legal Services) Nick Watson, Barrister, LLB, MBA; E-mail nick.watson@leics.mcs.gov.uk

Loughborough (2049), Melton, Belvoir and Rutland (2045)

Magistrates' Court Wood Gate, Loughborough, Leicestershire LE11 2XB; Tel 01509 215715; Fax 01509 261714
Director of Legal Services Nick Watson, Barrister, LLM, MBA; E-mail nick.watson@leics.mcs.gov.uk

Lincolnshire MCC

Justices' Chief Executive's Office 2nd Fl, 15 Newland, Lincoln, Lincolnshire LN1 1XG; Tel 01522 514200; Fax 01522 512633
Justices' Chief Executive Dennis Martin, Barrister; E-mail dennis.martin@lincolnshire.mcs.gov.uk

Boston (2073), Skegness (2082), The Wolds (2078)

Magistrates' Court Park Avenue, Skegness, Lincolnshire PE25 1BH; Tel 01754 762692; Fax 01754 767318
Justices' Clerk P.J. Wydell, Solicitor;
E-mail paul.wydell@lincolnshire.mcs.gov.uk

Bourne and Stamford (2074), Elloes (2076), Grantham (2077), Sleaford (2080)

Magistrates' Court Harlaxton Road, Grantham, Lincolnshire NG31 7SB; Tel 01476 563438; Fax 01476 567200
Justices' Clerk John Pilkington, Barrister, LLB

Gainsborough (2075)

Magistrates' Court Roseway, Gainsborough, DN21 2B3; Tel 01427 615612; Fax 01427 610338
Justices' Clerk Peter Veits, Barrister

Lincoln District (2079)

Magistrates' Court 358 High St, Lincoln, Lincolnshire LN5 7QA; E-mail lincoln@lincolnshire-magistrates.org.uk; Tel 01522 528218; Fax 01522 560139
Justices' Clerk Peter Veits, Barrister

London MCC

Justices' Chief Executive's Office Greater London Court Authority, 185 Marylebone Rd, London NW1 5QJ; Tel (General Enquiries) 0845 601 3600; (Headquarters) 020 7506 3010; Fax (Headquarters) 020 7223 9481
Justices' Chief Executive Maj. Gen. Truluck, C.B., C.B.E.

Acton (2723)

Magistrates' Court Winchester St, Acton, London W3 8PB; Tel 020 8992 9014; Fax 020 8993 9647
Justices' Clerk Howard Dingwall, Barrister, MA, LLB

Barking and Dagenham (2814)

Magistrates' Court East St, Barking, London IG11 8EW; Tel 020 8594 5311; Fax 020 8594 4297
Justices' Clerk Robin Wright, Barrister

Barnet (2725)

Magistrates' Court 7c High St, Barnet, Greater London
EN5 5UE; Tel 020 8441 9042; Fax 020 8441 6753
Justices' Clerk John Clark, Solicitor

Bexley (2728)

Magistrates' Court Norwich Pl, Bexleyheath, Kent
DA6 7NB; Tel 020 8304 5211; Fax 020 8303 6849
Justices' Clerk Carolyn Pilmore-Bedford, Solicitor

Bow Street (2641)

Magistrates' Court 28 Bow St, London WC2E 7AS; Tel 020
7853 9201; Fax 020 7853 9290
Justices' Clerk Gaynor Houghton-Jones, Barrister, LLB;
E-mail gaynor.houghton-j@glmca.mcs.gov.uk

Brent (2762)

Magistrates' Court 448 High Rd, Church End, London
NW10 2DZ; Tel 020 8955 0555; Fax 020 8955 0543
Justices' Clerk Peter Lydiate, Barrister, LLB;
E-mail pwh.lydiate@glmca.mcs.gov.uk

Brentford (2769)

Magistrates' Court Market Place, Brentford, London
TW8 8EN; Tel 020 8568 9811; Fax 020 8560 3578
Justices' Clerk Alan Baldwin, Solicitor

Bromley (2727)

Magistrates' Court 1 London Rd, Bromley, Kent BR1 1RA;
E-mail justices.clerk@bromley.olmcs-law.co.uk; Tel 020 8325
4000; Fax 020 8325 4006
Justices' Clerk Robin Haynes, Solicitor, MIPD

Camberwell Green (2656)

Magistrates' Court 15 D'Eynsford Rd, Camberwell Grn,
London SE5 7UP;
E-mail beverley.morse@glmca.mcs.gov.uk; Tel 020 7805
9801; Fax 020 7805 9895
Justices' Clerk Beverley Morse, Barrister, LLM (Cantab)

City of London (2631)

Magistrates' Court The Justice Rooms, 1 Queen Victoria St,
London EC4N 4XY; Tel 020 7332 1820; Fax 020 7332 1493
Justices' Clerk Julian Wignall, Barrister, MBA;
E-mail julian.wignall@glmca.mcs.gov.uk

Croydon (2732)

Magistrates' Court Barclay Rd, Croydon, Surrey CR9 3NG;
E-mail clare.bridges@croydon.olmcs-law.co.uk; Tel 020 8686
8680; Fax 020 8680 9801
Justices' Clerk Clare Bridges, Barrister, BSc(Hons)

Ealing (2734)

Magistrates' Court Green Man La, West Ealing, London
W13 0SD; Tel 020 8579 9311; Fax 020 8579 2985
Justices' Clerk Howard Dingwell, Barrister, MA, LLB

Enfield (2757)

Magistrates' Court Lordship La, Tottenham, London
N17 6RT; Tel 020 8808 5411; Fax 020 8885 4343
Justices' Clerk Andrew Shepstone, Solicitor, MA (Cantab);
E-mail andrew.shepstone@glmca.mcs.gov.uk

Greenwich (2643), Woolwich (2653)

Magistrates' Court 9–10 Blackheath Rd, London SE10 8PG;
Tel 020 8276 1301; Fax 020 8276 1396
Justices' Clerk Barbara Barnes, Barrister

Haringey (2742)

Magistrates' Court Bishops Rd, Highgate, London N6 4HS;
Tel 020 8340 3472; Fax 020 8348 3343
Justices' Clerk Graham Fillingham, Solicitor;
E-mail graham.fillingham@glmca.mcs.gov.uk
Magistrates' Court Lordship La, Tottenham, London
N17 6RT; Tel 020 8808 5411; Fax 020 8365 0436

Harrow Gore (2760)

Magistrates' Court PO Box 164, Rosslyn Cres, Harrow,
Greater London HA1 2JY; Tel 020 8427 5146; Fax 020 8863
9518
Justices' Clerk Gordon Cropper, Solicitor, LLB, MSc;
E-mail gordon.cropper@glmca.mcs.gov.uk

Havering (1837)

Magistrates' Court Main Rd, Romford, Essex RM1 3BH;
Tel 01708 771771; Fax 01708 771777
Justices' Clerk Tom Ring, Barrister;
E-mail tom.ring@glmca.mcs.gov.uk

Hillingdon (2766)

Magistrates' Court Harefield Rd, Uxbridge,
Greater London UB8 1PQ; Tel 01895 814646; Fax 01895
274280
Justices' Clerk Martin Hamilton, Barrister, MA (Oxon);
E-mail martin.hamilton@glmca.gov.uk

Hendon (2741)

Magistrates' Court The Hyde, Hendon, Greater London
NW9 7BY; Tel 020 8441 9042; Fax 020 8205 4595
Justices' Clerk John Clark, Solicitor

Highbury Corner (2663)

Magistrates' Court 51 Holloway Rd, London N7 8JA;
Tel 020 7506 3102; 020 7506 3103; Fax 020 7506 3192
Justices' Clerk Janice Woolley, Solicitor;
E-mail janice.wallace@glmca.mcs.gov.uk

Horseferry Road (2660)

Magistrates' Court 70 Horseferry Rd, London SW1P 2AX;
E-mail horseferry@ilmc6.freeserve.co.uk; Tel 020 7805 1101;
Fax 020 7805 1190
Justices' Clerk Gaynor Houghton-Jones, Barrister, LLB;
E-mail gaynor.houghton-j@glmca.mcs.gov.uk

Hounslow (2769)

Magistrates' Court Hanworth Rd, Feltham, Greater London
TW13 5AF; Tel 020 8751 3727; Fax 020 8844 1779
Justices' Clerk Alan Baldwin, Solicitor

Inner London and City Family Proceedings Court

59–65 Wells St, London W1A 3AE; Tel 020 7805 3401;
Fax 020 7805 3491
Justices' Clerk Audrey Damazer, Barrister, BA;
E-mail audrey.damazer@glmca.mcs.gov.uk

Kingston upon Thames (2812)

Magistrates' Court 19 High St, Kingston upon Thames, Surrey KT1 1JW; E-mail admin@kingmags.infotrade.co.uk; Tel 020 8546 5603; Fax 020 8547 3551
Justices' Clerk Andrew Vickers, Barrister, BA

Marylebone (2646)

Magistrates' Court 181 Marylebone Rd, London NW1 5QJ; Tel 020 7506 3701; Fax 020 7724 9163
Justices' Clerk Edward Houghton, Barrister, MA (Cantab); E-mail edward.houghton@glmca.mcs.gov.uk

Merton (2763)

Magistrates' Court Alexandra Rd, Wimbledon, London SW19 7JP; Tel 020 8946 8622; Fax 020 8946 7030
Justices' Clerk Eric Packer, Solicitor, LLB; E-mail eric.packer@glmca.mcs.gov.uk

Newham (2721)

Magistrates' Court 389–397 High St, London E15 4SB; Tel 020 8522 5000; Fax 020 8519 1657
Justices' Clerk Robin Wright, Barrister; E-mail robin.wright@glmca.mcs.gov.uk

Redbridge (2815)

Magistrates' Court 850 Cranbrook Rd, Barkingside, Ilford, Essex IG6 1HW; Tel 020 8551 4461; Fax 020 8550 2101
Justices' Clerk Kevin Moore, Barrister; E-mail kevin.moore@redbridge.glmca.mcs.gov.uk

Richmond upon Thames (2768)

Magistrates' Court Parkshot, Richmond, Surrey TW9 2RF; Tel 020 8948 2101; Fax 020 8332 2628
Justices' Clerk David Lowdell, Solicitor, BA

South Western (2649)

Magistrates' Court 176a Lavender Hill, Battersea, London SW11 1JU; Tel 020 7805 1401; Fax 020 7805 1409
Justices' Clerk John Mulhern, Barrister, LLB
Inner London Youth Panel Youth Centre 4

Sutton (2733)

Magistrates' Court Shotfield, Wallington, Surrey SM6 0JA; E-mail john.sunderland@sutton.olmcs-law.co.uk; Tel 020 8770 5950; Fax 020 8770 5977
Justices' Clerk John Sunderland, Solicitor, LLB; E-mail john.sunderland@glmca.mcs.gov.uk

Thames (2650)

Magistrates' Court 58 Bow Rd, London E3 4DJ; Tel 020 8271 1201; Fax 020 8271 1208
Justices' Clerk Keith Griffiths, Solicitor
Inner London Youth Panel Youth Centre 1

Tower Bridge (2651)

Magistrates' Court 211 Tooley St, London SE1 2JY; Tel 020 7805 9801; Fax 020 7805 9895
Justices' Clerk Beverley Morse, Barrister, LLM (Cantab)
Inner London Youth Panel

Waltham Forest (2813)

Magistrates' Court 1 Farnan Ave, Walthamstow, London E17 4NX; Tel 020 8527 8000; Fax 020 8527 9063
Justices' Clerk Peter Cozens, Solicitor

West London (2658)

Magistrates' Court 181 Talgarth Rd, London W6 8DN; Tel 020 8700 9301; Fax 020 8700 9303
Justices' Clerk Helen Parry, Barrister; E-mail helen.parry@glmca.mcs.gov.uk
Inner London Youth Panel Youth Centre 3

Merseyside MCC

Justices' Chief Executive's Office 2nd Fl, Port of Liverpool Bldg, Pierhead, Liverpool, Merseyside L3 1BY; E-mail jce@mcc.mcs.gov.uk; Tel 0151 474 8080; Fax 0151 474 8081
Justices' Chief Executive Malcolm Marsh, Solicitor, LLB

Knowsley (2266)

Magistrates' Court Latham Rd, Huyton, Merseyside L36 9XY; Tel 0151 481 4400; Fax 0151 481 0483
Principal Legal Adviser Gillian Johnston, Solicitor, LLB(Hons)

Liverpool (2267)

Magistrates' Court 107–111 Dale St, Liverpool, Merseyside L2 2JQ; E-mail keith.townend@mmcc.mcs.gov.uk; Tel 0151 243 5500; Fax 0151 243 5562
Principal Legal Adviser Keith Townend, Solicitor

North Sefton (2269)

Magistrates' Court Albert Rd, Southport, Merseyside PR9 0LJ; Tel 01704 534141; Fax 01704 500226
Principal Legal Adviser Susan Perry, Solicitor, LLB(Hons), MA; E-mail susan.perry@mmcc.mcs.gov.uk

South Sefton (2270)

Magistrates' Court 29 Merton Rd, Bootle, Merseyside L20 3BJ; Tel 0151 933 6999; Fax 0151 922 4285
Principal Legal Adviser Susan Perry, Solicitor, LLB(Hons), MA; E-mail susan.perry@mmcc.mcs.gov.uk

St. Helens (2286)

Magistrates' Court Corporation St, St. Helens, Merseyside WA10 1SZ; E-mail gillian.johnston@mmcc.mcs.gov.uk; Tel 01744 620244; Fax 01744 759697
Principal Legal Adviser Gillian Johnston, Solicitor, LLB(Hons)

Wirral Borough (2271)

Magistrates' Court Sessions Crts, Chester St, Birkenhead, Merseyside L41 5HW; E-mail sarah.pemberton@mmcc.mcs.gov.uk; Tel 0151 647 2345; Fax 0151 666 2783
Principal Legal Adviser Sarah Pemberton, Solicitor

Norfolk MCC

Justices' Chief Executive's Office 1st Fl, The Courthouse, Old Bury Rd, Thetford, Norfolk IP24 3AQ; Tel 01842 757300; Fax 01842 763084
Justices' Chief Executive Martin Sale, Barrister; E-mail martin.sale@norfolk.mcs.gov.uk

Central Norfolk (1442), South Norfolk (1446), West Norfolk (1447)

The Court House College La, King's Lynn, Norfolk P630 1PQ; Tel 01553 770120; Fax 01553 775098
Justices' Clerk Vacancy,

Great Yarmouth (1391), North Norfolk (1444)

Magistrates' Court North Quay, Great Yarmouth, Norfolk NR30 1PW; Tel 01493 849800; Fax 01493 852169
Justices' Clerk David Ratcliffe, Solicitor, LLB;
E-mail david.ratcliffe@norfolk.mcs.gov.uk

Norwich (1385)

The Magistrates' Court Bishopgate, Norwich, Norfolk NR3 1UP; Tel 01603 679500; Fax 01603 663263
Justices' Clerk David Carrier, Barrister, DMS;
E-mail david.carrier@norfolk.mcs.gov.uk

Northamptonshire MCC

Justices' Chief Executive's Office Regent's Pavillion, Summerhouse Rd, Moulton Pk, Northampton, NN3 6BJ; Tel 01604 497000; Fax 01604 497001
Justices' Chief Executive Neil Clarke, Solicitor, Council Member

Northumbria MCC

Justices' Chief Executive's Office Northumbria Magistrates' Courts Service, PO Box 793, Market St, Newcastle upon Tyne, Tyne and Wear NE99 1XJ; Tel 0191 245 6212; Fax 0191 260 2724
Justices' Chief Executive J.S. Young, Barrister, LLB

Alnwick (2347)

Magistrates' Court Lloyd's Bank Chambers, 24 Bondgate Within, Alnwick, Northumberland NE66 1TD; Tel 01665 602727; Fax 01665 510247
Justices' Clerk David Pryer, Barrister, MIMgt;
E-mail david.pryer@newcastle.gov.uk

Berwick-upon-Tweed (2348)

Magistrates' Court 44–48 Hide Hill, Berwick-upon-Tweed, Northumberland TD15 1AB; Tel 01289 306885; Fax 01289 302735
Justices' Clerk David Pryer, Barrister, MIMgt;
E-mail david.pryer@newcastle.gov.uk

Gateshead (2850)

Magistrates' Court PO Box 26, Warwick St, Gateshead, Tyne and Wear NE8 1DT;
E-mail southtyneside.magistrates@newcastle.gov.uk;
Tel 0191 477 5821; Fax 0191 478 7825
Justices' Clerk Chris Livesley, Solicitor, BA(Hons)

Houghton-le-Spring (2854)

Magistrates' Court Dairy La, Houghton-Le-Spring, Tyne and Wear DH4 5BL; Tel 0191 584 2392; Fax 0191 584 5809
Justices' Clerk Peter Rowbottom, Barrister, LLB, MBA, MIMgt

Newcastle-upon-Tyne (2851)

Magistrates' Court PO Box 191, Market St East, Newcastle upon Tyne, Tyne and Wear NE99 1TB; Tel 0191 232 7326; Fax 0191 221 0025
Justices' Clerk Rosemary Watson

North Tyneside (2852)

Magistrates' Court 153 Tynemouth Rd, North Shields, Tyne and Wear NE30 1AG; Tel 0191 296 0099; Fax 0191 296 2478
Justices' Clerk Rosemary Watson

South East Northumberland (2349)

The Law Courts Bedlington, Northumberland NE22 7LX; Tel 01670 531100; Fax 01670 820133
Justices' Clerk David Pryer, Barrister, MIMgt;
E-mail david.pryer@newcastle.gov.uk

South Tyneside (2853)

Magistrates' Court Millbank, Secretan Way, South Shields, Tyne and Wear N633 1RG; Tel 0191 427 4400; Fax 0191 427 4499
Justices' Clerk Chris Livesley, Solicitor, BA(Hons)

Sunderland (2855)

Magistrates' Court Gillbridge Ave, Sunderland, Tyne and Wear SR1 3AP; Tel 0191 514 1621; Fax 0191 565 8564
Justices' Clerk Peter Rowbottom, Barrister. LLB, MBA, MIMgt

Tynedale (2346)

The Court House Beaumont Street, Hexham, Northumberland NE46 3NB;
E-mail david.pryer@newcastle.gov.uk; Tel 01434 603248; Fax 01434 609378
Justices' Clerk David Pryer, Barrister, MIMgt

North Yorkshire MCC

Justices' Chief Executive's Office The Court Hse, Church Hill, Easingwold, North Yorkshire YO61 3JX; Tel 01347 821776; Fax 01347 823776
Justices' Chief Executive Paul Bradley, Barrister, LLB, DMS;
E-mail paul.bradley@magistrates.northyorks.gov.uk

Harrogate (2527)

Magistrates' Court PO Box 72, Victoria Ave, Harrogate, North Yorkshire HG1 1LS; Tel 01423 722000; Fax 01423 722001
Justices' Clerk Gordon Lees, Barrister, BA(Law);
E-mail gordon.lees@magistrates.northyorks.gov.uk

Northallerton and Richmond (2543)

Magistrates' Court 3 Racecourse La, Northallerton, North Yorkshire DL7 8QZ; Tel 01609 788200; Fax 01609 783509
Justices' Clerk Gordon Lees, Barrister, BA(Law);
E-mail gordon.lees@magistrates.northyorks.gov.uk

Scarborough (2536)

Magistrates' Court Northway, Scarborough, North Yorkshire YO12 7AE; Tel 01723 340200; Fax 01723 353250
Justices' Clerk Gordon Lees, Barrister, BA(Law);
E-mail gordon.lees@magistrates.northyorks.gov.uk

Selby (2537)

Magistrates' Court New La, Selby, North Yorkshire YO8 0QW; Tel 01757 293500; Fax 01757 293501
Justices' Clerk Gordon Lees, Barrister, BA(Law);
E-mail gordon.lees@magistrates.northyorks.gov.uk

Skipton (2538)

Magistrates' Court Otley St, Skipton, North Yorkshire BD23 1RQ; Tel 01765 794791; Fax 01765 701169
Justices' Clerk Gordon Lees, Barrister, BA(Law);
E-mail gordon.lees@magistrates.northyorks.gov.uk

York (2541)

Magistrates' Court Clifford St, York YO1 9RE; Tel 01904 615200; Fax 01904 615201
Justices' Clerk Gordon Lees, Barrister, BA(Law);
  E-mail gordon.lees@magistrates.northyorks.gov.uk

Nottinghamshire MCC

Justices' Chief Executive's Office Nottingham Magistrates' Court, Carrington St, Nottingham NG2 1EE;
E-mail jce.nottsmags@virgin.net; Tel 01159 558301;
Fax 01159 558177
Justices' Chief Executive Anthony Debruslais, Barrister, LLB

Mansfield (2566)

Magistrates' Court Rosemary St, Mansfield, Nottinghamshire NG19 6EE; Tel 01623 451500; Fax 01623 451648
Justices' Clerk Graham Hooper, Barrister, LLB, DMS;
  E-mail gbh.jc@virgin.net

Newark (2567)

Magistrates' Court Magnus St, Newark, Nottinghamshire NG24 1LD; Tel 01636 688200; Fax 01636 688222
Justices' Clerk Graham Hooper, Barrister, BA(Law);
  E-mail gbh.jc@virgin.net

Nottingham (2568)

Magistrates' Court Carrington St, Nottingham, Nottinghamshire NG2 1EE; Tel 01159 558111; Fax 01159 558139
Justices' Clerk Graham Hooper, Barrister, LLB, DMS;
  E-mail gbh.jc@virgin.net

Retford (2553), Worksop (2560)

Magistrates' Court 30 Potter St, Worksop, Nottinghamshire S80 2AJ; Tel 01909 486111; Fax 01909 473521
Justices' Clerk Graham Hooper, Barrister, LLB, DMS;
  E-mail gbh.jc@virgin.net

South Yorkshire MCC

Justices' Chief Executive's Office Unit 9, Meadow Crt, Almos Rd, Sheffield, South Yorkshire S9 1BX; Tel 0114 280 0900; Fax 0114 280 0901
Justices' Chief Executive Stephen Caven, Solicitor, BA(Hons), MBA;
  E-mail stephen.caven@symcc.mcs.gov.uk

Barnsley (2770)

Magistrates' Court PO Box 17, West Gate, Barnsley, South Yorkshire S70 2DW; E-mail barnsleymags@freenet.co.uk; Tel 01226 320000; Fax 01226 320048
Justices' Clerk David M. White, Barrister, LLB, MSc, FCMT;
  E-mail david.white@symcc.mcs.gov.uk

Doncaster (2771)

Magistrates' Court PO Box 49, College Rd, Doncaster, South Yorkshire DN1 3HT; Tel 01302 347303; Fax 01302 327906
Justices' Clerk Andrew M. Davison, Barrister;
  E-mail andrew.davison@symcc.mcs.gov.uk

Rotherham (2772)

Magistrates' Court PO Box 15, The Statutes, Rotherham, South Yorkshire S60 1YW; Tel 01709 788412; Fax 01709 788440
Justices' Clerk Andrew M. Davison, Barrister;
  E-mail andrew.davison@symcc.mcs.gov.uk

Sheffield (2773)

Magistrates' Court Castle St, Sheffield, South Yorkshire S3 8LU; Tel 0114 276 0760; Fax 0114 272 0129
Justices' Clerk David M. White, LLB, MSc, FCMT;
  E-mail david.white@symcc.mcs.gov.uk

Staffordshire MCC

Justices' Chief Executive's Office MCC Administration Centre, PO Box 1353, The Court Hse, Ryecroft, Newcastle under Lyme, Staffordshire ST5 2DG; Tel 01782 741700; Fax 01782 719735
Justices' Chief Executive Peter Woolliscroft, Solicitor;
  E-mail p.g.wooliscroft@staffsmcc.org.uk

Burton upon Trent (2780), Cannock and Seisdon (2859), Lichfield and Tamworth (2860), Mid Staffordshire and Rugeley (2799)

Southern Courts and Administration Centre South Walls, Stafford, Staffordshire ST16 3DW; Tel 01785 223144; Fax 01785 258508
Justices' Clerk Andrew Marshall, Barrister

Stoke on Trent (2781), North Staffordshire (2798)

Northern Courts and Administration Centre Baker St, Fenton, Stoke-on-Trent ST4 3BX; Tel 01782 845353; Fax 01782 744782
Justices' Clerk Mike Benson, Solicitor

Suffolk MCC

Justices' Chief Executive's Office Magistrates' Court, Old Shire Hall, Honey Hill, Bury St. Edmunds, Suffolk IP33 1HF; Tel 01284 352300; Fax 01284 352343
Justices' Chief Executive John Rodley;
  E-mail john.rodley@suffolkmcs.gov.uk

Haverhill and Sudbury (2864), North East Suffolk (2863), North West Suffolk (2862), South East Suffolk (2866), St. Edmundsbury and Stowmarket (2865)

Magistrates' Court Old Shire Hall, Honey Hill, Bury St. Edmunds, Suffolk IP33 1HF; Tel 01284 352300; Fax 01284 352343
Justices' Clerk Christopher Bowler, Barrister, LLB, DMS;
  E-mail christopher.bowler@suffolkmcc.mcs.gov.uk

Surrey MCC

Justices' Chief Executive's Office Court Hse, London Rd, Dorking, Surrey RH4 1SX; Tel 01306 885544; Fax 01306 877447
Justices' Chief Executive Sheridan Greenland

North Surrey (2845)

Magistrates' Court PO Box 5, Knowle Grn, Staines, Greater London TW18 1XR; Tel 01784 459261; Fax 01784 466257
Director (Legal Services) John Baker, Barrister;
  E-mail john.baker@surreymcc.gov.uk

North West Surrey (2846)

Magistrates' Court Station Approach, Woking, Surrey
GU22 7YL; Tel 01483 714950; Fax 01483 767849
Director (Legal Services) John Baker, Barrister

South East Surrey (2847)

Magistrates' Court Hatchlands Rd, Redhill, Surrey
RH1 6DH; Tel 01737 765581; Fax 01737 764972
Head (Legal Services) Elaine Wozniak, Solicitor;
E-mail elaine.wozniak@surreymcc.mcs.gov.uk

South West Surrey (2848)

Magistrates' Court PO Box 36, Mary Rd, Guildford, Surrey
GU1 4AS; Tel 01483 534811; Fax 01483 304377
Head (Legal Services) Lise Merie Buckingham, Barrister,
LLB(Hons), DMS,MBA;
E-mail lise.buckingham@surreymcc.mcs.gov.uk

Sussex MCC

Justices' Chief Executive's Office The Secretariat, The
Court Hse, Friars' Wlk, Lewes, East Sussex BN7 2PG;
Tel 01273 486455; Fax 01273 486470
Justices' Chief Executive Victoria Wallace

Arundel (2927), Chichester (2936)

Magistrates' Court 6 Market St, Chichester, West Sussex
PO19 1YE;
E-mail justicesclerk.chichester@westsussex.gov.uk;
Tel 01243 817000; Fax 01243 533655
Director (Legal Services) Philip Vahey, Barrister, MBA;
E-mail philip.vahey@sussexmcc.mcs.gov.uk

Brighton and Hove (1604)

Magistrates' Court Edward St, Brighton, Brighton and
Hove BN2 2LG; Tel 01273 670888; Fax 01273 790260
Director (Legal Services) Philip Vahey, Barrister, MBA;
E-mail philip.vahey@sussexmcc.mcb.gov.uk

Crawley (2929)

Magistrates' Court County Bldgs, Woodfield Rd, Crawley,
West Sussex RH10 1XF; Tel 01293 895315; Fax 01293
895113
Director (Legal Services) Philip Vahey, Barrister, MBA;
E-mail philip.vahey@sussexmcc.mcs.gov.uk

Eastbourne and Hailsham (1605)

Magistrates' Court Old Orchard Rd, Eastbourne,
East Sussex BN21 4UN; Tel 01323 727518; Fax 01323
649372
Director (Legal Services) Philip Vahey, Barrister, MBA;
E-mail philip.vahey@sussexmcc.mcs.gov.uk

Hastings and Rother (1606)

Magistrates' Court Bohemia Rd, Hastings, East Sussex
TN34 1ND; Tel 01424 437644; Fax 01424 429878
Director (Legal Services) Philip Vahey, Barrister, MBA;
E-mail philip.vahey@sussexmcc.mcs.gov.uk

Horsham (2930)

Magistrates' Court Hurst Rd, Horsham, West Sussex
RH12 2ET; Tel 01403 252391; Fax 01403 217612
Director (Legal Services) Philip Vahey, Barrister, MBA;
E-mail philip.vahey@sussexmcc.mcs.gov.uk

Lewes and Crowborough (1607)

Magistrates' Court Friar's Walk, Lewes, East Sussex
BN7 2PG; Tel 01273 478889; Fax 01273 480413
Director (Legal Services) Philip Vahey, Barrister, MBA;
E-mail philip.vahey@sussexmcc.mcs.gov.uk

Mid Sussex (2932)

Magistrates' Court Bolnore Rd, Haywards Heath, West
Sussex RH16 4BA;
E-mail justicesclerk.haywardsheath@westsussex.gov.uk;
Tel 01444 472603; Fax 01444 472639
Director (Legal Services) Philip Vahey, Barrister, MBA;
E-mail philip.vahey@sussexmcc.mcs.gov.uk

Worthing and District (2937)

Magistrates' Court PO Box 199, Christchurch Rd, Worthing,
West Sussex BN11 1JE;
E-mail justicesclerk.worthing@westsussex.gov.uk; Tel 01903
210981; Fax 01903 820074
Director (Legal Services) Philip Vahey, Barrister, MBA;
E-mail philip.vahey@sussexmcc.mcs.gov.uk

Thames Valley MCC

Justices' Chief Executive's Office Waverley Hse, Queens
Ave, Bicester, Oxfordshire OX6 8NZ; Tel 01869 853100;
Fax 01869 853103
Justices' Chief Executive Colin Clifford, Barrister, MBA;
E-mail colin.clifford@tv.mcs.gov.uk

Berkshire, Reading and West Berkshire (1076)

Magistrates' Court Civic Centre, Reading RG1 7TQ;
Tel 01889 552 600; Fax 01889 508173
Justices' Clerk Gillian Andrews, Barrister;
E-mail gill.andrews@tv.mcs.gov.uk

Buckinghamshire, Central Buckinghamshire (1129)

Magistrates' Court Walton St, Aylesbury, Buckinghamshire
HP21 7QZ; E-mail esavage@thamesvalley-mcs.gov.uk;
Tel 01296 554300; Fax 01296 554340
Justices' Clerk Philip Knowles, Barrister, LLB;
E-mail philip.knowles@tv.mcs.gov.uk

East Berkshire (1072)

Magistrates' Court Chanley Pk, Off Windsor Rd, Slough
SL1 2HJ; Tel 01889 552600; Fax 01889 508173
Justices' Clerk Gillian Andrews, Barrister;
E-mail gill.andrews@tv.mcs.gov.uk

Milton Keynes (1124)

Magistrates' Court 301 Silbury Blvd, Milton Keynes
MK9 2AJ; Tel 01296 554300; Fax 01296 554340
Justices' Clerk Philip Knowles, Barrister, LLB;
E-mail philip.knowles@tv.mcs.gov.uk

Northern Oxfordshire (2775)

Magistrates' Court Warwick Rd, Banbury, Oxfordshire
OX16 7AW; Tel 01865 448011; 01865 448012; Fax 01865
448013
Justices' Clerk Su Lutter; E-mail su.lutter@tv.mcs.gov.uk

Oxford, Oxfordshire and Southern Oxfordshire (2777)

Magistrates' Court PO Box 37, Speedwell St, Oxford,
Oxfordshire OXF 1RZ; Tel 01865 448011; 01865 448012;
Fax 01865 448013
Justices' Clerk Su Lutter; E-mail su.lutter@tv.mcs.gov.uk

Wycombe and Beaconsfield (1130)

Magistrates' Court Easton St, High Wycombe, Buckinghamshire HP11 1LR; Tel 01296 554300; Fax 01296 554340
Justices' Clerk Phillip Knowles, Barrister, LLB; E-mail philip.knowles@tv.mcs.gov.uk

Warwickshire MCC

Justices' Chief Executive's Office PO Box 16, 14 Hamilton Terr, Leamington Spa, Warwickshire CV32 4XG; Tel 01926 438730; Fax 01926 335051
Justices' Chief Executive Vivienne McGhee, Solicitor, LLB; E-mail vivienne.mcghee@warwickshire.mcs.gov.uk

Warwickshire (2904)

Magistrates' Court Vicarage St, Nuneaton, Warwickshire CV11 4DN; Tel 024 7628 2750; Fax 024 7604 2466
Justices' Clerk Mike Watkins, Solicitor, LLB, MCIPD, MIMgt

West Mercia MCC

Justices' Chief Executive's Office Magistrates' Courts Service, PO Box 2676, Comberton Place, Kidderminster, DY10 1WE; E-mail westmerciamcc@ereal.net; Tel 01562 514000; Fax 01562 514009
Justices' Chief Executive Nick Jones, Barrister, LLB, MA, MIPD

Bridgnorth (3274), Ludlow (3276), Telford (3282)

Magistrates' Court Telford Sq, Malinsgate, Telford, Shropshire TF3 4HX; Tel 01952 204500; Fax 01952 204554
Justices' Clerk Paul Bushell, Solicitor, LLB, MCMI

Drayton (3275), Oswestry (3277), Shrewsbury (3279)

Magistrates' Court Telford Sq, Malinsgate, Telford, TF3 4HX; Tel 01952 204500; Fax 01952 204554
Justices' Clerk Paul Bushell, Solicitor, LLB, MCMI

Herefordshire (1841)

Magistrates' Court The Court House, Bath St, Hereford, Herefordshire HR1 2HE; Tel 01562 514000; Fax 01562 514111
Justices' Clerk Paul Bushell, Solicitor, LLB, MCMI

North Worcester, Bromsgrove and Redditch (1840), Severnminster (1842)

Magistrates' Court Comberton Place, Kidderminster, DY10 1QQ; Tel 01562 514000; Fax 01562 514111
Justices' Clerk Paul Bushell, Solicitor, LLB, MCMI

South Worcester (1843)

Magistrates' Court The Law Courts, Ombersley St, Droitwich, WR9 8RY; Tel 01905 771089; Fax 01905 794684
Justices' Clerk John Stephenson, Solicitor, BA

West Midlands MCC

Justices' Chief Executive's Office 4 Newton St, Birmingham, West Midlands B4 6NE; Tel 0121 212 6789; Fax 0121 212 6787
Justices' Chief Executive Alan Eccles, Barrister

Aldridge and Brownhills (2917), Dudley (2911), Stourbridge and Halesowen (2912), Walsall (2918), Warley (2914), West Bromwich (2915), Wolverhampton (2919)

The Law Courts North St, Wolverhampton, West Midlands WV1 1RA; Tel 01902 773151; Fax 01902 427875
Justices' Clerk Vacancy

Birmingham (2909)

Victoria Law Courts Corporation Street, Birmingham, West Midlands B4 6QJ; Tel 0121 212 6611; Fax 0121 212 6624
Justices' Clerk Tony Heath, Solicitor, OBE, MA; E-mail anthony.heath@westmidlands.mcs.gov.uk

Coventry (2910), Solihull (2916), Sutton Coldfield (2909)

Magistrates' Court Little Park St, Coventry, West Midlands CV1 2SQ; Tel 024 7650 0614; Fax 024 7650 0618
Justices' Clerk John Griffin; E-mail john.griffin@westmidlands.mcs.gov.uk

West Yorkshire MCC

Justices' Chief Executive's Office Colbeck Hse, Bradford Rd, Birstall, Batley, West Yorkshire WF17 9NR; Tel 01924 424030; Fax 01924 427910
Justices' Chief Executive Stuart Baker, Barrister; E-mail stuart.baker@wy.mcs.gov.uk

Batley and Dewsbury (2996)

Magistrates' Court Grove St, Dewsbury, West Yorkshire WF13 1JP; Tel 01924 468287; Fax 01924 430483
District Legal Director Michelle Parry-Sharp, Solicitor

Bradford (2978)

Magistrates' Court PO Box 187, The Tyrls, Bradford, West Yorkshire BD1 1JL; Tel 01274 390111; Fax 01274 391731
District Legal Director Fiona Philpott, Barrister

Calderdale (2997)

Magistrates' Court PO Box 32, Harrison Rd, Halifax, West Yorkshire HX1 2AN; Tel 01422 360695; Fax 01422 347874
District Legal Director Frank Gray, Solicitor

Huddersfield (2987)

Magistrates' Court Civic Centre, PO Box B37, Huddersfield, West Yorkshire HD1 2NH; Tel 01484 423552; Fax 01484 430085
District Legal Director Michelle Parry-Sharp, Solicitor

Keighley (2979)

Magistrates' Court Bradford Rd, Bingley, West Yorkshire BD16 1YA; Tel 01274 568411; Fax 01274 551289
District Legal Director Fiona Philpott, Solicitor

Leeds District (2992)

The Magistrates' Court PO Box 97, Westgate, Leeds, West Yorkshire LS1 3JP; Tel 0113 245 9653; Fax 0113 244 4700
District Legal Director Mrs H.J. Gill, Solicitor

Pontefract (2994)

Magistrate's Court 2 Front St, Pontefract, West Yorkshire WF8 1BW; Tel 01977 723600; Fax 01977 723610
District Legal Director Raymond Goodman, Solicitor

2

Wakefield (2995)

Magistrates' Court Cliff Pde, Wakefield, West Yorkshire WF1 2TW; Tel 01924 303460; Fax 01924 303465
District Legal Director Raymond Goodman, Solicitor

Wiltshire MCC

Justices' Chief Executive's Office Wiltshire Magistrates' Courts Service, PO Box 13, Salisbury, Wiltshire SP1 2XQ; Tel 01722 415433; Fax 01722 335700
Justices' Chief Executive Paul Wilcock, Solicitor, DML, MIMgt; E-mail gp.wilcock@wiltsmcc.mcs.gov.uk

North West Wiltshire (3026)

The Court House Pewsham Way, Chippenham, Wiltshire SN15 3BF; Tel 01249 463473; Fax 01249 444319
Justices' Clerk David Brewer, Barrister, BA(Law); E-mail david.brewer@wiltsmcc.mcs.gov.uk

South East Wiltshire (3027)

Magistrates' Court 43–55 Milford St, Salisbury, Wiltshire SP1 2BP; Tel 01722 333225; Fax 01722 413395
Justices' Clerk David Brewer, Barrister, BA(Law); E-mail david.brewer@wiltsmcc.mcs.gov.uk

Swindon (3015)

Magistrates' Court Princes St, Swindon SN1 2JB; Tel 01793 527281; Fax 01793 488525
Justices' Clerk David Brewer, Barrister, BA(Law); E-mail david.brewer@wiltsmcc.mcs.gov.uk

Wales

Dyfed Powys MCC

Justices' Chief Executive's Office 4–5 Quay St, Carmarthen, Carmarthenshire SA31 3JT; Tel 01267 221658; Fax 01267 221812
Justices' Chief Executive Peter Townsend, Barrister

Carmarthen (3138), Llanelli (3122), Dinefwr (3140)

Magistrates' Court Town Hall Sq, Llanelli, Carmarthenshire SA15 3AW; Tel 01554 757201; Fax 01554 759669
Justices' Clerk Stephen Wale, Barrister

Ceredigion (3135)

Magistrates' Court 2 Alban Sq, Aberaeron, Ceredigion SA46 0DB; Tel 01545 570886; Fax 01545 540295
Justices' Clerk Stephen Wale, Barrister

De Brycheiniog (3350); Radnorshire and North Brecknock (3351)

Magistrates' Court Captain's Walk, Brecon, Powys LD3 7HS; Tel 01874 622993; Fax 01874 622441
Justices' Clerk Stephen Whale, Barrister

De Maldwyn (3352), Welshpool (3346)

Magistrates' Court Back La, Newtown, Powys SY16 2NJ; Tel 01686 627150; Fax 01686 628304
Justices' Clerk Stephen Whale, Barrister

North Pembrokeshire (3139), South Pembrokeshire (3142)

Magistrates' Court Penffynnon, Hawthorn Rise, Haverfordwest, Pembrokeshire SA61 3BQ; Tel 01437 766451; Fax 01437 768662
Justices' Clerk Stephen Wale, Barrister

Gwent MCC

Justices' Chief Executive's Office Gwent Hse, Gwent Sq, Cwmbran, Torfaen NP44 1PL; E-mail jce@gwent-magistrates.co.uk; Tel 01633 645000; Fax 01633 645015
Justices' Chief Executive Martin N.E. Speller, CBE, BSc (Hons), FIMgt; E-mail martin.speller@gwent.mcs.gov.uk

North West Gwent (3209)

Magistrates' Court Tredegar, Blaenau Gwent NP22 3XR; Tel 01633 645130; Fax 01633 645177
Justices' Clerk Eddie Harding, Barrister, MIMgt; E-mail eddie.harding@gwent.mcs.gov.uk

South East Gwent (3210)

Magistrates' Court Pentonville, Newport, NP20 5XQ; Tel 01633 645030; Fax 01633 645077
Justices' Clerk David Hulme, Solicitor; E-mail david.hulme@gwent.mcs.gov.uk

North Wales MCC

Justices' Chief Executive's Office 16 Ebberston Road West, Rhos on Sea, LL28 4AP; Tel 01492 541573; Fax 01492 541661
Justices' Chief Executive and Joint Justices' Clerk John Grant Jones, Solicitor; E-mail johngrant@nwmcc.mcs.gov.uk

Aberconwy (3237), Colwyn (3052), Denbighshire (3061)

Magistrates' Court Conwy Rd, Llandudno, Gwynedd LL30 1GA; Tel 01492 871333; Fax 01492 872321
Justices' Clerk Iolo Thomas, Solicitor, LLB

Anglesey (3229), Bangor (3222), Caernarfon and Gwynfrai (3234), Merionydd (3235), Pwllheli and Portmadog (3236)

Magistrates' Court 10–12 Market St, Caernarfon, LL55 1RT; E-mail gdavies@northwales.mags.org.uk; Tel 01286 675200; Fax 01286 678691
Justices' Clerk Iolo Thomas, Solicitor, LLB

Flintshire (3059), West Maelor (3058)

The Law Courts Boyhyfryd, Wrexham LL12 7BP; E-mail collettep@northwales.mags.org.uk; Tel 01978 310106; Fax 01978 358213
Justices' Clerk George Tranter, Solicitor, MA

South Wales MCC

Justices' Chief Executive's Office 47 Charles St, Cardiff CF10 2GD; Tel 029 2030 0250; Fax 029 2030 0240
Justices' Chief Executive Gillian Baranski, Barrister, LLB, MBA

Cardiff (3348)

Magistrates' Court Fitzalan Pl, Cardiff CF24 0RZ; Tel 029 2046 3040; Fax 029 2046 0264
Justices' Clerk Martyn Waygood, Solicitor

Cynon Valley (3262)

The Court House Cwmbach Rd, Aberdare, Rhondda, Cynon, Taff CF44 0ND; Tel 01685 883688; Fax 01685 876045
Justices' Clerk Steven Miller, Solicitor

Merthyr Tydfil (3264)

Magistrates' Court Glebeland Pl, Merthyr Tydfil CF47 8BU; Tel 01685 721731; Fax 01685 723919
Justices' Clerk Steven Miller, Solicitor

Miskin (3265)

Magistrates' Court Union St, Pontypridd, Rhondda, Cynon, Taff CF37 1SD; Tel 01443 480750; Fax 01443 485472
Justices' Clerk Steven Miller, Solicitor

Neath (3359)

Magistrates' Court Fairfield Way, Neath, Neath Port Talbot SA11 1RF; E-mail neathporttalbot@swmcc.co.uk; Tel 01639 765900; Fax 01639 641456
Justices' Clerk Jim Hehir, Solicitor,

Newcastle and Ogmore (3266)

Magistrates' Clerk's Office Sunnyside, Bridgend CF31 4AJ; Tel 01656 766431; Fax 01656 668981
Justices' Clerk Anthony Seculer, Barrister, BSc

Port Talbot (3357)

Magistrates' Court Cramic Way, Port Talbot, SA13 1RU; E-mail neathporttalbot@swmcc.co.uk; Tel 01639 889494; Fax 01639 889599
Justices' Clerk Jim Hehir, Solicitor

Swansea (3360)

Magistrates' Court Grove Pl, Swansea SA1 5DB; Tel 01792 655171; Fax 01792 651066
Justices' Clerk Justin Barron, Barrister

Vale of Glamorgan (3349)

Magistrates' Court Thompson St, Barry, Vale of Glamorgan CF63 4SX; Tel 01446 737491; Fax 01446 732743
Justices' Clerk Anthony Seculer, Barrister, BSc; E-mail anthony.seculer@southwales.mcs.gov.uk

COUNTY COURTS

England

Accrington

Bradshawgate Hse, 1 Oak St, Accrington, Lancashire BB5 1EQ; Tel 01254 237490; Fax 01254 393869

Aldershot and Farnham

78–86 Victoria Rd, Aldershot, Hampshire GU11 1SS; URL www.courtservice.gov.uk; Tel 01252 21639; 01252 331607; Fax 01252 345705; TelexDX 98530 Aldershot 2

Altrincham

Ashton La, Sale, Cheshire M33 1WX; Tel 0161 975 4760

Ashford

The Court Hse, Tufton St, Ashford, Kent TN23 1QQ; Tel 01233 632464

Aylesbury

2nd Fl, Heron Hse, Aylesbury, Buckinghamshire HP20 2NQ; URL www.open.gov.uk/lcd; Tel 01296 393498; Fax 01296 397363; TelexDX 97820 Aylesbury 3

Banbury

35 Parsons St, Banbury, Oxfordshire OX16 5BW; Tel 01295 265799; Fax 01295 277025; TelexDX 701967 Banbury 2

Barnet

St. Mary's Crt, Regents Park Rd, Finchley Central, London N3 1BQ; Tel 020 8343 4272; Fax 020 8343 1324; TelexDX 122570 Finchley (Church End)

Barnsley

12 Regent St, Barnsley, South Yorkshire S70 2EW; URL www.courtservice.gov.uk; Tel 01226 203471; Fax 01226 779126

Barnstaple

7th Fl, Civic Centre, North Wlk, Barnstaple, Devon EX31 1DY; Tel 01271 372252; Fax 01271 322968; TelexDX 98560 Barnstaple 2

Barrow-in-Furness

Government Bldgs, Michaelson Rd, Barrow-in-Furness, Cumbria LA14 2EZ; Tel 01229 820046; 01229 827150 (Bailiffs) 01229 877352; Fax 01229 430039; TelexDX 65210 Barrow-in-Furness 2

Basildon

The Gore, Basildon, Essex SS14 2BU; Tel 01268 458000; Fax 01268 458100

Basingstoke

3rd Fl, Grosvenor Hse, Basing View, Basingstoke, Hampshire RG21 4HG; E-mail basingstoke.city.cm@courtservice.gsi.gov.uk; Tel 01256 318200; Fax 01256 318225; TelexDX 98570 Basingstoke 3

Bath

Cambridge Hse, Henry St, Bath, Bath and North East Somerset BA1 1DJ; URL www.courtservice.gov.uk; Tel 01225 310282; Fax 01225 480915; TelexDX 98580 Bath 2

Bedford

29 Goldington Rd, Bedford, Bedfordshire MK40 2NN; Tel 01234 760400; Fax 01234 327431; TelexDX 97590 Bedford 3

Berwick-upon-Tweed

Norham Hse, 15 Walkergate, Berwick-upon-Tweed, Northumberland TD15 1DS; Tel 01289 305053 Principal Office–Morpeth (Wed only).

Birkenhead

76 Hamilton St, Birkenhead, Merseyside CH41 5EN; Tel 0151 647 8826; Fax 0151 647 3501

Birmingham

33 Bull St, Birmingham, West Midlands B4 6DS; Tel 0121 681 4441; Fax 0121 681 3001; 0121 681 3002; TelexDX 701987 Birmingham 7

Blackburn

64 Victoria St, Blackburn BB1 6DJ; Tel 01254 680640; 01254 680654; Fax 01254 692712; TelexDX 702650 Blackburn 4

Blackpool

The Law Courts, Chapel St, Blackpool FY1 5RJ; Tel 01253 293178; Fax 01253 295255

Bodmin

Cockswell Hse, Market St, Bodmin, Cornwall PL31 2HJ; Tel 01208 74224; Fax 01208 77255

Bolton

Bolton Combined Court Centre, The Law Courts, Blackhorse St, Bolton, Lancashire BL1 1SU; Tel 01204 392881; Fax 01204 363204; 01204 373706

Boston

55 Norfolk St, Boston, Lincolnshire PE21 6PE; Tel 01205 366080; Fax 01205 311692

Bournemouth

Deansleigh Rd, Bournemouth BH7 7DS; Tel 01202 502800; Fax 01202 502801

Bow

96 Romford Rd, Stratford, London E15 4EG; Tel 020 8555 3421; Fax 020 8503 1152; TelexDX 97490 Stratford (London) 2

Bradford

Bradford Combined Court Centre, The Law Courts, Exchange Sq, Drake St, Bradford, West Yorkshire BD1 1JA

Brecknock

Cambrian Way, Brecon, Powys LD3 7HR; Tel 01874 622671; Fax 01874 611607; TelexDX 124340 Brecon 2

Brentford

Alexandra Rd, High St, Brentford, Greater London TW8 0JJ; Tel 020 8580 7300; Fax 020 8568 2401; TelexDX 97840 Brentford 2

Brighton

William St, Brighton, Brighton and Hove BN2 0RF; Tel 01273 674421; Fax 01273 602138; TelexDX 98070 Brighton 3
Brighton Family Centre, 1 Edward St, Brighton, Brighton and Hove BN2 0JD; Tel 01273 811333; Fax 01273 607638

Bristol

Greyfriars, Lewins Mead, Bristol BS1 2NR; Tel 0117 929 4414; Fax 0117 925 0912; 0117 925 6172

Bromley

Court Hse, College Rd, Bromley, Kent BR1 3PX; URL www.courtservice.gov.uk; Tel (Civil Section) 020 8290 9620; (Family Section) 020 8290 9630; Fax 020 8313 9624; TelexDX 98080 Bromley 2

Burnley

Burnley Combined Court Centre, The Law Courts, Hammerton St, Burnley, Lancashire BB11 1XD; Tel 01282 416899; Fax 01282 414911

Burton-upon-Trent

165 Station St, Burton-upon-Trent, Staffordshire DE14 1BP; Tel 01283 568241; Fax 01283 517245; TelexDX 702044 Burton-on-Trent 3

Bury

Tenterden St, Bury, Lancashire BL9 0HJ; Tel 0161 764 1344; Fax 0161 763 4995; TelexDX 702615 Bury 2

Bury St. Edmunds

Triton Hse, (Entrance B), St. Andrew's St North, Bury St. Edmunds, Suffolk IP33 1TR; URL www.courtservice.gov.uk; Tel 01284 753254; Fax 01284 702687; TelexDX 97640 Bury St. Edmunds 3

Buxton

1–3 Hardwick St, Buxton, Derbyshire SK17 6DH; Tel 01298 23734; Fax 01298 73281; TelexDX 701970 Buxton 2

Cambridge

Bridge Hse, Bridge St, Cambridge, Cambridgeshire CB2 1UA; Tel 01223 224500; Fax 01223 224590; TelexDX 97650 Cambridge 3

Canterbury

Canterbury Combined Court Centre, Law Court, Chaucer Rd, Canterbury, Kent CT1 1ZA; Tel 01227 819200; TelexDX 99710 Canterbury 3

Carlisle

Carlisle Combined Court Centre, Courts of Justice, Earl St, Carlisle, Cumbria CA1 1DJ; URL www.courtservice.gov.uk; Tel 01228 528182; Fax 01228 590588

Central London

13–14 Park Cres, London W1B 1HT; URL www.courtservice.gov.uk; Tel 020 7917 5000; Fax 020 7917 5014

Chelmsford

London Hse, New London Rd, Chelmsford, Essex CM2 0QR; Tel 01245 264670; 01245 281386; 01245 350718; Fax 01245 496216; TelexDX 97660 Chelmsford 4

Cheltenham

The Court Hse, County Court Rd, Cheltenham, Gloucestershire GL50 1HB; Tel 01242 519983; Fax 01242 252741; TelexDX 98630 Cheltenham 4

Chester

Trident Hse, Little St. John St, Chester, Cheshire CH1 1SN; Tel 01244 404200; Fax 01244 404300

Chesterfield

St. Mary's Gate, Chesterfield, Derbyshire S41 7TD; Tel 01246 501200; Fax 01246 501205

Chichester

Chichester Combined Court Centre, The Courthouse, Southgate, Chichester, West Sussex PO19 1SX; Tel 01243 520700; Fax 01243 533756; TelexDX 97460 Chichester 2

2

Chorley

59 St. Thomas's Rd, Chorley, Lancashire PR7 1JE; Tel 01257 262778

Clerkenwell

33 Duncan Terr, Islington, London N1 8AN; URL www.courtservice.gov.uk; Tel 020 7359 7347; Fax 020 7354 1166; TelexDX 58284 Islington

Colchester

Faulkland Hse, 25 Southway, Colchester, Essex CO3 3EG; Tel 01206 572743; Fax 01206 369610; TelexDX 97670 Colchester 3

Coventry

Coventry Combined Court Centre, 140 Much Park St, Coventry, West Midlands CV1 2SN; Tel 024 7653 6166; Fax (Civil and Family) 024 7652 0443; (Criminal) 024 7625 1083; TelexDX 710580 Coventry 5

Crewe

The Law Courts, Civic Centre, Crewe, Cheshire CW1 2DP; Tel 01270 212255; Fax 01270 216344; TelexDX 702504 Crewe 2

Croydon

The Law Courts, Altyre Rd, Croydon, Surrey CR9 5AB; Tel 020 8410 4797; Fax 020 8760 0432

Darlington

4 Coniscliffe Rd, Darlington DL3 7RL; Tel 01325 485854; (Bailiff's Office) 01325 463224; Fax 01325 362829; TelexDX 65109 Darlington 3

Dartford

Court Hse, Home Gdns, Dartford, Kent DA1 1DX; Tel 01322 629820; Fax 01322 270902; TelexDX 98090 Dartford 2

Derby

Derby County Court, Morledge, Derby DE1 2XE; Tel 01332 622600; Fax 01332 622543; TelexDX 11526 Derby 2

Dewsbury

County Court Hse, Eightlands Rd, Dewsbury, West Yorkshire WF13 2PE; Tel 01924 465860; 01924 466135; Fax 01924 456419; TelexDX 702086 Dewsbury 2

Doncaster

74 Waterdale, Doncaster, South Yorkshire DN1 3BT; Tel 01302 381730; Fax 01302 768090; TelexDX 702089 Doncaster 4

Dudley

Harbour Bldgs, Waterfront West, Brierley Hill, West Midlands DY5 1LN; Tel 01384 480799; Fax 01384 4 82799

Eastbourne

4 The Avenue, Eastbourne, East Sussex BN21 3SZ; Tel 01323 735195; Fax 01323 638829; TelexDX 98110 Eastbourne 2

Edmonton

Court Hse, 59 Fore St, London N18 2TN; Tel 020 8807 1666; Fax 020 8803 0564; TelexDX 36206 Edmonton 1

Epsom

The Parade, Epsom, Surrey KT18 5DN; Tel 01372 721801; Fax 01372 726588; TelexDX 97850 Epsom 3

Evesham

1st Fl, 87 High St, Evesham, Worcestershire WR11 4EE; Tel 01386 442287; Fax 01386 49203

Exeter

The Castle, Exeter, Devon EX4 3PS; Tel 01392 210655

Gateshead

5th Fl, Chad Hse, Gateshead, Tyne and Wear NE8 3HY; Tel 0191 477 2445; Fax 0191 477 8562; Minicom 0191 478 1476

Gloucester

Kimbrose Way, Gloucester, Gloucestershire GL1 2DE; Tel 01452 529351; TelexDX 98660 Gloucester 5

Grantham

10 Guildhall St, Grantham, Lincolnshire NG31 6NJ; Tel 01476 563638; Fax 01476 570181; TelexDX 701931 Grantham 2

Gravesend

26 King St, Gravesend, Kent DA12 2DU; Tel 01474 321771; Fax 01474 534811; TelexDX 98140 Gravesend 2

Great Grimsby

Great Grimsby Combined Court Centre, Town Hall Sq, Grimsby, North East Lincolnshire DN31 1HX; Tel 01472 311811; Fax 01472 312039; TelexDX Grimsby 3

Guildford

The Law Courts, Mary Rd, Guildford, Surrey GU1 4PS; Tel 01483 595200; Fax 01483 300031; TelexDX 97860 Guildford 5

Halifax

Prescott St, Halifax, West Yorkshire HX1 2JJ; Tel 01422 344700; Fax 01422 360132; TelexDX 702095 Halifax 2

Harlow

Gate Hse, The High, Harlow, Essex CM20 1UW; Tel 01279 443291; 01279 635628; Fax 01279 451110; TelexDX 97700 Harlow 2

Harrogate

2 Victoria Ave, Harrogate, North Yorkshire HG1 1EL; Tel 01423 503921; Fax 01423 528679; TelexDX 702098 Harrogate 3

Hartlepool

1st Fl, The Law Courts, Victoria Rd, Hartlepool TS24 8BS; Tel 01429 268198; Fax 01429 862550; TelexDX 65121 Hartlepool 2

Hastings

The Law Courts, Bohemia Rd, Hastings, East Sussex TN34 1QX; Tel 01424 435128; Fax 01424 421585; TelexDX 98150 Hastings 2

Haywards Heath

Milton Hse, Milton Rd, Haywards Heath, Sussex
RH16 1YZ; Tel 01444 456326/7; Fax 01444 415282;
TelexDX 98160 Haywards Heath 3

Hereford

1st Fl, Barclays Bank Chambers, 1-3 Broad St, Hereford,
Herefordshire HR4 9BA; Tel 01432 357233; Fax 01432
352593; TelexDX 701904 Hereford 2

Hertford

4th Fl, Sovereign Hse, Hale Rd, Hertford, Hertfordshire
SG13 8DY; Tel 01992 503954; Fax 01992 501274; TelexDX
97710 Hertford 2

High Wycombe

The Law Courts, Easton St, High Wycombe,
Buckinghamshire HP11 1LR; Tel 01494 436374; Fax 01494
459430; TelexDX 97880 High Wycombe 3

Hitchin

Park Hse, 1–12 Old Park Rd, Hitchin, Hertfordshire
SG5 1LX; URL www.courtservice.gov.uk; Tel 01462
443750; 01462 443751; Fax 01462 443758; TelexDX 97720
Hitchin 2

Horsham

The Law Courts, Hurst Rd, Horsham, West Sussex
RH12 2EU; Tel 01403 252474; Fax 01403 258844; TelexDX
98170 Horsham 2

Huddersfield

Queensgate Hse, Queensgate, Huddersfield, West
Yorkshire HD1 2RR; URL www.courtservice.gov.uk;
E-mail huddersfield.cty@courtservice.gsi.gov.uk;
Tel 01484 421043; 01484 535085; Fax 01484 426366;
TelexDX 703013 Huddersfield 2

Huntingdon

Ground Fl, Godwin Hse, Huntingdon, Cambridgeshire
PE29 3BD; Tel 01480 450932; Fax 01480 435397; TelexDX
96650 Huntingdon 2

Ilford

Buckingham Rd, Ilford, Essex IG1 1BR; Tel 020 8478 1132;
Fax 020 8553 2824; TelexDX 97510 Ilford 3

Ipswich

8 Arcade St, Ipswich, Suffolk IP1 1EJ; Tel 01473 214256

Keighley

Yorkshire Bank Chambers, North St, Keighley, West
Yorkshire BD21 2SH; Tel 01535 602803; Fax 01535
610549

Kendal

The Court Hse, County Court, Kendal, Cumbria LA9 4NF;
Tel 01539 721218; Fax 01539 733840; TelexDX 63450
Kendal 2

Kettering

Dryland St, Kettering, Northamptonshire NN16 0BE;
Tel 01536 512471

King's Lynn

Chequer Hse, 12 King St, King's Lynn, Norfolk PE30 1ES;
Tel 01553 772067; Fax 01553 769824; TelexDX 97740
Kings Lynn 2

Kingston upon Hull

Kingston upon Hull Combined Court Centre, Lowgate,
Hull, Kingston upon Hull HU1 2EZ; Tel 01482 586161;
Fax 01482 588527; TelexDX 703010 Hull 5

Kingston upon Thames

St. James Rd, Kingston upon Thames, Surrey KT1 2AD;
Tel 020 8546 8843; Fax 020 8547 1426

Lambeth

Court Hse, Cleaver St, Kennington Rd, London SE11 4DZ;
URL www.courtservice.gov.uk; Tel 020 7091 4410; 020
7091 4420; Fax 020 7735 8147; TelexDX 33254

Lancaster

2nd Fl, Mitre Hse, Lancaster, Lancashire LA1 1UZ;
Tel 01524 68112; Fax 01524 846478

Leeds

Leeds Combined Court Centre, The Courthouse, 1 Oxford
Row, Leeds, West Yorkshire LS1 3BG;
URL www.courtservice.gov.uk; Tel 0113 283 0040;
TelexDX 703016 Leeds 6

Leicester

PO Box 3, 90 Wellington St, Leicester LE1 6ZZ; Tel 0116 222
2323; Fax 0116 222 3450; TelexDX 17401 Leicester 3

Leigh

22 Walmesley Rd, Leigh, Lancashire WN7 1YF; Tel 01942
673639; Fax 01942 681216

Lewes

Lewes Combined Court Centre, The Law Courts, High St,
Lewes, East Sussex BN7 1YB; Tel 01273 480400;
Fax (County) 01273 485270; (Crown) 01273 485269;
TelexDX 97395 Lewes 4

Lincoln

Lincoln County Court, 360 High St, Lincoln, Lincolnshire
LN5 7PS; Tel 01522 883000; Fax 01522 883003; TelexDX
703230 Lincoln 6

Liverpool

Liverpool Combined Court Centre, Queen Elizabeth II Law
Courts, Derby Sq, Liverpool, Merseyside L2 1XA;
Tel 0151 473 7373; Fax (County Court Process) 0151 471
1095; (Crown Court) 0151 258 1587; (Family Process)
0151 227 2806

Lowestoft

Lyndhurst, 28 Gordon Rd, Lowestoft, Suffolk NR32 1NL;
Tel 01502 573701; 01502 586047; Fax 01502 569319;
TelexDX 97750 Lowestoft 2

Ludlow

9–10 King St, Ludlow, Shropshire SY8 1QW; Tel 01584
872091; Fax 01584 877606; TelexDX 702013 Ludlow 2

2

Luton

5th Fl, Cresta Hse, Alma St, Luton LU1 2PU; Tel 01582
506700; Fax 01582 506701; TelexDX 97760 Luton 4

Macclesfield

2nd Fl, Silk Hse, Park Grn, Macclesfield, Cheshire
SK11 7NA; Tel 01625 422872; 01625 432492; Fax 01625
501262; TelexDX 702498 Macclesfield 3

Maidstone

Maidstone Combined Court Centre, The Law Courts,
Maidstone, Kent ME16 8EQ; Tel 01622 202000; Fax 01622
202002; TelexDX 130065 Maidstone 7

Manchester

Manchester County Court, Courts of Justice, Crown Sq,
Manchester M60 9DJ; Tel 0161 954 1800;
Fax (Enforcement) 0161 839 2756; (Family) 0161 819 1172

Mansfield

Beech Hse, 58 Commercial Gate, Mansfield,
Nottinghamshire NG18 1EU; Tel 01623 656406; TelexDX
702180 Mansfield 3

Mayor's and City of London

Guildhall Bldgs, Basinghall St, London EC2V 5AR; Tel 020
796 5400

Medway

Anchorage Hse, 47–67 High St, Chatham, Kent ME4 4DW;
Tel 01634 810720; Fax 01634 811332; TelexDX 98180
Chatham 4

Melton Mowbray

Crown Hse, 50–52 Scalford Rd, Melton Mowbray,
Leicestershire LE13 1JY; Tel 01664 568336; Fax 01664
480241; TelexDX 701937 Melton Mowbray 2

Milton Keynes

351 Silbury Blvd, Witan Gate East, Milton Keynes
MK9 2DT; Tel 01908 302800; TelexDX 136266

Morpeth

Fountain Hse, New Market, Morpeth, Northumberland
NE61 1LA; Tel 01670 512221; Fax 01670 504188; TelexDX
65124 Morpeth 2

Nelson

Phoenix Chambers, 9-13 Holme St, Nelson, Lancashire
BB9 9SU; Tel 01282 601177; Fax 01282 619557; TelexDX
702560 Nelson 2

Newark

Crown Bldg, 41 Lombard St, Newark, Nottinghamshire
NG24 1XN; Tel 01636 703607; Fax 01636 613726; TelexDX
701928 Newark 2

Newbury

Kings Road West, Newbury, West Berkshire RG14 5XU;
Tel 01635 40928; Fax 01635 37704; TelexDX 30816
Newbury 1

Newcastle upon Tyne

The Law Courts, Quayside, Newcastle upon Tyne, Tyne
and Wear NE1 3LA; Tel 0191 201 2000; Fax 0191 201
2001; TelexDX 65128 Newcastle-upon-Tyne 2

Newport (IoW)

Newport (IOW) Crown and County Courts, 1 Quay St,
Newport, Isle of Wight PO30 5YT; Tel 01983 526821;
Fax 01983 821039; TelexDX 98460 Newport (IOW) 2

North Shields

Northumbria Hse, Norfolk St, North Shields, Tyne and
Wear NE30 1EX; Tel 0191 257 5866; Fax 0191 296 4268;
TelexDX 65137 North Shields 2

Northampton

Northampton Combined Court Centre, 85–87 Lady's La,
Northampton, Northamptonshire NN1 3HQ; Tel 01604
470400; Fax 01604 232398; TelexDX 703131
Northampton 6

Northwich

25–27 High St, Northwich, Cheshire CW9 5DB; Tel 01606
42554; Fax 01606 331490; TelexDX 702515 Northwich 3

Norwich

Norwich Combined Court Centre, The Law Courts,
Bishopsgate, Norwich, Norfolk NR3 1UR; Tel 01603
728200; Fax 01603 760863; TelexDX 97385 Norwich 5

Nottingham

Nottingham County Court, 60 Canal St, Nottingham
NG1 7EJ; Tel 0115 910 3500; Fax 0115 910 3510

Nuneaton

Heron Hse, Newdegate St, Nuneaton, Warwickshire
CV11 4EL; Tel 024 7638 6134; Fax 024 76352769; TelexDX
701940 Nuneaton 2

Oldham

New Radcliffe St (off Rochdale Rd), Oldham, Lancashire
OL1 1NL; Tel 0161 290 4200; Fax 0161 290 4222

Oxford

St. Aldates, Oxford, Oxfordshire OX1 1TL;
URL www.courtservice.gov.uk; Tel 01865 264200;
TelexDX 96451 Oxford 4

Penrith

The Court Hse, Lowther Terr, Penrith, Cumbria CA11 7QL;
Tel 01768 862535; Fax 01768 899700

Penzance

Trevear, Alverton, Penzance, Cornwall TR18 4GH;
Tel 01736 362987; Fax 01736 330595

Peterborough

Peterborough Combined Court Centre, Crown Bldgs,
Rivergate, Peterborough PE1 1EJ; Tel 01733 349161;
Fax 01733 557348; TelexDX 702302 Peterborough 8

Plymouth

Plymouth Combined Court Centre, The Law Courts,
Armada Way, Plymouth PL1 2ER; Tel 01752 677400;
Fax (County) 01752 208286; (Crown) 01752 202292

Pontefract

Horsefair Hse, Horsefair, Pontefract, West Yorkshire
WF8 1RJ; E-mail ponte.cty.cm@courtservice.gsi.gov.uk;
Tel 01977 702357; Fax 01977 600204; TelexDX 703022
Pontefract 2

Poole

Law Courts, Civic Centre, Poole BH15 2NS; Tel 01202
741150; TelexDX 98700 Poole 4

Portsmouth

Portsmouth Combined Court Centre, The Courts of Justice,
Winston Churchill Ave, Portsmouth PO1 2EB; Tel 023
9289 3000; Fax 023 9282 6385; TelexDX 98490
Portsmouth 5

Rawtenstall

1 Grange St, Rawtenstall, Lancashire BB4 7RT; Tel 01706
214614; Fax 01706 219814; TelexDX 702565

Reading

160–163 Friar St, Reading RG1 1HE; Tel 0118 987 0500;
Fax 0118 939 1892; 0118 959 9827; TelexDX 98010
Reading 6

Redditch

Court Office, 13 Church Rd, Redditch, Worcestershire
B97 4AB; Tel 01527 67822; Fax 01527 65791; TelexDX
701880 Redditch 2

Reigate

Law Courts, Hatchlands Rd, Redhill, Surrey RH1 6BL;
Tel 01737 763637; (Bailiffs) 01737 761925; Fax 01737
766917; TelexDX 98020

Romford

2a Oaklands Ave, Romford, Essex RM1 4DP; Tel 01708
775353; Fax 01708 756653; TelexDX 97530 Romford 2

Rotherham

County Court, Portland Hse, Mansfield Rd, Rotherham,
South Yorkshire S60 2BX; Tel 01709 364786; Fax 01709
838044; TelexDX 703025 Rotherham 4

Rugby

5 Newbold Rd, Rugby, West Midlands CV21 2RN; Tel 01788
542543; Fax 01788 550212; TelexDX 701934 Rugby 2

Runcorn

The Law Courts, Halton Lea, Runcorn, Cheshire WA7 2HA;
Tel 01928 716533; Fax 01928 701692; TelexDX 702466
Runcorn 3

St. Albans

Victoria Hse, Victoria St, St. Albans, Hertfordshire AL1 3TJ;
Tel 01727 856925

St. Helens

Rexmore Hse, 1st Fl, St. Helens, Merseyside WA10 1SE;
Tel 01744 27544; Fax 01744 20484; TelexDX 702570 St
Helens 2

Salford

Prince William Hse, Peel Cross Rd, Salford, Lancashire
M5 4RR; Tel 0161 745 7511; Fax 0161 745 7202; TelexDX
702630 Salford 5

Salisbury

Salisbury Combined Court Centre, Courts of Justice,
Alexandra Hse, St. John St, Salisbury, Wiltshire SP1 2PN;
Tel 01722 325444; Fax 01722 412991; TelexDX 98500
Salisbury 2

Scarborough

Pavillion Hse, Valley Bridge Rd, Scarborough, North
Yorkshire YO11 2JS; Tel 01723 366361; Fax 01723 501992;
TelexDX 65140 Scarborough 2

Scunthorpe

Crown Bldg, Comforts Ave, Scunthorpe, Lincolnshire
DN15 6PR; Tel 01724 289111; Fax 01724 291119

Sheffield

50 West Bar, Sheffield, South Yorkshire S3 8PH; Tel 0114 281
2400; Fax 0114 281 2425

Shoreditch

19 Leonard St, London EC2A 4AL; Tel 020 7253 0956;
Fax 020 7490 5613; TelexDX 121000 Shoreditch 2

Shrewsbury

4th Fl, Cambrian Business Centre, Chester St, Shrewsbury,
Shropshire SY1 1NA

Skegness

Town Hall Annexe, North Parade, Skegness, Lincolnshire
PE25 1DA; Tel 01754 762429; Fax 01754 761165; TelexDX
701919 Skegness 2

Skipton

The Old Courthouse, Otley St, Skipton, North Yorkshire
BD23 1EH; Tel 01756 793315; Fax 01756 799989; TelexDX
703031 Skipton 2

Slough

The Law Courts, Windsor Rd, Slough SL1 2HE; Tel 01753
690300; Fax 01753 575990; TelexDX 98030 Slough 3

South Shields

25–26 Market Pl, South Shields, Tyne and Wear NE33 1AG;
Tel 0191 456 3343; Fax 0191 427 9503; TelexDX 65143
South Shields 3

Southampton

Southampton Combined Court Centre, The Courts of
Justice, London Rd, Southampton SO15 2XQ;
URL www.courtservice.gov.uk; Tel 023 8021 3200;
Fax 023 8021 3222

Southend

Tylers Hse, Tylers Ave, Southend on Sea, Southend
SS1 2AW; Tel 01702 601991; Fax 01702 603090; TelexDX
97780 Southend on Sea 2

Southport

The Duke's Hse, 34 Hoghton St, Southport, Merseyside PR9
0PU; Tel 01704 531541; Fax 01704 542487; TelexDX 702580

Stafford

Stafford Crown Court and County Court, The Law Courts,
Victoria Sq, Stafford, Staffordshire ST16 2QQ; Tel 01785
610730; Fax (County) 01785 213250; (Crown) 01785
610779; TelexDX 703190 Stafford 4

Staines

The Law Courts, Knowle Grn, Staines, Greater London
TW18 1XH; Tel 01784 459175; Fax 01784 460176; TelexDX
98040 Staines 2

Stockport

Heron Hse, Wellington St, Stockport, Cheshire SK1 3DJ;
Tel 0161 474 7707; Fax 0161 476 3129

Stoke-on-Trent

Stoke-on-Trent Combined Court, Bethesda St, Hanley,
Stoke-on-Trent ST1 3BP; Tel 01782 854000; Fax (County)
01782 854046; (Crown) 01782 854021

Stourbridge

7 Hagley Rd, Stourbridge, West Midlands DY8 1QL;
Tel 01384 394232; Fax 01384 441736; TelexDX 701889
Stourbridge 2

Stratford-upon-Avon

5 Elm Crt, Arden St, Stratford-upon-Avon, Warwickshire
CV37 6PA; Tel 01789 293056; Fax 01789 414973; TelexDX
701998 Stratford-upon-Avon 3

Swindon

Swindon Combined Court Centre, The Law Courts, Islington
St, Swindon SN1 2HG; URL www.courtservice.gov.uk;
Tel 01793 690500; Fax (County Court) 01793 690555;
(Crown Court) 01793 690535

Tameside

PO Box 166, Henry Sq, Ashton-under-Lyne, Lancashire
OL6 7TP; Tel 0161 331 5614; Fax 0161 331 5649

Tamworth

The Precinct, Lower Gungate, Tamworth, Staffordshire
B79 7AJ; Tel 01827 62664; Fax 01827 65289

Taunton

The Court Service, Taunton County Court, Shire Hall,
Taunton, Somerset TA1 4EU; Tel 01823 335972; Fax 01823
351337; TelexDX 98410 Taunton 2

Teesside

Teesside Combined Court Centre, Russell St,
Middlesbrough TS1 2AE; Tel 01642 340000; Fax 01642
340002; TelexDX 65152 Middlesbrough 2

Telford

Telford Sq, Malinsgate Town Centre, Telford, Shropshire
TF3 4JP; Tel 01952 291045; Fax 01952 291601; TelexDX
701976 Telford 3

Thanet

Capital Hse, Northdown Rd, Margate, Kent CT9 1EQ;
Tel 01843 221722; 01843 228771; Fax 01843 224313;
TelexDX 98210 Cliftonville 2

Torquay and Newton Abbot

Nicholson Rd, Torquay, Torbay TQ2 7AZ; Tel 01803 616791;
Fax 01803 616795; TelexDX 98740 Torquay 4

Truro

Truro Combined Court Centre, Courts of Justice, Truro,
Cornwall TR1 2PB; Tel 01872 222340; Fax 01872 222348

Tunbridge Wells

Merevale Hse, 42–46 London Rd, Tunbridge Wells, Kent
TN1 1DP; Tel 01892 515515; Fax 01892 513676; TelexDX
98220 Tunbridge Wells 3

Uxbridge

501 Uxbridge Rd, Hayes, Greater London UB4 8HL; Tel 020
8561 8562; Fax 020 8561 2020

Wakefield

Crown Hse, 127 Kirkgate, Wakefield, West Yorkshire
WF1 1JW; Tel 01924 370268; TelexDX 703040 Wakefield 3

Walsall

Bridge Hse, Bridge St, Walsall, West Midlands WS1 1JQ;
E-mail enquiries@walsallcountycourt.gsi.gov.uk;
Tel 0845 351 3513; Fax 0845 351 3514; TelexDX 701943
Walsall 2

Wandsworth

76–78 Upper Richmond Rd, Putney, London SW15 2SU;
Tel 020 8333 4351; 020 8333 4352; Fax 020 8877 9854;
TelexDX 97540 Putney 2

Warrington

The Law Courts, Legh St, Warrington WA1 1UR; Tel 01925
256700

Warwick

Warwick Combined Court Centre, Northgate, Warwick,
Warwickshire CV34 4RB; Tel 01926 492276; Fax 01926
411855; TelexDX 701964 Warwick 2

Watford

Cassiobury Hse, 11–19 Station Rd, Watford, Hertfordshire
WD1 1EZ; Tel 01923 249666; Fax 01923 251317; TelexDX
122740 Watford 5

Wellingborough

Lothersdale Hse, West Villa Rd, Wellingborough,
Northamptonshire NN8 4NF; Tel 01933 226168;
Fax 01933 272977; TelexDX 701883 Wellingborough 2

West London

43 North End Rd, West Kensington, London W14 8SZ;
Tel 020 7602 8444; 020 7602 8446; Fax 020 7602 1820;
TelexDX 97550 West Kensington 2

Weston-super-Mare

Regent Hse, High St, Weston-super-Mare, North Somerset
BS23 1JF; Tel 01934 626967; 01934 627787; Fax 01934
643028

Weymouth

Weymouth and Dorchester Combined Court Centre,
Westway Hse, Westway Rd, Weymouth, Dorset
DT4 8TE; Tel 01305 752510; Fax 01305 788293; TelexDX
98820 Weymouth 3

Wigan

Crawford St, Wigan, Greater Manchester WN1 1NG;
Tel 01942 246481; Fax 01942 829164

Willesden

9 Acton La, Harlesden, London NW10 8SB; Tel 020 8963
8200; Fax 020 8453 0946; TelexDX 97560 Harlesden 2

Winchester

Winchester Combined Court Centre, The Law Courts,
Winchester, Hampshire SO23 9EL; Tel 01962 841212;
Fax 01962 853821; TelexDX 98520 Winchester 3

Wolverhampton

Wolverhampton Combined Court Centre, Pipers Row, Wolverhampton, West Midlands WV1 3LQ; Tel 01902 481000; Fax 01902 481001; TelexDX 702019 Wolverhampton 4

Woolwich

The Court Hse, Powis St, London SE18 6JW; Tel 020 8854 2127; 020 8854 8048; Fax 020 8316 4842; TelexDX 123450 Woolwich 8

Worcester

Shirehall, Foregate St, Worcester, Worcestershire WR1 1EQ; Tel 01905 730800; Fax 01905 730801; TelexDX 716262 Worcester 1

Workington

Langdale Hse, Gray St, Workington, Cumbria CA14 2PA; Tel 01900 603967; Fax 01900 68001; TelexDX 63650 Workington 2

Worksop

8 Slack Walk, Worksop, Nottinghamshire S80 1LN; Tel 01909 472358; Fax 01909 530181; TelexDX 702190 Worksop 2

Worthing

The Law Courts, Christchurch Rd, Worthing, West Sussex BN11 1JD; Tel 01903 206721; Fax 01903 235559; TelexDX 98230 Worthing 4

Yeovil

22 Hendford, Yeovil, Somerset BA20 2QD; Tel 01935 474133; Fax 01935 410004; TelexDX 98830 Yeovil 2

York

Piccadilly Hse, 55 Piccadilly, York YO1 9WL; Tel 01904 629935; Fax 01904 679963; TelexDX 65165 York 4

Wales

Aberdare

Crown Bldg, Green St, Aberdare, Rhondda, Cynon, Taff CF44 7DW; Tel 01685 874779; Fax 01685 883413; TelexDX 99600 Aberdare 2

Aberystwyth

Edleston Hse, Queens Rd, Aberystwyth, Ceredigion SY23 2HP; Tel 01970 636370; Fax 01970 625985; TelexDX 99561 Aberystwyth 2

Blackwood

County Court Office, Blackwood Rd, Blackwood, Caerphilly NP12 2XB; Tel 01495 223197; Fax 01495 220289; TelexDX 99470 Blackwood 2

Bridgend

Crown Bldgs, Angel St, Bridgend CF31 4AS; Tel 01656 768881; Fax 01656 647124; TelexDX 99750 Bridgend 2

Caernarfon

The Court Hse, Llanberis Rd, Caernarfon, Gwynedd LL55 2DF; Tel 01286 678911; Fax 01286 678965; TelexDX 702483 Caernarfon 2

Cardiff

Civil Justice Centre, 2 Park St, Cardiff CF1 1ET; URL www.courtservice.gov.uk/wales; E-mail cardffctycso@courtservice.gsi.gov.uk; Tel 029 2037 6400; Fax 029 2037 6475; TelexDX 99500 Cardiff 6

Carmarthen

The Old Vicarage, Picton Terr, Carmarthen, Carmarthenshire SA31 1BJ; Tel 01267 228010; Fax 01267 221844; TelexDX 99570 Carmarthen 2

Conwy and Colwyn

36 Princes Dr, Colwyn Bay, LL29 8LA; Tel 01492 530807; Fax 01492 533591; TelexDX 702492 Colwyn Bay 2

Haverfordwest

Penffynnon, Hawthorn Rise, Haverfordwest, Pembrokeshire SA61 2AZ; Tel 01437 772060; Fax 01437 769222; TelexDX 99610 Haverfordwest 2

Llanelli

2nd Fl, Court Bldgs, Town Hall Sq, Llanelli, Carmarthenshire SA15 3AL; Tel 01554 757171; Fax 01554 758079; TelexDX 99510 Llanelli 2

Llangefni

County Court Bldgs, Glanhwfa Rd, Llangefni, Isle of Anglesey LL77 7EN; Tel 01248 750225; Fax 01248 750778; TelexDX 702480 Llangefni 2

Merthyr Tydfil

Merthyr Tydfil Combined Court Centre, The Law Courts, Glebeland Pl, Merthyr Tydfil CF47 8BH; Tel (County Court) 01685 358200; Fax 01685 359727; TelexDX 99582 Merthyr Tydfil 2

Mold

Law Courts, County Civic Centre, Mold, Flintshire CH7 1AE; Tel 01352 700313; Fax 01352 700297; TelexDX 702521 Mold 2

Neath and Port Talbot

Forster Rd, Neath, Neath Port Talbot SA11 3BN; URL www.courtservice.gov.uk/circuit_home.htm; Tel 01639 642267; Fax 01639 633505; TelexDX 99550 Neath 2

Newport

3rd Fl, Olympia Hse, Upper Dock St, Newport NP20 1PQ; Tel 01633 227150; Fax 01633 263820; TelexDX 99480 Newport 4

Pontypool

Court Offices, Park Rd, Riverside, Pontypool, Torfaen NP4 6NZ; Tel 01495 762248; Fax 01495 762467; TelexDX 117500

Pontypridd

The Courthouse, Courthouse St, Pontypridd, Rhondda, Cynon, Taff CF37 1JR; Tel (Bailiff's Office) 01443 402135; (General Office) 01443 402471; Fax 01443 480305; TelexDX 99620 Pontypridd 2

Rhyl

The Courthouse, Clwyd St, Rhyl, Denbighshire LL18 3LA; Tel 01745 330216; Fax 01745 336726; TelexDX 702489 Rhyl 2

Swansea

Caravella Hse, Quay West, Quay Pde, Swansea SA1 1SP;
Tel 01792 510350; Fax 01792 473520; TelexDX 99740
Swansea 5

Welshpool and Newtown

The Mansion Hse, Severn St, Welshpool, Powys SY21 7UX;
Tel 01938 550004; Fax 01938 555395; TelexDX 702524
Welshpool 2
Principal Office – Welshpool.
All correspondence and enquiries should be addressed to
the Welshpool office.

Wrexham

2nd Fl, Crown Bldgs, 31 Chester St, Wrexham LL13 8XN;
URL www.open.gov.uk-lcd; Tel 01978 351738; Fax 01978
290677; TelexDX 702463 Wrexham 2

NORTHERN IRELAND MAGISTRATES' AND COUNTY COURTS

The Business Managers assigned to courts in Northern
Ireland administer support to the judiciary.

Ards Division (9002)

Bangor Court Office The Court Hse, 6 Quay St, Bangor,
County Down BT20 5EA; Tel 028 9147 2626; Fax 028 9127
2667
Contact Jim Millar

Downpatrick Court Office The Courthouse, English St,
Downpatrick, County Down BT30 6AD; Tel 028 4461 4621;
Fax 028 4461 4621
Contact Jim Millar

Newtownards Court Office The Court Hse, Regent St,
Newtownards, BT23 4LP; Tel 028 9181 4343; Fax 028 9181
8024
Business Manager P. Kelly

Armagh and South Down Division

Armagh Court Office The Court Hse, The Mall, Armagh,
County Armagh BT61 9DJ; Tel 028 3752 2816; Fax 028 3752
8194

Banbridge Court Office The Court Hse, Victoria St,
Banbridge, County Down BT32 3DH; Tel 028 4062 3622;
Fax 028 4062 3059

Newry Court Office The Court Hse, 23 New St, Newry,
County Down BT35 6JD; Tel 028 3025 2040; Fax 028 3026
9830

Antrim Division

Ballymena Court Office The Court Hse, Albert Pl,
Ballymena, County Down BT43 5BS; Tel 028 2564 9416;
Fax 028 2565 5371
Contact Kay Heggarty

Coleraine Court Office The Courthouse, 46a Mountsandel
Rd, Coleraine, County Antrim BT51 1NY; Tel 028 7034 3437;
Fax 020 7032 0156
Contact Kay Heggarty

Larne Court Office The Court Hse, Victoria Rd, Larne,
B740 1RN; Tel 028 2827 2927; Fax 028 2827 6414
Contact Kay Heggarty

Belfast Division (9007)

Laganside Court 45 Oxford St, Belfast BT1 3LL; Tel 028 9032
8594
Contact Mandy Kilpatrick

Craigavon Division (9016)

Craigavon Court Office The Court Hse, Central Way,
Craigavon, BT64 1AP; Tel 028 3834 1324; Fax 028 3834
1243
Contact George Russell

Lisburn Court Office The Court Hse, Railway St, Lisburn,
BT28 1XR; Tel 028 9267 5336; Fax 028 9260 4107
Contact George Russell

Fermanagh and Tyrone Division

Dungannon Court Office The Courrt Hse, Chapel St,
Dungannon, County Fermanagh; Tel 028 8676 2637; Fax 028
8676 2868
Contact Margaret Elliott

Enniskillen Court Office The Court Hse, East Bridge St,
Enniskillen, County Fermanagh BT74 7BP; Tel 028 6632
2356; Fax 028 6632 3636
Contact Margaret Elliott

Omagh Court Office The Court Hse, High St, Omagh,
BT78 1DU; Tel 028 8224 2056; Fax 028 8225 1198
Contact Margaret Elliott

Strabane Court Office The Court Hse, Derry Rd, Strabane,
BT82 8D7; Tel 028 7138 2544; Fax 028 7138 3209
Contact Margaret Elliott

Londonderry Division

Limavady Court Office The Court Hse, Main St, Limavady,
BT49 0EY; Tel 028 7772 2688; Fax 028 7776 8794
Contact Paula McCourt

Londonderry Court Office The Court Hse, Bishop St,
Londonderry, County Londonderry BT48 6PQ; Tel 028 7136
3448; Fax 028 7137 2059
Contact Paula McCourt

Magherafelt Court Office The Court Hse, Hospital Rd,
Magherafelt, BT45 5DG; Tel 028 7963 2121; Fax 028 7963
4063
Contact Paula McCourt

SHERIFF COURTS SCOTLAND

Scotland is divided into six Sheriffdoms, including 51
Sheriff courts. Each of these has a Sheriff principal who
controls the conduct of the courts and hears civil appeals.
The work of the courts falls into three Categories: Civil,
Criminal and Commissary.

Grampian, Highland and Islands

Sheriff Principal's Chambers, Sheriff Court Hse, Aberdeen
AB10 1WP; Tel 01224 648316; TelexDXAB61
Sheriff Principal Sir Stephen S.T. Young, Bt QC

Aberdeen

Sheriff Court Hse, Castle St, Aberdeen AB9 1AP; Tel 01224
657200; Fax 01224 627185
Sheriff C.J. Harris, QC
Sheriff Mrs A.M. Cowan
Sheriff A.S. Jessop
Sheriff J.K. Tierney

Sheriff P.P. Davies
Sheriff G.K. Buchanan
Sheriff D.J. Cusine
Sheriff (Floating) K.M. Stewart

Banff

Sheriff Court Hse, Banff, Aberdeenshire AB45 1AU;
Tel 01261 812140; Fax 01261 818394; TelexDX 1325
Sheriff K.A. McLernan

Dingwall

Sheriff Court Hse, Dingwall, Highland IV15 9QX; Tel 01349
863153; Fax 01349 865230; TelexDX 52084
Sheriff A.L. MacFadyen

Dornoch

Sheriff Court Hse, Dornoch, Highland IV25 3SD; Tel 01862
810224; Fax 01862 810958
Sheriff Vacancy

Elgin

Sheriff Court Hse, Elgin, Moray IV30 1BU; Tel 01343
542505; Fax 01343 542505; TelexDX 520652
Sheriff I.A. Cameron

Fort William

Sheriff Court Hse, Fort William, Highland PH33 6EE;
Tel 01397 702087; Fax 01397 706214; TelexDX 531405 Fort
William
Sheriff Vacancy

Inverness

Sheriff Court Hse, Inverness, Highland IV2 3EG; Tel 01463
230782; Fax 01463 710602; TelexDX IN25
Sheriff A. Pollock
Sheriff D. Booker-Milburn

Kirkwall

Sheriff Court Hse, Kirkwall, Orkney Islands KW15 1PD;
Tel 01856 872110; Fax 01856 874835
Sheriff C.S. Mackenzie

Lerwick

Sheriff Court Hse, Lerwick, Shetland Isles ZE1 0HD;
Tel 01595 693914; Fax 01595 693340
Sheriff C. S. MacKenzie

Lochmaddy

Sheriff Court Hse, Lochmaddy, Western Isles PA82 5AE;
Tel 01876 500340; Fax 01876 500432
Sheriff Vacancy

Peterhead

Sheriff Court Hse, Queen St, Peterhead, Aberdeenshire AB42
6TP; Tel 01779 476676; Fax 01779 472435; TelexDX 1376
Sheriff M. Garden

Portree

Sheriff Court Hse, , Portree, Highland IV51 9EG; Tel 01478
612191; Fax 01478 613203
Sheriff Vacancy

Stonehaven

Sheriff Court Hse, Stonehaven, Aberdeenshire AB39 2JH;
Tel 01569 762758; Fax 01569 762132; TelexDX 521023
Sheriff Vacancy

Stornoway

Sheriff Court Hse, Stornoway, Western Isles HS1 2JF;
Tel 01851 702231; Fax 01851 704296
Sheriff Vacancy

Tain

Sheriff Court Hse, Tain, Highland IV19 1AB; Tel 01862
892518; Fax 01862 893348
Sheriff Vacancy

Wick

Sheriff Court Hse, Wick, Highland KW1 4AJ; Tel 01955
602846; Fax 01955 602846
Sheriff D.O. Sutherland

Tayside, Central and Fife

Sheriff Court Hse, Tay St, Perth, Perth and Kinross
PH2 8NL; Tel 01738 620546; Fax 01738 445181; TelexDX
PE20
Sheriff Principal R.A. Dunlop, QC

Alloa

Sheriff Court Hse, Alloa, Clackmannanshire FK10 1HR;
Tel 01259 722734; Fax 01259 219470; TelexDX 560433
Sheriff W.M. Reid

Arbroath

Sheriff Court Hse, Arbroath, Angus DD11 1HL; Tel 01241
876600; Fax 01241 874413; TelexDX 442 Arbroath
Sheriff C.N.R. Stein

Cupar

Sheriff Court Hse, Cupar, Fife KY15 4LX; Tel 01334 652121;
Fax 01334 656807; TelexDX 560545
Sheriff G.J. Evans

Dundee

Sheriff Court Hse, Dundee DD1 9AD; Tel 01382 229961;
Fax 01382 202006; TelexDX DD33
Sheriff A.L. Stewart, QC
Sheriff R.A. Davidson
Sheriff J.P. Scott
Sheriff I.D. Dunbar
Sheriff L. Wood
Sheriff F.R. Crowe

Dunfermline

Sheriff Court Hse, , 1–6 Carnegie Dr, Dunfermline, Fife
KY12 7HJ; Tel 01383 724666; Fax 01383 621205; TelexDX
DF17
Sheriff I.C. Simpson
Sheriff Mrs I.G. McColl
Sheriff D.N. Mackie
Sheriff R.J. MacLeod

Falkirk

Sheriff Court Hse, Camelon, Falkirk FK1 4AR; Tel 01324
620822; Fax 01324 678238; TelexDX FA17
Sheriff A.V. Sheehan
Sheriff A.J. Murphy
Sherriff C. Caldwell

Forfar

Sheriff Court Hse, Forfar, Tayside DD8 3LA; Tel 01307
462186; Fax 01307 462268; TelexDX 503674
Sheriff K.A. Veal

Kirkcaldy

Sheriff Court Hse, Whytescauseway, Kirkcaldy, Fife KY1
1XQ; Tel 01592 260171; Fax 01592 642361; TelexDX KY17
Sheriff   F.J. Keane
Sheriff   G.W.M. Liddle
Sheriff   B.G. Donald

Perth

Sheriff Court Hse, Perth, Perth and Kinross PH2 8NL;
Tel 01738 620546; Fax 01738 623601; TelexDX PE20
Sheriff   M.J. Fletcher
Sheriff   D.C.W. Pyle
Sheriff   L.D.R. Foulis

Stirling

Sheriff Court Hse, Stirling FK8 1NH; Tel 01786 462191;
Fax 01786 470456; TelexDX ST15
Sheriff   R.E.G. Younger
Sheriff   A.W. Robertson

Lothian and Borders

Sheriff Principal's Chambers, Sheriff Court Hse, Edinburgh
EH1 1LB; Tel 0131 225 2525; Fax 0131 225 2288
Sheriff Principal   I.D. MacPhail

Edinburgh

Sheriff Court Hse, 27 Chambers St, Edinburgh EH1 1LB;
Tel 0131 225 2525; Fax 0131 225 4422; TelexDX ED308
Sheriff   R.G. Craik, QC
Sheriff   I.A. Poole
Sheriff   R.J.D. Scott
Sheriff   A.M. Bell
Sheriff   J.M.S. Horsburgh, QC
Sheriff   J.A. Farrell
Sheriff   A. Lothian
Sheriff   C.N. Stoddart
Sheriff   M. McPartlin
Sheriff   J.D. Allan
Sheriff   N.M.P. Morrison, QC
Sheriff   M.M. Stephen
Sheriff   M.L.E. Jarvie, QC
Sheriff   N.J. MacKinnon
Sheriff   Mrs K.E.C. Mackie
Sheriff   D.W.M. McIntyre
Sheriff   K.M. Mciver
Sheriff   J.C. McSherry

Haddington

Sheriff Court Hse, Haddington, East Lothian EH41 3NH;
Tel 01620 822936; Fax 01620 826350; TelexDX 540732
Sheriff   G.W.S. Presslie

Jedburgh

Sheriff Court Hse, Jedburgh, Scottish Borders TD8 6AR;
Tel 01835 863231; Fax 01835 864110; TelexDX 581222
Sheriff   T.A.K. Drummond, QC

Linlithgow

Sheriff Court Hse, Linlithgow, West Lothian EH49 7EQ;
Tel 01506 842922; Fax 01506 848457; TelexDX 540881
Sheriff   M.G.R. Edington
Sheriff   G.R. Fleming, QC
Sheriff   P. Gillam
Sheriff   W.D. Muirhead

Peebles

Sheriff Court Hse, Peebles, Scottish Borders EH45 8SW;
Tel 01721 720204; Fax 01721 729583; TelexDX 540971
Sheriff   Vacancy

Selkirk

Sheriff Court Hse, Selkirk, Scottish Borders TD7 4LE;
Tel 01750 21269; Fax 01750 22884; TelexDX 581011
Sheriff   Vacancy

Glasgow and Strathkelvin

Sheriff Principal's Chambers, Sheriff Court Hse, Glasgow
G5 9DA; Tel 0141 429 8888; Fax 0141 418 5185; Tel exDX
GW213
Sheriff Principal   E.F. Bowen, QC

Glasgow and Strathkelvin

Sheriff Court Hse, Glasgow G5 9DA; Tel 0141 429 8888;
Fax 0141 418 5244; TelexDX 6W213
Sheriff   B. Kearney
Sheriff   S. Cathcart
Sheriff   B.A. Lockhart
Sheriff   A.W. Noble
Sheriff   A.L.A. Duncan
Sheriff   R.E.A. Rae, QC
Sheriff   Ms L.M. Ruxton
Sheriff   A.C. Henry
Sheriff   J.K. Mitchell
Sheriff   A.G. Johnston
Sheriff   S.A.O. Raeburn, QC
Sheriff   D. Convery
Sheriff   Mrs F.L. Reith, QC
Sheriff   I.H.L. Miller
Sheriff   I. Peebles, QC
Sheriff   J.D. Friel
Sheriff   C.W. McFarlane, QC
Sheriff   P.M.M. Bowman
Sheriff   J.A. Taylor
Sheriff   H. Matthews, QC
Sheriff   J.A. Baird
Sheriff   D.M. MacNeil, QC
Sheriff   C.A.L. Scott
Sheriff   W.J. Totten
Sheriff   M.G. O'Grady, QC
Sheriff   W.H. Holligan
Sheriff   A.C. Normand

North Strathclyde

Sheriff Principal's Chambers, Sheriff Court Hse, Paisley,
Renfrewshire PA3 4DD; Tel 0141 887 5291; Fax 0141 889
1748; TelexDX PA48
Sheriff Principal   B.A. Kerr, QC

Campbeltown

Sheriff Court Hse, Campbeltown, Argyll and Bute
PA28 6AN; Tel 01586 552503; Fax 01586 554967
Sheriff   Vacancy

Dumbarton

Sheriff Court Hse, Dumbarton, West Dunbartonshire G82
1QR; Tel 01389 763266; Fax 01389 764085; TelexDX 597
Sheriff   T. Scott
Sheriff   S.W.H. Fraser
Sheriff   J.T. Fitzsimons

Dunoon

Sheriff Court Hse, Dunoon, Argyll and Bute PA23 8BQ;
Tel 01369 704166; Fax 01369 702191; TelexDX 591655
Sheriff   C.M.A.F. Gimblett

Greenock

Sheriff Court Hse, 1 Nelson St, Greenock, Inverclyde PA15
1TR; Tel 01475 787073; Fax 01475 729746; TelexDX GR16
Sheriff   Mrs M. Swanney
Sheriff   J.P. Herald
Sheriff   J. Canavan

Kilmarnock

Sheriff Court Hse, Kilmarnock, East Ayrshire KA1 1ED;
Tel 01563 520211; Fax 01563 543568; TelexDX KK20
Sheriff Ms I.S. McDonald
Sheriff T.M. Croan
Sheriff C.G. McKay

Oban

Sheriff Court Hse, Albany St, Oban, Renfrewshire
PA34 4AL; Tel 01631 562414; Fax 01631 562037; TelexDX
0B8
Sheriff W.D. Small

Paisley

Sheriff Court Hse, 106 Renfrew Rd, Paisley, Renfrewshire
PA3 4DD; Tel 0141 887 5291; Fax 0141 887 6702; TelexDX
PA48
Sheriff G.C. Kavanagh
Sheriff J. Spy
Sheriff D.J. Pender
Sheriff W. Dunlop
Sheriff N. Douglas
Sheriff A.M. Cubie
Sheriff C.W. Pettigrew
Sheriff S.M. Sinclair
Sheriff S. Waldron

Rothesay

Sheriff Court Hse, Rothesay, Argyll and Bute PA20 9HA;
Tel 01700 502982; Fax 01700 504112; TelexDX 590655
Sheriff Vacancy

South Strathclyde, Dumfries and Galloway

Sheriff Principal's Chambers, Sheriff Court Hse, Airdrie,
North Lanarkshire ML6 6EE; Tel 01236 751121; Fax 01236
750980; TelexDX 570416
Sheriff Principal J.C. McInnes, QC

Airdrie

Sheriff Court Hse, Graham St, Airdrie, North Lanarkshire
ML6 6EE; Tel 01236 751121; Fax 01236 747497; TelexDX
570416
Sheriff R.H. Dickson
Sheriff M.M. Galbraith
Sheriff J.C. Morris, QC
Sheriff A.D. Vannet

Ayr

Sheriff Court Hse, Ayr, South Ayrshire KA7 1DR; Tel 01292
268474; Fax 01292 282442; TelexDX AY16
Sheriff N. Gow, QC
Sheriff C.B. Miller
Sheriff J. McGowan

Dumfries

Sheriff Court Hse, Dumfries, Dumfries and Galloway
DG1 2AN; Tel 01387 262334; Fax 01387 262357; TelexDX
580617 Dumfries
Sheriff K.G. Barr
Sheriff K.A. Ross

Hamilton

Sheriff Court Hse, Hamilton, South Lanarkshire ML3 6AA;
Tel 01698 282957; Fax 01698 284403; TelexDX HA16
Sheriff S.C. Pender
Sheriff J. Powrie
Sheriff W.E. Gibson
Sheriff D.C. Russell
Sheriff J.H. Stewart

Sheriff H.S. Neilson
Sheriff D.M. Bicket
Sheriff T. Welsh, QC
Sheriff C.A. Kelly
Sheriff J. Montgomery
Sheriff H.K. Small
Sheriff M.T. Smart

Kirkcudbright

Sheriff Court Hse, Kirkcudbright, Dumfries and Galloway
DG6 4JW; Tel 01557 330574; Fax 01557 331764; TelexDX
812 Kirkcudbright
Sheriff Vacancy

Lanark

Sheriff Court Hse, Lanark, Dumfries and Galloway
ML11 7NE; Tel 01555 661531; Fax 01555 664319; TelexDX
832 Lanark
Sheriff Ms N.C. Stewart

Stranraer

Sheriff Court Hse, Stranraer, Dumfries and Galloway
DG9 7AA; Tel 01776 702138; Fax 01776 706792; TelexDX
581261 Stranraer
Sheriff J.R. Smith

CROWN PROSECUTION SERVICE

The Crown Prosecution Service is responsible for the
independent review and conduct of criminal proceedings
instituted by police forces in England and Wales (with the
exception of cases conducted by the Serious Fraud Office
and certain minor offences). The Director of Public
Prosecutions is the Head of Service and discharges his
statutory functions under the superintendence of the
Attorney General. The Service comprises a Headquarters
and 42 areas co-terminus with police Areas in England and
Wales. Each of the Areas is supervised by a Chief Crown
Prosecutor, assisted by an Area Business Manager.
Headquarters 50 Ludgate Hill, London EC4M 7EX;
URL www.cps.gov.uk; E-mail enquiries@cps.gov.uk;
Tel (Public Enquiry Point) 020 7796 8500; (Switchboard)
020 7796 8000; TelexDX 300850 Ludgate EC4
Director (Public Prosecutions) Ken Macdonald, QC
Chief Executive Richard Foster

Headquarters

Covering complex and serious cases from all Police Forces
and Constabularies in England and Wales.
50 Ludgate Hill, London EC4M 7EX; Tel 020 7796 8000;
Fax 020 7796 8651; TelexDX 300850 Ludgate EC4
Director (Business Information Systems) Claire Hamon;
Tel 020 7759 7531
Director (Casework) Chris Newell; Tel 020 7796 8554
Director (Finance) John Graham; Tel 020 7796 8071
Director (Human Resources) Angela O'Connor; Tel 020 7796
8014
Director (Policy) Garry Patten; Tel 020 7796 8124
Head (Communications Division) Sue Cunningham; Tel 020
7796 8464

Area Offices

Crown Prosecution Service Avon and Somerset

Covering Avon and Somerset Constabulary.

2nd Fl, Froomsgate Hse, Rupert St, Bristol BS1 2QJ;
Tel 0117 930 2800; Fax 0117 930 2806; TelexDX 78120
Bristol
Chief Crown Prosecutor   David Archer
Area Manager (Business)   Sarah Trevelyan

Crown Prosecution Service Bedfordshire

Covering Bedfordshire Police.
Sceptre Hse, 7–9 Castle St, Luton LU1 3AJ; Tel 01582
816600; Fax 01582 816678; TelexDX 120503 Luton 6
Chief Crown Prosecutor   Richard Newcombe
Area Business Manager   Mark Fleckney

Crown Prosecution Service Cambridgeshire

Covering Cambridgeshire Constabulary.
Justinian Hse, Spitfire Cl, Ermine Bus Pk, Huntingdon,
Cambridgeshire PE29 6XY; Tel 01480 825200; Fax 01480
825205; TelexDX 123223 Huntingdon 5
Chief Crown Prosecutor   Richard Crowley
Area Business Manager   Adrian Mardell

Crown Prosecution Service Cheshire

Covering Cheshire Constabulary.
2nd Fl, Windsor Hse, Pepper St, Chester, Cheshire
CH1 1TD; Tel 01244 408600; Fax 01244 408658; TelexDX
20019 Chester
Chief Crown Prosecutor   Barry Hughes
Area Business Manager   Angela Garbett

Crown Prosecution Service Cleveland

Covering Cleveland Police.
5 Linthorpe Rd, Middlesbrough TS1 1TX; Tel 01642 204500;
Fax 01642 204503; TelexDX 60551 Middlesbrough 12
Chief Crown Prosecutor   David Magson
Area Business Manager   Margaret Phillips

Crown Prosecution Service Cumbria

1st Fl, Stocklund Hse, Castle St, Carlisle, Cumbria CA3 8SY;
Tel 01228 882900; Fax 01228 882910; TelexDX 63032
Carlisle
Chief Crown Prosecutor   David Farmer
Area Business Manager   John Pears

Crown Prosecution Service Derbyshire

Covering Derbyshire Constabulary.
7th Fl, St. Peter's Hse, Gower St, Derby DE1 1SB; Tel 01332
614000; Fax 01332 614009; TelexDX 17506 Derby 2
Chief Crown Prosecutor   David Adams
Area Business Manager   Chris Mitchell

Crown Prosecution Service Devon and Cornwall

Covering Devon and Cornwall Constabulary.
Hawkins Hse, Pynes Hill, Rydon La, Exeter, Devon
EX2 5SS; Tel 01392 288000; Fax 01392 288008; TelexDX
135606 Exeter 16
Chief Crown Prosecutor   Andrew Cresswell
Area Business Manager   John Nettleton

Crown Prosecution Service Dorset

Covering Dorset Police.
1st Fl, Oxford Hse, Oxford Rd, Bournemouth BH8 8HA;
Tel 01202 498700; Fax 01202 798701; TelexDX 7699
Bournemouth
Chief Crown Prosecutor   John Revell
Area Business Manager   Jason Putman

Crown Prosecution Service Durham

Covering Durham Constabulary.

Elvet Hse, Hallgarth St, Durham, County Durham
DH1 3AT; Tel 0191 383 5800; Fax 0191 383 5801; TelexDX
60227 Durham
Chief Crown Prosecutor   Jeff Corrighan
Area Business Manager   Karen Pearson

Crown Prosecution Service Dyfed Powys

Covering Dyfed Powys Police.
Heol Penlanffos, Tanerdy, Carmarthen, SA31 2EZ; Tel 01267
242100; Fax 01267 242111; TelexDX 51411 Carmarthen
Chief Crown Prosecutor   Simon Rowlands
Area Business Manager   Jeff Thomas

Crown Prosecution Service Essex

Covering Essex Police.
County Hse, 100 New London Rd, Chelmsford, Essex
CM2 0RG; Tel 01245 455800; Fax 01245 455809; TelexDX
139160 Chelmsford 11
Chief Crown Prosecutor   John Bell
Area Business Manager   Susan Stovell

Crown Prosecution Service Gloucestershire

Covering Gloucestershire Constabulary.
2 Kimbrose Way, Gloucester, Gloucestershire GL1 2DB;
Tel 01452 872400; Fax 01452 872406; TelexDX 7544
Gloucester
Chief Crown Prosecutor   Withiel Cole
Area Business Manager   Will Hollins

Crown Prosecution Service Greater Manchester

Covering Greater Manchester Police.
8th Fl, Sunlight Hse, PO Box 237, Quay St, Manchester
M60 3PS; Tel 0161 827 4700; Fax 0161 827 4930; TelexDX
710288 Manchester 3
Chief Crown Prosecutor   Tony Taylor
Area Business Manager   Kevin Fox

Crown Prosecution Service Gwent

Covering Gwent Police.
6th Fl, Chartist Tower, Upper Dock St, Newport NP9 1DW;
Tel 01633 261100; Fax 01633 261106; TelexDX 33232
Newport (Gwent)
Chief Crown Prosecutor   Chris Woolley
Area Business Manager   Helen Phillips

Crown Prosecution Service Hampshire and Isle of Wight

Covering Hampshire Police.
3rd Fl, Black Horse Hse, 8–10 Leigh Rd, Eastleigh,
Hampshire SO50 9FH; Tel 023 8067 3800; Fax 023 8067
3854; TelexDX 34149 Eastleigh
Chief Crown Prosecutor   Vacancy
Area Business Manager   Denise Bailey

Crown Prosecution Service Hertfordshire

Covering Hertfordshire Police.
Queen's Hse, 58 Victoria St, St. Albans, Hertfordshire
AL1 3HZ; Tel 01727 798700; Fax 01727 798795; TelexDX
120650 St Albans 7
Chief Crown Prosecutor   Charles Ingham
Area Business Manager   Linda Fox

Crown Prosecution Service Humberside

Covering Humberside Police.
2nd Fl, King William Hse, Market Pl, Lowgate, Hull,
Kingston upon Hull HU1 1RS; Tel 01482 621000;
Fax 01482 621002; TelexDX 11922 Hull
Chief Crown Prosecutor   Bob Marshall
Area Business Manager   Caron Skidmore

Crown Prosecution Service Kent

Covering Kent County Police.
Priory Gate, 29 Union St, Maidstone, Kent ME14 1PT;
Tel 01622 356300; Fax 01622 356374; TelexDX 4830
Maidstone
Chief Crown Prosecutor   Elizabeth Howe
Area Business Manager   Ken Mitchell

Crown Prosecution Service Lancashire

Covering Lancashire Constabulary.
3rd Fl, Unicentre, Lord's Walk, Preston, Lancashire
PR1 1DH; Tel 01772 208100; Fax 01772 208144; TelexDX
710054 Preston 10
Chief Crown Prosecutor   Dickie Dickenson
Area Business Manager   Ian Farrell (Acting)

Crown Prosecution Service Leicestershire

Covering Leicestershire Constabulary
Princes Crt, 34 York Rd, Leicester LE1 5TU; Tel 0116 204
6700; Fax 0116 204 6777; TelexDX 10899 Leicester 1
Chief Crown Prosecutor   Martin Howard
Area Business Manager   Vacancy

Crown Prosecution Service Lincolnshire

Covering Lincolnshire Police.
Crosstrend Hse, 10a Newport, Lincoln, Lincolnshire
LN1 3DF; Tel 01522 585900; Fax 01522 585958; TelexDX
15562 Lincoln 4
Chief Crown Prosecutor   Alison Kerr
Area Business Manager   Andrew Illingworth

Crown Prosecution Service London

Covering Metropolitan Police and City of London Police.
2nd Pl, The Flagship, 142 Holborn, London EC1N 2NG;
Tel 020 7796 8000; Fax 020 7796 8540; TelexDX 300850
Ludgate EC4
Chief Crown Prosecutor   Dru Sharpling
Area Business Manager   Alex Machray

Crown Prosecution Service Merseyside

Covering Merseyside Police.
7th Fl (South), Royal Liver Bldg, Pier Head, Liverpool,
Merseyside L3 1HN; Tel 0151 239 6400; Fax 0151 239
6420; TelexDX 00596 Liverpool 4
Chief Crown Prosecutor   John Holt
Area Business Manager   Deborah King

Crown Prosecution Service Norfolk

Covering Norfolk Constabulary.
Haldin Hse, Old Bank of England Crt, Queen St, Norwich,
Norfolk NR2 4SX; Tel 01603 693000; Fax 01603 693001;
TelexDX 5299 Norwich
Chief Crown Prosecutor   Peter Tidey
Area Business Manager   Catherine Scholefield

Crown Prosecution Service Northamptonshire

Covering Northamptonshire Police.
Beaumont Hse, Cliftonville, Northampton,
Northamptonshire NN1 5BE; Tel 01604 823600;
Fax 01604 823651; TelexDX 18512 Northampton
Chief Crown Prosecutor   Colin Chapman
Area Business Manager   Fiona Campbell

Crown Prosecution Service Northumbria

Covering Northumbria Police.
St. Ann's Quay, 122 Quayside, Newcastle upon Tyne, Tyne
and Wear NE1 3BD; Tel 0191 260 4200; Fax 0191 260
4241; TelexDX 62565 Jesmond
Chief Crown Prosecutor   Nicola Reasbeck
Area Business Manager   Adele Clarke

Crown Prosecution Service North Wales

Covering North Wales Police.
Bromfield Hse, Ellice Way, Wrexham LL13 7YW; Tel 01978
346000; Fax 01978 346001; TelexDX 26684 Wrexham
Chief Crown Prosecutor   Paul Whittaker
Area Business Manager   Angela Walsh

Crown Prosecution Service North Yorkshire

Covering North Yorkshire Police.
6th Fl, Ryedale Bldg, 60 Piccadilly, York YO1 1NS; Tel 01904
731700; Fax 01904 731764; TelexDX 61531 York
Chief Crown Prosecutor   Bob Turnbull
Area Business Manager   Liam Carroll

Crown Prosecution Service Nottinghamshire

Covering Nottinghamshire Police.
2 King Edward Crt, King Edward St, Nottingham
NG1 1EL; Tel 0115 852 3300; Fax 0115 852 3380; TelexDX
10161 Nottingham
Chief Crown Prosecutor   Kate Carty
Area Business Manager   Gail Pessol

Crown Prosecution Service South Wales

Covering South Wales Police.
20th Fl, Capital Hse, Greyfriars Rd, Cardiff CF10 3PL;
Tel 029 2080 3900; Fax 029 2080 3930; TelexDX 33056
Cardiff 1
Chief Crown Prosecutor   Huw Heycock
Area Business Manager   Edwina Sherwood

Crown Prosecution Service South Yorkshire

Covering South Yorkshire Police.
Greenfield Hse, 32 Scotland St, Sheffield, South Yorkshire
S3 7DQ; Tel 0114 229 8600; Fax 0114 229 8607; TelexDX
711830 Sheffield 18
Chief Crown Prosecutor   Judith Walker
Area Business Manager   Christopher Day

Crown Prosecution Service Staffordshire

Covering Staffordshire Police.
11a Princes St, Stafford, Staffordshire ST16 2EU;
Tel 01785 272200; Fax 01785 272299; TelexDX 25304
Stafford 2
Chief Crown Prosecutor   Harry Ireland
Area Business Manager   Brian Laybourne

Crown Prosecution Service Suffolk

Covering Suffolk Constabulary.
Saxon Hse, 1 Cromwell Sq, Ipswich, Suffolk IP1 1TS;
Tel 01473 282100; Fax 01473 282101; TelexDX 3266
Ipswich
Chief Crown Prosecutor   Chris Yule
Area Business Manager   Caroline Hodson

Crown Prosecution Service Surrey

Covering Surrey Police.
One Onslow St, Guildford, Surrey GU1 4YA; Tel 01483
468200; Fax 01483 468202; TelexDX 122041 Guildford 10
Chief Crown Prosecutor   Sandie Hebblethwaite
Area Business Manager   Martyn Wray

Crown Prosecution Service Sussex

Covering Sussex Police.
City Gate, 185 Dyke Rd, Brighton, Brighton and Hove
BN3 1TL; Tel 01273 765600; Fax 01273 765605; TelexDX
2754 Brighton 1
Chief Crown Prosecutor   Gary Perry (Acting)
Area Business Manager   Iain Everett

Crown Prosecution Service Thames Valley

Covering Thames Valley Police.
The Courtyard, Lombard St, Abingdon, Oxfordshire
OX14 5SE; Tel 01235 551900; Fax 01235 551901; TelexDX
35859 Abingdon
Chief Crown Prosecutor Simon Clements
Area Business Manager Graham Choldcroft

Crown Prosecution Service Warwickshire

Covering Warwickshire Constabulary.
Rossmore Hse, 10 Newbold Terr, Leamington Spa,
Warwickshire CV32 4EA; Tel 01926 455000; Fax 01926
455002; 01926 455003; TelexDX 11881 Leamington Spa
Chief Crown Prosecutor Mark Lynn
Area Business Manager Ian Edmondson

Crown Prosecution Service West Mercia

Covering West Mercia Constabulary.
Artillery Hse, Heritage Way, Droitwich, Worcestershire
WR9 8YB; Tel 01905 825000; Fax 01905 825100; TelexDX
179491 Droitwich 4
Chief Crown Prosecutor Jim England
Area Business Manager Laurence Sutton

Crown Prosecution Service West Midlands

Covering West Midlands Police.
14th Fl, Colmore Gate, 2 Colmore Row, Birmingham, West
Midlands B3 2QA; Tel 0121 262 1300; Fax 0121 262 1500;
TelexDX 719540 Birmingham 45
Chief Crown Prosecutor David Blundell
Area Business Manager Mike Grist

Crown Prosecution Service West Yorkshire

Covering West Yorkshire Police.
Oxford Hse, Oxford Rd, Leeds, West Yorkshire LS1 3BE;
Tel 0113 290 2700; Fax 0118 290 2701; TelexDX 26435
Leeds Park Square
Chief Crown Prosecutor Neil Franklin
Area Business Manager Jean Ashton

Crown Prosecution Service Wiltshire

Covering Wiltshire Constabulary.
2nd Fl, Fox Talbot Hse, Bellinger Cl, Malmesbury Rd,
Chippenham, Wiltshire SN15 1BN; Tel 01249
766100; Fax 01249 766101; TelexDX 98644
Chippenham 2
Chief Crown Prosecutor Nick Hawkins
Area Business Manager Karen Sawitzki

CHILDREN AND FAMILY COURT ADVISORY AND SUPPORT SERVICE

England

Avon (Bath and North East Somerset, Bristol, North Somerset and South Gloucestershire)

Unit 9, York Crt, Wilder St, Bristol BS2 8QH; Tel 0117 923
2070; Fax 0117 923 9075
Service Manager Vicki Siggens;
E-mail vicki.siggens@cafcass.gov
Service Manager T. Simpson

Bedfordshire

Social Services Communications, County Hall, Bedford,
Bedfordshire MK42 9AP; E-mail fd96@dial.pipex.com;
Tel 01234 408024; Fax 01234 228137
Manager (Personnel) Sandra Thacker

Buckinghamshire

Clyde Hse, 10 Milburn Ave, Oldbrook, Milton Keynes
MK6 2WA; Tel 01908 359420; Fax 01908 359421
Team Manager Christine Smart

New Cambridgeshire and Peterborough City Council

Cambridgeshire and Peterborough, PO Box 10, Cambridge,
Cambridgeshire CB3 0SX
Contact Tessa K. Bailey

Cornwall

Adoption and Family Finding Unit, 13 Treyew Rd, Truro,
Cornwall TR1 2BY; Tel 01872 270251; Fax 01872 260557

Cumbria

2nd Fl, Capital Bldg, Hilltop Heights, Carlisle, Cumbria
CA1 2NS; URL www.cafcass.gov.uk; Tel 01228 549130;
Fax 01228 510911
Service Manager Ian Gopsill;
E-mail ian.gopsill@cafcass.gov.uk

Derby and Derbyshire

3–5 Brimington Rd, Chesterfield, Derbyshire S41 7UG;
Tel 01246 221082; Fax 01246 278118
Team Manager Jill Hopkins;
E-mail jill.hopkins@cafcass.gov.uk

Devon

Minerva Hse, Pynes Hill, Exeter, Devon EX2 5JL; Tel 01392
354600; Fax 01392 447369
Service Manager Martin J. Gladwin;
E-mail martin.gladwin@cafcass.gov.uk

Durham County and Darlington

Rock Hse, Finchale Rd, Durham, County Durham
DH1 5HE; Tel 0191 386 6847; Fax 0191 386 5724
GALRO Panel Manager E. Hall

East Sussex

East Sussex County Council, Pelgham Hse, Lewes,
East Sussex BN7 1UN; Tel 01273 481946; Fax 01273
473321
Manager A. Flynn

Essex, Southend and Thurrock

90 Victoria Rd, Chelmsford, Essex CM1 1RD; Tel 01245
255660
Essex, Southend and Thurrock Manager A. Grocott;
E-mail adrian.grocott@essex.gov.uk

Gloucestershire

Northgate Hse, 19 London Rd, Gloucester, Gloucestershire
GL1 3HB
Team Manager Deborah Steele
Team Manager S. Tate

Greater Manchester

Bury, Oldham and Rochdale

Broadfield Hse, 91 Manchester Rd, Rochdale, Lancashire
OL11 4JG; Tel 01706 525774; Fax 01706 347985
Team Manager   Steve Huzzard

Manchester

Gateway Hse, Piccadilly South, Manchester M60 7LP;
Tel 0161 237 2157; Fax 0161 237 2597
Team Manager   Carole Lewis; Tel 0161 237 2534

Stockport (Tameside and Trafford)

1st Fl, Edward Hse, Edward St, Stockport, Greater
Manchester SK1 3DQ
Manager   Paul Doherty (Acting)

Bolton, Salford and Wigan (Children and Family Court Advisory and Support Service)

PO Box 114, Ince, Wigan, Greater Manchester WN3 4WW;
Tel 01942 828437; Fax 01942 828444
Team Manager   Chris Rivers;
E-mail chris.rivers@cafcass.gov.uk

Hertfordshire

3rd Fl, Swingate Hse, Dane St, Stevenage, Hertfordshire
SG1 1XH; Tel (General Enquiries) 01438 741100

Humberside (Joint Panel with Kingston-upon-Hull, East Riding of Yorkshire, North Lincolnshire and North East Lincolnshire)

20 The Weir, Hessle, Kingston upon Hull HU13 0RU;
Tel 01482 640228; Fax 01482 649199
Manager   H. Van Greuning

Isle of Wight

Children Services Centre, Atkinson Dr, Newport, Isle of
Wight PO36 2LS; Tel 01983 525790
*Services Manager (Joint Commissioning Children Services and
Looked-After Children)*   Mary Brunson

Kent

Public Law Office, Sessions Hse, County Rd, Maidstone,
Kent ME14 1XQ; E-mail joy.owen@cafcass.gov.uk;
Tel 01622 694284
Service Manager   Joy Owen;
E-mail joy.owen@cafcass.gov.uk; Fax 01622 696061

Lancashire

711 Cameron Hse, White Cross, South Rd, Lancaster,
Lancashire LA1 4XQ; Tel 01524 586300; Fax 01524
581455
Office Manager   S. Forrester
Team Manager   Mrs Terry Nash

Leicestershire (Joint Panel with Leicester City and Rutland)

Riverside, 49 Western Blvd, Leicester LE2 7HN; Tel 0116
249 5600; Fax 0116 247 0175
Manager   Kevin Smith; E-mail kevin.smith@cafcass.gov.uk

Lincolnshire

Hamilton Hse, 1–3 Clasketgate, Lincoln, Lincolnshire
LN2 1JG; URL www.catcass.gov.uk; Tel 01522 580750
Service Manager   Roger Sharp

London Boroughs

Inner and North London (Barking and Dagenham, Barnet,
Brent, Camden, City of London, Ealing, Enfield,
Greenwich, Hackney, Hammersmith, Haringey, Harrow,
Havering, Hillingdon, Hounslow, Islington, Kensington
and Chelsea, Lambeth, Lewisham, Newham, Redbridge,
Southwark, Tower Hamlets, Waltham Forest, Wandsworth,
Westminster).

Public Law Group

13th Fl, Archway Tower, 2 Junction Rd, London N19 5HQ;
URL www.cafcass.gov.uk; Tel 020 7210 4100; Fax 020
7210 4477

South London

PO Box 504, Sutton, Surrey SM1 1AE; Tel 020 8770 4518;
Fax 020 8770 4517
Manager   Victoria Philipson;
E-mail victoria.philipson@cableinet.co.uk

Merseyside

Sefton

PO Box 16, Liverpool, Merseyside L22 0QR; Tel 0151 285
5022; Fax 0151 285 5023
Manager   S. Ashton

Merseyside (Consortium: Wirral, Knowsley, St. Helens and Liverpool)

PO Box 234, Liverpool, Merseyside L69 4PB; Tel 0151 708
7906; Fax 0151 708 7931
Manager   C.R. Derby

Norfolk

Adoption and Family Finding Unit, 3 Unthank Rd,
Norwich, Norfolk NR2 2PA;
E-mail adoption.unit.socs@norfolk.gov.uk; Tel 01603
617796
Team Manager   Sally Stoker

North Yorkshire and York

PO Box 130, Haxby, York YO32 3XH; Tel 01904 762997
Manager   Kathryn Clark;
E-mail kathryn.clark@northyorks.gov.uk

Northamptonshire

PO Box 301, 9 Guildhall Rd, Northampton,
Northamptonshire NN1 1BJ; Tel 01604 602163; Fax 01604
603531
Manager   J. Chappell;
E-mail jchappell@northamptonshire.gov.uk

Nottingham

2a Castlebridge Office Village, Castle Marina Rd,
Nottingham NG7 1TD;
E-mail neville.hall@cafcass.gov.uk; Tel 0115 853 2500;
Fax 0115 941 0929
Team Manager   N. Hall

Shropshire, Telford and Wrekin

PO Box 457, Telford, Shropshire TF3 4WJ; Tel 01952 202040;
Fax 01952 200385
Manager   Vacancy

South Yorkshire

Victoria Pl, 34 Godstone Rd, Rotherham, South Yorkshire
S60 2PU; E-mail galro@rotherham.gov.uk; Tel 01709
839655; Fax 01709 839690
Manager   A. Slade

Staffordshire

Marsh Crt, Tillington St, Stafford, Staffordshire ST16 2RE;
Tel 01785 785816; Fax 01785 785817
Team Manager   John Mason;
E-mail john.mason@cafcass.gov.uk

Surrey

PO Box 52, Guildford, Surrey GU4 7WL; Tel 01483 455268;
Fax 01483 574528

Tees-Hartlepool Panel

78 Borough Rd, Middlesbrough TS1 2JH;
E-mail galro@hartlepool.gov.uk; Tel 01642 232023;
Fax 01642 249010
Manager   W.D. Walton

West Midlands

Birmingham

Milton Grange, 16 Handsworth Wood Rd, Birmingham,
West Midlands B20 2DR; Tel 0121 686 4045; Fax 0121 303
7208

Black Country (Joint Panel with Sandwell, Dudley, Walsall and Wolverhampton)

PO Box 8547, West Bromwich, West Midlands B70 8EA;
Tel 0121 569 5667; Fax 0121 569 5447
Manager   G. Wheeler

Coventry, Warwickshire and Solihull

PO Box 149, Coventry, West Midlands CV1 5TX;
E-mail barnes@surfacs.demon.co.uk; Tel 02476 833473;
Fax 02476 833426
Manager   Colin Barnes

West Yorkshire

PO Box 92, Kenburgh Hse, 289 Manor Row, Bradford,
West Yorkshire BD1 4WR; Tel 01274 386100; Fax 01274
735019
Manager   E. Greenwell

Worcestershire

Social Service Department, County Hall, Worcester,
Worcestershire WR5 2HA; Tel 01905 763763
Unit Manager (Child Protection/Planning and Review)
Alan Ferguson

Wales

West Glamorgan

76a Walter Rd, Swansea SA1 4QA; Tel 01792 460179;
Fax 01792 460193
Manager   Maggie Rees

West Wales

33 Quay St, Carmarthen, Carmarthenshire SA31 3JT;
Tel 01267 231199; Fax 01267 238811
Contact   Maggie Rees

North Wales

Heulwen, Glyn y Marl Rd, Llandudno Junction, Conwy
LL31 9NS; Tel 01492 581975; Fax 01492 582806
Team Manager   Jane Williams

South East Wales

1st Fl, 110b Merthyr Mawr Rd, Bridgend CF31 3NY;
Tel 01656 647272; Fax 01656 647341
Manager   J. Doughty

Cardiff and the Vale

Cardiff CF2 1RZ; Tel 029 2049 5382
Manager   D. Valle

CHILDREN'S PANELS – SCOTLAND

Following are the various positions relating to the
Children's Panels in Scotland. The Children's Panels deal
only with those cases in which formal proceedings are
raised by the Children's Reporter. The role of the Children's
Panel Advisory Committee is to monitor the appointment,
training and performance of Children's Panel members.

Aberdeen City

Chair   P. Simpson
2 Albyn Pl, Aberdeen AB10 1YH
Depute   C. Grant
Depute   K. Douglas

Aberdeenshire

E-mail childrenspanel@aberdeenshire.gov.uk
Chair   W. Smail
Aberdeenshire Children's Panel, St. Leonards, Sandyhill
Rd, Banff, Aberdeenshire AB45 1BH;
E-mail childrenspanel@aberdeenshire.gov.uk

Angus

Chair   I. Ingram
Fariways, 9 Seaton Rd, Arbroath, Angus DD11 5DX
Depute   C. Robertson
Depute   C. Urquhart

Argyll and Bute

Chair   P.J. Korbel
Cornwall Hse, Tabent, Argyll and Bute PA2D 6TW
Deputy   J. Fergussion
Deputy   M. Mowatt

Clackmannanshire

Chair   J. Wheeler
30 Polwarth Ave, Brightons, Falkirk FK2 0HL
Deputy   A. Craig

Dumfries and Galloway

Chair   D. McGregor
Scaurbrae, Speddoch, Dumfries, Dumfries and Galloway
DG2 9TZ
Deputy   D. Johnstone

Dundee

Chair   Fiona Mackenzie
21 City Sq, Dundee DD1 3BY; Tel 01382 434515
Deputy   Lina Notarangelo
Deputy   L. Stevenson

East Ayrshire

Chair L. Holbein
44 Woodlands Grn, Kilmarnock, East Ayrshire KA3 1TZ
Deputy M. Lopez

East Lothian

Chair M.N. Husband
The Kipper Hse, Woodbush, Dunbar, East Lothian
 EH42 1HB
Deputy D. Turner
9 Seton Crt, Port Seton, East Lothian EH32 0TU

East Renfrewshire

East Renfrewshire Council, Eastwood Pk, Rouken Glen Rd,
 Giffnock, East Renfrewshire G46 6UG
Joint Panel Chair Lil Miller

Falkirk

Chair G. Anderson
12a Arnothill Gdns, Falkirk FL1 5BQ
Joint Deputy T. McPherson
Joint Deputy R. Myles

Fife

Chair L. Smith
13 Greenacres, Kingseat, Dunfermline, Fife KY12 0RW
Deputy A.C. Morrison
Deputy A. Graham

Glasgow

Chair M.M.B. Pagani
15 Mansionhouse Rd, Mount Vernon, Glasgow G32 0RP
Deputy Hugh McNaughtan
364 Kingsbridge Dr, Glasgow G73 2BX
Deputy Christine Mackechhie
230 Knightswood Rd, Glasgow G13 2EY

Highland

Chair Edith Blake
The Children's Panel Office, The Highland Council,
 Inverness, Highland IV3 5NX; Tel 01463 702190;
 Fax 01463 702190
Deputy Rhona Morrison

Inverclyde

Chair J.R. Smith
44 Divert Rd, Gourock, Inverclyde PA19 1EE
Deputy K. Johnston

Midlothian

Chair S. Peart
The Old Golf Hse, Newbattle, Dalkeith, Midlothian
 EH22 3LX
Deputy P.J. Farrer

Moray

Chair G. Hamilton
East Lodge, Seapark, Kinloss, Moray IV36 0TT
Deputy M. Black

North Ayrshire

Chair Nora Parkinson
Deputy Margaret Murie

North Lanarkshire

Chair D.B. Geddes
64 Douglas St, Viewpark, Uddington, Glasgow G71 5EE
Deputy A. Robertson

Orkney

Chair N. Shearer
8 Quilco, Dounby, Orkney Islands KW17 2HW
Deputy P. Bennett

Perth and Kinross

Chair J. Mackintosh
6 Glebe Sq, Comrie, Fife PH6 2EN
Deputy D. Barnes

Renfrewshire

Chair M. Allison
49 Paisley Rd, Renfrew, Renfrewshire PA4 8HG

Scottish Borders

Chair A.S. Hemming
5 Bedrule, Denholm, Hawick, Scottish Borders TD9 8TE;
 Tel 01450 870192
Deputy Mrs Meg Reid
Deputy Teyl de Bordes

Shetland

Chair A. Simpson
2 Burgh Rd, Lerwick, Shetland Isles ZE1 0LB
Deputy A. Hamilton

South Ayrshire

Chair M.A. McMillan
Rowanlea, 41 Ottoline Dr, Troon, South Ayrshire
 KA10 7AN
Deputy F. McAlister

South Lanarkshire

Chair J. Sanson
10 Ivanhoe Crt, Carluke, South Lanarkshire ML8 5DQ
Deputy M. Bates

Stirling

Chair E. Hay
10 Bohun Crt, Wallace Pk, Stirling FK7 7UT
Deputy G. McBride

West Dunbartonshire

Chair Prof R.S. Phillips
15 Ardlui Gdns, Milngavie, West Dunbartonshire G62 7RL
Deputy D. Beveridge
61a Bonhill Rd, Dumbarton, West Dunbartonshire
 G82 2DR
Deputy M. Kinns
Glenavon, Back Rd, Clynder, West Dunbartonshire
 G84 0QQ
Deputy M. Palmer
14 Abercromby Cres, Helensburgh, West Dunbartonshire
 G84 9DX

West Lothian

Chair Father A. Chambers
83 Kenilworth Rise, Dedridge, Livingston, EH54 6JL
Deputy Lady R. Cullen
Deputy M. Crighton

Western Isles

Chair   E.A. MacLeod
8 Churchill Dr, Stornoway, Isle of Lewis HS1 2NP
Depute Chair   D.D. MacIver

SCOTTISH CHILDREN'S REPORTER ADMINISTRATION

The Scottish Children's Reporter Administration was created under the Local Government etc. (Scotland) Act 1994, and became fully operational on 1 April 1996. Its main responsibilities are to: facilitate the work of Children's Reporters for children; deploy and manage staff to carry out that work; provide suitable accommodation for children's hearings.
Ochil Hse, Springkerse Bus Pk, Stirling FK7 7XE;
   URL www.childrens-reporter.org;
   E-mail info@childrens-reporter.org;
   Tel 01786 459500;
   Fax 01786 459532
Chair   Douglas Bulloch
Principal Reporter   A.D. Miller

Stirling and Clackmannanshire

17 Gladstone Pl, Stirling FK8 2NG; Tel 01786 476400;
   Fax 01786 476418
Authority Reporter   Pauline Proudfoot

Falkirk

Campfield Hse, Wellside Pl, Falkirk FK1 5RL; Tel 01324
   626996; Fax 01324 626911
Authority Reporter   E. Cameron

North Lanarkshire – Bellshill

70 North Rd, Bellshill, North Lanarkshire ML4 1EN;
   Tel 01698 746771; Fax 01698 748142
Authority Reporter   Paul J. Harkness

East Region

Angus

Merrin Hse, 50 East Abbey St, Arbroath, Angus DD11 1EN;
   Tel 01241 873194; Fax 01241 431069
Authority Reporter   Rachel Burn

City of Dundee

3rd Fl, 91 Commercial St, Dundee DD1 2AF; Tel 01382
   433420; Fax 01382 433284
Authority Reporter   Rachael Burn

Fife

Albany Hse, 3 North St, Glenrothes, Fife KY7 5NA;
   Tel 01592 414919; Fax 01592 414903
Authority Reporter   S. Lynch

Perth and Kinross

52 Kinnoull St, Perth, Perth and Kinross PH1 5EZ; Tel 01738
   620950; Fax 01738 627684
Authority Reporter   N. Ritchie

West Region

Merchant Exchange, 10–20 Bell St, Candleriggs, Glasgow
   G1 1LG; Tel 0141 567 7900; Fax 0141 567 7969
Reporter Manager   Tom Philliben
Authority Reporter (Glasgow East)   J. McLafferty; Tel 0141
   567 7909; Fax 0141 567 7901
Authority Reporter (Glasgow South)   J. Doherty; Tel 0141 567
   7939; Fax 0141 567 7902
Authority Reporter (Glasgow North)   Iain Gault; Tel 0141 567
   7928; Fax 0141 567 7904

North Region

47–49 Academy St, Inverness, Highland IV1 1LP; Tel 01463
   245307; Fax 01463 245328
Reporter Manager   E. Grant

Aberdeenshire

8 Albyn Pl, Aberdeen AB10 1YH; Tel 01224 654105;
   Fax 01224 637472
Authority Reporter   Jillian Richards

City of Aberdeen

2 Albyn Pl, Aberdeen AB10 1YH; Tel 01224 654114;
   Fax 01224 640782
Authority Reporter   E. Templeton

Highland – Inverness

47–49 Academy St, Inverness, Highland IV1 1LP; Tel 01463
   245310; Fax 01463 245309
Authority Reporter   Hazel Marr

Moray

23a High St, Elgin, Moray IV30 1EE; Tel 01343 550015;
   Fax 01343 551856
Authority Reporter   J. Hammond

Orkney Islands

11 East Rd, Kirkwall, Orkney Islands KW15 1HZ; Tel 01856
   873238; Fax 01856 873387
Authority Reporter   M. Gordon

Shetland Islands

13 Hill La, Lerwick, Shetland Isles ZE1 0HA; Tel 01595
   692436; Fax 01595 696763
Authority Reporter   A. Cluness

Western Isles

10 Harbour View, Cromwell Quay, Stornoway, Western
   Isles HS1 2DF; Tel 01851 706317; Fax 01851 702189
Authority Reporter   S. Marshall

Edinburgh

1 Fountainhall Rd, Edinburgh EH9 2NL; Tel 0131 667 0284;
   Fax 0131 662 4640
Reporter Manager   M. Schaffer
Authority Reporter   G. Bell

Scottish Borders

12 Ettrick Terr, Selkirk, Scottish Borders TD7 4LE; Tel 01750
   20372; Fax 01750 23063
Authority Reporter   P. Walker

City of Edinburgh – West

1 Fountainhall Rd, Edinburgh EH9 2NL; Tel 0131 667 9431;
Fax 0131 663 4640
Authority Reporter Gordon Irvine

Mid/East Lothian

1 Loch Rd, Tranent, East Lothian EH33 2JX; Tel 01875
613355; Fax 01875 616178
Authority Reporter Celia McCracken

West Lothian

5 Edinburgh Rd, Bathgate, West Lothian EH48 1BA;
Tel 01506 632741; Fax 01506 631077
Authority Reporter A. Wright

Central West Region

66 Burnbank Rd, Hamilton, South Lanarkshire ML3 9AL;
Tel 01698 281903; Fax 01698 283227
Reporter Manager B. Lister

Dumfries and Galloway

3 Newall Terr, Dumfries, Dumfries and Galloway
DG1 1LN; Tel 01387 255734; Fax 01387 263411
Authority Reporter D. Weston (Acting)

East Ayrshire

2 Bridge La, Kilmarnock, East Ayrshire KA1 1QH; Tel 01563
555838; Fax 01563 555841
Authority Reporter J. Scanlon

South Ayrshire

11 Alloway Pl, Ayr, South Ayrshire KA7 2AA; Tel 01292
286386; Fax 01292 282905
Authority Reporter J. Scanlon

East Kilbride

Dava Hse, 43 Brousterhill, East Kilbride, South Lanarkshire
G74 1AG; Tel 013552 32145; Fax 013552 64690
Authority Reporter D. Jones

East Dunbartonshire

Merchant Exchange, 10–20 Bell St, Glasgow G1 1LG;
Tel 0141 567 7957; Fax 0141 567 7978
Authority Reporter M. Small

Argyll and Bute

Manse Brae, Lochgilphead, Argyll, Argyll and Bute
PA31 8QX; Tel 01546 606937; Fax 01546 606947
Authority Reporter S. Hunter

East Renfrewshire/Renfrewshire

10 Glen La, Paisley, Renfrewshire PA3 2HU; Tel 0141 889
9171; Fax 0141 889 5413
Authority Reporter L. King
Authority Reporter C. Welsh

Inverclyde

1–3 Brisbane St, Greenock, Inverclyde PA16 8LH; Tel 01475
720221; Fax 01475 724525
Authority Reporter K. Ritchie

North Ayrshire

1st Fl, Rivergate Hse, Rivergate, Irvine, North Ayrshire
KA12 8EH; Tel 01294 278151; Fax 01294 312132
Authority Reporter I. Mitchell

West Dunbartonshire

55 Church Crt, Dumbarton, West Dunbartonshire G82 1SU;
Tel 01389 764268; Fax 01389 742131
Authority Reporter C. Docherty

Government Departments for Wales, Scotland and Northern Ireland

3

- **Government Departments Wales**
  National Assembly for Wales
  National Assembly's Training and Education Department
  Care Standards Inspectorate for Wales
  Establishment Group
  Finance Group
  Health Protection and Improvement Directorate
  Local Government (Welsh Office)
  NHS Wales Department
  The Wales Office
  Office of the Chief Medical Officer
  Social Services Inspectorate for Wales
- **Government Departments Scotland**
  The Scottish Executive
  The Scottish Executive Enterprise and Lifelong Learning Department
  The Scottish Executive Education Department
  The Scottish Executive Justice Department
  The Scottish Executive Health Department
  Non-Departmental Public Bodies
- **Government Departments Northern Ireland**
  The Northern Ireland Office
  Department of Health, Social Services and Public Safety
  Department for Social Development

Government Departments for Wales, Scotland and Northern Ireland

GOVERNMENT DEPARTMENTS WALES

National Assembly for Wales

New Crown Bldg, Cathays Pk, Cardiff CF10 3NQ;
URL www.wales.gov.uk;
E-mail assembly.info@wales.gov.uk; Tel (Information Line) 029 2089 8200; (Switchboard) 029 2082 5111;
Fax 029 2089 8630

First Minister Rhodri Morgan
Deputy First Minister, Minister (Rural Development and Wales Abroad) Michael German, OBE
Minister (Economic Development) Andrew Davies
Minister (Education and Lifelong Learning) Jane Davidson
Minister (Health and Social Services) Jane Hutt
Minister (Open Government and Assembly Business) Carwyn Jones
Minister (Finance, Local Government and Public Services) Sue Essex
Minister (Environment, Planning and Countryside) Carwyn Jones
Minister (Culture, Welsh Language and Sport) Alun Pugh
Responsibility in Wales for health and personal social services; education except for terms and conditions of service of teachers, and for student awards; the Welsh language, arts and culture; local government; housing; water and sewerage; environmental protection; sport; agriculture and fisheries; forestry; land use, including town and country planning; countryside and nature conservation; new towns; ancient monuments and historic buildings; roads; tourism; training and the careers service; financial assistance to industry; urban programme in Wales; operations of the European Regional Development Fund in Wales and other European Community matters; non-departmental public bodies; civil emergencies and all financial aspects of these matters.

National Assembly's Training and Education Department

Director (Training and Education Department) (Grade 3) Richard J. Davies
Head (Youth Policy Division) Liz Williams
Head (Higher Education Division) Derek Adams
Head (Pupil Support Division) Alan Lansdown
Head (Schools Management Division) Elizabeth Taylor
Head (Standards and Performance Division) Keith Davies
Head (Lifelong Learning Division) Neil Thomas
Head (Training, Skills and Careers Policy Division) Richard Keveren
Head (Teaching and Leadership Division) Mike Harper

Care Standards Inspectorate for Wales (CSIW)

Heol Billingshey, Parc Nantgarw, Nantgarw, Nr Cardiff, CF15 7QZ; URL www.wales.gov.uk/csiw;
E-mail csiw_national_office@wales.gsi.gov.uk; Tel 01443 848450

Chief Executive Rob Pickford
Responsible for the regulation of social care, early years and private and voluntary health care in Wales.

Establishment Group

Director (Personnel Management) (Grade 3) P.R. Gregory
Counsel General W. Roddick
Senior Economic Adviser (Grade 5) M. Phelps
Chief Statistician (Grade 5) K. Chamberlain
Contact (Personnel Management) (Grade 5) S. Rees
Contact (Welsh Historic Monuments–Executive Agency) (Grade 5) T. Cassidy
Contact (Management Services) (Grade 5) R. Hughes

Finance Group

Principal Finance Officer (Grade 3) David Richards;
E-mail david.richards@wales.gsi.gov.uk
Finance Services (Grade 5) Laurie Pavelin;
E-mail laurie.pavelin@wales.gsi.gov.uk

Health Protection and Improvement Directorate

Chief Medical Officer (Grade 3) Dr R. Hall
Chief Dental Officer P. Langmaid
Chief Scientific Adviser Dr J.A.V. Pritchard
Deputy Chief Pharmaceutical Adviser C.M.W. Howells

Local Government (Welsh Office)

Head of Group (Grade 3) A. Peat
Local Government Finance Division (Grade 5) M. Chown
Social Care Policy Division (Grade 5) M.J. Shanahan
Housing Department (Grade 5) J. Bader
Social Services Inspectorate G. Williams

NHS Wales Department

Director Ann Lloyd; E-mail ann.lloyd@wales.gsi.gov.uk
Head (Central Support Team) Tim Kirby;
E-mail tim.kirby@wales.gsi.gov.uk
Head (NHS Performance, Quality and Regulation) John Hill-Tout; E-mail john.hilltout@wales.gsi.gov.uk

Head (NHS Finance Division)   Vacancy; Tel 029 2082 3137
Head (NHS Human Resources Division) (Grade 4)   Mr S.
  Redmond; E-mail stephen.redmond@wales.gsi.gov.uk
Head (Primary and Community Health Division)
  John Sweeney (Acting);
  E-mail john.sweeney3@wales.gsi.gov.uk
*Head (Health Information, Management and Technology and
  Estates) (Grade 5)*   John Morgan;
  E-mail john.morgan@wales.gsi.gov.uk
Head (Family Health Division)   R. Kennedy
Head (Health Information, Management Technology and Estates)
  John Skinner; E-mail protem113@wales.gsi.gov.uk
Head (NHS Quality Division)   B. Fuge
Head (NHS Health Services Policy)   J. Gregory
Chief Nursing Officer   Rosemary Kennedy;
  E-mail rosemary.kennedy@wales.gsi.gov.uk

REGIONAL DIRECTORS

North Wales   Derek Griffin Regional Office responsible for:
  Conwy, Denbighshire, Flintshire, Gwynedd, Isle of
  Anglesey, Wrexham.
Bromfield Hse, Queens La, Bromfield Ind Est, Mold,
  CH7 1XB; Tel 01352 706945
South East Wales   Sonia Mills Regional Office responsible
  for: Blaenau Gwent, Caerphilly, Cardiff, Merthyr Tydfil,
  Monmouthshire, Newport, Rhondda Cynon Taff,
  Torfaen, Vale of Glamorgan.
2nd Fl, Brecon Hse, Mamhilad Park Est, Pontypool,
  NP4 0YP; Tel 01495 758042
Mid and West Wales   Stuart Marples Regional Office
  responsible for: Bridgend, Carmarthenshire,
  Ceredigion, Neath Port Talbot, Pembrokeshire,
  Powys, Swansea.
2nd Fl, St. David's Hospital, Jobswell Rd, Carmarthen,
  Carmarthenshire SA31 3YH; Tel 01267 225225

National Public Health Service

c/o Velindre NHS Trust, Velindre Rd, Whitchurch, Cardiff
  CF4 2TL; URL www.nphs.wales.nhs.uk; Tel 029 2061
  5888
Director   Dr Cerilan Rogers
Regional Director of Public Health (South East Wales)
  Dr Sharon Hopkins
Regional Director of Public Health (Mid and West Wales)
  Dr William Richie
Regional Director of Public Health (North Wales)
  Dr Sandra Payne
From the 31st March 2003, the five Health Authorities in
Wales were dissolved. Their work and resources have been
transferred to this single organisation covering the whole of
Wales.

The Wales Office

Gwydyr Hse, Whitehall, London SW1A 2ER; Tel 020 7270
  0549; Fax 020 7270 0561
Secretary of State for Wales   The Rt Hon Peter Hain, MP
Parliamentary Under-Secretary of State   Don Touhig, MP
The Secretary of State for Wales is the member of the UK
cabinet who takes the lead in matters connected with the
Government of Wales Act and the transfer of functions to
the Assembly. The Secretary of State is responsible for
consulting the Assembly on the government's legislative
programme. Parliament will vote the Main Estimate for
Wales to the Secretary of State – he or she will pass it on to
the Assembly as a grant in aid.

Office of the Chief Medical Officer

Chief Medical Officer   Dr Ruth Hall;
  E-mail ruth.hall@wales.gsi.gov.uk
Chief Dental Officer   Dr Paul Langmaid;
  E-mail paul.langmaid@wales.gsi.gov.uk

Deputy Chief Pharmaceutical Adviser
  Darwen Wynne-Howells;
  E-mail darwen.wynne-howells@wales.gsi.gov.uk
Chief Scientific Advisor   Vacancy; Tel 029 2082 3912
Chief Environmental Officer   Ronnie Alexander;
  E-mail ronnie.alexander@wales.gsi.gov.uk

Social Services Inspectorate for Wales (SSIW)

New Crown Bldg, Cathays Pk, Cardiff CF10 3NQ;
  Tel (Information Line) 029 2089 8200; (Switchboard) 029
  2082 5111; Fax 029 2089 8630
Chief Inspector   Graham Williams
Deputy Chief Inspector (Services for Adults and Resources)
  Bob Woodward
Deputy Chief Inspector (Children and Family Services)
  Maria Michael
Deputy Chief Inspector (Inspection Unit)   Richard Tebboth
SSIW, through its inspection and development
programme, seeks to promote the provision by social
services authorities in Wales of high quality services to
service users and carers. These should be based on
consistent standards of professional practice and should
satisfy the test of Best Value. SSIW does not adjudicate on
outcomes of individual cases as concerns about these
should be referred to the local complaint process or to the
Local Ombudsman in Wales.
SSIW also contributes its professional expertise and
practical experience of Management in social services
authorities to inform the development of the Assembly's
policies in this field.

GOVERNMENT DEPARTMENTS SCOTLAND

The Scottish Executive

St. Andrew's Hse, Edinburgh EH1 3DG;
  URL www.scotland.gov.uk; E-mail ceu@scotland.gov.uk;
  Tel 0131 556 8400
First Minister   Jack McConnell, MSP
  Responsible for the development, implementation and
  presentation of Scottish Executive policies. Responsible
  for home affairs, including civil law and criminal justice,
  criminal justice social work services, police, fire and
  prisons.
*Deputy First Minister and Minister (Enterprise and Lifelong
  Learning)*   Jim Wallace, QC, MSP
  Responsible for justice, youth justice, victim support,
  criminal justice, social work, police, prisions, courts, law
  reform including civil law and fire services.
Deputy Minister (Enterprise and Lifelong Learning)
  Lewis Macdonald, MSP
  Deputy to the Minister for Enterprise and Lifelong
  Learning, with particular responsibility for training,
  further and higher education and the delivery of the
  new deal.
Minister (Education and Young People)   Peter Peacock, MSP
  Responsible for pre-school and school education,
  children and young people, culture and the arts, the
  built heritage, architecture, sport and lottery funding.
Deputy Minister (Education and Young People)
  Ewan Robson, MSP
  Deputy to the Minister for Children and Education with
  responsibility for pre-school and school education,
  children and young people.
Minister (Tourism, Culture and Sport)   Frank McAveety,
  MSP Responsible for culture and the arts, the built
  heritage, architecture, sport and lottery funding.

Minister (Justice)   Cathy Jamieson, MSP
   Responsible for the economy, business and industry
   including Scottish Enterprise, Highlands and Islands
   Enterprise, tourism, trade and inward investment,
   further and higher education, the science base, lifelong
   learning and training.
Minister (Health and Community Care)   Malcolm Chisholm,
   MSP
   Responsible for health policy, the National Health
   Service in Scotland, community care, and food safety.
Deputy Minister (Health and Community Care)
   Tom McCabe, MSP
   Deputy to the Minister for Health and Community Care
   with particular responsibility for community care.
Minister (Parliamentary Business)   Patricia Ferguson, MSP
   Responsible for Parliamentary Affairs and the
   management of Executive business in the Parliament.
   Labour Business Manager.
Deputy Minister (Parliamentary Business)   Tavish Scott, MSP
   Deputy to the Minister for Parliament, with particular
   responsibility for the Parliamentary handling of the
   legislative programme. Liberal Democrat Business
   Manager.
Minister (Environment and Rural Development)   Ross Finnie,
   MSP
   Responsible for policy in relation to rural development,
   including agriculture, fisheries and forestry,
   environment and natural heritage.
Deputy Minister (Environment and Rural Development)
   Allan Wilson, MSP
   Deputy to the Minister for Rural Development with
   particular responsibility for fisheries, forestry and
   research. Assists the Minister for Rural Affairs on policy
   in relation to rural development.
Minister (Communities)   Margaret Curran, MSP
   Responsible for social inclusion, local government and
   housing. Lead responsibility for Executive policy on
   equality issues and the voluntary sector.
Deputy Minister (Communities)   Mary Mulligan, MSP
   Deputy to the Minister for Communities with particular
   responsibility for social inclusion. Responsible for
   co-ordination of Executive policy on equality and the
   voluntary sector.
Minister (Transport)   Nicol Stephen, MSP
   Responsible for transport including the development for
   integrated transport policies, public transport, road and
   rail services, air and ferry services.
Minister (Finance and Public Services)   Andy Kerr, MSP
Deputy Minister (Finance and Public Services)
   Peter Peacock, MSP
   Responsible for Scottish Budget, public service delivery,
   modernising government, including civil service.
Lord Advocate   Colin Boyd, QC
   Legal advice to the Scottish Executive; prosecution in the
   Scottish criminal courts; tribunals.
Solicitor General   Elsh Angiolini
   Assists the Lord Advocate, with particular responsibility
   for prosecutions.

The Scottish Executive Enterprise and Lifelong Learning Department

Meridan Crt, Glasgow G2 6AT; Tel 0141 248 4774
Minister (Enterprise and Lifelong Learning)   Iain Gray, MSP
Deputy Minister   Lewis Macdonald, MSP; Tel 0131 244
   7005
Secretary and Head of Department   E.W. Frizzell, CB
Private Secretary to E.W. Frizzell   D. Sheldon; Tel 0141 242
   5704
Head (Lifelong Learning Group)   E. Weeple; Tel 0141 242
   0206
Head (New Deal Group)   M.F. Foulis; Tel 0131 244 0777
Head of Division (Transitions to Work)   I. McGhee
Head of Division (New Deal)   A. MacLeod
The Scottish Executive Enterprise and Lifelong Learning

Department (SEELLD) Administer: Government policy for
industry and energy issues, enterprise, the new deal
initiative, lifelong learning, further and higher education
skills, training and qualifications and careers guidance.

The Scottish Executive Education Department

Victoria Quay, Edinburgh EH6 6QQ; Tel 0131 556 8400; 0845
   774 1741; Fax 0131 244 8240
Head of Department   Mike Ewart
Head (Schools Group)   Philip Rycroft; Tel 0131 244 7108
Head of Division (Schools Division)   Colin Reeves
Head of Division (Pupil Support and Inclusion)
   Joanna Young
Head of Division (New Educational Developments)
   Eleanor Emberson
Head of Division (Teachers' Division)   Donald Henderson
Head of Division (Additional Support Needs)   Mike Gibson
Head of Division (Qualifications, Assessment and Curriculum)
   Francesca Odowska
Head of Group (Tourism, Culture and Sport)   John Mason
Head of Division (Sports, Arts and Culture)   Bob Irvine
Head of Division (Tourism and Architectural Policy)
   John Brown
Head of Group (Children and Young People)   Colin MacLean
Head of Division (Children and Families)   Sarah Smith
Head of Division (Early Education and Childcare)   Val Cox
Head of Division (Young People and Looked-After Children)
   Rachel Gwyon
Head of Division (Information Analysis and Communication)
   Alan Johnston
Head of Group (Social Work Services Inspectorate)
   Angus Skinner
Head of Division (Social Work Services Inspectorate)
   Kate Vincent
HM Inspectorate of Education/HM Senior Chief Inspector
   Graham Donaldson
Chief Executive (Historic Scotland)   Graeme Munro

Early Education and Childcare Division

Divisional Contact   Fay Meharry;
   E-mail fay.meharry@scotland.gsi.gov.uk; Tel 0131 244
   0962; Fax 0131 244 0978

Children and Families Division

Divisional and Action Team   Anne Fraser;
   E-mail anne.fraser@scotland.gsi.gov.uk; Tel 0131 244
   0209; Fax 0131 244 0978
Sure Start Scotland is the responsibility of the Children and
Families Division.

Young People and Looked-after Children Division

Divisional Contact   Ian McDougall;
   E-mail ian.mcdougall@scotland.gsi.gov.uk; Tel 0131 244
   5410; Fax 0131 244 3547

Information Analysis and Communication Division

Divisional Contact   Douglas Ansdell;
   E-mail douglas.ansdell@scotland.gsi.gov.uk; Tel 0131
   244 0914; Fax 0131 244 5581

The Scottish Executive Justice Department

St. Andrew's Hse, Regent Rd, Edinburgh EH1 3DG;
   E-mail ps.jd@scotland.gov.uk; Tel 0131 244 2120
Private Secretary   S. Rogerson
Group Head   C.M. Baxter

Group Head M. Brannan
Group Head V. Macniven
Head of Division (Police Division 1) D. Henderson
Head of Division (Police Division 2) Vacancy
Head of Division (Fire Services) I.A. Snedden, OBE
Head of Division (Civil Contingencies) J.F. Rowell, OBE
Head of Division (Community Justice Services)
  Mrs E.Y. Carmichael
Head of Division (Criminal Justice) Dr R. Scott
Head of Division (Single Agency Project Team) I. Walford
Head of Division (Criminal Procedures) Mrs W.A. Dickson
Head of Division (Parole and Life Sentence Review) A.L. Quinn
Head of Division (Civil Law) Mrs R.N. Menlowe
Head of Division (Civil Justice and International) P. Cackette
Head of Division (Access to Justice and European Co-ordination)
  C. Irnrie
Head of Division (Judicial Appointments and Finance)
  D. Stewart

Scotland Prison Service

Calton Hse, 5 Redheughs Rigg, Edinburgh EH12 9HW;
  Tel 0131 556 8400
Chief Executive Tony Cameron
Director (Strategy and Business Performance) K. Thomson
Director (Human Resources) Miss B. Allison
Director (Rehabilitation and Care) A. Spencer
Director (Finance and Business Services) W. Pretswell
Director (Scottish Police College) L.D. Garbutt, QPM
Director (Training) R. Virtue
Operations Director (South and West) M. Duffy
Operations Director (North and East) P. Withers
Head (Communications) Tom Fox
HM Chief Inspector of Constabulary for Scotland
  Sir Roy Cameron, QPM, BA, MPhil
HM Chief Inspector of Prisons for Scotland Rev A. McLellan
HM Chief Inspector of Fire Services D. Davis, OBE
HM Inspector of Fire Services A. Whitton

The Scottish Executive Health Department

St. Andrew's Hse, Edinburgh EH1 3DE; Tel 0131 244 2440;
  Fax 0131 244 2162
Chief Executive Trevor Jones
Private Secretary Gill Wylie
Chief Medical Officer Dr E. Armstrong, FRCO(Ed),
  FRCP(Glas), FRCGP

Directorate of Strategy and Performance Management

Director (Strategy and Performance Management)
  Dr K. Woods
Assistant Secretary T. Teale

Directorate of Primary Care

Director (Primary Care) A. Robson
Assistant Secretary Wilma Dickson
Assistant Secretary Hamish Wilson
Principal E. Mitchell

Directorate of Finance

Director M.J. Aldinalse
Senior Principal D.J. Palmer
Principal C.A. Naldrett
Principal B. Crawford
Principal S. Melling

Human Resources Directorate

Director G. Marr
Assistant Director J.A. McGregor

Assistant Director Robin Naysmith
Principal Dr I. Clayden
Principal G. Selkirk

Clinical Resources and Audit Group

Assistant Secretary Elaine Tait
Chief Medical Officer Prof Sir David Carter
Chief Nursing Officer Anne Jarvie

Public Health Policy Division 1

Chief Medical Officer and Head (Public Health Policy Unit)
  Prof Sir David Carter
Under-Secretary N. Munro
Assistant Secretary J. Brown
Principal J. Niven
Principal A. Oliver
Principal F. Tyrell
Principal N. Kernohan

Public Health Policy Division 2

Senior Principal E. Mackay
Principal B. Callaghan

Pharmaceutical Services

Chief Pharmacist W. Scott
Deputy Chief Pharmacist (Senior Principal) P. Warrington

Scottish Public Pensions Agency

St. Margaret's Hse, 151 London Rd, Edinburgh EH8 7TG;
  Tel 0131 244 3339
Chief Executive Ralph Garden
*Director (Information Technology and Corporate Development
  Project Manager)* John Nelson
Manager (NHS Pension Scheme) G. Taylor
Director (Policy) G. Mowat
Director (HR and FM and STSS Manager) M. McDermott
Administration of NHS and teachers' pension schemes,
public services superannuation and premature retirement
compensation policy and legislation for local government,
NHS, teachers, DAFS, police and firemen's schemes, and
for minor pension schemes, general co-ordination and
divisional training.

Non-Departmental Public Bodies

Scottish Children's Reporters Administration

Ochil Hse, Spring Kerse Bus Pk, Stirling SK7 7XE;
  E-mail info@childrens-reports.org; Tel 01786 459500;
  Fax 01786 459532
Principal Reporter Alan Miller
Carries out the Principal Reporters statutory functions
relating to care and justice for children in the Scottish
Childrens Hearings System.

GOVERNMENT DEPARTMENTS NORTHERN IRELAND

The Northern Ireland Office

Secretary of State for Northern Ireland The Rt Hon Paul
  Murphy, MP
Minister of State Jane Kennedy, MP
Parliamentary Under Secretary Des Browne, MP

London Office
11 Millbank, London SW1P 4QE; Tel 020 7210 3000

Belfast
Castle Bldgs, Stormont, Belfast BT4 3SG; Tel 028 9052 0700

Department of Health, Social Services and Public Safety

Castle Buildings, Stormont, Belfast, BT4 3SJ;
URL www.dhsspsni.gov.uk; Tel 028 9052 0500; Fax 028 9052 0572
Minister   Angela Smith, MP
Permanent Secretary   Clive Gowdy, CB
Chief Executive (Health Estates)   Ronnie Brown
Manager (Planning and Resource Group)   Don Hill
Manager (Health and Personal Social Services)   Paul Simpson
Chief Medical Officer   Dr Henrietta Campbell
Chief Inspector (Social Services Inspectorate)   Paul Martin
Chief Nursing Officer   Judith Hill
Chief Dental Officer   Doreen Wilson
Chief Pharmaceutical Officer   Dr Norman Morrow

Department for Social Development

The Department for Social Development in Northern Ireland and its Agencies have a wide ranging remit with direct responsibility for, or exercising control over, a wide range of functions.
7th Fl, Churchill Hse, Victoria Sq, Belfast BT1 4SD;
URL www.dsdni.gov.uk; Tel 028 9056 9100; Fax 028 9056 9240
Minister   John Spellar; Tel 028 9056 9216; Fax 028 9056 9244
Permanent Secretary   J.G. Hunter; Tel 028 9056 9203; Fax 028 9056 9243
The department functions include: Urban Regeneration, Voluntary and Community Sector, Housing, Social Policy and Legislation, Social Security, Child Support, State, Occupational and Personal Pensions, Policy and Legislation.

URBAN REGENERATION AND COMMUNITY DEVELOPMENT

Deputy Secretary (Senior Civil Service)   J. McGrath
Director (Senior Civil Service) (Belfast Regeneration Office)   M. Thompson
Director (Senior Civil Service) (North West Development Office)   D. O'Hare
Director (Senior Civil Service) (Regional Development Office and Lands Service)   E. Hayes
Director (Voluntary and Community Unit)   D. Wall
Contact (Urban Regeneration Strategy Directorate)   H. Johnston

RESOURCES, HOUSING AND SOCIAL SECURITY GROUP

Deputy Secretary   D. Baker
Director (Housing)   D. Crothers
Director (Social Security Policy and Legislation)   J. O'Neill
Director (Personnel)   T. O'Reilly

CENTRAL POLICY AND CO-ORDINATION UNIT

Director   P. Angus

SOCIAL SECURITY OFFICES

Antrim
20 Castle St, Antrim, County Antrim BT41 4JE; Tel 028 9442 6500; Fax 028 9442 6555

Armagh
Crown Bldgs, Alexander Rd, Armagh, County Armagh BT61 7JH; Tel 028 3752 9777; Fax 028 3752 9726

Ballymena
Twickenham Hse, 59–71 Mount St, Ballymena, County Antrim BT43 6BT; Tel 028 2566 2700; Fax 028 2566 2777

Ballymoney
11 St. John St, Ballymoney, County Antrim BT53 6DT; Tel 028 2766 0100; Fax 028 2766 0147

Ballynahinch
18 Crossgar Rd, Ballynahinch, County Down BT24 8XP; Tel 028 9756 0500; Fax 028 9756 0555

Banbridge
Crown Bldgs, Castlewellen Rd, Banbridge, County Down BT32 4AZ; Tel 028 4062 0800; Fax 028 4062 0888

Bangor
Crown Bldgs, 110 Hamilton Rd, Bangor, BT20 4LS; Tel 028 9127 9500; Fax 028 9127 9095

Carrickfergus
Davys St, Carrickfergus, County Antrim BT38 8DJ; Tel 028 9335 1811; Fax 028 9335 6940

Coleraine
Crown Bldgs, Artillery Rd, Coleraine, County Londonderry BT52 2AA; Tel 028 7034 1000; Fax 028 7034 1126
Manager   Anne Smiley

Cookstown
38–40 Fairhill Rd, Cookstown, County Tyrone BT80 8AG; Tel 028 8676 8000; Fax 028 8676 8001

Corporation Street
24–42 Corporation St, Belfast, BT41 4JD; Tel 028 9025 1411

Downpatrick
9–11 Mount Cres, Downpatrick, County Down BT30 6AU; Tel 028 4461 1300; Fax 028 4461 1333

Dungannon
Crown Bldgs, 13 Thomas St, Dungannon, County Tyrone BT70 1EN; Tel 028 8775 4754; Fax 01868 754854

Enniskillen
Crown Bldgs, Queen Elizabeth Rd, Enniskillen, County Fermanagh BT74 7JD; Tel 028 6634 3333; Fax 028 6634 3211

Falls Road
19 Falls Rd, Belfast BT12 4PH; Tel 028 9054 2800

Foyle
Crown Buildings, Asylum Rd, Londonderry, County Londonderry BT48 7EA; Tel 028 7131 9500; Fax 028 7126 0105
Manager   Una Breslin
Manager   Linda Pollock

Holywood Road
106–108 Holywood Rd, Belfast BT4 1JU; Tel 028 9052 8900

Kilkeel
Newry St, Kilkeel, BT34 4DR; Tel 028 4176 1400; Fax 028 4176 1422

Larne
Crown Bldgs, 59 Pound St, Larne, County Antrim BT40 1SB; Tel 028 2826 3200; Fax 028 2826 3211

Limavady
9 Connell St, Limavady, County Londonderry BT49 0TZ; Tel 028 7776 0500; Fax 028 7776 0555
Manager   Gerry Carlin

3

Lisburn
71 Bow St, Lisburn, County Antrim BT28 1BB; Tel 028 9262 3333; Fax 028 9262 3400

Lisnagelvin
2 Crescent Rd, Londonderry, BT47 2NJ; Tel 028 7131 9300; Fax 028 7131 9407

Lurgan
Alexandra Cres, Lurgan, Craigavon, County Armagh BT66 6BB; Tel 028 3831 5600; Fax 028 3831 5666

Magherafelt
31 Station Rd, Magherafelt, County Londonderry BT45 5DJ; Tel 028 7930 2000; Fax 028 7931 5666

Newcastle
Crown Bldgs, 31 Valentia Pl, Newcastle, County Down BT33 OEJ; Tel 028 4372 1600; Fax 028 4372 1610

Newry
28 Canal St, Newry, County Down BT35 8GB; Tel 028 3026 5522; Fax 028 3022 53076

Newtownards
East St, Newtownards, County Down BT23 3EL; Tel 028 9181 2581; Fax 028 9052 8723

Omagh
Crown Bldgs, 7 Mountjoy Rd, Omagh, County Tyrone BT79 7BB; Tel 028 8225 4222; Fax 028 8225 4333

Portadown
Jervis St, Portadown, Craigavon, County Armagh BT62 3AD; Tel 028 3839 7200; Fax 028 3839 7223

Strabane
Urney Rd, Strabane, County Tyrone BT82 9BX; Tel 028 7138 1000; Fax 028 7138 1053; Minicom 028 7138 1053

EXECUTIVE AGENCIES

Northern Ireland Child Support Agency
Gt Northern Tower, 17 Gt Victoria St, Belfast, BT2 7AD; Tel 0845 713 9896 (Customer Helpline)
Area Offices are located at the following Social Security Offices: Antrim; Corporation Street; Falls Road; Foyle; Holywood Road; Newry; Omagh.

Northern Ireland Social Security Agency
1st Fl, Churchill Hse, Belfast BT1 4SS; URL www.ssani.gov.uk
Chief Executive Chris Thompson

Allied Government Departments and Offices

4

- The Office of the Deputy Prime Minister
- Other Government and Public Offices England
- Other Government and Public Offices Wales
- Other Government and Public Offices Scotland
- Other Government and Public Offices Northern Ireland

Allied Government Departments and Offices

THE OFFICE OF THE DEPUTY PRIME MINISTER

26 Whitehall, London SW1A 2WH;
  URL www.odpm.gov.uk; Tel 020 7944 4400
Deputy Prime Minister and First Secretary of State
  The Rt Hon John Prescott, MP
Minister (Local Government and the Regions)
  The Rt Hon Nick Raynsford, MP
Minister (Regeneration and Regional Development)
  The Rt Hon Lord Jeff Rooker
Parliamentary Under Secretary of State Phil Hope, MP
Parliamentary Under Secretary of State Yvette Cooper, MP
The Office of the Deputy Prime Minister (ODPM) is responsible for the following policy areas: Housing, Homelessness, Planning, Fire, Health and Safety, Local Government and Local Government Finance, Regional Policy, Regional Co-ordination, Neighbourhood Renewal, Sustainable Communities, Urban Policy, and Social Exclusion.

Corporate Strategy and Resources Directorate

Director Peter Unwin
The Corporate Strategy and Resources Directorate provides policy advice to the Deputy Prime Minister on a wide range of issues in liaison with other government departments. In particular, the directorate supports the Deputy Prime Minister on devolution, English regional policy, international and environmental issues (including climate change), and on matters of public expenditure. It is also responsible for Finance, Corporate Business and Delivery, Human Resources and Information Management.

Analysis and Research Directorate

Eland Hse, Bressenden Pl, London SW1E 5DU
Deputy Director Vacancy

CENTRAL ECONOMIC ADVICE DIVISION

Divisional Manager Michael Kell
Provides economic advice.

RESEARCH ANALYSIS AND EVALUATION DIVISION

Contact Waqar Ahmad
Chief Social Scientist: Adviser to the department on social science issues; HOP Social Research Officer; management of housing and urban research programme; research-based advice and support to housing, homlessness, urban and planning policies; co-ordination of RAE work for urban environment and personnel. ODPM research management; ODPM policy evaluation and research responsibility; social research capacity; strategic research overview.

Housing, Homelessness and Planning Group

Eland Hse, Bressenden Pl, London SW1E 5DU
Director General Genie Turton

Equality and Diversity Unit

Eland Hse, Bressenden Pl, London SW1E 5DU
Divisional Manager Shelagh Prosser
To help the ODPM meet the aim of achieving diversity in employment practices, policies, programmes and service delivery.

Local and Regional Government Group

Eland Hse, Bressenden Pl, London SW1E 5DU
Director General Neil Kinghan
Responsible for Local Government Performance, Local Government Practice, Local Government Finance, Regional Policy and Local Governance and Fire, Health and Safety.

Fire, Health and Safety Directorate

Portland Hse, Stag Pl, London SW1E 5LP
Director Clive Norris
Divisional Manager (Built Environment Division)
  Paul Everall
Divisional Manager (Fire Policy Division) Diana Kahn
Divisional Manager (Fire Research Division) David Peace
Responsibility for: building regulations to ensure the health and safety of people in and around buildings, by providing functional requirements for building design and construction. Environmental issues relevant to the construction industry are promoted through the Regulations, for example improving energy efficiency. The Regulations also contribute to meeting the needs of disabled people.

HM FIRE SERVICE INSPECTORATE

Portland Hse, Stag Pl, London SW1E 5LP
Chief Inspector of the Fire Service Graham Meldrum
The role of the Fire Service Inspectorate is to inspect all fire brigades in England and Wales to ascertain how they are discharging their functions under the Fire Services Act 1947 and the Fire Precautions Act 1971 and meeting their responsibilities under the Health and Safety at Work Act, Equal Opportunities Act and other relevant legislation.

Local Government Directorate of Practice

Divisional Manager (Local Government Capacity and Modernisation Division) Geoff Tierney
Divisional Manager (Local Government Intervention Division) Robert Whittaker
Divisional Manager (Local Government Regional Team) Vacancy

Local Government Finance Directorate

Ashdown Hse, 123 Victoria St, London SW1E 6DE
Director Bob Linard
Divisional Manager (Modernisation and Grant Distribution Division) Robert Davies
Divisional Manager (Taxation, Valuation and General Division) Andrew Morrison
Divisional Manager (Statistics, Payments and IT Division) Meg Green
Divisional Manager (Capital Finance and Accountancy Advice Division) Pam Williams
Divisional Manager (Local Government Pensions Division) Terry Crossley

Local Government Performance Unit

Director Philip Ward
Divisional Manager (Local Government Legislation Division) Kevin Lloyd
Divisional Manager (Local Government Public Service Agreements Division) Richard Gibson
Divisional Manager (Local Government Quality and Performance Division) Richard Footitt
The LGPU has been created to handle the significant new responsibilities for improved local government performance flowing from the Local Government White Paper. It will ensure the ODPM's readiness to handle the first round of Comprehensive Performance Assessments of County and Unitary Authorities by the Audit Commission.

Regional Policy and Local Governance Directorate

Director Richard Allen
Divisional Manager (Democracy and Local Government Division) Paul Rowsell
Divisional Manager (Regional Economic Performance Division) Philip Cox
Contact (Regional Assemblies Division) Ian Scotter
RPLG's responsibilities are: to develop and deliver Ministers' policies on regional governance in England; to co-ordinate the customer role for ODPM vis-a-vis the Government Offices and the Regional Co-ordination Unit; to advise Ministers on the regional aspects of policy generally, including ODPM PSA 2 on regional economic performance.

Neighbourhood Renewal Unit

Eland Hse, Bressenden Pl, London SW1E 5DU
Director General Joe Montgomery
Promoting effective and joined-up policy making across Whitehall Departments to meet the ambitious deprivation-related targets and commitments for the National Strategy for Neighbourhood Renewal.

Neighbourhood Renewal Operations Directorate

Director Alan Riddell
Divisional Manager (Neighbourhood Renewal Implementation Division) Jon Bright
Divisional Manager (Neighbourhood Renewal Programmes Division) Graham Duncan
Contact (Neighbourhood Renewal Research Division) Raj Patel
Government and communities transforming neighbourhoods.

Neighbourhood Renewal Strategy Directorate

Director Lindsay Bell
Divisional Manager (Neighbourhood Renewal Delivery Division) Vacancy
Divisional Manager (Neighbourhood Renewal Communications Division) Sarah Clifford
Divisional Manager (Whitehall Advice and Co-ordination Division) Martin Joseph
Delivery of PSA1. To monitor and help departments on floor targets for deprived areas and to encourage mainstreaming.

Regional Co-ordination Unit (RCU)

Riverwalk Hse, 157–161 Millbank, London SW1P 4RR
Director General Rob Smith
The RCU has four key aims: better co-ordination of area-based initiatives; greater involvement of the Government Offices (GOs) in policy making; making the GOs the key representatives of Government in the regions; and establishing the RCU as the unified head office for the GOs.

Government Offices for the Regions

The Government Offices are key agents of Government for the English Regions, aiming to ensure effective delivery of Government programmes regionally and locally. Work with regional partners, including local authorities, Regional Development Agencies and other organisations.
Aiming to bring together the activities and interests of different Government departments within a single organisation, the Government Offices.

GOVERNMENT OFFICE FOR THE EAST OF ENGLAND

Eastbrook, Shaftesbury Rd, Cambridge, Cambridgeshire CB2 2DF; URL www.go-east.gov.uk; Tel 01223 372500; Fax 01223 372501
Regional Director Caroline Bowdler
Areas of responsibility
Bedfordshire; Cambridgeshire; Essex; Hertfordshire; Norwich; Suffolk

GOVERNMENT OFFICE FOR THE EAST MIDLANDS

The Belgrave Centre, Stanley Pl, Talbot St, Nottingham NG1 5GG; URL www.go-em.gov.uk; Tel 0115 971 9971; Fax 0115 971 2404
Regional Director Jane Todd
Areas of responsibility
Derbyshire; Leicestershire; Lincolnshire; Northamptonshire; Nottinghamshire; Rutland

GOVERNMENT OFFICE FOR LONDON

Riverwalk Hse, 157–161 Millbank, London SW1P 4RR; URL www.go-london.gov.uk; Tel 020 7217 3328; Fax 020 7217 3450
Regional Director Liz Meek
Areas of responsibility
Greater London

GOVERNMENT OFFICE FOR THE NORTH EAST

Welbar Hse, Gallowgate, Newcastle upon Tyne, Tyne and Wear NE1 4TD; URL www.go-ne.gov.uk; Tel 0191 201 3300; Fax 0191 202 3830
Regional Director Jonathon Blackie
Areas of responsibility
Cleveland; Durham; Northumbria; Tyne and Wear

GOVERNMENT OFFICE FOR THE NORTH WEST

Sunley Tower, Piccadilly Plaza, Manchester M1 4BE;
URL www.go-nw.gov.uk; Tel 0161 952 4000; Fax 0161 952 4099

Cunard Bldg, Pier Head, Water St, Liverpool, Merseyside L3 1QB; Tel 0151 224 6300; Fax 0151 224 6470

Regional Director   Keith Barnes

Areas of responsibility

Cheshire; Cumbria; Greater Manchester; Knowsley; Lancashire; Liverpool; Sefton; St. Helens; The Wirral

GOVERNMENT OFFICE FOR THE SOUTH EAST

Bridge Hse, 1 Walnut Tree Cl, Guildford, Surrey GU1 4GA; URL www.go-se.gov.uk; Tel 01483 882255; Fax 01483 882259

Regional Director   Paul Martin

Areas of responsibility

Buckinghamshire; Oxfordshire; Berkshire; Hampshire; Isle of Wight; West Sussex; East Sussex; Surrey; Kent

GOVERNMENT OFFICE FOR THE SOUTH WEST

2 Rivergate, Temple Quay, Bristol BS1 6ED;
URL www.gosw.gov.uk; Tel 0117 900 1700; Fax 0117 900 1900

Mast Hse, Shepherds Wharf, 24 Sutton Rd, Plymouth, PL4 0HJ; URL www.gosw.gov.uk; Tel 01752 635000; Fax 01752 227647

Castle Hse, Pydar St, Truro, Cornwall TR1 2UD; Tel 01872 264500; Fax 01872 264503

Regional Director   Jane Henderson

Areas of responsibility

Bath; Bournemouth; Bristol; Cornwall; Devon; Dorset; Gloucestershire; Isles of Scilly; Poole; Somerset; Swindon; Wiltshire

GOVERNMENT OFFICE FOR THE WEST MIDLANDS

77 Paradise Circus, Queensway, Birmingham, West Midlands B1 2DT; URL www.go-wm.gov.uk; Tel 0121 212 5050; Fax 0121 212 1010

Regional Director   Graham Garbutt

Areas of responsibility

Metropolitan Districts of Birmingham, Coventry, Dudley, Sandwell, Solihull, Walsall and Wolverhampton; the Unitary Authorities of Stoke-on-Trent and Telford and Wrekin; the Counties of Warwickshire, Staffordshire, Shropshire, Herefordshire and Worcestershire

GOVERNMENT OFFICE FOR YORKSHIRE AND THE HUMBER

City Hse, New Station St, Leeds, West Yorkshire LS1 4US; URL www.goyh.gov.uk; Tel 0113 280 0600; Fax 0113 283 6394

25 Queen St, Leeds, West Yorkshire LS1 2TW

Regional Director   Felicity Everiss

Areas of responsibility

The Humber; North Yorkshire; South Yorkshire; West Yorkshire

Social Exclusion Unit

Eland Hse, London SW1E 5DU;
URL www.socialexclusionunit.gov.uk; Tel 020 7276 2055

Director   Claire Taylor

Divisional Manager (Business Development Division and Impacts and Trends Division)   Sally Burlington

Divisional Manager (Business Development Division and Impacts and Trends Division)   Vanessa Scarborough

Divisional Manager (Children in Care Division)   Cath Shaw

Divisional Manager (External Relations Division and Implementation Division)   Jos Joures

Divisional Manager (Transport and Social Exclusion Division and Employment and Enterprise Division)   Marcus Bell

Divisional Manager (Mental Health Division)   Ruth Stanier

The Social Exclusion Unit remit is to help improve government action to reduce social exclusion by producing 'joined-up solutions to joined-up problems'. It works mainly on specific projects, chosen following consultation with other ministers and suggestions from interested groups.

Legal Group

Eland Hse, Bressenden Pl, London SW1E 5DU

Director General   David Hogg

Director (Legal Directorate)   Sandra Unerman
Responsibility for: the provision of legal services on Housing, Planning, Homelessness, Urban Policy, Local Government, Devolution, Regional Government, Neighbourhood Renewal, Fire and Safety, Commercial and Establishment matters.

Divisional Manager (Employment and Commercial)   Fred Croft
Responsibility for: the provision of legal advice on procurement and other contract and commercial matters; Employment Matters (including litigation): TUPE; Data Protection: Freedom of Information; and Health and Safety.

Divisional Manager (Constitutional and Regional Government)   Donatella Phillips
Responsibilty for: devolution, human rights co-ordination, regional development, regional government and compulsory purchase.

Divisional Manager (Legislative Unit)   David Ingham

Residential Property Tribunal Service

Senior President   Siobhan McGrath

The Residential Property Tribunal Service serves the private rented and leasehold housing market in England by providing an accessible, efficient and informal tribunal service which enables disputes between parties to be settled simply and quickly.

OTHER GOVERNMENT AND PUBLIC OFFICES ENGLAND

Acas

Brandon Hse, 180 Borough High St, London SE1 1LW;
URL www.acas.org.uk

Chair   Rita Donaghy

Head (Mediation)   Terry Lippiatt

Head (Communication)   Mary-Ann Auckland

See local phone book for nearest Acas office.

Armed Forces Social Work

Royal Air Force

Wing Commander RAF Community Support, Headquarters Personnel and Training Command, Gloucestershire GL3 1EZ; URL rafcom.co.uk; E-mail cspt@gtnet.gov.uk

The Naval Personal and Family Service (NPFS)

Office of the Second Sea Lord and Commander-in-Chief, Naval Home Command, Portsmouth PO1 3LS; Tel 023 9272 7254; Fax 023 9272 0086
Assistant Director (NPFS) Capt J.C. Scoles, OBE, MSc, DipSW, FInstMgt, Royal Navy
Employs naval and civilian qualified social work staff in support of the naval command system and to work with naval personnel and their families both in the UK and overseas. The majority of staff are based in the major RN port areas, i.e. Portsmouth, Plymouth and Faslane.

AREA OFFICES

Eastern Area

Swiftsure Block, HMS Nelson, Portsmouth PO1 3HH; Tel 023 9272 2712; 023 9272 3533
Area Officer (NPFS) East S. Owens-Cairns, MA, MSc, Dip in Applied Social Studies

Northern Area

Triton Hse, Churchill Sq, Helensburgh, Argyll and Bute G84 9HL; Tel 01436 672798
Area Officer (NPFS) North H. Muir, BSc, CQSW, DipAS

Western Area

Fenner Block, HMS Drake, Devonport, Devon PL2 2BG; Tel 01752 555041
Area Officer (NPFS) West Vacancy

Soldiers, Sailors, Airmen and Families Association (SSAFA – Forces Help)

Queen Elizabeth The Queen Mother Hse, 19 Queen Elizabeth St, London SE1 2LP; URL www.ssafa.org.uk; E-mail services-support@ssafa-forces-help.org.uk; Tel 020 7403 8783; Fax 020 7403 8815
Director (Social Work) R. Swindley
Enquiries (Staff Officer, Social Work) D. Toni
SSAFA–Forces Help employs British qualified social work staff to work with the families of service people based in the UK, western Europe, Gibraltar and Cyprus. In western Europe, SSAFA also operates as a registered adoption agency. In the UK, SSAFA social work staff are based at the larger Army garrisons and certain RAF stations and carry an advisory role.

Audit Commission

1 Vincent Sq, London SW1P 2PN; URL www.audit-commission.gov.uk; E-mail enquiries@audit-commission.gov.uk; Tel 020 7828 1212; Fax 020 7976 6187
Controller Steve Bundrel
Chair Jame Strachan
Deputy Chair Adrienne Fresko

Commission for Health Improvement

1st Fl, Finsbury Tower, 103–105 Bunhill Row, London EC1Y 8TG; URL www.chi.nhs.uk; Tel 020 7448 9200; Fax 020 7448 9222
Chief Executive Dr Peter Homa, CBE

Commission for Patient and Public Involvement in Health

PO Box 11442, Birmingham, West Midlands B2 4WP; URL www.cppih.org; E-mail communications@cppih.nhs.uk; Tel 0845 120 7111; Fax 0121 345 6130

Contact Laura McMurtrie
Contact Sharon Grant
The Commission for Patient and Public Involvement in Health was set up in January 2003. It is an independent, non-departmental public body, sponsored by the Department of Health, with a remit to ensure that the public is involved in decision making about health and the provision of health services.
It aims to ensure that the voices of both public and patients are heard in health matters. Working closely with a range of groups, including those who are already involved in healthcare, government and non-government organisations and the voluntary sector, the Commission is setting up Public and Patient Involvement (PPI) Forums across England.

East Anglia Region

Ground Fl, Block 7, The Westbrooke Centre, Cambridge CB4 1FA; Tel 0845 120 2093; Fax 0845 120 2094

East Midlands Region

5th Fl, Pearl Assurance Hse, Friar La, Nottingham NG1 6BT; Tel 0115 851 1300; Fax 0115 851 1388

London Region

Ground Fl, 163 Evershold St, London NW1 1BU; Tel 0207 788 4900; Fax 0207 788 4988

North East Region

Richmond Hse, Ground Fl, The Watermark, Metro Riverside Pk, Riverside Way, Gateshead NE11 9SZ; Tel 0191 448 4300; Fax 0191 448 4388

North West Region

4 Mandarin Crt, Centre Pk, Lakeside Dr, Warrington WA1 1GG; Tel 0192 554 3000; Fax 0192 554 3088

South East Region

Ground Fl, Victoria Hse, London Sq, Guildford NW1 1BU; Tel 0148 369 8000; Fax 0148 369 8088

South West Region

Lynx Hse, Pynes Hill Office Campus, Rydon La, Exeter EX2 7AN; Tel 0139 233 2100; Fax 0139 233 2188

West Midlands Region

9th Fl, Ladywood Hse, 45 Stephenson St, Birmingham B2 4DY; Tel 0121 222 4400; Fax 0121 222 4488

Yorkshire and Humberside Region

Nelson Hse, Quayside Bus Pk, George Mann Rd, Leeds LS10 1DJ; Tel 0113 227 2400; Fax 0113 227 2488

Connexions

Connexions Service National Unit, Department for Education and Skills, Moorfoot, Sheffield, S1 4PQ
Chief Executive Anne Weinstock
Contact (Government Office North East) Eric Bannister
Contact (Government Office North West) Tony McGee
Contact (Government Office Yorkshire and the Humber) Derek Ireland
Contact (Government Office West Midlands) John Robertson

Contact (Government Office East Midlands) Peter Ward
Contact (Government Office East of England) Roger Allen
Contact (Goverment Office London) Cheryl Rose
Contact (Government Office South West) Nita Murphy
Connexions is a Governmental advice and guidance service for 13–19 year olds.

Criminal Injuries Compensation

All applications for compensation for personal injury arising from crimes of violence in England, Scotland and Wales are dealt with at the locations shown below. (Separate arrangements apply in Northern Ireland). Applications received after 1 April 1996 are assessed under a Tariff-based Scheme, made under the Criminal Injuries Compensation Act 1995, by the Criminal Injuries Compensation Authority (CICA). There is a separate avenue of appeal to the independent Criminal Injuries Compensation Appeals Panel (CICAP).

Criminal Injuries Compensation Authority (CICA)

Morley Hse, 26–30 Holborn Viaduct, London EC1A 2JQ; URL www.cica.gov.uk; Tel 020 7842 6800; Fax 020 7436 0804
Chief Executive Howard Webber
Deputy Chief Executive Edward McKeown
Head (Legal Services) Anne M. Johnstone
Head (Communications) Alison Rothwell; Tel 020 7842 6808
Also at
Tay Hse, 300 Bath St, Glasgow, Scotland G2 4JR, Tel 0141 331 2726, Fax 0141 331 2287.

Criminal Injuries Compensation Appeals Panel (CICAP)

11th Fl, Cardinal Tower, 12 Farringdon Rd, London EC1M 3HS; URL www.cicap.gov.uk; E-mail info@cicap.gov.uk; Tel 020 7549 4600; Fax 020 7549 4643
Chair Roger Goodier
Deputy Chair Suzan Matthews, QC
Chief Executive and Secretary to the Panel Roy Burke

The Disability Rights Commission

Arndale Hse, Manchester M4 3AQ; URL www.drc-gb.org; Tel (Helpline) 08457 622633; Fax (Helpline) 08457 778878
Chair Bert Massie
Chief Executive Bob Niven
The Disability Rights Commission (DRC) is an independent body, established by an Act of Parliament to eliminate discrimination against disabled people and promote equality of opportunity.

Equal Opportunities Commission

Arndale Hse, Arndale Centre, Manchester M4 3EQ; URL www.eoc.org.uk; E-mail info@eoc.org.uk; Tel 0845 601 5901; Fax 0161 838 8303
Chair Julie Mellor
Chief Executive Caroline Slocock
Helpline 0900–1700 Monday to Friday.

General Social Care Council (GSCC)

General Social Care Council (GSCC), Goldings Hse, 2 Hay's La, London SE1 2HB; URL www.gscc.org.uk; E-mail info@gscc.org.uk; Tel 020 7397 5100
Chief Executive Lynne Berry
Chair Rodney Brooke

Government Actuary's Department

New King's Beam Hse, 22 Upper Ground, London SE1 9RJ; URL www.gad.gov.uk; E-mail <firstname>.<surname>@gad.gov.uk; Tel 020 7211 2600; Fax 020 7211 2630; 020 7211 2640
Government Actuary C.D. Daykin

Health and Safety Commission (HSC)

Rose Crt, 2 Southwark Bridge, London SE1 9HS; Tel 020 7717 6000; Fax 020 7717 6644
Chair Bill Callaghan
Secretary to the Commission Mark Dempsey
The Commission is responsible to the appropriate minister for the administration of the Health and Safety at Work etc Act 1974; it also reviews health and safety legislation and submits proposals for new or revised regulations. The HSC appointed, with effect from 1 January 1975, the three members of the HSC, a body corporate, which, together with its officers and servants, is responsible for implementing the provisions of the HSW Act 1974 and which reports to the Commission.

Health and Safety Executive (HSE)

Director General Timothy Walker
Deputy Director General (Operations) J. McCracken
Deputy Director General (Policy) Kate Timms
Director (Field Operations) Dr A. Ellis
Director (Hazardous Installations Directorate) Chris Willby
Director (Policy Group) Sandra Caldwell
Director (Policy Group) Nick Starling
Director (Railways Inspectorate) Alan Osborne
Director (Resources and Planning Directorate) V. Dews
Director (Nuclear Safety Directorate) L. Williams
Chief Executive (Health and Safety Laboratory) D. Buchanan
Director (Operational Policy Division) Phil Scott
Director (Corporate and Science Analytical Support Directorate) Dr Paul Davies
Director (Strategy and Intelligence Division) Brian Etheridge
The Health and Safety Executive is the HSC's major instrument. Through its inspectorates it enforces health and safety law in the majority of industrial premises, to protect both work-people and the public. The Executive advises the Commission in its major task of laying down safety standards through regulations and practical guidance for very large numbers of industrial processes, liaising as necessary with government departments and other institutions. The Executive is also the licensing authority for nuclear installations. In carrying out its functions the Executive acts independently of government guided only by the Commission as to general health and safety policy.

HSE MAIN OFFICES AND REGIONAL ORGANISATION

In each main office there are groups of inspectors and medical doctors specialising in specific industries to be found in the area. Each office will accept messages and enquiries for technical or interpreted advice, complaints, etc, which will be referred to the inspector/doctor as quickly as possible.

London and South East Regional Office

Rose Crt, 2 Southwark Bridge, London SE1 9HS; Tel 020 7717 6000

East and South East Regional Office

14 Cardiff Rd, Luton LU1 1PP; Tel 01582 444200; Fax 01582 444320

Midlands Regional Office

1 Hagley Rd, Birmingham, West Midlands B16 8HS;
Tel 0121 607 6200; Fax 0121 607 6349

Yorkshire and North East Regional Office

Marshall's Mill, Marshall St, Leeds, West Yorkshire
LS11 9YJ; Tel 0113 283 4200; Fax 0113 283 4382

North West Regional Office

Grove Hse, Skerton Rd, Manchester M16 0RB; Tel 0161 952
8200; Fax 0161 952 8222

Wales and West Regional Office

Phase 1, Government Bldgs, Ty Glas, Llanishen, Cardiff
CF14 5SH; Tel 029 2026 3000; Fax 029 2026 3120

Scotland Regional Office

Belford Hse, 59 Belford Rd, Edinburgh EH4 3UE; Tel 0131
247 2000; Fax 0131 247 2121

INFORMATION SERVICES

Public Enquiries

HSE Information Services, Caerphilly Business Pk,
Caerphilly CF83 3GG; URL www.hse.gov.uk;
E-mail hseinformationservices@natbrit.com; Tel 08701
545500; Fax 029 2085 9260; Minicom 029 2080 8537

National Care Standards Commission

Headquarters, St. Nicholas Bldg, St. Nicholas St, Newcastle
upon Tyne, NE1 1NB; URL www.carestandards.org.uk;
Tel 0191 233 3600; Fax 0191 233 3569
Chair   Anne Parker
Chief Executive   Ron Kerr, CBE
Director (Children's Rights)   Roger Morgan, OBE
Director (Adult Services)   Heather Wing, OBE
Director (Private and Voluntary Health Care)   Ros Gray
Director (Corporate Policy)   Patricia Davis
Director (Legal)   Richard Slack
Director (Finance)   Terence McCrady
The National Care Standards Commission was established
in April 2002 as a non-departmental public body to take on
the regulation of Social Care and private and voluntary
health care in England. As an executive non-departmental
public body, the NCSC has some independence from the
Department of Health, with an independent Chair, Chief
Executive and Board. The Commission is set targets and is
monitored by the Department of Health Ministers.
Inspectors and support staff have transferred from Health
Authorities and local authorities to the NCSC to regulate
the following services: Care Homes, Children's Homes,
Domiciliary Care Agencies, Residential Family Centres,
Voluntary Adoption Agencies, Independent Fostering
Agencies, Private and Voluntary Hospitals and Clinics,
Nurses' Agencies and Day Centres. It also inspects: local
authority fostering, local authority adoption and welfare
aspects of boarding schools. The Commission regulates and
inspects these services against national minimum
standards. The Commission also investigates complaints
against registered services and reports to the Secretary of
State on the range and quality of regulated services.
For a list of offices in your region contact the Commission
directly or visit its website.

Office for National Statistics

1 Drummond Gate, London SW1V 2QQ;
URL www.statistics.gov.uk;
E-mail info@statistics.gov.uk; Tel 020 7533 6261; Fax 020
7533 5880

Ombudsmen

Commission for Local Administration in England (The Local Government Ombudsmen)

Millbank Tower, Millbank, London SW1P 4QP;
URL www.lgo.org.uk;
E-mail enquiries.london@lgo.org.uk; Tel 020 7217 4620;
Fax 020 7217 4621; Telex DX 2376 Victoria 1
Chair and Local Government Ombudsman   Tony Redmond
Responsibility for: London boroughs north of the River
Thames (including Richmond but not Harrow or Tower
Hamlets), Essex, Kent, Surrey, Suffolk, East and West
Sussex, Hertfordshire, Buckinghamshire, Berkshire and
Coventry City.
Vice-Chair and Local Government Ombudsman
Patricia Thomas
Resposible for: Cheshire, Derbyshire, Nottinghamshire,
Lincolnshire, and the North of England (except the cities
of York and Lancaster).
Beverley Hse, 17 Shipton Rd, York YO30 5FZ; Tel 01904
663200; Fax 01904 663269
Local Government Ombudsman   Jerry White
Responsible for: London boroughs south of the River
Thames and Harrow, the cities of York and Lancaster;
and the rest of England not covered by Mr Redmond
and Mrs Thomas.
The Oaks No2, Westwood Way, Coventry, West Midlands
CV4 8JB; Tel 024 7669 5999; Fax 024 7669 5902
The Commission, established under the Local Government
Act 1974, investigates complaints from citizens alleging
injustice caused by maladministration by local authorities.
There are three local commissioners (local government
ombudsmen) each of whom investigates complaints arising
in a particular area of the country. A free booklet about the
service is called 'Complaint about the council? How to com-
plain to the Local Government Ombudsman', available from
council offices, citizens' advice bureaux or direct from the
Commission's offices. The local government ombudsmen can
investigate complaints about education matters. Education
matters form about 9% of the total number of complaints
received and about 26% of reports issued by the ombudsmen. Reports of investigations of education complaints are
available from the Commission's offices in London.

Parliamentary Commissioner for Administration (Parliamentary Ombudsman) and Health Service Commissioner for England and Wales (Health Service Ombudsman)

Millbank Tower, Millbank, London SW1P 4QP;
URL www.ombudsman.org.uk;
E-mail opca.enquiries@ombudsman.gsi.gov.uk; Tel 0845
015 4033; Fax 020 7217 4947
Health Service Ombudsman (Wales), 5th Fl, Capital Tower,
Greyfriars Rd, Cardiff CR1 3AG; Tel 0845 601 0987;
Fax 029 2022 6909
The Parliamentary Ombudsman investigates complaints
from individuals, which must be referred by a Member of
Parliament, that they have suffered an injustice caused by
maladministration on the part of central government depart-
ments, agencies and certain non-departmental public bodies.
The Health Service Ombudsman considers complaints
from members of the public about the National Health
Service (NHS) which have not been dealt with to the
satisfaction of the complainant by the body concerned. The
Ombudsman is completely independent of the NHS and
Government. Complaints may be about hospitals, family
health services, ancillary services such as physiotherapy,
and actions arising from the clinical judgement of
practitioners. The Ombudsman also considers complaints
about failures to provide information.
The complaint needs to be taken up locally first. Most
complaints are settled quickly this way. Complaints to the
Ombudsman should be made no later than a year from the
date of the incident or from the date on which the complainant became aware that he or she had cause for complaint.

Women's National Commission

Cabinet Office, 35 Great Smith St, London SW1P 3BQ;
URL www.thewne.org.uk; E-mail wnc@cabinet-office.x.gsi.gov.uk
Chair   Baroness Crawley
Director   Janet Veitch
Remit
To ensure that the informed opinions of women are given their due weight in the deliberations of government.

Youth Justice Board for England and Wales

11 Carteret St, London SW1H 9DL;
URL www.youth-justice-board.gov.uk; Tel 020 7271 3033; Fax 020 7271 3030
Chair   Vacancy
Chief Executive   Mark Perfect
The Youth Justice Board for England and Wales is an executive non-departmental public body. The aim of the Youth Justice Board is to prevent offending by children and young people. It delivers this by: preventing crime and the fear of crime; identifying and dealing with young offenders; reducing re-offending.
The Youth Justice System comprises Youth Offending Teams, the police, youth courts and the institutions in which young people are held in custody.

OTHER GOVERNMENT AND PUBLIC OFFICES WALES

Equal Opportunities Commission

Windsor Hse, Windsor La, Cardiff CF10 3GE; Tel 029 2034 3552; Fax 029 2064 1079
A Public Body set up by Parliament in 1975. It works to remove unlawful discrimination on grounds of sex and to promote equal opportunities for women and men.

Health Commission Wales

The Stables, Hensol Hospital, Pontyclun, CF72 8YS;
Tel 01656 753009
This organisation was established on 1st April 2003 to plan and pay for certain specialised health services across Wales. These include cardiac surgery, emergency ambulance services and some children's services.

Ombudsmen

Commission for Local Administration in Wales

Derwen Hse, Court Rd, Bridgend CF31 1BN;
URL www.ombudsman-wales.org;
E-mail enquiries@ombudsman-wales.org; Tel 01656 661325; Fax 01656 673279
Ombudsman   Vacancy

Health Service Commissioner for Wales

5th Fl, Capital Tower, Greyfriars Rd, Cardiff CF10 3AG;
URL www.ombudsman.org.uk;
E-mail whsc.enquiries@ombudsman.gsi.gov.uk; Tel 029 2039 4621

Care Council for Wales/Cyngor Gofal Cymru

6th Fl, West Wing, South Gate Hse, Wood St, Cardiff CF10 1EW; URL www.ccwales.org.uk;
E-mail info@ccwales.org.uk; Tel 029 2022 6257; Fax 029 2038 4764
Chief Executive   Rhian Huws Williams
The Care Council has the responsibility for: agreeing codes of practice which apply to social care workers and employers across the social care sector; setting up a register of social care workers to improve public protection, making sure that registrants found unfit to work in the sector are prevented from working in the sector; ascertaining training needs and promoting training across the social care sector; regulating social work qualifying and post qualifying training.

4

OTHER GOVERNMENT AND PUBLIC OFFICES SCOTLAND

Criminal Injuries Compensation Authority

Tay Hse, 300 Bath St, Glasgow G2 4LN;
URL www.cica.gov.uk; Tel 0141 331 2726; Fax 0141 331 2287
Chief Executive   H. Webber
Deputy Chief Executive   E. McKeown

Mental Welfare Commission for Scotland

K Fl, Argyle Hse, 3 Lady Lawson St, Edinburgh EH3 9SH;
Tel 0131 222 6111; Fax 0131 222 6112; 0131 222 6113
Chair   Ian Miller, OBE
Director   Dr J.A.T. Dyer, MBchB, MRCPsych
Secretary   Alison McRae
Assistant Secretary   C.L. Burns
Aims to protect the mentally disordered by the investigation of irregularities, by visiting patients and by reporting to the appropriate authorities.

Ombudsmen

Scottish Public Services Ombudsman

4–6 Melvile St, Edinburgh EH3 7NS;
URL www.scottishombudsman.org.uk;
E-mail enquiries@scottishombudsman.org.uk; Tel 0870 011 5378; Fax 0870 011 5379
Ombudsman   Prof Alice Brown
Deputy   Eric Drake
Jurisdiction over the functions of the Scottish Executive, NDPBs, Local Government, Health Service and Housing Associations.

The Scottish Commission for the Regulation of Care (The Care Commission)

Compass Hse, 11 Riverside Dr, Dundee DD1 4NY;
URL www.carecommission.com; Tel 01382 207100;
Fax 01382 207 289
Chief Executive   Jacquie Roberts
Director (Operations)   David Wiseman
The Scottish Care Commission, sponsored by Health Ministers, became operational from 1 April 2002. It was set up by the Regulation of Care (Scotland) Act 2001 to regulate a wide range of care services affecting around 500,000 people in Scotland.

The Scottish Social Services Council

Compass Hse, 11 Riverside Dr, Dundee DD1 4NY;
URL www.sssc.uk.com; Tel 01382 207101; Fax 01382 207
215
Chief Executive Carole Wilkinson
The Scottish Social Services Council, sponsored by
Education Ministers, became operational on 1st October
2001. It was set up by the Regulation of Care (Scotland) Act
2001 to regulate the Social Services Workforce and their
education and training.

OTHER GOVERNMENT AND PUBLIC OFFICES NORTHERN IRELAND

Ombudsmen

Office of the Northern Ireland Ombudsman

Progressive Hse, 33 Wellington Pl, Belfast BT1 6HN;
URL www.ni-ombudsman.org.uk;
E-mail ombudsman@ni-ombudsman.org.uk; Tel 028
9023 3821; Fax 028 9023 4912

Northern Ireland Ombudsman T. Frawley
The Northern Ireland Ombudsman is a popular title for
two statutory offices: the Assembly Ombudsman for
Northern Ireland; and the Northern Ireland Commissioner
for Complaints. The Assembly Ombudsman investigates
complaints of alleged maladministration against Northern
Ireland government departments and their agencies. The
Commissioner for Complaints investigates complaints of
alleged maladministration against public bodies in
Northern Ireland.

Northern Ireland Social Care Council

7th Fl, Millennium Hse, 19–25 Great Victoria St, Belfast
BT2 7AQ; URL www.niscc.info;
E-mail info@niscc.n-i.nhs.uk; Tel 028 9041 7600; Fax 028
9041 7601
*Chief Executive (Non Departmental Public Body for Regulation
of Social Care)* Brendan Johnston
NISCC is the regulatory body for the social care
workforce in Northern Ireland. It registers social care
workers and regulates standards of practice, education
and training for everyone involved in social care
services.

Local Authority Associations

5

■ **Representative Bodies**

Local Authority Associations

Representative Bodies

Association of Directors of Social Services (ADSS)

URL www.adss.org.uk
President   David Behan
London Borough of Greenwich, Nelson Hse, 50 Wellington St, London SE18 6PY; Tel 020 8921 3059; Fax 020 8921 3112
Senior Vice-President   David Behan
London Borough of Greenwich, Nelson Hse, 50 Wellington St, London SE18 6PY; Tel 020 8921 3059; Fax 020 8921 3112
Honorary Secretary   Liz Railton
Essex County Council, PO Box 11, County Hall, Chelmsford, Essex CM1 1LX; Tel 01245 431893; Fax 01245 431889
Honorary Treasurer   Terry Butler
Hampshire County Council, The Castle, Winchester, Hampshire SO23 8UQ; Tel 01962 847287; Fax 01962 877681
Policy Adviser   Drew Clode
48 Park Ave North, London N8 7RT; E-mail drew@adss.demon.co.uk; Tel 020 8348 5023; Fax 020 8340 6005

Regional Representatives

East Midlands Regional Representatives
Nottingham City Council, 14 Hounds Gate, Nottingham NG1 7BE; Tel 0115 915 7000; Fax 0115 915 7014
Director (Social Services)   Paul Snell

Greater London Regional Representatives
Corporation of London, Milton Crt, Moor La, London EC2Y 9BL; Tel 020 7332 1210; Fax 020 7588 9173
Director (Social Services)   Pam Donnellan

North West Regional Representatives
Civic Centre, Millgate, Wigan, Greater Manchester WN1 1AZ; E-mail b.walker@wiganmbc.gov.uk; Tel 01942 827782; Fax 01942 404113
Contact   B. Walker (Wigan)

Northern Ireland Regional Representatives
North and West Belfast H&SS Trust, Glendinning Hse, 6 Murray St, Belfast BT1 6DP; Tel 028 9032 7156; Fax 028 9032 9599
Director (Social Services)   Noel Rooney

Northern Regional Representatives
Darlington Borough Council, Town Hall, Darlington DL1 5QT; E-mail colin.morris@darlington.gov.uk; Tel 01325 388098; Fax 01325 388090
Contact   Colin Morris

South West Regional Representatives
Plymouth City Council, Civic Centre, Plymouth PL1 2EW; E-mail pullanj@plymouth.gov.uk; Tel 01752 307343; Fax 01752 307330
Contact   J. Graham

South East Regional Representatives
Royal Borough of Windsor and Maidenhead, Town Hall, St. Ives Rd, Maidenhead, Windsor and Maidenhead SL6 1RF; E-mail hilary.simon@sbwm.gov.uk; Tel 01628 796159; Fax 01628 796256
Contact   Hilary Simon

East Regional Representatives
Suffolk County Council, St. Paul Hse, County Hall, Rope Wlk, Ipswich, Suffolk IP4 1LH; Tel 01473 583427; Fax 01473 583402
Contact   W. Bulpin (Suffolk)

Wales Regional Representatives
Torfaen County Borough Council, County Hall, Croesyceiliog, Cwmbran, Torfaen NP44 2WN; Tel 01633 648616; Fax 01633 648746
Director (Social Services)   Gary Birch

West Midlands Regional Representatives
Dudley Metropolitan Borough Council, Ednam Hse, St. James' Rd, Dudley, West Midlands DY1 3JJ; E-mail directorssd@mbc.dudley.gov.uk; Tel 01384 815801; Fax 01384 815865
Contact   C. Williams (Dudley)

Yorkshire and Humberside Regional Representatives
Leeds City Council, Merrion Hse, 110 Merrion Centre, Leeds, West Yorkshire LS2 8QB; E-mail keith.murray@leeds.gov.uk; Tel 0113 247 8700; Fax 0113 247 7228
Contact   K. Murray (Leeds)

Association of Directors of Social Work

ADSW Office, Council Offices, Almada St, Hamilton, South Lanarkshire ML3 0AA; URL www.adsw.org.uk; E-mail adsw@southlanarkshire.gov.uk
President and Head (Operations)   Duncan Macaulay
The City of Edinburgh Council, Shrubhill Hse, 7 Shrub Pl, Edinburgh EH7 4PB
Secretary   Brian Fearon

Association of London Government (ALG)

59½ Southwark St, London SE1 0AL; URL www.alg.gov.uk; E-mail info@alg.gov.uk; Tel 020 7934 9999; Fax 020 7934 9991
Chair   Sir Robin Wales (Lab)
Head (Health and Social Care)   Mark Brangwyn; E-mail mark.brangwyn@alg.gov.uk; Tel 020 7934 9794

Convention of Scottish Local Authorities

President (South Lanarkshire) Cllr Pat Watters
Vice-President (Midlothian) Vacancy
Vice-President (Orkney) Vacancy
Chief Executive Rory Mair
Social Affairs Spokesperson (South Ayrshire) Cllr Rita Miller

Local Government Association

Local Government Hse, Smith Sq, London SW1P 3HZ;
URL www.lga.gov.uk; E-mail info@lga.gov.uk; Tel 020
7664 3131; Fax 020 7664 3030
President Lord Ouseley
Chair Cllr Sir Jeremy Beecham
Vice-Chair Harry Jones, CBE (Lab)
Vice-Chair Sandy Bruce-Lockhart (Con)
Deputy Chair Chris Clark (LD)
Deputy Chair Milner Whiteman (Ind)
Chief Executive Brian Briscoe
Director (Education and Social Policy) John Ransford
Director (Strategy and Communications) Phil Swann
Director (Economic and Environmental Policy) Sarah Wood
Director (Central Services) John Rees
Director (Information, Research and Intelligence) Nick Cull
The Local Government Association was formed by the
merger of the Association of County Councils, the
Association of District Councils and the Association of
Metropolitan Authorities on 1 April 1997. The LGA has just
under 500 members, including 238 shire district councils;
36 metropolitan district councils; 34 county councils; 46
new unitary authorities; 33 London authorities; and 22

Welsh authorities. In addition, the LGA represents police
authorities, fire authorities and passenger transport
authorities. The LGA provides the national voice for local
communities in England and Wales; its members represent
over 50 million people, employ more than two million staff
and spend over £70 billion on local services. Local
authorities have a unique role in leading communities and
working with the private and voluntary sectors to solve
national problems at local level.

Local Government Association (NILGA)

123 York St, Belfast BT15 1AB; E-mail office@nilga.org;
Tel 028 9024 9286; Fax 028 9023 3328
President Cllr Pat Mallon
Chief Executive Heather Moorhead, BSc, MBA

National Association of Local Councils

Representing Parish and Town Councils in England and
Community and Town Councils in Wales.
109 Gt Russell St, London WC1B 3LD;
URL www.nalc.gov.uk; E-mail nalc@nalc.gov.uk; Tel 020
7637 1865; Fax 020 7436 7451
Chief Executive John Findlay
Policy Officer Michael Green
Communications Officer Sam Heath
Head (Communications) Alan Jones
The Association offers legal, technical, financial, policy
media and advice to its member councils and represents
nationally their concerns on policies.

Local Government England

6

- **Main Council Information**
- **Social Services Department**
  including related services and key personnel
- **Education Department**
  including Special Needs Education

Key

(110)	Number of pupils
Mixed	Takes boys and girls
Boys	Takes boys only
Girls	Takes girls only
11–18	Age range of pupils

Abbreviations

ADHD	Attention Deficit Hyperactivity Disorder
ASD	Autism Spectrum Disorder
EBD	Emotional Behavioural Difficulties
LD	Learning Difficulties
LI	Language Impairment
MH	Mentally Handicapped
MLD	Moderate Learning Difficulties
PH	Physically Handicapped
PHAB	Physically Handicapped and Able-Bodied
PMLD	Profound and Multiple Learning Difficulties
PS	Partially Sighted
PtHg	Partially Hearing
SCU	Special Care Unit
SEBD	Severe Emotional Behaviour Difficulties
SEN	Special Educational Needs
SLD	Severe Learning Difficulties
SLDD	Students with Learning Difficulties and Disabilities
SMH	Severely Mentally Handicapped

Local Government England

AVON COUNTY COUNCIL

In April 1996 Avon County Council, Bath City Council, Bristol City Council, Kingswood Borough Council, Northavon District Council, Wansdyke District Council and Woodspring District Council were replaced by Bath and North East Somerset District Council, Bristol City Council, North Somerset District Council and South Gloucestershire Council – each responsible for all local government services in its area. These councils are listed alphabetically in this chapter.

BARNSLEY METROPOLITAN BOROUGH COUNCIL

www.barnsley.gov.uk

Population 218 000
Political Composition: Lab: 47, Con: 5, LD: 4, Ind: 9, No party: 1.
Town Hall, Barnsley, South Yorkshire S70 2TA;
    URL www.barnsley.gov.uk;
    E-mail terrygriffiths@barnsley.gov.uk; Tel 01226 770770
Chief Executive   Phil Coppard
Borough Secretary   Andrew Frosdick
Executive Director (Finance)   Steve Pick
Executive Director (Social Services)   Graham Gatehouse
Executive Director (Education)   Edna Sutton
Executive Director (Environmental Services)   Roy Garbett (Acting)
Executive Director (Development)   David Kennedy

Social Services Department

Wellington Hse, 36 Wellington St, Barnsley, South Yorkshire S70 1WA; Tel 01226 775656; Fax 01226 772399
Cabinet Spokesperson (Social Services)   Cllr A. Gardiner
Support Member (Social Services)   Cllr C. Jenkinson
Executive Director (Social Services)   Graham Gatehouse
Executive Head (Children's Services)   Janet Donaldson
Executive Head (Learning Disabilities)   Jenny Anderton
Manager (Mental Health Services)   Kath Harris
Senior Operations Manager (Quality and Service Development)   Ray Woodhams
Senior Operations Manager (Service Provision)   Pat Jupp
Principal Officer (Child Protection)   George Gilmore

AREA OFFICES

Athersley Children and Families

(Athersley, Darton, North West); Tel 01226 775180; Fax 01226 775199
Sector Manager   S. Cooke
Team Leader (Children and Families)   L. Jackson

Brierley Children and Families

(Cudworth, Brierley, Shafton and Grimethorpe)
Brierley Hall, Church St, Barnsley, South Yorkshire S72 9HT; Tel 01226 775930; Fax 01226 775929
Sector Manager   S. Cooke
Team Leader (Children and Families)   L. Dolphin

Goldthorpe Children and Families

(Goldthorpre, Dearne South, Thurnscoe)
Goldthorpe Town Hall, Goldthorpe, Rotherham, South Yorkshire S63 9EJ; Tel 01226 775011; Fax 01226 772029
Sector Manager   P. Williams
Team Leader (Children and Families)   H. White

Hoyland Children and Families

(Hoyland East, Hoyland West, Penistone East, Penistone West)
Hoyland Town Hall, Hoyland, Barnsley, South Yorkshire S74 9AD; Tel 01226 775441; Fax 01226 775458
Sector Manager   S. Cooke
Team Leader (Children and Families)   H. Grisewood

Lundwood Children and Families

(Lundwood, Ardsley, Monk Bretton, Park Kendray)
Lundwood Health Centre, Littleworth La, Barnsley, South Yorkshire S71 5RG; Tel 01226 298508; Fax 01226 770406
Sector Manager   P. Williams
Team Leader (Children and Families)   K. Smith

Wombwell Children and Families

(Darfield, Wombwell North, Wombwell South, Great Houghton and Little Houghton)
Hoyland Town Hall, Hoyland, Barnsley, South Yorkshire S74 9AD; Tel 01226 775474; Fax 01226 775458
Sector Manager   S. Cooke
Team Leader (Children and Families)   P. Armitage

Worsbrough Children and Families

(Park, South West, Central and Dodworth); Tel 01226 772423; Fax 01226 772404
Sector Manager   P. Williams
Team Leader (Children and Families)   K. Fletcher

6

Brierley Community Care Team

Brierley Hall, Church St, Brierley, Barnsley, South Yorkshire S72 9HT; Tel 01226 775901; Fax 01226 775929
Team Leader G. Swann
Team Leader L. Peterson
(covering Brierley, Darfield, Wombwell North, Cudworth, Grimethorpe, Little Houghton, Great Houghton, Shafton)

Darton Community Care Team

Darton Council Offices, Huddersfield Rd, Darton, Barnsley, South Yorkshire S75 5NB; Tel 01226 775480; Fax 01226 775481
Team Leader G. Shaw
(covering Darton, Dodworth, North West)

Goldthorpe Community Care Team

Goldthorpe Town Hall, Goldthorpe, Rotherham, South Yorkshire S63 9EJ; Tel 01226 775011; Fax 01226 775029
Team Leader K. Houghton
(covering Dearne South, Dearne Thurnscoe, Wombwell South, Jump, Hemmingfield)

Penistone Community Care Team

Penistone Town Hall, Penistone, Sheffield, South Yorkshire S36 6DY; Tel 01226 774242; Fax 01226 761019
Team Leader M. Ellam
(covering Penistone East/West, Hoyland East/West)

Worsbrough Community Care Team

Saville Hse, Park Rd, Worsbrough, Barnsley, South Yorkshire S70 5DE; Tel 01226 296610; Fax 01226 770408
Team Leader A. Baker
(covering Park, South West, Worsbrough, Ardsley)

HOSPITAL TEAMS

Barnsley District General Hospital 49–51 Gawber Rd, Barnsley, South Yorkshire S75 2EP; Tel 01226 730000 ext 2222; Fax 01226 200019
Team Manager R. Tulley
Mount Vernon Hospital Team Mount Vernon Rd, Barnsley, South Yorkshire S70 4DP; Tel 01226 777843
Team Manager R. Tulley

EMERGENCY DUTY TEAM

Carlton Hse, Carlton St, Cudworth, Barnsley, South Yorkshire S72 8ST; Tel 01226 715656; Fax 01226 715239
Team Manager C. Woolfe

INTENSIVE PREVENTION TEAM

Ground Fl, Wellington Hse, 36 Wellington St, Barnsley, South Yorkshire S70 1WA; Tel 01226 775878; Fax 01226 775886
Team Leader P. Howell

CHILD AND ADOLESCENT UNIT

New St Clinic, New St, Barnsley, South Yorkshire S70 2LP; Tel 01226 730000 ext 3163; Fax 01226 777905

CHILD PROTECTION TEAM

2–3 Burleigh Crt, Barnsley, South Yorkshire S70 1XY; Tel 01226 772400; Fax 01226 772398
Principal Officer (Child Protection) G. Gilmore

REGISTERED DAY NURSERIES/PLAYGROUPS/CHILDMINDERS

Details on application.

DISABLED CHILDREN'S TEAM

Birk Hse, Calder Cres, Kendray, Barnsley, South Yorkshire S70 3JF; Tel 01226 775390; Fax 01226 775399
Manager (Children's Services – Disabled Children) C. Nicklin

CHILDREN'S RESOURCE CENTRES

John Street Children's Resource Centre 43 John St, Great Houghton, South Yorkshire S72 0EA; Tel 01226 753744; Fax 01226 759472
Resource Centre Manager F. Tennison
Rockingham Street Children's Resource Centre 77–81 Rockingham St, Barnsley, South Yorkshire S71 1JU; Tel 01226 296471; Fax 01226 248279
Resource Centre Manager J. Jones
Needlewood Children's Resource Centre Keresforth Hill Rd, Barnsley, South Yorkshire S70 6RF; Tel 01226 205497
Resource Centre Manager B. Hoofe

KERESFORTH RESOURCE CENTRE FOR CHILDREN WITH SPECIAL NEEDS/DISABILITIES

14a Keresforth Cl, Off Broadway, Barnsley, South Yorkshire S70 6RS; Tel 01226 248096
Resource Centre Manager D. Wharton
(9)

SUMMERWELL RESOURCE CENTRE FOR CHILDREN WITH LEARNING DISABILITIES/SPECIAL NEEDS

Summerwell, Newsome Ave, Wombwell, South Yorkshire S73 8QS; Tel 01226 755558; Fax 01226 755566
Resource Centre Manager J. Davies (Acting)

ADOPTION/FOSTERING TEAM

Ground Fl, Wellington Hse, 36 Wellington St, Barnsley, South Yorkshire S70 1WA; Tel 01226 775872; Fax 01226 775864
Team Leader P. Dempsey

YOUTH OFFENDING TEAM

Phase 1 and 2, County Way, Barnsley, South Yorkshire S70 2DT; Tel 01226 774977; Fax 01226 774968
YOT Manager C. Barnes
Operations Manager T. Hart

FAMILY CENTRES

Barnardo's Family Centre Priory Campus, Pontefract Rd, Barnsley, South Yorkshire S71 5PN; Tel 01226 770169
NCH St. Edwin's Family Centre NHS Keresforth Centre, 5 Keresforth Cl, Barnsley, South Yorkshire S70 6RS; Tel 01226 241171
Thurnscoe Family Centre (in association with the Children's Society), Station Hse, Station Rd, Thurnscoe, South Yorkshire S63 0BX; Tel 01709 880682

PHYSICAL AND SENSORY DISABILITY TEAM

The Social Centre, Moorland Ave, Barnsley, South Yorkshire S70 6PH; Tel 01226 282025; Fax 01226 730935
Team Leader L. Phillips

SUBSTANCE MISUSE SERVICES

Unit 1 and 2, Burleigh Crt, Barnsley, South Yorkshire S70 1XY; Tel 01226 787316; Fax 01226 787315

COMMUNITY LEARNING DISABILITY TEAM

Birk House Calder Cres, Kendray, Barnsley, South Yorkshire S70 3JF; Tel 01226 775377; Fax 01226 775399
Team Leader S. Moylan

LEARNING AND DEVELOPMENT DAY SERVICES FOR ADULTS WITH LEARNING DISABILITIES

Barnsley Central, Dodworth and Penistone Employment Skills Learning and Development Units Woodland Dr, Barnsley, South Yorkshire S70 6QN; Tel 01226 281063

Barnsley North, Cudworth and Brierley Learning and Development Units St. Helen's Way, Monk Bretton, Barnsley, South Yorkshire S71 2PS; Tel 01226 292008; Fax 01226 770914

Dearne Unit King St, Goldthorpe, Rotherham, South Yorkshire S63 3EY; Tel 01709 896850; Fax 01709 891465

Learning and Development Services Management Team St. Helen's Resource Centre, St. Helen's Way, Monk Bretton, Barnsley, South Yorkshire S71 2PS; Tel 01226 285056; Fax 01226 770914
Manager (Day Services) G. Sanderson (Acting)

Wombwell and Darfield, Hoyland and Birdwell Sheltered Workshops and Specialised Resources Learning and Development Units Off Bondfield Cres, Wombwell, Barnsley, South Yorkshire S73 8TL; Tel 01226 753441; Fax 01226 757361

COMMUNITY MENTAL HEALTH TEAM

The Assertive Outreach Team Keresforth Centre, Off Broadway, Barnsley, South Yorkshire S70 6RS; Tel 01226 289135; Fax 01226 289143
Team Leader K. Ware

Barnsley District General Hospital Community Mental Health Team Gawber Rd, Barnsley, South Yorkshire S75 2EP; Tel 01226 730000 ext 2295; Fax 01226 289330
Manager (Mental Health Services) K. Harris

Kendray Hospital Doncaster Rd, Kendray, Barnsley, South Yorkshire S70 6RS; Tel 01226 777814; Fax 01226 201435

REHABILITATION TEAMS

Central Team Littleworth Crt, Littleworth La, Lundwood, South Yorkshire; Tel 01226 248610; Fax 01226 246457
Team Leader J. Jinks

Community Health Rehabilitation Team The Lodge, Kendray Hospital, Doncaster Rd, Barnsley, South Yorkshire S70 6RS; Tel 01226 286634; Fax 01226 201435
Manager D. Hignett

Dearne Valley Team 16 School St, Darfield, Barnsley, South Yorkshire S73 9ET; Tel 01226 752839
Team Leader D. Hanna

North Team 31 Greenside Ave, Mapplewell, Barnsley, South Yorkshire S75 6BB; Tel 01226 390370; Fax 01226 390127
Team Leader D. Quayle

South Team The Summer Lane Centre, Summer La, Wombwell, Barnsley, South Yorkshire S73 8QH; Tel 01226 341374; Fax 01226 755326
Team Leader D. Thompson

SUPPORTED LIVING TEAM

St. Helen's Resource Centre, St. Helens Way, Monk Bretton, Barnsley, South Yorkshire S71 2PS; Tel 01226 285056; Fax 01226 770914
Locality Manager Katrina Latham

EQUIPMENT AND ADAPTATIONS

2nd Fl, Wellington Hse, 36 Wellington St, Barnsley, South Yorkshire S70 1WA; Tel 01226 775800; Fax 01226 772399
Manager (Equipment and Adaptations) J. Grace

DAY CENTRE FOR PEOPLE WITH MENTAL HEALTH PROBLEMS

Moorland Court Day Centre 33 Gawber Rd, Barnsley, South Yorkshire S75 2AH; Tel 01226 730433; Fax 01226 771526
Resource Centre Manager J. Dacre

DAY CENTRE FOR ADULTS WITH PHYSICAL AND SENSORY DISABILITIES

Laithes Day Centre Laithes La, Athersley, Barnsley, South Yorkshire S71 3AF; Tel 01226 290650; Fax 01226 204508

Social Centre Moorland Ave, Barnsley, South Yorkshire S70 6PH; Tel 01226 785485; Fax 01226 299932
Resource Centre Manager J. Coulling

DAY CENTRES FOR THE ELDERLY

Greenside Day Centre Greenside Hse, Greenside Ave, Mapplewell, South Yorkshire S75 6BB; Tel 01226 386600; Fax 01226 391332

Highfield Grange Day Centre John St, Wombwell, South Yorkshire S73 8LW; Tel 01226 755480; Fax 01226 756986

Highgate Social Centre Saltersbrook, Highgate, South Yorkshire S63 9AR; Tel 01709 880989; Fax 01709 880989

TRANSPORT FOR USERS OF SERVICES

Moorland Ave, Barnsley, South Yorkshire S70 6PH; Tel 01226 287582; Fax 01226 202229
Transport Manager K. O'Donnell

6

Education Department

Berneslai Cl, Barnsley, South Yorkshire S70 2HS; URL www.barnsley.gov.uk; Tel 01226 773500
Executive Director (Education) J. Potter
Assistant Director (Strategic Planning and Evaluation) M. Thompson
Assistant Director (Community Learning) A. Meakin

SPECIAL DAY SCHOOL

Greenacre School Keresforth Hill Rd, Barnsley, South Yorkshire S70 6RG; E-mail greenacreschool@barnsley.org; Tel 01226 287165; Fax 01226 295328
Headteacher J. Short

BATH AND NORTH EAST SOMERSET DISTRICT COUNCIL

www.bathnes.gov.uk

Political Composition: LD: 30, Con: 26, Lab: 6, Independent Labour: 4.
Guildhall, High St, Bath, Bath and North East Somerset BA1 5AW; URL www.bathnes.gov.uk; Tel 01225 477000
Chief Executive J. Everitt
Director (Operations) P. Rowntree
Strategic Director (Social and Housing Services) J. Ashman
Strategic Director (Economic and Environmental Development) C. Thomas
Corporate Director S. Berry
Head (Human Resources) W. Harding

Social and Housing Services

PO Box 3343, Bath, Bath and North East Somerset BA1 2ZH; Tel 01225 477000; Fax 01225 477890
Strategic Director (Social and Housing Services) Jane Ashman

New Executive Council

Executive Member (Social Services) Cllr Francine Haeberling
Executive Member (Housing and Community Safety) Cllr Vic Pritchard

Children and Families Services

Head (Children and Families Services) M. Lindsay
Group Manager (Children and Families) Charlie Moat
Group Manager (Children and Families) Trina Shane
Planning Manager (Children and Families) L. Price

Adult Services

Head (Adult Services) N. Harris
Group Manager (Mental Health) Anne Kendall
Group Manager (Adults – Learning Difficulties)
   Sandra Lovern
Group Manager (Assessment and Commissioning) Jeff Saffin
Manager (Strategic Planning) Pam Richards

Housing and Supported Living Services

Head (Housing and Supported Living Services) Jane Shayler
Group Manager (Housing Regeneration) Colin Keane
Group Manager (Housing and Supported Living Services)
   Sarah Shatwell
Group Manager (Elderly Persons' Homes) Y. Case

Education Service

PO Box 25, Riverside, Temple St, Keynsham, Bristol
   BS31 1DN; URL www.bathnes.gov.uk; Tel 01225 477000
Director (Education) Alison Delyth (Acting)
Assistant Director (Strategy and Management) Susan Wheeler
*Assistant Director (Young People and Community Education
   Services)* Gail Quinton
Youth and Community PYCO Gareth Jones
Manager (Human Resources) Christine McKinley (Acting)
Team Leader (Education Finance) Richard Morgan
Team Leader (Children's Support Services)
   Georgie Mackintosh
Team Leader (Special Education Needs) Fran Newport
Principal Educational Psychologist Norman Donovan

SPECIAL SCHOOLS

Fosse Way School Longfellow Rd, Midsomer Norton, Bath,
Bath and North East Somerset BA3 4BL; Tel 01761 412198
Headteacher D. Gregory
   MLD

Lime Grove School Lime Grove Gdns, Pulteney Rd, Bath,
Bath and North East Somerset BA2 4HE; Tel 01225 424732
Headteacher J.D. Pulham
   SLD

Royal United Hospital School Cynthia Mossman Hse,
Combe Pk, Bath, Bath and North East Somerset BA1 3NJ;
Tel 01225 824223
Headteacher L. Harris

Summerfield School Weston Park East, Bath, Bath and
North East Somerset BA1 2UY; Tel 01225 423607
Headteacher G. Williams
   MLD

Wansdyke School Frome Rd, Odd Down, Bath, Bath and
North East Somerset BA2 5RF; Tel 01225 832212
Headteacher G. Rees
   EBD

BEDFORDSHIRE COUNTY COUNCIL
www.bedfordshire.gov.uk

In April 1997 Luton became a unitary authority. The rest of
Bedfordshire retains a two-tier structure. Luton is listed
alphabetically within this chapter. Bedfordshire County
Council is a commissioner and provider of Social Services.
Population 382 120

Political Composition: Con: 26, Lab: 13, LD: 9, Ind: 1
County Hall, Cauldwell St, Bedford, Bedfordshire
   MK42 9AP; URL www.bedfordshire.gov.uk; Tel 01234
   363222; Fax 01234 228619
Chair of the County Council Cllr J. Scott
Chief Executive D. Wilkinson

Social Services

Strategic Director (Social Services) Lyn Burns
Strategic Director (Learning) David Doran
Head (Strategy and Policy) Sandra Fielding
Children's centres are now managed by NCH.

TRAINING

Responsible for training professional and support staff in
the department. Tel 01234 228808
Head (Human Resources) Vince Hislop

NORTH DIVISION

OFFICES

Ampthill Office Houghton Lodge, Houghton Cl, off Oliver
St, Ampthill, Bedfordshire MK45 2TG; Tel 01525 840543;
Fax 01525 840551

Bedford Office Kingsway, Bedford, Bedfordshire
MK45 2TG; Tel 01234 345331; Fax 01234 353263

Biggleswade Office 142 London Rd, Biggleswade,
Bedfordshire SG18 8EL; Tel 01767 224224; Fax 01767 315955

Mid Beds Area

RESIDENTIAL CARE ESTABLISHMENT FOR CHILDREN WITH LEARNING DISABILITIES

Maythorn, The Lawns, The Baulk, Biggleswade,
   Bedfordshire; Tel 01767 313612
Contact L. Eaton
   (14)

DAY CARE ESTABLISHMENTS FOR PEOPLE WITH LEARNING DISABILITIES

London Road 142 London Rd, Biggleswade, Bedfordshire
SG18 8EH; Tel 01767 313436
Contact V. Leggatt
   (151)

Silsoe Horticultural Centre Holly Wlk, Silsoe, Bedfordshire
MK45 4EB; Tel 01525 860999
Contact M. Haynes
   (30)

RESIDENTIAL CARE ESTABLISHMENTS FOR PEOPLE WITH LEARNING DISABILITIES

Cherrytrees Kytelands Rd, Biggleswade, Bedfordshire
SG18 8NX; Tel 01767 313370
Contact V. Leggatt
   (25)

Group Home 7 The Rowlands, Biggleswade, Bedfordshire
SG18 8NY
   (4)

Group Home Cherrytrees, Kytelands Rd, Biggleswade,
Bedfordshire SG18 8NX
   (3)

DAY CARE ESTABLISHMENT FOR ELDERLY PEOPLE

Ampthill Social Centre Houghton Cl, Oliver St, Ampthill,
Bedfordshire MK45 2TG; Tel 01525 405368
Contact S. Lawrence

North Beds Area

DAY CARE ESTABLISHMENTS FOR PEOPLE WITH LEARNING DISABILITIES

Bedford Centre 115 Barkers La, Bedford, Bedfordshire MK41 9RR; Tel 01234 356535
(130)

Kempston Centre Carnell Cl, Kempston, Bedford, Bedfordshire MK42 7HP; Tel 01234 853973
Contact J. Presland
(130)

RESIDENTIAL CARE ESTABLISHMENTS FOR PEOPLE WITH LEARNING DISABILITIES

Orchard House 92 Brookfield Rd, Bedford, Bedfordshire MK41 9LJ; Tel 01234 344448
Contact Fiona Mackirdy
(24)

Group Home (The Hollies) The Hollies, Orchard Hse, 92 Brookfield Rd, Bedford, Bedfordshire MK41 9LJ
(3)

Group Home (Hazel House) Hazel Hse, C10, Orchard Hse, 92 Brookfield Rd, Bedford, Bedfordshire MK41 9LJ
(3)

Group Home (Meadway) 28–39 Meadway, Bedford, Bedfordshire MK41 9HU
(7)

Group Home (Owen) 32 Owen Cl, Kempston, Bedford, Bedfordshire MK42 7EA
(3)

HOSTEL FOR ADULTS WITH MULTIPLE DISABILITIES

George Beal Hse, off William Rd, Kempston, Bedford, Bedfordshire MK42 7HL; Tel 01234 857300
Contact Kate Walker
(16)

ESTABLISHMENTS FOR PEOPLE RECOVERING FROM MENTAL ILLNESS

The Barford Avenue Centre 29 Barford Ave, Bedford, Bedfordshire MK42 0DS; Tel 01234 215610; Fax 01234 857300
Contact Paul Feary
Day care (20)

Kimbolton Road Centre 42 Kimbolton Rd, Bedford, Bedfordshire MK40 2NX
(7)

ESTABLISHMENT FOR PEOPLE WITH PHYSICAL DISABILITIES

Sunflower Hse, Woodcote, Putnoe, Beford, Bedfordshire MK41 8EJ; Tel 01234 219403
Contact S. Capel-Jones
Contact J. Ward (job-share)
(6)

DAY CARE ESTABLISHMENTS FOR ELDERLY MENTALLY INFIRM

Bedford Social Centre Conduit Rd, Bedford, Bedfordshire MK40 1EG; Tel 01234 345439
Contact Nicola Tysoe

Goldington Social Centre 10 Barkers La, Bedford, Bedfordshire MK41 9LJ; Tel 01234 352210
Contact P. Naylor

SOUTH DIVISION

OFFICE

Dunstable Office Vernon Pl, Dunstable, Bedfordshire LU5 4EZ; Tel 01582 665861; Fax 01582 476134

DAY CARE ESTABLISHMENT FOR PEOPLE WITH LEARNING DISABILITIES

Townsend Centre Portland Cl, Houghton Regis, Bedfordshire LU5 5BA; Tel 01582 699246
Contact M. Hawkin
(98)

RESIDENTIAL CARE ESTABLISHMENTS FOR PEOPLE WITH LEARNING DISABILITIES

Downing View 1–3 Loring Rd, Dunstable, Bedfordshire LU6 1DZ; Tel 01582 604416
Contact R. Mead
(25)

Hostel for Adults with Multiple Disabilities Linsell Hse, Ridgeway Ave, Dunstable, Bedfordshire LU5 4QJ; Tel 01582 699438
Contact Sarah McLinden
(16)

RESIDENTIAL CARE ESTABLISHMENTS FOR PEOPLE RECOVERING FROM MENTAL ILLNESS

Steppingstones 29 Lancot Dr, Dunstable, Bedfordshire LU6 2AP; Tel 01582 605881
Manager T. Chapman
(16)

Group Home 29 Lancot Dr, Dunstable, Bedfordshire LU6 2AP
(3)

ESTABLISHMENT FOR PEOPLE WITH PHYSICAL DISABILITIES

Sheltered Workshop Ludun Workshops, Liscombe Rd, Dunstable, Bedfordshire LU5 4PL; Tel 01582 660261
Contact B. Jenkins

DAY CARE ESTABLISHMENT FOR ELDERLY MENTALLY INFIRM

Houghton Regis Social Centre Parkside Dr, Houghton Regis, Bedfordshire LU5 5PX; Tel 01582 865700
Contact Y. Heley

Education

County Hall, Cauldwell St, Bedford, Bedfordshire MK42 9AP; Tel 01234 363222; Fax 01234 228441; 01234 228993
Strategic Director (Learning) David Doran

SCHOOLS FOR CHILDREN WITH MODERATE LEARNING DIFFICULTIES

Grange School Halsey Rd, Kempston, Bedford, Bedfordshire MK42 8AU; Tel 01234 407100; Fax 01234 407110
Headteacher Mrs E. Zapiec
(162)

Hitchmead School Hitchmead Rd, Biggleswade, Bedfordshire SG18 0NL; Tel 01767 601010; Fax 01767 601010
Headteacher P. Latter
(100)

Weatherfield School Brewers Hill Rd, Dunstable, Bedfordshire LU6 1AF; Tel 01582 605632; Fax 01582 605632
Headteacher C. Peters
(141)

SCHOOLS FOR CHILDREN WITH SEVERE LEARNING DIFFICULTIES

Glenwood School Beech Rd, Dunstable, Bedfordshire LU6 3LY; Tel 01582 667106; Fax 01582 699538
Headteacher Mrs S. Crosbie
(120)

Hillcrest School Ridgeway Ave, Dunstable, Bedfordshire
LU5 4QL; Tel 01582 661983; Fax 01582 673705
Headteacher P. Skingley
(73)

Rainbow School Chestnut Ave, Bromham, Bedford,
Bedfordshire MK43 8HP; Tel 01234 822596; Fax 01234
826093
Headteacher Ms G. Pilling
(74)

Sunnyside School The Baulk, Biggleswade, Bedfordshire
SG18 0PT; Tel 01767 222662; Fax 01767 222662
Headteacher Ms G. Pilling
(69)

SCHOOL FOR CHILDREN WITH PHYSICAL DIFFICULTIES

Ridgeway School Hill Rise, Kempston, Bedford,
Bedfordshire MK42 7EB; Tel 01234 402402; Fax 01234
402410
Headteacher G. Allard
(73)

**SCHOOL FOR CHILDREN WITH EMOTIONAL AND BEHAVIOURAL
DIFFICULTIES**

Oak Bank School Sandy La, Leighton Buzzard,
Bedfordshire LU7 8BE; Tel 01525 374559; Fax 01525 867375
Headteacher Mr P. Cohen
(38)

PUPIL REFERRAL UNITS

Greys House Manor Dr, Kempston, Bedford, Bedfordshire
MK42 7AB; Tel 01234 408477; Fax 01234 408478
Head (Pupil Referral Unit) Sue, Raffe
9–13

**Manor Education Centre for Pregnant Schoolgirls and Young
Mothers** Manor Dr, Kempston, Bedford, Bedfordshire
MK42 7AB; Tel 01234 408477; Fax 01234 408478

Raleigh Education Centre Ampthill Rd, Bedford,
Bedfordshire MK42 9HE; Tel 01234 408477; Fax 01234
408478
15–16

Student Support Centre Houghton Regis Campus, Parkside
Dr, Houghton Regis, Dunstable, Bedfordshire LU5 5PY;
Tel 01582 865532
13–15

BERKSHIRE COUNTY COUNCIL

In April 1998 Berkshire County Council was replaced by
Bracknell Forest, Reading, Slough, West Berkshire, Windsor
and Maidenhead and Wokingham Councils, each
responsible for local government services in its area. These
councils are listed alphabetically in this chapter.

BIRMINGHAM CITY COUNCIL
www.birmingham.gov.uk

Population 1 014 400
Political Composition: Lab: 57, Con: 35, LD: 23, People's
Justice: 2
The Council Hse, Victoria Sq, Birmingham, West Midlands
B1 1BB; URL www.birmingham.gov.uk;
E-mail assist@birmingham.gov.uk; Tel 0121 303 9944;
Fax 0121 303 2258
The Lord Mayor Cllr Theresa Stewart

Chief Executive Stewart Dobson (Acting)
Director (Finance and Performance) Sarah Wood
Director (Transportation) David Pywell
Director (Environmental and Consumer Services)
David Bowman
Director (Housing) David Thompson
Director (Social Services) Sandra Taylor
Director (Planning and Architecture, Birmingham)
Emrys Jones (Acting)
Director (Leisure and Culture) Viv Griffiths (Acting)
Director (Economic Development) Paul Spooner
Director (Corporate and Democratic Services)
Stewart Dobson
Chief Personnel Officer Andy Albon

Social Services Department

Louisa Ryland Hse, 44 Newhall St, Birmingham, West
Midlands B3 3PL; Tel 0121 303 2946; 0121 303 4125
Emergencies only outside office hours 0121 475 4806
Chair (Social Services and Health Advisory Team)
Cllr Susannah McCorry
The Council Hse, Victoria Square, Birmingham, West
Midlands B1 1BB; Tel 0121 303 2015
Director (Social Services) Sandra Taylor; Tel 0121 303 2992
Assistant Director Area Services (Deputy Director)
Pauline Newman; Tel 0121 303 4086
Assistant Director (Area Services) Lynda Bull; Tel 0121 303
4006
Assistant Director (Resources) Terry Pinfold; Tel 0121 303
2367
Assistant Director (Adult Services) Mike Boyle; Tel 0121 303
2428
Assistant Director (Children's Services) Andrea Hickmen;
Tel 0121 303 4861
Head (Human Resources) Frank Took; Tel 0121 303 4417;
Fax 0121 303 1351
Principal Equalities Officer Rajpal Virdee; Tel 0121 303 3687;
Fax 0121 303 2769
Service Manager (Home Care (Adult Services)) P. Mtize;
Tel 0121 303 2202
Service Manager (Elderley Resources (Adult Services))
Hazel McAkteer; Tel 0121 303 2202
Service Manager (Specific Needs (Adult Services))
Lucy Ashton; Tel 0121 303 2202
Service Manager (Residential South (Children's Services))
Vacancy; Tel 0121 303 2281
Service Manager (Children and Families (Children's Services))
I. Bell; Tel 0121 351 3881

Social Services and Health Advisory Team
Members
Lab: Susannah McCorry, Ian McArdle, David Williams,
Dorothy Wallace.
Con: Len Clark, Anne Underwood.
LD: Sue Anderson.

Healthy, Caring and Inclusive City Overview
Scrutiny Committee
Chair Hugh McCallion (Lab)
Vice-Chair Paul Pyke (Lab)
Members
Lab: Roy Benjamin, Douglas McCarrick, John Robinson,
Mike Nangle, Tony Kennedy.
Con: Jane James, Margaret Scrimshaw, Len Gregory.
LD: Les Byron, Mohammed Massoon.

AREA OFFICES AND SUB-OFFICES

Edgbaston and Northfield Constituency
Tel 0121 303 1888
Area Manager (Social Services) Andrew Ferguson

Edgbaston Area Office Attwood Hse, 72 High St, Harbourne, Birmingham, West Midlands B17 9NJ; Tel 0121 303 1888; Fax 0121 303 9088

Longbridge Area Office 1431 Bristol Rd South, Northfield, Birmingham, West Midlands B31 2SU; Tel 0121 303 9500; Fax 0121 303 1327

Northfield Area Office 1102 Bristol Rd South, Northfield, Birmingham, West Midlands B31 2RE; Tel 0121 303 5350; Fax 0121 303 5761

Selly Oak and Hall Green Constituency

Tel 0121 303 5050; Fax 0121 303 5198
Area Manager (Social Services) Vacancy

Hall Green Area Office Windsor Hse, 11a High St, Kings Heath, Birmingham, West Midlands B14 7BB; Tel 0121 303 3571; Fax 0121 303 0923

Selly Oak Area Office 4a Hazelwell St, Stirchley, Birmingham, West Midlands B30 2JU; Tel 0121 303 5050; Fax 0121 303 5198

Ladywood and Perry Barr Constituency

Tel 0121 303 4362
Area Manager (Social Services) Yvette Waide

Ladywood Area Office All Saints Rd, Hockley, Birmingham, West Midlands B18 5QB; Tel 0121 303 4362; Fax 0121 303 0543

Ladywood Sub-Office 12 Dawson Rd, Handsworth, Birmingham, West Midlands B21 9HS; Tel 0121 303 6381; Fax 0121 303 8877

Perry Barr Area Office 392 Kingstanding Rd, Kingstanding, Birmingham, West Midlands B44 8LD; Tel 0121 303 6343; Fax 0121 303 0782

Perry Bar Sub-Office Hawthorne Hse, 58 Hamstead Hall Rd, Handsworth Wood, Birmingham, West Midlands B20 1HX; Tel 0121 303 2121; Fax 0121 303 0381

Hodge Hill and Yardley Constituency

Tel 0121 303 6541
Area Manager (Social Service) Glynis Hovell

Hodge Hill Area Office St. Peters College, Bridge Rd, Saltley, Birmingham, West Midlands B8 3TE; Tel 0121 303 6062; Fax 0121 303 8966

Yardley Area Office Silvermere Centre, Silvermere Rd, Yardley, Birmingham, West Midlands B26 3XA; Tel 0121 303 6541; Fax 0121 303 8530

Small Heath and Sparkbrook Constituency

Tel 0121 303 2334

Small Heath Area Office (Children) 156 High St, Aston, Birmingham, West Midlands B6 4UX; Tel 0121 303 2334; Fax 0121 303 9040

Small Heath Area Office (Adults) Sycamore Centre, Sycamore Rd, Aston, Birmingham, West Midlands B6 5HU; Tel 0121 303 4003; Fax 0121 303 5605

Sparkbrook Area Office Greencoat Hse, 261–271 Stratford Rd, Birmingham, West Midlands B11 1QS; Tel 0121 303 7070; Fax 0121 303 0619

Sutton and Erdington Constituency

Tel 0121 303 7737
Area Manager (Social Services) John Creber

Erdington Area Office 250 Reservoir Rd, Erdington, Birmingham, West Midlands B23 6DE; Tel 0121 303 7737; Fax 0121 303 9658

Sutton Coldfield Area Office The Council Hse, King Edward Sq, Sutton Coldfield, West Midlands B73 6AN; Tel 0121 303 9221; Fax 0121 303 9277

CHILDREN'S HOME WITH EDUCATION

The Uplands, 33 Green Hill, Blackwell, Bromsgrove, West Midlands B60 1BL; Tel 0121 447 7744

CHILDREN'S HOMES

Bournbrook Road Children's Home 67 Bournbrook Rd, Selly Oak, Birmingham, West Midlands B29 7BX; Tel 0121 472 5012

Braymoor Road Children's Home 18 Braymoor Rd, Tile Cross, Birmingham, West Midlands B33 0LR; Tel 0121 779 2213

Chamberlain Road Children's Home 7 Chamberlain Rd, Kings Heath, Birmingham, West Midlands B13 0QP; Tel 0121 444 1200

Church Lane Children's Home 150 Church La, Birmingham, West Midlands B20 2RT; Tel 0121 554 8665

Clissold Street Children's Home 63 Clissold St, Hockley, Birmingham, West Midlands B18 7HQ; Tel 0121 523 9939

Earlswood Secure Unit Gravelly Hill, North 18, Birmingham, West Midlands B23 6BQ; Tel 0121 382 5121; Fax 0121 377 6727

Fairfield Children's Home 20 Dudley Park Rd, Acocks Grn, Birmingham, West Midlands B27 62R; Tel 0121 706 3536

Fountain Road Children's Home 33 Fountain Rd, Edgbaston, West Midlands B17 8NP; Tel 0121 429 4815

Herons Way Children's Home 51 Herons Way, Selly Oak, Birmingham, West Midlands B29 6TR; Tel 0121 472 5338

Highters Close Children's Home 27 Highters Cl, Warstock, Birmingham, West Midlands B14 4NN; Tel 0121 474 5547

Kings Lodge Children's Home 143 Kingstanding Rd, Birmingham, West Midlands B44 8JU; Tel 0121 356 4570

Leach Green Lane Children's Home 307 Leach Green La, Rednal, West Midlands B45 8DR; Tel 0121 457 8112

Millmead Road Children's Home 36–38 Millmead Rd, Wesley Castle, West Midlands B32 3AX; Tel 0121 427 3029

Millmead Road Children's Home 52 Millmead Rd, Bartley Green, West Midlands B32 3AY; Tel 0121 427 2528

Mulberry House Children's Home Mulberry Hse, 37 Park Hill, Moseley, West Midlands B13 8DR; Tel 0121 449 2160

Oakhill House Children's Home Oakhill Hse, 31 Meadow Rd, Harborne, Birmingham, West Midlands B17 8DH; Tel 0121 434 4567; Fax 0121 434 3364

St. Athan's Croft Children's Home St. Athan's Croft, 34 Castlevale, West Midlands B35 7LS; Tel 0121 747 8270

South Acre Children's Home 6 Victoria Ave, Halesowen, West Midlands B62 9BL; Tel 0121 422 4907

Stuarts Road Children's Home 8 Stuarts Rd, Yardley, West Midlands B33 8UQ; Tel 0121 783 2658

Sutton Road Children's Home 45 Sutton Rd, Erdington, West Midlands B23 6QH; Tel 0121 373 8486

HOMES FOR CHILDREN WITH DISABILITIES

Charles House Children's Home Charles Hse, 501 Rednal Rd, West Heath, West Midlands B38 8HS; Tel 0121 458 3733
   Short stay–learning difficulty

Edgwood Road Children's Home 95–101 Edgwood Rd, Hawkesley, West Midlands B38 9RU; Tel 0121 433 4316

Jubilee House Children's Home Jubilee Hse, 89 Cambourne Cl, Aston, Birmingham, West Midlands B6 5ER; Tel 0121 328 0176
   Learning or physical disabilities

Packington Avenue Children's Home 308 Packington Ave, Shard End, Birmingham, West Midlands B34 7RT; Tel 0121 747 5478

6

Reynoldstown Road Children's Home 86 Reynoldstown Rd, Bromford Bridge, Birmingham, West Midlands B36 8UG; Tel 0121 747 9330
Learning difficulties.

Warwick House Children's Home Warwick Hse, 948 Warwick Rd, Acocks Grn, Birmingham, West Midlands B27 6QG; Tel 0121 706 0248
Learning difficulties.

YOUTH OFFENDING TEAMS

All Saints Street Juvenile Justice Team Hockley, Birmingham, West Midlands B18 7RJ; Tel 0121 554 6201; Fax 0121 523 8231

Common Lane Juvenile Justice Team 15 Common La, Washwood Heath, Birmingham, West Midlands B8 2US; Tel 0121 327 2727; Fax 0121 327 3182

Highgate Centre 157–159 St. Luke's Rd, Highgate, Birmingham, West Midlands B5 7DA; Tel 0121 464 1570; Fax 0121 464 1595

Halescroft Square Juvenile Justice Team Shenley Hill, Northfield, Birmingham, West Midlands B31 1HD; Tel 0121 476 5111; Fax 0121 411 2198

Pype Hayes Youth Justice Team Pype Hayes Hall, Pype Hayes Pk, Birmingham, West Midlands B24 0HG; Tel 0121 303 0252; Fax 0121 464 0921

Services for People with Specific Needs

DAY CENTRES FOR PEOPLE WITH LEARNING DISABILITIES

Alderman Bowen Day Centre 125 Broadway Ave, Birmingham, West Midlands B9 5YD; Tel 0121 766 7382
East

Aldridge Road Day Centre 127 Aldridge Rd, Perry Barr, Birmingham, West Midlands B42 2ET; Tel 0121 356 5161
West

Bell Barn Day Centre 70 Spring Rd, Edgbaston, Birmingham, West Midlands B15 2HA; Tel 0121 446 4540
Central

Collingwood Day Centre 25 West Heath Rd, Birmingham, West Midlands B31 3TN; Tel 0121 477 8022
South

Eastview House Day Centre Eastview Hse, Shooters Hill, off Eastview Rd, Birmingham, West Midlands B72 1HX; Tel 0121 355 3021
North

Ebrook Day Centre Shooter's Hill, Eastview Rd, Sutton Coldfield, West Midlands B72 1HX; Tel 0121 355 5736
North

Employment Preparation Team 61 Inkerman St, Nichells, Birmingham, West Midlands B7 4SB; Tel 0121 303 8479; Fax 0121 303 4837

Harbourne Day Centre 370 West Blvd, Harbourne, Birmingham, West Midlands B32 2PP; Tel 0121 426 1752; Fax 0121 426 6455
Central

Hockley Day Centre 27 All Saints Rd, Hockley, Birmingham, West Midlands B18 5QB; Tel 0121 464 1281
West

Linkway Day Centre Kennedy Hse, Bottecourt Rd, West Midlands B29 5TE; Tel 0121 427 6760
South

Moseley Day Centre 1 Amesbury Rd, Moseley, Birmingham, West Midlands B13 8LD; Tel 0121 303 0249
South

Sparkbrook Resource Centre 362 Moseley Rd, Birmingham, West Midlands B12 9AZ; Tel 0121 303 0752
Central

Strawberry Studio Day Centre Bierton Rd Centre for the LD, Bierton Rd South, Yardley, West Midlands B25 8PQ; Tel 0121 303 6364

Tyburn Road Day Centre 581 Tyburn Rd, Erdington, Birmingham, West Midlands B24 9RX; Tel 0121 303 9747
North

RESIDENTIAL HOMES FOR PEOPLE WITH LEARNING DISABILITIES

Alderlea Residential Home 32 Middle Park Rd, Birmingham, West Midlands B29 4BJ; Tel 0121 475 1683

Allenscroft Road Residential Home 153 Allenscroft Rd, Kings Heath, Birmingham, West Midlands B14 6RP; Tel 0121 444 7097

Berners Street Residential Home 30 Berners St, Lozells, Birmingham, West Midlands B19 2DR; Tel 0121 551 5051

Elms Residential Home 20–22 Alwold Rd, Weoley Castle, West Midlands B29 5RT; Tel 0121 427 6234

Firs Residential Home 31 Springfield St, Ladywood, Birmingham, West Midlands B18 7AU; Tel 0121 454 4651

Holland Street Residential Home 76 Holland St, Sutton Coldfield, West Midlands B72 1RR; Tel 0121 354 2789

Howard House 2 Villa Wlk, Birmingham, West Midlands B19 2XJ; Tel 0121 554 0296

Laurels Residential Home 65 Frederick Rd, Stechford, Birmingham, West Midlands B33 8AE; Tel 0121 784 5222

Limes Residential Home 65–67 Cadnam Cl, Harborne, Birmingham, West Midlands B17 0PX; Tel 0121 472 7169

Poplars Residential Home 889 Chester Rd, Birmingham, West Midlands B24 0BS; Tel 0121 373 0288

Sellywick Road Residential Home 16 Sellywick Rd, Birmingham, West Midlands B29 7JA; Tel 0121 472 8266; Fax 0121 472 8878

Willows Residential Home 1 Park Rd, Hockley, Birmingham, West Midlands B18 5JH; Tel 0121 554 1427

DAY CENTRES FOR PEOPLE WITH MENTAL HEALTH PROBLEMS

Albert Road Day Centre 198 Albert Rd, Birmingham, West Midlands B21 9JT; Tel 0121 523 4133

Bierton Road Day Centre Bierton Road School, Birmingham, West Midlands B25 8PY; Tel 0121 789 9724

Hawkesley Day Centre 2 Stockmans Cl, King's Norton, West Midlands B38 9TS; Tel 0121 459 6872

Main Street Mental Health Resource Centre 86 Main St, Sparkbrook, Birmingham, West Midlands B11 1RS; Tel 0121 773 2922

Saltley Day Centre St. Mary's and St. John's Church Hall, 12 Naseby Rd, Birmingham, West Midlands B8 3HE; Tel 0121 327 3223; Fax 0121 326 7806

Springfields Day Centre Church of Prophecy, Broad Rd, Birmingham, West Midlands B27 7UZ; Tel 0121 678 4050

Summerhill Centre 23 Summerhill Terr, Birmingham, West Midlands B1 3RA; Tel 0121 233 3072; Fax 0121 236 6814

Tudor Rose Centre Frankley Community High School, New St, Frankley, West Midlands B45 0EU; Tel 0121 457 9669; Fax 0121 453 7177

Yewcroft Resource Centre Court Oak Rd, Harborne, Birmingham, West Midlands B17 9AB; Tel 0121 678 3550

ACCOMMODATION FOR PEOPLE WITH MENTAL HEALTH PROBLEMS

The Rowans Home 192 Herbert Rd, Small Heath, Birmingham, West Midlands B10 0PR; Tel 0121 773 5993
Contact B. Broomes

Southfield Home 90 Gillott Rd, Edgbaston, Birmingham, West Midlands B16 0ES; Tel 0121 454 3427; Fax 0121 454 1544

DAY CENTRES FOR PEOPLE WITH A PHYSICAL DISABILITY

Bordesley Green Day Centre 31 Broadway Ave, Birmingham, West Midlands B9 5LY; Tel 0121 773 1823

Elwood Day Centre 270 Reservoir Rd, Erdington, Birmingham, West Midlands B23 6DE; Tel 0121 382 7328

The Fairway Day Centre 2 The Fairway, off Wychall La, Birmingham, West Midlands B38 8XJ; Tel Direct Meals Kitchen 0121 459 4811 Office 0121 459 4994

Prospect Hall Day Centre 12 College Wlk, Birmingham, West Midlands B29 6LE; Tel 0121 472 5115

Skipton Road Day Centre 14 Skipton Rd, Birmingham, West Midlands B16 8JJ; Tel 0121 303 0160

HOME FOR PEOPLE WITH A PHYSICAL DISABILITY

The Beeches, 43 Frances Rd, Ladywood, Birmingham, West Midlands B16 8SX; Tel 0121 454 2986

DAY CENTRES FOR ELDERLY PEOPLE

African-Caribbean Day Centre for the Elderly Kings Heath Community Centre, 8 Heathfield Rd, Birmingham, West Midlands B14 7DB; Tel 0121 443 1047

Annie Wood House Day Centre for the Elderly 131 Alma Way, Newtown, Birmingham, West Midlands B19 2LS; Tel 0121 523 0928
Manager Ruth Lawrence

Baker Street Day Centre for the Elderly 1 Baker St, Small Heath, Birmingham, West Midlands B10 9QX; Tel 0121 772 3682
Manager Madhavi Honap

Barncroft Day Centre for the Elderly 574 College Rd, Erdington, Birmingham, West Midlands B44 0JD; Tel 0121 373 2325

Bequest Hall Day Centre for the Elderly 41 Dimmingsdale Bank, Woodgate Valley, Birmingham, West Midlands B32 1ST; Tel 0121 421 7928

Briarscroft Day Centre for the Elderly 127 Crossfield Rd, Birmingham, West Midlands B33 9QB; Tel 0121 246 4000

Bushmere Day Centre for the Elderly 137 Edenbridge Rd, Hall Grn, Birmingham, West Midlands B28 8PN; Tel 0121 678 3755

Callowbrook Day Centre for the Elderly 96 The Roundabout, Northfield, Birmingham, West Midlands B31 2TX; Tel 0121 477 5151

Chamberlain House Day Centre for the Elderly 2 Yew Tree Rd, Moseley, Birmingham, West Midlands B13 8QG; Tel 0121 303 0879

Edwin Arrowsmith Day Centre for the Elderly 8 Payton Rd, Handsworth, Birmingham, West Midlands B21 0HP; Tel 0121 523 3145

Evergreen Day Centre for the Elderly Richard Lawn Hse, 102 St. Vincent St, Birmingham, West Midlands B16 8EB; Tel 0121 236 8671

Isis Day Centre for the Elderly 171 Nineveh Rd, Handsworth, Birmingham, West Midlands B21 0SY; Tel 0121 523 3116

George Canning Day Centre for the Elderly 40–42 Old Moat Way, Ward End, Birmingham, West Midlands B8 2DL; Tel 0121 322 2342

Livingstone Day Centre for the Elderly 50 Livingstone Rd, Perry Bar, Birmingham, West Midlands B20 2LL; Tel 0121 356 7136

Lyttleton House Day Centre for the Elderly 1 Ormond Rd, Frankley, Rubery, West Midlands B45 0JD; Tel 0121 460 1150

Magnolia Day Centre for the Elderly 73 Conybere St, Birmingham, West Midlands B12 0YL; Tel 0121 440 2875

Marsh Lane Day Centre for the Elderly 79 Marsh La, Erdington, Birmingham, West Midlands B23 6HY; Tel 0121 685 6805

Maypole Grove Day Centre for the Elderly 20 Maypole Gr, Warstock, Birmingham, West Midlands B14 4LP; Tel 0121 430 7070

Milan Asian Day Centre for the Elderly 37 Broadway Ave, Birmingham, West Midlands B9 5LY; Tel 0121 766 6923

Normanhurst Day Centre for the Elderly 40 Sutton Rd, Erdington, Birmingham, West Midlands B23 5QT; Tel 0121 384 7093

Park Hill Day Centre for the Elderly 7 Park Hill Dr, Handsworth Wood, Birmingham, West Midlands B20 1DU; Tel 0121 523 4766

Ruby Rhydderch Day Centre for the Elderly 2 Ipstones Ave, Stechford, Birmingham, West Midlands B33 2DZ; Tel 0121 789 7566

Sahara Asian Day Centre for the Elderly 46 Tern Gr, Kings Norton, Birmingham, West Midlands B38 9DN; Tel 0121 486 2963

St. Stephens Day Centre for the Elderly 171 Nineveh Rd, Birmingham, West Midlands B21 0SY; Tel 0121 255 7685

Shakti Asian Day Centre for the Elderly 117 Highgate St, Birmingham, West Midlands B12 0XR; Tel 0121 440 3338

Victor Yates (Chinese Cheing Ching Day Centre) Boulton Est, Camden St, Birmingham, West Midlands B18 7PW; Tel 0121 554 4997

Weatherdale Unit Day Centre for the Elderly 31 Weather Oak, Harborne, Birmingham, West Midlands B17 9DD; Tel 0121 427 1607

Weatheroak Day Centre for the Elderly Cotteridge Church, 24 Pershore Rd South, Birmingham, West Midlands B30 3EJ; Tel 0121 678 3570

Yardley Grange Calabash Day Centre for the Elderly 389 Church Rd, Yardley, Birmingham, West Midlands B33 9PA; Tel 0121 784 1636
Manager Jackie Wilson

DAY CENTRE FOR SINGLE HOMELESS

23 Summer Hill Terr, Birmingham, West Midlands B1 3RA; Tel 0121 233 3072

REHABILITATION UNIT FOR PEOPLE WITH SIGHT LOSS

Duchess Rd Rehabilitation Unit for People with Sight Loss, 78–81 Duchess Rd, Birmingham, West Midlands B16 8JD; Tel 0121 445 0045

FAMILY CENTRES

Belgravia Close Family Centre 65 Belgravia Cl, Birmingham, West Midlands B5 7LP; Tel 0121 440 1432

Cape Street Family Centre 42 Cape St, Winson Grn, Birmingham, West Midlands B18 4LE; Tel 0121 454 6595

Louise Road Family Centre 21 Louise Rd, Handsworth, Birmingham, West Midlands B21 0RY; Tel 0121 250 3717

Windsor Street South Family Centre 16 Windsor St South, Nechells, Birmingham, West Midlands B7 4HY; Tel 0121 685 5510

Education Service

Council Hse Extension, Margaret St, Birmingham, West Midlands B3 3BU; Tel 0121 303 2590; Fax 0121 303 1318
Chief Education Officer Tony Howell

EDUCATION WELFARE SERVICE

Central Area Education Welfare Service St. Andrew's School, St. Andrew's Rd, Birmingham, West Midlands B9 4NG; Tel 0121 303 1200; Fax 0121 303 1211
Area Manager Debbie Henry

6

North Area Education Welfare Service The Council Hse, King Edwards Sq, Sutton Coldfield, West Midlands B73 6AN; Tel 0121 303 8900; Fax 0121 303 1448
Area Manager Wal Holmes

South Area Education Welfare Service Martineau Centre, 74 Balden Rd, Harborne, Birmingham, West Midlands B32 2EH; Tel 0121 303 8050; Fax 0121 303 8054
Area Manager Sue Clarke

EDUCATION PSYCHOLOGY SERVICE

Room 326, Third Fl, Education Offices, Margaret St, Birmingham, West Midlands B3 3BU; Tel 0121 303 6689; Fax 0121 303 3716
Strategic Manager (Inclusion)/Chief Educational Psychologist Chris Atkinson
Deputy Chief Educational Psychologist Francis Mallon

Martineau Centre Balden Rd, Harborne, Birmingham, West Midlands B32 2EH; Tel 0121 303 1166; Fax 0121 303 1168
Senior Educational Psychologist Hugh Williams
Senior Educational Psychologist Linda Wynne

Psychology Service 8a The Gdns, Fentham Rd, Erdington, Birmingham, West Midlands B23 6AG; Tel 0121 303 0100; Fax 0121 303 0094
Senior Educational Psychologist Amanda Daniels
Senior Educational Psychologist Jill Copley

COURT CHILD EMPLOYMENT

35–50 Orphanage Rd, Erdington, West Midlands B24 9HL; Tel (Child Employment) 0121 303 5123; (Court Office) 0121 303 5124; (Children in Entertainment) 0121 303 5125; Fax 0121 303 5122

HOSPITAL SCHOOLS AND SPECIAL UNITS

City Hospital Ward 10, Dudley Rd, Birmingham, West Midlands B18 7QH; Tel 0121 507 5578; 0121 507 5579; Fax 0121 507 5579
Ward Manager Linda Freakley

Diana Princess of Wales Children's Hospital Steelhouse La, Birmingham, West Midlands B4 6NH; Tel 0121 333 8792; Fax 0121 333 8791
Senior Head (Education) Colin Lees

Good Hope Hospital Harvey Ward, Rectory Rd, Birmingham, West Midlands B75 7RR; Tel 0121 378 2211 ext 3124; Fax 0121 378 6156
Senior Head (Education) Diane Hoban

Heartlands Hospital New Paediatric Unit Bordesley Green Rd, Birmingham, West Midlands B9 5SS; Tel 0121 424 3824; Fax 0121 424 1827
Senior Head (Education) Diane Hoban

Northfield Centre George Auden Site, Bell Hill, Birmingham, West Midlands B31 1LD; Tel 0121 475 3826 0121 477 0362; Fax 0121 475 1167
Senior Head (Education) Anthea Owen

Parkway Centre St. Thomas Centre, Bell Barn Rd, Birmingham, West Midlands B15 2AF; Tel 0121 666 6409; Fax 0121 666 6956
Head (Education) Steve Hill (Acting)

Referrals and Home Teaching St. Thomas Centre, Bell Barn Rd, Birmingham, West Midlands B15 2AF; Tel 0121 666 6409; Fax 0121 666 6936
Senior Head (Education) Steve Penny

Willows Centre Queensbridge Rd, Birmingham, West Midlands B13 8QB; Tel 0121 449 3322; Fax 0121 442 2274
Head (Education) Clive Hartwell

Woodlands Hospital Ward 11, Bristol Rd South, Birmingham, West Midlands B31 2AP; Tel 0121 685 4246; 0121 685 4247; Fax 0121 685 4247
Ward Manager Caroline Vale

Yardley Green Hospital Site Yardley Green Rd, Birmingham, West Midlands B9 5PX; Tel 0121 753 3831; Fax 0121 772 3184
Senior Head (Education) Diane Hoban

SPECIAL SCHOOLS

Baskerville Residential School Fellows La, Birmingham, West Midlands B17 9TS; E-mail enquiry@baskvill.bham.sch.uk; Tel 0121 427 3191; Fax 0121 428 2204
Headteacher Rosemary Adams
Autism

Beaufort School 16 Coleshill Rd, Birmingham, West Midlands B36 8AA; E-mail enquiry@beaufort.bham.sch.uk; Tel 0121 783 3886; Fax 0121 783 6994
Headteacher Nick Rigby (Acting)

Braidwood School Perry Common Rd, Birmingham, West Midlands B23 7AT; E-mail enquiry@brdwood.bham.sch.uk; Tel 0121 373 5558; Fax 0121 382 5844
Headteacher Fiona Ison-Jacques
Deafness

Brays School Brays Rd, Birmingham, West Midlands B26 1NS; E-mail enquiry@brays.bham.sch.uk; Tel (Outreach Department) 0121 742 7203; 0121 743 5730; 0121 743 7005; Fax 0121 742 1567
Headteacher Mr M.J. Chinner
PH

Bridge School 290 Reservoir Rd, Erdington, Birmingham, West Midlands B23 6DE; E-mail enquiry@bridgesp.bham.sch.uk; Tel 0121 373 8265; Fax 0121 377 7619
Headteacher Steve White

Calthorpe School Sports College Darwin St, Birmingham, West Midlands B12 0TJ; E-mail enquiry@calthorp.bham.sch.uk; Tel 0121 773 4637; Fax 0121 773 0708
Headteacher Graham Hardy

Cherry Oak School 60 Frederick Rd, Birmingham, West Midlands B29 6PB; E-mail enquiry@cherryoak.bham.sch.uk; Tel 0121 464 2037; Fax 0121 464 5219
Headteacher Lesley Fowler

Dame Ellen Pinsent School Ardencote Rd, Birmingham, West Midlands B13 0RW; E-mail enquiry@depinsnt.bham.sch.uk; Tel 0121 444 2487; Fax 0121 444 7295
Headteacher Sylvia Rodgers

Fox Hollies School 419 Fox Hollies Rd, Birmingham, West Midlands B27 7QA; E-mail enquiry@foxholli.bham.sch.uk; Tel 0121 464 6566; Fax 0121 464 4148
Headteacher Kathryn O'Leary

Hallmoor School Hallmoor Rd, Birmingham, West Midlands B33 9QY; E-mail enquiry@hallmoor.bham.sch.uk; Tel 0121 783 3972; Fax 0121 783 3481
Headteacher Susan Charvis

Hamilton School Hamilton Rd, Birmingham, West Midlands B21 8AH; E-mail enquiry@hamilton.bham.sch.uk; Tel 0121 554 1676; Fax 0121 554 4808
Headteacher Nigel Carter

Hunter's Hill (Residential) School Spirehouse La, Blackwell, Bromsgrove, West Midlands B60 1QD; E-mail enquiry@hunthill.bham.sch.uk; Tel 0121 445 1320; Fax 0121 445 2496
Headteacher K. Lewis

James Brindley School Administration Office, St. Thomas Centre, Bell Barn Rd, Birmingham, West Midlands B15 2AF; E-mail enquiry@jamesbrindley.bham.sch.uk; Tel 0121 666 6409; Fax 0121 666 6956
Headteacher Lynne John

Kingstanding School Old Oscott Hill, Birmingham, West Midlands B44 9SP; E-mail enquiry@kingstnd.bham.sch.uk; Tel 0121 360 8222; Fax 0121 366 6394
Headteacher Michele Pipe

Langley School Lindridge Rd, Birmingham, West Midlands B75 7HU; E-mail enquiry@langley.bham.sch.uk; Tel 0121 329 2929; Fax 0121 311 1513
Headteacher Alan Reid

Lindsworth School North Rowden Dr, King's Norton, West Midlands B23 5UL; E-mail lindsworth.north@lindsworth.bham.sch.uk; Tel 0121 250 5151; Fax 0121 250 5153
Headteacher Mike Clarke

Lindsworth School South Monyhull Hall Rd, King's Norton, West Midlands B30 3QA; E-mail reception.school@lindsworth.bham.sch.uk; Tel 0121 693 5363; Fax 0121 693 5369
Headteacher Mike Clarke

Longmoor School and Residential Unit Coppice View Rd, Sutton Coldfield, Birmingham, West Midlands B73 6UE; E-mail enquiry@longmoor.bham.sch.uk; Tel 0121 353 7833; Fax 0121 353 9228
Headteacher Veronica Jenkins

Longwill School Bell Hill, Northfield, Birmingham, West Midlands B31 1LD; E-mail peter.plant@longwill.bham.sch.uk; Tel 0121 475 3923; Fax 0121 476 6362
Headteacher Peter Plant
Deafness

Mayfield School Finch Rd, Birmingham, West Midlands B19 1HP; E-mail paul.jenkins@mayfield.bham.sch.uk; Tel 0121 464 4278; Fax 0121 464 4279
Headteacher Paul Jenkins

The Pines School Dreghorn Rd, Birmingham, West Midlands B36 8LL; E-mail enquiry@pinessp.bham.sch.uk; Tel 0121 464 6136; Fax 0121 464 3149
Headteacher S.G. Tuft

Priestley Smith School Perry Common Rd, Birmingham, West Midlands B23 7AT; E-mail clewis@priestly.bham.sch.uk; Tel 0121 373 5493; Fax 0121 382 5471
Headteacher Christopher Lewis
PS

Queensbury School Wood End Rd, Birmingham, West Midlands B24 8BL; E-mail enquiry@queenbry.bham.sch.uk; Tel 0121 373 5731; Fax 0121 478 1585
Headteacher William Warriner

Selly Oak School Oak Tree La, Birmingham, West Midlands B29 6HZ; E-mail enquiry@sellyoak.bham.sch.uk; Tel 0121 472 0876; Fax 0121 415 5379
Headteacher R. Dowling

Skilts (Residential) School Gorcott Hill, nr Redditch, Birmingham, West Midlands B98 9ET; E-mail enquiry@skilts.bham.sch.uk; Tel 01527 853851; Fax 01527 857949
Headteacher Charles Herriotts

Springfield House (Residential) School Kenilworth Rd, Knowle, Solihull, West Midlands B93 0AJ; E-mail enquiry@spfldhs.bham.sch.uk; Tel 01564 772772; Fax 01564 771767
Headteacher Pat Jacques
Various specialisms

Uffculme School Queensbridge Rd, Birmingham, West Midlands B13 8QB; E-mail enquiry@uffculme.bham.sch.uk; Tel 0121 464 5250; Fax 0121 464 2207
Headteacher Alex Macdonald

Victoria School Bell Hill, Northfield, Birmingham, West Midlands B31 1LD; E-mail enquiry@victoria.bham.sch.uk; Tel 0121 476 9478; Fax 0121 411 2357
Headteacher Jim Kane
PH

Wilson Stuart School Perry Common Rd, Birmingham, West Midlands B23 7AT; E-mail enquiry@wilsonst.bham.sch.uk; Tel 0121 373 4475; Fax 0121 373 9842
Headteacher Anne Tomkinson
PH

BLACKBURN WITH DARWEN BOROUGH COUNCIL
council.blackburnworld.com

In April 1998 both Blackburn with Darwen and Blackpool Councils became unitary authorities and are listed alphabetically within this chapter. The rest of Lancashire retains a two-tier structure.
Political Composition: Lab: 36, Con: 16, LD: 8, BNP: 1, Ind: 1.
Town Hall, Blackburn BB1 7DY;
URL council.blackburnworld.com;
E-mail phil.watson@blackburn.gov.uk; Tel 01254 585585; Fax 01254 680870
Chief Executive Phillip Watson

6

Social Services Department
Jubilee Hse, Jubilee St, Blackburn BB1 1ET;
URL www.socialservices.blackburnworld.com;
E-mail stephen.sloss@blackburn.gov.uk; Tel 01254 583328; (Emergencies (out-of-office hours)) 01254 587547; Fax 01254 587591
Director Stephen Sloss
Deputy Director Vacancy
Assistant Director (Adults) D. Kerambrum
Assistant Director (Strategy and Support) C. Shaw
Assistant Director (Children and Families) B. Peake

Social Services Executive Group
Executive Member Maureen Bateson
9 Kings Rd, Darwen, Blackburn; Tel 01254 201889
Members of the Executive Group
M. Rishton, Y. Jan-Virmani.

AREA OFFICE
Darwen Social Services
Town Hall, Darwen, Blackburn BB3 1BQ; Tel 01254 222191
Emergency Duty Team Queens Park Hospital, Blackburn BB2 1SN; Tel 01254 587547
Contact Lynne Simpson

DAY NURSERIES
Albion Street Day Nursery Albion St, Blackburn BB2 4LX; Tel 01254 53640
Contact Christine Smalley
(52)

Churchill House Day Nursery Churchill Rd, Blackburn BB1 5NX; Tel 01254 52816
Contact A. Gleade
(42)

Hancock Street Day Nursery Hancock St, Blackburn BB2 2LZ; Tel 01254 54755
Contact Dinah Wilson
(50)

Lincoln Road Day Nursery Lincoln Rd, Blackburn BB1 1TP; Tel 01254 698613
Contact E. Kilshaw
(52)

CHILDREN WITH DISABILITIES

Jubilee Hse, Jubilee St, Blackburn BB2 3HH; Tel 01254 587732
Contact Margaret Adams
Children's special needs community support.

CHILDREN'S COMMUNITY HOMES

Anchor Avenue Children's Home 21–23 Anchor Ave, Darwen, Blackburn BB3 0AZ; Tel 01254 761827
(6)

Cherry Tree Lane Children's Home Cherry Tree La, Cherry Tree, Blackburn BB2 5NX; Tel 01254 202405
(8)

Hamer Avenue Children's Home 17–19 Hamer Ave, Blackburn BB1 3NR; Tel 01254 661044

Lytham Road Leaving Care Team 128–130 Lytham Rd, Blackburn BB2 3EB; Tel 01254 55356
Contact Jenny Dillon

Whalley New Road Children's Home 594 Whalley New Rd, Blackburn BB1 9AZ; Tel 01254 248565
Contact S.M. Martin
(5)

SHORT TERM CARE UNIT FOR CHILDREN WITH DISABILITIES

The Gatehouse, 70 Whalley New Rd, Blackburn BB1 6JT; Tel 01254 57361
(6)

YOUTH OFFENDING TEAM

Bank Hse, Wellington St, St. John's, Blackburn BB1 8AF; Tel 01254 299800
Contact Dave Fleming

FAMILY DAY CENTRES

Lord Street Children's Centre Lord St, Darwen, Blackburn BB3 0HD

Roman Road Family Centre Fishmoor Dr, Blackburn BB2 3UY; Tel 01254 680650
Contact D. Whelan
(76)

Seven Trees Children's Centre Whalley St, Blackburn BB1 6NZ; Tel 01254 681972
Contact Sheila Moss
(30)

MULTIPURPOSE DAY CENTRE

Mill Hill Sheltered Workshop and Resource Centre Mill Hill, Blackburn, BB2 2RB; Tel 01254 605940
Contact John Almond

DISPERSED HOUSING

Blackburn Supported Living Mowbray Lodge, Blackburn BB2 1SN; Tel 01254 504460
Contact T. Edmunson

Darwen Supported Living Darwen, Blackburn BB3 3LD; Tel 01254 504460
Contact Gary Cornwell

Tower View Day Service Marsh House La, Darwen, Blackburn BB3 3JB; Tel 01254 703721
Contact S. Almond
Services for adults with learning disabilities.
(5)

DAY CENTRES FOR PEOPLE WITH LEARNING DISABILITIES

Mount Pleasant Resource Centre Larkhill, Blackburn BB1 5BN; Tel 01254 662011
Contact Y. Statham
Mental health day centre/drop-in centre.
(30)

Mowbray Lodge Day Centre Park Lee Rd, Blackburn BB2 3ES; Tel 01254 57725
Contact Louise Griffin
(82)

Stansfield Centre Stansfield St, Blackburn BB2 2NG; Tel 01254 54293
Contact D. Ford
(50)

SERVICES FOR PEOPLE WITH MENTAL HEALTH PROBLEMS

Blackburn Community Mental Health Team Clarence Hse, Clarence St, Blackburn BB1 8AN; Tel 01254 342700
Contact L. Griffiths

Darwen Community Mental Health Team 175a Blackburn Rd, Darwen, Blackburn BB3 1HL; Tel 01254 771779
Contact A. Mellor

Hope Street Supported Tenancy Scheme 6 Hope St, Blackburn BB2 1DY; Tel 01254 55627
Contact L. Smith

Supported Tenancy Scheme 84 Haslingden Rd, Blackburn BB2 3HW; Tel 01254 580038
Contact Sue Johnson

DAY CENTRE FOR OLDER PEOPLE

Ardley Day Centre Bent St, Blackburn BB2 1NG; Tel 01254 661823
Contact Margaret Golding
(100)

RESIDENTIAL HOMES FOR OLDER PEOPLE

There are six local authority homes for older people and one rehabilitation unit. Tel 01254 587991
Contact Lynne Haworth

REHABILITATION FOR PEOPLE WITH SENSORY IMPAIRMENT

Swallow Drive Resource Centre Blakewater Lodge, Swallow Dr, Blackburn BB1 6LE; Tel 01254 260230
Contact Sheila Latham; Tel 01254 587849

Education and Lifelong Learning Department

Town Hall, Blackburn BB1 7DY; Tel 01254 585194; Fax 01254 698388
Director (Education and and Lifelong Learning)
Peter Morgan

SPECIAL SCHOOLS

Blackburn Fernhurst School Heys La, Blackburn, Lancashire BB2 4NW; Tel 01254 261655; Fax 01254 673375
Headteacher Drew Crawshawe

Blackburn Broadlands School Roman Rd, Blackburn BB1 2LA; Tel 01254 56044; Fax 01254 278760
Headteacher D.H. Mitchell

Blackburn Crosshill School Shadsworth Rd, Blackburn BB1 2HR; Tel 01254 265728; 01254 667713; Fax 01254 664449
Headteacher M.J. Hatch

Blackburn Newfield School Roman Rd, Blackburn BB1 2LA; Tel 01254 588600; Fax 01254 588601
Headteacher J.B. Barrie

Blackburn Partial Hearing SERF (Primary) School Lower Darwen CP, Milking La, Lower Darwen, Blackburn BB3 0RB; Tel 01254 55639; Fax 01254 668065

Blackburn Partial Hearing SERF (Secondary) School Queens Park CH, Shadsworth Rd, Blackburn BB1 2HT; Tel 01254 580665; Fax 01254 697072

Darwen Sunnyhurst Centre Salisbury Rd, Darwen, Blackburn BB3 1HZ; Tel 01254 702317; Fax 01254 761235
Headteacher Brian Peacock

SCHOOL SUPPORT AGENCY

Special Educational Needs Support Service Education – Lifelong Learning, Jubilee Hse, Jubilee St, Blackburn BB1 1ET; Tel 01254 587268
Contact Viviene Smith

BLACKPOOL BOROUGH COUNCIL
www.blackpool.gov.uk

In April 1998 Blackpool and Blackburn both became unitary authorities. The rest of Lancashire retains a two-tier structure.
Political Composition: Lab: 25, Con: 15, LD: 4
Town Hall, Blackpool FY1 1AD;
     URL www.blackpool.gov.uk; Tel 01253 477477;
     Fax 01253 477101
Chief Executive Steve Weaver, DipCRP
Head (Corporate Policy) Tony Williams; Tel 01253 477111
Head (Tourism) Jane Seddon
Corporate Director (Business Services) Julian Kearsley

Housing and Social Services Department

Progress Hse, Clifton Rd, Blackpool FY4 4US;
     E-mail social.services@blackpool.gov.uk; Tel 01253 477666; Fax 01253 477577
Director (Housing and Social Services) S.R. Pullan
Assistant Director (Children's Services) S. Sutherland
Assistant Director (Adults) J. Jaynes
Assistant Director (Landlord Services) P. Jefferson
Assistant Director (Policy, Planning and Support) Vacancy
Assistant Director (Housing Business Support) V. Bowen

Executive

Lab: 14, Con: 3, LD: 1
10 Lynwood Ave, Layton, Blackpool FY3 7DG; Tel 01253 397913
Portfolio Holder for Social Services and Health S. Wright (Lab)
Portfolio Holder for Lifelong Learning and Children's Services Cllr Ivan Taylor
179 Devonshire Rd,, Blackpool FY3 7DD
Members of the Executive
Lab: Cllr E. Collett, Cllr R. Fisher, Cllr P. Jackson, Cllr D. Owen.
LD: Cllr R. Wynne.

Public Contact Office

South King St, Blackpool FY1 4TR; Tel 01253 477666

CHILD DEVELOPMENT AND SPECIAL NEEDS CENTRE

138 Stonyhill Ave, Blackpool FY3 9HF

CHILDREN'S COMMUNITY HOMES

Argosy Avenue Children's Home 3 Argosy Ave, Grange Pk, Blackpool FY3 7NN; Tel 01253 476940
Contact Barbara Eggleton
Independence training unit.
     (5)

Bispham Road Children's Home 331 Bispham Rd, Blackpool FY2 0HH; Tel 01253 476770
     (6)

Blackpool Resource and Reception Centre (a split site facility) 138 Stonyhill Ave, Blackpool FY3 9HF; Tel 01253 343306; 01253 355526; Fax 01253 351727

COMMMUNITY HOME FOR CHILDREN WITH DISABILITIES

Westbury Lodge Community Home 160 Whitegate Dr, Blackpool FY2 1HF; Tel 01253 477794
Service Manager Billy Grace
A residential setting providing short breaks for children/young people with disabilities.
     (18)

YOUTH JUSTICE CENTRE

Devonshire Centre 307–309 Church St, Blackpool FY1 3PF; Tel 01253 392323
Contact Mary Storey
     (8)

FAMILY CENTRES

Bispham Family Centre 333 Bispham Rd, Bispham, Blackpool FY2 0HH; Tel 01253 358809
Contact Angela Chapman
     (50)

Whitegate Day Family Centre rear 162 Whitegate Dr, Blackpool FY3 9HF; Tel 01253 768104
Contact Angela Chapman
Includes children with special needs.
     (50)

DAY CENTRES FOR PEOPLE WITH LEARNING DISABILITIES

Langdale Day Centre Langdale Rd, Blackpool FY4 4RR; Tel 01253 763578
Contact Vera Atkinson
     (90)

The Beeches Day Centre 292 Central Dr, Blackpool FY1 5JW; Tel 01253 477774
Contact Brenda Smith
Community Support Team.
     (21)

DAY CENTRE FOR PEOPLE WITH PHYSICAL AND SENSORY DISABILTIES

Whitegate Drive Resources Centre 259 Whitegate Dr, Blackpool FY3 9JL; Tel 01253 768873
Contact Christine Prestwood
Includes individual planning, training and skills development, community and social integration for people with physical disabilities.
     (100)

DAY CENTRE FOR OLDER PEOPLE

Highfield Day Centre Highfield Rd, South Shore, Blackpool FY4 3JU; Tel 01253 476460
Contact Ann Armstrong
     (50)

RESIDENTIAL HOMES FOR OLDER PEOPLE

Contact Christine Prestwood
There are two local authority homes for older people plus two specialist resource centres.

Education, Leisure and Cultural Services Department

Progress Hse, Clifton Rd, Blackpool FY4 4US; Tel 01253 477477; Fax 01253 476504
Director (Education, Leisure and Cultural Services) David Lund, BEd(Hons), MSc

6

SPECIAL SCHOOLS

Highfurlong School Blackpool Old Rd, Blackpool FY3 7LR;
Tel 01253 392188; Fax 01253 305600
Headteacher E.V. Jackson
Chair of Governors P. Higham
Mixed

Park School Whitegate Dr, Blackpool FY3 9HF;
E-mail keith.berry@park.blackpool.sch.uk; Tel 01253
764130; Fax 01253 791108
Headteacher K. Berry
Chair of Governors J.M. Allcock

Woodlands Special School Whitegate Dr, Blackpool
FY3 9HF;
E-mail samuel.forde@woodlands.blackpool.sch.uk;
Tel 01253 316722; Fax 01253 316723
Headteacher Sam Forde
Chair of Governors M. Laye

HEARING IMPAIRED CHILDREN (DAY UNIT)

Blackpool SERF for the Hearing Impaired (Primary) c/o
Waterloo Primary School, Waterloo Rd, Blackpool
FY4 3AG; Tel 01253 315370

SPEECH AND LANGUAGE UNIT

Speech and Language SERF c/o Stanley Infants School,
Wordsworth Ave, Blackpool FY3 9UR; Tel 01253 763601

CHILD DEVELOPMENT CENTRE

Child Development and Family Support Centre Blenheim
Hse, 145–147 Newton Dr, Blackpool FY3 8LZ; Tel 01253
397006; Fax 01253 379008

BOLTON METROPOLITAN BOROUGH COUNCIL

www.bolton.gov.uk

Population 266 100
Political Composition: Lab: 27, Con: 19, LD: 14
Civic Centre, Bolton, Greater Manchester BL1 1RU;
URL www.bolton.gov.uk; Tel 01204 333333; Fax 01204
331042
Mayor Cllr C. Morris
Leader of the Council Cllr R.L. Howarth
Chief Executive Bernard Knight
Director (Finance) S.M. Arnfield, IPFA
Director (Central Services) P. Wilson
Director (Commercial Services) A. Fisher
Director (Environment) R. Jefferson, MA, MPhil, MRTPI
District Medical Officer P. Elton

Social Services Department

Le Mans Cres, Civic Centre, Bolton, Greater Manchester
BL1 1SA; URL www.bolton.gov.uk;
E-mail social.services@bolton.gov.uk; Fax 01204 337269;
Minicom 01204 365963
Director (Social Services) Andy Robertson, BSc, MA,
CQSW
Director (Commissioning and Redesign) John Rutherford
Assistant Director (Children and Families Services)
L. Jones
Assistant Director (Business Services) C. Fish
Assistant Director (Adult Services) A. Kilpatrick
Senior Principal Officer (Children) Peter Jones
Principal Officer (Adults' First Contact) C. King

Principal Officer (Older People) Marie Moore
Principal Officer (Welfare Rights) S. Brown
Principal Officer (Disability Services) M. Tynan
Head (Provider Services for Older People) Angela Gannon
Team Leader (Family Placement Team) N. Robinson
Information Co-ordinator Barbara Thomley
Planning Officer (Management, Information and Research)
Margaret Ranyard
Customer Relations Officer Andrew Platt

TRAINING

Responsible for training professional and support staff in
the department.
Thomasson Training Centre, Devonshire Rd, Bolton,
Greater Manchester BL1 4PG; Tel 01204 337600
Principal Officer (Staff Development) Gill Stopforth

Social Services Committee

Con: 16, Lab: 31, LD: 13; Tel 01204 331098
Cabinet Member (Social Services and Health)
Cllr Madeline Murray
Opposition Leader Cllr Allan Rushton (Con)
Opposition Leader Cllr Barbara Ranson (LD)
Chair (Policy Development Group – Children)
Cllr Prentice Howarth
Chair (Policy Development Group – Health)
Cllr Margaret Clare

DISTRICT OFFICES

North East

Nessford Hse, Bolton, Greater Manchester BL2 2LS;
Tel (Children) 01204 337400; (Adults) 01204 33767

South East

Town Hall, Market St, Farnworth, Greater Manchester
BL4 7PD; Tel (Children) 01204 333555; (Adults) 01204
337738
Great Lever Health and Social Services Centre Rupert St,
Bolton, Greater Manchester BL3 6RN; Tel 01204 337743;
Fax 01204 362415; Minicom 01204 365964
Royal Bolton Hospital (Team for Older People) Minerva
Rd, Farnworth, Greater Manchester BL4 0JR; Tel 01204
390614
Team Leader T. Morris
Team Leader A. Callaghan

West

Town Hall, Market St, Westhoughton, Greater Manchester
BL5 3AW; Tel (Emergency Duty Team) 01204 337777;
01942 634560; Fax 01942 634560; Minicom 01942
840164

HEADQUARTERS AND WEST DISTRICT

Le Mans Cres, Civic Centre, Bolton, Greater Manchester
BL1 1SA; URL bolton.gov.uk;
E-mail social.services@bolton.gov.uk; Tel 01204 337210

FAMILY SUPPORT CENTRES

New Bury Family Support Centre 106–108 St. James St, New
Bury, Bolton, Greater Manchester BL4 9RG; Tel 01204
337384
Contact Chris Callaghan
(48)

Harvey Early Years Centre Pilkington St, Bolton, Greater
Manchester BL3 6HP; Tel 01204 337390
Contact M. Blowe
(50)

RESOURCE CENTRE FOR CHILDREN WITH DISABILITIES

Elizabeth Ashmore Hse Resource Centre for Children with Disabilities, Chorley New Rd, Bolton, Greater Manchester BL1 5BS; Tel 01204 337100
Contact Hilda Bolton

Children and Families Resource Centre Woodlands, Manchester Rd, Bolton, Greater Manchester BL3 2PQ; Tel 01204 337451; Fax 01204 337489
Principal Officer (Childrens Resources) Paul Biancardi; Tel 01204 337453
Principal Officer (Child Protection) Jane Middison; Tel 01204 337470
Principal Officer (Advice and Assessment) Tom O'Loughlin; Tel 01204 337460
Principal Officer (Family Support) Elizabeth Mannion; Tel 01204 337463

AFTER CARE TEAM

The Woodlands, Manchester Rd, Bolton, Greater Manchester BL3 2QP
Contact Janet Howells
Learning care.

LEARNING DISABILITIES

Falcon View Cotton St, Bolton, Greater Manchester BL1 3JN; Tel 01204 337500
(North East Day Services).
Contact A. McGann

The Harrowbys Mill St, Farnworth, Bolton, Greater Manchester BL4 7BH; Tel 01204 337633
(South East Day Services).
Contact Joan Howarth

West Day Services 13–15 Market St, Westhoughton, Greater Manchester BL5 3AH; Tel 01942 634575
(West Day Services)
Contact R. Bruce

SERVICES FOR PEOPLE WITH LEARNING DISABILITIES

Senior Principal Officer (Learning Disabilities)
Isobel Southern (Acting)
22 Longworth Rd, Horwich, Greater Manchester BL6 7BA; Tel 01204 337799
Principal Officer (Mental Health) J. Buckley
Park Hse, Laurel St, Bolton, Greater Manchester BL1 4RB; Tel 01204 337550

BOLTON EMPLOYMENT DEVELOPMENT SERVICE

Office Unit 3, Bolton Market, Bolton, Greater Manchester BL1 1TQ; Tel 01204 337523

DAY CENTRES FOR PEOPLE WITH LEARNING DISABILITIES, MENTAL HEALTH PROBLEMS AND PHYSICAL DISABILITIES

Learning Disabilities Day Centre 124 Newport St, Bolton, Greater Manchester BL3 6AB; Tel 01204 337064
Contact R. Bruce

Jubilee Centre Darley St, Bolton, Greater Manchester BL1 3DX; Tel 01204 337808
Contact D. Flounders
Physical Disabilities.

Park Lodge Day Centre Queens Pk, Park Rd, Bolton, Greater Manchester BL1 4RU; Tel 01204 337062
Contact D. Rowley
Mental Health.

NETWORK SUPPORTING PEOPLE WITH LEARNING DISABILITIES

North East District Network Back Olga St, Bolton, Greater Manchester BL1 3LZ; Tel 01204 337510
Contact Eileen Bennett

West District Network 22 Longworth Rd, Bolton, Greater Manchester BL6 7BA; Tel 01204 337087
Contact John Berry

South East District Network Harrowbys, Mill St, Farnworth, Bolton, Greater Manchester BL4 7BA; Tel 01204 337639 01204 363679
Contact J. Greenhalgh

NETWORK SUPPORTING PEOPLE WITH MENTAL HEALTH PROBLEMS

Mental Health Network 1st Fl, 6–12 New La, Bolton, Greater Manchester BL2 5NB; Tel 01204 337825; Fax 01204 337819
Contact D. Hudson

OLDER PEOPLE PROVIDER

Rupert St, Bolton, Greater Manchester BL3 6RN; Tel 01204 398331
Head (Provider Services) Angela Gannon
Group Manager (Residential and Community Care Centres) Jean Herod

SERVICES TO PEOPLE WITH VISUAL OR DUAL SENSORY IMPAIRMENT

The Jubilee Centre, Darley St, Bolton, Greater Manchester BL1 3DX; Tel 01204 337814; Fax 01204 337817
Contact Richard Bounds

COMMUNITY CARE CENTRES

Alderbank Community Care Centre Melville Rd, Kearsley, Greater Manchester BL4 8JD; Tel 01204 337791
Contact K. Wolstenholme

Horwich Day Centre Cedar Ave, Horwich, Greater Manchester BL6 6EU; Tel 01204 337700
Contact Paula Christian

Lilian Hamer Community Care Centre Deane Rd, Bolton, Greater Manchester BL3 5NR; Tel 01204 337581
Contact Jane Bowbaker

WINIFRED KETTLE COMMUNITY CARE CENTRE

Leigh Rd, Westhoughton, Greater Manchester BL5 2NE; Tel 01942 634566
Contact Alison Leaver

ACCOMMODATION FOR OLDER PEOPLE

There are 12 local authority homes for the elderly, two nursing homes, 33 residential homes (including one voluntary home) and 18 dual registered homes.

ADULT PLACEMENT SERVICE

Falcon View, Cotton St, Bolton, Greater Manchester BL1 3JN; Tel 01204 337764; Fax 01204 337527
Contact I. Southern
Contact Gina Stokes

DAY CENTRE FOR OLDER PEOPLE

Firwood Day Centre Crompton Way, Bolton, Greater Manchester BL2 2PE; Tel 01204 337733
Contact P. Lyons

HIGH DEPENDENCY SHELTERED HOUSING

Campbell House Campbell St, Farnworth, Bolton, Greater Manchester BL4 4HP; Tel 01204 337013
Contact Janine Smethurst

Eldon Street Sheltered Housing off Tonge Moor Rd, Bolton, Greater Manchester BL2 2JA; Tel 01204 337012
Contact Janet Halliwell (Acting)

Merton Sheltered Housing 2 Northwood Cres, off Deane Rd, Bolton, Greater Manchester BL3 5SE; Tel 01204 337008

6

SUPPORT SERVICES

Mayor St, Bolton, Greater Manchester BL3 5DT; Tel 01204 337615

Catering Services, c/o Le Mans Cres, Civic Centre, Bolton, Greater Manchester BL1 1SA, Tel 01204 391262.

Education and Culture Department

PO Box 53, Paderborn Hse, Bolton, Greater Manchester BL1 1JW; URL www.boltonlea.org.uk; Tel 01204 333333; Fax 01204 332228

Director (Education and Culture)   M. Blenkinsop, MSc
Deputy Director   B. Shaw
Assistant Director (Policy and Resources Division)   C. Swift, BA, MEd, CertEd
Assistant Director (Access and Inclusion Division)   S. Fazal
Assistant Director (Heritage, Information and Arts)   Stephanie Crossley; Fax 01204 332225
Head (Museums Services)   Steve Garland, AMA, MBA; Fax 01204 391352
Manager (School Finance Unit)   C. Davies
Head (Youth Service)   R. Miller
Manager (Personnel Unit)   Kathryn Ball
Manager (ICT Unit)   G.D. Smith, MMS, DMS; Tel 01204 332323; Fax 01204 332300
Manager (Special Needs and Transport Service)   C.F. Chisholm, BA
Manager (Pupil and Student Services)   V. Fogg
Manager (Strategic Services)   T. Sinkinson
Manager (Asset Management Unit)   J. Fletcher
Manager (Training)   Vacancy
Management Information Officer   John Curtis
Chief Adviser   S. Lowndes
Principal Educational Psychologist   P. Nicklin, MA
EBD Co-ordinator   J. Trevena
Principal Education Social Worker   I. Price, MA, MSc

EDUCATION SOCIAL WORK SERVICE

Castle Hill Centre, Castleton St, Bolton, Greater Manchester BL2 2JW

EDUCATIONAL PSYCHOLOGY SERVICE

Castle Hill Centre, Castleton St, Bolton, Greater Manchester BL2 2JW; Tel 01204 332201

SPECIAL SCHOOLS

Firwood School   Crompton Way, Bolton, Greater Manchester BL2 3AS; Tel 01204 333044; Fax 01204 333045
Headteacher   Dr J. Steele
(71)

Green Fold School   Highfield Rd, Farnworth, Greater Manchester BL4 0RA; Tel 01204 333750; Fax 01204 333751
Headteacher   Mrs C.E. Chapman
(67)

Ladywood School   Masefield Rd, Little Lever, Bolton, Greater Manchester BL3 1NG; Tel 01204 333400; Fax 01204 333405
Headteacher   Mrs S.E. McFarlane
(84)

Lever Park School   Stocks Park Dr, Horwich, Greater Manchester BL6 6DE; Tel 01204 332666; Fax 01204 332667
Headteacher   Mr S.W. MacIvor
(44)

Ramworth School   Armandale Rd, Bolton, Greater Manchester BL3 4TP; Tel 01204 333600; Fax 01204 333602
Headteacher   Mr W.T. Bradbury
(124)

Thomasson Memorial School   Devonshire Rd, Bolton, Greater Manchester BL1 5DH; Tel 01204 333118; Fax 01204 333119
Headteacher   W. Wilson
(47)

BOURNEMOUTH BOROUGH COUNCIL
www.bournemouth.gov.uk

Population 163 600
Political Composition: Con: 16, LD: 33, Lab: 3, Ind: 2
Town Hall, Bourne Ave, Bournemouth BH2 6DY;
URL www.bournemouth.gov.uk;
E-mail paul.godier@bournemouth.gov.uk; Tel 01202 451451
Chief Executive   Paul Godier

Social Services Directorate

24 Christchurch Rd, Bournemouth BH1 3ND;
URL www.bournemouth.gov.uk;
E-mail socialservices@bournemouth.gov.uk;
Tel 01202 458000; Fax 01202 458730; Minicom 01202 458720

Director (Social Services)   Pam Donnellan
Head (Strategic Services)   Phil Hodges
Head (Adult Services)   Vacancy
Head (Children's Services)   Kevin Jones
Manager (Performance Information)   Claire Foreman
Manager (Finance and Resources)   Steve Charlesworth
Manager (Staff Development)   Marton MacDonald
5 Hyde Rd, Bournemouth BH10 5JJ; Tel 01202 582137
Service Manager (Fieldwork Services)   Linda Irving
Service Manager (Resources Post Care and Youth Support Services)   Shannon Clarke
Service Manager (Health and Disability)   Geoff Colvin
Service Manager (Elderly/ESMI)   Richard Bush
Service Manager (Mental Health/Learning Disability/Addictions)   Peter Munns
Principal Officer (Childrens' Services)   Rita Crown
Policy Development Officer (Children)   Sheena Parkin
Psychologist   Margaret Manning

Social Services Committee

LD: 5, Con: 7, Lab: 1, Ind: 1
Town Hall, Bourne Ave, Bournemouth BH2 6DY;
URL www.bournemouth.gov.uk
Chair   John Millward (LD)
Vice-Chair   Ben Grower (Lab)
Members of the Committee
LD: Jill Abott, Angela Manton, William Mason, Emily Morrell-Cross.
Con: William Carey, Stephen Chappell, Jackie Harris, Bruce Heath, Howard Henning, Margaret Rose, Barbara Siberry.
Lab: Peter Brushett.
Ind: Anne Ray.

AREA OFFICES

Bournemouth Central 9 Madeira Rd, Bournemouth BH1 1QN; Tel 01202 458000; Fax 01202 458010; Minicom 01202 458750

North Bournemouth 27 Slades Farm Rd, Ensbury Pk, Bournemouth BH10 4ES; Tel 01202 456700; Fax 01202 456701

CHILDREN'S HOMES

Milton House Children's Home 53 Wellington Rd, Bournemouth BH8 8JJ; Tel 01202 290781; Fax 01202 314927
Contact   Claire Williams

Poole Lane Children's Home 224 Poole La, Bournemouth BH11 9DS; Tel 01202 575354; Fax 01202 590611

YOUTH OFFENDING TEAM

Bournemouth and Poole Youth Offending Team 9 Madeira Rd, Bournemouth BH1 1QN; Tel 01202 458000; Fax 01202 458010
Service Manager   Pauline Batstone

FAMILY CENTRES

Bournemouth Family Centre 246 Kinson Rd, Bournemouth BH10 5EP; Tel 01202 546049; Fax 01202 548048
Contact   Rosemary Hobson
Family Assessment Services 79 Lansdowne Rd, Bournemouth BH1 1RP; Tel 01202 551757; Fax 01202 293552
Contact   Coral Hatton

SHORT STAY UNIT

Mayfield Short Stay Unit 50 Chatsworth Rd, Bournemouth BH8 8SN; Tel 01202 531365; Fax 01202 531419

SOCIAL AND EDUCATIONAL CENTRE

Forest View Social and Educational Centre Elliott Rd, West Howe, Bournemouth BH11 8LQ; Tel 01202 575806; Fax 01202 582857
Contact   David Harley

WORKSHOP FOR PEOPLE WITH A PHYSICAL DISABILITY/LEARNING DISABILITY

Dorset Enterprises and CES Elliott Rd, West Howe, Bournemouth BH11 8JP; Tel 01202 577966; Fax 01202 570049
Contact   Bill Gaskins

DAY CENTRES FOR PEOPLE WITH MENTAL HEALTH PROBLEMS

Beechwood, The Boscombe Centre 2a Owls Rd, Boscombe, Bournemouth BH5 1AA; Tel 01202 302910; Fax 01202 302017
The Winton Centre 528 Wimborne Rd, Bournemouth BH9 2EX; Tel 01202 531339

DAY CENTRE FOR DISABLED PEOPLE

The Boscombe Centre 2a Owls Rd, Bournemouth BH15 1AA; Tel 01202 309745; Fax 01202 302017
Contact   Margaret Parker

RESIDENTIAL HOMES FOR PEOPLE WITH LEARNING DIFFICULTIES

April Court Residential Home Poole La, Kinson, Bournemouth BH11 9DS; Tel 01202 576110
Contact   Lindsay Divall
Sevenoaks Residential Home 287 Windham Rd, Bournemouth BH1 4RE; Tel 01202 396691
Contact   Barbara Maynard
Wallfield Residential Home Castlemain Ave, Bournemouth BH6 5EJ; Tel 01202 428048; Fax 01202 293365
Contact   Zuhal Zeptekin

ACCOMMODATION FOR PEOPLE WITH MENTAL HEALTH NEEDS

Leven House 11 Leven Ave, Bournemouth BH4 9LH; Tel 01202 764415; Fax 01202 764041
Contact   Carol Monahan

DAY CENTRES FOR OLDER PEOPLE

Alumhurst Day Centre Alumhurst Rd, Westbourne, Bournemouth BH4 8ER; Tel 01202 761183; Fax 01202 762492
Contact   Shirley Young
Darracott Day Centre Darracott Rd, Pokesdown, Bournemouth BH5 2AY; Tel 01202 427933; Fax 01202 431195
Contact   Irene Draper

Malvern Day Centre 1005 Wimborne Rd, Bournemouth BH9 2BS; Tel 01202 537239; Fax 01202 526244
Contact   Carol Spriggs
Northbourne Day Centre 1354 Wimborne Rd, Bournemouth BH10 7AP; Tel 01202 576658; Fax 01202 591805
Contact   Joyce Sweeney
Nortoft Day Centre Nortoft Rd, Bournemouth BH8 8QR; Tel 01202 558608; Fax 01202 295346
Contact   Donna Nortcliffe
Seabourne Day Centre Seabourne Rd, Pokesdown, Bournemouth BH5 2HA; Tel 01202 421612; Fax 01202 424479
Contact   Ann Kennett
Springbourne Day Centre 291 Holdenhurst Rd, Bournemouth BH8 8BA; Tel 01202 393041; Fax 01202 301696
Contact   Paula Elcock
Wallisdown Heights Day Centre 119 Canford Ave, Wallisdown, Bournemouth BH11 8SH; Tel 01202 537884; Fax 01202 526198
Contact   Linda Ames-Lines

6

Education Directorate

Dorset Hse, 20–22 Christchurch Rd, Bournemouth BH1 3NL; URL www.bournemouth.gov.uk; Tel 01202 456223; Fax 01202 456191
Director (Education)   Pratap Deshpande

SPECIAL SCHOOL

Linwood School Alma Rd, Bournemouth BH9 1AJ; Tel 01202 525107; Fax 01202 525107
Headteacher   Steve Brown
(172)

BRACKNELL FOREST BOROUGH COUNCIL
www.bracknell-forest.gov.uk

In April 1998 Bracknell Forest became a unitary authority. Berkshire County Council was replaced by Bracknell Forest, Reading, Slough, West Berkshire, Windsor and Maidenhead and Wokingham.
Easthampstead Hse, Town Sq, Bracknell, Bracknell Forest RG12 1AQ; URL www.bracknell-forest.gov.uk; Tel 01344 424642; Fax 01344 352810
Chief Executive   Timothy Wheadon
Director (Leisure Services)   Vincent Paliczka
Director (Environment)   John Osborne
Director (Corporate Services)   Gill Steward

Social Services and Housing Department

Time Sq, Market St, Bracknell Forest; Tel Emergency Tel (out-of-office hours) 01344 786543; Fax 01344 351596
Director (Housing and Social Services)   Daphne Obang
Assistant Director (Housing Services)   Tom Hogan
Assistant Director (Strategy, Commissioning and Resources)   Vincent Badu
Assistant Director (Adult Services)   Simon Pearce
Head (Children's Services)   Alex Walters
Manager (Business)   Annal Nayyar

Social Care and Housing Portfolio Holder

Chair   Cllr Dr Gareth Barnard (Con)

RESIDENTIAL ACCOMMODATION FOR YOUNG PEOPLE WITH LEARNING DISABILITIES

Larchwood, 10 Portman Cl, Bracknell, Bracknell Forest RG42 1NE; Tel 01344 452315; Fax 01344 360405
Unit Manager Morag Campion
Seven respite care places

CHILD CARE AND FAMILY CENTRE

Bracknell Family Centre Wick Hill Cottage, Warfield Rd, Bracknell, Bracknell Forest RG12 2JA; Tel 01344 868729; Fax 01344 304335
Unit Manager Jane Beckwith

CHILD PROTECTION CO-ORDINATOR

Time Square Market St, Bracknell, Bracknell Forest RG12 1JD; Tel 01344 351523
Contact Penny Reuter

YOUTH OFFENDING TEAM

Bracknell Youth Support Team 76 Binfield Rd, Bracknell, Bracknell Forest RG42 2AR; Tel 01344 354300; Fax 01344 354310
Contact Karen Roberts

FAMILY PLACEMENT SERVICE (FOSTERING AND ADOPTION)

Bracknell Family Placement Team Time Sq, Market St, Bracknell, Bracknell Forest RG12 1JD; Tel 01344 351556; 01344 351557
Team Manager Diane Grist

HOME CARE

Bracknell Social Services Home Care Time Sq, Market St, Bracknell, Bracknell Forest RG12 1JD; Tel 01344 351446 01344 351473
Service Manager M. McMahon
Manager (Purchasing) Alison Cronin
Manager (Operations) Jean Strawson
Manager (Intermediate Care Team) Jayne Rigg

DAY CENTRE FOR PEOPLE WITH A PHYSICAL DISABILITY

Downside Resource Centre Wildridings Rd, Bracknell, Bracknell Forest RG12 7WP; Tel 01344 450230; Fax 01344 306639
Unit Manager Jane Brown
40 places five days per week
(40)

COMMUNITY TEAM FOR PEOPLE WITH LEARNING DISABILITIES

Bracknell Community Team for People with Learning Disabilities Waymead, St. Anthony's Cl, Bracknell, Bracknell Forest RG42 2EB; Tel 01344 861070; Fax 01344 400420
Team Manager Yvonne Tester

DAY CENTRES FOR ADULTS WITH LEARNING DISABILITIES (ADULT SPECIAL NEEDS UNIT ATTACHED TO DAY CENTRE)

Bracknell Resource and Opportunity Centre Eastern Rd, Bracknell, Bracknell Forest RG12 2UP; Tel 01344 423758; Fax 01344 302464
Unit Manager K. Probert
(125)

ACCOMMODATION FOR ADULTS WITH LEARNING DISABILITIES

Holbeck Home 150–151 Holbeck, Gt Hollands, Bracknell, Bracknell Forest RG12 8XE; Tel 01344 482333
Unit Manager V. Moore
(8)

Waymead Home St. Anthony's Cl, Bracknell, Bracknell Forest RG42 2EB; Tel 01344 451285
The project is jointly funded with Berkshire Health Authority.
Unit Manager (STC) D. Lacey
Ten places short stay.
Eight places long stay.
(18)

COMMUNITY MENTAL HEALTH TEAM

Bracknell Community Mental Health Team Time Sq, Market St, Bracknell, Bracknell Forest RG12 1JD; Tel 01344 351693
Contact Barbara Rodriguez

UNSTAFFED GROUP HOMES FOR PEOPLE WITH MENTAL HEALTH NEEDS

Bracknell has six group homes with a total of 15 places.
Contact Julian Emms; Tel 01344 351427

DAY CARE FOR ELDERLY PEOPLE

Heathlands Day Centre Crossfell Wildridings, Bracknell, Bracknell Forest RG12 7RX; Tel 01344 425650; Fax 01344 302427
Unit Manager L. Parsons
12 places (+three without transport) five days per week and alternate weekends.

Johnstone Court Day Centre Portman Cl, Bracknell, Bracknell Forest RG12 1NE; Tel 01344 452312; Fax 01344 307156
Unit Manager Evon Williams (Acting)
65 places five days a week
(65)

RESIDENTIAL ESTABLISHMENTS FOR ELDERLY PEOPLE

There are two local authority homes for elderly people with 71 permanent places, four short stay places and eight enhanced care places.

Education Department

Seymour Hse, 38 Broadway, Bracknell, Bracknell Forest RG12 1AU; URL www.bracknell-forest.gov.uk; E-mail education@bracknell-forest.gov.uk; Tel 01344 354000
Director (Education) Tony Eccleston

HOME AND HOSPITAL TEACHING SERVICE

West Rd, Old Wokingham Rd, Wokingham RG40 3BT; URL www.bracknell-forest.gov.uk; E-mail head@office.colleghall-pru.bracknell-forest.sch.uk; Tel 0118 989 3378
Co-ordinator Marion Bent

EDUCATIONAL PSYCHOLOGY SERVICE

Seymour Hse, 38 Broadway, Bracknell, Bracknell Forest RG12 1AU; URL www.bracknell-forest.gov.uk; E-mail education@bracknell-forest.gov.uk; Tel 01344 354018
Principal Educational Psychologist Anthony Riches

Crown Wood Language and Literacy Centre Crown Wood Primary School, Opladen Way, Bracknell, Bracknell Forest RG12 0PE; E-mail crownwood.bracknell-forest.sch.uk; Tel 01344 424203
Co-ordinator Susan Duffus
Language and literacy.

Kennel Lane School Kennel La, Bracknell, Bracknell Forest RG42 2EX; E-mail kennellane.bracknell-forest.sch.uk; Tel 01344 483872
Headteacher Andrea de Bunsen

Meadow Vale Special Resource Meadow Vale Primary School, Moordale Ave, Bracknell, Bracknell Forest RG42 1SY; E-mail meadowvale.bracknell-forest.sch.uk; Tel 01344 421046
Headteacher N. Duncan
Speech and language

The Pines Special Resource The Pines Junior School, Hanworth Rd, Bracknell, Bracknell Forest RG12 7YJ; E-mail pines-jun.bracknell-forest.sch.uk; Tel 01344 426413
Headteacher Kathleen Nugent
MLD

Ranelagh School Special Resource Ranelagh School, Ranelagh Dr, Bracknell, Bracknell Forest RG12 9DA; E-mail ranelagh.bracknell-forest.sch.uk; Tel 01344 421233
Headteacher K.M. Winrow

Social and Communications Resource Centre Great Hollands Infant School, Wordsworth, Bracknell, Bracknell Forest RG12 8WQ; E-mail gtholl-info.bracknellforest.sch.uk; Tel 01344 421340
Headteacher Eileen Rogers (Acting)

Kennel Lane School Kennel La, Bracknell, Bracknell Forest RG42 2EX; Tel 01344 483872
Headteacher Andrea de Bunsen

CITY OF BRADFORD METROPOLITAN DISTRICT COUNCIL
www.bradford.gov.uk

Population 480 750
City Hall, Bradford, West Yorkshire BD1 1HY;
URL www.bradford.gov.uk;
E-mail ian.stewart@bradford.gov.uk; Tel 01274 432111;
Fax 01274 432065
Chief Executive Ian Stewart
Assistant Chief Executive (Education, Community and Social Care) M. Carriline
Director (Social Services) A. O'Sullivan
Olicana Hse, Bradford, West Yorkshire BD1 5RE

Social Services Department

Olicana Hse, Chapel St, Bradford, West Yorkshire BD1 5RE;
URL www.bradford.gov.uk; Tel 01274 432918
Director (Social Services) A. O'Sullivan
Manager (Promotions) Prue Chennells
Department Officer (Policy and Information) Roger Hey

TRAINING

The following have responsibility for professional and support staff in the department.
West Riding Hse, Cheapside, Bradford, West Yorkshire BD1 4LH; Tel 01274 432798; Fax 01274 736247
Manager (Department Training) Chris Turner
Principal Training Officer (Children and R&QA)
Vacancy
Principal Training Officer (Adults) Vacancy

Overview and Scrutiny Committee (Health, Housing and Social Care)

Con: 4, Lab: 4, LD: 1
Lead Member (Health, Housing and Social Care)
Kris Hopkins (Con)
c/o J. Barter, Department of Social Services, Bradford, West Yorkshire BD1 5RE;
E-mail joanne.barter@bradford.gov.uk; Tel 01274 432900; Fax 01274 432905
Chair G. Thornton

3 Oakworth Grange, Oakworth, Keighley, West Yorkshire BD22 7JL; E-mail kris.hopkins@bradford.gov.uk
Members of the Committee
Lab: Amir Hussain, L. Joyce, M.S. Love, T.M. Salam.
Con: V. Binney, M. Hussain, C.G. Powell, D. Servant.

CONSTITUENCY OFFICES

Children's Division

Bradford North Romanby Shaw, Greengates, Bradford, West Yorkshire BD10 0EH; Tel 01274 435600; Fax 01274 614178

Bradford South 297 Rooley La, Bradford, West Yorkshire BD5 8LY; Tel 01274 435901; Fax 01274 742378

Bradford West No 6 Hse, Springfield Complex, Squire La, Bradford, West Yorkshire BD9 6RA; Tel 01274 435800; Fax 01274 491189

Keighley Cooke St, Keighley, West Yorkshire BD21 3PB; Tel 01535 618123; Fax 01535 611845

Shipley 39 Kirkgate, Shipley, West Yorkshire BD 18 3QZ; Tel 01274 437123; Fax 01274 532476

Services for Adults

North Bradford Area Blakehill Grange, 438 Killinghall Rd, Bradford, West Yorkshire BD2 4SL; Tel 01274 435100; Fax 01274 626614

South and West Area Harbourne, Brearcliffe Dr, Wibsey, Bradford, West Yorkshire BD6 2LE; Tel 01274 435400; Fax 01274 693501

City Team 215 Lumb La, Bradford, West Yorkshire BD8 7SG; Tel 01274 435200; Fax 01274 494298

Airedale Area The Oaks Resource Centre, Oakworth Rd, Keighley, West Yorkshire BD21 1QB; Tel 01535 618400; Fax 01535 690698

Disabilities Services

Myrtle Park Town Hall, Bingley, West Yorkshire BD16 2LQ; Tel 01274 438700; Fax 01274 510348

Owlet Road 21 Owlett Rd, Windhill, Shipley, West Yorkshire BD18 2LU; Tel 01274 435043; Fax 01274 532488

Hospitals – Social Work Offices

Airedale General Hospital Skipton Rd, Steeton, Keighley, West Yorkshire BD20 6TD; Tel 01535 651194; Fax 01535 651196

Bradford Royal Infirmary Duckworth La, Bradford, West Yorkshire BD9 6RJ; Tel 01274 364292; 01274 364293; Fax 01274 364345

St. Luke's Hospital Little Horton La, Bradford, West Yorkshire BD5 0NA; Tel 01274 365118; Fax 01274 365112

CHILD PROTECTION UNIT

Olicana Hse, 2nd Fl, Chapel St, Bradford, West Yorkshire BD1 5RE; Tel 01274 434341; Fax 01274 434345

ADOPTIONS AND FOSTERING UNIT

35 Saltaire Rd, Shipley, West Yorkshire BD18 3HH; Tel 01274 434331

COMMUNITY HOMES FOR CHILDREN

First Avenue Children's Home Killinghall Rd, Bradford, West Yorkshire BD3 7JE; Tel 01274 664459
(9)

Meadow Lea Children's Home 45 Hawksworth Dr, Menston, West Yorkshire LS29 6HP; Tel 01943 873050
(12)

6

Newholme Children's Home   Cavendish Rd, Idle, Bradford, West Yorkshire BD10 9LE; Tel 01274 619230
  (6)

Tyson House Children's Home   87 Park Rd, Bradford, West Yorkshire BD5 0SG; Tel 01274 731014; Fax 01274 742943
  (15)

Woodroyd Terrace Children's Home   29 Woodroyd Terr, West Bowling, Bradford, West Yorkshire BD5 8PQ; Tel 01274 723335
  (6)

HOMES FOR CHILDREN WITH SPECIAL NEEDS

Brunswick Road Children's Home   Brunswick Rd, Greengates, Bradford, West Yorkshire BD10 8BP; Tel 01274 614763

Clockhouse Project   Oakworth Rd, Keighley, West Yorkshire BD21 1QX; Tel 01535 691637

St. Stephen's Hostel   122 St. Stephen's Rd, West Bowling, Bradford, West Yorkshire BD5 7TB; Tel 01274 728337

FAMILY CENTRES

Albion Family Centre   70–72 Albion Rd, Idle, Bradford, West Yorkshire BD10 9QL; Tel 01274 611513

Farcliffe Family Centre   Toller La, Bradford, West Yorkshire BD8 8QA; Tel 01274 543636

Burnettfields Family Centre   c/o 42 Greaves St, Bradford, West Yorkshire BD5 7PE; Tel 01274 571555

Low Fold Family Centre   Exley Rd, Keighley, West Yorkshire BD21 1LT; Tel 01535 603894; Fax 01535 691349

Owlet Family Centre   Owlet Pk, Owlet Rd, Shipley, West Yorkshire BD18 2LU; Tel 01274 530877; Fax 01274 530879

BRADFORD AND DISTRICT YOUTH OFFENDING TEAM

Barkerend Base   181a Barkerend Rd, Bradford, West Yorkshire BD3 9AP; Tel 01274 728392; Fax 01274 742371

Fraternal House   45 Cheapside, Bradford, West Yorkshire BD1 4HP; Tel 01274 703760; Fax 01274 703761

Shipley Base   140 Manor La, Shipley, West Yorkshire BD18 3RJ

RESOURCE CENTRES

The Oaks Resource Centre   Oakworth Rd, Keighley, West Yorkshire BD21 1QB; Tel 01535 618400

Whetley Hill Resource Centre   3 Whetley Hill, Bradford, West Yorkshire BD8 8NL; Tel 01274 495442

OCCUPATIONAL THERAPISTS

Southern Team/Central Team   Bankfield Hse, Unit 1, Imex Business Centre, Carbottom Rd, Bradford, West Yorkshire BD5 9AG; Tel 01274 435252; Fax 01274 521337

Northern Team   Town Hall, Myrtle Pk, Bradford, West Yorkshire BD16 2LQ; Tel 01274 758760

DAY CENTRES

Beckfield Day Centre   70 Bolton La, Bradford, West Yorkshire BD2 4BN; Tel 01274 203003

Broadstones Day Centre   Gillingham Grn, Holmewood, Bradford, West Yorkshire BD4 9DT; Tel 01274 687164; Fax 01274 687205

Gulberg Community Resource Centre   Park La, Bradford, West Yorkshire BD5 0JL; Tel 01274 370180; Fax 01274 737956

Milton House Day Centre   1 Avenham Way, Brookfield Rd, Bradford, West Yorkshire BD3 0RN; Tel 01274 393586 01274 394411

Morley Street Resource Centre (Sensory Needs)   Centre for the Blind, 124 Morley St, Bradford, West Yorkshire BD7 1BB; Tel 01274 435001

Neville Grange Day Centre   off Queens Rd, Saltaire, Shipley, West Yorkshire BD18 4SJ; Tel 01274 532546; Fax 01274 587850

Norman Lodge Day Centre   1a Glenroyd Ave, Cleckheaton Rd, Bradford, West Yorkshire BD6 1DL; Tel 01274 606314 Residential 01274 691520

Thompson Court Day Centre   Morton La, Crossflatts, Bingley, West Yorkshire BD16 2EP; Tel 01274 561965

Weymouth Avenue Day Centre   2a Weymouth Ave, Allerton, Bradford, West Yorkshire BD15 7JJ; Tel 01274 488266

ACCOMMODATION FOR THE ELDERLY

There are 14 local authority homes offering over 501 places.

MEALS SERVICES

Social Services Catering Department (Community Meals); Tel 01274 437935

Education Bradford

Future Hse, Bolling Rd, Bradford, West Yorkshire BD4 7EB; E-mail info@eb.serco.com; Tel 01274 385500; Fax 01274 385586
Managing Director   Mark Pattison
Director (Education Department, Client Side)   Phil Green
Director (Achievement)   Teresa Whitfield
Director (Finance)   Darren Turnpenney
Director (Traded Services)   Steve Humphreys
Achievement Support Manager (South Area)   Pauline Armour; Tel 01274 375761
Achievement Support Manager (West Area)   Ros Garside
Achievement Support Manager (Keighley, Ilkley and Bingley Area)   Dave Jobbings
Achievement Support Manager (Shipley/North)   Kay Priestley

HOME AND HOSPITAL EDUCATION SERVICE

Administration Base   Lister Lane School, Lister La, Bradford, West Yorkshire BD2 4LL; E-mail office@listerlane.ngfl.ac.uk; Tel 01274 777106
Contact   G. Freeth

SPECIAL SCHOOLS

Bolling School   Annerley St, Bradford, West Yorkshire BD4 7SY; E-mail office@bolling.ngfl.ac.uk; Tel 01274 721962; Fax 01274 721962
Headteacher   Mrs S.M. Gill
  (77)

Braithwaite School   Braithwaite Rd, Keighley, West Yorkshire BD22 6PR; E-mail office@braithwaitet.ngfl.ac.uk; Tel 01535 603041; Fax 01535 691227
Headteacher   Mrs P.A. Pearson
  (77)

Branshaw School   Oxford St, Keighley, West Yorkshire BD21 1QX; E-mail joan.graveson@branshaw.ngfl.ac.uk; Tel 01535 662739; Fax 01535 663834
Headteacher   Mrs J. Graveson
  (40)

Chapel Grange School   Rhodesway, Bradford, West Yorkshire BD8 0DQ; E-mail bubble@chapelgrg.ngfl.ac.uk; Tel 01274 773307; Fax 01274 774088
Headteacher   Hilary Morrison
  (97)

Greenfield School   Boothroyd Dr, Idle, Bradford, West Yorkshire BD10 8LU; E-mail office@greenfield.ngfl.ac.uk; Tel 01274 614092; Fax 01274 613840
Headteacher   Mrs J. Taylor
  (63)

Haycliffe School Haycliffe La, Bradford, West Yorkshire BD5 9ET; E-mail haycliffe@haycliffe.ngfl.ac.uk; Tel 01274 576123; Fax 01274 770555
Headteacher K.G. Fair
(120)

Heaton Royds School Redburn Dr, Shipley, Bradford, West Yorkshire BD18 3AZ;
E-mail office@heatonroyds.ngfl.ac.uk; Tel 01274 583759; Fax 01274 589397
Headteacher Mrs M. Fowler
(40)

Lister Lane School Lister La, Bradford, West Yorkshire BD2 4LL; E-mail office@listerlane.ngfl.ac.uk; Tel (Support Service) 01274 777106; (Hospital Education) 01274 777107; (Physiotherapy) 01274 777108; Fax 01274 773623
Headteacher W.G. Freeth
(73)

Netherlands Avenue School and Community Nursery
Netherlands Ave, Bradford, West Yorkshire BD6 1EA;
E-mail office@netherlands.ngfl.ac.uk; Tel 01274 677711; Fax 01274 673108
Headteacher G. Bowden
(130)

Temple Bank School Daisy Hill La, Bradford, West Yorkshire BD9 6BN;
E-mail ethurtle@templebank.bradford.sch.uk; Tel 01274 776566; Fax 01274 776599
Headteacher R.C. Neal
(59)

Thorn Park School Thorn La, Bingley Rd, Bradford, West Yorkshire BD9 6RR;
E-mail dave.muir@thornpark.ngfl.ac.uk; Tel 01274 773770; Fax 01274 770387
Headteacher D. Muir
(71)

Wedgwood School and Community Nursery Landscove Ave, Holmewood, Bradford, West Yorkshire BD4 0NQ;
E-mail wedgw@legend.co.uk; Tel 01274 687236; Fax 01274 686735
Headteacher Mrs J. Godward
(93)

RESOURCED MAINSTREAM SCHOOLS

Bradford Cathedrral Community College Lister Ave, Bradford, West Yorkshire BD4 7QT;
E-mail sam.burnham@bccc.ngfl.ac.uk; Tel 01274 773320; Fax 01274 773321
Contact D. Brett
PH

Denholme Primary School Minorca Mount, Denholme, Bradford, West Yorkshire BD13 4AY;
E-mail office@denholme.ngfl.ac.uk; Tel 01274 832123; Fax 01274 831730
Head Mr P. Terry
Autism

Green Lane Primary School Green La, Manningham, Bradford, West Yorkshire BD8 8HT;
E-mail kevin.holland@greenlane.ngfl.ac.uk; Tel 01274 774644; Fax 01274 774655
Contact K.P. Holland
Severe speech and language difficulties.

Barkerend Primary School Hendford Dr, Pollard Pk, Bradford, West Yorkshire BD3 0QT;
E-mail office@barkerend.ngfl.ac.uk; Tel 01274 773003; Fax 01274 773966
Headteacher Mr R. Kunicki
SEN Nursery

Canterbury Children's Centre Basil St, Bradford, West Yorkshire BD5 9HL; E-mail s.hogan@canterbury.ngfl.ac.uk; Tel 01274 574539; Fax 01274 574522
Headteacher Ms S. Hogan
SEN Nursery

Eastwood Primary School Victoria Ave, Keighley, West Yorkshire BD21 3JL;
E-mail eastwoodprimary@hotmail.com; Tel 01535 610212; Fax 01535 210238
Headteacher Mrs L. Godden
SEN Nursery

Girlington Primary School Girlington Rd, Bradford, West Yorkshire BD8 9NR;
E-mail sue.wood@girlington.ngfl.ac.uk; Tel 01274 493543; Fax 01274 543874
Headteacher Mrs S.M. Wood
Hearing

Grange Technology College Haycliffe La, Bradford, West Yorkshire BD5 9ET;
E-mail admin@grangetc.org.uk; Tel 01274 775335; Fax 01274 775665
Headteacher Mr J. Player
Autism and Related Communication Difficulties

Hirst Wood Nursery School Clarence Rd, Shipley, West Yorkshire BD18 4NJ;
E-mail office@hirstwood.ngfl.ac.uk; Tel 01274 584368; Fax 01274 584368
Headteacher Mrs R. Morgan

Miriam Lord Community Primary School Church St, Manningham, Bradford, West Yorkshire BD8 8RE;
E-mail office@miriamlord.ngfl.ac.uk; Tel 01274 496611; Fax 01274 771874
Headteacher Mrs S.E. Clark
SEN Nursery

Nab Wood School Cottingley New Rd, Bingley, West Yorkshire BD16 1TZ;
E-mail info@admin.nabwood.ngfl.ac.uk; Tel 01274 567281; Fax 01274 510688
Headteacher Mrs H. Lynch
Hearing Difficulties

Strong Close Nursery Airedale Rd, Keighley, West Yorkshire BD21 4LW;
E-mail kath.williams@strongclose.ngfl.ac.uk; Tel 01535 605272; Fax 01535 605272
Headteacher Ms K. Williams
Hearing Difficulties

Thackley Primary School Town La, Thackley, Bradford, West Yorkshire BD10 8PJ;
E-mail admin@thackleyschool.com; Tel 01274 414437; Fax 01274 414438
Headteacher Mrs L. Tidy
SEN Nursery

Thornton Primary School Thornton Rd, Bradford, West Yorkshire BD13 3NN;
E-mail office@thorntonpri.ngfl.ac.uk; Tel 01274 833839; Fax 01274 831910
Headteacher Mrs D. Waring
SEN Nursery

Beckfoot Grammar School Wagon La, Bingley, West Yorkshire BD16 1EE;
E-mail admin@beckfoot.bradford.sch.uk; Tel 01274 771444; Fax 01274 771145
Headteacher D.J. Horn
Physical Difficulties

PUPIL REFERRAL UNITS

Aireview Pupil Referral Unit Aireview Centre, Baker St, Saltaire, West Yorkshire BD18 3JE;
E-mail office@aireview.ngfl.ac.uk; Tel 01274 437298; Fax 01274 437399
Headteacher Mr E. Gardner

City Pupil Referral Unit Ellar Carr Rd, Thackley, Bradford, West Yorkshire BD10 0TD;
E-mail elaine.collins@ellarcarr.ngfl.ac.uk; Tel 01274 612176; Fax 01274 619050
Headteacher Ms E. Collins
Head (KS3 Centre) Mrs S. Todd

6

City Pupil Referral Unit (KS4) Firth Bldgs, Wrose Brow, Shipley, West Yorkshire BD18 2NT; Tel 01274 599784; Fax 01274 531507
Head of Centre Mrs A. McCullough

City Pupil Referral Unit (College Provision) Room Q3C, Old Bldg, BICC, Great Horton Rd, Bradford, West Yorkshire BD7 1AY; Tel 01274 431665; Fax 01274 738723
Head of Centre Mr J. Linney

Jesse Street Pupil Referral Unit Jesse St, Bradford, West Yorkshire BD8 0JQ; E-mail office@prejesse.ngfl.ac.uk; Tel 01274 491986; Fax 01274 548343
Head Mrs K. Royston (Acting)

Newlands (Pregnant Schoolgirl Unit) Carlton Bolling College, Undercliffe Rd, Bradford, West Yorkshire BD3 3QS; Tel 01274 626458; Fax 01274 630635
Head of Unit Mrs S. Ahir
Head of Unit Mrs H. English

Primary Pupil Referral Unit Avenue Rd, West Bowling, Bradford, West Yorkshire BD5 8DB; E-mail catherine.carroll@primarypru.ngfl.ac.uk; Tel 01274 735298; Fax 01274 733795
Headteacher Mrs S. Smith

BRIGHTON AND HOVE CITY COUNCIL
www.brighton-hove.gov.uk

Population 250 000
Political Composition: Lab: 24, Con: 20, Green Party: 6, LD: 3, Ind: 1.
Kings Hse, Grand Ave, Hove, Brighton and Hove BN3 2SL; URL www.brighton-hove.gov.uk; E-mail katherine.travis@brighton-hove.gov.uk; Tel 01273 290000
Chief Executive David Panter
Deputy Chief Executive and Director (Corporate Services) A. McCarthy

Social Care Services

Brighton and Hove City Council, PO Box 2501, Kings Hse, Grand Ave, Hove, Brighton and Hove BN3 2SS; URL www.brighton-hove.gov.uk; E-mail infoline@brighton-hove.gov.uk; Tel 01273 290000; (Information Line Enquiries) 01273 295555; (Emergency Duty Service Mon–Thur 1700–0830, Fri 1630–Mon 0830) 07699 391462; Fax 01273 295041 (Information Line) 01273 296372; (Emergency Duty Team) 01273 814699; Minicom 01273 296333; Tel (Out of hours) 01273 295650; (Child Protection Register Enquiries) 01273 295999; Fax 01273 295998 (Out of hours) 01273 692079; Tel (Learning and Development) 01273 296184; Fax 01273 296186; Tel (Finance Referral Line) 01273 295660; Fax 01273 295672
Human Resources Tel 01273 295098; Fax 01273 295100
Customer Services Unit Tel 01273 296415; Fax 01273 296372
Executive Councillor (Social Care and Health) Cllr Gerry Kielty; Tel 01273 291167
Statutory Director (Social Services) Jenny Clark
Director (Housing and City Support) Ian Long (Acting)
Director (Children, Families and Schools) David Hawker
Press Officer Brian Walsh; Tel 01273 291040; Fax 01273 291048

Children, Families and Schools

Brighton and Hove Council, Kings Hse, Grand Ave, Hove, Brighton and Hove BN3 2SU; Tel 01273 293598 01273 293687; Fax 01273 293588
Director (Children, Families and Schools) David Hawker

Children, Families and Schools Sub-Committee
SPECIAL DAY SCHOOLS

Alternative Centre for Education Queensdown School Rd, off Lewes Rd, Brighton, Brighton and Hove BN1 7LA; Tel 01273 604472; Fax 01273 621811
Headteacher M. Whitby
Mixed 5–16 EBD (27)

Castledean School Lynchet Cl, Hollingdean, Brighton, Brighton and Hove BN1 7FP; Tel 01273 702112; Fax 01273 702121
Headteacher S. Furdas
Mixed 2–11 MLD (49)

Downs Park School Foredown Rd, Portslade, Brighton and Hove BN41 2FU; Tel 01273 417448; Fax 01273 439619
Headteacher A. Fulton
Mixed 5–16 MLD (68)

Downs View School Warren Rd, Brighton, Brighton and Hove BN2 6BB; Tel 01273 601680; Fax 01273 699420
Headteacher J. L. Reed
Mixed 2–19 SLD (59)

Hillside School Foredown Rd, Portslade, Brighton and Hove BN41 2FU; Tel 01273 416979; Fax 01273 417512
Headteacher R.J. Wall
Mixed 2–19 SLD (37)

Patcham House School 7 Old London Rd, Brighton, Brighton and Hove BN1 8XR; Tel 01273 551028; Fax 01273 550465
Headteacher S. Lamb
Mixed 5–16 PH (40)

Uplands School Lynchet Cl, Hollingdean, Brighton, Brighton and Hove BN1 7FP; Tel 01273 558623; Fax 01273 558622
Headteacher P. Atkins
Mixed 11–16 MLD (113)

BRISTOL CITY COUNCIL
www.bristol-city.gov.uk

Political Composition: Lab: 31, LD: 28, Con: 11
The Council Hse, College Grn, Bristol BS1 5TR; URL www.bristol-city.gov.uk; Tel 0117 922 2000
Head (Paid Service) Carew Reynell

Social Services and Health Department

Headquarters, PO Box 30, Amelia Crt, Bristol BS99 7NB; URL www.bristol-city.gov.uk/socialservices; E-mail socialservices@bristol-city.gov.uk; Tel (Emergency Duty Team (available only outside office hours)) 01454 615165; 0117 903 7860
Director (Social Services and Health) B. McKitterick
Divisional Director (Contracting and Quality) A. Edgington
Divisional Director (Mental Health and Learning Difficulties) Dot Smith
Divisional Director (Children's Services) Annie Hudson
Divisional Director (Services for Older People and Disabled Adults) John Merriman

Social Services Executive Team
Executive Member Cllr Graham Robertson

AREA OFFICES
North Bristol Area Offices

Lyddington Road Area Office Monks Pk, Bristol BS7 0UU; Tel 0117 903 1150

Ridingleaze Area Office Lawrence Weston, Bristol BS11 0QE; Tel 0117 903 1700

Upper Belgrave Road Area Office Clifton, Bristol BS8 2XR; Tel 0117 903 1526; Minicom 0117 903 1526

East Bristol Area Offices

Avonvale Road Area Office Redfield, Bristol BS5 9RH; Tel 0117 955 8231; Minicom 0117 935 1377

Beam Street Area Office Barton Hill, Bristol BS5 9QR; Tel 0117 903 7500

South Bristol Area Offices

Broadwalk Area Office Knowle, Bristol BS4 2QY; Tel 0117 903 1414

Redhouse Area Office Heggard Cl, Withywood, Bristol BS13 7SE; Tel 0117 903 1900

Symes House Area Office Peterson Sq, Hartcliffe, Bristol BS13 0EE; Tel 0117 964 2593

CHILD AND FAMILY SUPPORT CENTRES

Rodbourne Road Family Centre 148 Rodbourne Rd, Westbury-on-Trym, Bristol BS10 5AN; Tel 0117 903 8380
   (18)

Vowell Close Family Centre 23 Vowell Cl, Hartcliffe, Bristol BS13 9HS; Tel 0117 964 7278
   (18)

COMMUNITY HOMES

Bishopthorpe Road Community Home 45 Bishopsthorpe Rd, Westbury-on-Trym, Bristol BS10 5AB; Tel 0117 903 8088
   (6)

Briar Way Community Home 22 Briar Way, Fishponds, Bristol BS16 4EA; Tel 0117 903 1440

Capgrave Crescent Community Home 111 Capgrave Cres, St. Anne's, Bristol BS4 4TN; Tel 0117 903 1060
   Girls (6)

Lacey Road Community Home 97 Lacey Rd, Stockwood, Bristol BS14 8NB; Tel 01275 837363
   (6)

Rochester Road Community Home 36 Rochester Rd, St. Anne's, Bristol BS4 4QQ; Tel 0117 977 3348
   (6)

Romney Avenue Community Home 23 Romney Ave, Lockleaze, Bristol BS7 9ST; Tel 0117 951 5051
   (6)

Silbury Road Community Home 63a Silbury Rd, Ashton Vale, Bristol BS3 2QE; Tel 0117 966 3335

Witch Hazel Road Community Home 2 Witch Hazel Rd, Hartcliffe, Bristol BS13 0QE; Tel 0117 903 8996
   (6)

DAY CENTRES FOR THE MENTALLY ILL

Eastville Day Centre East Pk, Eastville, Bristol BS5 6YA; Tel 0117 951 0324
   (60)

Greville Day Centre Lacey Rd, Stockwood, Bristol BS14 8LN; Tel 01275 832973

Wellhay Resource Centre Brentry, Bristol BS10 6QH; Tel 0117 950 7564
   (10)

RESOURCE AND ACTIVITY CENTRES FOR PEOPLE WITH LEARNING DIFFICULTIES

Bush Resource and Activity Centre New Fosseway Rd, Hengrove, Bristol BS14 9XA; Tel 01275 835902
   (150)

Dovercourt Road Resource and Activity Centre Horfield, Bristol BS7 9SF; Tel 0117 969 1141
   (100)

Lanercost Road Resource and Activity Centre Southmead, Bristol BS10 6HZ; Tel 0117 903 8640
   (180)

Snowdon Road Centre Snowdon Rd, Fishponds, Bristol BS16 2EQ; Tel 0117 965 3812
   (125)

HOMES AND HOSTELS FOR PEOPLE WITH LEARNING DIFFICULTIES

Bush Short-Stay Hostel New Fosseway Rd, Hengrove, Bristol BS14 9XA; Tel 01275 838672
   (14)

Concord Lodge Kellaway Ave, Horfield, Bristol BS7 8SU; Tel 0117 924 3037
   (25)

Longhills Hostel 160 Whitefield Rd, Speedwell, Bristol BS5 7TZ; Tel 0117 965 2144

Newland Road Hostel 199 Newland Rd, Withywood, Bristol BS13 9DT; Tel 0117 964 1350
   (8)

School Road Community Home 40 School Rd, Bristol BS4 4NN; Tel 0117 977 1326
   (8)

DAY CENTRES FOR DISABLED PEOPLE

Bristol 600 Day Centre Langhill Ave, Inns Crt, Bristol BS4 1TN; Tel 0117 964 5833
(Clubs and handicraft classes for blind people are also held at the Centre)
   (150)

Lockleaze Blake Centre Gainsborough Sq, Lockleaze, Bristol BS7 9XA; Tel 0117 903 8454
   (150)

RESIDENTIAL HOME FOR DISABLED PEOPLE

The Bristol Home Gainsborough Sq, Lockleaze, Bristol BS7 9XA; Tel 0117 903 9050

ELDERLY PERSONS' HOMES

There are 13 local authority elderly persons' homes.

HOMES FOR ELDERLY MENTALLY INFIRM PEOPLE

Birchwood Home 35 Birchwood Rd, St. Anne's, Bristol BS4 4QL; Tel 0117 971 2266

Coombe Home 321 Camford La, Westbury-on-Trym, Bristol; Tel 0117 968 5211

Gleeson House Goffenton Dr, Oldbury Crt, Bristol BS16 2QD; Tel 0117 965 1889

Greville Home Lacey Rd, Stockwood, Bristol BS14 8LN; Tel 01276 837034

Rockwell Home Corbett Cl, Lawrence Weston, Bristol BS37 7BA; Tel 0117 982 5693

Education and Lifelong Learning Department

PO Box 57, Bristol BS99 7EB; URL www.bristol-lea.org.uk; E-mail john-gaskin@bristol-city.gov.uk; Tel 0117 903 7960; Fax 0117 903 7963
Director (Education and Lifelong Learning) John Gaskin
Head of Service (School Improvement and Educational Achievement) Sally Boulter
Head of Service (Education Resources and Support Services) John Holland

6

Head of Service (Education Inclusion and Regeneration)
Vanessa Harvey-Samuel
Head of Service (Education Policy and Planning)
Anne Papathomas
International Development and External Funding Jill Ritchie
Manager (Planning and Development) Trish Martin
Manager (Personnel) Merlyn Ipinson-Fleming
Manager (Education Resources) Andrew Birch
Manager (Community Education) Bob Woodward
Manager (IT) Derek Hart
Senior Education Officer (SEN Policy and Research)/PEP
Chris Stevens

SPECIAL SCHOOLS

Briarwood School Briar Way, Fishponds, Bristol BS16 4EA;
Tel 0117 965 7536
Headteacher David Hussey
SLD

Bristol Gateway School Stafford Rd, St. Werburgh's, Bristol
BS2 9UR; Tel 0117 377 2275; Fax 0117 377 2283
Headteacher Mike Lewis

Claremont School Henleaze Pk, Henleaze, Bristol BS9 4LR;
Tel 0117 924 7527
Headteacher Bob Coburn
PD

Elmfield School Greystoke Ave, Westbury-on-Trym, Bristol
BS10 6AY; Tel 0117 903 0366
Headteacher Ros Way
Deafness

Florence Brown School Leinster Ave, Knowle, Bristol
BS4 1NN; Tel 0117 966 8152
Headteacher Peter Evans
MLD/PD

Fulford School Fulford Rd, Hartcliffe, Bristol BS13 0PD;
Tel 0117 964 9806
Headteacher Sue Johnson
EBD

Kingsdon Manor School Kingsdon, Somerton, Somerset
TA11 7JZ; Tel 01935 840323
Headteacher John Holliday
Senior boys EBD

Kingsweston School Napier Miles Rd, Kingsweston, Bristol
BS11 0UT; Tel 0117 903 0400
Headteacher David Capel
Mixed MLD, SLD

New Fosseway School New Fosseway Rd, Hengrove,
Bristol BS14 9LN; Tel 0117 903 0220
Headteacher John Hiscox
Mixed All ages SLD

Notton House School 28 Notton, Lacock, Wiltshire
SN15 2NF; Tel 01249 730407
Headteacher Gerry Gamble
EBD

Woodstock School Rectory Gdns, Henbury, Bristol
BS10 2AH; Tel 0117 377 2175; Fax 0117 377 2177
Headteacher Graham Parsons
Primary-aged pupils. EBD

BUCKINGHAMSHIRE COUNTY COUNCIL

www.buckscc.gov.uk

In April 1997 Milton Keynes became a unitary authority.
The rest of Buckinghamshire Council retains a two-tier
structure, and employs over 11 000 people.
Population 468 720 (estimate)
Political Composition: Con: 40, LD: 9, Lab: 5

County Hall, Aylesbury, Buckinghamshire HP20 1UA;
URL www.buckscc.gov.uk; Tel 01296 395000
Chair of the Council Richard Pushman
Chief Officer Chris Williams
Strategic Manager (Resources) Ian Trenholm
Strategic Manager (Planning and Transportation)
Janet Relfe
Head (Legal Administration) Anne Davies
Head (Communication) Mike McCabe
Head (Human Resources) Ian Crich
Head (Trading Standards) Phil Dart
Head (Contracts) Graham Foulkes
Head (IT Services) W.K. Boxhall, MIDPM
Head (Finance) Martin Shefferd

Social Services

County Hall, Walton St, Aylesbury, Buckinghamshire
HP20 1YU; URL www.buckscc.gov.uk; Tel 01296 395000;
Duty Team (out-of-office hours) 01494 817750; Fax 01296
383182; Minicom 01296 392488
*Strategic Manager (Children and Young People)/Director (Social
Services)* John Beckerleg
Strategic Manager (Adult Social Care) Rita Lally
Head (Social Care for Children and Families) Clive Lee
Head (Learning Disability, Mental Health and Commissioning)
Jacqueline Pratt
Head (Older People and Physical Disabilities)
Trevor Boyd
*Head (Finance and Business Support for Children and
Families)* Alan Mander
Head (Finance and Business Support for Adult Social Care)
Elaine Kilkenny
Executive Manager (Integrated Learning Disability Services)
Stuart Mitchelmore
Executive Manager (Integrated Commissioning for Adults)
Kate Kennally
Group Manager (Children in the Community)
Heather Clarke
Group Manager (Older People) Dwina Wheatley
Manager (Older People – Strategy and Commissioning)
Varsha Raja
*Manager (Policy, Performance and Information – Children and
Young People)* David Shaw
*Manager (Adult Social Care and Resources – Policy Performance
and Information)* Brian Newton
Project Manager (Supporting People) Val Chambers
Joint Manager (Communication) Sharon Suich
Joint Manager (Communication) Barbara Loxton
Performance Manager (Adult Social Care)
Paul Greenhalgh
Manager (Complaints and Feedback) Daniele Manktelow
Policy Manager (Adult Social Care) Hedy Richards
Manager (Management Information and Research)
Cecile Colghet
Manager (Accountancy) Gavin Kinsman
Manager (Finance Support) John Bodie
Manager (Admin) Linda Gerhardt
Manager (ICT) Cath Birch
Manager (Human Resources) Richard Ayres
Senior Human Resources Officer (Training) Frances Mills

Emergency Duty Team Katherine Knapp Hse, Stretton Cl,
High Wycombe, Buckinghamshire HP7 0JD; Tel 01494
817750

DIVISIONAL OFFICES

Aylesbury Vale Area Office

Social Services Department, County Offices, Aylesbury,
Buckinghamshire HP20 1YU; Tel 01296 383999;
Fax 01296 383182; Minicom 01296 382488
*Senior Manager (Integrated Learning Disability Services –
Aylesbury and Buckingham)* Neil Fillingham
Area Manager (Older People and Home Care)
Wendy Price

Community Team Manager (Learning Disability)
Jeanette Hewitt
Team Manager (Physical and Sensory Disabilities – Aylesbury and Chiltern and South Bucks) Mary Williams
Service Manager (Children in Need) Diana Large
Service Manager (Children's Referral and Assessment)
Dan Russell

Chiltern and South Buckinghamshire Area Office

Social Services Department, County Offices, Amersham, Buckinghamshire HP6 5BN; Tel 01494 729000; Fax 01494 722154; Minicom 01494 432010
Community Team Manager (Learning Disability) Vacancy
Service Manager (Placement, Permanency and Adoption)
Carole Atkins
Manager (Review and Audit – Children) Mary Davern
Area Manager (Older People and Home Care) Sue Aston

Wycombe Area Office

Social Services Department, Easton St, High Wycombe, Buckinghamshire HP11 1NH; Tel 01494 442277; Fax 01494 475077; Minicom 01494 475253
Group Manager (Physical Disability) Beryl Ramsey
Group Manager (Looked After Children) Theresa Leavy (Acting)
Area Manager (Older People and Home Care) Janette Black
Senior Manager (Integrated Learning Disability Services – Wycombe and Amersham) Ian Harrison
Community Team Manager (Learning Disability)
Mandy Batten
Team Manager (Physical and Sensory Disability) Pam Rose
Service Manager (Children with Disabilities) Kathy Forbes
Service Manager (Children's Care Services) Margaret Doe
Service Manager (Leaving Care) Kathy Richards (Acting)

CHILDREN'S RESIDENTIAL UNITS

Chiltern View Residential Unit Nalders Rd, Chesham, Buckinghamshire HP5 3DF; Tel 01494 580613
Manager Marian Jones

Churchill Avenue Children's Home 1a Churchill Ave, Aylesbury, Buckinghamshire HP21 8LZ; Tel 01296 415279
Manager Margaret Birkett

FAMILY CENTRES

Castlefield Family Centre 19–21 Laburnum Gr, Castlefield, High Wycombe, Buckinghamshire HP12 3LS; Tel 01494 532406
Manager Dawn Willis

Desborough Road Family Centre Richardson St, High Wycombe, Buckinghamshire HP11 2SB; Tel 01494 445964
Manager Adele Bassett

Winterton Drive Family Centre Winterton Dr, Aylesbury, Buckinghamshire HP21 9BD; Tel 01296 421828
Manager Monica Gilbey

HOSTEL FOR ADULTS WITH LEARNING DISABILITIES

Seeleys House Campbell Dr, Knotty Grn, Beaconsfield, Buckinghamshire HP9 1TF; Tel 01494 677902
Unit Co-ordinator Wendy Rutland

MENTAL HEALTH SERVICES

Group Manager (Mental Health) Judith Burton (based in Amersham)
Community Services Manager (Aylesbury) Lyn Scott
Team Manager (High Wycombe) Mary Fountain
Team Manager (Amersham) Rosemary Tolley
Team Manager (Aylesbury) Pam Peake

RESOURCE CENTRES – DAY AND COMMUNITY SUPPORT SERVICES

Benjamin Road Day Service 2 Benjamin Rd, High Wycombe, Buckinghamshire HP13 6SP; Tel 01494 463429
Unit Co-ordinator Sue Smith

Bierton Hill Centre 3 Bierton Hill, Aylesbury, Buckinghamshire HP20 1EE; Tel 01296 23508
Resource Centre Manager Derek Randall

Burnham Resource Centre Minniecroft Rd, Burnham, Slough, Buckinghamshire SL1 7DE; Tel 01628 666111
Resource Centre Manager Pam Wheeler

Endeavour Centre Cameron Rd, Chesham, Buckinghamshire HP5 3BP; Tel 01494 783675
Resource Centre Manager Carol Larter

Hartwell Centre Thame Rd South, Aylesbury, Buckinghamshire HP22 8TS; Tel 01296 485088
Resource Centre Manager Sylvia Pyott

Princes Risborough Resource Centre Clifford Rd, Princes Risborough, Buckinghamshire HP27 0DU; Tel 01844 347851
Resource Centre Manager Derek Randall

Seeleys House Campbell Rd, Knotty Grn, Beaconsfield, Buckinghamshire HP9 1TF; Tel 01494 677902
Resource Centre Manager Pam Wheeler

Southern Day Services Orchard Hse, Cressey Rd, High Wycombe, Buckinghamshire HP12 4PR; Tel 01494 476133
Day Care Manager Anne Fitzpatrick

Stokebury Day Centre London Rd West, Amersham, Buckinghamshire HP7 0EZ; Tel 01494 729439
Unit Co-ordinator Buddug Chapman

Thrift Farm Resource Centre Buckingham Rd, Whaddon, Milton Keynes MK17 0EQ; Tel 01908 501733
Resource Centre Manager Jenni Burton

Well Street Centre Well St, Buckingham, Buckinghamshire MK18 1EN; Tel 01280 823564
Resource Centre Manager Jenni Burton

West End Hall Day Service Project, West End Rd, High Wycombe, Buckinghamshire HP11 2QB; Tel 01494 444383
Unit Co-ordinator Nyoka Clouden

Winslow Day Service Winslow Centre, Park Rd, Winslow, Buckinghamshire MK18 3DN; Tel 01296 383570
Resource Centre Manager Jenni Burton

WROC Hillcrest Coronation Rd, High Wycombe, Buckinghamshire HP12 3RP; Tel 01494 526375
Resource Centre Manager Mireille Letchford

WROC Micklefield Road 5 Micklefield Rd, High Wycombe, Buckinghamshire HP13 7JE; Tel 01494 443530
Resource Centre Manager Mireille Letchford

WROC Spring Valley Day Centre Spring Valley Dr, Hughendon Valley, High Wycombe, Buckinghamshire HP14 4LR; Tel 01494 56202
Resource Centre Manager Mireille Letchford

WROC Verney Avenue Special Needs Unit Verney Ave, High Wycombe, Buckinghamshire HP12 3NE; Tel 01494 461041
Resource Centre Manager Mireille Letchford

Wycombe Hills Day Services Orchard Hse, Cressex Rd, High Wycombe, Buckinghamshire HP12 4PR; Tel 01494 476139
Manager (Day Care) Pat Moore

RESIDENTIAL UNITS PROVIDING RESPITE CARE FOR CHILDREN WITH DISABILITIES

Merryfields Children's Home Cressex Rd, High Wycombe, Buckinghamshire HP12 4PR; Tel 01494 444138
Manager Marion Millward

Walton Grove Children's Home 1 Walton Gr, Aylesbury, Buckinghamshire HP21 7SL; Tel 01296 399473
Manager Vacancy

6

Schools Portfolio/Children and Young People Portfolio

County Hall, Walton St, Aylesbury, Buckinghamshire HP20 1UZ; Tel 01296 395000
Strategic Director (Children and Young People)
   John Beckerleg
Strategic Manager (Schools)/Chief Education Officer
   Sue Imbriano
Head (Youth and Community)   Liz Lawrence
Head (Special Educational Services)   Vacancy

Aylesbury Vale Area

HOSPITAL CLASS

Stoke Mandeville Hospital, Aylesbury, Buckinghamshire HP21 8AL; Tel 01296 315067
Teacher   Joanna Jones

SPECIAL DAY SCHOOLS

Furze Down School   Verney Rd, Winslow, Buckingham, Buckinghamshire MK18 3BL;
E-mail office.furzedown@easymail.rmplc.co.uk; Tel 01296 713385; Fax 01296 714420
Headteacher   Vacancy
   (99)

Kynaston School   Stoke Leys Cl, Aylesbury, Buckinghamshire HP21 9ET;
E-mail office@kynaston.bucks.sch.uk; Tel 01296 427221; Fax 01296 433700
Headteacher   Ron Westwood (Acting)
   (46)

Park School   Stocklake, Aylesbury, Buckinghamshire HP20 1DP; E-mail admin@park.bucks.sch.uk; Tel 01296 423507; Fax 01296 433353
Headteacher   Ruth Cutler
   (79)

Stoke Leys School   Stoke Leys Cl, Aylesbury, Buckinghamshire HP21 9ET;
E-mail office@stokeleys.bucks.sch.uk; Tel 01296 427441; Fax 01296 427441
Headteacher   Ron Westwood
   (66)

RESIDENTIAL SPECIAL SCHOOLS

Pebble Brook School   Churchill Ave, Aylesbury, Buckinghamshire HP21 8LZ;
E-mail office@pebblebrook.bucks.sch.uk; Tel 01296 415761 01296 415762; Fax 01296 434442
Headteacher   Donna Jolly
   (66)

Wendover House School   Church La, Wendover, Aylesbury, Buckinghamshire HP22 6NL;
E-mail office@wendoverhouse.bucks.sch.uk; Tel 01296 622157; 01296 623691; Fax 01296 622628
Headteacher   Nigel Morris
   Residential only. (69)

PUPIL REFERRAL UNITS

Aylesbury Vale Pupil Referral Unit (Primary)   Unit 1, Abbey Centre, Weedon Rd, Aylesbury, Buckinghamshire HP19 9NS; E-mail office@aylesburyvale-pri.bucks.sch.uk; Tel 01296 488447; Fax 01296 381506
Head of Centre   Gillian Davies

Aylesbury Vale Pupil Referral Unit (Secondary)   Unit 8, Abbey Centre, Weedon Rd, Aylesbury, Buckinghamshire HP19 9NS;
E-mail admin1@aylesburyvale-sec.bucks.sch.uk; Tel 01296 431989; Fax 01296 339125
Headteacher   Tom Millea

Chiltern/South Buckinghamshire Area

Council Offices, King George V Rd, Amersham, Buckinghamshire HP6 5BY; Tel 01494 732292; Fax 01494 732294

SPECIAL DAY SCHOOLS

Heritage House School   Cameron Rd, Chesham, Buckinghamshire HP5 3BP;
E-mail office@heritagehouse.bucks.sch.uk; Tel 01494 771445; Fax 01494 775892
Headteacher   Mike Barrie
   (79)

Special Needs Resource Centre   Unit 6, Abbey Centre, Weldon Rd, Aylesbury, Buckinghamshire HP19 9NS; Tel 01296 431716; Fax 01296 397698
Manager   Jenny Bennett

RESIDENTIAL SPECIAL SCHOOLS

Alfriston School   Penn Rd, Beaconsfield, Buckinghamshire HP9 2TS; E-mail office@alfriston.bucks.sch.uk; Tel 01494 673740; Fax 01494 670177
Headteacher   Valerie Gordon
   (124)

Prestwood Lodge School   Nairdwood La, Prestwood, Great Missenden, Buckinghamshire HP16 0QQ;
E-mail office.prestwoodlodge@easymail.rmplc.co.uk; Tel 01494 863514; Fax 01494 866154
Headteacher   Mike MacCourt
   (61)

Stony Dean School   Orchard End Ave, off Pineapple Rd, Amersham, Buckinghamshire HP7 9JP;
E-mail office@stonydean.bucks.sch.uk; Tel 01494 762538; Fax 01494 765631
Headteacher   Graham Newsholme
   (129)

PUPIL REFERRAL UNIT

The Oaks Pupil Referral Unit   Elangeni School Site, Woodside Ave, Amersham, Buckinghamshire HP6 6EG;
E-mail office@theoaks-pru.bucks.sch.uk; Tel 01494 721925
Headteacher   Olive Harrison

Wycombe Area

HOSPITAL CLASS

Wycombe General Hospital, Children's Ward 7, High Wycombe, Buckinghamshire HP11 2TT; Tel 01494 425503
Teacher-in-Charge   Anne Steiner

SPECIAL DAY SCHOOLS

Maplewood School   Faulkner Way, Downley, High Wycombe, Buckinghamshire HP13 5HB;
E-mail office@maplewood.bucks.sch.uk; Tel 01494 465609; 01494 525728
Headteacher   John Rumble
   16+ (72)

Westfield School   Highfield Rd, Bourne End, Buckinghamshire SL8 5BE;
E-mail office.westfield@easymail.rmplc.co.uk; Tel 01628 533125; Fax 01628 523345
Headteacher   Geoff Allen
   (35)

RESIDENTIAL SPECIAL SCHOOL

Chiltern Gate School   Verney Ave, High Wycombe, Buckinghamshire HP12 3NE;
E-mail office@chilterngate.bucks.sch.uk; Tel 01494 532621; Fax 01494 441478
Headteacher   Gordon Philips
   (109)

PUPIL REFERRAL UNITS

Woodlands Pupil Referral Unit (Primary) Philip Rd, High Wycombe, Buckinghamshire HP13 7JS; E-mail office@woodlands.bucks.sch.uk; Tel 01494 523874
Headteacher Maggie Farmer

The Wycombe Grange Pupil Referral Unit (Secondary) 56 Amersham Hill, High Wycombe, Buckinghamshire HP13 6PQ; E-mail office@wycombegrange-pru.bucks.sch.uk; Tel 01494 445815; Fax 01494 465860
Headteacher George Lloyd

Special Needs Resource Centre c/o Highcrest Community School, Hatters La, High Wycombe, Buckinghamshire HP13 7NQ; E-mail snrcwycombe@dial.pipex.com; Tel 01494 463266; Fax 01494 521753
Manager Jackie Finch

BURY METROPOLITAN BOROUGH COUNCIL
www.bury.gov.uk

Population 181 900
Political Composition: Lab: 28, Con: 16, LD: 4
Town Hall, Knowsley St, Bury, Greater Manchester BL9 0SW; URL www.bury.gov.uk; E-mail b.hargreaves@bury.gov.uk; Tel 0161 253 5000; Fax 0161 253 5079
Athenaeum Hse, Market St, Bury, Greater Manchester BL9 0BN; Tel 0161 253 5000
Chief Executive Mark Sanders, MBA, BSc(Hons)
Deputy Chief Executive Mike Kelly
Assistant Chief Executive Carolyn Wilkins
Director (Finance and E-Government) Mike Owen, IPFA
Director (Personnel) Guy Berry
Lester Hse, 21 Broad St, Bury, Greater Manchester BL9 0DA
Director (Legal and Democratic Services) Jayne Hammond
Director (Education and Culture) Harold Williams
Director (Social Services, Health and Housing) Eleni Ioannides

Social Services

Castle Bldgs, Market Pl, Bury, Greater Manchester BL9 0LT; URL www.bury.gov.uk; Tel 0161 253 5000; Fax 0161 253 5494
Director (Social Services, Health and Housing) Eleni Ioannides
Assistant Director (Children's Services) Judith Longhill
Assistant Director (Adult Services) Pat Horan
Head (Strategy and Planning) Linda Jackson
Resource Manager Monica Crossley
Resource Manager Sue Tattersall
Resource Manager Andy Crawford
Service Manager (Assessment and Care Management) Allan Calvert (Acting)
Service Manager (Learning Disability) E. McKeown (Acting)
Service Manager (Looked After Children) E. Shingler
Service Manager (Child Protection and Reviewing) Julie Owen
Service Manager (Assessment and Fieldwork) K. Todrick
Service Manager (Family Support and Disability) Joyce Berry
Service Manager (Disability Services) L. Hughes
Principal Officer (Finance) D.R. Pooler
Principal Officer (Income and Financial Assessment) H. Marrow
Principal Personnel Officer Carol Mangnall

TRAINING

Responsible for training professional and support staff in the department.
Seedfield Resource Centre, Parkinson St, Bury, Greater Manchester BL9 6NY; Tel 0161 253 6896
Manager (Development and Training) L. Jackson

Heads of Committees

Cabinet Portfolio Member (Health, Housing and Social Services – Executive Committee Head Spokesperson) Cllr M. Connolly
Chair (Review Panel) Cllr T. Isherwood

AREA OFFICES

Central/South – Adults 7 Whittaker St, Radcliffe, Manchester M26 9TD; Tel 0161 253 7190; Fax 0161 723 3327

North – Adults and Children Craig Hse, 5 Bank St, Bury, Greater Manchester BL9 0BA; Tel (Adults) 0161 253 5451; (Children) 0161 253 5454; Fax (Children) 0161 253 6011; (Adults) 0161 253 6267

South – Children and Families The Uplands, Bury New Rd, Whitefield, Greater Manchester M25 6QT; Tel 0161 253 7333; Fax 0161 253 7535

HOSPITAL SOCIAL WORKERS

Fairfield General Hospital Rochdale Old Rd, Bury, Greater Manchester BL9 7TD; Tel 0161 705 3582; 0161 705 3590; Fax 0161 705 6414
Team Manager (Fieldwork) Sue Fagelman

CHILDREN AND FAMILY CENTRES

Chesham Children and Family Centre 190 Chesham Rd, Bury, Greater Manchester BL9 6HA; Tel 0161 253 6565
Manager (Early Years Family Support) Nicola Freschini

Family Advice Support Team 18 Ribchester Dr, Bury, Greater Manchester BL9 9JT; Tel 0161 253 5200
Manager (Family Support) Kath McFarlane

Home and School Support Project Whitefield Community Primary School, Victoria Ave, Whitefield, Greater Manchester M45 6DP; Tel 0161 767 8361
Project Co-ordinator Colin Lyne; Tel 0161 778 3526

Ribchester Drive Children's Home 22 Ribchester Dr, Bury, Greater Manchester BL9 9JT; Tel 0161 253 6567
Team Manager Lynda Heitzman (Acting)

Victoria Children and Family Centre Victoria St, Radcliffe, Greater Manchester M26 0BD; Tel 0161 253 7166
Manager Alison Smith
(50)

ADOLESCENT SERVICES

Seedfield Resource Centre Parkinson St, Bury, Greater Manchester; Tel 0161 253 6862
Team Manager Philip Jones

FAMILY PLACEMENT

18–20 St. Mary's Pl, Bury, Greater Manchester BL9 0DZ; Tel 0161 253 5457
Service Manager E. Shingler
Team Manager Diana Powell; Tel 0161 253 5464

ADULT EDUCATION CENTRES

Bury Employment Support Training 24 Ribchester Dr, Bury, Greater Manchester BL9 9JT; Tel 0161 705 2010
Manager Huw Davies

Wheatfields Adult Education Centre Victoria Ave, Whitefield, Greater Manchester M25 6DP; Tel 0161 253 7572
Manager Anne Stansfield
(60)

6

William Kemp Heaton Centre (Including Special Care Unit)
St. Peter's Rd, Bury, Greater Manchester BL9 9RP; Tel 0161 253 6561
Officer-in-Charge Steve Hampson
(58)

DAY CENTRES FOR PEOPLE WITH LEARNING DIFFICULTIES

Learning Disabilities Development Service The Uplands, Bury New Rd, Whitefield, Greater Manchester M45 8QT; Tel 0161 253 7545
Service Manager E. McKeown
Manager (Day Service Resource) Melanie Cocker

Whittle Pike Day Centre Hazel St, Ramsbottom, Greater Manchester BL0 9PT; Tel 01706 822747
Officer-in-Charge Rob Laing
(60)

MENTAL HEALTH TEAM

Lord Street Mental Health Team 1a Lord St, Radcliffe, Manchester M26 3AF; Tel 0161 253 7100; Fax 0161 253 7133
Service Manager Pauline Ambrey
Service Manager Paul Bardsley

MENTAL HEALTH DAY CENTRES

Haworth Close Day Centre 1 Haworth Cl, off Bronte Ave, Bury, Greater Manchester BL9 9SB; Tel 0161 253 6558
Manager Lesley Fleming
(20)

Knowle Hill View Victoria Ave, Whitefield, Greater Manchester M25 6DP; Tel 0161 253 6559
Manager Lesley Fleming
(27)

Woodbury Day Centre Wesley St, Tottington, Greater Manchester BL8 3NN; Tel 01204 887424
Manager Peter Miller
(20)

DISABILITY SERVICES

Seedfield Resource Centre, Parkinson St, Bury, Greater Manchester BL9 6NY; Tel 0161 253 6858
Service Manager Lynda Hughes

DAY CARE CENTRES FOR THE ELDERLY

Grundy Day Care Centre Wellington Rd, Bury, Greater Manchester BL9 9AH; Tel 0161 253 6555
Manager Tricia Fern
(70)

Pinfold Lane Day Care Centre
Manager Irene Sargeant (Acting)

Seedfield Day Care Centre Parkinson St, Bury, Greater Manchester BL9 6NY; Tel 0161 253 6876
Manager Derek Melia
(24)

SHORT STAY HOME FOR THE ELDERLY

Beech Grove Home Chesham Rd, Bury, Greater Manchester BL9 6HA; Tel 0161 253 6552
Manager Marie Glynn

ACCOMMODATION FOR THE ELDERLY

Service Manager Steve Beale
There are nine homes providing long stay and respite care.

COMMUNITY DRUG AND ALCOHOL TEAM

Tenterden Street Drug and Alcohol Team Woolstenholme Hse, 4 Tenterden St, Bury, Greater Manchester BL9 0EG; Tel 0161 253 6488; Fax 0161 253 6546
Service Manager I. Goodey

WRVS

43 Knowsley St, Bury, Greater Manchester; Tel 0161 761 1549; 0161 764 4467
Officer-in-Charge Michelle Holt

EMERGENCY DUTY SERVICE

Bradley Fold, Bolton, Greater Manchester; Tel 0161 253 6606

Education and Culture Department

Athenaeum Hse, Market St, Bury, Greater Manchester BL9 0BN; Tel 0161 253 5652; Fax 0161 253 5653
Director (Education and Culture) Harold Williams, BEd, MA
Head (Access and Inclusion) T. Dawson
Service Manager (Special Educational Needs Service)/Principal Educational Psychologist L. Walker
Manager (Social Inclusion Service) A. Cogswell, BA(Hons)

SPECIAL DAY SCHOOLS

Elms Bank Community High School Ripon Ave, Whitefield, Greater Manchester M25 6PJ;
E-mail s3517011@yahoo.co.uk; Tel 0161 766 1597
Headteacher L. Lines, BA
Secondary Learning Difficulty

Millwood School Fletcher Fold Rd, Bury, Greater Manchester BL9 9RX; E-mail s3517010@yahoo.co.uk; Tel 0161 253 6083
Headteacher B.J. Emblem, MEd, DipSpEd
Primary Learning Difficulty

SCHOOL WITH RESOURCED PROVISION FOR HEARING-IMPAIRED CHILDREN

The Elton High School Walshaw Rd, Bury, Greater Manchester BL8 1RN; E-mail s3514004@yahoo.co.uk; Tel 0161 763 1434

SCHOOLS WITH RESOURCE PROVISION FOR PUPILS WITH MODERATE LEARNING DISABILITIES

Castlebrook High School Parr La, Bury, Greater Manchester BL9 8OP; E-mail s3514031@yahoo.co.uk; Tel 0161 796 9820

Radcliffe High School Abden St, Radcliffe, Greater Manchester M26 3AT; E-mail s3514018@yahoo.co.uk; Tel 0161 723 3110

Tottington High School Laurel St, Tottington, Bury, Greater Manchester BL8 3LY; E-mail s3514020@yahoo.co.uk; Tel 01204 882327

ACCESS AND INCLUSION SERVICE

Learning Support Service Seedfield Centre, Parkinson St, Bury, Greater Manchester BL9 6NY; Tel 0161 253 6418
Hospital tuition, home tuition, SpLD, literacy support, travellers service, specialist advisory teaching team.

English Language Teaching Service Seedfield Centre, Parkinson St, Bury, Greater Manchester BL9 6NY; Tel 0161 253 6424

Portage Service Seedfield Centre, Parkinson St, Bury, Greater Manchester BL9 6NY; Tel 0161 253 6131

Pupil Learning Centre New Summerseat Hse, Summerseat La, Bury, Greater Manchester BL0 9UD; Tel 01204 885275
Head of Centre K. Chantrey

Sensory Support Service c/o Radcliffe High School, Abden St, Radcliffe, Greater Manchester M26 0AW; Tel 0161 724 8337

CHILDREN'S DISABILITY SERVICE

Seedfield Centre, Parkinson St, Bury, Greater Manchester BL9 6NY; Tel 0161 253 6881

CALDERDALE METROPOLITAN BOROUGH COUNCIL
www.calderdale.gov.uk

Population 192 400
Political Composition: Lab: 10, Con: 25, LD: 16, Ind: 1;
BNP: 2
The Town Hall, Halifax, West Yorkshire HX1 1UJ;
URL www.calderdale.gov.uk; Tel 01422 357257;
Fax 01422 393102
Chief Executive Paul Sheehan
Deputy Chief Executive Carol White
Group Director (Corporate Services Directorate)
Catherine Parkinson
Group Director (Community Services Directorate)
Rose Wheeler
Group Director (Health and Social Care Directorate)
Philip Lewer
Group Director (Regeneration and Development Directorate)
Janet Waggott
Chief Finance Officer Pete Smith

Social Services

1 Park Rd, Halifax, West Yorkshire HX1 2TU;
URL www.calderdale.gov.uk; Tel 01422 363561;
(Emergency) 01422 365101; Fax 01422 393815
Head (Adult Services) Phil Shire
Head (Planning, Performance and Quality) Vacancy
Head (Children's Services) Vacancy
Head (Finance and Business Services) Robin Clark
Service Manager (Home Care) Margaret Moss

TRAINING

Responsible for training professional and support staff.
Senior Training Officer Col Bell

Cabinet

Leader Cllr Ford
14 Westfield Dr, Lightcliffe, Halifax, West Yorkshire
HX3 8AW
Deputy Leader Cllr Foran
7b Stratton Cl, Rastrick, Brighouse, West Yorkshire HD6 3SW
Portfolio Holder (Health and Social Care) Cllr Greason
14 Westfield Dr, Lightcliffe, Halifax, West Yorkshire
HX3 8AW
Members Cabinet (Social Services Committee)
Lab: Cllr Rivron.
Con: Cllr Mrs Hardy, Cllr Kirton, Cllr Whittaker.
LD: Cllr Battye, Cllr Coles, Mrs Jennings.

LOCALITY TEAMS

Lower Calder Locality Team Lawson Rd, Brighouse, West
Yorkshire HD6 1NY; Tel 01484 710821
South Halifax Locality Team 1 Park Rd, Halifax, West
Yorkshire HX1 2TU; Tel 01422 363561
Calder Valley – Elland Locality Team Southgate, Elland,
West Yorkshire HX5 0BW; Tel 01422 373491
Halifax Locality Team Ovenden Hall, Ovenden Rd, Halifax,
West Yorkshire HX3 5QS; Tel 01422 353279
North Halifax Locality Team 1 Park Rd, Halifax, West
Yorkshire HX1 2TU; Tel 01422 363561

HOSPITAL SOCIAL WORKERS

Calderdale Royal Hospital Salterhebble Hill, Halifax, West
Yorkshire; Tel 01422 357171

COMPLAINTS AND COMPLIMENTS; TEL 01422 393883
Head (Complaints and Compliments) Alan Taylor

CHILD PROTECTION REGISTER

C/o Headquarters 1 Park Rd, Halifax, West Yorkshire
HX1 2TU; Tel 01422 363561
Principal Officer (Child Protection) Paul Davy
Senior Reviewing Officer John Murray

COMMUNITY HOMES

There are three Children's Homes plus one respite unit.
Alloefield View Children's Home 57 Alloefield View,
Illingworth, Halifax, West Yorkshire; Tel 01422
244558
Cousin Lane Children's Home 91 Cousin La, Oveden,
Halifax, West Yorkshire; Tel 01422 244113
West Garth Children's Home 79 Victoria Rd, Elland,
Halifax, West Yorkshire; Tel 01422 373097

FAMILY PLACEMENT SERVICE

Social Services Department Lawson Rd, Brighouse, West
Yorkshire HD6 1NY; Tel 01484 710821
Manager (Locality Services Admin) L. O'Farrell

HALIFAX AREA DAY SERVICES

Chatham Street Centre Hope St, Halifax, West Yorkshire
HX1 5DW; Tel 01422 361086
Locality Manager Christine Gleeson
The Grove Day Services Savile Park Rd, Halifax, West
Yorkshire HX1 2EN

LOWER VALLEY DAY SERVICES

Lower Edge Centre Lower Edge Rd, Rastrick, Brighouse,
West Yorkshire HD6 3LD; Tel 01484 714683
Locality Manager Brian Mitchell
The Grove Respite Centre Savile Park Rd, Halifax, West
Yorkshire WX1 2EN; Tel 01422 362048
Unit Manager Geraldine Wood

UPPER VALLEY DAY SERVICES

Royd Square Special Care Unit Bond St, Hebden Bridge,
West Yorkshire HX7 7DE; Tel 01422 846045; Fax 01422
846045
Manager Sue Shaw

INDEPENDENT LIVING SCHEME

c/o Chatham St, Centre Hope St, Halifax, West Yorkshire
HX1 5DW; Tel 01422 323821; Fax 01422 323821
Unit Manager Christine Gleeson

SHARED HOUSES

Shared houses and supported living for people with mental
health problems.
Union Housing Scheme 23 Union Street South, Halifax,
West Yorkshire HX1 2LE; Tel 01422 340373; 01422
340444
28 places in eight houses around Calderdale with
varying levels of staff support to suit the needs of
residents.
6–8 Bank Villas Sowerby Bridge, Halifax, West Yorkshire
HX6 3BH; Tel 01422 835542
(8)
Making Space Unity Crt, Crowtrees, Rastrick, West
Yorkshire; Tel 01925 571680
(5)

6

CARE IN THE COMMUNITY FOR ADULTS WITH MENTAL HEALTH PROBLEMS

Wards End Day Services 14 Wards End, Halifax, West Yorkshire; Tel 01422 349528
Unit Manager Kevin Jukes

DAY CENTRE FOR PEOPLE WITH MENTAL HEALTH PROBLEMS

Ebenezer Centre St. James Rd, Halifax, West Yorkshire HX1 1YS; Tel 01422 342654
Unit Manager Libby Smith

ACCOMMODATION FOR PEOPLE WITH MENTAL HEALTH PROBLEMS

Lyndhurst Home 72 Victoria Rd, Elland, West Yorkshire HX5 0QF; Tel 01422 372808
Unit Manager Trevor Cox

Housing Support c/o Housing Advice Centre, Crossley St, Halifax, West Yorkshire; Tel 01442 393309; Fax 01442 393334
Manager (Housing Support Scheme) Rhian Barnabas

CARE IN THE COMMUNITY UNIT HOMES – UNION HOUSING

Huddersfield Road Unit Home 317 Huddersfield Rd, Halifax, West Yorkshire; Tel 01422 323244

Moorside Gardens Unit Home 14 Moorside Gdns, Ovenden, Halifax, West Yorkshire; Tel 01422 381926

Pye Nest Gardens Unit Home 126 Pye Nest Gdns, Halifax, West Yorkshire; Tel 01422 365741

Rooley Bank Unit Home 5–7 Rooley Bank, Sowerby Bridge, West Yorkshire; Tel 01422 836077

Rugby Terrace Unit Home 19–21 Rugby Terr, Ovenden, Halifax, West Yorkshire; Tel 01422 340177

Stretchgate Lane Unit Home 71–73 Stretchgate La, Pellon, Halifax, West Yorkshire; Tel 01422 340620

Whitwell Green Lane Unit Home 92–94 Whitwell Green La, Elland, West Yorkshire; Tel 01422 377583

RESIDENTIAL HOMES FOR THE ELDERLY

Team Manager (Older People and Disabilities) Vacancy
Headquarters
There are eight homes for the elderly.

MEALS SERVICES

Co-ordination 1 Park Rd, Halifax, West Yorkshire HX3 0HJ; Tel 01422 393819
Contact Helen Sutcliffe

Schools and Children's Services Directorate

Northgate Hse, Northgate, Halifax, West Yorkshire HX1 1UN; URL www.calderdale.gov.uk;
E-mail schoolsandchildrensservicesdirectorate@calderdale.gov.uk; Tel 01422 357257; Fax 01422 392515
Group Director (Schools and Children's Services) Ian Dodgson (Acting)
Principal Psychologist Keith Venables
Principal Education Welfare Officer John Taylor
Principal Officer (Children's Services Unit) Viv Murray

SPECIAL SCHOOLS

Highbury School Lower Edge Rd, Rastrick, Brighouse, West Yorkshire HD6 3LD; Tel 01484 716319; Fax 01484 721893
Headteacher P. Sellers
(37)

Ravenscliffe High School Skircoat Grn, Halifax, West Yorkshire HX3 0RZ; Tel 01422 358621; Fax 01422 329621
Headteacher M. Hirst
(111)

Wood Bank School Luddendenfoot, Halifax, West Yorkshire HX2 6PB; Tel 01422 884170; Fax 01422 884671
Headteacher J.D. Ingham
(41)

CAMBRIDGESHIRE COUNTY COUNCIL
www.cambridgeshire.gov.uk

In April 1998 Peterborough became a unitary authority and is listed alphabetically within this chapter. The rest of Cambridgeshire retains a two-tier structure.
Population 559 300 (mid 2001 estimate)
Political Composition: Con: 34, LD: 16, Lab: 9
Shire Hall, Castle Hill, Cambridge, Cambridgeshire
CB3 0AP; URL www.cambridgeshire.gov.uk;
E-mail charterline@cambridgeshire.gov.uk; Tel 01223 717111; Fax 01223 717201
Chair of the County Council Cllr Robin Driver
Chief Executive Ian Stewart
Director (Resources) Mike Parsons

Social Services Department

Castle Crt, Shire Hall, Castle Hill, Cambridge, Cambridgeshire CB3 0AP;
URL www.cambridgeshire.gov.uk/sub/ssd/index.htm;
E-mail maureen.charles@cambridgeshire.gov.uk;
Tel (Emergency) 01733 561370; 01223 717182; Fax 01223 717307
Director (Social Services) Eric Robinson
Assistant Director (Resources) Adrian Loades
Assistant Director (Children's Services) Colin Green
Assistant Director (Health) Helen Taylor (Job Share)
Assistant Director (Health) Charlotte Black (Job Share)
Assistant Director (Adult Services) Graham Wrycroft
Manager (Information Systems and Research) John Leigh
Manager (Communications and Customer Relations) Paul Ainsworth
Head (Policy and Performance) Hugh Gault
Head (Economic and Community Development) Simon Smith

TRAINING

Responsible for training professional and support staff in the department.
Manager (Training) Vacancy

AREA TEAMS

Cambridge Adults 110a Arbury Rd, Cambridge, Cambridgeshire CB4 2JF;
URL www.cambridgeshire.gov.uk; Tel 01223 718215; Fax 01223 718012

Cambridge Children Bldg 100, Rustat Hse, 60 Clifton Rd, Cambridge, Cambridgeshire CB1 7EG;
URL www.cambridgeshire.gov.uk; Tel 01223 718211; Fax 01223 718212

East Cambridgeshire Adults Julius Martin La, Soham, Cambridgeshire CB7 5EQ;
URL www.cambridgeshire.gov.uk; Tel 01353 725060; Fax 01353 725072

South Fenland and East Cambridgeshire Children The Grange, Nutholt La, Ely, Cambridgeshire CB7 4PL;
URL www.cambridgeshire.gov.uk; Tel 01353 667911; Fax 01353 616957

Huntingdonshire Adults Walden Hse, Market Hill, Huntingdon, Cambridgeshire PE29 6NX; URL www.cambridgeshire.gov.uk; Tel 01480 375501; Fax 01480 375611

Fenland Adults Fenland Hall, County Rd, March, Cambridgeshire PE15 8ND; URL www.cambridgeshire.gov.uk; Tel 01354 654321; Fax 01354 659179

North West Cambridgeshire Children Walden Hse, Market Hill, Huntingdon, Cambridgeshire PE29 6NX; URL www.cambridgeshire.gov.uk; Tel 01480 375501; Fax 01480 375520

St. Neots Children 6 Marshall Rd, St. Neots, Huntingdon, Cambridgeshire PE19 1NU; URL www.cambridgeshire.gov.uk; Tel 01480 376500; Fax 01480 376531

South Cambridgeshire Adults Comberton Rd, Toft, Cambridge, Cambridgeshire CB3 7RY; URL www.cambridgeshire.gov.uk; Tel 01223 264466; Fax 01223 263111

South Cambridgeshire Children 18–20 Signet Crt, Swann's Rd, Cambridge, Cambridgeshire CB5 8LA; URL www.cambridgeshire.gov.uk; Tel 01223 718011; Fax 01223 718012

North Fenland Children 100 Churchill Rd, Wisbech, Cambridgeshire PE13 2DE; URL www.cambridgeshire.gov.uk; Tel 01945 481100; Fax 01945 476219

HOSPITAL SOCIAL WORKERS

Children's Hospital Team 28 Long Rd, Cambridge, Cambridgeshire CB2 2PS; URL www.cambridgeshire.gov.uk; Tel 01223 714444; Fax 01223 714445
Douglas Hse, The Cedars Room, 18 Trumpington Rd, Cambridge, Cambridgeshire CB2 2AH; Tel 01223 568808; Fax 01223 568815
Team Manager Jackie Day

Cambridge Hospital Team 28 Long Rd, Cambridge, Cambridgeshire CB2 2PS; URL www.cambridgeshire.gov.uk; Tel 01223 714440; Fax 01223 714441
Team Manager Sarah Parkinson

South Mental Health Team Social Services, Fulbourn Hospital, Cambridge, Cambridgeshire CB1 5EF; URL www.cambridgeshire.gov.uk; Tel 01223 218695; Fax 01223 218760
Team Manager (Adult Mental Health) Mary Gregg

Huntingdon Fenland Mental Health Team Walden Hse, Market Hill, Huntingdon, Cambridgeshire PE29 6NX; URL www.cambridgeshire.gov.uk; Tel 01480 375519; Fax 01480 375665
Team Manager Pat Gale

Huntingdon/Fenland Hospital Team Hinchingbrooke Hospital, Hinchingbrooke Pk, Huntingdon, Cambridgeshire PE29 6NT; URL www.cambridgeshire.gov.uk; Tel 01480 416087; Fax 01480 416696
Team Manager Clare Welton

FAMILY CENTRES

The Family Unit 38 Buttsgrove Way, Oxmoor, Huntingdon, Cambridgeshire PE29 1LY; URL www.cambridgeshire.gov.uk; Tel 01480 376404; Fax 01480 376409
Manager Wendi Ogle-Welbourn

St. Neots Family Centre 6 Marshall Rd, St. Neots, Cambridgeshire PE19 1NU; Tel 01480 376531; Fax 01480 376531
Manager Wendi Ogle-Welbourn
(24)

Malta Road Family Centre Malta Rd, Cambridge, Cambridgeshire CB1 3PZ; Tel 01223 247092; Fax 01223 242280
Manager Fran Stellitano
(24)

ACCOMMODATION FOR CHILDREN

Fitzwilliam Road Children's Home 1 Fitzwilliam Rd, Cambridge, Cambridgeshire CB2 2BN; Tel 01223 368145; Fax 01223 368145
Manager Monty Legg
(6)

The Hawthorns Adolescent Unit 10 Haviland Way, Cambridge, Cambridgeshire CB4 2RA; Tel 01223 351994; Fax 01223 351994
Manager Rose-Anne Jacobs
(10)

Victoria Road Children's Home 78 Victoria Rd, Wisbech, Cambridgeshire PE13 2QF; Tel 01945 583506; Fax 01945 466831
Manager W. Bowen
(7)

HOSTELS FOR CHILDREN WITH LEARNING DISABILITIES

Hill Rise Children's Hostel Buttsgrove Way, Huntingdon, Cambridgeshire PE18 7LY; Tel 01480 398027; Fax 01480 376409
Manager J. Larkin
(4)

Norwich Road Children's Hostel 204 Norwich Rd, Wisbech, Cambridgeshire PE13 3TD; Tel 01945 584994; Fax 01945 466849
Manager Jim Gallagher
(5)

Haviland Way Children's Hostel 33 Haviland Way, Cambridge, Cambridgeshire CB4 2RE; Tel 01223 712162; Fax 01223 712164
Manager S. Draper
(12)

HOME FOR YOUNG PEOPLE WITH LEARNING DISABILITIES

Harston, Cambridgeshire CB2 5QH; Tel 01223 874590; Fax 01223 874100
Manager H. Jarvis
(4)

FAMILIES AND YOUNG PEOPLE SERVICES (LEAVING CARE)

38 Buttsgrove Way, Huntingdon, Cambridgeshire PE29 1LY; Tel 01480 376404; Fax 01480 376409
Manager Wendi Ogle-Welbourn

DAY CENTRES FOR PEOPLE WITH MENTAL HEALTH PROBLEMS

Cambridge Clubhouse 47 Norfolk St, Cambridge, Cambridgeshire CB1 2LD; Tel 01223 359561
Manager Carol Morgan
(15)

The Croylands Centre Croylands, 30 Cambridge Rd, Ely, Cambridgeshire CB7 4HL; Tel 01353 667974
Manager P. Martin
(20)

Dartford Centre Old School Bldgs, Dartford Rd, March, Cambridgeshire PE15 8AN; Tel 01354 659265
Manager John Carter

Spiers Project 189 High St, Sawston, Cambridgeshire CB2 4HY; Tel 01223 718951
Operating at Melbourn, Comberton, Gramlingay and Sawston.
Manager D. Bance

DAY CENTRES FOR PEOPLE WITH LEARNING DISABILITIES

Bargroves Day Centre Cromwell Rd, St. Neots, Cambridgeshire PE19 2EY; Tel 01480 398058; Fax 01480 473197
Manager K. Liddle
    Trainees (60)

Sawston Day Centre 187 High St, Sawston, Cambridgeshire CB2 4HJ; Tel 01223 712727; Fax 01223 712731
Manager Matthew Minks
    (10)

Horizon Resource Centre Coldhams La, Cambridge, Cambridgeshire CB1 3HY; Tel 01223 568811; Fax 01223 566175
Contact Stuart Edwards
Contact Debbie Yearsley
    Trainees (80)

Larkfield Resource Centre High Barns, Ely, Cambridgeshire CB7 4SB; Tel 01353 661128
Contact Mark Briggs
Contact M. Grzybek
    (80)

Marwick Centre Marwick Rd, March, Cambridgeshire PE15 8PH; Tel 01354 653284
Manager N. Bull
    Trainees (90)

St. Michael's Resource Centre Ambury Rd, Huntingdon, Cambridgeshire PE29 1JE; Tel 01480 398050; Fax 01480 398051
Manager K. Liddle
    Trainees (80)

RESOURCE CENTRES FOR PEOPLE WITH LEARNING DISABILITIES

CATS 1 Bull La, St. Ives, Huntingdon, Cambridgeshire PE17 4AX; Tel 01480 375200
Manager K. Liddle

Connections School La, Fulbourn, Cambridge, Cambridgeshire CB1 5BH; Tel 01223 881251
Manager Pam Wilson

Gate Lodge Resource Centre c/o The Bargroves, Cromwell Rd, St. Neots, Cambridgeshire PE19 2EY; Tel 01480 475211
Manager Karen Liddle

HOSTELS FOR PEOPLE WITH LEARNING DISABILITIES

Jasmine House 1a Upherds La, Ely, Cambridgeshire CB6 1BA; Tel 01353 662261
Manager Linda Peckett

Elm Road Hostel 53 Elm Rd, March, Cambridgeshire PE15 8PQ; Tel 01354 654146
Manager Alan Briscoe

Laxton Way Hostel 20 Laxton Way, Cambridge, Cambridgeshire CB4 2LB; Tel 01223 424541
Manager Jillian Skinner

Russell Street Hostel 44 Russell St, Cambridge, Cambridgeshire CB2 1HT; Tel 01223 712259
Manager Sarah Swallowe

St. Luke's Close Hostel 6 St. Luke's Cl, Huntingdon, Cambridgeshire PE29 2JT; Tel 01480 456941
Manager Annika Short

Wagstaff Close Hostel 8b Wagstaff Cl, Cambridge, Cambridgeshire CB4 2PS; Tel 01223 426368
Manager Jane Leighton

DAY SUPPORT SERVICES TO PHYSICALLY HANDICAPPED DISABLED PEOPLE

The Enterprise Centre Haggis Gap, Fulbourn, Cambridgeshire CB1 5HD; Tel 01223 568859
Manager Lisa Fordham

WORK CENTRE FOR PHYSICALLY DISABLED AND OLDER PEOPLE

Chrysalis Centre Community Education, Huntingdonshire College, Huntingdon, Cambridgeshire PE29 1BL; Tel 01480 452069
Manager V. Peel
    (20)

Victoria Lodge 9 Larksfield, Wisbech, Cambridgeshire PE13 2UW; Tel 01945 581510
Manager Nigel Bull
    22 residents

ACCOMMODATION FOR THE ELDERLY

The Department has recently transferred all but one of its residential homes for older people to the independent sector.

Education, Libraries and Heritage Department

Castle Crt, Shire Hall, Shire Hill, Cambridge,
    Cambridgeshire CB3 0AP; Tel 01223 717990
Director A. Baxter
Assistant Director (Schools Quality Assurance) Linda Bird
Assistant Director (Schools Quality Assurance) Mike Edey
Assistant Director (Planning and Review) A. Williams
Assistant Director (Pupil Support) B. Gale
Assistant Director (Resources) K. Manley

SPECIAL SCHOOLS

Green Hedges School Bar La, Stapleford, Cambridgeshire CB2 5BJ; E-mail office@greenhedges.cambs-schools.net; Tel 01223 508608; Fax 01223 508678
Headteacher G. Newell
    Mixed 2–19 PMLD/SLD (70)

Highfield School Downham Rd, Ely, Cambridgeshire CB6 1BD; E-mail office@highfield.cambs-schools.net; Tel 01353 662085; Fax 01353 662096
Headteacher J. Moran
    Mixed 2–19 MLD/SLD/PMLD (100)

Meadowgate School Meadowgate La, Wisbech, Cambridgeshire PE13 2JH;
E-mail office@meadowgate.cambs-schools.net; Tel 01945 461836; Fax 01945 589967
Headteacher R.M. Blunt
    Mixed 2–19 MLD/SLD/PMLD (120)

Rees Thomas School Downhams La, Cambridge, Cambridgeshire CB4 1YB;
E-mail office@reesthomas.cambs-schools.net; Tel 01223 712100; Fax 01223 712101
Headteacher P. Smith
    Mixed 2–19 MLD/SLD/PMLD (60)

Samuel Pepys School Pepys Rd, St. Neots, Huntingdon, Cambridgeshire PE19 2EW;
E-mail office@pepysroad.cambs-schools.net; Tel 01480 375012; Fax 01480 375012
Headteacher J. Weston
    Mixed 2–16+ MLD/SLD/PMLD (95)

Spring Common School American La, Huntingdon, Cambridgeshire PE18 7TY;
E-mail office@springcommon.cambs-schools.net; Tel 01480 377403; Fax 01480 377406
Headteacher C. Owens
    Mixed 2–19 MLD/SLD/PMLD (145)

The Lady Adrian School Courtney Way, Cambridge, Cambridgeshire CB4 2EE;
E-mail office@ladyadrian.cambs-schools.net; Tel 01223 508793; Fax 01223 508796
Headteacher K. Taylor
    Mixed 7–16 MLD (Day) (135)

The Habour School Station Rd, Wilburton, Ely,
Cambridgeshire CB6 3RR;
E-mail office@manorely.cambs-schools.net; Tel 01353
740229; Fax 01353 740632
Headteacher J. Currie
  Boys 5–16 EBD (71)

The Windmill School Fulbourn, Cambridge,
Cambridgeshire CB1 5EE;
E-mail office@windmill.cambs-schools.net; Tel 01223
712210; Fax 01223 712212
Headteacher K. Kemp
  Mixed 2–19 MLD/SLD/PMLD (64)

CHESHIRE COUNTY COUNCIL
www.cheshire.gov.uk

Population 668 000
County Hall, Chester, Cheshire CH1 1SF;
  URL www.cheshire.gov.uk;
  E-mail info@cheshire.gov.uk; Tel 01244 602424;
  Fax 01244 603800
Chief Executive Jeremy Taylor
Director (Environment) Peter Cocker
Director (Policy and Performance) Paul Heath

Social Services Department

Tel 01244 603224; (Emergency) 01606 76611; Fax 01244
  603815; (Emergency) 01606 781368
Director (Social Services) John Weeks
County Manager (Policy) J. Townsend
Senior Manager (Performance Assurance Service)
  C. Reynolds
Group Personnel Officer J. Maloney
Senior Manager (Communication and Executive Support)
  S. Ritchie
County Care Manager (Services to Adults Purchasing)
  H. Black
County Care Manager (Children's Services) A. Webb
County Care Manager (Older People Services) S. Connolly
County Care Manager (Adults Provision) T. Mann

TRAINING

Responsible for training professional and support staff in
the department.
County Hall, Chester, Cheshire CH1 1BW; Tel 01244 603243
Manager (Training) C. Burkett

Social Services Advisory Committee

Con: 7, Lab: 4, LD: 1
3 Hartford Cl, Dingle Meadow, Sandbach, Cheshire
  CW1 1ZU
Chair N.T. Price (Con)
Executive Member L.G. Hardwick (Con)
Members of the Committee
Lab: B. Doyle, B. Jones, D.J. Newton MA, K.A. Whittle.
Con: D. Andrews, M. Asquith, M. Grange, R. Parker,
N.T. Price, A. Tyrrell, W. Wolstencroft.
LD: S.R. Proctor.

LOCAL OFFICES

West Cheshire

Chester Local Office Goldsmith Hse, Hamilton Pl, Chester,
Cheshire CH1 1SE; Tel 01244 603400
Ellesmere Port Local Office Coronation Rd, Ellesmere Port,
Cheshire CH65 9AA; Tel 0151 357 4500

FAMILY CENTRES

Hatton Road Family Centre (0–5 yrs) 70–72 Hatton Rd,
Blacon, Chester, Cheshire CH1 5EE; Tel 01244 373603
Team Leader S. Hesketh
The Park Family Centre Stanney La, Ellesmere Port,
Cheshire CH65 9AE; Tel 0151 355 1500
Team Leader S. Hesketh

Central Cheshire

County Offices Watling St, Northwich, Cheshire CW9 5ET;
Tel 01606 814900
Delamere House Delamere St, Crewe, Cheshire CW1 2LL;
Tel 01270 505100

FAMILY CENTRE

Small Oaks Family Centre Cheviot Sq, Mount Pleasant,
Over, Winsford, Cheshire CW7 1QS; Tel 01606 815693;
Fax 01606 861913
Team Leader A. Chisnall

East Cheshire

County Offices Chapel La, Wilmslow, Cheshire SK9 1PU;
Tel 01625 534700
Riverside Mountbatten Way, Congleton, Cheshire
CW12 1DG; Tel 01260 285400

FAMILY CENTRES

Bradshaw House Family Centre 21 Lawton St, Congleton,
Cheshire CW12 1RU; Tel 01260 273282
Team Leader N. Layfield
Donagh Close Family Centre 4 Donagh Cl, Macclesfield,
Cheshire SK10 3HP; Tel (Hurdsfield) 01625 501855; 01625
829046
Team Leader Mark Stanley
Ethel Elks Family Centre Salisbury Ave, Crewe, Cheshire
CW2 6JW; Tel 01270 257328
Contact M. Greenwood
Middlewich Family Centre c/o Chadwick Fields,
Coronation Rd, Middlewich, Cheshire CW10 0DL;
Tel 01606 837443
Team Leader M. Goddard
Poolswood Nursery Centre Clarke Terr, Macclesfield,
Cheshire SK11 7QD; Tel 01625 425473
Team Leader J. Lewis

COMMUNITY HOMES

Children's Centre 38a Armthorpe Dr, Little Sutton,
Cheshire CH66 3RF; Tel 0151 339 5303
Team Leader K. Roberts
  (24)
Macclesfield Children's Centre Priors Hill, Kennedy Ave,
Macclesfield, Cheshire SK10 3HQ; Tel 01625 615262
Team Leader M. Greaves
The Meadows Community Home Meadow Dr, Barnton,
Northwich, Cheshire CW8 4PH; Tel 01606 815775;
Fax 01606 815774
Team Leader A. Lamb
Sunnyside Community Home 259–261 Nantwich Rd, Crewe,
Cheshire CW2 6NX; Tel 01270 560306; Fax 01270 650417
Team Leader Jo Sheard
Team Leader A. Mason

DAY CARE FOR CHILDREN WITH DISABILITIES

Pinewood Centre Darnhall School La, Winsford, Cheshire
CW7 1JR; Tel 01606 815660
Team Leader M. Watkins

COUNTY CHILDREN'S CENTRE

Redsands Crewe Rd, Willaston, Nantwich, Cheshire
CW5 6NE; Tel 01270 664116; Fax 01270 664116
Manager   G. Green

RESIDENTIAL ACCOMMODATION FOR CHILDREN WITH DISABILITIES

19b Bridge Meadow, Great Sutton, Cheshire CH66 2LE;
   Tel 0151 356 0487
Team Leader   Martin Watkins

**RESIDENTIAL NETWORKS FOR ADULTS WITH LEARNING
DISABILITIES**

Acorn Macon Hse, Macon Way, Crewe, Cheshire CW1 6DR;
Tel 01270 588881; Fax 01270 251137
Team Leader   J. Latham

Adult Services Dover Dr, Ellesmere Port, Cheshire
CH65 9DN; Tel 0151 355 5761
Team Leader   K. Fleming

CENTRES FOR ADULTS WITH A DISABILITY

Danewalk Centre Watling St, Northwich, Cheshire
CW9 5ET; Tel 01606 815043; Fax 01606 815043
Team Leader   M. Goddard

Hilary Centre Salisbury Ave, Crewe, Cheshire CW2 6JW;
Tel 01270 214599; Fax 01270 257951
Team Leader   M. Goddard

Mayfield Centre Mayfield Terr, off Mayfield Ave,
Macclesfield, Cheshire SK11 7TG; Tel 01625 613269
Team Leader   J. Walker

Poole Centre New Grosvenor Rd, off Grace Rd, Ellesmere
Port, Cheshire CH65 2HB; Tel 0151 355 9255
Team Leader   D. Davies

DAY CENTRES FOR ADULTS WITH SEVERE LEARNING DIFFICULTIES

Carter House Day Centre Rear of 48 Lawton St, Congleton,
Cheshire CW12 1RS; Tel 01260 278485; Fax 01260 298563
Team Leader   H. Coombes

Castleleigh Day Centre David St, Northwich, Cheshire
CW8 1HE; Tel 01606 783979; Fax 01606 784284
Team Leader   M. Insley

Cheyne Hall Centre 113 Beam St, Nantwich, Cheshire
CW5 5NF; Tel 01270 610106; Fax 01270 610107
Team Leader   P. Ogle

Coronation Centre Coronation Rd, Ellesmere Port, Cheshire
L69 9AB; Tel 0151 355 8311
Team Leader   N. Higham

Dean Row Centre Dean Row Rd, Wilmslow, Cheshire
SK9 2HA; Tel 01625 539018
Team Leader   A. Palin

Macon House Day Centre Macon Way, Crewe, Cheshire
CW1 6DR; Tel 01270 588881; Fax 01270 253981
Team Leader   J. Latham

Meadowbank Lodge Day Centre Grange La, Winsford,
Cheshire; Tel 01606 550564; Fax 01606 556943
Team Leader   V. Prince

Mulberry Centre Sealand Rd, Chester, Cheshire; Tel 01244
373059
Team Leader   S. Hughes

Old Fire Station Day Centre Chester Way, Northwich,
Cheshire CW9 5JA; Tel 01606 49276
Team Leader   M. Insley

Old Vicarage Day Centre Waterloo Rd, Castle, Northwich,
Cheshire CW8 1EH; Tel 01606 871993; Fax 01606 871993
Team Leader   J. Whitehead

The Peatfields Centre Park La, Macclesfield, Cheshire
SK11 8JR; Tel 01625 426344
Team Leader   G. Higgins

Sandbach House Day Centre 36 Crewe Rd, Sandbach,
Cheshire CW11 4NE; Tel (office) 01270 753400; Fax 01270
759445
Team Leader   H. Coombes

Stanley Centre Stanley Hse, Knutsford, Cheshire
WA16 0BX; Tel 01625 534875
Contact   L. Mullins

**SUPPORTED HOUSING AND DAY SERVICES FOR PEOPLE WITH
MENTAL HEALTH PROBLEMS**

Greenleaves Crewe Rd, Sandbach, Cheshire CW11 4NE;
Tel 01270 761655
Team Leader   D. Watson

Nantwich Road 291 Nantwich Rd, Crewe, Cheshire
CW2 6PF; Tel 01270 665120
Team Leader   K. Gray

The Moss, Mental Health Provider Team c/o 6 Congleton
Rd, Macclesfield, Cheshire SK11 4UE; Tel 01625 534700
Team Leader   Marie Stephenson

DAY CARE NETWORK FOR OLDER PEOPLE

Davenham Day Centre Royal Gdns, By Pass Rd, Northwich,
Cheshire CW9 8AY; Tel 01606 47750; Fax 01606 350727
Network Team Leader   G. Davies

Fellowship House Park Rd, Congleton, Cheshire
CW12 1DP; Tel 01260 280486
Co-ordinator   D. McCoy
Tue, Thu.

Hurdsfield Social Services Activity Centre Nicholson Cl,
Hurdsfield, Macclesfield, Cheshire SK10 2BQ; Tel 01625
501855
Co-ordinator   M. Stanley
Mon, Fri; Tue for older people with learning difficulties.

Jubilee House St. Paul's St, Crewe, Cheshire CW1 2QA;
Tel 01270 256430; Fax 01270 501286
Team Leader   S. Groom

CENTRES FOR OLDER PEOPLE AND ADULTS WITH A DISABILITY

Canal Street House Day Centre Canal St, Chester, Cheshire
CH1 4EJ; Tel 01244 311772
Team Leader   D. Davies

Chadwick Fields Centre (ESMI Provision) Coronation Rd,
Middlewich, Cheshire CW10 0DL; Tel 01606 833151
Team Leader   M. Goddard

Salinae Centre Lewin St, Middlewich, Cheshire
CW10 9DG; Tel 01606 836588
Team Leader   S. Groom

MULTIPURPOSE DAY CENTRE

The Redesmere Centre Redesmere Rd, Handforth,
Wilmslow, Cheshire SK9 3RX; Tel 01625 251251
Team Leader   P. Gratrix

COMMUNITY SUPPORT CENTRES

Bexton Court Centre Bexton Rd, Knutsford, Cheshire
WA16 0BZ; Tel 01565 651725
Team Leader   S. Bryan
Team Leader   A. Dodd
Business Support Officer   K. Spurr

Curzon House Centre Curzon St, Saltney, Chester, Cheshire
CH4 8BP; Tel 01244 680025
Team Leader   J. Black
Team Leader   P. Sandland
Business Support Officer   Vacancy

Cypress House Centre South Acre Dr, Handforth,
Wilmslow, Cheshire SK9 3HN; Tel 01625 532779
Centre Team Leader   T. Farrington
Business Support Officer   K. Spurr

Hallwood Court Community Support Centre Bridge St, Neston, Wirral CH64 9UH; Tel 0151 353 0460

Hollins View Centre Clarke Terr, off Byron St, Macclesfield, Cheshire SK11 7QD; Tel 01625 534700
Team Leader (Centre) A. Jones
Team Leader (Community) L. Murphy
Business Support Officer K. Spurr

Leftwich Green Community Support Centre Old Hall Rd, Leftwich, Northwich, Cheshire CW9 8BE; Tel 01606 42033; Fax 01606 330116
Team Leader G. Bradley
Team Leader D. Wilson
Co-ordinator A. Carter

Lightfoot Lodge Centre Lightfoot St, Hoole, Chester, Cheshire CH2 3AD; Tel 01244 347555
Team Leader M. Riley
Team Leader M. Smith
Co-ordinator A. Carter

Lincoln House Samuel St, Crewe, Cheshire CW1 3WH; Tel 01270 580240; Fax 01270 501471
Team Leader (Community) A. Butler
Team Leader (Residential) N. Chapman
Business Support Officer A. Montague

Mountview Centre Melton Dr, Congleton, Cheshire CW12 4YF; Tel 01260 272925; Fax 01260 297386
Team Leader (Centre) K. Bebe
Team Leader (Community) B. Williams-Powell
Business Support Officer A. Montague

Santune House Rope La, Shavington, Crewe, Cheshire CW2 5DT; Tel 01270 665691; Fax 01270 650118
Team Leader (Residential) A. Naylor
Care Co-ordinator A. Gibson
Care Co-ordinator J. Locke

Sutton Beeches Centre Alvanley Rd, Ellesmere Port, Cheshire CH66 3JZ; Tel 0151 339 6589
Team Leader K. Allchin
Team Leader G. Brown
Business Support Officer Vacancy

Education Department

County Hall, Chester, Cheshire CH1 1SQ;
E-mail educationhq@cheshire.gov.uk; Tel 01244 602330; Fax 01244 603821
Director (Education) D. Cracknell
County Manager (Schools) J. Feenan
County Manager (Education Standards) Maggie Atkinson
County Manager (Learning Support) M. Gledhill
Senior Educational Psychologist (West Cheshire/Chester/Ellesmere Port and Neston) P. Bragg
Senior Educational Psychologist (Mid Cheshire (Crewe Area Office)) Yvonne Hugman
Senior Educational Psychologist (Mid Cheshire Service Development, Mid Cheshire (Vale Royal)) H. Madden
Senior Educational Psychologist (East Cheshire (Macclesfield)) E.P. Powell

AREA EDUCATION OFFICES

West Cheshire Learning Support Service Area Education Office, Stanney La, Ellesmere Port, Cheshire CH65 6QL; Tel 0151 357 6489 0151 357 6876
Area Manager (Learning Support) Brian McDevitt

Mid Cheshire Learning Support Service Area Education Office, Delamere Hse, Crewe, Cheshire CW1 2LL; Tel 01270 505226 01270 505253
Area Manager (Learning Support) L. Trump

East Cheshire Learning Support Service Area Education Office, Chapel La, Wilmslow, Cheshire SK9 1PU; Tel 01625 534700
Area Manager (Learning Support) F. Bradley

Learning Support Service Education Department, County Hall, Chester, Cheshire CH1 1SQ;
E-mail simcoed@cheshire.gov.uk; Tel 01244 602378

Cheshire Parent Partnership Service The Professional Centre, Woodford Lodge, Winsford, Cheshire CW7 4EH; Tel 01606 814372

West Cheshire

Stanney La, Ellesmere Port, Wirral CH65 6QL; Tel 0151 357 6822

SPECIAL SCHOOLS

Capenhurst Grange School Chester Rd, Great Sutton, Cheshire CH66 2NA;
E-mail head@capenhurstgrange.school.cheshire.org.uk;
Tel 0151 339 5141; Fax 0151 348 0348
Headteacher Mrs C. Creasy
(50)

Dee Banks School Dee Banks, Sandy La, Chester, Cheshire CH3 5UX;
E-mail head@deebanks.school.cheshire.org.uk; Tel 01244 324012; Fax 01244 346723
Headteacher Christine Newall
Mixed (72)

Dorin Park School Wealstone La, Upton, Chester, Cheshire CH2 1HD;
E-mail head@dorinpark.school.cheshire.org.uk; Tel 01244 381951; Fax 01244 390422
Headteacher P. Kidman
Mixed PH (115)

Hinderton School Capenhurst La, Whitby, Wirral CH65 7AQ; E-mail head@hinderton.school.cheshire.org.uk;
Tel 0151 355 2177; Fax 0151 355 2177
Headteacher L. McCallion
Mixed (35)

East Cheshire

Chapel La, Wilmslow, Cheshire SK9 1PU; Tel 01625 534700; Fax 01625 434852

SPECIAL SCHOOLS

Park Lane School Park La, Macclesfield, Cheshire SK11 8JR; E-mail head@parklane.school.cheshire.org.uk;
Tel 01625 423407; Fax 01625 511191
Headteacher D. Calvert
Mixed (84)

St. John's Wood Community School Longridge, Knutsford, Cheshire WA16 8PA; Tel 01565 634578; Fax 01565 750187
Headteacher P. Evans
2–16 EBD (15)

Mid Cheshire (Crewe/Nantwich and Vale Royal) Area

Delamere Hse, Delamere St, Crewe, Cheshire CW1 2LL; Tel 01606 814900

SPECIAL SCHOOLS

Adelaide School Adelaide St, Crewe, Cheshire CW1 3DT;
E-mail head@adelaidestreet.school.cheshire.org.uk;
Tel 01270 255661; Fax 01270 584577
Headteacher L. Willday
Mixed (23)

Cloughwood School Stones Manor La, Hartford, Northwich, Cheshire CW8 1NU;
E-mail head@cloughwood.school.cheshire.org.uk; Tel 01606 76671; Fax 01606 783486
Headteacher D.H. Smith
Boys EBD (65)

6

Greenbank Residential School Green Bank La, Hartford, Northwich, Cheshire CW8 1LD;
E-mail head@greenbank.school.cheshire.org.uk; Tel 01606 76521; Fax 01606 783736
Headteacher Mrs B. Freake
  Mixed 7–16+ MLD and SLD 84 residential plus 6 day

Hebden Green Community Special School Woodford La West, Winsford, Cheshire CW7 4EJ; Tel 01606 59422 01606 594221; Fax 01606 861549
Headteacher A.W. Farren
  Mixed 2–19 (Day, Boarders) (120)

Oaklands School Montgomery Way, Winsford, Cheshire CW7 1NU; E-mail head@oaklands.school.cheshire.org.uk; Tel 01606 551048; Fax 01606 861291
Headteacher K.D. Boyle
  Mixed (112)

Rosebank School Townfield La, Barnton, Northwich, Cheshire CW8 4QP;
E-mail head@rosebank.school.cheshire.org.uk; Tel 01606 74975; Fax 01606 783564
Headteacher Vacancy
  Mixed 2–19 Diagnostic/assessment (Day)

The Russett School Middlehurst Ave, Weaverham, Northwich, Cheshire CW8 3BW;
E-mail head@russett.school.cheshire.org.uk; Tel 01606 853005; Fax 01606 854669
Headteacher Mrs H.M. Watts
  Mixed (116)

Springfield School Crewe Green Rd, Crewe, Cheshire CW1 5HS;
E-mail head@springfieldce.school.cheshire.org.uk; Tel 01270 582446; Fax 01270 258281
Headteacher M. Swaine
  Mixed (100)

SOCIAL SERVICES CENTRE

Redlands Children's Centre, Crewe Rd, Nantwich, Cheshire CW5 6NQ; Tel 01270 664116; Fax 01270 664116
Headteacher R. Grimwood
Social Services Residential Children's Centre

CLEVELAND COUNTY COUNCIL

In April 1996 Cleveland County Council, Hartlepool Borough Council, Langbaurgh-on-Tees Borough Council, Middlesbrough Borough and Stockton-on-Tees Borough Council were replaced by Hartlepool Borough Council, Middlesbrough Council, Redcar and Cleveland Borough Council and Stockton-on-Tees Borough Council – each responsible for all local government services in its area. These councils are listed alphabetically in this chapter.

CORNWALL COUNTY COUNCIL

www.cornwall.gov.uk

Population 494 655 (Aug 2000)
Political Composition: LD: 36, Ind: 25, Lab: 9, Con: 9
County Hall, Treyew Rd, Truro, Cornwall TR1 3AY;
  URL www.cornwall.gov.uk;
  E-mail enquiries@cornwall.gov.uk; Tel 01872 322000;
  Fax 01872 270340
Leader John Lobb
Chair P.C. Tregunna
Chief Executive Peter Stethridge
County Treasurer Frank Twyning
Engineering and Architectural Design Nick Powell
Head (IT) Stuart Pryer
Director (Planning, Transport and Estates) Richard Fish

Social Services Department

E-mail enquiries.social@cornwall.gov.uk; Tel 01208 251300;
  Fax 01208 251300
Portfolio Holder (Individual Services – Adults) G.M. Nicholls
Portfolio Holder (Individual Services – Children) N.C. Walker
Director (Social Services) D. Law (Acting); Tel 01872 323612; Fax 01872 323665
Deputy Director (Social Services) D. Law; Tel 01872 323611
Deputy Director (Social Services) J.R. Gould; Tel 01872 323637
Assistant Director (Community Care) S. Whitehead
Cathedral Cl, Truro, Cornwall TR1 2TE; Tel 01872 278533
Assistant Director (Purchasing and Service Development)
  D.R. Richards; Tel (Direct Line) 01872 323619
Manager (Training Information) N. Bell; Tel (Direct Line) 01872 323620
Senior Operations Manager (LD and Elderly) M. Faulds; Tel 01872 322679
Divisional Manager (East) (Children's Services) L. Taylor
Priory Hse, Priory Rd, Bodmin, Cornwall PL31 2AD; Tel 01208 74491
Divisional Manager (Mid) (Children's Services)
  F. Fitzpatrick
Penwinnick Hse, Trewhiddle, St. Austell, Cornwall PL25 5BZ; Tel 01726 63582
Divisional Manager (West) (Children's Services) J. Kerrison
The White Hse, 24 Bassett Rd, Camborne, Cornwall TR14 8SL; Tel 01209 714721
Manager (Financial Administration) G. Goodier
Priory Hse, Priory Rd, Bodmin, Cornwall; Tel 01208 74491
Manager (Financial Administration) J. Ferris
The Whitehouse, 26 Bassett Rd, Camborne, Cornwall; Tel 01209 714721
Manager (Financial Administration) E. Singer
Cathedral Cl, Truro, Cornwall; Tel 01872 278533
Manager (Financial Administration) P. Maycock; Tel (Direct Line) 01872 323616
Manager (Financial Administration) S. Oakes
Senior Team Leader (Personnel) N. Nightingale; Tel (Direct Line) 01872 323657
Contracts and Service Development Officer Mike Langshaw; Tel 01872 323632
Senior Manager (Mental Health) A. Carron; Tel 01872 323459

Social Services Committee

LD: 4, Ind: 4, Lab: 1, Con: 1
Portfolio Holder (Individual Services – Adults) G.M. Nicholls (LD)
13 Tavistock Rd, Launceston, Cornwall PL15 9HF; Tel 01566 773566
Portfolio Holder (Individual Services – Children) N.C. Walker (LD)
Trevean Farm, Penzance, Cornwall TR20 9PF; Tel 01736 762340
Members of the Executive Committee
LD: D.M. Ansari, W.J. Lobb, G.M. Nicholls, N.C. Walker.
Ind: B.M.M. Biscoe, P.A. Lyne, W.H. Roberts.
Lab: J. Ferrett.
Con: R.E. Hichens.

LOCAL OFFICES

Caradon Local Office

Wesbourne Hse, West St, Liskeard, Cornwall PL14 6BY; Tel 01579 342919

NORTH CORNWALL

Priory Hse, Priory Rd, Bodmin, Cornwall PL31 2AD; Tel 01208 74491

Carrick Local Office

Cathedral Cl, Truro, Cornwall TR1 2TE; Tel 01872 278533

RESTORMEL

Penwinnick Hse, Trewhiddle Rd, St. Austell, Cornwall
PL25 5BZ; Tel 01726 63582

Kerrier Local Office

The White Hse, 24 Basset Rd, Camborne, Cornwall
TR14 8SL; Tel 01209 714721

PENWITH

Roscadghill Parc, Heamoor, Penzance, Cornwall TR18 3QX;
Tel 01736 365714

ADOPTION

Adoption and Family Finding Unit 13 Treyew Rd, Truro,
Cornwall TR1 2BY; Tel 01872 270251

NON-RESIDENTIAL FAMILY CENTRES

Bodmin Family Centre Old Police Station, Pound La,
Bodmin, Cornwall PL31 2BT; Tel 01208 77662
Contact R. Blackburn (in association with NCH)

Camborne Resource Centre Trevithick Rd, Camborne,
Cornwall TR14 8LQ; Tel 01209 719058

Falmouth Resource Centre Park Terr, Falmouth, Cornwall
TR11 2DJ; Tel 01326 312493

Newquay Resource Centre 28 Mount Wise, Newquay,
Cornwall TR7 2BJ; Tel 01637 872070

St. Austell Resource Centre Woodland Rd, St. Austell,
Cornwall PL25 4RA; Tel 01726 74969

RESIDENTIAL FAMILY CENTRES

Pendean Residential Centre West St, Liskeard, Cornwall
PL14 6BT; Tel 01579 342259
Centre Manager R. Hickman

Penelvan Residential Centre 22 Roskear, Camborne,
Cornwall TR14 8BM; Tel 01209 713206
Centre Manager M. Allen

Thornton House Residential Centre 22 Clinton Rd, Redruth,
Cornwall TR15 2QE; Tel 01209 314693
Centre Manager B. Girvan

INTERMEDIATE TREATMENT CENTRE

Dreadnought Centre Carn Brea La, Pool, Redruth, Cornwall
TR15 3DS; Tel 01209 218764
Contact G. Perrins (in association with Dreadnought
Council)

HOSTELS FOR THOSE WITH LEARNING DISABILITIES

Chy Koes Hostel Woodland Rd, St. Austell, Cornwall
PL25 4QZ; Tel 01726 76045
Officer-in-Charge Anne Davies

Lowena Hostel Truro, Cornwall TR1 1HZ; Tel 01872
270013
Officer-in-Charge J. Jackson

St. Christopher's Hostel Lower Cardrew La, Redruth,
Cornwall TR15 2QE; Tel 01209 314970
Officer-in-Charge C. Jennings

Tregarne Hostel North St, St. Austell, Cornwall PL25 5QE;
Tel 01726 72429
Officer-in-Charge E. Steel

TRAINING CENTRES – LEARNING DISABILITY

Blantyre Training Centre Truro Rd, St. Austell, Cornwall
PL25 5HJ; Tel 01726 72583
Officer-in-Charge M. Trevail

Bude Day Centre (Pathfields) Stratton Footpath, Bude,
Cornwall; Tel 01288 356235
Centre Manager T. Trago

Echo Centre Barras Pl, Liskeard, Cornwall PL14 6AX;
Tel 01579 347836
Manager John Sherwood

Frank Johns Care Centre 56–58 Queensway, Bodriggy,
Hayle, Cornwall TR27 4NR; Tel 01736 754545
Manager Pauline Viner

John Daniel Centre Heamoor, Penzance, Cornwall
TR20 8PT; Tel 01736 368531
Centre Manager A.S. Tyson

Kehelland Horticultural Centre Ltd Kehelland, Camborne,
Cornwall TR14 0DD; Tel 01209 718975
Manager C. Williamson

Launceston Day Centre 14a Newport Ind Est, Launceston,
Cornwall PL15 8EX; Tel 01566 776422
Centre Manager J.A. Blank

Morley Tamblyn Lodge Training Centre Lodge Hill,
Liskeard, Cornwall PL14 4EN; Tel 01579 345858
In-House Manager J. Poole

Murdoch and Trevithick Adult Training Centre Lower
Cardrew La, Redruth, Cornwall TR15 1LZ; Tel 01209
215552
In-House Manager G. McReady

The Priory Centre Pound La, Bodmin, Cornwall PL31 2BT;
Tel 01208 73623
Centre Manager V. Putt

DAY CENTRES FOR PEOPLE WITH MENTAL HEALTH PROBLEMS

Anchor Day Centre 106 Killigrew St, Falmouth, Cornwall
TR11 3PT; Tel 01326 315822
Co-ordinator Julie Acton

Boundervean Day Centre 6 Pendarves Rd, Camborne,
Cornwall TR14 7QE; Tel 01209 613006
Co-ordinator John Landy

Caradon Day Centre The Coach Hse, Trevillis Hse, Lodge
Hill, Liskeard, Cornwall PL14 4EJ; Tel 01579 347651
Co-ordinator Dave Rowe

Fountain House Day Centre 1 Eastbourne Rd, St. Austell,
Cornwall PL25 4SZ; Tel 01726 76299
Co-ordinator Joe Hunt

Pathfields Day Centre Pathfields, St. Hilary's, Bude,
Cornwall EX23 8DW; Tel 01288 355695
Co-ordinator Lynn Attwater

Penzance Day Centre Richmond Hse, Tolver Pl, Tolver Rd,
Penzance, Cornwall TR18 2AJ; Tel 01736 350752
Co-ordinator Patty Barlow

Roswyth Day Centre 4 Cheltenham Pl, Newquay, Cornwall
TR7 1BA; Tel 01637 873122
Co-ordinator Lyn Morgan

Stepping Stones Day Centre 5 Ferris Town, Truro, Cornwall
TR1 3JG; Tel 01872 241783
Co-ordinator Eileen McDevitt

Education, Arts and Libraries

County Hall, Truro, Cornwall TR1 3AY;
E-mail general@educationcornwall.gov.uk; Tel 01872
322000; Fax 01872 323818
Executive Portfolio Holder (Lifelong Learning)
Mrs D. Ansair
Director (Education, Arts and Libraries) G. Aver
Deputy Director (Education, Arts and Libraries) D. Ashton
Assistant Director (Individual Needs Policy) Vacancy
Head (Child and Family Services) S.J. Colwill
County Manager (Youth Service) J. Appleton
Head (Audiology Service) B. Vann
Head (Visually Impaired Service) J. Stacey

SPECIAL SCHOOLS

The Curnow Community Special School Drump Rd, Redruth, Cornwall TR15 1LU; E-mail enquiries@curnow.cornwall.sch.uk; Tel 01209 215432; Fax 01209 314205
Headteacher Mrs C. Simpson, MPhil
(117)

Doubletrees School St. Blazey Gate, Par, Cornwall PL24 2DS; E-mail enquiries@doubletrees.cornwall.sch.uk; Tel 01726 812757; Fax 01726 812896
Headteacher M. Mcgee (Acting)
(112)

Doubletrees Hostel St Blazey Gate, Par, Cornwall PL24 2DS; Tel 01726 812758
SLD (30)

Nancealverne School Madron Rd, Penzance, Cornwall TR20 8TP; E-mail enquiries@nancealverne.cornwall.sch.uk; Tel 01736 365039; Fax 01736 331941
Headteacher Mrs F. Cock
(76)

Pencalenick School St. Clement, Truro, Cornwall TR1 1TE; E-mail enquiries@pencalenick.cornwall.sch.uk; Tel 01872 520385; Fax 01872 520729
Headteacher A. Barnett
Mixed Senior (131)

Counselling and Assessment Unit Royal Cornwall Hospital (City), Infirmary Hill, Truro, Cornwall TR1 1NR; Tel 01872 74242
Contact Mrs M. Henwood
(12)

COVENTRY CITY COUNCIL
www.coventry.gov.uk

Population 304 400
The Council Hse, Coventry, West Midlands CV1 5RR;
URL www.coventry.gov.uk;
E-mail godiva@coventry.gov.uk;
E-mail ssymonds@coventry.gov.uk; Tel 024 7683 3333;
Tel 024 7683 1088; Fax 024 7683 1079
Lord Mayor Cllr Dave Chater
Leader of the Council Cllr N. Nolan
Chief Executive and Town Clerk Stella Manzie; Tel 024 7683 1100; Fax 024 7683 3680
City Secretary Chris Hinde; Tel 024 7683 3020; Fax 024 7683 3070
Strategic Director (Resources) P. Cordle, IPFA; Tel 024 7683 3000; Fax 024 7683 3171
Head (Communications) A. McLean; Tel 024 7683 3700; Fax 024 7683 3770
Strategic Director (Social Inclusion) J. Smith

Social Services and Planning Department

Council Hse, Earl St, Coventry, West Midlands CV1 5RS;
Tel 024 7683 3333; Fax 024 7683 3501
Cabinet Member (Social Services) Cllr K. Maton; Tel 024 7683 3333
Cabinet Member (Community Housing) Cllr Heather Parker; Tel 024 7683 3333
Head (Business Improvement Group) Sally Burton
Head (Adult Services Group) B. Chauhan
Service Manager (Financial Services) J. Barr
Service Manager (Human Resources) Sue Matthews
Service Manager (Information Management) T. Ledwidge; Tel ext 3532
Service Manager (Information Management) D. Stainforth

Service Manager (Commissioning Services) K. Edwards; Tel ext 3488
Principal Assistant (Promotions) Jon Hawtin

Adult Services

ASSESSMENTS (ADULTS AND OLDER PEOPLE)
Wilfred Spencer Centre, Whitaker Rd, Coventry, West Midlands; Tel 024 7667 3048
Manager (Operational Service – Older People) Gina Rigby
Manager (Operational Service – Adults) Mark Godfrey

OLDER PEOPLE – PROVIDER SERVICES
Service Manager Maureen Womble (Acting)
Primrose Hill Lodge, Aylesford St, Coventry, West Midlands; Tel 024 7655 5361
Manager (Supported Living) Rae Butterill (Acting); Tel 024 7655 5361
Manager (Supported Living) Martyn Wilkins; Tel 024 7652 0329
Manager (Community Support) Jan Malosti; Tel 024 7655 5361

DAY CARE AND/OR RESIDENTIAL
Senior Resource Manager Sandra Walton; Tel 07951 285548

Children's Services

FAMILY PLACEMENT SERVICES
Family Placement Unit, Stoke Hse, Lloyd Cres, Coventry, West Midlands CV2 5NY; Tel 024 7665 9009
Manager (Service Group) John McConnochie

VOLUNTEER UNIT
Remembrance Hse, Remembrance Rd, Coventry, West Midlands CV3 3DG; Tel 024 7630 1051
Team Leader Estella Nesden

Community Support Services
Holbrooks Health Centre, 303 Holbrook La, Coventry, West Midlands CV6 4DG; Tel 024 7668 0600
Senior Resource Manager Mark Blackburn

LOCALITY SERVICES – CHILDREN AND FAMILIES
Manager (Service East) Allen Torrance
SM Office, Wilfred Spencer Centre, Whittaker Rd, Coventry, West Midlands CV5 9JE; Tel 024 7671 7707
Manager (Service West) Shirley Price
SM Office, 57 Ribble Rd, Coventry, West Midlands CV3 1AW; Tel 024 7663 6035

Coundon/Allesley/Radford/Holbrooks/Tile Hill/Canley

Coundon Family Centre Moseley Ave, Coventry, West Midlands CV6 1AB; Tel 024 7660 1414
Manager (Fieldwork) Ann Hossack

Foleshill/Hillfields

FOLESHILL FAMILY CENTRE
454 Foleshill Rd, Coventry, West Midlands CV6 5LB; Tel 024 7666 1131; Tel 024 7660 1414
Manager (Fieldwork) Tony Rae (Acting) (based at Croydon)

Stoke Aldermoor/Upper Stoke/Wyken

Whitworth Avenue Stoke Aldermoor, Coventry, West Midlands CV3 1EP; Tel 024 7645 8336
Manager (Fieldwork) Debbie Carter

Willenhall/Earlsdon/Cheylesmore

Stretton Avenue Willenhall, Coventry, West Midlands CV3 3AH; Tel 024 7630 2444
Manager (Fieldwork) Jivan Sembi (based at Stoke Aldermoor)

Wood End/Bell Green

Bay Tree Close Wood End, Coventry, West Midlands CV2 1HP; Tel 024 7661 4232
Manager (Fieldwork) Debbie Carter

RESIDENTIAL FAMILY CENTRE

Monkswood 50–80 Monkswood Cres, Coventry, West Midlands; Tel 024 7661 8020
Team Leader Maureen McNamara

CHILDREN'S REGISTRATION AND REVIEWING SERVICE

Broadgate Hse, 4th Fl, Coventry, West Midlands CV1 1NG; Tel 024 7683 3443
Manager Birgitta Lundberg

CHILDREN'S RESIDENTIAL SERVICES

The Grange Children's Home Brownshill Green Rd, Keresley, Coventry, West Midlands CV6 2EG; Tel 024 7633 6212
Team Leader Trevor Ronneback

Stoke House Lloyd Cres, off Harry Rose Rd, Coventry, West Midlands; Tel 024 7645 1010
Team Leader Dave Brackford

Wistaria Lodge Earlsdon Ave, South, Coventry, West Midlands; Tel 024 7671 5027
Team Leader Dave Saunders

CHILDREN WITH LEARNING DIFFICULTIES SHORT STAY HOME

Broad Park Hse, Broad Park Rd, Henley Grn, Coventry, West Midlands; Tel 024 7661 5254
Unit Manager Lena Lole

CHILDREN'S SERVICES (LOOKED AFTER)

Stoke Hse, Lloyd Cres, Coventry, West Midlands CV2 5NY; Tel 024 7645 4550
Service Manager Stephan Hope

CHILDREN'S DISABILITY TEAM

Willenhall Fieldwork Office, Stretton Ave, Willenhall, Coventry, West Midlands; Tel 024 7645 2157
Team Leader Brian Kerrigan

YOUTH OFFENDING SERVICE

Little Park St Police Station, Coventry, West Midlands; Tel 024 7653 9031
Service Manager Andy Pepper

Fieldwork Teams

Canley/Tile Hill/Coundon/Allesley – West Team 312 Charter Ave, Canley, Coventry, West Midlands; Tel 024 7646 6851
Team Manager Sally Caren

Holbrooks/Radford/Hillfields/Foleshill – North Team Telfer Rd, Coventry, West Midlands; Tel 024 7659 5125
Team Manager Colin Bingham

Wyken/Walsgrave/Wood End/Bell Green/Upper Stoke/Stoke Aldermoor – East Team Vincent Wyles Hse, Attoxhall Rd, Coventry, West Midlands; Tel 024 7663 5744
Team Manager Cindy Clarke

HOSPITAL SERVICES

Ward H1, Phase IV Wallsgrave Hospital, Clifford Bridge Rd, Coventry, West Midlands; Tel 024 7653 8979
Team Leader S. Browning

Community Mental Health Teams

City Wide New Referrals Social Services Caludon Centre, Walsgrave Hospital, Coventry, West Midlands; Tel 024 7653 5158

East Community Mental Health Team 18a Riley Sq, Bell Grn, Coventry, West Midlands; Tel 024 7666 6697

North Community Mental Health Team Lamb St Centre, Lamb St, Coventry, West Midlands; Tel 024 7625 8222

West Community Mental Health Team The Cedars, Torrington Hse, Coventry, West Midlands; Tel 024 7647 0350

Community Mental Health Team (Older People) Halpin Ward, Gulson Hospital, Coventry, West Midlands; Tel 024 7684 4144; Tel 024 7660 2020
Fieldwork Manager Bridget Macy

PHYSICAL DISABILITIES

Centre for Integrated Living Faseman Ave, Tile Hill, Coventry, West Midlands CV4 9RB; Tel 024 7647 1411
Fieldwork Manager (Physical Disability) Lyn Martin
Fieldwork Manager (Learning Disability) Dorothy Hall
Manager (Disability Development) M. Ridcout

PEOPLE WITH SENSORY IMPAIRMENT

Centre for Integrated Living, Faseman Ave, Coventry, West Midlands CV4 9RB; Tel 024 7647 1411
Fieldwork Manager Lyn Martin
Fieldwork Manager Dorothy Hall

LEARNING DIFFICULTIES

Logan Assessment Service Logan Rd, Henley Grn, Coventry, West Midlands; Tel 024 7660 4608
Team Leader Tracy Sherrington (Acting)

RESIDENTIAL ESTABLISHMENTS FOR PEOPLE WITH LEARNING DIFFICULTIES AND PHYSICAL DISABILITIES

Dick Crossman House 1 Dunsmore Ave, Willenhall, Coventry, West Midlands; Tel 024 7630 1931; 024 7669 5605

Jackers Road Home Cressage Rd, Fern Cl, Coventry, West Midlands; Tel 024 7636 6416; 024 7669 5605

Maurice Edelman House Moat House La, Coventry, West Midlands; Tel 024 7667 3010; 024 7669 5605

Woodway Lane House 474 Woodway La, Coventry, West Midlands; Tel 024 7661 8288

RESIDENTIAL ESTABLISHMENT FOR PEOPLE WITH MENTAL ILL HEALTH

Axhomle Hse, Axholme Rd, Coventry, West Midlands; Tel 024 7645 7788; Fax 024 7671 3644
Service Group Manager Lynne Black

DAY SERVICES FOR PEOPLE WITH MENTAL ILL HEALTH

Lamb Street Centre Lamb St, Coventry, West Midlands; Tel 024 7625 8170; Fax 024 7671 3644
Service Group Manager Lynne Black

WILFRED SPENCER CENTRE

Woodside, Torrington Hse, Torrington Ave, Tile Hill, Coventry, West Midlands; Tel 024 7646 7222
Service Group Manager Maureen Womble

6

TRANSPORT SERVICES

Whitely Depot, London Rd, Coventry, West Midlands;
Tel 024 7683 3466
Manager (Transport Services)   Alan Charlish

EMPLOYMENT SUPPORT AGENCY

189 Princethorpe Way, Coventry, West Midlands; Tel 024
7681 5590

RESOURCE BASES FOR PEOPLE WITH LEARNING DIFFICULTIES/ PHYSICAL DISABILITIES

Wilfred Spencer Centre Whittaker Rd, Coventry, West
Midlands CV5 9JE; Tel 024 7669 1947

Princethorpe Way 193 Princethorpe Way, Coventry, West
Midlands; Tel 024 7645 4111

Watcombe Centre Watcombe Rd, Coventry, West Midlands;
Tel 024 7661 2132

INTERPRETATION AND TRANSLATION UNIT

35 Vine St, Coventry, West Midlands; Tel 024 7622 5853; 024
7622 7505
Senior Interpreter/Translator   Sam Chakraverty

Education Service

New Council Offices, Earl St, Coventry, West Midlands
CV1 5RS; E-mail cathy.goodwin@coventry.gov.uk;
Tel 024 7683 1511; Fax 024 7683 1620
Director (Education and Libraries)   Roger Edwardson
Departmental Manager (Human Resources)
Christopher Burrows
Principal Officer (Finance)   Charles Aplin
Head (Policy and Performance)   Jos Parry
Head (Management Services)   C. West
Head (Services for Schools)   Ruth Snow
Head (Services for Communities)   Brian Parker

Community Education Area Offices

EAST DISTRICT

c/o Willenhall Education, Employment and Training Centre
Robin Hood Rd, Willenhall, Coventry, West Midlands
CV3 3AN; Tel 024 7651 1228; Fax 024 7651 1309
Strategic Officer   David Knaggs
Service Manager (Children and Families)   Chris Ashton
Service Manager (Adult)   Sue Wyatt
Service Manager (Youth)   Howard Day

WEST DISTRICT

Allesley Further Education Centre Birmingham Rd,
Allesley, Coventry, West Midlands CV5 9GR; Tel 024 7640
5700; Fax 024 7640 5701
Strategic Officer   Kevin Crawford
Service Manager (Adult)   Lynne Amery
Service Manager (Children and Families)   Linda Holmes
Service Manager (Youth)   Hilary Snell

CENTRAL DISTRICT

Southfields Old School South St, Coventry, West Midlands
CV1 5EJ; Tel 024 7622 3831; Fax 024 7663 2573
Strategic Officer   Alan Newbold
Service Manager (Adult)   Ros Bell
Service Manager (Youth)   C. Bowen
Service Manager (Children and Families)   Jane Goodyer

EDUCATIONAL PSYCHOLOGY SERVICE

9 North Ave, Stoke Pk, Coventry, West Midlands CV2 4DH;
Tel 024 7645 9718; Fax 024 7644 5211

SPECIAL DAY SCHOOLS

Alice Stevens School Ashington Gr, Coventry, West
Midlands CV3 4DE; Tel 024 7630 3776; Fax 024 7630 6173
Headteacher   R.I. McAllister, MEd
MLD (169)

Baginton Fields School Sedgemoor Rd, Coventry, West
Midlands CV3 4EA; Tel 024 7630 1904; 024 7630 3854;
Fax 024 7630 4247
Headteacher   S. Grant
SLD (96)

Corley (Coventry) School Corley, Coventry, West Midlands
CV7 8AZ; Tel 01676 540218; Fax 01676 542577
Headteacher   R. Nason
MLD (70)

Dartmouth School Tiverton Rd, Wyken, Coventry, West
Midlands CV2 3DN; Tel 024 7644 4141; Fax 024 7645 3838
Headteacher   Andrew Robbie
Boys EBD (60)

Deedmore School Pettitor Cres, Coventry, West Midlands
CV2 1EW; Tel 024 7661 2271; Fax 024 7660 3986
Headteacher   Y. McCall, BA, BPhil
MLD (67)

Hawkesbury Fields School rear of 176–8 Alderman's Green
Rd, Coventry, West Midlands CV2 1PL; Tel 024 7636 7075;
Fax 024 7664 5388
Headteacher   H. Bishton, BEd, MBA(Ed)
SLD (57)

The Meadows School Hawthorn La, Coventry, West
Midlands CV4 9PB; Tel 024 7646 2335; Fax 024 7646 9866
Headteacher   J. Murland
EBD (40)

Sherbourne Fields School Rowington Cl, off Kingsbury Rd,
Coventry, West Midlands CV6 1PS; Tel 024 7659 1501;
Fax 024 7659 0517
Headteacher   D.F. Southeard
Physically Disabled (122)

Three Spires School Kingsbury Rd, Coventry, West
Midlands CV6 1PJ; Tel 024 7659 4952; Fax 024 7659 3798
Headteacher   Jackie Brook
MLD (70)

Tiverton School Rowington Cl, off Kingsbury Rd,
Coventry, West Midlands CV6 1PS; Tel 024 7659 4954;
Fax 024 7659 1575
Headteacher   A. Chave, BPhil(Ed)
SLD (39)

Wainbody Wood School Stoneleigh Rd, Coventry, West
Midlands CV4 7AB; Tel 024 7641 8755; Fax 024 7669 0809
Headteacher   M. Chilvers (Acting)
EBD (49)

SPECIAL DEAF UNIT

Howes Primary School Palermo Ave, Coventry, West
Midlands CV3 5EH; Tel 024 7641 1711
Headteacher   P. Davies, CertEd

Visual Impairment Resource Base

Alderman Callow School and Community College Mitchell
Ave, Coventry, West Midlands CV4 8DY; Tel 024 7642 2212;
024 7646 7779
Headteacher   R. Whittall, BA

SPECIAL RESIDENTIAL SCHOOLS

Corley (Coventry) School Corley, Coventry, West Midlands
CV7 8AZ; Tel 01676 540218
Headteacher   R. Nason
(16)

The Meadows School Hawthorn La, Coventry, West
Midlands CV4 9PB; Tel 024 7646 2335
Headteacher   J. Murland
Boys EBD

SPEECH AND LANGUAGE SERVICE

c/o Manor Park Primary School Ulverscroft Rd, Coventry, West Midlands CV3 5EZ; Tel 024 7650 2927
Headteacher H. Hill

SPECIAL UNITS

Pre-School Education Service Pre-school Unit, Annie Osborn Primary School, Coventry, West Midlands CV2 1HQ; Tel 024 7661 8202; Fax 024 7661 8242
Headteacher J. Friswell

Sensory Support Service – Howes (Primary) Hearing Impaired Unit Palermo Ave, Coventry, West Midlands CV3 5EH; Tel 024 7641 7415; Fax 024 7641 7415
Head of Service Peter McCann
Head of School Mrs P. Davies

Sensory Support Service – Stoke Park (Secondary) Hearing Impaired Unit Dane Ave, Coventry, West Midlands CV2 4JW; Tel 024 7641 7415; 024 7665 8914; Fax 024 7641 7415
Head of Service Peter McCann
Head of School Mr W.T. Wolger

Sensory Support Service – Alderman Callow Visual Impairment Resource Base Alderman Callow School and Community College, Mitchell Ave, Coventry, West Midlands CV4 8DY; Tel 024 7641 7415; 024 7642 2212; Fax 024 7641 7415
Head of Service Peter McCann
Head of School Mr R. Whittle

Autism Support Team c/o Corley School, Corley, Coventry, West Midlands CV7 8AZ; Tel 01676 541249; Fax 01676 549116
Headteacher Jo Tasker

CUMBRIA COUNTY COUNCIL
www.cumbria.gov.uk

Population 491 400
Political Composition: Lab: 40, Con: 33, LD: 10, Ind: 1
The Courts, Carlisle, Cumbria CA3 8LZ;
URL www.cumbria.gov.uk; Tel 01228 606369; Fax 01228 606372
Chief Executive L.E.J. Victory; Tel 01228 606301; Fax 01228 606302
Head (Member Services) D. Claxton
Head (Legal Services) B. Walker
Director (Corporate Finance) R.F. Mather, BSc, IPFA; Tel 01228 606260; Fax 01228 606264
Director (Social Services) M. Siegal, BA
3–7 Victoria Pl, Carlisle, Cumbria CA1 1EJ; Tel 01228 607110; Fax 01228 607108
Director (Community Economy and Environment) R. Howard
Citadel Chambers, Carlisle, Cumbria CA3 8SG; Fax 01228 606698
Manager (Property Client Unit) J. Mitchell, BA, DMS
18–19 Portland Sq, Carlisle, Cumbria CA1 1QQ; Fax 01228 606016
Chief Fire Officer and Director (Safety Services) J.M. Elliott, CertEd, MIFire, EMBIM
County Fire Services Headquarters, Station Rd, Cockermouth, Cumbria; Tel 01900 822503; Fax 01900 824940

Social Services Department

3 Victoria Pl, Carlisle, Cumbria CA1 1EH;
E-mail social.services@cumbriacc.gov.uk;
Tel (Emergency) 01228 526690; 01228 607080; Fax 01228 607108

Director (Social Services) Jean Bradshaw (Acting)
Head (Performance Unit) C. Pritchard (Acting)
Head (Adult Services) J. McMullon
Head (Departmental Management Services) S. Don
Head (Children and Family Services) P. Moore
Manager (Customer Services (Information)) Peter Knock
Manager (Information Systems) M.L. Thomas
Press and Media Officer Lorraine Hunter

TRAINING AND STAFF DEVELOPMENT

The following have responsibility for training professional and support staff in the department.
3 Victoria Pl, Carlisle, Cumbria CA1 1EH; Tel 01228 607080
Co-ordinator (NVQ) Wendy Shaw
Co-ordinator (Training and Staff Development) Christine Chenery
Training and Staff Development Officer (Child and Family Care) J. Cheal
Training and Staff Development Officer (Adult Services) Lynn Heath
Training and Development Officer (Adult Services) Liz Sharp
Learning Centre Co-ordinator for Professional and Post-Qualifying training (Practice Teachers, Social Workers) Vacancy

6

Cabinet

17 Wolsty Cl, Stanwix, Carlisle, Cumbria CA3 0PB;
E-mail john.mallinson@cumbriacc.gov.uk
Care and Social Services J. Mallinson (Con)

DIVISIONS

East Cumbria

Civic Centre Carlisle, Cumbria CA3 8QG; Tel 01228 607080; Fax 01228 607064

Friargate Penrith, Cumbria CA11 7NX; Tel 01768 242200; Fax 01768 242260

South Cumbria

County Offices Kendal, Cumbria LA9 4RQ; Tel 01539 773300; Fax 01539 773354

Brogden Street Ulverston, Cumbria LA12 7AH; Tel 01229 894000

Market Street Barrow-in-Furness, Cumbria LA14 2LH; Tel 01229 894000; Fax 01229 894869

West Cumbria

Council Offices Wigton, Cumbria CA7 9QD; Tel 01963 43238

New Oxford Street Workington, Cumbria CA14 2LW; Tel 01900 325300; Fax 01900 325368

Somerset House Duke St, Whitehaven, Cumbria CA28 7SQ; Tel 01946 852800; Fax 01946 852822

Town Hall Main St, Egremont, Cumbria CA22 2DB; Tel 01946 820270

HOSPITAL SOCIAL WORKERS

Cumberland Infirmary Carlisle, Cumbria CA2 7HY; Tel 01228 523444

Furness General Hospital Dalton La, Barrow-in-Furness, Cumbria; Tel 01229 870870

Carleton Clinic Carlisle, Cumbria; Tel 01228 602000

West Cumberland Hospital Homewood Rd, Hensingham, Whitehaven, Cumbria; Tel 01946 693181

Westmorland General Hospital Burton Rd, Kendal, Cumbria; Tel 01539 732288

COMMUNITY HOMES

The Grange Community Home 16 Wood St, Carlisle, Cumbria; Tel 01228 607188
(8)

Huntley Avenue Community Home 21 Huntley Ave, Penrith, Cumbria; Tel 01768 242263

Overend Road Community Home 30 Overend Rd, Hensingham, Whitehaven, Cumbria; Tel 01946 852864
(8)

Sedbergh Drive Community Home 3 Sedbergh Dr, Kendal, Carlisle, Cumbria; Tel 01539 773367
(8)

Westrigg Road Community Home 54 Westrigg Rd, Carlisle, Cumbria; Tel 01228 607189
(8)

FAMILY CENTRES

Carleton Road Family Centre 11 Carleton Rd, Workington, Cumbria CA14; Tel 01900 325380
Contact P. Robson
(30)

The Family Centre Ennerdale Ave, Botcherby, Carlisle, Cumbria; Tel 01228 607184
Contact R. Sharp

Morton Park Family Centre Wigton Rd, Carlisle, Cumbria; Tel 01228 607085
Contact R. Sharp
(45)

Ormsgill Family Centre Millstone Ave, Barrow-in-Furness, Cumbria; Tel 01229 894797
Contact J.E. Shakeshaft
(50)

Education Department

5 Portland Sq, Carlisle, Cumbria CA1 1PU;
    URL www.cumbria.gov.uk/education;
    E-mail education@cumbriacc.gov.uk; Tel 01228 606877;
    Fax 01228 606896
Corporate Director (Education) Victoria Ashfield
Head (Access and Inclusion) Mr M. Watmough
County Inspector Adviser (Special Educational Needs)
    Ms J. Armstrong
Senior Education Officer (Attendance and Exclusion)
    Mrs L. Rundle
Principal Educational Psychologist Mr D. Thomson

SPECIAL SCHOOLS

George Hastwell School Moor Tarn La, Walney, Barrow-in-Furness, Cumbria LA14 3LW;
E-mail admin@ghastwell.cumbria.sch.uk; Tel 01229 475253;
Fax 01229 471418
Headteacher B.J. Gummett
(Day)

James Rennie School California Rd, Kingstown, Carlisle, Cumbria CA3 0BX;
E-mail adminoffice@jamesrennie.cumbria.sch.uk; Tel 01228 607559; Fax 01228 607563
Headteacher S.J. Bowditch
(Day)

Mayfield School Moresby Rd, Hensingham, Whitehaven, Cumbria CA28 8TU;
E-mail admin@mayfeld.cumbria.sch.uk; Tel 01946 852676;
Fax 01946 852677
Headteacher Ms S. Leathers
(Day)

Sandgate School Sandylands Rd, Kendal, Cumbria LA9 6JG; E-mail office@sandgate.cumbria.sch.uk; Tel 01539 773636; Fax 01539 792101
Headteacher T. Robson
(Day)

Sandside Lodge School Sandside Rd, Ulverston, Cumbria LA12 9EF; E-mail admin@sandsidelodge.cumbria.sch.uk; Tel 01229 894180; Fax 01229 894180
Headteacher Mrs J. Billingham
(Day)

DARLINGTON BOROUGH COUNCIL
www.darlington.gov.uk

Came into effect April 1997
Population 97 800
Political Composition: Lab: 35, Con: 16, LD: 2
Town Hall, Darlington DL1 5QT;
    URL www.darlington.gov.uk;
    E-mail policy_unit@darlington.gov.uk; Tel 01325 380651;
    Fax 01325 382032

Social Services Department

Central Hse, Gladstone St, Darlington DL3 6JX; Tel 01325 346200; Fax 01325 346474
Director (Social Services) Colin Morris
Assistant Director (Operations) Ewen Weir;
    E-mail ewen.weir@darlington.gov.uk; Tel 01325 346244;
    Fax 01325 346266
Assistant Director (Partnerships) Ian Tucker;
    E-mail ian.tucker@darlington.gov.uk; Tel 01325 346229
Assistant Director (Performance and Development)
    Angela Ratcliffe;
    E-mail angela.ratcliffe@darlington.gov.uk; Tel 01325 346288
Manager (Strategic and Operational Finance)
    Neville Simpson;
    E-mail neville.simpson@darlington.gov.uk; Tel 01325 388097
Performance and development, operations, partnerships, administration and finance.

Social Affairs and Health Scrutiny Committee

Chair Cllr B. Dixon
Members
Broxsome, Buckle, Copeland, Flowers, Jones, Roberts, Scott, Thomas, Vasey, Walker, Scott, Smith, Shaiton, Thistlethwaite, Thomas, J.C. Vasey, L. Vasey, Walker, Wallis.

HOSPITAL SOCIAL WORKERS

Darlington Memorial Hospital Hollyhurst Rd, Darlington DL3 6HX; Tel 01325 380100; Fax 01325 743284

CHILDREN'S UNIT

Salters Lane Children's Unit 92 Salters Lane South, Darlington; Tel 01325 362293; 01325 469410
Contact Jean Langthorne
(10)

YOUTH OFFENDING AND COMMUNITY SAFETY SERVICE

Central House Annexe, Gladstone St, Darlington DL3 6JX;
    E-mail andy.errington@darlington.gov.uk; Tel 01325 346723
Head of Service Andy Errington

FAMILY RESOURCE CENTRE

Harewood Hse, 14 Harewood Hill, Darlington; Tel 01325 254377; 01325 254378

LEARNING DISABILITIES SECTION

Upperthorpe, Darlington DL3 7PZ;
E-mail nicola.bailey@darlington.gov.uk; Tel 01325 364694
Head (Learning Disability) Nicola Bailey

HOME FOR PEOPLE WITH LEARNING DISABILITIES

Brinkburn Lodge, 83 Brinkburn Rd, Darlington; Tel 01325 468877

MENTAL HEALTH SECTION

4 Woodlands Rd, Darlington DL3 7PJ;
E-mail ian.franks@darlington.gov.uk; Tel 01325 350501
Team Leader Ian Franks

ADULT TRAINING CENTRES

Beck Hse, Faverdale Ind Est, Darlington; Tel 01325 469080
Manager (Day Services) Malcolm Powton
(110)

HOMES FOR ELDERLY PEOPLE

There are four homes for elderly people under the control of Darlington Council.

Education Department

Town Hall, Darlington DL1 5QT;
URL www.darlington.gov.uk; Tel 01325 388689;
Fax 01325 388883
Assistant Director (Client Services) Paul Campbell

DERBY CITY COUNCIL

www.derby.gov.uk

Came into effect April 1997
Population 236 261
Political Composition: Lab: 27, Con: 11, LD: 12, Ind: 1
The Council Hse, Corporation St, Derby DE1 2FS;
URL www.derby.gov.uk; Tel 01332 293111; Fax 01332 255500

Social Services Department

Middleton Hse, 27 St. Mary's Gate, Derby DE1 3NS;
URL www.derby.gov.uk; Tel ((Derby Care Line 1700–0900 (daily, weekends and Bank Holidays)) 01332 256066 (0900–1700); 01332 717777; Fax (Derby Care Line) 01332 292165 (0900–1700); 01332 716767; Tel (Child Protection Register Enquiries) 01332 717818
Cabinet Member (Social Care and Health) Cllr Roy Webb
14 Calder Cl, Allestree, Derby DE22 2SH; Tel 01332 550668
Chair (Social Care and Health Commission) Cllr Fareed Hussain
37 Empress Rd, Derby DE23 6TD; Tel 01332 296134
Director (Social Services) Margaret McGlade
Assistant Director (Community Care) Mick Connell
Assistant Director (Children – Assessment and Care Planning) Rachel Dickinson
Assistant Director (Children – Resources and Projects) Keith Woodthorpe
Assistant Director (Resources and Performance Management) Ian Orrell

Social Services Committee

Con: 12, Lab: 25, Liberal: 13, Ind: 1
Cabinet Member (Social Care and Health) Cllr Roy Webb
Chair (Social Care and Health Commission)
Cllr Fareed Hussain
Members
Cllr R.J. Allen, Cllr S. Amra, Cllr M. Hird, Cllr Hilary Jones, Cllr D. Roberts, Cllr Robin Turner, Cllr P. Willitts, Cllr L. Wilson Croft

DERBY CITY LOCAL OFFICES

St. Mary's Gate Office

29 St. Mary's Gate, Derby DE1 3NU; Tel 01332 717777;
Fax 01332 717277; Minicom 01332 206180

Perth Street Office

Perth St, Chaddesden, Derby DE21 6XX; Tel 01332 717777;
Fax 01332 717747; Minicom 01332 206182

Rosehill Street Office

71–73 Rosehill St, Derby DE23 8FZ; Tel 01332 717777;
Fax 01332 717188; Minicom 01332 206184

Stanley Road Office

Stanley Rd, Alvaston, Derby DE24 0EX; Tel 01332 717777;
Fax 01332 718099; Minicom 01332 751681

Osmaston Road Office

218a Osmaston Rd, Derby DE23 8JX; Tel 01332 717777;
Fax 01332 717150; Minicom 01332 206184

CHILDREN'S UNITS

Child Protection Office Eastmead, 107 Duffield Rd, Derby DE22 1AE; Tel 01332 717818; Fax 01332 717819

Child Sexual Abuse Unit 42 Leopold St, Derby DE1 2HF; Tel 01332 717575

Moorfield Children's Unit 400 Sinfin La, off Redwood Rd, Derby DE2 9HN; Tel 01332 718725
(24)

YOUTH OFFENDING SERVICES

St. Peters Hse, Gower St, Derby DE1 9BR; Tel 01332 717525;
Fax 01332 369297

FAMILY CENTRES

Ashtree Family Support Service Ashtree Hse, 218 Osmaston Rd, Derby DE23 8JX; Tel 01332 717640; (Project) 01332 717641

Bute Walk Family Centre 22 Bute Wlk, Chaddesden, Derby DE21 6BN; Tel 01332 717477

Chesapeake Family Resource Centre 22 Chesapeake Rd, Chaddesden, Derby DE21 6RB; Tel 01332 718308

Coronation Avenue Family Centre 55 Coronation Ave, Alvaston, Derby DE24 0LR; Tel 01332 718100

Cricklewood Family Centre 19 Cricklewood Rd, Mackworth, Derby DE22 4DP; Tel 01332 717470

Elmhurst Family Centre Lonsdale Pl, Uttoxeter Rd, Derby DE22 3LP; Tel 01332 717655

Queensferry Gardens Family Centre 86 Queensferry Gdns, off Sinfin Ave, Allenton, Derby DE24 9JS; Tel 01332 718410

Vicarage Road Family Centre 12 Vicarage Rd, Mickleover, Derby DE3 5EA; Tel 01332 718929; (Disabled Children's Team) 01332 718940; Fax (Disabled Children's Team) 01332 718950

6

COMMUNITY LIVING TRAINING UNIT

Community Living Resource Team (Beaufort Street) 69 Beaufort St, Chaddesden, Derby DE21 6AY; Tel 01332 717480

Porter Road Resource Team 91 Porter Rd, Derby; Tel 01332 718715

The Target Project 64 Birdcage Wlk, Mackworth, Derby DE22 4LD; Tel 01332 718900 (no staff based on site)

DAY CENTRES FOR PEOPLE WITH LEARNING DIFFICULTIES

Humbleton View Rough Heanor Rd, Mickleover, Derby DE3 5AZ; Tel 01332 718919; Fax 01332 718923

Wetherby Centre Gosforth Rd, off Ascot Dr, Derby DE24 8HU; Tel 01332 717600; (Community Team) 01332 717621; Fax 01332 717624

HOSTELS FOR PEOPLE WITH LEARNING DIFFICULTIES

Ashlea Hostel 53 Coronation Ave, Alvaston, Derby DE24 0LR; Tel 01332 718105 (23)

The Knoll Hostel 241 Village St, Derby DE23 8DD; Tel 01332 718708; Fax 01332 718707 (24)

MENTAL HEALTH PROJECTS

Community Care Day Service 126 Osmaston Rd, Derby DE1 2RF; Tel 01332 717507; Fax 01332 717666

Community Support Team 63 Duffield Rd, Derby, Derbyshire DE22 1AA; Tel 01332 717507; Fax 01332 717512

DAY SERVICES FOR PEOPLE WITH PHYSICAL DISABILITIES

Alternative Living Scheme 32 Newdigate St, Derby DE23 8UY; Tel 01332 718700; Fax 01332 717801; Minicom 01332 271176

Rycote Resource Centre (Leonard Cheshire) Parker St, Derby DE1 3HF; Tel 01332 717507; Fax 01332 204082

Unit for Deaf People The Coach Hse, 29 Kedleston Rd, Derby DE22 1FL; Tel 01332 717567; Fax 01332 717571; Minicom 01332 344358

Early Years Centre for Young Deaf Children and their Families 41 Brentford Dr, Mackworth, Derby DE22 4BP; Tel 01332 717517; Fax 01332 717517; Minicom 01332 717518

DAY SERVICES FOR ELDERLY PEOPLE

Morleston Street Day Centre Derby; Tel 01332 717630

Whitaker Centre Whitaker Rd, Derby DE23 6AR; Tel 01332 717500

HOMES FOR ELDERLY PEOPLE

There are nine homes for the elderly run by Derby City Council.

RESOURCE CENTRES FOR ELDERLY PEOPLE

Arthur Neal House Hanwell Way, Mackworth, Derby DE22 4AD; Tel 01332 717457

Perth House Athlone Cl, Chaddesden, Derby DE21 4BP; Tel 01332 717550

Education Service

Middleton Hse, 27 St. Mary's Gate, Derby DE1 3NN; Tel 01332 716924; Fax 01332 716920
Education, Attendance and Welfare Officer Julie Mullard
Education Officer (Pupil Services) Liz Beswick
Principal Educational Psychologist Mick Pitchford

SPECIAL SCHOOLS

Ivy House School 249 Osmaston Rd, Derby DE23 8LG; Tel 01332 344694; Fax 01332 344658
Headteacher P. Sillitoe
(72)

St. Andrew's School St. Andrew's View, Breadsall Hilltop, Derby DE21 4EW; Tel 01332 832746; Fax 01332 830115
Headteacher M. Dawes
(71)

St. Clare's School Rough Heanor Rd, Mickleover, Derby DE3 5AZ; Tel 01332 511757; Fax 01332 519968
Headteacher C. McKenna
(108)

St. Giles' School Hampshire Rd, Chaddesden, Derby DE21 6BT; Tel 01332 343039; Fax 01332 207321
Headteacher P.J. Walsh
(75)

St. Martins School Wisgreaves Rd, Alvaston, Derby DE24 8RQ; Tel 01332 571151; Fax 01332 758608
Headteacher P. Ormerod
(84)

SPECIAL UNITS

Ronnie Mackeith Centre for Child Development Derby City General Hospital Trust, Uttoxeter Rd, Derby DE22 3NE; Tel 01332 340131 ext 6917
Teacher-in-Charge L. Harahan

Special Educational Needs Support Service Kingsmead Centre, Bridge St, Derby DE1 3LB; Tel 01332 716000; Fax 01332 716006
Head of Service A. Jenner (Acting)

DERBYSHIRE COUNTY COUNCIL
www.derbyshire.gov.uk

The County Council retains its two-tier structure; however in April 1997 Derby City Council became a separate unitary authority and is responsible for all its local government services – Derby City Council is listed alphabetically in this chapter.
Population 735 000
Political Composition: Lab: 43, Con: 13, LD: 7, Ind: 1
County Hall, Matlock, Derbyshire DE4 3AG;
    URL www.derbyshire.gov.uk; Tel 01629 580000;
    Fax 01629 585279
Chatsworth Hall, Matlock, Derbyshire DE4 3FW;
    URL www.derbyshire.gov.uk
Chair of the County Council Cllr Charles Cutting
Chief Executive A.R.N. Hodgson
County Treasurer P. Swaby
Director (Corporate Resources) G. Tommy

Social Services Department

County Hall, Matlock, Derbyshire DE4 3AG; Tel 01629 580000; Fax 01629 772213
Child Protection Register Enquiries P. Memmory
Cabinet Member for Health and Socal Services Cllr A. Western
Director (Social Services) B. Buckley
Head of Service (Older People) K. Hickey
Head of Service (Disabilities) A. Milroy
Head of Service (Children) I. Johnson
Head (Quality Assurance) M. McElvaney
Head (Organisational Effectiveness and Development) S. Dring

Departmental Staff Development Officer P. Jelf
Procedures and Information Officer Pam Brassington (Acting)
Head (Planning and Projects – Adults) J. Matthews

TRAINING

Responsible for training professional and support staff in the department.
Training Section, Long Cl, Ripley, Derbyshire; Tel 01773 728230
Departmental Staff Development Officer P. Jelf

AREA OFFICES

Area 1: High Peak Office Talbot St, Glossop, Derbyshire SK13 7DG; Tel 01457 728888

Area 2: Chesterfield Office West St, Chesterfield, Derbyshire S41 7QT; Tel 01246 347777

Area 3: Derbyshire Dales Office Portland Hse, Clifton Rd, Matlock, Derbyshire DE4 3PW; Tel 01629 772323

Area 4: North-East Derbyshire Office High St, Clay Cross, Chesterfield, Derbyshire S45 9EA; Tel 01246 348888

Area 5: Bolsover Office Oxcroft La, Bolsover, Chesterfield, Derbyshire S44 6DJ; Tel 01246 348400

Area 6: Amber Valley Office Long Cl, Cemetery La, Ripley, Derbyshire DE5 3HY; Tel 01773 728000

Area 7: Erewash Office Rutland Mill, Market St, Ilkeston, Derbyshire DE7 5RU; Tel 0115 909 8585

Area 8: South Derbyshire Office Civic Way, Swadlincote, Derbyshire DE11 0AQ; Tel 01283 238000

HOSPITAL SOCIAL WORKERS

Chesterfield and North Derbyshire Royal Hospital Calow, Chesterfield, Derbyshire S44 5BL; Tel 01246 277271; Fax 01246 274259

Derbyshire Royal Infirmary NHS Trust, London Rd, Derby DE1 2QY; Tel 01332 347141; Fax 01332 254923

Derby City General Hospital NHS Trust Uttoxeter Rd, Derby DE22 3NE; Tel 01332 625574; Fax 01332 625641
Service Manager Covering also Derbyshire Children's Hospital, Derby.

Kingsway Hospital Kingsway, Derby DE22 3LY; Tel 01332 624569; Fax 01332 623744
Service Manager Covering also Kingsway Hospital, Derby; Tel 01332 362221; and Aston Hall Hospital, Ashton-on-Trent, Derby; Tel 01332 792412.

Hospitals covered by Area Social Services Offices
Area 3 – Derbyshire Dales
St Oswald's Hospital, Ashbourne, Derbyshire
Area 4 – North East Derbyshire
Clay Cross Community Hospital.
Area 5 – Bolsover
Bolsover Hospital
Area 6 – Amber Valley
Heanor District Hospital, Babington Hospital, Belper, Derbyshire
Area 8 – Erewash
Ilkeston Community Hospital; Ilkeston Maternity Hospital

FAMILY SUPPORT CENTRES

Bolsover Family Support Centre 4 High St, Bolsover, Chesterfield, Derbyshire S44 6HF; Tel 01246 348500

North East Derbyshire Family Support Centre The Grange Hse, 88 Southgate, Eckington, Derbyshire S21 4FT; Tel 01246 348640

Charnos Family Support Centre Whitworth Rd, Ilkeston, Derbyshire DE7 5NU; Tel 0115 909 8130

Cotmanhay Family Support Centre 49–51 Dovedale Circle, Cotmanhay, Ilkeston, Derbyshire DE7 8SG; Tel 0115 909 8125

Gamesley Early Excellence Centre (Joint User with Education Department) Winster Mews, Gamesley, Glossop, Derbyshire SK13 0LU; Tel 01457 728950

Long Eaton Family Support Centre Lime Terr, off King St, Long Eaton, Nottingham NG10 4LF; Tel 0115 909 8705

Redhouse Family Support Centre 109 Mansfield Rd, Alfreton, Derbyshire DE55 7JP; Tel 01773 728335

Shirebrook Family Support Centre Byron St, Shirebrook, Derbyshire NG20 9PJ; Tel 01623 58805

Staveley Family Support Centre Leyfield Hse, Lowgates, Staveley, Derbyshire S43 3TR; Tel 01246 348030

Victoria Family Support Centre Victoria St, Glossop, Derbyshire SK13 8HT; Tel 01457 728920

CHILDREN'S CENTRE

125c Market St, Clay Cross, Chesterfield, Derbyshire S45 9LX; Tel 01246 348734; Fax 01246 348705 (25)

FAMILY CENTRES

Albany House Albany St, Ilkeston, Derbyshire DE7 5AE; Tel 0115 909 8120

Fernslope Family Centre Chesterfield Rd, Belper, Derbyshire DE5 1FD; Tel 01773 728700

Gamesley Centre 1–4 Matlock Bank, Gamesley Est, Glossop, Derbyshire SK13 6SX; Tel 01457 728977

Glenholme Family Centre Dove La, Long Eaton, Nottingham NG10 4LP; Tel 0115 909 8700

Linden House Church St, Swadlincote, Derbyshire DE11 8LF; Tel 01283 238130

Mundy Street Family Centre 1 Mundy St, Heanor, Derbyshire DE75 7EB; Tel 01773 728407

Newbold Resource Centre 267 Newbold Rd, Chesterfield, Derbyshire S41 7AL; Tel 01246 347500

Spire Lodge Family Centre 91a Sheffield Rd, Chesterfield, Derbyshire S41 7HJ; Tel 01246 347535

Top Road Family Centre 25 Top Rd, Calow, Chesterfield, Derbyshire S44 5SY; Tel 01246 347625

YOUTH OFFENDING SERVICE

Cobden Road Youth Offending Team Chesterfield, Derbyshire S40 4TD; Tel 01246 347615

Kents Bank Road Youth Offending Team Buxton, Derbyshire; Tel 01298 308400

Naylor House Youth Offending Team Mundy St, Ilkeston, Derbyshire DE7 8DH; Tel 0115 909 8170

DAY SERVICES FOR PEOPLE WITH LEARNING DIFFICULTIES

Alderbrook Centre Buxton Rd, Chinley, Derbyshire SK12 6DR; Tel 01663 508300 (125)

Ashbrook Centre Cuttholme Rd, Chesterfield, Derbyshire S40 2RD; Tel 01246 347575 (200)

Bankcroft Centre Cokayne Ave, Ashbourne, Derbyshire DE6 1EJ; Tel 01335 238040 (40)

Bolsover Day Services Oxcroft La, Bolsover, Chesterfield, Derbyshire S44 6DJ; Tel 01246 348535

Bolsolver Day Services Project Community Centre Carter La, Mansfield, Nottinghamshire N620 8PE; Tel 01623 588060

6

Eaton Vale Centre Briar Gate, Long Eaton, Nottingham NG10 4BQ; Tel 0115 909 8715
(100)

Newhall Centre Meadow La, Newhall, Swadlincote, Derbyshire DE11 0UW; Tel 01283 238150
(100)

Parkwood Centre Alfreton Pk, Alfreton, Derbyshire DE5 7AL; Tel 01773 728366
(190)

Ringwood Centre Victoria St, Brimington, Chesterfield, Derbyshire S43 1HY; Tel 01246 347545
(200)

Whitemoor Centre 100 John O'Gaunts Way, Belper, Derbyshire DE56 0DB; Tel 01773 728717
(175)

Wilson Avenue Centre 1–3 Wilson Ave, Clowne, Chesterfield, Derbyshire S43 4NH; Tel 01246 348114

HOSTELS FOR PEOPLE WITH LEARNING DIFFICULTIES

Newhall Hostel Plummer Rd, Newhall, Swadlincote, Derbyshire DE11 0QX; Tel 01283 238145
(26)

Parkwood Hostel Alfreton Pk, Alfreton, Derbyshire DE5 7AL; Tel 01773 728350
(22)

Petersham Centre Petersham Rd, Long Eaton, Nottinghamshire NG10 4DD; Tel 0115 909 8735
(22)

Victoria Street Hostel 9 Victoria St, Brimington, Chesterfield, Derbyshire S43 1HY; Tel 01246 347590
(22)

COMMUNITY LIVING TRAINING UNIT

Hadfield Road Community Living Project 141–143 Hadfield Rd, Hadfield, Glossop, Derbyshire SK13 2DR; Tel 01457 728930

Hasland Community Living Unit 55–57 Mansfield Rd, Hasland, Chesterfield, Derbyshire S41 0JE; Tel 01246 347600

Park Road Community Living Project 28–30 Pk Rd, Chapel-en-le-Frith, High Peak, Derbyshire SK23 0LP; Tel 01298 308177

MENTAL HEALTH SERVICES PROJECTS

Chesterfield Support Network Chesterfield Community Centre, Tontine Rd, Chesterfield, Derbyshire S40 1GU; Tel 01246 347555

RESOURCE CENTRES FOR ELDERLY PEOPLE

Ambervale Resource Centre Cemetery La, Ripley, Derbyshire DE5 3HY; Tel 01773 728160

Eccles Fold Resource Centre Eccles Fold, Chapel-en-le-Frith, High Peak, Derbyshire SK23 9TJ; Tel 01298 308181

Gernon Manor Resource Centre Dagnall Gdns, Bakewell, Derbyshire DE45 1EN; Tel 01629 778400

Holmlea Resource Centre Waverley St, Tibshelf, Derbyshire DE55 5PS; Tel 01773 728606

The Leys Resource Centre Old Derby Rd, Ashbourne, Derbyshire DE6 1BT; Tel 01335 238001

Lincote Centre Wideshaft, Swadlincote, Derbyshire DE11 8LQ; Tel 01283 238135

Shirevale Elderly Resource Centre Rockley Way, Shirebrook, Mansfield, Nottinghamshire NG20 8PD; Tel 01623 588020

Underhall Resource Centre Two Dales, Matlock, Derbyshire DE4 2SD; Tel 01623 778511

Valley View Resource Centre Pleasant View, Bolsover, Chesterfield, Derbyshire S44 6NB; Tel 01246 348525

ACCOMMODATION FOR ELDERLY PEOPLE

There are 32 local authority homes for older people.

Education Department

County Hall, Matlock, Derbyshire DE4 3AG; Tel 01629 580000
Chief Education Officer Roger Taylor

DEVON COUNTY COUNCIL
www.devon.gov.uk

The County Council retains its present two-tier structure. However in April 1998 Plymouth and Torbay became separate unitary authorities and are responsible for their own local government services – they are listed alphabetically in this chapter.
Population 697 700 (2002)
Political Composition: LD: 21, Con: 23, Lab: 5, Lib: 2, Ind: 3.
County Hall, Exeter, Devon EX2 4QD;
URL www.devon.gov.uk; E-mail plloyd@devon.gov.uk; Tel 01392 382000; Fax 01392 382286
Chair of the Council Lt Col Anthony Drake
Chief Executive P. Jenkinson
County Solicitor R. Gash
Director (Resources) Jan Stanhope
Director (County Environment) Edward Chorlton, CEng, MICE, FIHT, ACIArb, EurIng
Chief Purchasing Officer P. Dummett, IPFA

Social Services Directorate

County Hall, Topsham Rd, Exeter, Devon EX2 4QR;
URL www.devon.gov.uk/socserve;
E-mail sshq@devon.gov.uk; Tel 01392 382331; Fax 01392 382363
Director (Social Services) David Johnstone
Assistant Director (Strategic and Corporate Services) Alan Wooderson
Assistant Director and Head (Children's Service) Anne Whiteley
Deputy Director Dave Padfield
Manager (Learning and Development) Debbie Haskins
Head (Performance Review) Geoff Evans
Manager (HR Operations) Jackie Wilson

Community Services Overview/Scrutiny Committee

LD: 5, Lab: 1, Con: 5, NAG: 1
Members of the Committee
LD: H.R. Barton, B.H. Berman, R. Connelly, J. Rawlinson, Mrs M.A. Rogers.
Con: S. Barker, E.J. Berry, A.J. Collins, Mrs C. Marsh, J.O. Yabsley.
Lab: C.G. Gale.
NAG Mrs M.E. Turner.

Emergency Duty Service Unit 2, Alley Crt, Eagle Way, Sowton Ind Est, Exeter, Devon EX2 7HY; Tel 0845 6000388

ADMINISTRATIVE OFFICES

East Devon

Fostering and Adoption, Youth Justice, Child Protection, Training.
Ivybank, 45 St. David's Hill, Exeter, Devon EX4 4DN; Tel 01392 384955; Fax 01392 384990

DISTRICT OFFICES

East Devon Social Services District Town Hall, St. Andrew's Rd, Exmouth, Devon EX8 1AW; Tel 01392 385700; Fax 01392 385772

Honiton (Adults) Honiton, St. Michael's, Orchard Way, Honiton, Devon EX14 1HU; Tel 01392 385800; Fax 01392 385811

Sidmouth-Ottery St. Mary (Child Care) St. Saviour's, Exeter Rd, Ottery St. Mary, Devon EX11 1RE; Tel 01392 385980; Fax 01392 385953

Okehampton Jacobspool Hse, No 11 West St, Okehampton, Devon EX20 1LJ; Tel 01392 383848; Fax 01392 386748

Mid Devon District (I) Phoenix La, Tiverton, Devon EX16 6LB; Tel 01392 384100; Fax 01392 384141
Mid Devon District (II) Market St, Crediton, Devon EX17 2AJ; Tel 01392 384100; Fax 01363 384177

EXETER DISTRICT CHILD CARE

Children and Families Assessment George St, Exeter, Devon EX1 1AD; Tel 01392 384444

Children with Disabilities Team Magdalen Hse, 56 Magdalen Rd, Exeter, Devon EX2 4TL; Tel 01392 383773

Youth Justice Team Ivybank, St. David's Hill, Exeter, Devon; Tel 01392 384978; Fax 01392 384985

EXETER DISTRICT ADULT SERVICES CARE MANAGEMENT TEAMS

Exeter East St. Edmund's Crt, 16 Okehampton St, Exeter, Devon EX4 1DU; Tel 01392 384444

Exeter Hospital Team RD&E (Wonford) Hospital, Barrack Rd, Exeter, Devon EX2 5DW; Tel 01392 402244

Exeter West St. Edmund's Crt, 16 Okehampton St, Exeter, Devon EX4 1DU; Tel 01392 384444

EAST DEVON DISTRICT CARE MANAGEMENT TEAMS

Town Hall, St. Andrew's Rd, Exmouth, Devon EX8 1AW; Tel 01392 385700

East Devon District (Honiton Adults) St. Michael's, Community Centre, Honiton, Devon; Tel 01392 385800

East Devon District (Ottery St. Mary) St. Saviour's, Exeter Rd, Ottery St. Mary, Devon EX11 1RE; Tel 01392 385980

Honiton Joint Agency Community Team (Mental Health) Churchill Hse, Church Hill, Honiton, Devon EX14 8D3; Tel 01404 540100

Honiton Learning Disability Community Team The Jerrard Wing, Honiton Hospital, Marlpitts Rd, Honiton, Devon EX14 8DD; Tel 01404 540500

OKEHAMPTON/CREDITON DISTRICT CARE MANAGEMENT TEAMS

Jacobspool Hse, 11 West St, Okehampton, Devon EX20 1LJ; Tel 01392 383848

TIVERTON DISTRICT CARE MANAGEMENT TEAMS

Phoenix La, Tiverton, Devon EX16 6LB; Tel 01392 384100
Team Manager (Adult and Learning Disability)
Laraine Hale

Mental Health Leigh Hse, St. Andrew St, Tiverton, Devon EX16 6PL; Tel 01884 235710

Post Hill Centre Post Hill, Twyford Clinic, Tiverton, Devon EX16 6QY; Tel 01884 259464

RESIDENTIAL CHILD CARE

Atkinson Secure Unit Beacon La, Exeter, Devon EX4 8NA; Tel 01392 251449; Fax 01392 251449

Brookhayes Community Home, Pilton La, Exeter, Devon EX1 3RA; Tel 01392 468111; Fax 01392 460012

Devon Action for Youth Devon Action for Youth, Brookhayes, Exeter, Devon EX1 3RA; Tel 01392 430027

Elizabeth Avenue Community Home 34–36 Elizabeth Ave, Exeter, Devon EX4 7EQ; Tel 01392 255832; Fax 01392 423942

Rifford Road Community Home 15–19 Rifford Rd, Exeter, Devon EX2 5JT; Tel 01392 278015; Fax 01392 496150

St. Leonard's Community Home Brewin Rd, Tiverton, Devon EX16 5DL; Tel 01884 253036; Fax 01884 257290

ADULT SERVICES

c/o Alphin House Mill La, Alphington, Exeter, Devon EX2 8SG; Tel 01392 251728; Fax 01392 493461

Buddle Lane Family Centre Locarno Rd, St. Thomas, Exeter, Devon EX4 1QD; Tel 01392 279361; Fax 01392 423240

Doyle Centre Salterton Rd, Exmouth, Devon EX8 2NS; Tel 01395 264789

Exeter Disabilities Group Nichols Centre, Polsloe Rd, Exeter, Devon EX21 2HN; Tel 01392 274981

Fairbanks Family Centre 90 Polsloe Rd, Exeter, Devon EX1 2HW; Tel 01392 423441

Orchard Lea Orchard Way, Cullompton, Devon EX15 1EJ; Tel 01884 33375; Fax 01884 35060

East Devon Family Support Services (Community) Littleham Primary School, Elm La, Exmouth, Devon EX8 2QY; Tel 01395 225984

St. Michael's Community Care Centre Orchard Way, Honiton, Devon EX14 8HH; Tel 01392 385800; Fax 01404 47505
Domiciliary Services St. Michael's Community Care Centre, Devon; Tel 01392 385888; Fax 01404 47505
Senphy Centre St. Michael's Community Care Centre, Devon; Tel 01392 385865; Fax 01404 44577

Sensory Impairment Services Magdalen Hse, 56 Magdalen Rd, Exeter, Devon EX2 4TL; Tel 01392 383730; Fax 01392 383767

Tavistock Family Centre Abbey Rise, Whitchurch Rd, Tavistock, Devon PL19 9AS; Tel 01822 610945

Wardhayes Residential Home Simmons Rd, Okehampton, Devon EX20 1PT; Tel 01837 52487

North Devon

Civic Centre, Barnstaple, Devon EX31 1EE; Tel 01271 388473; Fax 01271 382451

DISTRICT OFFICES

Tawside District St. George's Rd, Barnstaple, Devon EX32 7AU; Tel 01271 388010; Fax 01271 327375

Children's and Families' (Mental Health Team) Civic Centre, Barnstaple, Devon EX31 1EE; Tel 01271 388646; Fax 01271 388451

North Devon District Hospital Barnstaple, Devon; Tel 01271 322474 ext 8692; Fax 01271 25985

Torridge District Abbotsham Rd, Bideford, Devon EX39 3AT; Tel 01237 475693; Fax 01237 422234

BARNSTAPLE

St. George's Rd, Barnstaple, Devon EX32 7AU; Tel 01271 388010

Civic Centre Barnstaple, Devon; Tel 01271 388680; Fax 01271 388721

Hospital Social Work Office North Devon District Hospital, Raleigh Pk, Barnstaple, Devon EX31 4JB; Tel 01271 322474; Fax 01271 25985

6

TORRIDGE DISTRICT CARE MANAGEMENT TEAMS

Abbotsham Rd, Bideford, Devon EX39 3AT; Tel 01392 388990

Bridgeland Street Care Management Team 14 Bridgeland St, Bideford, Devon; Tel 01237 475693

Community Services North Devon

ADULT SERVICES

Civic Centre, North Walk, Barnstaple, Devon EX31 1EA; Tel 01271 388749
Resource Manager (East/North) (Adults)   Ian Rice

ADULT SERVICES

Civic Centre North Wlk, Barnstaple, Devon EX31 3EE; Tel 01271 388752; Fax 01271 329332

Ashcryst Centre Hospital La, Whipton, Exeter, Devon EX1 3RB; Tel 01392 208389

NORTH DEVON DISABILITY SERVICES

Greenfields, Derby Rd, Barnstaple, Devon; Tel 01271 343709; Fax 01271 328027

Alexandra Road Mental Health Centre Alexandra Rd, Barnstaple, Devon; Tel 01271 322943; Fax 01271 328040

Greenfields Derby Rd, Barnstaple, Devon; Tel 01271 343709

Highbridge House Limes Hill, Torrington, Devon; Tel 01805 622755

Holsworthy Social Care Centre Well Pk, Holsworthy, Devon; Tel 01409 254729

Old Rectory Centre Abbotsham Rd, Bideford, Devon; Tel 01237 471001

Silver Hill Lodge Sowden La, Barnstaple, Devon; Tel 01271 343623; Fax 01271 24104

Torrington Group Home 5 Palmer Crt, Torrington, Devon; Tel 01805 623860

Two Lanes Community Resource Centre Belvedere Rd, Ilfracombe, Devon; Tel 01271 866176; Fax 01271 863985

Well Park Community Resource Centre Well Pk, Western Rd, Holsworthy, Devon; Tel 01409 254531

South Devon

CHILD PROTECTION TEAM

Parkers Barn, Culverdale, Totnes, Devon; Tel 01803 869380

DISTRICT OFFICES

Teignbridge District Teign Hse, Kingsteignton Rd, Newton Abbot, Devon TQ12 2QG; Tel 01392 384900; Fax 01392 384903

Newton Abbot District Kingsteignton Rd, Newton Abbot, Devon TQ12 2QG; Tel 01392 384900; Fax 01392 384903

South Hams District Parkers Barn, Culverdale, Totnes, Devon TQ9 5UF; Tel 01392 386000; Fax 01803 869303

Butterpark Brook Rd, Ivybridge, Devon PL21 0AX; Tel 01752 891030; Fax 01752 891001

Combe Royal Stentiford Hill, Kingsbridge, Devon TQ7 4HD; Tel 01752 891050

SOUTH HAMS AND DISTRICT CARE MANAGEMENT TEAMS

Totnes and Dartmouth Adult Team, Parkers Barn, Totnes, Devon TQ9 5UF; Tel 01803 869300

Kingsbridge and Ivybridge Adult Team Combe Royal, Stentiford Hill, Kingsbridge, Devon; Tel 01752 891050

South Hams District Adult and Child and Family Team Butterpark, Brook Rd, Ivybridge, Devon; Tel 01752 891030

CHILD CARE SERVICES

Parkers Barn Culverdale, Totnes, Devon TQ9 5UF; Tel 01392 386000; Fax 01803 869303

Windmill House Ashburton Rd, Totnes, Devon TQ9 5JT; Tel 01803 867847; Fax 01803 867535

CSD/SOUTH HAMS PURCHASING UNIT

Parkers Barn, Culverdale, Totnes, Devon TQ9 5UF; Tel 01392 386000; Fax 01803 869303

Parkers Barn Community Resource Centre Culverdale, Totnes, Devon TQ9 5UF; Tel 01392 386000; Fax 01803 869303

Orchard House Family Centre 21 Ashburton Rd, Newton Abbot, Devon TQ12 1RX; Tel 01626 360737; Fax 01626 332746

Teignbridge and South Hams Youth Support Sun Crt, 16 Wolborough St, Newton Abbot, Devon TQ12 1JJ; Tel 01626 202828

ADULT SERVICES

Mapleton Residential Home Ashburton Rd, Newton Abbot, Devon TQ12 1RB; Tel 01626 353261; Fax 01626 333925

West Devon

DISTRICT OFFICES

Tavistock District Abbey Rise, Whitchurch Rd, Tavistock, Devon PL19 9AS; Tel 01392 386990

TAVISTOCK DISTRICT CARE MANAGEMENT TEAMS

Abbey Rise, Whitchurch Rd, Tavistock, Devon PL19 9AS; Tel 01392 386990

INDUSTRIAL SERVICES GROUP

Group Office, 22 Marsh Grn Rd, Exeter, Devon EX2 8PQ; Tel 01392 221046; Fax 01392 495369
General Manager   Bill Hande

Barnstaple Industrial Services Riverside Rd, Pottington Ind Est, Barnstaple, Devon EX31 1GN; Tel 01271 345109

Exeter Industrial Services 22 Marsh Grn Rd, Marsh Barton, Exeter, Devon EX2 8PQ; Tel 01392 438329

Sheltered Placement Scheme 22 Marsh Grn Rd, Marsh Barton, Exeter, Devon EX2 8PQ; Tel 01392 221046

COMMUNITY LEARNING DISABILITIES TEAMS

Alexandra Road Community Learning Disabilities Team 19c Alexandra Rd, Barnstaple, Devon; Tel 01237 475693

East Devon District Office Town Hall, St. Andrews Rd, Exmouth, Devon EX8 1AW; Tel 01392 385700

Honiton Learning Disability Community Team The Jerrard Wing, Honiton Hospital, Honiton, Devon EX14 8DD; Tel 01404 540500

Community Learning Disability Services Twyford Clinic, Belmont Rd, Tiverton, Devon EX16 6QY; Tel 01884 259464

Teign House Kingsteignton Rd, Newton Abbot, Devon TQ12 2QG; Tel 01392 384900

Teign View 16 Orchard Gdns, Teignmouth, Devon TQ14 8DS; Tel 01626 775951

DAY CENTRES FOR PEOPLE WITH LEARNING DISABILITIES

Doyle Community Resource Centre Salterton Rd, Exmouth, Devon EX8 2NS; Tel 01395 264789

Gifty Steer Resource Centre Crediton Hospital, Western Rd, Crediton, Devon; Tel 01363 775588

Highbridge House Community Resource Centre Limers Hill, Torrington, Devon EX38 8AX; Tel 01805 622755

Honiton Day Services Newholme, Northcott La, Honiton, Devon EX14 8NH; Tel 01404 44420

Kingsteignton Adult Training Unit 6 Pottery Rd, Kingsteignton, Newton Abbot, Devon; Tel 01626 363715

Kingsteignton Community Resource Centre Greenhill Rd, Kingsteignton, Newton Abbot, Devon; Tel 01626 365996; Fax 01626 331443

Launch Pad Day Centre Sandhill St, Ottery St. Mary, Devon; Tel 01404 815669

Molly Owen Community Resource Centre Westbridge Ind Est, Pixon La, Tavistock, Devon PL19 8DE; Tel 01822 612981

Newcombes Centre Belle Pde, Crediton, Devon; Tel 01363 773746

Nichols Centre 89 Polsloe Rd, Exeter, Devon; Tel 01392 274971

Outlook Lodge 11a Eastcliff Rd, Dawlish, Devon; Tel 01626 863831; Fax 01626 866131

Phillips Resource Centre Lyme Cl, Axminster, Devon EX13 5BA; Tel 01297 33793

Ropewalk Resource Centre Ropewalk, Kingsbridge, Devon; Tel 01548 853163

Silverhill Lodge Sowden La, Barnstaple, Devon; Tel 01271 343623

The Leaze Day Centre Tors Rd, Okehampton, Devon EX20 1EF; Tel 01837 54133

The Old Rectory Centre Abbotsham Rd, Bideford, Devon EX39 3AB; Tel 01237 471001; Fax 01237 425505

Totnes Community Resource Centre Parkers Barn, Culverdale, Totnes, Devon TQ9 5UF; Tel 01803 869390

Treetops Day Centre Exwick Rd, Exeter, Devon EX4 2BJ; Tel 01392 251726

Tumbly Hill Day Centre Kiln Hse, Squares Quay, Kingsbridge, Devon TQ7 1HN; Tel 01548 853033

Two Lanes Community Resource Centre Belvedere Rd, Ilfracombe, Devon EX34 9JH; Tel 01271 866176

Well Park Community Resource Centre 1 Well Pk, Western Rd, Holsworthy, Devon EX22 6DH; Tel 01409 254531

RESIDENTIAL HOMES FOR PEOPLE WITH LEARNING DISABILITIES

Haldon View 1 Beech Ave, Exeter, Devon EX4 6HE; Tel 01392 411229

Silver Hill Lodge Sowden La, Barnstaple, Devon EX32 6AJ; Tel 01271 343623

Pine Park House Pine Park Rd, Honiton, Devon EX14 2HR; Tel 01404 42549

Torrington Group Home 5 Palmer Crt, Torrington, Devon EX38 7NF; Tel 01805 623860

Welland House Chaddiford La, Barnstaple, Devon EX32 1RF; Tel 01271 345692 (respite care for children).

SENSORY DISABILITY WORKERS

East Devon District Town Hall, St. Andrew's Rd, Exmouth, Devon EX8 1AW; Tel 01392 385700

Magdalen Road 56 Magdalen Rd, Exeter, Devon; Tel 01392 383730

Tiverton District Office Phoenix La, Tiverton, Devon EX16 6LB; Tel 01392 384100

DAY CENTRES FOR PEOPLE WITH PHYSICAL OR SENSORY DISABILITIES

Acorn Centre George St, Exeter, Devon EX1 1DA; Tel 01392 384481

Alexandra Lodge 5 Old Rd, Tiverton, Devon EX16 1HQ; Tel 01884 243819

Exmouth Day Services at Marjorie Moore Centre Mudbank La, Exmouth, Devon EX8 3EG; Tel 01395 227134

DAY SERVICES MANAGER, PHYSICAL HANDICAP (HONITON/SIDMOUTH)

St. Michael's Day Centre Orchard Way, Honiton, Devon EX14 1HU; Tel 01404 42764

RESIDENTIAL HOME FOR PEOPLE WITH PHYSICAL OR SENSORY DISABILITIES

Danby House Mudbank La, Exmouth, Devon EX8 2BS; Tel 01395 265210; Fax 01395 265210

DAY CENTRES FOR PEOPLE WITH MENTAL HEALTH PROBLEMS OR SUBSTANCE ABUSE PROBLEMS

Alexandra Road Mental Health Centre 19c Alexandra Rd, Barnstaple, Devon EX34 8BA; Tel 01271 322943

Mental Health Drop In Day Services NSF 1, St. James' St, Okehampton, Devon EX20 1DW; Tel 01837 55440

Victory Centre 52 Magdalen St, Exeter, Devon EX2 4LT; Tel 01392 383788

COMMUNITY MENTAL HEALTH TEAMS

Cabot House 69 Fore St, Totnes, Devon TQ9 5NJ; Tel 01803 866225

Civic Centre Barnstaple, Devon; Tel 01271 388685

The Courteney Scheme Joint Agency EMI St. John's Crt, St. John's Rd, Exmouth, Devon; Tel 01395 263768

Exmouth Joint Agency Community Team (Mental Health) 34 Danby Terr, Exmouth, Devon; Tel 01395 280300

Honiton Joint Agency Community Team (Mental Health) Churchill Hse, Church Hill, Honiton, Devon; Tel 01404 540100

Leigh House St. Andrew's St, Tiverton, Devon; Tel 01884 235710

Teign View 16 Orchard Gdns, Teignmouth, Devon TQ14 8DS; Tel 01626 775951

DAY CENTRES FOR ELDERLY PEOPLE

Bodley Day Centre Wayside Cres, Exeter, Devon EX1 3LS; Tel 01392 462473; Fax 01392 464899

Mariner's Close Day Centre Mariner's Cl, Braunton, Devon EX33 2BY; Tel 01271 815263

Burrow House Day Centre Oaktree Gdns, Highfield Rd, Ilfracombe, Devon EX34 9JP; Tel 01271 863685

Davey Court Day Unit Buckingham Cl, Exmouth, Devon EX8 3EG; Tel 01395 273860; Fax 01395 222316

Exebank Day Centre Mudbank La, Exmouth, Devon EX8 3EG; Tel 01395 271692; Fax 01395 222854

Harewood House Care Centre 66 Plymouth Rd, Tavistock, Devon PL19 8BU; Tel 01822 613130

Hartland Day Centre and Springfield Day Centre Chanters Rd, Bideford, Devon EX39 2QN; Tel 01237 475240; Fax 01237 471012

Hatherleigh Road Day Centre Hatherleigh Rd, St. Thomas, Exeter, Devon; Tel 01392 259947

Poppy Day Centre Wardhayes, Simmons Way, Okehampton, Devon EX20 1PT; Tel 01837 52487

Rosebank Day Centre Derby Rd, Barnstaple, Devon EX32 7EZ; Tel 01271 378651

Rushbrook Day Centre Station Rd, Totnes, Devon TQ9 5HW; Tel 01803 862678

6

St. Lawrence Respite and Day Centre Churchill Dr, Crediton, Devon EX17 2EF; Tel 01363 773173

St. Michael's Community Centre Orchard Way, Honiton, Devon; Tel 01392 385850

Sycamores Resource Centre Mount Pleasant Rd, Exeter, Devon EX4 7AE; Tel 01392 496690; Fax 01392 413598

Teignmouth Day Centre Beechcroft, Salisbury Terr, Teignmouth, Devon; Tel 01626 773739

Woodland Vale Day Centre New St, Torrington, Devon EX38 8DL; Tel 01805 622206; Fax 01805 622713

Education, Arts and Libraries Directorate

County Hall, Topsham Rd, Exeter, Devon EX2 4QG;
URL www.devon.gov.uk; E-mail edmail@devon.gov.uk;
Tel 01392 382059; Fax 01392 382203
Director   Phil Norrey
Deputy Director and Head (Policy and Strategy)   Vacancy
Head (Services to Individuals)   Vacancy
Principal Educational Psychologist   Christopher Aston

SPECIAL SCHOOLS

Barnstaple, Lampard-Vachell School St. John's La, Barnstaple, Devon EX32 9DD; Tel 01271 345416; Fax 01271 345416
Headteacher   M. Buckland
6–16 MLD

Barnstaple, Pathfield School Abbey Rd, Pilton, Barnstaple, Devon EX31 1JU; Tel 01271 342423; Fax 01271 323252
Headteacher   S. Williams
3–19 SLD/PMLD

Dartington, Bidwell Brook School Shinner's Bridge, Dartington, Totnes, Devon TQ9 6JU; Tel 01803 864120; Fax 01803 868025
Headteacher   S.M. Love
3–16 SLD

Dawlish, Oaklands Park School John Nash Dr, Dawlish, Devon EX7 9SF; Tel 01626 862363; Fax 01626 888566
Headteacher   R.W. Pugh
5–17 SLD

Dawlish, Ratcliffe School John Nash Dr, Dawlish, Devon EX7 9RZ; Tel 01626 862939; Fax 01626 888101
Headteacher   C. White
8–17 EBD

Exeter, Barley Lane School Barley La, St. Thomas, Exeter, Devon EX4 1TA; Tel 01392 430774; Fax 01392 433193
Headteacher   M. Davis
9-14 EBD

Exeter, Ellen Tinkham School Hollow La, Exeter, Devon EX1 3RW; Tel 01392 467168; Fax 01392 464011
Headteacher   J. Warne
3–16 SLD/PMLD

Exeter, Southbrook School Bishop Westall Rd, Exeter, Devon EX2 6JB; Tel 01392 258373; Fax 01392 494036
Headteacher   H. Green
6–16 MLD

Exmouth, Hill Crest School St. John's Rd, Exmouth, Devon EX8 4ED; Tel 01395 263480; Fax 01395 225357
Headteacher   G. Adler
11–16 EBD

Honiton, Mill Water School Littletown, Honiton, Devon EX14 2ER; Tel 01404 43454; Fax 01404 43402
Headteacher   S. Leathlean
3–16 MLD/SLD

Marland School Peters Marland, Torrington, Devon EX38 8QQ; Tel 01805 601324; Fax 01805 601298
Headteacher   S. Parker (Acting)
11–16

HEALTH PROVISIONS

Exeter Child Guidance Clinic 97 Heavitree Rd, Exeter, Devon; Tel 01392 76348
Counsultant Psychiatrist   Dr P. Kay
Counsultant Psychiatrist   Dr M. Roberts

North Devon Family Consultancy Barnstaple Health Centre, Vicarage St, Barnstaple, Devon; Tel 01271 71761
Consultant Psychiatrist   Dr P. Knight
Consultant Psychiatrist   Dr S. White

HOSTEL FOR CHILDREN WITH EMOTIONAL AND BEHAVIOURAL DIFFICULTIES

The Gables, Willand, Cullompton, Devon EX15 2PL;
Tel 01884 33241; Fax 01884 35288
Warden   P. Hurring
Boys 7–12, Girls 5–18

DONCASTER METROPOLITAN BOROUGH COUNCIL
www.doncaster.gov.uk

Population 292 877
Political Composition: Lab: 45, LD: 8, Ind: 1, Con: 7, Community Candidate: 2
2 Priory Pl, Doncaster, South Yorkshire DN1 1BN;
URL www.doncaster.gov.uk; Tel 01302 734444; Fax 01302 734040
Chief Executive   Vacancy
Community Care Commissioning   Sarah Rogerson
Community Care Provision   Joan Beck
Children and Families   Bronwyn Sanders

Social Services Department

The Council Hse, PO Box 251, Doncaster, South Yorkshire DN1 3DA; Tel 01302 737777; Fax 01302 737778; (Emergency) 01302 737852
Executive Director (Social Services)   Mervyn Thomas, MA, BA, BA, CQSW;
E-mail mervyn.thomas@doncaster.gov.uk
Head of Service (Community Care Commissioning)
S. Rogerson, BSoc.Sc, CQSW, DipASS, CHS, DMS
Head of Service (Policy and Performance)   L.S. Warren, MA, CQSW
Head of Service (Children and Families)   B. Saunders, MBA, BA, CQSW
Head of Service (Community Care Provision)   J. Beck
Services Manager (Children and Families)   A.P. Percival (Responsible for Children's Services Districts 1 and 2 and Child Protection)
Services Manager (Children and Families)   R. Dobbing (Responsible for Children's Services District 3 and Childrens Resources)
Services Manager   C. Pattison (Responsible for Children's Services District 4 and 5 and Emergency Social Services Team)
Services Manager   P. Collier (Responsible for Adult Services Districts 1 and 2 Mental Health and Mental Handicap)
Services Manager   M. Cartlidge (Responsible for Adult Services District 3. Adaptations and Equipment Services and Community Development and Sensory Impairment)
Services Manager   B. Henson (Responsible for Adult Services Districts 4 and 5 and Hospital Social Work Team)
Manager   Linda Hill (Responsible for Children and Youth Justice Social Care)
Manager (Adult and Elderly)   Alan Machin (Responsible for Adult and Elderly Social Care)

Service Manager (Policy and Practice Development)
 Jayne Miller
Service Manager (Business Systems)   N. Thompson
Service Manager (Business Support)   Vacancy

Social Services Board

Con: 1, Lab: 9, LD: 3, Community Candidate: 1
Chair   J. Hardy (Lab)
Vice-Chair   S. Bolton (Lab)
Members of the Committee
Lab: Roni Chapman, Keith Coulton, Maureen Edgar, Elizabeth Jeffries, Michael McAteer, John Mounsey, Malcolm Wood.
Con: Yvonne Woodcock.
Lib Dem: Paul Coddington, Peter Firth, Karen Page.
Community Candidate: Michael Breen.

REGISTRATION INSPECTION AND COMPLAINTS UNIT

Rosemead, May Ave, Balby, South Yorkshire DN4 9AE; Tel 01302 850921
Principal Inspector   J. Skidmore

DISTRICT OFFICES

District 1

Council Offices, 1 Main St, Mexborough, South Yorkshire S64 9LU; Tel 01302 735700; Fax 01302 735734

Districts 2–3

The Council House PO Box 251, Doncaster, South Yorkshire DN1 3DA; Tel 01302 737777; Fax 01302 737778

District 5

Council Offices, Thorne Hall, Doncaster, South Yorkshire DN8 5LE; Tel 01405 812147; Fax 01405 735959

HOSPITAL SOCIAL WORK

Doncaster Royal Infirmary Armthorpe Rd, Doncaster, South Yorkshire; Tel 01302 366666; Fax 01302 320098

CHILD CARE UNITS

Amersall Road Centre 167 Amersall Rd, Scawthorpe, Doncaster, South Yorkshire; Tel 01302 780125
Contact   M. Wainwright
 (9)

Croasdale Gardens Centre 1 Croasdale Gdns, Carcroft, Doncaster, South Yorkshire DN6 8BT; Tel 01302 722034
Contact   C. Wilson
 (10)

Cromwell Drive Centre 4 Cromwell Dr, Sprotbrough, Doncaster, South Yorkshire DN5 8DE; Tel 01302 788076
Contact   L. Oliver

Morrison Drive Centre 14 Morrison Dr, Rossington, Doncaster, South Yorkshire DN11 0BB; Tel 01302 868319
Contact   P. Sabaiba
 (9)

Pinewood Avenue Centre 69 Pinewood Ave, Armthorpe, Doncaster, South Yorkshire DN3 2HA; Tel 01302 831295
Contact   Vacancy
 (9)

Tickhill Square Centre 36 Tickhill Sq, Denaby, Doncaster, South Yorkshire; Tel 01302 770263
Contact   John Robinson

HOMES FOR MENTALLY HANDICAPPED CHILDREN

Newlands Home 20 Avenue Rd, Doncaster, South Yorkshire DN2 4NQ; Tel 01302 327695
Contact   H. Todd
 (8)

Oaklands Avenue Home 17 Oaklands Ave, Hatfield, Doncaster, South Yorkshire DN7 6JL; Tel 01302 840340
Contact   J. Johnson
 (14)

St. Wilfrids Hostel 74 Church La, Bessacarr, Doncaster, South Yorkshire DN4 6QD; Tel 01302 536843
Contact   A. McKenzie
 (6)

YOUTH JUSTICE SERVICE

May Avenue, Balby, Doncaster, South Yorkshire DN4 9AE; Tel 01302 311115
Contact   M. Summers

DAY CENTRES

Askarne Centre The Lake Side, Spa Pool Rd, Doncaster, South Yorkshire; Tel 01302 707791
Contact   S. Higginson

Beechfield Family Centre Chequer Rd, Doncaster, South Yorkshire DN1 2AF; Tel 01302 361597

Benefits Advice and Tribunal Unit The Guildhall Advice Centre, 1st Fl, Doncaster, South Yorkshire DN1 1QW; Tel 01302 734823; Fax 01302 735269

Don View Day Centre 22 Thellusson Ave, Scawsby, South Yorkshire

East Dene Centre Lansdowne Rd, Intake, Doncaster, South Yorkshire; Tel 01302 734069
Manager   P. Pegg

Edlington Neighbourhood Family Centre Cross St, Edlington, South Yorkshire DN12 1LG; Tel 01709 770687

Elm Green Lane Day Centre Elm Green La, Conisbrough, South Yorkshire; Tel 01709 862187

Glebe House Haynes Rd, Thorne, South Yorkshire DN8 5HU; Tel 01405 740819

Mexborough Day Centre Harlington Rd, Mexborough, South Yorkshire; Tel 01709 585224
 (80)

Mexborough Toy Library Highwoods Rd, Mexborough, South Yorkshire; Tel 01709 570164

Rockleigh Family Centre Whitelea Rd, Mexborough, South Yorkshire S64 9QY; Tel 01709 570159

Stainforth Family Centre The Old School Hse, Thorne Rd, Stainforth, South Yorkshire DN7 5BQ; Tel 01302 844157

Stapleton Centre Stapleton Rd, Warmsworth, South Yorkshire; Tel 01302 734977
Manager   E. Whitworth
 (40)

Stirling Social Centre Milton Wlk, Doncaster, South Yorkshire; Tel 01302 363201
 (200)

Windsor Centre Warmsworth Rd, Doncaster, South Yorkshire; Tel 01302 853420

SOCIAL EDUCATION CENTRES FOR MENTALLY HANDICAPPED ADULTS

Adwick Social Education Centre Village St, Adwick-le-Street, Doncaster, South Yorkshire; Tel 01302 721494
 (75)

Cedar Social Education Centre Cedar Ave, Balby, Doncaster, South Yorkshire; Tel 01302 853298
 (75)

Conisbrough Social Education Centre Old Rd, Conisbrough, Doncaster, South Yorkshire; Tel 01709 862097
 Special Care Unit (25) (100)

Danum Light Industries Cedar Rd, Balby, Doncaster, South Yorkshire; Tel 01302 854531

6

Hayfield Social Education Centre Hayfield La, Finningley, South Yorkshire DN9 3NB; Tel 01302 772726

Thorne Social Education Centre Coulman Rd, Thorne, Doncaster, South Yorkshire; Tel 01405 812065
Special Care Unit (6) (60)

HOSTELS FOR PEOPLE WITH MENTAL HEALTH PROBLEMS

Cherry Grange Hostel Pickering Rd, Bentley, Doncaster, South Yorkshire DN5 0ME; Tel 01302 874898
(12)

East Avenue Hostel 23 East Ave, Stainforth, Doncaster, South Yorkshire DN7 5HH; Tel 01302 843187
(10)

Mill Stream View Hostel Mill La, Adwick-le-Street, Doncaster, South Yorkshire; Tel 01302 721408
(24)

Priestly Close Hostel 30–32 Priestly Cl, Balby, Doncaster, South Yorkshire; Tel 01302 853421
(9)

Ravenfield Lodge Denaby Ave, Conisbrough, Doncaster, South Yorkshire; Tel 01709 862290
(27)

Warmsworth Road Hostel 58 Warmsworth Rd, Balby, Doncaster, South Yorkshire; Tel 01302 853042
(13)

West End Lane Hostel 104–106 West End La, Rossington, Doncaster, South Yorkshire; Tel 01302 868164
(10)

Wickett Hern Road Hostel 123 Wickett Hern Rd, Armthorpe, Doncaster, South Yorkshire DN3 3TB; Tel 01302 831969
Contact H. Willis

COMMUNITY MENTAL HEALTH TEAM (NORTH)

34 Nether Hall Rd, Doncaster, South Yorkshire; Tel 01302 366666
Care Manager R. Dunlop

COMMUNITY MENTAL HEALTH TEAM (CENTRAL)

East Dene Centre, Lansdowne Rd, Doncaster, South Yorkshire DN2 6QN; Tel 01302 734050
Care Manager T. Johnson

COMMUNITY MENTAL HEALTH TEAM (SOUTH)

Stapleton Resource Centre, Stapleton Rd, Warmsworth, South Yorkshire; Tel 01302 734795

ACCOMMODATION FOR THE ELDERLY

(incuding provision for the elderly mentally infirm)
There are 12 local authority homes accommodating 412 old people.

RESIDENTIAL PROVISION FOR OLDER PEOPLE WITH LEARNING DIFFICULTIES

Don View, 22 Thellusson Ave, Scawsby, South Yorkshire DN5 8NQ; Tel 01302 785257

MEALS SERVICE

Metro Catering.

Directorate of Education and Culture

PO Box 266, The Council Hse, Doncaster, South Yorkshire DN1 3AD; Tel 01302 737222; Fax 01302 737223
Executive Director (Education and Culture) M.S. Eales
Head of Service (Inclusion Services) T. Common
Head of Service (Education Standards) C.A. Gruen

Principal Education Welfare Officer Mrs G. Morgan

SPECIAL SCHOOLS

Anchorage School (Lower Site) Cusworth La, York Rd, Doncaster, South Yorkshire DN5 8JL; Tel 01302 391007; Fax 01302 390329
Headteacher J. Taylor, MA
Mixed (156)

Athelstane School Old Rd, Conisbrough, Doncaster, South Yorkshire DN12 3LR; Tel 01709 864978; Fax 01709 770172
Headteacher G. Davies
Mixed (101)

Cedar School Cedar Rd, Balby, Doncaster, South Yorkshire DN4 9HT; Tel 01302 853361; Fax 01302 853922
Headteacher T.M. Kellett, BA
(70)

Chase School Ash Hill, Hatfield, Doncaster, South Yorkshire DN7 6JH; Tel 01302 844883; Fax 01302 841052
Headteacher G.C. Williams
(82)

Fernbank School Village St, Adwick-le-Street, Doncaster, South Yorkshire DN6 7AA; Tel 01302 723571; Fax 01302 724196
Headteacher M.J. Wright
(71)

Rossington Hall School Great North Rd, Rossington, Doncaster, South Yorkshire DN11 0HS; Tel 01302 868365; Fax 01302 865620
Headteacher S. Leone
Mixed

Sandall Wood School Leger Way, Doncaster, South Yorkshire DN2 6HQ; Tel 01302 322044; Fax 01302 739927
Headteacher C.M. Ray
PH (73)

Highfields Youth and Community Centre Highfields, Doncaster, South Yorkshire DN6 7JE; Tel 01302 724340
M. Evans

Mexborough Youth Centre New Oxford Rd, Mexborough, South Yorkshire S64 0JL; Tel 01709 583175
S. Wilson

Moorends Youth Centre Northgate, Moorends, Doncaster, South Yorkshire DN8 4LX; Tel 01405 813523
K. Watson

Wadworth Youth Club Community Centre, Wadworth, Doncaster, South Yorkshire

Windmill Youth Centre Windmill Ave, Conisbrough, Doncaster, South Yorkshire; Tel 01709 862955

DORSET COUNTY COUNCIL
www.dorsetcc.gov.uk

The County Council retains its two-tier structure. However in April 1997 Bournemouth and Poole became separate unitary authorities and are listed alphabetically in this chapter.
Political Composition: LD: 14, Con: 23, Lab: 4, Ind: 1
County Hall, Colliton Pk, Dorchester, Dorset DT1 1XJ;
URL www.dorsetcc.gov.uk;
E-mail help@dorsetcc.gov.uk; Tel 01305 251000;
Fax 01305 224839
Chief Executive David Jenkins, MA
Leader of the County Council Timothy Palmer
Director (Resources) Peter Lewis
Director (Environmental Services) Miles Butler
Head (Financial Services) Paul Kent, IPFA

Social Service Directorate

E-mail countyhallsocialservices@dorsetcc.gov.uk; Tel 01305
251000; Fax 01305 224325
Chair (Social Services Committee) Mrs A. Warman
Bedlam, 25 Heath Rd, St. Leonards, Ringwood, Dorset
BH24 2PZ; Tel 01425 476319
Vice-Chair Mrs R.M. Ash
Agememnon, Thornhill Rd, Stalbridge, Sturminster,
Newton, Dorset DT10 2PS; Tel 01963 363422
Director (Social Services) David Joannides; Tel 01305
224317; Fax 01305 224642
Head (Community Care Services) Jeremy Deane
Head (Support Services) Steve Clements
Head (Children's Services) Jackie Last
Manager (Community Services) Roderick Knight
Manager (Community Services) Christine Burch
Manager (Community Services) Andrew Archibald
Manager (Provider Services) Nigel Coles
Manager (Personnel and Training) Rowland Hartle
Manager (Finance) Val Morton
Manager (Strategic Commissioning and Performance Review)
Gill Slade
Manager (Transport and Catering Services) Julie Caswell
Policy Officer (Looked After Children) Peter Todd
Policy Officer (Elderly and Mental Health) Brian Goodrum
Policy Officer (Families and Young People) Liz Chekanoff
Policy Officer (Children in Need/Child Protection)
Tanya Foley
Policy Officer (Disability Services) C. Kippax
Co-ordinator (Quality Projects) Jerry Brady
Co-ordinator (Drug Action Team) Lee Bayliss

Social Services Committee

LD: 4, Con: 8, Lab: 1, Ind: 1
Chair Mrs A. Warman
Vice-Chair Mrs R.M. Ash
Members of the Committee
Con: S.A. Brown, T.B. Coombs, D.W. Hiett, R.W. Mason,
D.A. Mildenhall, A. Warman.
Lab: H.L. Priest.
Ind: L.H.Ames.
LD: B.G. Cooper, B. Fox-Hodges, L.M. Jones,
M.B. Osner.

STAFF DEVELOPMENT UNIT

Pippins', Hanham Rd, Wimborne, Dorset; Tel 01202 883194;
Tel 01202 883894
Principal Training Officer Helen Sotheran

LOCAL OFFICES

Bridport Local Office The Grove, Rax La, Bridport, Dorset
DT6 3JL; Tel 01308 422234; Fax 01308 427421
Manager (Community Services) A. Archibald
Manager (Resources) Graham Pritchard

Dorchester Local Office Acland Rd, Dorchester, Dorset
DT1 1SH; Tel 01305 251414; Fax 01305 251034
Assistant Manager (Community Services) David Fry
Manager (Resources) Marianne Turton

North Dorset Local Office Bath Rd, Sturminster Newton,
Dorset DT10 1DR; Tel 01258 472652; Fax 01258 473161
Manager (Community Services) Christine Burch

Purbeck Local Office Bonnets La, Wareham, Dorset
BH20 4HB; Tel 01929 553456; Fax 01929 556319
Manager (Community Services) Roderick Knight
Manager (Resources) Chris Bowley

Sherborne Local Office The Shielings, The Ave, Sherborne,
Dorset DT9 3AJ; Tel 01935 814104; Fax 01935 817207
Resource Manager I. Solly

Weymouth and Portland Local Offices Jubilee Pk, Jubilee Cl,
Weymouth, Dorset DT4 7BG; Tel 01305 760139; Fax 01305
774622
Service Manager (Childcare) Ian Huckle

Christchurch Local Office 32 Jumpers Rd, Christchurch,
Dorset BH23 2JT; Tel 01202 474106; Fax 01202 478081
Assistant Manager (Community Services) R. Last
Ferndown Local Office Victoria Rd, Penny's Walk,
Ferndown, Dorset BH22 9JY; Tel 01202 877445
Service Manager (Child Care) Pam Hewett

COMMUNITY HOMES

Maumbury House Community Home South Court Ave,
Dorchester, Dorset DT1 2DA; Tel 01305 251449; Fax 01305
257068
Manager Jim Collins
(8)

Westmoors Community Home 266 Station Rd, West Moors,
Ferndown, Dorset BH22 0JF; Tel 01202 854796; Fax 01305
268045

YOUTH JUSTICE CENTRE

Youth Justice West Southwinds, Cranford Ave, Weymouth,
Dorset DT4 7TL; Tel 01305 760336; Fax 01305 761423
Team Manager Patrick Goldsmith

FAMILY CENTRES

Stour View Family Centre Bath Rd, Sturminster Newton,
Dorset DT10 1DR; Tel 01258 473932; Fax 01258 473407
Manager Linda White

Weymouth Family Centre Cromwell Rd, Weymouth, Dorset
DT4 0JH; Tel 01305 784764; Fax 01305 782801
Manager Chris Bourne

ADOPTION AND FOSTERING UNIT

Princes Hse, Princes St, Dorchester, Dorset; Tel 01305
251414; Fax 01305 251034

SOCIAL AND EDUCATIONAL CENTRES

Bridport Centre Flood La, Bridport, Dorset; Tel 01308
422666; Fax 01308 427326
Manager Jacky Walters
(80)

The Juniper Centre 32a Jumpers Rd, Christchurch, Dorset
BH23 2JT; Tel 01202 486114; Fax 01202 482377
Manager N. Bunting
(70)

Stourcastle Centre Stour View Cl, Sturminster Newton,
Dorset DT10 1JF; Tel 01258 472957; Fax 01258 471364
Manager Frances Musty
(93)

The Ridgeway Centre 54 Links Rd, Granby Ind Est,
Weymouth, Dorset DT4 0PF; Tel 01305 760917; Fax 01305
783802
Manager Jenny Taylor
(120)

RESIDENTIAL HOMES FOR PEOPLE WITH LEARNING DIFFICULTIES

Alexandra Road Home 25–27a Alexandra Rd, Weymouth,
Dorset; Tel 01305 760663; Fax 01305 770236
Manager Dan Crone
(26)

The Beeches Fairfield Bungalows, Blandford, Dorset
DT11 7HX; Tel 01258 453436; Fax 01258 451540
Manager Sue Tuck
(25)

Carlton Road Home 5 Carlton Rd North, Weymouth,
Dorset; Tel 01305 760729; Fax 01305 788557
Manager Simon Martin
(23)

Douglas Jackman House 1 Weymouth Ave, Dorchester,
Dorset DT1 1QR; Tel 01305 251598; Fax 01305 268972
Manager Gill Joslin
(20)

6

RESIDENTIAL HOME FOR CHILDREN WITH LEARNING DIFFICULTIES

The Cherries Home 19 Mount Pleasant, Avenue South, Weymouth, Dorset DT3 5JF; Tel 01305 760701; Fax 01305 773041
Manager Jim Collins
(14)

DAY CENTRE FOR PEOPLE WITH A MENTAL ILLNESS

Leon Centre 307a Chickerell Rd, Weymouth, Dorset DT4 0QU; Tel 01305 760039
Manager Caroline Biswell
(22)

DAY CENTRE FOR PEOPLE WITH A PHYSICAL DISABILITY

The Acorns Grosvenor Rd, Weymouth, Dorset DT4 7QL; Tel 01305 760583; Fax 01305 786139
Manager Jackie Rockett

DAY CENTRES FOR OLDER PEOPLE

Beaminster Day Centre St. Mary's Gdns, Beaminster, Dorset; Tel 01308 863944
Manager Mairi Manvell

Blandford Day Centre Fairfield Bungalows, Blandford, Dorset DT11 7HW; Tel 01258 453436
Manager Frances Musty
Mon, Tue, Thur and Sat (15)

Christchurch Day Centre 250 Lymington Rd, Highcliffe, Christchurch, Dorset BH23 5ET; Tel 01425 278644; Fax 01425 279809
Manager Jane Allman
(40)

Dorchester Day Centre Acland Rd, Dorchester, Dorset DT1 1FH; Tel 01305 269073; Fax 01305 216670
Manager Carol Murphy

Fairfield Day Centre East St, Fortuneswell, Portland, Dorset DT5 1NF; Tel 01305 821337; Fax 01305 826130
Manager Trudy Comben
Mon, Wed, Thu and Fri
Separate am and pm sessional attendance 50

Ferndown Day Centre Library Rd, Ferndown, Wimborne, Dorset BH22 9JP; Tel 01202 894426; Fax 01202 891337
Manager Lynn Werkmeister
(55)

Lyme Regis Day Centre Halletts Crt, Queens Walk, Lyme Regis, Dorset; Tel 01297 442480
Manager Mairi Manvell

Rawson Court High St, Gillingham, Dorset SP8 4RZ; Tel 01747 824686
Manager Liz Redman
Mon and Fri only

Shaftesbury Day Centre Trinity Centre, Bimport, Shaftesbury, Dorset SP7 8BW; Tel 01747 854959
Manager Liz Redman
Separate am and pm sessional attendance.

The Shielings Day Centre The Avenue, Sherborne, Dorset; Tel 01935 816321
Manager Viv Fowles
(18)

Stour View Day Centre Bath Rd, Sturminster Newton, Dorset DT10 1DR; Tel 01258 473152
Manager Fran DeMonti
(15)

Swanage Day Centre High St, Swanage, Dorset BH19 2NB; Tel 01929 422804; Fax 01929 425492
Manager Kate Hesketh
(35)

ACCOMMODATION FOR OLDER PEOPLE

There are seven local authority homes for older people.

Education Directorate

County Hall, Dorchester, Dorset DT1 1XJ;
URL www.dorsetcc.gov.uk; Tel 01305 251000; Fax 01305 224499
Director (Education) David Goddard

SPECIALIST MAINSTREAM BASES FOR MODERATE LEARNING DIFFICULTIES

Beaminster School Newtown, Beaminster, Dorset DT8 3EP; URL www.stmarysbeaminster.dorset.sch.uk; E-mail office@stmarysbeaminster.dorset.sch.uk; Tel 01308 862633
Heateacher M. Best
Mixed 11–16+ MLD

St. Mary's CE Primary School Clay La, Beaminster, Dorset DT8 3BY; URL www.stmarysbeaminster.dorset.sch.uk; E-mail office@stmarysbeaminster.dorset.sch.uk; Tel 01308 862201
Headteacher C.F. Longridge
Mixed 7–11 MLD

SPECIAL SCHOOLS

Bridport, Mountjoy School Flood La, Bridport, Dorset DT6 3QG; URL www.mountjoy.dorset.sch.uk; E-mail office@mountjoy.dorset.sch.uk; Tel 01308 422250
Headteacher S.G. Hosking
2–19 SLD

Dorchester, Penwithen School Winterborne Monkton, Dorchester, Dorset DT2 9PS; URL www.penwithen.dorset.sch.uk; E-mail office@penwithen.dorset.sch.uk; Tel 01305 266842
Headteacher S. Downes
11–16 EBD

Penwithen Hostel Winterborne Monkton, Dorchester, Dorset DT2 9PS; URL www.penwithen.dorset.sch.uk; E-mail office@penwithen.dorset.sch.uk; Tel 01305 264315
Head of Care A. Bowerman
11–16 EBD

Sturminster Newton, Yewstock School Honeymead La, Sturminster Newton, Dorset DT10 1EW; URL www.sturminsternewton.dorset.sch.uk; E-mail office@snhs.dorset.sch.uk; Tel 01258 472796
Headteacher J. Davis
2–19 MLD and SLD

Weymouth, Wyvern School 307a Chickerell Rd, Weymouth, Dorset DT4 0QU; URL www.wyvern.dorset.sch.uk; E-mail office@wyvern.dorset.sch.uk; Tel 01305 783660
Headteacher H. MacKenzie
2–19 SLD

PUPIL REFERRAL UNITS

Dorchester Learning Centre The Old Rectory, Winterborne Monkton, Dorchester, Dorset DT2 9PS; URL www.dorchester-lc.dorset.sch.uk; E-mail john.h.taylor@dorsetcc.gov.uk; Tel 01305 250860; Fax 01305 250860
Contact J. Taylor

Sherborne Pupil Referral Unit Simons Rd, Sherborne, Dorset DT9 4DN; E-mail j.s.ardundal@dorsetcc.gov.uk; Tel 01935 814582
Contact A. Arundel

Wimborne Learning Centre School La, Wimborne, Dorset BH21 1HQ; URL www.wimborne-lc.dorset.sch.uk/; E-mail b.smith@dorsetcc.gov.uk; Tel 01202 886947
Contact Barry Smith

HOME TUITION BASES

Christchurch Home Tuition Base The Court Hse, Bargates, Christchurch, Dorset BH23 1PY; Tel 01202 471410
Contact Pam Pyke

Southill Home Tuition Base Southill Youth Centre, Radinpole La, Southill, Weymouth, Dorset DT4 9; Tel 01305 771324
Contact Vacancy; Tel 01305 224422

CHILDREN'S EDUCATION UNIT

Allington Ward, West Dorset Hospital, Damers Rd, Dorchester, Dorset DT1 2JX; Tel 01305 254287
Teacher-in-Charge Harriet Finbow

DUDLEY METROPOLITAN BOROUGH COUNCIL
www.dudley.gov.uk

Population 305 155
Political Composition: Lab: 30, Con: 31, LD: 10, BNP: 1.
Directorate of Education and Lifelong Learning, The Council Hse, Priory Rd, Dudley, West Midlands DY1 1HF; URL www.dudley.gov.uk; Tel 01384 814225; (Out of hours) 01384 818182
Mayor Cllr Mrs R. Tomkinson
Director (Urban Environment) R.W. Johnson
Director (Housing) J. Stringer
Director (Finance) M.S. Williams;
E-mail director.finance@dudley.gov.uk; Tel 01384 814800
Director (Law and Property) J.P. Polychronakis
Head (Environmental Services) N. Powell
Head (Personnel and Support Services) S.G.F. Woodall
Head (Highways) J. Anderson

Directorate of Social Services

Ednam Hse, St. James' Rd, Dudley, West Midlands DY1 3JJ; URL www.dudley.gov.uk/socialservices; E-mail social.services@dudley.gov.uk; Tel (Emergency) 01384 456111; 01384 815822; Fax 01384 815865; Tel 01384 815821
Lead Member (Social Services) Peter Miller (Con)
The Council Hse, Dudley, West Midlands DY1 1HS; URL www.dudley.gov.uk; E-mail internet.itsd@dudley.gov.uk; Tel 01384 818181
Director (Social Services) Linda Warren
Assistant Director (Adult Care Services) Valerie Beint
Assistant Director (Children and Family Services) Pauline Sharratt
Assistant Director (Business Services) Hilary Jackson
Assistant Director (Direct Care Services) Richard Carter (Acting)
Manager (Race, Equality and Communication Services) Resham Sandhu;
E-mail sreqcservissed@mbc.dudley.gov.uk; Tel 01384 813670
Manager (YOT) Mike Galikowski; Tel 01384 813267
Manager (Review and Commissioning) Christine Ballinger
Team Manager (Human Resources) Andrew Packer
Principal Service Manager (Children and Family Services) Jane Prashar
Information Officer Gus Swanson; Tel 01384 815870
Senior Officer (Business Services – Public Information) Barry Hutchinson; Tel 01384 815875

TRAINING

Responsible for training professional and support staff in the department.
Parkes Hall Centre, Parkes Hall Rd, Woodsetton, Dudley, West Midlands DY1 3RJ;
E-mail hrgroup.ssd@mbc.dudley.gov.uk; Tel 01384 813130
Team Manager (Human Resources) A. Packer

DISTRICT OFFICES

Brierley Hill District Office Cottage St, Brierley Hill, West Midlands DY5 1RE; Tel 01384 813000
Dudley District Office 23–25 St. James's Rd, Dudley, West Midlands DY1 1HP; Tel 01384 813200
Halesowen District Office Great Cornbow, Halesowen, West Midlands B63 3AF; Tel 01384 815900
Sedgley District Office The Ladies Walk Centre, Ladies Wlk, Sedgley, West Midlands DY3 3AU; Tel 01384 813250
Stourbridge District Office Wollescote Hall, Wollescote Rd, Stourbridge, West Midlands; Tel 01384 813150

HOSPITAL SOCIAL WORKERS

Guest Hospital Tel 01384 244819
Social Services Manager (General Hospitals) Tony Ivko

COMMUNITY HOMES

Parkes Street Community Home Parkes St, Brierley Hill, West Midlands DY5 3DW; Tel 01384 813481
(15)
Rydal Children's Home 14 St James's Rd, Dudley, West Midlands DY1 3JD; Tel 01384 813625
(12)
Tipton Road Community Home 18 Tipton Rd, Sedgley, Dudley, West Midlands DY3 1HB; Tel 01384 813610
(12)

OCCUPATIONAL AND INDUSTRIAL CENTRES FOR THE HANDICAPPED

Coseley Employment Preparation Unit; Old Meeting Rd, Coseley, West Midlands WV14 8HH; Tel 01384 813653
People with a learning disability.

HOMES FOR ADULTS WITH A LEARNING DISABILITY

Glebelands Residential Home Kempton Way, off Heath Farm Rd, Stourbridge, West Midlands DY8 3AZ; Tel 01384 813590
LD
Grange House Residential Home Parkway Rd, Dudley, West Midlands DY1 2QA; Tel 01384 813545
LD

DAY CENTRES FOR PEOPLE WITH MENTAL HEALTH PROBLEMS

Hill House Day Centre High St, Amblecote, Stourbridge, West Midlands DY8 4D9; Tel 01384 440808
Woodside Centre Highgate Rd, Holly Hall, Dudley, West Midlands DY2 0F2; Tel 01384 813415

DAY CENTRES FOR THE PHYSICALLY HANDICAPPED AND THE HEARING IMPAIRED

Bridge House Day Centre Bayer St, Coseley, Dudley, West Midlands WV14 9DS; Tel 01384 813450
PH
Queen's Cross Day Centre Wellington Rd, Queen's Cross, Dudley, West Midlands DY1 1RB; Tel 01384 813460

SOCIAL EDUCATION CENTRES

Amblecote Social Education Centre King William St, Amblecote, West Midlands DY8 4ES; Tel 01384 813300
Audnam Social Education Centre High St, Audnam, Wordsley, West Midlands DY8 4AG; Tel 01384 813640
Lower Gornal Social Education Centre Holloway St, Lower Gornal, West Midlands DY3 2EF; Tel 01384 813350
Contact Peter O'Connor

6

Stourbridge Social Education Centre Mere Rd, Norton, Stourbridge, West Midlands DY8 3AY; Tel 01384 813530

DAY CENTRES FOR THE ELDERLY

Brettell Lane Day Centre King William St, Amblecote, Stourbridge, West Midlands DY8 4ES; Tel 01384 813315

Brett Young Day Centre Old Hawne La, Halesowen, West Midlands B63 3TB; Tel 01384 813600

Roseville House Day Centre Tunnel St, Coseley, West Midlands WV14 9DE; Tel 01384 813645

DAY CENTRE FOR OLDER PEOPLE WITH LEARNING DIFFICULTIES/ MENTAL HEALTH PROBLEMS

Poplars Centre LMHU Little Cottage St, Brierley Hill, West Midlands DY5 1RG; Tel 01384 482333
Manager Bev Nicholls

ACCOMMODATION FOR OLDER PEOPLE

There are nine local authority homes for older people; 11 sheltered housing schemes.

ACCOMMODATION FOR ELDERLY WITH A VISUAL HANDICAP

Beacon Centre Wolverhampton, Dudley and Districts Institute for the Blind, Dudley, West Midlands WV4 6AZ; Tel 01907 373041 Day and night line 01902 880111

MEALS SERVICES

Services operated in conjunction with the WRVS, 69 Market St, Stourbridge, West Midlands; Tel 01384 394704.

Education Offices

Westox Hse, 1 Trinity Rd, Dudley, West Midlands DY1 1JQ; Tel 01384 818181; Fax 01384 814216
Director (Education and Lifelong Learning) John Freeman
Assistant Director (School Effectiveness) John Slater
Assistant Director (Resources and Planning) Richard Stiff
Assistant Director (Access and Inclusion) Sharon Menghini
Assistant Director (Libraries) Chris Wrigley
Manager (Pupil Support Service) Kelvin Peel, MEd
Principal Educational Psychologist Howard Marsh, BSc(Psych), DipEdPsych
Principal Education Social Worker Dave Corbett

SPECIAL SCHOOLS AND SPECIAL EDUCATIONAL PROVISION

The Brier School Cottage St, Brierley Hill, Dudley, West Midlands DY5 1RE; Tel 01384 816000; Fax 01384 816001
Headteacher D.K. Postlethwaite
5–16

Gig Mill Language Unit Based at Gig Mill Primary School, The Broadway, Stourbridge, West Midlands DY8 3HL; Tel 01384 818605
Teacher-in-Charge R.W. Jennings

Hasbury Language Unit Based at Hasbury Primary School, Hagley Rd, Halesowen, West Midlands B63 4QD; Tel 0121 550 7597; 01384 818665
Teacher-in-Charge L. Marston

Highgate Language Unit Based at Highgate Primary School, Highgate Rd, Dudley, West Midlands; Tel 01384 818252
Teacher-in-Charge A. Evans

Old Park School Corbyn Rd, Russells Hall Est, Dudley, West Midlands DY6 9AW; Tel 01384 818905; Fax 01384 818906
Headteacher Mrs G. Cartwright (Acting)
3–19

Pens Meadow School Ridge Hill, Brierley Hill Rd, Dudley, West Midlands DY8 5ST; Tel 01384 818945; Fax 01384 818946
Headteacher K. Grew
3–19

Pre-School Assessment Unit Based at Bromley Pensnett Primary School, Bromley, Brierley Hill, West Midlands DY5 4PJ; Tel 01384 816865; Fax 01384 816868
Teacher-in-Charge K. Manders

Rosewood School Overfield Rd, Russells Hall Est, Dudley, West Midlands DY1 2NX; Tel 01384 816800; Fax 01384 816801
Headteacher C. Murphy (Acting)
11–16

School Counselling Service The Education Centre, Church St, Pensnett, Dudley, West Midlands DY5 4EY; Tel 01384 814239
Headteacher J. Newton

The Sutton School Scotts Green Cl, Russells Hall Est, Dudley, West Midlands DY1 2DU; URL www.sutton.dudley.gov.uk/; Tel 01384 818670; Fax 01384 818671
Headteacher David Bishop-Rowe
11–16

The Woodsetton School Tipton Rd, Woodsetton, Dudley, West Midlands DY3 1BY; Tel 01384 818265; Fax 01384 818266
Headteacher P. Rhind-Tutt
4–11

COMMUNITY CENTRES

Brockmoor Community Centre Pensnett Rd, Brierley Hill, West Midlands DY6 3JJ; Tel 01384 78722
Secretary Mrs K. Grainger

Dingle Community Centre Madeley Rd, Kingswinford, West Midlands DY6 8PF; Tel 01384 270289
Secretary Jean Willder

Hawbush Community Centre Brettell La, Brierley Hill, West Midlands DY5 3LT; Tel 01384 79188
Secretary Mrs J. Styles

Kingswinford Community Association High St, Kingswinford, West Midlands DY6 8AP; Tel 01384 273625
Community Worker L. Plant

Lye Community Centre Crosswalks Rd, Lye, Stourbridge, West Midlands DY9 8BH; Tel 01384 813960
Keyholder Pauline Weston
Secretary Jean Stanley

Nine Locks Community Centre Hill St, Brierley Hill, West Midlands DY5 2UE; Tel 01384 79799; 01384 822603
Chair I. Korin

Pensnett Community Centre High St, Pensnett, Brierley Hill, West Midlands DX5 4JQ; Tel 01384 79521
Secretary Gill Robins

Wall Heath Community Centre Enville Rd, Wallheath, Dudley, West Midlands DY2 0JT; Tel 01384 273744
Chair H. Walker

Woodside Community Centre Highgate Rd, Dudley, West Midlands DY2 0SN; Tel 01384 75814
Secretary Gill Robins

Wordsley Community Centre The Green, Wordsley, Stourbridge, West Midlands DY8 5BN; Tel 01384 273186
Chair and Treasurer Mr B. Blakeway

Wrens Nest Community Centre Summer Rd, Wrens Nest, Dudley, West Midlands DY1 3PD; Tel 01384 212885
Manager (Community Centre) Vacancy

HOME AND HOSPITAL TUITION SERVICE

Office: Saltwells Education Development Centre Bowling Green Rd, Dudley, West Midlands DY2 9LY; Tel 01384 813740
Head of Service C. Mountford

LEARNING SUPPORT SERVICE

Saltwells Education Development Centre Bowling Green Rd, Dudley, West Midlands DY2 9LY; Tel 01384 813731
Head of Service D. Foxall

ETHNIC MINORITY ACHIEVEMENT SERVICE

Saltwells Education Development Centre Bowling Green Rd, Dudley, West Midlands DY2 9LY; Tel 01384 813731

PHYSICAL AND SENSORY SERVICE

Church St, Brierley Hill, West Midlands DY5 4EY; Tel 01384 818001
Head of Service Vacancy

Unit for Secondary School Children Redhill School, Junction Rd, Stourbridge, West Midlands DY1 2DU; Tel 01384 816359
Head (Resource Base) S.D. Whitlow

DURHAM COUNTY COUNCIL
www.durham.gov.uk

The County Council retains its two-tier structure. However in April 1997 Darlington became a separate unitary authority and is responsible for all its local government services – Darlington is listed alphabetically in this chapter. Population 491 100
Political Composition: Lab: 53, Ind: 2, LD: 4, Con: 2
County Hall, Durham, County Durham DH1 5UG;
URL www.durham.gov.uk; Tel 0191 383 3000; Fax 0191 383 4500
Chief Executive K.W. Smith, IPFA

Social Services Department

E-mail ssis@durham.gov.uk; Tel 0191 383 3000; Fax 0191 383 4182
Director (Social Services) Peter M. Kemp, OBE;
E-mail peter.kemp@durham.gov.uk; Tel 0191 383 3296; Fax 0191 383 3685
Head (Strategic Planning and Finance) Karen Gater;
E-mail karen.gater.gov.uk; Tel 0191 383 3388; Fax 0191 383 3685
Head (Community Support) Peter Brookes;
E-mail peter.brookes@durham.gov.uk; Tel 0191 383 4960
Head (Youth Offending) Christina Blythe;
E-mail christina.blythe@durham.gov.uk; Tel 0191 383 4173; Fax 0191 383 4362
Head (Children and Family Services) Debbie Jones;
E-mail debbie.jones@durham.gov.uk; Tel 0191 383 3322
Head (Adult Commissioning) John Thornberry;
E-mail john.thornberry@durham.gov.uk; Tel 0191 383 5144
Head (County Durham Care) Duncan Callum; Tel 0191 383 5103

Cabinet

Leader Ken Manton (Lab); Tel 0191 383 3000; Fax 0191 383 3000
Deputy Leader Don Ross (Lab)
Members with special responsibility for Social Services issues
Cllr A. Barker, Cllr Smith.

QUALITY AND PERFORMANCE

County Hall, Durham, County Durham DH1 5UG; Tel 0191 383 3304; Fax 0191 383 4182
This Branch is split into four divisions.

Human Resource Management
Dealing with workforce planning, recruitment and selection, salaries and wages, health and safety, staff development and training and staff care.

Information and Communications Services
Covering information technology, information to the public, management information, publicity and communications.

Quality and Performance
Dealing with policy development, performance monitoring and review, customer relations and complaints.

Education Department

County Hall, Durham, County Durham DH1 5UJ;
URL www.durham.gov.uk; Tel 0191 383 3000
Director (Education) Keith Mitchell, BA, LLB, PGCE
Deputy Director (Education) N. Charlton, BA(Hons), CertEd
Head (Special Educational Needs) D. Sayer
Head (School and Governor Support Service) H.H. Wills, CertEd, MA
Head (Learning Support Service) L. Gregory
Head (Education ITSS) B.P. Whitehead, CIPFA
Head (Access and Inclusion) M.E. Clare, BEd
Head (Education Services) A.J. Johnson, BA
Head (Education Resources) P. Barclay, DMA
Head (Education Standards) V.R. Ashfield, BA, MEd, MA
Operations Manager (Attendance and Exclusions) I. Shanks
Manager (School Places and Capital Budget) J.K. Banks, BA, MEd, DLC, ACP
Manager (Community Education) P.B. Robinson, BA
Manager (Finance and Staffing) J.W. Bowman, CIPFA
Manager (Technical Support Service) A. Peart
Chief Inspector D.G. Ford, CertEd, BA, AdvDipEd
Senior Inspector J. Stephenson, CertEd, AdvCert, English/Maths
Senior Inspector P. Livsey, BA, MEd
Senior Inspector T.E. Robshaw, BSc
Senior Inspector M. Pinch, ACP, BEd, BSc, MPhil, DipManEd, CertEd
Inspector R. Lilley, BSc(Hons), PGCE
Inspector T. Hemsley, BEd, MEd
Inspector T. Woods, BEd(Hons)
Inspector J. Farrow
Inspector P. Smith, BEd, MEd
Inspector J. Mitcheson
Inspector J. Chidgey, BA, CertEd, MEd
Inspector L. Halliday
Inspector R. Higgs, BEd, MEd
Inspector S. Fall
Inspector L. Richardson, CertEd, BA, MA(Ed)
Inspector A. Firth, BEd(Hons), MA
Inspector K. Hinton, BSc, MA
Inspector L. Aers, MA
Inspector M. Tones, BEd(Hons), CertEd, NDA
Inspector G. Stephenson, BA, CertEd, FCP
Inspector B. Hudson, BEd(Hons), CertEd, MA
Inspector E. Graham, BEd, CertEd
Inspector M. Bell, BA(Hons), Dipman Stud
Inspector M. Bennett
Inspector C. Earlam, BA, PGCE, Dip in AdvEd Studies(DAES), MPhil
Senior Policy Officer N. Reed, BSc, MA(Ed), PhD, PGCE
Departmental Performance and Review Officer S. Moulton, BSc(Hons), MSc, PGCE
Principal Educational Psychologist/Head (SEN Assessment and Review) D.A. Smith, BTech, MEd, PGCE
Area Senior Educational Psychologist J. Little, BA, Dip(Ed Psych)
Area Senior Educational Psychologist J. Sharpe, BSc, MSc(Ed Psych)
Area Senior Educational Psychologist M. Taylor, BA, Dip(Ed Psych)
Area Senior Educational Psychologist P. Withnall, BSc, MSc(Ed Psych)

6

Specialist Senior Educational Psychologist (Early Years)
M. Portwood, BA, MSc(Ed Psych)
Specialist Senior Educational Psychologist (Early Years)
P. Nagel, BA, MSc
Specialist Senior Educational Psychologist (Social Services)
I. Keddie, BSc, MSc(Ed Psych)
Specialist Senior Educational Psychologist (Emotional and Behavioural) R. Ford, BA, MSc(Ed Psych)
Specialist Senior Educational Psychologist (Sensory Impairment)
H. Flack, BSc, MSc(Ed Psych)
Specialist Senior Educational Psychologist (Speech and Language) J. Crawford, BA, MSc(Ed Psych)
Specialist Senior Educational Psychologist (CAMHS)
S. Woodcock, BA, MSc(Ed Psych)
Specialist Senior Educational Psychologist (CAMHS)
K. Hibbert
Specialist Educational Psychologist (Emotional and Behavioural)
A. Cartwright, MEd, MSc
Educational Psychologist P. Mullholland, BSc(Hons)
Educational Psychologist R.E. Leonard, BA(Hons)
Educational Psychologist L. Tustin, MSc(Ed Psych), BSc(Hons)
Educational Psychologist L. Siddle, BA, MSc (Ed Psych), MEd
Educational Psychologist C. Hutchinson, BA, MSc(Ed Psych)
Educational Psychologist J. Moore, BSc, MSc(Ed Psych)
Educational Psychologist J. Davies, BSc(Psych)
Educational Psychologist C. Shearer, BSc, MSc(Ed Psych)
Educational Psychologist S. Storr, BA, MSc
Educational Psychologist D. Guy, BA, Dip(Ed Psych)
Early Years Inclusion Co-ordinator D. Hodgson, BA, MA(EdPsych)
Early Years Inclusion Co-ordinator J. O'Neil, BA(Hons), MSc(Ed Psych)
Senior Schools Officer D. Marshall, BSc, MSc, PGCE
Senior Schools Officer K. Bates, BSc, MSc
Senior Schools Officer W. Watson

SPECIAL SCHOOLS

Durham Trinity (Bek Premises) School Hartside, Durham, County Durham DH1 5RH; Tel 0191 384 5288

Durham Trinity (Flambard Premises) School Aykley Heads, Durham, County Durham DH1 5TS; Tel 0191 386 4612
Headteacher J. Connolly

Durham Trinity (Kirkham Premises) School Aykley Heads, Durham, County Durham DH1 5TS; Tel 0191 384 7658

Elemore Hall Residential School Littletown, Sherburn, County Durham DH6 1QD; Tel 0191 372 0275
Headteacher R.J. Royle

Ferryhill Rosebank School Rutherford Terr, Broom, Ferryhill, County Durham DL17 8AN; Tel 01740 651555
Headteacher S. Stubbs

Glen Dene School Crawlaw Rd, Easington Colliery, Peterlee, County Durham SR8 3BQ; Tel 0191 527 0304
Headteacher E.W. Baker

Hare Law School Catchgate, Annfield Plain, Stanley, County Durham DH9 8DT; Tel 01207 234547
Headteacher P.H. Eagle

The Meadows School Whitworth La, Spennymoor, County Durham DL16 7QW; Tel 01388 811178
Headteacher G. Harris

Murphy Crescent School Bishop Barrington Campus, Woodhouse La, Bishop Auckland, County Durham DL14 6LA; Tel 01388 451199
Headteacher M. Wilson

Newton Aycliffe Walworth School Bluebell Way, Newton Aycliffe, County Durham DL5 7LP; Tel 01325 300194
Headteacher A.S. Dawson
(Day and residential)

Pupil Referral Unit Broom, Ferryhill, County Durham DL17 8AN; Tel 01740 656040
Contact K. Summerbell

Villa Real School Villa Real, Consett, County Durham DH8 6BH; Tel 01207 503651
Headteacher F. Wood

Warwick Road School Warwick Rd, Bishop Auckland, County Durham DL14 6LS; Tel 01388 602683
Headteacher G. Price

Whitworth School Rock Rd, Spennymoor, County Durham DL16 7DB; Tel 01388 816061
Headteacher L.E. Ablett

Windlestone Hall School Rushyford, Chilton, Ferryhill, County Durham DL17 0LX; Tel 01388 720337
Headteacher P.M. Jonson
(Residential)

EAST RIDING OF YORKSHIRE COUNCIL

www.eastriding.gov.uk

Population 314 113
Political Composition: Lab: 8, Con: 28, LD: 23, Ind: 6, SDP: 2.
County Hall, Beverley, East Riding of Yorkshire HU17 9BA;
URL www.eastriding.gov.uk;
E-mail info@eastriding.gov.uk; Tel 01482 887700
Chief Executive D. Stephenson
Director (Finance and Information Technology) J. Butler
Director (Law, Administration, Planning and Property)
N. Pearson
Director (Personnel and Performance) E. Heath
Director (Operational Services) H. Roberts

Social Services, Housing and Public Protection

Tel 01482 887700; Fax 01482 396003
Director (Social Services, Housing and Public Protection)
Tony Hunter
Head (Social Services) Jack Blackmore
Performance Manager (Adults – North) Liz Warrllow
Performance Manager (Children – North) Heather Flynn
Performance Manager (Adults – South) Connie Young
Performance Manager (Children – South) Jane Stow
Manager (Strategic Development – North) Martin Farran
Manager (Strategic Development – South) Paul Dyson
Manager (Strategic Development – Children's Services)
Ann Gladwin
Manager (Strategic Development – Adult Services) Rita Hunt
Manager (Integrated, Social and Health Care) Derek Newton;
E-mail derek.newton@herch-tr.nhs.uk
Manager (Family Support) Phil Burns
Manager (Early Years and Child Development) Bridget
Bennett; Tel 01482 679921
Manager (Business Development and Monitoring)
Sukhdev Dosanjh
Manager (Information) Pete Baldwin
Management Information Officer Sue Marson
Senior Officer (Welfare Rights) Penny Fox
Co-ordinator (Domestic Violence Response) Liz Turnbull
Gypsy Liaison Officer Alex Nail

Improved Health

Con: 5, LD: 4, Lab: 2, Ind:1, Co-opted Members: 3
Members
Lab: Cllr Clark, Cllr O'Neil.
Con: Cllr Blake-James, Cllr Engall, Cllr Chapman, Cllr Darley, Cllr Jackson.
LD: Cllr Kingston, Cllr J. Kitchen, Cllr Kay, Cllr Walker.
Ind: Cllr Suggit.
Co-opted Member: M. Wilkinson, P. Stocks, Vacancy.

NATIONAL CARE STANDARDS COMMISSION

Unit 3, First Fl, Hesslewood Country Park Offices, Ferriby Rd, Hessle, East Riding of Yorkshire HU13 0PB

HOSPITAL TEAM

Castle Hill Hospital Social Services Hospital Team, Castle Hill, Cottingham, East Riding of Yorkshire HU16 5JQ; Tel 01482 623056; Fax 01482 623062
Manager (Hospital Team) Ann Cross

EMERGENCY DUTY TEAM

100 Lairgate, Beverley, East Riding of Yorkshire HU17 8JQ; Tel 01482 880826; Fax 01482 880827
Team Leader Alan Cooper

CHILDCARE AND PROTECTION CO-ORDINATORS

Manor Rd, Beverley, East Riding of Yorkshire HU17 7BT
Co-ordinator (Childcare and Protection – Children's Services) Louise Kitcher
Co-ordinator (Childcare and Protection – South) Barbara Starns
Co-ordinator (Childcare and Protection – North) Rita Pygott

KINGSTON UPON HULL AND EAST RIDING OF YORKSHIRE AREA CHILD PROTECTION COMMITTEE

Aneurin Bevan Lodge, 140 Hotham Rd North, Kingston upon Hull HU5 4RJ; Tel 01482 846082; Fax 01482 846063
Manager Kathy Rowe

CHILD CARE RESOURCES

31–31a Lairgate, Beverley, East Riding of Yorkshire HU17 8ET; Tel 01482 396672; Fax 01482 396642
Manager (Child Care Resources) Annie Shaw
Multi-agency Family Support Services (North) George St, Bridlington, East Riding of Yorkshire YO15 3PS; Tel 01262 602612; Fax 01262 409516
Unit Manager Vacancy
Multi-agency Family Support Service (West) Carlisle Hse, Carlisle St, Goole, East Riding of Yorkshire DN14 5DS; Tel 01405 768153; Fax 01405 766462
Unit Manager Janet Gravel
Multi-agency Family Support Services (East) George St, Hedon, East Riding of Yorkshire HU12 8JH; Tel 01482 899962; Fax 01482 899680
Unit Manager Polly Campbell

CHILDREN'S RESIDENTIAL HOMES

Cardigan Road Children's Home 117 Cardigan Rd, Bridlington, East Riding of Yorkshire YO15 3LP; Tel 01262 672504; Fax 01262 400792
Home Manager Bob Pattison
The Croft Children's Home 83 Kilnwick Rd, Pocklington, East Riding of Yorkshire YO4 2LJ; Tel 01759 303325; Fax 01759 304158
Home Manager Martin Kelly
Manor Way Children's Home 99 Manor Way, Anlaby, East Riding of Yorkshire HU10 3TN; Tel 01482 657985
Home Manager Rickey Burrett

MULTI-AGENCY YOUTH OFFENDING TEAM

Council Offices, Main St, Skirlaugh, East Riding of Yorkshire HU11 5HN; Tel 01482 396623; Fax 01482 396622
Manager (Youth Offending Team) Darren O'Neill

CARE MANAGEMENT AND COMMISSIONING TEAMS

Care Management and Commissioning Team (West – District 1) The Health Centre, George St, Pocklington, East Riding of Yorkshire YO42 2DF; Tel 01759 304699; 01759 350704; Fax 01759 306915
(Wolds/Dales)

Team Leader (Childcare) Judy Hill
Team Leader (Adults) Pam Mellor
Care Management and Commissioning Team (West – District 2) Council Offices, Church St, Goole, East Riding of Yorkshire DN14 5BG; Tel 01482 396842; Fax 01482 396843
(Goole/Howden)
Team Leader (Childcare) Viv Rathmell
Team Leader (Adults) Chris Wright
Care Management and Commissioning Team (East – District 3) 3 Eastgate, Hessle, East Riding of Yorkshire HU13 9NA; Tel 01482 640131; Fax 01482 642425
(Beverley Rural/Haltemprice)
Team Leader (Childcare) Sheila McMillan
Team Leader (Adults) Pat Youle
Care Management and Commissioning Team (East – District 4) Council Offices, Skirlaugh, East Riding of Yorkshire HU11 5HN; Tel 01482 396532; Fax 01482 396533
(Beverley Minster/South Holderness)
Team Leader (Childcare) Margaret Longhorn
Team Leader (Adults) Vacancy
Care Management and Commissioning Team (North – District 5) Council Offices, Westgarth, Driffield, East Riding of Yorkshire YO25 6TP; Tel 01377 256394; Fax 01377 240369; 01482 396782
Bayle View, Long La, Bridlington, East Riding of Yorkshire YO16 5AZ; Tel 01262 401488; Fax 01262 403664
(Driffield/Bridlington North)
Team Leader (Childcare) Vacancy
Team Leader (Adults) Garry Briggs
Care Management and Commissioning Team (North – District 6) Town Hall, Quay Rd, Bridlington, East Riding of Yorkshire YO16 4LP; Tel 01262 422611; Fax 01262 422615
(Bridlington/South/North Holderness)
Team Leader (Childcare) Bill Harris
Team Leader (Adults) Angela Hallett

REHABILITATION AND OCCUPATIONAL THERAPY SERVICES

Occupational Therapy Team Manor Rd, Beverley, East Riding of Yorkshire HU17 7BT; Tel 01482 888830; Fax 01482 882824
Senior Occupational Therapist Vicky Taylor

SENSORY IMPAIRED SERVICE AND PHYSICAL DISABILITY TEAM

Sensory Impaired Team Manor Rd, Beverley, East Riding of Yorkshire HU17 7BT; Tel 01482 888830; Fax 01482 882824
Social Worker for Deaf People Lyn Stanton
Physical Disability Team
Specialist Worker for Physically Disabled Steve Gray

PRIORITY CARE TEAMS

Priority Care Team (Beverley Minster/South Holderness) Council Offices, Skirlaugh, East Riding of Yorkshire HU11 5HN; Tel 01482 396612; Fax 01482 883862
Team Leader Julie Bottom (Acting)
Priority Care Team (East Beverley Rural/Haltemprice) Minster Towers, Lord Roberts Rd, Beverley, East Riding of Yorkshire HU17 0BE; Tel 01482 886087; Fax 01482 886089
Team Leader Julie Bottom (Acting)
Priority Care Team (North – Bridlington North/Driffield) 47–49 Manorfield Rd, Driffield, East Riding of Yorkshire YO25 7JE; Tel 01377 255345; Fax 01377 272074
Team Leader Helen Greenwood
Priority Care Team (North – Bridlington South/North Holderness) Applegarth La, Bridlington, East Riding of Yorkshire YO16 5LS; Tel 01262 400133; Fax 01262 400132
Team Leader Helen Greenwood
Priority Care Team (West Goole/Howden) 1 Staff Hse, Ilkeston Ave, Goole, East Riding of Yorkshire DN14 6PZ; Tel 01405 768544; Fax 01405 766617
Team Leader Julie Bottom

6

Priority Care Team (West Wolds/Dales) Wold Haven, Burnby La, Pocklington, East Riding of Yorkshire YO42 2QD; Tel 01759 305618; Fax 01759 306219
Team Leader Julie Bottom

EAST RIDING LIFELINE

Lifeline Control Centre 100 Lairgate, Beverley, East Riding of Yorkshire HU17 8JQ; Tel 01482 862417; 01482 881059; Fax 01482 861176
Manager (Lifeline Operation) Janet Huitt

Lifeline Control Centre 3 Chantry Crt, Bridlington, East Riding of Yorkshire YO16 5NB; Tel 01262 605467; Fax 01262 401448
Manager (Lifeline Operation) Janet Huitt

PHYSICAL DISABILITY RESIDENTIAL UNIT

Applegarth Physical Disability Unit Applegarth La, Bridlington, East Riding of Yorkshire YO16 7NE; Tel 01262 672952; Fax 01262 401013
Unit Manager Shirley McLaughlin

LEARNING DISABILITY SERVICES

Beverley Learning Disability Resource Centre The Lilacs, Grovehill Rd, Beverley, East Riding of Yorkshire HU17 0JJ; Tel 01482 867283
Team Leader Rose Parvin

Bridlington Outreach Bayle View, Long La, Bridlington, East Riding of Yorkshire YO16 5AZ; Tel 01262 602549
Team Leader John Fortnum

Grovehill Centre Grovehill Rd, Beverley, East Riding of Yorkshire HU17 0JJ; Tel 01482 869002
Unit Manager Kevin Holder

Holderness Day Services and Outreach Services c/o Victoria Ave Day Centre, Victoria Ave, Withernsea, East Riding of Yorkshire HU19 2LH; Tel 01964 614496
Unit Manager Kevin Holder

Holderness Learning Disability (Hornsea Area) Hornsea Resources Centre, Parva Rd, Hornsea, East Riding of Yorkshire HU18 1PS; Tel 01964 537369; Fax 01964 537380
Unit Manager Kevin Holder

The Laurels, Residential and Respite Services Grovehill Rd, Beverley, East Riding of Yorkshire HU17 0JJ; Tel 01482 867283
Team Leader Rose Parvin

The Lilacs, Community Services Grovehill Rd, Beverley, East Riding of Yorkshire HU17 0JJ; Tel 01482 869935; Fax 01482 860162
Team Leader Rose Parvin

Priory View Centre Marton Rd, Bridlington, East Riding of Yorkshire YO16 2AH; Tel 01262 602477
Team Leader John Fortnum

Rawcliffe Centre Station Rd, Rawcliffe, Goole, East Riding of Yorkshire DN14 8QP; Tel 01405 839410
Team Leader Helen Clarke

MENTAL HEALTH RESOURCE TEAMS

Belgravia Mental Health Resources Centre 6–7 Belgravia, Goole, East Riding of Yorkshire DN14 5BU; Tel 01405 720780
Team Leader Vacancy

Outreach 3 Eastgate, Hessle, East Riding of Yorkshire HU13 9NA; Tel 01482 640131
Team Leader Vacancy

Bridlington Mental Health Resources Team Crystal Villa, 15 St. John's Ave, Bridlington, East Riding of Yorkshire YO16 4NW; Tel 01262 401292
Manager (Operational Services) Lynn Hood

Beverley Mental Health Resources Team 65 Keldgate, Beverley, East Riding of Yorkshire; Tel 01482 861103
Manager (Operational Services) Mike Gray

MULTIPURPOSE RESOURCE CENTRES

Burlington Day Centre Long La, Bridlington, East Riding of Yorkshire YO16 5AZ; Tel 01262 671115
Unit Manager Maureen Emanuel

Chapel Meadows Day Centre Chapel Meadows Community Room, Gilberdyke, East Riding of Yorkshire HU15 2UN; Tel 01430 441569
Supervisor Gordon Johnson

Driffield Day Centre Scarborough Rd, Driffield, East Riding of Yorkshire YO25 5DS; Tel 01377 255084; Fax 01377 249479
Day Centre Co-ordinator Gary Sharples

Samman Road Day Centre and Mobile Rural Day Centre Samman Rd, Beverley, East Riding of Yorkshire HU17 0BS; Tel 01482 871132; Fax 01482 887073
Centre Co-ordinator Richard Fasnacht

Victoria Avenue Day Centre Victoria Ave, Withernsea, East Riding of Yorkshire HU19 2LH; Tel 01964 614496
Centre Co-ordinator Brian Dobson

Wold Haven Day Centre 36 Burnby La, Pocklington, East Riding of Yorkshire YO4 2QD; Tel 01759 304259
Supervisor Ros Sherratt

Woodlands Day Centre Woodlands Ave, Goole, East Riding of Yorkshire DN14 6RU; Tel 01405 763321; Fax 01405 760920
Supervisor (Day Centre) John Duncan

RESIDENTIAL HOMES FOR OLDER PEOPLE

There are three Local Authority residential homes for older people in the area.

Directorate of Lifelong Learning

Tel 01482 392000; Fax 01482 392002
Director (Lifelong Learning) Jon Mager;
    E-mail jon.mager@eastriding.gov.uk
Head (School Improvement) Philip Holmes
Head (Inclusion and Resources) D. Shaw
Head (Libraries and Community Services) M. Godwin
Manager (School Governance, Research and Information)
    Stephen Kuhn
Manager (Resources) H. Jackson
Manager (Inclusion and Special Educational Needs)
    R. Thompson
Manager (Libraries, Museums and Archives) A. Moir
Manager (Community Education) Margaret Walker

SPECIAL SCHOOLS

Bridgeview School Ferriby Rd, Hessle, East Riding of Yorkshire HU13 0HR; E-mail bridgeview@eril.net; Tel 01482 640115
Headteacher R. Coates (Acting)

Driffield Kings Mill School Victoria Rd, Driffield, East Riding of Yorkshire YO25 6UG; E-mail kingsmill@eril.net; Tel 01377 253375
Headteacher Ms S.J. Young

Ganton School Springhead Ave, Willerby Rd, East Riding of Yorkshire HU5 5YJ; E-mail ganton@eril.net; Tel 01482 564646
Headteacher P.J. Glover

Riverside School Ainsty St, Goole, East Riding of Yorkshire DN14 5JS; E-mail riverside@eril.net; Tel 01405 763925
Headteacher L. Jarred

St. Anne's School St. Helen's Dr, Welton, Brough, East Riding of Yorkshire HU15 1NR; Tel 01482 667379
Headteacher M. Stubbins

South Wolds School Dalton Holme, Beverley, East Riding of Yorkshire HU17 7PB; E-mail office@bgs.karoo.co.uk; Tel 01430 810641
Headteacher J. McGill

EAST SUSSEX COUNTY COUNCIL
www.eastsussexcc.gov.uk

East Sussex retains its two-tier structure. However in April 1997 Brighton and Hove became a unitary authority and is listed alphabetically in this chapter.
Population 493 100 (excluding Brighton and Hove)
County Hall, St. Anne's Cres, Lewes, East Sussex BN7 1SG;
  URL www.eastsussexcc.gov.uk;
  E-mail education@eastsussexcc.gov.uk; Tel 01273 481000;
  Fax 01273 481261
Chief Executive Mrs C. Miller
Director (Education) Ms A.D. Stokoe
Director (Corporate Resources) S. Nolan
Director (Law and Performance Management)
  Andrew Ogden
Director (Transport and Environment) R. Wilkins, MSc,
  CEng, MICE, MinstWM, MIHT
Head (Libraries, Information and Arts) Ms D. Thorpe, BA,
  MPhil, ALA
Head (Trading Standards) D. Marshall, BA, DMS, MITSA,
  DCA
County Emergency Planning Officer I. Loughborough,
  MBE

Social Services Department

PO Box 5, County Hall, St. Anne's Cres, Lewes, East Sussex
  BN7 1SW; URL www.eastsussexcc.gov.uk;
  E-mail information.line@eastsussexcc.gov.uk; Tel 01273
  481000; Fax 01273 481261
Lead Councillor for Social Services Cllr Keith Glazier
c/o Pelham Hse, St. Andrew's La, Lewes, East Sussex;
  Tel 01273 481000
Director (Social Services) David Archibald
Child Protection Register Enquiries Tel 01323 769018
*County Council Inspection Unit (Adults – National Care
  Standards Commission)* Tel 01323 636200
Directorate Support Tel 01273 481000
Manager (Training) Tel 01273 481000
Personnel (Recruitment) Tel 01273 481000
Finance Officer Tel 01273 481000
Emergency Duty Team (out of hours) Tel 07699 391462
All enquiries about local services, teams and
establishments should be directed to the Information Line
on 0845 601 0664. Minicom service available.

Education and Libraries Department

PO Box 4, County Hall, St. Anne's Cres, Lewes, East Sussex
  BN7 1SG; URL www.eastsussexcc.gov.uk; Tel 01273
  481000; Fax 01273 481261
Director (Education and Libraries) Denise Stokoe
Assistant Director (Children and Young People) P.A. Weston,
  MSc
Head (Teaching Support Services) J. Amos, MA, AMBDA
  (Acting)

Sussex Careers Services Ltd

Education Business Centre, The Rise, Portslade, Brighton
  and Hove BN41 2QR; Tel 01273 704100
Chief Executive S. Gauntlett

SPECIAL DAY SCHOOLS

Cuckmere House School Eastbourne Rd, Seaford, East
Sussex BN25 4BA;
E-mail office@cuckmerehouse.e-sussex.sch.uk; Tel 01323
893319; Fax 01323 896457
Headteacher Ms D.S. Cross (Acting)
  9–16 EBD (33)

The South Downs Community Special School Beechy Ave,
Eastbourne, East Sussex BN20 8NU;
E-mail office@downs.e-sussex.sch.uk; Tel 01323 730302;
Fax 01323 640544
Headteacher Mrs A. Gidlow
  Mixed 2–9 MLD (56)

Glyne Gap School Hastings Rd, Bexhill, East Sussex
TN40 2PU; E-mail office@glynegap.e-sussex.sch.uk;
Tel 01424 217720; Fax 01424 734962
Headteacher J.A. Hassell
  Mixed 5–19 SLD (94)

Grove Park School Church Rd, Crowborough, East Sussex
TN6 1BN; E-mail office@grove-park.e-sussex.sch.uk;
Tel 01892 663018; Fax 01892 653170
Headteacher Ms C.A. Moody
  Mixed 2–19 SLD (55)

Hazel Court Secondary School Larkspur Dr, Eastbourne,
East Sussex BN23 8EJ; Tel 01323 465720; Fax 01323
740121
Headteacher P. Gordon
  SLD

The Lindfield School Lindfield Rd, Eastbourne, East Sussex
BN22 0BQ; E-mail office@lindfield.e-sussex.sch.uk;
Tel 01323 502988; Fax 01323 500433
Headteacher E. Brooke (Acting)
  Mixed 5–16 MLD (66)

New Horizons Behaviour Support Centre Beauchamp Rd, St.
Leonards, East Sussex TN38 9JU;
E-mail office@newhorizons.e-sussex.sch.uk; Tel 01424
855665; Fax 01424 855117
Headteacher Mrs L. Myles (Acting)
  Mixed 7–16 EBD (43)

St. Anne's School Rotten Row, Lewes, East Sussex BN7 1LJ;
E-mail office@st-annes.e-sussex.sch.uk; Tel 01273 473018;
Fax 01273 480435
Headteacher Ms G. Ingold
  Mixed 5–16 MLD (101)

Saxon Mount School Edinburgh Rd, St. Leonards, East
Sussex TN38 8DA; E-mail office@saxon.e-sussex.sch.uk;
Tel 01424 426303; Fax 01424 444115
Headteacher Ms L. Carlyle
  Mixed 11–16 MLD (106)

Torfield School Croft Rd, Hastings, East Sussex TN34 3JT;
E-mail office@torfield.e-sussex.sch.uk; Tel 01424 428228;
Fax 01424 712322
Headteacher Ms C.M. McCarthy
  Mixed 2–11 MLD (122)

SPECIAL RESIDENTIAL SCHOOL

St. Mary's School Horam, Heathfield, East Sussex
TN21 0BT; E-mail office@st-marys-horam.e-sussex.sch.uk;
Tel 01435 812278; Fax 01435 813019
Headteacher D.F. Bashford
  Mixed 11–16 MLD/EBD (Boarding) (57)

SECONDARY SCHOOLS WITH SPECIAL NEEDS UNITS

Bexhill High School Gunters La, Bexhill, East Sussex
TN39 4ED; E-mail office@bexhillhigh.e-sussex.sch.uk;
Tel 01424 730100
Special unit: special facility for pupils with specific learning
difficulties.

Claverham Community College North Trade Rd, Battle, East
Sussex TN33 0HT;
E-mail office@claverham.e-sussex.sch.uk; Tel 01424
772155
Special unit: hearing support facility.

Filsham Valley School Edinburgh Rd, St. Leonards, East
Sussex TN38 8DA;
E-mail office@filshamvalley.e-sussex.sch.uk; Tel 01424
446247
Special unit for pupils with severe physical difficulties.

6

Hailsham Community College Battle Rd, Hailsham, East Sussex BN27 1DT;
E-mail office@hailshamcc.e-sussex.sch.uk; Tel 01323 841468
Special unit: special facility for pupils with specific learning difficulties.

Priory School Mountfield Rd, Lewes, East Sussex BN7 2XD; E-mail office@priory.e-sussex.sch.uk; Tel 01273 476231
Special unit: hearing support facility.

Seaford Head Community College Arundel Rd, Seaford, East Sussex BN25 4LX;
E-mail office@seafordhead.e-sussex.sch.uk; Tel 01323 891623
Special unit: special facility for pupils with specific learning difficulties.

Willingdon Community School Broad Rd, Lower Willingdon, Eastbourne, East Sussex BN20 9QX;
E-mail office@willingdon.e-sussex.sch.uk; Tel 01323 485254
Special unit: hearing support facility.

PRIMARY SCHOOLS WITH SPECIAL NEEDS UNITS

Elphinstone Community School Parker Rd, Hastings, East Sussex TN34 2DE;
E-mail office@elphinstone.e-sussex.sch.uk; Tel 01424 425670
Autistic spectrum disorder unit.

Little Ridge Community Primary School Little Ridge Ave, St. Leonards, East Sussex TN37 7LR;
E-mail admin@littleridge.e-sussex.sch.uk; Tel 01424 752266
Speech and language unit.

Manor Primary School Downsview Cres, Manor Est, Uckfield, East Sussex TN22 1UB;
E-mail office@manor.e-sussex.sch.uk; Tel 01825 763041; Fax 01825 768107
Hearing support facility.

Robsack Wood Community Primary School Whatlington Way, St. Leonards, East Sussex TN38 9RB;
E-mail office@robsack-wood.e-sussex.sch.uk; Tel 01424 853521
Special facility for hearing support.

Wallands Community Primary School Gundreda Rd, Lewes, East Sussex BN7 1PU;
E-mail office@wallandscp.e-sussex.sch.uk; Tel 01273 472776
Speech and language unit.

West St. Leonards Community Primary School Harley Shute Rd, St. Leonards, East Sussex TN38 8BX;
E-mail office@west-st-leonards.e-sussex.sch.uk; Tel 01424 422080
Severe physical and sensory disabilities.

Willingdon Primary School Rapsons Rd, Willingdon, Eastbourne, East Sussex BN20 9RJ;
E-mail office@willingdon.e-sussex.sch.uk; Tel 01323 482619; Fax 01323 482619; Minicom 01323 482619
Hearing support facility.

ESSEX COUNTY COUNCIL
www.essexcc.gov.uk

In April 1998 both Southend and Thurrock councils became unitary authorities and are listed alphabetically within this chapter. The rest of Essex retains a two-tier structure.
Population 1 316 300
County Hall, Chelmsford, Essex CM1 1LX;
URL www.essexcc.gov.uk;
E-mail corp.comms@essexcc.gov.uk; Tel 01245 492211; Fax 01245 352710
Chair of the Council Anthony Peel, MA, LMRTPI
Chief Executive K.W.S Ashurst, MA(Oxon), MSocSci, FCMI

Deputy Chief Executive (Finance and Performance) A. Hudson, BA(Hons)
Deputy Chief Executive (Planning and Environment) M. Burchell, MA, MRTPI
Head (Human Resources) Mrs L. Pitt, FIPD, MIMgt

Social Services Department

PO Box 297, County Hall, Chelmsford, Essex CM1 1YS; Tel 01245 492211; Fax 01245 268580
Director (Social Services) M. Leadbetter
Head (Community Care Services) R. Rennie
Head (Children and Families Service) R. Vincent
Head (Inspection) D. Gane
Head (Finance) C. Feehily

TRAINING

Responsible for training professional and support staff in the department.
Manager (Organisational and Staff Development) A. Mack

Social Services Committee

LD: 6, Con: 16, Lab: 9
Chair J.W. Pike (Con)
21 Boisfield Terr, Halstead, Essex CO9 2DF
Vice-Chair E.A. Dines (Con)
Midlands Farm, Grange Rd, Tillingham, Essex CM0 7UA
Members of the Committee
Con: T.M. Chapman, W.E. Cole, W.J.C. Dick, E.A. Dines, J.M. Gray, E.M. Hart, C. Jessop, C.B. Manning-Press, D.W. Morris, J.W. Pike, I. Pummell, J.M. Reeves, K. Twitchen, R.C. Wallace, J.A.W. Whitehead, R.M. Williams.
Lab: C.J. Baker, F.E.T. Card, G.J. Huckle, M.D. Juliff, E.I.V. Morris, S.D. Nandanwar, R.G. Smith, B.L. Stapleton, D.E. Williams.
LD: J.E. Beard, E.B. Davis, K. Jones, P.L. Pascoe, D.E.A. Rice, R.V. Yates.

Local Offices

Basildon Local Office Ely Hse, Ely Way, Basildon, Essex SS14 2BQ; Tel 01268 643333; Fax 01268 643346

Braintree Local Office Tabor Hse, 5 Coggeshall Rd, Braintree, Essex CM7 9DB; Tel 01376 555400; Fax 01376 551558

Brentwood Local Office Coptfold Hse, 2 New Rd, Brentwood, Essex CM14 2BU; Tel 01277 221444; Fax 01277 239186

Castle Point Local Office 535 London Rd, Thundersley, Essex SS7 1AB; Tel 01268 565999; Fax 01268 758798

Chelmsford Local Office (Highfield) Highfield, Moulsham St, Chelmsford, Essex CM2 9AF; Tel 01245 493622; Fax 01245 496007

Chelmsford Local Office (Montrose Rd) 3a Montrose Rd, Chelmsford, Essex CM2 6TE; Tel 01245 235500; Fax 01245 450437

Clacton Local Office Magnet Hse, Jackson Rd, Clacton, Essex CO15 9AF; Tel 01255 253300; Fax 01255 253301

Colchester Local Office (East Hill House) East Hill Hse, 76 High St, Colchester, Essex CO1 1UF; Tel 01206 761954; 01206 763267; Fax 01206 760388

Colchester Local Office (Rose House) Rose Hse, St. Albrights, Colchester, Essex CO3 5NG; Tel 01206 769017; 01206 769018; Fax 01206 369113

Dunmow Local Office 2–2a Twyford Crt, High St, Dunmow, Essex CM6 1AE; Tel 01371 876551; Fax 01371 874157

Epping Forest Local Office (Croft House) Croft Hse, Goldings Hill, Loughton, Essex IG10 2DJ; Tel 020 8508 9311; Fax 020 8508 9311

Epping Forest Local Office (Sun Street) 46a Sun St, Waltham Abbey, Essex EN9 1GJ; Tel 01992 701188; Fax 01992 701168

Harlow Local Office (Willowfield House) Willowfield Hse, Tendring Rd, Harlow, Essex CM18 6SE; Tel 01279 434641; Fax 01279 635186

Harlow Local Office (Westfield House) Westfield Hse, Tendring Rd, Harlow, Essex CM18 6TA; Tel 01279 426102; Fax 01279 431902

Maldon Local Office Carmelite Hse, White Horse La, Maldon, Essex CM9 7FU; Tel 01621 854011; Fax 01621 851639

Rayleigh Local Office 134 High St, Rayleigh, Essex SS6 7BX; Tel 01268 778282; Fax 01268 772408

Saffron Walden Local Office 37 Fairycroft Rd, Saffron Walden, Essex CB10 1ND; Tel 01799 513132; Fax 01799 525890

HOSPITAL SOCIAL WORKERS

Basildon Hospital Nethermayne, Basildon, Essex SS16 5NL; Tel 01268 533911
Senior Social Worker E. Greenwood
Senior Social Worker R. Oldfield

Broomfield Hospital Chelmsford, Essex; Tel 01245 440761
Team Leader S. Willis

Princess Alexandra Hospital Hamstel Rd, Harlow, Essex CM20 1QX; Tel 01279 444455
Principal Social Worker H. Carr-West

FAMILY CENTRES AND DAY NURSERIES

Brook Street Day Nursery Old Rectory Rd, Brook St, Colchester, Essex CO1 2U2; Tel 01206 792541

Clacton Family Centre 5 Russell Rd, Clacton-on-Sea, Essex CO15 6BE; Tel 01255 429171

The Gables Family Centre 116 High St, Maldon, Essex CM9 7BS; Tel 01621 858958

The Mulberry Tree 76 High St, Colchester, Essex CO1 1UF; Tel 01206 572558

Rainbow Centre 14 Quendon Rd, Basildon, Essex SS14 3PD; Tel 01268 530222

Willowbrook Centre Church Rd, Basildon, Essex SS14 2EX; Tel 01268 521898

Witham Family Centre Stefre Hse, White Horse La, Witham, Essex CM8 2BU; Tel 01376 501526

Writtle Wick Family Centre (Under Eights) 62 Chignal Rd, Chelmsford, Essex CM1 2JB; Tel 01245 352784

CHILDREN'S HOMES

Brocklesmead Children's Home 432 Brocklesmead, Harlow, Essex; Tel 01279 444354

Chignal Road Children's Home 48 Chignal Rd, Chelmsford, Essex; Tel 01245 269878

Clacton Family Centre 5 Russell Rd, Clacton-on-Sea, Essex CO15 6BE; Tel 01255 429171

Cripsey Avenue Children's Home 3 Cripsey Ave, Shelley, Ongar, Essex CM5 0AT; Tel 01277 362509

The Gables Children's Home 116 High St, Maldon, Essex CM9 7BS; Tel 01621 858958

Lane Cottage Children's Home Green La, Walton-on-Naze, Essex CO14 8HA; Tel 01255 675638

Lionmede Family Centre 216 Springfield Rd, Chelmsford, Essex CM2 6BN; Tel 01245 353789

New Century Road Children's Home 93 New Century Rd, Laindon, Basildon, Essex SS15 6AQ; Tel 01268 543432

The Old Manse Children's Home New St, Dunmow, Essex CM6 1BH; Tel 01371 872110

Patricia Gardens Children's Home 12 Patricia Gdns, South Grn, Billericay, Essex CM11 2QR; Tel 01277 624793

Rainbow Centre 14 Quendon Rd, Basildon, Essex SS14 3PD; Tel 01268 530222

Richmond Avenue Children's Home 17 Richmond Ave, South Benfleet, Essex; Tel 01268 759251

Witham Family Centre Stefre Hse, White Horse La, Witham, Essex CM8 2BU

ADOLESCENT SERVICE UNIT

Cedar Centre 1 Beverley Rd, Colchester, Essex CO3 3NG; Tel 01206 768067

DAY CARE CENTRES FOR ADULTS WITH LEARNING DISABILITIES

Ashleigh Centre Whitmore Way, Basildon, Essex SS14 2NN; Tel 01268 282834; 01268 526342

Chapter House Day Care Centre Carmelite Way, Maldon, Essex CM9 7FX; Tel 01621 841121

Chelmsford Training Centre Ravensbourne Dr, Chelmsford, Essex CM1 2SL; Tel 01245 257155

Church Farm Day Service 4 Church Farm, Naylands Rd, Colchester, Essex CO4 5JJ; Tel 01206 853104
Contact T. Hogan

Concord Special Care Unit Whitmore Way, Basildon, Essex SS14 2NN; Tel 01268 284006

Diana Golding Centre 103 Coggeshall Rd, Braintree, Essex CM7 9EP; Tel 01376 552886

Garden House Community Base Hyth Quay, Colchester, Essex CO2 8JF; Tel 01206 869761

Hesten Lodge Day Care Centre 311 Church Rd, Thundersley, Essex SS7 3HT

Leywood Training Centre Leywood Cl, Braintree, Essex CM7 6NP; Tel 01376 323711

Little Clacton Resource Centre Harwich Rd, Little Clacton, Essex CO16 9ND; Tel 01255 860868

Loughton Training Centre Torrington Dr, Loughton, Essex IG10 3DT; Tel 020 8508 4537

Mile End Training Centre Turner Rd, Colchester, Essex CO4 5LB; Tel 01206 852156

Norman House Day Care Centre 28 Rocheway, Rochford, Essex SS4 1DQ; Tel 01702 543051
Contact G. Fisher

Oakwood Crafts Oakwood Bus Pk, Stephenson Road West, Clacton, Essex; Tel 01255 436967

Oakwood Crafts 2 Harwich Rd, Little Clacton, Essex; Tel 01255 860550

Pyenest Day Services and Special Needs Unit Pyenest Rd, Harlow, Essex CM19 4HL; Tel 01279 308130

Red House Day Care Centre School Rd, Messing, Colchester, Essex CO5 9TH; Tel 01621 815219

Roundwood Day Care Centre Church St, Bocking, Braintree, Essex CM7 5LJ; Tel 01376 551728

Saffron Walden Day Care Centre 39 Audley Rd, Saffron Walden, Essex CB11 3HD; Tel 01799 522496

Shernbroke Road Special Care Unit 1–6 Shernbroke Rd, Waltham Abbey, Essex EN9 3JF; Tel 01992 700545
Contact G. Elliot

Walter Boyce Centre Warley Hill, Brentwood, Essex CM13 3AP; Tel 01277 228571

DAY CARE CENTRES FOR ADULTS WITH MENTAL HEALTH PROBLEMS

Coombe Wood Workshop 1 Websters Way, Rayleigh, Essex SS6 8JQ; Tel 01268 774612

Netteswell Work Centre Netteswell Hall Annexe, Park La, Harlow, Essex CM20 2QH; Tel 01279 421223

RESIDENTIAL CARE HOMES FOR ADULTS WITH LEARNING DISABILITIES

Berecroft Residential Care Home 317 Berecroft, Harlow, Essex; Tel 01279 410859

Bridgemarsh Residential Care Home 184 Main Rd, Broomfield, Chelmsford, Essex CM1 5AJ; Tel 01245 440858

Holliwell Lodge Residential Care Home 81 New Farm Rd, Stanway, Essex CO3 5PG; Tel 01206 578218

Magdalen Close Residential Care Home 1–8 Magdalen Cl, Clacton, Essex; Tel 01255 432951

Mellow Purgess Residential Care Home 5 Mellow Purgess End, Laindon, Basildon, Essex SS1 5PX; Tel 01268 412934

Nether Priors Residential Care Home Colchester Rd, Halstead, Essex CO9 2ET; Tel 01787 477432

Pyefleet Lodge Residential Care Home Leywood Cl, Cressing Rd, Braintree, Essex CM7 6NP; Tel 01376 324350

Shernbroke Road Hostel 1–6 Shernbroke Rd, Waltham Abbey, Essex EN9 3JF; Tel 01992 700545
Contact   G. Elliot

DAY CARE CENTRES FOR ADULTS WITH PHYSICAL AND SENSORY DISABILITIES

Bader House Witchards, Basildon, Essex SS16 5BP; Tel 01268 523269

Barn Mead Occupational Centre Partridge Rd, Harlow, Essex CM18 6TT; Tel 01279 439356

Castle Point Activity Centre Little Gypps Rd, Canvey Island, Essex SS8 9GH; Tel 01268 683530

Chelmsford Occupational Centre Highfield Centre, Moulsham St, Chelmsford, Essex CM2 9AF; Tel 01245 352250

Woodlands Multi-Purpose Centre Recreation Rd, Colchester, Essex CO1 2HJ; Tel 01206 799705
Contact   S. Howell

RESIDENTIAL CARE HOME FOR ADULTS WITH PHYSICAL SENSORY DISABILITIES

Chigwell House 79 High Rd, Chigwell, Essex IG7 6DS; Tel 020 8500 1799

SECURE UNIT

Leverton Secure Unit Dark La, Great Warley, Brentwood, Essex CM14 5LL; Tel 01277 222785

DAY CENTRES AND LUNCHEON CLUBS FOR THE ELDERLY

Provided by District Authorities and Voluntary Organisations.

ACCOMMODATION FOR THE ELDERLY

There are 39 local authority residential homes for the elderly. List available from Social Services Inspection Unit, Kensal Hse, Chelmsford, Essex.

DAY CENTRE FOR OLDER PEOPLE WITH MENTAL HEALTH PROBLEMS

Merefield Day Centre Partridge Rd, Harlow, Essex CM18 6TD; Tel 01279 411795

MULTIPURPOSE CENTRES

Saffron Walden Adult Resource Centre 39 Audley Rd, Saffron Walden, Essex CB11 3HE; Tel 01799 522496

Woodland Multipurpose Centre Recreation Rd, Colchester, Essex CO1 2HJ; Tel 01206 799705

MEALS SERVICES

Provided to all those people assessed as needing a meals service, and fully funded by the County Council from April 1995. Meals are supplied through the District and Borough Councils, working with the WRVS in many areas.

Learning Services Directorate

PO Box 47, Chelmsford, Essex CM2 6WN;
   URL www.essexcc.gov.uk;
   E-mail learning@essexcc.gov.uk; Tel (Education Helpline) 01245 436231; 01245 492211; Fax 01245 492759
Director (Learning Services) Mr P. Lincoln
Head (Post-16 Education and Lifelong Learning) David Holling

SPECIAL SCHOOLS

Castledon School Bromfords Dr, Wickford, Essex SS12 0PW; E-mail admin@castledon.essex.sch.uk; Tel 01268 761252; Fax 01268 571861
Headteacher   Mrs M. Angele
   MLD

Cedar Hall School Hart Rd, Thundersley, Benfleet, Essex SS7 3UQ; E-mail admin@cedarhall.essex.sch.uk; Tel 01268 774723; Fax 01268 776604
Headteacher   Mr P. Whelan
   MLD

The Edith Borthwick School Fennes Rd, Church St, Bocking, Braintree, Essex CM7 5LA;
URL www.edithborthwick-spec.essex.sch.uk;
E-mail admin@edithborthwick.essex.sch.uk; Tel 01376 529300; Fax 01376 529316
Headteacher   Mrs J. Baker
   MSD

The Endeavour School Hogarth Ave, Brentwood, Essex CM15 8BE; URL www.endeavour.essex.sch.uk;
E-mail admin@endeavour.essex.sch.uk; Tel 01277 217330; Fax 01277 225157
Headteacher   Mr M. Southgate
   MLD

Glenwood School Rushbottom La, New Thundersley, Benfleet, Essex SS7 4LW;
E-mail admin@glenwood.essex.sch.uk; Tel 01268 792575; Fax 01268 750907
Headteacher   Mrs J. Salter
   SLD

Harlow Fields School Tendring Rd, Harlow, Essex CM18 6RN; E-mail admin@harlowfields.essex.sch.uk; Tel 01279 423670; Fax 01279 431412
Headteacher   Dr B. Thomas
   MSD

The Hayward School Maltese Rd, Chelmsford, Essex CM1 2PA; E-mail admin@hayward.essex.sch.uk; Tel 01245 258667; Fax 01245 347126
Headteacher   Mr M. Reeve
   MLD

The Heath School Winstree Rd, Stanway, Colchester, Essex CO3 5QE; E-mail admin@heath.essex.sch.uk; Tel 01206 571379; Fax 01206 578591
Headteacher   Mr S. Grant
Residential
   Secondary EBD

Homestead School School Rd, Langham, Colchester, Essex CO4 5PA; URL www.homestead.essex.sch.uk;
E-mail admin@homestead.essex.sch.uk; Tel 01206 272303; Fax 01206 272927
Headteacher   Mr W. Lampard
Residential
   Secondary EBD

Kingswode Hoe School Sussex Rd, Colchester, Essex
CO3 3QJ; E-mail admin@kingswode.essex.sch.uk; Tel 01206
576408; Fax 01206 571477
Headteacher Mrs E. Drake
   MLD

The Leas School Leas Rd, Clacton-on-Sea, Essex
CO15 1DY; E-mail admin@leas.essex.sch.uk; Tel 01255
426288; Fax 01255 473629
Headteacher Mr J. Edwards
   MLD

Lexden Springs School Halstead Rd, Colchester, Essex
CO3 9AB; E-mail admin@lexdensprings.essex.sch.uk;
Tel 01206 563321; Fax 01206 570758
Headteacher Mr S.H. Goldsmith
   SLD

Market Field School School Rd, Elmstead Market,
Colchester, Essex CO7 7ET;
E-mail admin@marketfield.essex.sch.uk; Tel 01206 825195;
Fax 01206 825234
Headteacher Mr G. Smith
   MLD

Ramsden Hall School Ramsden Heath, Billericay, Essex
CM11 1HN; E-mail admin@ramsdenhall.essex.sch.uk;
Tel 01277 624580; Fax 01277 631373
Headteacher Mr S. Grant
   Secondary EBD

Oak View School Whitehills Rd, Loughton, Essex IG10 1TS;
E-mail admin@oakview.essex.sch.uk; Tel 020 8508 4293;
Fax 020 8502 1864
Headteacher Mr S.P. Armstrong
   MSd

Southview School Conrad Rd, Witham, Essex CM8 2TA;
E-mail admin@southview.essex.sch.uk; Tel 01376 503505;
Fax 01376 503460
Headteacher Mr G.W. Currie
   PNI

Thriftwood School Slades La, Galleywood, Chelmsford,
Essex CM2 8RW; E-mail admin@thriftwood.essex.sch.uk;
Tel 01245 266880; Fax 01245 490691
Headteacher Mrs S. Davies
   MLD

Wells Park School and Training Centre School La,
Lambourne Rd, Chigwell, Essex IG7 6NN;
E-mail admin@wellspark.essex.sch.uk; Tel 020 8502 6442;
Fax 020 8502 6729
Headteacher Mr D.C. Wood
Residential
   Primary EBD

The Windsor School Ogilvie Hse, 114 Holland Rd, Clacton-
on-Sea, Essex CO15 6HF;
E-mail admin@windsor.essex.sch.uk; Tel 01255 424412;
Fax 01255 475938
Headteacher Mrs J. Hodges
   SLD

Woodlands School Patching Hall La, Chelmsford, Essex
CM1 4BX; URL www.woodlands-spec.essex.sch.uk;
E-mail admin@woodlandsschool.essex.sch.uk; Tel 01245
355854; Fax 01245 491749
Headteacher Mr O. Caviglide
   SLD

ADULT COMMUNITY LEARNING

Basildon Adult Community College Lifelong Learning
Centre, Broadmayne, Ely Way, Basildon, Essex SS14 2EQ;
E-mail basildonacc@essexcc.gov.uk; Tel 01268 520599;
Fax 01268 524362
Principal Ros Sanders

Castlepoint and Rochford Adult Community College
Rocheway, Rochford, Essex SS4 1DQ; Tel 01702 544900;
Fax 01702 541293
Principal Nicola Davidson

The Adult Community College, Chelmsford Beeches Cl,
Chelmsford, Essex CM1 2SB;
URL www.adultcollege-chelm.ac.uk;
E-mail accchelm@essexcc.gov.uk; Tel 01245 263013;
Fax 01245 494364
Principal Maurice Flude

The Adult Community College, Colchester Grey Friars,
High St, Colchester, Essex CO1 1UG;
E-mail grey.friars.college@essexcc.gov.uk; Tel 01206 542242;
Fax 01206 574853
Principal Alan Skinner

East Essex Adult Community College The Friary, Carmelite
Way, Maldon, Essex CM9 5FJ;
URL www.eastessexacc.co.uk;
E-mail eeacc@essexcc.gov.uk; Tel 01621 853337; Fax 01621
850286
Principal Jackie Short

Mid Essex Adult Community College Bishops Hill, Rayleigh
Rd, Hutton, Brentwood, Essex CM13 1BD;
URL www.meacc.ac.uk; E-mail meacc@essexcc.gov.uk;
Tel 01277 218593; Fax 01277 230471
Principal Irene Davis

North and West Essex Adult Community College Rivermill
Centre, Hodings Rd, Harlow, Essex CM20 1NW;
URL www.nweacc.ac.uk;
E-mail enquiry@nweacc.ac.uk; Tel 01279 427711;
Fax 01279 430031
Principal Maggie Evans

North Essex Adult Community College John Bramston
School, Spinks La, Witham, Essex CM8 1EP;
E-mail neacc@essexcc.gov.uk; Tel 01376 516533; Fax 01376
513099
Principal Sue Bellamy

The Pioneer School Church Rd, Basildon, Essex SS14 2NQ;
Tel 01268 522077; Fax 01268 533214
Headteacher Mrs S. Horsted

Tendring Adult Community College Green Lodge, 180 Old
Rd, Clacton, Essex CO15 3AY;
E-mail tencol@essexcc.gov.uk; Tel 01255 424151; Fax 01255
436765
Principal Christine Bradshaw

Wansfell College Theydon Bois, Epping, Essex CM16 7LF;
URL www.wansfellcollege.net;
E-mail education@wansfellcollege.net; Tel 01992 813027;
Fax 01992 814761; Textphone 01992 613762
Principal Marilyn Taylor

6

GATESHEAD COUNCIL
www.gateshead.gov.uk

Population 200 200
Political Composition: Lab: 46, LD: 20
Civic Centre, Regent St, Gateshead, Tyne and Wear
NE8 1HH; URL www.gateshead.gov.uk;
E-mail enquiries@gateshead.gov.uk; Tel 0191 433 3000;
Fax 0191 478 3495
Leader Cllr Mike Henry
Mayor Cllr David Lynn
Chief Executive L.N. Elton
Director (Finance and ICT) D. Coates
Director (Legal and Corporate Services) R.M. Kelly, LLB,
   Solicitor
Director (Community Based Services) S. Bramwell, BA,
   FCIH
Director (Development and Enterprise) D. Quinn
Director (Local Environmental Services) B. Hallimond,
   MInstWM
Director (Human Resources) J. Parkinson, MA, MBA,
   MIPD

Community Based Services

Tel 0191 433 3000; Fax 0191 477 6544
Cabinet Member (Social Support)　Cllr G. Spring
49 Grange Est, Kibblesworth, Gateshead, Tyne and Wear
　NE11 0TG; Tel 01207 561166
Cabinet Member (Children and Young People)
　Cllr Linda Green
161 Sherburn Way, Wardley, Tyne and Wear NE10 8TZ;
　Tel 0191 438 0625
Cabinet Member (Health)　Cllr D. Napier
6 Heatherwell Grn, Felling, Tyne and Wear NE10 9HB;
　Tel 0191 438 1495
Group Director　Steve Bramwell
Director (Social Services)　Simon Hart
Head of Service (Performance Review)　Fiona Rackstraw
Head of Service (People with Disabilities)　Margaret Whellans
Head of Service (Older People)　Rosemary Luckett
Head of Service (Children and Families)　Keith Moore
Manager (Planning and Development)　M. Brown
The Department is divided into four areas: Children and
Families; Older People and Physically Disabled; Mental
Health and Learning Disabilities; Planning and Support.

TRAINING

The following have responsibility for training professional
and support staff in the department.
CBS Training, Council Offices, Prince Consort Rd,
　Gateshead, Tyne and Wear NE8 4HJ; Tel 0191 435 3000;
　Fax 0191 477 6645
Manager (Training)　Vacancy; Tel 0191 433 8255; Fax 0191
　478 4979
Staff Development Officer (Children and Families)　L. Lyons

Cabinet

Lab: 10, LD: 3
Chair　M. Henry (Lab)
7 Woodbine Terr, Gateshead, Tyne and Wear NE8 1RU
Members of the Cabinet
Lab: D. Bollands, M. Graham, L. Green, M. Henry, J.
McElroy, J.I. Mearns, P.J. Mole, M. McNestry, D. Napier,
G. Spring.

AREA OFFICES

Division – Children and Families

Civic Centre, Regent St, Gateshead, Tyne and Wear
　NE8 1HH; Tel 0191 433 300; Fax 0191 477 6092
Head of Service　Keith Moore

SUB–OFFICES

Blaydon District Office　Council Office, Shibdon Rd,
Blaydon, Tyne and Wear NE21 5LS; Tel 0191 414 2822;
Fax 0191 414 7434

Felling District Office　Booth St, Felling, Gateshead, Tyne
and Wear NE10 9EW; Tel 0191 469 7411; Fax 0191 495
2110

Wrekenton District Office　Social Advice Centre, The High
St, Gateshead, Tyne and Wear NE9 7JR; Tel 0191 487 3421;
Fax 0191 491 4360

Family Support Services

Council Offices, Prince Consort Rd, Gateshead, Tyne
　and Wear NE8 1HJ; Tel 0191 433 3000; Fax 0191 477
　6645

Division – Older People and Physically Disabled

Council Offices, Prince Consort Rd, Gateshead, Tyne and
　Wear NE8 1HJ; Tel 0191 433 3000; Fax 0191 477 8343
Head of Service　R. Luckett

SUB–OFFICES

Blaydon District Office　Council Office, Shibdon Rd,
Blaydon, Tyne and Wear NE21 5LS; Tel 0191 414 2822;
Fax 0191 414 7434

Felling District Office　Booth St, Felling, Gateshead, Tyne
and Wear NE10 9EW; Tel 0191 469 7411; Fax 0191 495 2110

Whickham District Office　Council Offices, Front St,
Newcastle upon Tyne, Tyne and Wear NE16 4EG; Tel 0191
488 7141; Fax 0191 488 3428

SOCIAL WORK BASES

Disabilities　Civic Centre, Regent St, Gateshead, Tyne and
Wear NE8 1HH; Tel 0191 433 3000; Fax 0191 478 2224
Head of Service　Margaret Whellans

Gateshead Group of Hospitals　Queen Elizabeth Hospital,
Sheriff Hill, Gateshead, Tyne and Wear NE9 6SX; Tel 0191
403 2200; Fax 0191 491 5903
Head of Service　R. Luckett

COMMUNITY HOMES

Blaydon Community Home　30 Linden Rd, Blaydon, Tyne
and Wear NE21 5BA; Tel 0191 414 2354; Fax 0191 414 1981
Officer-in-Charge　Deb Noble
　(6)

Crawcrook Community Home　53a Edendale Est, Crawcrook,
Ryton, Tyne and Wear NE40 4PX; Tel 0191 413 2711;
Fax 0191 413 1849
Officer-in-Charge　V. Taylor
　(6)

Grove House Community Home　East Park Rd, Gateshead,
Tyne and Wear NE9 6AX; Tel 0191 478 7124; Fax 0191 477
7625
Officer-in-Charge　C. Hodgkinson
　(7)

Hallgarth Community Home　37 Hallgarth, Leam Lane Est,
Gateshead, Tyne and Wear NE10 8XJ; Tel 0191 469 2747;
Fax 0191 469 1265
Officer-in-Charge　Heather Hill
　(6)

Lyndhurst Community Home　42 Eskdale Gdns, Lyndhurst
Est, Gateshead, Tyne and Wear NE9 6NS; Tel 0191 487 6620
Contact　L. Cogan
　(7)

YOUNG PEOPLE'S SERVICE

224–230 High Street　Gateshead, Tyne and Wear; Tel 0191
478 5288; Fax 0191 477 6349

FAMILY CENTRES

Beacon Lough Family Centre　38 Kendal Cres, Beacon
Lough, Gateshead, Tyne and Wear NE9 6YB; Tel 0191 482
2375
Officer-in-Charge　Mandy Hudspeth

Birtley Family Centre　14–16 Birch Terr, Birtley, Chester-Le-
Street, County Durham DH3 1JL; Tel 0191 410 4107
Officer-in-Charge　M. Martin

Bleach Green Family Centre　4–6 Cypress Rd, Winlaton,
Blaydon, Tyne and Wear NE21 5BL; Tel 0191 414 1966
Officer-in-Charge　S. Lightfoot

Deckham Family Centre　195–201 Split Crow Rd, Deckham,
Gateshead, Tyne and Wear NE8 3UB; Tel 0191 477 1864
Officer-in-Charge　Karen Cree

Dunston Pre-school Centre　Ellison Rd, Dunston,
Gateshead, Tyne and Wear NE11 9SS; Tel 0191 460 5000
Officer-in-Charge　M. Spurr

Highfield Family Centre　66–68 Whinfield Terr, Highfield,
Rowlands Gill, Tyne and Wear NE39 2JY; Tel 01207 544175
Officer-in-Charge　Eileen Coates; Tel 0191 490 1616

Wrekenton Family Centre 107 Lanchester Ave, Springwell Est, Gateshead, Tyne and Wear NE9 7AN; Tel 0191 482 5602
Officer-in-Charge H. Youngman

DAY CARE CENTRES FOR PEOPLE WITH LEARNING DIFFICULTIES

Birtley Adult Training Centre Harras Bank, Birtley, Chester-Le-Street, County Durham DH3 2AJ; Tel 0191 410 2159
Manager J. Hood (Acting)
(74)

Chase Park Day Centre Chase Pk, Whickham, Newcastle upon Tyne, Tyne and Wear NE16 4EE; Tel 0191 488 3261
Manager S. Gray (Acting)
(16)

Felling Community Base 3 Harlequin Lodge, Felling, Gateshead, Tyne and Wear NE10 0HF; Tel 0191 495 0611
Manager M. Batey (Acting)
(20)

Marquisway Day Centre Team Valley Trading Est, Gateshead, Tyne and Wear NE11 0RS; Tel 0191 487 4611; Fax 0191 487 4194
Manager A. McGinley
(130)

New Road Day Centre Team Valley Trading Est, Gateshead, Tyne and Wear NE11 0JU; Tel 0191 487 9263; Fax 0191 487 4193
Manager A. Bruce
(70)

Winlaton Community Base Community Centre, North St, Winlaton, Tyne and Wear NE21 6BY; Tel 0191 414 4213; Fax 0191 499 0785
Manager G. Maughan
(22)

Wrekenton Community Base Community Centre, High St, Wrekenton, Tyne and Wear NE9 7JR; Tel 0191 482 3767; Fax 0191 482 6701
Manager K. Atkinson (Acting)
(20)

GREENSFIELD BUSINESS CENTRE (DIRECT EMPLOYMENT SERVICE)

Mulgrave Terr, Gateshead, Tyne and Wear NE8 1PQ; Tel 0191 477 2958; Fax 0191 277 6888
Co-ordinator L. Wightman
(45)

HOSTELS FOR LEARNING DIFFICULTIES

There are 24 independent registered and 16 small homes providing 176 places.

Blake Avenue Hostel 6–8 Blake Ave, Whickham, Newcastle upon Tyne, Tyne and Wear NE16 4BZ; Tel 0191 488 7598; Fax 0191 496 0996
Manager J. Neill
(5)

Fennel Hostel 1a Fennel, Beacon Lough, Gateshead, Tyne and Wear NE9 7DT; Tel 0191 487 9963; Fax 0191 487 4182
Manager D. Smith
(7)

The Hermitage Hostel Front St, Whickham, Newcastle upon Tyne, Tyne and Wear NE16 4JQ; Tel 0191 488 7372; Fax 0191 488 1330
Manager S. Gillender
(13)

Windermere Gardens Hostel 30 Windermere Gdns, Whickham, Newcastle upon Tyne, Tyne and Wear NE16 4ET; Tel 0191 488 2934; Fax 0191 488 8656
Manager J. Grigg
(3)

DAY CENTRES FOR PEOPLE WITH MENTAL HEALTH PROBLEMS

Blaydon Centre St Cuthberts Way, Blaydon, Tyne and Wear NE21 5QD; Tel 0191 499 0014; Fax 0191 414 7041
Manager V. Mitchinson (Acting)
(50)

Carlisle House Day Centre 2–4 Cambridge Terr, Gateshead, Tyne and Wear NE8 1RP; Tel 0191 478 4192; Fax 0191 490 1073
Manager A. Geddes
(45)

Heworth Centre Colepeth, Felling, Gateshead, Tyne and Wear NE10 9DU; Tel 0191 495 2399; Fax 0191 469 1268
Manager F. Parker
(45)

ACCOMMODATION FOR PEOPLE WITH MENTAL HEALTH PROBLEMS

There are seven independent registered homes providing 93 places.

Bircholme The Drive, Durham Rd, Gateshead, Tyne and Wear NE9 5BL; Tel 0191 487 8156; Fax 0191 487 4189
Officer-in-Charge W. Monaghan
(11)

DAY CENTRE FOR THE ELDERLY

Worcester Green Day Centre Worcester Grn, Gateshead, Tyne and Wear NE8 1NH; Tel 0191 477 1346
Manager B. Hodgson
(35)

MENTAL HEALTH SUPPORT SERVICES

Boxlaw Independent Living Scheme 4 Boxlaw, Gateshead, Tyne and Wear NE9 6ST; Tel 0191 482 0559; Fax 0191 491 5991
Manager K. Straher
(16)

Coverdale Independent Living Scheme 72 Coverdale, Gateshead, Tyne and Wear NE10 8HX; Tel 0191 469 1617; Fax 0191 495 2099
Manager S. Leeder
(15)

Winlaton Independent Living Scheme 8 North St, Winlaton, Tyne and Wear NE21 6BX; Tel 0191 414 0904; Fax 0191 414 2559
Manager L. Herron
(15)

RESIDENTIAL HOMES FOR THE ELDERLY

There are 11 local authority old people's homes providing a total of 388 places and 25 independent registered homes providing 709 places. There are also eight small homes within Nursing Homes providing 24 places.

MEALS SERVICES

Contact Social Services Department District Office

Learning and Culture

Civic Centre, Regent St, Gateshead, Tyne and Wear NE8 1HH; Tel 0191 433 3000; Fax 0191 490 1168
Group Director (Learning and Culture) and Director (Education) B.H. Edwards, BEd, MEd
Head (Access and Inclusion) D. Mitchell, BA, LTCL
Chief Education Welfare Officer K. Johnson, CQSW
Principal Educational Psychologist R.A. Campion, MA, MSc
Principal Officer (Community Education) Vacancy

PUPIL REFERRAL UNIT

Millway Centre Millway, Gateshead, Tyne and Wear NE9 5PQ; Tel 0191 420 0606; Fax 0191 420 0608
Teacher-in-Charge E.C. Bell (Acting)

PUPIL SERVICES

Civic Centre, 6 Regent St, Gateshead, Tyne and Wear NE8 1HH; Tel 0191 477 1011

SPECIAL SCHOOLS

The Cedars School Ivy La, Gateshead, Tyne and Wear NE9 6QD; Tel 0191 487 7591; Fax 0191 482 0926
Headteacher E. Bartley
2–16 PH

Dryden School Shotley Gdns, Gateshead, Tyne and Wear NE9 5UR; Tel 0191 420 3811; 0191 420 3812; Fax 0191 420 3701
Headteacher G. Foster
11–19

Eslington Primary School Leafield Hse, Portobello Rd, Birtley, Chester-le-Street, Tyne and Wear DH3 2LR; Tel 0191 410 8538
Headteacher R. Young

Furrowfield School Whitehills Dr, Felling, Gateshead, Tyne and Wear NE10 9RZ; Tel 0191 469 9499; Fax 0191 420 0905
Headteacher S. Roberts
Boys 11–16

Gibside School Burnthouse La, Whickham, Newcastle upon Tyne, Tyne and Wear NE16 5AT; Tel 0191 441 0123; Fax 0191 441 0124
Headteacher P.A. Gilbert
4–11

Hill Top School Wealcroft, Felling, Gateshead, Tyne and Wear NE10 8LT; Tel 0191 469 2462
Headteacher E. Colquhoun
11–16

Shipcote Centre PRU Edendale Terr, Gateshead, Tyne and Wear NE8 4JW; Tel 0191 477 4835; Fax 0191 477 1663
P. Whitfield

GLOUCESTERSHIRE COUNTY COUNCIL

www.gloscc.gov.uk

Population 564 000
Political Composition: LD: 16, Con: 27, Lab: 19, Others: 1
Shire Hall, Gloucester, Gloucestershire GL1 2TR;
    URL www.gloscc.gov.uk; E-mail gcc@gloscc.gov.uk;
    Tel 01452 425000
Chair of the County Council Cllr Mike Skinner
Chief Executive Joyce Redfearn
Executive Director (Environment) Peter Bungard
Bearland Wing, Shire Hall, Gloucester, Gloucestershire GL1 2TH
Executive Director (Resources) Stephen Wood
Press Officer Sarah Wood

Social Services Department

Bearland Wing, Shire Hall, Gloucester, Gloucestershire GL1 2TR; Tel 01452 426000; Fax 01452 425149
Executive Director (Social Services) Margaret Sheather
Head of Service (Children and Families) M. Swann
Head of Service (Adult Care) Kim Carey
Manager (Finance) S. Fossali
Manager (Personnel and Staff Development) J. Walters
Manager (Planning and Policy) A. Cathles
Manager (IT and Systems) C. Chambers
Manager (Performance) N. Berry
Manager (Countywide Services) T. Reid (Based at Shire Hall)
Manager (Information) M. Guest
Manager (Administrative Services) D. Burgess
Communications Officer S. Wood

TRAINING

Responsible for training professional and support staff in the department.
Manager (Training) B. Wiltshire; Tel 01452 425135

Cabinet

LD: 5, Lab: 5
Leader Cllr Clarke
Deputy Leader Cllr Boait
Portfolio Holder (Children and Families) Cllr Rutter
Portfolio Holder (Adult Care) Cllr Hendry

AREA OFFICES

Cheltenham

Sandford Park Hse, 39–41 London Rd, Cheltenham, Gloucestershire; Tel 01242 532500; Fax 01242 532519
County Manager (Mental Health) T. Williams

COTSWOLDS AREA OFFICE

The Old School, 46 Lewis La, Cirencester, Gloucestershire GL7 1QX; Tel 01285 881000

NORTH COTSWOLDS FIELDWORK OFFICE

Victoria Hse, Stow-on-the-Wold, Gloucestershire; Tel 01451 832272

Gloucester

Quayside Hse, Lower Quay St, Gloucester, Gloucestershire; Tel 01452 426000; Fax 01452 425148
County Manager (Learning Disabilities)
    Andy Rowadowski
County Manager (Learning Disabilities) Amanda Blackton
Manager (Community Care and Locality Development – Gloucester) R. McDowell

FOREST OF DEAN AREA OFFICE

Dean Hse, Station St, Cinderford, Gloucestershire GL14 2JF; Tel 01594 820500; Fax 01594 820510

STROUD AND DURSLEY AREA OFFICE

The Health Centre, Beeches Grn, Stroud, Gloucestershire; Tel 01453 760500; Fax 01453 756472
Manager (Fieldwork Services) C. Sands
Manager (Fieldwork Services) S. Butcher
Sub-Office
Dursley Boulton La, Dursley, Gloucestershire; Tel 01453 546182; Fax 01453 548026

NORTH TEWKESBURY AREA OFFICE

Church St, Tewkesbury, Gloucestershire GL20 5SW; Tel 01684 275852; Fax 01684 275849
Manager (Community Care and Locality Development – Cheltenham and Tewkesbury) J. Kearsley

SOUTH TEWKESBURY AREA OFFICE

Block B, Spur 2, Elmbridge Crt, Gloucester, Gloucestershire GL3 1AG; Tel 01452 410345; Fax 01452 410567

HOSPITAL SOCIAL WORK SERVICES

Social Services Department, Gloucester Royal Hospital, Gloucester, Gloucestershire; Tel 01452 528555
District General Hospitals at Gloucester and Cheltenham. Also at Standish, Cirencester and Tewkesbury, Stroud Green, Delancey, Moreton-in-Marsh and Bourton-on-the Water. A limited service is provided to other peripheral hospitals in conjunction with community based social workers.

FAMILY CENTRES (INCLUDING PRE-SCHOOL DAY CARE)

Russet House Family Centre Russet Cl, Tuffley, Gloucester, Gloucestershire GL4 0RG; Tel 01452 528955
Manager S. Aitken

Whaddon Family Centre Clyde Cres, Cheltenham, Gloucestershire; Tel 01242 513010
Manager P. Sweet
Manager S. Collins

CHILDREN AND FAMILIES (RESIDENTIAL)

Cheltenham Children's Resource Centre Hales Mead, Hales Cl, Cheltenham, Gloucestershire GL52 6TE; Tel 01242 227446

Children's Resource Centre Shepherd End, Shepherd Rd, Tuffley, Gloucester, Gloucestershire GL33 3AL; Tel 01452 525727
Manager (Partnership and Development) R. Townsend
Manager (Looked After Children) C. Shea

Enderley Children's Resource Centre Amberley, Gloucestershire GL5 5AW; Tel 01453 872515

Gloucester Children's Resource Centre The Trees, Jordan's Brook Hse, North Upton La, Gloucester, Gloucestershire GL33 3AL; Tel 01452 618691
Contact D. Needleman

Lynton Children's Resource Centre 34 Podsmead Rd, Gloucester, Gloucestershire GL1 5PA; Tel 01452 523210

Matlock House Children's Resource Centre 1 Barnwood Rd, Gloucester, Gloucestershire GL2 0RU; Tel 01452 414491

Pengwern Pitville Circus Rd, Cheltenham, Gloucestershire GL52 2PZ; Tel 01242 517928
Manager A. Green

SPECIAL FOSTER HOMES

The Department has a number of schemes for the special fostering of children and adolescents.

ADULT OPPORTUNITY CENTRES

Chipping Campden Adult Opportunity Centre Pear Tree Cl, Chipping Campden, Gloucestershire; Tel 01386 841139
Manager S. Randell
Manager V. Mathews

Cirencester Resource and Information Centre Chesterton Halt, Meadow Rd, Cirencester, Gloucestershire; Tel 01285 658576
Manager Vacancy

Gloucester Adult Opportunity Centre Eastbrook Rd, Gloucester, Gloucestershire; Tel 01452 522591
Manager R. Harwood

Lydney Adult Opportunity Centre Fairtide Centre, Naas La, Lydney, Gloucestershire GL15 5AT; Tel 01594 844636
Manager L. Tocknell

Oakley Adult Opportunity Centre Isbourne Rd, Whaddon, Cheltenham, Gloucestershire GL52 5QG; Tel 01242 221725
Manager Vacancy

Parkside Adult Opportunity Centre Princess Elizabeth Way, Cheltenham, Gloucestershire GL51 7PA; Tel 01242 527101
Manager K. Salter

The Royal Forest Centre Valley Rd, Cinderford, Gloucestershire GL14 2LJ; Tel 01594 822088
Manager L. Davis

Stroud Adult Opportunity Centre Beeches Grn, Stroud, Gloucestershire GL5 4AE; Tel 01453 763484
Manager L. Hurlock

Tewkesbury Adult Opportunity Centre The Birches, Station Rd, Tewkesbury, Gloucestershire GL20 5DR; Tel 01684 293096
Manager M. Evans

SHELTERED WORKSHOPS

Alpha Workshops Valley Rd, Cinderford, Gloucestershire GL14 2LJ; Tel 01594 822089

Prospect Works Sudmeadow Rd, Gloucester, Gloucestershire GL2 5HS; Tel 01452 520438

DAY CENTRES FOR PEOPLE WITH MENTAL HEALTH PROBLEMS

Grafton Road Day Centre Melray, 20 Grafton Rd, Gloucester, Gloucestershire; Tel 01452 311599
Manager V. Underwood

Milsom Street Day Centre Milsom St, Cheltenham, Gloucestershire; Tel 01242 512812
Manager C. Jones

Weston Road Day Centre 78 Weston Rd, Gloucester, Gloucestershire; Tel 01452 300631
Manager V. MacDougall

The White House Day Centre Stow Rd, Moreton-in-Marsh, Gloucestershire GL56 0DW; Tel 01608 652232
Manager V. MacDougall (Acting)

Worcester House Day Centre Pittville Circus Rd, Cheltenham, Gloucestershire; Tel 01242 525320
Manager A. Ayrton (Acting)

HOMES FOR PEOPLE WITH LEARNING DIFFICULTIES

Cathedral View Archdeacon St, Gloucester, Gloucestershire GL1 2QX; Tel 01452 302807
Manager D. Ewers

Long House 6 Whitehouse Pk, Caincross, Stroud, Gloucestershire GL5 4LD; Tel 01453 765647
Manager A. Sutton

Severnleigh Naas La, Lydney, Gloucestershire; Tel 01594 841086
Manager L. Davis

The Vicarage Andover Rd, Cheltenham, Gloucestershire GL50 2TS; Tel 01242 521918
Manager J. Metcalfe

RESOURCES FOR PEOPLE WITH PHYSICAL DISABILITIES

Foxes Bridge Day Centre Valley Rd, Cinderford, Gloucestershire GL14 2LJ; Tel 01594 825484
Manager G. Hardy

Hatherley Road Day Centre Hatherley Rd, Gloucester, Gloucestershire GL1 4PW; Tel 01452 520390
Manager S. Middleton

Newholme Victoria Rd, Cirencester, Gloucestershire GL1 1LY; Tel 01285 653533
Manager P. Fordyce

Prestbury Road Day Centre 236 Prestbury Rd, Cheltenham, Gloucestershire GL52 3ET; Tel 01242 584470
Manager C. Porter

Wheatridge Court (Residential) 40 Shergar Cl, Abbeydale, Gloucester, Gloucestershire GL4 9FD; Tel 01452 500669
Manager L. Gamm

RESOURCES FOR OLDER PEOPLE

Glebe House Day Centre Fairmead Est, Cam, Gloucestershire GL11 5JS; Tel 01453 548523

Great Western Court 33a Millbrook St, Gloucester, Gloucestershire GL1 4DP; Tel 01452 423495
Manager A. Neilens

Tewkesbury Day Centre Station Rd, Tewkesbury, Gloucestershire GL20 5DR; Tel 01684 296238
Manager S. Allen

ACCOMMODATION FOR OLDER PEOPLE

One local authority home for elderly; 23 residential homes with Coverage Care Ltd an independent industrial and Provident Society.

6

Education Offices

Shire Hall, Westgate St, Gloucester, Gloucestershire
GL1 2TP; E-mail edu@gloscc.gov.uk; Tel 01452 425300;
Fax 01452 425496
Executive Director Jo Davidson

YOUTH AND COMMUNITY SERVICE

Head (Youth and Community Service) M. Counsell, BEd
Chequers Bridge Centre, Painswick Rd, Gloucester,
Gloucestershire GL4 9PR; Tel 01452 425420; Fax 01452
426375

SPECIAL DAY SCHOOLS

Alderman Knight School Ashchurch Rd, Tewkesbury,
Gloucestershire GL20 8JJ;
E-mail admin@aldermanknight.gloucs.sch.uk; Tel 01684
295639; Fax 01684 295639
Headteacher I.T. Walsh, BA, CertEd, DipSpEd
(80)

Battledown Children's Centre Harp Hill, Battledown,
Cheltenham, Gloucestershire GL52 6PZ;
E-mail admin@battledown.gloucs.sch.uk; Tel 01242 525472;
Fax 01242 257557
Headteacher E.M. Rook, AdDip(SpNeeds)
(48)

Belmont School Warden Hill Rd, Cheltenham,
Gloucestershire GL51 3AT;
E-mail admin@belmont.gloucs.sch.uk; Tel 01242 216180;
Fax 01242 227827
Headteacher Mrs H.A. Maddison
(57)

Bettridge School Warden Hill Rd, Cheltenham,
Gloucestershire GL51 3AT;
URL www.bettridgeschool.ik.org;
E-mail admin@bettridge.gloucs.sch.uk; Tel 01242 514934;
Fax 01242 514934
Headteacher M. Saunders, BEd(Hons)
(87)

Dean Hall School Speech Hse Rd, Coleford,
Gloucestershire GL16 7EJ;
URL www.deanhallschool.ik.org;
E-mail school@deanhall.gloucs.sch.uk; Tel 01594 822175;
Fax 01594 826472
Headteacher J.N. Haddock, BA, BEd
(50)

The Milestone School Longford La, Gloucester,
Gloucestershire GL2 9EU;
URL www.themilestoneschool.ik.org;
E-mail milestone@rmplc.co.uk; Tel 01452 500499; Fax 01452
500602
Headteacher L. Shea
(278)

Oakdene School Dockham Rd, Cinderford,
Gloucestershire GL14 2AN;
URL www.oakdeneschool.ik.org;
E-mail head@oakdene.gloucs.sch.uk; Tel 01594 822693;
Fax 01594 822693
Headteacher Mrs E. Oates (Acting)
(33)

Paternoster School Watermoor Rd, Cirencester,
Gloucestershire GL7 1JS; URL www.paternoster.ik.org;
E-mail admin@paternoster.gloucs.sch.uk; Tel 01285 652480;
Fax 01285 642490
Headteacher P. Barton, CertEd, DipSpecEd
(43)

Sandford School Seven Springs, Cheltenham,
Gloucestershire GL53 9NG;
E-mail admin@sandford.gloucs.sch.uk; Tel 01242 870224;
Fax 01242 870331
Headteacher S. Jones
(84)

SPECIAL DAY AND RESIDENTIAL SCHOOLS

Amberley Ridge School Rodborough, Stroud,
Gloucestershire GL5 5DB;
E-mail mac@the-bridge.demon.co.uk; Tel 01453 872536;
Fax 01453 872557
Headteacher D. McDonald, BEd, CertEd
(31)

Cam House School Drake La, Cam, Dursley,
Gloucestershire GL11 5HD;
URL www.camhouseschool.ik.org;
E-mail admin@camhouse.gloucs.sch.uk; Tel 01453 542130;
Fax 01453 547067
Headteacher Mrs B. Turner
(54)

Coln House School Horcott Rd, Fairford, Gloucestershire
GL7 4DB; E-mail admin@colnhouseschool.org.uk; Tel 01285
712308; Fax 01285 713011
Headteacher C. Clarke
(50)

TUITION CENTRES

The Hatherley Centre Lismore Hse, 3 Horton Rd,
Gloucester, Gloucestershire GL1 3PX;
E-mail thehatherley@easymail.rmplc.co.uk; Tel 01452
309510

St. George's Centre 140b St. George's Rd, Cheltenham,
Gloucestershire GL50 3EL;
E-mail stgeorgescentre@easymail.rmplc.co.uk; Tel 01242
581519; Fax 01242 578836

Whitminster Centre Roxburgh Hse, Nelson St, Stroud,
Gloucestershire GL5 2HP;
E-mail whitminstercentre@easymail.rmplc.co.uk; Tel 01453
767293

GREATER MANCHESTER METROPOLITAN AREA

The following Metropolitan Councils comprise the Greater
Manchester Metropolitan Area and may be found in
alphabetical order within this chapter: Bolton, Bury,
Manchester, Oldham, Rochdale, Salford, Stockport,
Tameside, Trafford, Wigan.

ASSOCIATION OF GREATER MANCHESTER AUTHORITIES

Wigan Investment Centre, Waterside Dr, off Swan Meadow
Rd, Wigan, Greater Manchester WN3 5BA;
URL agma.gov.uk; E-mail j.hawkins@wiganmbc.gov.uk;
Tel 01942 705719; Fax 01942 705728
Chair Cllr Peter Smith (Wigan MBC)
Secretary Stephen Jones (Chief Executive, Wigan MBC)

HALTON BOROUGH COUNCIL
www.halton.gov.uk

Political Composition: Con: 2, LD: 7, Lab: 47
Municipal Bldg, Kingsway, Widnes, Halton WA8 7QF;
URL www.halton.gov.uk; Tel 0151 424 2061
Chief Executive Mike Cuff
Executive Director (Social Care, Housing and Health)
Diana Terris
Leader of The Council Cllr T. McDermott
Executive Director (Environment and Development) R. Tregea
Executive Director (Resources and Corporate Services) A. Hill
Executive Director (Neighbourhood Services) C. Soper

Social Care, Housing and Health Directorate

Halton Borough Council, Grosvenor Hse, Halton Lea, Runcorn, Halton WA8 2WD; Tel 0151 424 2061; Fax 01928 704375
Executive Director (Social Care, Housing and Health) Diana Terris
Operational Director (Policy and Support) Dwayne Johnson
Operational Director (Children's Services) Kath O'Dwyer
Operational Director (Adult Services) John Webb
Operational Director (Older People's Services) Peter Barron

Social Care and Health

Lab: 9, LD: 1, Runcorn Labour Group: 1
Chair T. McInerney (Lab)
Vice-Chair K. Morley (Lab)
Members of the Board
Lab: I. Ashley, A. Cole, A. Gerrard, S. Osborne, K. Philbin, L. Temple, D. Reynolds.
LD: J. Morley.
Runcorn Labour: B. McClure.

SUB-OFFICE

John Briggs Hse, Gerrad St, Widnes, Halton WA8 6BE; Tel 0151 424 2061; (Emergency Duty) 01606 76611

CHILDREN AND FAMILY CENTRES

Glendale Family Centre Wren Cl, Palacefields Ave South, Runcorn, Halton; Tel 01928 716988
Contact S. Garner

Inglefield and Braemar The Butts, Castlefields Ave North, Runcorn, Halton WA7 2LH; Tel 01928 561591
Contact V. Webb

Peelhouse Family Centre Peelhouse La, Widnes, Halton; Tel 0151 420 7767
Contact J. Perry

ADULT AND OLDER PEOPLE'S COMMUNITY DAY CENTRES

Astmoor Day Services Chadwick Rd, Astmoor Ind Est, Runcorn, Halton WA7 1PW; Tel 01928 567271
Contact M. Walker

Bridgewater Day Centre Castlefields Ave North, Runcorn, Halton WA7 2HT; Tel 01928 564199
Contact D. Richards

Pingot Day Centre Dundalk Rd, Widnes, Halton WA8 8DF; Tel 0151 424 2284

ADULT AND OLDER PEOPLE'S RESIDENTIAL HOMES

Bredon Hostel Lapwing Gr, off Palacefields Ave, Runcorn, Halton WA7 2TJ; Tel 01928 713261
Contact K. Howard

Croftwood Centre Whitchurch Way, Halton Lodge, Runcorn, Halton; Tel 01928 576049
Contact F. Coy

Oakmeadow Centre Peelhouse La, Widnes, Halton; Tel 0151 424 9185
Contact M. Hartley

Education and Social Inclusion Directorate

Grosvenor Hse, Halton Lea, Runcorn, Halton WA7 2WD; E-mail hbeduct@halton-borough.gov.uk; Tel 0151 424 2061; Fax 0151 471 7321
Executive Director Graham Talbot
Senior Educational Psychologist D.J. Baldwin

SPECIAL DAY SCHOOLS

Ashley School Cawfield Ave, Widnes, Halton WA8 7HG; Tel 0151 424 4892; Fax 0151 424 5980
Headteacher L. King
Mixed MLD

Brookfields School Moorfield Rd, Widnes, Halton WA8 0JA; Tel 0151 424 4329; Fax 0151 495 3460
Headteacher A. Chrysaffi
Mixed SLD

Cavendish School Lincoln Cl, Runcorn, Cheshire WA7 4YX; Tel 01928 561706; Fax 01928 566088
Headteacher Mrs C. Dickinson
Mixed SLD

Chesnut Lodge School Green La, Widnes, Cheshire WA8 7HF; Tel 0151 424 0679; Fax 0151 495 2141
Headteacher S. Lancaster
Mixed (75)

HAMPSHIRE COUNTY COUNCIL
www.hants.gov.uk

6

The county has a two-tier structure: the county council and 11 district councils.
Population 1.25 million
The Castle, Winchester, Hampshire SO23 8UQ; URL www.hants.gov.uk; Tel 01962 841841; Fax 01962 847189
Chief Executive Peter Robertson, LLB

Social Services Department

Trafalgar Hse, The Castle, Winchester, Hampshire SO23 8UQ; URL www.hants.gov.uk; E-mail socialservices@hants.gov.uk; Tel 01962 847208; Fax 01962 847159
Executive Member (Social Care) Cllr Felicity Hindson
Chair (Social Services Policy Review Committee) Cllr Patricia Banks
Director (Social Services) Terry Butler, CBE, MA
Deputy Director John Clifton
Assistant Director (Older People) Andrew Brooker
Assistant Director (Adults) Jill Stannard
Assistant Director (Resources) David Ward
Assistant Director (Children and Families) Steve Love
County Manager (Older People – Strategy) Claire Foreman
County Manager (Performance Management) Karen Robinson
County Manager (Supporting People) Alan Hagger
County Manager (Older Persons Residential Homes) Vincent Oliver
County Manager (Older People – Operational) Chris Taylor
Head of Service (Home Care) Vacancy
County Manager (Learning Disability – Strategy) Claire Bruin
County Manager (Physical Disability) Glyn Jones
County Manager (Mental Health – Strategy) Graham Collingridge
County Manager (Mental Health – Operational) Ruth Dixon
County Manager (Children and Families – Strategy) Graham Wright
County Manager (Children and Families) Kate Hart
Communications Officer Frances Kemble
County Manager (Learning Disability – Operational) Derek Oliver
Head (Finance) Gordon Shinn
Head (Personnel and Training) Pauline Lucas
Partnership Manager (North Hampshire PCT) Christina Sells
Partnership Manager (Eastleigh and Test Valley South PCT) Pauline Owen
Partnership Manager (Blackwater Valley and Hart PCT) Helen Clanchy

Partnership Manager (Fareham and Gosport PCT)
  Nicky Pendleton
Partnership Manager (Mid-Hants PCT) Vacancy
County Manager (Delayed Transfers of Care) Colin Hardy
Race Policy Adviser Mohammed Mossadaq
Manager (Complaints and Customer Care) Irene Unwin

TRAINING

Responsible for training professional and support staff in
the department.
Head (Personnel and Training) Pauline Lucas

LOCAL OFFICES

Aldershot Office The Old Town Hall, Grosvenor Rd,
Aldershot, Hampshire GU11 3DP; Tel 01252 314221;
Fax 01252 327755

Alton Office Park Hse, High St, Alton, Hampshire
GU34 1EN; Tel 01420 544255; Fax 01420 543451

Andover Office Chantry Hse, Chantry Way, Andover,
Hampshire SP10 1LT; Tel 01264 387400; Fax 01264 387401

Basingstoke Office Sun Alliance Hse, 37–41 Wote St,
Basingstoke, Hampshire RG21 1LU; Tel 01256 362000;
Fax 01256 320884

Eastleigh Office Russell Hse, 26–28 Romsey Rd, Eastleigh,
Hampshire SO50 9AN; Tel 023 8061 8722; Fax 023 8065
2420

Fareham Office Fareham Health Centre, Civic Way,
Fareham, Hampshire PO16 7EP; Tel 0845 600 4555;
Fax 01329 826569

Gosport Office 133 Stoke Rd, Gosport, Hampshire
PO12 1SD; Tel 0845 600 4555; Fax 023 9251 1797

Havant Office Town End Hse, PO Box 61, Havant,
Hampshire PO9 1UB; Tel 023 9247 1644; Fax 023 9249 8959

Hythe Office West Shore Hse, West St, Southampton
SO45 6AA; Tel 023 8084 6953; Fax 023 8084 0270

Lymington Office Avenue Rd, Lymington, Hampshire
SO41 9YB; Tel 01590 625000; Fax 01590 625005

Petersfield Office Tilbrook Hse, 2–4 Grenehurst Way,
Petersfield, Hampshire GU31 4AZ; Tel 01730 265462;
Fax 01730 231637

Romsey Office Former Magistrates Court, Church St,
Romsey, Hampshire SO51 8AQ; Tel 01794 526000; Fax 01794
526001

Winchester Office Corinium Hse, 10–14 Andover Rd,
Winchester, Hampshire SO23 7BX; Tel 01962 869313;
Fax 01962 878537

SECURE UNIT

Swanwick Lodge Secure Unit Glen Rd, off Swanwick La,
Southampton SO3 7DT; Tel 01489 581913
  Mixed

CHILDREN'S HOMES (GROUP 2 UNITS)

Bournemouth Road Children's Home 49 Bournemouth Rd,
Chandlers Ford, Eastleigh, Hampshire SO53 3DJ; Tel 023
8025 1341

Cambridge Road Children's Home 2 Cambridge Rd,
Aldershot, Hampshire GU11 3JZ

Crossways Children's Home Hatch La, Old Basing,
Basingstoke, Hampshire RG24 0DL; Tel 01256 473899
  (12)

Cypress Lodge Children's Home 181 Winchester Rd,
Basingstoke, Hampshire RG21 1YF; Tel 01256 461785
  (7)

Glendalyn Children's Home Fernhill La, New Milton,
Hampshire BH25 5SX; Tel 01425 615373
  (13)

Godbey House Children's Home 380 Seafront, Hayling
Island, Hampshire PO11 0BD; Tel 023 9246 2939
  (20)

Milesdown Children's Home Winton Cl, Winchester,
Hampshire SO22 6AB; Tel 01962 854070
  (15)

Stonecroft Children's Home 8 Leigh Rd, Havant,
Hampshire PO9 2ET; Tel 023 9247 2300
  Boys

The Mead Children's Home King St, Odiham, Hampshire
RG25 1NF; Tel 01256 712646
  (12)

Woodend Children's Home 26 Shepherds Row, Andover,
Hampshire SP10 2QQ; Tel 01264 323710
  (9)

HOMES FOR CHILDREN WITH LEARNING DISABILITIES

Merrydale Children's Home Church La, Kings Worthy,
Winchester, Hampshire SO23 7QS; Tel 01962 881564
  (16)

Verdi Close Children's Home 44 Verdi Cl, Basingstoke,
Hampshire; Tel 01256 355949
  (12)

YOUTH OFFENDING TEAMS

Manager Phil Sutton
25 High St, Winchester, Hampshire SO23 9BL; Tel 01962
876100

Basingstoke Youth Offending Team 80 Culver Rd, Basingstoke, Hampshire; Tel 01256 464034; Fax 01256 327210

Intensive Supervision and Surveillance Programme
Ashville Hse, 260–262 Havant Rd, Cosham, Portsmouth
PO6 1PA; Tel 023 9228 3900; Fax 023 9238 1318

Isle of Wight Youth Offending Team 62 Crocker St,
Newport, Isle of Wight PO30 5DA; Tel 01983 522799;
Fax 01983 523175

Portsmouth Youth Offending Team Derby Hse, Orkney Rd,
Cosham, Portsmouth PO6 3LU; Tel 023 9237 0013; Fax 023
9220 0374

Southampton Youth Offending Team 33 Selbourne Ave,
Harefield, Southampton SO2 5DQ; Tel 023 8046 3336;
Fax 023 8047 0060

DAY SERVICES FOR ADULTS WITH LEARNING DISABILITIES

Aldershot Day Services Church La East, Aldershot,
Hampshire GU11 3SS; Tel 01252 323178
  (109)

Alton Day Services Chawton Park Rd, Alton, Hampshire
GU34 1RQ; Tel 01420 82504
  (140)

Andover Day Services Portway Ind Est, East Portway,
Andover, Hampshire SP10 3LU; Tel 01264 364549
  89 including ten special care

Apex Centre Civic Offices, Harlington Way, Fleet,
Hampshire GU13 8BB; Tel 01252 624534
  (40)

Basingstoke Day Services Ashwood Way, Winklebury,
Basingstoke, Hampshire RG23 8AA; Tel 01256 465725
  130 including 15 special care

Bishopstoke Day Services Church Rd, Bishopstoke,
Hampshire SO50 6DR; Tel 023 8061 4879
  (186)

Fareham Day Services Meon Hse, 9 High St, Fareham,
Hampshire PO16 7AN; Tel 01329 827626
  (110)

Gosport Day Services 185 Brockhurst Rd, Gosport,
Hampshire PO12 3AY; Tel 023 9258 0635
  (65)

The Grove Hinton Fields, Kingsworthy, Winchester, Hampshire SO23 7QS; Tel 01962 886764

Havant Day Services Barncroft Way, Leigh Pk, Havant, Hampshire PO9 3AL; Tel 023 9248 3672
225 including 50 special care.

Locksheath Day Services Bridge Centre, 21–23 Cold East Way, Southampton SO3 6AT; Tel 01489 574241

New Forest Day Services Forest Pines, New Milton, Hampshire BH25 5SX; Tel 01425 617321
132 including 35 special care.

Romsey and Waterside Day Services Jacobs Gutter La, Hounsdown, Southampton SO40 9FT; Tel 023 8086 2597
(107)

DAY CENTRES FOR PEOPLE WITH MENTAL HEALTH PROBLEMS

Aldershot Mental Health Day Services 169 Victoria Rd, Aldershot, Hampshire GU11 1JU; Tel 01252 331134

Andover Mental Health Day Services 68b Junction Rd, Andover, Hampshire SP10 3QX; Tel 01264 336638

Basingstoke Mental Health Day Services 3 Vyne Rd, South View, Basingstoke, Hampshire RG21 2NL; Tel 01256 363010

Fareham Mental Health Day Services 219 West St, Fareham, Hampshire PO16 0ET; Tel 01329 825922

Havant Mental Health Day Services 110a–110c West St, Havant, Hampshire PO9 1LE; Tel 023 9249 8333

HOMES AND HOSTELS FOR PEOPLE WITH LEARNING DISABILITIES

Croft House Redlands La, Fareham, Hampshire PO14 1EY; Tel 01329 280600
(27)

Fernmount House Forest Pines, New Milton, Hampshire BH25 5SS; Tel 01425 611558

Highfield House 118 Church Rd, Bishopstoke, Eastleigh, Hampshire S050 6DQ; Tel 023 8062 0177

Homewood Enham La, Charlton, Andover, Hampshire SP10 4AN; Tel 01264 324200
(16)

Itchen Mead Church Rd, Bishopstoke, Hampshire SO50 6DR; Tel 023 8061 2922
(30)

Meadowcroft Whitchurch Cl, Aldershot, Hampshire GU11 3RU; Tel 01252 313470
(24)

Merryfield Inwood Rd, Liss, Hampshire GU33 7LY; Tel 01730 893087
(7)

Orchard Close 28 Westfield Ave, Hayling Island, Hampshire PO11 9AG; Tel 023 9246 4457
Short stay holiday home. (25)

Poynings Ashwood Way, Winklebury, Basingstoke, Hampshire RG23 8AA; Tel 01256 325316
(22)

DAY CENTRES FOR PEOPLE WITH A PHYSICAL DISABILITY

Audleys Close Centre Alton Rd, Cliddesden, Basingstoke, Hampshire RG25 2JT; Tel 01256 326404
(80)

Hexagon Centre Suffolk Cl, Eastleigh, Hampshire SO53 3GZ; Tel 023 8026 0616; 023 8026 0617
(90)

HOSTEL FOR PEOPLE WITH A PHYSICAL DISABILITY

John Darling Mall Selborne Dr, Boyatt Wood, Eastleigh, Hampshire SO50 4SE; Tel 023 8061 3101
(24+ Special Housing Units).

DAY CENTRES FOR OLDER PEOPLE

Bulmer House Day Centre Ramshill, Petersfield, Hampshire GU31 4AP; Tel 01730 261744
(30)

Calmore Day Centre Calmore Dr, Totton, Southampton SO40 2ZX; Tel 023 8086 4852
(30)

Cranleigh Paddock Day Centre Calpe Ave, Lyndhurst, Hampshire SO43 7EP; Tel 023 8028 3602
(10)

Kingsworthy Day Centre Church La, Kingsworthy, Winchester, Hampshire SO23 7QS; Tel 01962 881257
(20)

Linden House Day Centre New St, Lymington, Hampshire SO4 9BP; Tel 01590 679623
(16)

The Masters House Centre Great Well Dr, Romsey, Hampshire SO51 7QN; Tel 01794 523990
(25)

Newman Bassett EPRC Warwick Rd, Winklebury, Basingstoke, Hampshire RG23 8EA; Tel 01256 329641
(37)

HOMES FOR OLDER PEOPLE

There are 26 homes for the elderly.

6

Hampshire County Council, Education

County Office, The Castle, Winchester, Hampshire SO23 8UG; URL www.hants.gov.uk; Tel 01962 841841; Fax 01962 842355
CEO Andrew J. Seber, MA, PGCE
Deputy County Education Officer Assistant CEO (Standards and Improvement) John Clarke, MA, PGCE, MEd

SPECIAL SCHOOLS (AGES 2–19)

Henry Tyndale Special School Ship La, Farnborough, Hampshire GU14 8BX; Tel 01252 544577
Headteacher Rob Thompson
2–19 LD, ASD (109)

Icknield Special School River Way, Andover, Hampshire SP11 6LT; Tel 01264 365297
Headteacher Stephen Steer-Smith
2–19 SLD (72)

Limington House Special School St. Andrew's Rd, Basingstoke, Hampshire RG22 6PS; Tel 01256 322148
Headteacher Petra Smillie
2–19 SLD (80)

The Meadow Special School Mill Chase Rd, Bordon, Hampshire GU35 0HA; Tel 01420 474396; Fax 01420 488329
Headteacher Margaret Mann (Acting)
4–16 MLD and ASD (115)

Rachel Madocks School Eagle Ave, Cowplain, Waterlooville, Hampshire PO8 9XP; Tel 023 9224 1818; Fax 023 9226 9521
Headteacher Mrs Chrys Browne
2–19 SLD (70)

St. Francis Special School Patchway Dr, Oldbury Way, Fareham, Hampshire PO14 3BN; Tel 01329 845730; Fax 01329 847217
Headteacher Sue Chalmers
2–19 SLD and ASD (98)

Salterns Special School Commercial Rd, Totton, Southampton SO40 3AF; Tel 023 8086 4211; Fax 023 8087 2174
Headteacher Nicola Dando
3–19 SLD (54)

Whitedown Special School Albert Rd, The Butts, Alton, Hampshire GU34 1LP; Tel 01420 82201; Fax 01420 542837
Headteacher Barbara Livings
2–19 SLD (43)

SPECIAL SCHOOLS (PRIMARY)

Forest Edge Special School Lydlynch Rd, Totton, Southampton SO40 3DW; Tel 023 8086 4949
Headteacher Rosemary Wiles
4–11 MLD, ASD (60)

Heathfield Special School Oldbury Way, Fareham, Hampshire PO14 3BN; Tel 01329 845150; Fax 01329 846548
Headteacher Stella Muirhead
2–11 MLD, PD, ASD (120)

Maple Ridge Special School Maple Cres, Basingstoke, Hampshire RG21 5SX; Tel 01256 323639; Fax 01256 841059
Headteacher Jenny Martin
4–11 MLD, ASD (65)

Medecroft Opportunity Centre Sparkford Rd, Winchester, Hampshire SO22 4NJ; Tel 01962 860393
Headteacher Olivia Peak
2–5 (33)

Norman Gate Special School Vigo Rd, Andover, Hampshire SP10 1JZ; Tel 01264 323423
Headteacher Christine Gaylor
2–11 MLD, ASD (50)

Riverside Special School Scratchface La, Purbrook, Waterlooville, Hampshire PO7 5QD; Tel 023 9225 0138
Headteacher David Jones
3–11 MLD, ASD (104)

Saxon Wood Special School Rooksdown, Barron Pl, Basingstoke, Hampshire RG24 9NH; Tel 01256 356635
Headteacher Paul Skinner
2–11 PD (42)

Shepherds Down Special School Shepherds La, Compton, Winchester, Hampshire SO21 2AJ; Tel 01962 713445
Headteacher Tony Gazzard
4–11 MLD, ASD (130)

Waterloo School Warfield Ave, Waterlooville, Hampshire PO7 7JJ; Tel 023 9225 5956
Headteacher Pete Greenwood
4–11 EBD (42)

Wolverdene Special School 22 Love La, Andover, Hampshire SP10 2AF; Tel 01264 362350
Headteacher Richard Ford
5–11 EBD (45)

SPECIAL SCHOOLS (SECONDARY)

Baycroft Special School Gosport Rd, Stubbington, Fareham, Hampshire PO14 2AE; Tel 01329 664151
Headteacher Rob Hendry
11–16 MLD, ASD (184)

Dove House Special School Sutton Rd, Basingstoke, Hampshire RG21 5SU; Tel 01256 351555; Fax 01256 329749
Headteacher Colin House
11–16 MLD, ASD (105)

Glenwood Special School Washington Rd, Emsworth, Hampshire PO10 7NN; Tel 01243 373120; Fax 01243 373103
Headteacher Philip Johnson
11–16 MLD (100)

Hawthorns Special School Pack La, Basingstoke, Hampshire RG22 5TH; Tel 01256 336601
Headteacher John Burton
10–16 EBD (56)

Lakeside Special School Winchester Rd, Chandlers Ford, Hampshire SO53 2DW; Tel 023 8026 6633
Headteacher Gareth Evans
11–16 EBD (63)

Osborne School Andover Rd, Winchester, Hampshire SO23 7BU; Tel 01962 851583; 01962 854537; Fax 01962 849419
Headteacher Rod Wakelam, DipSpEd, MEd
11–19 MLD, ASD (143)

Lord Wilson Special School Coldeast Way, Sarisbury Grn, Southampton SO31 7AT; Tel 01489 582684; Fax 01489 582115
Headteacher Lynda Strodder
Boys 11–16 EBD (42)

The Mark Way Special School Batchelors Barn Rd, Andover, Hampshire SP10 1HR; Tel 01264 351835; Fax 01264 366276
Headteacher Tony Oakley
11–16 MLD and ASD (75)

Oak Lodge Special School Roman Rd, Dibden Purlieu, Southampton SO45 4RQ; Tel 023 8084 7213; Fax 023 8084 5112
Headteacher Beverley Hawker
11–16 MLD, ASD (100)

Samuel Cody Special School Lynchford Rd, Farnborough, Hampshire GU14 6BJ; Tel 01252 314720; Fax 01252 341869
Headteacher Anna Dawson
11–16 MLD, ASD (80)

Sundridge Special School Silvester Rd, Cowplain, Waterlooville, Hampshire PO8 8TR; Tel 023 9226 1234
Headteacher Keith Davis
11–16 EBD (35)

HARTLEPOOL BOROUGH COUNCIL

www.hartlepool.gov.uk

Political Composition: Lab: 33, LD: 11, Con: 7, Ind: 7 + elected Mayor (Ind)
Civic Centre, Victoria Rd, Hartlepool TS24 8AY;
    URL www.hartlepool.gov.uk; Tel 01429 266522;
    Fax 01429 523599
Director (Environment and Development) Paul Magee
Public Relations Officer Alastair Rae

Social Services Department

PO Box 96, Civic Centre, Hartlepool TS24 8BR;
    E-mail social.services@hartlepool.gov.uk; Tel 01429 266522; Fax 01429 523908
Director (Social Services) Mike Lauerman
Senior Assistant Director/Deputy Ian McMillan
Assistant Director (Resources and Review)
    Sallyanne Johnson
Assistant Director (Children and Families) Peter Seller;
    Tel 01429 523956
Manager (Strategy and Resource) Margaret Hunt; Tel 01429 523928
Manager (Commissioning and Review) Margaret Messer
Head (Learning Disabilities and Mental Health Services)
    David Jones; Tel 01429 523911
Head (Older People and Physical Disabilities Services)
    Sandra Robinson

Social Services Committee

Chair Clouth (Lab)
Vice-Chair Worthy (Lab)
Members of the Committee
Lab: Bently, Body, Doyle, English, Griffin, C. Richardson, Sleet, Smith, Todd, Wallace, Wilkinson.

ADULT SERVICES

Civic Centre Victoria Rd, Hartlepool TS24 8AY; Tel 01429 266522; Fax 01429 523908

CHILDREN AND FAMILY SERVICES

Aneurin Bevin House Avenue Rd, Hartlepool; Tel 01429 266522; Fax 01429 52306; (Child Protection) 01429 523905

COMMUNITY MENTAL HEALTH TEAM

Stewart House Community Mental Health Team 49–53 Church St, Hartlepool; Tel 01429 424392; Fax 01429 424599

DUTY TEAM

Civic Centre Victoria Rd, Hartlepool TS24 8AY; Tel 01429 266522; Fax 01429 523907

FAMILY RESOURCE CENTRES

Family Resource Centre Kilmarnock Rd, Hartlepool TS25 2AR; Tel 01429 265741
Family Resource Centre 43 Murray St, Hartlepool TS26 8PQ; Tel 01429 281944
Family Resource Centre Somersby Cl, 71–72 Millpool Cl, Hartlepool TS24 0TH; Tel 01429 284574

DAY NURSERY

Kilmarnock Road Day Nursery Hartlepool; Tel 01429 265741

COMMUNITY HOME

Flint Walk Community Home 198 Flint Wlk, Hartlepool TS26 0TL; Tel 01429 273132

CHILDREN AND FAMILIES DISABILITY TEAM

Lynn Street Research Centre Lynn St, Hartlepool TS24 7LX; Tel 01429 284597; Fax 01429 282400

HOME FOR CHILDREN WITH DISABILITIES

Exmoor Green Children's Home 16 Exmoor Grn, Hartlepool TS26 0XE; Tel 01429 232634

YOUNG PERSON'S TEAM

Station Lane Seaton Carew, Hartlepool; Tel 01429 275144; Fax 01429 860670

HOMES FOR PEOPLE WITH LEARNING DISABILITIES

Briarfields Home Elwick Rd, Hartlepool TS26 0BE; Tel 01429 274685
Fairlawn Home Grange Rd, Hartlepool TS26 8LU; Tel 01429 266747

DAY SERVICES FOR PEOPLE WITH LEARNING DISABILITIES

Warren Road Hartlepool; Tel 01429 264661
Assessment Team Lynn St Resource Centre, Lynn St (South), Hartlepool TS24 7LX; Tel 01429 286122; Fax 01429 282400

EMPLOYMENT SERVICES FOR PEOPLE WITH LEARNING DISABILITIES

Employment Link Lynn St Resource Centre, Lynn St (South), Hartlepool TS24 7LX; Tel 01429 282400; Fax 01429 282444

ACCOMMODATION FOR PEOPLE WITH MENTAL HEALTH PROBLEMS

The Firs 26 Westbourne Rd, Hartlepool TS25 5RH; Tel 01429 232861

DAY SERVICE FOR PEOPLE WITH MENTAL HEALTH PROBLEMS

Brooklyn Centre 156 Grange Rd, Hartlepool; Tel 01429 866001

DAY SERVICE FOR PEOPLE WITH PHYSICAL DISABILITIES

Havelock Centre Burbank St, Hartlepool TS24 7LT; Tel 01429 260583

HOMES FOR OLDER PEOPLE

There are five local authority homes for older people.

Education Department

Civic Centre, Victoria Rd, Hartlepool TS24 8AY;
E-mail education@hartlepool.gov.uk; Tel 01429 266522;
Fax 01429 523750
Director (Education) Jeremy Fitt
Assistant Director (Policy, Planning, Children's Services)
Adrienne Simcock
Assistant Director (Resources and Support Services)
Gill Rollings
Assistant Director (Educational Achievement) John Collings

SPECIAL SCHOOLS

Catcote School Catcote Rd, Hartlepool TS25 4EZ; Tel 01429 264036; Fax 01429 234452
Headteacher Robin Campbell
Secondary Full Range

Springwell School Wiltshire Way, Hartlepool TS26 0TB; Tel 01429 280600; Fax 01429 260493
Headteacher Alan Lacey
Primary

6

HEREFORDSHIRE COUNCIL
www.herefordshire.gov.uk

In April 1998, Hereford and Worcester County Council split to form a Unitary Council in Herefordshire with two-tier local government continuing in Worcestershire. They are listed alphabetically within this chapter.
Population 169 313
Political Composition: Con: 21, Ind: 17, LD: 16, Lab: 4
Brockington, 35 Hafod Rd, Hereford, Herefordshire
HR1 1SH; URL www.herefordshire.gov.uk;
E-mail info@herefordshire.gov.uk; Tel 01432 260000
Chief Executive Neil Pringle
Chair Cllr Peter Harling
Director (Environment) Graham Dunhill
Director (Policy and Community) Jane Jones
Leader of the Council Cllr Roger Phillips

Directorate of Social Services and Housing

Garrick Hse, Widermarsh St, Hereford, Herefordshire
HR4 9EU; Tel 01432 260000; (Emergency Duty Team
1700–0900 Mon–Fri; 1600–0900 Weekends) 01905 358116
Director (Social Care and Strategic Housing) Sue Fiennes;
Tel 01432 260039
Cabinet Member (Social Care) Cllr Olwyn Barnett
Cabinet Member (Housing) Cllr David Short, MBE
Head (Social Care – Children) Henry Lewis; Tel 01432 261603
Head (Social Care – Adults) Stephanie Canham; Tel 01432 260320

Head (Strategic Housing) Richard Gabb; Tel 01432 261902
Head (Business Services) Sue Alexander; Tel 01432 260069
Service Manager (Older People/Physical Disabilities)
Daphne Welch; Tel 01432 261602
Service Manager (Internal Resources and Service Re-design)
Suzanne Hughes; Tel 01568 616397
Children's Services Manager (Resources) Jon Dudley;
Tel 01432 260327
Children's Services Manager (Operations) Steve Merrell;
Tel 01432 261605
Service Manager (Learning Disabilities) Lydia Bailey;
Tel 01568 616397
Manager (Mental Health) Mike Thomas; Tel 01432 270243

Area Offices

Bromyard Area Office Council Offices, 1 Rowberry St,
Bromyard, Herefordshire HR7 4DX; Tel 01432 260000

Hereford Area Office Council Offices, Bath St, Hereford,
Herefordshire HR1 2HQ; Tel 01432 261626

Hereford Area Office (Hospital Based) County Hospital,
Stonebow Rd, Hereford, Herefordshire HR1 2ER; Tel 01434
355444 Ext 5142

Ledbury Area Office Ledbury Community Health and Care
Centre, Market St, Ledbury, Herefordshire HR8 2AA;
Tel 01531 638410

Leominster Area Office The Old Priory, off Church St,
Leominster, Herefordshire HR6 8DA; Tel 01432 383349

Ross-on-Wye Area Office Berkeley Lodge, 27 New St, Ross-
on-Wye, Herefordshire HR9 7DA; Tel 01432 383251

MENTAL HEALTH SERVICE

Moor House Widemarsh Common, Hereford,
Herefordshire HR4 9NA; Tel 01432 262850

CHILDREN'S RESOURCE SERVICE (FOSTERING AND ADOPTION)

Moor House Widemarsh Common, Hereford,
Herefordshire HR4 9NA; Tel 01432 262834

WORCESTERSHIRE AND HEREFORDSHIRE YOUTH OFFENDING TEAM

1–3 Daws Rd, Hereford, Herefordshire HR1 2JJ; Tel 01432
383300

CHILDREN AND FAMILY CENTRE

Hollybush Family Centre (Family Resource) Hollybush
Wlk, Hereford, Herefordshire HR2 6AF; Tel 01432 269437

RESIDENTIAL RESOURCES FOR PEOPLE WITH LEARNING DISABILITIES

Ivy Close 1–4 Ivy Cl, Ledbury Rd, Hereford, Herefordshire
HR1 1RJ; Tel 01432 274311

RESPITE RESOURCES FOR PEOPLE WITH LEARNING DISABILITIES

Windsor Place Ryelands Rd, Leominster, Herefordshire
HR6 8NZ; Tel 01568 613098

RESOURCES FOR PEOPLE WITH LEARNING DISABILITIES

Green Fingers Horticultural Team Marshfield Centre,
Ryelands Rd, Leominster, Herefordshire HR6 8NZ;
Tel 01568 614772
Approximately (60)

The Paint Box 37 West St, Leominster, Herefordshire
HR6 8EP; Tel 01568 611869

Ryefield Centre Grammar School Cl, Ross-on-Wye,
Herefordshire HR9 7QD; Tel 01989 768273 01989 768711
Multi-purpose Resource Centre for all People with
Disabilities.

Workmatch Art and Craft Workshops Bramley Bus Pk,
Waterworks La, Worcester Rd, Leominster, Herefordshire
HR6 8AX; Tel 01568 614444

DAY OPPORTUNITIES RESOURCES FOR PEOPLE WITH LEARNING DISABILITIES

St. Owen's Centre Symonds St, Hereford, Herefordshire
HR1 2HA; Tel 01432 355005

Widemarsh Workshop Widemarsh Common, Hereford,
Herefordshire HR4 9NA; Tel 01432 354250; 01432 354259

RESIDENTIAL HOMES FOR OLDER PEOPLE

There are seven homes for older people including day
centres.

BUSINESS SERVICES

Finance and information, joint review, personnel, training,
and development and support services.

National Care Standards Commission

CENTRAL UNIT

178 Widemarsh St, Hereford, Herefordshire HR4 9HN;
Tel 01432 845700
Area Manager Doug Mason

Education Directorate

Hereford Education and Conference Centre, PO Box 185,
Blackfriars St, Hereford, Herefordshire HR4 9ZR;
Tel 01432 260900; Fax 01432 260957
Director (Education) Dr E. Oram
Head (Children's and Students' Services) Anne Heath
Manager (Pupil, School and Parent Support)
Dennis Longmore
Manager (Special Educational Needs) Linda Nash
Organiser (Physical and Sensory Support Services) Jan Hughes

SPECIAL SCHOOLS

Barrs Court School Barrs Court Rd, Hereford,
Herefordshire HR1 1EQ; Tel 01432 265035; Fax 01432
353988
Headteacher S.J. Ashley

Blackmarston School Honddu Cl, Redhill, Hereford,
Herefordshire HR2 7NX; Tel 01432 272376; Fax 01432
272376
Headteacher Mrs S. Bailey

The Brookfield School Grandstand Rd, Hereford,
Herefordshire HR4 9NG; Tel 01432 265153; Fax 01432
275067
Headteacher O.R. Evans

Westfield School (including Early Years Centre) Westfield
Wlk, Leominster, Herefordshire HR6 8HD; Tel 01568
613147; Fax 01568 613147
Headteacher Mrs S. Harns (Acting)

HERTFORDSHIRE COUNTY COUNCIL
www.hertsdirect.org

Population 1 004 600
Political Composition: Con: 40, Lab: 27, LD: 10
County Hall, Pegs La, Hertford, Hertfordshire SG13 8DF;
URL www.hertsdirect.org;
E-mail hertsdirect@hertscc.gov.uk
Council Chair Keith Emsall

Chief Executive   Caroline Tapster (Acting)

Hertfordshire County Council launched two new services in April 2001: Children, Schools and Families; and Adult Care Services. The Director of Adult Care Services continues to have overall responsibility for Social Care within the Authority.

Adult Care Services

Tel (Customer Service Centre) 01438 737400; Fax 01438 737334

Director   Sarah Pickup (Acting)

Assistant Director (Services for Older People and Physically Disabled People)   David Robinson

Assistant Director (Performance and Commissioning)   Diane Grinstead

Assistant Director (Services for Learning Disabilities and Mental Health)   Cathy Kerr

Assistant Director (Resources)   Mike Curtis

Head (Policy and Performance)   Greg Haritson

Head (Finance)   Ralph Paddock

Head (Management Information Unit)   Gary Newton

Head (Human Resources)   John Cooper

Head (Joint Commissioning)   Paul Atkins

Head (Social Care Practice)   Mark Jordan

Head (Continuing Health Care)   Mike Horne

Head (Quality Assurance and Complaints)   Meg Carter

Head (Contracts)   Erin McAllister

Manager (Planning and Commissioning Mental Health)   Jonathan Wells

Manager (Planning and Commissioning E&PD)   Peter Ruane

Manager (Planning and Commissioning LD)   Judith Jackson

Policy Manager (Users and Carers)   Tim Anfilogoff

Service Manager (Community Services LD)   Peter Loose

Service Manager (Residential and Day Services)   Janice Maher

Development Manager (Physical and Sensory Services)   Gill Manning-Smith; Tel 01442 405681

AREA TEAMS

Elderly and Physically Disabled

DACORUM

Tel 01442 405685

Area Manager   Arold Sanin

HERTSMERE

Tel 020 8327 4868

Area Manager   Adrian Smith

NORTH HERTFORDSHIRE AND STEVENAGE

Tel 01438 737007

Area Manager   Monica Mace

SOUTH EAST HERTFORDSHIRE

Tel 01992 411120

Area Manager   Mark Janes

ST. ALBANS CITY AND DISTRICT

Tel 01727 755323

Area Manager   Trish Orne

WATFORD AND THREE RIVERS

Tel 01923 354558

Area Manager   Seona Gordon

WELWYN/HATFIELD

Tel 01707 283931

Area Manager   Liddy Lawrence

Children, Schools and Families

The Children, Schools and Families service (CSF) combines the county's LEA responsibilities and social services for children; Tel (Customer Services Centre) 01438 737500

Director   John Harris

Deputy Director   Vacancy

Deputy Director   John Evans

Assistant Director (School Standards and Curriculum)   Gill Jones (Acting)

Assistant Director (Planning)   Jim Dalton

Assistant Director (Local Services)   Cheryl Hopkins

Assistant Director (Operations)   Alan Sapsford

Assistant Director (Development)   Diana Searle

Assistant Director (Resources)   Lesley Brockington

Assistant Director (Youth Justice Service)   Tom Rees

Head (Human Resources)   Vacancy

Head (Conciliation and Appeals)   Mark Roberts

Head (Learning and Development)   Hannes de Bruin (Acting)

Head (Care Practice)   Janet Rothwell

Head (Education Welfare Service)   Lesley Hewitt

Head (Child Protection)   Carol Taylor

Head (Looked after Children)   Maureen Phillips

Head (School Funding)   Claire Cook

Head (Youth Services)   Chris Garcia

Head (Inspection and Registration – Health and Hertfordshire County Council)   Jane Bandcroft (Acting)

Senior Development Manager (Service Quality)   Roger de Ste Croix (Acting)

Senior Development Manager (Early Years and Early Intervention)   Helen Ashdown

Senior Development Manager (Young People and Transitions)   Andrew Wellington

Senior Planning Manager (Property)   John Procter

Senior Planning Manager (Needs Commissioning and Outsourcing)   Denise Radley

Senior Planning Manager (School Places)   Lindsay Martin

Manager (Education Psychology)   Elaine Redmayne

Manager (Assessment and Review)   Vacancy

Manager (Education Access)   Vacancy

Senior Adviser (School Improvement)   Jenny Newman

Adviser (School Development)   Clive Mitchell

QUADRANT TEAMS

North

The Old Grammar School, Broadway, Letchworth, Hertfordshire SG6 3TD

Manager   Mike Benaim

East

County Hall, Pegs La, Hertford, Hertfordshire SG13 8DF

Manager   Helen Nys

South

Langleybury School Site, Hunton Bridge, Langleybury, Kings Langley, Hertfordshire WD4 8RW

Manager   David Ring

West

4 Porters Wood, St. Albans, Hertfordshire AL3 6ST

Manager   Paul Wedgbury

SPECIAL SCHOOLS FOR CHILDREN WITH LEARNING DIFFICULTIES

Amwell View School St. Margarets, Stanstead Abbotts, Hertfordshire SG12 8EH; Tel 01920 870027

Headteacher   J.S. Liversage

2–19+ (Day)

Breakspeare School Gallows Hill La, Abbots Langley, Watford, Hertfordshire WD5 0BU; Tel 01923 263645

Headteacher   G. Williamson

3–19 (Day)

6

The Collett School Lockers Park La, Hemel Hempstead, Hertfordshire HP1 1TQ; Tel 01442 398988
Headteacher Ms E. Gardner
Mixed 5–16 MLD (Day)

Garston Manor School Horseshoe La, Garston, Watford, Hertfordshire WD25 7HR; Tel 01923 673757
Headteacher D. Harrison
Mixed 11–16 MLD (Day)

Greenside School Shephall Grn, Stevenage, Hertfordshire SG2 9XS; Tel 01438 315356
Headteacher D.J. Victor
5–19 SLD (Day)

Lakeside School Lemsford La, Welwyn Garden City, Hertfordshire AL8 6YW; Tel 01707 327410
Headteacher J. Chamberlain
2–19 SLD (Day)

Pinewood School Hoe La, Ware, Hertfordshire SG12 9PB; Tel 01920 412211
Headteacher G.R. Rodbard
11–16 MLD (Day, Boarders)

St. Luke's School Crouch Hall La, Redbourn, Hertfordshire AL3 7ET; Tel 01582 626727
Headteacher P. Johnson
9–16 MLD (Day)

The Valley School Valley Way, Stevenage, Hertfordshire SG2 9AB; Tel 01438 747274
Headteacher R.A. Stabler
Mixed 11–16 (Day)

Watling View School Watling View, St. Albans, Hertfordshire AL1 2NU; Tel 01727 850560
Headteacher S.M. Gardner
5–19 SLD (Day)

Woodfield School Malmes Croft, Leverstock Grn, Hemel Hempstead, Hertfordshire HP3 8RL; Tel 01442 253476
Headteacher J. Johnson
5–19 SLD (Day)

SCHOOLS FOR CHILDREN WITH EMOTIONAL AND BEHAVIOURAL DIFFICULTIES

Batchwood School Townsend Dr, St. Albans, Hertfordshire AL3 5RP; Tel 01727 765195
Headteacher K. Putman
11–16 EBD (Day)

Boxmoor House School Box La, Hemel Hempstead, Hertfordshire HP3 0DF; Tel 01442 256915
Headteacher D.E. Pawson
11–16 EBD (Day, Boarders)

Brandles School Weston Way, Baldock, Hertfordshire SG7 6EY; Tel 01462 892189
Headteacher C. Mepham
11–16

Falconer School Falconer Rd, Bushey, Watford, Hertfordshire WD23 3AT; Tel 020 8950 2505
Headteacher J.S.B. Page
10–16 EBD (Day, Boarders)

Hailey Hall School Hailey La, Hertford, Hertfordshire SG13 7PB; Tel 01992 465208
Headteacher S. Watt
11–16 (Day, Boarders)

Haywood Grove School St. Agnells La, Hemel Hempstead, Hertfordshire HP2 7BG; Tel 01442 250077
Headteacher I.M. Bennett
5–11

SCHOOLS FOR CHILDREN WITH HEARING IMPAIRMENT

Heathlands School Heathlands Dr, St. Albans, Hertfordshire AL3 5AY; Tel 01727 868596
Headteacher Mrs M. Davis
under 5–16 (Day, Boarders)

Knightsfield School Knightsfield, Welwyn Garden City, Hertfordshire AL8 7LW; Tel 01707 376874
Headteacher L. Leith
10–18 (Day, Boarders)

SCHOOLS FOR CHILDREN WITH PHYSICAL IMPAIRMENT

Lonsdale School Webb Rise, Stevenage, Hertfordshire SG1 5QU; Tel 01438 357631
Headteacher Mrs P. Clark
5–19 (Day, Boarders)

Meadow Wood School Coldharbour La, Bushey, Hertfordshire WD23 3NU; Tel 020 8420 4720
Headteacher Miss J. Shiel
5–11 (Day)

HUMBERSIDE COUNTY COUNCIL

In April 1996, Humberside County Council, Beverley Borough Council, Boothferry Borough Council, Cleethorpes Borough Council, East Yorkshire Borough Council, Glanford Borough Council, Great Grimsby Borough Council, Holderness Borough Council, Hull City Council and Scunthorpe Borough Council were replaced by East Riding of Yorkshire Council, Kingston upon Hull City Council, North Lincolnshire Council and North East Lincolnshire Council – each responsible for all local government services in its area. These councils are listed alphabetically in this chapter.

ISLE OF WIGHT COUNCIL
www.iwight.com

Political Composition: LD: 19, Con: 12, Ind: 12, Lab: 5
County Hall, Newport, Isle of Wight PO30 1UD;
URL www.iwight.com; Tel 01983 821000; Fax 01983 823333
Director (Education and Community Development) and Head (Paid Service) Alen Kaye
There is a general email address:
<firstname>.<surname>@iow.gov.uk

Social Services and Housing Directorate

17 Fairlee Rd, Newport, Isle of Wight PO30 2EA;
E-mail glen.garrod@iow.gov.uk
Director (Social Services and Housing) G. Garrod
Head (Housing) M. Pearl
Head (Children's Services) J. Doyle
Head (Policy Performance and Resources) D. Cousins
Head (Adults) S. Weller

Social Services, Housing and Benefits Select Committee

Chair Ian Stephens
Members of the Committee
Buster Bartlett, Terry Butckers, Deborah Gardiner, Charles Hancock, Gordon Kendall, Anthony Mundy, Erica Oulton, Colin Richards, Ian Stephens, Jill Wareham, David Williams.

TRAINING

Responsible for training professional and support staff in the Directorate.

HOSPITAL TEAM LEADER

St. Mary's Hospital, Newport, Isle of Wight; Tel 01983 524081
Service Manager (Hospital)   C. Way, CQSW

DAY CARE AND SHORT STAY HOME FOR CHILDREN WITH A MENTAL HANDICAP

Westminster House   Westminster La, Newport, Isle of Wight; Tel 01983 526310
Officer-in-Charge   Jeremy Baker
Residential (8)

CHILDREN'S SERVICE CENTRE

Atkinson Dr, Newport, Isle of Wight PO30 2LS; Tel 01983 525790
Head (Children's Services)   J. Doyle

VOLUNTARY DAY CENTRE FOR THE ELDERLY

WRVS, Newport St, Ryde, Isle of Wight

ACCOMMODATION FOR THE ELDERLY

There are two local authority residential homes.

MEALS SERVICES

Operated by the WRVS as agent for the Council.

LOCAL OFFICES

Social Services Centre (Cowes)   J.S. White Bldg, Medina Rd, Cowes, Isle of Wight PO31 2EX; Tel 01983 291144
Head (Adults)   S. Weller

Social Services Centre (Newport)   147 High St, Newport, Isle of Wight; Tel 01983 823440
Service Manager (Adults)   M. Henson
Service Manager (Admin and Finance)   R. Webb

Social Services Centre (Ryde)   Town Hall, Lind St, Ryde, Isle of Wight PO33 2NQ; Tel 01983 566011
Service Manager (Learning Disabilities)   Daron Perkins

Social Services Centre (Sandown)   The Barrack Block, The Broadway, Sandown, Isle of Wight PO36 9BS; Tel 01983 408448
Service Manager (Adults)   M. Henson

Education Offices

County Hall, Newport, Isle of Wight PO30 1UD;
URL www.iwight.com; E-mail david.pettitt@iow.gov.uk;
Tel 01983 821000
Director (Education and Community Development)
David Pettitt, BA, MA(Ed)
Principal Youth and Community Officer   G. Weech, BA
Principal Education Officer   R. Faulkner, BA, MSc
Senior Education Officer and Principal Educational Psychologist
R.W. Denman, BSc, ABPS

CHILD GUIDANCE CLINIC

Senior Education Officer and Principal Educational Psychologist
R.W. Denman, BSc, ABPS

SPECIAL DAY SCHOOLS

Medina House School   School La, Newport, Isle of Wight PO30 2HS; E-mail pdench@lineone.net; Tel 01983 522917; Fax 01983 526355
Headteacher   J. Hudson, MBA(Ed)
(84)

Watergate School   Watergate Rd, Newport, Isle of Wight PO30 1XW; E-mail admin.watergate@lineone.net; Tel 01983 524634; Fax 01983 533911
Headteacher   Mark Bell
(153)

KENT COUNTY COUNCIL
www.kent.gov.uk

In April 1998 Medway Town Council became a unitary authority and is listed alphabetically within this chapter. The rest of Kent retains a two-tier structure.
Population 1 330 000
Political Composition: Con: 52, Lab: 22, LD: 10
Sessions Hse, County Hall, Maidstone, Kent ME14 1XQ;
URL www.kent.gov.uk; Tel 01622 671411; Fax 01622 690892
Chief Executive   M. Pitt
Strategic Director (Resources)   D. Lewis, CPFA
Director (Strategic Planning)   Pete Raine

Social Services Department

Sessions Hse, County Hall, Maidstone, Kent ME14 1XQ;
URL www.kent.gov.uk;
E-mail social.services@kent.gov.uk; Tel 01622 671411;
Fax 01622 694910; Minicom 01622 696393
Strategic Director (Social Services)   Peter Gilroy
Director (Operations)   Oliver Mills
Assistant Director (Resources)   C. Highwood
Head (Policy and Standards Contracting)   Cathi Sacco
Policy Manager (Public Involvement)   Anthony Mort
Directorate Personnel Manager   M. Bell

Social Care and Community Health Policy Overview Committee

Cabinet Member   Mr P.W.A. Lake (Con)
Chair   Mr M.J. Angell (Con)
Vice-Chair   Mr M.J. Fittock (Lab)
Members of the Committee
Con: Mrs A.D. Allen, M.J. Angell, Mr J.A. Davies, Mr J.B. O'Fullarton, Mr D.A. Hirst, Mr J.D. Kirby, Mrs J. Newman, Dr T.R. Robinson, Mr J.D. Simmonds, Mr M.V. Snelling, Mr R. Tolputt.
Lab: Mrs J.E. Butcher, Mr M.J. Fittock, Mr K. Sansum, Mrs P.M. Stevens.
LD: Mrs M.E. Featherstone, Mr G. Rowe.

NHS Overview and Scrutiny Committee

Chair   Dr T. Robinson (Con)
Vice-Chair   Mr R.W. Ford
Members of the Committee
Conservative: Mrs A.D. Allen, Mr A.R. Chell, Dr T. Robinson, Mr J.D. Simmonds, Mr M.V. Snelling, Mr R. Tolputt.
Labour: Mr M.J. Fittock, Mr R.W. Ford, Mr K. Sansum.
LD: Mr G. Rowe.

ADOPTION TEAMS

West Kent Adoption Team   17 Kings Hill Ave, West Malling, Kent ME19 4UL; Tel 01732 525323

Mid/East Kent Adoption Team   Kroner Hse, Eurogate Bus Pk, Ashford, Kent TN24 8XU; Tel 01233 898630

COUNTY BENEFITS SERVICE

Sessions Hse, County Hall, Maidstone, Kent ME14 1XQ;
Tel 01622 694862; Fax 01622 694911
Manager   Christine Grosskopf

OCCUPATIONAL THERAPY BUREAU

Occupational Therapy and Sensory Disabilities Unit   Invicta Hse, County Hall, Maidstone, Kent ME14 1XX; Tel 01622 221832; Fax 01622 221853; Minicom 01622 221826
Head   Jan Harker

6

Mid Kent Area 2 Bishops Terr, Bishops Way, Maidstone, Kent ME14 1LA; Tel 01622 691640; Fax 01622 772291
Queens Hse, Guildhall St, Folkestone, Kent CT20 1DX; Tel 01303 224370; Fax 01303 224375
Principal Occupational Therapist Sue Stower

East Kent Area Ladesfield RCC, Vulcan Cl, Whitstable, Kent CT5 4LZ; Tel 01227 592410; Fax 01227 592417
Cairn Ryan, 101–103 London Rd, Kearnsey, Dover, Kent CT16 3AA; Tel 01304 828555; Fax 01304 828572
Avenue of Remembrance, Sittingbourne, Kent ME10 4DD; Tel 01795 473333; Fax 01795 437256
Principal Occupational Therapist Elizabeth Stenhouse

West Kent Area Joynes Hse, New Rd, Gravesend, Kent DA11 0AT; Tel 01474 328664; Fax 01474 358125
17 Kings Hill Ave, Kings Hill, West Malling, Kent ME19 4UL; Tel 01732 525000; Fax 01732 525309
Principal Occupational Therapist Carol Coyne

COUNTY DUTY SERVICE

Tel (Out of hours) 08457 626777; 01233 639677

DEAF SERVICES BUREAU

Headquarters, Invicta Hse, County Hall, Maidstone, Kent ME14 1XX; Tel 01622 671411; Fax 01622 221853; Minicom 01622 221826
Manager Beryl Palmer

East Kent Deaf Services Bureau Cairn Ryan, 101–103 London Rd, Kearnsey, Dover, Kent CT16 3AA; Tel 01304 671411; Fax 01304 828504; Minicom 01304 827862

Medway Deaf Services Bureau OT and Deaf Services, Compass Centre, Pembroke, Chatham Maritime, Kent ME4 4YH; Tel 01634 306000; Fax 01634 331200; Minicom 01634 331257

Mid Kent Deaf Services Bureau Kroner Hse, Eurogate Bus Pk, Ashford, Kent TN24 8XU; Tel 01233 639677; Fax 01233 898514; Minicom 01233 898513

West Kent Deaf Services Bureau 17 Kings Hill Ave, Kings Hill, Kent ME19 4UL; Tel 01732 525000; Fax 01732 525395; Minicom 01732 525394

KENT QUALIFIED

Suite 8, 30 Churchill Sq, Kings Hill, West Malling, Kent ME19 4YU; Tel 01732 872294; Fax 01732 871978

SUPPORT LINE

Gibson Dr, Commercial Services Bldg, Kings Hill, West Malling, Kent ME19 4QG; Tel 01622 605539

MENTAL HEALTH SERVICES

17 Kings Hill Ave, Kings Hill, West Malling, Kent ME19 4UL; Tel 01732 525000; Fax 01732 525309
Service Manager Mark Brampton

Ashford Western Avenue Day Services, Western Ave, Ashford, Kent TN23 1LX; Tel 01233 204026

Canterbury and Coastal Intake Durham Hse, 69 Canterbury Rd, Herne Bay, Kent CT6 5SA; Tel 01227 594888

Dartford St. Lawrence Hse, 48a West Hill, Dartford, Kent DA1 2HT; Tel 01322 277744

Dover Colman Hse, Brookfield Ave, Dover, Kent CT20 2HA; Tel 01304 216666

Gravesend 6 High St, Gravesend, Kent DA11 0BQ; Tel 01474 534200

Maidstone (North) The Pagoda, Hermitage Lne, Maidstone, Kent ME16 9PD; Tel 01622 724200

Maidstone (South) Kingswood CMHC, 180–186 Union St, Maidstone, Kent ME14 1EY; Tel 01622 766900

Shepway 2–4 Radnor Park Ave, Folkestone, Kent CT19 5HN; Tel 01303 222424

South West Kent c/o Dry Hill Road CMHC, 6 Dry Hill Rd, Tonbridge, Kent TN9 1LX; Tel 01732 360032

South West Kent c/o Braeside, Pembury Hospital, Tunbridge Wells, Kent TN2 4QJ; Tel 01892 823545

South West Kent c/o St. Johns CMCH, St. Johns Rd, Sevenoaks, Kent TN13 3LR; Tel 01732 470840

Swale Mental Health Unit, Memorial Hospital, Bell Rd, Sittingbourne, Kent ME10 4DT; Tel 01795 418300 2022

Swanley 17 High St, Swanley, Kent; Tel 01322 669899

Thanet The Old Police Station, Cavendish Rd, Ramsgate CT11 9AN; Tel 01843 855200

Substance Misuse (West) 17 Kings Hill Ave, Kings Hill, West Malling, Kent ME19 4UL; Tel 01732 525000

Substance Misuse (East) The Cottage, Vulcan Cl, Borstal Hill, Whitstable, Kent CT5 4LL; Tel 01227 277287

AREA OFFICES

West Kent Area Offices
17 Kings Hill Ave, Kings Hill, West Malling, Kent ME19 4UL; Tel 01732 525000; Fax 01732 525309
Area Director Andrew Ireland
Head (Children's Services) Kay Weiss
Head (Adult Services) Chris Belton
Head (Contracting and Planning Unit) Jan Bumstead
Area Manager (Finance) Vacancy
Area Manager (Personnel and Development) Graham Funnell

LOCAL OFFICES

Dartford Local Office St. Lawrence Hse, 48a West Hill, Dartford, Kent DA1 2HG; Tel 01322 277744; Fax 01322 289343

Gravesend Local Office Joynes Hse, New Rd, Gravesend, Kent DA11 0AT; Tel 01474 328664; Fax 01474 320741

Sevenoaks Local Office Tricon Hse, Old Coffee House Yard, London Rd, Sevenoaks, Kent TN13 1AH; Tel 01732 585320; Fax 01732 743275

Swanley Local Office The Willows, Hilda May Ave, Swanley, Kent BR8 7BT; Tel 01322 611000; Fax 01322 616449

Tonbridge Local Office Croft Hse, East St, Tonbridge, Kent TN9 1HP; Tel 01732 362344; Fax 01732 770319

Tunbridge Wells Local Office Montague Hse, 9 Hanover Rd, Tunbridge Wells, Kent TN1 1ET; Tel 01892 515045; Fax 01892 549804

FAMILY CENTRES

Adolescent Resource Centre 5 Manor Rd, Gravesend, Kent DA12 1AA; Tel 01474 354204; Fax 01474 335874
Contact Lorraine Shorey

Dartford Family Centre 2 Essex Rd, Dartford, Kent DA1 2AU; Tel 01322 279170
Contact Liz Allen

Denton Multicultural Family Centre Lower Range Rd, Denton, Gravesend, Kent DA12 2QL; Tel 01474 365891
Contact Nicki Vass

Grove Hill Road Family Support Centre 39a Grove Hill Rd, Tunbridge Wells, Kent; Tel 01892 513221

Homefinding Team 17 Kings Hill Ave, Kings Hill, West Malling, Kent ME19 4UL; Tel 01732 525000

Larkfield Family Support Centre 72 Martins Sq, Larkfield, Aylesford, Kent ME20 6QN; Tel 01732 841863

Northcourt Family Centre Dickens Rd, Gravesend, Kent DA12 2JY; Tel 01474 365510
Contact Mary Fathers

Swanley Family Centre The Willows, Hilda May Ave, Swanley, Kent BR8 7BT; Tel 01322 611000; Fax 01322 616449
Contact Christine Lines

Wallis Park Family Centre off College Rd, Wallis Pk, Northfleet, Kent; Tel 01474 353872
Contact Juliet Broadley

LEARNING DISABILITIES

Home Support Network Joynes Hse, New Rd, Gravesend, Kent DA11 0AT; Tel 01474 328664
Contact Mark Walker

Dartford Social Education Centre Brent Way, Dartford, Kent DA2 6DA; Tel 01322 274014
Contact Rose Johnson

Gravesend Social Education Centre Haig Gdns, Trinity Rd, Gravesend, Kent DA12 1NA; Tel 01474 358802
Contact Y. Jacquelin

Yew Tree Centre Brent Way, Dartford, Kent DA2 6DA; Tel 01322 292538
Contact Maureen Pritchard

SERVICES FOR THE ELDERLY

Dene Holm LSC Dene Holm Rd, Northfleet, Kent DA11 8JY; Tel 01474 567532
Manager Elizabeth Kinge

Edward Moore House LSC Trinity Rd, Gravesend, Kent DA12 1LX; Tel 01474 321360
Manager Rose Debling

Guru Nanak Day and Family Centre 11 The Gr, Gravesend, Kent DA12 1DX; Tel 01474 537781
Manager Shaminder Bedi

Leyton House LSC Common La, Wilmington, Dartford, Kent DA2 7BA; Tel 01322 221129
Manager Joy Fletcher

The Limes LSC Brent La, Dartford, Kent DA1 1QN; Tel 01322 224584
Manager Marianne Weller

Manorbrooke LSC Bevis Cl, Stone, Dartford, Kent DA2 6HB; Tel 01322 223628
Manager Patricia Isted

Milan Day Centre Westgate Rd, Dartford, Kent DA1 2AR; Tel 01322 290960
Manager Shaminder Bedi

The Mount Day Centre Barn End La, Wilmington, Kent DA2 7PP; Tel 01322 225170
Manager Sue Giblin

Stanley Morgan House LSC Barn End La, Wilmington, Kent DA2 7PX; Tel 01322 226849
Manager Sue Giblin

Valley Lodge LSC Valley Dr, Gravesend, Kent DA12 5UA; Tel 01474 566490
Manager Rosie Wijeyawardena

HOSPITAL TEAMS

Darenth Valley Hospital Darenth Wood Rd, Dartford, Kent DA2 8AB; Tel 01322 428601; Fax 01322 428707
Team Leader Jean Townsend

Kent and Sussex Hospital Mount Ephraim, Tunbridge Wells, Kent TN4 8AT; Tel 01892 526111
Team Leader Jerry Wilson

Pembury Hospital Pembury Rd, Tunbridge Wells, Kent TN2 4QJ; Tel 01892 823535
Team Leader Jerry Wilson

REGISTERED CARE CENTRES

Bowles Lodge All Saints Rd, Hawkhurst, Kent TN18 4HT; Tel 01580 752775; Fax 01580 754622
Contact B. Seal

Leyton House Common La, Wilmington, Kent DA2 7BA; Tel 01322 221129; Fax 01322 284581
Contact J. Fletcher

The Limes Brent La, Dartford, Kent DA1 1QN; Tel 01322 224584; Fax 01322 284702
Contact M. Weller

Manorbrooke Bevis Cl, Srone, Dartford, Kent DA2 6HB; Tel 01322 223628; Fax 01322 284638
Contact P. Isted

Stanley Morgan Barne End La, Wilmington, Kent DA2 7PX; Tel 01322 226849; Fax 01322 284634
Contact S. Giblin

FOSTERING SERVICE

West Kent Fostering Team 17 Kings Hill Ave, Kings Hill, West Malling, Kent ME19 4UL; Tel 01732 525349; Fax 01732 525315

Mid Kent Area Offices

Area Director Steve Leidecker
Head (Children's Services) Cathy Yates
Head (Adult Services) Anne Tidmarsh
Head (Contracting and Planning) Michael Herbert
Area Manager (Finance) Kathryn Beldon
Area Manager (Personnel and Development)
Lorna Williamson

LOCAL OFFICES

Ashford Local Office ~~Swanton Hse, Elwick Rd, Ashford,~~ Kent; Tel 01233 625233; Fax 01233 628903

Folkestone Local Office Queen's Hse, Guildhall St, Folkestone, Kent CT20 1DU; Tel 01303 253476; Fax 01303 220751

Maidstone Local Office Bishop's Terr, Bishop's Way, Maidstone, Kent ME14 1LA; Tel 01622 691640; Fax 01622 691135

LEARNING DISABILITY (CHILDREN)

The Willows, Hilda May Ave, Swanley, Kent BR8 7BT; Tel 01322 611000; Fax 01322 616449

FOSTERING SERVICE

Mid Kent Fostering Team Kroner Hse, Eurogate Bus Pk, Ashford, Kent TN24 8XU; Tel 01233 898634; Fax 01233 898638

FAMILY SUPPORT CENTRE

Northumberland Road Family Support Centre 16 Northumberland Rd, Maidstone, Kent; Tel 01622 756496

DAY SERVICES – ADULTS

Horizons Day Opportunities Service Westerham Rd, Brasted, Kent TN16 1HJ; Tel 01959 563545
Manager John Walker

Maidstone Day Opportunities Centre Boughton La, Maidstone, Kent ME17 4NA; Tel 01622 743459
Manager F. McGibbon

Princess Christian Farm Riding La, Hildenborough, Tonbridge, Kent TN11 9LP; Tel 01732 838408

Tunbridge Wells Day Opportunities Service Langton Rd, Tunbridge Wells, Kent; Tel 01893 525802

LEARNING DISABILITY – RESIDENTIAL (ADULTS)

The Hedgerows Home 1 and 2 The Hedgerows, Station Rd, Staplehurst, Kent TN12 0QQ; Tel 01580 893269
Manager S. Pattenden

6

Tonen ln
01233
20585
8

Mountwood Hostel Westerham Rd, Brasted, Kent TN16 1HJ; Tel 01959 563413
Manager S. Bullen

Rusthall Elms Hostel Langton Rd, Tunbridge Wells, Kent TN3 0DP; Tel 01892 535623

REGISTERED CARE CENTRES

Broadmeadow Lucy Ave, Folkestone, Kent CT19 5TX; Tel 01303 252047; Fax 01303 259481
Contact J. Ross

Dorothy Lucy Centre Northumberland Rd, Maidstone, Kent ME15 7TA; Tel 01622 678071; Fax 01622 762877
Contact J. Parsooraman

Heathside Day Care Centre Heath Rd, Coxheath, Maidstone, Kent ME17 4AH; Tel 01622 741924

Lawrence House 15 St. Marks Cl, Folkestone, Kent CT20 3LY; Tel 01303 248177; Fax 01303 252191
Contact C. Hillen

The Lindens St. Benets Way, Tenterden, Kent TN30 6QQ; Tel 01580 764737; Fax 01580 766305
Contact P. Hales

Whitegates Whitegates Cl, Hythe, Kent CT21 6BD; Tel 01303 266277; Fax 01303 261585
Contact S. Harrison

East Kent Area Offices

St. Peters Hse, Dane Valley Rd, St. Peters, Broadstairs, Kent CT10 3JJ; Tel 01843 860000; Fax 01843 864874
Area Director B. Anderson
Head (Children's Services) D. Guy
Head (Adult Services) B. Henry
Head (Contracting and Planning) M. Dorman
Area Manager (Finance) M. Godden
Area Manager (Personnel and Development) G. Vary

FOSTERING SERVICE

East Kent 1 Fostering Team Canterbury Local Office, 70 Stour St, Canterbury, Kent CT1 2NW; Tel 01227 451741; Fax 01227 762218
Covers Canterbury and Swale areas

East Kent 2 Fostering Team 26 High St, Margate, CT9 1DS; Tel 01843 290778; Fax 01843 231736
Covers Thanet and Dover areas

FAMILY SUPPORT SERVICES

Beaver Centre 135 Beaver La, Ashford, Kent; Tel 01233 622533; Fax 01233 640978
Contact M. Sanderson

Brockman Cranbourne, Cheriton High St, Folkestone, Kent CT18 8AN; Tel 01303 279051; Fax 01303 271472
Contact R. Ross

Canterbury Family Support Centre Kingsmead Primary School, St. Johns Pl, Northgate, Canterbury, Kent CT1 1BD; Tel 01227 592720; Fax 01227 592723

Poltons Vale View Rd, Dover, Kent CT17 9NP; Tel 01304 211925; Fax 01304 212445
Contact G. Holland

Swale Family Centre Greenporch Cl, Milton Regis, Sittingbourne, Kent ME10 2HA; Tel 01795 426373; Fax 01795 420437

Thanet Family Support Centre Perkins Ave, Margate, Kent CT9 4AV; Tel 01843 226430; Fax 01843 296588

Westchurch House Godfrey Walk, Ashford, Kent TN23 1XJ; Tel 01233 639535; Fax 01233 612724
Contact M. Sanderson

ADULTS WITH A LEARNING DISABILITY

Ashford SEC St. Stephen's Wlk, Ashford, Kent TN23 5BD; Tel 01233 621189
Contact A. Ward

Faversham Day Opportunities Centre Lower Rd, Faversham, Kent ME13 7NT; Tel 01795 532802
Manager S. King

Folkestone SEC Military Rd, Folkestone, Kent CT20 3SP; Tel 01303 249197
Contact S. Uden

Osborne Court Lower Rd, Faversham, Kent ME13 7NT; Tel 01795 533352
Manager V. Smith

Walmer SEC Liverpool Rd, Walmer, Kent CT14 7NW; Tel 01304 363443
Contact N. Wellard

ADULTS WITH MENTAL HEALTH PROBLEMS

Braethorpe Day Centre Gore Hill, Canterbury Rd, Ashford, Kent TN24 8QF; Tel 01233 625371
Contact P. Choules

Community Support Scheme The Health Centre, Maison Dieu Rd, Dover, Kent CT16 1RH; Tel 01304 202525
Contact L. Hardward
Contact T. Ripley

Resource House 11 Victoria Cres, Dover, Kent CT16 1DU; Tel 01304 225037
Contact R. Hewitt

LEARNING AND PHYSICALLY-DISABLED ADULTS

Ashford Independent Living Scheme The Nest, Rear of Fairlawns, Ashford, Kent TN23 2LY; Tel 01233 640488
Contact L. Reynolds

Dover and Deal Independent Living Scheme Health Centre, Maison Dieu Rd, Dover, Kent CT16 1RH; Tel 01303 202525
Contact D. Grossmann

Meadowside Liverpool Rd, Walmer, Kent CT14 7NW; Tel 01304 363445
Contact J. Wilson

Shepway Independent Living Scheme Grove Rd, Cranbourne, Folkestone, Kent CT18 8AN; Tel 01303 279001
Contact P. Watson

DISABLED AND CARERS IN COMMUNITY

The Bridge Resource Centre Whitegates Cl (off Stade St), Hythe, Kent CT6 6DS; Tel 01303 260689
Contact J. Stokes

The Nest Resource Centre Rear of Fairlawns, Kingsnorth Rd, Ashford, Kent TN23 2LY; Tel 01233 641931

The Well Resource Centre Winchelsea St, Dover, Kent CT17 9ST; Tel 01304 241740
Contact M. Moss

REGISTERED CARE CENTRES

Appleton Lodge Rumfield Rd, Broadstairs, Kent CT10 2PW; Tel 01843 867858; Fax 01843 602344
Contact A. Locke

Blackburn Lodge The Broadway, Sheerness, Kent ME12 1RA; Tel 01795 667035; Fax 01795 668141
Unit Manager M. Marks

Campfield Reynolds Cl, Herne Bay, Kent CT6 6DS; Tel 01227 366965; Fax 01227 364754
Contact S. Mcgrath

Cornfields Cranley Cl, Whitfield, Dover, Kent CT16 3NW; Tel 01304 820019; Fax 01304 826255
Contact M. Heathcote

Doubleday Lodge Glebe La, Sittingbourne, Kent ME10 4JW; Tel 01795 423444; Fax 01795 470457
Unit Manager J. Langthorne

Kiln Court Lower Rd, Faversham, Kent ME13 7NY; Tel 01795 532183; Fax 01795 530942
Contact J. Jones

Ladesfield Vulcan Cl, Whitstable, Kent CT5 4LZ; Tel 01227 261090; Fax 01227 266201
Contact B. Cooper

Sampson Court Mongeham Rd, Mongeham, Deal, Kent CT14 9PD; Tel 01304 360909; Fax 01304 381933
Contact C. Heffernan

Wayfarers St. Bart's Rd, Sandwich, Kent CT13 0AW; Tel 01304 614255; Fax 01304 620130
Contact P. Woodcock

LOCAL OFFICES

Canterbury Local Office Social Services Department, 70 Stour St, Canterbury, Kent CT1 2NW; Tel 01227 451741; Fax 01227 762218

Dover Local Office Social Services Department, 3–4 Cambridge Terr, Dover, Kent CT16 1JT; Tel 01304 204915; Fax 01304 242783

Social Services Help Desk Thanet District Council Offices, PO Box 9, Cecil St, Margate, Kent CT9 1XZ; Tel 01843 577276

Swale Local Office Social Services Department, Ave of Remembrance, Sittingbourne, Kent ME10 4DD; Tel 01795 473333; Fax 01795 420016

Thanet Local Office Social Services Department, St. Peters Hse, Dane Valley Rd, Broadstairs, Kent CT10 3JJ; Tel 01843 860000; Fax 01843 864874

Whitstable Local Office Acorn Hse, John Wilson Ind Pk, Thanet Way, Whitstable, Kent CT5 3QT; Tel 01277 771686; Fax 01227 771737.

6

Education and Libraries

Sessions Hse, County Hall, Maidstone, Kent ME14 1XQ; Tel 01622 671411; Fax 01622 694186; Minicom 01622 605720
Strategic Director (Education and Libraries)
Graham Badman
Assistant Director (Pupils and Students)
Joanna Wainwright, MA, AIMgt
Assistant Director (Policy and Service Development)
Marilyn Hodges, BA(Hons), CertEd, FAE, MIMgt (Acting
Assistant Director (Resources) Grahame Ward, BSc(Hons), IPFA
Assistant Director (School Effectiveness) Trevor Sandford, MA, MEd, FRSA
Assistant Director (Schools and Early Years) Ian Craig, BA, MBA, FRSA
County Officer (Community Services) Yinnon Ezra, BA(Hons), MILAM, FRSA
Head (Arts and Libraries) Richard Ward, MLIB, ALA
Head (Youth and Community) Mick Price, BA, PGCE, Dip Youth and Community, AdDipEdMgt
Head (Sports Development) Chris Hespe, BSc(Hons) MA, DMS, PGCE, MILAM, MIMgt
Head (Finance) Keith Abbott
Head (AEN and Resources Service Unit) Colin Feltham
Head (Language and Traveller Achievement Service) Jenny Robson
Joint Head (Behaviour Service) Sue Fenton-Smith (Acting)
Joint Head (Behaviour Service) Glynis Eley (Acting)
Head (Physical and Sensory) Lynne Williams (Acting)
Head (Pre-School AEN) Elizabeth Astridge
Head (Cognition and Learning) Chris Berry

Head (Psychology Service) Alan Macgregor, MEd, CPsychol, AFBPsS
Head (Education Welfare) Carole Bowes
Head (Early Years) Alex Gamby
Assistant Head (Psychology (West Kent)) Rosemary Rees
Manager (Capital Projects) Nick Tricker
Manager (Provision and Planning) Mike Thompson
Manager (Client Services) Mark Sleep
Manager (Awards) Nick Jordan
Children's Officer Rosemary Dillon
Principal Adviser (School Improvement) Mike Dowden, MA, LLB, MRD
Principal Adviser (Advisory Services) Elizabeth Lewis, BA
Principal Adviser (Primary) Mike Aylen, BA, MA
Principal Adviser (Special Support) John Woodroffe, BEd(Hons), MA
Principal Adviser (Secondary) Gordon Bernard, BA(Hons), MA, MBA, MIL(Secondary)
Principal Adviser (SEN) John Moore, BEd(Hons), MEd, CertEd
Strategic Adviser (Personnel and Development) Rob Semens
IS Support Clive Bonner
Senior Educational Psychologist (Complex Learning (West Kent)) Denise Ford
Senior Educational Psychologist (West Kent) Jey Monson (Associate Tutor UCL)
Senior Educational Psychologist (West Kent) Lucille Galli-Phillips
Senior Educational Psychologist (West Kent) Doreen Hipsley
Senior Educational Psychologist (West Kent – Early Years) Sandy Coates
Senior Educational Psychologist (West Kent – Able) Rosie Hitching
Assistant Head (Mid-Kent – Psychology) Trisha McCaffrey
Senior Educational Psychologist (Mid Kent) Julia Johns
Senior Educational Psychologist (EBD – Mid Kent) Sarah Hindle
Assistant Head (East Kent -Psychology Service) Val Collman
Senior Educational Psychologist (East Kent – EBD) Jane Birnie
Senior Educational Psychologist (East Kent – Complex Learning) Tricia Eastgate
Senior Educational Psychologist (East Kent – CPD) Andy Heather
Senior Educational Psychologist (East Kent – SI/PD) Paul Withington
Principal Education Welfare Officer (West Kent) Kate Pawson
Senior Education Welfare Officer (West Kent) Eleanor Morgan
Education Welfare Officer (West Kent – Social Inclusion) Clair Brough
Education Welfare Officer (West Kent – Travellers) Sue Toms
Education Welfare Officer (West Kent – Behaviour Service) Sheridan Whitfield
Rapid Response Project (West Kent) Elizabeth Turner
Primary Prevention Officer (West Kent) Liberty Hand
Child Employment Officer (West Kent) Andrew Swan
Principal Education Welfare Officer (Mid Kent) Sylvia Jones
Education Welfare Officer (Mid Kent – Rapid Response) Heather Ham
Child Employment Officer (Mid Kent) Shelley Davies
Primary Prevention Officer (Mid Kent) Penny Tanner
Senior Education Welfare Officer (Mid Kent) Debbie Spice
Education Welfare Officer (Mid Kent – Behaviour Service) Louise Peregrina
Senior Education Welfare Officer (East Kent) Ian Younie
Child Employment Officer (East Kent) Kerry Miles
Senior Education Welfare Officer (East Kent) Lindy Whitfield
Education Welfare Office (East Kent – Asylum Seekers) Romana Ghorbani
Education Welfare Officer (East Kent – Behaviour Service) Janet Elgar
Service Education Welfare Officer (East Kent – Behaviour Service) Elaine Keeping
Education Welfare Officer (East Kent – Travellers) Judith Willis

PSYCHOLOGY SERVICE

West Kent Area Education Offices, 39 Grove Hill Rd, Tunbridge Wells, Kent TN1 1SL; Tel 01892 523342; Fax 01892 511529; Minicom 01892 520986

Joynes House New Rd, Gravesend, Kent DA11 0AT; Tel 01474 564701; Fax 01474 320395; Minicom 01474 564701

Mid Kent Bishop's Terr, Bishop's Way, Maidstone, Kent ME14 1AF; Tel 01622 671411; Fax 01622 605163

Shorncliffe Road Psychology Service 3 Shorncliffe Rd, Folkestone, Kent; Tel 01303 850789; Fax 01303 245015

East Kent John Wilson Business Pk, Thanet Way, Whitstable, Kent CT5 3QZ; Tel 01227 772992; Fax 01227 772290

HOSPITAL SPECIAL SCHOOLS

East Kent Hospital School Service City New Hospital, Canterbury, Kent CT2 8PT; Tel 01227 781548; Fax 01227 781548
Headteacher Ms R. Eastwood
  Mixed

West Kent Hospital School Service City View, Canterbury, Kent CT2 8PT; Tel 01227 781548; Fax 01227 781548
Headteacher J. Locke
  Mixed

SPECIAL DAY SCHOOLS

Bower Grove School Fant La, Maidstone, Kent ME16 8NL; Tel 01622 726773; Fax 01622 729315
Headteacher T.N. Phipps
  Mixed MLD

Five Acre Wood School Boughton La, Maidstone, Kent ME15 9QL; Tel 01622 743925; Fax 01622 744828
Headteacher J.E. Kratochvil
  Mixed SLD

The Foreland School Lanthorne Rd, Broadstairs, Kent CT10 3NX; Tel 01843 863891; Fax 01843 860710
Headteacher P.S. Hare
  Mixed SLD

Grange Park School Birling Rd, Leybourne, Maidstone, Kent ME19 5QA; Tel 01732 842144
Headteacher Mrs J. Hanley
  Mixed SLD (31)

Harbour School Elms Vale Rd, Dover, Kent CT17 9PS; Tel 01304 201964; Fax 01304 225000
Headteacher A. Berresford
  Mixed MLD

Highview School Moat Farm Rd, Folkestone, Kent CT19 5DJ; Tel 01303 258755
Headteacher C. Hurling
  Mixed MLD

The Ifield School Cedar Ave, Gravesend, Kent DA12 5JT; Tel 01474 365485; Fax 01474 569744
Headteacher S.M. Harrison
  Mixed MLD

Milestone School Ash Rd, New Ash Grn, Dartford, Kent DA3 8JZ; Tel 01474 709420; Fax 01474 707170
Headteacher E. Flanagan
  Mixed SLD

Oakley School Penbury Rd, Tunbridge Wells, Kent TN2 4NE; Tel 01892 823096; Fax 01892 823836
Headteacher M. Absolom
  Mixed Communication Disorders, SLD (55)

The Orchard School Cambridge Rd, Canterbury, Kent CT1 3QQ; Tel 01227 769220; Fax 01227 781589
Headteacher B.S. Shelley
  Mixed MLD

Ridge View School Cage Green Rd, Tonbridge, Kent TN10 4PT; Tel 01732 771384; Fax 01732 770344
Headteacher A. Carver
  Mixed SLD

Rowhill School Stock La, off Gerdview Dr, Dartford, Kent DA2 7BZ; Tel 01322 225490; Fax 01322 291433
Headteacher S. McGuiness
  Mixed MLD

St. Anthony's School St. Anthony's Way, Margate, Kent CT9 3RA; Tel 01843 292015; Fax 01843 231574
Headteacher R.A. O'Dell
  Mixed MLD

St. Bartholomew's School Attlee Way, North St, Sittingbourne, Kent ME10 2HE; Tel 01795 477888; Fax 01795 478833
Headteacher Ms J. Hurstfield (Acting)
  Mixed SLD

St. Nicholas School Holme Oak Cl, Nunnery Fields, Canterbury, Kent CT1 3JJ; Tel 01227 464316; Fax 01227 781589
Headteacher D. Lewis
  Mixed SLD

St. Thomas' School Swanstree Ave, Sittingbourne, Kent ME10 4NL; Tel 01795 477788; Fax 01795 477771
Headteacher P.J. Rankin
  Mixed MLD

The Wyvern School Hythe Rd, Ashford, Kent TN24 0XL; Tel 01233 621302; Fax 01233 660621
Headteacher D. Spencer
  Mixed MLD/SLD (146)

SPECIAL BOARDING SCHOOLS (SOME WITH DAY PLACES)

Broomhill Bank School Broomhill Rd, Rusthall, Tunbridge Wells, Kent TN3 0TB; Tel 01892 510440; Fax 01892 502460
Headteacher P.A. Barnett
  Girls MLD

Foxwood School Seabrook Rd, Hythe, Kent CT21 5QJ; Tel 01303 261155; Fax 01303 262355
Headteacher C. Soulsby
  Mixed SLD Day places (132)

Furness School Rowhill Rd, Hextable, Swanley, Kent BR8 7RP; Tel 01322 662937; Fax 01322 615033
Headteacher R.J. Chapman
  Mixed EBD

Gap House School 1 South Cliffe Pde, Broadstairs, Kent CT10 1TJ; Tel 01843 861679; Fax 01843 868828
Headteacher I.P. Cooke
  Mixed Speech and language handicapped

Halstead Place School Church Rd, Halstead, Sevenoaks, Kent TN14 7HQ; Tel 01959 533294; Fax 01959 533705
Headteacher T. Fox (Acting)
  Mixed EBD

Laleham School Northdown Park Rd, Margate, Kent CT9 2TP; Tel 01843 221946; Fax 01843 231368
Headteacher K. Mileham
  Mixed SLD

Portal House School Sea St, St. Margaret's-at-Cliffe, Dover, Kent CT15 6AR; Tel 01304 853033; Fax 01304 853526
Headteacher L. Sage
  Mixed EBD

Stone Bay School Stone Rd, Broadstairs, Kent CT10 1EB; Tel 01843 863421; Fax 01843 866652
Headteacher R. Edey
  Mixed SLD

Swinford Manor School Great Chart, Ashford, Kent TN23 3BT; Tel 01233 622958; Fax 01233 662177
Headteacher R. Law (Acting)
  Boys EBD

Valence School Westerham, Kent TN16 1QN; Tel 01959 562156; Fax 01959 565046
Headteacher R. Gooding
  Mixed PH

PUPIL REFERRAL UNITS

Barn End Centre High Rd, Wilmington, Kent DA2 7DP; Tel 01322 228395; Fax 01322 294717
Contact N. Mason

Beaver Education Project Beaver Centre, 135 Beaver La, Ashford, Kent TN23 2NX; Tel 01233 622533; Fax 01233 640978
Contact J. Hurn

Brook Education Centre Parkfield Rd, Folkestone, Kent CT19 5BY; Tel 01303 221350; Fax 01303 221372
Contact Mrs H. Craggs (Acting)

The Cedars Pupil Referral Unit Bower Mount Rd, Maidstone, Kent ME16 8AU; Tel 01622 753772; Fax 01622 693622
Contact R. Brown

Centre Class Swanley School Youth Wing, St. Mary's Rd, Swanley, Kent BR8 7TE; Tel 01322 665209
Contact S. Fenton-Smith

Charles Street Centre Charles St, Southborough, Tunbridge Wells, Kent TN4 0DS; Tel 01892 534589; Fax 01892 534589
Contact M. Bell

Charlton Court Pupil Referral Unit East Sutton, Maidstone, Kent ME17 3DQ; Tel 01622 842424; Fax 01622 844220
Contact Mrs N. Coulling

Northwood Centre Highfield Rd, Ramsgate, Kent CT12 6QB; Tel 01843 592152
Team Leader L. Noble

Phoenix Centre Woodview Site, Main Rd, Dartford, Kent DA3 7PW; Tel 01474 705377
Contact A. Gritten

The Ridgeway Study Support Centre Southborough, Tunbridge Wells, Kent TN4 0AB; Tel 01892 519841; Fax 01892 519841
Contact Mrs J. Kenny

KINGSTON UPON HULL CITY COUNCIL

www.hullcc.gov.uk

Population 269 144
Political Composition: Lab: 23, LD: 29, Ind: 5, Con: 2
Guildhall, Alfred Gelder St, Kingston upon Hull HU1 2AA; URL www.hullcc.gov.uk; Tel 01482 300300
Leader of the Council Cllr S. Butterworth
Managing Director Jim Brooks
Group Director (Regeneration and Development) Andrew Flockhart (Acting)
Group Director (Community Services) Tom Hogan
Group Director (Hull City Services) David Purchon (Acting)

Social Services Department

Brunswick Hse, Strand Cl, Beverley Rd, Kingston Upon Hull HU2 9DB; URL www.hullcc.gov.uk/socialservices; Tel 01482 300300; Fax 01482 616162
Corporate Director Ken Foote
Assistant Director (Adult Services) Alec Pearson
Assistant Director (Children and Family Services) Margaret Dennison
Liaison Officer Clare Bradley

Cabinet Committee

Social and Health Care S. Wandby (Lab)
Social and Health Care P. Clarke (Lab)
Housing S. Bayes (Lab)

Members of the Cabinet Committee
Lab: Bayes, Clarke, Gemmell, Glew, Hale, Inglis, Lavery, McVie, Waudby, Wilson.
Ind: Jarris.

HOSPITAL SOCIAL WORK TEAMS

Hull Royal Infirmary Anlaby Rd, Kingston upon Hull HU3 2JZ; Tel 01482 605220

Hull Women and Children's Hospital Anlaby Rd, Kingston upon Hull HU3 2JZ; Tel 01482 675698

Princess Royal Hospital Saltshouse Rd, Kingston upon Hull HU8 9HE; Tel 01482 676607

AREA OFFICES

Childcare Resources Unit

The Gleneagles Centre, East Carr Rd, Kingston upon Hull HU8 9UB; Tel 01482 300300; Fax 01482 712438
Principal Childcare Manager (Resources) Alan McKenzie
Principal Childcare Manager (West Hull) Sue Atkins
Principal Childcare Manager (East Hull) Jon Plant

Adult Services Locality Managers

Locality Manager Roger Grey
Locality Manager Linda Bowen
Locality Manager Gary Jones
Locality Manager Claire Brown

CHILDREN'S HOMES

Aneurin Bevan Lodge Children's Home 140 Hotham Rd North, Kingston upon Hull HU5 4RJ; Tel 01482 300300; Fax 01482 848516

Elgar Road Children's Home 2 Elgar Rd, Anlaby Park Road North, Kingston upon Hull HU4 7NX; Tel 01482 300300; Fax 01482 573784
Community Home temporarily at 49a Kinloss Garth, Bransholme, Kingston upon Hull, HU7 4LY; Tel 01482 833101; Fax 01482 834688.

Hessle Road Children's Home 1123 Hessle Rd, Kingston upon Hull HU4 6SB; Tel 01482 300300; Fax 01482 569997
Community home

Kinloss Garth Children's Home 49a Kinloss Garth, Bransholme, Kingston upon Hull HU7 4LY; Tel 01482 300300; Fax 01482 834688

Lime Tree Court Children's Home Bellfield Hse, Middlesex Rd, Kingston upon Hull HU8 0RB; Tel 01482 300300; Fax 01482 796667
LD

Marlborough Avenue Children's Home 71 Marlborough Ave, Princes Ave, Kingston upon Hull HU5 3JR; Tel 01482 300300; Fax 01482 449983

Milne Road Children's Home 8 Milne Rd, Kingston upon Hull HU9 4UB; Tel 01482 300300; Fax 01482 791828
Community home

Wansbeck Road Children's Home 10 Wansbeck Rd, Longhill Est, Kingston upon Hull HU8 9SL; Tel 01482 300300; Fax 01482 817627
Community home

CHILDREN AND FAMILY TEAMS

East Area John Havelot Hse, Grange Rd, Kingston upon Hull HU9 4LQ; Tel 01482 300300; Fax 01482 781196

East Area (Contact Team) Bellfield Hse, Middlesex Rd, Kingston upon Hull HU8 0RB; Tel 01482 300300; Fax 01482 715156

North Carr Area 74 Goodhart Rd, Bransholme, Kingston upon Hull HU7 4AP; Tel 01482 300300; Fax 01482 838401

6

North Hull Endike Resource Centre, Endike La, Kingston upon Hull HU6 7UR; Tel 01482 300300; Fax 01482 616445

Park Area 449 Holderness Rd, Kingston upon Hull HU8 8JS; Tel 01482 300300; Fax 01482 786025

Riverside Area The Myton Centre, William St, Kingston upon Hull HU1 2SP; Tel 01482 300300; Fax 01482 326860

West Hull Pickering Centre, Pickering Rd, Kingston upon Hull HU4 7AD; Tel 01482 300300; Fax 01482 573361

Wyke Area 50 Pearson Pk, Kingston upon Hull HU5 2TG; Tel 01482 300300; Fax 01482 444145

Emergency Duty Team Anevrin Bevan Lodge, 140 Hotham Road North, Kingston upon Hull HU5 4RJ; Tel 01482 788080; Fax 01482 841544

COMMUNITY SUPPORT TEAMS

Bransholme Community Support Team Nicholson Hse, 97 Mirfield Gr, Kingston upon Hull HU9 4QR; Tel 01482 300300; Fax 01482 708883

Central Hull Support Team Rokeby Resource Centre, 3 Rokeby Ave, Kingston upon Hull HU4 7ND; Tel 01482 300300; Fax 01482 571609

Community Team Learning Disability (CTLD) Salingar Hse, 2 Logan Cl, Kingston upon Hull HU7 4PG; Tel 01482 300300; Fax 01482 831987

East Hull Community Support Team Nicholson Hse, 97 Mirfield Gr, Kingston upon Hull HU9 4QR; Tel 01482 300300; Fax 01482 708883

North Hull Community Support Team Rokeby Resource Centre, 3 Rokeby Ave, Kingston upon Hull HU4 7ND; Tel 01482 300300; Fax 01482 571609

West Hull Rokeby Resource Centre, 3 Rokeby Ave, Kingston upon Hull HU4 7ND; Tel 01482 300300; Fax 01482 571609

MENTAL HEALTH SERVICES

Based at Hull and ER Community Health Trust, Victoria Hse, Park St, Kingston upon Hull HU2 8TD; Tel 01482 617941

Assertive Outreach Team John Symans Hse, Park Row, Park St, Kingston upon Hull HU2 8TD; Tel 01482 335670

Central Hull Mental Health Resource Centre Waterloo Centre, Brunswick Ave, Kingston upon Hull HU2 9AY; Tel 01482 326261; Fax 01482 326261

East Hull Mental Health Resource Centre 605 Holderness Rd, Kingston upon Hull HU8 9AJ; Tel 01482 321703; Fax 01482 336926

North Hull Mental Health Resource Centre Dales Hse, 304 Cottingham Rd, Kingston upon Hull HU6 8QA; Tel 01482 336687; Fax 01482 336195

Bransholme Mental Health Resource Centre Stroud Cres, Bransholme, Kingston upon Hull HU7 4DQ; Tel 01482 335750; Fax 01482 336931

West Hull Mental Health Resource Centre Westlands Community Unit, Wheeler St, Kingston upon Hull HU3 5QE; Tel 01482 574555; Fax 01482 336935

RESOURCE CENTRES FOR LEARNING DISABLED

East Hull Learning Disability Resource Centre Leads Rd, Sutton, Kingston upon Hull HU7 4XS; Tel 01482 300300; Fax 01482 836196
LD

West Hull Resource Centre 2056–2058 Hessle High Rd, Kingston upon Hull HU13 9NW; Tel 01482 300300; Fax 01482 644923

DISABILITY SERVICES

George Ashton Centre Ashton Cl, Ellerburn Ave, Kingston upon Hull HU6 9RJ; Tel 01482 300300; Fax 01482 801960
PD

Ings Lodge 30 Middlesex Rd, Bellfield Ave, Kingston upon Hull HU8 0RB; Tel 01482 300300; Fax 01482 714333
LD

Physical Disability Day Resource Arthur Richardson Centre, Savoy Rd, Kingston upon Hull HU8 0TX; Tel 01482 300300; Fax 01482 374508
PD

Vocational Training Centre (Holden) Leads Rd, Kingston upon Hull HU7 4XS; Tel 01482 300300; Fax 01482 836196

CARE MANAGEMENT TEAMS (ADULTS)

Central Hull Care Management Team 48 Pearson Pk, Kingston upon Hull HU5 2TG; Tel 01482 300300; Fax 01482 494296

East Hull Care Management Team Pashby Hse, 69 James Reckitt Ave, Kingston upon Hull HU8 7TH; Tel 01482 300300; Fax 01482 701786

North Hull 49 Kinloss Garth, Bransholme, Kingston upon Hull HU7 4YG; Tel 01482 300300; Fax 01482 822766

West Hull Care Management Team Lindsey Pl, Arcon Dr, Kingston upon Hull HU4 6AJ; Tel 01482 300300; Fax 01482 355035

DAY CENTRES FOR ELDERLY PEOPLE

Bellfield Day Centre Middlesex Rd, Kingston upon Hull HU8 0RB; Tel 01482 300300; Fax 01482 715737

Bethune Avenue Day Centre Bethune Ave, Kingston upon Hull HU4 7EL; Tel 01482 300300; Fax 01482 648532

Buckingham Street Day Centre Buckingham St, Holderness Rd, Kingston upon Hull HU8 8UG; Tel 01482 300300; Fax 01482 616454

Fernleigh Day Centre Waterloo St, Kingston upon Hull HU2 9LG; Tel 01482 300300; Fax 01482 620626

Partnership Day Services Buckingham St, Holderness Rd, Kingston upon Hull HU8 8UG; Tel 01482 300300; Fax 01482 616454

Pennine Multipurpose Day Centre Pennine Way, Bransholme, Kingston upon Hull HU7 5YU; Tel 01482 300300 01482 830435

ADULT RESOURCE CENTRES AND RESIDENTIAL HOMES

Alderson Resource Centre Linnaeus St, Anlaby Rd, Kingston upon Hull HU3 2PD; Tel 01482 300300; Fax 01482 581918
Resource centre for older people.

Catherine Ellis Resource Centre Catherine Ellis Hse, Ashton Cl, Kingston upon Hull HU6 9RJ; Tel 01482 300300; Fax 01482 805209

Highfield Resource Centre Wawne Rd, Sutton, Kingston upon Hull HU7 4YG; Tel 01482 300300; Fax 01482 833588

Rokeby Resource Centre 3 Rokeby Ave, Kingston upon Hull HU4 7ND; Tel 01482 300300; Fax 01482 571609

ELDERLY RESIDENTIAL

There are four homes for the elderly.

CENTRE FOR MULTIPURPOSE USE

Pennine Day Centre Pennine Way, Bransholme, Kingston upon Hull HU7 5YU; Tel 01482 300300; Fax 01482 830435

Welfare Rights Team Pickering Centre, Pickering Rd, Kingston upon Hull HU4 7AD; Tel 01482 300300; Fax 01482 564461

OTHER SERVICES

Adoption Service Gleneagles Centre, East Carr Rd, Kingston upon Hull HU8 9LB; Tel 01482 300300; Fax 01482 789282

Area Child Protection Committee Aveurin Bevan Lodge, 140 Hotham Rd North, Kingston upon Hull HU5 4RJ; Tel 01482 846082; Fax 01482 846063

Attendance Centre Newland Homes, Cottingham Rd, Kingston upon Hull HU6 7RJ; Tel 01482 440259

Disability Services Bellfield Hse, Middlesex Rd, Kingston upon Hull HY8 0RB; Tel 01482 300300; Fax 01482 714180

Fostering Team Gleneagles Centre, East Carr Rd, Kingston upon Hull HU8 9LB; Tel 01482 300300; Fax 01482 798670

Specialist Substance Misuse Service Albion St, Kingston upon Hull HU1 3TG; Tel 01482 336790; Fax 01482 336916

Sutton Place Safe Centre 347 Saltshouse Rd, Kingston upon Hull HU8 9HR; Tel 01482 300300; Fax 01482 712173

Training and Development Section Coronation Road North, Kingston upon Hull HU5 5RL; Tel 01482 300300; Fax 01482 616643

Youth Offending Team Myton Centre, Porter St, Kingston upon Hull HU1 2RE; Tel 01482 609991; Fax 01482 609983

Learning Services

Essex Hse, Manor St, Kingston upon Hull HU1 1YD; Tel 01482 613007; Fax 01482 613407
Corporate Director (Learning and Culture)
   Helen McMullen
Deputy Director (Education)   S. Gardner
Assistant Director (Achievements and Standards)
   Dr A. Swallow
Assistant Director (Finance and Information)   M. Fox
Education Officer (Schools)   C. Herrick
Education Officer (Schools)   J. Pearce

SPECIAL SCHOOLS

Frederick Holmes School Inglemire La, Kingston upon Hull HU6 8JJ; Tel 01482 804766; Fax 01482 806967
Headteacher   D.M. Boyes

Northcott School Dulverton Cl, Bransholme, Kingston upon Hull HU7 4EL; Tel 01482 825311; Fax 01482 822253
Headteacher   M. Johnson

Teskey-King School Inglemire La, Kingston upon Hull HU6 8JH; Tel 01482 854588; Fax 01482 855496
Headteacher   L.A. Purvis

Tweendykes School Tweendykes Rd, Kingston upon Hull HU7 4XJ; Tel 01482 826508; Fax 01482 839597
Headteacher   K.J. Ogilvie

KIRKLEES METROPOLITAN COUNCIL

www.kirkleesmc.gov.uk

Population 390 900
Political Composition: Lab: 25, LD: 29, Con: 15, Green: 3
Civic Centre 3, Market St, Huddersfield, West Yorkshire HD1 1WG; URL www.kirkleesmc.gov.uk; Tel 01484 221000; Fax 01484 221777
Chief Executive   T. Elson
Executive Director   R.W. Vincent
Executive Director   R. Pelty
Executive Director   D. Sequerra
Manager (Group Personnel)   D. Crowther
Oldgate Hse, 2 Oldgate, Huddersfield, West Yorkshire HD1 6QF; Tel 01484 221000; Fax 01484 225360

Solicitor to the Council   J. Emms
Civic Centre, 2nd Fl, High St, Huddersfield, West Yorkshire HD1 2TG; Tel 01484 221000; Fax 01484 221423

Social Services

Oldgate Hse, 2 Oldgate, Huddersfield, West Yorkshire HD1 6QF; URL www.kirklees.gov.uk; E-mail social.services@kirklees.gov.uk; Tel 01484 223000 Emergency Tel (Out-of-office hours) 01924 326489; Fax 01484 326410; Minicom 01484 324293
Director (Social Affairs and Health)   Philip Cotterill; Tel 01484 225078
Assistant Director (Children and Families)   Paul Johnson; Tel 01484 225331
Assistant Director (Community Care Services)   Keith Smith; Tel 01484 225321
Assistant Director (Performance and Strategic Development)   Mark Greaves; Tel 01484 225145
Principal Officer (Equal Opportunities)   David Bundy; Tel 01484 225027
Group Manager (Personnel)   David Crowther; Tel 01484 225118
Group Manager (Finance)   John Dixon; Tel 01484 225144
General Manager (Training)   Iain Baines; Tel 01484 223722
Unit Manager (Strategic Co-ordination)   Matthew Holland; Tel 01484 225138

Cabinet Member

Cllr S.A. Smithson (LD)
Members Services, Crown Crt Bldgs, Princess St, Huddersfield, West Yorkshire HD1 2TT; Tel 01484 221801

ACCESS SERVICE

Service Information Point – Cleckheaton Town Hall, Church St, Cleckheaton, West Yorkshire BD19 3RH; Tel 01924 335072; Fax 01924 335014

Service Information Point – Dewsbury The Walsh Bldg, Town Hall Way, Dewsbury, West Yorkshire WF12 8EQ; Tel 01924 325050; Fax 01924 325077

Service Information Point – Huddersfield Civic Centre, High St, Huddersfield, West Yorkshire HD1 1DH; Tel 01484 223000; Fax 01484 226214

COMMUNITY CARE SERVICES

Oldgate Hse, 2 Oldgate, Huddersfield, West Yorkshire HD1 6QF; Tel 01484 225331; Fax 01484 225188
Assistant Director   Keith Smith
Divisional Manager (Mental Health and Learning Difficulties Service)   Paul Davies
Briarcourt, Occupation Rd, Huddersfield, West Yorkshire HD3 3EE; Tel 01484 223798; Fax 01484 223549
Divisional Manager (North Kirklees)   Janice Simpson
13a Westfield Rd, Mirfield, West Yorkshire WF14 9PW; Tel 01924 326497
Divisional Manager (South Kirklees)   Jane Sharkey
2nd Fl, 6–8 St. Peter's St, Huddersfield, West Yorkshire HD1 1DH; Tel 01484 225330

CARE MANAGEMENT

13a Westfields Rd, Mirfield, Huddersfield, West Yorkshire WF14 9PW
Senior Group Manager (North Kirklees)   Julia Suddick; Tel 01924 326414; Fax 01924 326410
Group Manager   Vacancy

Batley and Spen Office Lydgate Hse, Soothill La, Batley, West Yorkshire WF17 6EZ; Tel 01924 326125
Team Manager   Tim Sanders
Senior Practitioner   Susan Preece

6

CARE MANAGEMENT – SOUTH KIRKLEES

6–8 St. Peter's St, Huddersfield, West Yorkshire HD1 1DH; Tel 01484 226937; Fax 01484 226214
Senior Group Manager (South Kirklees)   Diane Green
Group Manager   Paul Hollingdale

South   Slaithwaite Town Hall, Carr La, Slaithwaite, Huddersfield, West Yorkshire HD7 5AF; Tel 01484 222547; Fax 01484 222554
Team Manager   Annette Armstrong
Senior Practitioner   Alison Cornelly

Central   Eastlawns, 21 Thomas St, Huddersfield, West Yorkshire HD3 3JJ; Tel 01484 222055

HOME CARE SERVICES

13a Westfields Rd, Mirfield, Huddersfield, West Yorkshire WF14 9PW
Manager (Home Care Team, North Kirklees)   Debra Mallinson (Acting); Tel 01924 326449
Group Manager (South Kirklees Home Care)   Helen Clay; Tel 01484 226246; Fax 01484 226214
Manager (Home Care Team, South Kirklees)   Bev Moore; Tel 01484 226254

LEARNING DISABILITIES MANAGEMENT

Briarcourt, 28 Occupation Rd, Lindley, Huddersfield, HD3 3EE
Manager (Learning Disabilities Services)   Jill Robson; Tel 01484 226530
Group Manager (Learning Disabilities and Residential Services)   Jane Greaves; Tel 01484 226539

Social Work Team – North Kirklees   Cullingworth St, Staincliffe, Dewsbury, West Yorkshire WT13 4AN; Tel 01924 816275; Fax 01924 816082
Team Manager   Walter O'Neill

Social Work Team – South Kirklees   Greenhead Resource Unit, 24 Greenhead Rd, Huddersfield, West Yorkshire HD1 4EN; Tel 01484 347600; 01484 347601; Fax 01484 347618
Team Manager   Andrew Smith
Manager (Resource Unit)   Coral Buchanan

Assessment and Development Unit   Lobley St, Heckmondwicke, West Yorkshire WF16 0ES; Tel 01924 325657
Manager   Sue Taylor

ADULT PLACEMENT TEAM

Briarcourt, 28 Occupation Rd, Lindley, Huddersfield, West Yorkshire HD3 3EE; Tel 01484 226527 01484 226528
Contact   Les Mitchell

MENTAL HEALTH

Briarcourt, 28 Occupation Rd, Lindley, Huddersfield, West Yorkshire HD3 3EE
Care Manager (Professional Development)   John Young; Tel 01484 226524
Manager (Community Options)   Frances Barnes; Tel 01484 226525; Fax 01484 223540

MENTAL HEALTH – SOUTH KIRKLEES

St. Luke's Hospital, Crosland Moor, Huddersfield, West Yorkshire HD4 5RQ
General Manager (Forensic Services)   Sue Threadgold (Castle Hill Unit); Tel 01484 343010
Locality Manager (Community Mental Health Team, South West)   Lynne Holtom (Old Nursing School); E-mail lynne.holtom@cht.nhs.uk; Tel 01484 343810; Fax 01484 343800
Locality Manager (Community Mental Health Team, North East)   Patrick Darkwa (Old Nursing School); E-mail patrick.darkwa@cht.nhs.uk; Tel 01484 343302; Fax 01484 343800

Manager (Clinical Services and Assertive Outreach Team)   Alex Doran; Tel 01484 347739; Fax 01484 350669
Manager (Adult Mental Health Services, South Kirklees)   Vacancy
Manager (Care)   Joe Hodgson; Tel 01484 343314; Fax 01484 343666

MENTAL HEALTH – NORTH KIRKLEES

Ravensleigh Cottage, 28 Oxford Rd, Dewsbury, West Yorkshire WF13 4LN
General Manager (Community Services – Adults)   Mike Young; E-mail mike.young@dewsbury.nhs.uk; Tel 01924 516155; Fax 01924 516151
General Manager (NHS Adult Services)   Clive Leggett; Tel 01924 516150
Manager (Assertive Outreach Team) and Locality Manager   Sue Harrison (Acting) (Ravensleigh Resource Unit); Tel 01924 516160; Fax 01924 516163
Care Manager/CPA   Chris Vickerman
Batley Enterprise Centre, 513 Bradford Rd, Batley, West Yorkshire WF17 8LL; Tel 01924 326951; Fax 01924 326956

OUT OF HOURS SERVICE

Team Manager   Duncan Fairwater (Acting)

CHILDREN AND FAMILIES

Assistant Director   Paul Johnson
Oldgate Hse, 2 Oldgate, Huddersfield, West Yorkshire HD1 5QF; Tel 01484 225331; Fax 01484 225188
Divisional Manager   Phil Tomlinson
Westfields, Westfields Rd, Mirfield, Huddersfield, West Yorkshire WF14 9PW; Tel 01924 483721; Fax 01924 486080
Unit Manager (Quality Protects)   Aziz Daji
Westfields, Westfields Rd, Mirfield, Huddersfield, West Yorkshire WF14 9PW; Tel 01924 326081
Manager (Family Support)   Clare Mulgan
Westfields, Westfields Rd, Mirfield, West Yorkshire WF14 9PW; Tel 01924 483728; Fax 01924 483720
Manager (Residential and After Care)   Allan Pearson
Westfields, Westfields Rd, Mirfield, West Yorkshire WF14 9PW; Tel 01924 483750; Fax 01924 486080
Manager (Children with a Disability)   Vacancy
13a Westfields Rd, Mirfield, West Yorkshire WF14 9PW; Tel 01924 326433
Manager (Child Protection and Review)   Phil Holmes
Westfields, Westfields Rd, Mirfield, West Yorkshire WF14 9PW; Tel 01924 483745
Manager (Family Placement)   Sarah Patrick
Westfields, Westfields Rd, Mirfield, West Yorkshire WF14 9PW; Tel 01924 483702; Fax 01924 483720
Manager (Youth Offending Team)   Richard Smith
Somerset Bldg, Church St, Huddersfield, West Yorkshire HD1 1DD; Tel 01484 226935; Fax 01484 226938
Manager (Pathways Team)   Robert Eabry
Sandymount, 300 Blackmoorfoot Rd, Huddersfield, West Yorkshire HD4 5QU; Tel 01484 222152; Fax 01484 222170
Manager (Planning and Strategic Development)   Lorraine Crossland
Westfields, Westfields Rd, Mirfield, Huddersfield, West Yorkshire WF14 9PW; Tel 01924 483721; Fax 01924 486080
Community Manager (North Kirklees)   Pauline McCarton
13a Westfields Rd, Mirfield, Huddersfield, West Yorkshire WF14 9PW; Tel 01924 326081; Fax 01924 326080
Community Manager (South Kirklees)   Catherine Harrison
Oakmead, 1c Lidget St, Lindley, Huddersfield, West Yorkshire HD3 3JB; Tel 01484 414846
Equality Officer (Equal Opportunities)   Denise MacDonald
Westfields, Westfields Rd, Mirfield, West Yorkshire WF14 9PW; Tel 01924 483761

COMMUNITY HOMES (CHILDREN)

Copthorne House Community Home   6 Copthorne Gdns, Bradley, Huddersfield, West Yorkshire HD2 1RH; Tel 01484 223441

Eddercliffe Crescent Community Home 20 Eddercliffe Cres, Littletown, Liversedge, West Yorkshire WF15 6LR; Tel 01924 325120
Residential Manager Diane Latouche (Acting)

Elm Grove Community Home Heckmondwike, West Yorkshire WF16 9DN; Tel 01924 325365

Grosvenor House Community Home 76 Grosvenor Rd, Dalton, Huddersfield, West Yorkshire HD5 9HX; Tel 01484 223189

Healds Road Community Home 105 Healds Rd, Dewsbury, West Yorkshire WF13 4HT; Tel 01924 324845
Residential Manager Angela Harman

Orchard View Community Home 13b Westfields Rd, Mirfield, Huddersfield, West Yorkshire WF14 9PW; Tel 01924 482100

Woodlands Community Home 1b Lidget St, Lindley, Huddersfield, West Yorkshire HD3 3JB; Tel 01484 222277
Residential Manager Vic Szczesnowicz

FAMILY CENTRES

Southgate Family Centre Southgate, Huddersfield, West Yorkshire HD1 1SR; Tel 01484 223543

Walpole Family Centre 61–65 Walpole Rd, Crosland Moor, Huddersfield, West Yorkshire HD4 5EX; Tel 01484 222173

Westtown Family Centre Boothroyd La, High St, Dewsbury, West Yorkshire WF13 2RQ; Tel 01924 325129

Windy Bank Family Centre 13–15 Eleventh Ave, Windy Bank Est, Liversedge, West Yorkshire WF15 8LL; Tel 01274 335266
Unit Leader Pauline Bunch
Unit Leader Ruth O'Connor

RESIDENTIAL CARE HOMES

Group Manager J. Grier
13a Westfields Rd, Mirfield, Huddersfield, West Yorkshire WF14 9PW; Tel 01924 326419

Westmoor House Residential Care Home 175 Staincliffe Rd, Dewsbury, West Yorkshire WF13 4EF; Tel 01924 325185; Fax 01924 325193

Woodwell House Residential Care Home Mayman La, Batley, West Yorkshire WF17 7TB; Tel 01924 326278; Fax 01924 326277

PERFORMANCE AND STRATEGIC DEVELOPMENT

Oldgate Hse, 2 Oldgate, Huddersfield, West Yorkshire HD1 6QF; Tel 01484 225145; Fax 01484 225188
Assistant Director Mark Greaves
Head (Quality and Professional Development) Gary McBrien; Tel 01484 225331
Unit Manager (Service Review Team) Nazir Mira
Oldgate Hse, 2 Oldgate, Huddersfield, West Yorkshire HD1 6QF; Tel 01484 225095; Fax 01484 225335
Unit Manager (Quality and Professional Development) Vacancy; Tel 01484 225180
Unit Manager (Information Systems Unit) Lise Elliott
Oakmead, 1c Lidget St, Huddersfield, West Yorkshire HD3 3JB; Tel 01484 222089
Team Manager (Working in Partnership Team) Fiona Weir
6–8 St. Peter's St, Huddersfield, West Yorkshire; Tel 01484 226927
Team Manager (Working in Partnership Team) Fiona Weir (Job Share)
6–8 St. Peter's St, Huddersfield, West Yorkshire; Tel 01484 226928
Manager (Community Care Development) John Doyle
Oldgate Hse, 2 Oldgate, Huddersfield, West Yorkshire HD1 6QF; Tel 01484 225363
Manager (Business Development) Gary Blakely; Tel 01484 225050

Manager (Finance) Alan Fletcher; Tel 01484 225150; Fax 01484 225360
Principal Officer (Strategic Co-ordination) Maxine Stead; Tel 01484 225170
Senior Officer (Finance) Mark Eustwood
5th Fl, Oldgate Hse, Huddersfield, West Yorkshire HD1 6QF; Tel 01484 222086
Senior Officer (Assessment) Y. Kay
Oakmead, 1c Lidget St, Huddersfield, West Yorkshire HD3 3JB; Tel 01484 222027
Officer (Complaints and Compliments) Yasmin Mughal; Tel 01484 225115

Education Service

Oldgate Hse, 2 Oldgate, Huddersfield, West Yorkshire HD1 6QW; E-mail gavin.tonkin@kirklees.gov.uk; Tel 01484 225242; Fax 01484 225237
Assistant Director (Pupil Support) Liz Dobie
Manager (Education Access) J. Wilson, BSc(Hons), CQSW, DipFT, CMS
Head (Resources) D.A. Gerrard

EDUCATION SOCIAL WORK SERVICE

North Team Town Hall Annexe, Brunswick St, Batley, West Yorkshire WF17 5DT; E-mail jennie.hill@kirklees.gov.uk; Tel 01924 326004; Fax 01924 326016

South Team and Headquarters Upperhead Row, Huddersfield, West Yorkshire HD1 2JL; E-mail anne.mallinson@kirklees.gov.uk; Tel 01484 221919; Fax 01484 221788

Service for Pupils with Emotional and Behavioural Difficulties Field Hill Centre, Batley, West Yorkshire WF17 0BQ; E-mail val.porter@kirklees.gov.uk; Tel 01924 326220; Fax 01924 326222

ETHOS (FORMERLY H.H. TEACHING SERVICES)

The KESS Centre, Rawthorpe High School Campus, Huddersfield, West Yorkshire HD5 9NY; E-mail angela.firth@kirklees.gov.uk; Tel 01484 226500; Fax 01484 226515
Head of Service G. Sunderland
Senior Teacher S. Stainton, MA

Dewsbury District Hospital Ward 7, Dewsbury, West Yorkshire; Tel 01924 465105
Contact J. Kay

Huddersfield Royal Infirmary Ward 17, The Royal Infirmary, Huddersfield, West Yorkshire; Tel 01484 422191 2479
Contact A. Crawshaw

SERVICE FOR HEARING-IMPAIRED CHILDREN

Rawthorpe High School Campus Rawthorpe High School Campus, Huddersfield, West Yorkshire HD5 9NY; Tel 01484 226500; Fax 01484 226515
Head of Service G. Sunderland
Senior Teacher J. Parkin

SERVICE FOR VISUALLY IMPAIRED CHILDREN

Rawthorpe Campus Rawthorpe High School Campus, Huddersfield, West Yorkshire HD5 9NY; Tel 01484 226500; Fax 01484 226515
Head of Service G. Sunderland
Senior Teacher L. Swan

SERVICE FOR AUTISTIC CHILDREN

Tel 01484 226500; Fax 01484 226515
Head of Service G. Sunderland
Advisory Teacher E. Marper

6

PSYCHOLOGICAL SERVICE – CHILD AND FAMILY GUIDANCE SERVICE

Civic Centre 1 High St, Huddersfield, West Yorkshire HD1 2NF;
E-mail huddersfield.psychology@kirklees.gov.uk; Tel 01484 221472; Fax 01484 221491
Contact J. Bamford

Child and Family Guidance Centre Temple Rd, Dewsbury, West Yorkshire WF13 3QD;
E-mail dewsbury.psychology@kirklees.gov.uk; Tel 01924 324850; Fax 01924 324870

SPECIAL DAY SCHOOLS

Fairfield School Dale La, Heckmondwike, West Yorkshire WF16 9PA;
E-mail head.fairfields@kirklees-schools.org.uk; Tel 01924 325700; Fax 01924 325702
Headteacher Ms S. Williams (Acting)
3–19

Hartshead Moor School Halifax Rd, Cleckheaton, West Yorkshire BD19 6LP;
E-mail office.hartsheadmoor@kirklees-schools.org.uk; Tel 01274 335223; Fax 01274 335225
Headteacher I. McDonald, BSc, MA, PGCE, NPQH) (Acting
5–16

Highfields School Cemetery Rd, Edgerton, Huddersfield, West Yorkshire HD1 5NF;
E-mail office.highfields@kirklees-schools.org.uk; Tel 01484 226659; Fax 01484 226660
Headteacher R.T. Ware
3–19

Longley School Smithy La, Huddersfield, West Yorkshire HD5 8JE; E-mail office.longley@kirklees-schools.org.uk;
Tel 01484 223937; Fax 01484 511520
Headteacher M. Riaz (Acting)
5–16

Lydgate School Kirkroyds La, New Mill, Huddersfield, West Yorkshire HD9 1LS;
E-mail office.lydgate@kirklees-schools.org.uk; Tel 01484 222484; Fax 01484 222485
Headteacher B. Goler, DipEd, BA, MEd
5–16

Ravenshall School Ravensthorpe Rd, Thornhill Lees, Dewsbury, West Yorkshire WF12 9EE;
E-mail office.ravenshall@kirklees-schools.org.uk; Tel 01924 325234; Fax 01924 325235
Headteacher C. Newby
11–16

Turnshaws School Turnshaws Ave, Kirkburton, Huddersfield, West Yorkshire HD8 0TJ;
E-mail tss@turnshaws.kirklees.sch.uk; Tel 01484 222760; Fax 01484 222761
Headteacher Mrs G. Taylor, MA, DipSEN
Mixed 3–19

SPECIAL RESIDENTIAL AND DAY SCHOOL

Nortonthorpe Hall School Busker La, Scissett, Huddersfield, West Yorkshire HD8 9JU;
E-mail office.nortonthorpe@kirklees-schools.org.uk;
Tel 01484 222921; Fax 01484 222966
Headteacher M.P. Ironmonger, BA, MA(EdMan)
Mixed

SPECIAL EDUCATIONAL NEEDS ADMINISTRATION TEAM

Civic Centre I High St, Huddersfield, West Yorkshire HD1 2NF; E-mail janet.swann@kirklees.gov.uk; Tel 01484 221474; Fax 01484 221491
Assistant Education Officer (SEN) J. Swann

KNOWSLEY METROPOLITAN BOROUGH COUNCIL
www.knowsley.gov.uk

Population 153 094
Political Composition: Lab: 55, LD:11
PO Box 21, Huyton, Knowsley, Merseyside L36 9YU;
    URL www.knowsley.gov.uk;
    E-mail knowsley@connect.org.uk; Tel 0151 489 6000
Chief Executive Steve Gallagher, BA, MBA, CQSW;
    Tel 0151 443 3772; Fax 0151 443 3030
*Director (Planning and Development) and Deputy Chief
    Executive* G.A. Smith, BSc, Dip Ms, (CEng), MICE, MIHT
Director (Finance) and Deputy Chief Executive
    Steve Houston
Director (Leisure and Community Services) John Bell, BSc, MSocSci, MILAM

Social Services Department

PO Box 23, Huyton, Merseyside L36 9YY; Tel 0151 443 3439
Chief Executive (Health and Social Care) Anita Marsland
Assistant Director (Business Management) Vacancy

TRAINING

Responsibility for training professional and support staff in the department.
Training Section, Training and Conference Centre, Huyton, Merseyside
Manager (Training and Development) Caroline Murphy; Tel 0151 443 3580
Training Officer (Adults) Linda Reid; Tel 0151 443 3578
Training Officer (Child Care/Protection) Tracey Hollyhead; Tel 0151 443 3579
*Training Officer/NVQ Co-ordinator/Practice Teacher
    Co-ordinator* R. Barnes; Tel 0151 443 3577

Cabinet Member with Portfolio for Health and Social Care

Ken Keith (Lab)

Child Care

Kirby Municipal Bldgs, Cherryfield Dr, Kirkby, Merseyside; Tel 0151 443 4187
Assistant Director (Children and Families) Moya Sutton
Service Manager (Children and Families) M.D. Parker
Service Manager (Children and Families) Vacancy

SOCIAL WORK TEAMS – CHILD CARE

Child Protection Unit Municipal Bldgs, Cherryfield Dr, Kirkby, Merseyside L32 1TX; Tel 0151 443 4080

Halewood Child Care 5–21 Ravenscourt Shopping Pde, Halewood, Halewood, Merseyside L26 0TS; Tel 0151 443 2110

Huyton Team 1 Page Moss One-Stop Shop, 603 Princess Dr, Page Moss, Liverpool, Merseyside L14 9ND; Tel 0151 443 5021

Huyton Team 2 Municipal Bldgs, Archway Rd, Huyton, Merseyside L36 9YY; Tel 0151 443 3797

Kirkby Team Municipal Bldgs, Cherryfield Dr, Kirkby, Merseyside L32 1TX; Tel 0151 443 4252

Prescot/Whiston Child Care Prescot One-Stop Shop, Prescot Shopping Centre, Prescot, Merseyside; Tel 0151 443 4515

CHILDREN'S COMMUNITY HOMES

Bedford Close Children's Home 6 Bedford Cl, Huyton, Merseyside; Tel 0151 443 3968
Manager J. Whitfield

Brook Cottages Community Home 2 Liverpool Rd, Prescot, Merseyside L34 1NL; Tel 0151 443 4650
Manager D. Tagoe

FAMILY SUPPORT UNITS

Halewood Family Support Unit Leathers La, Halewood, Merseyside L27 0TD; Tel 0151 486 4597
Manager (part-time) Doreen McGhee

Highfield Family Support Unit 45 William Roberts Ave, Kirkby, Merseyside L33 1YA; Tel 0151 443 4205
Manager J. McIntyre

Page Moss Family Support Unit Princess Dr, Huyton, Merseyside; Tel 0151 443 3547
Manager J. Parry

Whiston Family Support Unit Old Colliery Rd, Whiston, Prescot, Merseyside L35 3SX; Tel 0151 443 4517
Manager (part-time) Doreen McGhee

RESPITE HOME

Children's Outreach Residential Service Huyton Family Centre, Church Rd, Huyton, Merseyside L36 5SH; Tel 0151 443 3013
Manager L. Kilshaw

FAMILY PLACEMENT TEAM

Astley Hse, Huyton, Merseyside L36 8HY; Tel 0151 443 3958

Adult Care

25 Derby Rd, Huyton, Merseyside; Tel 0151 443 3450
Assistant Director (Adults of Employment Age) A. Kilpatrick
Service Manager (Care Management Adults) L. Hill

SOCIAL WORK TEAMS – ADULTS

Delfby Crescent Mental Health Resource Centre Delfby Cres, Southdene, Knowsley, Merseyside L32 8TN; Tel 0151 443 4051
Manager P. Robertson

Halewood Social Work Team 5–21 Ravenscourt Shopping Pde, Leathers La, Halewood, Merseyside L26 0UP; Tel 0151 443 2122

Huyton Learning Disability Service Astley Hse, Astley Rd, Knowsley, Merseyside L14 9NQ; Tel 0151 482 1136
Manager D. Hughes

Huyton Social Work Team Municipal Bldgs, PO Box 28, Huyton, Merseyside L36 9YY; Tel 0151 443 3714

Kirkby Social Work Team Municipal Bldgs, Cherryfield Dr, Kirkby, Merseyside L32 1TX; Tel 0151 443 4173

Knowsley Community Partnership Scheme Astley Hse, Astley Rd, Knowsley, Merseyside L14 9NQ; Tel 0151 482 1136
Scheme Manager R. Springett

Montgomery Road Mental Health Resource Centre Montgomery Rd, Huyton, Knowsley, Merseyside L36 7AH; Tel 0151 443 3626
Manager P. Robertson

Prescot Locality Centre 16 Park Rd, Prescot, Merseyside L34 3LR; Tel 0151 443 4611
Manager C. Bayliss

Prescot/Whiston Social Work Team Prescot One-Stop Shop, Prescot Shopping Centre, Prescot, Merseyside L35 5GA; Tel 0151 443 4613

Whiston Hospital Warrington Rd, Prescot, Merseyside L35 5DR; Tel 0151 430 1669

Older People's Unified Service (OPUS)

Municipal Bldgs, Huyton, Kirkby, Merseyside L36 9YY; Tel 0151 443 3926
Assistant Director (Service Provision – Adults) B. Spoors
Service Manager D. Ralph
Service Manager B. Riddell

CARE MANAGEMENT – ADULTS DIVISION

Disability Service Team Kirkby Municipal Bldgs, Cherryfield Dr, Kirkby, Merseyside L32 1TX; Tel 0151 443 4429
Derby Road Welfare Rights Officers 25 Derby Rd, Huyton, Merseyside; Tel 0151 443 3711

SPD ADULTS DIVISION

Disability Resource Centre Stockbridge Village Centre, Roughsedge Hey, Stockbridge Village, Liverpool, Merseyside L28 1NW; Tel 0151 489 0270

DAY RESOURCE CENTRES

Halewood Resource Centre Arncliffe Rd, Halewood, Merseyside L25 9PB; Tel 0151 443 2049; 0151 443 2050
Manager H. Jackson

Huyton Resource Centre Princess Dr, Huyton, Merseyside L14 9NQ; Tel 0151 489 4816
Manager D. Hughes

Vocational Support Service Sedburn Rd, Southdene, Kirkby, Merseyside L32 7PB; Tel 0151 549 1446
Manager J.G. Bailey

Westvale Resource Centre Mercer Ave, Kirkby, Merseyside L32 9TU; Tel 0151 546 9703

RESOURCE CENTRES FOR THE ELDERLY

Huyton Resource Centre Tarbock Rd, Huyton, Merseyside L36 5XW; Tel 0151 443 3619
Manager S. Howard

Kirkby Resource Centre James Holt Ave, Westvale, Kirkby, Merseyside L32 5TA; Tel 0151 443 4215
Manager M. Fitzpatrick

MEALS SERVICE

Connaughtons Staff Hse 2, Tarbock Rd, Huyton, Merthyr Tydfil L36 5XW
Manager J. Lavery; Tel 0151 443 3608
Details of local luncheon or old people's clubs are available from the Service Provision Division.

Education Department

Huyton Hey Rd, Huyton, Merseyside L36 5YH; Tel 0151 489 6000
Director (Education) Steve Munby

SPECIAL SCHOOLS

The Elms School Whitethorn Dr, Stockbridge Village, Knowsley, Merseyside L28 1RX;
E-mail theelms.de@knowsley.gov.uk; Tel 0151 477 8350
Headteacher Mrs L. Lowe

Highfield Service Centre Baileys La, Halewood, Merseyside L26 0TY; E-mail highfield.de@knowsley.gov.uk; Tel 0151 486 4787
Headteacher Tom Smith

Knowsley Central Primary Support Centre Mossbrow Rd, Huyton, Merseyside L36 7SY;
E-mail knowsleycentral.de@knowsley.gov.uk; Tel 0151 477 8450
Headteacher Patricia Thomas

Knowsley Northern Primary Support Centre Bramcote Wk, Northwood, Kirkby, Merseyside L33 9UR;
E-mail knowsleynorthern.de@knowsley.de.gov.uk; Tel 0151 477 8140
Headteacher Barbara Twiss

Knowsley Southern Primary Support Centre Arncliffe Rd, Halewood, Knowsley, Merseyside L25 9QE;
E-mail knowsleysouthern.de@knowsley.gov.uk; Tel 0151 486 5514
Headteacher Eric Smith

Parkfield Service Centre Bracknell Ave, Southdene, Knowsley, Merseyside L32 9PW;
E-mail parkfield.de@knowsley.gov.uk; Tel 0151 477 8382
Headteacher Pat Tunna

Springfield School Cawthorne Cl, Southdene, Kirkby, Merseyside L32 3XQ;
E-mail springfield.de@knowsley.gov.uk; Tel 0151 549 1425
Headteacher Ian Cordingley

EDUCATION WELFARE OFFICE

Huyton Hey Road Huyton, Knowsley, Merseyside L36 6YH; Tel 0151 443 3236
Principal Manager (Social Inclusion) Wendy Middlemas

LANCASHIRE COUNTY COUNCIL
www.lancashire.gov.uk

In April 1998 both Blackburn with Darwen and Blackpool councils became unitary authorities and are listed alphabetically within this chapter. The rest of Lancashire retains a two-tier structure.
Population 1 134 974
Political Composition: Lab: 43, Con: 27, LD: 6, Green: 1, Other: 1
PO Box 78, County Hall, Preston, Lancashire PR1 8XJ;
    URL www.lancashire.gov.uk;
    E-mail corporate.communications@css.lancscc.gov.uk;
    Tel 01772 254868; Fax 01772 533553
Chief Executive C.J. Trinick
Director (Education and Cultural Services) Sue Mulvany
Director (Resources) and Deputy Chief Executive Jim Edney;
    Tel 01772 534702; Fax 01772 534701
Director (Environment) G.P. Harding, BEng, CEng, FICE, FIHT, MIMgt
PO Box 9, Guild Hse, Preston, Lancashire PR1 8RD

Social Services Directorate

PO Box 162, East Cliff County Offices, Preston, Lancashire PR1 3EA; Tel (Out of Office Hours) 01772 534868
Director (Social Services) Richard Jones
Assistant Director (Special Projects) J.J. Slater
Head (Strategy and Planning) B. McPherson
Head (Adult Services) O. Carroll
Head (Children and Families) G. Rigg
Head (Business Information) Dave Burnham (Acting)
Head (Finance and Administration) R. Hulme
Head (Human Resources) D.M. Fairclough
Head (Policy and Review) Larry Barker (Acting)
Head (Contracts) Mike Webster
Head (IT) David Lewis (Acting)
Head (Quality Development) L. Barker
Manager (Executive Support) Mike Stewart

Cabinet Members
Cllr C.W. Cheetham (Lab)
30 Lowcroft, Ashurst, Skelmersdale, Lancashire WN8 6TZ;
    E-mail chris.cheetham@cclancscc.gov.uk
Cllr C. Grunshaw (Lab);
    E-mail clive.grunshaw@cclancscc.gov.uk

SOCIAL SERVICES OFFICES

Lancaster and Morecambe

Kensington Road Offices 6–8 Kensington Rd, Morecambe, Lancashire LA4 5LX; Tel 01524 418565

White Cross Office South Rd, Lancaster, Lancashire LA1 4XQ; Tel 01524 66246

Wyre and Fylde

Estates Office Hastings Pl, Lytham St. Annes, Lancashire FY8 5LZ; Tel 01253 738111

Four Lane Ends Office Fleetwood Rd, South, Thornton-Cleveleys, Lancashire FY5 5EB; Tel 01253 866130

Station Road Office 29 Station Rd, Kirkham, Lancashire PR4 2HB; Tel 01772 685318

Preston and South Ribble

Bhailok Court Office Pole St, Preston, Lancashire PR1 1DX; Tel 01772 263689

East Cliff Office PO Box 162, East Cliff County Offices, Preston, Lancashire PR1 3EA; Tel 01772 264404

Greenbank Street Office 155 Greenbank St, Preston, Lancashire PR1 7JS; Tel 01772 404404

Chorley and West Lancashire

Balfour Court Office 4–5 Balfour Crt, Leyland, Preston, Lancashire PR25 2TF; Tel 01772 904600

Brindle Road Office Bamber Bridge, Preston, Lancashire PR5 6UQ; Tel 01772 904650

Peter House Office Peter St, Chorley, Lancashire PR7 2RP; Tel 01257 516000

West Lancashire

Birkrigg Office Digmoor Shopping Pde, 200–206 Birkrigg, Skelmersdale, Lancashire WN8 9HW; Tel 01695 724451

JDO, Greetby Buildings Derby St, Ormskirk, Lancashire L39 2BP; Tel 01695 585800

Ribble Valley and Hyndburn

Blackburn Road Office 4 Blackburn Rd, Rishton, Lancashire BB1 4BS; Tel 01254 887124

Joint Divisional Offices off Pimlico Rd, Clitheroe, Lancashire BB7 2BL; Tel 01200 425146

Union Street Offices 44 Union St, Accrington, Lancashire BB5 1PL; Tel 01254 398731

Burnley and Rossendale

Chaddesley House Office Manchester Rd, Burnley, Lancashire BB11 1HW; Tel 01282 425961

Oakenhead Office Haslingden Old Rd, Rawtenstall, Rossendale, Lancashire BB4 8RR; Tel 01706 211221

Pendle

Carr Road Office 7–11 Carr Rd, Nelson, Lancashire BB9 7JS; Tel 01282 661366

Market Place Office 2a Market Pl, Colne, Lancashire BB8 0HY; Tel 01282 866706

Staff Training Centre

Moor Street Human Resources Unit (Employee Development) Moor St, Kirkham, Preston, Lancashire PR4 2AU; Tel 01772 685214

OBSERVATION AND ASSESSMENT CENTRE FOR CHILDREN

Easden Clough Morse St, Burnley, Lancashire BB10 4PB; Tel 01282 436327
Manager E. Loyd
(24)

CHILD DEVELOPMENT AND SPECIAL NEEDS CENTRES

Bickerstaffe House 53 Garstang Rd, Preston, Lancashire PR1 1LB; Tel 01772 562547
Manager E. Dewhurst
Special needs, child and family consultation service.

Broadoaks Child Development Centre Broad Sq, Balcarres Rd, Leyland, Preston, Lancashire PR25 3ED; Tel 01772 621062
Manager A. Davidson

The Bungalow Respite Care Unit 82a Blackbull La, Preston, Lancashire PR2 3PY; Tel 01772 716252
Manager K. Edmondson
Respite home for children with special needs.

Grimshaw Lane Centre 77a Grimshaw La, Ormskirk, Lancashire L39 1PA; Tel 01695 572861
Manager J. McKenna
Children with learning disabilities.
(4)

Holly House Child Development Centre 6 Blackburn Rd, Rishton, Lancashire BB1 4BS; Tel 01254 888503
Manager D. Bennett
Special needs/intake according to need.

Long Copse Centre 46 Long Copse, Astley Village, Chorley, Lancashire PR7 1TH; Tel 01257 264485
Manager K. Hughes
Children with learning disabilities.
(4)

Ormskirk District Hospital Wigan Rd, Ormskirk, Lancashire L39 2AZ; Tel 01695 577111
Manager C.S. Carlson
Child development centre.

Reedley Cottages Reedley Hall, Colne Rd, Burnley, Lancashire BB10 2LW; Tel 01282 602245
Manager J. May
Respite home/child development centre/special needs (places according to need).

CHILDREN'S COMMUNITY HOMES

Alexandra House Community Home Westbourne Dr, Lancaster, Lancashire LA1 5EE; Tel 01524 37606
Manager E.M. Reakes
Respite homes (PH) for children with special needs.
(7)

Barnacre Road Community Home 2 Barnacre Rd, Longridge, Lancashire PR3 2PD; Tel 01772 782569
Manager J. Shorrock
(8)

Belvedere Road Community Home 39 Belvedere Rd, Thornton-Cleveleys, Lancashire FY5 5DF; Tel 01253 823774
Manager J. Redmond
(7)

Blake Gardens Community Home 14 Blake Gdns, Great Harwood, Lancashire BB6 7JX; Tel 01254 886292
Manager C. Pattinson
(7)

Bowerham Road Community Home 262 Bowerham Rd, Lancaster, Lancashire LA1 4LR; Tel 01524 66171
Manager J. Redpath
Children with LD.
(8)

Briars Hey School Orchard Hse Secure Unit, Mill La, Rainhill, Merseyside L35 6NE; Tel 0151 4309677
Headteacher Louise Tierney
Community home for girls, with education on the premises.
(36)

Carr Street Children's Home 1–5 Carr St, Preston, Lancashire PR1 4HR; Tel 01772 259874
Manager J. Milligan
(11)

Crestmoor Children's Resource Unit Unity Way, off Haslingden Old Rd, Rawtenstall, Rossendale, Lancashire BB4 8RR; Tel 01706 217389
Manager/Network Co-ordinator L. Mills
(21)

Derwent Road Community Home 22 Derwent Rd, Chorley, Lancashire PR7 2JR; Tel 01257 263563
Manager P. Halsall
(7)

Dyke Nook Community Home Whalley Rd, Accrington, Lancashire BB5 8RR; Tel 01254 233547
Manager T. Sutherland
(12)

Elm House Children's Home Lime Gr, Skelmersdale, Lancashire WN8 8ET; Tel 01695 725886
Contact J. Dawson (Acting)
(12)

Garth House Resource and Reception Centre 25 Sandycroft, off Farringdon La, Preston, Lancashire PR2 6LP; Tel 01772 795081
Manager A. Tew
Daycare/teaching/youth setting.
(25)

Glendale Community Home 4 Glendale Cl, Leyland, Preston, Lancashire PR25 3DN; Tel 01772 432694
Manager P. Smith
(20)

Grange Avenue Community Home 61 Grange Ave, Riblbleton, Preston, Lancashire PR2 6PR; Tel 01772 792631
Manager D. Worden
(7)

Hala Grove Community Home 24 Hala Gr, Lancaster, Lancashire LA1 4PS; Tel 01524 65640
Manager E. Wallis
(8)

The Haven Community Home 235 Brunshaw Rd, Burnley, Lancashire BB10 4QR; Tel 01282 428078
Officer-in-Charge Mrs E. Howard
(12)

Haverholt Close Community Home 24a Haverholt Cl, Colne, Lancashire BB8 9SN; Tel 01282 864967
Manager Susan Henks
Small children's home.
(11)

Kingsfold Drive Community Home 33 Kingsfold Dr, Penwortham, Preston, Lancashire PR1 9DN; Tel 01772 743937
Manager A.L. Shenton
(8)

Lancaster Resource/Reception Centre 73 Slyne Rd, Lancaster, Lancashire LA1 2JH; Tel 01524 68076
Manager Gary Pickles
(15)

Larches Avenue Community Home 4 Larches Ave, Ashton, Preston, Lancashire PR2 1LN; Tel 01772 726147
Manager S. Dawson
(8)

6

Maplewood House Community Home Ash Gr, off Collins Rd, Preston, Lancashire PR5 6GY; Tel 01772 336384
Manager C. Greenhalgh
Home for children with severe learning disabilities.
(18)

Marl Hill Crescent Community Home 61 Marl Hill Cres, Moor Nook, Ribbleton, Preston, Lancashire PR2 6LJ; Tel 01772 791786
Manager K. Banks
Residential, with some daycare / teaching.
(8)

Old Vicarage Community Home Whalley Rd, Padiham, Burnley, Lancashire BB12 8JX; Tel 01282 771415
Manager G. Wilkinson
(14)

Warwick Avenue Community Home 4 Warwick Ave, Clayton-le-Moors, Accrington, Lancashire BB5 5RN; Tel 01254 233451
Manager L. Smith
Small children's home.
(8)

Watling Street Road Children's Resource Unit 113a Watling Street Rd, Fulwood, Preston, Lancashire PR2 8BQ; Tel 01772 774952
Manager K. Coulton
Adolescent boys' hostel.
(8)

The Willows Community Home 354 Birley Wood, Skelmersdale, Lancashire W98 9BL; Tel 01695 554020
Manager M. Lees
(18)

FAMILY DAY CENTRES

The Hawthorns Day Centre Gloucester Rd, Chorley, Lancashire PR7 3HN; Tel 01257 279360
Manager M. Thompson
(50)

Skerton Family Day Centre Sefton Dr, Lancaster, Lancashire LA1 2QD; Tel 01524 841256
Manager T. Burzacki
Joint family day centre.
(50)

Sydney Street Day Centre Sydney St, St. Annes-on-Sea, Lytham St. Annes, Lancashire FY8 1TR; Tel 01253 722278
Manager V. Powell
Family day centre (with indeterminate number of places according to need).

Tup Bridge Day Centre Newchurch Rd, Rawtenstall, Rossendale, Lancashire BB4 7QX; Tel 01706 223805
Manager P. Butler
Manager M. Francioli
Multidisciplined planned care development.
(50)

RESOURCE CENTRES FOR PEOPLE WITH DISABILITIES

Hyndburn Resource Centre Nelson St, Accrington, Lancashire BB5 2HQ; Tel 01254 384297
Manager Maureen Lord
Day services for people with physical and sensory disabilities.
(65)

Marsden Resource Centre Rigby St, Nelson, Lancashire BB9 7AA; Tel 01282 692502
Manager D. MacLean
Day services for people with physical and sensory disability.
(65)

Moor Lane Resource Centre Moor La, Preston, Lancashire PR1 3JQ; Tel 01772 556064
Manager M. Peckett
(150)

Oakenhead Resource Centre Haslingden Old Rd, Rawtenstall, Rossendale, Lancashire BB4 8RR; Tel 01706 211124
Manager Ann Smith
Day services for people with physical and sensory disability.
(60)

Temple Street Resource Centre Temple St, Burnley, Lancashire BB11 3BD; Tel 01282 434341
Manager J. Ackroyd
Day services for people with physical and sensory disabilities.
(150)

COMMUNITY RESOURCE CENTRES

The Knoll Resource Centre Westbourne Rd, Lancaster, Lancashire LA1 5EF; Tel 01524 585788
Contact Julie Dockerty

Mental Health Resource Centre (Pathways), St. Aidan's Rd, Bamber Bridge, Preston, Lancashire PR5 6GD; Tel 01772 324285
Social Worker K. Harrison (part-time)
Social Worker M. Downes (part-time)
Social workers attached to multidisciplinary team for people with ME.

Resource Centre 166 Bacup Rd, Rawtenstall, Rossendale, Lancashire BB4 7PA; Tel 01706 225833
Manager K. Hacking
For mentally ill people; jointly managed with Cherry Cres.

Ribblebank Resource Centre Gerrard St, Preston, Lancashire PR1 8NQ; Tel 01772 886885
Manager S. Nunes
LD
(45)

Westfield Resource Centre West Paddock, Leyland, Lancashire PR25 1HR; Tel 01772 622777
Social Worker M. Downes (part-time)
Social worker attached to multidisciplinary team working for people with ME.

CORE AND CLUSTER UNITS

Hyndburn Supported Living Service 98–100 Gloucester Ave, Accrington, Lancashire BB5 4BG; Tel 01254 395060
Team Leader H. Cooney
Support adult (LD) people in Hyndburn Housing Scheme.
(30)

Ribble Valley Supported Living Service off Pimlico Rd, Clitheroe, Lancashire BB7 2BL; Tel 01200 429270
Team Leader A. Russell
(5)

DAY CENTRES FOR PEOPLE WITH LEARNING DISABILITIES

Bankside Day Centre Weldbank La, Chorley, Lancashire PR7 3NQ; Tel 01257 264173
Manager Kim Howarth
Day centre for LD including 10 special needs (on same campus as Welbank Hostel).
(107)

Brownedge Centre Brownedge La, Bamber Bridge, Preston, Lancashire PR5 6TA; Tel 01772 315282
Manager T. Horne
(30)

Bymbrig Day Centre Co-operative St, Bamber Bridge, Preston, Lancashire PR5 6FH; Tel 01772 335351
Manager B. Emerson
(50)

Cedar Crescent Resource Centre 2 Cedar Cres, Kirkham, Lancashire PR4 2TY; Tel 01772 671949
Manager Pat Hirst
(12)

Connolly Day Centre Steeple View, Ashton, Preston, Lancashire PR2 2PQ; Tel 01772 724792
Manager Pat Bound
Provides outreach service.
(30)

Crossways Day Centre West Paddock, Leyland, Lancashire PR25 2HR; Tel 01772 423612
Manager Sue Donovan
Includes 15 special care places, 10 place horticultural unit at Lynnhurst.
(85)

Deepdale Day Centre Sir Tom Finney Way, Preston, Lancashire PR1 6JA; Tel 01772 795444
Manager Sue Langdale
(90)

Ecroyd Day Centre Gibfield Rd, Colne, Lancashire BB8 8JT; Tel 01282 865344
Manager H. Warren (Acting)
Additional 10 special care.
(75)

Enfield Centre Church La, Altham West, Accrington, Lancashire BB5 4DE; Tel 01254 232018
Manager J. McLoughlin
Additional 12 special care.
(78)

Ewood Day Centre Clod La, Haslingden, Rossendale, Lancashire BB4 6LR; Tel 01706 213869
Manager Judith Eardley
Additional 10 special care.
(75)

Fernandes Centre North St, Burnley, Lancashire BB10 1LU; Tel 01282 436807
Manager Sandra Dixon
Day services for mentally ill people and luncheon club for elderly people.
(25)

Larkholme Lodge Day Centre Larkholme Ave, Fleetwood, Lancashire FY7 7PN; Tel 01253 874778
Contact M. Hickey
Additional 12 special care.
(78)

Lynnhurst Horticultural Project Stanifield La, Farington, Leyland, Lancashire PR25 4UA; Tel 01772 456857
Manager S. Donovan
Horticultural project under auspices of Crossways Day Centre.
(10)

Meadowbank Day Centre Mount Pleasant St, Burnley, Lancashire BB11 1LW; Tel 01282 427003
Manager B. Ingham
Additional 10 special care.
(100)

Moss Lea Day Centre off Aughton St, Ormskirk, Lancashire L39 3BS; Tel 01695 574544
Manager Gillian Holt
LD includes 10 special care places; also outreach and community placement work.
(83)

Park View Centre Haven Rd, Lytham, Lancashire FY8 5DJ; Tel 01253 734884
Manager A.C. Esslinger
LD and PH/additional 10 special care.
(60)

Pendleton Brook Day Centre George St, Clitheroe, Lancashire BB7 1BU; Tel 01200 428153
Manager J. Hallam
Additional 20 special care.
(30)

Riverview Centre Langdale Rd, Lancaster, Lancashire LA1 1DL; Tel 01524 60872
Manager Harry Lowder
Additional 12 special care.
(60)

Springbank Day Centre West St, Padiham, Burnley, Lancashire BB12 8JD; Tel 01282 772087
Manager Janet Keys
(60)

Stanley Villas Day Centre 63 Albert Rd, Colne, Lancashire BB8 0BP; Tel 01282 869073
Manager D. Polding
Day services for mentally ill people. Additional 20 places for elderly.
(20)

Sunnybank Day Centre Marquis St, Kirkham, Lancashire PR4 2HY; Tel 01772 684622
Manager P. Kindred
Additional 10 special care.
(50)

Thorpe View Centre Thorpe Ave, Torrisholme, Morecambe, Lancashire LA4 6NG; Tel 01524 414784
Manager H. Lowder
Additional 12 special care.
(65)

Whiteledge Centre Spencers La, Skelmersdale, Lancashire WN8 9JS; Tel 01695 723447
Manager C. Collins (Acting)
LD includes 13 special care places.
(71)

DAY CENTRE FOR PHYSICALLY AND SENSORY HANDICAPPED PEOPLE

Chatsworth Resource Centre Chatsworth Ave, Fleetwood, Lancashire FY3 8AT; Tel 01253 873159
Manager F. Cairney
Planned activity programme in centre and in community.
(65)

SPECIAL CARE UNITS FOR LEARNING DISABILITIES

Meadowfield Rehabilitation Unit 17–19 Meadowfield, Fulwood, Preston, Lancashire PR2 8FX; Tel 01772 860621
Manager Lesley Dixon
Special care unit for LD.
(8)

Moor Park Special Care Unit 19 Moor Park Ave, Preston, Lancashire PR1 6AS; Tel 01772 556200
Manager Lesley Dixon
(18)

ADULT HOSTELS FOR LEARNING DISABILITIES

Broadwater House Hostel Larkholme Ave, Fleetwood, Lancashire FY7 7PN; Tel 01253 874027
Manager Susan Grey
Additional two short term.
(23)

The Heights Community Support Team Aughton View, off Aughton St, Ormskirk, Lancashire L39 3BS; Tel 01695 578131
Team Leader J. Lambert
Dispersed housing (West Lancashire) – hospital resettlement for LD.
(31)

Holmewood View Hostel Clod La, Haslingden, Rossendale, Lancashire BB4 6LR; Tel 01706 214311
Officer-in-Charge J. Selby
Additional three short term.
(24)

Malham Place Hostel 17–19 Malham Pl, Croasdale Ave, Preston, Lancashire PR2 6UB; Tel 01772 700664
Contact Helen Graham
Offers one special care/respite place.
(9)

Preston Community Support Team 34 Porter St, Preston, Lancashire PR1 6QN; Tel 01772 250308
Manager Gary Brown
(8)

6

Priding House Hostel Co-operative St, Bamber Bridge,
Preston, Lancashire PR5 6FH; Tel 01772 335581
Manager Linda Kellett
Offers five special care/respite places.
(27)

West Lancashire Resettlement Team Aughton View, off
Aughton St, Ormskirk, Lancashire L39 3BS; Tel 01695
578131
Team Leader Robin Vian

HOMES FOR THE MENTALLY ILL

Weldbank Hostel and Dispersed Housing Bungalow 2,
Weldbank Hse, Chorley, Lancashire PR7 3NQ; Tel 01257
262280
Manager David Lupton
(28)

Wordsworth Terrace Hostel 52–58 Wordsworth Terr,
Chorley, Lancashire PR6 7AG; Tel 01257 266081
Manager Phil Holmes
Community support team/substantially male service users.
(12)

INDEPENDENCE UNIT FOR THE MENTALLY ILL

Lynnhurst (Hostel) Stanifield La, Farington, Leyland,
Lancashire PR25 4UA; Tel 01772 421564
Contact D. Fletcher-Jones
Includes one emergency place.
(12)

HOMES FOR THE MENTALLY INFIRM

Castleford Day Centre Queens Rd, Clitheroe, Lancashire
BB7 1AR; Tel 01200 443507
Officer-in-Charge E. Pollard
Additional day centre for elderly people; 10 units sheltered
housing.
(45)

Riverview House Langdale Rd, Lancaster, Lancashire
LA1 1DL; Tel 01524 60871
Manager Claire Darwen
LD, additional four short term.
(22)

HOME FOR THE PHYSICALLY AND SENSORILY HANDICAPPED

Lakeland View Laidleys Wlk, Fleetwood, Lancashire
FY7 7JL; Tel 01253 874900
Manager L. Bowden
Additional 10 short term; provides 120 meals on wheels per
week, respite, rehab, daycare.
(40)

DAY CENTRES FOR THE ELDERLY

Cartmel Day Centre Euston Rd, Morecambe, Lancashire
LA4 5NR; Tel 01524 421701
Manager Adah Lishman
(65)

Derby Day Centre Derby St, Ormskirk, Lancashire
L39 2BW; Tel 01695 578452
Manager Jean Despres
(60)

Fosterfield Day Centre Eaves La, Chorley, Lancashire
PR6 0EY; Tel 01257 275183
Manager C. Tudor
Open seven days per week and Friday evenings.
(60)

Leyland Day Centre King St, Leyland, Lancashire
PR25 2LE; Tel 01772 435997
Manager Denny Lindley
30 places and 10 drop-in.
(40)

Sulyard Street Day Centre Sulyard St, Lancaster, Lancashire
LA1 1PX; Tel 01524 381164
Manager Carole Harrison
(35)

HOMES FOR THE ELDERLY

There are 54 local authority homes for elderly people.

Education and Cultural Services Directorate

Business Services Division

County Director J. Bennett (Acting); Tel 01772 261646;
Fax 01772 261331
Manager (County Schools Personnel Services) D. Hewitt;
Tel 01772 261776
Manager (Schools Financial Services) A. Taylor; Tel 01772
261726
Manager (Competiton and Miscellaneous Services) R. Kerfoot;
Tel 01772 261627
Manager (Buildings and Development) J. Newton; Tel 01772
261602
Manager (Budget and Financial Services) J. England;
Tel 01772 261733
Co-ordinator (Performance and Management Review)
C. Garbutt; Tel 01772 261683
Manager (Committee and Office Services Team) A. Cooper;
Tel 01772 261316
Manager (School Policy and Operations) S.J. Mercer;
Tel 01772 261925
Manager (Personnel Services) P. Durham; Tel 01772
263899

Advisory Service

Head (Advisory Service) S. Mulvany;
E-mail sue.mulvany@ed.lancscc.gov.uk; Tel 01772
261652; Fax 01772 261900
Senior Adviser (Special Educational Needs) S. Riley (Acting);
Tel 01772 262713; Fax 01772 261640
Manager (Enterprise and Partnership Strategy) P. Carter;
E-mail paul.carter@ed.lancscc.gov.uk; Tel 01772 261644;
Fax 01772 262436
Manager (Business Development) Laurie Scullard;
E-mail laurie.scullard@ed.lancscc.gov.uk; Tel 01772
261772; Fax 01772 261918
Strategy Manager Janice Marston Standards Fund, EDP,
Finance and Information Systems, Administration and
Finance; E-mail janice.marston@ed.lancscc.gov.uk;
Tel 01772 261904; Fax 01772 261617
Principal Adviser (Foundation, Primary and Management)
L. Crouan; E-mail louis.crouan@ed.lancscc.gov.uk;
Tel 01772 261635; Fax 01772 261617
Principal Adviser (Enterprise and Intervention) G. Dunn;
E-mail graham.dunn@ed.lancscc.gov.uk; Tel 01772
261663; Fax 01772 261525
Principal Adviser (Secondary, Post-16 and Curriculum)
Angela Rawson (Acting);
E-mail angela.rawson@ed.lancscc.gov.uk; Tel 01772
261610; Fax 01772 261576
Senior Adviser Graham Fielden (Acting);
E-mail graham@ict.lancsngfl.ac.uk; Tel 01257 516072;
Fax 01257 516074
Senior Adviser (English Literacy) Lyn Ranson (Acting);
Tel 01257 516060; Fax 01257 516103
Senior Adviser (School and Community Partnership) S. Siner;
E-mail susan.siner@ed.lancscc.gov.uk; Tel 01257 239914;
Fax 01257 239901
Senior Adviser (Maths, Numeracy and Key Skills) G. Bagnall;
E-mail gordon.bagnall@ed.lancscc.gov.uk; Tel 01257
516102 01524 585812; Fax 01257 516103

Senior Adviser (Extended Core and Foundation Curriculum)
S. Styles History, Geography, Science, Modern Foreign
Languages, Design Technology, PE, Art;
E-mail sue.styles@ed.lancscc.gov.uk; Tel 01772 261666;
Fax 01772 261576

Lifelong Learning Division

Head (Lifelong Learning Division) R. Wand; Tel 01772
264004
Manager (County Library Services) D. Lightfoot; Tel 01772
264010
County Museums Officer E. Southworth; Tel 01772 264061
County Archivist B. Jackson; Tel 01772 263026
County Arts Officer L. Prue; Tel 01772 263584
Information Systems Officer D. Carr; Tel 01772 261682
Manager (County Adult and Continuing Education Service)
R. Hooper; Tel 01772 261608
County Youth and Community Officer J. Goffee; Tel 01772
261792

Pupil Services Division

Head (Pupil Services Division) J.K. Wales; Tel 01772 261650;
Fax 01772 261900
Head (Outreach Services) S. Fagg; Tel 01772 261730
Head (SEN Assessment and Educational Psychology Services)
D. Webster; Tel 01772 261661
*Head (Policy and Planning – SEN, Early Years and Behaviour
Support)* G. Hiscox; Tel 01772 261760
Manager (County Access Team) T. Clark; Tel 01772 261655
County Education Welfare Officer A. Hazell; Tel 01772
261613

Performance Management and Review

Team Leader C. Garbutt; Tel 01772 261683
Senior Performance Management Officer S. Blakey; Tel 01772
262764
Performance Management Officer K. Taylor; Tel 01772
262838

AREA OFFICES

Area Office (East)

The Globe Centre, St. James' Sq, Accrington, Lancashire
BB5 0RE; Tel 01254 220500; Fax 01254 220501
*District Team Manager (Hyndburn Youth and Community
Service)* B. Emmett; Tel 01254 876295
District Team Manager (Burnley Youth and Community Service)
L. Rushton; Tel 01282 831040
District Team Manager (Pendle Youth and Community Service)
J. Mason; Tel 01282 862850
*District Team Manager (Ribble Valley Youth and Community
Service)* W. Taylor; Tel 01200 443466
Area Team Leader (Committee and Office and Services Group)
D. Greaves; Tel 01254 220520
Area Team Leader (School Personnel Group) W. Hindle;
Tel 01254 220510
Area Team Leader (School Financial Services Group)
C. Shepherd; Tel 01254 220555
*Area Team Leader (School Policy and Operations Group –
Governor Services)* J. Halshaw; Tel 01254 220503
Area Education Welfare Officer Vacancy
*Senior Education Welfare Officer (Hyndburn, Ribble Valley and
Rossendale)* F. Molloy; Tel 01254 220726
*Senior Education Welfare Officer (Burnley, Pendle and
Rossendale)* M. Sunderland; Tel 01282 612043
*Assistant Principal Educational Psychologist and Area
Assessment Manager* K. Fallon; Tel 01254 220526
Area Officer (Pupil Access Officer) P. Bainbridge; Tel 01254
220706
Assistant Youth and Community Officer C. Reeve; Tel 01254
876295
Senior Adviser (Primary School SSG) S. Cowan; Tel 01254
220530

Area Office (North)

Area Education Office, PO Box 606, White Cross Education
Centre, Quarry Rd, Lancaster, Lancashire LA1 3SQ;
Tel 01524 63243; Fax 01524 581149
*District Team Manager (Lancaster Youth and Community
Service)* J. Gordon; Tel 01524 35099
District Team Manager (Wyre Youth and Community Service)
M. Piela; Tel 01253 893102
District Team Manager (Fylde Youth and Community Service)
M. Stott; Tel 01772 682548
Area Team Leader (Committee and Office Services Group)
G. Gaunt; Tel 01524 581204
Area Team Leader (School Personnel Services Group)
D. Singleton; Tel 01524 581102
Area Team Leader (School Financial Services Group)
R. Livesey; Tel 01524 581101
Senior Area Education Welfare Officer (Lancaster Team)
Kate Gaskell; Tel 01524 585855
Senior Education Welfare Officer (Poulton Team)
Nweeda Khan; Tel 01253 887738
*Assistant Principal Educational Psychologist and Area
Assessment Manager* J. Bradshaw; Tel 01524 581240
Area Pupil Access Officer D. Ormerod; Tel 01524 581213
Area Manager (North Youth and Community Service)
Vacancy
Area Team Leader (Advisory Division) J. Hewitt; Tel 01524
585868

Area Office (South)

Joint Divisional Office, East Cliff, Preston, Lancashire
PR1 3JT; Tel 01772 262719
*District Team Manager (South Ribble Youth and Community
Service)* C. Fenning; Tel 01772 621125
District Team Manager (Preston Youth and Community Service)
M. Raithatha; Tel 01772 261805
District Team Manager (Chorley Youth and Community Service)
G. Murdoch; Tel 01257 268251
*District Team Manager (West Lancashire – Youth and
Community Service)* K. Gillies; Tel 01695 585761
Area Team Leader (Committee and Office Services Group)
D. Wilde; Tel 01772 262718
Area Team Leader (School Personnel Group) C. Allison;
Tel 01772 262106
Area Team Leader (School Financial Services Group) N. Smith;
Tel 01772 262054
*Area Team Leader (School Policy and Operations Group
(Governor Services))* B. Golding; Tel 01772 262162
Senior Education Welfare Officer (Ormskirk Team) A. Kay;
Tel 01695 585752
Area Education Welfare Officer (Chorley Team) G. Vickers;
Tel 01257 239934
*Assistant Principal Educational Psychologist and Area
Assessment Manager* B. Probin; Tel 01772 261597
Area Pupil Access Officer L. Philipson; Tel 01772 261797
Assistant County Youth and Community Officer C. Grant;
Tel 01772 261761
*Senior Adviser and Team Leader (Primary Schools SSG and
Early Years)* T. Thornton; Tel 01257 239928

SPECIAL DAY SCHOOLS/UNITS

Beacon School Tanhouse Rd, Skelmersdale, Lancashire
WN8 6BA; Tel 01695 721066; Fax 01695 732932
Headteacher Mr J.H. Taylor
Mixed

Black Moss School School La, Chapel Hse, Skelmersdale,
Lancashire WN8 8EH; Tel 01695 721487; Fax 01695
559078
Headteacher Mr P.F. Boycott
Mixed 4–18 MLD

Brookfield School, Poulton-le-Fylde Fouldrey Ave,
Poulton-le-Fylde, Lancashire FY6 7HE; Tel 01253 886895;
Fax 01253 882845
Headteacher Mr I.M. Thomas
11–16 EBD

6

Burnley Calder View Community Special School March St, Burnley, Lancashire BB12 0BU; Tel 01282 433946; Fax 01282 839141
Headteacher Mrs F. Entwistle
Mixed 5–16 MLD

Burnley Primrose Hill School Harrogate Cres, Burnley, Lancashire BB10 2NX; Tel 01282 424216; Fax 01282 831419
Headteacher Mr G. McCabe
Mixed 3–16 PD

Burnley Westway School March St, Burnley, Lancashire BB12 0BU; Tel 01282 704499; Fax 01282 704500
Headteacher Mrs J. Grecic
Mixed 3–19 SLD

Chorley Astley Park School Harrington Rd, Chorley, Lancashire PR7 1JZ; Tel 01257 262227; Fax 01257 269074
Headteacher Mr J. McAndrew
Mixed 4–16 MLD

Colne Gibfield School Gibfield Rd, Colne, Lancashire BB8 8JT; Tel 01282 865011; Fax 01282 859096
Headteacher Mr P.D. Wright
Mixed 5–16 MLD

Elms School Moor Pk, Preston, Lancashire PR1 6AU; Tel 01772 792681; Fax 01772 654940
Headteacher Mr S. Artis
Mixed 2–19 SLD

Great Arley School Holly Rd, Thornton, Cleveleys, Lancashire FY5 4HH; Tel 01253 821072; Fax 01253 865073
Headteacher Mrs J.L. Johns
Mixed 4–16 MLD

Great Harwood North Cliffe School Blackburn Old Rd, Great Harwood, Blackburn BB6 7UW; Tel 01254 885245; Fax 01254 877953
Headteacher Mr R.L. Whitaker
Mixed 5–16 MLD

Kingsbury School School La, Chapel Hse, Skelmersdale, Lancashire WN8 8EH; Tel 01695 722991; Fax 01695 51428
Headteacher Mr J. Hajnrych
Mixed 2–19 SLD

Kirkham Pear Tree School Station Rd, Kirkham, Preston, Lancashire PR4 2HA; Tel 01772 683609; Fax 01772 681553
Headteacher Mrs J. Cook
Mixed 2–19 SLD

Lancaster The Loyne School Sefton Dr, Lancaster, Lancashire LA1 2PZ; Tel 01524 64543; Fax 01524 845118
Headteacher Mrs C.M. Murphy
Mixed 2–19 SLD

Lostock Hall Moor Hey School Far Croft, Leyland Rd, Lostock Hall, Preston, Lancashire PR5 5SS; Tel 01772 336976; Fax 01772 696670
Headteacher Mr C.W.T. Wilson
Mixed 4–16 MLD

Mayfield School Gloucester Rd, Chorley, Lancashire PR7 3HN; Tel 01257 263063; Fax 01257 263072
Headteacher Mr P. Monk
Mixed 2–19 SLD

Moorbrook School Ainslie Rd, Fulwood, Preston, Lancashire PR2 3DB; Tel 01772 774752; Fax 01772 713256
Headteacher Mrs W. Fisher (Acting)
Mixed 11–16 EBD

Moorfield School Moor Pk, Preston, Lancashire PR1 6AA; Tel 01772 795378; Fax 01772 651472
Headteacher Mr P. Johnson
Mixed 3–19 PD

Morecambe and Heysham Morecambe Road School Morecambe Rd, Morecambe, Lancashire LA3 3AB; Tel 01524 414384; Fax 01524 426339
Headteacher Mr T.G. Pickles
Mixed 3–16 MLD

Nelson Townhouse School Town Hse Rd, Nelson, Lancashire BB9 8DG; Tel 01282 614013; Fax 01282 691970
Headteacher Mrs D. Morris
Mixed 2–19 SLD

Oswaldtwistle Broadfield School Fielding La, Oswaldtwistle, Accrington, Lancashire BB5 3BE; Tel 01254 381782; Fax 01254 396805
Headteacher Mrs J.E. White
Mixed 5–16 MLD

Oswaldtwistle White Ash School Thwaites Rd, Oswaldtwistle, Accrington, Lancashire BB5 4QG; Tel 01254 235772; Fax 01254 385652
Headteacher Mr B. Frew
Mixed 2–19 SLD

Rawtenstall Cribden House Community Special School Haslingden Rd, Rawtenstall, Rossendale, Lancashire BB4 6RX; Tel 01706 213048; Fax 01706 210553
Headteacher J. Lord
Boys 5–11 EBD

Rossendale Tor View School Clod La, Haslingden, Rossendale, Lancashire BB4 6LR; Tel 01706 214640; Fax 01706 215797
Headteacher Mr A. Squire
Mixed 5–19 MLD and SLD

Sherburn School Moor Pk, Preston, Lancashire PR1 6AA; Tel 01772 795749; Fax 01772 652096
Headteacher Mr M. Moss
Mixed 4–16 MLD

Thornton, Cleveleys Red Marsh School Holly Rd, Thornton, Cleveleys, Lancashire FY5 4HH; Tel 01253 868451; Fax 01253 868451
Headteacher Miss D. Halpin
Mixed 2–19 SLD

Walton-le-Dale, The Coppice School Ash Gr, Bamber Bridge, Preston, Lancashire PR5 6GY; Tel 01772 336342; Fax 01772 620826
Headteacher Mrs A. Jenkins
Mixed 2–19 SLD

RESIDENTIAL SPECIAL SCHOOLS

Bleasdale House School 27 Emesgate La, Silverdale, Carnforth, Lancashire LA5 0RG; Tel 01524 701217; Fax 01524 702044
Headteacher Mrs L. Ormrod
Mixed 2–19 SLD

Massey Hall School Halfacre La, Thelwall, Warrington WA4 3JQ; Tel 01925 752016; Fax 01925 756308
Headteacher Mr C.F. Gleave
Mixed 11–16 EBD

Wennington Hall School Wennington, Lancaster, Lancashire LA2 8NS; Tel 015242 21333; Fax 015242 22140
Headteacher Mr J. Prendergast
Boys 11–16 EBD

COMPLEX LEARNING DIFFICULTIES SERVICE

Hillside School, Longridge Ribchester Rd, Longridge, Preston, Lancashire PR3 3XB; Tel 01772 782205; Fax 01772 782471
Headteacher Mr G. Fitzpatrick
Mixed

PUPIL REFERRAL SERVICE (PRS)/LANCASHIRE EDUCATION MEDICAL SERVICE (LEMS)

8 East Cliff, Preston, Lancashire PR1 3JE; Tel 01772 261853; Fax 01772 262214
PRS/LEMS Manager C. Potter

PORTAGE SERVICES

Lancaster c/o Ridge CP School, Keswick Rd, Lancaster, Lancashire LA1 3LE; Tel 01524 847140; Fax 01524 847140
Contact Claire Goss

LANCASHIRE EDUCATION MEDICAL SERVICE

East Lancashire Education Medical Service The Globe, St. James Sq, Accrington, Lancashire BB5 0RE; Tel 01254 220785; Fax 01254 220787
Contact K. Mendoros

North Lancashire Education Medical Service Storey Hse, White Cross Est, South Rd, Lancaster, Lancashire LA1 4XQ; Tel 01524 585838
Contact D. Wood

South Lancashire Education Medical Service Joint Divisional Offices, 5th Fl, East Cliff, Preston, Lancashire PR1 3JT; Tel 01772 261572
Contact P. Probin

PUPIL REFERRAL SERVICE AREA TEAMS

Primary North Ringway Pupil Referral Unit, Ringway, Thornton-Cleveleys, Lancashire FY5 2NL; Tel 01253 850714
Contact S. Bonney

Secondary North 33 Hornby Rd, Caton, Lancaster, Lancashire LA2 9QW; Tel 01524 771632/3
Contact L. McKee

Primary South Centurion Hse, Leyland, Lancaster, Lancashire PR5 2GR; Tel 01772 455649
Contact K. Loten

Secondary South Minster Lodge Pupil Referral Unit, Ruff La, Ormskirk, Lancashire L39 4QX; Tel 01695 575486
Contact G. Lucy (Acting)

Primary East Rishton Pupil Referral Unit, 7 Station Rd, Blackburn, Lancashire BB1 4HF; Tel 01254 887116
Contact B. Whittaker (Acting)

Secondary East Rawtenstall Education Office, 1 Grange St, Rawtenstall, Lancashire BB4 7RT; Tel 01706 211149
Contact P. Cooper

PUPIL REFERRAL SERVICE/LANCASHIRE EDUCATION MEDICAL SERVICE INCLUDING CAMHS – SOUTH AREA

PUPIL REFERRAL UNITS

Burnley Pupil Referral Unit Swindon St, Burnley, Lancashire BB1 4PF; Tel 01282 434253; Fax 01282 434253
Headteacher Mrs J. Smith

Golden Hill Pupil Referral Unit Earnshaw Dr, Leyland, Preston, Lancashire PR5 1QS; Tel 01772 904780; Fax 01772 904781
Headteacher Mrs S. Parr
Mixed 5–11

Lancaster Pupil Referral Unit Bowerham Rd, Lancaster, Lancashire LA1 4HT; Tel 01524 671614; Fax 01524 841239
Headteacher Mr D. Ramsbottom
Mixed 5-11

Larches House Pupil Referral Unit
Contact Mr M. Frost
9–16

Marles Hill Pupil Referral Unit 150 Wheatley Lane Rd, Barrowford, Nelson, Lancashire BB9 6QQ; Tel 01282 615862; Fax 01282 603372
Headteacher Mrs D. Learoyd
11–16

Minster Lodge Pupil Referral Unit Ruff La, Ormskirk, Lancashire L39 4QX; Tel 01695 575486; Fax 01695 575150
Headteacher Mr D. Owen (Acting)
11–16

Pendle Pupil Referral Unit Hendon Brook, Townhouse Rd, Nelson, Lancashire BB9 8BP; Tel 01282 693432
Headteacher Mrs G.B. Laycock
Mixed 5–11

Preston Pupil Referral Unit Cromwell Rd, Ribbleton, Preston, Lancashire PR2 6YD; Tel 01772 796603; Fax 01772 652263
Headteacher Mrs J. Holmes
5–11

Rishton Pupil Referral Unit 7 Station Rd, Rishton, Blackburn BB1 4HF; Tel 01254 887116; Fax 01254 887116
Headteacher Mrs B. Whittaker
5–11

Rossendale Pupil Referral Unit Burnley Rd, Rawtenstall, Lancashire BB4 8HY; Tel 01706 215977; Fax 01706 215500
Headteacher Mrs L. Hurley
5–11

Thornton Cleveleys Ringway Ringway, Thornton-Cleveleys, Lancashire FY5 2NL; Tel 01253 821516; Fax 01253 850842
Contact S.L. Whittaker
EBD

LEEDS CITY COUNCIL
www.leeds.gov.uk

6

Population 727 500 (approx)
Political Composition: Lab: 52, Con: 22, LD: 20, Green: 3, Ind: 2
Civic Hall, Leeds, West Yorkshire LS1 1UR;
    URL www.leeds.gov.uk; Tel 0113 234 8080
Lord Mayor Cllr D.E. Hudson
Chief Executive Paul Rogerson
Deputy Chief Executive D. Page
Deputy Chief Executive P.R. Cook
Director (Legal and Democratic Services) Nicole Jackson
Director (Leisure Services) J. Davies
Director (City Services) R. Brown
Director (Leeds Development Agency) J.D. Ansbro
Director (Housing Services) E. Bowen
Director (Planning) J. Lynch
Director (Highways and Transportation) J. McArthur
Director (Community Planning and Regulations) A. Taylor
Chief Financial Officer A. Gay

Social Services Department

110 Merrion Centre, Leeds, West Yorkshire LS2 8QB;
    URL www.leeds.gov.uk; Tel 0113 247 8630; Fax 0113 247 7779
Director (Social Services) Keith Murray
Chief Officer (Support Services) Ray France
Chief Officer (Adult Services) Mike Evans
Chief Officer (Strategy and Performance) John England
Head of Service (Learning Disabilities) D. Rosser
Manager (Community Services) A. Pugh
Manager (Personnel) Eileen Stanton
Manager (Residential and Day Care – Adults) P. Hardy
Manager (Residential and Day Care – Children) Eric Shedlow
Manager (Community Services) Anthony Griffin (Acting)
Manager (Performance Review) Liz Bradbury
Manager (Strategic Planning) D. Holmes
Manager (Fostering and Adoptions Resource Team) Rodger Walker
Manager (Communications) Mike Sells

TRAINING

The following have responsibility for training professional and support staff in the department.
Manager (Training) T. Cartmell; Tel 0113 247 8562
Senior Officer (Training) Anne Moseley
Senior Officer (Training) Averil Rushton
Training and Development Officer (Mental Health)
    C. Murphy; Tel 0113 247 8564

Training and Development Officer (Children) Helen Evans;
Tel 0113 247 8603
Training and Development Officer (Older People) M. Lawson;
Tel 0113 224 3519
Training and Development Officer (Child Protection)
Angie Waterton; Tel 0113 224 3520

Social Services Committee

Lab: 7, Con: 1, LD: 1
Chair B. Walker (Lab)
Civic Hall, Leeds, West Yorkshire LS1 1UR
Deputy Chair A. Hudson (Lab)
Members of the Committee
Lab: M. Bedford, S. Bradley, E. Minkin, T. Murray,
K. Wakefield.
Con: A. Carter.
LD: M. Harris.

AREA OFFICES

Armley Area Office

Redcourt, Church Rd, Leeds, West Yorkshire LS12 1TY;
Tel 0113 214 3500; Fax 0113 214 3513

Belle Isle Office

92 Windmill Rd, Leeds, West Yorkshire LS10 3HJ; Tel 0113
214 1740; Fax 0113 214 1770

Bramley Area Office

2 Westover Rd, Bramley, Leeds, West Yorkshire LS13 3PG;
Tel 0113 214 6014; Fax 0113 214 6028

Crossgates Area Office

Library Bldgs, Farm Rd, Leeds, West Yorkshire LS15 7LB;
Tel 0113 247 7250; Fax 0113 247 7227

Garforth Office

Main St, Garforth, Leeds, West Yorkshire LS25 1DU;
Tel 0113 247 7033; Fax 0113 247 7031

Hough Lane Office

Hough Lane Centre, Bramley, Leeds, West Yorkshire
LS13 3RD; Tel 0113 214 6001; Fax 0113 214 6013

Hunslet Hall Area Office

Hunslet Hall, Disraeli Terr, Leeds, West Yorkshire
LS11 6UA; Tel 0113 214 1600; Fax 0113 214 1603

Middleton Advice Centre

2 Acre Rd, Leeds, West Yorkshire LS10 4DD; Tel 0113 214
1884; Fax 0113 214 1731

Morley Area Office

Morley District Council Offices, Morley Town Hall, Leeds,
West Yorkshire LS27 9DY; Tel 0113 247 7194; Fax 0113
247 7154
Area Manager M. Harrison

Otley Office

8 Boroughgate, Otley, West Yorkshire LS21 3AM; Tel 0113
247 7715; Fax 0113 247 7798

Pudsey Office

Pudsey Town Hall, Pudsey, Leeds, West Yorkshire
LS28 7BN; Tel 0113 247 7784; Fax 0113 247 7776

Rawdon Area Office

Micklefield Hse, Rawdon, Leeds, West Yorkshire LS19 6DF;
Tel 0113 247 7605; Fax 0113 247 7651

Rothwell Office

Civic Bldgs, Marsh St, Rothwell, West Yorkshire LS26 0AE;
Tel 0113 247 7085; Fax 0113 247 7076

Roundhay Road Area Office

79 Roundhay Rd, Leeds, West Yorkshire LS7 4AA; Tel 0113
247 7400; Fax 0113 247 7358
Area Manager J. Coleman

Seacroft Area Office

Irford Hse, Seacroft Centre, Leeds, West Yorkshire
LS14 0PA; Tel 0113 214 4254; Fax 0113 214 4264

Stanningley Office

10 Gladstone Terr, Leeds, West Yorkshire LS28 6NE;
Tel 0113 214 6060; Fax 0113 214 6046

West Park Area Office

West Park Curriculum Centre, Spen La, Leeds, West
Yorkshire LS16 5BE; Tel 0113 274 9492; Fax 0113 274 9493

Wetherby Office

Council Offices, Westgate, Wetherby, West Yorkshire
LS22 4NL; Tel 0113 224 3490; Fax 0113 247 7258

White Rose House Area Office

Buckingham Hse, 41 Headingley La, Leeds, West Yorkshire
LS6 1BL; Tel 0113 247 7424; Fax 0113 247 7459

York Towers Area Office

383 York Rd, Leeds, West Yorkshire LS9 6AT; Tel 0113 214
3400; Fax 0113 214 3401
Area Manager P. Dwyer

ONE STOP CENTRES

Osmonthorpe One Stop Centre 81a Wykebeck Mount,
Leeds, West Yorkshire LS9 0JE; Tel 0113 247 7699; Fax 0113
247 8872
Manager (Customer Services) D. Sayers
The Centre is a joint venture and includes: Housing,
Community Benefits and Rights and the Community
Mental Health Service.

South Seacroft One Stop Service 91–95 Moresdale La,
Leeds, West Yorkshire LS14 6GG; Tel 0113 247 8833;
Fax 0113 247 5009
Manager (Customer Services) P. Cunningham
The Centre includes the Community Mental Health
Service, the local GP's Surgery and a chemist. Welfare
Rights advice is also available Mon, Weds and Fri.

HOSPITAL SOCIAL WORK STAFF

Chapel Allerton Hospital Leeds, West Yorkshire; Tel 0113
392 4850
Principal Social Worker G. Chapman

Cookridge Hospital Leeds, West Yorkshire; Tel 0113 392
4234
Principal Social Worker G. Sharp

High Royds Hospital Menston, Leeds, West Yorkshire
LS29 6AQ; Tel 01943 876151
Health Team Manager D. Wright; Tel 01943 876151 ext 6343

Ida and Robert Arthington Hospital Hospital La, Leeds,
West Yorkshire LS16 6QA; Tel 0113 267 3411

Leeds Chest Clinic 74 New Briggate, Leeds, West Yorkshire LS1 6PH; Tel 0113 295 1100; Fax 0113 293 0536

Leeds General Infirmary Great George St, Leeds, West Yorkshire LS1 3EX; Tel 0113 392 6851
Health Team Manager J. Khan

Meanwood Park Hospital Leeds, West Yorkshire; Tel 0113 275 8721

St. James's Hospital Beckett St, Leeds, West Yorkshire LS9 7TF; Tel 0113 206 4391
Health Team Manager P. Heydon

Seacroft and Killingbeck Hospitals Leeds, West Yorkshire; Tel 0113 264 8164
Principal Social Worker A. Gore

Wharfedale General Hospital, Otley Branch Newall Carr Rd, Otley, Leeds, West Yorkshire LS21 2LY; Tel 01943 3923037
Principal Social Worker G. Chapman

CRISIS SERVICE

Leeds Crisis Centre 3 Spring Rd, Headingley, Leeds, West Yorkshire LS6 1AD; Tel 0113 275 5898
Places available for other authorities.

REGIONAL SECURE UNIT

Regional Secure Unit East Moor La, Adel, Leeds, West Yorkshire LS16 8EB; Tel 0113 261 0031; Fax 0113 267 7218
Principal F. Njie

DAY CENTRES

Firthfields Day Centre Conisborough La, Garforth, Leeds, West Yorkshire LS25 2LR; Tel 0113 232 0550

Laurel Bank Day Centre 100 Middleton Park Ave, Leeds, West Yorkshire LS10 4HY; Tel 0113 271 4706
(50)

Rose Farm Day Centre Cornwall Cres, Rothwell, Leeds, West Yorkshire LS26 0RA; Tel 0113 282 2228
(30)

Rowan Gardens Day Centre Broom Pl, Leeds, West Yorkshire LS10 3JP; Tel 0113 271 9711

Springfield Day Centre Cottingley Dr, Leeds, West Yorkshire LS11 0JP; Tel 0113 277 1472

SMALL CHILDREN'S HOMES

Bodmin Road Children's Home 4 Bodmin Rd, Beeston, Leeds, West Yorkshire LS10 4PJ; Tel 0113 214 1707
(6)

Cranmer Bank Children's Home 21 Cranmer Bank, Moortown, Leeds, West Yorkshire LS17 5LE; Tel 0113 268 5519
(8)

Easdale Close Children's Home 9 Easdale Cl, Seacroft, Leeds, West Yorkshire LS14 6QF; Tel 0113 214 4174; 0113 214 4175
(6)

Ganners Green Children's Home 9 Ganners Grn, Bramley, Leeds, West Yorkshire LS13 2PB; Tel 0113 257 6191
(6)

Iveson Approach Children's Home 22 Iveson Approach, Leeds, West Yorkshire LS16 6NT; Tel 0113 230 0753
(6)

Lambrigg Crescent Children's Home 25 Lambrigg Cres, Seacroft, Leeds, West Yorkshire LS14 6JH; Tel 0113 214 4174
(6)

Lingfield Approach Children's Home 14a Lingfield Approach, Moortown, Leeds, West Yorkshire LS17 7HL; Tel 0113 268 6511
(6)

Luttrell Crescent Children's Home 23 Luttrell Cres, Leeds, West Yorkshire LS16 6LU; Tel 0113 267 8361
(6)

St. Catherine's Drive Children's Home 79 St. Catherine's Dr, Bramley, Leeds, West Yorkshire LS13 2JY; Tel 0113 257 6104
(6)

LARGE CHILDREN'S HOMES

Holmfield Children's Home 1 North Hill Rd, Leeds, West Yorkshire LS6 2EN; Tel 0113 230 2950
(14)

Inglewood Children's Home 2 Whiteley Croft Garth, Otley, Leeds, West Yorkshire LS21 3NT; Tel 01943 467213
(16)

Wood Lane Children's Home 15 Wood La, Headingley, West Yorkshire LS6 2AT; Tel 0113 275 4028

HOMES FOR CHILDREN WITH LEARNING DIFFICULTIES

Broom Court Children's Home Broom Pl, Leeds, West Yorkshire LS10 3JP; Tel 0113 277 2958
(14)

Pinfolds Children's Home Pinfold Sq, Field Terr, Leeds, West Yorkshire LS15 7RE; Tel 0113 260 5061
(15)

Wesley Street Group Home 25–27 Wesley St, Morley, West Yorkshire LS27 6EE; Tel 0113 252 2105

LEAVING CARE PROJECT

Leaving Care Support Team 9 Foxcroft Cl, Leeds, West Yorkshire LS6 3NT; Tel 0113 214 4566; Fax 0113 275 5946
(6)

HOMES FOR ADULTS WITH LEARNING DIFFICULTIES

Baileys House Bailey Hill, Leeds, West Yorkshire LS14 6PS; Tel 0113 214 4170
(24)

Delph Manor Delph View, Leeds, West Yorkshire LS6 2PE; Tel 0113 214 5279
(24)

Healey Croft Westerton Rd, West Ardsley, Wakefield, West Yorkshire WF3 1NR; Tel 0113 253 2184
(31)

Joseph Street Home 7 Joseph St, Hunslet, Leeds, West Yorkshire LS10 3BE; Tel 0113 276 0319

Mawcroft Grange Mawcroft Grange Dr, Apperley La, Rawdon, West Yorkshire LS19 6DA; Tel 0113 250 6826
(25)

Roos Court 35 Batchelor La, Horsforth, Leeds, West Yorkshire LS18 5NA; Tel 0113 258 1226

Rossedene Railsfield Way, Bramley, Leeds, West Yorkshire LS13 3AU; Tel 0113 256 7277
(24)

Templar's Croft Audby La, Wetherby, Leeds, West Yorkshire LS22 7FD; Tel 01937 584127
(30)

Windlesford Green Holmsley La, Woodlesford, Leeds, West Yorkshire LS26 8RY; Tel 0113 282 6114
(25)

SHELTERED WORKSHOP

Roseville Enterprises 65 Roundhay Rd, Leeds, West Yorkshire LS7 3BQ; Tel 0113 214 3151

DAY CENTRES FOR PEOPLE RECOVERING FROM MENTAL ILLNESS

Roundhay Road Day Centre 79 Roundhay Rd, Leeds, West Yorkshire LS7 4AA; Tel 0113 247 7309
(50)

6

Stocks Hill Day Centre Chapel La, Leeds, West Yorkshire LS12 2DJ; Tel 0113 279 3836
(50)

The Vale Day Centre Church St, Leeds, West Yorkshire LS10 2AP; Tel 0113 271 3337
(60)

ACCOMMODATION FOR PEOPLE RECOVERING FROM MENTAL ILLNESS

Bewerley Croft Northcote Dr, Beeston, Leeds, West Yorkshire LS11 6NJ; Tel 0113 246 8741

Cottingley Court Cottingley Approach, Leeds, West Yorkshire LS11 0HP; Tel 0113 270 7901

Lee Grange Westerton Rd, West Ardsley, Wakefield, West Yorkshire WF3 1BD; Tel 0113 204 9100

Spen Croft Spen La, Leeds, West Yorkshire LS16 5EJ; Tel 0113 214 4647

ADULT TRAINING CENTRES

Bramley Training Centre Railsfield Rise, Leeds, West Yorkshire LS13 3AA; Tel 0113 256 8686
(150)

Horsforth Training Centre Church La, Horsforth, Leeds, West Yorkshire LS18 5LA; Tel 0113 258 4966
Including an adult special care day unit (25) (105)

Moor End Training Centre Tulip St, off Beza Rd, Leeds, West Yorkshire LS10 2BR; Tel 0113 270 7920
(150)

Potternewton Work Skills Centre Potternewton View, Leeds, West Yorkshire LS7 2DW; Tel 0113 262 6549

Ramshead Wood Training Centre Ramshead Approach, Leeds, West Yorkshire LS14 1HH; Tel 0113 214 4168
Including an adult special care day unit (25) (150)

Rothwell Training Centre Holmsley La, Woodlesford, Leeds, West Yorkshire LS26 8RY; Tel 0113 282 6042
(80)

West Ardsley Training Centre Westerton Rd, West Ardsley, Wakefield, West Yorkshire WF3 1NR; Tel 0113 253 7719
Includes special care unit (25) (135)

Wetherby Training Centre Sandbeck Way, Wetherby, Leeds, West Yorkshire LS22 7DN; Tel 01937 585717
(100)

HOME FOR PEOPLE WITH A PHYSICAL DISABILITY

Cliffdene Cliff Rd, Leeds, West Yorkshire LS6 2NR; Tel 0113 278 7013
(26)

DAY CENTRES FOR OLDER PEOPLE

Bramley Lawn Centre Rossefield Approach, Bramley, Leeds, West Yorkshire LS13 3RG; Tel 0113 255 2404

Calverlands Day Centre Church La, Horsforth, Leeds, West Yorkshire LS18 5LA; Tel 0113 239 0265

Doreen Hamilton Centre Rookwood Rd, Leeds, West Yorkshire LS9 0NH; Tel 0113 249 1169

Farfield Day Centre Farfield Ave, Leeds, West Yorkshire LS28 5HD; Tel 0113 255 1355

Firthfields Day Centre Dover St, Conisborough La, Leeds, West Yorkshire LS25 2LP; Tel 0113 232 0551

Frederick Hurdle Day Centre Reginald Terr, Leeds, West Yorkshire LS7 3EZ; Tel 0113 262 2861

The Green Day Centre Baileys La, Seacroft, Leeds, West Yorkshire LS14 6JL; Tel 0113 214 4167

Holbeck Day Centre Holbeck Moor Rd, Leeds, West Yorkshire LS11 9QL; Tel 0113 242 2027

Hyde Park Day Centre Woodsley Rd, Leeds, West Yorkshire LS3 1DX; Tel 0113 245 4870

Laurel Bank Day Centre 100 Middleton Park Ave, Leeds, West Yorkshire LS10 4HY; Tel 0113 271 4707

Lincoln Fields Day Centre Cromwell St, Leeds, West Yorkshire LS9 7SG; Tel 0113 243 4032

Middlecross Day Centre Simpson Gr, Leeds, West Yorkshire LS12 1QG; Tel 0113 231 0357

Naburn Court Day Centre Naburn Approach, Leeds, West Yorkshire LS14 2DF; Tel 0113 214 4165

Queenswood Day Centre 244 Queenswood Dr, Leeds, West Yorkshire LS6 3ND; Tel 0113 275 8525

Radcliffe Lane Day Centre Pudsey, Leeds, West Yorkshire LS28 8AB; Tel 0113 255 4737

Richmond Hill Day Centre Walter Cres, Richmond Hill, Leeds, West Yorkshire LS9 8RZ; Tel 0113 248 1383

Rose Farm Day Centre Cornwall Cres, Rothwell, Leeds, West Yorkshire LS26 0RA; Tel 0113 282 2228

Siegen Manor Day Centre Wesley St, Morley, Leeds, West Yorkshire LS27 9EE; Tel 0113 253 6116

Springfield Day Centre Cottingley Dr, Leeds, West Yorkshire LS11 0JP; Tel 0113 277 0950

Stocks Hill Day Centre Chapel La, Armley, Leeds, West Yorkshire LS12 2DJ; Tel 0113 279 3836

The Vale Day Centre Church St, Hunslet, Leeds, West Yorkshire LS10 2AP; Tel 0113 271 3337

Woodhouse Day Centre Pennington St, Leeds, West Yorkshire LS6 2JP; Tel 0113 242 5709

Wykebeck Valley Day Centre Wykebeck Valley Rd, Leeds, West Yorkshire LS9 6NR; Tel 0113 248 3842

ACCOMMODATION FOR OLDER PEOPLE

There are 24 local authority homes for older people, five voluntary homes and over 100 local authority sheltered housing schemes.

ACCOMMODATION FOR ELDERLY PEOPLE WITH MENTAL HEALTH PROBLEMS

Aged persons' homes for people with dementia or severe confusion (referral via social worker).

Musgrave Court Home Crawshaw Rd, Pudsey, Leeds, West Yorkshire LS28 7UB; Tel 0113 214 6186

Middlecross Home Simpson Gr, Leeds, West Yorkshire LS12 1QG; Tel 0113 279 8484

MEALS SERVICES

Department of Social Service 110 Merrion Centre, Leeds, West Yorkshire LS2 8QB; Tel 0113 247 8630

Jewish Welfare Board 311 Stonegate Rd, Leeds, West Yorkshire LS17 6AS; Tel 0113 268 4211

Education Leeds

Merrion Hse, 110 Merrion Centre, Leeds, West Yorkshire LS2 8DT; Tel 0113 247 5590; Fax 0113 247 5611
Chief Executive Chris Edwards
Assistant Chief Executive (Social Inclusion) Sonia Sharp
Strategic Manager (Human Resources) P. Toner
Strategic Manager (Behaviour and Attendance) Carol Jordan

EDUCATION PSYCHOLOGY SERVICE

Principal Educational Psychologist Tom Kelly

SPECIAL SCHOOLS

Broomfield School Broom Pl, Leeds, West Yorkshire
LS10 3JP; Tel 0113 214 1708
Headteacher D.M.W. Dewhirst, BA
 Nursery unit

Elmete Wood School Elmete La, Leeds, West Yorkshire
LS8 2LJ; Tel 0113 214 4190
Headteacher W.J. Chatwin

Grafton School Craven Rd, Leeds, West Yorkshire LS6 2SN;
Tel 0113 293 0323
Headteacher M. Purches
 Motor development unit attached.

Green Meadows School Bradford Rd, Guiseley, West
Yorkshire LS20 8PP; Tel 01943 876362 01943 878536
Headteacher Diane E. Seed
 Nursery unit attached.

John Jamieson School Hollin Hill Dr, Leeds, West
Yorkshire LS8 2PW; Tel 0113 293 0236
Headteacher Sally Joy
 Nursery unit attached.

Milestone School 4 Town St, Stanningley, West Yorkshire
LS28 6HL; Tel 0113 214 6107
Headteacher Peter Miller

Penny Field School Tongue La, Leeds, West Yorkshire
LS6 4QE; Tel 0113 214 4510
Headteacher H.M. Barrett

Stonegate School Stonegate Rd, Leeds, West Yorkshire
LS6 4QJ; Tel 0113 214 4521
Headteacher P.W. Bailey

Victoria Park School Victoria Park Gr, Leeds, West
Yorkshire LS13 2RD; Tel 0113 214 4512
Headteacher P. Miller

West Oaks School Westwood Way, Boston Spa, West
Yorkshire LS23 6DX; Tel 01937 844772
Headteacher H. McEwan
 Nursery unit attached.

LEICESTER CITY COUNCIL
www.leicester.gov.uk

Leicester City Council covers an area of approximately
7337 hectares. The Council became a unitary authority on
1 April 1997, providing all Local Government services to its
citizens.
Please contact the Council directly for current personnel
and departmental information.
New Walk Centre, Welford Pl, Leicester LE1 6ZG;
 URL www.leicester.gov.uk; Tel 0116 254 9922

Social Care and Health Directorate

New Walk Centre, Welford Pl, Leicester, Leicestershire
 LE1 6ZG; E-mail cozea001@leicester.gov.uk; Tel 0116 252
 8300; Fax 0116 224 7147
Corporate Director (Social Care and Health) Andrew Cozens
Service Director (Older People) Elaine Yardley
Service Director (Adults) Bhupen Dave
Service Director (Children and Family Resources)
 Kim Bromley-Derry
Service Director (Children and Family Assessment and Strategy)
 Andrew Bunyan
Service Director (Resources) David Oldershaw
Service Manager (Home Care) Maureen Dover
The Rowans, Collegiate St, Leicester; Tel 0116 221 1511;
 Fax 0116 221 1535
Service Manager (Residential Care/Older People)
 Pravin Lukka

The Rowans, Collegiate St, Leicester, Leicestershire;
 Tel 0116 221 1555; Fax 0116 221 1550
Service Manager (Learning Disabilities) Dave Durrant
Greyfriars, Leicester LE1 5PH; Tel 0116 256 5142; Fax 0116
 256 5058
Service Manager (Planning and Service Development)
 Sue Batty
Town Hall, Town Hall Sq, Leicester; Tel 0116 225 4769;
 Fax 0116 225 4754
Service Manager (Access/Older People) Mary McCausland
The Rowans, Collegiate St, Leicester; Tel 0116 256 8301;
 Fax 0116 256 5058
Service Manager (Mental Health – Older People)
 Bindu Parmar; Tel 0116 256 5291; Fax 0116 256 5058
Service Manager (Promoting Independence) Deborah Perry
Grey Friars, Leicester LE1 5PH; Tel 0116 256 8301; Fax 0116
 256 5058
Head (Learning Disabilities Services) Shaun O'Leary;
 Tel 0116 256 5149; Fax 0116 256 5058
Service Manager (Health Action Zone/Health Partnerships)
 Mandy Goode
The Rowans, Collegiate St, Leicester; Tel 0116 221 1564;
 Fax 0116 221 1550
Principal Officer (Children Looked After) Julie Jordan
Eagle Hse, Friar La, Leicester; Tel 0116 299 5881
Principal Officer (Children Looked After) Maggie McGrath;
 Tel 0116 299 5879
Service Manager (Child Protection and Independent Review)
 Pat Nawrockyi; Tel 0116 225 4706; Fax 0116 225 4746
Service Manager (Placements) Mark Tingley; Tel 0116 299
 5878; Fax 0116 299 5887
Service Manager (Children Residential) Mike Evans
Eagle Hse, Friar La, Leicester; Tel 0116 299 5875; Fax 0116
 299 5887
Service Manager (Children's Duty and Assessment Service)
 Kathy Summerton
Grey Friars, Leicester LE1 5PH; Tel 0116 256 5082; Fax 0116
 256 5067
Service Manager (Child Care) Carol Shaw
1 Grey Friars, Leicester LE1 5PM; Tel 0116 256 8292;
 Fax 0116 256 5192
Service Manager (Child Care Operations) Andy Smith
Beaumont Way, Leicester LE4 1EL; Tel 0116 299 5707;
 Fax 0116 299 5777
Service Manager (Child Care Operations) Dave Starling
Grey Friars, Leicester LE1 5PH; Tel 0116 256 5023; Fax 0116
 256 5192
Service Manager (Children and Family Resources)
 Bernice Bennett
Hillview, 1b Blackmore Dr, Leicester LE3 1LP; Tel 0116 285
 8032; Fax 0116 285 9077
Service Manager (Youth Offending Team) Mary Campagnac
Eagle Hse, Friar La, Leicester; Tel 0116 299 5843; Fax 0116
 233 6003
Service Manager (Children's Services Planning Unit)
 Hilal Barwany
Town Hall, Town Hall Sq, Leicester; Tel 0116 225 4723
*Service Manager (Disabled Children Co-ordination, Health
 Action Zone)* Chris Bush
Fosse Neighbourhood Centre, Mantle Rd, Leicester
 LE35 5HQ; Tel 0116 223 2290
Service Manager (Drugs Action Team) Kate Galoppi
Troon Bus Pk, Humberstone La, Leicester; Tel 0116 258
 8988; Fax 0116 258 8722
Manager (Emergency Duty Team) George Giez
Grey Friars, Leicester LE1 5PH; Tel 0116 256 8299; Fax 0116
 256 8269

CHILDREN AND FAMILY CENTRES

Belgrave Family Centre Cossington St, Leicester LE4 6JD;
Tel 0116 266 1894; Fax 0116 268 1618

Bishopdale Family Centre Bishopdale Rd, Beaumont Leys,
Leicester LE4 0SR; Tel 0116 235 7756

Charnwood Family Centre Kingfisher Ave, Charnwood Est,
Leicester LE5 3SS; Tel 0116 253 1319; Fax 0116 251 8326

6

Johnston Family Centre Catesby St, Leicester LE3 5PB; Tel 0116 251 9992; Fax 0116 285 6079

Jubilee Family Centre Gallards Hill, Leicester LE3 1QQ; Tel 0116 285 5871

Mayfield Centre Mayfield Rd, Leicester LE3 1LR; Tel 0116 254 8855; Fax 0116 247 1052

St. Andrew's Family Centre 25 Grisedale Cl, St. Andrew's Est, Leicester LE2 7HG; Tel 0116 254 1013

St. Christopher's Family Centre The Crossway, Saffron La, Leicester LE2 6QW; Tel 0116 283 2662

St. Peter's Family Centre 20 Barnard Cl, St. Peter's Est, Leicester LE2 0TX; Tel 0116 262 0710; Fax 0116 251 8859

DAY SERVICES FOR PEOPLE WITH LEARNING DIFFICULTIES

Fosse Day Centre Aylestone Rd, Leicester LE2 7LF; Tel 0116 247 0020; Fax 0116 247 0020

Hastings Road Day Centre 120 Hastings Rd, Leicester LE5 0HL; Tel 0116 276 2856

Layton House Resource Centre Frewin St, Leicester LE5 0PA; Tel 0116 221 1300

DAY CENTRES FOR PEOPLE WITH MENTAL HEALTH DIFFICULTIES

Martin House Day Centre 341 London Rd, Leicester LE2 3JX; Tel 0116 270 9423; Fax 0116 270 0169

Nia Day Centre The Rowans, College St, Leicester LE2 0JJ; Tel 0116 221 1556

Roshni Project Day Centre West End Neighbourhood Centre, Andrews St, Leicester LE3 5PA; Tel 0116 262 7897; Fax 0116 253 2013

Visamo Day Centre Herrick Lodge Orchardson Ave, Leicester LE4 3DP; Tel 0116 251 5421; Fax 0116 251 5421

West End Day Centre Andrewes Day Centre, Andrewes St, Leicester LE3 5PA; Tel 0116 253 2013; Fax 0116 253 2013

DAY FACILITIES FOR PEOPLE WITH PHYSICAL OR SENSORY DISABILITY

Douglas Bader Centre Malabar Rd, St. Matthew's, Leicester LE1 2LJ; Tel 0116 262 8754

COMMUNITY HOMES

Barnes Heath House Community Home Humphries Cl, Rowlatts Hill, Leicester LE5 4LU; Tel 0116 276 3783; Fax 0116 274 0743

Dunblane Avenue Community Home 31 Dunblane Ave, Leicester; Tel 0116 268 2821; Fax 0116 286 2823

Netherhall Road Community Home 15 Netherhall Rd, Leicester; Tel 0116 276 9349; Fax 0116 274 3107

Tatlow Road Community Home 2 Tatlow Rd, Braunstone Frith, Leicester LE3 8NF; Tel 0116 287 3755; Fax 0116 287 1422

Wigston Lane Community Home 124 Wigston La, Aylestone, Leicester LE2 8TN; Tel 0116 244 0564; Fax 0116 244 0554

Wigston Lane Community Home 126 Wigston La, Leicester; Tel 0116 244 0110; Fax 0116 283 3498

HOME FOR PEOPLE WITH LEARNING DIFFICULTIES

Beaumanor House 34 Robert Hall St, Abbey La, Leicester LE4 5RB; Tel 0116 266 4833; Fax 0116 266 4833

DAY SERVICES FOR OLDER PEOPLE

Wycliffe Day Centre Butterwick Hse, Tiling Rd, Leicester LE4 0SY; Tel 0116 235 1269

ELDERLY PERSONS' HOMES

There are ten homes for the elderly.

Education and Lifelong Learning Department

Leicester City Council, Marlborough Hse, Leicester LE2 7AA; E-mail educa226@mailhub1.leicester.gov.uk; Tel 0116 252 7807; Fax 0116 233 2685
Corporate Director (Education and Lifelong Learning)
  Steven Andrews

SPECIAL SCHOOLS

Ash Field School Broad Ave, Leicester LE5 4PY; E-mail office@ashfield.leicester.sch.uk; Tel 0116 273 7151; Fax 0116 273 9962
Headteacher Mr D. Bateson
  PD

Cherryleas Assessment Centre Westcotes Dr, Leicester LE3 0QU; Tel 0116 254 8834
Headteacher D. Mackey
Teacher-in-Charge Vacancy

Children's Hospital School Infirmary Sq, Leicester LE1 5WW; E-mail office@chslri.demon.co.uk; Tel 0116 258 5330; Fax 0116 247 1060
Headteacher A.C. Osborne Hospital School Foundation

Ellesmere College Ellesmere Rd, Leicester LE3 1BE; E-mail fmoir@ellesmere.leics.sch.uk; Tel 0116 289 4242; Fax 0116 289 4121
Headteacher Mrs F. Moir (Secondary)
  MLD

Emily Fortey School Glenfield Rd, Leicester LE3 6DG; E-mail headteacher@emilyfortey.leicester.sch.uk; Tel 0116 285 7395; Fax 0116 254 6493
Headteacher Mr M. Thompson
SLD Foundation

Keyham Lodge School Keyham La, Leicester LE2 1FG; E-mail freda@keyhamlodge.leicester.sch.uk; Tel 0116 241 6852; Fax 0116 241 6852
Headteacher Ms D. Fox
  EBD

Millgate Centre 18a Scott St, Leicester LE2 6DW; Tel 0116 270 4922; Fax 0116 270 8753
Headteacher Ms K.M. Howells
  Boys EBD (Day, Boarding)

Nether Hall School Netherhall Rd, Leicester LE5 1DT; E-mail netherhallschool@hotmail.com; Tel 0116 241 7258; Fax 0116 241 7259
Headteacher Mr P. Goodchild
  SLD

Oaklands School Whitehall Rd, Leicester, Leicestershire LE5 6GJ; E-mail admin@oaklands.leicester.sch.uk; Tel 0116 241 5921; Fax 0116 243 3259
Headteacher Mr A. Moran
Primary
  MLD

Piper Way Primary School Glenfield Rd, Leicester LE3 6DN; E-mail piperway@aol.com; Tel 0116 285 6181; Fax 0116 285 8298
Headteacher Mrs A. Standley

Western Park School Western Pk, Leicester LE3 6HX; E-mail westernpark@webleicester.co.uk; Tel 0116 285 8225; Fax 0116 285 6208
Headteacher Ms J. Booth
  Delicate

SPECIAL UNITS ATTACHED TO MAINSTREAM SECONDARY SCHOOLS

Babington Community Technology College Strasbourg Dr, Leicester LE4 0SZ; E-mail admin@babingtoncc.leics.sch.uk; Tel 0116 222 1616; Fax 0116 222 1620
Headteacher Mrs J. Smith
  Visual Impairment

Crown Hills Schools and Community College Gwendolen Rd, Leicester LE5 5FT;
E-mail gacoleby@crownhills.leicester.sch.uk; Tel 0116 273 6893; Fax 0116 273 0413
Headteacher Mr G.A. Coleby
Hearing impairment

LEICESTERSHIRE COUNTY COUNCIL
www.leics.gov.uk

The county retains its two-tier structure; however on 1 April 1997 Leicester City and Rutland became separate unitary authorities and are listed alphabetically in this chapter.
Population 610 300
Political Composition: Con: 28, Lab: 15, LD: 10, Other: 1
County Hall, Glenfield, Leicester LE3 8RA;
URL www.leics.gov.uk;
E-mail information@leics.gov.uk; Tel 0116 232 3232; Fax 0116 265 6260
Chair of the Council David Knaggs
Chief Executive John Sinnott; Tel 0116 265 6001
County Solicitor and Head (Chief Executive's Department) Elizabeth McCalla; Tel 0116 265 6006
Director (Resources) Alan Youd; Tel 0116 265 7830
Director (Highways, Transportation and Waste Management) Bruce Jamieson; Tel 0116 265 7000
Director (Community Services) Alan Morrison; Tel 0116 265 7372

Social Services Department

County Hall, Glenfield, Leicester LE3 8RL;
URL www.leics.gov.uk;
E-mail social-services@leics.gov.uk; Tel 0116 232 3232

Management Team
Director Tony Harrop
Senior Assistant Director John Kershaw
Assistant Director (Children and Family Services) Flick Schofield
Assistant Director (Mental Health and Learning Disability Services) Tim Watts
Assistant Director (Services for Older People and People with Disability) Sheila Rochester
Head (Finance) Paul Simpson

Children and Family Services
Service Manager (Placements) Penny Hajek
Service Manager (Quality Projects) Helen Millar
Service Manager (Early Years and Family Support) Rob Wade
Service Manager (Child Protection and Review) Bob Parker
Service Manager (Child Care Operations) Alison Talleth
Gladstone Ave, Loughborough, Leicestershire
Service Manager (Child Care Operations) Vanessa Bishop
Bassett St, South Wigston, Leicester, Leicestershire
Principal Officer (Family Placements) Cath Sartoris
Principal Officer (Placements) Michael Nerini

Access and Care Management Services
Head (Partnerships and Diversity) Barry Davies
Head (Quality and Performance Management) Liz Clark
Service Manager (Access – Intermediate Care) Jan Futter
Pennine Hse, Loughborough, Leicestershire
Service Manager (Access – Lead: Children's Services) Jane Scannell
Leicester Rd, Melton Mowbray, Leicestershire
Service Manager (Learning Disabilities/Mental Health) Tony Howlett
Bassett St, South Wigston, Leicester, Leicestershire

Service Manager (Older People and Disabled People) Mark Goddin
Bassett St, South Wigston, Leicester
Manager (Staff Development) Jennifer Penfold
Manager (Human Resources) Jo Boulton
Principal Personnel Officer Steve Kelly
Principal Officer (Resources) Julian Haywood

Provider Services
Service Manager (Home Care, Sensory Disability) Jane Dabrawska
34 Asfordby Rd, Melton Mowbray, Leicestershire
Service Manager (Residential, Day Care Services) Sue Disley Hinckley
Service Manager (Learning Disability Services) Roger Kirby
Garden St, Thurmaston, Leicestershire

Complaints and Commendations
Complaints Officer Teresa Oldman Rothley
Rothley Hse, Coalville, Leicestershire

LOCAL OFFICES

Asfordby Road Local Office 34 Asfordby Rd, Melton Mowbray, Leicestershire LE13 0HR; Tel 01664 410080; Fax 01664 410702

Bassett Street South Wigston, Leicestershire LE18 4PE; Tel 0116 278 7111; Fax 0116 278 0761

Brooklands Local Office Northampton Rd, Market Harborough, Leicestershire LE16 9HN; Tel 01858 465331; Fax 01858 431104

County Buildings Leicester Rd, Melton Mowbray, Leicestershire LE13 0DA; Tel 01664 564698; Fax 01664 564390

Gladstone Avenue Local Office 2 Gladstone Ave, Loughborough, Leicestershire LE11 1NP; Tel 01509 610311; Fax 01509 210175

High Street Local Office 3 High St, Coalville, Leicestershire LE67 3EA; Tel 01530 275200; Fax 01530 815155

Pennine House 2 Lemington St, Loughborough, Leicestershire LE11 1HH; Tel 01509 266641; Fax 01509 210167

Rothley House Local Office Coalville Bus Pk, Coalville, Leicestershire LE67 3NR; Tel 01530 513785

Upper Bond Street Local Office 27 Upper Bond St, Hinckley, Leicestershire LE10 1RH; Tel 01455 636964; Fax 01455 250450

HOSPITAL TEAMS

Glenfield Hospital Groby Rd, Leicester LE3 9QP
Leicester General Hospital Gwendolen Rd, Leicester LE5 4PW
Leicester Royal Infirmary Infirmary Sq, Leicester LE1 5WW

ADOPTION TEAM

Eagle Hse, 11 Friar La, Leicester LE1 5RB; Tel 0116 299 5899; Fax 0116 299 5900

THERAPEUTIC SOCIAL WORK TEAM FOR CHILDREN AND YOUNG PEOPLE

8 St. Martin's, Leicester LE1 5DD; Tel 0116 253 1191; Fax 0116 256 8365

EMERGENCY TEAM

Team Manager G. Giez

FAMILY PLACEMENT TEAM AND LEAVING CARE TEAM

Bassett St, South Wigston, Leicestershire LE18 4PE; Tel 0116 275 9255 0116 275 9315; Fax 0116 278 0761

6

FAMILY CENTRES

Coalville and Area High St, Coalville, Leicestershire LE67 3EA; Tel 01530 838502; Fax 01530 510242
(50)

Hinckley and Area Granville Rd, Hinckley, Leicestershire LE10 0PP; Tel 01455 637485; Fax 01455 619368
(50)

Loughborough and Area Regent St, Loughborough, Leicestershire LE11 5BA; Tel 01509 267360 01509 610566
(50)

CHILDREN'S RIGHTS SERVICE

Rothley Hse, Coalville Bus Pk, Coalville, Leicestershire LE67 3NR; Tel 01530 513817; Fax 01530 513872
Children's Rights Officer   Elaine Constable

COMMUNITY HOMES

Blaby Community Home Old Hospital Site, Hospital La, Blaby, Leicester LE8 4FE; Tel 0116 275 9150; Fax 0116 275 9153

Littlehill House Community Home 107 Moat St, Wigston, Leicestershire LE8 2GE; Tel 0116 288 9709; Fax 0116 288 3192
(12)

London Road Community Home 43 London Rd, Coalville, Leicestershire
(10)

LEICESTER, LEICESTERSHIRE AND RUTLAND YOUTH OFFENDERS INTERVENTION TEAM

26 Station Rd, Wigston, Leicestershire LE18 2DH; Tel 0116 288 1844; Fax 0116 257 1525

DAY SERVICES FOR PEOPLE WITH LEARNING DISABILITIES

Coalville Community Resource Centre Comet Way, Coalville, Leicestershire LE67 5FS; Tel 01530 814020; Fax 01530 817097

Leicester Road Centre Melton Mowbray, Leicestershire LE13 0DA; Tel 01664 565644; Fax 01664 481724
(60)

Mountsorrel Day Centre Marsh Rd, Mountsorrel, Loughborough, Leicestershire LE12 7JP; Tel 0116 230 3112; Fax 0116 230 3301
(150)

Millfield Centre 30 Frederick Ave, Hinckley, Leicestershire LE10 0EX; Tel 01455 610723; Fax 01455 610730
(150)

Roman Way Day Centre 36 Roman Way, Market Harborough, Leicestershire LE16 7PQ; Tel 01858 433221; Fax 01858 433221

Wigston Day Centre 78 West Ave, Wigston, Leicestershire LE18 2FB; Tel 0116 288 7845; Fax 0116 257 0858
(200)

HOMES FOR PEOPLE WITH LEARNING DISABILITIES

Cossington Road Home 227 Cossington Rd, Sileby, Leicestershire LE12 7RR; Tel 01509 816240

Hamilton Court Home 50 Smith Cres, Coalville, Leicestershire LE67 4JE; Tel 01530 831767; Fax 01530 835046
(15)

Respite Care Unit 44 Smith Cres, Coalville, Leicestershire LE67 4JE; Tel 01530 815887; Fax 01530 835046

Silverdale Home Scalford Rd, Melton Mowbray, Leicestershire LE13 1JZ; Tel 01664 566834; Fax 01664 566834
(20)

The Trees Deveron Way, Hinckley, Leicestershire LE10 0XD; Tel 01455 615523; Fax 01455 614317
(26)

Waterlees House Aylestone La, Wigston, Leicestershire LE18 1AB; Tel 0116 288 9502; Fax 0116 288 6704
(20)

COMMUNITY RESOURCE SERVICES – ADULT MENTAL HEALTH

Albert Street Centre Albert St, Loughborough, Leicestershire LE11 2DW; Tel 01509 266260; Fax 01509 219463

Centre 88 Countesthorpe Community College, Winchester Rd, Countesthorpe, Leicestershire LE8 3PR; Tel 0116 278 0228; Fax 0116 278 0228

Grange Day Centre Marlene Reid Centre, Belvoir Rd, Coalville, Leicestershire LE67 3PH; Tel 01530 811174
(25)

Market Harborough Resource Centre 1 Bowden La, Market Harborough, Leicestershire LE16 7JD; Tel 01858 434763 01858 461398

Melton Mental Health Project 34 Asfordby Rd, Melton Mowbray, Leicestershire LE13 0HJ; Tel 01664 410080; Fax 01664 410702

Westfield Day Centre Rosemary Way, Hinckley, Leicestershire LE10 0LN; Tel 01455 238633
(20)

MENTAL HEALTH HOSTEL

Huncote Road Mental Health Hostel 52 Huncote Rd, Narborough, Leicester LE9 5GN; Tel 0116 286 6024; Fax 0116 284 1396
(25)

DAY SERVICES FOR PEOPLE WITH PHYSICAL/SENSORY DISABILITIES

Charnwood Day Centre Mobile Units, Burleigh College, Loughborough, Leicestershire LE11 0SQ; Tel 01509 268647
(20)

Coalville Community/Resource Centre Comet Way, Coalville, Leicestershire LE67 5FS; Tel 01530 814020

Groby Community College Ratby La, Groby, Leicestershire LE6 0GE; Tel 0116 287 9829; Fax 0116 287 0189
(30)

Norman Way Day Centre Melton Mowbray, Leicestershire LE13 1JE; Tel 01664 566895; Fax 01664 561717
(30)

DAY SERVICES FOR OLDER PEOPLE AND OLDER PEOPLE WITH MENTAL HEALTH DIFFICULTIES

Brooklands Gardens Walcote Rd, Market Harborough, Leicestershire LE16 9DL; Tel 01858 410093
(25)

Castle View Day Centre Watling St, Mountsorrel, Leicestershire LE12 7BD; Tel 0116 237 4408; Fax 0116 237 5373

Curtis Weston House Aylestone La, Wigston, Leicester LE8 1AB; Tel 0116 288 7331; Fax 0116 288 7799

Hood Court North St, Ashby-de-la-Zouch, Leicestershire LE65 5HY; Tel 01530 412835; Fax 01530 412835
(25)

The Limes Derby Rd, Hinckley, Leicestershire LE10 1QS; Tel 01455 230436
(15)

The Pavilions Central Ave, Lutterworth, Leicestershire LE17 4PA; Tel (Tues, Wed and Thurs pm only) 01455 558643

Victoria Centre Albert St, Loughborough, Leicestershire LE11 2DW; Tel 01509 610674; Fax 01509 219463
(24)

Vine House Loughborough Rd, Shepshed, Leicestershire
LE12 9DN; Tel (Fri only) 01509 505079
(10)

ELDERLY PERSONS' HOMES

Contact communications and consultation team for details
on Tel 0116 256 7404.

ADULT PLACEMENT TEAM

8 Garden St, Thurmaston, Leicestershire LE4 8D3; Tel 0116
260 4660; Fax 0116 260 4611

Education Department

County Hall, Glenfield, Leicester LE3 8RF;
    URL www.leics.gov.uk/education;
    E-mail education@leics.gov.uk; Tel 0116 265 6631
Director (Education) Mrs J. Strong, BSc, MEd

LEICESTERSHIRE EDUCATIONAL PSYCHOLOGY SERVICE

Education Dept, County Hall, Leicester LE3 8RF; Tel 0116
    265 6699
Principal Educational Psychologist T. Holme

SPECIAL SCHOOLS

Ashmount School Ashmount, 9 Beacon Rd, Loughborough,
Leicestershire LE11 2BG;
E-mail office@ashmount.leics.sch.uk; Tel 01509 268506;
Fax 01509 231605
Headteacher Kate Waplington

Craven Lodge School Burton Rd, Melton Mowbray,
Leicestershire LE13 1DJ;
E-mail office@cravenlodge.leics.sch.uk; Tel 01664 562246;
Fax 01664 480043
Headteacher Peter Coopey
Junior
    Mixed (Weekly boarding)

Dorothy Goodman School Middlefield La, Hinckley,
Leicestershire LE10 0RB;
URL www.dorothygoodman.ik.org;
E-mail office@dorothygoodman.leics.sch.uk; Tel 01455
634582; Fax 01455 613667
Headteacher Tony Smith

Forest Way School Cropston Dr, Coalville, Leicestershire
LE67 4HS; E-mail forestway@forestway.leics.sch.uk;
Tel 01530 831899; Fax 01530 814069
Headteacher Lynn Slinger

Maplewell Hall School Maplewell Rd, Woodhouse Eaves,
Loughborough, Leicestershire LE12 8QY;
E-mail admin@maplewell.leics.sch.uk; Tel 01509 890237;
Fax 01509 891197
Headteacher Susan Yarnall
Secondary
    Mixed (Day and weekly boarding)

Menphys Centre Launceston Rd, Wigston, Leicester,
Leicestershire LE18 2FZ;
E-mail menphyscentre@freeserve.com; Tel 0116 288 9977;
Fax 0116 288 9448
Contact Christine Silver

The Mount School The Mount, Leicester Rd, Melton
Mowbray, Leicestershire LE13 0DA;
URL www.webstore-ed.net/melton;
E-mail admin@themount.leics.sch.uk; Tel 01664 562418;
Fax 01664 410281
Headteacher Peter Henshaw

Wigston Birkett House Community Special School
Launceston Rd, Wigston Magna, Leicestershire LE18 2FZ;
E-mail office@birketthouse.leics.sch.uk; Tel 0116 288 5802;
Fax 0116 257 1932
Headteacher Steve Welton

LINCOLNSHIRE COUNTY COUNCIL
www.lincolnshire.gov.uk

Population 611 900
Political Composition: Con: 49, Lab: 21, LD: 4, Ind: 3
County Offices, Newland, Lincoln, Lincolnshire LN1 1YL;
    URL www.lincolnshire.gov.uk;
    E-mail steve.jackson@lincolnshire.gov.uk; Tel 01522
552222; Fax 01522 552323
Chief Executive Davie Bowles
County Treasurer Pete Moore
Director (Highways and Planning) R. Wills
Chief Property Officer Tony Wilkins

Social Services Directorate

Orchard Hse, Orchard St, Lincoln, Lincolnshire LN1 1BA;
    URL www.lincolnshire.gov.uk;
    E-mail ssdcommunications@lincolnshire.gov.uk;
    Tel (Emergency Duty) 01529 413366; Fax 01522 554006
Director (Social Services) M. Bukowski
Information Contact Peter Dugmore

6

TRAINING

The following have responsibility for training professional
and support staff in the department.
Manager (Human Resources) S. Nearney; Tel 01522 554034
*Senior Training Officer (Child Care and Vocational Assessment
Team)* R. Burn; Tel 01522 554088
Senior Training Officer (Adult Community Care Team)
    N. Marshall; Tel 01522 554093

AREA OFFICES

Boston Area Office County Hall, Boston, Lincolnshire
PE21 6LX; Tel 01205 310010 ext 2277; Fax 01522 554331

Gainsborough Area Office 156 Trinity St, Gainsborough,
Lincolnshire DN21 1JP; Tel 01427 615331; Fax 01427 810617

Grantham Area Office Grange Hse, 46 Union St, Grantham,
Lincolnshire NG31 6NZ; Tel 01476 561061; Fax 01476
567572

Horncastle Area Office Homeleigh, Foundry St, Horncastle,
Lincolnshire LN9 6AQ; Tel 01522 554621; Fax 01522 524489

Lincoln Area Office Orchard Hse, Orchard St, Lincoln,
Lincolnshire LN1 1BA; Tel 01522 554135; Fax 01522 554489

Louth Area Office Eastfield Hse, Eastfield Rd, Louth,
Lincolnshire LN11 7AN; Tel 01507 600800; Fax 01522 554433

Market Rasen Area Office 20 King St, Market Rasen,
Lincolnshire LN8 3JH; Tel 01673 842537; Fax 01673 842300

North Hykeham Area Office Richmond Hse, Richmond Dr,
North Hykeham, Lincolnshire LN6 8QY; Tel 01522 689000;
Fax 01522 696460

Skegness Area Office 2 Ida Rd, Skegness, Lincolnshire
PE25 2AR; Tel 01754 764271; Fax 01754 769808

Sleaford Area Office Council Offices, Eastgate, Sleaford,
Lincolnshire NG34 7EB; Tel 01529 414144; Fax 01529 307728
ext 2299

Spalding Area Office The Vista, Churchgate, Spalding,
Lincolnshire PE11 2RA; Tel 01775 725751; Fax 01775 710991

Stamford Area Office 38 North St, Stamford, Lincolnshire
PE9 2YN; Tel 01780 751821; Fax 01780 754533

HOSPITAL SOCIAL WORKERS

Grantham and Kesteven Hospital Social Work Department,
Manthorpe Rd, Grantham, Lincolnshire NG31 8DG;
Tel 01476 565232

John Coupland Hospital Social Work Department, Ropery Rd, Gainsborough, Lincolnshire; Tel 01427 816500

Lincoln County Hospital Social Work Department, Greetwell Rd, Lincoln, Lincolnshire LN2 5QY; Tel 01522 512512

Louth County Hospital Social Work Department, High Holme Rd, Louth, Lincolnshire; Tel 01507 600100

Pilgrim Hospital Social Work Department, Sibsey Rd, Boston, Lincolnshire PE21 9QS; Tel 01205 364801

Skegness and District Hospital Social Work Department, Dorothy Ave, Skegness, Lincolnshire; Tel 01754 898941

FAMILY CENTRES

Albion Street Centre 67 Albion St, Spalding, Lincolnshire; Tel 01775 722471

The Beacon Centre Sandon Cl, Grantham, Lincolnshire; Tel 01476 564283

Fenside Family Centre 64 Fenside Rd, Boston, Lincolnshire PE21 8JH; Tel 01205 355630

Grantham Family Centre 42 Earlsfield La, Grantham, Lincolnshire; Tel 01476 563984

Hartsholme Family Centre Carrington Dr, Lincoln, Lincolnshire; Tel 01522 689576

Haven Cottage Church Rd, Boston, Lincolnshire; Tel 01205 361388

Mablethorpe Family Centre The Old School, High St, Mablethorpe, Lincolnshire; Tel 01507 479594

Northolme Day Centre 33 Northolme, Gainsborough, Lincolnshire; Tel 01427 613232

Roseberry House Family Centre Roseberry Ave, Skegness, Lincolnshire; Tel 01754 766763

St. Giles Family Centre Lamb Gdns, Lincoln, Lincolnshire; Tel 01522 567040

THE WARREN FAMILY CENTRE

North Warren Rd, Gainsborough, Lincolnshire; Tel 01427 678061

Virginia House 10 Virginia Dr, Louth, Lincolnshire LN11 8BD; Tel 01507 602399

SOCIAL EDUCATION CENTRES

Chappell Centre Pinchbeck Rd, Spalding, Lincolnshire PE11 1QF; Tel 01775 769721

Fen Lane Social Education Centre Fen La, North Hykeham, Lincolnshire LN6 8UZ; Tel 01522 686427

Gainsborough Enterprises Social Education Centre Unit 17, Corringham Rd Ind Est, Gainsborough, Lincolnshire DN21 1QB; Tel 01427 614388

Interskills Warwick Rd, Louth, Lincolnshire; Tel 01507 607914

Long Leys Social Education Centre Long Leys Rd, Lincoln, Lincolnshire; Tel 01522 528087

Louth Social Education Centre Birch Rd, Louth, Lincolnshire; Tel 01507 602410

DAY CENTRES FOR PEOPLE WITH MENTAL HEALTH PROBLEMS

Acorn Day Centre St. Mary's Old School Bldg, Horncastle Rd, Boston, Lincolnshire PE21 9BU; Tel 01205 359158

Jubilee Centre East Rd, Sleaford, Lincolnshire; Tel 01529 303309

The Oaks Day Centre Skegness and District Hospital, Dorothy Ave, Skegness, Lincolnshire; Tel 01754 612039

ACCOMMODATION FOR PEOPLE WHO ARE PHYSICALLY AND/OR MENTALLY HANDICAPPED

PHYSICALLY HANDICAPPED ADULTS

Bodmin Moor Close Home 8 Bodmin Moor Cl, North Hykeham, Lincoln, Lincolnshire; Tel 01522 694421

DISABLED CHILDREN

The Beacon Sandon Cl, Grantham, Lincolnshire NG31 9AX; Tel 01476 564283

ADULTS WITH LEARNING DISABILITIES

The Avenue Home 34 The Ave, Gainsborough, Lincolnshire; Tel 01427 614982

Broughton Gardens Home Broughton Gdns, Brant Rd, Lincoln, Lincolnshire; Tel 01522 536102

Clifton Road Home 21 Clifton Rd, Boston, Lincolnshire; Tel 01205 367141

Garfits Lane Home 3 Garfits La, Boston, Lincolnshire; Tel 01205 352856

Glendon Close Home 3 Glendon Cl, Lincoln, Lincolnshire; Tel 01522 512662

Hervey Road Home 24 Hervey Rd, Sleaford, Lincolnshire; Tel 01529 304957

Nettleham Home Brackenwood, Lincoln Rd, Nettleham, Lincolnshire; Tel 01522 880206

Nettleham Road Home 232 Nettleham Rd, Lincoln, Lincolnshire; Tel 01522 880207

Oxford Street Home 9 Oxford St, Grantham, Lincolnshire; Tel 01476 579606

77–79 Queen Elizabeth Road Ernine Est West, Lincoln, Lincolnshire; Tel 01522 532182

Unit Office 122 Boultham Park Rd, Lincoln, Lincolnshire; Tel 01522 885600

Westlode 34–36 Westlode St, Spalding, Lincolnshire; Tel 01775 769065

MENTALLY ILL ADULTS

The Crescent 17 The Cres, Horncastle, Lincolnshire; Tel 01507 608959

Work Skills 5a St. Catherines, Lincoln, Lincolnshire; Tel 01522 530643

DAY CENTRES FOR PEOPLE WITH PHYSICAL DISABILITIES

Ancaster Day Centre Ancaster, Boundary St, Lincoln, Lincolnshire LN5 8NJ; Tel 01522 611109

Holmeleigh Day Centre Foundry St, Horncastle, Lincolnshire; Tel 01507 523891

Stamford Day Centre 33 Ryhall Rd, Stamford, Lincolnshire; Tel 01780 482641

MULTIPURPOSE DAY CENTRES (VOLUNTARY SUPPORT)

Butterfield Centre North Rd, Bourne, Lincolnshire; Tel 01778 421422

Dorothy Avenue Day Centre Skegness, Lincolnshire; Tel 01754 766763

Ivo Day Centre Albion St, Spalding, Lincolnshire; Tel 01775 768888

Link Day Centre Virginia Dr, Louth, Lincolnshire; Tel 01507 605649

Ruskin Court Day Centre Ruskin Rd, Mablethorpe, Lincolnshire; Tel 01507 472055

MEALS ON WHEELS

Social Services Dept, Orchard Hse, Lincoln, Lincolnshire LN1 1BA; Tel 01522 554075

AGE CONCERN

The Day Centre, Park St, Lincoln, Lincolnshire; Tel 01522 527694

Education and Cultural Services Directorate

County Offices, Newland, Lincoln, Lincolnshire LN1 1YQ; Tel 01522 552222; Fax 01522 553257
Director (Education and Cultural Services)
    Dr Cheryle Berry
Head (Service for Sensory Impaired) T.A. Moodley
Head (Behavioural Support Service) S. Fenton-Smith
Head (SEN Support Services) D. Fish
Manager (Special Needs Services) Peter Broster
Manager (Service Development) Carl Baker
Traveller Education Service P. Ingall

COUNTY PSYCHOLOGY SERVICE

Council Offices Sleaford, Lincolnshire NG34 7EB; Tel 01529 414144

County Hall Boston, Lincolnshire PE21 6LX; Tel 01205 310010

Eastfield House Eastfield Rd, Louth, Lincolnshire LN11 7AN; Tel 01507 600800

49 Newland Lincoln, Lincolnshire LN1 1YQ; Tel 01522 552222

HOSPITAL SCHOOLS

The Ash Villa School Willoughby Rd, Rauceby Hospital, Sleaford, Lincolnshire NG34 8PP;
E-mail neil.barton@ashvilla.lincs.sch.uk; Tel 01529 488066; Fax 01529 488239
Headteacher N. Barton (Acting)
    Mixed 8–16

Pilgrim Hospital School and Lincolnshire Hospital Education Service 4th Fl, Sibsey Rd, Boston, Lincolnshire PE21 9QS; E-mail enquiries@pilgrimhospital.lincs.sch.uk; Tel 01205 364801 ext 2641; Fax 01205 368151
Headteacher Mrs C. Seymour
    Mixed All ages

SPECIAL SCHOOLS

Ambergate School Dysart Rd, Grantham, Lincolnshire NG31 7LP; E-mail amy.hodson@ambergate.lincs.sch.uk; Tel 01476 564957; Fax 01476 573870
Headteacher R. McCrossen
    Mixed 5–16

The Beckett School White's Wood La, Gainsborough, Lincolnshire DN21 1TW;
E-mail susan.hayter@beckett.lincs.sch.uk; Tel 01427 612139; Fax 01427 616776
Headteacher Mrs S.M. Hayter
    Mixed 2–19

The Eresby School Eresby Ave, Spilsby, Lincolnshire PE23 5HU; E-mail enquiries@eresby.lincs.sch.uk; Tel 01790 752441; Fax 01790 754223
Headteacher Mrs J. McPherson
    Mixed 2–19

The Fortuna Primary School Kingsdown Rd, Doddington Pk, Lincoln, Lincolnshire LN6 0FB; Tel 01522 705561; Fax 01522 705563
Headteacher Jo Richardson

Gosberton House School Westhorpe Rd, Gosberton, Spalding, Lincolnshire PE11 4EW;
E-mail louise.stanton@gosberton-house.lincs.sch.uk; Tel 01775 840250; Fax 01775 841017
Headteacher Ms L. Stanton
    3–11

Garth School Pinchbeck Rd, Spalding, Lincolnshire PE11 1QF; E-mail linda.dawson@garth.lincs.sch.uk; Tel 01775 725566; Fax 01775 768829
Headteacher L. Dowson
    Mixed 2–19

John Fielding School Ashlawn Dr, Boston, Lincolnshire PE21 9PX; E-mail sandra.meakin@john-fielding.lincs.sch.uk; Tel 01205 363395; Fax 01205 357696
Headteacher Linda Clarke (Acting)
    Mixed 2–19

The Lady Jane Franklin School Partney Rd, Spilsby, Lincolnshire; Tel 01790 753902
Headteacher David Fuller
    Mixed 6–16

The Phoenix School Great North Rd, Grantham, Lincolnshire; Tel 01476 574112
Headteacher Bill Bush

Priory School Neville Ave, Spalding, Lincolnshire PE11 2EH; E-mail enquiries@priory.lincs.sch.uk; Tel 01775 724080; Fax 01775 713860
Headteacher B.J. Howes
    Mixed 11–16

Queen's Park School South Pk, Lincoln, Lincolnshire LN5 8EW; E-mail dale.robinson@queens.park.lincs.sch.uk; Tel 01522 878121; Fax 01522 878113
Headteacher Dale Robinson
    Mixed 2–19

St. Bernard's School Wood La, Louth, Lincolnshire LN11 8RS; E-mail enquiries@st-bernards.lincs.sch.uk; Tel 01507 603776; Fax 01507 603914
Headteacher M.A. Warren
    2–19

St. Christopher's School Hykeham Rd, Lincoln, Lincolnshire LN6 8AR;
E-mail enquiries@st-christopher.lincs.sch.uk; Tel 01522 528378; Fax 01522 521110
Headteacher Mr D. Metcalfe (Acting)
    Mixed 3–16

St. Francis School Wickenby Cres, Lincoln, Lincolnshire LN1 3TJ; E-mail admin@st-francis.lincs.sch.uk; Tel 01522 526498; Fax 01522 569128
Headteacher Mrs A. Hoffmann
    Mixed

St. Lawrence School Bowl Alley La, Horncastle, Lincolnshire LN9 5EJ;
E-mail enquiries@st-lawrence-special.lincs.sch.uk; Tel 01507 522563; Fax 01507 522974
Headteacher D. Smith
    5–16

Sandon School Sandon Cl, Sandon Rd, Grantham, Lincolnshire NG31 9AX;
E-mail janet.roddis@sandon.lincs.sch.uk; Tel 01476 564994; Fax 01476 592195
Headteacher Janet Roddis
    2–19

William Harrison School Middlefield La, Gainsborough, Lincolnshire DN21 1PU;
E-mail sheenagh.scott@william.harrison.lincs.sch.uk; Tel 01427 615498; Fax 01427 615498
Headteacher Dr M.J. Blackband
    Mixed 3–16

The Willoughby School South Rd, Bourne, Lincolnshire PE10 9JE; E-mail willoughbyspec@supanet.com; Tel 01778 425203; Fax 01778 425284
Headteacher Adam Booker
    Mixed 2–19

6

Emotional/Behavioural Difficulties

Head (Emotional and Behavioural Support) C. Fenton-Smith; Tel 01522 553390

The Acting Head of Emotional and Behavioural Support Service, C. Fenton-Smith, can be contacted on Tel 01522 553390.

Learning Support Service Tel 01522 553265

Head of Service D. Fish; Tel 01522 553265

The Learning Support Service is a delegated service from which primary schools can purchase time to provide professional advice or teaching support in respect of children with learning difficulties (i.e. specific learning difficulties).

Headteachers can contact Head of Service.

Sensory Impaired Service

Head T.A. Moodley; Tel 01522 553364

Ethnic Minority Achievement Service

Teacher and Co-ordinator J. Chandar-Nair; Tel 01427 787190

Traveller Education Service

Head P. Ingall; Tel 01522 553320

Gifted and Talented Support Service

Teacher/Co-ordinator M. Stopper; Tel 01427 788056

LIVERPOOL CITY COUNCIL

www.liverpool.gov.uk

Population 457 000

Political Composition: LD: 73, Lab: 20, Liberal: 2, Ward Lab: 3, Ind: 1

Municipal Bldgs, Dale St, Liverpool, Merseyside L69 2JG; URL www.liverpool.gov.uk; E-mail phil.wall@liverpool.gov.uk; Tel 0151 233 3000

Lord Mayor E. Clein

Chief Executive David Henshaw

Supported Living and Community Safety Portfolio

1st Fl, Millennium Hse, 60 Victoria St, Liverpool, Merseyside L1 6JQ; Tel 0151 233 4415; Fax 0151 233 4496

Executive Director Tony Hunter

Assistant Executive Director (Children's Services) Peter Duxbury

Assistant Executive Director (Adult Services) Vacancy

Assistant Executive Director (Community Safety) John Slayers

Head (Youth Offending) Aileen Shepherd

Group Manager (Family Placement) Alan Renshall

Group Manager (Assessment) Liz Mekki

Group Manager (Residential Services) James Clarke

Group Manager (Fostering, Adoption and Disabled Children's Services) Christine Banim

Group Manager (Mental Health and Drug/Alcohol Service) Dave Gardiner

Group Manager (Adult Strategic Commissioning) Paul Clitheroe

Group Manager (Assessment and Care Management) Barbara Hitchins

Group Manager (Assessment and Care Management) Brendan Doyle

Group Manager (Supporting People with Disabilities) Kathy Roberts

Group Manager (Support Services) Liz Hill

Group Manager (Children's Services – Performance Management) Terry Hawkins

Group Manager (Operation Manager – Youth Offending Service) Mark McCausland

Group Manager (Policy and Development – Youth Offending Service) Angela Parton

Group Manager (Community Safety) Vacancy

Police LA Liaison Officer (Community Safety) Mike Creer

HOSPITAL SOCIAL WORK TEAMS

Aintree Hospital Social Work Department, Eskdale Hse, Longmoor La, Liverpool, Merseyside L9 7AL; Tel 0151 525 5980

Team Manager Sarah D'Arcy

Team Manager John Davies

Alder Hey Hospital Eaton Rd, Liverpool, Merseyside L12 2AP; Tel 0151 228 4811

Manager (Social Work Team) Linda Fletcher

Mossley Hill Hospital Social Work Department, Park Ave, Liverpool, Merseyside L18 8BU; Tel 0151 250 6057

Operational Manager Joe Doherty

Liverpool Women's Hospital Crown St, Liverpool, Merseyside L8 7SS; Tel 0151 708 9988

Manager Vacancy

Royal Hospital Social Work Department, Prescott St, Liverpool, Merseyside L7 8XP; Tel 0151 706 2858

Operational Manager John Foster

CHILDREN AND FAMILIES

Aigburth Drive Family Centre 30 Aigburth Dr, Liverpool, Merseyside L17 4JH; Tel 0151 233 4099

Manager (Family Centre) Wanda Bentley

Belvedere Road Family Centre 7–9 Belvedere Rd, Liverpool, Merseyside L8; Tel 0151 233 4878

Manager Bill Piper

Family Advisory Centre 6 Chatsworth Dr, Liverpool, Merseyside L7 6PT; Tel 0151 233 6241

Team Manager David Webb

Family Support Centre Sefton Grange, Croxteth Dr, Liverpool, Merseyside L17 3EZ; Tel 0151 233 1694

Family Placement Sefton Grange, Croxteth Dr, Liverpool, Merseyside L17 3EZ; Tel 0151 530 1151

Manager Yvonne Griffin Hall

Langtry Family Centre Langtry Rd, Liverpool, Merseyside L4; Tel 0151 233 1171

Manager Helen Tweedle

SOCIAL WORK TEAMS

Ash Cottage Newhall Campus, Liverpool, Merseyside L10 1LD; Tel 0151 233 5064

Manager Christine Bates

Belle Vale Office Naylorsfield Dr, Liverpool, Merseyside L25 2RH; Tel 0151 233 1580

Long Lane Office The Old School Bldg, Long La, Liverpool, Merseyside L9 6DN; Tel 0151 523 8855

Manager (Social Work Resource) Mike Evans

Wellington Road Office Wellington Rd, Liverpool, Merseyside L8 4OX; Tel 0151 233 1712

Manager (Social Work Resource) Tony Bates

RESIDENTIAL ESTABLISHMENTS FOR CHILDREN

Alder Road Children's Home 42 Alder Rd, Liverpool, Merseyside L12 2AY; Tel 0151 228 1222

Unit Manager Vacancy

Gladstone House Dyson Hall, Higher La, Liverpool, Merseyside L9 7HB; Tel 0151 233 1485

Manager (Residential Unit) Jane Darlington

Prescot Drive Children's Home 6–8 Prescot Dr, Liverpool, Merseyside L6 8PB; Tel 0151 254 1399

Manager (Residential Unit) Graham Brandwood

Warnerville Road Children's Home 2 Warnerville Rd, Liverpool, Merseyside L13 4BG; Tel 0151 228 1222

LEAVING CARE TEAM

Sefton Grange, Croxteth Dr, Liverpool, Merseyside L17 3EL; Tel 0151 233 1435
Manager (Social Work Resource) Karen Fletcher

Besford House Besford Rd, Liverpool, Merseyside L25 2XD; Tel 0151 498 4281
Contact M. Coffey
(23)

Preesall Way Home 6–8 Preesall Way, Liverpool, Merseyside L11 0DU; Tel 0151 546 0051
Contact S. Williams

Stillington Street Home 69–71 Stillington St, Liverpool, Merseyside L8 9XA; Tel 0151 727 4591
Contact M. Akabuko

CHILD PROTECTION TEAM

Brougham Terr, 1–7 West Derby Rd, Liverpool, Merseyside L6 1AE; Tel 0151 225 4904
Team Manager Ali Mekki

Canning Street Day Centre 56 Canning St, Liverpool, Merseyside L8 7NR; Tel 0151 709 7914
Contact Dave Leigh
(18)

Crown Street Day Centre Liverpool, Merseyside L7 3PY; Tel 0151 708 0245
Contact Jackie Ellis
(50)

South Drive Day Centre 29 South Dr, Liverpool, Merseyside L15 8JJ; Tel 0151 734 1544
Contact Debbie Morgan

Unicorn Road Day Centre Liverpool, Merseyside L11 4TS; Tel 0151 549 2260
Contact Pat Maddox

YOUTH OFFENDING TEAMS

Referral and Resource Team Broughton Terr, 1–7 West Derby Rd, Liverpool, Merseyside L6 1AE; Tel 0151 225 6025
Team Manager Dave Ballard

Central Youth Offending Team Croxteth Dr, Liverpool, Merseyside L17 3AL; Tel 0151 233 1918
Team Manager Paul Byrne (Acting)

Norh Youth Offending Team 2 Lancaster St, Liverpool, Merseyside L9 1BQ; Tel 0151 530 1051
Team Manager Rachel Harding (Acting)

South Youth Offending Team 89 St. Mary's Rd, Liverpool, Merseyside L19 2NL; Tel 0151 494 3627
Team Manager Pat Keegan

SERVICES FOR ADULTS

DAY CENTRES

100 Walton Village, Liverpool, Merseyside L4 6TL; Tel 0151 525 2109
Contact Joe Willman
(50)

Alderwood Centre Bridge Chapel Centre, Heath Rd, Liverpool, Merseyside L19; Tel 0151 494 2174
Manager Bridie Freeman

Cottage 10 Day Centre Newhall Campus, Longmoor La, Liverpool, Merseyside L10; Tel 0151 521 4654
Manager Noreen Graham

Central, Hawthorne House New Hall, Longmoor La, Liverpool, Merseyside L10 1OD; Tel 0151 523 5630; 0151 525 0567; 0151 525 3431; 0151 525 8126
Contact S. Fox

Fairfield Social Education Centre Sheil Rd, Liverpool, Merseyside L6 3AA; Tel 0151 260 2277
Contact Eileen Smith
(120)

Social Education Centre and Workshop Holt Hall, Caldway Dr, Liverpool, Merseyside L27 0YB; Tel 0151 488 6106
Contact M. Forfyth
(186)

Crown Street Resource Centre Crown St, Liverpool, Merseyside L7 3LZ; Tel 0151 708 0245
Manager Gary Alman

Kempston Street Centre 101–103 Kempston St, Liverpool, Merseyside; Tel (Voice and text) 0151 298 2055
Contact Jan Lockyer

Fax/Crox Day Centre Newhall Campus, Long La, Liverpool, Merseyside L10; Tel 0151 525 8126
Manager Isobel James

Joseph Gibbons Day Centre Livingstone Dr, Liverpool, Merseyside L17 4LR; Tel 0151 727 0689
Manager Bernice Charlesworth

Knotty Ash Day Centre East Prescot Rd, Liverpool, Merseyside L14 3NA; Tel 0151 220 3031
Manager Jackie Corkhill

Mobile Meals Service City Cleansing Depot, H BLock, Liverpool, Merseyside L6 4DJ; Tel 0151 225 5234
Contact Tom Sweeney

Lancaster Centre 170 Rice La, Liverpool, Merseyside L9 1DG; Tel 0151 523 6801
Manager Norah Hartless

Lime Court Day Centre Upper Baker St, Liverpool, Merseyside L6 1NE; Tel 0151 263 8338
Manager John Fielding

Men's Direct Access Centre 11 Green La, Liverpool, Merseyside L13; Tel 0151 228 1327
Manager Paul Gallagher

Norris Green Day Centre Falklands Approach, Parthenon Dr, Liverpool, Merseyside L11 5BS; Tel 0151 256 8119
Manager Lorraine Russell

Sheila Kay Day Centre High Park St, Liverpool, Merseyside L8 8DX; Tel 0151 727 5850
Manager Billy Ware

South Drive Centre Eden Vale, 29 South Dr, Liverpool, Merseyside L15 8JJ; Tel 0151 734 1544
Manager Debbie Morgan

Speke Resource Centre Parklands, Conleach Rd, Liverpool, Merseyside L24 0TW; Tel 0151 223 2294
Manager Judith Miller-Jones

Unicorn Road Day Centre Unicorn Rd, Liverpool, Merseyside; Tel 0151 549 2260
Manager Pat Maddox

Venmore Community Care Centre Hartnup St, Anfield, Liverpool, Merseyside L5 1UW; Tel 0151 263 2888
Manager Ann Marie, Little

SUPPORTED ACCOMMODATION

Sheltered Housing Office 99 Queen's Rd, Liverpool, Merseyside L6 2NF; Tel 0151 233 4059
Manager Darrell Stephen

Amethyst Close 14 Amethyst Cl, Liverpool, Merseyside L6 5LT; Tel 0151 260 6055
Group Leader (Supported Accommodation) Shirley Woodhouse

Barton Road 10–10a Foley Cl, Liverpool, Merseyside L4 1UY; Tel 0151 933 7064
Group Leader (Supported Accommodation) Jean Sheridan

Bentley Road 11 Bentley Rd, Liverpool, Merseyside L8 0SY; Tel 0151 726 9506
Group Leader (Supported Accommodation) Ruth Billows

Canova Close 24 Canova Cl, Liverpool, Merseyside L27 4BB; Tel 0151 498 4343
Group Leader (Supported Accommodation) Tracey Donnell

6

Cherry Mill 7–9b Upper Park St, Liverpool, Merseyside
L8 0HD; Tel 0151 709 3413
Group Leader (Supported Accommodation) Gareth Griffiths

Cottage 9 Newhall Campus, Liverpool, Merseyside L10;
Tel 0151 525 1842
Group Leader (Supported Accommodation) Michelle Doyle
Group Leader (Supported Accomodation) Bev Farrell

Derby Road 76 Derby Rd, Liverpool, Merseyside L19 9AW;
Tel 0151 494 2871
Group Leader (Supported Accommodation) Tracey Donnell

Jade Road 9–11 Jade Rd, Liverpool, Merseyside L6 5HP;
Tel 0151 264 0901
Group Leader (Supported Accommodation)
Shirley Woodhouse

Mere View 10–12 Hodder Rd, Liverpool, Merseyside
L5 0PZ; Tel 0151 260 6616
Group Leader (Supported Accommodation) Jean Sheridan

Rufford Road 7 Rufford Rd, Liverpool, Merseyside L6 3BD;
Tel 0151 260 6668
Group Leader (Supported Accommodation) John Cooper

Rumney Place 4–6 Rumney Pl, Liverpool, Merseyside
L4 1XA; Tel 0151 933 8033
Group Leader (Supported Accommodation) Gareth Griffiths

Upper Baker Street 20–22 Upper Baker St, Liverpool,
Merseyside L6 1LX; Tel 0151 263 5694
Group Leader (Supported Accommodation) John Cooper

HOME CARE

Belle Vale Office Naylorsfield Dr, Liverpool, Merseyside
L25 2RH; Tel 0151 233 1516
Manager (Home Care) Helen Hannigan

Boaler Street APH Boaler St, Liverpool, Merseyside
L6 9AE; Tel 0151 261 9031
Manager (Home Care) Cathy Cross

Leighton Dene Long La, Liverpool, Merseyside L9 6DW;
Tel 0151 525 7734
Manager (Home Care) Carol Alker

Spellow Lane Office Customer Focus Centre, 42 Spellow
La, Liverpool, Merseyside L4 4DE; Tel 0151 2333 3107
Manager (Home Care) Alan Dennis

Wavertree Road Office 80 Wavertree Rd, Liverpool,
Merseyside L7 1PH; Tel 0151 225 6628
Manager (Home Care) Donna Burnett

ASYLUM SEEKERS/HOMELESSNESS

Sheltered Housing Office, 99 Queen's Rd, Liverpool,
Merseyside L6 2NF; Tel 0151 233 4073
Manager Cecil Edey

REFUGEE AND ASYLUM SEEKERS SUPPORT TEAM

4 Moss Gr, Liverpool, Merseyside L8 0SA; Tel 0151 734
0070
Team Manager Karl Oram

ADULT PROTECTION

Brougham Terr, 1–7 West Derby Rd, Liverpool, Merseyside
L6 1AE; Tel 0151 225 6007
Manager Kevin Felton

MOBILE NIGHT TEAM

Old Swan Health Centre, Liverpool, Merseyside; Tel 0151
285 3752
Assistant Manager Diane Jones

HOUSING ADVICE TEAM

2nd Fl, Millenium Hse, 60 Victoria St, Liverpool,
Merseyside L1 6JQ; Tel 0151 233 5393
Manager (Housing Advice) Paula Kinnane Walls

SUPPORTING PEOPLE TEAM

Brougham Terr, 1–7 West Derby Rd, Liverpool, Merseyside
L6 1AE; Tel 0151 225 6045
Team Manager John Laverick

SUPPORTED EMPLOYMENT TEAM

Brougham Terr, 1–7 West Derby Rd, Liverpool, Merseyside
L6 1AE; Tel 0151 225 4900
Team Manager (Supported Employment) Natalie Maxham

DRUG AND ALCOHOL TEAM

Brougham Terr, 1–7 West Derby Rd, Liverpool, Merseyside
L6 1AE; Tel 0151 225 6027
Team Manager Alan Sloan

MENTAL HEALTH TEAMS

Rathbone Hospital Social Work Department, Mill La,
Liverpool, Merseyside L9 7JP; Tel 0151 250 3050
Team Manager Hilary Thomas

Arundel House Sefton General Hospital Site, Smithdown
Rd, Liverpool, Merseyside L15 2LF; Tel 0151 330 8032
Team Manager Alan O'Leary

Education, Lifelong Learning and Leisure

4th Fl, 4 Renshaw St, Liverpool, Merseyside L1 4NX;
Tel 0151 233 2822
Director (Education) Colin Hilton
Principal Educational Welfare Officer R. Collinson
Principal Educational Psychologist Judy Poole

HOSPITAL SCHOOL

Alder Hey Hospital School Eaton Rd, Liverpool, Merseyside
L12 2AP; Tel 0151 228 4811 ext 2461; Fax 0151 252 5366
Headteacher P. Morrison

SPECIAL DAY SCHOOLS

Ashfield School Alice Elliott Site, Childwall Abbey Rd,
Liverpool, Merseyside L16 5EY
Headteacher J. Ashley
Health

Clifford Holroyde School Thingwall La, Liverpool,
Merseyside L14 7NX; Tel 0151 228 9500; Fax 0151 228 9318
Headteacher Ms E. Dwyer

Ernest Cookson School Mill La, Liverpool, Merseyside
L12 7JA; Tel 0151 220 1874; Fax 0151 252 1238
Headteacher S. Roberts

Greenways School Beechwood Rd South, Liverpool,
Merseyside L19 0LD
Headteacher Mrs D. Williams (Acting)
Assessment

Harold Magnay School Woolton Hill Rd, Liverpool,
Merseyside L25 6JA; Tel 0151 428 6305; Fax 0151 428 1103
Headteacher M. Little
Mixed PH

Margaret Beavan School Almonds Grn, Liverpool,
Merseyside L12 5HP; Tel 0151 226 1306; Fax 0151 256 7432
Headteacher R.A. Holm
MLD

Meadow Bank School Sherwoods La, Liverpool,
Merseyside L10 1LW; Tel 0151 525 3451; Fax 0151 524 1284
Headteacher C. Clancy
MLD

Mersey View School Minehead Rd, Liverpool, Merseyside
L17 6AX; Tel 0151 427 1863; Fax 0151 494 3091
Headteacher C. Muscatelli
MLD

Millstead School Old Mill La, Liverpool, Merseyside L15 8LW; Tel 0151 722 0974; Fax 0151 722 5852
Headteacher M. Lucas

Palmerston School c/o Lee Manor High School, Childwall Valley Rd, Liverpool, Merseyside L27 3YA; Tel 0151 487 8399; Fax 0151 421 0985
Headteacher J.F. Wright
SLD

Princes School Selborne St, Liverpool, Merseyside L8 1YQ; Tel 0151 709 2602; Fax 0151 709 2627
Headteacher V. Healey
SLD

Redbridge School Sherwoods La, Liverpool, Merseyside L10 1LW; Tel 0151 525 5733; Fax 0151 524 0435
Headteacher S. Coates
SLD

Sandfield Park School Sandfield Wlk, Liverpool, Merseyside L12 1LH; Tel 0151 228 0324; Fax 0151 252 1273
Headteacher J. Hudson
PH

Watergate School Speke Rd, Liverpool, Merseyside L25 8QA; Tel 0151 428 5812; Fax 0151 421 1433
Headteacher P. Richardson
MLD

White Thorn School Ranworth Sq, Liverpool, Merseyside L10 1LW; Tel 0151 498 4811; Fax 0151 498 4868
Headteacher J. Roberts

SPECIAL RESIDENTIAL SCHOOLS

Abbots Lea School Beaconsfield Rd, Woolton, Merseyside L25 6EE; Tel 0151 428 1161; Fax 0151 428 6180
Headteacher C. Boycott
Autism

Lower Lee School Beaconsfield Rd, Liverpool, Merseyside L25 6EF; Tel 0151 428 4071; Fax 0151 428 4737
Headteacher P. Wright (Acting)

LUTON BOROUGH COUNCIL
www.luton.gov.uk

Came into effect April 1997.
Population 183 100
Political Composition: Lab: 36, LD: 9, Con: 3
Town Hall, Luton LU1 2BQ; URL www.luton.gov.uk; Tel 01582 546000; Fax 01582 546223
Chief Executive Darra Sinah

Social Services Department

Unity Hse, 111 Stuart St, Luton LU1 5NP; Tel 01582 547500; Fax 01582 547733
Corporate Director (Housing and Social Services) Hugh Dunnachie
Head (Resources and Performance Review) Bob Ashforth; Tel 01582 547501
Head (Children and Family Services) Wes Cuell; Tel 01582 547502
Head of Services (Community Care) Paul Jenkins; Tel 01582 547503
Care Manager (Family Support and Child Protection) Jane Webb; Tel 01582 547561
Care Manager (Family Support and Child Protection) Lyn Hartnell; Tel 01582 547562
Service Manager (Disabled Children and Support Services) Hilary Griffiths Job share; Tel 01582 547595
Service Manager (Disabled Children and Support Services) Brendan Timon Job share; Tel 01582 547622

Service Manager (Family Support and Child Protection) Richard Fountain; Tel 01582 547560
Service Manager (Looked After Children) Jenny Coles; Tel 01582 547647
Manager (Standards and Performance) Rachel Jones; Tel 01582 547564
Team Manager (Adoption and Permanent Family Placement) Carol Hughes; Tel 01582 547584
Team Manager (Family Finding and Foster Carer Support) Lynne Howells; Tel 01582 547633
Team Manager (Initial Assessment Team) Carole Barker; Tel 01582 547653
Duty Adults' Services Tel 01582 547659; Tel 01582 547660
Service Manager (Home Care and Warden Services) Jill Jackson; Tel 01582 547794
Service Manager (Assessment and Care Management) Linda Coady; Tel 01582 547676
Service Manager (Strategy Planning and Partnerships (OPS)) Marina Mele; Tel 01582 547691
Service Manager (Learning Disability) Bernie Middlehurst; Tel 01582 547538
Service Manager (Mental Health) Anthony Cole
Service Manager (Physical Disability and Sensory Impairment) Wendy Toomey; Tel 01582 547776
Service Manager (Residential/Daycare (OPS)) Shirley Owens; Tel 01582 547779
Occupational Therapy Team Leader Sheila Scoot; Tel 01582 547715
Occupational Therapy Team Leader Vacancy; Tel 01582 547716

Social Services Committee

Lab: 11, LD: 3, Con: 1
Executive Member for Care and Health Jenny Davies
Vice-Chair Mohammed Ashraf (Lab)

South Bedfordshire Youth Offending Team and Independent Living Unit 16 Rothesay Rd, Luton
Head (Youth Offending Services) Mike Thomas; Tel 01582 736522
Team Manager (16+) Johnathan Whalley
45–47 Grosvenor Hse, Luton; Tel 01582 547900

DAY CARE CENTRE FOR CHILDREN

Alder Cres, Solway Rd, Luton
Officer-in-Charge Vacancy; Tel 01582 494762

CHILDREN'S HOME

Buckle Close Children's Home 2 Buckle Cl, Northwell Dr, Luton LU3 3SZ
Officer-in-Charge Maggie Walsh; Tel 01582 597028

YOUNG PEOPLE'S RESOURCE CENTRE

50 Parys Rd, Birdsfoot La, Luton LU3 2EW
Officer-in-Charge J. Harrington; Tel 01582 572145

HOME FOR CHILDREN WITH LEARNING DISABILITIES

Fairway Children's Home 111 London Rd, Luton LU1 3RH
Officer-in-Charge Lyn Hartnell; Tel 01582 736966

FAMILY RESOURCE CENTRES

Leagrave Family Resource Centre 35 Mayne Ave, Luton LU4 9LR
Manager Rosemary Moss; Tel 01582 582962

Manor Family Resource Centre Chase St, Luton LU1 3QZ
Manager Diane Foyle; Tel 01582 415401

DAY CARE CENTRES FOR PEOPLE WITH LEARNING DISABILITIES

Bramingham Centre Weltmore Rd, Luton LU3 2TN
Unit Manager Marilyn George; Tel 01582 573408

6

Downside Day Care Centre Oakwood Ave, Dunstable, Bedfordshire
Unit Manager Sandra Jenkins; Tel 01582 660655

ASSESSMENT AND REHAB TEAM

The Acorns, 7 School La, Luton LU4 9QS
Unit Manager Kay McCarthy; Tel 01582 505508

SUPPORTED LIVING FOR PEOPLE WITH LEARNING DISABILITIES

The Acorns 7 School La, Luton LU4 9QS
Unit Manager Barbara Hobbs; Tel 01582 599807
Wauluds House Wauluds Bank Dr, Marsh Farm, Luton LU3 3LZ
Unit Manager Barbara Hobbs; Tel 01582 507032

SERVICES FOR DEAF PEOPLE

Alban Neve Centre for the Deaf 46 Old Bedford Rd, Luton LU2 7NX
Unit Manager Christopher Reid; Tel 01582 483417

CENTRES FOR PEOPLE WITH A PHYSICAL DISABILITY

Disability Resource Centre Adult Physical Disability Team, Poynters Rd, Dunstable, Bedfordshire; Tel 01582 470900
Adult Physical Disability Team
Team Manager Christine Langley
Downlands Day Centre 39 Leicester Rd, Luton LU4 8SF
Unit Manager Polly Edwards; Tel 01582 595746

HOME FOR PEOPLE WITH A PHYSICAL DISABILITY

The Oaks 8 School La, Luton LU4 9QS
Unit Manager Rick Forryan; Tel 01582 599993

DAY CARE CENTRES FOR OLDER PEOPLE

African Caribbean Elders Day Centre Old School Hse, Trinity Rd, Luton LU3 1TP; Tel 01582 504840
Manager Rita Watling
Farley Day Centre Whipperley Ring, Luton LU1 5QY
Manager Jackie Smith; Tel 01582 413961
Hockwell Ring Day Centre 2 Hockwell Ring, Luton LU4 9NG
Manager Elizabeth Kelly; Tel 01582 502116
Milan Centre 161 Dunstable Rd, Luton 1BW 2BW
Manager Lali Nandi; Tel 01582 401533
St. Monica's Day Centre 45 St. Ives Cl, St. Monica's Ave, Luton L43 1PP
Manager Diane Catley; Tel 01582 425661
Stopsley Day Centre 562 Hitchin Rd, Luton LU2 7UG
Manager Ann Conway; Tel 01582 732850
Sundon Park Day Centre 210 Sundon Park Rd, Luton LU3 3DN
Manager Val Smith; Tel 01582 599310

HOMES FOR OLDER PEOPLE

There are three homes for older people.

Lifelong Learning Department

Luton Borough Council, Unity Hse, 111 Stuart St, Luton LU1 5NP; E-mail education@luton.gov.uk; Tel 01582 546000; Fax 01582 548454
Corporate Director (Lifelong Learning) T. Dessent

SPECIAL SCHOOLS

Lady Zia Wernher School Ashcroft Rd, Luton LU2 9AY; Tel 01582 728705
Headteacher J. Jackson
(87)

Richmond Hill School Sunridge Ave, Luton LU2 7JL; Tel 01582 721019
Headteacher J. Jackson (Acting)
(120)
Woodlands Secondary School Northwell Dr, Luton LU3 3SP; Tel 01582 572880
Headteacher H.A. Hardie
(156)

MANCHESTER CITY COUNCIL
www.manchester.gov.uk

Population 392 908
Political Composition: Lab: 76, LD: 22, Other: 1
Town Hall, PO Box 532, Manchester M60 2LA;
URL www.manchester.gov.uk; Tel 0161 234 5000;
Fax 0161 234 3207
Lord Mayor Cllr A. Jones
Chief Executive Howard Bernstein
City Architect R. King
City Treasurer R. Paver
Director (Art Galleries and Museums) V. Tandy
Director (Libraries) V. Rosin
Director (Housing) S. Rumbelow
Director (City Works and Environmental Development) P. North

Social Services Department

PO Box 536, Town Hall Extension, Manchester M60 2AF;
URL www.manchester.gov.uk/ssd; Tel 0161 234 5000;
Emergency Unit (Out-of-office hours) 0161 274 3099
Director (Social Services) Heather Stephens
Assistant Director (Older People's Services)
Claudette Webster (Acting)
Assistant Director (Finance) Carol Wright
Assistant Director (Children and Families) Vacancy
Assistant Director (Adults) Paul Cassidy
Manager (Manchester Advice) Blake Dobson

TRAINING

Responsible for training professional and support staff in the department.
Training Section, c/o PO Box 536, Manchester M60 2AF;
Tel 0161 234 5000

Social Services Committee

Lab: 20, LD: 5
Executive Member (Health and Social Care) S. Cooley (Lab)
Deputy A. Trotman (Lab)
Members of the Committee
Lab: A. Burns, B. Curley, G. Evans, B. Harrison, R. Leese, P. Murphy, S. Murphy, C. Nangle, M. Pagel, I. Rizvi, K. Robinson, D. Shaw, J. Smith, M. Smitheman, A. Spinks, V. Stevens, B. Stone.
LD: S. Ashley, J. Bridges, A. Jones, J. Pearcey, S. Weale.

DISTRICT OFFICES

North

Beswick District Office 1 Campion Walk, Bradford, Manchester M11 3SB; Tel 0161 223 9641
Harpurhey District Office Rochdale Rd, Manchester M9 1DD; Tel 0161 205 7321

Central

Longsight District Office Stockport Rd, Manchester M12 4LL; Tel 0161 225 9293

Moss Side District Office Bold St, Alexandra Park Est, Manchester M16 7AD; Tel 0161 226 8131

South

Chorlton District Office 102 Manchester Rd, Chorlton, Manchester M21 9SZ; Tel 0161 881 0911

Wythenshawe District Office Etrop Way, Civic Centre, Manchester M22 5RE; Tel 0161 499 2121

RESIDENTIAL UNITS (CHILDREN AND YOUNG PEOPLE)

Burton Road Residential Unit 31 Burton Rd, Withington, Manchester M20 9FA; Tel 0161 445 5712

Glendene Residential Unit Greenbrow Rd, Newall Grn, Manchester M23 8RE; Tel 0161 437 8388

Lynwood Residential Unit Holme Rd, Didsbury, Manchester M20 8TX; Tel 0161 434 4057

Seymour Green Residential Unit 40 Seymour Grn, Crumpsall, Manchester M8 6BR; Tel 0161 740 6224

Woodland's Residential Unit Carlton Rd, Whalley Range, Manchester M16 8BB; Tel 0161 226 8228

COMMUNITY HOME WITH EDUCATION

Broome Hse, 779 Wilmslow Rd, Manchester M20 8RW; Tel 0161 445 8883

YOUTH JUSTICE CENTRES

Frank Kelly Centre Greenbrow Rd, Nowall Grn, Manchester M23 8RE; Tel 0161 437 3069

Parkway Centre Chichester Rd, Manchester M15 5PA; Tel 0161 226 9714

Ridgeway Centre 9–15 Stilton Dr, Beswick, Manchester M11 3SB; Tel 0161 223 0488

HOSPITAL SOCIAL WORK TEAMS

Manchester Royal Infirmary Oxford Rd, Manchester M13 9WL; Tel 0161 276 4153
Team Manager R. Dumpleton

North Manchester General Hospital Delauneys Rd, Manchester M8 6RB; Tel 0161 720 2510
Team Manager L. Siddall

Wythenshawe Hospital Clay La, Manchester M23 9LT; Tel 0161 291 2275
Team Manager B. Staniforth

COMMUNITY RESOURCE CENTRES

Bradford Centre Raglan Cl, Bradford, Manchester M11 3TH; Tel 0161 223 4673
Elderly disabled

Claremont Community Resource Centre Rolls Cres, Hulme, Manchester M15 5FS; Tel 0161 226 3420

Hall Lane Community Resource Centre 159 Hall La, Baguley, Manchester M23 8WD; Tel 0161 945 7609

Heathfield Community Resource Centre Heathfield St, Newton Heath, Manchester M40 6LF; Tel 0161 688 0560

Hillside Community Resource Centre Rudcroft Cl, Chorlton-on-Medlock, Manchester M13 9TN; Tel 0161 273 2016

Minehead Centre Minehead Ave, Withington, Manchester M20 8FW; Tel 0161 446 2551

Openshaw Centre Oldfield, 10 Catherine St, Manchester M11 1NS; Tel 0161 301 1480
Elderly

Woodville Community Resource Centre Shirley Rd, Cheetham, Manchester M8 7NE; Tel 0161 740 3134

DAY CENTRES FOR PEOPLE WITH MENTAL HEALTH PROBLEMS

Harpurhey Centre 93 Church La, Harpurhey, Manchester M9 1NH; Tel 0161 205 0118
Mentally ill

Victoria Park Centre 70 Daisy Bank Rd, Victoria Pk, Manchester M14 5QN; Tel 0161 224 1308
Mentally ill (30)

DAY CENTRES FOR PEOPLE WITH LEARNING DISABILITIES

Crossacres Resource Centre Peel Hall Rd, Crossacres, Wythenshawe, Greater Manchester M22 5DG; Tel 0161 499 3375

Forrester House Day Centre 50 Blackwin St, Manchester M12 5JY; Tel 0161 223 4025

Mill House Resource Centre Nathans Rd, Banchill, Wythenshawe, Greater Manchester M22 9GH; Tel 0161 498 9773

Northfield Day Centre Northfield Rd, Manchester M40 0RL; Tel 0161 681 3510

NETWORK SCHEMES

There are eight Network Support Schemes for adults with a learning disability.

ACCOMMODATION FOR PEOPLE WITH MENTAL HEALTH PROBLEMS

There are 18 minimum support homes throughout the city for people with mental health problems; Tel (Mental Health Partnership) 0161 205 1483

HOME FOR PARTIALLY RECOVERED ALCOHOLICS

Newbury, 80 Daisy Bank Rd, Manchester M14 5GJ; Tel 0161 224 5729
(16)

ELDERLY PERSONS' HOME

There is one elderly persons' home.

Education Offices

Overseas Hse, Quay St, Manchester M3 3BB; URL www.manchester.gov.uk/education; Tel 0161 234 7270; Fax 0161 234 7147
Chief Education Officer Mick Waters; Tel 0161 234 7001; Fax 0161 234 7007
Head (Learning Support Strategy) Jenny Andrews (Acting); Tel 0161 234 7154; Fax 0161 234 7073
Chief Education Welfare Officer Simon Ashley; Tel 0161 234 7177; Fax 0161 234 7218
Chief Educational Psychologist Maria Heffernan
Central District Centre, Westwood St, Moss Side, Manchester M14 4SW; Tel 0161 226 5404; Fax 0161 226 2821

PUPIL REFERRAL SERVICE

Education Offices, Overseas Hse, Quay St, Manchester M3 3BB; Tel 0161 234 7240; Fax 0161 234 7107
Head (Exclusions and Education) Chris Read

EDUCATIONAL PSYCHOLOGY SERVICE

Central District Centre Westwood St, Moss Side, Manchester M14 4SW; Tel 0161 226 5404; Fax 0161 226 2821
District Senior Educational Psychologist Patricia Carter

North District Centre 2 Thornaby Wlk, Harpurhey, Manchester M9 5GE; Tel 0161 205 2857; Fax 0161 205 0893
District Senior Educational Psychologist Jennifer Noble

South District Centre Yew Tree La, Northern Moor, Wythenshawe, Manchester M23 9EA; Tel 0161 998 4130; 0161 998 4897; Fax 0161 945 8482
District Senior Educational Psychologist Karen Hazzan (Acting)

EDUCATION WELFARE SERVICE

East/West Manchester District Education Welfare Office, The Waldway, 537a Stockport Rd, Manchester M12 4LJ; Tel 0161 225 0293; 0161 225 0304; Fax 0161 225 3476
District Manager (East) Michael Heaney
District Manager (West) Sue Toke

North Manchester District The Old Rectory, 337 St. Mary's Rd, Moston, Greater Manchester M40 0EW; Tel 0161 682 9054; Fax 0161 682 9054
District Manager David Hinde

South Manchester District 2nd Fl, Hale Top Hse, Wythenshawe, Manchester M22 5SD; Tel 0161 499 1451; Fax 0161 437 6920
District Manager Beverley Howard

HOSPITAL SCHOOL AND HOME TUITION SERVICE

Manchester Hospital Schools and Home Teaching Service Charlestown Rd, Blackley, Manchester M9 7AA; Tel 0161 220 5118; Fax 0161 220 5600
Head Helen E. Jones

Leo Kelly Centre Monton St, Greenheys, Manchester M14 4LT; Tel 0161 226 1367; Fax 0161 232 1969

Newbrook School Newholme Rd, West Didsbury, Manchester M20 2XZ; Tel 0161 445 5172; Fax 0161 438 0058

SPECIAL DAY SCHOOLS

Barlow Hall Primary School and Assessment Unit Darley Ave, Chorlton-cum-Hardy, Manchester M21 2JA; Tel 0161 881 1934; Fax 0161 861 8367
Headteacher Tony Scally
  Assessment unit

The Birches School Newholme Rd, West Didsbury, Manchester M20 2XZ; Tel 0161 448 8895; Fax 0161 445 4970
Headteacher Marie L. Morgan
  SLD

Camberwell Park School Bank House Rd, Blackley, Manchester M9 8LT; Tel 0161 740 1897; Fax 0161 740 3473
Headteacher Pam Stanier
  SLD

Ewing School Central Rd, West Didsbury, Manchester M20 4ZA; Tel 0161 445 0745; Fax 0161 438 0510
Headteacher Pat Derbyshire
  (58)

Gorton Brook School Belle Vue St, Gorton, Manchester M12 5PW; Tel 0161 223 1822; Fax 0161 223 2731
Headteacher Ivor John
  MLD

Grange School 77 Dickenson Rd, Rusholme, Manchester M14 5AZ; Tel 0161 248 4841; Fax 0161 248 6715
Headteacher Ann Fitzpatrick
  Complex Learning Difficulties (45)

Greenbrow Infant School and Assessment Unit Greenbrow Rd, Newall Grn, Wythenshawe, Manchester M23 2UE; Tel 0161 437 3331; Fax 0161 436 5331
Headteacher Susan Johnson
  Assessment unit

Harpur Mount Primary School and Assessment Unit Beech Mount, Harpurhey, Manchester M9 5XS; Tel 0161 205 4993
Headteacher Pat A. Turner
  Assessment unit

Lancasterian School and Barrier Free Partnership Elizabeth Slinger Rd, West Didsbury, Manchester M20 2XA; Tel 0161 445 0123; Fax 0161 445 6826
Headteacher Carole Cooper (Acting)
  PH (145)

Meade Hill School Middleton Rd, Crumpsall, Manchester M8 4NB; Tel 0161 795 8445; Fax 0161 795 6241
Headteacher Bob Paprosky
  Social and emotional difficulties

Medlock Valley High School Palmerston St, Ancoats, Manchester M12 6PT; Tel 0161 274 4667; Fax 0161 274 4566
Headteacher Sandra Hibbert
  MLD

Melland High School Holmcroft Rd, Gorton, Manchester M18 7NG; Tel 0161 223 9915; Fax 0161 230 6919
Headteacher Judith O'Kane
  SLD

Newbrook School Newholme Rd, West Didsbury, Manchester M20 2XZ; Tel 0161 445 5172; Fax 0161 438 0058
Headteacher Susan Parsons
  Hearing impaired

Piper Hill High School 200 Yew Tree La, Northenden, Manchester M23 0FF; Tel 0161 998 4068; Fax 0161 945 6625
Headteacher Linda Jones (Acting)
  SLD

Richmond Park School Cochrane Ave, Longsight, Manchester M12 4FA; Tel 0161 273 4894; Fax 0161 273 8341
Headteacher Joan Holt
  MLD

Rodney House School 388 Slade La, Burnage, Manchester M19 2HT; Tel 0161 224 2774; Fax 0161 225 5186
Headteacher Mary Isherwood
  Assessment unit (45)

Roundwood School Roundwood Rd, Northenden, Manchester M22 4AB; Tel 0161 998 4138; Fax 0161 946 0495
Headteacher Sandra Hibbert
  MLD

Shawgrove School Cavendish Rd, West Disbury, Manchester M20 1QB; Tel 0161 445 9435; Fax 0161 445 0386
Headteacher Hugh Taylor
  Vision impaired

Southern Cross School Barlow Hall Rd, Chorlton-cum-Hardy, Manchester M21 7JJ; Tel 0161 881 2695; Fax 0161 861 7190
Headteacher Michael J. Howard
  Social and emotional difficulties

Woodside School Crossacres Rd, Peel Hall, Wythenshawe, Manchester M22 5DR; Tel 0161 437 5697; Fax 0161 498 0297
Headteacher John E. Law
  MLD

RESIDENTIAL SCHOOL

Buglawton Hall School Buxton Rd, Congleton, Cheshire CW12 3PQ; Tel 01260 274492; Fax 01260 288313
Headteacher Ken Williams
  Social and emotional difficulties

INDEPENDENCE DEVELOPMENT SERVICE FOR CHILDREN WITH DISABILITIES

Abraham Moss Centre, Cresent Rd, Crumpsall, Manchester M8 5UF; Tel 0161 908 8360; Fax 0161 908 8370
Manager Jan Line; Tel 0161 980 8361

BEHAVIOUR SUPPORT NEEDS

Peacock Centre, Peacock Cl, Gorton, Manchester M18 8AX; Tel 0161 223 3158; Fax 0161 223 1653
District Co-ordinator Elaine Hillary

ETHNIC MINORITY ACHIEVEMENT SERVICE

Palmerston St, Ancoats, Manchester M12 6PE; Tel 0161 273 4232; Fax 0161 274 3427
Head (Pupil Achievement) Pinaki Ghoshal

LEARNING SUPPORT NEEDS

Westwood St, Moss Side, Manchester M14 4PH; Tel 0161
226 0843; Fax 0161 226 0211
Head of Service Amanda Corcoran
Head of Service Lynda Karalis (Acting)

TRAVELLER EDUCATION SERVICE

Parkside Centre, Sheepfoot La, Prestwich, Manchester
M25 0BW; Tel 0161 740 1465; Fax 0161 721 4220
Head of Service Brenda Dawnes

MEDWAY COUNCIL
www.medway.gov.uk

In April 1998 Medway became a unitary authority. The rest
of Kent retains a two-tier structure.
Political Composition: Con: 38, Lab: 25, LD: 15, Ind LD: 2
Civic Centre, Strood, Rochester, Medway ME2 4AU;
URL www.medway.gov.uk; Tel 01634 306000
Mayor Cllr N. Bowler
Portfolio Holder (Health and Community) Cllr H. Doe
Chief Executive Judith Armitt
Leader of Conservative Group Cllr Rodney Chambers
Leader of Labour Group Cllr Paul Godwin
Leader of Liberal Democrat Group Cllr Geoff Juby
Leader of Independent Liberal Democrat Group Cllr Ian Burt
Director (Development and Environment) Dr Richard
  Simmons
Director (Finance and Corporate Services) Neil Davies
Director (Health and Community Services) Ann Windiate
Director (Education and Leisure) Rose Collinsa

Social Services Department

Compass Centre, Pembroke, Chatham Maritime, Medway
ME4 4YH; Tel 01634 306000; Fax 01634 331200;
Minicom 01634 331257
Director (Health and Community Services) Ann Windiate
Assistant Director (Adults) Dave Wilkinson
Assistant Director (Children and Families) Helen Davies
Assistant Director (Strategy and Support) Geoff Ettridge
Manager (Finance) David Taffs
Manager (Contracts) Brain Wintle-Smith
Manager (Access and Information) Wilma Whitall
Manager (Customer Relations – Complaints)
  Julie Rimmington
Adviser (Information and Technology) Darren Gunn

AREA OFFICES

Gillingham Local Office

Kingsley Hse, 37–39 Balmoral Rd, Gillingham, Medway
ME7 4PF; Tel 01634 331927; Fax 01634 331926;
Minicom 01634 331339
Access and Information Officer Lin Wilson
Access and Information Officer Joy Godfrey

Strood Local Office

Greatfield Lodge, Darnley Rd, Strood, Medway ME2 2UU;
Tel 01634 294356; Fax 01634 294357
Access and Information Officer Dee Davie

Children and Families Division

Assistant Director (Children and Families Services)
  Helen Davies; Tel 01634 306000
Manager (Service Standards – Looked After Children) Ian Dixon
*Manager (Service Standards – Child Protection and Family
  Support)* Deirdre Tonkin

Principal Officer (Young Offenders) Ian Sparling
Service Provider Manager Didge Eldred
Chatham Teams Based at, Compass Centre, Chatham
Maritime, Chatham, Medway ME4 4YH; Tel 01634 306000;
Fax 01634 331200
Team Manager (Family Assessment Team) Nigel Honan;
Tel 01634 331229
Team Manager (Child Care) Debbie Thornelow; Tel 01634
33156
Gillingham Kingsley Hse, 37–39 Balmoral Rd, Gillingham,
Medway ME7 4PF; Tel 01634 331927; Fax 01634 331926
Operational Manager Karen Bays; Tel 01634 331902
Team Manager (Children with a Disability)
  Eileen Hollingsworth
Team Manager (Gillingham East) Jeanette Scott
Team Manager (Gillingham West) Kath Thomas
Rochester/Strood Teams Based at Greatfield Lodge,
Darnley Rd, Rochester, Medway ME2 2UU; Tel 01634
294356; Fax 01634 294357
Team Manager (Rochester North) David Ross
Team Manager (Rochester South) Tony Dickinson

CHILDREN AND ADOLESCENTS MENTAL HEALTH SERVICE
(DEPARTMENT OF CHILD AND FAMILY PSYCHIATRY)

Department of Children and Family Psychiatry, The
  Childrens Centre, Canada Hse, Gillingham, Medway
  ME7 4JL
Senior Practitioner Chris Cahill; Tel 01634 854547

YOUNG OFFENDERS TEAM

Adolescent Resource Centre, 67 Balfat Rd, Chatham,
  Medway ME4 6QO; Tel 01634 818753; Fax 01634 849660
Principal Officer Ian Sparling

Services for Children and Families

67 Balfour Rd, Chatham, Medway ME4 6QU; Tel 01634
  406981; Fax 01634 409122
Service Manager Didge Eldred

RESIDENTIAL SERVICES

The Old Vicarage Upnor Rd, Lower Upnor, Rochester,
Medway ME2 4UX; Tel 01634 294409; Fax 01634 294423
Unit Manager Patrick Burns

Patrixborne Adolescent Unit 46 Patrixborne Ave,
Gillingham, Medway ME8 6UF; Tel 01634 232282
Unit Manager Bob Barnes

COMMUNITY SUPPORT SERVICES

Adolescent Resource Centre 67 Balfour Rd, Chatham,
Medway ME4 6QU; Tel 01634 818753; Fax 01634 849660
Unit Manager Joyce Kreit

Chatham Family Centre Wayfield Rd, Chatham, Medway;
Tel 01634 300302
Unit Manager Hilary Young

Gillingham Family Care Workers Kingsley Hse, 37–39
Balmoral Rd, Gillingham, Medway ME7 4PF; Tel 01634
331954; 01634 331961; Fax 01634 331926

Rochester Family Care Workers Wayfield Centre, Wayfield
Rd, Chatham, Medway; Tel 01634 300302

Strood Family Centre Darnley Rd, Strood, Medway
ME2 2UL; Tel 01634 291391
Unit Manager Judith Marshall

HOMEFINDING SERVICES

Compass Centre Pembroke, Chatham Maritime, Chatham,
Medway ME4 4YH; Tel 01634 306000; Fax 01634 331200
Manager (Fostering) Clive Eggleton
Manager (Adoption) Lesley Penna
Manager (Adoption) Mandy Lowe

6

Adults Division

Assistant Director (Adult Services) Dave Wilkinson; Tel 01634 306000
Principal Officer (Lead for Older People) Karen Seymour
Principal Officer (Lead for People with a Disability) Val Bridges
Principal Officer (Mental Health) Nigel Gregory
Service Provider Manager (Lead for Learning Disability and Mental Health) Liz Nicholas
Service Provider Manager (Lead for Older People and Physical Disability Services) Rita Bishop
Principal Occupational Therapist Jackie Challis Job share.
Principal Occupational Therapist Amanda Dean Job share.

GILLINGHAM CARE MANAGEMENT

Principal Officer Val Bridges; Tel 01634 331474

Gillingham East Kingsley Hse, 37–39 Balmoral Rd, Gillingham, Medway ME7 4PF; Tel 01634 331927; Fax 01634 331926
Team Manager Carole Turner; Tel 01634 331910

Gillingham West Kingsley Hse, 37–39 Balmoral Rd, Gillingham, Medway ME7 4PF; Tel 01634 331927; Fax 01634 331926
Team Manager Carol O'Meara; Tel 01634 331978

ROCHESTER AND CHATHAM CARE MANAGEMENT

Principal Officer Karen Seymour; Tel 01634 331487

Central Team (Rochester) Compass Centre, Pembroke, Chatham Maritime, Medway ME4 4YH; Tel 01634 306000; Fax 01634 331200
Team Manager Andre Fox; Tel 01634 331341

East Team (Chatham) Riverside 1, Dock Rd, Chatham, Medway ME4 4SL; Tel 01634 331820; Fax 01634 331851
Team Manager Tricia Mercer; Tel 01634 331862

West Team (Strood) Shaws Wood, Mill Rd, Strood, Medway ME2 3BU; Tel 01634 295589; Fax 01634 718370
Team Manager Nigel Spicer

HEALTH CARE TEAM

Hospital Team Medway Maritime Hospital, Windmill Rd, Gillingham, Medway; Tel 01634 825286; Fax 01634 825285
Team Manager Anthea Winter

PALLIATIVE CARE TEAM

Wisdom Hospice Centre for Palliative Care Services, St. William's Way, Rochester, Medway ME1 2NU; Tel 01634 830456; Fax 01634 845890
Senior Practitioner Nan McMurray

MENTAL HEALTH TEAMS

Gillingham Mental Health Team Kingsley Hse, 37–39 Balmoral Rd, Gillingham, Medway ME7 4PF; Tel 01634 331927; Fax 01634 331926
Team Manager Edwina Morris; Tel 01634 331938

Mental Health Team Compass Centre, Pembroke, Chatham Maritime, Medway ME4 4YH; Tel 01634 306000; Fax 01634 331200
Principal Officer Nigel Gregory; Tel 01634 331216

Rochester and Chatham Mental Health Team (includes the Departmental Substance Misuse Care Managers) Compass Centre, Pembroke, Chatham Charitime, Medway ME4 4YH; Tel 01634 306000; Fax 01634 331200
Team Manager Steve Morris; Tel 01634 331441

OCCUPATIONAL THERAPY SERVICE

Occupational Therapy Services Compass Centre, Pembroke, Chatham Maritime, Medway ME4 4YH; Tel 01634 331272

Principal Occupational Therapist Jackie Challis; Tel 01634 331272; Fax 01634 331542
Principal Occupational Therapist Amanda Dean

DEAF SERVICES

Compass Centre Pembroke, Chatham Maritime, Chatham, Medway ME4 4YH; Tel 01634 331262; Fax 01634 331542
Services for the Blind
Services for people who are blind or have a visual impairment are provided by Kent Association for the Blind. Kent Association for the Blind; Tel 01634 722766

SERVICES FOR ADULTS

Service Provider Manager (Learning Disability and Mental Health Services) Liz Nicholas; Tel 01634 331269
Service Provider (Older People and Physical Disability Services) Rita Bishop; Tel 01634 331310
Manager (Home Care) Ellen Murphy; Tel 01634 818859

RESIDENTIAL AND DAY SERVICES FOR OLDER PEOPLE

Platters Farm Lodge Highfield Rd, Rainham, Medway ME8 0EQ; Tel 01634 377579; Fax 01634 260791
Unit Manager Jenny Broom

Nelson Court Nelson Terr, Luton, Chatham, Medway ME5 7JZ; Tel 01634 845337; Fax 01634 819316
Unit Manager Jan Newall

Robert Bean Lodge Pattens La, Rochester, Medway ME1 2QT; Tel 01634 831122; Fax 01634 831113
Unit Manager Rodney Peal

Shaws Wood Home Mill Rd, Strood, Medway ME2 3BU; Tel 01634 723203/4; Fax 01634 723203
Unit Manager Viv Simmons

HOME CARE SERVICES FOR OLDER PEOPLE

Robert Bean Lodge Pattens La, Rochester, Medway ME1 2QT; Tel 01634 818859; Fax 01634 831113
Home Care Manager Ellen Murphy

SERVICES FOR ADULTS WITH PHYSICAL DISABILITIES

Balfour Day Centre Pattens La, Rochester, Medway ME1 2RB; Tel 01634 845940; Fax 01634 814475
Unit Manager Derek Gooch
Unit Manager Jackie Welch

DAY SERVICES FOR ADULTS WITH LEARNING DISABILITIES

Access to Employment Strood Day Opportunities Centre, Darnley Rd, Strood, Medway ME2 2EU; Tel 01634 294964; Fax 01634 295513
Unit Manager Jane Love

Chatham Day Opportunities Centre 20 Manor Rd, Chatham, Medway ME4 5AG; Tel 01634 826453; Fax 01634 826465
Unit Manager Inge Johnson

Enhanced Care Unit The Balfour Centre, Pattens La, Rochester, Medway ME1 2RB; Tel 01634 819899; Fax 01634 295513
Unit Manager Dennis Hilliard

Gillingham Day Opportunities Centre 48a Canterbury St, Gillingham, Medway ME7 5UN; Tel 01634 580080; Fax 01634 580158
Unit Manager Inge Johnson

Strood Day Opportunities Centre Darnley Rd, Strood, Medway ME2 2EU; Tel 01634 719793; Fax 01634 295513
Unit Manager Jane Love

RESIDENTIAL SERVICES FOR ADULTS WITH LEARNING DISABILITIES

Foxbury Manor Respite Care Unit 36a Birling Ave, Rainham, Medway
Unit Manager Denise Watkins

Napier Road Home 43 Napier Rd, Gillingham, Medway;
Tel 01634 571751
Manager Denise Watkins

SERVICES FOR PEOPLE WITH MENTAL HEALTH PROBLEMS

Compass Centre Pembroke, Chatham Maritime, Chatham,
Medway ME4 4YH; Tel 01634 306000; Fax 01634 331200
Service Provider Manager Liz Nicholas
Community Residential Manager Richard Ford
Community Residential Manager Norma Lawson
Community Resource Manager (Chatham/Gillingham)
Jenny Bartlett
Montgomery Ave, Chatham, Medway; Tel 01634 829922
Community Resource Manager (Rochester/Gillingham)
Jackie Sloan
Chaucer Centre, 1a and 1b Chaucer Rd, Gillingham,
Medway; Tel 01634 573194

OTHER SERVICES

The Community Interpreting Service Compass Centre,
Pembroke, Chatham Maritime, Medway ME4 4YH;
Tel 01634 306000; Fax 01634 331200
Manager Elizabeth Bird; Tel 01634 331286

Out of Hours Service Kiln Crt, Lower Rd, Faversham,
Medway ME13 7NY; Tel (Office hours) 01795 590555; (Out
of hours) 0345 626777; Fax (Office hours) 01795 590973
Medway Operational Manager James Sinclair

Registration and Inspection Unit Riverside 1, Dock Rd,
Chatham, Medway ME4 4SL; Tel 01634 331841; Fax 01634
331843
Manager (Registration and Inspection) Alan Barwood

SUPPORT SERVICES

Assistant Director (Support Services) Geoff Ettridge
Compass Centre, Pembroke, Chatham Maritime, Chatham,
Medway ME4 4YH; Tel 01634 306000; Fax 01634 331200

Customer Services
Manager (Access and Information) Wilma Whitall
Manager (Customer Relations) Julie Rimmington

Finance Team
Manager (Finance) David Taffs; Tel 01634 306000
Manager (Budget) Paul Worden
Manager (Exchequer Services) Chris Gell
Financial Management and Information Officer
Jon Crockford

Other Support Services
Manager (Information and Technology) Darren Gunn;
Tel 01634 331517

Personnel and Training Section
Adviser (Health and Safety) Alastair Barker; Tel 01634
331437

Education and Leisure Department

Civic Centre, Strood, Rochester, Medway ME2 4AU;
Tel 01634 306000; Fax 01634 331117
Director (Education and Leisure) Rose Collinson

SPECIAL SCHOOLS

Abbey Court Community School Rede Crt Rd, Strood,
Rochester, Medway ME2 3SP; E-mail courtabbey@aol.com;
Tel 01634 718153; Fax 01634 295369
Headteacher Karen Joy
Mixed 5–16 SLD

Bradfields School Churchill Ave, Chatham, Medway
ME5 0LB; E-mail staffordfields@supernet.com; Tel 01634
683990; Fax 01634 683571
Headteacher Peter J. Harris
Mixed 11–16 MLD

MERSEYSIDE METROPOLITAN AREA

The following Metropolitan Councils comprise the
Merseyside Metropolitan Area and may be found in
alphabetical order within this chapter: Knowsley,
Liverpool, St. Helens, Sefton, Wirral.

MERSEYSIDE CO-ORDINATING COMMITTEE

Committee Services, Liverpool City Council, Liverpool,
Merseyside L69 2DH; URL www.liverpool.gov.uk;
E-mail mike.storey@liverpool.gov.uk
Chair Cllr Marie Rinner St. Helens MBC
Secretary to Co-ordinating Committee David Henshaw;
E-mail david.henshaw@liverpool.gov.uk; Tel 0151 225
2334

MIDDLESBROUGH COUNCIL
www.middlesbrough.gov.uk

6

Population 144 000
Political Composition: Lab: 41, LD: 7, Con: 4, Ind: 1
Town Hall, PO Box 99a, Middlesbrough TS1 2QQ;
URL www.middlesbrough.gov.uk; Tel 01642 245432
Managing Director John E. Foster
Leader of the Council K. Walker
Corporate Director (Education and Leisure) Dr C. Berry
Corporate Director (Social and Housing Services)
A. Snowden

Training

3rd fl, Civic Centre, Middlesbrough TS1 2QH
Human Resource and Workforce Development Manager
C. O'Donovan

Welfare Rights Unit

3rd fl, Civic Centre, Middlesbrough; Tel 01642 245432;
Fax 01642 262822
Senior Welfare Rights Officer S. Nelson

Social Services

PO Box 234, Civic Centre, Middlesbrough TS1 2XH;
E-mail jan_douglas@middlesbrough.gov.uk; Tel 01642
729500; Fax 01642 729969
Executive Director (Social Services) Jan Douglas

Executive Board

Lab: 31, LD: 6, Con: 7, Ind: 4
Social Care Executive Member Cllr B. Thompson
Members of the Executive Board
Cllr B. Brady, Cllr B. Coppinger, Cllr D. Budd, Cllr B. Kerr,
Cllr R. Lowes, Cllr B. Thompson, Cllr P. Thompson,
Cllr N. Walker.

LOCAL OFFICES

Adults

PO Box 234, Civic Centre, Middlesbrough TS1 2XH;
Tel 01642 726004; Fax 01642 828641
Service Manager (Adults) N. Marshall
Service Manager (Adults) Y. Morren

Children's and Families' Services

Sandringham Hse, Park End, Middlesbrough; Tel 01642
  300870; Fax 01642 300849
Service Manager (Children and Families)   D. Waites
Service Manager (Children and Families)   S. Robinson

HOSPITAL SOCIAL WORKERS

South Cleveland Middlesbrough; Tel 01642 850850

CENTRE FOR CHILDREN WITH DISABILITIES

Gleneagles Resource Centre Gleneagles Rd,
Middlesbrough; Tel 01642 829437
   (10)

CENTRE FOR PEOPLE WITH DISABILITIES

Lansdowne Centre Lansdowne Rd, Middlesbrough;
Tel 01642 246610
   (80)

HOMES FOR PEOPLE WITH LEARNING DIFFICULTIES

Cumberland House Chelmsford Rd, Middlesbrough;
Tel 01642 814029
   (24)
St. Pauls Road Home 4 St. Pauls Rd, Middlesbrough;
Tel 01642 241620
   (30)

DAY SERVICES FOR PEOPLE WITH MENTAL HEALTH PROBLEMS

**Lothian Road Day Service for People with Mental Health
Problems** 90–92 Lothian Rd, Middlesbrough; Tel 01642
217399
Parklands Intermediate Care Services Homerton Rd,
Pallister Pk, Middlesbrough TS3 8PN; Tel 01642
246648
Woodside EMI Resource Centre Marton Rd,
Middlesbrough

ACCOMMODATION FOR PEOPLE WITH MENTAL HEALTH PROBLEMS

Sunningdale Road 11a Sunningdale Rd, Middlesbrough;
Tel 01642 826111
   (26)

SHELTERED WORKSHOP

Ayresome Industries, Letitia St, Middlesbrough; Tel 01642
   224606

DAY SERVICE FOR PEOPLE WITH LEARNING DISABILITIES

Erimus Day Centre Barrington Cres, Thorntree,
Middlesbrough; Tel 01642 248315

DAY CENTRES FOR THE ELDERLY

Albert Cocks Day Centre Rainham Cl, Thorntree,
Middlesbrough TS3 9HQ; Tel 01642 287399
Kirkley Lodge Day Centre Dalby Way, Coulby Newham,
Middlesbrough TS1 5NQ; Tel 01642 590283
Newport Day Centre 2 St. Pauls Rd, Middlesbrough
TS1 5NQ; Tel 01642 353498
North Ormesby Day Centre Derwent St, North Ormesby,
Middlesbrough; Tel 01642 226105

ELDERLY PERSON'S HOMES

There are four residential homes for the elderly.

Education Service

PO Box 69, Vancouver Hse, Gurney St, Middlesbrough
  TS1 1EL; Tel 01642 245432; Fax 01642 726984
Corporate Director   Dave Johnson (Acting)
Head (Planning and Information)   Sue Goodhall
Head (Inclusion)   Dave Johnson
Senior Adviser (Secondary)   Kevin Buckle
Senior Adviser (SEN, Equal Opportunities and EMAG)
  June Kearns
General Adviser (Primary, Early Years, Baseline)
  Valerie Whittington

PSYCHOLOGICAL SERVICES

Education and Leisure Service, PO Box 69, Vancouver Hse,
  Gurney St, Middlesbrough TS1 1EL
Principal Education Psychologist   Janet Philpott

SPECIAL SCHOOLS FOR PUPILS WITH LEARNING DIFFICULTIES

Holmwood School Saltersgill Ave, Middlesbrough TS4 3JS;
Tel 01642 819157; Fax 01642 829981
Headteacher   J. Appleyard
  Primary MLD
Priory Woods School Tothill Ave, Middlesbrough TS3 0RH;
Tel 01642 321212; Fax 01642 326800
Headteacher   B. Knill
  SLD
Tollesby School Saltersgill Ave, Middlesbrough TS4 3JS;
Tel 01642 815765; Fax 01642 823628
Headteacher   J. Whittingham, BPhil
  Secondary MLD

SPECIAL SCHOOL FOR HEARING IMPAIRED AND AUTISM

Beverley School Beverley Rd, Middlesbrough TS4 3LQ;
Tel 01642 277444; Fax 01642 277453
Headteacher   N. Carder
   (94)

MILTON KEYNES COUNCIL
www.mkweb.co.uk

The structure of the Council is designed to align the
services the Council offers to the user groups. This means
that personal social services are combined with other
functions. Personal social services for children are
delivered through the Learning and Development
Directorate along with education, economic development
and leisure services, all being focused predominantly on
children and younger people. Similarly, personal social
services for adults are supplied by the Neighbourhood
Services Directorate along with housing, benefits and
community alarm services.
Population 212 810 (April 2001)
Political Composition: Lab: 15, LD: 27, Con: 7, Ind: 1,
Vacancy: 1
Civic Offices, 1 Saxon Gate East, Milton Keynes MK9 3EJ;
  URL www.mkweb.co.uk; Tel (Out of hours Emergency
  Social Worker) 01908 265545; 01908 691691; Fax 01908
  253556; Minicom 01908 252727
Chief Executive   John Best
Strategic Director (Neighbourhood Services)   Kate Page
  (Designated Director of Social Services)
Strategic Director (Learning and Development)   Vanessa Gwynn
Director (Housing)   John Holman
Head (Commissioning and Customer Care)   David Moore
  (Acting)
Head (Integrated Commissioning)   Jennifer Cook
Head (Adult Social Care)   Alistair Gibbons
Head (Children's Services)   Paul Sutton

Head (Education) James McElligot
Manager (Social Work) John Heseltine
Manager (Older People's Services) Sue Graham
Manager (Service Development – Children's Services)
  Lois Russell
Manager (Service Development – Neighbourhood Services)
  Simon Ablett
Manager (Mental Health Services) Chris Moody
Manager (Performance and Quality) Jane Reed
*Manager (Children's Services (Children Assessment and
  Protection)* Amanda Farr
*Manager (Children's Services (Placement and Young People's
  Service))* Sue Maddox
*Manager (Children's Service – Conferences, Review and Service
  Development)* Karen Rogers
Manager (Youth Offending Team) Lee Westlake
There is a general e-mail address:
<firstname>.<lastname>@milton-keynes.gov.uk

Committees

Social Care, Housing and Health Overview Committee

Lab: 3, LD: 5, Con: 1
Chair Cllr Stephen Coventry
Vice-Chair Cllr Donald Hoyle
Members of the Committee
Cllr Burke, Cllr Carrington, Cllr Sandra Clark, Cllr Long,
Cllr Pugh, Cllr Saunders, Cllr Tamagnini-Barbosa.

Learning Community and Economic Development Overview Committee

Lab: 3, LD: 6, Co-opted Members: 4, Con: 2
Chair Vacancy
Vice-Chair Cllr Dransfield
Members of the Committee
Co-opted: Carrington, Sandra Clark, Stephen Clark, Crooks,
Drewett, Gerrella, Jury, Lloyd, Pendry.

Learning and Development Directorate

Services for Children.
PO Box 106, Saxon Crt, Avebury Blvd, Milton Keynes
  MK9 3ZE; URL www.mkweb.co.uk; Tel 01908 253465;
  Fax 01908 253254

UNDER FIVES RESOURCE CENTRE

Simpson Under Fives Resource Centre 211 Simpson Rd,
Simpson, Milton Keynes MK6 3AD; Tel 01908 670673
Centre Manager Linda Hoggan

CHILDREN'S HOMES

Halswell Place Children's Home 13 Halswell Pl, Middleton,
Milton Keynes MK10 9BL; Tel 01908 675258
Unit Manager Sue White

HOMES FOR CHILDREN WITH A LEARNING DISABILITY

Furze House Children's Home 1 Dulverton Dr, Furzton,
Milton Keynes MK4 1EA; Tel 01908 502529
Officer-in-Charge Anne Roberts

Westminster Drive Children's Home 147–149 Westminster
Dr, Bletchley, Milton Keynes MK3 6LP; Tel 01908 644982
Officer-in-Charge Louise Joyner

YOUTH OFFENDING TEAM

Manor Road Centre Oakwood Dr, Bletchley, Milton Keynes
MK2 2JG; Tel 01908 271562
Team Manager Lee Westlake

FAMILY CENTRE

Moorlands Family Centre 53–56 Wastel, Beanhill, Milton
Keynes MK6 4LW; Tel 01908 679819
Centre Manager Gill Smith

SPECIAL DAY SCHOOLS

The Redway School Farmborough, Netherfield, Milton
Keynes MK6 4HG; Tel 01908 200000; Fax 01908 206420
Headteacher Richard Fraser
  (110)

Slated Row School Old Wolverton Rd, Wolverton, Milton
Keynes MK12 5NJ; Tel 01908 316017; Fax 01908 315082
Headteacher Liz Bull
  (154)

RESIDENTIAL SPECIAL SCHOOLS

The Gatehouse School Crosslands, Stantonbury, Milton
Keynes MK14 6AX; Tel 01908 313903; Fax 01908 221195
Headteacher Jan Park
(Day, Boarders)
  (10) (10)

Romans Field School Shenley Rd, Bletchley, Milton Keynes
MK3 7AW; Tel 01908 376011; Fax 01908 645320
Head Wayne Marshall
(Day, Boarders)
  (52)

The Walnuts School Old Grove Way, Simpson, Milton
Keynes MK6 3AF; Tel 01908 670032; Fax 01908 232774
Headteacher Nick Jackman
  (Day, Boarders) (44)

White Spire School Rickley La, Bletchley, Milton Keynes
MK3 6EW; Tel 01908 373266; Fax 01908 643057
Headteacher Peter Jones
  (Day, Boarders) (155)

OTHER SPECIAL NEEDS PROVISION

Educational Support Service Queensway Centre,
Queensway, Bletchley, Milton Keynes MK2 2HB;
E-mail queenswaycentre(educationsupport)@
milton-keynes.gov.uk; Tel 01908 375072; Fax 01908
630280
Senior Co-ordinator (Support Service) Andy Nicholson

Primary Behaviour Support Service Galley Hill Education
Centre, Galley Hill, Stony Stratford, Milton Keynes
MK11 1PA; Tel 01908 254535
Head (Primary Behaviour Support) Cathy Baker

Pupil Referral Unit – Main Centre Manor Rd Centre,
Bletchley, Milton Keynes MK2 2HP; Tel 01908 368268;
Fax 01908 370154
Headteacher Moyra Forrester

Pupil Resource Base Galley Hill Education Centre, Galley
Hill, Stony Stratford, Milton Keynes MK11 1PA; Tel 01908
254535
Head (Primary Behaviour Support) Cathy Baker

Tuition Service Fenny Hse, Queensway, Bletchley, Milton
Keynes MK2 2HB;
E-mail shelagh@fenny.milton-keynes.sch.uk; Tel 01908
646034; Fax 01908 646034
Headteacher Shelagh Bainbridge

Young People Out of School (YPOS) Holne Chase Centre,
Buckingham Rd, Bletchley, Milton Keynes MK3 5HP;
Tel 01908 657823; Fax 01908 649893
Senior Project Worker Claire Coltman

Neighbourhood Services Directorate

Services for Adults.

6

DAY CENTRES FOR PEOPLE WITH A LEARNING DISABILITY

Surrey Road Day Centre 5 Surrey Rd, Bletchley, Milton Keynes MK3 7HD; Tel 01908 372811

Tower Drive Day Centre Tower Dr, Neath Hill, Milton Keynes MK14 6HY; Tel 01908 604290
Unit Co-ordinator Richard Franklin

Whaddon Way Special Needs Unit 296 Whaddon Way, Bletchley, Milton Keynes MK3 7JR; Tel 01908 271450

DAY CENTRE FOR ADULTS WITH MENTAL HEALTH PROBLEMS

Keystone Day Centre Cripps Lodge Resource Centre, Broadlands, Milton Keynes MK6 4JJ; Tel 01908 835881
Manager Marc Hamilton (Acting)

DAY CENTRE FOR ELDERLY PEOPLE WITH MENTAL HEALTH PROBLEMS

Redwood Unit Day Centre Cripps Lodge Resource Centre, Broadlands, Milton Keynes MK6 4JJ; Tel 01908 835892
Centre Manager Anne Walker

HOMES FOR ELDERLY PEOPLE

There is one home run by Milton Keynes Council.

NEWCASTLE UPON TYNE CITY COUNCIL

www.newcastle.gov.uk

Population 293 600
Civic Centre, Barras Bridge, Newcastle upon Tyne, Tyne and Wear NE1 8PR; URL www.newcastle.gov.uk; Tel 0191 232 8520; Fax 0191 211 4972
Lord Mayor Cllr Margaret Carter
Leader of the Council Cllr A. Flynn
Chief Executive Ian Stratford
Head (Legal Services) Val Dodds
Head (Design Services) M. McHale
City Treasurer Paul Woods
Director (Community and Housing) Vacancy
Director (Enterprise Environment and Culture)
  Steve Dunlop

Social Services Directorate

Civic Centre, Newcastle upon Tyne, Tyne and Wear NE1 8PA; URL www.newcastle.gov.uk; E-mail socialservices.customer@newcastle.gov.uk; Tel (24 hours) 0191 232 8520; Fax 0191 211 4955; Textphone 0191 211 6388
Joint Inspection Unit, Newburn Rd, Newburn, Newcastle upon Tyne, Tyne and Wear NE15 8QJ; Tel 0191 277 2566
Director (Social Services) Tom Dervin
Locality Director (Mental Health – Newcastle)
  Ruth Hofbauer; Tel 0191 223 2529; Fax 0191 223 2469
Head (Commissioning (Adults)) Vacancy
Head (Children's Services) Ruth Rogan
Head (Business Services) Lynn Stephenson
Head (Performance) Caroline Thomas; Tel 0191 232 8520
Head (Financial Services) Adam Fletcher
Manager (Welfare Rights and Supporting People)
  Nick Whitton
Manager (Older People) Cathy Bull
Manager (Disability) Becky Lyons
Manager (Accommodation – Care Services) Vacancy,
Manager (Planning and Contract Compliance)
  Patricia Hopkinson,

Manager (Customer Services and Marketing) Meg Woollam
Manager (Accommodation – Children) Vacancy
Manager (Quality Standards – Children's Services)
  Veronica Grant
Manager (Staff Development and Staffing) Jill Watson
Manager (Support Services – Buildings) Denise Stead
Manager (Support Services) Margaret Croney; Tel 0191 278 8159; Fax 0191 278 8188
Manager (Support Services) Margaret Curry
Manager (Support Services) Elaine Blair; Tel 0191 295 5535
Manager (Information and Communication Systems)
  Vacancy
Manager (Day Services) Cath Williams
Manager (Development and Best Value) Tony Metcalf; Tel 0191 232 8520
Performance Manager Caroline Thomas; Tel 0191 232 8520
Commissioning Manager (Childcare) Sharon Williams; Tel 0191 286 3311

Social Services and Health Portfolio

Cabinet Member Cllr O'Shea (Lab)

Social Services Committee

Chair Cllr Malcolm (Lab)

DUTY TEAMS

Social Work Duty Team for Children's Services (covering Wards: Byker, Jesmond, Dere, Heaton, Monkchester, Sandyford, Walker, Walkergate)

Walker Social Work Office, Airey Terr, Newcastle upon Tyne, Tyne and Wear NE6 3HR; Tel 0191 295 5535; Fax 0191 263 9292
Customer Service Duty Point for Children's Services (East).

Social Work Office – Children with Disabilities

23 Raby Cross, Byker, Newcastle upon Tyne, Tyne and Wear NE6 2FF; Tel 0191 278 2898; Fax 0191 278 2900

Social Work Duty Team for Adult Services (covering Wards: Dene, Jesmond, Heaton, Sandyford, Byker, Monkchester, Walkergate, Walker, South Gosforth, Grange, Kenton, Fawdon and Castle)

5 Lansdowne Terr East, Gosforth, Newcastle upon Tyne, Tyne and Wear NE3 1HF; Tel 0191 277 2077; Fax 0191 273 3430
Customer Service Duty Point for Adult Services (East and North).

Social Work Duty Team for Children's Services (covering Wards: Benwell, Elswick, Fenham, Moorside, West City, Wingrove)

Cruddas Park Social Work Office, Park Rd, Newcastle upon Tyne, Tyne and Wear NE4 7RW; Tel 0191 277 2500; Fax 0191 273 2399
Customer Service Duty Point for Children's Services (Inner West and Central).

Social Work Duty Team for Adult Services (covering Wards: Moorside, West City, Wingrove, Fenham, Elswick, Benwell, Scotswood, Lemington, Newburn, Denton, Westerhope, Woolsington and Blakelaw)

Council Offices, Newburn Rd, Newcastle upon Tyne, Tyne and Wear NE15 8QJ; Tel 0191 277 2555; Fax 0191 277 2550
Customer Service Duty Point for Adult Services (West and Central).

Social Work Office

Shieldfield Centre, 4–8 Clarence Wlk, Newcastle upon Tyne, Tyne and Wear NE2 1AL; Tel 0191 278 8100; Fax 0191 278 8188

Social Work Duty Team for Children's Services (covering wards: Blakelaw, Denton, Lemington, Newburn, Scotswood, Westerhope, Woolsington, South Gosforth, Grange, Kenton, Fawdon and Castle)

Sheriff Leas, Springfield Rd, Newcastle upon Tyne, Tyne and Wear NE5 3DS; Tel 0191 286 3311; Fax 0191 271 6865
Customer Service Duty Point for Children's Services (Outer West and North).

HOSPITAL SOCIAL WORK TEAMS

Fleming Nuffield Unit (for Children and Young People)
Burdon Terr, Newcastle upon Tyne, Tyne and Wear NE2 3AE; Tel 0191 232 5131; Fax 0191 281 6103
Team Manager Vacancy

Freeman Road Hospital Freeman Rd, Newcastle upon Tyne, Tyne and Wear NE7 7DN; Tel 0191 223 1025; Fax 0191 285 3455
Team Manager Elizabeth Howliston
Team Manager Stewart Pattinson

Newcastle General Hospital Westgate Rd, Newcastle upon Tyne, Tyne and Wear NE4 6BE; Tel 0191 273 8811; Fax 0191 273 2533
Team Manager Brenda Rickleton

Royal Victoria Infirmary Queen Victoria Rd, Newcastle upon Tyne, Tyne and Wear NE1 4LF; Tel 0191 232 5131; Fax 0191 230 2866
Team Manager Terri Randall

St. Nicholas Hospital Clinical Services Centre, Jubilee Rd, Newcastle upon Tyne, Tyne and Wear NE3 3XT; Tel 0191 223 2507; Fax 0191 285 3466
Team Manager A. West

ADULT PLACEMENTS

Shieldfield Centre, 4–8 Clarence Wlk, Newcastle upon Tyne, Tyne and Wear NE2 1AL; Tel 0191 278 8106; Fax 0191 278 8118
Team Manager Cath Williams

ADOPTION UNIT

Shieldfield Terr, 4–8 Clarence Wlk, Newcastle upon Tyne, Tyne and Wear NE2 1AL; Tel 0191 278 8200; Fax 0191 278 8188

FOSTERING SERVICE

Shieldfield Centre, 4–8 Clarence Wlk, Newcastle upon Tyne, Tyne and Wear NE2 1AL; Tel 0191 278 8359; Fax 0191 278 8330

COMMUNITY HOME

Clavering Resource Centre Axwell Park Est, Blaydon, Tyne and Wear NE21 6RN; Tel 0191 414 6311; Fax 0191 414 4572

RESIDENTIAL ESTABLISHMENTS FOR CHILDREN AND YOUNG PEOPLE

East View Home 12 Earsdon Cl, Newcastle upon Tyne, Tyne and Wear; Tel 0191 267 9268; Fax 0191 267 0360

Hartburn Walk Home 5 Hartburn Wlk, Newcastle upon Tyne, Tyne and Wear; Tel 0191 271 3393; Fax 0191 271 3392

Iona Place Home 8 Iona Pl, Fairhaven Est, Newcastle upon Tyne, Tyne and Wear NE6 3PU; Tel 0191 262 6011; Fax 0191 262 6011

Slatyford Lane Home 12 Slatyford La, Newcastle upon Tyne, Tyne and Wear; Tel 0191 274 3279; Fax 0191 275 0400

NON-RESIDENTIAL ESTABLISHMENT FOR CHILDREN AND YOUNG PEOPLE

Leaving Care Team Rivedell, Melbourne St, Newcastle upon Tyne, Tyne and Wear NE1 2JQ; Tel 0191 261 7589; Fax 0191 221 0912

Shared Care Children Shieldfield Centre, 4–8 Clarence Wlk, Newcastle upon Tyne, Tyne and Wear NE2 1AL; Tel 0191 278 8345; Fax 0191 278 8330

YOUTH OFFENDING TEAM

Block D, 4th Fl, Jesmond Quadrant, 3 Archbold Terr, Sandyford, Newcastle upon Tyne, Tyne and Wear NE2 1BZ; Tel 0191 277 7377; Fax 0191 277 7399
Manager R. Stapley

FAMILY CARE CENTRE

Family Support Service Craigside Hse, Heaton, Newcastle upon Tyne, Tyne and Wear NE6 1SE; Tel 0191 278 8500; Fax 0191 278 8511

CENTRE FOR PEOPLE WITH DISABILITIES

Westerhope Centre Pilton Mews, Westerhope, Newcastle upon Tyne, Tyne and Wear NE5 4PQ; Tel 0191 286 1236; Fax 0191 271 3296
Team Leader Steve Williamson

INDEPENDENT LIVING SCHEME FOR PEOPLE WITH A LEARNING DISABILITY

Linbridge Drive Newcastle upon Tyne, Tyne and Wear NE5 5DQ; Tel 0191 264 6197
Team Leader Chris Johnson

CENTRES FOR PEOPLE WITH A LEARNING DISABILITY

Wingrove Road Centre 35 Wingrove Rd, Fenham, Newcastle upon Tyne, Tyne and Wear NE4 9BP; Tel 0191 272 4011
Team Leader Bob Linton

SHORT-TERM CARE FACILITY FOR ADULTS WITH A LEARNING DISABILITY

Clayton Road Centre 62 Clayton Rd, Jesmond, Newcastle upon Tyne, Tyne and Wear NE2 1TL; Tel 0191 281 1956
Team Leader Frank Martin

DAY SERVICES FOR PEOPLE WITH DISABILITIES

Capability's 13 Heaton Rd, Newcastle upon Tyne, Tyne and Wear NE6 1SA; Tel 0191 224 4022
Team Leader J. Collinson

Employment and Community-Based Opportunities Team (ECBOT) Shieldfield Centre, 4–8 Clarence Wlk, Newcastle upon Tyne, Tyne and Wear NE2 1AL; Tel 0191 278 8117; Fax 0191 278 8118
Team Leader J. Collinson

Welford Centre Jubilee Rd, Gosforth, Newcastle upon Tyne, Tyne and Wear NE3 3UR; Tel 0191 285 9957; Fax 0191 285 3940
Team Leader K. Inglis

RESOURCE CENTRES FOR PEOPLE WITH MENTAL HEALTH PROBLEMS

Scrogg Road Centre 49–51 Scrogg Rd, Newcastle upon Tyne, Tyne and Wear; Tel 0191 265 6310; Fax 0191 276 2725
Manager Jane Bowie

6

Summerhill Centre 269–271 Westgate Rd, Newcastle upon Tyne, Tyne and Wear NE4 6AH; Tel 0191 232 7872; Fax 0191 221 1257
Officer-in-Charge Yvonne Robson

RESOURCE CENTRES FOR OLDER PEOPLE

Chirton Resource Centre Headlam Way, Byker, Newcastle upon Tyne, Tyne and Wear NE6 2DX; Tel 0191 276 2195; Fax 0191 224 1929
Resource Manager Jane Breheny

Connie Lewcock Resource Centre West Denton Rd, Newcastle upon Tyne, Tyne and Wear NE15 7LQ; Tel 0191 264 3439; Fax 0191 267 1169
Resource Manager Lynn Dugan

Harehills Resource Centre Burnfoot Way, Newcastle upon Tyne, Tyne and Wear NE3 3AL; Tel 0191 284 7117; Fax 0191 284 0773
Resource Manager Simon Mulligan

Napier Resource Centre Napier St, Newcastle upon Tyne, Tyne and Wear NE2 1XJ; Tel 0191 232 2424
Resource Manager Gary Gilchrist

RESOURCE CENTRE FOR OLDER PEOPLE WITH MENTAL HEALTH PROBLEMS

Byker Lodge Resource Centre Bolam Way, Byker, Newcastle upon Tyne, Tyne and Wear NE6 2AT; Tel 0191 265 2448; Fax 0191 224 2259
Resource Manager Chris Dugdale
(35)

Education Offices

City Education Dept, Civic Centre, Barras Bridge, Newcastle upon Tyne, Tyne and Wear NE1 8PU; Tel 0191 232 8520
Director (Education and Libraries) Philip Turner
Director (Education and Libraries – Information Services) Tony Durcan
Head (Planning and Resource Management) Marian Howett
Head (Access and Inclusion Division) Duncan Nicholson
Head (Educational Achievement and Strategic Planning) Roger Edwardson
Principal Educational Psychologist S. Ridgway

CHILD AND FAMILY GUIDANCE CLINIC

College Street Centre College St, Newcastle upon Tyne, Tyne and Wear; Tel 0191 232 2555

SPECIAL SCHOOLS

Hadrian School Betram Cres, Newcastle upon Tyne, Tyne and Wear NE15 6PY; Tel 0191 273 4440; Fax 0191 226 1150
Headteacher Elizabeth Turnbull
2–11

Sir Charles Parson School Westbourne Ave, Newcastle upon Tyne, Tyne and Wear NE6 4ED; Tel 0191 263 0261; Fax 0191 263 8897
Headteacher John Preston
11–19

Thomas Bewick School Hillhead Parkway, Newcastle upon Tyne, Tyne and Wear NE15 1DS; Tel 0191 267 5435; Fax 0191 267 9857
Headteacher Richard Heard
5–19

Trinity School Central Administration, Condercum Rd, Newcastle upon Tyne, Tyne and Wear NE4 8XJ; Tel 0191 226 1500; Fax 0191 226 1226
Headteacher Dave Edmondson
5–16+

Denview Site Freeman Rd, Newcastle upon Tyne, Tyne and Wear NE3 1SZ; Tel 0191 284 3533; Fax 0191 213 1171
Teacher-in-Charge Mary Kiernan
Kenton Lodge Site Kenton Rd, Newcastle upon Tyne, Tyne and Wear NE3 4PD; Tel 0191 285 5392; Fax 0191 213 1730
Teacher-in-Charge Leo McLaughlin
Oakfield College Site Condercum Rd, Newcastle upon Tyne, Tyne and Wear NE4 8XJ; Tel 0191 273 5558; Fax 0191 272 2677
Deputy Headteacher Bill Curley

NORFOLK COUNTY COUNCIL
www.norfolk.gov.uk

Population 797 900 (2001 census)
Political Composition: Con: 47, Lab: 26, LD: 11
County Hall, Martineau La, Norwich, Norfolk NR1 2DH; URL www.norfolk.gov.uk; E-mail information@norfolk.gov.uk; Tel 01603 222222; Fax 01603 222959
Chair of the County Council Neville Chapman
Chief Executive T.J. Byles, BA, DMS
Director (Finance) R.D. Summers, CPFA, FCCA
Director (Planning and Transportation) T. Malynn, BEng(Hons), MBA, CEng, MICE
Director (Corporate Resources) Paul Adams

Social Services Department

County Hall, Martineau La, Norwich, Norfolk NR1 2SQ; Tel 01603 222141; Fax 01603 223096; Minicom 01603 223242
Director (Social Services) Lisa Christensen
Senior Assistant Director Paul Adams
Joint Director (Learning Disability Services) Amanda Reynolds
Assistant Director (Children and Families) Rosemary Claridge
Assistant Director (Community Care) Glen Garrod
Deputy Assistant Director (Children and Families) Geoff Gildersleeve
Head (Finance and Administration) Jacqui Lomas
Head (Performance Management) L. Rainger
Communications and Publicity Officer Dan Pritchard
Service Development Manager (Adults) Graham Robinson

TRAINING

Responsible for training professional and support staff in the department.
Principal Officer (Training and Staff Development) Vacancy
County Hall Annex, Martineau La, Norwich, Norfolk NR1 2SQ; Tel 01603 223156; Fax 01603 222479
Principal Officer (Mental Health) Sue Brown
15 Hooper La, Norwich, Norfolk NR3 4ED; Tel 01603 495129

Social Services and Health Review Panel

Chair R. Monbiot (Con)
Members of the Panel
J. Caldwell, M.J. Clarke, J. Eells, J. Fowler, D. Forgan, S. Gurney, R. Johnson, C.M. Mowle, H.N. Panting, J. Perry-Warner, D. Rye, T. Stickle, C.M. Ward, S. Whitaker, A.J. Wright.

DISTRICT OFFICES

Norwich District Office

Carrow Hse, 301 King St, Norwich, Norfolk NR1 2TN; Tel 01603 223500; Fax 01603 223513
District Manager (Community Care) S. Morton
Service Manager (Children's Support Service) P. Currie

NORWICH RECEPTION AND REFERRAL TEAM

Norwich Sub-Office (Reception and Referral Team)
Norwich, Norfolk NR2 1NR; Tel 01603 223500; Fax 01603 762445

Eastern District (HQ)

Ferryside, High Rd, Gorleston, Great Yarmouth, Norfolk NR31 0PH; Tel 01493 664282; Fax 01493 442283
District Manager (Community Care)   H. Wynn

EASTERN DISTRICT SUB-OFFICES

Great Yarmouth Child and Family Care Sub-Office
The Hollies Addison Rd, Gorleston, Great Yarmouth, Norfolk NR31 0PA; Tel 01493 665605; Fax 01493 442454
Great Yarmouth Sub-Office
Nelson House 31–33 South Quay, Great Yarmouth, Norfolk NR30 2RG; Tel 01493 850317; Fax 01493 854851
Service Manager (Children's Assessment Service)   Laura Sutton

Northern District (HQ)

Northfield Rd, North Walsham, Norfolk NR28 0AS; Tel 01692 500550; Fax 01692 500536
Area Director (Social Care)   Karen Wadham
District Manager (Community Care)   Bryony Dennison
Service Manager (Looked After Children)   Malcolm Griffiths

NORTHERN DISTRICT SUB-OFFICE

Northern Norfolk Sub-Office (Fakenham) 28 Norwich Rd, Fakenham, Norfolk; Tel 01328 863241; Fax 01328 855060

BRADSHAW DISTRICT OFFICE

Blithemeadow Crt, Falcon Road East, Norwich, Norfolk NR7 8PU; Tel 01603 787363; Fax 01603 788264
District Manager (Community Care)   Debbie Olley

Southern District (HQ)

Carrow Hse, 301 King St, Norwich, Norfolk NR1 1TS; Tel 01603 224100; Fax 01603 224108
Director (Social and Intermediate Care)   Hilary Mills
South District Sub-Office Elm Rd, Thetford, Norfolk; Tel 01842 754484; Fax 01842 761740
Sub-Office (Child and Family Care) 74 Pople St, Wymondham, Norfolk NR18 0LP; Tel 01953 602071; Fax 01953 601427

SOUTHERN DISTRICT SUB-OFFICE

31 Norwich St, Dereham, Norfolk NR19 1DH; Tel 01362 694711; Fax 01362 694483

Western District (HQ)

Grey Friars Hse, Birch Tree Cl, King's Lynn, Norfolk PE30 3SS; Tel 01553 669300; Fax 01553 769241
District Manager (Community Care)   T. Conn
Service Manager (Family Intervention Service)
   Sandra Summerfield

WESTERN DISTRICT SUB-OFFICES

Western District Sub-Office Howdale Rd, Downham Market, Norfolk PE38 9EU; Tel 01366 382911; Fax 01366 388329
Western District Sub-Office Valentine Rd, Hunstanton, Norfolk PE36 5EF; Tel 01485 533409; Fax 01485 535460

PRINCIPAL HOSPITAL SOCIAL WORK TEAMS

Norfolk and Norwich University Hospital Colney La, Colney, Norwich, Norfolk NR4 7UZ; Tel 01603 286274; Fax 01603 287466

James Paget Hospital Lowestoft Rd, Gorleston, Great Yarmouth, Norfolk NR31 6LA; Tel 01493 452123; Fax 01493 452895
Queen Elizabeth District General Hospital Gayton Rd, King's Lynn, Norfolk PE30 4ET; Tel 01553 613806; Fax 01553 613573
St. Michaels Hospital Cawston Rd, Aylsham, Norwich, Norfolk NR11 6NA; Tel 01263 732341; Fax 01263 735029

RESOURCES FOR CHILDREN AND FAMILIES

Unthank Centre 3a Unthank Rd, Norwich, Norfolk NR2 2PA; Tel 01603 630661; Fax 01603 764903

CHILD CARE INFORMATION SERVICE

The Unthank Centre, 3a Unthank Rd, Norwich, Norfolk NR2 2PA; Tel 01603 622292; Fax 01603 764903

RESOURCE CENTRES

East Hills Road Resource Centre 81 East Hills Rd, New Costessey, Norwich, Norfolk NR5 0PD; Tel 01603 742262
Manager   Cathy Stoneman
   (6)
Ferry Road Resource Centre Ferry Rd, West Lynn, Norfolk PE34 3NB; Tel 01553 772853; Fax 01553 776271
Manager   Pamela Sandell
   (9)
Garfield House Resource Centre 15 Norwich Rd, East Dereham, Norfolk NR20 3AE; Tel 01362 693250
Manager   Rachel Cowdry
   (6)
Harvey Lane Resource Centre 16 Harvey La, Norwich, Norfolk NR7 0BN; Tel 01603 437811; Fax 01603 702972
Contact   Stewart Betts
The Hollies Centre Addison Rd, Gorleston, Great Yarmouth, Norfolk NR31 0PA; Tel 01493 665605; Fax 01493 442454
   (6)

HOMES FOR CHILDREN WITH LEARNING DISABILITIES

Marsh Fields Resource Centre Ferry Rd, West Lynn, King's Lynn, Norfolk PE34 2NB; Tel 01553 773322; Fax 01553 776271
Manager   Helen Jackson
   (6)
Repton House Resource Centre Parkside Dr, Old Catton, Norwich, Norfolk NR6 7DP; Tel 01603 423429; Fax 01603 482619
Manager   N. Loone
   (6)

ADOPTION AND FAMILY FINDING UNIT

Unthank Road Unit 5 Unthank Rd, Norwich, Norfolk; Tel 01603 617796 01603 617797; Fax 01603 615567

COUNTY LEAVING CARE TEAM

Leaving Care Team The Oaks, 16 Harvey La, Norwich, Norfolk NR7 0BN; Tel 01603 437811; Fax 01603 702972

RESOURCES FOR ADULTS WITH LEARNING DISABILITIES

DAY CARE FOR ADULTS WITH LEARNING DISABILITIES

Caister Day Centre High St, Caister-on-Sea, Norfolk NR30 5EH; Tel 01493 722552; Fax 01493 377929
Norwich Special Needs Unit Blackhorse Centre, Hooper La, Norwich, Norfolk NR3 4ED; Tel 01603 413324; Fax 01603 486669

6

HOMES FOR ADULTS WITH LEARNING DISABILITIES

Faro Lodge Gaywood Hall Dr, King's Lynn, Norfolk PE30 4ED; Tel 01553 679233; Fax 01553 677263
(27)

Rayleen Home Flowerpot La, Long Stratton, Norfolk NR15 2TS; Tel 01508 530820
(5)

DAY SERVICES

Attleborough Day Services Station Rd, Attleborough, Norfolk NR17 2AT; Tel 01953 453373; Fax 01953 457254
Special care unit (6) (92)

Dereham Day Services Rash's Grn, Dereham, Norfolk NR19 1JG; Tel 01362 697915/6; Fax 01362 698903
Special care unit (8) (92)

Great Yarmouth Day Services Suffolk Rd, Great Yarmouth, Norfolk NR31 0LJ; Tel 01493 664658; Fax 01493 443229
Special care unit (104)

Holt Day Services Charles Rd, Holt, Norfolk NR25 6DA; Tel 01263 712451; Fax 01263 711144
Special care unit (10) (96)

Kings Lynn Day Services Bryggen Rd, King's Lynn, Norfolk PE30 2HZ; Tel 01553 773449; Fax 01553 773449
Special care unit (120)

Norwich Day Services 120 Ipswich Rd, Norwich, Norfolk NR4 6QS; Tel 01603 458643; Fax 01603 452276
Autistic unit Special care unit (6) (120)

Sprowston Day Services Church La, Sprowston, Norfolk NR7 8AY; Tel 01603 410377; Fax 01603 403923
Special care unit (6) (130)

RESOURCES FOR ADULTS WITH MENTAL HEALTH PROBLEMS

DAY FACILITIES FOR PEOPLE WITH MENTAL HEALTH PROBLEMS

Broadland MH Support Team (E and F) 2 Blithemeadow Ct, Sprowston, Norwich, Norfolk NR7 8PU; Tel 01603 424932
Northern Norfolk MHSG (A, B and D) 1 St. Mary's Rd, Cromer, Norfolk NR27 9DJ; Tel 01263 512234
Southern Norfolk MH Support Group (M) Ventura Hse, 101 Norwich Rd, Watton, Norfolk IP25 6DH; Tel 01953 885412
Southern Norfolk MH Support Group (O, P and N) Flowerpot La, Long Stratton, Norfolk NR15 2TS; Tel 01508 430920

ACCOMMODATION FOR PEOPLE WITH MENTAL HEALTH PROBLEMS

Hawthorne Road Home 38 Hawthorne Rd, Gorleston, Great Yarmouth, Norfolk NR31 8ES; Tel 01493 440325; Fax 01493 442531
(6)

St. Catherine's Way Home 1b St. Catherines Way, Gorleston, Great Yarmouth, Norfolk NR31 7QB; Tel 01493 653756
(6)

RESOURCES FOR ADULTS WITH PHYSICAL DISABILITIES

HOME FOR YOUNGER PHYSICALLY DISABLED ADULTS

Local Authority

Bishop Herbert House Globe Pl, Vauxhall St, Norwich, Norfolk NR2 2SG; Tel 01603 620710; Fax 01603 623654

DAY CENTRE FOR PHYSICALLY DISABLED ADULTS

Vauxhall Centre Johnson Pl, Norwich, Norfolk NR2 2JA; Tel 01603 626014; Fax 01603 610632

RESOURCES FOR ELDERLY PEOPLE

Laburnum Grove Day Centre Elm Rd, Thetford, Norfolk NR24 3HL; Tel 01842 753185

DAY CENTRES AND LUNCHEON CLUBS FOR ELDERLY PEOPLE

Crossroads Day Centre Grimston Rd, South Wootton, Norfolk PE30 3HU; Tel 01553 672753

Essex Rooms Luncheon Club Essex Rooms, Essex St, Norwich, Norfolk NR2 2BL; Tel 01603 610799

Garnham Day Centre Back Chapel La, Gorleston, Great Yarmouth, Norfolk NR31 6NY; Tel 01493 650167

The Lawns Day Centre Caister Rd, Gt Yarmouth, Norfolk NR30 4DQ; Tel 01493 859589

Mousehold Day Centre Heathfield, Cannell Grn, Norwich, Norfolk NR3 1TT; Tel 01603 621910

St. Augustine's Place Day Centre Addison Rd, Gorleston, Great Yarmouth, Norfolk NR31; Tel 01493 442810

Silver Rooms Luncheon Club Silver Rd, Norwich, Norfolk NR3 4TB; Tel 01603 618721

ACCOMMODATION FOR ELDERLY PEOPLE

There are 32 residential local authority homes for elderly people with 980 places and seven housing with care schemes with housing associations.

MEALS SERVICE

The Social Services Department in conjunction with the following voluntary organisations: WRVS, Norfolk, Norwich and Great Yarmouth branches; Age Concern, Norwich.

COUNTY SENSORY SUPPORT TEAM

30 Unthank Rd, Norwich, Norfolk NR2 2PA; Tel 01603 622331; Fax 01603 619711; Minicom 01603 760534

Education Department

County Hall, Martineau La, Norwich, Norfolk NR1 2DL;
URL www.esinet.norfolk.gov.uk;
E-mail education.enquiries.edu@norfolk.gov.uk;
Tel 01603 222146; Fax 01603 222119

SPECIAL SCHOOLS

Alderman Jackson School Marsh La, Gaywood, King's Lynn, Norfolk PE30 3AE;
URL www.aldermanjackson.norfolk.sch.uk;
E-mail office@aldermanjackson.norfolk.sch.uk; Tel 01553 672779 01553 674281; Fax 01533 670344
Headteacher Mrs D. McCarthy
Mixed 4–19 (Day) (52)

Chapel Road School Chapel Rd, Attleborough, Norfolk NR17 2DS; URL www.chapelroad.norfolk.sch.uk;
E-mail office@chapelroad.norfolk.sch.uk; Tel 01953 453116; Fax 01953 455931
Headteacher Mrs K. Heap
Mixed 4–19 (Day) (49)

The Clare School South Park Ave, Norwich, Norfolk NR4 7AU; URL www.clare.norfolk.sch.uk;
E-mail office@clare.norfolk.sch.uk; Tel 01603 454199; Fax 01603 250736
Headteacher C. Hocking, BSc
Mixed 4–19 (Day) (82)

Eaton Hall School Pettus Rd, Norwich, Norfolk NR4 7BU; URL www.eatonhall.norfolk.sch.uk;
E-mail office@eatonhall.norfolk.sch.uk; Tel 01603 457480; Fax 01603 456211
Headteacher J. Lees
Boys 7–16 (Day, Boarders) (40)

The Ethel Tipple School Winston Churchill Dr, Fairstead, King's Lynn, Norfolk PE30 4RP; URL www.etheltipple.norfolk.sch.uk; E-mail office@etheltipple.norfolk.sch.uk; Tel 01553 763679; Fax 01553 770321
Headteacher Mr G. Wilkinson
  Mixed 7–16 (Day) (83)

Fred Nicholson School Westfield Rd, Dereham, Norfolk NR19 1JB; URL www.frednicholson.norfolk.sch.uk; E-mail office@frednicholson.norfolk.sch.uk; Tel 01362 693915; Fax 01362 693298
Headteacher Mr M. Clayton
  Mixed 7–16 (Day, Boarders) (84)

Hall School St. Faith's Rd, Old Catton, Norwich, Norfolk NR6 7AD; URL www.hall.norfolk.sch.uk; E-mail office@hall.norfolk.sch.uk; Tel 01603 466467; Fax 01603 466407
Headteacher Mrs A. Ruthven
  Mixed 3–19 (Day) (68)

Harford Manor School Ipswich Rd, Norwich, Norfolk NR2 2LN; URL www.harfordmanorspecial.norfolk.sch.uk; E-mail office@harfordmanor.norfolk.sch.uk; Tel 01603 451809; Fax 01603 453508
Headteacher Mr G. Kitchen
  Mixed 4–19 (Day) (60)

John Grant School St. George's Dr, Caister-on-Sea, Great Yarmouth, Norfolk NR30 5QW; URL www.johngrant.norfolk.sch.uk; E-mail office@johngrant.norfolk.sch.uk; Tel 01493 720158; Fax 01493 728616
Headteacher Mr G. Hampson
  Mixed 4–19 (Day) (87)

The Parkside School College Rd, Norwich, Norfolk NR2 3JA; URL www.parkside.norfolk.sch.uk; E-mail office@parkside.norfolk.sch.uk; Tel 01603 441126; 01603 441127; Fax 01603 441128
Headteacher Mr B. Payne
  Mixed 7–16 (Day) (136)

Sheringham Woodfield School Holt Rd, Sheringham, Norfolk NR26 8ND; Tel 01263 820520; Fax 01263 820521
Headteacher Mrs D. Whitham
  Mixed 4–19 (Day) (28)

Sidestrand Hall School Cromer Rd, Sidestrand, Cromer, Norfolk NR27 0NH; URL www.sidestrandhall.norfolk.sch.uk; E-mail office@sidestrandhall.norfolk.sch.uk; Tel 01263 578144; Fax 01263 579287
Headteacher Mrs S. Fee
  Mixed 7–16 (Day, Boarders) (104)

PUPIL REFERRAL UNITS

Bawdeswell Pupil Referral Unit Fakenham Rd, Bawdeswell, Dereham, Norfolk NR20 4PR; Tel 01362 688762
Head of Centre Julian Spetch

Greenwood Pupil Referral Unit Greenwood Rd, Tuckswood Est, Norwich, Norfolk NR4 6BN; Tel 01603 45819; Fax 01603 259466
Area Headteacher Mrs L. Jones

King's Lynn Centre Providence St, King's Lynn, Norfolk PE30 5ET; Tel 01553 775184
Head of Centre Geoff Melia

North Walsham Pupil Referral Unit North Walsham Centre, Manor Rd, North Walsham, Norfolk NR28 9HG; Tel 01692 404919; Fax 01692 404919
Head of Centre Sue Kirrage

Norwich Centre 113 Aylsham Rd, Norwich, Norfolk NR2 2HY; Tel 01603 408036; Fax 01603 408036
Head of Centre Tony Webb

Thetford Pupil Referral Unit Elm Road Centre, Elm Rd, Thetford, Norfolk IP24 3HL; Tel 01842 762289; Fax 01842 820103
Head of Centre Toni Rainbow

Westwood Pupil Referral Unit 111 Newmarket Rd, Norwich, Norfolk NR2 2HT; Tel 01603 455531; Fax 01603 501818
Head of Centre Mr T. Burt

NORTH EAST LINCOLNSHIRE COUNCIL

www.nelincs.gov.uk

Population 157 983
Political Composition: Con: 16, LD: 15, Lab: 7, Ind: 4.
Municipal Offices, Town Hall Sq, Grimsby, North East Lincolnshire DN31 1HU; URL www.nelincs.gov.uk; E-mail sue.turner@nelincs.gov.uk; Tel 01472 313131
Chief Executive Jim Leivers
Leader of the Council Cllr Keith Brookes

6

Community Care Directorate

Fryston Hse, Fryston Corner, Grimsby, North East Lincolnshire DN34 5BB; Tel 01472 325500; (Emergency Duty Team (covering North and North East Lincolnshire)) 01652 651628; Fax 01472 325462
Director Peter Hay
Assistant Director (Community Service) Andrea Pope-Smith
Assistant Director (Learning and Child Care) Jayne Martin
Business Support Manager (Finance and Information) Vacancy
The Elms, 22 Abbey Rd, Grimsby, North East Lincolnshire DN32 0HW; Tel 01472 325500; Fax 01472 325506
Business Support Manager (Policy, Administration and Training) Rosy Pope
Community Care Manager (Finance) Dave Cook
Manager (Management Information) Penny Hill
Manager (Customer Services) Christine Jackson
Training and Commissioning Officer Barbara Marshallsay
Business Development Unit Kathryn Irwin-Banks
The Council is a Unitary Authority created in April 1996 during the local government reorganisation of Humberside. The Authority's activities are divided into four programme areas. Social Services is within the 'Environment, Housing and Social Services' programme area. The Department undertakes the full range of duties and responsibilities of a social services department.

Cabinet Members

Cllr K.M. Bradley, Cllr M. Burnett, Cllr P.J. Ramsden, Cllr A. Wallace.

Policy

Business Support, The Elms, 22 Abbey Rd, Grimsby, North East Lincolnshire DN32 0HW; Tel 01472 325412

CHILD PROTECTION AND PLANNING SERVICE

Fryston Hse, Fryston Corner, Grimsby, North East Lincolnshire; Tel 01742 325500
Contact Jill Alderson

CHILD CARE

Fryston Hse, Grimsby, North East Lincolnshire; Tel 01472 325500
Service Manager (Children's Resources) Marilyn Josetsen
Service Manager (Children's Services Fieldwork) Matthew Sampson

ADULT COMMISSIONING

Care Management Team West, Hereford Centre, Hereford Ave, Grimsby, North East Lincolnshire; Tel 01472 325181

Care Management Team East, St. Hugh's Ave, Cleethorpes, North East Lincolnshire; Tel 01472 325353
Manager (Community Services) Matun Wawryk

CHILD CARE TEAMS

The Cedars Eastern Inway, Grimsby, North East Lincolnshire DN34 5HH; Tel 01472 325151
Principal Care Manager (Referral and Assessment) Sue Proudlove

St. Hughes Avenue Cleethorpes, North East Lincolnshire DN35 8ED; Tel 01472 325363
Principal Care Manager Paul Cordy

HOSPITAL SOCIAL WORK TEAM

Diana, Princess of Wales Hospital Scartho Rd, Grimsby, North East Lincolnshire DN33 2BA; Tel 01472 874111
Community Service Manager (Health and Rehabilitation) Andrew Humphrey

COMMUNITY SUPPORT TEAM

36 Brighowgate, Grimsby, North East Lincolnshire DN32 0QP; Tel 01472 325435
Team Leader Jane Fox

The Willows Respite and Rehabilitation Centre Barmouth Dr, Grimsby, North East Lincolnshire DN37 9EA; Tel 01472 325444

OCCUPATIONAL THERAPY SERVICES

William Molson Centre, Kent St, Grimsby, North East Lincolnshire DN32 7DJ; Tel 01472 325222

CHILD CARE UNITS

FAMILY RESOURCE TEAMS

Crosland Road Resource Team Grimsby, North East Lincolnshire; Tel 01472 325111

Wootton Road Resource Team 19 Wootton Rd, Grimsby, North East Lincolnshire; Tel 01472 325171

FOSTERING AND ADOPTION SERVICE

St. James Hse, 2nd Fl, St. James Sq, Grimsby, North East Lincolnshire DN31 1EP; Tel 01472 325555

YOUTH OFFENDING TEAM

46 Heneage Rd, Grimsby, North East Lincolnshire DN32 9ES; Tel 01472 325252

COMMUNITY HOMES

Cromwell House 495 Cromwell Rd, Grimsby, North East Lincolnshire DN37 9BN; Tel 01472 325311

Cromwell Road Community Home 419 Cromwell Rd, Grimsby, North East Lincolnshire DN33 9ES; Tel 01472 325646

Wootton Road Community Home 17 Wootton Rd, Grimsby, North East Lincolnshire DN37 9ES; Tel 01472 325570

CHILDREN'S DISABILITY SERVICE

The Bungalow, 495 Cromwell Rd, Grimsby, North East Lincolnshire DN37 9BN; Tel 01472 325607

ADULTS' UNITS

COMMUNITY MENTAL HEALTH UNIT

21 Eleanor St, Grimsby, North East Lincolnshire DN32 9EA; Tel 01472 325282
Principal Care Manager Jon Wilson

Hostel 7–9 Selge Way, Grimsby, North East Lincolnshire DN33 1RN; Tel 01472 872795

COMMUNITY RESOURCE TEAM (DISABILITY)

William Molson Centre, Kent St, Grimsby, North East Lincolnshire DN31 2BN; Tel 01472 325323

LEARNING DISABILITIES DAY RESOURCE CENTRES

Cromwell Resource Centre 402 Cromwell Rd, Grimsby, North East Lincolnshire DN31 2BN; Tel 01472 325595

Queen St. Resource Centre Queen St, Grimsby, North East Lincolnshire DN31 1QG; Tel 01472 325575

LEARNING DISABILITIES RESIDENTIAL RESOURCE CENTRE

Farnhurst Residential Resource Centre 5 Eleanor St, Grimsby, North East Lincolnshire; Tel 01472 325264

MULTIPURPOSE CENTRE FOR OLDER PEOPLE

Bert Boyden Centre 34 Carver Rd, Immingham, North East Lincolnshire DN40 1DS; Tel 01469 516019

DAY RESOURCES FOR OLDER PEOPLE

Curzon Centre Coulbeck Dr, Cleethorpes, North East Lincolnshire DN35 9HW; Tel 01472 325063

RESIDENTIAL RESOURCES FOR OLDER PEOPLE

The Beacon Respite and Rehabilitation Centre Solomon Crt, Cleethorpes, North East Lincolnshire DN35 9HL; Tel 01472 325405

Directorate of Learning and Child Care

Eleanor St, Grimsby, North East Lincolnshire DN32 9DU; Tel 01472 323090; Fax 01472 323020
Director (Learning and Childcare) G. Hill, BSc, MSc(Ed), PGCE
Deputy Director (Learning) P. Lacey
Deputy Director (Childcare) Vacancy
Assistant Director (Support Services) Sarah Mann
Assistant Director (Inclusion) P. Elwis
Service Manager (Fieldwork) Matthew Sampson
Service Manager (Resources) Darren Hale
Principal Education Officer (Schools Services) A. Green, BPharm, MEd
Principal Education Officer (Special Educational Needs) Vacancy
Principal Education Officer (Continuing Education and Training) A. Butler, BA, MA, PGCE
Principal Educational Psychologist A. Reynolds
Principal Education Welfare Officer S. Nixon
Principal Youth Officer D. Mitchell

SPECIAL SCHOOLS

Cambridge Park School Cambridge Rd, Grimsby, North East Lincolnshire DN34 5EB;
E-mail office@cambridgepark.ne-lincs.sch.uk; Tel 01472 230110; Fax 01472 230113
Headteacher G. Kendall

Humberston Park School St. Thomas' Cl, Humberston, Grimsby, North East Lincolnshire DN36 4HS;
E-mail office@humberstonpark.ne-lincs.sch.uk; Tel 01472 590645; Fax 01472 590643
Headteacher A.A. Zielinski

OTHER ESTABLISHMENTS

Phoenix House Pupil Referral Unit, Harold St, Grimsby, North East Lincolnshire DN32 7NQ; E-mail office@phoenix.sch.dccl.net; Tel 01472 351412; Fax 01472 351412
Headteacher H. Hawkes

NORTH LINCOLNSHIRE COUNCIL
www.northlincs.gov.uk

Political Composition: Lab: 23, Con: 19
Pittwood Hse, Ashby Rd, Scunthorpe, North Lincolnshire DN16 1AB; URL www.northlincs.gov.uk; Tel 01724 296296; Fax 01724 281705
Chief Executive Dr Michael Garnett; Tel 01724 296001; Fax 01724 296005
Director (Environment and Public Protection) Eddie Lodge; Tel 01724 297601; Fax 01724 297899
Director (Corporate Affairs) Simon Driver; Tel 01724 296011; Fax 01724 296031
Director (Community Services) Tom Moore
Community Services Department, Cottage Beck Rd, Scunthorpe, North Lincolnshire DN16 1TS; Tel 01724 297800; Fax 01724 296372
Assistant Director (Property Services) Tom Hogg
Hewson Hse, Station Rd, Brigg, North Lincolnshire; Tel 01724 296700; Fax 01724 296770

Directorate of Social and Housing Services

The Angel, Market Pl, Brigg, North Lincolnshire DN20 8LD; URL www.northlincs.gov.uk; Tel 01724 296401; (Emergency Duty Team (Mon–Fri 1700–2400; Sat, Sun, Bank Holidays 0900–2400)) 01652 651628; Fax 01724 296404; (Emergency Duty Team) 01482 875742
Director (Social and Housing Services) Mike Hunter
Assistant Director (Performance and Operational Support) A. Pate
Assistant Director (Adults) Eric Dews
Assistant Director (Children and Families) N. Richardson
Assistant Director (Housing) R. Birchett
Manager (Performance) M. Pinnock
Manager (Adult Services) M. Briggs
Manager (Adult Commissioning) K. Martin
Principal Childcare Manager (Resources) Denise Hyde
Principal Childcare Manager (Fieldwork) Dave Basker
Service Manager (Older People) Pam Tomlinson
The Lilacs Resource Centre, Warwick Rd, Scunthorpe, North Lincolnshire DN16 1HH
Service Manager (Learning Disability) Julie Clark
The Hollies Resource Centre, Normanby Rd, Scunthorpe, North Lincolnshire DN15 6AR
Service Manager (Disability/Older People) Gina Goodwin
The Lilacs Resource Centre, Warwick Rd, Scunthorpe, North Lincolnshire DN16 1HH
Service Manager (Mental Health/Substance Misuse) Graeme Fagan
297–299 Ashby High St, Scunthorpe, North Lincolnshire DN16 2RY
Service Manager (Supported Employment) Alan Diggles
Standfield Resource Line, B-Line Industries, Scunthorpe, North Lincolnshire DN15 9YJ
The Department manages its services through separate adult and child care structures which are split into purchaser and provider services.

TRAINING
Training and Development Officer B. Mellors

Social Services Committee

Lab: 10, Con: 6
Chair J. Waldron (Lab)
24 Crowberry Dr, Scunthorpe, North Lincolnshire DN16 3DE
Vice-Chair Janet Metcalfe
21 Newbigg, Crowle, North Lincolnshire DN17 4EZ
Members of the Committee
Lab: A. Deas, F.G. Delaney, B.P. Martin, G.P. Philips, M. Simpson, M.J. Todd, J. Waldron, J. Wardle, D. Whiteley.
Con: G.E. Appleyard, S.J. Bromby, P. Clark, S.M.H. Herring, E.M. Redfern, D.M. Stewart.

CHILDREN AND FAMILIES SERVICES

Community Support Team Ariadne Hse, 23 Manby Rd, Scunthorpe, North Lincolnshire DN17 2JR; Tel 01724 842727

Glanford District Office Willow Dr, East Gr, Barton-upon-Humber, North Lincolnshire DN18 2HE; Tel 01652 632517

Scunthorpe North District Office 5–7 Cliff Gdns, Scunthorpe, North Lincolnshire DN15 7PH; Tel 01724 296500

Scunthorpe South District Office 1–3 Cliff Gdns, Scunthorpe, North Lincolnshire DN15 7PH; Tel 01724 296500

ADULT SERVICES

Glanford Care Management District Merchants Court Office Suite, 59 Wrawby St, Brigg, North Lincolnshire DN20 8JE; Tel 01652 655252

Scunthorpe Hospital Social Work Team Scunthorpe District General Hospital, Cliff Gardens, Scunthorpe, North Lincolnshire DN15 7BH; Tel 01724 290096

Scunthorpe North Care Management District 5–7 Cliff Gdns, Scunthorpe, North Lincolnshire DN15 7PH; Tel 01724 296550

Scunthorpe South Care Management District 145 Cherry Gr, Ashby, Scunthorpe, North Lincolnshire DN16 2NT; Tel 01724 282145

Community Support Team The Lilacs, Warwick Rd, Scunthorpe, North Lincolnshire DN16 1HH; Tel 01724 282632

CHILDREN'S OBSERVATION AND ASSESSMENT CENTRE

The Grove, 38 West St, Scawby, North Lincolnshire DN20 9AN; Tel 01652 656005

CENTRE FOR CHILDREN WITH LEARNING DISABILITIES

The Cygnets Normanby Rd, Scunthorpe, North Lincolnshire DN15 6AR; Tel 01724 281542

CHILDREN'S COMMUNITY HOMES

Cambridge House Community Home Cambridge Ave, Bottesford, Scunthorpe, North Lincolnshire DN16 3LG; Tel 01724 852577

Fieldside House Community Home Epworth, Doncaster, North Lincolnshire DN9 1DR; Tel 01427 874799

The Grove Community Home 38 West St, Scawby, North Lincolnshire DN20 9AN; Tel 01652 650130

Poplar Drive Community Home 13 Poplar Dr, Brigg, North Lincolnshire; Tel 01652 653492

CENTRE FOR YOUNG PEOPLE WITH PHYSICAL DISABILITIES

Minster Centre, 45 Minster Rd, Scunthorpe, North Lincolnshire DN15 7EP; Tel 01724 863324

6

CHALLENGING BEHAVIOUR SERVICE

c/o The Hollies, Normanby Rd, Scunthorpe, North Lincolnshire DN15 6AR; Tel 01724 870200

CENTRES FOR ADULTS WITH LEARNING DISABILITIES

Brigg Resource Centre Horstead Ave, Brigg, North Lincolnshire DN20 8PX; Tel 01652 653384

Dryden Road Centre 55–57 Dryden Rd, Scunthorpe, North Lincolnshire; Tel 01724 281016

The Hollies Resource Centre Normanby Rd, Scunthorpe, North Lincolnshire DN15 6AR; Tel 01724 271982

SUPPORTED EMPLOYMENT

B-Line Industries, 4 Cupola Way, Scunthorpe, North Lincolnshire DN15 8LJ; Tel 01724 282836

SANDFIELD MENTAL HEALTH RESOURCE CENTRE

297–299 Ashby High St, Scunthorpe, North Lincolnshire DN16 2RY; Tel 01724 278070

MULTIPURPOSE DAY CENTRES

Burnham Road Day Centre 36 Burnham Rd, Epworth, North Lincolnshire DN19 1BY; Tel 01427 873709

Tofts Road Centre Tofts Rd, Barton-upon-Humber, North Lincolnshire DN18 5NG; Tel 01652 634554

OCCUPATIONAL THERAPY SERVICE

Hewson House Station Rd, Brigg, North Lincolnshire DN20 8XJ; Tel 01652 296616

OUTREACH SERVICES

c/o The Hollies, Normanby Rd, Scunthorpe, North Lincolnshire DN15 6AR; Tel 01724 870790

SCOTTER DISPERSED HOUSING TEAM

West Common La, Scunthorpe, North Lincolnshire DN17 1DS; Tel 01724 855051

WEST STREET FAMILY CENTRE

7 West St, Scunthorpe, North Lincolnshire DN15 6HS; Tel 01724 858692

ELDERLY PEOPLE'S DAY CENTRES

Alvingham Road Day Centre Alvingham Rd, Scunthorpe, North Lincolnshire DN16 2DP; Tel 01724 851946

The Lilacs Resource Centre Warwick Rd, Scunthorpe, North Lincolnshire DN16 1HH; Tel 01724 869635

ELDERLY PEOPLE'S RESIDENTIAL HOMES

There are three elderly people's residential homes in the area.

Directorate of Education and Personal Development

PO Box 35, Hewson Hse, Brigg, North Lincolnshire DN20 8XJ; URL www.northlincs.gov.uk; E-mail epd.enquiries@northlincs.gov.uk; Tel 01724 297240; Fax 01724 297242
Director (Education and Personal Development)
  Dr Trevor Thomas
Assistant Director (Learning Services) David Lea
Assistant Director (Personal Development) Gareth Roberts
Assistant Director (Schools and Directorate Services)
  Dr Brian E. Roberts
Assistant Director (Inclusion SEN) Angela Brooks
Senior Education Officer (Schools) Vacancy

Senior Adviser (Secondary) Vacancy
Manager (Directorate Finance and Information)
  Adrian J. Williamson
Principal Educational Psychologist Dr Tony Branwhite

SPECIAL SCHOOLS

St. Hugh's School Bushfield Rd, Scunthorpe, North Lincolnshire DN16 1NB; Tel 01724 842960
Headteacher Mrs G. Volans (Acting)

St. Luke's School Burghley Rd, Scunthorpe, North Lincolnshire DN16 1JD; Tel 01724 844560
Headteacher Dr Rob W. Ashdown

OTHER ESTABLISHMENTS

Adult Education Service Lincoln Gdns, Scunthorpe, North Lincolnshire DN16 2ED; Tel 01724 849996
Head John Lowden

Bilingual Support Service Crosby Primary School, Frodingham Rd, Scunthorpe, North Lincolnshire DN15 7NL; Tel 01724 280207
Head (Service) June Sherlock

Careers Centre 60 Oswald Rd, Scunthorpe, North Lincolnshire DN15 7PQ; Tel 01724 282200
Head P.L. Madden

Education Business Patnership South Leys Campus, Enderby Rd, Scunthorpe, North Lincolnshire DN17 2JL; Tel 01724 862309; Fax 01724 270563
Head Roger Jenman

Education Development Centre South Leys Campus, Enderby Rd, Scunthorpe, North Lincolnshire DN17 2JL; Tel 01724 862309; Fax 01724 270563
Head (Centre) Pam Baker

Educational Psychology Service Hewson Hse, PO Box 35, Brigg, North Lincolnshire DN20 8XJ; Tel 01724 297252
Head Dr Tony Branwhite

John Leggott College West Common La, Scunthorpe, North Lincolnshire DN17 1DS; Tel 01724 282998; Fax 01724 281631
Head David P. Linnell

North Lindsey College Kingsway, Scunthorpe, North Lincolnshire DN17 1AH; Tel 01724 281111; Fax 01724 281308
Head Dr R. Bennett

Pupil Referral Unit Mill Brook, School Rd, Scunthorpe, North Lincolnshire DN16 2TD; Tel 01724 864329; Fax 01724 281704
Head (Service) Trish Barthorpe

Pupil Referral Unit Holme Valley Primary School, Timberland, Scunthorpe, North Lincolnshire DN16 3SL
Head (Service) Trish Barthorpe

Special Educational Needs Support Service South Leys Campus, Enderby Rd, Scunthorpe, North Lincolnshire DN17 2JL; Tel 01724 864098
Head (Service) Trish Barthorpe

Young Parents' Unit Henderson Ave, Scunthorpe, North Lincolnshire DN15 7RW; Tel 01724 278668
Head (Centre) Coleen Langton

NORTH SOMERSET DISTRICT COUNCIL

www.n-somerset.gov.uk

Political Composition: Con: 24, LD: 23, Lab: 10, Ind: 2, Green: 1
Town Hall, Weston-super-Mare, North Somerset BS23 1ZY; URL www.n-somerset.gov.uk; Tel 01934 888888; Fax 01934 888832

Housing and Social Services

Tel 01934 634542
Assistant Director (Housing) Stuart Palmer;
E-mail stuart.palmer@n.somerset.gov.uk

Social Services Committee

Chair Ashton (Con)
Vice-Chair Peddlesden (Con)
Members of the Committee
Con: Ashton, Baker, Crutchley, Daws, Greenland, Peddlesdon, Pepporall, Kas, Roberts, Terry.
LD: Brown, Cummings, Steadman.
Lab: Bateman, Nobbs, Parker, Stevens.
Ind: Shopland.

DISTRICT OFFICES

North Woodspring 7 Clevedon Wlk, Nailsea, Bristol BS19 2QS; Tel 0117 985 1231

South Woodspring Town Hall, Oxford St, Weston-super-Mare, North Somerset BS23 1TG; Tel 01934 627611

RESOURCE AND ACTIVITY CENTRES

The Meridens 7–9 Albert Quadrant, Weston-super-Mare, North Somerset BS23 2QY; Tel 01934 641050
(53)

Scottish Horn Centre Station Rd, Nailsea, Bristol BS48 1BZ; Tel 01275 857599
(20)

Strode Road Centre 21 Strode Rd, Clevedon, North Somerset BS21 6QB; Tel 01275 342069
(15)

William Knowles Resource and Activity Centre Winterstoke Rd, Weston-super-Mare, North Somerset BS24 9AA; Tel 01934 627392
(120)

DAY CENTRE FOR DISABLED PEOPLE

Winterstoke Day Centre, Winterstoke Rd, Weston-super-Mare, North Somerset BS23 3YG; Tel 01934 626333
(30)

RESIDENTIAL HOMES FOR OLDER PEOPLE

There are five Local Authority homes for older people.

Education Department

PO Box 51, Town Hall, Weston-super-Mare, North Somerset BS23 1ZZ; Tel (Governor support helpline) 01934 634778; (Governor support helpline) 01275 884225; 01934 888829; Fax 01934 888834
Director (Education) Colin Diamond
Head (Resources) Roger Eggleton
Head (Inclusion Services) Kate East
Head (School Improvement) Debbie Magill
Head (Policy and Pupil and Student Services) Craig Bolt
Head (Support Services) Dave Williams
Principal Educational Psychologist and Manager (Inclusion Support Service) Carol Franzen
Principal Education Welfare Officer Colin Tinkell
Manager (Special Educational Needs) Jane Routledge

SPECIAL SCHOOLS (DAY)

Baytree School Baytree Rd, Weston-super-Mare, North Somerset BS22 8HG; Tel 01934 625567
Headteacher C. Penney
3–19 SLD

Ravenswood School Pound La, Nailsea, Bristol BS19 1EY; Tel 01275 854134; Fax 01275 810876
Headteacher A. Wakelam (Acting)
3–19 SLD, MLD

Westhaven School Uphill, Weston-super-Mare, North Somerset BS23 4UT; Tel 01934 632171; Fax 01934 645596
Headteacher Jennifer Moss
7–16 MLD

NORTH TYNESIDE COUNCIL
www.northtyneside.gov.uk

Population 193 600
Political Composition: Lab: 39, Con: 13, LD: 8
Town Hall, High St East, Wallsend, Tyne and Wear NE28 7RR; URL www.northtyneside.gov.uk; Tel 0191 200 6565; Fax 0191 200 7273
Mayor Cllr David Charlton
Executive Director Anne Marie Carrie
Executive Director John Jackson
Executive Director Victor Gallant
Executive Director Martin Swales
Executive Director David Wright
Executive Director Brian Doughty
Head (Policy) Anthony Clark; Tel 0191 200 6855; Fax 0191 200 7273
Head (Customer Services) Mike Robson; Tel 0191 200 7779; Fax 0191 200 7861
Head (Environmental Services) Martin Swales
PO Box 113 Station Rd, Killingworth, Newcastle upon Tyne, Tyne and Wear NE12 0WJ; Tel 0191 219 2323; Fax 0191 200 2345
Head (Legal) Carol Dunn; Tel 0191 200 5317; Fax 0191 200 5858
Head (Information Technology) Malcolm Scaife; Tel 0191 200 5232; Fax 0191 200 6096
Head (Corporate Finance) Charles Oakley; Tel 0191 200 7043; Fax 0191 200 6953
Head (Community Services) Brian Topping; Tel 0191 200 5173; Fax 0191 200 5799
Head (Housing Management) Derek Adcock; Tel 0191 200 7641; Fax 0191 200 7860
Head (Building Services) Keith Harris; Tel 0191 219 2233; Fax 0191 219 2225
Head (Development) Mike Halsey; Tel 0191 219 2320; Fax 0191 219 2345
Head (Schools Services) Jill Alexander; Tel 0191 200 5018; Fax 0191 200 5060

Social Services (Adults)

Great Lime Rd, West Moor, Newcastle upon Tyne, Tyne and Wear NE12 7DQ; Tel (Standby out-of-hours) 0191 200 6800; 0191 200 8181; Fax 0191 200 8151
Head (Adults) Sue Ramprogus
Locality Director (Learning Disability Services) Diane Holmes
Manager (Community Disability Service) Derna Campbell
Manager (Community and Hospital Social Work Service) Pauline Smith
Manager (Mental Health Services) Warren Austin
Manager (Administration and Finance) Sheila Watson

Policy and Resources Cabinet

Chief Executive John Marsden
Mayor Linda Arkley
Deputy Mayor Cllr Lawrence Goveas
Members of the Cabinet
Cllr Mrs L. Arkley, Cllr Mrs J.M. Bell, Cllr E. Hodson, Cllr Mrs Kje Johnston, Cllr Macculay, Cllr M. McIntyre, Cllr K. Mewett.

CENTRAL SERVICES

Cleveland Centre Cleveland Rd, North Shields, Tyne and Wear NE29 0NG; Tel 0191 200 6185

Community Disability Services Rehabilitation Department, North Tyneside General Hospital, North Shields, Tyne and Wear NE29 8NH; Tel 0191 293 2774; Fax 0191 293 2770
Manager Derna Campbell

Community Learning Disability Team Parkside Hse, Elton St, Wallsend, Tyne and Wear NE28 6BR; Tel 0191 200 6500; Fax 0191 200 7028
Team Leader (Employment Services) Sue Stamp
Team Leader (Social Care) Alison Cockayne
Team Leader (Day Care Services) Mike Davide

Disability Resource Centre Longbenton Community College, Hailsham Ave, Newcastle upon Tyne, Tyne and Wear; Tel 0191 200 7885

Home Services
Manager Vacancy

Medical Social Work Team North Tyneside General Hospital, Rake La, North Shields, Tyne and Wear NE29 8NH; Tel 0191 293 2719; Fax 0191 296 5088
Manager Verner Taylor

Mental Health Services
Manager Warren Austin

Norcraft Centre Planet Pl, George Stephenson Ind Est, Newcastle upon Tyne, Tyne and Wear NE12 0DY; Tel 0191 200 8383; Fax 0191 200 8387

RESPITE UNIT FOR YOUNG ADULTS

Fordley Respite Unit 15 Annitsford Dr, Fordley, Dudley, Tyne and Wear NE23 7AP; Tel 0191 200 8001
Assistant Manager Gordon Meek

INDUSTRIAL UNIT FOR THE DISABLED

Northtyne Products Unit 13–14, Point Pleasant Trading Est, Wallsend, Tyne and Wear; Tel 0191 200 7159
Manager Bill Craig

RESIDENTIAL/RESPITE FOR PEOPLE WITH LEARNING DISABILITIES

Aldercare Home Parkside Hse, Elton St, Wallsend, Tyne and Wear; Tel 0191 200 6500; Fax 0191 200 7028
Manager (Independent Living Services) Hannah Prescott

Bamburgh Crescent Home 10 Bamburgh Cres, Shiremoor, Newcastle upon Tyne, Tyne and Wear; Tel 0191 200 8624
Assistant Manager Chris Browell

Blanchland Wing John Spence Community High School, Blanchland Terr, North Shields, Tyne and Wear; Tel 0191 200 6251
Co-ordinator Kevin Baldwin

Cleveland Centre Cleveland Rd, North Shields, Tyne and Wear; Tel 0191 200 6185
Co-ordinator Vacancy

Norcraft Home Planet Pl, George Stephenson Ind Est, Newcastle upon Tyne, Tyne and Wear; Tel 0191 200 8383
Manager Ralph Smith

West Farm Road Home West Farm Rd, Wallsend, Tyne and Wear NE28 7AY; Tel 0191 200 7161
Assistant Manager Susan Redpath

Wilson Terrace Home Forest Hall, 22–23 Wilson Terr, Newcastle upon Tyne, Tyne and Wear; Tel 0191 200 8295
Assistant Manager Janet Howell

DISABILITY RESOURCE SERVICE

Marden House Solway Ave, Cullercoats, North Shields, Tyne and Wear; Tel 0191 200 6179
Co-ordinator Steve Walker

Preston Day Centre Solway Ave, Cullercoats, North Shields, Tyne and Wear; Tel 0191 200 6260; Fax 0191 200 5755
Unit Leader Jon Routledge

Resource Centre Longbenton Community High School, Hailsham Ave, Longbenton, Tyne and Wear; Tel 0191 200 7885
Co-ordinator Chris Hedworth

RESIDENTIAL HOMES FOR OLDER PEOPLE

There are six residential homes for elderly people.

LOCAL VOLUNTEER SERVICE

North Tyneside Voluntary Organisations Development Agency (VODA) Linskill Centre, Linskill Terr, North Shields, Tyne and Wear; Tel 0191 200 5790

Social Services (Children's)

Camden Hse, Camden St, North Shields, Tyne and Wear NE30 1NW; Tel 0191 200 6161; Fax 0191 200 6089
Head (Children's Services) Helen Watson
Independent Chair (Quality Assurance) Mike Sutherland
Education Welfare Service, Stephenson Hse, North Shields, Tyne and Wear NE30 1QA; Tel 0191 200 5784; Fax 0191 200 5616
Manager (Children and Families) Paul Cook
Manager (Finance and Administration) Ray Duddy
Manager Jen Harrison
Youth Court Services, 153 Tynemouth Rd, North Shields, Tyne and Wear NE30 1ED; Tel 0191 200 6008; Fax 0191 200 6009
Manager (Placement and Day Services) Fred Lillie
Manager (Performance and Quality Assurance) Carole Goodman
Employee Development Officer Dawn Parkin

EXTENDED HOURS SCHEME

Coquet Coquet Park First School, Coquet Ave, Whitley Bay, Tyne and Wear; Tel 0191 251 0394
5–12 (24)

Denbigh Denbigh Community First School, Denbigh Ave, Wallsend, Tyne and Wear NE28 0DS; Tel 0191 234 4912
5–12 (16)

Greenfields Greenfields Comm Primary School, Wideopen, Newcastle upon Tyne, Tyne and Wear NE13 6NB; Tel 0191 236 4531
5–12 (24)

Moor Edge Moor Edge First School, Garth 6, Killingworth, Tyne and Wear; Tel 0191 200 8287
5–12 (26)

Riverside Riverside Early Years Centre, Minton La, North Shields, Tyne and Wear NE29 6DQ; Tel 0191 200 5506
5–13 (24)

Southridge Southridge First School, Cranleigh Pl, Whitley Bay, Tyne and Wear NE25 9UD; Tel 0191 251 0767
5–12 (24)

Education Service

Stephenson Hse, Stephenson St, North Shields, Tyne and Wear NE30 1QA; Tel 0191 200 5022; Fax 0191 200 6090
Director (Education and Cultural Services) Anne-Marie Carrie
Chief Education Officer and Head (Education and Cultural Services) Gill Alexander, BA, MA
Head (Education, Finance and Support) Mark Longstaff

Head (Education, Strategy and Achievement)   Peter Parish, MA
Head (Pupil and Student Services)   John Scott, MA
Education Officer (Special Needs)   Pat MacDonald
Education Officer (Special Needs) and Manager (Statutory Assessment and Review)   Glynis McManus
Principal Educational Psychologist   Kath McAulay
Chapel La Education Centre, Chapel La, Monkseaton, Whitley Bay, Tyne and Wear NE25 8AD; Tel 0191 200 1441

LEARNING SUPPORT SERVICE

Hadrian Education Centre, Addington Dr, Wallsend, Tyne and Wear NE28 9RT; Tel 0191 200 6981
Manager   John Waldron

BEHAVIOUR AND ATTENDANCE SUPPORT SERVICE

Hadrian Education Centre, Addington Dr, Wallsend, Tyne and Wear NE28 9RT; Tel 0191 200 8641
Manager (Acting)   Hazel Brown

SPECIAL DAY SCHOOLS

Ashleigh School Charlotte St, North Shields, Tyne and Wear NE30 1BP; Tel 0191 200 6339
Headteacher   R. Harrison
  SLD/AUT

Glebe School Woodburn Dr, Whitley Bay, Tyne and Wear NE26 3HW; Tel 0191 200 8776
Headteacher   L. Turner, BA
  Primary MLD/AUT

Parkside School Mullen Rd, High Farm, Wallsend, Tyne and Wear NE28 9HA; Tel 0191 200 7254
Headteacher   H.M. Jones, MA
  SLD/AUT

Silverdale School Mitford Gdns, Howden, Wallsend, Tyne and Wear NE28 8QN; Tel 0191 200 5982
Headteacher   Bill Lennox
  ESBD

Southlands School Beach Rd, Tynemouth, North Shields, Tyne and Wear NE30 2QR; Tel 0191 200 6348
Headteacher   D.J. Erskine, BEd
  Secondary MLD

Woodlawn School Langley Ave, Whitley Bay, Tyne and Wear NE25 9DF; Tel 0191 200 8729
Headteacher   B.W. Hickman
  PH

DEAF AND PARTIAL HEARING UNITS (SCHOOL BASED)

Marden High School Hartington Rd, North Shields, Tyne and Wear NE30 3RZ; Tel 0191 200 6357

Monkhouse Primary School Wallington Ave, North Shields, Tyne and Wear NE30 3SH; Tel 0191 200 6350
Teacher-in-Charge   E. Rigby

LANGUAGE UNITS

Goathland Primary School Goathland Ave, Longbenton, Newcastle upon Tyne, Northumberland NE12 8LH; Tel 0191 200 7427
Headteacher   Mrs S. A. Tickell, BPhil

Waterville Primary School Waterville Rd, North Shields, Tyne and Wear NE29 6SL; Tel 0191 200 6351
Headteacher   Mrs P.A. Duncan, MPhil

LANGUAGE/AUTISM UNIT

Norham Community Technology College Alnwick Ave, North Shields, Tyne and Wear NE29 7BU; Tel 0191 200 5062
Principal   Mrs L. Halbert

NORTH YORKSHIRE COUNTY COUNCIL
www.northyorks.gov.uk

Political Composition: Con: 42, LD: 17, Lab: 12, Ind: 3
County Hall, Northallerton, North Yorkshire DL7 8AD;
  URL www.northyorks.gov.uk;
  E-mail chief.exec@northyorks.gov.uk; Tel 01609 780780;
  Fax 01609 780447
Chief Executive   J. Walker
Director (Financial Services)   J.S. Moore

Social Services Directorate

County Hall, Northallerton, North Yorkshire DL7 8DD;
  Tel (Emergency Duty Team (for whole County)) 01904 762314; 01609 780780; Fax 01904 760198
Director (Social Services)   R.K. Archer
Unit Manager (Directorate Support)   T. Rose
Head (Children and Families Services)   P. Davies
Head (Community Care)   S. Breen
Head (County Care)   N. Revely
Manager (Human Resources)   C. McCarty
Manager (Finance and Administration)   J. Foster
Manager (Human Resources)   R. Ashman
Manager (Finance)   Lisa Gallow
2 West Parade Rd, Scarborough, North Yorkshire YO12 5ED; Tel 01723 508007
Manager (Emergency Duty Team Unit)   S. Clark; Tel 01904 762314; Fax 01904 760198
Unit Manager (Contracting)   J. Johnson
Senior Officer (Business Support)   S. Chandler
Principal Officer (Adoption)   Helen Shakespeare
Principal Officer (Business Support)   N. Sutton
Principal Officer (Business Support)   T. O'Brien
Principal Officer (Disability)   J. Cocker

TRAINING

Responsible for training professional and support staff in the department.
Manager (Training)   Tim Clark
Training Matters, Willow Tree Hse, York YO3 3NS; Tel 01904 766142; Fax 01904 769363

CHILDREN AND FAMILIES BUSINESS UNIT

Children's Services

Group Manager (East)   D. Molesworth
Ryedale Hse, Malton, North Yorkshire YO17 0HH; Tel 01653 600666; Fax 01653 698133
Group Manager (West)   V. Hobman
4 Stockwell La, Knaresborough, North Yorkshire HG5 0DA; Tel 01423 799400; Fax 01423 779407
Group Manager (Central)   K. Podmore

CHILDREN'S SERVICES SERVICE MANAGERS

Armoury House Otley St, Skipton, North Yorkshire BD23 1EL; Tel 01756 793042; Fax 01756 799987
Service Manager   A. Hodgson

The Broadway Centre 9 The Broadway, Colburn, Catterick Garrison, North Yorkshire DL9 4RF; Tel 01748 832600; 01748 832692; Fax 01748 834930
Service Manager   L. Phythian

Brook Lodge Union La, Selby, North Yorkshire YO8 0BA; Tel 01757 705421; Fax 01757 213965
Service Manager   D. Yellen

6

The Close 58 Northallerton Rd, Brompton, Northerallerton, North Yorkshire DL6 2QH; Tel 01609 779922; Fax 01609 778906
Service Manager T. Whitfield

Dean Road Centre 16 Dean Rd, Scarborough, North Yorkshire; Tel 01723 508100; Fax 01723 500396
Service Manager (Scarborough South) M. Gittins
Service Manager (Scarborough North) M. Chance

Haywra Street Centre 1 Haywra St, Harrogate, North Yorkshire; Tel 01423 505049; Fax 01423 561550
Service Manager Nick O'Brien

Ryedale House Old Malton Rd, Malton, North Yorkshire; Tel 01653 600666; Fax 01653 698133
Service Manager T. Cherry

Sharow View 75 Allhallowgate, Ripon, North Yorkshire HG1 4LE; Tel 01765 605135; Fax 01765 607837
Service Manager L. Ingleson

Children and Families Initial Assessment Team 16 Dean Rd, Scarborough, North Yorkshire YO12 7SN; Tel 01723 352579; Fax 01723 500396
Service Manager Wendy Jones

Children with Disabilities

Morton-on-Swale 8 St. Helen's Cl, Morton-on-Swale, North Yorkshire DL7 9TT; Tel 01609 772127; Fax 01609 778424
Service Manager Cath Kemp

Scarborough 14 Dean Rd, Scarborough, North Yorkshire YD12 7SN; Tel 01723 501155
Service Manager P. Marr

Stockwell Lane 4 Stockwell La, Knaresborough, North Yorkshire; Tel 01423 799400; Fax 01423 799407
Service Manager D. Hammal

Child Placement

4 Stockwell La, Knaresborough, North Yorkshire HG5 0DA; Tel 01423 799409; Fax 01423 799440
Group Manager J. Heron

CHILD PLACEMENT SERVICE MANAGERS

Dean Road 16 Dean Rd, Scarborough, North Yorkshire; Tel 01723 508117; Fax 01723 500396
Service Manager R. Shannon
Service Manager N. Roberts
The Cl, Northallerton Rd, Northallerton, North Yorkshire DL6 2QH; Tel 01609 779922; Fax 01609 778906

Stockwell Lane 4 Stockwell La, Knaresborough, North Yorkshire; Tel 01423 799450; Fax 01423 799407
Service Manager S. Leahy

Residential and Daycare Establishments

FAMILY CENTRES

Family Support Centre Hipswell Rd, Hipswell, Catterick Garrison, North Yorkshire DL9 4AT; Tel 01748 833890
Family Support Worker Manager J. Taylor

Family Support Centre 31 Trinity Rd, Scarborough, North Yorkshire YO11 2TD; Tel 01723 500172
Family Support Worker Manager Vacancy

Westbourne House Family Support Centre Westbourne Rd, Selby, North Yorkshire YO8 9BZ; Tel 01757 213399
Family Support Worker Manager C. Foster

CHILDREN'S RESOURCE CENTRES

Children's Resource Centre 6 St. Helen's Cl, Station La, Northallerton, North Yorkshire DL7 9TT; Tel 01609 776602
Manager J. Tyre
Residential (8 + 1 emergency bed)

The Ghyll Resource Centre Cawder La, Skipton, North Yorkshire BD23 2QQ; Tel 01756 792949
Manager G. Harvey
Respite (6)

Nidderdale Children's Resource Centre Ripon Rd, Killinghall, North Yorkshire HG3 2AY; Tel 01423 506196; Fax 01423 508190
Manager J. Hoyle
(8)

CHILDREN'S CENTRES

Forest Lane Children's Centre 2 Forest La, Starbeck, Harrogate, North Yorkshire HG2 7DX; Tel 01423 880872; Fax 01423 885557
Manager D. Hodgson

Stepney Road Children's Centre 53–55 Stepney Rd, Scarborough, North Yorkshire YO12 5BT; Tel 01723 373891; Fax 01723 373891
Manager I. Simpson
(7)

Woodleigh Children's Centre 34–40 Woodfield Sq, Harrogate, North Yorkshire HG1 4LY; Tel 01423 505360; Fax 01423 509048
Manager D. Hodgson

COMMUNITY CARE BUSINESS UNIT

Jesmond Hse, 33 Victoria Ave, Harrogate, North Yorkshire HG1 5QE; Tel 01423 561951; Fax 01423 508779
General Manager (SW) Hilary Edwards
General Manager M. Hunt
2 West Parade Rd, Scarborough, North Yorkshire YO12 5ED; E-mail michael.hunt@northyorks.gov.uk; Tel 01723 508006; Fax 01723 379683

SERVICE MANAGERS

Disabilities Resource Centre Dunslow Rd, Cayton Low Rd Ind Est, Scarborough, North Yorkshire YO11 3UD; Tel 01723 587002; Fax 01723 585417
Service Manager Jon Cleary

Jesmond House 33 Victoria Ave, Harrogate, North Yorkshire HG1 5QE; Tel 01423 561951; Fax 01423 508779
Area Manager Linda Denham
Area Manager (Learning Disability) Raepl Edwards

The Old School East Rd, Northallerton, North Yorkshire DL7 1NQ; Tel 01609 771953; Fax 01609 778488
Area Manager J. Pudney
Area Manager (Learning Disability) Ian Peasley

Mental Health

Hambleton/Richmondshire 12 Friarage St, Northallerton, North Yorkshire DLE 1DP; E-mail paul.farrimond@hrpct.nhs.uk; Tel 01609 763417; Fax 01609 763409
Director Paul Farrimond

Harrogate/Craven The Hamlet, Hornbeam Pk, Harrogate, North Yorkshire HG2 8RE; E-mail david.brown@chrd-pct.nhs.uk; Tel 01423 815150; Fax 01423 859600
Director (Mental Health) David Brown

Scarborough and Rydale Teny NHS Trust, The Lodge, Cross Lane Hospital, Scarborough, North Yorkshire YO12 6DN; E-mail john.ballatt@tney.northy.nhs.uk; Tel 01723 343556; Fax 01723 343534
Director John Ballatt

MENTAL HEALTH UNIT RESOURCE CENTRES

Belmont Road Centre 34 Belmont Rd, Harrogate, North Yorkshire HG2 0LR; Tel 01423 502581; Fax 01423 520465
Service Manager P. Nagel

Trafalgar Square Centre 2 Trafalgar Sq, Scarborough, North Yorkshire YO12 2PY; Tel 01723 375694

NORTH EAST CENTRES

Advanced Work Unit Units 1 and 2, Wareham Rd, Scarborough, North Yorkshire YO11 3UW; Tel 01723 584093; Fax 01723 585110

Ashlands Centre Ashlands Rd, Northallerton, North Yorkshire DL6 1HL; E-mail ashlands.centre@nyccss.btinternet.com; Tel 01609 772461

Ashlands Outreach 59 Newbiggin, Richmond, North Yorkshire; E-mail ashlands.outreach@nyccss.btinternet.com; Tel 01748 850031

Burnside Hostel 1 Burnside, Eastfield, Scarborough, North Yorkshire YO11 3LH; E-mail burnside.resource@nyccss.btinternet.com; Tel 01723 583802

Cauwood Centre Old Malton Rd, Malton, North Yorkshire YO17 0EY; E-mail cauwood@nyccss.btinternet.com; Tel 01653 696588

Elder Street Day Centre 10 Elder St, Scarborough, North Yorkshire YO11 1DZ; Tel 01723 500788

Eskholme Day Centre 1 Upgang La, Whitby, North Yorkshire YO21 3DR; Tel 01747 604601

Resource Centre 65a Valley Rd, Northallerton, North Yorkshire DL6 1SH; Tel 01609 760337

Scarborough Training Centre Salter Rd, Eastfield, Scarborough, North Yorkshire YO11 3BY; E-mail stc.scarborough@nyccss.btinternet.com; Tel 01723 583017

Trafalgar Square Centre 2 Trafalgar Sq, Scarborough, North Yorkshire; Tel 01723 375694

SOUTH WEST CENTRES

The Belmont Road Centre 34 Belmont Rd, Harrogate, North Yorkshire HG2 0LR; Tel 01423 502581

Harrogate Centre 68a High St, Starbeck, Harrogate, North Yorkshire HG2 7LW; E-mail starbeck.centre@nyccss.btinternet.com; Tel 01423 887461

Resource Centre for People with Learning Disabilities 30 Duke St, Settle, North Yorkshire BD24 9DN; Tel 01720 824099

Resource Centre for People with Learning Disabilities 80 High St, Starbeck, Harrogate, North Yorkshire HG2 7LW; Tel 01423 883301

Resource Unit for People with Learning Disabilities 24 Gargrave Rd, Skipton, North Yorkshire BD23 1QV; E-mail gargrave.road@nyccss.btinternet.com; Tel 01756 700720

Ripon Day Centre Sharow View, 75 Allhallowgate, Ripon, North Yorkshire HG4 1LE; Tel 01765 605109

Selby and District Day Centre 75 Brook St, Selby, North Yorkshire YO8 0AL; Tel 01757 705421

Snaygill Centre Keighley Rd, Skipton, North Yorkshire BD23 2QS; E-mail snaygill.centre@nyccss.btinternet.com; Tel 01756 792787

AREA MANAGERS

Frenchgate 91 Frenchgate, Richmond, North Yorkshire; Tel 01748 824444; 01748 824445; Fax 01748 826011
Area Manager P. Richardson

Harrogate General Hospital 13 Wettecly Rd, Harrogate, North Yorkshire HG2 0UB; Tel 01423 553120; Fax 01423 553701

Assistant Care Manager F. Dracup
Assistant Care Manager L. Allott

The Old School Kirkgate, Sherburn in Elmet, North Yorkshire LS25 6BL; Tel 01977 684545; Fax 01977 681576
Area Manager O. Joistdahl

Otley Street 45 Otley St, Skipton, North Yorkshire; Tel 01756 794777; Fax 01756 796120
Area Manager C. Haslam

Ryedale House Old Malton Rd, Malton, North Yorkshire YO17 0HH; Tel 01653 600666; Fax 01653 698133
Area Manager A. Hall

Springhill Close 19 Springhill Cl, Scarborough, North Yorkshire; Tel 01723 501144; Fax 01723 368005
Area Manager M. Glover

COUNTY CARE

Jesmond House 80 High St, Storbeck, North Yorkshire; Tel 01423 883301
Locality Manager Jayne Marshall

Manor Road Easingwold, North Yorkshire; Tel 01347 821651; Fax 01347 823136
Area Group Manager D. Buckley Richmondshire

West Parade Road 2 West Parade Rd, Scarborough, North Yorkshire; Tel 01723 508006; Fax 01723 379683
Locality Manager S. Barrett Scarborough South

County Care

Allhallowgate 75 Allhallowgate, Ripon, North Yorkshire; Tel 01765 605135
Locality Manager Debbie Jon Malachuski
Locality Manager Jacki Bradfield

Holly Garth 17 Holly Gr, Thorpe Willoughby, North Yorkshire; Tel 01757 708656
Locality Manager (Selby) Martin Kearns

Jesmond House 80 High St, Storbeck, North Yorkshire; Tel 01423 883301
Locality Manager Jayne Marshall
Area Group Manager (Harrogate/Craven) Tony McIntyre; Tel 01423 561951

Manor Road Easingwold, North Yorkshire; Tel 01347 821651; Fax 01347 823136
Area Group Manager (Hambleton/Richmondshire) D. Buckley

Oak Mount Thirsk Rd, Northallerton, North Yorkshire; Tel 01609 780146
Locality Manager (Hambleton) Ken Aspnall

Otley Street 45 Otley St, Skipton, North Yorkshire; Tel 01756 794777; Fax 01756 796120
Locality Manager C. Mawdsley-Stone

Richmond House Reeth Rd, Richmond, North Yorkshire; Tel 01748 822103
Locality Manager (Richmondshire) Mike O'Neill

Ryedale House Malton, North Yorkshire; Tel 01653 600666
Locality Manager (Ryedale) Shoona Patterson

West Parade Road 2 West Parade Rd, Scarborough, North Yorkshire; Tel 01723 508006; Fax 01723 379683
Locality Manager (Scarborough) S. Barratt
Locality Manager (Scarborough North) Judith Stark

Education Department

Management Team and Heads (Units).
County Hall, Northallerton, North Yorkshire DL7 8AE; E-mail education@northyorks.gov.uk; Tel 01609 780780; Fax 01609 778611
Director (Education) C. Welbourn, MA, FRSA

Head (Pupil and Parent Services Unit)   G. McQueen, BEd, MA
Head (Policy and Development Unit)   B. Jones, BA
Head (Education Finance Unit)   G.C. Bateman, IPFA
Head (Continuing Education Unit)   C.J McGee, BA
Chief Adviser   J. Owen (Acting)

PUPIL AND PARENT SERVICES UNIT

Manager (Development and Quality Assurance)   A.P. Terry, BA
Manager (Special Educational Needs)   M. Bennett
Manager (Access)   P.L. Mellor, MA, MEd
Principal Education Psychologist   M. Cotton

LOCAL OFFICES

Harrogate Local Office

Local Education Office, Ainsty Rd, Harrogate, North Yorkshire HG1 4XU; URL www.northyorks.gov.uk/pps; E-mail pps.harrogate@northyorks.gov.uk; Tel 01423 700100; Fax 01423 700101

Scarborough/Ryedale Local Office

Local Education Office, Valley Bridge Pde, Scarborough, North Yorkshire YO11 2PL; URL www.northyorks.gov.uk/pps; E-mail pps.scarborough@northyorks.gov.uk; Tel 01723 361376; Fax 01723 501496

SPECIAL SCHOOLS

Baliol School Cautley Rd, Sedbergh, Cumbria LA10 5LQ; Tel 01539 620232; Fax 01539 621275
Headteacher   A.E. Anderson, MEd

Brompton Hall School Brompton by Sawdon, Scarborough, North Yorkshire YO13 9DB; Tel 01723 859121; Fax 01723 850239
Headteacher   M. Mihkelson, MA

Brooklands School Burnside Ave, Skipton, North Yorkshire BD23 2DB; Tel 01756 794028; Fax 01756 794200
Headteacher   K. Shorrock

The Dales School Morton-on-Swale, Northallerton, North Yorkshire DL7 9QW; Tel 01609 772932; Fax 01609 780278
Headteacher   W.F. Rab, MEd

The Forest School Park La, Knaresborough, North Yorkshire HG5 0DQ; Tel 01423 864583; Fax 01423 861145
Headteacher   Mrs M. Uden

Mowbray School Masham Rd, Bedale, North Yorkshire DL8 2SD; Tel 01677 422446; Fax 01677 426056
Headteacher   Mr J. Tearle

Netherside Hall School Threshfield, Skipton, North Yorkshire BD23 5PP; Tel 01756 752324; Fax 01756 753227
Headteacher   Mr M. Charlton

Springhead School Barry's La, Seamer Rd, Scarborough, North Yorkshire YO12 4HA; Tel 01723 367829; Fax 01723 360021
Headteacher   Mrs C.D. Wilson

Springwater School High St, Starbeck, Harrogate, North Yorkshire HG2 7LW; Tel 01423 883214; Fax 01423 881465
Headteacher   Mrs G.M. Cook, MEd

Welburn Hall School Kirkbymoorside, York YO62 7HQ; Tel 01751 431218; Fax 01751 433157
Headteacher   J.V. Hall

The Woodlands School Woodlands Dr, Scarborough, North Yorkshire YO12 6QN; Tel 01723 373260; Fax 01723 371715
Headteacher   P. Edmondson

NORTHAMPTONSHIRE COUNTY COUNCIL
www.northamptonshire.gov.uk

Population 629 676 (2001 census)
Political Composition: Lab: 39, Con: 33, LD: 1
County Hall, PO Box 163, Northampton, Northamptonshire NN1 1AX;
URL www.northamptonshire.gov.uk;
E-mail genie.northamptonshire.gov.uk; Tel 01604 236236; Fax 01604 236223
Chair of the Council   Patricia Cass; E-mail pcass@northamptonshire.gov.uk; Tel 01604 236002
Chief Executive   Peter Gould; E-mail pgould@northamptonshire.gov.uk; Tel 01604 236050
Corporate Director (Business Management)   Alistair Neill; E-mail aneil@northamptonshire.gov.uk
Strategic Director (Social Care and Health)   Ian Winter; E-mail iwinter@northamptonshire.gov.uk; Tel 01604 237804

Social Care and Health Directorate

County Hall, PO Box 233, Northampton, Northamptonshire NN1 1AZ; URL northamptonshire.gov.uk;
E-mail swilts@northamptonshire.gov.uk; Tel 01604 237804; (Out of Hours Team) 01604 626938; Fax 01604 237600
Corporate Director (Social Care and Health)   Stephen Wilds
County Manager (Commissioning Planning and Policy)   P. McCarthy
County Manager (Social Servcies – Children's Services)   S. Bresnahan
Oxford Hse, West Villa Rd, Wellingborough, Northamptonshire NN8 4JR; Tel 01933 220730; Fax 01933 443103
County Manager (Adult Services)   Fiona Seymour
Oxford Hse, West Villa Rd, Wellingborough, Northamptonshire NN8 4JR; Tel 01933 220720; Fax 01933 443929
Assistant Director (Finance and Support Services)   Vacancy
John Dryden Hse, PO Box 225, Northampton, Northamptonshire NN4 7DF; Tel 01604 236439; Fax 01604 236421
Manager (Performance and Change)   G. Jarvis; Tel 01604 237287; Fax 01604 237600

Adult Services Provision

Oxford Hse, West Villa Rd, Wellingborough, Northamptonshire NN8 4JR; Tel 01933 220720; Fax 01933 443929
County Manager   Fiona Seymour
Operations Manager   Andy Jewers
Operations Manager   Brian Frisby; Tel 01933 220750; Fax 01933 275267
Head (Learning Disabilities)   N. Parkes
Property Management Officer   Richard Beeby
9 Guildhall Rd, Northampton, Northamptonshire; Tel 01604 236447; Fax 01604 237718

CHILDREN AND FAMILIES TEAMS

Daventry South Northamptonshire Daventry, North St, Towcester, Northamptonshire NN111 5PN; Tel 01327 300567; Fax 01327 300447

Kettering/Corby Local Office Grafton Crt, Kettering Parkway, Kettering Venture Pk, Kettering, Northamptonshire NN15 6XR; Tel 01536 313000; Fax 01536 313075

Northampton East Eaton Brook Clinic, Chedworth Cl, Eaton Brook, Northampton, Northamptonshire NN3 6HW; Tel 01604 411911; Fax 01604 416816

Wellingborough Oxford Hse, West Villa Rd, Wellingborough, Northamptonshire NN8 4JR; Tel 01933 220700; Fax 01933 443103

DIVISIONS

Children's Services

Oxford Hse, West Villa Rd, Wellingborough, Northamptonshire NN8 4JR; Tel 01933 220730; Fax 01933 443103
County Manager (Services to Children and Families)
S. Bresnahan

Commissioning and Policy

Manager (Commissioning and Contracting) Jim Golcher; Tel 01604 237014; Fax 01604 236103

Daventry/South Northamptonshire Care Management Team Danetre Lodge, 34 London Rd, Daventry, Northamptonshire NN11 4DY; Tel 01327 313200; Fax 01327 313220

Kettering/Corby Care Management Team Grafton Crt, Kettering Parkway, Kettering Venture Pk, Kettering, Northamptonshire NN15 6XR; Tel 01536 313110; Fax 01536 313115

Northampton Care Management Team John Dryden Hse, PO Box 225, Northampton, Northamptonshire NN4 7DF; Tel 01604 236147; Fax 01604 237669

Wellingborough/East Northamptonshire Care Management Team Oxford Hse, West Villa Rd, Wellingborough, Northamptonshire NN8 4JR; Tel 01933 220710; Fax 01933 270123

HOSPITAL SOCIAL WORKERS

Kettering General Hospital Trust Rothwell Rd, Kettering, Northamptonshire NN16 8UZ; Tel 01536 492131; Fax 01536 493782

Northampton General Hospital Trust Cliftonville, Northampton, Northamptonshire NN1 5BD; Tel 01604 545360; Fax 01604 545591

COMMUNITY MENTAL HEALTH TEAMS – NORTHAMPTON

ASW Services South 3rd Fl, Campbell Hse, Northampton, Northamptonshire NN1 3EB; Tel 01604 656065; Fax 01604 656062

Corby Community Mental Health Team Cottingham Rd, Corby, Northamptonshire NN17 1TD; Tel 01536 206868; Fax 01536 407723

Daventry Community Mental Health Team North St, 34 London Rd, Daventry, Northamptonshire NN11 5PH; Tel 01327 313200; Fax 01327 313220

Kettering Community Mental Health Team 75 London Rd, Kettering, Northamptonshire NN15 7QU; Tel 01536 414207; Fax 01536 412815

Accommodation Team Fl 1, Oxford Hse, West Villa Rd, Wellingborough, Northamptonshire NN8 4JR

Rushden Community Mental Health Team Rushden Hospital, Wymington Rd, Rushden, Northamptonshire NN10 9JS; Tel 01933 412912; Fax 01933 413706

South Northamptonshire Community Mental Health Team Mill Hse, Chantry La, Towcester, Northamptonshire NN12 7YY; Tel 01327 351822; Fax 01327 353123

Wellingborough Community Mental Health Team Oxford Hse, West Villa Rd, Wellingborough, Northamptonshire NN8 4JR; Tel 01933 220727; Fax 01933 443929

CHILD AND FAMILY CONSULTATION SERVICE

Northampton 8 Notre Dame Mews, Northampton, Northamptonshire NN1 2BG; Tel 01604 604608; Fax 01604 604531

Kettering 10 Headlands, Kettering, Northamptonshire NN15 7HP; Tel 01536 518022; Fax 01536 517002

CHILD PROTECTION REGISTER AND CONFERENCE SERVICE

Robert St, Northampton, Northamptonshire NN1 3AR; Tel 01604 259200; Fax 01604 234767

CHILDREN'S CENTRES

Gainsborough Road Centre Corby, Northamptonshire; Tel 01536 400063; Fax 01536 403369

Northwood Centre Holmecross Rd, Thorplands, Northampton, Northamptonshire NN3 8AW; Tel 01604 790073; Fax 01604 671187

RESIDENTIAL UNITS FOR CHILDREN

Raven House 53–55 Rockingham Rd, Corby, Northamptonshire NN17 1AJ; Tel 01536 403341; Fax 01536 406828

St. John's House St. John's Centre, St. John's Rd, Tiffield, Towcester, Northamptonshire NN12 8AA; Tel 01604 858187; Fax 01604 857370

St. John's Centre St. John's Rd, Tiffield, Towcester, Northamptonshire NN12 8AA; Tel (secure unit) 01604 858113; 01604 859411; Fax 01604 859580
Mixed education provision secure unit.

Welford House Residential Unit 275 Welford Rd, Kingsthorpe, Northampton, Northamptonshire NN2 8PW; Tel 01604 846212; Fax 01604 841812

YOUTH OFFENDING TEAM

Youth Offending Team North 73–75 London Rd, Kettering, Northamptonshire NN15 7PQ; Tel 01536 415767; Fax 01536 411352

Youth Offending Team South 63 Billing Rd, Northampton, Northamptonshire NN1 5DB; Tel 01604 602400; Fax 01604 639231

RESIDENTIAL UNITS FOR CHILDREN WITH DISABILITIES

Evenley Road Residential Unit 22–24 Evenley Rd, Northampton, Northamptonshire; Tel 01604 842296

John Greenwood Shipman Children's Centre Farmbrook Cl, Billingbrook Rd, Northampton, Northamptonshire; Tel 01604 499717; Fax 01604 790309

Northampton Road Residential Unit 82 Northampton Rd, Wellingborough, Northamptonshire; Tel 01933 225289; Fax 01933 270012

RESIDENTIAL UNITS FOR ADULTS WITH PHYSICAL/LEARNING DISABILITIES

Cranwell Resource Centre 47 Doddington Rd, Wellingborough, Northamptonshire NN8 2LY; Tel 01933 276739; Fax 01933 272132

Eleanor Lodge Residential Unit 25 Camborne Cl, Gloucester Ave, Northampton, Northamptonshire NN4 8PH; Tel 01604 764583; Fax 01604 768920

Elm Bank Community Unit Northampton Rd, Kettering, Northamptonshire NN15 7JZ; Tel 01536 416409; Fax 01536 416369

Norborough House Residential Unit Coverack Cl, Delapre, Northampton, Northamptonshire NN4 8PQ; Tel 01604 665920; Fax 01604 665921

6

Pine Lodge Residential Unit Motala Cl, Viking Way, Corby, Northamptonshire NN18 9EJ; Tel 01536 742043; Fax 01536 741713

Quarry House Residential Unit Port Rd, New Duston, Northampton, Northamptonshire NN5 6NS; Tel 01604 757778; Fax 01604 757595

Saunders Close Residential Unit 94 Saunders Cl, Kettering, Northamptonshire; Tel 01536 410340; Fax 01536 481089

St. Lucia House Residential Unit 54 The Ave, Cliftonville, Northampton, Northamptonshire NN1 5BT; Tel 01604 630521; Fax 01604 626221

RESIDENTIAL UNITS FOR PEOPLE WITH MENTAL HEALTH PROBLEMS

Lindfield Community Mental Health Centre 445 Wellingborough Rd, Northampton, Northamptonshire NN1 4EZ; Tel 01604 631362; Fax 01604 259594

Meadhurst Residential Unit 116 Rockingham Rd, Kettering, Northamptonshire NN16 9AF; Tel 01536 415340; Fax 01536 415340

Moray Lodge Residential Unit Peveril Rd, Duston, Northampton, Northamptonshire NN5 6JW; Tel 01604 753887; Fax 01604 750728

Robin Lane 55–57 Robin La, Hemmingwell Est, Wellingborough, Northamptonshire NN8 4TJ; Tel 01933 277306

NORDIS INDUSTRIES

Cornhill Cl, Lodge Farm Ind Est, Northampton, Northamptonshire NN5 7UB; Tel 01604 596910; Fax 01604 758470

EMPLOYMENT AND DISABILITY SERVICES

10 London Rd, Kettering, Northamptonshire NN15 7QU; Tel 01536 412802; Fax 01536 412856

DAY CENTRES FOR OLDER PEOPLE AND ADULTS WITH DISABILITIES

Cliftonville Day Centre (Age Concern) Cliftonville Rd, Northampton, Northamptonshire NN1 5BU; Tel 01604 36145; Fax 01604 604283
   Elderly
Cliftonville 'Choices' Cliftonville Road, Northampton, Northamptonshire; Tel 01604 628952; Fax 01604 239509

Community Day Services Team 10 London Rd, Kettering, Northamptonshire NN15 7QU; Tel 01536 310103; Fax 01536 412856

Elm Bank Day Centre Northampton Rd, Kettering, Northamptonshire NN15 7JZ; Tel 01536 410330; Fax 01536 482991

Four Seasons Day Centre (Age Concern) School La, Kettering, Northamptonshire NN16 0DH; Tel 01536 84259; Fax 01536 84259

Gladstone Centre Gladstone Rd, Northampton, Northamptonshire NN5 7EJ; Tel 01604 752611; Fax 01604 580936

Henley Centre Saunders Cl, George St, Kettering, Northamptonshire NN16 0AP; Tel 01536 410339; Fax 01536 485053

Nene Centre Bedford Rd, Northampton, Northamptonshire NN4 7AD; Tel 01604 621361; Fax 01604 259522

Oakley Grange Centre Oakley Rd, Corby, Northamptonshire NN18 9NP; Tel 01536 207950; Fax 01536 207951

Riverside Resource Centre Islington Rd, Towcester, Northamptonshire NN12 6AU; Tel 01327 359252; Fax 01327 358093

St. David's Day Centre 1a Drayton Wlk, Northampton, Northamptonshire NN2 7SD; Tel 01604 713922; Fax 01604 711158

Sanders Gate Centre 93–97 Sanders Rd, Finedon Road Ind Est, Wellingborough, Northamptonshire NN8 4NL; Tel 01933 276861; Fax 01933 272052

Shire Lodge Day Centre Sheaf Cl, Lodge Farm Ind Est, Northampton, Northamptonshire NN5 7UL; Tel 01604 755128; Fax 01604 586010

Stone House Day Centre South Rd, Corby, Northamptonshire NN17 1XB; Tel 01536 400401; Fax 01536 443326

Willows Day Centre Robert St, Simon de Senlis Ct, Northampton, Northamptonshire NN1 3AE; Tel 01604 230711; Fax 01604 630783

RESIDENTIAL UNITS FOR OLDER PEOPLE

There are 23 homes for older people.

MEALS SERVICES

Contact H. Lemmon; Tel 01604 236096; Fax 01604 237481
Northamptonshire County Council

SENSORY IMPAIRMENT UNIT

Oxford House West Villa Rd, Wellingborough, Northamptonshire NN18 4JR; Tel 01933 220727; Fax 01933 279828; Minicom 01933 223551
Unit Manager Lynne Griffiths

VOLUNTARY SERVICES OFFICER

AIDS/HIV Service Fl 2, Oxford Hse, Wellingborough, Northamptonshire NN8 4JR; Tel 01933 220720; Fax 01933 443929

County Hall PO Box 177, Northampton, Northamptonshire NN1 1AY; Tel 01604 237170; Fax 01604 237600

Schools Services

Please note that the Department operates on a split site. The Director is based at the County Hall address.
PO Box No 149, County Hall, Northampton, Northamptonshire NN1 1AU;
   E-mail education@northamptonshire.gov.uk; Tel 01604 236252; Fax 01604 237121; 01604 237011
Spencer Centre, Lewis Rd, Northampton, Northamptonshire NN5 7BJ; Tel 01604 237465
Director (Schools Services) Andrew Sortwell; Tel 01604 236252
Director (Children and Families Service) C. Danks; Tel 01604 237863
Assistant Director (School Improvement) J. Martin
Principal Youth Officer G. Stewart; Tel 01604 236601; Fax 01604 237441
Education Officer Promoting Equalities (Multi-cultural Education Service) Roger Tweed; Tel 01604 236213
Principal Psychologist D.J. Lucas, BSc(Econ), DipEdPsych, DipYLO; Tel 01604 236201
Principal Education Welfare Officer Anna-Marie Mullan; Tel 01604 236203

HOSPITAL EDUCATION SERVICE

Kettering General Hospital Cromwell St, Northampton, Northamptonshire; Tel 01604 239730
Headteacher Lyn Mayer

MAINSTREAM SCHOOLS WITH DESIGNATED SPECIAL PROVISION

Barry Primary School Barry Rd, Northampton, Northamptonshire NN1 5JS; Tel 01604 234574
Headteacher Mrs L. Pugh
   Significant physical difficulties.

Beanfield Infant School Farmstead Rd, Corby, Northamptonshire NN18 0LS; Tel 01536 202982
Headteacher Carolyn Wilson
SLD/MLD including autism spectrum disorders. (incl. Junior) (38)

Beanfield Junior School Farmstead Rd, Corby, Northamptonshire NN18 0U; Tel 01536 203907
Headteacher Ray James (Acting)
SLD/MLD includes autism spectrum disorders. (incl. infants) (38)

Boothville Middle School Esher Crt, The Arbours, Northampton, Northamptonshire NN3 3RG; Tel 01604 406746

Croyland Primary School Croyland Rd, Wellingborough, Northamptonshire NN8 2AX; Tel 01933 224169
Headteacher Helen Tite
7–11 Provision for children with speech and language difficulties. Wheelchair access. (3)

Croyland Nursery School Croyland Rd, Wellingborough, Northamptonshire; Tel 01933 279681
Headteacher C. Whelan
3–4 Provision for children with speech and language difficulties. Wheelchair access. (8)

Daventry Falconers Hill Community Junior School Ashby Rd, Daventry, Northamptonshire NN11 5QE; Tel 01327 703132
Headteacher Ms P.A. Marston
General and specific learning difficulties. (12)

Daventry Grange Infant School Staverton Rd, Daventry, Northamptonshire NN11 4HW; Tel 01327 703597
Headteacher Mrs P.L. Long
Nursery provision for children with specific speech and language difficulties. (8)

Daventry Southbrook Infant and Nursery School Hawke Rd, Southbrook Estate, Daventry, Northamptonshire NN11 4U; Tel 01327 703440
Headteacher Lorraine Felstead
Nursery and infant provision for children with general and specific learning difficulties. Also for children with communication difficulties. (15)

Denfield Park Junior School Victoria Rd, Rushden, Northamptonshire NN10 0DA; Tel 01933 355961
Headteacher Angela Griffiths
7–11 LD (10)

East Hunsbury Primary School Penvale Rd, Northampton, Northamptonshire NN4 0QW; Tel 01604 677970
Headteacher Rita Arundel
SLD (38)

Emmanuel Middle School Billing Brook Rd, Lings, Northamptonshire NN3 8NL; Tel 01604 408033
Headteacher Alison Byrne
General and specific learning difficulties. (16)

Greenoaks Primary School Bective Rd, Northampton, Northamptonshire NN2 7TD; Tel 01604 715249
Headteacher Julie Hill
Communications difficulties (autism spectrum). (29)

Hayway Infant School Hayway, Rushden, Northamptonshire NN10 9AG; Tel 01933 355260
Headteacher Mrs J. Clemence
Provision for children with learning difficulties. (7)

Headlands Primary School Bushland Rd, Northampton, Northamptonshire NN3 2NS; Tel 01604 407098
Headteacher Mrs G. Roy
(Day)
Mixed 3–5 Nursery provision SLD (28)

Henry Gotch Infant School Windmill Ave, Kettering, Northamptonshire NN15 7EA; Tel 01536 482462
Headteacher Heather Donoyou
Nursery provision for children with speech difficulties and language. (8)

Kingsthorpe Grove Primary School Kingsthorpe Gr, Northampton, Northamptonshire NN2 6NS; Tel 01604 714674
Headteacher Mrs J.E. Brothers
Severe communication difficulties (autism spectrum). (10)

Mereway Community College Mereway, Northampton, Northamptonshire NN4 8EJ; Tel 01604 702620; Fax 01604 701668
Headteacher Mike Hart
General and specific learning difficulties. (24)

Nicholas Hawksmoor Primary School Balmoral Cl, Towcester, Northamptonshire NN12 7JA; Tel 01327 351466
Headteacher R.F. Edwards
Nursery provision for children with specific speech and language difficulties. (8)

Queen Eleanor Primary School Queen Eleanor Rd, Northampton, Northamptonshire NN4 8NN; Tel 01604 761200
Headteacher Mrs K. Graystone
Resourced provision for deaf children whose main form of communication is British Sign Language. (6)

Simon de Senlis Primary School Hildrop Rd, East Hunsbury, Northampton, Northamptonshire NN4 0PH; Tel 01604 661011
Headteacher R.E. Sansom
MLD/SLD (15)

Southbrook Junior School Hawke Rd, Southbrook Est, Daventry, Northamptonshire NN11 4U; Tel 01327 703512
Headteacher Mrs J.M. Mitchell-Kings
7–11 Provision for children with general and specific learning difficulties. Also for children with communication difficulties. (10)

Southfield Primary School Banbury Rd, Brackley, Northamptonshire NN13 6AU; Tel 01280 709792
Headteacher David Norwood
General and specific learning difficulties. Also for children with communication difficulties. Nursery provision for children with specific speech and language difficulties. (14)

Spring Lane Primary School Spring La, Northampton, Northamptonshire NN1 2JW; Tel 01604 639114
Headteacher D.J. McAlpine
Speech and Language provision. (25)

Studfall Infant School Rowlett Rd, Corby, Northamptonshire NN17 2BP; Tel 01536 203524
Headteacher Mrs A. Brinkman
Provision for children with learning difficulties includes autism spectrum disorders. Resourced provision for deaf children whose main form of communication is British Sign Language. (21)

Studfall Junior School Rowlett Rd, Corby, Northamptonshire NN17 2BT; Tel 01536 202621
Headteacher P.S. Rangecroft
Provision for children with learning difficulties. Resourced provision for deaf children whose main form of communication is British Sign Language. (33)

Thorplands Primary School Farm Field Crt, Thorplands, Northampton, Northamptonshire NN3 8AQ; Tel 01604 493384
Headteacher Mrs M. Slaymaker
General and specific learning difficulties. (10)

Unity College Trinity Ave, Northampton, Northamptonshire NN2 6JW; Tel 01604 713621
Headteacher Sharon Goode
Hearing difficulties provision. (7)

Vernon Terrace Primary School Vernon Terr, Northampton, Northamptonshire NN1 5HE; Tel 01604 633894
Headteacher Mrs M. Starkey
Hearing difficulties provision. (7)

6

Whitehills Nursery School Acre La, Spring Pk,
Northampton, Northamptonshire NN2 8DF; Tel 01604
842957
Headteacher Jan Waller
Speech and language difficulties. (8)

EDUCATION ESTABLISHMENTS FOR PUPILS WITH SPECIAL NEEDS

Billing Brook School Penistone Rd, Lumbertubs,
Northampton, Northamptonshire NN3 4EZ; Tel 01604
773910
Headteacher D. Scott
Mixed 3–16 Learning difficulties/autism (Day) (144)

Fairfields School Trinity Ave, Northampton,
Northamptonshire NN2 6JN; Tel 01604 714777
Headteacher Mrs Coralie Murray
3–11 SLD/MLD/PMLD, Day (72)

Friars School Friar's Cl, Wellingborough,
Northamptonshire NN8 2LA; Tel 01933 304950
Headteacher Pat Norton
Mixed 11–16 Learning difficulties (Day) (140)

Greenfields School Harborough Rd, Northampton,
Northamptonshire NN2 8LR; Tel 01604 843657
Headteacher Mrs J. Moralee
Mixed 11–19 SLD/PMLD/autism (Day) (70)

Isebrook School Eastleigh Rd, Kettering,
Northamptonshire NN15 6PT; Tel 01536 503296; Fax 01536
503298
Headteacher K.J. McHenry
Mixed 11–16 Moderate learning difficulties/physical
handicap/autism. (Day) (82)

Kings Meadow School Manning Rd, Moulton Leys,
Northampton, Northamptonshire NN3 7XD; Tel 01604
673780
Headteacher B. Kettleborough
5–11 EBD, Day (40)

Kingsley School Churchill Way, Kettering,
Northamptonshire NN15 5DP; Tel 01536 316880 01536
516948; Fax 01536 415755
Headteacher Janet Thompson
Mixed 3–11 incl. 30 hospital and 28 neighbourhood
nursery Physically handicapped/autism/MLD/SLD/
PMLD/hospital provision (Day) (130)

Maplefields School School Pl, Gainsborough, Corby,
Northamptonshire NN18 0QP; Tel 01536 409040
Headteacher Mrs Morgan
4–11 EBD, Day (40)

Northgate School Queen's Park Pde, Northampton,
Northamptonshire NN2 6LR; Tel 01604 714098
Headteacher Rod Conway
Mixed 11–16 Learning difficulties (Day) (112)

The Orchard School Beatrice Rd, Kettering,
Northamptonshire NN16 9QR; Tel 01536 501430
Headteacher Mr. R. Barrett
Mixed 11–16 EBD (Day) (58)

Raeburn School Raeburn Rd, Northampton,
Northamptonshire NN2 7EU; Tel 01604 460017
Headteacher D. Lloyd
Mixed 11–16 EBD (Day) (50)

Wren Spinney Community Special School Westover Rd, off
Westhill Dr, Kettering, Northamptonshire NN15 0AP;
Tel 01536 481939
Headteacher Mrs D. Withers
3–19 SLD/PMLD/autism (Day) (60)

INCLUSION AND PUPIL SUPPORT SERVICE

Principal Educational Psychologist D.J. Lucas, BSc(Econ),
DipEdPsych

Daventry/South West Area Team Cliftonville Centre,
Cliftonville Middle School, Northampton,
Northamptonshire NN1 5BW; Tel 01604 636777; Fax 01604
636888

Area Team Leader and Senior Educational Psychologist
A. Cuthill

Kettering/Corby Area Team William Knibb Centre,
Montagu St, Kettering, Northamptonshire NN16 8AE
Area Co-ordinator Anne Hodson; Tel 01536 514244; 01536
82487; Fax 01536 414809

Northampton Area Team Springfield Cliftonville,
Northampton, Northamptonshire NN1 5BE; Tel 01604
630082 01604 632814; Fax 01604 630283
Area Co-ordinator Gary Sturgess

Wellingborough and North East Area Team Fairlawn Centre,
Spring Gdns, Wellingborough, Northamptonshire
NN8 2AA; Tel 01933 440289; Fax 01933 226744
Area Co-ordinator Anthea Raddan

UNITS FOR HEARING IMPAIRED CHILDREN

Avondale Infant School Laburnum Cres, Kettering,
Northamptonshire NN16 9PH; Tel 01536 512040
Headteacher B.A. Hunnable
Mixed 3–7 Hearing Impaired Day

Avondale Junior School Laburnum Cres, Kettering,
Northamptonshire NN16 9PH; Tel 01536 316860
Headteacher C.H. Jervis, BEd, ACP
Mixed 7–11 Hearing Impaired Day

Boothville Middle School Esher Crt, Northampton,
Northamptonshire NN3 3RG; Tel 01604 406746
Headteacher D. Atkinson
Mixed 9–13 Hearing Impaired Day

Latimer School Castle Way, Barton Seagrave, Kettering,
Northamptonshire NN15 6SW; Tel 01536 720300
Headteacher C. Grimshaw
Mixed 11–18 Hearing Impaired Day

Trinity School Trinity Ave, Northampton,
Northamptonshire NN2 6JW; Tel 01604 713621
Headteacher M.R. Hart, MA
Mixed 13–18 Hearing Impaired Day

NORTHUMBERLAND COUNTY COUNCIL
www.northumberland.gov.uk

Population 310 000
Political Composition: Lab: 38, Con: 17, LD: 9, Ind: 3
County Hall, Morpeth, Northumberland NE61 2EF;
URL www.northumberland.gov.uk; Tel 01670 533000;
Fax 01670 533253
Chair of the County Council Ian Swithenbank
Chief Executive Alan Clarke
Director (Finance) Clive Burns
County Manager (Planning and Environment) H.A. Fawcett

Northumberland Care Trust and Social Services Department

Tel 01670 533824 Emergency Tel (Out-of-office hours) 0845
6005252; Fax 01670 533892; Minicom 01670 515131
Director (Social Services) E. Hill
Divisional Director (Children's Division)
Jan Van Wagtendonk

Northumberland Care Trust

Social Care and Planning Directorate, Merley Croft,
Loansdean, Morpeth, Northumberland NE61 2DL;
Tel 01670 394400; Fax 01670 394501
Director (Social and Planning) David Parkin

BLYTH VALLEY LOCALITY DIRECTORATE

Richard Stannard Hse, 40 Bridge St, Blyth,
Northumberland NE24 2AG; Tel 01670 782300;
Fax 01670 782303

CENTRAL NORTHUMBERLAND LOCALITY DIRECTORATE

Wansbeck Bus Pk, Rotary Pk, Ashington, Northumberland
NE63 8QZ; Tel 01670 394700; Fax 01670 394709

NORTH LOCALITY DIRECTORATE

Lee Moor Bus Pk, Rennington, Alnwick, Northumberland
NE66 3RL; Tel 01665 572200; Fax 01665 572112

WEST LOCALITY DIRECTORATE

The Courtyard, Hexham General Hospital, Hexham,
Northumberland NE46 1QJ; Tel 01434 656200; Fax 01434
656202

TRAINING

Responsible for training professional and support staff in
the department.
*Principal Officer (Training and Staff Development, Social
Services)* E. Phillips
Staff Development Unit, Hansbeck Hse, Morpeth,
Northumberland NE61 2NF; Tel 01670 534435
*Principal Officer (Training and Staff Development,
Northumbrland Care Trust)* J. Jennison

Executive Member: Primary Health and Social Care

Executive Member L.B. Smith
48 Terrier Cl, Bedlington, Northumberland NE22 5JR;
Tel 01670 825186
Portfolio Assistant T.S. Wilson
122 Disraeli St, Blyth, Northumberland NE24 1JB; Tel 01670
364765
Community health, the elderly, disabled adults, health
partnerships, community care, welfare rights.

Executive Member: Childrens Services

Executive Member J. Wright
Portfolio Assistant J.M. Carlin
Children's mainstream school services, pre-school
education, school children with disabilities, family services,
youth services, training and vocational education, non-
vocational education, Sure Start, youth offending, adoption
and permanency.

DISTRICT OFFICES

Central Division

Ashington District Office South View, Ashington,
Northumberland NE63 0SF; Tel 01670 815060
Manager (Children's Services) Guy Kirk

Bedlington District Office 1 Beech Gr, Bedlington,
Northumberland NE22 5DA; Tel 01670 822423

Morpeth District Office 94 Newgate St, Morpeth,
Northumberland NE61 1BU; Tel 01670 516131
Service Manager Russ Stamp

Newbiggin District Office Gisbon St, Newbiggin-by-the-Sea,
Northumberland NE64 6UZ; Tel 01670 810600

North Division

Alnwick District Office 38 Green Batt, Alnwick,
Northumberland NE66 1TU; Tel 01665 603411

Berwick District Office Waltergate, Berwick,
Northumberland TD15 1DB; Tel 01289 334000

South Division

Blyth District Office Compass Hse, 68 Bridge St, Blyth,
Northumberland NE24 2SA; Tel 01670 354316
Service Manager Dennis Gibson

Cramlington District Office Civic Precinct, Forum Way,
Cramlington, Northumberland NE23 6SH; Tel 01670
712925
Manager (Children's Services) Vacancy

West Division

Hexham District Office Priory Bldgs, Beaumont St,
Hexham, Northumberland NE46 3NE; Tel 01434 603582
Manager (Children's Services) Denis Robinson

Prudhoe District Office Oaklands Hse, Front St, Prudhoe,
Northumberland NE42 5DQ; Tel 01661 832758

HOSPITAL SOCIAL WORKERS

Alnwick Infirmary

Berwick Infirmary Berwick-upon-Tweed, Northumberland
TD15 1LT; Tel 01289 307484

Blyth Community Hospital Thoroton St, Blyth,
Northumberland NE24 5TR; Tel 01670 396400

Hexham General Hospital Hexham, Northumberland
NE46 1QJ; Tel 01434 655655

Morpeth Cottage Hospital Gt North Rd, Morpeth,
Northumberland NE61 2BT; Tel 01670 395600

Northgate Hospital Morpeth, Northumberland NE61 3BP;
Tel 01670 394000

Prudhoe Hospital Prudhoe, Northumberland NE42 5NT;
Tel 01670 394000

St. George's Hospital Morpeth, Northumberland
NE61 2NU; Tel 01670 512121

Wansbeck General Hospital Woodhorn La, Ashington,
Northumberland NE63 9JJ; Tel 01670 521212

COMMUNITY HOMES

Allerhope Home 65 Allerhope, Cramlington,
Northumberland; Tel 01670 713627
Unit Manager Andy Campbell

Reavley Avenue Home 21 Reavley Ave, Bedlington,
Northumberland; Tel 01670 823167
Unit Manager Steve Williamson

Thornbrae Community Home Alnmouth Rd, Alnwick,
Northumberland NE66 2PS; Tel 01665 602687
Unit Manager C. Woonton

RESIDENTIAL ESTABLISHMENT FOR CHILDREN

Netherton Park Community Home and School Stannington,
Morpeth, Northumberland NE61 6DE; Tel 01670 785959
Manager Yvonne Martin

INTERMEDIATE TREATMENT

Riverside Centre Youth Offending Team North Seaton Ind
Est, Ashington, Northumberland NE63 0YB; Tel 01670
852225
Contact Geoff Buckley

TRAINING CENTRES FOR ADULTS WITH LEARNING DISABILITIES

Alnwick Adult Training Centre Howling La, Alnwick,
Northumberland NE66 1DJ; Tel 01665 602181
Unit Manager Stephanie Stafford

Berwick Adult Training Centre St. Mary's Castlegate,
Berwick, Northumberland TD15 1JT; Tel 01289 305105
Unit Manager Claire O'Gorman

6

Blyth Adult Training Centre Kitty Brewster Trading Est, Blyth, Northumberland NE24 4RG; Tel 01670 353276
Unit Manager Sean Brennan

Cramlington Adult Training Centre Blyth Rd, South Nelson Ind Est, Cramlington, Northumberland NE23 9HL; Tel 01670 717701
Unit Manager Peter Douglas

Hexham Adult Training Centre Haugh Lane Ind Est, Hexham, Northumberland NE46 3PU; Tel 01434 605245
Unit Manager Christine Hope

RESIDENTIAL ESTABLISHMENTS FOR PERSONS WITH LEARNING DISABILITIES

Alnbank Home Alnmouth Rd, Alnwick, Northumberland NE66 2PR; Tel 01665 603584
Unit Manager Dot Kent

Glebe Road Home 69 Glebe Rd, Bedlington, Northumberland NE22 6JT; Tel 01670 823831
Unit Manager Cynthia Pegg
(26)

DAY CARE ESTABLISHMENTS

Amble Day Centre Charles Rd, Amble, Northumberland NE65 0RA; Tel 01665 710829
Manager M. Silverton

Bedlington Day Centre Town Centre, Bedlington, Northumberland NE22 5UQ; Tel 01670 823728
Manager Tony Lundy

Foundry House Day Centre The Oval, Stead La, Bedlington, Northumberland NE22 5HS; Tel 01670 536401
Manager Dawn Hill

Greenholme Day Centre Haltwhistle, Northumberland NE49 9DP; Tel 01434 321494
Unit Manager Christine North

Ponteland Day Centre Callerton La, Ponteland, Northumberland NE20 9EY; Tel 01661 820385
Manager Anne Craggs

Tynedale House Day Centre Tynedale Dr, Blyth, Northumberland NE24 4LH; Tel 01670 364660
Unit Manager Malcolm Fairbairn

HORTICULTURAL SKILLS UNIT

Hepscott Pk, Stannington, Morpeth, Northumberland NE61 6NF; Tel 01670 511463
Contact Clive Moon

MEALS SERVICE

Age Concern Wansbeck Business Centre, Wansbeck Bus Pk, Rotary Way, Ashington, Northumberland NE63 8QZ; Tel 01670 528220

WRVS Suite 2, Hubbway Hse, Bassington La, Cramlington, Northumberland NE23 8AD; Tel 01670 700910

Education Directorate

County Hall, Morpeth, Northumberland NE61 2EF; Tel 01670 533000; Fax 01670 533605 01670 533750
Director (Education) B. Edwards (Acting)
Senior Education Officer D.M. Jenkins
Senior Education Officer J.P. Clark
Senior Education Officer M.J. Trimming
Senior Education Officer M.A. Tomkinson
Finance Officer A. Mason
Adviser (Special Needs) S. Pinner

EDUCATION WELFARE OFFICES

County Hall, Morpeth, Northumberland NE61 2EF; Tel 01670 533000; Fax 01670 533750
Principal Education Welfare Officer M.R. Macdonald

Alnwick Education Welfare Office 54 Bondgate Within, Alnwick, Northumberland NE66 1JD; Tel 01665 605428; Fax 01665 606121
Senior Education Welfare Officer M.F. Forrest

Blyth Education Welfare Office 107a Waterloo Rd, Blyth, Northumberland NE24 1AD; Tel 01670 361874; Fax 01670 369236
Senior Education Welfare Officer L.M. McAvoy

Hexham Education Welfare Office The Gatehouse, Wanless La, Hexham, Northumberland NE46 1BU; Tel 01434 605973; Fax 01434 600357
Senior Education Welfare Officer S. Lister

Morpeth Education Welfare Office Newgate Hse, 94 Newgate St, Morpeth, Northumberland NE61 1BU; Tel 01670 511474; Fax 01670 517616
Senior Education Welfare Officer A. Cunningham

PSYCHOLOGICAL SERVICES

Tyne House Hepscott Pk, Stannington, Morpeth, Northumberland NE61 6NF; Tel 01670 534300; Fax 01670 534327
Principal Educational Psychologist B.V. Daly
Senior Educational Psychologist J. Taylor

SPECIAL SCHOOLS

Atkinson House School Pit La, Seghill, Cramlington, Northumberland NE23 7EB; Tel 0191 298 0838; Fax 0191 298 0448
Headteacher R. McGlashan
Boys 11–16

Barndale House School Barndale Hse, Howling La, Alnwick, Northumberland NE66 1DQ; Tel 01665 602541; Fax 01665 606370
Headteacher J.P. Chappells, BA
Mixed 5–16 (30)

Cleaswell Hill School School Ave, Guide Post, Choppington, Northumberland NE62 5DJ; Tel 01670 823182; Fax 01670 823182
Headteacher R. Hope
Mixed 4–16

Cramlington Hillcrest School East View Ave, East Farm, Cramlington, Northumberland NE23 1DY; Tel 01670 713632; Fax 01670 737920
Headteacher C. Gibson
Mixed 10–16

The Grove School Grove Gdns, Tweedmouth, Berwick-upon-Tweed, Northumberland TD15 2EN; Tel 01289 306390; Fax 01289 306994
Headteacher E. Brown
Mixed 5–16

Hexham Hackwood Park School Gallows Bank, Hexham, Northumberland NE46 1AU; Tel 01434 604039; Fax 01434 604039
Headteacher J. Wells
Mixed 4–16

Hexham Priory School Dene Pk, Hexham, Northumberland NE46 1HN; Tel 01434 605021; Fax 01434 609022
Headteacher M. Thompson
Mixed 3–16

Morpeth Collingwood School Stobhillgate, Morpeth, Northumberland NE61 2HA; Tel 01670 516374; Fax 01670 510973
Headteacher C. Hetherington
Mixed

SCHOOLS RESOURCED FOR CHILDREN WITH LEARNING DIFFICULTIES

Abbeyfields County First School Abbots Way, Morpeth, Northumberland NE61 2LZ; Tel 01670 513582

Berwick County High School Adams Dr, Berwick-upon-Tweed, Northumberland TD15 2JF; Tel 01289 305083; Fax 01289 302681

Berwick County Middle School Lovaine Terr, Berwick-upon-Tweed, Northumberland TD15 1LA; Tel 01289 306140; Fax 01289 306140

Berwick St. Mary's C of E Controlled First School Newfields Est, Berwick-upon-Tweed, Northumberland TD15 1SP; Tel 01289 306170

Hirst County High School Lichfield Cl, Ashington, Northumberland NE63 9RX; Tel 01670 816111; Fax 01670 522565

Seaton Hirst County Middle School Norwich Cl, Ashington, Northumberland NE63 9SA; Tel 01670 815444; Fax 01670 853199

Dr Thomlinson's C.E. Special Agreement Middle School Silverton La, Rothbury, Morpeth, Northumberland NE65 7RH; Tel 01669 620287; Fax 01669 621919

SERVICES FOR COMMUNICATION DISORDERED PUPILS

Till House Centre Hepscott Pk, Morpeth, Northumberland NE61 6NF; Tel 01670 534344; Fax 01670 534343
Head of Service S. Grigor

UNITS FOR COMMUNICATION DISORDERED PUPILS

Abbeyfields County First School Abbots Way, Morpeth, Northumberland NE61 2LZ; Tel 01670 513582

Hexham East County First School Beaufront Ave, Hexham, Northumberland NE46 1JD; Tel 01434 603467; Fax 01434 603467

CENTRES AND UNITS FOR HEARING-IMPAIRED CHILDREN

Blyth Horton Grange First School Blyth, Northumberland NE24 4RE; Tel 01670 353503; Fax 01670 354276

Cramlington County High School Highburn, Cramlington, Northumberland NE23 6BN; Tel 01670 712311; Fax 01670 730598

Southlands County Middle School Westloch Rd, Cramlington, Northumberland NE23 6LW; Tel 01670 714475; Fax 01670 734968

Till House Hepscott Pk, Stannington, Morpeth, Northumberland NE61 6NF; Tel 01670 534313; Fax 01670 534343
Head of Service P. Loftus

OUTDOOR EDUCATION CENTRE

Ford Castle Residential Centre Ford, Berwick-upon-Tweed, Northumberland TD15 2PX; Tel 01890 820257

REGIONAL SERVICE FOR VISUALLY IMPAIRED CHILDREN

Firfield Community High School, Firfield Rd, Newcastle upon Tyne, Tyne and Wear NE5 3HU; Tel 0191 286 3211
Head of Service D. Robson

NOTTINGHAM CITY COUNCIL
www.nottinghamcity.gov.uk

In April 1998 Nottingham City Council became a unitary authority. The rest of Nottinghamshire retains a two-tier structure and is listed alphabetically within this chapter.
Population 284 300
Political Composition: Lab: 40, Con: 11, LD: 4
The Guildhall, Nottingham NG1 4BT;
URL www.nottinghamcity.gov.uk; Tel 0115 915 5555; Fax 0115 915 4636
Chief Executive Vacancy

Social Services Department

14 Hounds Gate, Nottingham NG1 7BE; Tel 0115 915 5500; (Emergency Team) 0115 915 9299; Fax 0115 915 7014
Director (Social Services) Paul Snell
Assistant Director (Children and Families (Asssessment)) Sue Gregory (Acting)
Assistant Director (Children and Families (Resources)) Margaret Mackechnie
Assistant Director (Planning and Policy) Brian Cox
Assistant Director (Adult Services) Paul Slade
Head (Support Services) Jeff Grant

Lead Member

Lab: 11, Con: 3, LD: 1
Executive Member (Housing and Social Care) D. Trimble (Lab)
The Council Hse, The Market Sq, Nottingham NG1 2DT
Chair (Social Care Policy Development and Review) Vacancy

TRAINING

Responsible for training professional and support staff in the Department Staff Development Unit.
14 Hounds Gate, Nottingham NG1 7BE; Tel 0115 915 5500
Head (Staff Development) Sanbjit Hayre

MEDICAL SOCIAL WORK DEPARTMENTS

City Hospital Valebrook Hse, Hucknall Rd, Nottingham NG5 1PB; Tel 0115 969 1169; Fax 0115 962 7686
Manager (Hospital Services) M. Bravant

Harvey Court Queen's Medical Centre, Social Work Dept, Nottingham NG7 2UH; Tel 0115 924 9924; Fax 0155 942 3180
Manager (Hospital Social Services) Lis Henry
Manager (Hospital Social Services) Vacancy

SOCIAL WORK OFFICES – CHILDREN AND FAMILIES

Bridgeway Centre 1 Bridgeway Centre, The Meadows, Nottingham NG2 2JG; Tel 0115 915 5500

City Hospital – Children and Families City Hospital, Social Work Department, Nottingham NG5 1PB; Tel 0115 969 1169; Fax 0115 962 7755
Service Manager Andrew Brunt
Harvey Crt, University Hospital, Queens Medical Centre, Nottingham NG7 2UH

The Clocktower 8–22 Commercial Rd, Bulwell, Nottingham NG6 8HA; Tel 0115 915 5500

Gilead Street Office 1 Gilead St, Bullwell, Nottingham NG6 8NA; Tel 0115 915 5500

Players Court Player St, Radford, Nottingham NG7 5LZ; Tel 0115 915 5500

Queens Medical Centre – Children and Families University Hospital, Queens Medical Centre, Nottingham NG7 2UH; Tel 0115 924 9924; Fax 0115 942 3180
Service Manager Andrew Brunt
Harvey Crt, University Hospital, Queens Medical Centre, Nottingham NE7 2UH

York House 2nd Fl, Mansfield Rd, Nottingham NG1 3NS; Tel 0115 915 5500

FOSTERING AND ADOPTION

Mansfield Road 126 Mansfield Rd, Nottingham NG1 3HL; Tel 0115 915 5500

York House 2nd Fl, Mansfield Rd, Nottingham NG1 3NS; Tel 0115 915 5500

SUPPORT AFTER ADOPTION

Strelley Road 14 Strelley Rd, Nottingham; Tel 0115 915 5500

SOCIAL WORK OFFICES – ADULTS

Ashbourne House 49 Forest Road East, Nottingham NG1 4HT; Tel 0115 915 5500

Manor Farm 45 Strelley Rd, Nottingham NG8 1PN; Tel 0115 915 5500

Mansfield Road Office 136 Mansfield Rd, Nottingham NG1 3HL; Tel 0115 915 5500

Medway Street Radford, Nottingham NG8 1PN; Tel 0115 915 5500

CHILDREN AND FAMILIES AREA TEAMS

Abbey, Clifton East and West, and Wilford Team York Hse, 2nd Fl, Mansfield Rd, Nottingham NG1 3NS
Service Manager Pete McEntee; Tel 0115 915 5500

Aspley Team 387 Woodborough Rd, Nottingham NG3 5GX
Service Manager Tracey Newcomb (Acting); Tel 0115 915 5500

Basford and Bestwood Team The Denewood Centre, Denewood Cres, Bilborough, Nottingham NG8 3DH
Service Manager Pat O'Brien
Clock Tower, Bulwell, Nottingham; Tel 0115 915 5500

Bilborough, Beechdale and Wollaton Team The Denewood Centre, Denewood Cres, Bilborough, Nottingham NG8 3DH
Service Manager Tracey Newcomb (Acting); Tel 0115 915 5500

Bulwell East and West Team 1 Gilead St, Bulwell, Nottingham NG6 8NA
Service Manager Pat O'Brien
Clock Tower, Bulwell, Nottingham; Tel 0115 915 5500

Byron and Portland Team The Clock Tower, 18–22 Commercial Rd, Bulwell, Nottingham NG6 3HA
Service Manager Pat O'Brien; Tel 0115 915 5500

Central Duty Team Players Crt, Player St, Radford, Nottingham NG7 5LZ
Service Manager Tracey Newcomb (Acting); Tel 0115 915 5500

Forest, Mapperley and Sherwood Team The Denewood Centre, Denewood Cres, Bilborough, Nottingham NG8 3DH
Contact Pat O'Brien; Tel 0115 915 5500

Greenwood and Trent Team 126 Mansfield Rd, Nottingham NG1 3HL
Service Manager Pete McEntee; Tel 0115 915 5500

Lenton, Park and Bridge Team 1 Bridgeway Centre, The Meadows, Nottingham NG2 2JG; Tel 0115 915 5500
Service Manager Pete McEntee; Tel 0115 915 5500

Radford and Robin Hood Team York Hse, 2nd Fl, Mansfield Rd, Nottingham NG1 3NS
Service Manager Tracey Newcomb (Acting); Tel 0115 915 5500

St. Anns and Manvers Team 126 Mansfield Rd, Nottingham NG1 3HL
Service Manager Pete McEntee; Tel 0115 915 5500

Strelley Team The Denewood Centre, Denewood Cres, Bilborough, Nottingham NG8 3DH
Service Manager Tracey Newcomb (Acting); Tel 0115 915 5500

FAMILY CENTRES

Arnold Road Family Centre 514 Arnold Rd, Nottingham NG5 5HN; Tel 0115 967 0032
Manager Yvonne Tait

Bulwell Family Centre 22 Main St, Bulwell, Nottingham NG6 8QL; Tel 0115 927 8851
Manager Susan Parker

Garden Street Family Centre Garden St, Nottingham NG7 3HD; Tel 0115 978 2253
Manager Angela Daniel

Highwood Family Centre Beechdale Rd, Nottingham NG8 3AJ; Tel 0115 915 3144
Manager Isalyn Martin

Larkdale Contact Centre North Sherwood St, Nottingham NG1 4EZ; Tel 0115 947 0351
Manager Claudette McLennon

St. Ann's Family Centre Magson Cl, St. Ann's, Nottingham NG3 2GW; Tel 0115 958 1847
Manager Audrey Taylor

Sherwood Family Centre Spondon St, Nottingham NG5 4AB; Tel 0115 960 5346
Manager Sue Moore

Trent Family Centre Castlefields, The Meadow, Nottingham NG2 1HN; Tel 0115 986 0616; Fax 0115 986 0616
Manager Denise Phillips

CHILDREN'S COMMUNITY HOMES

Farmlands 12a Ranskill Gdns, Nottingham NG5 9DX; Tel 0115 915 9500

Hamilton Court Children's Home 23 Vivian Ave, Nottingham NG5 1AU; Tel 0115 915 9031

Red Tiles 9 Beckhampton Rd, Nottingham NG5 5SP; Tel 0115 967 6172

Wollaton House Children's Home 43 Radford Bridge Rd, Nottingham NG8 1NB; Tel 0115 928 1689

Woodborough Road Children's Home 387 Woodborough Rd, Nottingham NG3 5GX; Tel 0115 915 7537

Wood Nook Children's Home 229 Beechdale Rd, Nottingham NG8 3EZ; Tel 0115 915 7607

RESIDENTIAL ESTABLISHMENT FOR CHILDREN WITH LEARNING DIFFICULTIES

Crocus Fields Arkwright Wlk, Meadows, Nottingham NG2 2HN; Tel 0115 915 3884
Service Manager Ted Townsend

YOUTH COURT SERVICES

Youth Offending Team 2 Isabella St, Nottingham NG1 6AT; Tel 0115 841 3008

CHILDREN AND YOUNG PEOPLE DISABILITY REGISTER

The Lindens 379 Woodborough Rd, Nottingham; Tel 0115 977 2547

OCCUPATIONAL THERAPY SERVICE

City Division (East) 45–47 Gregory Blvd, Nottingham; Tel 0115 915 5500

City Division (West) 2 Teams, Medway St, Radford, Nottingham NG8 1PN; Tel 0115 915 5500

DAY CENTRES FOR OLDER PEOPLE

Aidan Lion Day Centre Brambel Cl, Nottingham NG6 0QG; Tel 0115 978 0875

Fairham Day Centre Fairham Community College, Farnborough Rd, Clifton, Nottingham NG11 9AE; Tel 0115 974 4409

Long Meadows Day Centre Meadows Way, Nottingham NG2 3DZ; Tel 0115 986 9205

Nuffield House Day Centre 16 Claremont Rd, Nottingham NG5 1BH; Tel 0115 960 4970

Silver Birches Day Centre Zulu Rd, New Basford, Nottingham NG7 7EH; Tel 0115 978 2347

Wollaton Grange Day Centre Tremayne Rd, Nottingham NG8 4HQ; Tel 0115 928 9768

DAY CENTRES FOR OLDER PEOPLE – ATTACHED UNITS

Cherry Trees Resource Centre Fairlight Way, Nottingham NG5 5SZ; Tel 0115 926 5547

Oak Leaves Day Centre Acorn Day Centre, Dalkeith Terr, Nottingham NG7 5JG; Tel 0115 970 0558

The Oaks Day Centre Campbell St, St. Ann's, Nottingham NG3 1GZ; Tel 0115 950 3134

Willows Day Centre Ambergate Rd, Nottingham NG8 3GD; Tel 0115 929 3861

INDEPENDENT LIVING TEAM

Medway Street Radford, Nottingham NG8 1PN; Tel 0115 915 5500

VISUAL IMPAIRMENT TEAM

Middle Pavement 15 Middle Pavement, Nottingham; Tel 0115 950 2517

DEAF SERVICES TEAM

Goldsmith Street 4th Fl, 13 Goldsmith St, Nottingham; Tel 0115 947 5729
Service Manager Andrew Bount

DAY CENTRES FOR ADULTS WITH LEARNING DISABILITIES

Bestwood Day Centre Bestwood Rd, Nottingham NG6 8SS; Tel 0115 927 8345
Manager D. Boulton
(130)

Springwood Day Centre Ramson Dr, Mapperley, Nottingham NG3 5LR; Tel 0115 962 2611
Manager Maddie Lonergan (Acting)
SCU 25

RESIDENTIAL ESTABLISHMENTS FOR ADULTS WITH LEARNING DIFFICULTIES

Riverside Coventry Rd, Bulwell, Nottingham NG6 8RA; Tel 0115 927 7418
Manager M. Rickett
(26)

Woodborough Road Home 10 Woodborough Rd, Nottingham; Tel 0115 915 5500
Service Manager Ted Townsend

DAY CENTRE FOR ADULTS WITH PHYSICAL DISABILITIES

Acorn/Oak Leaves Day Centre Dalkeith Terr, Hyson Grn, Nottingham NG7 5JG; Tel 0115 915 5500
Manager Linda Silk

DAY CENTRE FOR ADULTS WITH MENTAL HEALTH PROBLEMS

Open Door Day Centre 19 Victoria Embankment, Nottingham NG2 2JY; Tel 0115 915 5500

COMMUNITY LEARNING DISABILITY TEAMS

Community Learning Disability Team East Hyson Green Office, 41 Gregory Blvd, Nottingham NG7 4HT; Tel 0115 915 5500

Community Learning Disability Team North Ashbourne Hse, 49 Forest Road East, Nottingham NG1 4HT; Tel 0115 915 5500

Community Learning Disability Team West Ashbourne Hse, 49 Forest Road East, Nottingham NG1 4HT; Tel 0115 915 5500

COMMUNITY MENTAL HEALTH TEAMS

Broxtowe Community Mental Health Team The Hope Centre, Dovecote Hse, Nottingham NG9 2NR; Tel 0115 943 0456

East and Carlton Community Mental Health Team Stonebridge Centre, Carlton Rd, Nottingham NG3 2FH; Tel 0115 948 3268

North and Hucknall Community Mental Health Team Rosebery Hse, Waterford St, Nottingham; Tel 0115 942 1414
Contact L. Metcalfe

North East and Arnold Community Mental Health Team Mandala Centre, Gregory Blvd, Nottingham; Tel 0115 960 6082

NOTTINGHAMSHIRE SIGN LANGUAGE INTERPRETING SERVICE

22 Forest Road West, Nottingham; Tel 0115 978 6984; Fax 0115 942 3729; Minicom 0115 978 6881

RESIDENTIAL ESTABLISHMENTS FOR OLDER PEOPLE

There are 12 residential establishments for older people.

Education Department

Sandfield Centre, Sandfield Rd, Lenton, Nottingham NG7 1QH; URL nottinghamcity.gov.uk/education; E-mail education@nottinghamcity.gov.uk
Director (Education) Heather Tomlinson
Special Schools
6 Day; 3 Hospital Schools

HOSPITAL EDUCATION

City Hospital Education Base Hucknall Rd, Nottingham NG5 1PB; Tel 0115 962 7600; Fax 0115 962 7931
Contact Roger Stephenson

Queens Medical Centre Education Base E Fl, East Block, Nottingham NG7 2UH; Tel 0115 970 9753; Fax 0115 924 4292
Contact Hazel Hoskins

Thorneywood Hospital Education Base Fairmead Cl, The Wells Rd, Nottingham NG3 3AL; Tel 0115 915 3862; Fax 0115 915 3863
Contact Paul Hickling

Inclusion Nottingham City Council, Sandfield Centre, Nottingham NG7 1QH; Tel 0115 915 0710; Fax 0115 915 0603

SPECIAL SCHOOLS

Aspley Wood School Robins Wood Rd, Aspley, Nottingham NG8 3LD; Tel 0115 913 1400 0115 913 1401; Fax 0115 913 1404
Headteacher B. Mole
Mixed All ages PH (Day) (17)

Nethergate School Swansdowne Rd, Clifton, Nottingham NG11 8HX; Tel 0115 915 2959; Fax 0115 915 2958
Headteacher S. Johnson-Marshall
Mixed All ages MLD (Day) (55)

Rosehill School St. Matthias Rd, St. Ann's, Nottingham NG3 2FE; Tel 0115 915 5815; Fax 0115 915 5816
Headteacher J.K. Pearson
Mixed All ages MLD + secondary autistic unit (Day) (33)

Shepherd School Harvey Rd, Bilborough, Nottingham NG8 3BB; URL www.shepherdschool.org.uk; Tel 0115 915 3265; Fax 0115 915 3264
Headteacher D.S. Stewart, BA(Hons)
All ages SLD (Day) (72)

Westbury Special School Chingford Rd, Bilborough, Nottingham NG8 3BT; Tel 0115 915 5858; Fax 0115 915 5857
Headteacher John Dyson
10–16 (Day)

6

Woodlands School Beechdale Rd, Aspley, Nottingham NG8 3EZ; Tel 0115 915 5734; 0115 915 5735; Fax 0115 915 5736
Headteacher S. Fee
Mixed All Ages MLD (Day) (121)

NOTTINGHAMSHIRE COUNTY COUNCIL
www.nottscc.gov.uk

Nottinghamshire County Council retains a two-tier structure but on 1 April 1998 Nottingham City Council became a unitary authority and is listed alphabetically within this chapter.
Population 748 300
Political Composition: Lab: 39, Con: 21, LD: 3
County Hall, West Bridgford, Nottingham NG2 7QP; URL www.nottscc.gov.uk; Tel 0115 982 3823; Fax 0115 981 7945
Chief Executive R. Latham
Director (Resources) A. Deakin
Director (Environment) Peter Webster
Trent Bridge Hse, Fox Rd, Nottingham, Nottinghamshire NG2 2JT; Tel 0115 982 3823; Fax 0115 945 5113

Social Services Department

County Hall, West Bridgford, Nottingham NG2 7QP; E-mail communications.ssd@nottscc.gov.uk; Tel (Emergency) 0115 844 7333; 0115 982 3823
Director (Social Services) R.S. Brook
Assistant Director (Commissioning – Adults) M. Dillon
Assistant Director (Resources) D. Pearson
Assistant Director (Direct Services – Children and Families) M. Eaden
Assistant Director (Commissioning – Children and Families) J. Pedley
Assistant Director (Direct Services – Adults) Vacancy
Assistant Director (Mental Health and Learning Disability) Joy Cooper

TRAINING

Responsible for training professional and support staff in the department.
Staff Development Unit, Ludlow Hse, West Bridgford, Nottingham NG2 6HF; Tel 0115 945 2764
Head (Staff Development) Judith Horsfall

Cabinet

Lab: 10
Chair M. Warner (Lab)
Vice-Chair D. Kirkham (Lab)
Members of the Cabinet
Lab: J.E. Anthony, C.J. Bromfield, T. Butler, J. Carter, D.J. Kirkham, V. Smailes, J. Stocks, M. Storey, M. Warner, C. Winterton.

LOCAL OFFICES

Ashfield Office

Meadow Hse, Littleworth, Mansfield, Nottinghamshire NG18 2TB; Tel 01623 433433
Locality Manager (Children and Families) N. Hanson

Bassetlaw Office

The Hurst, Cheapside, Worksop, Nottinghamshire S80 2HX; Tel 01909 472220
Locality Manager (Adults) D. Whitham

Broxtowe Office

Broadgate Hse, Humber Rd, Beeston, Nottinghamshire NG9 2EF; Tel 0115 917 5800

Gedling Office

Sir John Robinson Way, Arnold, Nottinghamshire NG5 6DB; Tel 0115 854 6000
Locality Manager (Adults) J. Lawson

Mansfield Office

Meadow Hse, Littleworth, Mansfield, Nottinghamshire NG18 2TB; Tel 01623 433433
Locality Manager (Adults) Paul McKay

Newark Office

20 Balderton Gate, Newark, Nottinghamshire NG24 1UW; Tel 01636 682700
Locality Manager (Children and Families) H. Ryan

Rushcliffe

The Hall, West Bridgford, Nottingham NG2 6AD; Tel 0115 914 1500
Locality Manager (Children and Families) C. Jones

CUSTOMER RELATIONS SERVICE

Melrose House Waverley St, Nottingham NG7 4HF; Tel 0115 979 1125
Head (Customer Relations Service) J. Pidgeon

MEDICAL SOCIAL WORK DEPARTMENTS

Ashfield Community Hospital Social Work Department, Portland St, Kikby-in-Ashfield, Nottinghamshire NG17 7AE; Tel 01623 784741; Fax 01623 784798

Bassetlaw District General Hospital Social Work Department, Kilton Hill, Worksop, Nottinghamshire S81 0BD; Tel 01909 500990; Fax 01909 480121

City Hospital Valebrook Hse, Hucknall Rd, Nottingham NG5 1PB; Tel 0115 840 5816

King's Mill Centre Mansfield Rd, Sutton-in-Ashfield, Nottinghamshire NG17 4JL; Tel 01623 622515; Fax 01623 627584
Team Manager M. Gregory

Mansfield Community Hospital Social Work Department, Stockwell Gate, Mansfield, Nottinghamshire NG18 5QJ; Tel 01623 785031; Fax 01623 785184

Newark Hospital Social Work Department, Boundary Rd, Newark, Nottinghamshire NG24 4DE; Tel 01636 681681; Fax 01636 685740

Queen's Medical Centre Social Work Department, Harvey Crt, Nottingham NG7 2UH; Tel 0115 924 9924; Fax 0115 924 3180

FAMILY CENTRES

Albion Centre Albion Cl, Worksop, Nottinghamshire S80 1RA; Tel 01909 475602

Beeston Family Centre Trevor Rd, Beeston, Nottinghamshire NG9 1GR; Tel 0115 925 6839

Dukeries Centre for Families Whinney La, New Ollerton, Newark, Nottinghamshire NG22 9TD; Tel 01623 862363

Eastwood Drop-in-Centre 1a Seymour Rd, Eastwood, Nottingham NG16 3ND; Tel 01773 535839

Gedling View Family Centre Church View, Gedling, Nottingham NG4 3HW; Tel 0115 961 8898

Kirkby Nursery Centre off Abbey Rd, Coxmoor Est, Kirkby-in-Ashfield, Nottinghamshire NG17 7NR; Tel 01623 462506

Newark Family Centre Gladstone Rd, Newark, Nottinghamshire NG24 4HZ; Tel 01636 610171

Sandy Bank Family Centre Bilborough Rd, Mansfield, Nottinghamshire NG18 2NZ; Tel 01623 631101

Spring Street Family Centre Spring St, Hucknall, Nottingham NG15 7BZ; Tel 0115 964 0513

Sutton Nursery Centre Westbourne View, Sutton-in-Ashfield, Nottinghamshire NG17 2HT; Tel 01623 450464

Swan Lane Family Centre Swan La, Mansfield Woodhouse, Mansfield, Nottinghamshire NG19 8BT; Tel 01623 420113

CHILDREN'S COMMUNITY HOMES

The Big House Church St, Edwinstowe, Nottinghamshire NG21 9QA; Tel 01623 822453
Respite care unit

Caudwell House Children's Home Upton Rd, Southwell, Nottinghamshire NG25 0PT; Tel 01636 813170

Ivy Lodge The Ridge, The Park, Mansfield, Nottinghamshire NG18 2AT; Tel 01623 622933

Lawn Place 2a Sandown Rd, Sutton-in-Ashfield, Nottinghamshire NG17 4LW; Tel 01623 555890

Minister View Children's Home Upton Rd, Southwell, Nottinghamshire NG25 0PT; Tel 01636 815450

Woodland View 28 Sparken Hill, Worksop, Nottinghamshire S80 1AP; Tel 01909 472679

MISCELLANEOUS CHILDREN'S UNITS

Adoption and Fostering Unit The Lindens, 379 Woodborough Rd, Nottingham NG3 5GX; Tel 0115 977 3459

Shine (formerly Children's Disability Register) West Bridgford Hse, Loughborough Rd, West Bridgford, Nottinghamshire NG2 7UN; Tel 0115 846 5616

YOUTH OFFENDING TEAMS

County House Dale Cl, 100 Chesterfield Rd South, Mansfield, Nottinghamshire NG19 7AQ; Tel 01623 452216

Newark Office County Offices, Newark, Nottinghamshire NG24 1UW; Tel 01636 682700

Retford Office Martlett School, Newgate St, Worksop, Nottinghamshire S80 2RW; Tel 01909 544500

COMMUNITY LEARNING DISABILITY TEAMS

Bassetlaw Community Learning Disability Team 53 Cheapside, Worksop, Nottinghamshire S80 2JD; Tel 01909 530205

Broxtowe Community Learning Disability Team Sunnyside Rd, Beeston, Nottinghamshire NG9 4FR; Tel 0115 943 1086

Central Nottinghamshire Community Learning Disability Team The Bungalow Complex, 68 Portland St, Kirkby-in-Ashfield, Nottinghamshire NG17 7AG; Tel 01623 785473

Gedling Community Learning Disability Team Sir John Robinson Way, Arnold, Nottingham NG5 6DB; Tel 0115 854 6000

Newark Community Learning Disability Team Byron Hse, Newark Hospital, Boundary Rd, Newark, Nottinghamshire NG24 4DE; Tel 01636 685927

Rushcliffe Community Learning Disability Team West Bridgford Hse, Loughborough Rd, Nottingham NG2 7UN; Tel 0115 846 5612

COMMUNITY MENTAL HEALTH TEAMS

Ashfield Community Mental Health Team New Street Health Centre, Sutton-in-Ashfield, Nottinghamshire NG17 1BW; Tel 01623 514632

Bassetlaw Community Mental Health Team Boundary Resource Centre, Watson Rd, Worksop, Nottinghamshire S80 2BL; Tel 01909 533800

Broxtowe and North West Mental Health Team The Hope Centre, Dovecote Hse, 38 Wollaton Rd, Beeston, Nottingham NG9 2NR; Tel 0115 943 0456

Mansfield Community Mental Health Team Heatherdene, Crow Hill Dr, Mansfield, Nottinghamshire NG19 7AE; Tel 01623 626147

Newark Community Mental Health Team Byron Hse, Newark Hospital, Boundary Rd, Newark, Nottinghamshire NG24 4DE; Tel 01636 685985

Rushcliffe Community Mental Health Team 32a George Rd, West Bridgford, Nottingham NG2 7QG; Tel 0115 945 5990

DAY CENTRES FOR ADULTS WITH LEARNING DIFFICULTIES

SCU denotes special care unit.

Barncroft Day Centre Sunnyside Rd, Beeston, Nottinghamshire NG9 4FR; Tel 0115 925 0172
  SCU (150)

Beck Meadow Day Centre Rolleston Dr, Arnold, Nottinghamshire NG5 7JH; Tel 0115 955 7655
  SCU (200)

Friary House Resource Centre 55 Whitfield St, Newark, Nottinghamshire NG24 1QX; Tel 01636 707611

Greenacre Day Centre Wingfield Ave, Worksop, Nottinghamshire S81 0TA; Tel 01909 476499
  SCU (150)

Redoaks Day Centre Southwell Road West, Rainworth, Mansfield, Nottinghamshire NG21 0HJ; Tel 01623 795991
  (150)

Whitewater Day Centre Main Rd, Boughton, Newark, Nottinghamshire NG22 9TD; Tel 01623 835186
  SCU (100)

Willow Wood Day Centre Sheepwash La, Sutton-in-Ashfield, Nottinghamshire NG17 5GG; Tel 01623 550376
  SCU (150)

DAY CENTRES FOR ADULTS WITH MENTAL HEALTH PROBLEMS

Boundary Resource Centre Watson Rd, Worksop, Nottinghamshire S80 2BL; Tel 01909 533800
  (62)

Rokerfield Resource Centre 401 Mansfield Rd, Sutton-in-Ashfield, Nottinghamshire NG17 4HJ; Tel 01623 623382
  (75)

PLACES AVAILABLE FOR TWO OTHER LOCAL AUTHORITIES

Residential and Community Support Team 29 Helmsley Rd, Rainworth, Nottinghamshire NG21 0DQ; Tel 01623 476939
Offering community support as well as residential services for people with learning difficulties.

OCCUPATIONAL AND INDUSTRIAL CENTRES FOR PEOPLE WITH DISABILITIES

Braille Bureau County Hall, West Bridgford, Nottinghamshire; Tel 0115 982 3823

Brook Farm Horticultural Centre Linby, Nottinghamshire NG15 8AE; Tel 0115 963 2638

County Visual Communications County Hall, West Bridgford, Nottinghamshire NG2 7QP; Tel 0115 982 3823 ext 3706

Sherwood Industries Southwell Road West, Rainworth, Mansfield, Nottinghamshire NG21 0HW; Tel 01623 792151
  (75)

RESIDENTIAL CENTRES FOR LEARNING DIFFICULTIES (OVER SCHOOL LEAVING AGE)

Dorket View Residential Centre Howbeck Rd, Arnold, Nottinghamshire NG5 8AA; Tel 0115 920 2771 (24)

Wincroft Residential Centre Wingfield Ave, Worksop, Nottinghamshire S81 0TA; Tel 01909 476490 (25)

Wynhill Court Residential Centre Wynhill Ct, Bingham, Nottingham NG13 8TE; Tel 01949 838492

OCCUPATIONAL THERAPY SERVICE

Ashfield Disability Services Team, Sutton Centre, High Pavement, Sutton-in-Ashfield, Nottinghamshire; Tel 01623 405300

Broadgate House Humber Rd, Beeston, Nottinghamshire NG8 2EF; Tel 0115 917 5800

Cheltermill House 38 Lombard St, Newark, Nottinghamshire NG24 1XP; Tel 01636 652040

Council Offices Sir John Robinson Way, Arnold, Nottingham NG5 6DB; Tel 0115 854 6000

The Hall Bridgford Rd, West Bridgford, Nottinghamshire NG2 6AD; Tel 0115 914 1500

Meadow House Littleworth, Mansfield, Nottinghamshire NG18 2TB; Tel 01623 433433

Queen's Buildings Potter St, Worksop, Nottinghamshire S80 2BZ; Tel 01909 533533

DAY CENTRES FOR PEOPLE WITH PHYSICAL DISABILITIES

Day Centre for the Elderly and People with Physical Disabilities Eastgate Resource Centre, Albion Cl, Worksop, Nottinghamshire S80 1RA; Tel 01909 474144

Day Centre for Physical Disabilities Dallas St Resource Centre, Dallas St, Mansfield, Nottinghamshire NG18 5SZ; Tel 01623 476880

Day Centre for Physical Disabilities Rushcliffe Resource Centre, Loughborough Rd, Nottingham NG2 7FA; Tel 0115 923 2353

Day Centre for Physical Disabilities Balderton Resource Centre, London Rd, Newark, Nottinghamshire NG24 3AL; Tel 01636 687444

Day Centre for the Elderly and People with Physical Disabilities High Pavement Resource Centre, High Pavement, Sutton-in-Ashfield, Nottinghamshire NG17 1EE; Tel 01623 457673

VISUAL IMPAIRMENT TEAM

Meadow Hse, Littleworth, Mansfield, Nottinghamshire NG18 2TB; Tel 01623 433433

DEAF SERVICES TEAM

County Deaf Team Meadow Hse, Littleworth, Little Mansfield, Nottinghamshire NG18 2TB; Tel 01623 433433

DAY CENTRES

Ascroft Day Centre Langton Rd, Sutton-in-Ashfield, Nottinghamshire NG17 1ER; Tel 01623 555634; Fax 01623 441662

Beauvale Court Day Centre Wellington Pl, Eastwood, Nottinghamshire NG16 3GB; Tel 01773 768183

Bishops Court Day Centre Tuxford Rd, Boughton, Newark, Nottinghamshire NG22 9HY; Tel 01623 862043

Dukeries Day Centre Dukeries Complex, Whinney La, New Ollerton, Nottinghamshire NG22 9TD; Tel 01623 862363

Four Seasons Day Centre Braywood Gdns, Millbrook Dr, Carlton, Nottingham NG4 3SR; Tel 0115 938 1363

James Hince Day Centre Windsor Gdns, Carlton-in-Lindrick, Worksop, Nottinghamshire S81 9BL; Tel 01909 540287

Kirklands Day Centre Fairhaven, Kirkby in Ashfield, Nottinghamshire NG17 7FW; Tel 01623 723946

Lawn View Day Centre c/o St. Michael's View, Hallcroft Rd, Retford, Nottinghamshire DN22 7NE; Tel 01777 708322

Leivers Court Day Centre Douro Dr, Arnold, Nottinghamshire NG5 8AX; Tel 0115 926 5643

Maun View Day Centre 261 Chesterfield Rd South, Mansfield, Nottinghamshire NG19 7EL; Tel 01623 423125; Fax 01623 412731

Moorlands Day Centre Moor La, Bingham, Nottinghamshire NG13 8AS; Tel 01949 836652

Patchills Day Centre Eaking Cl, Mansfield, Nottinghamshire NG18 3BS; Tel 01623 658280

Selston Day Centre Mathew Holland Complex, Selston, Nottinghamshire NG16 6BW; Tel 01773 580886

Springfield Day Centre Robin Hood Dr, Hucknall, Nottingham NG15 6HU; Tel 0115 963 3071

Woods Court Day Centre Walker Cl, Newark, Nottinghamshire NG24 4BP; Tel 01636 673548

RESIDENTIAL ESTABLISHMENTS FOR OLDER PEOPLE – ASHFIELD

There are four homes for the elderly in Ashfield/Mansfield locality.

RESIDENTIAL ESTABLISHMENTS FOR OLDER PEOPLE – BASSETLAW/NEWARK

There are six homes for the Elderly in Bassetlaw/Newark locality.

MEALS SERVICE

Ashfield, Mansfield and Newark areas administered from local offices. Other areas administered via Riverside Way: Tel 0115 986 2211.

RESIDENTIAL ESTABLISHMENTS FOR OLDER PEOPLE – BROXTOWE/GEDLING/RUSHCLIFFE

There are eight homes for the Elderly in Broxtowe/Gedling Rushcliffe locality.

SHELTERED HOUSING SCHEMES FOR THE ELDERLY

Sheltered housing is provided by the local housing authorities grant aided by the County Council. Enquiries should be directed to the respective authority.
Some sheltered housing is provided by local voluntary organisations including housing associations. Details of housing associations may be found in the Housing and Planning Year Book.

Education Department

Enquiries regarding Education within Nottinghamshire County Council Authority should initially be directed to Communications at the address below.
County Hall, West Bridgford, Nottingham NG2 7QP;
  URL www.nottinghamshire.gov.uk/learningandwork;
  E-mail communications@education.nottscc.gov.uk;
  Tel 0115 982 3823; Fax 0115 981 2824
Director (Education) P. Tulley

EDUCATIONAL PSYCHOLOGY SERVICE

Ashfield, Bassetlaw, Mansfield and Newark Meadow Hse, Littleworth, Mansfield, Nottinghamshire NG18 2TA; Tel 01623 433433; Fax 01623 433319
Senior Educational Psychologist (Bassetlaw and Newark) M. Collins

Broxtowe, Gedling and Rushcliffe Sir John Robinson Way, Arnold, Nottinghamshire NG5 6BN; Tel 0115 854 6000; Fax 0115 854 6037
Senior Educational Psychologist   C. Allward

SPECIAL SCHOOLS/INDIVIDUAL NEEDS CENTRES

Arnold Derrymount School Churchmoor La, Arnold, Nottinghamshire NG5 8HN; Tel 0115 953 4015; Fax 0115 953 4025
Headteacher   G. Read
Mixed All ages MLD (Day) (plus unit for hearing impaired) (72)

Ash Lea School Owthorpe Rd, Cotgrave, Nottinghamshire NG12 3PA; Tel 0115 989 2744; Fax 0115 989 3878
Headteacher   L. Skillington
Mixed All ages SLD (Day) (51)

Beech Hill School Fairholme Dr, Mansfield, Nottinghamshire NG19 6DX; Tel 01623 626008; Fax 01623 651459
Headteacher   M. Sutton
Mixed Secondary MLD (Day) (63)

Bracken Hill School Chartwell Rd, Kirkby in Ashfield, Nottinghamshire NG17 7HZ; Tel 01623 477268; Fax 01623 477298
Headteacher   A. Kawalek
Mixed All ages MLD and SLD 60 Day

Mansfield Yeoman Park School Park Hall Rd, Mansfield Woodhouse, Mansfield, Nottinghamshire NG19 8PS; Tel 01623 459540; Fax 01623 459526
Headteacher   P. Betts
Mixed All ages SLD (Day) (84)

Orchard School Town Site, Appletongate, Newark, Nottinghamshire NG24 1JR; Tel 01636 682255; Fax 01636 682266
Headteacher   S.P. Jefferies, DipEd
Mixed All ages MLD/SLD 75 day, 1 residential

Redgate School Somersall St, Mansfield, Nottinghamshire NG19 6EL; Tel 01623 455944; Fax 01623 455778
Headteacher   K.G. Fallows, MEd
Mixed Primary MLD (Day) (35)

Retford St. Giles School North Rd, Retford, Nottinghamshire DN22 7XN; Tel 01777 703683; Fax 01777 705324
Headteacher   C.M. Kirk
Mixed All ages MLD/SLD (Day) (66)

INDIVIDUAL NEEDS CENTRES FOR HEARING-IMPAIRED PUPILS

Arnold Derrymount School Churchmoor La, Arnold, Nottinghamshire NG5 8HN; Tel 0115 953 4015; Fax 0115 953 4025
Headteacher   G. Read
Unit for hearing-impaired pupils with learning difficulties.

Holgate Comprehensive School Hillcrest Dr, Nottingham NG15 6PX; Tel 0115 963 2104; Fax 0115 968 1993
Headteacher   R. Kenney

INDIVIDUAL NEEDS CENTRE FOR VISUALLY IMPAIRED CHILDREN

Bramcote Park School Bramcote, Beeston, Nottinghamshire NG9 3GD; Tel 0115 913 0013; Fax 0115 913 0012
Headteacher   P. Crompton

INDIVIDUAL NEEDS CENTRE FOR CHILDREN WITH PHYSICAL DIFFICULTIES

Colonel Frank Seely School Flatts La, Calverton, Nottinghamshire NG14 6JZ; Tel 0115 965 2495; Fax 0115 965 5723
Headteacher   K.R. Geary

OLDHAM METROPOLITAN BOROUGH COUNCIL
www.oldham.gov.uk

Population 219 720
Civic Centre, Oldham, Greater Manchester OL1 1XL; URL www.oldham.gov.uk; Tel 0161 911 3000; Fax 0161 911 4684
Mayor   Riaz Ahmad
Chief Executive   A.W. Kilburn
Executive Director (Housing)   H. Broadbent, BA(Hons)
Executive Director (Environment and Transportation)   P. Barrett, BEng, CEng, MICE, MIHT
Henshaw Hse, Cheapside, Oldham, Greater Manchester OL1 1NY
Executive Director (Corporate Services and Borough Treasurer) and Deputy Chief Executive   P. Fenton, CPFA
Executive Director (Operational Services)   M. Kelly, FCIOB, MInst, MIMgt, MIMBB
Assistant Director (Legal and Administration) and Solicitor to the Council   A. Harwood

Social Services Department

Civic Centre, West St, Oldham, Greater Manchester OL1 1UW; E-mail all.social.services@oldham.gov.uk; E-mail socs.general.enquiry@oldham.gov.uk; Tel (Out-of-office hours) 0161 628 5933; 0161 911 4768; Fax (Out-of-office hours) 0161 678 2904; 0161 911 4855
Chair (Social Services Committee)   Cllr Len Quinn
Executive Director (Social Services)   Veronica Jackson; E-mail socs.veronica.jackson@oldham.gov.uk; Tel 0161 911 4752; Fax 0161 911 4782
Assistant Director (Older People and Vulnerable Adults)   David Friday; E-mail socs.david.friday@oldham.gov.uk; Tel 0161 911 4779; Fax 0161 911 4782
Assistant Director (Strategy and Performance)   Vacancy; Tel 0161 911 4794; Fax 0161 911 4782
Assistant Director (Children, Learning Disability and Mental Health)   Linda Priest; E-mail socs.linda.priest@oldham.gov.uk; Tel 0161 911 4780; Fax 0161 911 4782

Cabinet

Social Services Executive Member (Health and Social Care)   Cllr Len Quinn
Chair (People and Communities Overview and Scrutiny Committee)   Cllr Alan Harrison
Chair (Learning Disability Partnership Board)   Cllr Derek Heffernan
Chair (Health and Social Care Modernisation Board)   Cllr Len Quinn

CHILDREN SERVICES

Marian Walker Hse, Frederick St, Oldham, Greater Manchester OL8 2SW; Tel 0161 626 4947; Fax 0161 652 2821
Head   Teresa Broadbent

FIELDWORK SERVICES

Royton Town Hall, Rochdale Rd, Royton, Oldham, Greater Manchester OL2 6QJ; Tel 0161 911 3730; Fax 0161 911 3737
Manager   David Lord

CENTRAL RESOURCES

Marian Walker Hse, Frederick St, Oldham, Greater Manchester OL8 2SW; Tel 0161 626 4947; Fax 0161 652 2821
Head   Steve Slater

AFTER CARE

Marian Walker Hse, Frederick St, Oldham, Greater
Manchester OL8 2SW; Tel 0161 626 4947; Fax 0161 652
2821
Manager   Julie Griffiths

FAMILY SUPPORT

Marian Walker Hse, Frederick St, Oldham, Greater
Manchester OL8 2SW; Tel 0161 626 4947; Fax 0161 652
2821
Service Manager   Gail Cassidy
Manager   Anne Wood

FAMILY SUPPORT UNITS

Coalshaw Green Family Centre   off Stanley Rd, Oldham,
Greater Manchester OL9 7HS; Tel 0161 624 5278; Fax 0161
633 7113
Senior Family Support Worker   Cheryl Boardman

Derker Family Support Unit   27 Whetstone Hill Rd, Oldham,
Greater Manchester OL1 4NA; Tel 0161 678 8979; Fax 0161
622 0379
Senior Family Support Worker   Kathleen Davies

Fitton Hill Family Support Unit   62 The Spur, Oldham,
Greater Manchester OL8 2NR; Tel 0161 626 5717; Fax 0161
633 1971
Senior Family Support Worker   Alison Walker

Heathcot Family Support Unit   1st Fl, 78 Windsor Rd,
Oldham, Greater Manchester OL8 1RP; Tel 0161 626 0535;
Fax 0161 785 0459
Senior Family Support Worker   Lynn Mills

Holts Family Support Unit   41–43 Course View, Holts,
Oldham, Greater Manchester OL4 5QA; Tel 0161 626 0534;
Fax 0161 652 8213
Senior Family Support Worker   Ruth Whitehead

Park View Family Centre   Kings Rd, Oldham, Greater
Manchester OL8 2BJ; Tel 0161 624 3267; Fax 0161 652 8211
Senior Family Support Worker   Bernadette Royales

Sure Start   31 Farm Rd, Limeside, Oldham, Greater
Manchester OL8 3PB; Tel 0161 633 1843; Fax 0161 620
5473
Manager   Donna McGlade (Acting)

CHILDREN'S RESOURCE CENTRE (CHILD PROTECTION)

Queens Road Resource Centre   79 Queen's Rd, Oldham,
Greater Manchester OL8 2BA; Tel 0161 628 7963; Fax 0161
652 2913
Co-ordinator   Margaret Raynor

RESIDENTIAL CARE

Blackshaw Lane Children's Home   1 Blackshaw La, Royton,
Oldham, Greater Manchester OL2 6NT; Tel 0161 620 1210;
Fax 0161 626 5298
Manager   Gary Sanders

Brierley Avenue Children's Home   60 Brierley Ave,
Failsworth, Oldham, Greater Manchester M35 9HA;
Tel 0161 681 2965; Fax 0161 681 2965
Manager   Andrew Taylor

Burnley Lane Children's Home   39 Burnley La, Chadderton,
Oldham, Greater Manchester OL9 0BT; Tel 0161 620 8506;
Fax 0161 627 2242
Manager   Sue Nadin

Hawthorn Crescent Children's Home   10 Hawthorn Cres,
Oldham, Greater Manchester OL8 2NH; Tel 0161 627 2454;
Fax 0161 627 2454
Manager   Joan Taylor

Johnson Avenue Children's Home   14–16 Johnson Ave,
Sholver, Oldham, Greater Manchester OL1 4RD; Tel 0161
633 1480; Fax 0161 633 1480
Manager   Gary Sanders

Netherhey Street Children's Home   43 Netherhey St,
Oldham, Greater Manchester OL8 2JG; Tel 0161 678 9160;
Fax 0161 624 0590
Manager   Sue Nadin

Newport Street Children's Home   105 Newport St, Oldham,
Greater Manchester OL8 1RE; Tel 0161 624 0163; Fax 0161
624 5349
Manager   Andrew Taylor

Respite Care   45 Netherhey St, Oldham, Greater
Manchester OL8 2JG; Tel 0161 633 6739; Fax 0161 633
6739
Manager   Jean Jones

CHILDREN WITH DISABILITIES

Fieldwork Services, Woodfield Centre, Manchester Rd,
Oldham, Greater Manchester OL8 4ET; Tel 0161 627
1749; Fax 0161 627 0388
Service Manager   Vacancy
Manager   Sue Rowlands

YOUTH OFFENDING TEAM

Brunswick Hse, Brunswick Sq, Union St, Oldham, Greater
Manchester OL1 1DE; Tel 0161 621 9500; Fax 0161 621
9501
Manager   Allan Broadbent

FOSTERING AND ADOPTION SERVICE

Marian Walker Hse, Frederick St, Oldham, Greater
Manchester OL8 2SW; Tel 0161 626 4947; Fax 0161 627
4969
Team Manager   Jenny Whitmore

ADULT SERVICES DIVISION

Failsworth Town Hall, Oldham Rd, Failsworth,
Manchester M35 0FJ; Tel 0161 683 2900; Fax 0161 683
2988
Head (Residential and Day Care Services)   Althea Rankin
Head (Assessment and Commissioning)   Dorothy Phillips

FIELDWORK SERVICES

Failsworth Town Hall, Oldham Rd, Failsworth, Manchester
M35 0FJ; Tel 0161 683 2900; Fax 0161 683 2988
Manager (Community Care)   Chris Moffatt
Manager (Community Care)   Glen Eyre

HOSPITAL SOCIAL WORK SERVICES

Royal Oldham Hospital, Rochdale Rd, Oldham, Greater
Manchester OL1 2JH; Tel 0161 627 8650; Fax 0161 627
8072
Manager (Community Care)   Joyce Lees (Acting)

HOME SUPPORT SERVICES

Home from Hospital Service   Royal Oldham Hospital,
Rochdale Rd, Oldham, Greater Manchester OL1 2JH;
Tel 0161 627 8650; Fax 0161 627 8072
Team Manager   Joyce Lees
Manager (Home Support)   Chris Stevens

District Home Support Service   Failsworth Town Hall,
Oldham Rd, Failsworth, Manchester M35 0FJ; Tel 0161 683
2900; Fax 0161 683 2988
Head   Colin Carey
Team Manager   Margaret Williams

BOROUGH WIDE UNDER 65S

The Link Centre, 140 Union St, Oldham, Greater
Manchester OL1 1DZ; Tel 0161 911 4799; Fax 0161 911
3803
Manager   Adele Major

PHYSICAL/SENSORY SERVICES

The Link Centre, 140 Union St, Oldham, Greater
Manchester OL1 TDZ; Tel 0161 911 4799; 0161 911 4800;
Fax 0161 911 3803
Team Manager   Barbara Christopher
Head   Janet Whitehead

LEARNING DISABILITY SERVICE

Broadway House   Broadway, Chadderton, Oldham, Greater
Manchester; Tel 0161 911 3868; Fax 0161 911 3870
Head   Beverley Maybury
Provider Manager   Rosemary Molyneux
Team Manager (Care Management)   Ken Stapleton

Respite Care Unit   High Barn St, Royton, Oldham, Greater
Manchester OL2 6DW; Tel 0161 633 3850; Fax 0161 627 5445
Manager   Sally Cripps

DAY SERVICES FOR PEOPLE WITH A LEARNING DISABILITY

Ena Hughes Centre   Ellesmere St, Failsworth, Manchester
M35 9AD; Tel 0161 684 7290
Locality Co-ordinator (Failsworth)   Margaret Neyman
Manager (Day Centre)   Mandy Mellett

Bentley Street   3 Bentley St, Chadderton, Oldham, Greater
Manchester OL9 6PS; Tel (Outreach) 0161 621 0294; 0161
785 3100; Fax 0161 785 3101
Locality Co-ordinator (Chadderton)   Joanne Knight (Acting)

Rock Street Day Centre   Rock St, Oldham, Greater
Manchester OL1 3UJ; Tel 0161 911 3787; Fax 0161 911 3788
Manager (Day Centre)   Anne Forrest
Locality Co-ordinator (Oldham)   Lilian Nelson

SUPPORTED LIVING

1 Royle Cl, Oldham, Greater Manchester OL8 2AP; Tel 0161
678 0266
Manager   Diane Prendergast

MENTAL HEALTH SERVICES – JOINT SERVICE – OLDHAM SOCIAL SERVICES AND OLDHAM NHS TRUST

Head (Mental Health Social Services)   Alan Chittenden
The Hollies, Frederick St, Oldham, Greater Manchester
OL8 4BD; Tel 0161 633 4612; Fax 0161 633 7855
Borough Director   Simon Pierce
Parklands Mental Health Unit, Royal Holdham Hospital,
Rochdale Rd, Oldham, Greater Manchester OL1 2JH;
Tel 0161 627 8039; Fax 0161 627 8039

FIELDWORK SERVICES

The Beeches, 5 Waterloo St, Oldham, Greater Manchester
OL1 1SP; Tel 0161 909 8060; Fax 0161 909 8092
The Hollies, Frederick St, Oldham, Greater Manchester
OL8 4BD; Tel 0161 633 4612; Fax 0161 633 7855
Team Manager (The Beeches)   Ian Walker
Team Manager (The Hollies)   Vacancy
Manager (Laurel Bank)   Barnard McIntyre (Acting)

DAY CENTRES – MENTAL HEALTH

The Hollies Day Centre   Frederick St, Oldham, Greater
Manchester OL8 4BD; Tel 0161 633 4612; Fax 0161 633 7855
Manager   Joe O'Grady

The Phoenix Centre   Phoenix St, Oldham, Greater
Manchester OL1 1DB; Tel 0161 911 3830; Fax 0161 911 3831
Manager   James Quigley

RESIDENTIAL CARE – MENTAL HEALTH

The Hollies, Frederick St, Oldham, Greater Manchester
OL8 4BD; Tel 0161 633 4612; Fax 0161 633 7855
Manager (Residential Services)   Carole Norris

Mayall Street Residential Unit   16 Mayall St, Oldham,
Greater Manchester; Tel 0161 624 1569
Manager   Glenys Brooks

Greenacres Lodge Residential Unit   Greenacres Rd,
Oldham, Greater Manchester; Tel 0161 627 2639
Manager   Christine Tierney

SUPPORTED HOUSING – MENTAL HEALTH

Keston Road Supported Housing   15 Keston Rd,
Watersheddings, Oldham, Greater Manchester OL1 4HL;
Tel 0161 652 4330; Fax 0161 652 4330
Manager   Glenys Brooks

Old Lane Supported Housing   147 Old La, Chadderton,
Oldham, Greater Manchester OL9 7JQ; Tel 0161 628 7839
Manager   June Rainford

RESETTLEMENT – MENTAL HEALTH

Furness Avenue Resettlement Scheme   123 Furness Ave,
Oldham, Greater Manchester OL8 2EB; Tel 0161 624 6409;
Fax 0161 633 8907
Manager   June Rainford

Majestic Mill Resettlement Scheme   Unit 1, Turner St, Lees,
Oldham, Greater Manchester OL4 3NT; Tel 0161 633 8907;
Fax 0161 633 8907
Manager   June Rainford

Substance Misuse   18 Union St, Oldham, Greater
Manchester OL1 1RU; Tel 0161 624 9595; Fax 0161 622 1749
Manager   Sue Doherty

DISABILITY SERVICES

The Link Centre, 140 Union St, Oldham, Greater
Manchester OL1 1DZ; Tel 0161 911 4799; Fax 0161 911
3803
Head   Janet Whitehead

DAY CENTRE FOR YOUNG PHYSICALLY DISABLED

The Link Centre, 140 Union St, Oldham, Greater
Manchester OL1 1DZ; Tel 0161 911 4786; Fax 0161 911
4789
Manager (Day Centre)   Derek Broadbent

DAY CARE FOR OLDER PEOPLE

Broadway Day Centre   Broadway Hse, Broadway, Oldham,
Greater Manchester; Tel 0161 911 3873; Fax 0161 911 3870
Manager   Carole Bardsley

Laurel Bank Day Centre   Kershaw St, Shaw, Greater
Manchester OL2 7AJ; Tel 01706 841983
Manager   June Richardson

SERVICES FOR OLDER PEOPLE

There are three local authority homes for older people and
two resource centres.

MENTAL HEALTH SERVICES FOR OLDER PEOPLE

Highbarn Hse, Highbarn St, Royton, Oldham, Greater
Manchester OL2 6DW; Tel 0161 911 3715; Fax 0161 911
3717
Team Manager (Dementia)   Gill Evans
Team Manager (Functional)   Jackie Crawley

OCCUPATIONAL THERAPY SERVICE

The Link Centre, 140 Union St, Oldham, Greater
Manchester OL1 1DZ; Tel 0161 628 6882; 0161 911 3782;
Fax 0161 911 3784
Manager (Occupational Therapy)   Anne Foley

TRAINING INTO EMPLOYMENT

Unit 1, Falcon Enterprise Centre, Victoria St, Chadderton,
Oldham, Greater Manchester OL9 0HB; Tel 0161 633
7754; Fax 0161 652 1135
Manager   Phil Sykes

6

Education and Leisure Services Department

PO Box 40, Civic Centre, Oldham, Greater Manchester
OL1 1XJ; Tel 0161 911 4260; Fax 0161 911 3221
*Chief Executive (Oldham Education, Business and Guidance
Services)* Tim Mitchell
Executive Director (Education and Leisure Services) Chris Berry
Assistant Director (Lifelong Learning and Culture) Nick Ford
Head (Education Out Of School) Janet Depledge
Head (Youth Service) Pam Griffin
Manager (Arts in the Community) Vacancy
School Development Adviser (Equal Opportunities/SEN)
Ian McPhail
Pre-School Special Needs Service Claire Ward

SPECIAL SCHOOLS AND UNITS

Hardman Fold School Dean St, Failsworth, Manchester
M35 0DQ; E-mail info@hardmanfold.oldham.sch.uk;
Tel 0161 688 7114; Fax 0161 684 7414
Headteacher R. Maycock, AdDipEd
EBD (Day and residential)

Hill Top School Arncliffe Rise, Pennine Meadow, Oldham,
Greater Manchester OL4 2LZ;
E-mail els.hilltop@oldham.gov.uk; Tel 0161 620 6070;
Fax 0161 624 3558
Headteacher G. Quinn, BEd, MEd
SLD

The Kingfisher Community Foxdenton La, Chadderton,
Oldham, Greater Manchester OL9 9QR;
E-mail info@kingfisher.oldham.sch.uk; Tel 0161 284 5335;
Fax 0161 284 5338
Headteacher Dominic Wall, BA
PH

Marland Fold School Rosary Rd, Oldham, Greater
Manchester OL8 2RP;
E-mail info@marlandfold.oldham.gov.uk; Tel 0161 911 3175;
Fax 0161 911 3177
Headteacher D. Leach, BEd
MLD

Park Dean School St. Martin's Rd, Oldham, Greater
Manchester OL8 2PY;
E-mail info@parkdean.oldham.sch.uk; Tel 0161 620 0231;
Fax 0161 633 9534
Headteacher Graham Quinn, BEd, MEd) (Acting
PH

Spring Brook School Hunt La, Chadderton, Oldham,
Greater Manchester OL9 0LS;
E-mail info@springbrook.oldham.sch.uk; Tel 0161 911 5007;
Fax 0161 911 5008
Headteacher Janet Jones
MLD

SPECIAL NEEDS SUPPORT SERVICES

Educational Psychology Service Centre for Professional
Development, Rosary Rd, Oldham, Greater Manchester
OL8 2QE; Tel 0161 911 4218; Fax 0161 911 3211
Senior Educational Psychologist Stephen Rooney

Hospital Teaching Service Northgate Hse, Firbank Rd,
Oldham, Greater Manchester OL2 6TU; Tel 0161 911 3233
Manager Mrs K. Williams

Secondary Special Needs Service GPD, Rosary Rd,
Oldham, Greater Manchester OL8 2QE; Tel 0161 911 3673
Manager P. Wilkinson, BA, MSc

Service for the Hearing Impaired Greenbank, Firbank Rd,
Royton, Oldham, Greater Manchester OL2 6TU; Tel 0161
911 3113
Contact J. Lally

Service for the Visually Impaired Greenbank, Firbank Rd,
Oldham, Greater Manchester OL2 6TU; Tel 0161 911 3114
Contact Mrs J. Sweeting, BEd

Social Services Teaching Team c/o Adolescent and Youth
Project, Marion Walker Hse, Oldham, Greater Manchester;
Tel 0161 626 4947
Deputy Teacher-in-Charge J. Hayes

OXFORDSHIRE COUNTY COUNCIL
www.oxfordshire.gov.uk

Population 627 500
Political Composition: Con: 26, Lab: 24, LD: 19, Green: 1
County Hall, New Rd, Oxford, Oxfordshire OX1 1ND;
URL www.oxfordshire.gov.uk;
E-mail online@oxfordshire.gov.uk; Tel 01865 792422;
Fax 01865 726155
Chair of the Council C. Shouler
Chief Executive R. Shaw
Assistant Chief Executive and Solicitor to the Council
C.J. Impey, LLB
Treasurer C. Gray, BA, IPFA
Director (Environmental Services) D.S.B. Young, BA,
MRTPI
Speedwell Hse, Speedwell St, Oxford, Oxfordshire
OX1 1NE
County Officer (Personnel) Sue Corrigan; Tel 01865 810280;
Fax 01865 815224

Social and Health Care

Yarnton Hse, Rutten La, Yarnton, Kidlington, Oxfordshire
OX5 1LP; URL www.oxfordshire.gov.uk;
E-mail social&healthcare@oxfordshire.gov.uk; Tel 01865
375515; (Emergency) 0800 833408; Fax 01865 841666
Director Charles Waddicote
Assistant County Treasurer Sean Collins
Head (Social Care for Children) Phil Hodgson
Head (Social Care for Adults) Lorna Brown
Head (Partnerships and Planning) N. Welch

Social Services Committee

Spokesperson Ted Cooper (Lab)
Spokesperson Judith Heathcoat (Con)
Spokesperson Janet Godden (LD)

TRAINING

Responsible for training professional and support staff in
the department.
Manager C. Laird
Yarnton Hse, Rutten La, Yarnton, Oxfordshire OX5 1LP;
Tel 01865 854431

AREA OFFICES

Calthorpe House Area Office Calthorpe St, Banbury,
Oxfordshire OX16 8EX; Tel 01865 375515

The Charter Area Office Broad St, Abingdon, Oxfordshire
OX14 3LT; Tel 01865 375515

Oxford City Office 134b Cowley Rd, Oxford, Oxfordshire
OX4 1JH; Tel 01865 375515

HEALTH SERVICES

Manager (Health Services – Adult) J. Lee
Oxford Radcliffe Trust, John Radcliffe Site, Headington,
Oxfordshire OX3 9DU; Tel 01865 221206
Manager (Children and Families Assessment Teams)
Noreen Collins
Yarnton Hse, Rutten La, Yarnton, Oxfordshire OX5 1LP;
Tel 01865 854462

Churchill Hospital Social and Health Care, Headington, Oxford, Oxfordshire OX3 7LJ; Tel 01865 225960; 01865 225961
Specialist Medicine

Horton NHS Trust Hospital Social and Health Care, Oxford Rd, Banbury, Oxfordshire OX16 9AL; Tel 01295 229140

Littlemore Hospital Oxfordshire Mental Health Care, Littlemore, Oxford, Oxfordshire OX4 4XN; Tel 01865 778911

Nuffield Orthopaedic Centre Social and Health Care, Windmill Rd, Headington, Oxfordshire OX3 7LD; Tel 01865 227633

Park Hospital Social and Health Care, Old Rd, Headington, Oxfordshire OX3 7LQ; Tel 01865 226348

Radcliffe Infirmary Trust Social and Health Care, Woodstock Rd, Oxford, Oxfordshire OX2 6HE; Tel 01865 228455

Warneford Hospital Social and Health Care, Headington, Oxford, Oxfordshire OX3 7JX; Tel 01865 226309

Young Disabled Unit The Churchill Hospital, Ritchie Russell Hse, Churchill Dr, Headington, Oxfordshire; Tel 01865 225544

CHILDREN'S HOME

Thornbury House Children's Home The Moors, Kidlington, Oxfordshire OX5 2AL; Tel 01865 373153
Manager Lindsay Truby (Acting)

RESOURCE CENTRE (CHILDREN WITH DISABILITIES)

St. Nicholas House Resource Centre St. Nicholas Rd, Littlemore, Oxfordshire OX4 4PN; Tel 01865 771124
Manager Bob Finch

FAMILY CENTRES

Barton, Open Door Burchester Ave, Headington, Oxfordshire OX3 9ND; Tel 01865 764952
Manager D. Mitchell

Britannia Road Family Centre Grove St, Banbury, Oxfordshire OX16 5DN; Tel 01295 266358
Manager Jan Capehorn

Cuddesdon Corner Family Centre 61–63 Cuddesdon Way, Blackbird Leys, Oxford, Oxfordshire OX4 6SB; Tel 01865 773263
Manager P. Welply

Florence Park Family Centre Rymers La, Oxford, Oxfordshire OX4 3JZ; Tel 01865 777286
Manager A. Machin

Kaleidoscope Family Centre Oxford Rd, Kidlington, Oxfordshire OX5 1AB; Tel 01865 372591
Manager S. Laverty

HOMES FOR ADULTS (LEARNING DISABILITY)

Cherwell and West Supported Living Scheme Greenwood Resource Centre, Warwick Rd, Banbury, Oxfordshire OX16 7PA; Tel 01295 254571
Manager J. Surplice

Marcham Home 19–20 Fettiplace Rd, Marcham, Abingdon, Oxfordshire OX13 6PL; Tel 01235 524933; Fax 01235 524566
Manager Trisha Selby

Marywood House Leiden Rd, The Slade, Headington, Oxfordshire OX3 8QX; Tel 01865 768883
Manager Aileen Bird

Stowford House Faringdon Rd, Shippon, Abingdon, Oxfordshire OX13 6NA; Tel 01235 524933
Manager Trisha Selby

Thorney Leys Home 8 Thorney Leys Pk, Witney, Oxfordshire OX28 4GE; Tel 01993 703953; Fax 01993 706907
Manager J. Surplice

ADULT DAY CENTRES (LEARNING DISABILITIES)

The Abbey Centre Audlett Dr, Abingdon, Oxfordshire OX14 3GD; Tel 01235 523065
Manager Robin Letchford

Blenheim Road Centre Blenheim Rd, Kidlington, Oxfordshire OX5 2HP; Tel 018675 377662
Manager J. Boyt

Charlton Centre Charlton Village Rd, Wantage, Oxfordshire OX12 7HG; Tel 01235 769261
Manager J. Parker

Cromwell Centre Highworth Rd, Farringdon, Oxfordshire SN7 7EG; Tel 01367 240853
Manager P. Clarke

Greenwood Day Services Parklands Hse, off Warwick Rd, Banbury, Oxfordshire OX16 7BA; Tel 01295 272306
Manager P. Turner

Moorland Centre 24 Dark La, Witney, Oxfordshire OX8 5LE; Tel 01993 703661
Manager G. Trevelyan

Oxford Options Resource Centre Horspath Driftway, Headington, Oxfordshire OX3 7JQ; Tel 01865 779570
Manager G. Trevelyan

Redlands Centre Neithrop Ave, Banbury, Oxfordshire OX16 7NT; Tel 01295 263594
Manager J. Boyt

South Oxfordshire Day Services High St, Wallingford, Oxfordshire OX10 0DB; Tel 01491 832373
Manager Mary Shortt

DAY CENTRES (ELDERLY)

Britannia Road Day Centre Grove St, Banbury, Oxfordshire OX16 8DN; Tel 01295 264068
Manager Jan Capehorn

The Charter Day Centre Broad St, Abingdon, Oxfordshire OX14 3LT; Tel 01235 521094
Manager M. Masawi

Wantage Day Centre Stirlings Cl, Garston La, Wantage, Oxfordshire OX12 7AQ; Tel 01235 765934
Manager Jackie Carmen

HOMES FOR ELDERLY PERSONS – CARE IN OXFORDSHIRE

There are 20 homes for elderly persons. For brochure Tel 01865 375515.

COMMUNITY MEALS – FROZEN

Social Services Department. For information please Tel 01865 375515.

MULTIPURPOSE DAY CENTRES

Bicester Day Centre Launton Rd, Bicester, Oxfordshire OX26 6DJ; Tel 01869 242808
Manager K. Hampton

Shotover Day Centre Craufurd Rd, Oxford, Oxfordshire OX4 2RA; Tel 01865 787315
Manager M. Jacobs

B AND H INDUSTRIES

Unit 5 Oxford Business Centre, Osney La, Oxford, Oxfordshire OX1 1TB; Tel 01865 791606
Manager B. Parsons

SENSORY IMPAIRMENT TEAM

The Charter Broad St, Abingdon, Oxfordshire OX14 3LT; Tel 01235 549399
Manager H. Grime

6

SHELTERED HOUSING

The responsibility of Oxford District Council; Cherwell District Council; South Oxfordshire District Council; Vale of White Horse District Council; West Oxfordshire District Council.

Learning and Culture

Macclesfield Hse, New Rd, Oxford, Oxfordshire OX1 1NA; URL www.oxfordshire.gov.uk; Tel 01865 815449; Fax 01865 791637
Director (Learning and Culture) Keith Bartley
Head (Children's Services) G. Tee
Head (School Development Service) R. Howard
Cricket Rd Centre, Cricket Rd, Oxford, Oxfordshire OX4 3DW

EDUCATIONAL PSYCHOLOGY SERVICE

Principal Educational Psychologist C. Sey; Tel 01865 815751; Fax 01865 815214
Senior Educational Psychologist (Southern Team) H. Squibb
Education Psychology Service, Faringdon Rd, off Wootton Rd, Abingdon, Oxfordshire OX14 1BH; Tel 01235 554554; Fax 01235 523421
Senior Educational Psychologist (City Team) D. Biddlestone
Education Psychology Service, L18, Cricket Rd Centre, Cricket Rd, Oxford, Oxfordshire OX4 3DW; Tel 01865 428011; Fax 01865 428020
Senior Educational Psychologist (Northern Team) A. Parsons
Educational Psychology Service, Woodgreen Hse, Hornbean Cl, off Broughton Rd, Banbury, Oxfordshire OX16 9RL; Tel 01295 252968; Fax 01295 255614
Education Psychology Service, 44 Church Grn, Witney, Oxfordshire OX8 6AW; Tel 01993 704174; Fax 01993 708326

EDUCATION SOCIAL WORK SERVICE

Social Inclusion Officer (Attendance and Reintegration) Barry Armstrong; Tel 01865 815956; Fax 01865 815214
Area Education Social Work Manager (Northern Area) Andy Whitehouse
The School Hse, Prescott Cl, Banbury, Oxfordshire OX16 0RD; Tel 01295 272525; Fax 01295 261590
Education Social Work Service, 44 Church Grn, Witney, Oxfordshire OX8 6AW; Tel 01993 776703; Fax 01993 708326
Area Education Social Work Manager (Oxford City Area) David Hayes
Education Social Work Service, Lawn Upton Hse, Littlemore, Oxford, Oxfordshire OX4 4PU; Tel 01865 718787; Fax 01865 749362
Area Education Social Work Manager (Southern Area) Shelagh Harlow
Education Social Work Service, 61a High St, Wallingford, Oxfordshire OX10 0DB; Tel 01491 833293; Fax 01491 833292
Education Social Work Service, Champion Hse, 12 Wootton Rd, Abingdon, Oxfordshire OX14 1JA; Tel 01235 555542; Fax 01235 537145
Senior Practitioner (Pupils with Emotional and Behavioural Difficulties) A. Whitehouse

PRE-SCHOOL TEACHER COUNSELLING SERVICE

Northern Team 44 Church Grn, Witney, Oxfordshire OX8 6AW; E-mail bernice.kurze@oxfordshire.gov.uk; Tel 01993 706460; Fax 01993 708326
Pre-School Teacher Counsellor Bernice Kurze

Oxford City L18, Cricket Rd Centre, Cricket Rd, Oxford, Oxfordshire OX4 3DW;
E-mail netta.buckett@oxfordshire.gov.uk; Tel 01865 428013; Fax 01865 428020
Pre-School Teacher Counsellor Netta Buckett

Southern Team Special Needs Resource Centre, Kingfisher School, Radley Rd, Abingdon, Oxfordshire OX14 3RR; E-mail hilary.clement@oxfordshire.gov.uk; Tel 01235 536026
Pre-School Teacher Counsellor Hilary Clements

OXFORDSHIRE HOSPITAL SCHOOL

Headteacher B. Jackson

The Highfield Family and Adolescent Unit
Contact D. Bingley

The John Radcliffe Hospital
Contact C. Hammersley Ward 4D; Tel 01865 221116
Contact M. Shawyer Ward 4B; Tel 01865 221102

Nuffield Orthopaedic Centre Headington, Oxfordshire OX3 7LD; Tel 01865 227554; Fax 01865 227554
Contact B. Jackson
  Orthopaedic and paediatric (60)

The Park Hospital for Children Old Rd, Headington, Oxford, Oxfordshire; Tel 01865 226216
Contact D. Jacob

The Radcliffe Infirmary Woodstock Rd, Oxford, Oxfordshire OX2 6HE
Contact M. Shawyer; Tel 01865 224644

SPECIAL SCHOOLS

Bardwell School Hendon Pl, Sunderland Dr, Bicester, Oxfordshire OX6 7RZ; E-mail office@bardwell.oxon.sch.uk; Tel 01869 242182; Fax 01869 243211
Headteacher C. Hughes

Fitzwaryn School Denchworth Rd, Wantage, Oxfordshire OX12 9ET; Tel 01235 764504; Fax 01235 768728
Headteacher M. Tighe
  Learning (Day) (70)

Frank Wise School Hornbeam Cl, Banbury, Oxfordshire OX16 9RL; E-mail frankwise@easynet.co.uk; Tel 01295 263520; Fax 01295 273141
Headteacher K.A. Griffiths
  (Day) (70)

Iffley Mead School Iffley Turn, Oxford, Oxfordshire OX4 4DU; Tel 01865 747606; Fax 01865 711134
Headteacher J. Headland
  Learning (Day) (106)

John Watson School Littleworth Rd, Wheatley, Oxfordshire OX33 1NN; E-mail enquiries@johnwatsonschool.co.uk; Tel 01865 872515; Fax 01865 452724
Headteacher S. Withey
  Learning (Day) (57)

Kingfisher School Radley Rd, Abingdon, Oxfordshire OX14 3RR; E-mail headteacher@kingfisher.oxon.sch.uk; Tel 01235 523843; Fax 01235 554051
Headteacher A. O'Meara
  Learning (Day) (96)

Mabel Prichard School St. Nicholas Rd, Littlemore, Oxford, Oxfordshire OX4 4PN;
E-mail headteacher@mabel-prichard.oxon.sch.uk; Tel 01865 777878; Fax 01865 775218
Headteacher J. Wallington
  Learning (49)

Northern House School South Pde, Oxford, Oxfordshire OX2 7JN; E-mail northern@rmplc.co.uk; Tel 01865 557004; Fax 01865 511210
Headteacher A. Battersby
  Management (Day) (78)

Ormerod School Waynflete Rd, Headington, Oxford, Oxfordshire OX3 8DD; Tel 01865 744173; Fax 01865 741489
Headteacher C. Peters
  PH (Day) (Day) (49)

Oxford, Northfield School Knights Rd, Blackbird Leys, Oxford, Oxfordshire OX4 5DQ; E-mail nfield@inc.co.uk; Tel 01865 771703; Fax 01865 773873
Headteacher M. Blencowe
Management (Day, Residential) (85)

Thornbury Education Unit 40 The Moors, Kidlington, Oxfordshire OX5 2AL; Tel 01865 373153; Fax 01865 842348
Headteacher J. Sampson

Springfield School 9 Moorland Cl, Witney, Oxfordshire OX8 5LN; Tel 01993 703963; Fax 01993 708796
Headteacher C. Niner
(Day) (87)

Woodeaton Manor School Woodeaton, Oxford, Oxfordshire OX3 9TS; E-mail mailus@woodeaton.oxon.sch.uk; Tel 01865 558722; Fax 01865 311561
Headteacher C. Grant
Mixed 6–16 Learning (Weekly Residential) (70)

SPECIAL NEEDS HOSTEL

Northfield Hostel Sandy Lane West, Littlemore, Oxford, Oxfordshire OX4 5LD; Tel 01865 775779
Manager M. Blencowe

PETERBOROUGH CITY COUNCIL
www.peterborough.gov.uk

In April 1998 Peterborough City Council became a unitary authority. The rest of Cambridgeshire retains a two-tier structure and is listed alphabetically within this chapter. Political Composition: Con: 21, Con Group 2: 8, Lab: 17, Ind Group: 1, Minority: 9, Vacancy: 1.
Town Hall, Bridge St, Peterborough PE1 1PJ;
URL www.peterborough.gov.uk; Tel 01733 747474
Chief Executive Gillian Beasley

Social Care Department

Bayard Pl, Broadway, Peterborough PE1 1FD;
URL www.adultsocialcare.org.uk; Tel (Emergency) 01733 561370; 01733 747474; Fax 01733 746050
Director (Adult Social Care) Ian Anderson
Head (Children's Social Care) Sheila Smith

Cabinet

Cabinet Member (Children's Services) Yvonne Lowndes (Con)
Cabinet Member (Adult Social Care) Michael Burton (Con)

DIVISIONAL OFFICES

Child Care Review Team – Staniland Court Suite 7, Staniland Crt, Werrington, Peterborough PE4 6NJ; Tel 01733 746225; Fax 01733 746230

Child Protection Team Suite 7, Staniland Crt, Werrington, Peterborough PE4 6NJ; Tel 01733 746211; Fax 01733 746230

Children in Need Herlington Herlington Hse, Benyon Gr, Orton Goldhay, Peterborough PE2 5SX; Tel 01733 746350; Fax 01733 746370

Children In Need Newark Newark Crt, 7 Newark Ave, Peterborough PE1 4NH; Tel 01733 746400; Fax 01733 746413

Intake and Assessment Children's Services Laxton Hse, 191 Lincoln Rd, Peterborough PE1 2PN; Tel 01733 746460; Fax 01733 746480

Community Team (Adults)

Sundance Hse, Staniland Way, Werrington, Peterborough PE4 6WR; Tel 01733 746126; Fax 01733 746140
Teams within this section include South and Access Team, Sensory Impairment, Older People's Mental Health Team, North West/North East Disability Team.

HEALTH TEAM PETERBOROUGH (ADULTS)

Peterborough District General Hospital, Social Services, Peterborough PE1 4DA; Tel 01733 874354; Fax 01733 346058

Health Team (Adults) Edith Cavell Hospital, Bretton Gate, Peterborough PE3 9G2; Tel 01733 875140; Fax 01733 875155

Mental Health Services Cambridgeshire and Peterborough Mental Health Partnership NHS Trust; Tel 01480 398500

Community Learning Disability Team

Room 206, Town Hall, Bridge St, Peterborough PE1 1HL; Tel 01733 452432; Fax 01733 456140

Looked After Children – Bretton Green

Units 2–3 Bretton Grn, Office Village, Bretton, Peterborough; Tel 01733 746278; Fax 01733 746251

Children's Services

RESIDENTIAL CARE

Dogsthorpe Road Children's Home 12 Dogsthorpe Rd, Peterborough; Tel 01733 746502; Fax 01733 746504
Manager Frankie Goat (Acting)

London Road Children's Home 165 London Rd, Fletton, Peterborough PE2; Tel 01733 746525; Fax 01733 746526
Manager Alan Pearson (Acting)

RESPITE CARE FOR CHILDREN WITH LEARNING DISABILITIES

The Manor Derby Dr, Peterborough PE1 4NG; Tel 01733 746533; Fax 01733 746534
Manager Brian Moss (Acting)

SECURE UNIT

Clare Lodge Secure Unit Welmore Rd, Glinton, Peterborough PE6 7LU; Tel 01733 253246; Fax 01733 253565
Manager Phil Tooze

FAMILY CENTRES

Gunthorpe Family Centre Gunthorpe Rd, Peterborough PE4 7DZ; Tel 01733 746529; Fax 01733 746530
Manager Tracy Foster

Welland Family Centre 141–145 Redmile Walk, Welland, Peterborough PE1 4TU; Tel 01733 746521; Fax 01733 746522
Manager Jenny Curtis

PREVENTION TEAM

Orchard St Resources Centre, Orchard St, Woodston, Peterborough PE2 9AH; Tel 01733 746508; Fax 01733 890073
Manager Karen Ferris

CHILDREN WITH A DISABILITY

Children's Community Disability Team Herlington Hse, Benyon Gr, Orton Goldhay, Peterborough PE2 5SX; Tel 01733 746371; Fax 01733 746370
Manager Val Callis (Acting)

ADOPTION AND FOSTERING SERVICES

Adoption and Fostering Team Suite 6, Staniland Crt, Werrington, Peterborough PE4 6NJ; Tel 01733 746179; Fax 01733 746196
Manager Vacancy

Services for Adults with a Disability

PETERBOROUGH DAY SERVICES

17 Fletton Ave, Peterborough PE1 8DX; Tel 01733 319954;
01733 890093; Fax 01733 890093
Manager (Day Services) Scott Hall

Kingfisher Centre The Cresset, Bretton, Peterborough
PE3 8DX; Tel 01733 746570; Fax 01733 746571
Assistant Manager (Learning Disability Team) Pat Wilson
Assistant Manager (Physical Disability Team) Zara Young

Kingsthorpe Lighthouse The Bungalow, Vawser Lodge,
Peterborough PE3 6JE; Tel 01733 893254
Assistant Manager Zara Young

Lincoln Road Centre (Physical and Learning Disability) 49
Lincoln Rd, Peterborough PE1 2RR; Tel 01733 746507;
Fax 01733 746506
Assistant Manager Julie Skelton

RESIDENTIAL SERVICES FOR ADULTS WITH LEARNING DISABILITIES

Yaxley Hostel (Respite Care) 2 Park Cl, Yaxley,
Peterborough PE7 3JW; Tel 01733 240830; Fax 01733
243124
Manager Sadie Manchett
Assistant Manager Ruth Dawson

Services for Elders

DAY CARE ESTABLISHMENTS FOR ELDERS

Cresset Day Centre Rightwell East, Bretton, Peterborough
PE3 8DX; Tel 01733 260696; Fax 01733 263176
Manager Andy Saw

The Fleet Day Centre Fleet Community Centre, Fleet Way,
Fletton, Peterborough PE2 8DL; Tel 01733 558181
Manager Andy Saw

Greenwood House – Residential Home and Day Centre
South Pde, Peterborough PE3 6BQ; Tel 01733 569362;
Fax 01733 569434
Manager Linda Wilson

Welland House Residential Home and Day Centre Poplar
Ave, Dogsthorpe, Peterborough PE1 4DG; Tel 01733 345421;
Fax 01733 563209
Manager Harvey Boome

HOME CARE MANAGEMENT OFFICE

Home Care Manager Sundance Hse, Staniland Way,
Werrington, Peterborough PE4 6WR; Tel 01733 746102;
01733 746108; Fax 01733 746113
Manager Andy Saw

Education and Children's Department

Bayard Pl, Broadway, Peterborough PE1 1FB;
URL www.thelearningcity.co.uk; Tel (Helpline) 01733
748444; Fax 01733 748002
Director (Education and Children) Ros Clayton

EDUCATIONAL PSYCHOLOGY SERVICE

Peterborough City Council (Education), Bayard Pl,
Broadway, Peterborough PE1 1FB; Tel 01733 748360
Principal Educational Psychologist Sue Dewar

SPECIAL SCHOOLS

Clayton School Orton Goldhay, Peterborough;
E-mail aab075@peterborough.gov.uk; Tel 01733 232346;
Fax 01733 230879
Headteacher Phil Pike

Heltwate School North Bretton, Peterborough PE3 8RL;
E-mail aab077@peterborough.gov.uk; Tel 01733 262878;
Fax 01733 331192
Headteacher D.R. Smith

Marshfields School Eastern Cl, Dogsthorpe, Peterborough
PE1 4PP; E-mail aab067@peterborough.gov.uk; Tel 01733
568058; Fax 01733 553855
Headteacher W. Spurgeon

St. George's School Lawn Ave, Dogsthorpe, Peterborough
PE1 3RB; E-mail aab079@peterborough.gov.uk; Tel 01733
562058; Fax 01733 312737
Headteacher Phil Pike

PLYMOUTH CITY COUNCIL
www.plymouth.gov.uk

In April 1998 Plymouth became a unitary authority along
with Torbay. The rest of Devon retains a two-tier structure
and is listed alphabetically within this chapter.
Political Composition: Con: 39, Lab: 21
Civic Centre, Royal Pde, Plymouth PL1 2EW;
URL www.plymouth.gov.uk;
E-mail pccmail@plymouth.gov.uk; Tel 01752 668000;
Fax 01752 304963
Chief Executive and Town Clerk Alison Stone, LlB
Director (Development) Richard Willoughby
Head (Finance) Alan Clifford

Department for Social and Housing Services

City of Plymouth, Civic Centre, Plymouth PL1 2AA;
URL www.plymouth.gov.uk/; Tel 01752 307329;
Fax 01752 307330
Director Lesley Reid
Head (Children and Families) Jane Hampton
Head (Community Care) Paul Francombe (Acting)
Head (Performance and Resources) Howard Tomlin (Acting)
Head (Housing) Giles Perritt

TRAINING

Manager (Staff Development) Kay Burkett
Civic Centre, Plymouth; Tel 01752 307867; Fax 01752 304900

PLYMOUTH WORK OPPORTUNITIES

Clittaford Rd, Southway, Plymouth; Tel 01752 306660;
Fax 01752 306650
Manager Martin Davies

Portfolio Members

Adult Social Services and Health Chris Pattison
Shadow Patrick Nicholson

LOCAL OFFICES

For Service Information please contact Local Office.
Home Care Service, Meals on Wheels Service, Occupational
Therapy Service, Playgroup/Childminders.

Emergency Out of Hours Team Midland Hse, Notte St,
Plymouth PL1 2EJ; Tel 01752 346984; Fax 01752 331193

Budshead Office Greville Hse, Budshead Way, Crownhill,
Plymouth; Tel 01752 784511; Fax 01752 769601

Devonport Office Wolseley, Wolseley Rd, Milehouse,
Plymouth; Tel 01752 305638; Fax 01752 305644

Efford Office Douglass Hse, Douglass Rd, Efford,
Plymouth; Tel 01752 308777; Fax 01752 388740

Estover Office Endeavour Hse, Parkway Crt, Parkway, Plymouth; Tel 01752 308888; Fax 01752 308886

Ham/Trelawney Office Wolseley, Wolseley Rd, Plymouth; Tel 01752 305638; Fax 01752 308936

Plympton Office Treverbyn Hse, 88 Plymbridge Rd, Plympton, Plymouth; Tel 01752 305250; Fax 01752 305267

Plymstock Office 9a Dean Hill, Plymstock, Plymouth; Tel 01752 405671; Fax 01752 482502

St. Budeaux Office Chaucer Hse, 83 Chaucer Way, Manadon, Plymouth; Tel 01752 305151; Fax 01752 305160

Waterfront Office Nykredit Hse, 26 Lockyer St, Plymouth; Tel 01752 305600; Fax 01752 305601

Home Care Offices

GREVILLE HOUSE

Budshead Way, Crownhill, Plymouth; Tel 01752 779987

PASTERNOSTER HOUSE

Efford La, Efford, Plymouth; Tel 01752 776339

PEIRSON HOUSE

Mulgrave St, Plymouth; Tel 01752 261617

STIRLING HOUSE

Honicknowle Grn, Plymouth; Tel 01752 704881

HOSPITAL SOCIAL WORK

Derriford Hospital, Plymouth; Tel 01752 792136; 01752 792137; Fax 01752 792829

Central Team Mount Gould Hospital, Mountgould, Plymouth; Tel 01752 272542

Mental Health Team Scott Hospital, Westbourne Unit, Plymouth; Tel 01752 550741

Services for Children/Families

ADOPTION/FOSTERING TEAM

Midland Hse, Notte St, Plymouth PL1 2EJ; Tel 01752 306800

FAMILY CENTRES

Maya Contact Centre Wolseley Rd, Plymouth; Tel 01752 306300

North Plymouth Family Centre Crownhill, Plymouth; Tel 01752 787800

Ringmore Way Family Centre 41 Ringmore Way, West Pk, Plymouth; Tel 01752 351070

Sunflower Family Centre Adelaide St, Stonehouse, Plymouth; Tel 01752 225943

RESIDENTIAL ESTABLISHMENTS

Hawkers Lodge Hawkers La, Plymouth PL3 4QA; Tel 01752 242381

Summerfield Lancaster Gdns, Whitleigh, Plymouth; Tel 01752 706478

YOUTH OFFENDING TEAM

3rd Fl, Midland Hse, North St, Plymouth PL1 2EJ; Tel 01752 306999; Fax 01752 306998

SERVICES FOR PEOPLE WITH LEARNING DIFFICULTIES

Colwill Lodge Respite Centre Leypark Wlk, Estover, Plymouth; Tel 01752 768646; Fax 01752 776255

Highbury Resource Centre 207 Outlands Rd, Milehouse, Plymouth; Tel 01752 783676; Fax 01752 786149

Manadon Day Centre Chaucer Way, Manadon, Plymouth; Tel 01752 780321; Fax 01752 780003

Mayflower Day Centre Courtfield Lodge, Manamead, Plymouth; Tel 01752 226055; Fax 01752 220478

Project Enterprise Unit 57, City Bus Pk, Plymouth; Tel 01752 605868; Fax 01752 607992

St. George's Community Resource Centre George Pl, Stonehouse, Plymouth; Tel 01752 664128; Fax 01752 256112

Welby Community Unit 203 Outlands Rd, Milehouse, Plymouth; Tel 01752 794544; Fax 01752 768226

West Plymouth Work Unit Unit 7, Kestrel Way, Honicknowle, Plymouth; Tel 01752 788097; Fax 01752 779221

Woodfield Resource Centre Taunton Ave, Whitleigh, Plymouth; Tel 01752 766816; Fax 01752 783952

SERVICES FOR PHYSICALLY OR SENSORY HANDICAPPED

Reach Centre Taunton Ave, Whitleigh, Plymouth; Tel 01752 782020; Fax 01752 768952

Services for Elderly People

COMMUNITY CARE CENTRES

Granby Way Community Care Centre Park Ave, Devonport, Plymouth; Tel 01752 563040; Fax 01752 605970

Paternoster Day Centre Efford La, Efford, Plymouth; Tel 01752 793596

Peirson Community Care Centre (Community Care Support Centre) Peirson Hse, Mulgrave St, Plymouth; Tel 01752 662394; Fax 01752 253494

Stirling Day Centre Stirling Hse, Honicknowle Grn, Plymouth; Tel 01752 790531

Whitleigh Whitleigh Grn, Whitleigh, Plymouth; Tel 01752 706470; Fax 01752 769882

Department for Lifelong Learning

City of Plymouth Council, Plymouth PL1 2AA; URL www.pgfl.plymouth.gov.uk; E-mail lifelong.learning@plymouth.gov.uk; Tel 01752 307400; Fax 01752 307403
Director (Lifelong Learning) Sohail Faruqi, BSc DipEd, MBA

SPECIAL SCHOOLS

Mount Tamar School Row La, St. Budeaux, Plymouth PL5 2EF; E-mail mount.tamar.school@plymouth.gov.uk; Tel 01752 365128; Fax 01752 351227
Headteacher B. Jones
  Mixed 6–16 EBD

Plymouth Hospital School Level 12, Derriford Hospital, Plymouth PL6 8DH; E-mail hospital.school@plymouth.gov.uk; Tel 01752 792476; Fax 01752 792476
Headteacher R. Bill
  Mixed 5–16

Plymouth, Courtlands School Widey La, Crownhill, Plymouth PL6 5JS; E-mail courtlands.school@plymouth.gov.uk; Tel 01752 776848; Fax 01752 769102
Headteacher G. Dunkerley
  Mixed 5–12 MLD

Plymouth, Hillside School Bodmin Rd, Whitleigh, Plymouth PL5 4DZ; E-mail hillside.school@plymouth.gov.uk; Tel 01752 773875; Fax 01752 775761
Headteacher D. Whitton
  Mixed 11–17 MLD

6

Plymouth, Mill Ford School Rochford Cres, Ernesettle, Plymouth PL5 2PY;
E-mail millford.school@plymouth.gov.uk; Tel 01752 300270; Fax 01752 300109
Headteacher J. Hill
   Mixed 3–19 SLD/PMLD

Plympton, Longcause Community School St. Maurice, Plympton, Plymouth PL7 1JB;
E-mail longcause.school@plymouth.gov.uk; Tel 01752 336881; Fax 01752 341151
Headteacher M. Jelly
   Mixed 4–16 MLD

Plymstock, Downham School Horn La, Plymstock, Plymouth PL9 9BR; URL www.downham.plymouth.sch.uk; E-mail downham.school@plymouth.gov.uk; Tel 01752 403214; Fax 01752 481539
Headteacher M.E. Maleham, MPhil
   Mixed 3–16 SLD

Woodlands School Bodmin Rd, Whitleigh, Plymouth PL5 4DZ; E-mail woodlands.school@plymouth.gov.uk; Tel 01752 300101; Fax 01752 300102
Headteacher M.A. Vatcher
   Mixed 3–17 PH

PUPIL REFERRAL UNITS

Plymouth Tuition Service; Young Mothers' Group Lancaster Gdns, Whiteleigh, Plymouth PL5 4AA;
E-mail plymouth.youngmothersgroup@plymouth.gov.uk; Tel 01752 786696
Headteacher J. Moir

Plymouth Tuition Service; Years 6–8 Mannamead Centre, 15 Eggbuckland Rd, Plymouth PL3 5HF;
E-mail perren.tracey@plymouth.gov.uk; Tel 01752 306269; Fax 01752 306269
Headteacher Perren Tracey

Plymouth Tuition Service; Years 9–11 Bretonside Tuition Centre, Martin's Gate, Bretonside, Plymouth PL4 0AT;
E-mail bretonside.tuition@plymouth.gov.uk; Tel 01752 229351; Fax 01752 229351
Headteacher N. Cook

BOROUGH OF POOLE

www.poole.gov.uk

Population 140 940
Political Composition: Con: 26, LD: 16.
Civic Centre, Poole BH15 2RU; URL www.poole.gov.uk;
   Tel 01202 633633; Fax 01202 633706
Chief Executive John McBride
Policy Director Fred Davies; E-mail f.davies@poole.gov.uk

Social Services Department

E-mail f.davies@poole.gov.uk; Tel 01202 633203; Fax 01202 633899
Policy Director (Social Services) Fred Davies
Adult Social Services (Commissioning) Unit Tel 01202 261132; Fax 01202 261141
Head (Service Unit) John Dermody
Principal Officer (Elderly Disability and Hospital)
   Angie Smith
Principal Officer (Mental Health, Disability and Hospital)
   Allan Brown
Principal Officer (Support Services) Malcolm Nichols
Principal Officer (Community Care) Eileen Dunnachie
Adult Social Services (Provider Unit) Tel 01202 261030; Fax 01202 261001
Head (Service Unit) Charlie Sheldrick

Manager (Community Services) Philip Mason; Tel 01202 261017
Principal Officer (Older People and Home Care) Jeff Russell
Principal Officer (Younger Adults) Peter Moore
Principal Officer (Finance and Support) Karen Withers
Contact (Children and Families Services) Tel 01202 714745; Fax 01202 715589
Service Unit Head Jan Thurgood; Tel 01202 714745; Fax 01202 715589
Principal Officer (Services Management) Gerry Moore
Principal Officer (Policy, Planning and Performance Management) Jan Sayers
Principal Officer (Finance, Administration and Systems)
   Gerald Lewis
Emergency Duty Service Mitchell Hse, 2 Mitchell Rd, Poole BH17 5SU; Tel 01202 668123; Fax 01202 670837

Care Theme Representative on the Executive Committee

Chair (Policy Advisory Group) Cllr C. Meachin (LD)
Vice-Chair (Policy Advisory Group) Cllr Mrs J. James (LD)
Chair (Overview and Scrutiny Committee)
   Cllr R. O'Mahoney (Lab)
Vice-Chair (Overview and Scrutiny Committee)
   Cllr C. Meachin (LD)
Members of the Policy Advisory Group
Con: Ms E. Atkinson, Mrs W. Beckwith, C. Bulteel, Mrs B. Grant-Braham.
LD: G. Curtis, Mrs J. Jones.
Lab: R. O'Mahoney.
Members of the Overview and Scrutiny Committee
Con: Mrs E. Atkinson, Mrs W. Beckwith, C. Bulteel.
LD: P. Dykes, Ms C. Ewart.

FAMILY CENTRE

Ted Webster Family Centre 519a Ashley Rd, Parkstone, Poole BH14 0BD; Tel 01202 745110; Fax 01202 718017
Manager Jill Aiken
   (50)

SOCIAL AND EDUCATION CENTRE

Seaview Centre Croft Rd, Parkstone, Poole BH12 3LD; Tel 01202 721590; Fax 01202 721609
Manager Russell Giles

RESIDENTIAL HOME FOR PERSONS WITH LEARNING DIFFICULTIES

Pergins Residential Home 21 Christopher Cres, Poole BH15 3HW; Tel 01202 678728; Fax 01202 665990
Manager Martin Ward

HEALTH, DISABILITY AND MENTAL HEALTH DAY SERVICES

Fourways Day Centre, Constitution Hill Rd, Poole BH14 0PZ; Tel 01202 262921; Fax 01202 669638
Manager Diana Wharam
   (90)

DAY CENTRES FOR THE ELDERLY

Garland Road Day Centre 55 Garland Rd, Poole BH15 2LD; Tel 01202 673632; Fax 01202 667816
Manager Jean Stainer
   (25)

Poole Day Centre 12a Commercial Rd, Poole BH14 0JW; Tel 01202 721722; Fax 01202 737078
Manager Jean Stainer
   (50)

RESIDENTIAL AND DAYCARE FOR OLDER PEOPLE

Mitchell Hse, 2 Mitchell Rd, Canford Heath, Poole BH17 7SU; Tel 01202 681446; Fax 01202 670837
Manager Sally Ann Stacey

HOME FOR THE ELDERLY

There is one home for the elderly run by Poole Council.

Education Service

Borough of Poole Civic Centre, Poole BH15 2RU; Tel 01202 633633

SPECIAL SCHOOLS

Hearing Impaired Unit c/o Sylvan First School, Livingstone Rd, Parkstone, Poole BH12 3DT; Tel 01202 743064; Fax 01202 716360
Headteacher Tanya Bunting

Langside School Langside Ave, Parkstone, Poole BH12 5BN; Tel 01202 518635; Fax 01202 531513
Headteacher J. Ashby
Independent

Longspee Special School Learoyd Rd, Canford Heath, Poole BH17 8PJ; Tel 01202 380266; Fax 01202 380270
Headteacher Eric Bell

Montacute Special School 3 Canford Heath Rd, Poole BH17 9NG; Tel 01202 693239; Fax 01202 657363
Headteacher M. Sammons
Foundation

Victoria Education Centre 12 Lindsay Rd, Branksome Pk, Poole BH13 6AS; Tel 01202 763697; Fax 01202 768078
Headteacher P. Warner
Independent

Winchelsea Special School Guernsey Rd, Parkstone, Poole BH12 4LL; Tel 01202 746240; Fax 01202 733024
Headteacher G. Moore

PORTSMOUTH CITY COUNCIL
www.portsmouth.gov.uk

Came into effect April 1997.
Population 188 800 (1999)
Political Composition: Con: 15, LD: 16, Lab: 11.
Civic Offices, Guildhall Sq, Portsmouth PO1 2AL;
    URL www.portsmouth.gov.uk;
    E-mail general@portsmouthcc.gov.uk; Tel 023 9282 2251
Chief Executive Nick Gurney

Social Services Department

Civic Offices, Guildhall Sq, Portsmouth PO1 2EP; Tel 023 9282 2251
Director (Social Services) Rob Hutchinson
Assistant Director (Children and Families) Pam Robinson
Assistant Director (Older Persons) Sarah Mitchell
Assistant Director (Adults) Mary Brunt
Assistant Director (Resources) Steve Dixon
Manager (Policy Development – Children and Families) Vaughan Tudor-Williams
Manager (Policy Development – Adults) Rob Watt
Manager (Personnel and Training) Pete Owen
Manager (Contracts, Projects and Premises) Ken Wise
Manager (Information and Planning) Nick Davey
Customer Relations and Complaints Officer Sam Midgley
Group Accountant (Devolved Unit) Carol Durrant
Child Protection and Development Officer Steve Hayes
Senior Manager (Family Support Services) Malcolm Childs; Tel 023 9283 9111
Senior Manager (Service Quality – Children and Families) Rose Storkey; Tel 023 9283 9111
Senior Manager (Looked After Children) Vanessa Courtney; Tel 023 9283 9111

Senior Manager (Fieldwork Services – Children and Families) Kevin Jones; Tel 023 9283 9111
Senior Manager (Older Persons) Chris Izard; Tel 023 9284 1168
Resources Manager (Adults) Sarah Vance; Tel 023 9220 0132
Commissioning Manager (Adults) Alan Windsor; Tel 023 9220 0132

Social and Health Care Committee

Chair Tom Blair
Vice-Chair Pam Webb
Members of the Committee
Alex Bentley, Malcolm Hey, Nicholas Lacey, Mike Park, Lauren Semke, Steve Wemyss.

AREA OFFICES

Services for Children and Families Merefield Hse, Nutfield Pl, Portsmouth PO1 4JZ; Tel 023 9283 9111

Services for Adults and Older People Medina Hse, 38 Medina Rd, Portsmouth PO6 3EX; Tel 023 9220 0132

Services for Adults and Older People Brankesmere, Queens Cres, Portsmouth PO5 3HS; Tel 023 9275 6321

HOSPITAL SOCIAL WORKERS

Queen Alexandra Hospital Southwick Hill Rd, Portsmouth PO6 3LY; Tel 023 9253 8200

St. James' Hospital Locksway Rd, Milton, Portsmouth PO4 8LD; Tel 023 9286 6251

St. Mary's Hospital Milton Rd, Portsmouth PO3 6AD; Tel 023 9277 8200

CHILDREN'S HOMES

Leverett House Children's Home 3 Yarborough Rd, Southsea, Hampshire PO5 3DX; Tel 023 9282 4770
    (16)

Lightfoot Lawn Children's Home Milton, Portsmouth PO4 8HX; Tel 023 9273 5327
    (10)

Seaway Crescent Children's Home 49–51 Seaway Cres, Milton, Portsmouth PO4 8LL; Tel 023 9273 1037
    (11)

Skye Close Children's Home Orkney Rd, Cosham, Portsmouth PO6 3LU; Tel 023 9237 8378

CENTRE FOR CHILDREN WITH A PHYSICAL DISABILITY

Beechside Respite Care Unit, 235 Havant Rd, Drayton, Portsmouth PO6 1DA; Tel 023 9264 2291
    (9)

FAMILY CENTRES

Battenburg Family Centre Battenburg Ave, North End, Portsmouth PO2 0SN; Tel 023 9266 1959

Buckland Family Centre Nessus St, Buckland, Portsmouth PO2 7HA; Tel 023 9269 3121

Hester Road Family Centre Hester Rd, Milton, Portsmouth PO4 8HB; Tel 023 9287 5294

DAY CENTRES FOR PEOPLE WITH A LEARNING DISABILITY

Horizon Day Centre Sundridge Cl, Cosham, Portsmouth PO6 3LP; Tel 023 9238 0455

Portsmouth Day Services Dundas Lane Centre, Quartermaine Rd, Portsmouth PO3 5QP; Tel 023 9261 9888

HOME FOR PEOPLE WITH A PHYSICAL DISABILITY

Corben Lodge Moorings Way, Portsmouth PO4 8QW; Tel 023 9273 1941
    (24)

6

HOSTEL FOR PEOPLE WITH A LEARNING DISABILITY

Russets Hostel Gatcombe Dr, Hilsea, Portsmouth PO2 0TX; Tel 023 9269 4423
(28)

CITY MENTAL HEALTH SERVICE

Community Support Services Campion Pl, 44–46 Elm Gr, Southsea, Portsmouth PO5 1JG; Tel 023 9273 7106

DAY CENTRES FOR THE ELDERLY

Longdean Day Centre Hillsley Rd, Paulsgrove, Portsmouth PO6 4NH; Tel 023 9238 3512
(35 places five days per week)

McDonald Watson Day Centre Nutfield Pl, Portsmouth PO1 4JE; Tel 023 9273 7758
(40 places five days per week)

Northern Parade Day Centre Doyle Ave, Hilsea, Portsmouth PO2 9NF; Tel 023 9266 7255
(32 places five days per week)

HOMES FOR THE ELDERLY

There are ten homes for the elderly run by Portsmouth City Council.

Education Authority

Portsmouth City Council, 4th Fl, Civic Offices, Guildhall Sq, Portsmouth PO1 2EA; Tel 023 9284 1209; Fax 023 9284 1208

SPECIAL SCHOOLS AND SCHOOLS WITH SPECIALIST PROVISION

Cliffdale Primary School Battenburg Ave, Portsmouth PO2 0SN; Tel 023 9266 2601; Fax 023 9266 0506
Headteacher Mrs J. Sansome
4–11 MLD

East Shore School Eastern Rd, Milton, Portsmouth PO3 6EP; Tel 023 9283 9331; Fax 023 9287 2504
Headteacher P. Clarke
3–19 SLD

The Futcher School Drayton La, Drayton, Portsmouth PO6 1HG; Tel 023 9237 5318; Fax 023 9237 5348
Headteacher J.C. Meek
3–16 PD

Redwood Park School Wembley Gr, Portsmouth PO6 2RY; Tel 023 9237 7500; Fax 023 9220 1104
Headteacher Mrs E. Nye
11–16 MLD

Waterside School Tipner La, Portsmouth PO2 8RA; Tel 023 9266 5664; Fax 023 9265 3333
Headteacher T.S. Stokes
11–16 EBD

The Willows Nursery School Battenburg Ave, Portsmouth PO2 0SN; Tel 023 9266 6918; Fax 023 9265 2247
Headteacher A. Swann
2–4 Special nursery

PUPIL REFERRAL UNITS

Highlands Centre at The Spinnaker Education Centre Penhale Rd, Portsmouth PO1 5EF; Tel 023 9281 6486; Fax 023 9281 6478
Teacher-in-Charge B. McDonagh

North End at The Spinnaker Education Centre Penhale Rd, Portsmouth PO1 5EF; Tel 023 9281 7766; Fax 023 9285 5061
Teacher-in-Charge Rose Allen

The Sevenoaks Centre Sundridge Cl, Cosham, Portsmouth PO6 3JL; Tel 023 9221 4492; Fax 023 9221 4509
Team Co-ordinator Sally Garret

READING BOROUGH COUNCIL
www.reading.gov.uk

In April 1998 Berkshire County Council was replaced by Bracknell Forest, Reading, Slough, West Berkshire, Windsor and Maidenhead and Wokingham, each responsible for local government services in their area. They are listed alphabetically within this chapter.
Political Composition: Lab: 36, LD: 6, Con: 3
Civic Centre, Reading RG1 7TD;
    URL www.reading.gov.uk;
    E-mail <firstname>.<surname>@reading.gov.uk;
    Tel 0118 939 0900; Fax 0118 958 9770; Minicom 0118 939 0700
Chief Executive Trish Haines
Leader of the Council David Sutton
Director (Environment) Tony Lear
Director (Arts and Leisure) Anita Cacchioli

Social Services and Housing

PO Box 2624, Reading RG1 7WB;
    URL www.reading.gov.uk; Tel 0118 939 0900; Fax 0118 958 9770
Director (Social Services and Housing) Eileen Means; Tel 0118 939 0094
Assistant Director (Housing) Debbie Ward; Tel 0118 939 0266; Fax 0018 939 0865
Head (Children and Families Services) Laura Eades; Tel 0118 939 0080; Fax 0118 939 0408
Head (Community Care) Anne Gay; Tel 0118 939 0081; Fax 0118 939 0408
Head (Strategy and Performance) Sarah Gee; Tel 0118 939 0973; Fax 0118 939 0786
Manager (Training) Russell Gabbini; Tel 0118 939 0900 ext 4064; Fax 0118 939 0470
Manager (Personnel) Annette Paterson; Tel 0118 939 0942; Fax 0118 939 0470
Manager (Housing Development) Vacancy; Tel 0118 939 0218; Fax 0118 939 0786

Social Services and Health Committee

Lab: 10, LD: 2, Con: 1
Chair Peter Ruheman (Lab)
66 Brooksby Rd, Tilehurst, Reading RG31 6LY; Tel 0118 941 5760
Vice-Chair Trish Thomas (Lab)
18 Rowley Rd, Reading RG2 0DR; Tel 0118 975 6601
Members of the Committee
Lab: G. Bello, C. Goodall, D. Lawrence, M. Lockey, J. Morris, M. Powers, A. Sheibani.
LD: B. Green, D. Ferriday.
Con: J. Skeates.

FAMILY SUPPORT TEAMS

Adolescent and Family Resource Team August Hse, 6 Brownlow Rd, Reading RG1 6NP; Tel 0118 901 5324; Fax 0118 901 5325
Team Manager Poppy Orfanos

Family Support Centre Amethyst La, Liebenrood Rd, Reading RG30 2EZ; Tel 0118 901 5320; Fax 0118 901 5321
Team Manager Chris Barefield (Acting)

Family Support Service PO Box 2624, Reading RG1 7WB; Tel 0118 939 0049; Fax 0118 939 0408
Service Manager Paul Kerswell

Referral and Assessment Team Civic Centre, Reading RG1 7TD; Tel 0118 955 3617; Fax 0118 955 3741
Team Manager Deborah Appelbee

LOOKED AFTER CHILDREN'S SERVICE

Fostering and Adoption Team Fountain Hse, Queenswalk, Reading RG1 7WB; Tel 0118 955 3740; Fax 0118 955 3746
Team Manager Judith Russell

Leaving Care 2–4 Western Elms Ave, Reading RG30 2AN; Tel 0118 901 5330; Fax 0118 901 5332
Team Manager Debbie Curd

Looked After Service PO Box 2624, Reading RG1 7WB; Tel 0118 939 0526; Fax 0118 939 0408
Service Manager Jean Ash

Looked After Team Fountain Hse, Queenswalk, Reading RG1 7WB; Tel 0118 955 3601; Fax 0118 955 3746
Team Mangaer Denise McKay (Acting)

CHILDREN WITH DISABILITIES

Disabled Children's Team Fountain Hse, Queenswalk, Reading RG1 7WB; Tel 0118 955 3647; Fax 0118 955 3741
Team Manager Shantie Critchley

Residential Team, Pinecroft 1 Monksbarn, Cressingham Rd, Reading RG2 7RU; Tel 0118 901 5339; Fax 0118 901 5385
Team Manager Matthew Randle

Residential Team, Cressingham 27 Cressingham Rd, Reading RG2 7RU; Tel 0118 901 5335; 0118 901 5336; Fax 0118 901 5338
Team Manager Pippa Hutchinson

Reviewing, Monitoring and User Participation PO Box 2624, Reading RG1 7WB; Tel 0118 939 0351; Fax 0118 939 0408
Service Manager Bridget Harnett

Youth Offending Team 34–36 Crown St, Reading RG1 2SE; Tel 0118 939 0420; Fax 0118 939 0935
Team Manager Phil Hutchins

OTHER SERVICES

Sheltered Housing PO Box 2624, Reading RG1 7WB; Tel 0118 939 0211; Fax 0118 939 0865
Team Manager Gill Rimmer

Transport 16 Bennet Rd, Reading RG30 0QX; Tel 0118 901 5366; Fax 0118 901 5366
Manager Colin Dee

SERVICES FOR PEOPLE WITH LEARNING DISABILITIES

Adults with Learning Difficulties PO Box 2624, Reading RG1 7WB; Tel 0118 939 0401; Fax 0118 939 0408
Locality Manager Lynn Harrington

Joint Community Team for People with Learning Disabilities PO Box 2624, Reading RG1 7WB; Tel 0118 955 3553; Fax 0118 955 3741
Team Manager Christine Edwards

DAY CENTRES (LEARNING DISABILITIES)

Reading Education and Training Centre 18 Bennett Rd, Reading RG2 0QX; Tel 0118 901 5344; Fax 0118 901 5345
Unit Manager Bobbie Richardson

Strathy Close Day Centre Craig Ave, Tilehurst, Reading RG30 2PP; Tel 0118 901 5346
Unit Manager Philip Browne

RESIDENTIAL HOME (LEARNING DISABILITIES)

Supported Living Team 188 Whitley Wood La, Reading RG2 8PR; Tel 0118 901 5347; Fax 0118 901 5347
Unit Manager Rob Lynch

SERVICES FOR ADULTS WITH MENTAL HEALTH NEEDS

PO Box 2624, Reading RG1 7WB; Tel 0118 939 0384
Locality Manager Suzanne Westhead

Community Alcohol and Drugs Team 342 Oxford Rd, Reading RG3 1AF; Tel 0118 958 9557; Fax 0118 950 8936

Joint Community Mental Health Team Compass Hse, Battle Hospital, Oxford Rd, Reading RG30 1AG; Tel 0118 959 2850; Fax 0118 959 2851
Joint Team Manager Jane McCausland

DAY CENTRE (MENTAL HEALTH)

Compass Opportunities Day Treatment Centre Compass Pl, Battle Hospital, Oxford Rd, Reading RG30 1AG
Joint Unit Manager Susanna Yeoman; Tel 0118 959 2800

RESIDENTIAL HOMES (MENTAL HEALTH)

Focus House 14–16 Castle St, Reading RG1 6AG; Tel 0118 901 5350; Fax 0118 901 5350
Unit Manager Nigel Leaney

COMMUNITY CARE SERVICES

Access Team Civic Centre, Reading RG1 7TD; Tel 0118 955 3621; Fax 0118 955 3741
Team Manager Bryan Bellis

Reading Abbey Community Care Teams Whitley Social Services Centre, 268 Northumberland Ave, Whitley, Reading RG2 7PJ; Tel 0118 931 2277; Fax 0118 931 0682
Team Manager Bryan Bellis

Reading Thames Community Care Teams Founatain Hse, Queenswalk, Reading RG1 7WB; Tel 0118 955 3553; Fax 0118 955 3741
Team Manager Regina Couibear

Services for Older People (Operational) PO Box 2624, Reading RG1 7WB; Tel 0118 939 0406; Fax 0118 939 0408
Services Manager Vacancy

DAY CENTRES (OLDER PEOPLE)

Albert Road Day Centre 1 Albert Rd, Caversham, Reading RG4 7AN; Tel 0118 901 5361; Fax 0118 901 5360
Co-ordinator (Activities) Yvonne Antrobus

Phoenix Day Centre Amethyst La, Liebenrood Rd, Reading RG30 2EZ; Tel 0118 901 5364; Fax 0118 901 5365
Unit Manager Peter Pratt

RESIDENTIAL HOMES (OLDER PEOPLE/DISABILITIES)

There are four local authority residential homes for older and disabled people.
Service Manager Paul Cooper
PO Box 2624, Reading RG1 7WB; Tel 01189 390406; Fax 01189 390408

Education and Community Services Directorate

Civic Centre, PO Box 2623, Reading RG1 7WA; Tel 0118 939 0923
Director (Education and Community Services) Andrew Daykin
Head (School Improvemet) Paul Sadler
Head (Services for Children and Young People) Melani Oliver
Head (Education Strategy and School Planning) Richard Parker
Head (Directorate Support Services) John Littlefair

EDUCATION WELFARE SERVICE

Reading Education Welfare Service York Hse, York Rd, Reading RG1 8DH; Tel 0118 901 5870
Senior Education Welfare Officer Mary Koudis

6

EDUCATION FOR CHILDREN OUT OF SCHOOL (ECOS)

Seagull Hse, Ross Rd, Reading RG1 8DY; Tel 0118 901 5583
Head of Service Zoe Lattimer
Pupils out of school are referred to ECOS for home teaching leading to return to school or admittance to a pupil referal unit/other special educational needs establishment.

EDUCATIONAL PSYCHOLOGY SERVICE

23 Craven Rd, Reading RG1 5LE; Tel 0118 901 5400

SPECIAL CLASSES AND UNITS

Horseshoes New Town School, School Terr, Reading RG1 3LS; Tel 0118 901 5508

Hugh Faringdon Special Resource Hugh Farrington Secondary School, Fawley Rd, Reading RG30 3EP; Tel 0118 957 4730
Headteacher P. Barras
Asperger syndrome

St. Michael's Resource St. Michael's School, Dee Rd, Tilehurst, Reading RG30 4AS; Tel 0118 901 5550

SPECIAL SCHOOLS

The Avenue School Basingstoke Rd, Reading RG2 0EN; Tel 0118 901 5554; Fax 0118 901 5558
Headteacher V.A. Brown

The Holy Brook School 145 Ashampstead Rd, Southcote, Reading RG30 3LT; Tel 0118 901 5489; Fax 0118 901 5488

Reading Alternative Special School 40 Christchurch Rd, Reading RG2 7AY; Tel 0118 901 5524; Fax 0118 901 5519
Secondary adjustment centre

PUPIL REFERRAL UNITS

Highways Pupil Referral Unit 999 Oxford Rd, Reading RG31 6TL; Tel 0118 941 1720; Fax 0118 941 1720

Seagull House Pupil Referral Unit Ross Rd, Reading RG1 8DZ; Tel 0118 901 5583

REDCAR AND CLEVELAND BOROUGH COUNCIL

www.redcar-cleveland.gov.uk

Population 139 000
Political Composition: Lab: 31, Con: 14, LD: 11, Ind: 3
Town Hall, Fabian Rd, South Bank, Middlesbrough TS6 9AR; URL www.redcar-cleveland.gov.uk; Tel 01642 444000; Fax 01642 444584
Chief Executive Colin Moore

Social Services Department

Seafield Hse, Kirkleatham St, Redcar, Redcar and Cleveland TS10 1SP; Tel 01642 771500; Fax 01642 771670
Director (Health and Social Care) Maurice Bates
Head (Children's Services) Barbara Shaw
Head (Commissioning) Nicola Bailey
Head (Partnership and Performance) Dave Appleton
Principal Officer (Finance and Management Information) Tim Graham
Principal Officer (Personnel) John Finlay

Cabinet Member Health and Social Care

Member Cllr Valerie Halton (Con)

AREA OFFICES

The Grange 153 Fabian Rd, Eston, Middlesbrough, Redcar and Cleveland TS6 9RH; Tel 01642 464610; Fax 01642 464305
Team Manager (Disability) N. Porter

Grosmont Resource Centre 20 Grosmont Cl, Redcar, Redcar and Cleveland TS10 4PJ; Tel 01642 495910; Fax 01642 491630
Manager (Accommodation and Support) Chris Daniel

HOSPITAL SOCIAL WORKERS

The Cottage Guisborough General Hospital, Northgate, Guisborough, Redcar and Cleveland; Tel 01287 284141; Fax 01287 630932

James Cook James Cook University Hospital, Marton Rd, Middlesbrough, Redcar and Cleveland; Tel 01642 850850; Fax 01642 854594

TARGET

16 Millbank Terr, Redcar, Redcar and Cleveland; Tel 01642 488433
Manager (Target Team) Sharon McBride

COMMUNITY HOMES

Bylands Community Home 31 Bylands Cl, Redcar, Redcar and Cleveland TS10 4EX; Tel 01642 483825

Cherry Tree House Community Home 27 Clynes Rd, Grangetown, Redcar and Cleveland TS6 7LZ; Tel 01642 453122

Rose Tree House Community Home 4 Derwent Rd, Skelton, Redcar and Cleveland TS12 2HW; Tel 01287 650476

HOME FOR CHILDREN WITH LEARNING DISABILITIES

St. Margaret's Way Resource Centre 45 St. Margaret's Way, Brotton, Redcar and Cleveland TS12 2UE; Tel 01287 677733; Fax 01287 678437

HOMES FOR PEOPLE WITH LEARNING DIFFICULTIES

Hollingside Home Albion Terr, Saltburn, Redcar and Cleveland TS12 1LS; Tel 01287 623994

Jervaulx Road Home 17 Jervaulx Rd, New Skelton, Redcar and Cleveland TS12 2NL; Tel 01287 653814

Norwood Home Albion Terr, Saltburn, Redcar and Cleveland TS12 1LT; Tel 01287 622310

CENTRES FOR ADULTS WITH LEARNING DISABILITIES

Grangetown Works Experience Centre Bolckow Rd, Grangetown, Redcar and Cleveland TS6 7AA; Tel 01642 467849

Skelton Social Skills Centre Hollybush Trading Est, Skelton, Redcar and Cleveland TS12 2LQ; Tel 01287 652333; Fax 01287 653359

Upsall Hall Rural Centre Swans Corner, Nunthorpe, Middlesbrough, Redcar and Cleveland TS7 0PG; Tel 01642 315481

DAY CENTRES FOR THE ELDERLY

North Skelton Day Centre Vaughan St, North Skelton, Redcar and Cleveland TS12 2AR; Tel 01287 653901

St. Germain's Day Centre Vicarage Dr, Marskey, Redcar and Cleveland; Tel 01287 485844

HOMES FOR THE ELDERLY

There are five homes for the elderly.

MEALS SERVICE

Frozen meals supplied.

Education Department

Education Department, PO Box 83, Redcar, Redcar and
Cleveland TS10 1YA; Tel 01642 444000; Fax 01642 444122
Director (Education)   Jenny Lewis; Fax 01642 771184
Assistant Director (Education – Parent and Student Services)
Simon Willson (Acting)
Assistant Director (Education – Lifelong Learning)
Catherine Hatch
Head (Special School Support)   Mike Cotton
*Head (Admissions, Welfare and Awards) and Principal
Education Social Worker*   Lynn Strachan
SEN Officer   Steven Harrison (Acting)

PSYCHOLOGICAL SERVICE

Redcar Education Department, Corporation Rd, Redcar,
Redcar and Cleveland TS10 1HA; Tel 01642 286644;
Fax 01642 282146

SPECIAL SCHOOLS FOR PUPILS WITH LEARNING DIFFICULTIES

Kilton Thorpe School Marshal Dr, Saltburn by the Sea,
Brotton, Redcar and Cleveland TS12 2UW; Tel 01287
677265; Fax 01287 201201
Headteacher   Mrs N. Robinson
Full range (78)

Kirkleatham Hall School Kirkleatham Village, Redcar,
Redcar and Cleveland TS10 4QR; Tel 01642 483009;
Fax 01642 480054
Headteacher   A.G. Naylor
Full range (123)

ROCHDALE METROPOLITAN BOROUGH COUNCIL
www.rochdale.gov.uk

Population 202 164
Political Composition: Lab: 31, LD: 21, Con: 8
PO Box 39, Municpal Offices, Rochdale, Greater
Manchester OL16 1LQ; URL www.rochdale.gov.uk;
E-mail council@rochdale.gov.uk; Tel 01706 647474;
Fax 01706 865450
The Mayor   Cllr Lil Murphy
Deputy Mayor   Cllr Sultan Ali
Chief Executive   Roger Ellis
Director (Technical Services)   P. Bleasdale, DipArch, RIBA
Electric Hse, Smith St, Rochdale, Greater Manchester
OL16 1YP; Tel 01706 647474
Director (Environment)   S. Beckwith
Director (Housing Services)   H. Eastham
Director (Recreation and Community Services)   A. Wiggans
Chief Officer (Direct Services)   J. Patterson
Folly Walk, Rochdale, Greater Manchester OL12 0UT;
Tel 01706 641170; Fax 01706 658407

Social Services Department

PO Box 67, Municpal Offices, Rochdale, Greater
Manchester OL16 1YQ; Tel 01706 647474
Director (Social Services)   I. Davey
Assistant Director (Community Care)   S. Netherwood
Assistant Director (Child Care)   S. Titcombe
Assistant Director (Professional and Technical Services)
T. Kitchin
Manager (Adult Services Resource)   K. Adamson
Manager (Registration and Inspection Unit)   M. Tomlinson
St. Albans Hse, Drake St, Rochdale, Greater Manchester;
Tel 01706 341411
Manager (Physical Disability)   V. Chadwick
Manager (Learning Disabilities Services)   M. O'Keefe

Manager (Mental Health Services)   B. Windle
Manager (Adult Services – Rochdale and Pennine Townships)
C. Beech
Manager (Adult Services – Middleton and Heywood Townships)
A. Topping
Manager (Childcare – Rochdale and Pennine Townships)
M. Cunningham
Manager (Childcare – Middleton and Heywood)   S.E. Dooks
Manager (Children Resources)   Vacancy
Manager (Strategic Planning)   D. Ledsham
Manager (Information Systems)   Laurence McGough
Communications Officer   Gabriel Murray

TRAINING

Responsible for training professional and support staff in
the department.
Manager (Human Resource)   S. Adamson
Social Services Training, Foxholes Hse, Rochdale, Greater
Manchester OL12 0ED; Tel 01706 710750

The Executive

Lab: 5, LD: 3, Con: 1
49 Partington St, Castleton, Rochdale, Greater Manchester
Lead Member (Social Services)   Colin Thompson (Lab)
41 Vicarage Road North, Rochdale, Greater Manchester
OL11 2TF
Members of the Executive Committee
Lab: Brett (Vice-Chair), Murphy, Roberts (Chair),
Robotham.
LD: Ashworth, Rowen, Smith.
Con: Dearnley.

AREA OFFICES

Denehurst House Area Office Denehurst Pk, Edenfield Rd,
Rochdale, Greater Manchester OL11 5AU; Tel 01706 644106
Area Team Manager (Adult Services – Pennine)   J. Maher
Area Team Manager (Adult Services – Rochdale North)
S. Collison
Area Team Manager (Adult Services – Rochdale South)
J. Hannaway

Lakeside Offices Bowness Rd, Middleton, Greater
Manchester M24 4NU; Tel 0161 643 1525
Area Team Manager (Adult Services)   C. Spankie
Area Team Manager (Child Care)   R. Helm

Peine House Area Office Hind Hill St, Heywood, Greater
Manchester OL10 1JZ; Tel 01706 867355
Area Team Manager (Child Care)   K. Shaw
Area Team Manager (Adult Services)   K. Hutton

Townhead Area Office John St, Rochdale, Greater
Manchester OL16 1LB; Tel 01706 865286
Area Team Manager (Child Care – Rochdale North)   E. King
Area Team Manager (Child Care – Rochdale South)   D. Fisher
Area Team Manager (Child Care – Pennine)   C. McCrystal

HOSPITAL SOCIAL WORKERS

Birch Hill Hospital, Rochdale, Greater Manchester;
Tel 01706 377777
Hospital Team Manager   V. Driver
Hospital Team Manager   P. Lavin

CHILDREN'S CONFERENCE AND REVIEW UNIT

Jacob Brights Children and Families Centre Whitworth Rd,
Rochdale, Greater Manchester OL12 6EP; Tel 01706 345275
Manager   K. Batt

CHILDREN'S HOMES

Furness Road Children's Home 5 Furness Rd, Middleton,
Greater Manchester M24 6FQ; Tel 0161 643 3936
Manager   A. Lancashire
(6)

6

Martin Lane Children's Home 39 Martin La, Rochdale, Greater Manchester OL12 7NU; Tel 01706 650491
Manager J. Spencer
(6)

Rugby Road Children's Home 180 Rugby Rd, Rochdale, Greater Manchester OL12 0DZ; Tel 01706 646507
Manager A. Lancashire
(+ 2 Emergency Beds) (6)

Whalley Road Children's Home 1 Whalley Rd, Middleton, Greater Manchester M24 6FP; Tel 0161 643 5049
Manager K. Robinson
(6)

CHILDREN AND FAMILY CENTRES

Ashbrook Centre Kitter St, Smallbridge, Rochdale, Greater Manchester OL12 9SF; Tel 01706 353481
Manager A. Thornley
(40)

Jacob Bright Centre Whitworth Rd, Rochdale, Greater Manchester OL12 6EP; Tel 01706 655709
Manager K. Wilkinson
(32)

Queen Street Centre Heywood, Greater Manchester OL10 4LF; Tel 01706 360265
Manager H. Hudson
(40)

Queensway Nursery Unit Hartley La, Rochdale, Greater Manchester OL11 2LR; Tel 01706 521006
Manager J. Sinacola
(12)

Stonepark Centre Derby St, Heywood, Greater Manchester OL10 4QJ; Tel 01706 366565
Manager C. Bowmer
(40)

Wardleworth Centre Ramsey St, Rochdale, Greater Manchester OL16 2BK; Tel 01706 630222
Manager R. Allat
(30)

FOSTERING AND ADOPTION UNIT

Family Placement Team, Foxholes Hse, Foxholes Rd, Rochdale, Greater Manchester OL12 0ED; Tel 01706 710750
Manager A. Tully

RESPITE UNIT FOR CHILDREN WITH LEARNING DIFFICULTIES

Bridgefold Lodge, Bridgefold Rd, Rochdale, Greater Manchester OL12 5BX; Tel 01706 342841
Manager M. Stanton

SOCIAL EDUCATION CENTRES

Burnside Centre 38 Burnside Cres, Middleton, Greater Manchester M24 5NN; Tel 0161 643 2689
Manager J. Walsh
(73)

Cherwell Centre Cherwell Ave, Heywood, Greater Manchester OL10 4SY; Tel 01706 369115
Manager C. Morphett
(60)

Greenfields Social Education Centre George St, Wardle, Rochester, Greater Manchester OL16 2RR; Tel 01706 378976
Manager J. Yuen
(64)

Innes Centre Ings La, Rochdale, Greater Manchester OL12 7DW; Tel 01706 46901
Manager C. Tattersall
(54)

ACCOMMODATION FOR PEOPLE WITH LEARNING DISABILITIES

Community Support Team 5th Fl, Telegraph Hse, Baillie St, Rochdale, Greater Manchester OL16 1LJ; Tel 01706 865233
Team Manager G. Holden

DAY CENTRES FOR PEOPLE WITH MENTAL HEALTH PROBLEMS

Hanson Corner Day Centre Hanson St, Middleton, Greater Manchester M24 2HD; Tel 0161 654 7060
Contact P. Styles

Richard Street Day Centre 44 Richard St, Rochdale, Greater Manchester OL11 1DY; Tel 01706 643954
Manager S. Coventry

ACCOMMODATION FOR PEOPLE WITH MENTAL HEALTH PROBLEMS

Community Restart Team 13–15 Darlington Rd, Queensway, Rochdale, Greater Manchester OL11 2LL; Tel 01706 658559
Team Manager P. Cooper

ACCOMMODATION FOR OLDER PEOPLE

There are seven local authority older persons' homes providing 243 places.

DAY CENTRES FOR OLDER PEOPLE

Riverside Day Centre Maden Sq, Littleborough, Greater Manchester OL15 9AJ; Tel 01706 378993
Manager L. Dewhurst
Physically handicapped

Ronald Gorton Centre Castlemere St, Rochdale, Greater Manchester; Tel 01706 642982
Manager R. Collinge
Older and physically disabled persons.

Wood Clough Day Centre Wood St, Middleton, Greater Manchester
Manager P. Robertshaw
Elderly

MEALS SERVICE

WRVS and old people's welfare committees are the agents for the Social Services Department.

RESOURCE CENTRE

Youth Offending Team Dunstenville Hse, Manchester Rd, Rochdale, Greater Manchester OL11 3RB; Tel 01706 643327
Manager R. Massiah

Education Service

PO Box 70, Municipal Offices, Smith St, Rochdale, Greater Manchester OL16 1YD; Tel 01706 647474; Fax 01706 658560
Executive Director (Education) T. Piggott
Head of Service (Learners and Young People) A. Tipton
Team Leader (Pupil Welfare and Inclusion) S. Dearden
Team Leader (Special Education) M. Boyle
Manager (Education Welfare) J. Vinter
Consultant (Behaviour Management Development Team) J. Hook

PSYCHOLOGICAL SERVICE

Fieldhouse School Greenbank Rd, Rochdale, Greater Manchester OL12 0HZ; Tel 01706 640477; Fax 01706 750455

SPECIAL SCHOOLS

Adlington Unit High Birch Special School, Bolton Rd, Rochdale, Greater Manchester OL11 4RA; Tel 01706 631752; Fax 01706 642663
Headteacher J. Herring
16–19

Alderman Kay School Tintern Rd, Hollin, Middleton, Greater Manchester M24 6JQ; Tel 0161 643 4917; Fax 0161 655 4081
Headteacher S. Pidgeon

Birtle View School George St, Heywood, Greater Manchester OL10 4PW; Tel 01706 368821; Fax 01706 620760
Headteacher A. Richardson

Brownhill School Heights La, Rochdale, Greater Manchester OL12 0PZ; Tel 01706 648990; Fax 01706 648537
Headteacher K. Connelly (Acting)

High Birch School Bolton Rd, Rochdale, Greater Manchester OL11 4RA; Tel 01706 631752; Fax 01706 642663
Headteacher J. Herring

Innes School Ings La, Rochdale, Greater Manchester OL12 7DW; Tel 01706 646605; Fax 01706 648783
Headteacher A. Wilson

Rydings School Great Howarth, Wardle Rd, Rochdale, Greater Manchester OL12 9HJ; Tel 01706 657993; Fax 01706 647112
Headteacher R.A. Jazwinski

SCHOOL SUPPORT SERVICES

Rochdale Additional Needs Service Hamer CP School, Albert Royds St, Rochdale, Greater Manchester OL16 2SU; Tel 01706 631520; 01706 633613; Fax 01706 869275
Head (Service) S. McKinlay

ROTHERHAM METROPOLITAN BOROUGH COUNCIL
www.rotherham.gov.uk

Population 253 207
Political Composition: Lab: 59, Con: 4, Ind: 3
The Crofts, Moorgate St, Rotherham, South Yorkshire S65 1UF; URL www.rotherham.gov.uk; E-mail chiefexecutive@rotherham.gov.uk; Tel 01709 382121
Chief Executive G. Fitzgerald
Executive Director (Resources) Carol Mills
Executive Director (Housing and Environmental Services) Tom Cray
Executive Director (Economic and Development Services) Adam Wilkinson
Head (Legal and Democratic Services) T.C. Mumford

Social Services Programme Area

Crinoline Hse, Effingham Sq, Rotherham, South Yorkshire S65 1AW; Tel (Emergency) 01709 364689; 01709 382121; Fax 01709 822325
Cabinet Member (Social Services) M.R. Kirk
14 Russell St, Rotherham, South Yorkshire; Tel 01709 368985
Executive Director (Social Services) J. Gomersall

Rotherham Metropilitan Borough Council Cabinet

Cabinet Member (Social Services) Kirk (Lab)
Members of the Cabinet
Lab: G. Boyes, S. Ellis, M.R. Kirk, T. Sharman, G. Smith, R. Stone, J.P. Wardle, J. Wright.

OFFICES

Central Locality Crinoline Hse, Effingham Sq, Rotherham, South Yorkshire S65 1AW; Tel 01709 382121; Fax 01709 822325

North Locality Town Hall, Wath, Rotherham, South Yorkshire S63 7RE; Tel 01709 873678; Fax 01709 876217

South Locality Maltby Civic Centre, High St, Rotherham, South Yorkshire S66 8LP; Tel 01709 812637; Fax 01709 790164

STRATEGIC SERVICES

Head of Centre Vacancy
Principal Officer (Workforce Planning and Staff Development) A. Beaumont
Performance Officer Mike Daniels

CHILDREN AND FAMILIES SERVICES

Head of Service Ms J. Jenkinson
Service Manager (South Locality) D. McGee
Service Manager (North Locality) P. Allen
Service Manager (Adoption and Fostering) G. Black
Service Manager (Health and Disabilities) B. Wood
Service Manager (Protection, Performance and Quality) P. Kelly
Training Gordon Jelley
Family Placement Service
Fostering and Adoption Service
Crinoline Hse, Effingham Sq, Rotherham, South Yorkshire S65 1AW; Tel 01709 382121; Fax 01709 823516
Youth Offending Service Moorgate Hse, 23 Moorgate Rd, Rotherham, South Yorkshire S60 2EN

CHILDREN'S ESTABLISHMENTS

Family Crisis Response Team 34 Godstone Rd, Moorgate Rd, Rotherham, South Yorkshire; Tel 01709 839655

Independent Training Unit Hollowgate Flats, Hollowgate, Rotherham, South Yorkshire; Tel 01709 370194

Long-Term Care Unit 18 St. Edmund's Ave, Thurcroft, Rotherham, South Yorkshire; Tel 01709 543734

Long-Term Care Unit 60 Studmoor Rd, Kimberworth Pk, Rotherham, South Yorkshire; Tel 01709 555420

Long-Term Care Unit 2 Goodwin Cres, Rotherham, South Yorkshire; Tel 01709 583539

Respite Care Unit Cherry Tree Hse, Orchard Children's Centre, Rotherham, South Yorkshire; Tel 01709 552235

Respite Care Unit for Children with Disabilities Bramley Hse, Orchard Children's Centre, Rotherham, South Yorkshire; Tel 01709 558997

Short-Term Assessment Unit 92 Creswick Rd, East Herringthorpe, Rotherham, South Yorkshire; Tel 01709 850541

ADULT SERVICES

Head of Service D. Hamilton
Service Manager (Older People) M. Smales (Acting)
Locality Manager (North) P. Billingsley
Locality Manager (Central) C. Jaques-Newton
Principal Officer (Adult Services) Gary Haigh (Acting)
Manager (Direct Provision for Older People) J. Harding; Tel 01709 382121

Community Mental Health Team 36 Godstone Rd, Moorgate, Rotherham, South Yorkshire; Tel 01709 838969; Fax 01709 839727

HOSPITAL SOCIAL WORK TEAM

Rotherham General Hospital, Rotherham, South Yorkshire; Tel 01709 820000; Fax 01709 824011

6

DAY CENTRES FOR PEOPLE WITH LEARNING DIFFICULTIES

Addison Day Centre Addison Rd, Maltby, South Yorkshire; Tel 01709 812358
   Extra care unit (27) (108)

Eastwood Day Centre Eastwood Trading Est, Chesterton Rd, Rotherham, South Yorkshire; Tel 01709 371701
   Special needs unit (15) (130)

The Oaks Day Centre Oak Rd, Wath upon Dearne, Rotherham, South Yorkshire; Tel 01709 872225
   High dependency unit (18) (95)

FLATLETS AND HOSTELS FOR THE REHABILITATION OF PEOPLE WITH LEARNING DISABILITY

Park Hill Lodge Larch Rd, Maltby, South Yorkshire; Tel 01709 813040
   Permanent + short stay (15)

Quarry Hill Road Hostel 58 Quarry Hill Rd, Wath, Rotherham, South Yorkshire; Tel 01709 873404

Treefield Close Hostel 1 Treefield Cl, Wingfield, Rotherham, South Yorkshire; Tel 01709 551325

HOSTELS FOR PEOPLE WITH LEARNING DISABILITY

Churchfields Hostel 6–8 Churchfields, Wickersley, Rotherham, South Yorkshire; Tel 01709 700258
   (3)

Eldon Road Hostel 54–56 Eldon Rd, Rotherham, South Yorkshire; Tel 01709 378495
   (3)

Elm Tree Road Hostel 17–19 Elm Tree Rd, Matby, Rotherham, South Yorkshire; Tel (Landlady) 01709 813825
   (5)

DAY CENTRE FOR PEOPLE WITH MENTAL HEALTH PROBLEMS

Clifton Court Day Centre Doncaster Rd, Rotherham, South Yorkshire; Tel 01709 378141

INDEPENDENT LIVING SCHEME FOR ADULTS WITH PHYSICAL DISABILITIES AND SENSORY IMPAIRMENT

Grafton Hse, Shaftsbury Sq, St. Ann's, Rotherham, South Yorkshire; Tel 01709 836139

DAYCARE AND SOCIAL CENTRE FOR THE ELDERLY, PEOPLE WITH A DISABILITY AND VISUALLY IMPAIRED

Millenium Day Centre, Badsley Moor La, Rotherham, South Yorkshire; Tel 01709 514003

RESIDENTIAL HOMES FOR THE ELDERLY

There are nine homes for the elderly.

DOMICILIARY SERVICES LAUNDRY CENTRE

Fitzwilliam Centre Doncaster Rd, Rotherham, South Yorkshire; Tel 01709 360553

Education, Culture and Leisure Services

Norfolk Hse, Walker Pl, Rotherham, South Yorkshire S65 1AS; Tel 01709 382121; Fax 01709 372056
Executive Director (Education, Culture and Leisure Services) Di Billups
Senior School Improvement Adviser Bob Toms
Principal Adviser (Inclusion) Helen Longland
Adviser (Young People's Services) George Simpson
Principal Educational Psychologist Steve Mulligan

DAY SPECIAL SCHOOLS AND HOSPITAL SPECIAL SCHOOLS

Abbey School Little Common La, Kimberworth, Rotherham, South Yorkshire S61 2RA; Tel 01709 740074; Fax 01709 553465
Headteacher J.S. Swain
   (135)

Green Arbour School Locksley Dr, Thurcroft, South Yorkshire S66 9NT; Tel 01709 542539; Fax 01709 703198
Headteacher Philip Gawthorpe
   (126)

Hilltop School Larch Rd, Maltby, South Yorkshire S66 8AZ; Tel 01709 813386; Fax 01709 798383
Headteacher P. Leach
   (92)

Kelford School Oakdale Rd, Kimberworth, Rotherham, South Yorkshire S61 2NU; Tel 01709 512088; Fax 01709 512091
Headteacher Mrs S.L. Greenhough
   (106)

Milton School Storey St, Swinton, Mexborough, South Yorkshire S64 8QG; Tel 01709 570246; Fax 01709 572009
Headteacher Martin Fittes
   (96)

Newman School East Bawtry Rd, Whiston, Rotherham, South Yorkshire S60 3LX; Tel 01709 828262; Fax 01709 821162
Headteacher Sue Garland-Grimes
   PH

Whiston Grange School East Bawtry Rd, Whiston, Rotherham, South Yorkshire S60 3LX; Tel 01709 828838; Fax 01709 828838
Headteacher Pam Storey
   (32)

OUTDOOR PURSUITS CENTRES

Habershon House Primrose Valley, Filey, North Yorkshire YO14 9QX; Tel 01723 512872; 01723 513194
Contact Christine Fitton

Ulley Water Activities Centre Ulley Reservoir, Aughton, Sheffield, South Yorkshire S26 3XL; Tel 01709 379960; 01709 828151; Fax 01709 379960
Contact Andy Rangecroft

RUTLAND COUNTY COUNCIL
www.rutnet.co.uk

Population 34 563
Political Composition: Con: 13, Ind: 6, LD: 4, Others: 2, Vacancy: 1.
Catmose, Oakham, Rutland LE15 6HP;
   URL www.rutnet.co.uk; Tel 01572 722577; Fax 01572 758375
Chair of the Council Mr C. Parsons
Chief Executive Keith Franklin
Director (Resources) Neil Taylor
Director (Environmental Services) Philip Trow

Social Services and Housing Department

Council Offices, Catmose, Oakham, Rutland LE15 6HP; Tel 01572 722577; Fax 01572 758375
Director (Social Services and Housing) Colin Foster
Head of Service (Adults) Joan Styran
Head (Service Children and Families) Steven Attwood
Head (Housing) John Bloxsom
Lead Officer (Learning Disabilities) Jean Billington
Lead Officer (Older Persons' Services) Sam Lloyd

Cabinet

Chair Mr H.E.G. Rees
Portfolio Holder (Social Services and Housing) Peter Golden

EMERGENCY DUTY TEAM (OUT OF HOURS)

This is a joint service managed by Leicester City Council Social Services Department.
Tel 0116 255 1606

CHILDREN AND FAMILIES TEAM

Social Services Office, Catmose, Rutland LE15 6HP

ADULT CARE TEAM

Social Services Office, Catmose, Rutland LE15 6HP

DAY SERVICE FOR PEOPLE WITH A LEARNING DISABILITY

Oakham Day Centre Barleythorpe Rd, Oakham, Rutland LE15 6NR; Tel 01572 723111

HOME FOR PEOPLE WITH A LEARNING DISABILITY

Pinewood 1 Cold Overton Rd, Oakham, Rutland LE15 6NT; Tel 01572 757225

ELDERLY PERSONS' HOME

The is one elderly persons' home under the control of Rutland Council.

HOUSING SERVICES

Catmose, Rutland LE15 6HP; Tel 01572 722577

Education, Youth and Culture Department

Council Offices, Catmose, Oakham, Rutland LE15 6HP; URL www.rutnet.gov.uk; Tel 01572 758481; Fax 01572 758479
Director (Education, Youth and Culture) Carol Chambers; E-mail cchambers@rutland.gov

---

ST. HELENS METROPOLITAN BOROUGH COUNCIL

www.sthelens.gov.uk

Population 176 000
Political Composition: Lab: 33, LD: 15, Con: 6
Town Hall, St. Helens, Merseyside WA10 1HP; URL www.sthelens.gov.uk; Tel 01744 456000; Fax 01744 456889
Mayor Cllr L. McGuire
Chief Executive C.A. Hudson, BA, IPFA
Assistant Chief Executive (Finance) I. Roberts

Social Services Department

The Gamble Bldg, Victoria Sq, St. Helens, Merseyside WA10 1DY; URL www.sthelens.gov.uk; E-mail contactcentre@sthelens.gov.uk; Tel (Emergency) 01744 22328; 01744 456000; Fax 01744 456551
Social Care and Health Portfolio Leader Cllr J. Fletcher
Town Hall, Victoria Sq, St. Helens, Merseyside WA10 1DY
Assistant Director (Vulnerable Adults) J. Wakefield
Director (Social Services) Sue Lightup

Assistant Director (Children's Services) Audrey Williamson
Assistant Director (Performance and Business Support) M. Wyatt
Assistant Director (Health and Social Care for Older People) Nick Dyer
Head (Personnel) Lesley Barry
Manager (Business Support) Caroline Wilson
Senior Systems Officer Joe Griffin
Chief Press and Public Relations Officer Chris Cahill
Customer User and Carer Development Carole Swift

Scrutiny Committee

Chair Cllr S. Banawick

TRAINING

Responsible for training professional and support staff in the department.
Principal Officer (Training) D. Broster
Training Section, Town Hall, St. Helens, Merseyside; Tel 01744 456084

LOCAL OFFICES

Derbyshire Hill Local Office 193 Newton Rd, Broad Oak, Merseyside; Tel 01744 677000; Fax 01744 677035

Haydock Local Office Church Rd, Haydock, Merseyside; Tel 01744 677627; Fax 01744 677663

Newton-le-Willows Local Office Town Hall, Earlestown, Newton-le-Willows, Merseyside; Tel 01744 677900

West Area Local Office Sunbury St, Thatto Heath, St. Helens, Merseyside; Tel 01744 677740

CHILD PROTECTION AND REVIEW UNIT

The Gamble Bldg, Victoria Sq, St. Helens, Merseyside WA10 1DY; Tel 01744 456965; Fax 01744 456946
Manager A. Lowe

CHILDREN'S HOMES

Abbeyford Children's Home Kingsley Rd, Abbeyford, Merseyside; Tel 01744 677545

Ghyll Grove Children's Home 14 Ghyll Gr, St. Helens, Merseyside

Red Bank Community Home Winwick Rd, Newton-le-Willows, Merseyside

Windle Hall Drive Children's Home 46 Windle Hall Dr, St. Helens, Merseyside

Windle Hall Drive Children's Home 161 Windle Hall Dr, St. Helens, Merseyside

YOUTH OFFENDING TEAM

Alexandra Hse, Borough Rd, St. Helens, Merseyside; Tel 01744 677048

CHILDREN WITH DISABILITIES

Willow Green Centre St. Helens, Merseyside (18)

ADOPTION AND FOSTER CARE SERVICE

73 Corporation St, St. Helens, Merseyside; Tel 01744 456528
Manager L. Harvey
Manager C. Taylor

LEARNING DISABILITY NETWORKS

27 Field Rd, Clock Face, St. Helens, Merseyside SA9 4QN; Tel 01744 677721
Manager S. Bickerton

6

DAY SERVICES FOR PEOPLE WITH LEARNING DIFFICULTIES

Kitchener Street Kitchener St, St. Helens, Merseyside;
Tel 01744 453595

Stephenson Rainhill, Merseyside; Tel 0151 426 0785
Manager F. Topping

DAY SERVICES FOR PEOPLE WITH MENTAL HEALTH PROBLEMS

Drop-in Centre Market Chambers, Earlestown, Newton-le-Willows, Merseyside; Tel 01925 292190
Development Worker Vacancy

Heath Park Lodge 5 Boroughs Trust, Thatto Heath, Merseyside; Tel 01744 813357
Manager Lindsey Foy

ACCOMMODATION FOR PEOPLE WITH MENTAL HEALTH PROBLEMS

Abbey House Abbey Rd, Merseyside; Tel 01744 451222
Manager Sharon Keene
(20)

CENTRE FOR DISABLED PEOPLE

Windle Pilkington House Merseyside; Tel 01744 677345
Manager Mark Burgess
(60)

DAY CENTRE FOR OLDER PEOPLE

Kershaw Centre Portland St, Newton-le-Willows, Merseyside; Tel 01744 677845
Manager Lorraine Flynn

ACCOMMODATION FOR OLDER PEOPLE

Manager M. Dibben
There are six homes with accommodation for 232 elderly people.

Community Education and Leisure Services Department

The Rivington Centre, Rivington Rd, St. Helens, Merseyside WA10 4ND; URL www.sthelens.gov.uk; Tel 01744 455328; Fax 01744 455350
Director (Community Education and Leisure Services) Susan Richardson
Head (Access and Inclusion) Steven Pugh; E-mail stevenpugh@sthelens.gov.uk; Tel 01744 455400; Fax 01744 455311
Principal Educational Psychologist L. Temple
Educational Advisory Unit, Gamble Ave, St. Helens, Merseyside WA10 6LR; Tel 01744 677216

SPECIAL DAY SCHOOLS AND UNITS

Hamblett School Rainford Rd, St. Helens, Merseyside WA10 6BX; Tel 01744 678770
Headteacher R. Brownlow
2–16

Hurst School Hard La, St. Helens, Merseyside WA10 6PN; Tel 01744 25643
Headteacher M.J. Carolan, BEd, MA
5–16

Mill Green School Mill La, Newton-le-Willows, Merseyside WA12 8BG; Tel 01744 678760
Headteacher P. Cronin
11–19

Penkford School Wharf Rd, Newton-le-Willows, Merseyside WA12 9XZ; Tel 019252 224195
Headteacher D. Hartley
5–16

St. Helens PACE Unit Derbyshire Hill Rd, St. Helens, Merseyside WA9 2LH; Tel 01744 677175
Head of Unit Mr Zygmunt Kulbacki
2–11

SERVICE FOR HEARING-IMPAIRED CHILDREN

Park Rd Centre, Park Rd, St. Helens, Merseyside; Tel 01744 677335
Head J.A. McGuffog

SERVICE FOR CHILDREN WITH VISUAL IMPAIRMENT

Park Road Centre, Park Rd, St. Helens, Merseyside; Tel 01744 677333
Manager P. Auckland

SALFORD CITY COUNCIL
www.salford.gov.uk

Population 224 828 (2001, Registrar General estimate)
Political Composition: Lab: 51, LD: 6, Con: 2, Ind: 1
Salford Civic Centre, Chorley Rd, Swinton, Salford, Greater Manchester M27 5DA; URL www.salford.gov.uk; Tel 0161 794 4711; Fax 0161 794 6595
Mayor Cllr J. King
Chief Executive J.C. Willis, BA(Econ), CPFA
Solicitor and Head (Law and Administration) A.R. Eastwood
Treasurer A. Westwood, CPFA
Director (Housing) H.W. Seaton, MIH
Turnpike Hse, 631 Eccles New Rd, Salford, Greater Manchester M5 2SW; Tel 0161 737 0551 ext 1201
Director (Development Services) M. Sykes, BA, DipTP, MRTPD

Community and Social Services Directorate

Crompton Hse, 100 Chorley Rd, Swinton, Greater Manchester M27 6BP; Tel 0161 793 2241; Fax 0161 794 0197
Director (Community and Social Services) Anne Williams, MA(Hons), MA Econ, CQSW
Deputy Director E. Murphy
Assistant Director (Children Commissioning) P. Woltman
Assistant Director (Adult Commissioning) J. Clark
Assistant Director (Performance and Customer Care) L. Jones, MA, BSc, CQSW, DipSS
Principal Manager (Care Services – Services to Adults and Older People) S. Wood-Townend
Beechfield Hse, Fourth Ave, Swinton, Greater Manchester M27 4LZ; Tel 0161 906 1531; Fax 0161 794 7722
Principal Care Services Manager (Adults and Older People) R. Blackstone
Beechfield Hse, Fourth Ave, Swinton, Greater Manchester M27 4LZ; Tel 0161 906 1533; Fax 0161 794 7722
Principal Officer (Children and Families) C. Williams
Avon Hse, Avon Cl, Little Hulton, Greater Manchester M28 6LA; Tel 0161 799 1762; Fax 0161 790 4892
Principal Officer (Child Protection and Reviewing Unit) A. Hampson
Avon Hse, Avon Cl, Little Hulton, Greater Manchester M28 6LA; Tel 0161 790 6332; Fax 0161 790 4892
Principal Manager (Occupational Therapy) L. Dixon
Burrows Hse, 10 Priestley Rd, Wardley Ind Est, Worsley, Greater Manchester M28 2LY
Team Leader (Sensory Disability) N. Erlich
White Moss, Bracken Ave, Walkden, Greater Manchester M28 3SS; Tel 0161 607 6999; Fax 0161 607 6900
Principal Officer (Policy and Publicity) Deborah Siddique; Tel 0161 793 2323; Fax 0161 794 0197

Principal Officer (Information Services) Wendy Threlfall
Crompton Hse, 100 Chorley Rd, Swinton, Greater
Manchester M27 6BP; Tel 0161 793 2296; Fax 0161 794
0197
Manager (Communication and Public Relations) Ian Andrew;
Tel 0161 793 3157

TRAINING

Responsible for training professional and support staff in
the department.
Senior Training Officer Sheila Dawson
Chaseley Field, Chaseley Rd, Salford, Greater Manchester
M6 7DZ; Tel 0161 745 7479; Fax 0161 743 0979

Cabinet

Lab: 18
Leader W. Hinds (Lab)
10 Chelford Dr, Swinton, Greater Manchester M27 8HJ
Deputy Leader J. Merry (Lab)
14 Cleveleys Gr, Salford, Greater Manchester M7 4DE
Arts and Leisure E. Sheehy
Arts and Leisure Mrs D. Miller
Community Social Service P. Connor
Community Social Service Mrs C. Hudson
Corporate Services D. Antrobus
Corporate Services J. Murphy
Development Services B. Warner
Development Services S. Miller
Education D. Daniels
Education K. Mann
Environmental Services D. Lancaster
Environmental Services J. Hunt
Housing J. Warmisham
Housing N. Clarke
Personnel Mrs M. Lea
Personnel V. Devine

Social Scrutiny Committee

Lab: 8, LD: 1, Con: 1
Chair W. Pennington
Members of the Committee
Lab: A. Clague, D. Eglin, Mrs D. Fernandez, J. Holt,
J. Hulmes, A. Leaston, K. Memory.
LD: B. Carson.
Con: Miss C. Upton.

COMMUNITY SOCIAL WORK TEAMS

Childhood Disability Services – Salford Families Project
222 Eccles Old Rd, Salford, Greater Manchester M6 8AL;
Tel 0161 707 0222; Fax 0161 707 9118
Project Leader G. Travis

Child Protection and Review Unit Avon Hse, Avon Cl, Little
Hulton, Greater Manchester M28 6LA; Tel 0161 790 6332;
Fax 0161 790 4892
Principal Manager A. Hampson

Salford Adolescent and Aftercare Service The Next Step
Project, 1a Garden St, Eccles, Greater Manchester M30 0EZ;
Tel 0161 707 9495; Fax 0161 707 5661
Project Manager Vacancy

Salford East Adult and Older People Social Work Team 78a
Great Clowes St, Salford, Greater Manchester M7 1SR;
Tel 0161 831 7484; Fax 0161 819 1541
Community Manager B. Gathercole

Salford East Children and Families Social Work Team 2
Police St, Pendleton, Salford, Greater Manchester M6 6PL;
Tel 0161 743 1000; Fax 0161 736 6829
Principal Manager Margaret Maudsley

Salford Mental Health Social Work Team Cleveland Hse,
224 Eccles Old Rd, Salford, Greater Manchester M6 8AL;
Tel 0161 789 5234; Fax 0161 707 9517
Principal Manager Marie Boles (Acting)

Salford West Adult and Older People Social Work Team 11
Corporation Rd, Eccles, Greater Manchester M30 0EQ;
Tel 0161 707 0704; Fax 0161 707 0709
Community Manager A. Whyte

Salford West Children and Families Social Work Team
Council Offices, Astley Rd, Irlam, Greater Manchester
M44 5LL; Tel 0161 606 6767; Fax 0161 777 6377
Principal Manager Judith Longhill

Salford West Children and Families Social Work Team
Brierley Hse, 335 Manchester Road East, Little Hulton,
Greater Manchester M28 9AR; Tel 0161 799 4404; Fax 0161
702 0608
Community Manager S. Hood

SOCIAL WORK SUPPORT TO HEALTH SERVICE

Community Drug Advice Service Town Hall Basement,
Eccles, Greater Manchester; Tel 0161 707 7188; Fax 0161 789
0360

Hope Hospital Stott La, Salford, Greater Manchester
M6 8HD; Tel 0161 787 4820; Fax 0161 707 9518
Principal Manager C. Entwistle

Manchester Children's Hospital NHS Trust Hospital Rd,
Pendlebury, Greater Manchester M27 4HA; Tel 0161 727
2271; Fax 0161 728 5232
Team Manager Kay George

The Mental Health Services of Salford NHS Trust Prestwich
Site, Bury New Rd, Prestwich, Greater Manchester
M25 3BL; Tel 0161 773 9121; Fax 0161 798 5776
Team Manager John Kinsella (Acting)

Salford Alcohol Service 6 Acton Sq, The Cres, Salford,
Greater Manchester M5 4NY; Tel 0161 745 7227; Fax 0161
736 3740

Salford Drug Service Bank Chambers, 11a Church St,
Eccles, Greater Manchester M30 0EL; Tel 0161 787 7813;
Fax 0161 787 7814

HOME FOR THE PHYSICALLY DISABLED

Willow Bank 20–22 Queensway, Clifton, Greater
Manchester M27 2QE; Tel (Day Centre) 0161 728 5844;
(Residential) 0161 794 6884
(24)

ECCLES AND IRLAM CHILDREN'S RESOURCE CENTRES

Park House Barton Moss Rd, Eccles, Greater Manchester
M30 7RL; Tel 0161 787 7626; Fax 0161 707 9512
Secure (20)

Liverpool Road Resource Centre 262 Liverpool Rd,
Patricroft, Eccles, Greater Manchester M30 0SD; Tel 0161
789 5641
Residential (5)

Silver Street Resource Centre 559 Silver St, Irlam, Greater
Manchester M44 6HT; Tel 0161 775 2683
Residential (6)

SALFORD CHILDREN'S RESOURCE CENTRES

Fitzwarren Court Resource Centre 85 Fitzwarren Crt,
Pendleton, Salford, Greater Manchester M6 5LN; Tel 0161
745 7425
Residential (16+ unit) (5)

Northfield Resource Centre 192 Moor La, Salford, Greater
Manchester M7 0PZ; Tel 0161 792 2578
Residential (4)

Youth OffendingTeam 10–12 Encombe Pl, Salford,
Greater Manchester M3 6FJ; Tel 0161 832 5382; Fax 0161 832
4306
Community support (18 educ) (20)

6

WORSLEY CHILDREN'S RESOURCE CENTRES

The Grange Resource Centre 29 Trippier Rd, Peelgreen, Eccles, Greater Manchester M30 7PT; Tel 0161 707 7441; Fax 0161 789 8078
Manager Mandy Dickins (Acting)
Residential (6)

Trafford Drive Resource Centre 66–68 Trafford Dr, Little Hulton, Worsley, Greater Manchester M28 6QB; Tel 0161 790 3546
Manager Irene Lee
Residential (5)

Whittle Street Resource Centre 90 Whittle St, Walkden, Worsley, Greater Manchester M28 5WY; Tel 0161 790 3327
Manager Ciaron Dillon
Residential (5)

DAY CARE (CHILDREN AND FAMILIES)

Belvedere Community Nursery Centre Belvedere Rd, Salford, Greater Manchester M6 5EJ; Tel 0161 737 3171
Manager Mrs A. More
(45)

Bradshaw Community Nursery Centre Devonshire St, Salford, Greater Manchester M7 4RF; Tel 0161 792 3271; Fax 0161 708 8313
Manager Ms Coward
(45)

Bradshaw Family Centre Rigby St, Salford, Greater Manchester M7 4BQ; Tel 0161 792 8586
Manager Mrs Mawdsley
(12)

Irlam Community Nursery Centre Fiddlers La, Irlam, Greater Manchester M44 6QE; Tel 0161 775 8884; Fax 0161 776 1483
Manager Mr M. Kirk
(45)

Little Hulton Community Early Years Centre Longshaw Dr, Little Hulton, Greater Manchester M28 0BP; Tel 0161 790 5359
Manager Mrs D. Jones
(45)

NCH Family Centre 18 Fiddlers La, Irlam, Greater Manchester M44 6HN; Tel 0161 775 5340
Manager Ms Evers

NCH Family Centre St. Marys Rd, Eccles, Greater Manchester M30 0AX; Tel 0161 789 0566
Manager J. Vickor

Ordsall Family Centre 1 Carmel Ave, Robert Hall St, Salford, Greater Manchester M5 3LR; Tel 0161 872 0382
Manager A. Hitchcock
(12)

Plum Tree Court Family Centre 11 Plum Tree Crt, Salford, Greater Manchester M6 5BB; Tel 0161 736 1185
Manager J. Cheetham
(12)

Wingate Road Family Centre 31 Wingate Rd, Little Hulton, Greater Manchester M28 6PP; Tel 0161 790 7210
Manager K. Joby
(12)

Winton Community Nursery Centre Brindley St, off Sutherland St, Winton, Greater Manchester M30 8AB; Tel 0161 788 0192; Fax 0161 789 5822
Manager Mrs T. Collins
(40)

DAY CARE (DISABILITIES)

Craig Hall Centre Preston Ave, Irlam, Greater Manchester M30 5BH; Tel 0161 775 1885
Manager K. Richardson
(100)

Dawson Street Centre off Swinton Hall Rd, Swinton, Greater Manchester M27 1FJ; Tel 0161 794 5771; Fax 0161 794 5771
Manager W. Skeer
(30)

Princes Park Horticultural Centre Princes Pk, Irlam, Greater Manchester M44 6BR; Tel 0161 775 0030
Manager R. Phelan
(15)

Salford Work Department Unit c/o Dawson St, off Swinton Hall Rd, Swinton, Greater Manchester M27 1FJ; Tel 0161 728 1945; Fax 0161 728 1945
Manager P. Higson

St. George's Centre Cromwell Rd, Salford, Greater Manchester M6 6SU; Tel 0161 737 6923; Fax 0161 743 9592
Manager P. Reddyoff
(150)

DAY CARE (LEARNING DISABILITIES)

Orchard Mount Centre Chorlton Fold, Monton, Eccles, Greater Manchester M30 9NA; Tel 0161 789 3913
Manager Mrs K. Richardson (Acting)
(85)

The Waterside Resource Unit Billy La, Clifton, Swinton, Greater Manchester M27 8GB; Tel 0161 794 6788
Manager A. Johnson
(90)

HOME FOR PEOPLE WITH LEARNING DISABILITIES

New Granville Home 10 Victoria Rd, Eccles, Greater Manchester M30 9HB; Tel 0161 789 1041
Contact Mrs F. Laurukenas-Sproston
Short stay (13)

DAY CENTRES FOR PEOPLE WITH MENTAL HEALTH PROBLEMS

Cromwell House Community Mental Health Centre Cromwell Rd, Eccles, Greater Manchester M30 0QT; Tel 0161 787 6000; Fax 0161 707 6006
Manager D. Booth
(40)

Duchy House Day Centre Duchy Rd, Salford, Greater Manchester M6 6WL; Tel 0161 737 5925
Manager Mrs Y. Russell-Coyles
(50)

Ramsgate House Day Centre 43 Ramsgate St, Salford, Greater Manchester M7 2YB; Tel 0161 708 9512; Fax 0161 708 9566
Manager E. Willoughby

ACCOMMODATION FOR PEOPLE WITH MENTAL HEALTH PROBLEMS

Holly Bank Home 40 Eccles Old Rd, Salford, Greater Manchester M6 8RA; Tel 0161 737 5439
(22)

Ingleside Home Oakwood Pk, Salford, Greater Manchester M6 7NQ; Tel 0161 736 2574
Manager J. Tierney
(12)

DAY CARE (PHYSICAL DISABILITIES)

Willow Bank Day Centre 20–22 Queensway, Clifton, Swinton, Greater Manchester M27 2QE; Tel 0161 728 5844
(28)

RESOURCE CENTRES FOR OLDER PEOPLE

Beechfield Resource Centre Cutnook La, Irlam, Greater Manchester M44 6JX; Tel 0161 775 4625; Fax 0161 775 4622
Manager J. Mann
(31)

Brynheys Resource Centre Cleggs La, Little Hulton, Worsley, Greater Manchester M28 9RS; Tel 0161 790 5651; Fax 0161 790 5678
Manager A. Raynor
(35)

DAY CARE (OLDER PEOPLE)

Alexandra House 395 Liverpool Rd, Eccles, Greater Manchester M30 7HB; Tel 0161 788 0636
Manager S. Skeer
(100)

Brierley House Day Centre Longshaw Dr, Little Hulton, Greater Manchester M28 6AR; Tel 0161 799 0656
Manager E. Thorpe
(100)

Humphrey Booth Day Centre Heath Ave, Lower Broughton, Salford, Greater Manchester M7 9WL; Tel 0161 834 2407
Manager L. Thornley
(100)

Humphrey Booth Day Centre (Ordsall) Taylorson St, Salford, Greater Manchester M5 3EX; Tel 0161 872 6491
Manager S. Ellis
(100)

Salford Methodist Community Church Social Centre
Pendleton Way, Salford, Greater Manchester M6 5RR;
Tel 0161 737 4500
(100)

Education and Leisure Department

Minerva Hse, Pendlebury Rd, Swinton, Salford, Greater Manchester M27 4EQ; Tel 0161 778 0123
Director (Education and Leisure) M. Carriline, MA(Cantab)
Deputy Director (Education and Leisure) and Head (Strategic Services) Vacancy
Principal Adviser and Head (Inspection and Advisory Service) Ann Hillerton
Principal Educational Psychologist D.M. O'Hara, MSc, BSc; Tel 0161 778 0382
Principal Education Welfare Officer Denise Lynch; Tel 0161 742 3923
Principal Youth and Community Officer Linda Pride (Acting); Tel 0161 778 0361

SPECIAL DAY SCHOOLS

Irwell, Park School Britannia St, Salford, Greater Manchester M6 6FX; Tel 0161 737 0024
Headteacher M. Ironmonger
Secondary EBD (29)

The Language Resource St. Philips C of E Primary School, Barrow St, Salford, Greater Manchester M3 5LF; Tel 0161 832 6637
Headteacher L. Connor
Language difficulties

New Croft High School Seedley Rd, Salford, Greater Manchester M6 5JL; Tel 0161 736 6415
Headteacher J.S. Chapman
Secondary SLD (74)

Oakwood High School Park La, Salford, Greater Manchester M6 7RQ; Tel 0161 736 3944
Headteacher J. Triska
Secondary MLD (157)

Royal Manchester Children's Hospital School Hospital Rd, Pendlebury, Swinton, Greater Manchester M27 4HA; Tel 0161 794 1151
Headteacher B.I. Purdy, BEd
(94)

Support Service Halton Hse, 36 Eccles Old Rd, Salford, Greater Manchester M6 8RA; Tel 0161 607 1677; Fax 0161 607 1697

Head of Service Debra Wailes
Support to children of all ages with special educational needs in mainstream schools and in the home.

SCHOOL PSYCHOLOGICAL CHILD GUIDANCE

Education Centre London St, Salford, Greater Manchester M6 6QT; Tel 0161 743 4210
Contact M. O'Hara, MSc, BGc

SANDWELL METROPOLITAN BOROUGH COUNCIL
www.sandwell.gov.uk

Population 293 742
Political Composition: Lab: 55, LD: 10, Con: 6, Ind: 1
Sandwell Council Hse, PO Box 2374, Oldbury, West Midlands B69 3DE; URL www.sandwell.gov.uk; Tel 0121 569 2200
Executive Director (Education and Lifelong Learning) Eric Griffiths
PO Box 41, Shaftesbury Hse, 402 High St, West Bromwich, West Midlands B70 9LT; E-mail lea_lifelonglearning@sandwell.gov.uk; Tel 0121 569 8205; Fax 0121 553 1528
Deputy Chief Executive Allison Fraser; Tel 0121 569 3500; Fax 0121 569 3130
Executive Director (Urban Form) Steve Gregory
Development Hse, PO Box 42, Lombard St, West Bromwich, West Midlands B70 8RU; Tel 0121 569 5060; Fax 0121 569 5193
Executive Director (Sandwell Direct) Brian Oakley
Environment Hse, PO Box 42, Lombard St, West Bromwich, West Midlands B70 8RU; Tel 0121 569 6184; Fax 0121 569 4280
Executive Director (Social Inclusion and Health) Angela Saganowska
Kingston Hse, 438 High St, West Bromwich, West Midlands B70 9LD; Tel 0121 569 5464; Fax 0121 569 5489
Head (Estate Management) P. Manley
Sandwell Council Hse, Oldbury, West Midlands B69 3DQ; Tel 0121 569 3900; Fax 0121 569 3938
Head (Environment Direct) Mike Baker
Environment Hse, PO Box 42, Lombard St, West Bromwich, West Midlands B70 8RU; Tel 0121 569 4118; Fax 0121 569 4104
Head (Building Services) Martin Garrington (Acting)
Municipal Bldgs, Barrs Rd, Cradley Heath, West Midlands B64 7JX; Tel 0121 569 4540; Fax 0121 569 4547
Head (Planning and Development Services) R. Lee
Development Hse, PO Box 42, Lombard St, West Bromwich, West Midlands B70 8RU; Tel 0121 569 4052; Fax 0121 569 4072
Head (Environmental Health and Trading Standards) Michael Parkes
Environment Hse, PO Box 42, Lombard St, Oldbury, West Midlands B70 8RU; Tel 0121 569 6628; Fax 0121 569 6556
Head (Information Technology) Vacancy
Sandwell Council Hse, PO Box 2372, Oldbury, West Midlands B69 3DF; Tel 0121 569 3357; Fax 0121 569 3493

Social Inclusion and Health

Kingston Hse, 438 High St, West Bromwich, West Midlands B70 9LD; Tel 0121 569 2200; Fax 0121 569 5755
Executive Director A. Saganowska
Head (Childcare Services) J. Skinner (Acting)
Head (Adult Commissioning) A. Dean (Acting)
Head (Business Support) H. Jivan-Patel
Head (Adult Providing) Vacancy

6

STAFF DEVELOPMENT AND TRAINING

Responsible for training professional and support staff in the department.
Principal Training Officer J. Wyke

Social Inclusion and Health Cabinet Advisory Team

Lab: 14, LD: 3
Cabinet Member D. Cooper
6 Crystal Hse, Oakfield Cl, Smethwick, West Midlands B66 3JT
Cabinet Advisory Team
Edis, Griffin, Hughes, James, Smith, Watkins, Webb.

CHILD CARE DIVISION

Children's Management Centre, Kingston Hse, West Bromwich, West Midlands B70 9LD; Tel 0121 569 5750
Divisional Manager S. Rowe
Manager (Strategic Partnership) J. Lees

ROWLEY AND TIPTON PRIMARY CARE GROUP

Short Term 5–6 Unity Wlk, Tipton, West Midlands; Tel 0121 569 5920; 0121 569 5921
Manager (Short-term Team) J. Levitt
Principal Social Worker Claudia Gordon (Acting)
Long Term Municipal Bldgs, Cradley Heath, West Midlands; Tel 0121 569 5625; 0121 569 5605
Manager (Long-term Team) A. Knight
Principal Social Worker C. Cunn (Acting)

WEDNESBURY AND WEST BROMWICH PRIMARY CARE GROUP

Short Term Rear of Town Hall, Lodge Rd, West Bromwich, West Midlands; Tel 0121 569 5412
Manager (Short-term Team) G. Saunders
Principal Social Worker Donessa Gray
Long Term Town Hall, Holyhead Rd, Wednesbury, West Midlands WS10 7DF; Tel 0121 556 7451
Manager (Long-term Team) D. Atkinson
Principal Social Worker B. McEvoy

SMETHWICK AND OLDBURY PRIMARY CARE GROUP

Short Term 253a High St, Smethwick, West Midlands B66 3NJ; Tel 0121 569 5585; 0121 569 5586
Manager (Short-term Team) E. Duffy
Principal Social Worker L. Brannigan
Long Term Metsec Bldg, Broadwell Rd, Oldbury, West Midlands B69 4HE; Tel 0121 565 5555
Manager (Long-term Team) B. Bassral
Principal Social Worker A. Grant

CHILD PROTECTION AND REVIEWING UNIT

Clifton Lane Stone Cross, West Bromwich, West Midlands B71 3AS; Tel 0121 569 5793
Manager A. Child

EMERGENCY DUTY TEAM

Regis Lodge George Ave, Rowley Regis, West Midlands B65 9BD; Tel 0121 588 7662
Team Manager M. Reynolds

HOMEFINDING TEAM

Hollies Family Centre, Coopers La, Smethwick, West Midlands B67 7DW; Tel 0121 569 5771
Service Manager (Permanency) G. Jones
Service Manager (Fostering Support) M. Gregory
Service Manager (Recruitment and Assessment) P. Gordon

AFTERCARE

Greenwood Ave, Oldbury, West Midlands B6B 8JE; Tel 0121 569 3741
Team Manager R. Adams

RESIDENTIAL UNITS

Comgreaves Residential Homes Comgreaves Rd, Cradley Heath, West Midlands B64 6BL; Tel 01384 410004
Resource Manager Sharon Pommills
Spon Lane Children's Home Grenville Dr, Smthwick, West Midlands B70 6AZ; Tel 0121 658 8276
Resource Manager Mark Wood
Tame Rise Residential Unit 27 Tame Rise, Warley, Oldbury, West Midlands B68 0JU; Tel 0121 422 9058
Currently closed for refurbishment.
Manager S. Pommilos (Acting)

CHILDREN WITH DISABILITIES TEAM

Clifton La, West Bromwich, West Midlands B71 3AS; Tel 0121 569 5736
Team Manager M. Chappell
Principal Social Worker E. Murray

FAMILY SUPPORT

Tanhouse Centre, Hamstead Rd, Great Barr, West Midlands B43 5EL; Tel 0121 569 5500
Team Manager T. Braithwaite

FAMILY CENTRES

Barnford Family Centre Causeway Green Rd, Warley, Oldbury, West Midlands B68 8LA; Tel 0121 552 5563
Manager L. Fortune
Coneygre Family Centre Sedgley Road East, Tipton, West Midlands DY4 8UH; Tel 0121 569 5950
Manager S. Cooke
The Hollies Family Centre Coopers La, Smethwick, Greater Manchester B67 7DW; Tel 0121 569 5780
Manager B. Greasby
Unity Family Centre Beeches Rd, West Bromwich, West Midlands B70 6HQ; Tel 0121 553 5587
Manager J. Wilson

JUVENILE SERVICES

Youth Offending Team SGS Bldg, Tipton Rd, Tividale, West Midlands B69 3HX; Tel 0121 557 8804
Team Manager K. Barham

ADULT COMMISSIONING DIVISION

Adult Commissioning Management Centre, Kingston Hse, West Bromwich, West Midlands B70 9LD
Divisional Manager (Disabilities) S. Rees; Tel 0121 569 5495
Divisional Manager (Elderly) P. Charnock (Acting); Tel 0121 569 5462
Divisional Manager (Carers) L. Brodrick; Tel 0121 569 5461
Oldbury Adults Team Metsec Bldgs, Broadwell Rd, Oldbury, West Midlands B69 4HE; Tel 0121 544 6029
Locality Manager A. Quinn
Rowley Adults Team Regis Lodge, George Ave, Rowley Regis, West Midlands B65 9BD; Tel 0121 569 5604
Locality Manager G. Champaneri
Smethwick Adults Team 253a High St, Smethwick, West Midlands B66 BNJ; Tel 0121 569 5595
Locality Manager H. Mangat
Tipton Adults Team 8 Unity Wlk, Tipton, West Midlands DY4 8QL; Tel (Homecare) 0121 569 5916; 0121 569 5932
Locality Manager M. Armstrong (Acting)

Wednesbury Adults Team Town Hall, Holyhead Rd, Wednesbury, West Midlands WS10 7DF; Tel 0121 505 5553
Locality Manager Y. Coleman

West Bromwich Adults Team Rear of Town Hall, off Lodge Rd, West Bromwich, West Midlands B70 8DT; Tel 0121 569 5554
Locality Team Manager K. Brown (Acting)

ADULT PROVIDER MANAGEMENT CENTRE

Stoney La, West Bromwich, West Midlands B71 4JA; Tel 0121 500 4850; Fax 0121 500 5844
Divisional Manager Sandra Lee (Acting)
Service Manager (Adults) Bev Williamson (Acting)
Service Manager (Elderly/EMI Services) Chris Guest
Service Manager (Home Care) Ada Rose
Co-ordinator (Leisure and Social Care Development) Alexis Ellis
The Crest, 107 All Saints Way, , West Bromwich, West Midlands B71 1RU; Tel 0121 588 2980

LEARNING DISABILITIES

Causeway Green Resource Centre Causeway Green Rd, Oldbury, West Midlands B68 8LD; Tel 0121 552 2580; Fax 0121 544 7714
Assistant Co-ordinator Jo Thomas

Hill Top Resource Centre Peter St, West Bromwich, West Midlands B70 0HT; Tel 0121 556 0131; Fax 0121 556 5596
Manager (Operations) Vacancy

Price Street Community Service Price St, Smethwick, West Midlands; Tel 0121 558 8917; Fax 0121 565 0469
Assistant Co-ordinator Debra Evans

Warstone House Salters La, West Bromwich, West Midlands B71 4BQ; Tel 0121 569 5382 (Adult Placement) 0121 569 5386; Fax 0121 569 5387
Homes Manager Joe Eslen

PHYSICAL DISABILITY/SENSORY IMPAIRMENT

Causeway Green Day Centre Causeway Green Rd, Oldbury, West Midlands B68 8LE; Tel 0121 552 5699; Fax 0121 544 7714
Co-ordinator Bev Hellend (Acting)

Independent Living Centre 100 Oldbury Rd, Smethwick, West Midlands; Tel 0121 558 5555
Senior Rehabilitation Officer Rachel Jennings

Personal Assistance Team The Crest, 107 All Saints Way, West Bromwich, West Midlands B71 1RU; Tel 0121 588 2826; Fax 0121 588 7990
Day Centre Officer Ann Turner

Stoney Lane Day Centre Stoney La, West Bromwich, West Midlands B71 4JA; Tel 0121 553 0067; Fax 0121 525 9202
Co-ordinator Bev Hellend (Acting)

Vision Services Day Centre 107 All Saints Way, West Bromwich, West Midlands B71 1RU; Tel 0121 588 2509; Fax 0121 588 7990
Senior Care Officer Carol Brown

MENTAL HEALTH

Beeches Enterprise Centre 23 Beeches Rd, West Bromwich, West Midlands B70 6QE; Tel 0121 569 5563; Fax 0121 553 4656
Co-ordinator Samantha Mattis

Park Corner 53 Walsall St, Wednesbury, West Midlands WS10; Tel 0121 505 1242; Fax 0121 556 4118
Assistant Co-ordinator Mary Thompson (Acting)

Vocational Services 23 Beeches Rd, West Bromwich, West Midlands B70 6QE; Tel 0121 525 3964; Fax 0121 553 4656
Co-ordinator Anne Jones

HOME CARE SERVICES

Holly Grange Mallin St, Smethwick, West Midlands B66 1QY; Tel (Home Care) 0121 555 4250; (VSA) 0121 555 4260; Fax 0121 555 4266
Grange Manager Malcolm Heath (Acting)

Manifoldia Grange Coyne Rd, off Moor St, West Bromwich, West Midlands B70 7JU; Tel 0121 553 6644; Fax 0121 500 4077
Co-ordinator Brenda Essom

Walker Grange Day Centre Central Ave, Tipton, West Midlands DY4 9RY; Tel 0121 520 0201; Fax 0121 521 5687
Co-ordinator Sue Roche (Acting)

RESIDENTIAL SERVICES FOR OLDER PEOPLE

There are nine residential homes for older people.

Education and Lifelong Learning

Shaftesbury Hse, PO Box 41, West Bromwich, West Midlands B70 9LT; URL www.lea.sandwell.gov.uk; E-mail lea_lifelonglearning@sandwell.gov.uk; Tel 0121 569 2200; Fax 0121 553 1528
Executive Director (Education and Lifelong Learning) E. Griffiths
Head (Education Inclusion) P. Cox
Head (Lifelong, Learning Libraries and Culture) K. Heyes
Head (School Improvement) P. Penn-Howard
Head (Strategy and Resources) M. Dudley
Principal Welfare Officer and Manager (Attendance Strategy) C. Elton

CHILD PSYCHOLOGY SERVICES

Connor Education Centre Connor Rd, West Bromwich, West Midlands B71 3DJ; Tel 0121 588 8337; Fax 0121 567 5520

Inclusion Support 12 Grange Rd, West Bromwich, West Midlands B70 8PD; Tel 0121 553 7411; Fax 0121 580 1522
Principal Educational Psychologist P.A. Evans (Acting)

SPECIAL SCHOOLS

The Meadows School Dudley Road East, Oldbury, West Midlands B69 3BU;
E-mail headteacher@themeadows.sandwell.sch.uk; Tel 0121 569 7080; Fax 0121 569 7081
Headteacher Ms A. Duncan

The Orchard School Coopers La, Smethwick, West Midlands B67 7DW; Tel 0121 558 1069; Fax 0121 565 0940
Headteacher Mrs H. Atkins

The Orchard School (Holly Lane) Holly La, Smethwick, West Midlands B66 1QN; Tel 0121 558 2560; Fax 0121 555 6034
Deputy Headteacher Mrs S. Chinner

Shenstone Lodge School Shenstone, Lichfield, Staffordshire WS14 0LB; Tel 01543 480369; Fax 01543 481104
Headteacher S.P. Butt
  (Residential)

The Westminster School (Tipton) Upper Church La, Tipton, West Midlands DY4 9PF;
E-mail headteacher@westminster.sandwell.sch.uk; Tel 0121 577 2528; Fax 0121 522 3456
Headteacher Mrs D. Williams

The Westminster School (West Bromwich) Westminster Rd, West Bromwich, West Midlands B71 2JN;
E-mail headteacher@westminster.sandwell.sch.uk; Tel 0121 588 2421; 0121 588 5434; Fax 0121 588 5451
Headteacher Mrs D. Williams

Whittington Grange School Burton Rd, Whittington, Lichfield, Staffordshire WS14 9NU; Tel 01543 432296; Fax 01543 433254
Headteacher Ms S. Lancaster
  (Residential)

6

SEFTON METROPOLITAN BOROUGH COUNCIL

Population 286 900
Political Composition: Lab: 25, LD: 21, Con: 17, Ind: 3
Mayor Cllr W. Jones
Director (Education) Mrs E. Simpson; Tel 0151 934 3201;
  Fax 0151 934 3239
Director (Legal) C. Elwood; Tel 0151 934 2032; Fax 0151 934
  2256
Director (Finance) T. Yates
Balliol Hse, Stanley Precinct, Bootle, Merseyside L20 3NQ;
  Tel 0151 922 4040; Fax 0151 934 4050
Strategic Director (Development and Environmental Services)
  A.R. Moore, FRICS
Balliol Hse, Stanley Precinct, Bootle, Merseyside L20 3NJ;
  Tel 0151 922 4040; Fax 0151 934 4220
Director (Housing) J. Robinson
Vermont Hse, 375 Stanley Rd, Bootle, Merseyside L20 3RY;
  Tel 0151 922 4040; Fax 0151 934 3611
Strategic Director (Personal Services) B. Marsh
Merton Hse, Stanley Rd, Bootle, Merseyside; Tel 0151 934
  3525; Fax 0151 934 3526

Social Services Department

Merton Hse, 7th Fl, Bootle, Merseyside L20 3UU;
  E-mail customer.services@social-services.sefton.gov.uk;
  Tel 0151 934 3737; Fax 0151 934 3755
*Spokesperson (Conservative Group) and Cabinet Member for
  Social Services* Cllr Parry
Spokesperson (LD Group) Cllr M. Dally
Spokesperson (Labour Group) Cllr D.A. Langley
Director (Social Services) Charlie Barker
Head (Adult Services) Peter Pattendon
Head (Central Services) Bob McConnell
Manager (Publicity) Lynn Billingham

TRAINING

Responsible for training professional and support staff in
the department.
Manager (Training) Anne Connor
Social Services, Training and Development Unit and NVQ
  Assessment Centre, Liverpool, Merseyside L21 2PE
*Staff Development Officer (Mental Health and Learning
  Disabilities)* Barbara Creghan (Job Share); Tel 0151 330
  5742; Fax 0151 330 5730
Staff Development Officer Vacancy
Staff Development Officer (Older People) Joan Coupe;
  Tel 0151 330 5747; Fax 0151 330 5730
Staff Development Officer (Children) Maureen Hart; Tel 0151
  330 5744; Fax 0151 330 5730
Staff Development Officer (Community Care) Vacancy

LOCAL OFFICES

Bryant House Local Office Liverpool Road North, Maghull,
Merseyside L31 2PA; Tel 0151 922 4040
Services for older people.

Hoghton Street Local Office 44 Hoghton St, Southport,
Merseyside; Tel 01704 533133
Services for children and families.

Litherland Town Hall Local Office Sefton Rd, Litherland,
Merseyside L21 7PD; Tel 0151 922 4040
Services for children and families.

Southport Local Office Shakespeare Centre, Unit 19,
Southport, Merseyside; Tel 01704 533133
Services for older people.

Sterrix Lane Local Office 80 Sterrix La, Litherland,
Merseyside L21 0DA; Tel 0151 922 4040
Services for children, children with disabilities.

Vermont House Local Office 375 Stanley Rd, Bootle,
Merseyside L20 3RY; Tel 0151 922 4040
Services for children and families.

Waterloo Town Hall St. Georges Rd, Waterloo, Merseyside
L22 1RD; Tel 0151 922 4040
Services for older people. Services for adults with
disabilities.

HOSPITAL SOCIAL WORKERS

Child Guidance Clinic 52 Hoghton St, Southport,
Merseyside PR9 0PN; Tel 01704 540911

Fazakerley Hospital Longmoor La, Liverpool, Merseyside
L9 7AL; Tel 0151 525 5980

Southport and Formby District General Hospital Town La,
Southport, Merseyside; Tel 01704 547471

Southport General Infirmary Scarisbrick New Rd,
Southport, Merseyside; Tel 01704 547471

CHILDREN'S HOMES

Cherry Road Children's Home 27 Cherry Rd, Ainsdale,
Southport, Merseyside; Tel 01704 77652
  (7)

Kirwan House Children's Home Fleetwood Rd, Southport,
Merseyside; Tel 01704 24953
  (12)

HOMES FOR ADULTS WITH LEARNING DISABILITIES

Buckley Hill House Buckley Hill La, Sefton Est, Bootle,
Merseyside L29 1YB; Tel 0151 924 3475
  (24)

The Meadows Home Sandbrook Rd, Ainsdale, Southport,
Merseyside; Tel 01704 78601

The Poplars Home Poplar St, Southport, Merseyside;
Tel 01704 535118

Springbrook Home 28 Meadow La, Ainsdale, Southport,
Merseyside; Tel 01704 79204
  Children (10)

ACCOMMODATION FOR PEOPLE WITH MENTAL HEALTH PROBLEMS

Lansdowne House Blundellsands Road East,
Blundellsands, Crosby, Merseyside; Tel 0151 931 2065
  (14)

DAY CENTRES FOR PEOPLE WITH LEARNING DISABILITIES

Brook Lea Adult Training Centre Pendle Dr, Litherland,
Merseyside; Tel 0151 924 2046
  (110)

The Dunnings Bridge Centre Dunnings Bridge Rd,
Netherton 10, Merseyside; Tel 0151 525 6686
  (145)

Southport Adult Training Centre Sandbrook Rd, Ainsdale,
Southport, Merseyside; Tel 01704 79839
  (90)

DAY CENTRES FOR PEOPLE WITH A PHYSICAL OR SENSORY DISABILITY

Bootle Day Centre 211 Linacre La, Bootle, Merseyside;
Tel 0151 922 2800
  (50)

Esplanade Day Centre Esplanade, Waterloo, Merseyside;
Fax 0151 949 0269

Mornington Road Centre Mornington Rd, Southport,
Merseyside; Tel 01704 545600
  (60)

Resource Centre Kilnyard Rd, Crosby, Merseyside; Tel 0151
924 3426
  Children

DAY CENTRES FOR OLDER PEOPLE

David Brown Day Centre Magdalene Sq, Bootle, Merseyside L30 5QH; Tel 0151 525 8351
(30)

Marshside Day Centre Marshside Rd, Southport, Merseyside PR9 9SX; Tel 01704 29093
(45)

The Orchards Day Centre Orchard La, Ainsdale, Southport, Merseyside PR8 3RA; Tel 01704 75239
(45)

DAY CENTRE FOR ELDERLY PEOPLE WITH MENTAL HEALTH PROBLEMS

Brookdale Care Unit Sandbrook Rd, Ainsdale, Southport, Merseyside PR8 3RG; Tel 01704 73122
(35)

Children, Schools and Families

Town Hall, Oriel Rd, Bootle, Merseyside L20 7AE;
URL www.sefton.gov.uk;
E-mail mike.dixon@csf.sefton.gov.uk; Tel 0151 922 4040;
Fax 0151 934 3349
Strategic Director (Children, Schools and Families)
Bryn Marsh
Director (Personal Services) David Alexander
Director (Schools and Young People) Mike Dixon
Head (Support and Operations) Wendy Holbeche
Head (STEPS Service) Eileen Oakes (Acting)
Head (STEPS Service) Daphne Mortimer (Acting)
Head (SEN Service) Colin Oxley
Head (Youth and External Funding Services) Eric Hughes
Adviser (Early Years) Gill Rice
Area Officer (Education Welfare) Julie Palin
Co-ordinator (Health Education) N. Scott
Adviser (Early Years) Tracey Bowden

EDUCATION WELFARE OFFICE

Town Hall, Bootle, Merseyside L20 7AE;
URL www.sefton.gov.uk;
E-mail welfare.officers@education.sefton.gov.uk;
Tel 0151 934 3359

SPECIAL SCHOOLS

Crosby High School De Villiers Ave, Crosby, Merseyside L23 2TH; Tel 0151 924 3671
Headteacher S.J. Dempsey
Mixed 6–15 MLD (Day)

Merefield School Westminster Dr, Southport, Merseyside PR8 2QZ; Tel 01704 577163; 01704 577164
Headteacher Ms A. Foster
3–19 SLD and Autism (Day)

Newfield School Edge La, Thornton, Merseyside L23 4TG; Tel 0151 924 9620
Headteacher Mrs S. Evans
Mixed 5–17 EBD (Day)

Presfield School Preston New Rd, Southport, Merseyside PR9 8PA; Tel 01704 227831
Headteacher Mr E.T. Powell
4–15 MLD (Day)

Rowan Park School Sterrix La, Litherland, Merseyside L21 0DB; Tel 0151 222 4894
Headteacher Mrs J. Kelly
Mixed 3–18 SLD and Autism

School of the Good Shepherd Sterrix La, Litherland, Merseyside L21 0DA; Tel 0151 928 6165
Headteacher Mr A.M. Sullivan
3–16 Learning difficulties associated with physical and medical disabilities.

SEFTON TEACHING AND EDUCATION PSYCHOLOGY SERVICE (STEPS)

Freshfield Primary School Base Watchyard La, Formby, Merseyside L37 3JY; E-mail steps@mersinet.co.uk; Tel 01704 385902
Head (STEPS Service) Eileen Oakes (Acting)
Head (STEPS Service) Daphne Mortimer (Acting)

SHEFFIELD METROPOLITAN CITY COUNCIL
www.sheffield.gov.uk

Population 513 100 (2001)
Political Composition: Lab: 49, LD: 36, Con: 1, Ind: 1
Town Hall, Sheffield, South Yorkshire S1 2HH;
URL www.sheffield.gov.uk;
E-mail first.point@sheffield.gov.uk; Tel 0114 272 6444
Lord Mayor Cllr D. Leek
Chief Executive R. Kerslake, BSc, IPFA

6

Social Services Directorate

Old Town Hall, Room 210, Sheffield, South Yorkshire S1 2HH; URL www.sheffield.gov.uk/services; Tel (Out-of-office hours) 0114 273 4446; (Children and Families Services) 0114 273 4855; (Adult Services) 0114 273 4908
Executive Director Penny Thompson; Tel 0114 273 4844
Deputy Director and Head (Strategy and Performance Review)
Sandie Keene
Fl 3, Redvers Hse, Sheffield, South Yorkshire S1 2JQ;
Tel 0114 273 4840
Head (Finance and Resources) Kevin Foster
Fl 3, Redvers Hse, Sheffield, South Yorkshire S1 2JQ;
Tel 0114 273 4687
Head (Children and Families) Penny Peysner
Fl 3, Redvers Hse, Sheffield, South Yorkshire S9 4JT;
Tel 0114 273 5116
*Head (Assessment and Care Mangement) and Manager
(Strategy and Operations)* Madeleine Fullerton
Fl 3, Redvers Hse, Sheffield, South Yorkshire S1 2JQ;
Tel 0114 273 4731

TRAINING

Manager (Employee Development Unit) Ann Harrison
Brockwood Park Training Centre, Station Rd, Sheffield, South Yorkshire; Tel 0114 269 1271

HOSPITAL SOCIAL WORK TEAMS

Children's Hospital Western Bank, Sheffield, South Yorkshire S10 2TH; Tel 0114 271 7310

Jessops Wing Leavygreave Rd, Sheffield, South Yorkshire S3 7RE; Tel 0114 226 8355

Northern General Hospital Herries Rd, Sheffield, South Yorkshire S5 7AU; Tel 0114 271 2466
Team Manager (Assessment and Integrated Care Services)
Kim Munks; Tel 0114 266 6896

Royal Hallamshire Hospital 6 Claremont Pl, Sheffield, South Yorkshire S10 2JF; Tel 0114 271 1900
Team Manager (HHSA/HICT) Carole Hastings; Tel 0114 271 5024

Ryegate Centre Tapton Crescent Rd, Sheffield, South Yorkshire S10 3TJ; Tel 0114 271 7633

Weston Park Hospital Whitham Rd, Sheffield, South Yorkshire S10 2ST; Tel 0114 267 0222

Nether Edge Psychiatric Unit Michael Carlisle Centre, Osborn Rd, Sheffield, South Yorkshire S11 9BJ; Tel 0114 271 8614

CHILDREN AND FAMILIES SERVICE

Head Penny Peysner
Fl 3, Redvers Hse, Sheffield, South Yorkshire; Tel 0114 273 5116
Service Manager (South West) Diane Williamson
Fl 7, Redvers Hse, Sheffield, South Yorkshire S1 2JQ; Tel 0114 273 5198
Service Manager (Family Placement) Nick Hughes
Fl 12, Castlemarket, Exchange St, Sheffield, South Yorkshire; Tel 0114 273 5155
Service Manager (Children with Disabilities) Chris Finnegan
Fl 7, Redvers Hse, Sheffield, South Yorkshire ST 2JQ; Tel 0114 273 5309
Service Manager (North East) Vicki Bennetts
Fl 4, Redvers Hse, Sheffield, South Yorkshire S1 2JQ; Tel 0114 273 4913
Service Manager (Child Protection and Reviewing) Trevor Owen
3 Palatine Chambers, Redvers Hse, Sheffield, South Yorkshire S1 2JQ; Tel 0114 273 4934
Service Manager (South East) Judith Dodd
The Old School, Station Rd, Sheffield, South Yorkshire S9; Tel 0114 203 4783
Service Manager (North West) Lisa Adams
Meade Hse, 96–100 Middlewood Rd, Sheffield, South Yorkshire S6; Tel 0114 203 9649
Service Manager (Family Placement) Nic Hughes
Fl 2 Castlemarket Bldg, Exchange St, Sheffield, South Yorkshire S1; Tel 0114 273 5155

ACCESS AND ASSESSMENT – CHILDREN

Service Manager (South East) Judith Dodd
Old School Hse, Darnall, Sheffield, South Yorkshire S9; Tel 0114 203 7483
Team Manager (First Point) Tommy Doyle
Fl 1, Howden Hse, Sheffield, South Yorkshire S1; Tel 0114 273 5682
Team Manager (North East) Karen Walker
Fl 4, Redvers Hse, Sheffield, South Yorkshire S1 2JQ; Tel 0114 273 4854
Team Manager (North East 4 Stephanie Watson
Fl 4, Redvers Hse, Sheffield, South Yorkshire S1 2JQ; Tel 0114 273 5560

LONG TERM CARE – CHILDREN

Project Officer (Children) David Beavers
Fl 4, Castle Market Bldgs, Sheffield, South Yorkshire S1 2HA; Tel 0114 273 4829
Team Manager (South East 1) Jacquie Stocks
The Old School, Station Rd, Sheffield, South Yorkshire S9 4JT; Tel 0114 203 7481
Team Manager (South East 4 PMN) Carol O'Neil
The Old School, Station Rd, Sheffield, South Yorkshire S9 4JT; Tel 0114 203 7487
Team Manager (South West 2 CIN) Phil Bradley
Fl 7, Redvers Hse, Sheffield, South Yorkshire S1 2JQ; Tel 0114 273 4916
Team Manager (South West 4 PMN) Ruth Fern
Fl 7, Redvers Hse, Sheffield, South Yorkshire S1 2JQ; Tel 0114 273 4912
Team Manager Vacancy
Meade Hse, 96–100 Middlewood Rd, Sheffield, South Yorkshire S6 4HA; Tel 0114 203 9629
Team Manager (North West 4 PMN) Susie Abraham
Meade Hse, 96–100 Middlewood Rd, Sheffield, South Yorkshire S6 4HA; Tel 0114 203 9630
Team Manager (South East 3 CIN) Paul Massey
The Old School, Station Rd, Sheffield, South Yorkshire S9 4JT; Tel 0114 203 7488
Team Manager (North West 1 CIN) Eileen Drury
Meade Hse, 96–100 Middlewood Rd, Sheffield, South Yorkshire S6 4HA; Tel 0114 203 9628
Team Manager (South West 3) Catherine Sikakana
Fl 7, Redvers Hse, Sheffield, South Yorkshire S1 2JQ; Tel 0114 273 4870

Team Manager (North West 2 CIN) Yasmin Farooq
Meade Hse, 96–100 Middlewood Rd, Sheffield, South Yorkshire S6 4HA; Tel 0114 203 9629
Team Manager (South West 1 CIN) Dave Nellist
Fl 7, Redvers Hse, Sheffield, South Yorkshire S1 2JQ; Tel 0114 273 6920

CHILDREN'S RESIDENTIAL SERVICES

Fl 2, Castle Market Bldg, Exchange St, Sheffield, South Yorkshire S1; Tel 0114 273 4956
Project Manager (Residential) Karen Standsberry
Ballifield Hall Residential Unit Redford Rd, Sheffield, South Yorkshire S13 9LF; Tel 0114 269 3095
Principal Karen Harrison
Barncliffe Residential Unit Redmires Rd, Sheffield, South Yorkshire S10 4LA; Tel 0114 230 1172
Principal Karen Harrison
Guildford House Residential Unit 300 Guildford View, Sheffield, South Yorkshire SZ2 2NZ; Tel 0114 276 0144
Principal Heather Gatley
Lydgate Residential Unit 2 Cross La, Sheffield, South Yorkshire S10 5FP; Tel 0114 268 5828
Principal Hazel Axon
Mather Road Residential Unit 45 Mather Rd, Sheffield, South Yorkshire S9 4GP; Tel 0114 204 7425
Principal Andrea Aram
Morland Drive Residential Unit 12 Morland Dr, Sheffield, South Yorkshire S14 1SY; Tel 0114 203 7808
Principal Ann Brown

RESIDENTIAL UNITS FOR CHILDREN WITH DISABILITIES

Chancet Wood Residential Unit Chancet Wood Dr, Sheffield, South Yorkshire S8 7TR; Tel 0114 274 6459
Principal Shirley Jones
Ringinglow Residential Unit 336 Ringinglow Rd, Sheffield, South Yorkshire S11 7PY; Tel 0114 235 1101; 0114 235 1102
Principal Sue Hatton
Rushley Meadows Residential Unit 1 Bannerdale Rd, Sheffield, South Yorkshire S7 2DJ; Tel 0114 255 0595
Principal Claire Blundell

SPECIALIST CHILDREN'S SERVICES

Fostering and Adoptions Services Fl 2 Castle Market Bldgs, Sheffield, South Yorkshire; Tel 0114 273 5155
Service Manager Nic Hughes
Family Placement Fl 2, Castle Market Bldgs, Sheffield, South Yorkshire; Tel 0114 273 4967
Contact Sue Massey
GALRO Victoria Pl, 34 Godstone Rd, Rotherham, South Yorkshire S60 2PU; Tel 01709 839655

YOUTH JUSTICE

Youth Offending Team 7 St. Peter's Cl, Sheffield, South Yorkshire S1 2EJ; Tel 0114 228 8555
Service Manager (Youth Offending) Malcolm Potter
Team Manager (Reparation) Ann Wilson
Team Manager (Remand and Bail Support) Gillian Ackerley
Aldine House (Secure Unit) 75 Limb La, Sheffield, South Yorkshire S17 3EX; Tel 0114 262 1160
Manager Francis N'Jie
Archway (Alternative to Custody) 104 Upperthorpe, Sheffield, South Yorkshire S6 3NE; Tel 0114 234 6992
Team Manager Tim Galton

RESIDENTIAL AND FAMILY SUPPORT SERVICE

Eastbank Family Support Unit Eastbank Rd, Sheffield, South Yorkshire S2 3PX; Tel 0114 203 9011
Principal Winston Campbell; Tel 0114 203 9009

DAY SERVICES FOR PEOPLE WITH LEARNING DISABILITIES

Fl 1, Howden Hse, Sheffield, South Yorkshire; Tel 0114 273 4835
Group Manager   Jim Harrap

Adsetts Day Service   Petre St, Sheffield, South Yorkshire S4 8DD; Tel 0114 243 2000; Fax 0114 243 1650
Area Manager (North East)   Vacancy
Area Manager   Josie Bolland
Area Manager   Carol Hickman

Beaumont Road   91 Beaumont Rd North, Sheffield, South Yorkshire S2 1RT; Tel 0114 203 7807
Area Manager (South East)   Alison Wylie
Assistant Area Manager   Jane Hobson

Blackstock   33 Blackstock Rd, Sheffield, South Yorkshire S14 1AB; Tel 0114 255 4754
Assistant Area Manager   Donna Turner

Crown Hill Workshop   Carlisle St, Sheffield, South Yorkshire S4 8DQ; Tel 0114 243 1712
Manager (Day Service)   Glyn Cook
Employment-based service.

Hallamgate Day Centre   16 Hallamgate Rd, Sheffield, South Yorkshire S10 5BT; Tel 0114 266 3134
Area Manager (South West)   Joan Richardson; Tel 0114 267 1813
Assistant Area Manager   Alan Johnson

High Green Day Service   Westwood Rd, Sheffield, South Yorkshire S30 8LE; Tel 0114 284 5354
Area Manager (North West)   Margaret Haddon

Owlerton Day Base   712a Penistone Rd, Sheffield, South Yorkshire S6 2DF
Assistant Area Manager   Peter Simmons; Tel 0114 203 9540

Stradbroke (Centre One)   133 Stradbroke Rd, Sheffield, South Yorkshire S13 3SL; Tel 0114 265 4654
Assistant Area Manager   Lisa Milton

Tannery Interlink   522–524 Stradbroke Rd, Sheffield, South Yorkshire S13 7GD; Tel 0114 269 6592
Assistant Area Manager   Phil Yelland

Warminister Day Centre   154 Warminister Rd, Sheffield, South Yorkshire S8 8PQ; Tel 0114 203 7211
Assistant Area Manager   Philip Sporne

Woodside   Woodside Local Day Base, Woodside La, Sheffield, South Yorkshire S3 9PB; Tel 0114 203 9320
Area Manager   Brian Hinchcliffe

ADULT SERVICES – MENTAL HEALTH

Fulwood Hse, Sheffield, South Yorkshire S10 3TH; Tel 0114 271 6383
Area Manager   Guy Hollingsworth

ASSESSMENT AND CARE MANAGEMENT – MENTAL HEALTH

Assistant Service Manager (North East – Mental Health)   Jo Jones
Northlands, Southey Hill, Sheffield, South Yorkshire S5 8BE; Tel 0114 271 6217
Assistant Service Manager (North West – Mental Health)   Kate Green
The Yews, Worrall Rd, Sheffield, South Yorkshire S30 3AU; Tel 0114 271 6100
Team Manager (South East – Mental Health)   Julie Hill
Eastglade Centre, 1 Eastglade Cres, Sheffield, South Yorkshire S12 4QN; Tel 0114 271 6451
Team Manager (South West – Mental Health)   John Heron
Argyll Hse, 9 Williamson Rd, Sheffield, South Yorkshire S11 9AR; Tel 0114 271 8654
Team Manager (Target Fund)   Chris Kearton
The Yews, Worrall Rd, Sheffield, South Yorkshire S30 3AU; Tel 0114 271 6107

MENTAL HEALTH SERVICES

City Road Day Service   555 City Rd, Sheffield, South Yorkshire S2 1GF; Tel 0114 264 4411
Principal   Greg Harrison

Howard Road Support Unit   178 Howard Rd, Sheffield, South Yorkshire S6 3RX; Tel 0114 233 5823
Principal   Paul Nicholson

Moncrieffe Day Service   9 Moncrieffe Rd, Sheffield, South Yorkshire S7 1HQ; Tel 0114 226 2500
Principal   Louise McQuinn

North East Community Mental Health Support Service   50–52 Lytton Rd, Parson Cross, Sheffield, South Yorkshire; Tel 0114 285 2252
Principal   Helen Cowhig

Pitsmoor Day Service   259 Pitsmoor Rd, Sheffield, South Yorkshire S3 9AQ; Tel 0114 203 9012
Principal   Derrick Longwright

Wainwright Crescent   48 Wainwright Cres, Sheffield, South Yorkshire S13 8EN; Tel 0114 265 2503
Principal   Janet Burke

ADULT SERVICES – DISABILITY

Head (Learning Disabilities)   Josie Bennett
Fl 2, Redvers Hse, Sheffield, South Yorkshire S1 2JQ; Tel 0114 273 4826
Manager (North West Disability Team)   Chris Read
Council Office, Salt Box La, Sheffield, South Yorkshire S35 8QS; Tel 0114 203 7084
Manager (South East Disability Team)   Sue Luckhurst
Crystal Peaks, 1–3 Peaks Mount, Sheffield, South Yorkshire S20 7PH; Tel 0114 248 1000
Manager (South West Disability Team)   Caroline Harris
Fl 1, Howden Hse, Sheffield, South Yorkshire S1 2SH; Tel 0114 273 4898
Team Manager (Sensory Impairment)   Norman Creighton
Fl 1, Howden Hse, Sheffield, South Yorkshire S1 2SH; Tel 0114 273 4955

DAY SERVICES FOR PEOPLE WITH PHYSICAL DISABILITIES

Foxwood Bungalow   3–5 Ridgeway Rd, Sheffield, South Yorkshire S12 2TW; Tel 0114 203 7810
Manager (Disability Day Service – South)   Sue Spooner
Team Leader   Marie Miller

Grange Crescent   105 Grange Cres, Sheffield, South Yorkshire S11 8AZ; Tel 0114 203 7209
Team Leader   Janet Harrington

Shiregreen Neighbourhood Centre   Beck Rd, Sheffield, South Yorkshire; Tel 0114 203 7010
Manager (Disability Day Service – North)   Gillian Robinson-Smith
Manager (Disability Day Service – North)   Paul Beastow

DISABILITY RESIDENTIAL UNITS

Grimesthorpe Road Residential Unit   144 Grimesthorpe Rd, Sheffield, South Yorkshire S4 7HE; Tel 0114 281 2261
Deputy Principal   Claire Bassinder

Oakwood View Residential Unit   328 Fulwood Rd, Sheffield, South Yorkshire S10 3BN; Tel 0114 230 4859
Deputy Principal   Liz Harding

Parson Cross Project   Parson Cross, 104 Holgate Rd, Sheffield, South Yorkshire S5 9FS; Tel 0114 273 7009
Manager   Christopher Wright

Rutland Road Residential Unit   275 Rutland Rd, Sheffield, South Yorkshire S3 9PZ; Tel 0114 281 2271
Manager (Operations)   Steve Danford

Upper Hanover Residential Unit   128 Upper Hanover St, Sheffield, South Yorkshire S3 7RF; Tel 0114 275 6263
Manager   Cath Egan Bennett

Walkley Residential Unit   16 Joseph Rd, Sheffield, South Yorkshire S6 3RZ; Tel 0114 285 3331
Manager   Carol Shaw

Warminster Road   136 Warminister Rd, Sheffield, South Yorkshire S8 8PQ; Tel 0114 281 2274
Manager   Mark Piper

6

ADULT SERVICES – OLDER PEOPLE

PURCHASING CARE MANAGEMENT

Crystal Peaks, 1–3 Peaks Mount, Sheffield, South Yorkshire S20 7PH
Service Manager (Purchasing Care) Kieth McKinstrie
Fl 1, Howden Hse, Sheffield, South Yorkshire S1 2SH; Tel 0114 273 4896

SPECIALIST ADULT SERVICES

Adult Abuse Policy Co-ordinator Fl 1, Redvers Hse, Sheffield, South Yorkshire S1 2JQ; Tel 0114 273 6870
City Wide Alarms 1st Fl, Priory Office, Darnall, South Yorkshire S9; Tel 0114 242 0351
Team Manager David Hudson

Emergency Duty Team
Contact John Hammerton; Tel 0114 273 4446

Education Department

Town Hall, Sheffield, South Yorkshire S1 2HH;
URL www.sheffield.gov.uk; Tel 0114 272 6444; Fax 0114 273 6279
Executive Director (Education) Jonathan Crossley-Holland
Deputy Director/Head of Service (Policy and Performance) S. Farnsworth
Head of Service (Access and Inclusion) Karen Worrall
Principal Education Psychologist John Coleman
Head of Service (Planning and Premises) Penny Pennington
Chief Education Welfare Officer Richard Deeks
Chief Executive (Sheffield Futures) Jim Reid

SCHOOL PSYCHOLOGICAL SERVICE

Bannerdale Centre 125 Carterknowle Rd, Sheffield, South Yorkshire S7 2EX; Tel 0114 250 6800; Fax 0114 250 6811
Manager John Coleman

SPECIAL SCHOOLS

Bents Green School Ringinglow Rd, Sheffield, South Yorkshire S11 7TB; Tel 0114 236 1737; 0114 236 3545; Fax 0114 262 1904
Headteacher A. Scott-Jones
Learning difficulties, day and residential (75)
Broad Elms School Broad Elms La, Sheffield, South Yorkshire S11 9RQ; Tel 0114 236 8277; Fax 0114 281 2899
Headteacher Mrs K. Taylor
Adjustment difficulties (36)
Dr John Worrall School Maltby St, Sheffield, South Yorkshire S9 2QA; Tel 0114 244 1762; Fax 0114 244 2185
Headteacher B.M. Burdon
MLD, behavioural difficulties (45)
East Hill Secondary School East Bank Rd, Sheffield, South Yorkshire S2 3PX; Tel 0114 276 0245; Fax 0114 272 8829
Headteacher K. Jenkins
MLD
Mossbrook Primary School Bochum Parkway, Sheffield, South Yorkshire S8 8JR; Tel 0114 237 2768; Fax 0114 283 9253
Headteacher M. Brough
Mixed Learning difficulties, day and residential (56)
Oakes Park School Hemsworth Rd, Sheffield, South Yorkshire S8 8LN; Tel 0114 255 4533; 0114 255 6754; Fax 0114 255 4533
Headteacher P. Johnson (Acting)
Mixed PH
Oakwood School Northern General Hospital, Herries Rd, Sheffield, South Yorkshire S5 7AU; Tel 0114 226 1691; Fax 0114 256 0369
Mixed Adjustment difficulties (26)

Sheffield Service for the Sensory Impaired (Visually Impaired) Hallam Primary School, Hallam Grange Cres, Sheffield, South Yorkshire S10 4BD; Tel 0114 263 0333; Fax 0114 230 9092
Teacher-in-Charge R. Flowerday
Mixed visually impaired (34)
Shirle Hill Hospital School Cherry Tree Rd, Sheffield, South Yorkshire S11 9AA; Tel 0114 271 6877; Fax 0114 271 6878
Headteacher G.D. Lewis, BEng
Mixed Adjustment difficulties (20)
Talbot Secondary School Matthews La, Sheffield, South Yorkshire S8 8JS; Tel 0114 250 7394; Fax 0114 250 7857
Headteacher J. Irwin
Mixed SLD

SPECIAL UNITS

Sensory Impaired Service c/o Hazlebarrow Primary School, Hazlebarrow Cres, Sheffield, South Yorkshire S8 8AQ; Tel 0114 237 7611; Fax 0114 237 4865
Teacher-in-Charge R. Flowerday

INTEGRATED RESOURCES

Abbeydale Grange School Hastings Rd, Sheffield, South Yorkshire S7 2GU; Tel 0114 255 7301; Fax 0114 250 8540
Headteacher C. Mallaband
Mixed MLD
Arbourthorne NI School Eastern Ave, Sheffield, South Yorkshire S2 2GQ; Tel 0114 239 8317; Fax 0114 249 5125
Headteacher S. Haigh
Nursery mixed
Fox Hill NIJ School Keats Rd, Sheffield, South Yorkshire S6 1AZ; Tel 0114 231 3469; Fax 0114 285 3661
Headteacher J. Willis
Mixed MLD
Greengate Lane NIJ School Greengate La, Sheffield, South Yorkshire S35 3GT; Tel 0114 284 8322; Fax 0114 284 8322
Headteacher M.E. Griffin
Mixed Primary SEN
Greystones IJ School Greystones Rd, Sheffield, South Yorkshire S11 7GL; Tel 0114 266 3413; Fax 0114 268 6235
Headteacher A. Anwyl
Mixed Hearing impaired
Hartley Brook NIJ School Hartley Brook Rd, Sheffield, South Yorkshire S5 0JF; Tel 0114 245 6882; Fax 0114 240 2544
Headteacher P. Martlew
Mixed SEN (incl nursery)
Hazlebarrow NIJ School Hazlebarrow Cres, Sheffield, South Yorkshire S8 8AQ; Tel 0114 237 5778
Headteacher J. Kilner
Mixed Hearing impaired
High Storrs School Ringinglow Rd, Sheffield, South Yorkshire S11 7LH; Tel 0114 267 0000; Fax 0114 266 3624
Headteacher E. Talmadge
Mixed Hearing impaired
King Ecgbert School Furniss Ave, Sheffield, South Yorkshire S17 3QN; Tel 0114 236 9931; Fax 0114 236 2468
Headteacher M.R. Evans
Mixed Communication difficulties
Nether Green J School Fulwood Rd, Sheffield, South Yorkshire S10 3QA; Tel 0114 230 2461; Fax 0114 263 0189
Headteacher P. Jenkins
SLD
Nook Lane J School Nook La, Stannington, Sheffield, South Yorkshire S6 6BN; Tel 0114 234 1097; Fax 0114 285 4392
Headteacher G. Hodges
Mixed SLD

Pipworth J and NI Schools Pipworth Rd, Sheffield, South Yorkshire S2 1AA; Tel 0114 239 1078; (NI) 0114 239 8432; Fax (Junior) 0114 239 1989
Headteacher (Junior) J. Storey
Headteacher (Nursery Infant) M. Davey
  Adjustment difficulties

Prince Edward School City Rd, Sheffield, South Yorkshire S12 2AA; Tel 0114 228 1900; Fax 0114 239 9307
Headteacher B. MaGeachie
  Mixed SEN

Sharrow J School South View Rd, Sheffield, South Yorkshire S7 1DB; Tel 0114 255 1704; Fax 0114 255 1704
Headteacher S. Jackson
  Mixed MLD

Silverdale School Bents Cres, Sheffield, South Yorkshire S11 9RT; Tel 0114 236 9991; Fax 0114 262 0627
Headteacher H. Storey
  Mixed Hearing impaired

Stradbroke NIJ School Richmond Rd, Sheffield, South Yorkshire S13 8LT; Tel 0114 239 9320; Fax 0114 239 3430
Headteacher B.M. Clarke
  Mixed MLD

Tapton School Darwin La, Sheffield, South Yorkshire S10 5RG; Tel 0114 267 1414; Fax 0114 294 1155
Headteacher J.E. Bardsley
  Mixed Visually handicapped

Wharncliffe Side NIJ School Brightholmlee La, Sheffield, South Yorkshire S35 0DD; Tel 0114 286 2379; Fax 0114 286 2379
Headteacher D. Bowes
  Mixed Nursery SEN

TEACHER AND REINTEGRATION SERVICE

Spring La Education Centre, Brimmesfield Rd, Sheffield, South Yorkshire S2 2JR; Tel 0114 253 1988; Fax 0114 253 1989
Headteacher P. Goode

Clifford Centre 2 Clifford Rd, off Psalter La, Sheffield, South Yorkshire S11 9AQ; Tel 0114 255 0741
Headteacher P. Goode (Acting)

Hospital and Home Education Service 24 Clarkhouse Rd, Sheffield, South Yorkshire S10 2LB; Tel 0114 268 3853
Headteacher A. Beamhall

SHROPSHIRE COUNTY COUNCIL
www.shropshireonline-cc.gov.uk

In April 1998 Telford and Wrekin Council became a unitary authority and is listed alphabetically within this chapter. The rest of Shropshire retains a two-tier structure.
Population 283 300 (2001)
Political Composition: Con: 18, Lab: 11, LD: 9, Progressive Ind: 4, Assoc. Ind Shropshire Cllrs: 2.
The Shirehall, Abbey Foregate, Shrewsbury, Shropshire SY2 6ND; URL www.shropshireonline-cc.gov.uk; Tel 01743 251000; Fax 01743 255901
Chair of the County Council Major A.H. Coles, MBE, TD Knowbury Hse, Knowbury, Ludlow, Shropshire SY8 3LQ; Tel 01584 890287
Chief Executive Carolyn Downs; Tel 01743 252702
Corporate Director (Community and Environment) Penny Spencer; Tel 01743 252302

Social Care and Health

The Shirehall, Abbey Foregate, Shrewsbury, Shropshire SY2 6ND; Tel (Emergency) 01743 244197; 01743 253729; Fax 01743 253727

Corporate Director (Social Care and Health) Jack Collier
Head (Business Support) Mike Harris; Tel 01743 253709
Head (Childrens Services) Terry Jones
Manager (Adults Services) John Hall; Tel 01743 253702
CSW, The Shirehall, Shrewsbury, Shropshire SY2 6ND; Tel 01743 253823
Divisional Manager (Planning and Commission) G. James, BA, BEd, PhD

DISTRICT SOCIAL SERVICES OFFICES

Bridgnorth District Office Whitburn Cottage, Whitburn Pl, Bridgnorth, Shropshire WV16 4QS; Tel 01746 761760

Ludlow District Office Fairview Hse, 47 Gravel Hill, Ludlow, Shropshire SY8 1QS; Tel 01584 876688
Children and Families Team.

Oswestry District Office Holbache Rd, Oswestry, Shropshire SY11 4RH; Tel 01691 652383
Elderly and Disability.

Shrewsbury District Office St. Michael's Hse, St. Michael's St, Shrewsbury, Shropshire SY1 2HE; Tel 01743 255754

Wem District Office Talbot Hse, 3 High St, Wem, Shropshire; Tel (Older People Services) 01939 234713 ; (Child Care) 01939 235353

HOSPITAL SOCIAL WORK TEAMS

Oswestry Hospital Social Work Team Robert Jones and Agnes Hunt Orthopaedic Hospital, Oswestry, Shropshire SY10 7AG; Tel 01691 404490
Manager Gled Cloherty

RSH Social Work Team Royal Shrewsbury Hospital, Mytton Oak Rd, Shrewsbury, Shropshire SY3 8XF; Tel 01743 261012
Manager Linda Burgham

ASSERTIVE OUTREACH TEAMS

Oswestry Assertive Outreach Team 71 Salop Rd, Oswestry, Shropshire SY11 2NQ; Tel 01691 656520
Contact Steve Lawrence
Intensive team support for people with severe mental health problems.

Shrewsbury Assertive Outreach Team Cambrian Hse, Chester St, Shrewsbury, Shropshire; Tel 01743 340155
Contact J. Taylor
  Intensive team support for people with severe mental health problems.

COUNTY ADOPTION TEAM

Observer House Holywell St, Abbey Foregate, Shrewsbury, Shropshire SY2 5DE; Tel 01743 241915

CHILDREN AND FAMILIES

Old Police Station, Whitburn St, Bridgnorth, Shropshire WV16 6QP; Tel 01746 711940
Contact Pete Murphy
  Ongoing cases only, refer others to Ludlow.

FAMILY RESOURCE CENTRES

Besford House Resource Centre 42 Trinity St, Belle Vue, Shrewsbury, Shropshire SY3 7PQ; Tel (Fostering, Teencare (West)) 01743 232398; (Child Care) 01743 368174

Bourne House Radbrook College Campus, Radbrook Rd, Shrewsbury, Shropshire SY3 9BL; Tel 01743 254800

The Wheatlands Family Resource Centre 77 The Wheatlands, Baschurch, Shrewsbury, Shropshire SY4 2DW; Tel 01939 260553
Contact J. Taylor
Contact N. Garratt
  Mixed (8)

6

YOUTH OFFENDING TEAM

Richmond Hse, Rutland, Harlescott, Shrewsbury,
   Shropshire SY1 3EG; Tel 01743 460560

RESIDENTIAL ESTABLISHMENTS FOR CHILDREN

Holmwood Home Clive Ave, Church Stretton, Shropshire
SY6 7BL; Tel 01694 722844

Path House Lower Gables, Lowr Galdeford, Ludlow,
Shropshire SY8 1SD; Tel 01584 879563
Contact   Robert Davidson

Robert House Hearne Way, Monkmoor, Shrewsbury,
Shropshire SY2 5SL; Tel 01743 357625

The Rowans 46 Upper Rd, Meole Brace, Shrewsbury,
Shropshire SY3 9JQ; Tel 01743 359897
Contact   K. Ford

CHILDREN WITH DISABILITIES

Richmond Hse, Rutland, Harlescott, Shrewsbury,
   Shropshire SY1 3QG; Tel 01743 460560
Contact   Mike Felstead

DAY CENTRE FOR THE PHYSICALLY HANDICAPPED

The Grange Centre Levens Dr, Lancaster Rd, Shrewsbury,
Shropshire SY1 3TQ; Tel 01743 443559
Contact   J. Barnett

LEAVING CARE TEAM

East Entrance, Suite 6, Prospect Hse, Belle Vue Rd,
   Shrewsbury, Shropshire SY3 7NR; Tel 01743 364025;
   Fax 01743 364037
Manager   Colin Wright

ESTABLISHMENTS FOR ADULTS WITH LEARNING DISABILITIES

Albert Road Shrewsbury, Shropshire SY14; Tel 01743 246208

Aquamira Home Primrose Dr, Sutton Pk, Shrewsbury,
Shropshire SY3 7TP; Tel 01743 355984
Contact   Wendy Thomas

Besford Hse 42 Trinity St, Bell Vue, Shrewsbury, Shropshire
SY3 7PQ; Tel 01743 253600
District Manager   Kath Edwards
Initial Assessment   Tim Gunner
Case Manager   Andy Nicholls
Manager (Resources)   Colin Wright

Church Stretton Day Services 44b Sandford Ave, Church
Stretton, Shropshire SY6 6BH; Tel 01694 723319
Contact   Carol Lucas

Eskdale House Eskdale Rd, Shrewsbury, Shropshire
SY2 5UD; Tel 01743 231303
Contact   D. Hill
   (34)

Friars Walk Resource Centre Bishop Mascall Centre,
Lower Caldeford, Ludlow, Shropshire SY8 1NT; Tel 01584
877706
Contact   Gavin Bayliss

Greenacres Rural Unit Fenemere La, Walford, Baschurch,
Shrewsbury, Shropshire SY4 2JA; Tel 01939 291109
Contact   Graham Archer

Innage Lane Centre 2 Innage La, Bridgnorth, Shropshire
WV16 4HW; Tel 01746 769438
Contact   Jo Walker
Contact   Doreen Simpkins

Kempsfield Hostel Primrose Dr, Sutton Pk, Shrewsbury,
Shropshire SY3 7TP; Tel 01743 246033
Contact   P. Morgan
   (25)

Maesbury Metals 22–23 Maes-yy-clwd, Maesbury Ind Est,
Oswestry, Shropshire; Tel 01691 670665

Market Drayton Day Services The Youth Centre, Drayton
Gr, Market Drayton, Shropshire TF9 3AD; Tel 01630 658213
Contact   Mary Johnson

Meole Brace Resource Centre Roman Rd, Shrewsbury,
Shropshire SY3 9JN; Tel 01743 360387
Contact   Graham Parker

Monkmoor Centre Eskdale Rd, Shrewsbury, Shropshire
SY2 5UD; Tel 01743 236868
Contact   Liz Hayward
   (96)

Oak Farm Station Rd, Ditton Priors, Bridgnorth, Shropshire
WV16 6SS; Tel 01746 712352
Contact   Stuart Toulson

Patchworks Unit 12, Radford Field, Maesbury Ind Est,
Oswestry, Shropshire; Tel 01691 671923
Contact   Bill Coxhead

Sabrina Court Longden, Coleham, Shrewsbury, Shropshire
SY3 7EL; Tel 01743 249145

Victoria Centre Victoria Rd, Oswestry, Shropshire
SY11 2HT; Tel 01691 652467
Contact   T. King
   (70)

COMMUNITY MENTAL HEALTH TEAMS

**Community Mental Health Team South East Shropshire –
Bridgnorth** Bridgnorth Hospital, Norghate, Bridgnorth,
Shropshire WV16 4EU; Tel 01746 768787; 01746 769531
Contact   Kevin Mansell

Community Mental Health Team South Shropshire – Ludlow
25 Corve St, Ludlow, Shropshire SY8 1DA; Tel 01584
878167
Contact   Jane Hambleton

Community Mental Health Team North Shrewsbury Hartleys
Business Centre, Monkmoor Rd, Shrewsbury, Shropshire
SY2 5ST; Tel 01743 243300
Contact   Ann Mitchell
Day Services (Monkmoor Haven)   Jonathan Taylor; Tel 01743
254064; 07789 932597
ENABLE (Support in finding employment)   Jonathan Allen;
Tel 01743 340035

**Community Mental Health Team North East Shropshire –
Market Drayton** The Portacabins, Market Drayton Cottage
Hospital, Market Drayton, Shropshire TF9 3DQ; Tel 01630
655066
Contact   N. Godman
Day Services (Mon and Wed)   Noreen Fletcher; Tel 01630
653678

**Community Mental Health Team North West Shropshire –
Oswestry** 71 Salop Rd, Oswestry, Shropshire SY11 2NQ;
Tel 01691 679500
Contact   Paul Cooper

MENTAL HEALTH ESTABLISHMENTS

Abbey Works Unit 11, Shire's Bus Pk, Abbey Foregate,
Shrewsbury, Shropshire SY2 5DE; Tel 01743 359737
Contact   Alan Baker

Craven Arms Community Centre Newington Way, Craven
Arms, Ludlow, Shropshire SY7 9PS; Tel 01588 673884
Contact   Margaret Reynolds

The Elms House off Belvidere Ave, Shrewsbury, Shropshire
SY2 5PE; Tel 01743 356127
Contact   J. McArdle
   Mixed (32)

Hartley Business Centre Monkmoor Rd, Shrewsbury,
Shropshire SY2 5ST

North West Shropshire Day Services Lorne Street Day
Centre, Cabin La, Oswestry, Shropshire SY11 1ND;
Tel 01691 655465
Contact   Steve Lawrence

Pathways Unit 11, Harlescott Barns, Harlescott La, Shrewsbury, Shropshire SY1 3SZ; Tel 01743 464293
Contact Michael Cainc

Radbrook Day Services Radbrook Rd, Shrewsbury, Shropshire; Tel 01743 254064
Contact E. Crisp

SERVICES FOR OLDER PEOPLE

Bradbury Day Centre Whitchurch Hospital, Whitchurch, Shropshire SY13 1NT; Tel 01948 664786; Fax 01948 662534
Contact Val Grocott (Acting)

Crowmoor House Frith Cl, Shrewsbury, Shropshire SY2 5XW; Tel 01743 235835
Contact Cate Wallington

Drawwell House 1–2 Drawwell Hse, Noble St, Wem, Shropshire SY4 5DP; Tel 01939 234713
Contact Vacancy
Disability Ged Cloherty

Ludlow Day Centre Helena La Hse, Hamlet Rd, Ludlow, Shropshire SY8 2NP; Tel 01584 878233
Contact Sandra Griffiths
Contact Linda Watkins; Tel 01584 872776
Disability Tony Watkins; Tel 01584 877189

Meres Day Centre Ellesmere Hse, Trimpley St, Ellesmere, Shropshire SY12 0HS; Tel 01691 622584
Contact Di Beasley

ACCOMMODATION FOR OLDER PEOPLE

There is one local authority residential elderly persons' homes.
Care for Older People.
District Social Work Teams will assess and advise on care requirements. Contact appropriate district team.

MEALS SERVICES

Assessment for Community meals is undertaken by the appropriate District Social Work Team. For general advice and information telephone 01743 253788.

Education Services Directorate

Shirehall, Abbey Foregate, Shrewsbury, Shropshire SY2 6ND; URL www.shropshireonline.gov.uk; E-mail education-dept@shropshire-cc.gov.uk; Tel 01743 254307; Fax 01743 254415
Corporate Director (Education Services) E. Nicholson, BPhil

EDUCATIONAL PSYCHOLOGICAL SERVICE

The Glebe Centre Glebe St, Wellington, Telford, Shropshire TF1 1JP; Tel 01952 522610

Education Welfare Service The Glebe Centre, Glebe St, Telford, Shropshire TF1 1JP; Tel 01952 522620
Principal Education Welfare Officer D. Simpkins

SPECIAL SCHOOLS

Severndale School Hearne Way, Monkmoor, Shrewsbury, Shropshire SY2 5SL; Tel 01743 281600; Fax 01743 352482
Headteacher C. Davies, BEd
Mixed SLD/PH (160)

Trench Hall School Tilley Grn, Wem, Shropshire SY4 5PJ; Tel 01939 232372
Headteacher R. Wilson
Mixed EBD (35)

SLOUGH BOROUGH COUNCIL
www.slough.gov.uk

In April 1998 Berkshire County Council was replaced by Bracknell Forest, Reading, Slough, West Berkshire, Windsor and Maidenhead and Wokingham each responsible for local government services in their area. They are listed alphabetically within this chapter.
Political Composition: Lab: 26, Con: 6, Ind: 4, Lib: 3, LD: 1, Vacancy: 1
Town Hall, Bath Rd, Slough SL1 3UQ;
URL www.slough.gov.uk; Tel 01753 552288; Fax 01753 692499; Minicom 01753 875030
Chief Executive Cheryl Coppell, BA(Econ)

Social Services Department

Town Hall, Bath Rd, Slough SL1 3UQ;
URL www.slough.gov.uk; Tel 01753 552288; (Out-of-hours from 1700 only) 01344 786543
Director (Social Services) Dawn Warwick
Assistant Director (Social Services Community Care) Frank Toner
Assistant Director (Social Services Children and Families) Ann Domeney
Assistant Director (Finance and Business Resources) Andrew Blake-Herbert
Assistant Director (Commissioning and Quality Standards) Dugald Millar

Social Services Cabinet

Commissioner (Health and Social Care) Arvind Dhaliwell (Lab)
Commissioner (Children and Young People) Muriel Gilmore (Lab)

RESIDENTIAL HOME FOR CHILDREN

Elmside 1 Yew Tree Rd, Slough SL1 2AA; Tel 01753 534733; Fax 01753 553087
Manager Val Drake
Group Manager (Resources and Reviewing) Nicky Rayner
Five short term places.
(8)

RESPITE UNIT FOR YOUNG PEOPLE WITH LEARNING DISABILITIES

Breakaway 2 Priors Cl, St. Laurence Way, Slough SL1 2BQ; Tel 01753 825365; Fax 01753 821368
Manager Helen Cornwall
Group Manager (Resources and Reviewing) Nicky Rayner
Seven bedded respite unit.

RESPITE CARE FOR YOUNG PEOPLE WITH LEARNING DISABILITIES

Home from Home Scheme Town Hall, Bath Rd, Slough SL1 3UQ; Tel 01753 690961; Fax 01753 690801
Manager Lesley Fitzgerald
Group Manager (Resources and Reviewing) Nicky Rayner
Short term breaks with specialist carers.

CHILD CARE AND FAMILY CENTRES

Slough Family Resource Centre Chalvey Pk, Slough SL1 2HX; Tel 01753 521448; Fax 01753 554126
Unit Manager Linda Ball
Group Manager (Resources and Reviewing) Nicky Rayner

CHILDREN'S SOCIAL WORK TEAMS

Access and Assessment Team Town Hall, Bath Rd, Slough SL1 2UQ; Tel 01753 690822; Fax 01753 690801
Manager Paul Bains
Group Manager (Fieldwork Services) Mark Evans

6

Adoption and Permanency Team Town Hall, Bath Rd, Slough SL1 3UQ; Tel 01753 690779; Fax 01753 690801
Manager Julia Brown
Group Manager (Resources and Reviewing) Nicky Rayner

Disabled Children's Team Town Hall, Bath Rd, Slough SL1 3UQ; Tel 01753 690778; Fax 01753 690801
Manager Sue Betts
Group Manager (Fieldwork Services) Mark Evans

Family Placement Team Town Hall, Bath Rd, Slough SL1 3UQ; Tel 01753 690961; Fax 01753 690801
Manager (Fostering) Lesley Fitzgerald
Group Manager (Resources and Reviewing) Nicky Rayner

Family Support Team Town Hall, Bath Rd, Slough SL1 3UQ; Tel 01753 690830; Fax 01753 690801
Manager Tina Ryan
Group Manager (Fieldwork Services) Mark Evans

LAC Reviewing Officers Town Hall, Bath Rd, Slough SL1 3UQ; Tel 01753 690906
LAC Reviewing Officer Jean Armsby
LAC Reviewing Officer Joan Guiles
Group Manager (Resources and Reviewing) Nicky Rayner

Looked After Children Team Town Hall, Bath Rd, Slough SL1 3UQ; Tel 01753 690831; Fax 01753 690801
Manager Bindiya Grewal
Group Manager (Fieldwork Services) Mark Evans

CHILD PROTECTION CO-ORDINATOR

Town Hall, Bath Rd, Slough SL1 3UQ; Tel 01753 872903
Manager Carolyn Beese-Jarvis
Manager Rona Walker
Group Manager (Resources and Reviewing) Nicky Rayner

YOUTH RESOURCE TEAM

Slough Youth Offending Team Partnership Hse, Chalvey Pk, Slough SL1 2HT; Tel 01753 522702
Manager Shelley Larose-Jones

RESIDENTIAL ACCOMMODATION FOR ADULTS WITH LEARNING DISABILITIES

Lavender Court 1 Priors Cl, St Laurence Way, Slough SL1 2BQ; Tel 01753 512368
Group Manager (Learning Disabilities) J. Bruynseels
Manager Peter Sutton
Long term residential care for Adults with Learning Disabilities.
(8)

SUPPORTED LIVING TEAMS

Cherwell Project 2 Victoria St, Slough SL1 2PR; Tel 01753 516985; Fax 01753 516985
Manager Pauline Grady
Group Manager (Learning Disabilities) John Bruynseels
Supported living for people with a learning disability.

Longcroft Supported Living Team 305 Langley Rd, Langley, Slough SL3 8DA; Tel 01753 690470
Group Manager (Physical Disabilities) Vicky Cooper
Supported living for older people.

Supported Living Team Flat 6, The Tower, Burlington Ave, Slough SL1 2LA; Tel 01753 787544; Fax 01753 757545
Manager Helen Proctor
Group Manager (Learning Disabilities) John Bruynseels
Supported living for people with learning disabilities and people with mental health problems.

RESPITE UNIT FOR PEOPLE WITH LEARNING DISABILITIES

Respond 3 Priors Cl, St. Laurence Way, Slough SL1 2BQ; Tel 01753 554435; 01753 577066
Manager Paul Nicholl
Group Manager (Learning Disabilities) John Bruynseels
Eight bedded unit, planned and emergency respite care.

DAY SERVICES FOR ADULTS WITH LEARNING DISABILITIES

Priors Day Services 4 Priors Cl, St. Laurence Way, Slough SL1 2BQ; Tel 01753 577066; Fax 01753 577068
Unit Manager Virginia Ashberry
Adults with severe learning disabilities/physical disabilities or sensory impairment.

Slough Day Service Elliman Resource Unit, Pursers Crt, off Elliman Ave, Slough SL2 5DL; Tel 01753 527344; Fax 01753 692683
Manager Elaine Gammond
Group Manager (Learning Disabilities) John Bruynseels
Day centre for adults with learning disabilities.

SHELTERED WORKSHOPS AND WORK CENTRES

Speedwell Enterprises Northampton Ave, Slough SL1 3BP; Tel 01753 572249; Fax 01753 511685
Manager Huw Griffiths
43 Workstep Programme places (Work Prepartion Programme), 40 Opportunity Group places (Work Preparation, Experience and Placement)

COMMUNITY TEAM FOR PEOPLE WITH LEARNING DISABILITIES

Slough CTPLD Town Hall, Bath Rd, Slough SL1 3UQ; Tel 01753 690860; Fax 01753 690413
Team Manager Gerry Crawford
Group Manager (Learning Difficulties) John Bruynseels

ADULT FAMILY PLACEMENT

Town Hall, Bath Rd, Slough SL1 3UQ; Tel 01753 690873; Fax 01753 690413
Manager Suma Saakwa-Mante
Group Manager (Learning Disabilities) John Bruynseels

MENTAL HEALTH SERVICES

Access Team New Horizons, Pursers Crt, off Elliman Ave, Slough SL2 1BX; Tel 01753 690950; Fax 01753 690949
Service Manager Gareth Davies
Locality Manager Ade Odunlade
Assessment, short term management and signposting for people presenting with mental health problems to services in Slough.

Assertive Outreach Team New Horizons, Pursers Crt, off Elliman Ave, Slough SL2 1BX; Tel 01753 477000; Fax 01753 690949
Team Leader Tony Dwyer
Locality Manager Ade Odunlade
Engaging service users presenting with mental health problems who will not work with established services.

Slough Community Mental Health Team New Horizons, Pursers Crt, off Elliman Ave, Slough SL1 1BX; Tel 01753 690950; Fax 01753 690949
Service Manager (Health) Jane Knowles
Team Manager (Social Services) Geoff Demby
Locality Manager Ade Odunlade

TRANSPORT CO-ORDINATOR

Tel 01753 552015; Fax 01753 692683
Transport Co-ordinator John Northam
Assistant Director (Finance and Business Resources) Andrew Blake-Herbert

DAY CENTRE FOR PEOPLE WITH PHYSICAL DISABILITIES

The New Phoenix Day Centre 307 Langley Rd, Langley, Slough SL3 8DA; Tel 01753 541103; Fax 01753 541103
Manager Rene Lipman
Group Manager (Physical Disabilities) Vicky Cooper
(22)

RESIDENTIAL ACCOMMODATION FOR OLDER PEOPLE

There are three local authority residential establishments for older people.

DAY CENTRES FOR OLDER PEOPLE

The Beeches Day Centre Newbeech, Long Readings La, Britwell, Slough SL2 1QP; Tel 01753 691212; Fax 01753 512326
Manager Kathy Laflin
Group Manager (Physical Disabilities) Vicky Cooper
20 day centre places, five days a week.

Wexham Day Centre Wexham Hse, Knolton Way, Wexham Crt, Slough SL2 5SQ; Tel 01753 524321; Fax 01753 531306
Manager Baljit Kaur
Group Manager (Physical Disabilities) Vicky Cooper
15 day centre places, 5 days a week.

OLDER PEOPLE'S INTERMEDIATE CARE

Intermediate Care Team Newbeech Hse, Long Readings La, Britwell, Slough SL2 1QE; Tel 01753 527252; Fax 01753 825866
Manager Teresa Wager
Group Manager (Physical Disabilities) Vicky Cooper
Facilities early discharge from hospitals and prevents hospital admissions. Includes six bedded unit.

OLDER PERSONS' OCCUPATIONAL THERAPY

Community Occupational Therapy Team Town Hall, Bath Rd, Slough SL1 3UQ; Tel 01753 690436
Manager Jenny Jarrett
Group Manager (Physical Disabilities) Vicky Cooper

HOME CARE

Slough Social Services Home Care Town Hall, Bath Rd, Slough SL1 3UQ; Tel 01753 690930; Fax 01753 823121
Home Care Manager Syliva Broadbridge
Home Care Manager Daryl Reading
Home Care Manager Yvonne Edwards
Group Manager (Older People's Services) George Howard

OLDER PEOPLE SOCIAL WORK TEAM

Community Social Work and Access Team Town Hall, Bath Rd, Slough SL1 3UQ; Tel 01753 690400; Fax 01753 960413
Manager Beth Booker
Group Manager (Older Peoples Services) George Howard
Older people and people with physical disabilities, 18+.

OLDER PEOPLE'S HOSPITAL SOCIAL WORK TEAMS

Upton Hospital Social Work Team Albert St, Slough SL1 2BJ; Tel 01753 635070; Fax 01753 635071
Assistant Team Manager Sue Nutter
Group Manager (Older Peoples Services) George Howard

Wexham Park/Heatherwood Hospital Social Work Team Wexham Park Hospital, Wexham St, Slough SL2 4HL; Tel 01753 633661; Fax 01753 633664
Manager Val Rigby
Group Manager (Older Peoples Services) George Howard

COMMISSIONING AND QUALITY STANDARDS

Quality Standards Team Town Hall, Bath Rd, Slough SL1 3UQ; Tel 01753 875698; Fax 01753 875764
Manager (Quality Standards) Gerry Brady
Responsible for performance management and quality assurance in Social Services. This includes completion of statutory returns, provision of management information, managing complaints and compliments, development and monitoring of service standards, co-ordinating service planning, planning and implementing quality audits and reviews and driving the performance and quality agenda across the department.

Joint Commissioning Team Beech Hse, Upton Hospital, Albert St, Slough SL1 2BJ; Tel 01753 635573; Fax 01753 635574

Manager (Strategic Commissioning) Jane Wood
Joint arrangement with Slough PCT with primary role of co-ordinating the development and implementation of NSF objectives and commissioning and contracting health and social care services for older people, children and young people, people with disabilities and mental illness, substance users and carers.

Learning and Cultural Services

Town Hall, Bath Rd, Slough SL1 3UQ; Tel 01753 875700; Fax 01753 875716
Chief Education Officer Christopher Spencer
Special Schools
2

HOME AND HOSPITAL TUITION

Wexham Park Hospital The School Room Paediatric Dept, Wexham St, Slough SL2 4HL; Tel 01753 634610
Head T. Nicholas

SCHOOL PSYCHOLOGICAL SERVICE

Education Psychological Service, Town Hall, Bath Rd, Slough SL1 3UQ; Tel 01753 787640; Fax 01753 787641
Head R. Crofts

CHILDREN WITH SPECIFIC LEARNING DIFFICULTIES (DAY UNITS)

Beechwood Special Resource Beechwood Secondary School, Long Readings La, Slough SL1 1QE; Tel 01753 520473
Headteacher J. Shepard
Mixed

Cippenham Junior School Elmshott La, Slough SL1 5RB; Tel 01628 604665
Headteacher H.P. Duffy
Mixed

Ryvers Primary Resource Trelawney Ave, Slough SL1 6HE; Tel 01753 544474
Headteacher A. Dean
Mixed (11)

The Westgate Resource Cippenham La, Slough SL1 5AH; Tel 01753 521320
Headteacher R. Thomas

DELICATE AND PHYSICALLY HANDICAPPED (DAY UNITS)

Priory School Orchard Ave, Slough SL1 6HE; Tel 01628 604767
Headteacher Ms J. Laver
Foundation (672)

HEARING IMPAIRED CHILDREN (DAY UNITS)

Foxborough Combined Common Rd, Slough SL3 8TX; Tel 01753 546376
Headteacher D.H. Richards
Mixed

Langleywood School Langleywood School, Langley Rd, Slough SL3 7EF; Tel 01753 541549
Headteacher Ms J.A. Alder

SPECIAL CLASSES AND RESOURCES

Chalvey Nursery Assessment Resource Chalvey Nursery, The Green, Slough SL1 2SP; Tel 01753 536293
Headteacher K. Makinson

St. Ethelbert's Language and Literacy Centre St. Ethelbert's RC Aided Combined School, Wexham Rd, Slough SL2 5QR; Tel 01753 522048
Headteacher T. Haggart (Acting)

6

SPECIAL SCHOOLS

Arbour Vale School Stoke Rd, Slough SL2 5AY; Tel 01753 525291
Headteacher Ms A. Beane

Littledown Special School Queens Rd, Slough SL1 3QW; Tel 01753 521734
Headteacher L. Redfern

METROPOLITAN BOROUGH OF SOLIHULL
www.solihull.gov.uk

Population 199 521
Political Composition: Con: 28, Lab: 13, LD: 10
Council Hse, PO Box 18, Solihull, West Midlands B91 3QS;
URL www.solihull.gov.uk;
E-mail chiefexecutive@solihull.gov.uk; Tel 0121 704 6000
Chief Executive Katherine Kerswell
Director (Finance and Information Technology) C. Whapent, CPFA) (Acting
Director (Housing and Regeneration) D. Wheatley, FCIH
Director (Environment Services) J.K. Wilson, MA, DipTP, MRTPI

Resources Directorate

Corporate Director (Finances) C. Whereat, CPFA
Head (Financial Strategy and Physical Resources) D. Hingley, CPFA
Head (Financial Operation) P. Field, CPFA
Manager (Building Design) S. Leigh, RIBA

Social Services Department

Council Hse, PO Box 32, Solihull, West Midlands B91 3QY;
URL www.solihull.gov.uk;
E-mail socialservices@solihull.gov.uk; Tel (Emergency) 0121 605 6060; 0121 704 6000
Director (Social Services) Michael Hake
Operations Director (Adult Care and Technology)
Peter Davidson; E-mail pdavidson@solihull.gov.uk
Operations Director (Children and Personnel)
Anne Plummer; E-mail aplummer@solihull.gov.uk
Head (Resource Management) Tony Richardson;
E-mail trichardson@solihull.gov.uk
Head (Performance Management) Ian Ash;
E-mail iash@solihull.gov.uk
Sector Manager (Specialist Services – Children) Jim Elliot;
E-mail jelliot@solihull.gov.uk
Sector Manager (Fieldwork – Children) Lynne Bickerdike (Acting); E-mail lbickerdike@solihull.gov.uk
Care Sector Manager (Commissioning) Vacancy
Service Manager (Learning Disabilities) Avice Taylor;
E-mail avicetaylor@solihull.gov.uk
Manager (Support Services) Sue Munbodh;
E-mail smunbodh@solihull.gov.uk
Manager (Policy and Quality – Children) Richard Keble;
E-mail rkeble@solihull.gov.uk
Policy and Review Officer (Adults) Val Dickens;
E-mail vdickens@solihull.gov.uk

Social Services Committee

Con: 6, Lab: 3, LD: 2
Chair Diana Holl-Allen (Con)
Fir Tree Cottages, Spencers La, Berkswell, Solihull, West Midlands CV7 7BY

Vice-Chair Rosemary Worsley (Con)
23 Bronte Farm Rd, Shirley, Solihull, West Midlands B90 3DE
Members of the Committee
Con: J.S. Bramham, Mrs S. Gomm, A.W. Martin, K.I. Meeson, R. Sleigh.
Lab: A.R. Harper, H.R. Hendry, A.S. Montgomerie.
LD: I.B. Chamberlain.

OFFICES

Orchard House Council Hse, PO Box 32, Solihull, West Midlands B91 3QY; Tel 0121 704 6755

SOCIAL WORK

Solihull Hospital, Lode La, Solihull, West Midlands B91 2JL; Tel 0121 711 4455

CHILDCARE NORTH

Chelmsley Wood Library, Stephenson Dr, Chelmsley Wood, West Midlands B37 5TA; Tel 0121 788 4300

CHILDCARE SOUTH

Old Council Hse, 21 Poplar Rd, Solihull, West Midlands B91 3AH; Tel 0121 704 6777; 0121 704 6778

SPECIALIST CHILDCARE

Craig Croft Centre, Craig Croft, Chelmsley Wood, Birmingham, West Midlands B37 7TR; Tel 0121 788 4200

ADULT CARE NORTH

Lowbrook, Chichester Gr, Chelmsley Wood, West Midlands B37 5RZ; Tel 0121 788 4474

LEARNING DISABILITIES

Oliver Hse, 4 Ivy Lodge Cl, Coleshill Rd, Marston Grn, West Midlands B37 7HL; Tel 0121 779 5860
Park View, Tudor Grange Pk, Monkspath Hall, Solihull, West Midlands B91 3LU; Tel 0121 704 7470

TRAINING

Keepers Lodge, Chelmsley Rd, Chelmsley Wood, West Midlands B37 7RS; Tel 0121 779 1713

Education and Children's Services Directorate

Council Hse, PO Box 20, Solihull, West Midlands B91 3QU;
Tel 0121 704 6656; Fax 0121 704 6669
Corporate Director (Education and Children's Services)
Kevin Crompton
Head (Social Regeneration and Learning Strategy)
P. Mayhew, MBA
Chief Education Welfare Officer S. Martin
Education Officer (Facilities) M.J. Luntley

EDUCATION PSYCHOLOGY SERVICE

Woodlands Centre, Lundy View, Birmingham, West Midlands B36 0LY; Tel 0121 770 6030; Fax 0121 770 7608
Principal Educational Psychologist A.G. Russell, BSc, DipEdPsych
Assistant Principal Educational Psychologist Christine Best, BA, MEd(EdPsych)
Senior Educational Psychologist Dr P. Timmins, BSc, MSc, PhD

EDUCATION WELFARE SERVICE

Woodlands Centre, Lundy View, Birmingham, West
Midlands B36 0LY; Tel 0121 788 1505; Fax 0121 779 7714
Chief Education Welfare Officer   S. Martin
Senior Education Welfare Officer   S. Wyatt, MEd, MSc
Senior Education Welfare Officer   I. Wyatt, BA, MPhil

Alderbrook School Blossomfield Rd, Solihull, West
Midlands B91 1SN; Tel 0121 704 2146
Headteacher   W. Sedgwick
   Secondary unit.

Langley School Kineton Green Rd, Solihull, West Midlands
B92 7ER; Tel 0121 706 9771
Headteacher   V. Duffy-Cross
   Secondary unit.

Lyndon School Daylesford Rd, Solihull, West Midlands
B92 8EJ; Tel 0121 743 3402
Headteacher   S. Westwood
   Secondary unit.

Reynalds Cross Unit Kineton Green Rd, Solihull, West
Midlands B92 7ER; Tel 0121 706 0627
Headteacher   K. Evans

Secondary Support Centre Langley School, Kineton Grn
Rd, Solihull, West Midlands; Tel 0121 706 9771
Headteacher   V. Duffy-Cross

Woodlands Centre Lundy View, Smith's Wood,
Birmingham, West Midlands B36 0LY; Tel 0121 770 6267;
Fax 0121 770 6267
Manager (Learning Support Service)   S. Colman

SPECIAL SCHOOLS

Forest Oak School Lanchester Way, Castle Bromwich,
Birmingham, West Midlands B36 9LF; Tel 0121 748 3411
Headteacher   P.L. Sankey
   Mixed MLD (97)

Hazel Oak School Hazel Oak Rd, Shirley, Solihull, West
Midlands B90 2AZ; Tel 0121 744 4162
Headteacher   P.A. Wright, MEd
   Mixed MLD (94)

Lanchester School Lanchester Way, Castle Bromwich,
Birmingham, West Midlands B36 9LF; Tel 0121 776 7465
Headteacher   S. Williams

Merstone School Exeter Dr, Marston Grn, Birmingham,
West Midlands B37 5NX; Tel 0121 788 8122
Headteacher   A. Mordey
   Mixed SLD (66)

Reynalds Cross School Kineton Grn Rd, Solihull, West
Midlands B92 7ER; Tel 0121 707 3012
Headteacher   K.D. Evans
   Mixed SLD (Day) (60)

SOMERSET COUNTY COUNCIL
www.somerset.gov.uk

Population 498 700 (2001 mid-year estimate)
Political Composition: LD: 29, Con: 24, Lab: 5
County Hall, Taunton, Somerset TA1 4DY;
   URL www.somerset.gov.uk; Tel 01823 355455;
   Fax (Committee Services) 01823 355258
Chair of the Council   R.J.E. Bush
Chief Executive   Alan Jones
Corporate Director (Central Services)   D. Taylor
Corporate Director (Treasury)   Chris Besland
Corporate Director (Economy, Transport and Environment)
   N. Farrow
Corporate Director (Culture and Heritage)   Mrs J. Murray
Corporate Director (Fire and Emergency Planning)   C. Kemp
Corporate Director (Performance Development)   R. Kershaw

Social Services Department

County Hall, Taunton, Somerset TA1 4DY;
   URL www.somerset.gov.uk;
   E-mail enquiries@somerset.gov.uk; Tel (Emergency)
   01458 253241; 01823 355455; Fax 01823 355156
Corporate Director (Social Services)   David Gwyther (Acting)
Assistant Director (Resources)   T. Gillham
Head (Adult Services)   Miriam Maddison
Strategic Commissioning Manager (Adult Services)
   D. Dixon
Head (Children and Families Services)   A. Weir
Joint Commissioning Manager (Mental Health)
   R. Hayward
Operations Manager (Learning Disabilities)   D. Dick
Manager (Quality Support Unit)   N. Pack
Manager (Human Resources)   M. Walsh
Public Information Officer   Janet Regis
Media Officer   Debbie Pugh-Jones
Social services and health services for people with mental
health problems are provided by a separate organisation:
Somerset Partnership NHS and Social Care Trust; Tel 01278
446151.

TRAINING

The following have responsibility for training professional
and support staff in the department.
Human Resources Team SSD   Tel 01823 355455; Fax 01823
   355156
Team Leader (Vocational Training)   Kim Westaway
Team Leader (Professional Training)   Tim Luxton
Team Leader (Professional Training)   Carole Owens
Staff Development Officer (Community Care)   E. Skinner
Staff Development Officer (Learning Disabilities)   F. Bunce
Staff Development Officer (Learning Disabilities)   P. Jessop
Staff Development Officer (Residential Childcare)
   M. Conneely-James
Staff Development Officer (Children and Families)
   N. Miller
Staff Development Officer (Foster Care)   B. Cosgrove
Staff Development Officer (Physical Disability)   Vacancy
Staff Development Officer (Health and Safety)   P. Tobin
Staff Development Officer (Community Care Assistant/NVQ)
   F. Kimpton
Staff Development Officer (NVQ)   W. Johnston
Staff Development Officer (Professional Training)
   Gill Calvin-Thomas
*Staff Development Officer (Somerset Child Protection
   Committee)*   S. Reimers

Care and Safety Panel

LD: 4, Con: 3, Lab: 1
Chair   C. Gordon (LD)
189 Greenway Rd, Taunton, Somerset TA2 6LQ; Tel 01823
   332592
Vice-Chair   R. Parsons (LD)
5 Fairford Cl, Highbridge, Somerset TA9 3JN; Tel 01278
   785427
Members of the Panel
LD: C. Lockey, H. Prior-Sankey.
Con: M. Healey, D. Huxtable, E. Weymouth.
Lab: D. Loveridge.

LOCAL OFFICES

CARE DIRECT

Offers information, advice and access to services to older
people and their carers for social care, health, social
security benefits and housing services. It is available 24
hours a day on freephone 0800 444 000.

Emergency Duty Team Bartletts Elm, Langport, Somerset
TA10 9SP; Tel 01458 253241; Fax 01458 251219
Service Manager   C. Woon

6

Mendip Area

Area Manager (Children and Families) J. Sellars
Area Manager (Physical Disabilities and Older People)
C. Humphrey
Service Manager (Children and Families – Frome)
C. Dryden
Service Manager (Children and Families – Glastonbury)
E. Evans
Service Manager (Learning Disabilities) M. Lock

Services for Adults with Learning Disabilities Community Team, Shepton Mallet Day Centre, Old Wells Rd, Shepton Mallet, Somerset BA4 5XN; Tel 01749 335400; Fax 01749 335401

Frome Office Public Offices, Christchurch Street West, Frome, Somerset BA11 1EF; Tel 01373 461162; Fax 01373 455111

Glastonbury Office 2 Orchard Crt, The Archers Way, Glastonbury, Somerset BA6 9LH; Tel 01458 831668; Fax 01458 837300

Somerset Coast Area (Sedgemoor and West Somerset)

Area Manager (Children and Families) A. Wells
Area Manager (Physical Disabilities and Older People)
Nyree Bevan
Service Manager (Children and Families – Bridgwater) S. Hird
Service Manager (Children and Families – Bridgwater)
C. Paterson
Service Manager (Learning Disabilities) S. Jones
Service Manager (Children and Families – Minehead)
A. Cole

Bridgwater Office Blake, Northgate, Bridgwater, Somerset TA6 3EU; Tel 01278 431111; Fax 01278 437237

Child and Family Therapeutic Services Petrel Hse, Broadway Pk, Bridgwater, Somerset TA6 5YA; Tel 01278 720275

Minehead Office Social Services Office, Townsend Rd, Minehead, Somerset TA24 5RJ; Tel 01643 706124; Fax 01643 708164

Services for Adults with Learning Disabilities Community Team, Enterprise Resource Centre, Bridgwater, Somerset TA6 3EU; Tel 01278 455571; Fax 01278 444522

Services for Children with Disabilities Chandos Hse, 6 Castle St, Bridgwater, Somerset TA6 3DB; Tel 01278 474303

South Somerset Area

Area Manager (Children and Families) F. Prime
Area Manager (Physical Disabilities and Older People)
B. Fitzpatrick
Service Manager (Children and Families – Yeovil)
C. Goldman
Service Manager (Children and Families – Yeovil)
T. Stafford
Service Manager (Children and Families – Chard) J. Okell
Service Manager (Learning Disabilities) D. Graham

Child and Family Therapeutic Services Balidon Centre, Summerlands, Yeovil, Somerset BA20 2BX; Tel 01935 479879

Chard Office Ravensworth, 30 Fore St, Chard, Somerset TA20 1PT; Tel 01460 65201; Fax 01460 63443

Services for Children with Disabilities Social Work Office, 5 Parfields, Preston Gr, Yeovil, Somerset BA20 2DV; Tel 01935 432239; Fax 01935 410174

Services for Adults with Learning Disabilities Community Team, Fiveways Resource Centre, Ilchester Rd, Yeovil, Somerset BA21 3BB; Tel 01935 470600; Fax 01935 470614

Services for Older People and Physically Disabled Adults I The Balsam Centre, Balsam Pk, Wincanton, Somerset BA9 9HB; Tel 01963 33337; Fax 01963 34324

Services for Older People and Physically Disabled Adults II Social Work Office, Crewkerne Hospital, Crewkerne, Somerset TA18 8BG; Tel 01460 76818; Fax 01460 78441

Services for Older People and Physically Disabled Adults III Social Work Office, Northmoor, Langport, Somerset TA10 9RR; Tel 01458 253162; Fax 01458 251762

Yeovil Office Maltravers Hse, Petters Way, Yeovil, Somerset BA20 1SP; Tel 01935 422111; Fax 01935 432515

Taunton Deane Area

Area Manager (Children and Families) F. Prime (Acting)
Area Manager (Physical Disability and Older People)
Farida Parkyn
Service Manager (Children and Families – Taunton)
D. Verwey
Service Manager (Children and Families – Taunton)
L. Bidmead
Service Manager (Learning Disabilities) S. Horne

Services for Children and Families Area Social Services Office, County Hall, Taunton, Somerset TA1 4DY; Tel 01823 335285; Fax 01823 357900

Services for Adults with Learning Disabilities Community Team, Six Acres Resource Centre, Roman Rd, Taunton, Somerset TA1 2BD; Tel 01823 257908; Fax 01823 353012

Services for Older People and Physically Disabled Adults I Halcon Centre, Huish Cl, Taunton, Somerset TA1 2EP; Tel 01823 338781; Fax 01823 325410

Services for Older People and Physically Disabled Adults II 21a Fore St, Wellington, Somerset TA21 8AA; Tel 01823 338781; Fax 01823 660324

HOSPITAL SOCIAL WORK SERVICE

Taunton and Somerset Hospital Musgrove Pk, Taunton, Somerset TA1 5DA; Tel (Children's Services) 01823 342366; (Adult Services) 01823 342367; Fax (Adult Services) 01823 330539; (Children's Services) 01823 342369
Team Leader (Adults) J. Haynes
Team Leader (Children and Families) A. Cackett

Yeovil District Hospital Higher Kingston, Yeovil, Somerset BA21 4AT; Tel (Adult Services) 01935 413119; (Children's Services) 01935 422111; Fax (Children's Services) 01935 432515; (Adult Services) 01935 474322
Team Manager M. Davis

DRUGS SERVICE

Service Manager Ben Thomas

Mendip Somerset Drugs Service, Priory Pk, Glastonbury Rd, Wells, Somerset BA5 1TH; Tel 01749 671583

Sedgemoor Somerset Drugs Service, Salmon Pde, Bridgwater, Somerset TA6 5PY; Tel 01278 434293

South Somerset Somerset Drugs Service, Summerlands Hospital, Preston Rd, Yeovil, Somerset BA16 2BX; Tel 01935 426170

Taunton Deane and West Somerset Somerset Drugs Service, 1st Fl, 34 North St, Taunton, Somerset TA1 1LW; Tel 01823 337800

CENTRES FOR CHILDREN AND FAMILIES

Friarn Centre Albert St, Bridgwater, Somerset TA6 3RG; Tel 01278 424942
Manager S. Hollock

The Hollies South St, Taunton, Somerset TA1 3AG; Tel 01823 333076; Fax 01823 330554
Manager L. Sweetland

Sydenham Family Centre Fairfax Rd, Bridgwater, Somerset TA6 4LS; Tel 01278 446771
Manager A.P. Walker

CHILDREN'S HOMES

Mendip Children's Centre 54 Whitewell Rd, Frome, Somerset BA11 4EH; Tel 01373 462563; Fax 01373 471350
Manager V. Smith

Sedgemoor Children's Resource Centre 4 Wembdon Rise, Bridgwater, Somerset TA6 7QU; Tel 01278 444495; Fax 01278 444885
Manager S. Travis

Staplegrove Road Children's Home 87 Staplegrove Rd, Taunton, Somerset TA1 1DN; Tel 01823 275356
Manager S. Kennedy

Taunton Children's Centre 94–96 Trull Rd, Taunton, Somerset TA1 4QW; Tel 01823 330291
Manager P. Alcock

Yeovil Children's Centre 1 Wyndham View, Yeovil, Somerset BA21 5DA; Tel 01935 423363
Manager L. Webster

UPLANDS

2 Bawdrip La, Bawdrip, Bridgwater, Somerset TA7 8PS; Tel 01278 683713
Manager S. Water

HOMES FOR CHILDREN WITH DISABILITIES

The Elms Curry Rivel, Langport, Somerset TA10 0JD; Tel 01458 251206; Fax 01458 251207
Manager Pauline Perrin

Parfields Children's Home 5 Parfields, Preston Gr, Yeovil, Somerset BA20 2DV; Tel 01935 474303
Manager N. Redding

Wardleworth Way Children's Home 15a Wardleworth Way, Wellington, Somerset TA14 6QG; Tel 01823 665787
Manager S. Harrison

YOUTH OFFENDING CENTRES

The Bridge Centre Westonzoyland Rd, Bridgwater, Somerset TA6 5BJ; Tel 01278 451204
Manager L. Hyde
Social Services Office, Blake, Bridgwater, Somerset TA6 3EU; Tel 01278 431111; Fax 01278 437237

Belvedere Road Centre Unit 3, Belvedere Trading Est, Taunton, Somerset TA1 1BH; Tel 01823 326731; Fax 01823 327042
Manager J. Berry

PROMISE 5 West End, Street, Somerset BA16 DLG; Tel 01458 440880
Manager J. Foley

YOUTH OFFENDING TEAM

Contact local social services office for operational staff.
County HQ, 5–7 West End, Street, Somerset BA16 0LG; Tel 01458 440820
Service Manager L. Barnett

DAY CENTRES FOR PHYSICALLY DISABLED ADULTS

Halcon Day Centre Huish Cl, Hamilton Rd, Taunton, Somerset TA1 2EP; Tel 01823 338781; Fax 01823 325410
Manager J. Simon

Highfield Day Centre Highfield Rd, Yeovil, Somerset BA21 4RJ; Tel 01935 425391
Associated satellite centres in Crewkerne, Chard, Langport, South Petherton and Yeovil.
Manager J. Duffy

Minehead Day Centre The Coach Hse, Wyndham Hse, Minehead, Somerset TA24 5PJ; Tel 01643 707086
Manager J. Melbourne

Mount Street Day Centre Mount St, Bridgwater, Somerset TA6 3ER; Tel 01278 445434
Manager C. Pether
Manager Y. Spraggs (Annexe); Tel 01278 423455

DAY SERVICES FOR PEOPLE WITH LEARNING DIFFICULTIES

Beckery Resource Centre Mill La, Glastonbury, Somerset BA6 9NP; Tel 01458 831729; Fax 01458 835783
Manager A. France

Dulverton Resource Centre 23 Jury Rd, Dulverton, Somerset TA22 9DX; Tel 01398 323652
Manager F. Hallam

Enterprise Resource Centre, Bridgwater Northgate, Bridgwater, Somerset TA6 3EU; Tel 01278 455571; Fax 01278 444522
Manager D. Winter

Enterprise Resource Centre, Frome Manor Rd, Frome, Somerset BA11 4BS; Tel 01373 461882
Manager D. Kingston

Fiveways Resource Centre Ilchester Rd, Yeovil, Somerset BA21 3BB; Tel 01935 420925
Manager P. Woodburn

The Laurel Resource Centre, Chard Wilkins Cl, Chard, Somerset TA20 1PB; Tel 01460 68500
Manager J. Holtom

Pepperall Resource Centre Pepperall Rd, Highbridge, Somerset TA9 3EE; Tel 01278 794625
Manager P. Schumann

St. James' Resource Centre Houndstone Cl, Long Mead, Yeovil, Somerset BA21 3GL; Tel 01935 433038
Manager C. Hamlin

Seahorse Resource Centre 9 Parkhouse Rd, Minehead, Somerset TA24 8AB; Tel 01643 705000
Manager F. Hallam

Shepton Mallet Day Centre Old Wells Rd, Shepton Mallet, Somerset BA4 5XN; Tel 01749 335400
Manager C. Chandler

Six Acres Resource Centre Roman Rd, Taunton, Somerset TA1 2BD; Tel 01823 257908
Manager F. Bunce

SUPPORTED EMPLOYMENT

Advanced Training Unit Unit 9–10, Dye Hse La, Glastonbury, Somerset BA6 9LZ; Tel 01458 835324
Manager A. France

Frome Garden Centre Manor Rd, Frome, Somerset BA11 4BS; Tel 01373 453094
Manager A. Marshall

Somerset County Enterprises Northgate, Bridgwater, Somerset TA6 3EU; Tel 01278 445446; Fax 01278 444892
Manager R. Liddle

Supported Employment Bureau College Hse, Broadway Pk, Bridgwater, Somerset TA6 5YA; Tel 01278 431635
Manager G. Milroy

West Huntspill Projects Old Pawlett Rd, West Huntspill, Highbridge, Somerset TA9 3RQ; Tel 01278 786240
Manager S. Elson

Workpower 22–25 Livingstone Way, Taunton, Somerset TA2 2BD; Tel 01823 254345
Manager D. Pike

SUPPORTED ACCOMMODATION FOR ADULTS WITH LEARNING DIFFICULTIES

Alfoxton Road Home 21 Alfoxton Rd, Bridgwater, Somerset TA6 7NN; Tel 01278 444942
Manager P. Cornish
Short stay

Ashbury Home Six Acres Cl, Roman Rd, Taunton, Somerset TA1 2BD; Tel 01823 327713
Manager D. Bleakley

6

The Brambles Home Six Acres Cl, Roman Rd, Taunton, Somerset TA1 2BD; Tel 01823 327714
Manager N. Taft

Eldermere Home Knowle La, Shepton Mallet, Somerset BA4 4PF; Tel 01749 344642
Manager J. Porter

Greengates Home 26 Fore St, North Petherton, Bridgwater, Somerset TA6 6PY; Tel 01278 662721
Manager J. Gillett

Jasmine Home Dod La, Glastonbury, Somerset BA6 8BZ; Tel 01458 832490
Manager B. Chant

The Maples Home Catherines Cl, Castle Cary, Somerset BA7 7HP; Tel 01963 351105
Manager G. Lane

Meadow View Home Six Acres Cl, Roman Rd, Taunton, Somerset TA1 2BD; Tel 01823 252662
Manager J. Pearce

Mountsfield Home 45 and 64 Mountsfield, Frome, Somerset BA11 2EP; Tel 01373 452815; 01373 466001
Manager K. Wilkinson

Newholme Home Bushy Cross La, Ruishton, Somerset TA3 5JT; Tel 01823 442298
Manager S. Law

Oak Bungalow Home Six Acres Cl, Roman Rd, Taunton, Somerset TA1 2BD; Tel 01823 327715
Manager J. Pearce

The Old Farmhouse Avishayes La, Chard, Somerset TA20 1RU; Tel 01460 66058
Manager L. Anderton

The Old Police House Catch Rd, Nunney, Somerset BA11 4NE; Tel 01373 836211
Manager S. Perry

The Old Vicarage Brook La, Cannington, Bridgwater, Somerset TA5 2HP; Tel 01278 653688
Manager C. Jay

Rossiters Hill Home 24 Rossiters Hill, Frome, Somerset BA11 2EP; Tel 01373 463627
Manager H. Plummer

Southway Drive Home 52 Southway Dr, Yeovil, Somerset BA21 3ED; Tel (Elliot Hse) 01935 426775; (Hardy Hse) 01935 426969; (Selwyn Hse) 01935 479143
Manager C. Bussell

Staplegrove Road Home 53 Staplegrove Rd, Taunton, Somerset TA1 1DG; Tel 01823 257001; 01823 257002
Manager N. John

Whitegables Home 36 Somerset Rd, Frome, Somerset BA11 2BB; Tel 01373 454040
Manager Y. Duddridge

RESIDENTIAL RESOURCE CENTRE

Halcon House Hostel Huish Cl, Hamilton Rd, Taunton, Somerset TA1 2EP; Tel 01823 353447
Manager L. Janes

DAY CENTRES FOR ELDERLY PEOPLE

Dulverton Day Centre c/o Hanover Ct Sheltered Housing Scheme, Kemps Way, Dulverton, Somerset TA22 9HZ; Tel 01398 324076
Manager B. Bindon
Tue, Fri

Evergreen Social Centre 50 The Mount, Taunton, Somerset TA1 3NR; Tel 01823 326870
Manager D. Stooke

Greenfields Day Centre c/o Ivy Hse, Friarn St, Bridgwater, Somerset TA6 3LH; Tel 01278 427129
Manager G. Lock
Tues, Thur and Fri

Ivy House Day Centre Friarn St, Bridgwater, Somerset TA6 3LH; Tel 01278 427129
Manager T. Cherry
Tue, Fri, weekends

The Parks Day Centre 4 The Parks, Minehead, Somerset TA24 8BS; Tel 01643 705374
Manager S. Roberts
Mon, Wed, Fri

South Street Centre Baptist Church Hall, South St, Wellington, Somerset; Tel 01823 663669
Manager J. Phillips
Mon, Wed

Wessex Centre Hannah More Cottage, Lower North St, Cheddar, Somerset; Tel 01934 742399
Manager M. Lewis
Thurs

SHELTERED HOUSING SCHEMES FOR ELDERLY PEOPLE

District councils provide 3955 units in the County.

DOMICILIARY MEALS SERVICES

The Meals on Wheels service is operated through voluntary agencies, including the British Red Cross Society and the WRVS.

Lifelong Learning Directorate

County Hall, Taunton, Somerset TA1 4DY;
 URL www.somerset.gov.uk/education;
 E-mail education@somerset.gov.uk; Tel 01823 355455;
 Fax 01823 355332
Corporate Director (Lifelong Learning) Michael Jennings
Deputy Director (Lifelong Learning) Jon Rose
Assistant Director (Education – Improvement and Effectiveness) Judith Richardson
Assistant Director (Education – Planning and Resources) Fiona Catcher
Group Manager (Service Development) Cynthia Starkey
Group Manager (SEN) and Educational Psychologist Michele Hitchcock
Group Manager (Youth Services) Elisabeth Piecha
Group Manager (Planning and Admissions) Julia Ridge
Head (Community Education) Stephen Lay

SPECIAL SCHOOLS

Avalon School Brooks Rd, Street, Somerset BA16 0PS; Tel 01458 443081; 01458 447380
Headteacher Mrs J. King

Avalon Special Needs Support Centre
Co-ordinator J. Henderson

Bartlett's Elm Community Special School Field Road, Langport, Somerset TA10 9SP; Tel 01458 252852
Headteacher Mr J.P. Lowe

Critchill School Nunney Rd, Frome, Somerset BA11 4LB; Tel 01373 464148; Fax 01373 453481
Headteacher Mr L. Rowsell

Critchill Learning Support Centre
Co-ordinator D. Hale

Elmwood School Hamp Ave, Bridgwater, Somerset TA6 6AP; Tel 01278 422866; Fax 01278 445157
Headteacher Mrs J.A. Tobin

Learning Support Centre
Co-ordinator J. Tobin

Fairmead School Mudford Rd, Yeovil, Somerset BA21 4NZ; Tel 01935 421295; Fax 01935 410552
Headteacher Mrs V.C. Brookham

Fairmead Learning Support Centre
Co-ordinator S. Thomas-Peter

Fiveways Special School Victoria Rd, Yeovil, Somerset
BA21 5AZ; Tel 01935 476227; Fax 01935 411287
Headteacher Mr M. Collis

Penrose School Albert St, Bridgwater, Somerset TA6 7ET;
Tel 01278 423660; Fax 01278 431075
Headteacher Mrs S. Neale

The Priory School Pickeridge Cl, Taunton, Somerset
TA2 7HW; Tel 01823 275569; Fax 01823 330277
Headteacher Vacancy

Selworthy School Selworthy Rd, Taunton, Somerset
TA2 8HD; Tel 01823 284970
Headteacher Mr D.J. Machell

OTHER SPECIAL EDUCATIONAL FACILITIES

The Mendip Centre Beckery New Rd, Glastonbury,
Somerset BA6 9NS; Tel 01458 835364; Fax 01458 835364
Head Ms S. Staples

The Monmouth Centre c/o The Methodist Church Hall, 5
Monmouth Street, Bridgwater, Somerset TA6 5EQ
Head Stuart Denro

Orchard Lodge Dene Rd, Cotford St Luke, Taunton,
Somerset TA4 1DB; Tel 01823 432673; Fax 01823 432541
Service Teacher Mrs K. Taylor

The Sedgemoor Centre Blake St, Bridgwater, Somerset
TA6 3NB; Tel 01278 421148
Head Mr C.R. Perry
EBD

Yeovil Centre Dampier St, Reckleford, Yeovil, Somerset
BA21 4EN; Tel 01935 410793/4
Head Mrs L. Knockton

SPECIAL EDUCATION

Multi-professional bases including learning support,
hearing impaired, psychology and behaviour support.
Area Base Team Leader Eric Stokes
Somerset Education Service, The Holway Centre, Taunton,
Somerset TA1 2JB; Tel 01823 334475; Fax 01823 323656
Area Base Team Leader Kate East
Somerset Education Services, Strode Hse, Street, Somerset
BA16 0HA; Tel 01458 441140; Fax 01458 441150
Area Base Team Leader Carol Franzen
Somerset Education Services, Chandos Hse, Bridgwater,
Somerset; Tel 01278 446445; Fax 01278 446199
Area Base Team Leader Stephen Lavington
Somerset Education Service, The Baldon Centre, Yeovil,
Somerset BA20 2BX; Tel 01935 476130; Fax 01935 414060

SOUTH GLOUCESTERSHIRE COUNCIL
www.southglos.gov.uk

Political Composition: LD: 33, Con: 21, Lab: 16
Castle St, Thornbury, South Gloucestershire BS35 1HF;
URL www.southglos.gov.uk;
E-mail mailbox@southglos.gov.uk; Tel 01454 868686
Chief Executive Amanda Phillips (Acting)

Social Services Department HQ

St. Lukes Cl, Emersons Way, Emersons Grn, Bristol
BS16 7AL; URL www.southglos.gov.uk; Tel 01454
865922; Fax 01454 865940
Director (Social Services) Bill Robbins
Assistant Director (Community Care) Jonathan Giles
Assistant Director (Child Care) Peter Murphy
Head (Inspection and Registration Unit) Roger Greenland
Tel 01454 865923; Fax 01454 865941

Manager (Children's Services – Fieldwork)
James McParland
Manager (Planning and Resources) Roger Hampson
Manager (Children's Services -Resources) Patrick Leightley
Manager (Performance) Claire Leandro
Manager (Training) Nick Thorne; Tel 01454 865918
Manager (Planning) Maggie Durnell
Manager (Care Management and Mental Health)
Steve Peacock
Manager (Personnel) Helen Scammell
Manager (Finance, Property and IT) Chris Manvell
Fiveways, New Cheltenham Rd, South Gloucestershire
BS15 4RR; Tel 01454 865999; Fax 01454 865998
Manager (Services for People with Learning Dificulties)
Kathy McKay
Manager (Adult Services) Peter Mulvaney
Team Manager (Home Care) Vacancy
Consumer Services Officer Karen Hawkes; Tel 01454 865924;
Fax 01454 865941
Children's Support Officer Trish McCrae
Partnership Officer (Children) Nigel Shipley
Partnership Officer (Children and Accidents) Kim Smith
Partnership Officer (Older People) Geoff Mark
Partnership Officer (Mental Health and Cancer)
Lindsay Davison
Partnership Officer (Physcial and Sensory Impairments)
Vacancy
Contracts Officer P. Feingold

Executive Committee
Members of the Committee
LD: Tony Davis, Ruth Davis, Neil Halsall, Pat Hockey,
Alan Lawrence, Maggie Tyrell.

Select Committee
Members of the Committee
LD: Linda Boon, Kay Crowe, Ken Dando, Mike Drew,
Shelia Mead, Mike Robbins, Sue Walker.
Lab: Mark Dean, June Lovell, Deanna MacRae,
Duncan Macrea.
Con: Sandra Grant, Allan Higgs.

CONTACT POINTS – CHILD CARE

Adolescent Services Team 43 The Park, Kingswood, South
Gloucestershire BS15 4BL; URL www.southglos.gov.uk;
Tel 01454 866303; Fax 01454 866306
Team Manager Peter Parry

Child Health and Disability Team The Health Resource
Centre, 2a Newton Rd, Bristol BS30 8EZ;
URL www.southglos.gov.uk; Tel 01454 866257; Fax 01454
866261
Team Manager Beverly Williams

Child Protection Manager Eclipse Hse, Unit 4, Eclipse
Office Pk, Staple Hill, South Gloucestershire BS16 5EL;
URL www.southglos.gov.uk; Tel 01454 865912; Fax 01454
866915
Team Manager Ruby Parry

Children's Assessment Team (Child Care Duty Desk)
Kingswood Office, Health Centre, Alma Rd, Kingswood,
South Gloucestershire BS15 4EJ;
URL www.southglos.gov.uk; Tel 01454 868501 01454
868502; Fax 01454 866210
Team Manager Frances Ware

Drug Action Team 48–50 Elm Pk, Filton, South
Gloucestershire BS34 7PH; URL www.southglos.gov.uk;
Tel 01454 868552; Fax 01454 868560
Team Manager David Warren

Family Placement Team The Health Resource Centre, 2a
Newton Rd, Bristol BS30 8EZ; URL www.southglos.gov.uk;
Tel 01454 866088; Fax 01454 866261
Team Manager Nasareen Ahmed

6

Family Support Manager Kingswood Office, Health Centre, Alma Rd, Kingswood, South Gloucestershire BS15 4EJ; URL www.southglos.gov.uk; Tel 01454 866051; Fax 01454 866100
Team Manager Verity Scott

Filton Community Team (Child Care) Filton Office, Conygre Hse, Conygre Rd, Filton, South Gloucestershire BS34 7DF; URL www.southglos.gov.uk; Tel 01454 866051; Fax 01454 866100
Team Manager Mike Connolly

Kingswood Community Team (Child Care) Kingswood Office, Health Centre, Alma Rd, Kingswood, South Gloucestershire BS15 4EJ; URL www.southglos.gov.uk; Tel 01454 866201; Fax 01454 866210
Team Manager Mark Jones

Secure Unit Emersons Grn La, Emersons Green, Bristol BS16 7AA; URL www.southglos.gov.uk; Tel 0117 970 2286; Fax 0117 970 2326
Operations Manager Mike Hardy

Under 11 Resource Centre Enmore Hse, Crt Rd, Kingswood, South Gloucestershire BS15 9QP; URL www.southglos.gov.uk; Tel 01454 866330
Manager Gill Summerill

Yate/Thornbury Community Team (Child Care) Yate Office, Council Offices, Chipping Sodbury, South Gloucestershire BS37 6JX; URL www.southglos.gov.uk; Tel 01454 866001; Fax 01454 866915
Team Manager Tina Wilson

Youth Offending Team 48–50 Elm Pk, Filton, South Gloucestershire BS34 7PH; URL www.southglos.gov.uk; Tel 01454 868558; Fax 01454 868560
Team Manager Steve Waters

CONTACT POINTS – ADULT CARE

Adult Care Management Newton House Resource Centre, Earlstone Cres, Bristol BS30 8AA; URL www.southglos.gov.uk; Tel 01454 866271; Fax 01454 866250
Team Manager Lesley Connell

Adult Care Management Thornbury Office, 32 Gloucester Rd, Thornbury, South Gloucestershire BS35 1DJ; URL www.southglos.gov.uk; Tel 01454 866140; Fax 01454 866135
Team Manager Nick Stephenson

Adult Duty Desk Kerr Hse, 50 Morley Rd, Staple Hill, South Gloucestershire BS16 4QS; URL www.southglos.gov.uk; Tel (0830–1630 Mon–Thur, 0830–1600 Fri) 01454 866270

Emergency Duty Team Oaklands Dr, Almondsbury, South Gloucestershire BS12 4AB; URL www.southglos.gov.uk; Tel (Daytime) 01454 615046; (Out of hours) 01454 615165; Fax 01454 615317
Team Manager Bob Hill

Hospital Social Work Teams Frenchay Hospital, Beckspool Rd, Frenchay, South Gloucestershire BS16 1LE; URL www.southglos.gov.uk; Tel 0117 975 3920; Fax 0117 970 2365
Team Manager Lynfa Vater
Team Manager Ron Cole

Manager of Homes for Older People and EMI Fiveways, New Cheltenham Rd, Kingswood, South Gloucestershire BS15 4RR; URL www.southglos.gov.uk; Tel 01454 865999; Fax 01454 865998
Team Manager Elaine Gibson

Manager of Resource and Activity Centres and Day Centres Fiveways, New Cheltenham Rd, Kingswood, South Gloucestershire BS15 4RR; URL www.southglos.gov.uk; Tel 01454 865999; Fax 01454 865998
Team Manager Keith Dickerson

Mental Health Kerr Hse Resource Centre, 50 Morley Rd, Staple Hill, South Gloucestershire BS16 4QS; URL www.southglos.gov.uk; Tel 01454 866214; Fax 01454 866031
Team Manager Kenny Braidwood

Occupational Therapy Fiveways, New Cheltenham Rd, Kingswood, South Gloucestershire BS15 4RR; URL www.southglos.gov.uk; Tel 01454 865999; Fax 01454 865998
Team Manager Maria Melbourne

Occupational Therapy Duty Desk The Health Resource Centre, 2a Newton Rd, Bristol BS30 8EZ; URL www.southglos.gov.uk; (Tel 0900–1630 Mon–Thur, 0900–1600 Fri) 01454 866328; Fax 01454 866326

Services for People with Learning Difficulties Team Fiveways, New Cheltenham Rd, Kingswood, South Gloucestershire BS15 4RR; URL www.southglos.gov.uk; Tel 01454 865999; Fax 01454 865998
Team Manager Jonathan Powell

RESOURCE AND ACTIVITY CENTRES

Almondsbury Resource and Activity Centre Oaklands Dr, Almondsbury, South Gloucestershire BS32 4AB; URL www.southglos.gov.uk; Tel 01454 866160; Fax 01454 615137
Manager Jenny Ireland

Blackhorse Resource and Activity Centre Blackhorse Rd, Mangotsfield, South Gloucestershire BS17 3AN; URL www.southglos.gov.uk; Tel 01454 866145
Manager Sarah Webb

Kingswood Resource and Activity Centre New Cheltenham Rd, Kingswood, South Gloucestershire BS15 4RR; URL www.southglos.gov.uk; Tel 01454 866150
Manager Sue Jenkins

Siblands Resource and Activity Centre Gillingstool, Thornbury, South Gloucestershire BS35 2EH; URL www.southglos.gov.uk; Tel 01454 866155
Manager Alison Lewthwaite

DAY CENTRE FOR DISABLED PEOPLE

Downend Day Centre Overndale Rd, South Gloucestershire BS16 2RQ; URL www.southglos.gov.uk; Tel 01454 866309
Manager Brenda Birkinshaw

RESIDENTIAL SERVICES FOR OLDER PEOPLE

Team Manager Elaine Gibson; Tel 01454 866117
There are seven homes for older people.

RESOURCE CENTRE FOR ELDERLY MENTALLY INFIRM PEOPLE (INCLUDING RESIDENTIAL)

Woodleaze Station Rd, Yate, South Gloucestershire BS37 4AF; URL www.southglos.gov.uk; Tel 01454 866043
Manager Pauline Hindle

Education Service

South Gloucestershire Offices, Bowling Hill, Chipping Sodbury, South Gloucestershire BS37 6JX; URL www.southglos.gov.uk; E-mail educ_service@southglos.gov.uk; Tel 01454 868686; Fax 01454 863263
Director (Education) Therese Gillespie
Deputy Director (Achievement and Inclusion) Jane Spouse
Manager (Early Years and Childcare) Gail Amphlett
Head (Central Teaching and Inclusion Support) Clare Steele
Head (Education Planning and Student Support) Pat Vedmore
Head (Special Educational Needs) Trevor Daniels
Principal Educational Psychologist Peter Wiggs
Principal Education Welfare Officer Fran Bennett

SPECIAL SCHOOLS

Culverhill School Kelston Cl, Yate, South Gloucestershire BS37 4SZ; E-mail head@culverhill.s-gloucs.sch.uk; Tel 01454 866930; Fax 01454 866931
Headteacher Miss N. Jones
  MLD

New Siblands School Easton Hill Rd, Thornbury, South Gloucestershire BS35 2JU;
E-mail head@newsiblands-spe.s-gloucs.sch.uk; Tel 01454 866754; Fax 01454 866759
Headteacher P. Casson
  SLD

Warmley Park School Tower Rd North, Warmley, South Gloucestershire BS30 8XL;
E-mail head@warmleypark.s-gloucs.sch.uk; Tel 01454 867272; Fax 01454 867273
Headteacher S. Morris
  SLD

SOUTH TYNESIDE COUNCIL

www.southtyneside.info

Population 154 697
Political Composition: Lab: 50, LD: 6, Other: 4
Town Hall and Civic Offices, Westoe Rd, South Shields, Tyne and Wear NE33 2RL;
  URL www.southtyneside.info; Tel 0191 427 1717;
  Fax 0191 455 0208
Chief Executive Irene Lucas
Executive Director (Resources) Julie Alderson
Executive Director (Corporate Development) Vacancy
Executive Director (Neighbourhood Services)
  Amanda Skelton

Social Care and Health Directorate

Kelly Hse, Campbell Park Hse, Hebburn, Tyne and Wear NE31 2SW;
  E-mail social.services@s-tyneside-mbc.gov.uk; Tel 0191 427 1717; Fax 0191 424 4624
Executive Director T. Doughty
Head (Children's Services) A. Dinning
Head (Resources and Business Services) K. Hannah
Head (Community Care) L. Dean
Manager (Childcare – Assessment and Commissioning)
  A. Scott
Manager (Childcare – Assessment and Commissioning)
  M. Scholes
Manager (Childcare – Business Services) E. Dunn
Manager (Childcare – Quality Standards) M. McCracken
Manager (Offendim Team) P. Bennett; Tel 0191 454 5686
Manager (Learning Disability) L. Bradford
Manager (Mental Health) M. Brown
Manager (Older People and Physical Disability – Assessments)
  L. Simpson
Manager (Commissioning and Quality) G. Purvis
Manager (Contracts) S. Woodhouse
Manager (Central Services) J. Garthwaite
Business Manager (Adult Services) B. Hodgson
Welfare Rights Co-ordinator M. Peel

TRAINING

The following have responsibility for training professional and support staff in the department.
Manager (Personnel and Development) P. Medd
Training Officer (Child Care, NVQ Development in Child Care, Practice Teaching) S. Statter
Training Officer (Child Protection – Child Care) P. Pick

AREA OFFICES

Central Area Office Landreth Hse, Boldon La, South Shields, Tyne and Wear; Tel 0191 427 1919
Team Manager (Community Care) N. Masters
Team Manager (Child Care) C. Pharcah

East Area Office Hosley Hill Sq, South Shields, Tyne and Wear; Tel 0191 497 4000
Team Manager (Child Care) M. Concannon
Team Manager (Community Care) C. English (Acting)

Hebburn Team Area Office

Hebburn Civic Centre, Campbell Park Rd, Hebburn, Tyne and Wear; Tel 0191 424 4040
Team Manager (Community Care) D. Bruce

Jarrow Team Area Office Jarrow Town Hall, Grange Road West, Jarrow, Tyne and Wear; Tel 0191 489 1141
Team Manager (Community Care) J. Tiernan
Team Manager (Child Care) M. Hope

North Area Office Bolingbroke St, South Shields, Tyne and Wear NE33 2SS; Tel 0191 427 1717
Team Manager (Community Care) D. Duke
Team Manager (Child Care) D. Martin

Eastern Team (Mental Health Services) 27–29 Market Pl, South Shields, Tyne and Wear; Tel 0191 424 4950
Team Manager M. Carney

South Community Mental Health Team Boker Lane Health Centre, Boker La, East Boldon, Tyne and Wear; Tel 0191 554 3200
Senior Practitioner C. May

West Community Mental Health Team Hebburn Health Centre, Campbell Park Rd, Hebburn, Tyne and Wear NE31 2SP; Tel 0191 451 6217
Team Manager S. Lewis

RESIDENTIAL ESTABLISHMENTS FOR CHILDREN

Henderson Road Home 23 Henderson Rd, Simonside, South Shields, Tyne and Wear NE34 9QN; Tel 0191 455 2016
Manager D. McGee (Acting)
  (6)

Lanark Drive Home 63 Lanark Dr, Jarrow, Tyne and Wear; Tel 0191 489 8291
Manager D. McGee
  (6)

Owen Drive Home 9 Owen Dr, West Boldon, East Boldon, Tyne and Wear NE36 0HP; Tel 0191 536 7197
Contact M. Webber
  (6)

FAMILY CENTRES

Family Support Group

Garrick Street Nursery Garrick St, South Shields, Tyne and Wear NE33 4JJ; Tel 0191 456 0728
Manager A. McLasham
  (31)

Jane Fry Nursery Flagg Crt, South Shields, Tyne and Wear NE33 2LS; Tel 0191 456 5418
Manager C. West
  (31)

RESOURCE UNITS – PEOPLE WITH LEARNING DISABILITIES

Balgownie Resource Centre Bede Burn Rd, Jarrow, Tyne and Wear; Tel 0191 483 5560
Manager D. Beeston

Campbell Park Road Resource Unit Hebburn, Tyne and Wear; Tel 0191 483 2004
Manager D. Sutherland
  Special care unit (15) (60)

Danesfield Flatlets Bede Burn Rd, Jarrow, Tyne and Wear
Manager M. Watters

6

West Walpole Street Resource Unit South Shields, Tyne and Wear; Tel 0191 455 6213
Manager J. Blythe
   Special care unit (15) (105)

LEARNING DISABILITY TEAM

Balgownie Hse, Bede Burn Rd, Jarrow, Tyne and Wear; Tel 0191 483 5560
Team Manager E.F. Kaye

HOSTEL FOR PEOPLE WITH LEARNING DISABILITIES

Wenlock Lodge Wenlock Rd, South Shields, Tyne and Wear; Tel 0191 455 3756

ESTABLISHMENTS FOR PEOPLE WITH MENTAL HEALTH PROBLEMS

Mental Health Resource Centre (Residential) 257 Stanhope Rd, South Shields, Tyne and Wear; Tel 0191 456 2363
   (11)
Mental Health Resource Centre (Day Care) Denis Johnson Centre, Temple Pk Rd, South Shields, Tyne and Wear; Tel 0191 455 9579
Joint Officer-in-Charge P. Docherty (Acting)
   (30)

DAY AND OCCUPATIONAL CENTRE FOR THE HANDICAPPED

John Wright Centre Flagg Crt, South Shields, Tyne and Wear; Tel 0191 456 3963; Minicom 0191 4277072

DAY AND EVENING CENTRES FOR THE ELDERLY

Bede Burn Day Centre Bede Burn Rd, Jarrow, Tyne and Wear; Tel 0191 489 8466
Manager E. Elrick
Father James Walsh Centre Hedgeley Rd, Hebburn, Tyne and Wear; Tel 0191 483 6850; Minicom 0191 4834461
Manager S. Garvin
Gainsborough Avenue South Shields, Tyne and Wear; Tel 01915 369319
Manager L. Whitfield
Hampden Street Centre South Shields, Tyne and Wear; Tel 0191 456 9639
Manager S. Holmes
The Lonnen Centre South Shields, Tyne and Wear; Tel 0191 456 5763
Manager H. Pollard
Perth Green Centre Jarrow, Tyne and Wear; Tel 0191 489 3883
Manager L. Bell (Acting)
Queens Road Day Centre Jarrow, Tyne and Wear; Tel 0191 489 9368
Manager J. Middleton
Wilfred Street Centre Boldon Colliery; Tel Boldon 366852
Manager E. Lincoln

ACCOMMODATION FOR THE ELDERLY

There are seven local authority homes for elderly people five of which are designated resource centres offering in total 246 long-term places and 25 respite places.

Lifelong Learning and Leisure Department

Town Hall and Civic Offices, Westoe Rd, South Shields, Tyne and Wear NE33 2RL; Tel 0191 427 1717; Fax 0191 427 0584
Executive Director B. Hughes
Head (Access and Inclusion) A. Bradley
Principal Educational Psychologist C.D.D. Matthew

Head (Lifelong Learning) R. McKay
Manager (Pupil Services) B. Davis
Manager (Pupil Services) S. Makin
Chief Education Welfare Officer J.A. Soulsby

EDUCATION WELFARE OFFICE

Jarrow Town Hall Jarrow, Tyne and Wear; Tel 0191 489 1141; Fax 0191 428 0416
Senior Education Welfare Officer R. Pickering

SCHOOL PSYCHOLOGICAL, CHILD GUIDANCE SERVICE AND SPECIAL NEEDS SUPPORT CENTRE

Chuter Ede Education Centre Galsworthy Rd, South Shields, Tyne and Wear; Tel 0191 519 1909; Fax 0191 519 0600

SPECIAL SCHOOLS

Bamburgh School Norham Ave, South Shields, Tyne and Wear NE34 7TD; Tel 0191 454 0671; Fax 0191 427 1931
Headteacher J.M. Fawcett
   (125)
Epinay School Clervaux Terr, Jarrow, Tyne and Wear NE32 5UP; Tel 0191 489 8949; Fax 0191 483 7417
Headteacher H. Harrison
   (103)
Greenfields School Victoria Rd East, Hebburn, Tyne and Wear NE31 1YQ; Tel 0191 489 7480; Fax 0191 483 7390
Headteacher M. Conway
   (45)
Margaret Sutton School Ashley Rd, South Shields, Tyne and Wear NE34 0PF; Tel 0191 455 3309; Fax 0191 422 0702
Headteacher A. Godfrey
   (99)
Oakleigh Gardens School Oakleigh Gdns, Cleadon, Sunderland, Tyne and Wear SR6 7PT; Tel 0191 536 2590; Fax 0191 519 0213
Headteacher M. Lockney
   (54)

SOUTH YORKSHIRE METROPOLITAN AREA

The following Metropolitan Councils comprise the South Yorkshire Metropolitan Area and may be found in alphabetical order within this chapter: Barnsley, Doncaster, Rotherham, Sheffield.

SOUTHAMPTON CITY COUNCIL

www.southampton.gov.uk

Political Composition: Lab: 22, LD: 16, Con: 7
Civic Centre, Southampton SO14 7LY;
   URL www.southampton.gov.uk; Tel 023 8022 3855
Chief Executive B. Roynon
Executive Director (Performance and Management) M. Smith

Health and Social Care Directorate

Tel 023 8083 2621
Executive Director (Health and Social Care) Dr John Beer
Head (Strategy and Social Development) Chris Hawker; Tel 023 8083 3209

Manager (Programme Support) Paul Williams; Tel 023 8083 3102

Manager (Human Resources) Ken Sikora; Tel 023 8083 3257

Head of Services (Children and Families) Carol Tozer; Tel 023 8083 3021

Service Manager (Prevention) Anne Davies; Tel 023 8083 4646

Service Manager (Support Services) Mair Thomas; Tel 023 8083 4660

Service Manager (Standards and Commissioning) Hilary Corrick; Tel 023 8083 3101

Head (Health and Community Care) Mark Charters; Tel 023 8083 3439

Service Manager (Commissioning Standards) Chris Martin; Tel 023 8083 4850

Service Manager (Intermediate Care) Jay Stickland; Tel 023 8083 4851

Assistant Head (Health and Community Care) Jane Brentor ; Tel 023 8083 3262

Service Manager (Locality Support Teams) Julia Clarke; Tel 023 8033 2861

Service Manager (Learning Disabilities) Ena Conway; Tel 023 8083 4787

Service Manager (Mental Health and Substance Misuse) Carole Binns; Tel 023 8024 1320

Service Manager (Policy and Performance) Rosey Wood; Tel 023 8083 4429

Health and Social Care

Cabinet Member (Health and Social Care) Virginia Moore (LD)

LOCAL OFFICES

Southampton Central Local Office Archers Hse, 1a Archers Rd, Southampton SO15 2LQ; Tel 023 8033 2861; Fax 023 8033 6762

Children Assessment Team 14 Cumberland Pl, Southampton; Tel 023 8083 3336

FAMILY CENTRES

Bitterne Family Centre 46 Peartree Ave, Bitterne, Southampton SO19 7JP; Tel 023 8044 3003

Derby Road Family Centre Derby Rd, Southampton SO2 0DZ; Tel 023 8022 8073

Forest View Family Centre 1 Sutherland Rd, Lordshill, Southampton SO16 8GA; Tel 023 8073 4592; Fax 023 8073 9380

CHILDREN'S HOMES

Coxford Road Children's Home 315 Coxford Rd, Lordswood, Southampton SO16 6LH; Tel 023 8079 9100 (10)

Porlock Road Children's Home 70 Porlock Rd, Millbrook, Southampton SO16 9JD; Tel 023 8091 5350

DAY SERVICES FOR ADULTS WITH A LEARNING DISABILITY

Southampton Day Services Auckland Rd, Millbrook, Southampton SO15 0SD; Tel 023 8077 2596
308 including ten special care

DAY CENTRE FOR PEOPLE WITH MENTAL HEALTH PROBLEMS

Bedford House Day Centre Amoy St, Southampton SO15 2DR; Tel 023 8063 7189

HOME AND HOSTEL FOR PEOPLE WITH LEARNING DISABILITIES

Kentish Road Hostel 32 Kentish Rd, Freemantle, Southampton SO15 3GX; Tel 023 8070 1227

DAY CENTRES FOR PEOPLE WITH A PHYSICAL DISABILITY

Sembal House Day Centre Handel Terr, The Polygon, Southampton SO15 2FH; Tel 023 8033 0286

CARE HOMES FOR OLDER PEOPLE

There are seven homes for older people.

Lifelong Learning and Leisure Directorate

5th Fl, Frobisher Hse, Southampton SO15 1BZ; URL www.southampton.gov.uk/education/; Tel 023 8022 3855

Executive Director Ian Sandbrook
Civic Centre, Southampton SO14 7LP

SPECIAL SCHOOLS

The Cedar Special School Redbridge La, Nursling, Southampton SO16 0XN; Tel 023 8073 4205; Fax 023 8073 8231
Headteacher B.C. Hart
3–16 PD

Netley Court School Victoria Rd, Southampton S031 5DR; Tel 023 8045 3259; Fax 023 8045 5438
Headteacher Ms J. Partridge

The Polygon Special School Handel Terr, Southampton SO15 2FH; Tel 023 8063 6776; Fax 023 8033 6066
Headteacher Mr L. Gent
EBD

Red Lodge School Vermont Cl, off Winchester Rd, Southampton SO16 7LT; Tel 023 8076 7660; Fax 023 8076 7643
Headteacher S. Mackie
11–16 MLD

Ridgeway House Special School Peartree Ave, Bitterne, Southampton SO19 7JL; Tel 023 8043 3875; Fax 023 8044 8897
Headteacher Ms J. Boyd (Acting)
2–19 SLD, Autism

Vermont School Vermont Cl, off Winchester Rd, Southampton SO16 7LT; Tel 023 8076 7988; Fax 023 8076 6902
Headteacher Mrs J. Wilson
EBD

PUPIL REFERRAL UNITS

Pupil Referral Unit and Exclusion Support Service 18 Melbourne St, Southampton SO14 5RB; Tel 023 8021 5320; Fax 023 8021 5329
Headteacher Mr A. Sumner

The Compass Pupil Referral Unit Warren Ave, Shirley Warren, Southampton SO16 6AH; Tel 023 8051 0202; Fax 023 8077 6523
Teacher-in-Charge Mr R. Gilroy

SOUTHEND-ON-SEA BOROUGH COUNCIL

www.southend.gov.uk

In April 1998 Southend and Thurrock both became unitary authorities. The rest of Essex retains a two-tier structure and is listed alphabetically within this chapter.
Civic Centre, Victoria Ave, Southend-on-Sea, Southend SS2 6ER; URL www.southend.gov.uk; Tel 01702 215 100
Director (Education and Library Service) Vacancy

6

Social Care Department

Civic Centre, PO Box 6, Victoria Ave, Southend-on-Sea, Southend SS2 6ER; URL www.southend.gov.uk; Tel (Emergency) 01245 434083; 01702 534646
Director (Social Care) John Nawrockyi
Director (Integrated Services) Penny Furness-Smith
Senior Assistant Director (Business Support) Philip Stepney
Assistant Director (Child Care Services) Meera Spillett
Manager (Support Services) Kathryn Ash
Manager (Training and Resources) Jim Gray
Manager (Quality Services) Nick Corrigan
Manager (Joint Commisioning) Vacancy
Manager (Children's Quality) Chris Munday

Child Care Services

Queensway Hse, Essex St, Southend-on-Sea, Southend SS2 5TB; Tel 01702 534725
Manager (Children's Services) Karen Reeve; Tel 01702 534416
Manager (Children's Resources) Mick Hamblion; Tel 01702 534406
Development Officer (Under Eights) Susan Green

ADOLESCENT SERVICES

After Care and Youth Support, 17 Weston Rd, Southend SS1 1AS; Tel 01702 330464
Manager John Stock

CHILD PROTECTION

Queensway Hse, Essex St, Southend SS2 5TB; E-mail angeladerry@southend.gov.uk; Tel 01702 534490

CHILD AND FAMILY CONSULTATION SERVICE

2nd Fl, Queensway Hse, Southend SS2 5TB; Tel 01702 577090

CHILDREN AND FAMILY SUPPORT

Queensway Hse, Essex St, Southend SS2 5TA; Tel 01702 534409; 01702 534412

FAMILY PLACEMENT AND FAMILY FINDERS (ADOPTION)

283 London Rd, Westcliff-on-Sea, Essex SS0 7BX; Tel 01702 354366
Manager Ian Marsh

SHARED CARE

Social Services Department, 535 London Rd, Thundersley, Essex SS7 1AB; Tel 01268 565999

TEAM FOR CHILDREN WITH DISABILITIES

93–99 Southchurch Rd, Southend SS2 3TB; Tel 01702 534256
Manager Neale Laurie

YOUTH OFFENDING TEAM

Broyton Hse, Victoria Ave, Southend; Tel 01702 330464
Manager Derek Eyre

Adult Services

Queensway Hse, Essex St, Southend SS2 5TB; Tel 01702 534408
Service Manager (Older People) Carol Cranfield
Service Manager (Learning Disability) Ruth Bull; Tel 01702 534404

TEAMS FOR OLDER PEOPLE (INCLUDING HOME CARE)

Queensway Hse, Essex St, Southend-on-Sea, Southend SS2 5TB; Tel 01702 534415 (West Team); 01702 534418 (East Team)

COMMUNITY TEAM FOR PEOPLE WITH LEARNING DISABILITIES

Queensway Hse, Essex St, Southend-on-Sea, Southend SS2 5TB; Tel 01702 534293

TEAM FOR PEOPLE WITH PHYSICAL AND SENSORY IMPAIRMENTS

93–99 Southchurch Rd, Southend-on-Sea, Southend SS2 3TB; Tel 01702 534272

OCCUPATIONAL THERAPY

93–99 Southchurch Rd, Southend SS2 3TB; Tel 01702 534207
Service Manager Karen Kabarowska

HOSPITAL HOME CARE TEAM

Southend General Hospital, Social Work Dept, Westcliff-on-Sea, Essex SS0 0RY; Tel 01702 221291

HOSPITAL SOCIAL WORK TEAM

Southend General Hospital, Social Work Department, Westcliff-on-Sea, Essex SS0 0RY; Tel 01702 221293

MENTAL HEALTH SERVICES

Director (Mental Health) Euan MacIntyre
South Essex Partnership NHS Trust, Dunton Crt, Laindon, Essex; Tel 01268 366000
Southend Mental Health Resource Centre Queensway Hse, 2nd Fl, Southend-on-Sea, Southend SS2 5TB; Tel 01702 577125
Shoebury Mental Health Ness Rd, Shoeburyness, Essex SS3 9DL; Tel 01702 577650
Roche Unit c/o District Office, Union La, Rochford, Essex; Tel 01702 578230
Mental Health for Older People Queensway Hse, Essex St, Southend SS2 5TB; Tel 01702 534405

FAMILY CENTRES

Marigold Centre Avenue Rd Family Unit, 62 Avenue Rd, Westcliff-on-Sea, Essex SS0 7DG; Tel 01702 337455
Team Leader Chris Reynolds
Queensway Day Nursery Queensway Hse, Essex St, Southend-on-Sea, Southend SS2 5TB; Tel 01702 615147
Manager Jackie Poole

HOMES FOR OLDER PEOPLE

Manager (Residential Homes) Louise Langley
Delaware Hse, Maplin Way, Shoeburyness, Essex SS3 9PS; Tel 01702 588859
There are three local authority homes for older people.

DAY CENTRES (ADULTS)

Avro Training Centre Avro Rd, Eastwood, Southend SS2 6UX; Tel 01702 545775
Unit Manager Henry Watson
Maybrook Training Centre 303 Southchurch Rd, Southend SS1 2PE; Tel 01702 301311
Unit Manager Vacancy
Queensway Resource Therapy Centre Queensway Hse, Essex St, Southend-on-Sea, Southend SS2 5TB; Tel 01702 534750
Unit Manager Irene Coles
Viking House Day Centre Avro Rd, Eastwood, Southend SS2 6UX; Tel 01702 545776
Unit Manager Henry Watson

DAY CENTRES (OLDER PEOPLE)

Leyland Day Centre Leyland Crt, 275 Southchurch Rd, Southend SS1 2LR; Tel 01702 468651

Priory Day Centre c/o Priory Hse, Burhill Chase, Southend
SS2 6PE; Tel 01702 343010
Day Care Officer Sheila Hussey

RESIDENTIAL UNITS (LEARNING DISABILITES)

Berland House 315 Southchurch Rd, Southend-on-Sea,
Southend SS1 2PE; Tel 01702 612064
Unit Manager Andy Woolliams

Saxon Lodge South St, Shoeburyness, Southend SS3 6HH;
Tel 01702 295001
Unit Manager Pauline Marshall

Shelford West St, Prittlewll, Southend SS2 6HH; Tel 01702
353843
Unit Manager John Hase

CENTRAL EQUIPMENT STORE

Unit 6, The Forum, Southend SS2 5TE; Tel 01702 618542
Store Manager Neil Keeler

COMMUNITY LIASION/DEVELOPMENT

Contact Maureen Frewin
SAVS., Southend-on-Sea, Southend; Tel 01702 619489

Education and Lifelong Learning Department

5th Fl, Civic Centre, Southend SS2 6ER;
E-mail maureencox@southend.gov.uk; Tel 01702 215048
Director (Education and Lifelong Learning) Lorraine O'Reilly
Special Schools
5

SPECIAL SCHOOLS

Kingsdown School Snakes La, Southend SS2 6XT; Tel 01702
527486; Fax 01702 526762
Headteacher J.F. Hagyard
Physically Disabled (Day) (13)

Lancaster School Prittlewell Chase, Westcliff-on-Sea, Essex
SS0 0RT; Tel 01702 342543; Fax 01702 352630
Headteacher Audrey Farrow

Priory School Burr Hill Chase, Southend SS2 6PE; Tel 01702
347490; Fax 01702 432164
Headteacher V. Wathen

St. Nicholas School Philpott Ave, Southend SS2 4RL;
Tel 01702 462322; Fax 01702 600487
Headteacher G.M. Houghton

The St. Christopher School (Special) Mountdale Gdns,
Leigh-on-Sea, Southend SS9 4AW; Tel 01702 524193;
Fax 01702 526761
Headteacher T. Wilson

STAFFORDSHIRE COUNTY COUNCIL

www.staffordshire.gov.uk

The county council retains its two tier structure. However
on 1st April 1997 Stoke-on-Trent became a separate unitary
authority and is responsible for all its local government
services – Stoke-on-Trent is listed alphabetically in this
chapter.
Population 800 000
Political Composition: Lab: 36, Con: 22, LD: 4
Staffordshire County Council, Martin St, Stafford,
Staffordshire ST16 2LH; URL www.staffordshire.gov.uk;
Tel 01785 223121; Fax 01785 215153
Chief Executive Nigel T. Pursey;
E-mail nigel.pursey@staffordshire.gov.uk

County Treasurer and Director (Finance) R.G. Tettenborn,
OBE, MA, CPFA; Tel 01785 223121
Director (Development Services) A.L. Murray, BSc(Hons),
DipTP, MRTPI
Head (Planning and Economic Services) F.A. Lockett,
BSc(Hons), DipTP, MRTPI, DMS,MIMgt
County Property and Estates Officer B.J. Cahill, BSc, DMA,
DipManSc

Social Services Department

St. Chads Pl, Stafford, Staffordshire ST16 2LR; Tel 01785
277088; Fax 01785 277004
Corporate Director (Social Care and Health) R.A. Lake;
Tel 01785 277000; Fax 01785 277127
*Assistant Director (Adult Services – Assessment and Care
Management)* G.P.M. Gilmore, BA(Hons), MSc, CQSW;
Tel 01785 277060; Fax 01785 277127
Assistant Director (Adult Services – Service Provision)
G.W. Pierpoint, BA(Hons), DMA; Tel 01785 277080;
Fax 01785 277127
Assistant Director (Children and Family Services)
R.C. Jarrett, CQSW, DMS; Tel 01785 277026; Fax 01785
277127
Assistant Director (Quality and Partnerships) T. Edwards,
BA(Hons), PhD; Tel 01785 277160; Fax 01785 277127
Deputy Director (Finance and Support) A. Lotinga,
BCom(Accounting)(Hons), IPFA; Tel 01785 277162;
Fax 01785 277127

6

Scrutiny Committee

Lab: 21, Con: 11, LD: 1
Leader of Social Services Cllr G.K. Bullock
Chair of Scrutiny Committee B. Cawley
Members of the Committee
M.J. Barber, C.A. Dean, B.J. Faulkner, R.L. Gorton,
D. Heptonstall, K. Hoare, M. Lovett, R.B. Mycock,
J. O'Leary, S.M. Oatley, G.E. Roberts.

AREA OFFICES

Biddulph Area Office Town Hall, High St, Biddulph, Stoke-
on-Trent ST8 6AR; Tel 01782 297810; Fax 01782 297815

Burntwood Area Office Sycamore Rd, Burntwood,
Staffordshire WS7 4RR; Tel 01543 510410; Fax 01543 510437

Burton Area Office 1–3 St. Paul's Sq, Burton upon Trent,
Staffordshire DE14 2EF; Tel 01283 239600; Fax 01283 239606

Cannock Area Office Ivy Hse, 202 Wolverhampton Rd,
Cannock, Staffordshire WS11 1AT; Tel 01543 510300;
Fax 01543 510350

Cheadle Area Office Council Offices, Leek Rd, Cheadle,
Staffordshire ST10 1JG; Tel 01538 483800; Fax 01538 483823

Codsall Area Office Histons Hill, Codsall, Staffordshire
WV8 1AA; Tel 01902 434000; Fax 01902 434005

Kidsgrove Area Office Town Hall, Liverpool Rd, Kidsgrove,
Staffordshire ST7 4EH; Tel 01782 296705; Fax 01782 296724;
Minicom 01782 296813

Leek Area Office County Services Bldg, Fountain St, Leek,
Staffordshire ST13 6JR; Tel 01538 483112; Fax 01538 483145

Newcastle Area Office The Holborn, Castle Hill Rd,
Newcastle-under-Lyme, Staffordshire ST5 2SX; Tel 01782
296005; Fax 01782 296024; Minicom 01782 296029

The Old House Area Office Eastern Ave, Lichfield,
Staffordshire WS13 7SQ; Tel 01543 510100; Fax 01543 510141

Rugeley Area Office Council Offices, Anson St, Rugeley,
Staffordshire WS15 2BH; Tel 01889 256016; Fax 01889
256034

Stafford Area Office The Business Centre, Madfield Retail
Pk, Foregate St, Stafford, Staffordshire ST16 2PA; Tel 01785
276800; Fax 01785 276880

Tamworth Area Office Marmion Hse, Lichfield St, Tamworth, Staffordshire B79 7BZ; Tel 01827 475506; 01827 475507; Fax 01827 475509; Minicom 01827 475510

Uttoxeter Area Office 63 High St, Uttoxeter, Staffordshire ST14 7JD; Tel 01889 256300; Fax 01889 256326

STAFF DEVELOPMENT UNIT

Tillington Dentre, Second Ave, Stafford, Staffordshire ST16 1PS; Tel 01785 355770; Fax 01785 355771

Hospital Social Work Departments and Related Services

Abbey Hulton Clinic Child and Adolescent Mental Health, Leek Rd, Abbey Hulton, Stoke-on-Trent; Tel 01782 538148; Fax 01782 538151

Argyle Street Clinic Child and Family Service, Argyle St, Glascote, Tamworth, Staffordshire B77 3EW; Tel 01827 51183; Fax 01827 312098

Bucknall Hospital Social Work Department, Eaves La, Bucknall, Stoke-on-Trent ST2 8LD; Tel 01782 275022; 01782 275023; Fax 01782 207532

Burton Hospital Social Work Dept, Burton Hospitals NHS Trust, Burton upon Trent, Staffordshire DE13 0RB; Tel 01283 566333; Fax 01283 516633

Cannock Chase Hospital Social Work Dept, Brunswick Rd, Cannock, Staffordshire WS11 2XY; Tel 01543 576920; Fax 01543 576929

Cross Street Clinic Cross St, Burton upon Trent, Staffordshire DE14 1EG; Tel (Children and Families) 01283 505820; 01283 516334; Fax 01283 510360

Hammerwich Hospital Lichfield and Burntwood Community Support Team, Hospital Rd, Burntwood, Staffordshire WS7 0EH; Tel 01543 686224; Fax 01543 672356

Horninglow Clinic Burton Community Care and Support Team, Carlton St, Burton upon Trent, Staffordshire DE13 0TF; Tel 01283 538030; Fax 01283 537801

North Staffordshire Hospital Social Work Department, Estates Bldg (A34 Site), City General Complex, Newcastle Rd, Stoke-on-Trent ST4 6QG; Tel 01782 552095; 01782 553148; 01782 553149; Fax 01782 633942

Queens Hospitals NHS Trust NHS Trust Social Work Department, nr Children's Clinic Queens Hospital, Belvedere Rd, Burton upon Trent, Staffordshire DE13 0RB; Tel 01283 566333 ext 4421; Fax 01283 561921

Sir Robert Peel Hospital Social Work Dept, Plantation La, Mile Oak, Tamworth, Staffordshire B79 3NG; Tel 01827 263800; Fax 01827 263844

St. Edward's Hospital Social Work Department, Cheddleton, Leek, Staffordshire ST13 7EB; Tel 01538 360421; Fax 01538 361644

St. Michael's Hospital Social Work Dept, 15 Trent Valley Rd, Lichfield, Staffordshire WS13 6EF; Tel 01543 414555; (Children and Families) 01543 416715; Fax 01543 410273

Stafford Central Clinic Child Development Centre, North Walls, Stafford, Staffordshire ST16 3AE; Tel 01785 223140; Fax 01785 224014

Stafford District General Hospital Social Work Dept, Weston Rd, Stafford, Staffordshire ST16 3SA; Tel 01785 257731; Fax 01785 230929

Wall Lane House Adolescent Mental Health Service, Young People's Unit, 1–2 Wall Lane Terr, Cheddleton, Leek, Staffordshire ST13 7GD; Tel 01782 275150; Fax 01538 360611

OTHER UNITS

Mid Staffordshire Mental Health Team The Lodge, Marston Dr, Stafford, Staffordshire ST16 3BU; Tel 01785 356738; Fax 01785 356751

Cherry Orchard House 35 Hospital St, Tamworth, Staffordshire B79 7EE; Tel 01827 308820; Fax 01827 313449

TRAINING

Responsible for training professional and support staff in the department.
Head of Staff Development and Principal Officer (Staff Development) J. Wiltshaw
Tillington Centre, Staff Development Unit, Stafford, Staffordshire ST16 1PS; Tel 01785 355770; Fax 01785 355771

Children and Family Services Division

SPECIALIST PLACEMENT TEAM

Corporation St, Stafford, Staffordshire ST16 3LX; Tel 01785 276969; Fax 01785 276928

COUNTY EQUIPMENT CENTRE

Unit 2–4, Greyfriars, Stafford, Staffordshire ST16 2RF; Tel 01785 356626; Fax 01785 356629; Minicom 01785 356628

CHILDREN AND FAMILY CENTRES

Burton Children and Family Centre 63 Branston Rd, Burton upon Trent, Staffordshire DE14 3BY; Tel 01283 239431

Cannock Children and Family Centre Crown Hse, Beecroft Rd, Cannock, Staffordshire WS11 1JP; Tel 01543 462580

Watling House Secure Unit Watling St, Gailey, Staffordshire ST19 5PR; Tel 01902 798220; Fax 01902 798224
Contact Steve Feaver

RESIDENTIAL UNITS FOR CHILDREN AND YOUNG PEOPLE

The Alders Residential Unit 146 Lichfield Rd, Tamworth, Staffordshire B79 2SF; Tel 01827 51408
Unit Manager Kath Payne
Short term care (10)

The Birches Residential Unit Sidmouth Ave, Newcastle, Staffordshire ST5 0QN
Unit Manager R. Porter
Short term care (7)

Coalpit Lane Residential Unit 53 Coalpit La, Brereton, Rugeley, Staffordshire WS15 1EW; Tel 01889 583020
Unit Manager P. Findon
Short term care (8)

Hawthorn Crescent Residential Unit 67 Hawthorn Cres, Burton upon Trent, Staffordshire DE15 9QP; Tel 01283 569386
Unit Manager Ann Hutt
Respite care (8)

Old Penkridge Road Residential Unit 35a Old Penkridge Rd, Cannock, Staffordshire WS11 1BY; Tel 01543 466933
Unit Manager A. Nicholls
Short term care (7)

Westmorland Avenue Residential Unit 31a Westmorland Ave, Kidsgrove, Staffordshire ST7 1AS; Tel 01782 783088
Unit Manager A. Werner
Settled care (6)

Wordsworth Close Residential Unit 3 Wordsworth Cl, Burton upon Trent, Staffordshire DE14 2RY; Tel 01283 568607
Unit Manager Jenny Nash
Remand and Intensive (4)

DISABILITY RESOURCE TEAMS

South Team Lombard Crt, Lombard St, Lichfield, Staffordshire WS13 6DF; Tel 01543 510800; Fax 01543 510817

North Team Town Hall, Liverpool Rd, Kidsgrove, Staffordshire ST7 4EH; Tel 01782 296800; Fax 01782 296812

Mid Team Harance Hse, Rumer Hill, Cannock, Staffordshire WS11 3ET; Tel 01543 512350; Fax 01543 512367; Minicom 01543 512366

Youth Offending Servce and Family Placement

North Team

Red Gables Family Placement Services, 59 High St, Uttoxeter, Staffordshire ST4 7JQ; Tel 01889 256400; Fax 01889 256410

Seabridge Community Education Centre Youth Offending Team, Seabridge Pk, Ashway, Westlands, Newcastle-under-Lyme, Staffordshire ST5 3UB; Tel 01782 297615; Fax 01782 297616

Mid Team

Priory House Beaconside, Stafford, Staffordshire ST18 0DD; Tel 01785 358310; Fax 01785 358311

South Team

The Old House Family Placement and Youth Offending Service, Eastern Ave, Lichfield, Staffordshire WS13 7SQ; Tel 01543 510100; Fax 01543 510141

Adult Services Division

ADULT DAY CENTRES AND DAY SERVICE UNITS

Burton Day Services Shobnall St, Burton upon Trent, Staffordshire DE14 2HE; Tel 01283 562794
Manager B. Kitchen
(80)

Chase Day Services Longford Rd, Cannock, Staffordshire WS11 3LG; Tel 01543 503069
Manager J. Cooper
(118)

Codsall Day Services Histons Hill, Codsall, Staffordshire WV8 1AA; Tel 01902 846764
Manager Wendy Cantliffe
(60)

Kidsgrove Day Services Gloucester Rd, Kidsgrove, Staffordshire ST7 1EH; Tel 01782 776606
Manager D. Kemp
(113)

Moorlands Day Services Buxton Rd, Leek, Staffordshire ST13 6NF; Tel 01538 382808
Manager W. Low
(113)

Lichfield Day Services Cherry Orchard, Lichfield, Staffordshire WS14 9AA; Tel 01543 262408
Manager N. Edge
(71)

Newcastle Day Services Wilmot Dr, Lower Milehouse, Newcastle-under-Lyme, Staffordshire ST5 9AZ; Tel 01782 622132
Manager W. Boyce
(90)

Stafford Day Services Lime Tree Ave, Stafford, Staffordshire ST16 2RR
Manager D. Brackstone
(130)

Tamworth Day Services Silica Rd, Amington Ind Est, Tamworth, Staffordshire B77 4DT; Tel 01827 57469
Manager V. Glenn
(65)

MULTIPURPOSE DAY CENTRES

Burton Day Centre Byrkley St, Burton upon Trent, Staffordshire DE14 2EG; Tel 01283 565973
Manager L. Grimley
(45)

Cheadle Day Centre 61 Charles St, Cheadle, Cheshire ST10 1EE; Tel 01538 757158
Manager J. Faulkner
(25)

Davy Unit Cannock Chase Hospital, Brunswick Rd, Cannock, Staffordshire WS11 2XY; Tel 01543 576110 ext 6112
Manager F. Cook
(60)

The Elkes Day Centre Holly Rd, Uttoxeter, Staffordshire ST14 7DX; Tel 01889 562836
Manager A. Noblett
(20)

Great Wyrley Day Centre 156 Walsall Rd, Great Wyrley, West Midlands WS6 6NG; Tel 01922 419829
Manager M. Horton
(85)

Leek Day Centre 109 Buxton Rd, Leek, Staffordshire ST13 6EH; Tel 01538 386696
Manager D. James
(30)

Lichfield Day Centre Braeburn Cl, Lichfield, Staffordshire WS13 6MY; Tel 01543 419131
Manager S. Deeming
(45)

May Place Day Centre Brampton Rd, Newcastle, Staffordshire ST5 0RQ; Tel 01782 712229
Manager L. Ward
(20)

Northfields Care Centre Stone Rd, Stafford, Staffordshire ST16 2RS; Tel 01785 248584
Manager F. Wilson
(50)

Oakdene Day Centre Sycamore Rd, Chasetown, Burntwood, West Midlands WS7 4RR; Tel 01543 673074
Manager L. Asbury
(60)

Priory Day Centre Lymewood Gr, Newcastle, Staffordshire ST5 2EH; Tel 01782 639516
Manager L. Ward
(60)

Quest Day Centre Marston Rd, Stafford, Staffordshire ST16 3BU; Tel 01785 356782
Manager D. Gascoigne

Stone Day Centre Berkeley St, Stone, Staffordshire ST15 8LS; Tel 01785 813882
Manager F. Wilson
(30)

Tamworth Day Centre Hockley Rd, Wilnecote, Tamworth, Staffordshire B77 5EB; Tel 01827 261677
Manager C. Price
(45)

Wombourne Day Centre Planks La, Wombourne, Staffordshire WV5 9HE; Tel 01902 897683
Manager Sandra Jenkinson
73

RESIDENTIAL ESTABLISHMENTS FOR PEOPLE WITH DISABILITIES

Brookside Giggety La, Wombourne, Staffordshire WV5 0AX; Tel 01902 894485
Unit Manager J. Crook
(18)

Brunswick House Brunswick Rd, Cannock, Staffordshire WS11 5RZ; Tel 01543 578018
Unit Manager S. Pilmore
(18)

Co-operative Street 40 Co-operative St, Stafford, Staffordshire ST16 3DA; Tel 01785 252645
Unit Manager K. Johns
(11)

Douglas Road 114 Douglas Rd, Newcastle-under-Lyme, Staffordshire ST5 9BJ; Tel 01782 711041
Unit Manager Caroline Brenner (Acting)
(14)

Glebelands Court Penkvale Rd, Moss Pit, Stafford, Staffordshire ST17 9EY; Tel 01785 252214
Unit Manager S. Roestenburg
  (12)

Gloucester Road 140 Gloucester Rd, Kidsgrove, Stoke-on-Trent ST7 1EL; Tel 01782 782596
Unit Manager S. Sproston
  (21)

Greenfields House Springfield Rd, Leek, Staffordshire ST13 6LQ; Tel 01538 385916
Unit Manager Annette Cocks
  (8)

Hawthorn House Burton Old Rd, Lichfield, Staffordshire WS13 6EN; Tel 01543 252211
Unit Manager Karen Webb
  (31)

Hunters Lodge Horninglow Rd, Burton upon Trent, Staffordshire DE14 2PY; Tel 01283 563509
Unit Manager Jane Pettite
  (18)

The Newlands Royal Wlk, Cheadle, Staffordshire ST10 1EL; Tel 01538 752210
Unit Manager S. Brookes
  (12)

Orchard House Clayton Rd, Newcastle-under-Lyme, Staffordshire ST5 3AF; Tel 01782 615522
Unit Manager S. Forester
  (17)

St. Luke's Close 26 St. Luke's Cl, Cannock, Staffordshire WS11 1BB; Tel 01543 579109
Unit Manager J. Morris
  (14)

Scotch Orchard 55 Scotch Orchard, Lichfield, Staffordshire WS13 6DE; Tel 01543 264755
Unit Manager Vacancy
  (12)

Springhill Mount Rd, Leek, Staffordshire ST13 7LX; Tel 01538 382860
Unit Manager L. Foden
  (24)

Stone Road 216–218 Stone Rd, Stafford, Staffordshire ST16 1NS; Tel 01785 242709
Unit Manager Bruce Smith
  (21)

RESIDENTIAL ESTABLISHMENTS FOR ELDERLY PEOPLE

There are 25 homes for elderly people run by Staffordshire Council.

MEALS ON WHEELS

St. Chads Pl, Stafford, Staffordshire ST16 2LR; Tel 01785 277133; Fax 01785 277004

Education Department

Education Office, Tipping St, Stafford, Staffordshire ST16 2DH; URL www.staffordshire.gov.uk; E-mail education@staffordshire.gov.uk; Tel 01785 223121; Fax 01785 278639
Corporate Director (Education and Lifelong Learning)
  Mrs J.C. Hawkins, BA
Principal Education Officer (Pupil and Student Services)
  Mrs J. Murphy
Chief Educational Psychologist R.G. Booth, BA(Hons)Psych, DipEdPsych
District Senior Educational Psychologist (Burton and Tamworth District) S. Williams
District Senior Educational Psychologist (Newcastle, Leek and Moorlands) P. Hodson, BA(Hons)Psych, MSc

District Senior Educational Psychologist (Stafford and South Staffs District) S. Laycock
District Senior Educational Psychologist (Lichfield and Cannock Chase District) A. Baddeley
Inspector (Special Schools) Ms J. Stevenson

COUNTY PSYCHOLOGICAL SERVICE

Flash Ley Resource Centre, Hawksmoor Rd, Stafford, Staffordshire ST17 9DR; Tel 01785 356871; Fax 01785 356940
District Senior Educational Psychologist S. Laycock

Specialist Support Service Flash Ley Resource Centre, Hawksmoor Rd, Stafford, Staffordshire ST17 4JX; Tel 01785 356917

SPECIAL DAY SCHOOLS

Beecroft Hill School Brunswick Rd, Cannock, Staffordshire WS11 2SF; E-mail headteacher@beecrofthill.staffs.sch.uk; Tel 01543 510216; Fax 01543 510222
Headteacher Mrs S. Ashley
  SLD

Blackfriars School Priory Rd, Newcastle-under-Lyme, Staffordshire ST5 2TF; E-mail headteacher@blackfriars.staffs.sch.uk; Tel 01782 297780; Fax 01782 297784
Headteacher C.E. Lilley
  PH

Chasetown Community School Church St, Chasetown, Walsall, West Midlands WS7 8QL; Tel 01543 686315; Fax 01543 675984
Headteacher L. James

Cherry Trees School Giggetty La, Wombourne, Wolverhampton, West Midlands WV5 0AX; E-mail headteacher@cherrytrees.staffs.sch.uk; Tel 01902 894484; Fax 01902 894484
Headteacher L.J. Allman
  SLD (21)

Coppice School Abbots Way, Newcastle-under-Lyme, Staffordshire ST5 2EY; E-mail headteacher@coppice.staffs.sch.uk; Tel 01782 297490; Fax 01782 297496
Headteacher A. Black
  MLD

Crown Special School Bitham La, Stretton, Burton upon Trent, Staffordshire DE13 0HB; E-mail headteacher@crown.staffs.sch.uk; Tel 01283 239700; Fax 01283 239701
Headteacher J. Harris
  SLD

Greenhall Community Special School Second Ave, Holmcroft, Stafford, Staffordshire ST16 1PS; E-mail headteacher@greenhall.staffs.sch.uk; Tel 01785 246159; Fax 01785 215490
Headteacher S.I. Barlow
  PH (42)

Marshlands School Lansdowne Way, Wildwood, Stafford, Staffordshire ST17 4RD; E-mail headteacher@marshlands.staffs.sch.uk; Tel 01785 356385; Fax 01785 356387
Headteacher Ms B.A. Whale
  SLD

Meadows School Tunstall Rd, Biddulph, Staffordshire ST8 7AB; E-mail headteacher@meadows.staffs.sch.uk; Tel 01782 297920; Fax 01782 297930
Headteacher C. Fielding
  MLD

Merryfields School Hoon Ave, May Bank, Newcastle-under-Lyme, Staffordshire ST5 9NY; E-mail headteacher@merryfields.staffs.sch.uk; Tel 01782 296076; Fax 01782 296082
Headteacher A. Bird
  SLD

Park School Solway Cl, Leyfields, Tamworth, Staffordshire B79 8EB; E-mail headteacher@park.staffs.sch.uk; Tel 01827 475690; Fax 01827 475697
Headteacher F. Bartlett
MLD

Queen's Croft Community School Birmingham Rd, Lichfield, Staffordshire WS13 6PJ; E-mail headteacher@queens.staffs.sch.uk; Tel 01543 510669; Fax 01543 510673
Headteacher J.F. Edwards
MLD

Quince Tree School Quince, Amington Heath, Tamworth, Staffordshire B77 4EN; E-mail headteacher@quincetree.staffs.sch.uk; Tel 01827 475740; Fax 01827 475746
Headteacher Mrs V.A. Vernon
SLD

Rocklands School Wissage Rd, Lichfield, Staffordshire WS13 6SW; E-mail headteacher@rocklands.staffs.sch.uk; Tel 01543 510760; Fax 01543 510762
Headteacher A. Dooley
SLD Autistic

Springfield School Springfield Rd, Leek, Staffordshire ST13 6LQ; E-mail headteacher@springfield.staffs.sch.uk; Tel 01538 383558; Fax 01538 383558
Headteacher I. Corden
SLD (32)

Stretton Brook School Bitham La, Stretton, Burton upon Trent, Staffordshire DE13 0HB; E-mail headteacher@bitham.staffs.sch.uk; Tel 01283 239161; Fax 01283 239168
Headteacher S.T. Gair
MLD

William Baxter Community School Stanley Rd, Hednesford, Staffordshire WS12 4JS; E-mail headteacher@williambaxter.staffs.sch.uk; Tel 01543 423714; Fax 01543 423714
Headteacher Mrs C.M. Allsop
MLD

SPECIAL RESIDENTIAL SCHOOLS

Cicely Haughton School Westwood Manor, Wetley Rocks, Stoke-on-Trent ST9 0BX; E-mail headteacher@cicelyhaughton.staffs.sch.uk; Tel 01782 550202; Fax 01782 550202
Headteacher N. Phillips
EBD

Horton Lodge School Rudyard, Leek, Staffordshire ST13 8RB; E-mail headteacher@hortonlodge.staffs.sch.uk; Tel 01538 306214; Fax 01538 306006
Headteacher C. Coles
PH

Loxley Hall School Stafford Rd, Loxley, Uttoxeter, Staffordshire ST14 8RS; E-mail loxley.hall@staffordshire.gov.uk; Tel 01889 256390; Fax 01889 256397
Headteacher W.M. Pearce
MLD, behavioural difficulties (59)

Saxon Hill School Kings Hill Rd, Lichfield, Staffordshire WS14 9DE; E-mail headteacher@saxonhill.staffs.sch.uk; Tel 01543 510615; Fax 01543 510626
Headteacher D.J. Butcher
PH

Walton Hall School Stafford Rd, Eccleshall, Stafford, Staffordshire ST21 6JR; E-mail office@waltonhall.staffs.sch.uk; Tel 01785 850420; Fax 01785 850225
Headteacher R.B. Goldthorpe
MLD

Wightwick Hall School Tinacre Hill, Compton, Wolverhampton, West Midlands WV6 8DA; E-mail headteacher@wightwickhall.staffs.sch.uk; Tel 01902 761889; Fax 01902 765080
Headteacher P.H.W. Archer, AdvDipEd
MLD Autistic (6)

STOCKPORT METROPOLITAN BOROUGH COUNCIL
www.stockport.gov.uk

Population 291 500
Political Composition: LD: 33, Lab: 17, Con: 8, Ind: 4, Free Social Democrats: 1.
Town Hall, Stockport, Greater Manchester SK1 3XE; URL www.stockport.gov.uk; E-mail mail@stockport.gov.uk; Tel 0161 474 4609; Fax 0161 476 2746
Chief Executive J. Schultz, MA, DipTP, MRTPI, MIMgt

Social Services

Ponsonby Hse, Edward St, Stockport, Greater Manchester SK1 3UR; URL www.stockport.gov.uk/socialservices; E-mail socialservices@stockport.gov.uk; Tel 0161 474 4609; (Emergency) 0161 718 2118; Fax 0161 476 2746; Textphone 0161 474 4619
Director (Social Services) Jean Daintith
Assistant Director (Finance, IT and Premises) Rodney D'Costa
Assistant Director (Adults) John Rutherford
Assistant Director (Children and Family) Michael Jameson
Assistant Director (Strategy and Performance) Terry Dafter

TRAINING

Responsible for training professional and support staff.
Staff Development Section, Dialstone Centre, Stockport, Greater Manchester SK2 7LL; Tel 0161 474 2137
Co-ordinator Liz Glynn
Co-ordinator Christine Ash

Executive Arrangements

Executive Member (Social Care and Health Portfolio) Martin Candler (LD)
38 Turncliff Cres, Stockport, Greater Manchester

ADULT SERVICES

DISABILITY SERVICES

6th Fl, Regal Hse, Stockport, Greater Manchester SK1 3DA; Tel 0161 477 3700
Service Manager Janet Beer

SERVICES FOR OLDER PEOPLE – ASSESSMENT AND CARE MANAGEMENT

Ashlea, 28 Manchester Rd, Stockport, Greater Manchester SK8 2NP; Tel 0161 428 3241
Council Offices, Memorial Pk, Stockport, Greater Manchester SK6 6BB; Tel 0161 427 7011
Service Manager Maggie Kufeldt
Service Manager Hilary Makepeace

LEARNING DISABILITY SERVICES

Oak Hse, 2 Gatley Rd, Stockport, Greater Manchester SK8 1PY; Tel 0161 491 4376
Head of Service Mike Corrigan

6

STRATEGY AND PERFORMANCE

6 Fl, Regal Hse, Stockport, Greater Manchester SK1 3DA;
Tel 0161 477 3700
Manager   Mike Illingworth

CHILDREN'S SERVICES

CHILDREN IN NEED

1 Baker St, Heaton Norris, Stockport, Greater Manchester
SK4 1QQ; Tel 0161 475 6799
Senior Service Manager   Gani Martins

REFERRAL AND ASSESSEMENT

Mount Tabor, Mottram St, Stockport, Greater Manchester
SK1 3PA; Tel 0161 474 4709
Service Manager   Sara Pearson

FAMILY SUPPORT

Baker St, Stockport, Greater Manchester SK4 1QQ; Tel 0161
475 6700
Service Manager   Jane Davies

CHILDREN LOOKED AFTER

Dialstone Centre, Lisburn La, Offerton, Stockport, Greater
Manchester SK2 7LL; Tel 0161 474 2100
Senior Service Manager   Brian Evans

PERMANENCE

Dialstone Centre, Lisburne La, Stockport, Greater
Manchester SK2 7LL; Tel 0161 474 2100
Service Manager   Mary Candlin

LOOKED AFTER SERVICE

Baker St, Stockport, Greater Manchester SK4 1QQ; Tel 0161
425 6700
Service Manager   Sue Westwood
Service Manager   Charlotte Ramsden

STRATEGY AND PERFORMANCE

6th Fl, Royal Hse, Stockport, Greater Manchester SK1 3DA;
Tel 0161 477 3700
Manager   Vacancy

CHILD PROTECTION AND REVIEW UNIT

Sanderling Bldg, Birdhall La, Stockport, Greater
Manchester SK3 0RS; Tel 0161 474 5658
Manager   Kate Rose

CHILDREN'S HOMES

Broadfield Children's Home   21 Egerton Rd, Davenport,
Stockport, Greater Manchester SK3 8SR; Tel 0161 483 2815
Dawlish Children's Home   19 Dawlish Ave, Brinnington,
Stockport, Greater Manchester SK5 8AX; Tel 0161 430 2723
Dial Park Children's Home   72 Dial Park Rd, Offerton,
Stockport, Greater Manchester SK2 7LT; Tel 0161 483 9258
Otterburn Place Children's Home   7 Otterburn Pl,
Crosswaite Rd, off Lisburne La, Stockport, Greater
Manchester SK2 5LD; Tel 0161 487 3885

FAMILY CENTRES

Brinnington Road Family Centre   334 Brinnington Rd,
Brinnington, Stockport, Greater Manchester SK5 8BX;
Tel 0161 430 4851
Queen's Road Family Centre   Queen's Rd, Hazel Gr,
Stockport, Greater Manchester SK7 4HX; Tel 0161 483 4237
Reddish Vale Family Support Team   Reddish Vale Early
Years Centre, Reddish Vale Rd, Stockport, Greater
Manchester SK5 7EU; Tel 0161 480 6713

DAY SERVICES FOR PEOPLE WITH LEARNING DISABILITIES

Cheadle Community Link   Park Rd, Cheadle, Stockport,
Greater Manchester SK8 2AN; Tel 0161 474 4756
Manager   Ann-Marie McIntyre
Employment Services (Work Link, Community Access)
Sanderling Bldg, Birdhall La, Stockport, Greater
Manchester SK3 0SB; Tel 0161 474 5903
Manager   Doug Cresswell
Heatons Community Link   Thornfield Rd, Heaton Moor,
Stockport, Greater Manchester SK4 3LD; Tel 0161 442 2286
Manager   Joe Carter

RESIDENTIAL HOME FOR PEOPLE WITH LEARNING DISABILITIES

Hulme Hall Close Residential Home   Hulme Hall Rd,
Cheadle Hulme, Stockport, Greater Manchester SK8 6JZ;
Tel 0161 486 9783

MENTAL HEALTH – RESIDENTIAL ESTABLISHMENT

Redcroft   43 Parsonage Rd, Heaton Moor, Greater
Manchester SK4 4JW; Tel 0161 432 1096

**DAY RESOURCES FOR PEOPLE WITH PHYSICAL/SENSORY
DISABILITIES**

Leyfield Centre (Primus)   Leyfield Ave, Romiley, Stockport,
Greater Manchester SK5 6BQ; Tel 0161 430 2891
Millbrook Centre   Millbrook St, Stockport, Greater
Manchester SK1 3NW; Tel 0161 480 1890

MENTAL HEALTH RESOURCE CENTRES

Councillor Lane Resource Centre   Cheadle, Stockport,
Greater Manchester SK8 2JS; Tel 0161 718 2203
Sector 3 Mental Health Resource Centre   Torkington Lodge,
Torkington Pk, Stockport, Greater Manchester SK7 4RQ;
Tel 0161 456 0200
York House Resource Centre   21 Heaton Moor Rd,
Stockport, Greater Manchester SK4 4LT; Tel 0161 442 7751

DAY CENTRES FOR ELDERLY/DISABLED PEOPLE

Ada Kay Centre   Park View, Annable Rd, Stockport, Greater
Manchester SK6 2DE; Tel 0161 430 3619
Arthur Greenwood Centre   Hipley Cl, Woodley, Stockport,
Greater Manchester SK6 1ES; Tel 0161 430 4871
Crescent Road Day Centre   Lower Brinnington, Stockport,
Greater Manchester SE1 2QQ; Tel 0161 480 5883
Highgate Centre   Bents Ave, Bredbury, Stockport, Greater
Manchester SK6 2LF; Tel 0161 430 2111
Kimberley Street Day Centre   Kimberley St, Cale Grn,
Stockport, Greater Manchester SK3 8EB; Tel 0161 480 6596
Marple Senior Citizens Hall   Memorial Pk, Marple,
Stockport, Greater Manchester SK6 6BA; Tel 0161 427 3632
New Bairstow Centre   Rupert St, Reddish, Stockport,
Greater Manchester SK5 6DL; Tel 0161 432 0834
Park View Centre   Hardman St, Chestergate, Stockport,
Greater Manchester SK3 0DH; Tel 0161 480 6735
Queens Court Day Centre   25 Church St, Marple, Stockport,
Greater Manchester SK6 6BS; Tel 0161 427 9639
Torkington Centre   Torkington Rd, Hazel Gr, Stockport,
Greater Manchester SK7 4PY; Tel 0161 483 7496

Education Services

Town Hall, Piccadilly, Stockport, Greater Manchester
SK1 3XE; E-mail education.division@stockport.gov.uk;
Tel 0161 480 4949; Fax 0161 953 0012
Principal Education Welfare Officer   P. Pugh
Principal Educational Psychologist   J. Davies

SPECIAL SCHOOLS

Castle Hill School Lapwing La, Brinnington, Stockport, Greater Manchester SK5 8LF; Tel 0161 494 6439
Headteacher M.E. Marra, BEd, MSc

Heaton School St. James' Rd, Heaton Moor, Stockport, Greater Manchester SK4 4RE; Tel 0161 432 1931
Headteacher E. Seers, BEd

Lisburne School Half Moon La, Offerton, Stockport, Greater Manchester SK2 5LB; Tel 0161 483 5045
Headteacher D.J. Woods

Oakgrove School Matlock Rd, Heald Grn, Stockport, Greater Manchester SK8 3BU; Tel 0161 437 4956; Fax 0161 283 6665
Headteacher A. Copley, BEd
4–10

Valley School Whitehaven Rd, Bramhall, Stockport, Greater Manchester SK7 1EN; Tel 0161 439 7343
Headteacher C. Goodlet, MEd, BEd

Windlehurst School Windlehurst Rd, Hawk Grn, Stockport, Greater Manchester SK6 7HZ; Tel 0161 427 4788; Fax 0161 484 5091
Headteacher Mr K. Lloyd
11–15

STOCKTON-ON-TEES BOROUGH COUNCIL

www.stockton.gov.uk

Political Composition: Lab: 28, Con: 13, Ind: 8, LD: 5
PO Box 11, Municipal Bldgs, Stockton-on-Tees TS18 1LD;
URL www.stockton.gov.uk;
E-mail stocktoncouncil@stockton.gov.uk; Tel 01642 393939; Fax 01642 393092; Minicom 01642 393010
Chief Executive George Garlick

Health and Social Care

Alma Hse, 6 Alma St, Stockton-on-Tees TS18 2AP;
E-mail socialservices@sbcss3.stockton-bc.gov.uk;
Tel 01642 393339; Fax 01642 393371
Corporate Director (Health and Social Care) A. Baxter
Director (Service Development – North Tees PCT)
Richard Webb
Head (Operations) Jane Humphreys
Head (Policy and Development) Tony Beckwith

TRAINING

Responsible for training professional and support staff in the department.
Ideal Hse, Allensway, Thornaby, Stockton-on-Tees;
Tel 01642 391680
Manager (Employee Development) A.P. Todd

WELFARE RIGHTS UNIT

Billingham Office Council Offices, Town Sq, Billingham, Stockton-on-Tees; Tel 01642 897170

CHILDREN'S COMMUNITY HOMES

Princess Avenue Children's Community Home 37 Princess Ave, Stockton-on-Tees; Tel 01642 393416
(8)
Vulcan Way Children's Community Home 149 Vulcan Way, Thornaby, Stockton-on-Tees; Tel 01642 391540
(8)

HOME FOR CHILDREN WITH LEARNING DISABILITIES

Hartburn Lodge Children's Home Harsley Rd, Hartburn, Stockton-on-Tees; Tel 01642 391700
(15)

HOMES FOR PEOPLE WITH LEARNING DISABILITIES

Lanark Close Home Elm Tree Farm, 1 Lanark Cl, Stockton-on-Tees; Tel 01642 391705
(18)
Oak Road Home 31 Oak Rd, Eaglescliffe, Stockton-on-Tees;
Tel 01642 391800

DAY CENTRE FOR ADULTS WITH LEARNING DISABILITIES

Allensway Centre 45 Allensway, Thornaby, Stockton-on-Tees; Tel 01642 391537
(100)

ACCOMMODATION FOR PEOPLE WITH MENTAL HEALTH PROBLEMS

Ware Street Home 5 Ware St, Stockton-on-Tees; Tel 01642 393405
(25)

DAY CENTRE FOR PEOPLE WITH PHYSICAL DISABILITIES

Alma Centre Alma St, Stockton-on-Tees; Tel 01642 391485
(80)

HOME FOR PEOPLE WITH PHYSICAL DISABILITIES

Blenheim Trenchard Ave, Thornaby, Stockton-on-Tees;
Tel 01642 391535
(30)

DAY CENTRES FOR THE ELDERLY

Parkfield Hall Day Centre Bowesfield La, Stockton-on-Tees;
Tel 01642 393410
(30)

Parkside Day Centre Melrose Ave, Billingham, Stockton-on-Tees; Tel 01642 397287

Tithebarn House Day Centre High Newham Rd, Hardwick, Stockton-on-Tees; Tel 01642 393412

Education, Leisure and Cultural Services

PO Box 228, Municipal Bldgs, Stockton-on-Tees TS18 1XE;
URL www.stockton-bc.gov.uk; Tel 01642 393939;
Fax 01642 383479
Corporate Director (Education, Leisure and Cultural Services)
Stanley Bradford, BSc, MA(Ed), MBA, CBiol, MIBiol, MIMgt
Head (Promoting Achievement) J. Morrison
Head (Planning and Performance) P.J. Walkley, BA
Manager (Special Education Needs) J. Ormond, CQSW, DipSW
General Adviser (SEN) M. McKenna, BA

EDUCATIONAL PSYCHOLOGICAL SERVICE

Wrensfield Hse, Wrensfield Rd, Stockton-on-Tees TS19 0AT;
Tel 01642 393947; Fax 01642 393944

SPECIAL UNIT FOR PUPILS WITH PHYSICAL HANDICAPS

Bishopsgarth Secondary School Harrowgate La, Stockton-on-Tees TS19 8TF; Tel 01642 586262; Fax 01642 570038
Headteacher J. Golds

6

SPECIAL SCHOOLS FOR PUPILS WITH LEARNING DIFFICULTIES

Abbey Hill School   Ketton Rd, Hardwick, Stockton-on-Tees TS19 8BU; Tel 01642 677113; Fax 01642 679198
Headteacher   M. Vening
   Secondary Full Range

Ash Trees School   Bowes Rd, Billingham, Stockton-on-Tees TS23 2BU; Tel 01642 563712; Fax 01642 563712
Headteacher   Iain Bowran
   Primary Full Range

Westlands School   Eltham Cres, Thornaby, Stockton-on-Tees TS17 9RA; Tel 01642 883030; Fax 01642 883070
Headteacher   J.E. Jefferson, BPhil(Ed), MA(Ed) Special Needs
   MLD Day (90), residential (50)

SPECIAL SCHOOL FOR PUPILS WITH EMOTIONAL AND BEHAVIOURAL DIFFICULTIES

Saltergill School   Worsall Rd, Kirklevington, Yarm, Stockton-on-Tees TS15 9QD; Tel 01642 782081; Fax 01642 783606
Headteacher   A. Riley
   Boys (Day, Boarders)

STOKE-ON-TRENT CITY COUNCIL
www.stoke.gov.uk

Political Composition: Lab: 27, Independent Group: 16, LD: 8, Con: 5, Ind (Non-aligned): 3, BNP: 1
Civic Centre, PO Box 636, Glebe St, Stoke-on-Trent ST4 1RN; URL www.stoke.gov.uk; E-mail enquiries@stoke.gov.uk; Tel 01782 234567; Fax 01782 232603
Council Manager   Dr Ita O'Donovan
Director (Regeneration and Community)   Robert Collins
Director (Urban Environment)   Philip Harper
Director (City Services)   Brian Nettleton, DMS, CEng, MICE, MIHT
Director (Corporate Resources)   Paul Brindley
Director (Housing and Consumer Protection)   Steve Robinson
City Secretary   Mark Winstanley

Social Services Department

Civic Centre, PO Box 755, Glebe St, Stoke-on-Trent ST4 1WB; URL www.stoke.gov.uk/socialcare; Tel 01782 235985; Fax 01782 235996; Minicom 01782 236133
Director (Social Services)   Phil Swann, BA, CQSW, DMS, MBA
Assistant Director (Adults)   Sarah Hill, MBA, BA(Hons), CQSW; Tel 01782 235901; Fax 01782 235996
Assistant Director (Children and Families)   Helen Oakley, BA(Hons), CQSW, MBA; Tel 01782 235902; Fax 01782 235996
Assistant Director (Support Services)   David Fish, DMS; Tel 01782 235903; Fax 01782 235996
Assistant Director (Planning and Commissioning)   Dave Trenery, BA, MA, CQSW; Tel 01782 235904; Fax 01782 235996
Head (Financial Support Unit)   Steve Rowley, CPFA; Tel 01782 235901; Fax 01782 235996

Social Services Executive Committee

Chair   A.E. James (Lab)
Members of the Committee
K. Ali, D. Bamford, J. Bowers, D. Capey, R. Conteh, G.B. Davies, J.G. Davis, Jean Edwards, J.A. Garner, B. Glover, R.N. Gore, R.M. Ibbs, P. Joynson, A.M. Knapper, J. Lamingman, J. Mayer, C. McLaren, M. Pyatt, M. Salih, D. Thomas, T.D. Tolley, C. Wood.

AREA OFFICES

Bucknall Area Office   Werrington Rd, Bucknall, Stoke-on-Trent ST2 9AF; Tel 01782 235384; Fax 01782 235283; Minicom 01782 235384

Hanley Area Office   Regent Centre, Regent Rd, Stoke-on-Trent ST1 3TD; Tel 01782 235100; Fax 01782 235166; Minicom 01782 235167

Longton Area Office   Drayton Rd, Longton, Stoke-on-Trent ST3 1BA; Tel 01782 234050; Fax 01782 234060; Minicom 01782 234055

Tunstall Area Office   Oldcourt St, Tunstall, Stoke-on-Trent ST6 5BL; Tel 01782 234235; Fax 01782 234255

CHILD CARE MONITORING UNIT

Tunstall Area Office, Oldcourt St, Tunstall, Stoke-on-Trent ST6 5BL; Tel 01782 234235; (Emergency Duty Team) Tel 01782 330221;Fax 01782 254255; Fax (Emergency Duty Team) 01782 235639; Minicom 01782 330221

PROVIDER UNIT

Heron Cross Hse, Grove Rd, Stoke-on-Trent ST4 3AY; Tel 01782 234555; Fax 01782 234556

FAMILY SUPPORT RESOURCE UNIT

380 Chell Heath Rd, Chell Heath, Stoke-on-Trent ST6 6DD; Tel 01782 235885; Fax 01782 235883

DISABILITY RESOURCES TEAM

Regent Centre, Regent Rd, Stoke-on-Trent ST1 3TD; Tel 01782 235200; Fax 01782 235206; Minicom 01782 235285

STAFF DEVELOPMENT UNIT

Civic Centre, Glebe St, Stoke-on-Trent ST4 1WB; Tel 01782 235945; Fax 01782 235996; Minicom 01702 236133
Manager   Sheila Wood

HOSPITAL SOCIAL WORKERS

Bucknall Hospital   Social Work Department, Eaves La, Bucknall, Stoke-on-Trent ST2 8LD; Tel 01782 275022; 01782 275023; Fax 01782 207532; Minicom 01782 235129

North Staffordshire Hospital   Social Work Department, Estates Bldg, City General Complex, Newcastle Rd, Stoke-on-Trent ST4 6QG; Tel 01782 552095; 01782 553148; 01782 553149; Fax 01782 714769

Customer Services   Civic Centre, Glebe St, Stoke-on-Trent ST4 1WB; Fax 01782 235920; Minicom 01782 236133

FAMILY SUPPORT CENTRES

Belgrave Family Support Centre   Belgrave Hse, Belgrave Ave, Stoke-on-Trent ST3 4EA; Tel 01782 234535

Burslem Sure Start Centre   Jenkins St, Burslem, Stoke-on-Trent ST6 4EL; Tel 01782 235667

Trent Vale Family Support Centre   Flash La, Trent Vale, Stoke-on-Trent ST4 5QZ; Tel 01782 235247

Tunstall Family Sure Start Centre   Oldcourt St, Tunstall, Stoke-on-Trent ST6 5BL; Tel 01782 234970; 01782 235480

CHILDREN'S HOMES

Chell Heath Road Children's Home   100 Chell Heath Rd, Chell Heath, Stoke-on-Trent ST6 6DD; Tel 01782 234488; Fax 01782 234491

Hollybank House Children's Home   Oakhill, Stoke-on-Trent ST4 5AS; Tel 01782 234276

The Pathway Project   36 Redhouse Cres, Longton, Stoke-on-Trent ST3 2QS; Tel 01782 233572

Pembridge Road Children's Home 14a Pembridge Rd, Blurton, Stoke-on-Trent ST7 3BX; Tel 01782 234970

Wood Street Children's Home 50 Wood St, Longton, Stoke-on-Trent ST3 1EL; Tel 01782 234282; Fax 01782 234286

RESOURCE CENTRE FOR CHILDREN WITH DISABILITIES

170 Weston Coyney Rd, Longton, Stoke-on-Trent ST3 6ER; Tel 01782 598330

LEAVING CARE/AFTER CARE TEAM

Leaving Care/After Care Team 245 Hartshill Rd, Stoke-on-Trent ST4 7NQ; Tel 01782 233575; Fax 01782 233577

Youth Offending Team Unit C, Melto Bus Pk, Clough St, Hanley, Stoke-on-Trent ST1 4AF; Tel 01782 235858; Fax 01782 235860

ADULT DAY SERVICES AND DAY CARE CENTRES

Bentilee Day Centre Dawlish Dr, Bentilee, Stoke-on-Trent ST2 0HW; Tel 01782 235656

Burslem Day Centre Baddeley St, Burslem, Stoke-on-Trent ST6 4EX; Tel 01782 233850

Fenton Day Centre City Rd, Fenton, Stoke-on-Trent ST4 2PP; Tel 01782 234300

Longton Day Centre Dylan Rd, Longton, Stoke-on-Trent ST3 1SR; Tel 01782 235850

Maryhill Day Centre (co-arrangement for Staffordshire County Council) Gloucester Rd, Kidsgrove, Stoke-on-Trent ST17 1EH; Tel 01782 786890

Newpak Products (co-arrangement for Staffordshire County Council) London Rd, Chesterton, Newcastle, Staffordshire ST5 7HT; Tel 01782 235900; Fax 01782 236900

Queensberry Day Centre Queensberry Rd, Normacot, Stoke-on-Trent ST3 1QZ; Tel 01782 235343

Stoke-on-Trent Workshops 211 City Rd, Fenton, Stoke-on-Trent ST4 2PN; Tel 01782 233900; Fax 01782 234900

Tunstall Day Centre Oldcourt St, Tunstall, Stoke-on-Trent ST6 5BL; Tel 01782 235636

HOMES FOR PEOPLE WITH DISABILITIES/MENTAL HEALTH DIFFICULTIES

Baden Road Home 6 Baden Rd, Smallthane, Stoke-on-Trent ST6 1SA

Duke Street Home 210 Duke St, Fenton, Stoke-on-Trent ST4 3DJ; Tel 01782 235640

Handley Drive Home 12 Handley Dr, Brindley Ford, Stoke-on-Trent ST8 7QZ; Tel 01782 517079

Hillcrest Street Home 23 Hillcrest St, Hanley, Stoke-on-Trent ST1 2AA; Tel 01782 234370

Pittsburgh House 741 Lightwood Rd, Longton, Stoke-on-Trent ST3 7HD; Tel 01782 235616

Travers Court Home Travers Crt, 134 City Rd, Fenton, Stoke-on-Trent ST4 2DY; Tel 01782 234863

RESIDENTIAL HOMES FOR THE ELDERLY

There are 14 local authority old people's homes.

SPECIALIST TEAMS

Learning Disability Team Longton Area Office, Drayton Rd, Longton, Stoke-on-Trent ST3 1BA; Tel 01782 234050; Fax 01782 234060; Minicom 01782 234055

Mental Health Team Dyke St, Hanley, Stoke-on-Trent ST1 2DF; Tel 01782 236130; Fax 01782 236131

Education Department

Civic Centre, Glebe St, Stoke-on-Trent ST4 1HH; URL www.stoke.gov.uk; Tel 01782 232014; Fax 01782 236803

Director (Education) Nigel Rigby

PSYCHOLOGICAL SERVICE

Education Psychological Service The Mount, Mount Ave, Penkhull, Stoke-on-Trent ST4 4SY; Tel 01782 234700

SPECIAL DAY SCHOOLS

Abbey Hill School Greasley Rd, Bucknall, Stoke-on-Trent ST2 8LG; Tel 01782 234727
Headteacher M Coutouvidis, BA(Hons)
MLD SLD (35) Autistic (18)

Aynsley Special School Aynsley's Dr, Blythe Bridge, Stoke-on-Trent ST11 9HJ; Tel 01782 392071
Headteacher Angela Hardstaff

Heathfield School Chell Heath Rd, Chell Heath, Stoke-on-Trent ST6 6PD; Tel 01782 234494
Headteacher Jean Colesby
SLD

Kemball School Duke St, Fenton, Stoke-on-Trent ST4 3NR; Tel 01782 234879
Headteacher Elizabeth Spooner
SLD

Middlehurst School Turnhurst Rd, Chell Heath, Stoke-on-Trent ST6 6NQ; Tel 01782 234612
Headteacher Jonathan May (Acting)
MLD

6

SUFFOLK COUNTY COUNCIL
www.suffolkcc.gov.uk

Population 673 600
Political Composition: Lab: 35, Con: 32, LD: 12, Ind: 1
St. Helen Crt, County Hall, Ipswich, Suffolk IP4 2JS; URL www.suffolkcc.gov.uk; Tel 01473 583000; Fax 01473 214549

Chair of the Council Harold Mangar
Chief Executive and Director (Resource Management)
M. Moore, CPFA
St. Giles Hse, County Hall, Ipswich, Suffolk IP4 2JP; Tel 01473 584960; Fax 01473 212429
Assistant Director (Legal and Audit, Scrutiny and Monitoring)
Eric Whitfield
County Director (Environment and Transport) P. Thompson, MSc, CEng, FICE
St. Edmund Hse, County Hall, Ipswich, Suffolk IP4 1LZ; Tel 01473 583305; Fax 01473 230078

Social Care Services Department

St. Paul Hse, Rope Walk, Ipswich, Suffolk IP4 1LH; URL www.suffolkcc.gov.uk/social-services; E-mail chris.lane@comms.suffolkcc.gov.uk; Tel 01473 583427; Fax 01473 583402

Executive Committee Member (lead responsibility for Social Care) Terry Green (Lab)
Executive Committee Member (lead responsibility for Social Care) Tony Lewis (Lab)
Director (Social Care Services) Anthony Douglas
Assistant Director (Older People) Peter Tempest
Assistant Director (Strategic Planning) Janet Dillaway
Assistant Director (Children) John Gregg
Assistant Director (Organisational Development) Paul Jell
Assistant Director (Resources) Mel Cassedy
Associate Director (Vulnerable Adults) John Lewis

Caring and Protecting Theme Panel

Chair Roger Belham (Lab)
7 Nunn's Yard, Camps Rd, Haverhill, Suffolk CB9 8HE
Members of the Panel
Lab: R. Bellham, M. Cherry, D. Lockwood, R. Tostevin.
Con: J. Storey, R.A. Ward.
LD: R. Harsawt, P.H. Howard, P. O'Brien.
Co-opted: C. Kerr, J. Martin.
Lab: 4, Con: 4, LD: 2

CUSTOMER FIRST

Whitehouse Rd, Ipswich, Suffolk IP1 5NX;
   E-mail customer.first@socserv.suffolkcc.gov.uk;
   Tel (Lines open Mon–Fri 0800–1845) 08456 023023

AREA OFFICES

Beccles Area Office The Old Surgery, 1a Market St, Beccles, Suffolk NR34 9AQ; Tel 01502 717373; Fax 01502 711233

Eye Area Office 6 Cross St, Eye, Suffolk IP23 7AB; Tel 01379 873111; Fax 01379 870513

Lowestoft Area Office Clapham Hse, Clapham Rd, Lowestoft, Suffolk NR32 1QX; Tel 01502 405176; Fax 01502 405111

Saxmundham Area Office County Bldgs, Street Farm Rd, Saxmundham, Suffolk IP17 1AL; Tel 01728 403100; Fax 01728 403113

Woodbridge Area Office Eden Lodge, Cuberland St, Woodbridge, Suffolk IP12 4AN; Tel 01394 625011; Fax 01394 625040

HOSPITAL SOCIAL WORKERS

The James Paget Hospital Lowestoft Rd, Great Yarmouth, Suffolk NR31 6LA; Tel 01493 452452

CHILDREN'S RESOURCE CENTRE

Grange Road Resource Centre 10 Grange Rd, Beccles, Suffolk; Tel 01502 712659

HOSTEL FOR PEOPLE WITH LEARNING DISABILITIES

Rotterdam Road Hostel John Turner Hse, Rotterdam Rd, Lowestoft, Suffolk; Tel 01502 405447
Includes Special Care Unit.

DAY CARE FOR PEOPLE WITH LEARNING DISABILITIES

Lowestoft Day Care Rotterdam Rd, Lowestoft, Suffolk; Tel 01502 405432

Saxmundham Day Care A12 Advanced Workshop, Saxmundham, Suffolk; Tel 01728 603567

Saxmundham Resources Centre Seaman Ave, Saxmundham, Suffolk; Tel 01728 603140

RESIDENTIAL HOMES FOR OLDER PEOPLE

There are nine homes for older people.

Western Division

AREA OFFICES

Bury Area Office Shire Hall, Bury St. Edmunds, Suffolk IP33 1RX; Tel 01284 352000; Fax 01284 352206

Haverhill Area Office Camps Rd, Haverhill, Suffolk CB9 8HF; Tel 01440 762051; Fax 01440 712082

Mildenhall Area Office Willow Hse, 45 St. Andrews St, Mildenhall, Suffolk IP27 7HB; Tel 01638 717006; Fax 01638 718982

Newmarket Area Office Dolford Hse, Exning Rd, Newmarket, Suffolk CB8 0EA; Tel 01638 686000; Fax 01638 606019

Stowmarket Area Office 127 Ipswich St, Stowmarket, Suffolk IP14 1BB; Tel 01449 626190; Fax 01449 626181

Sudbury Area Office Friars St, Sudbury, Suffolk CO10 6AA; Tel 01787 296060; Fax 01787 296048

HOSPITAL SOCIAL WORKERS

Newmarket Hospital Exning Rd, Newmarket, Suffolk CB8 7JG; Tel 01638 584051

The West Suffolk Hospital Hardwick La, Bury St. Edmunds, Suffolk IP33 2QZ; Tel 01284 713000

CHILDREN'S RESOURCE CENTRES

Hospital Road Resource Centre 67a Hospital Rd, Bury St. Edmunds, Suffolk IP33 3JY; Tel 01284 352670

Risbygate Street Resource Centre 77 Risbygate St, Bury St. Edmunds, Suffolk IP33 3AQ

FAMILY CENTRES

The Chestnuts Family Centre 3 Kings Hill, Sudbury, Suffolk CO10 0EH; Tel 01787 372670

High Street Family Centre 72 High St, Haverhill, Suffolk CB8 8AN; Tel 01440 714444

Violet Hill Road Family Centre Violet Hill Rd, Stowmarket, Suffolk IP14 1NL; Tel 01449 626200

HOSTEL FOR PEOPLE WITH LEARNING DISABILITIES

Chestnut House The Vinefields, Bury St. Edmunds, Suffolk; Tel 01284 352583

DAY CARE FOR PEOPLE WITH LEARNING DISABILITIES

Hollow Road Centre Hollow Rd, Bury St. Edmunds, Suffolk IP32 7AY; Tel 01284 352597

Advanced Work Unit Unit 9, Bury St. Edmunds, Suffolk IP32 7DS; Tel 01284 352605

Stowmarket Resource Centre Crown St, Stowmarket, Suffolk IP14 7AX; Tel 01449 626216

Sudbury Day Care Chilton Ind Est, Northern Rd, Sudbury, Suffolk CO10 6XQ; Tel 01787 296090

HOSTEL FOR ADULTS WITH MENTAL HEALTH PROBELMS

Westfield Hostel Hospital Rd, Bury St. Edmunds, Suffolk IP33 3GA; Tel 01284 352665

RESIDENTIAL HOMES FOR OLDER PEOPLE

There are eight homes for older people.

Southern Division

AREA OFFICES

East Ipswich Area Office 214b Sidegate La, Ipswich, Suffolk IP4 3DH; Tel 01473 588535; Fax 01473 588566

Felixstowe Area Office 108 Queens Rd, Felixstowe, Suffolk IP11 7PG; Tel 01394 625704; Fax 01394 625739

Hadleigh Area Office Corn Exchange, Market Pl, Hadleigh, Suffolk IP7 5DN; Tel 01473 823948; Fax 01473 824415

South and Centre Ipswich Area Office 17 Tower St, Ipswich, Suffolk IP1 3BE; Tel 01473 583594; Fax 01473 583675

HOSPITAL SOCIAL WORKERS

The Ipswich Hospital Heath Rd, Ipswich, Suffolk IP4 5PD; Tel 01473 712233; Fax 01473 703542

St. Clements Hospital 566 Foxhall Rd, Ipswich, Suffolk IP3 8LT; Tel 01473 276525; Fax 01473 276557
Mental Health Team.

CHILDREN'S RESOURCE CENTRES

Belstead Road Resource Centre 52 Belstead Rd, Ipswich, Suffolk IP2 8BA; Tel 01473 601505

Montgomery Road Resource Centre 76 Montgomery Rd, Ipswich, Suffolk IP2 8QE; Tel 01473 686539

Oak Cottage Resource Centre Oak Cottage, 4 Crabbe St, Ipswich, Suffolk IP4 5HS; Tel 01473 588527; Fax 01473 588530

FAMILY CENTRES

Grange Road Centre Grange Rd, Felixstowe, Suffolk IP11 8LA; Tel 01394 284431

Robert Milne Family Centre 333 Felixstowe Rd, Ipswich, Suffolk IP3 9BU; Tel 01473 724549
Run jointly with Ormiston Trust.

Shenstone Drive Centre 9 Shenstone Dr, Ipswich, Suffolk IP1 6NT; Tel 01473 588114

Stonelodge Lane West Centre Stonelodge La West, Ipswich, Suffolk IP2 9HN; Tel 01473 602150

DAY CARE FOR PEOPLE WITH LEARNING DISABILITIES

Humber Doucy La, Ipswich, Suffolk IP4 3PB; Tel 01473 588505

OCCUPATIONAL AND INDUSTRIAL CENTRE FOR PEOPLE WITH DISABILITY

White House Enterprises, Lovetofts Dr, Ipswich, Suffolk IP1 5NZ; Tel 01473 588115; Fax 01473 588116

RESIDENTIAL HOMES FOR OLDER PEOPLE

There are nine homes for older people.

SERVICES TO DEAF PEOPLE (COUNTY RESOURCE)

Whitehouse Office, Whitehouse Rd, Ipswich, Suffolk IP1 5NX; Tel 01473 583559

Education Offices

St. Andrew Hse, County Hall, Ipswich, Suffolk IP4 1LJ; Tel 01473 584800; Fax 01473 584624
Director (Learning) D.J.E. Thornton, MA, MEd (Acting
Deputy County Director (Education) D.J.E. Thornton, MA, MEd
Assistant Director (Learner Support) G. Nethercott
Manager (Special Needs) V. Harvey-Samuel
Manager (Children's Futures) B. Newton
Senior Education Officer (Community) R.D. Dool
Senior Education Officer (Policy and Planning) M. Brenner, BSc
Assistant Education Officer (Family Support) E. Maloney
County Educational Psychologist W.F. Herbert, BSc(Hons), MEd

CHILD GUIDANCE CLINICS

Cases referred to the Institute of Family Psychiatry.

AREA OFFICES

Northern Area

Adrian Hse, Alexandra Rd, Lowestoft, Suffolk NR32 1PL; Tel 01502 405218
Area Manager (Education) S. Simpkin

SPECIAL SCHOOLS

The Ashley School Ashley Downs, Lowestoft, Suffolk NR32 4EU; Tel 01502 565439; 01502 574847
Headteacher D. Field

Warren School Clarkes La, Lowestoft, Suffolk NR33 8HT; Tel 01502 561893
Headteacher C. Moore

Southern Area

St. Andrew Hse, County Hall, Ipswich, Suffolk IP4 1LJ; Tel 01473 584800
Area Manager (Education) J.H. Crompton, BA, DMA

SPECIAL SCHOOLS

Beacon Hill School Stone Lodge Lane West, Ipswich, Suffolk IP2 9HW; Tel 01473 601175
Headteacher D. Stewart, BEd

Belstead School Sprites La, Belstead, Ipswich, Suffolk IP8 3ND; Tel 01473 556200
Headteacher S. Chesworth

Heathside School Heath Rd, Ipswich, Suffolk IP4 5SN; Tel 01473 725508
Headteacher O. Doran

Thomas Wolsey School 642 Old Norwich Rd, Ipswich, Suffolk IP1 6LA; Tel 01473 467600
Headteacher N. McArdle, BEd

Western Area

Shire Hall, Bury St. Edmunds, Suffolk IP33 IRX; Tel 01284 352000
Area Manager (Education) T.H. Scherb, BA

SPECIAL SCHOOLS

Hampden House School 3 Cats La, Great Cornard, Sudbury, Suffolk CO10 6SF; Tel 01787 373583
Warden Mr Parker

Hillside School Hitchcock Pl, Sudbury, Suffolk CO10 1NN; Tel 01787 372808; Fax 01787 375249
Headteacher J.E. Freeman

Priory School Mount Rd, Bury St. Edmunds, Suffolk IP32 7BH; Tel 01284 761934; Fax 01284 725878
Headteacher L. Preece

Riverwalk School South Cl, Bury St. Edmunds, Suffolk IP32 3JZ; Tel 01284 764280; Fax 01284 705943
Headteacher B. Ellis

6

CITY OF SUNDERLAND
www.sunderland.gov.uk

Population 290 000
Political Composition: Lab: 62, Con: 11, LD: 2
Civic Centre, Sunderland, Tyne and Wear SR2 7DN; URL www.sunderland.gov.uk; Tel 0191 553 1000; Fax 0191 553 1099
Leader of the Council R. Symonds
Chief Executive Dr Colin Sinclair, PhD
Director (Corporate Services) Ian Whyte, CPFA
Director (Development and Regeneration) Phil Barrett, BEng, MICE, MIHT

Social Services Department

50 Fawcett St, Sunderland, Tyne and Wear SR1 1RF; E-mail directorate@ssd.sunderland.gov.uk; Tel 0191 553 1000; Fax 0191 553 7254
Director (Social Services) Dr Glenys Jones; Tel 0191 553 7180

Head of Service (Performance and Development)   Gill Wall;
Tel 0191 553 7179
Head (Adult Care Services)   J. Fisher; Tel 0191 553 7192
Head (Children's Services)   Barbara Williams; Tel 0191 553
7175

TRAINING

Responsible for training professional and support staff in
the department.
Head of Service   Gill Wall
50 Fawcett St, Sunderland, Tyne and Wear SR1 1RF;
Tel 0191 553 7073

Cabinet Members

Cabinet Member (Social Services)   Cllr Eric Timmins (Lab)
59 Raleigh Rd, Red Hse, Sunderland, Tyne and Wear
SR5 5RB
Deputy Cabinet Member (Social Services)   Cllrs Ronnie
Bainbridge (Lab)
12 Hawsker Cl, Ryhope, Sunderland, Tyne and Wear
SR3 2YD

AREA OFFICES

Headquarters

50 Fawcett St, Sunderland, Tyne and Wear SR1 1RF;
URL www.sunderland.gov.uk;
E-mail directorate@ssd.sunderland.gov.uk; Tel 0191 553
7128 0191 553 7129
Manager (Customer and Quality Services)   D. Elliott
Manager (Information Communications Technology)   Peter
Coates
Manager (Financial Support Services)   J. Hedley
Assistant Head (Joint Commissioning)   Debbie Burnicle
Assistant Head (Support at Home)   Pauline Blyth

Children's Services

Manager (Youth Offending Service)   Judith Hay
11 John St, Sunderland, Tyne and Wear SR1 1HT; Tel 0191
553 7370 0191 553 7371
Service Manager (Young People's Services)   Jill Varndell
13 Toward Rd, Sunderland, Tyne and Wear SR1 2QF;
Tel 0191 553 7350
Head (Case Management)   Ann White
Cassaton Hse, 43–49 Fawcett St, Sunderland, Tyne and
Wear; Tel 0191 566 1500
Children's Guardian Panel Manager   Val Smith
19 Villiers St, Sunderland, Tyne and Wear SR1 1EJ; Tel 0191
553 7881; 0191 553 7882
Divisional Manager (Services for Looked After Children)
Karen Wilson
Penshaw Hse, Station Rd, Penshaw, Houghton-Le-Spring,
Tyne and Wear OH4 7LB; Tel 0191 553 3108
Service Manager (Children with Disabilities)   Steve Fletcher
Broadway Hse, Springwell Rd, Grindon, Sunderland,
Tyne and Wear;
E-mail child.disability@ssd.sunderland.gov.uk; Tel 0191
553 5800

CHILDREN'S SERVICES – DIRECT SERVICES – RESIDENTIAL ESTABLISHMENTS

Avenue Vivian Centre   98 Avenue Vivian, Fence Hses,
Houghton-Le-Spring, Tyne and Wear DH4 6HZ; Tel 0191
382 3049
(5)

Columbo Road Centre   Hylton Castle, 7 Columbo Rd,
Sunderland, Tyne and Wear SR5 3SD; Tel 0191 553 5443
(8)

Cotswold Road Centre   59 Cotswold Rd, Hylton Castle,
Sunderland, Tyne and Wear SR5 3NE; Tel 0191 553 5441

Monument View Centre   Station Rd, Houghton-Le-Spring,
Tyne and Wear DH4 7LB; Tel 0191 382 3057

Revelstoke Road Centre   18 Revelstoke Rd, Red House Est,
Sunderland, Tyne and Wear SR5 5EP; Tel 0191 553 5435
(7)

Wellesley Centre   Links Rd, Blyth, Northumberland
NE24 3PF; Tel 01670 352773
(28)

SERVICES FOR LOOKED AFTER CHILDREN

Penshaw House   Station Rd, Penshaw, Tyne and Wear;
Tel 0191 382 3105/6
Team Manager (Placements)   Margaret Stafford

Adults' Services

Divisional Manager (Adult Care Direct Services)
L. Pickering
Leechmere Centre, Leechmere Ind Est, Sunderland, Tyne
and Wear SR2 9TQ; Tel 0191 553 6274
Divisional Manager   N. Taylor
Dock St, Tyne and Wear; Tel 0191 566 2000
Divisional Manager   J. Usher
Houghton Area Office, The Broadway, Houghton-Le-
Spring, Tyne and Wear DH4 4BB; Tel 0191 553 6420
Divisional Manager (Joint Equipment Loans Store)
I. Murton
Leechmore Ind Est, Leechmore, Sunderland, Tyne and
Wear SR2 9TQ; Tel 0191 521 9730
General Manager (Mental Health)   Gail Price
15–16 John St, Sunderland, Tyne and Wear SR1 1HT;
Tel 0191 553 8600

DIRECT SERVICES ADULT CARE

Bishopwearmouth Horticultural Nursery   Chester Rd, High
Barnes, Sunderland, Tyne and Wear SR4 7RF; Tel 0191 553
2811
Manager   John Grabham

Fulwell Day Centre   Fulwell Rd, Sunderland, Tyne and
Wear SR6 9QW;
E-mail fulwell.daycentre@ssd.sunderland.gov.uk; Tel 0191
553 2255
Manager   Vacancy
MH (135)

Nookside Day Centre   Nookside, Grindon, Sunderland,
Tyne and Wear SR4 8TQ;
E-mail nookside.daycentre@ssd.sunderland.gov.uk;
Tel 0191 553 5916
Contact   J. Walls

Sunderland People First   30 Roker Pk Rd, Roker,
Sunderland, Tyne and Wear; Tel 0191 549 8168

Washington Multipurpose Centre   Ayton Rd, Crowther Ind
Est, Washington, Tyne and Wear NE38 0AB; Tel 0191 553
3530
Contact   B.J. Mitchinson
(120)

Workline   Leechmore Training Centre, Carrmere Rd,
Leechmere Ind Est, Sunderland, Tyne and Wear; Tel 0191
553 6268

RESIDENTIAL SERVICES FOR ADULTS

Anthony Road Home   8 Anthony Rd, Farthingdon,
Sunderland, Tyne and Wear SR3 3HG; Tel 0191 553 5780

Aston Square Home   9 Aston Sq, Farringdon, Sunderland,
Tyne and Wear SR3 3HQ; Tel 0191 553 5950
Manager   C. McCaffery

Belford Road Home   Belford Rd, Ashbrooke, Sunderland,
Tyne and Wear SR22 7TJ; Tel 0191 553 2298

Blackwood Road Home   Down End Farm, Sunderland, Tyne
and Wear SR25 4PG; Tel 0191 553 6979

Castlereagh Residential Service 40 Castlereagh, Silksworth, Sunderland, Tyne and Wear SR3 1HL; Tel 0191 523 8571

Clarendon Square Residential Service 4 Clarendon Sq, Carley Hill, Sunderland, Tyne and Wear SR2 2NW; Tel 0191 548 9072

Coach Road Residential Services 131 Coach Rd, Usworth, Washington, Tyne and Wear NE37 2EN; Tel 0191 219 3634

Godfrey Road Home 12 Godfrey Rd, Grindon, Sunderland, Tyne and Wear SR4 9PU; Tel 0191 534 8850

Goodwood Road Residential Services 17 Goodwood Rd, Grindon, Sunderland, Tyne and Wear SR4 9QA; Tel 0191 553 6829

The Nook Lodge Nookside, Grindon, Sunderland, Tyne and Wear SR4 8PQ; Tel 0191 525 0279

Striding Edge Residential Services 137 Striding Edge, Blackfell, Washington, Tyne and Wear NE37 1HL

Swaledale Crescent Home 2–4 Swaledale Cres, Penshaw, Houghton-Le-Spring, Tyne and Wear DH4 7NT; Tel 0191 382 3015

Thrunton Court Residential Service 9 Thrunton Crt, Racecourse Est, Houghton-Le-Spring, Tyne and Wear DH5 8ET; Tel 0191 584 0723

Tilbury Road Residential Services 52 Tilbury Rd, Thorney Cl, Sunderland, Tyne and Wear SR3 4JT

Tilbury Road Home 72 Tilbury Rd, Thorney Cl, Sunderland, Tyne and Wear SR3 4LY; Tel 0191 553 4121

Trool Court Home 10 Trool Crt, Oxford Pk, Sunderland, Tyne and Wear S43 2LQ; Tel 0191 553 4114

Villette Lodge 1 Edith St, Hendon, Sunderland, Tyne and Wear SR2 8JS; Tel 0191 553 2165
Contact J. Stoves

SHORT BREAK SERVICES

The Close Rock Lodge Rd, Roker, Sunderland, Tyne and Wear SR6 9WH; Tel 0191 553 5425
Contact C. Norman

Doric View Station Rd, Penshaw, Houghton-Le-Spring, Tyne and Wear DH4 7LB; Tel 0191 382 3063
Contact J. Wright

ADULT CARE – DIRECT SERVICES – RESIDENTIAL SERVICES

Brunswick Road/Bodmin Square 3–15 Brunswick Rd, Town End Farm, Sunderland, Tyne and Wear SR5 4JJ; Tel 0191 553 6982

Cresswell Terrace Sunderland, Tyne and Wear SR2 7ER; Tel 0191 567 6517

Hillcrest Rehabilitation Unit 1 Elms West, Ashbrooke, Sunderland, Tyne and Wear SR2 7BY; Tel 0191 567 3118
Contact S. Miller

17 Longfellow Street Houghton-le-Spring, Tyne and Wear DH5 8LS; Tel 0191 584 7824

24 Rennie Road Red Hse, Sunderland, Tyne and Wear SR5 5EJ; Tel 0191 553 5437

ADULT CARE – DIRECT CARE – MENTAL HEALTH DAY CENTRES

Glebe Day Care Service Glebe Day Centre, Glebe Village, Washington, Tyne and Wear NE38 7PX; Tel 0191 219 3636
Contact P. Mitchison

Hetton Day Care Service Bog Row, The Quay, Hetton-le-Hole, Tyne and Wear DH5 9JN; Tel 0191 553 6647

HOMES FOR OLDER PEOPLE

There are six homes for older people.

Education

PO Box 101, Civic Centre, Sunderland, Tyne and Wear SR2 7DN; Tel 0191 553 1000; Fax 0191 553 1359
Director (Education) Barbara Comiskey, PhD, PGCE, BA
Head (Access and SEN) M.J. Craddock, MA, BPhil
Head (Quality and Development) T.H. Walsh, BA
Head (Strategy and Performance) D. Staples
Manager (Direct Education) P. Glass

EDUCATIONAL PSYCHOLOGY SERVICE

Educational Psychology Service Broadway Centre, Springwell Rd, Sunderland, Tyne and Wear SR4 8NW; Tel 0191 553 5695; Fax 0191 553 5716

Learning Support Service Stannington Gr, Sunderland, Tyne and Wear SR2 9JT; Tel 0191 553 2230; Fax 0191 553 2246

SPECIAL DAY SCHOOLS

Barbara Priestman School Meadowside, Sunderland, Tyne and Wear SR2 7QN; Tel 0191 553 6000; Fax 0191 553 6004
Headteacher W.F. Hitchcock, MA, BEd

Davenport School Old Durham Rd, Houghton-Le-Spring, Tyne and Wear DH5 8NF; Tel 0191 553 6572; Fax 0191 553 6575
Headteacher Mrs K. Elliott

Felstead School Fordfield Rd (North Side), Sunderland, Tyne and Wear SR4 0DA; Tel 0191 553 7635; Fax 0191 553 7640
Headteacher I. Reed, BEd

Hylton Castle Site Cheadle Rd, Sunderland, Tyne and Wear SR5 3NQ

Maplewood School Redcar Rd, Sunderland, Tyne and Wear SR5 5PA; Tel 0191 553 5587; Fax 0191 553 5585
Headteacher Mrs J. Wilson, MEd, BEd, DAES

Portland School Weymouth Rd, Chapelgarth, Sunderland, Tyne and Wear SR3 2NQ; Tel 0191 553 6050; Fax 0191 553 6048
Headteacher Mrs J.A. Chart, BPhil

Springwell Dene School Portland Rd, Sunderland, Tyne and Wear SR3 1SS; Tel 0191 553 6067; Fax 0191 528 2295
Headteacher Mrs M.D. Mitchell

Sunningdale School Shaftoe Rd, Sunderland, Tyne and Wear SR3 4HA; Tel 0191 553 5880; Fax 0191 553 5882
Headteacher J.F. McKnight, MEd, BEd

Wellbank School Wellbank Rd, Washington, Tyne and Wear NE37 1NL; Tel 0191 219 3860; Fax 0191 219 3861
Headteacher Mrs J.E. MacLeod

SPECIAL UNITS

Eastfield Unit Unit 3–4 Pallion West Ind Est, Sunderland, Tyne and Wear SR2 6ST; Tel 0191 553 2856
Head of Unit C.E. Bentley, BEd

Stannington Unit Stannington Gr, Sunderland, Tyne and Wear SR2 9JT; Tel 0191 553 2230
Head of Unit M. Stansfield, DAES

6

SURREY COUNTY COUNCIL
www.surreycc.gov.uk

Population 1 078 100
Political Composition: Con: 51, LD: 13, Lab: 6, Ind: 6
County Hall, Penrhyn Rd, Kingston upon Thames, Surrey KT1 2DN; URL www.surreycc.gov.uk; E-mail contact.centre@surreycc.gov.uk; Tel (Contact Centre) 08456 009 009; Minicom 020 8541 8914; Fax 020 8541 9004

Chair of the Council Brian Coffin
Chief Executive Paul Coen
Head (Legal Services and County Solicitor) Ann Charlton
Executive Director (Performance and Resources) Mike Taylor

Social Services Department

AC Crt, High St, Thames Ditton, Surrey KT7 0QA;
Tel (Emergency Response Team) 01483 563317; 020 8541
8527; Fax (Emergency Response Team) 01483 563349; 020
8541 8740
Director (Social Services) Sue Fiennes (Acting)
Head (Commissioning) Sue Chilton
Head (Local Services and Community Care) Vacancy
Head (Resources) Alan Rhodes
Head (Children's Services) Felicity Budgen
(based at Woking); Tel 01483 728022
Head (Adult Services) Roger Deacon
(based at Guildford); Tel 01483 484900
Head (Inspection and Registration) Heather Wing
(based at Guildford); Tel 01483 579808
Professional Officer (Director and Members) Anna Coss
Professional Officer (Director and Members) Graham Lindsay
Strategic Commissioning Manager (Older People)
Christina Sell
Strategic Commissioning Manager (Learning Disabilities)
Derek Oliver
Strategic Commissioning Manager (Mental Health) Liz Parkes
*Strategic Commissioning Manager (Physical and Sensory
Disabilities)* Julia Penfound
Strategic Commissioning Manager (Contracting) Graeme Plank
Strategic Commissioning Manager (Children) Judy Wright
Strategic Commissioning Manager (Children with Disabilities)
Phil Osborne
Manager (Quality Audit) Dave Wellbelove
Departmental Complaints Officer Elaine Goodier
Manager (Information and Communication) Liz Woods
Manager (Planning and Performance Review) Tim Quelch
Manager (Finance) Nick Gray
Manager (Human Resources) Charmian Robinson
Manager (Information) Wilmett Ovenstone
Manager (Support Services) Alison Braithwaite
Manager (Property) Rob Thorpe
Manager (SSID Information Development) Gary Creighton

Social Services Committee

Con: 11, LD: 4, Lab: 1, Ind/RA: 1, Ex Officios: 4
Chair Kay Hammond (Con)
18 Birchwood Cl, Horley, Surrey RH6 9TX
Vice-Chair Ken Pugh (Con)
27 Broomfield, Sunbury-on-Thames, Surrey TW16 6SN;
Tel 01483 770094
Members of the Committee
Con: Diana Bowes, J.G. Carruthers, Elizabeth Compton,
K. Hammond, K. Hartley, M.A. Klat, Peter Langham,
Edwyn Pelly, K.P.Pugh, Elise Whiteley.
LD: Margaret Hill, Penelope Horsfall JP, Mary Laker,
Maggie Martin.
Lab: Mark Hayhurst.
Ind/RA: Joan Haward.

ADULT SERVICES MANAGEMENT TEAM

Andrew's Hse, College Rd, Guildford, Surrey GU1 4RG;
Tel 01483 484900; Fax 01483 484929
Head (Adult Services) Roger Deacon
Adult Services Manager (Residential Care Older People)
Maureen Eales
*Adult Services Manager (Physical Sensory and Learning
Disabilities)* Nicholas Grealy
*Adult Services Project Manager (Learning Disabilities Day
Services)* Paul Leyland
Adult Services Manager (Domiciliary Care) Brenda Metcalfe
Adult Services Manager (Mental Health) Dave Sargeant
Manager (Support Services) David Watkins

CHILDREN'S SERVICES MANAGEMENT TEAM

Beaufort Hse, Mayford Grn, Woking, Surrey GU22 0PG;
Tel 01483 728022; Fax 01483 776326
Head (Children's Services) Felicity Budgen
Head (Early Years and Child Care Services) Sue Berelowitz
Children's Services Manager (Local Family Support)
Ruth Everley
Children's Services Manager (Local Family Support)
Lorna Scarlett
*Children's Services Manager (Child Protection and Independent
Review)* Simon Slater
Children's Services Manager (Specialist Services) Sally Farmer
Children's Services Manager (Placements and Resources)
Janet Forster
Project Manager (Education and Social Services Joint Strategy)
Nick Press
Manager (Support Services) Pamela Hart

LOCAL SERVICES AND COMMUNITY CARE
MANAGEMENT TEAMS

AC Crt, High St, Thames Ditton, Surrey KT7 0QA; Tel 020
8541 8530
Head (Local Services and Community Care) Vacancy
Manager (East – Local Services and Community Care)
Alan Warren
Manager (Specialist – Local Services and Community Care)
Daphne McEleny
Manager (West – Local Services and Community Care)
Pam Marsden
*Manager (Learning Disability – Local Services and Community
Care)* Yvonne Waltham
Manager (Support Services) Kevin Balchin

SOCIAL SERVICES CENTRES (FAMILY SUPPORT AND
COMMUNITY CARE)

Elmbridge

Manager (Community Care Team) Alison McLean (Based at
Molesey)
Team Manager (Family Support) Ros Morris (Based at
Walton)

MOLESEY SOCIAL SERVICES CENTRE

(Community Care only)
319b Walton Rd, West Molesey, Surrey KT8 2QG; Tel 020
8979 7515; Fax 020 8979 8415

WALTON AND WEYBRIDGE SOCIAL SERVICES CENTRE

Family Support only
185 Sidney Rd, Walton-on-Thames, Surrey KT12 3SD;
Tel 01932 253033; Fax 01932 228137

Epsom and Ewell

Manager (Family Support Team) Neil Kornfein
Manager (Community Care Team) Doug Ettridge

EPSOM AND EWELL SOCIAL SERVICES CENTRE

Town Hall, The Parade, Epsom, Surrey KT18 5BX; Tel 01372
740631; Fax 01372 720512

Guildford

Team Manager (Family Support Team) Neal Hester (Based at
Guildford)
Manager (Community Care Team) Colin Rowett (Based at
Guildford)

ASH SOCIAL SERVICES CENTRE

Community Care only
Ash St, Ash, Surrey GU12 6LF; Tel 01252 319288; Fax 01252
318532

GUILDFORD SOCIAL SERVICES CENTRE
41 Epsom Rd, Guildford, Surrey GU1 3LA; Tel 01483
579898; Fax 01483 450190

Mole Valley
Manager (Community Care Team)   Libby Ramsay (Based at
Dorking)
Manager (Family Support Team)   Peter Davison (Based at
Leatherhead)

DORKING SOCIAL SERVICES CENTRE
Pippbrook Hse, Reigate Rd, Dorking, Surrey RH4 1SH;
Tel 01306 888033; Fax 01306 742536

Reigate and Banstead
Manager (Family Support Team)   Sue Herbert (Based at
Redhill and Reigate)
Manager (Community Care Team)   Vacancy (Based at
Banstead)

BANSTEAD SOCIAL SERVICES CENTRE
Community Care only
The Squirrels, The Horseshoe, Banstead, Surrey SM7 2BQ;
Tel 01737 362597; Fax 01737 371809

HORLEY SOCIAL SERVICES CENTRE
Community Care only
Victoria Rd, Horley, Surrey RH6 7AB; Tel 01293 773687;
Fax 01293 822117

REDHILL AND REIGATE SOCIAL SERVICES CENTRE
Family Support only
Noke Dr, Redhill, Surrey RH1 4AX; Tel 01737 778675;
Fax 01737 778676

Runnymede
Manager (Family Support Team)   Pat Stubbs (Based at
Chertsey)
Manager (Community Care Team)   Helen Hutchings (Based
at Chertsey)

CHERTSEY AND ADDLESTONE SOCIAL SERVICES CENTRE
Heritage Hse, 93 Eastworth Rd, Chertsey, Surrey KT16 8DY;
Tel 01932 884610; Fax 01932 884671

EGHAM SOCIAL SERVICES CENTRE
Crown Hse, 137–139 High St, Egham, Surrey TW20 9HL;
Tel 01784 439565; Fax 01784 430724

Spelthorne
Manager (Family Support Team)   Sally Woodhead (Based at
Ashford)
Manager (Community Care Team)   Bob Moore (Based at
Staines)

ASHFORD SOCIAL SERVICES CENTRE
Family Support only
108 Vicarage Rd, Sunbury on Thames, Greater London
TW16 7QX; Tel 01784 765990; Fax 01784 780548

STAINES AND STANWELL SOCIAL SERVICES CENTRE
Community Care only
Burges Way, Knowle Grn, Staines, Greater London
TW18 1XD; Tel 01784 466280; Fax 01784 449306

Surrey Heath
Manager (Family Support Team)   Rosemary Horbury
Manager (Community Care Team)   Paula Uden
Manager (Family Support Team)   Julia Slater

CAMBERLEY AND FRIMLEY SOCIAL SERVICES CENTRE
157 Frimley Rd, Camberley, Surrey GU15 2PZ; Tel 01276
682716; Fax 01276 677565

Tandridge
Manager (Community Care Team)   Helen Oldman (Based at
Oxted)
Manager (Family Support Team)   Peter Richards (Based at
Caterham)

CATERHAM SOCIAL SERVICES CENTRE
Family Support only
129 Farningham Rd, Caterham, Surrey CR3 6LN; Tel 01883
347551; Fax 01883 348922

OXTED SOCIAL SERVICES CENTRE
Community Care only
14 Gresham Rd, Oxted, Surrey RH8 0BQ; Tel 01883 717311;
Fax 01883 730178

Waverley
Manager (Family Support Team)   Allan Rose (Based at
Farnham)
Manager (Community Care Team)   Pam Henderson (Based at
Godalming)

CRANLEIGH SOCIAL SERVICES CENTRE
Community Care only
Bloggs Way, off High St, Cranleigh, Surrey GU6 8AW;
Tel 01483 275376; Fax 01483 272594

FARNHAM SOCIAL SERVICES CENTRE
Family Support only
Suite B Gostrey Hse, Union Rd, Farnham, Surrey GU9 7QJ;
Tel 01252 733848; Fax 01252 713861

GODALMING SOCIAL SERVICES CENTRE
Community Care only
Bridge St (above the Library), Godalming, Surrey
GU7 1LA; Tel 01483 414131; Fax 01483 429716

HASLEMERE SOCIAL SERVICES CENTRE
Community Care only
Beech Rd, Haslemere, Surrey GU27 2RH; Tel 01428 661856;
Fax 01428 656046

Woking
Manager (Family Support Team)   Liz Crocker
Manager (Community Care Team)   Gary Bowman

WOKING SOCIAL SERVICES CENTRE
Trizancia Hse, 74 Chertsey Rd, Woking, Surrey GU21 5BJ;
Tel 01483 730461; Fax 01483 764411

Health-based Social Services Teams

Ashford and St Peters Hospitals
Manager (Community Care Team – Health)   Paul Greene
Incorporates Walton, Woking and Weybridge Hospitals
Social Services Department Ashford Hospital, London Rd,
Ashford, Greater London TW15 3AA; Tel 01784 884251;
Fax 01784 884293

Social Services Department St. Peter's Hospital, Guildford Rd, Chertsey, Surrey KT16 0QA; Tel 01932 722526; Fax 01932 722587

East Surrey Hospital Social Services Team, Canada Ave, Redhill, Surrey RH1 5RH; Tel 01737 231802; Fax 01737 231637s
Manager (Community Care Team – Health) Liz Uliasz
Incorporates: Caterham Dene, Dorking, Harrowlands Neuro Rehab and Oxted hospitals.

Epsom General Hospital Social Service Department, Dorking Rd, Epsom, Surrey KT18 7EG; Tel 01372 735297; 01372 735298; Fax 01372 735256
Manager (Community Care Team – Health) Colin McKinlay
Incorporates: Cobham Cottage, New Epsom and Ewell Cottage, Leatherhead, Molesey and West Park hospitals.

Frimley Park Hospital Social Service Department, Portsmouth Rd, Frimley, Surrey GU16 5UJ; Tel 01276 604604; Fax 01276 62824
Manager (Community Care Team – Health)
Geraldine Deith
Incorporates: Farnham Hospital.

Royal Surrey County Hospital Egerton Rd, Park Barn, Guildford, Surrey GU2 5XX; Tel 01483 464008; Fax 01483 451913
Manager (Community Care Team – Health) Griff Jones

Children's Services

CHILDREN WITH DISABILITIES TEAM (EAST)

5 Linkfield La, Redhill, Surrey RH1 1SX; Tel 01737 789094; Fax 01737 789095
Team Manager Jacqui Lendrim (Based at Reigate)

CHILDREN WITH DISABILITIES TEAM (WEST)

Team Manager Hazel Denman (Based at Ash)
Social Services Centre Ash St, Ash, Surrey GU12 6LF; Tel 01252 319288; Fax 01252 318532
Heritage House 93 Eastworth Rd, Chertsey, Surrey KT16 8DY; Tel 01932 844661; Fax 01932 884673

YOUTH OFFENDING TEAM (EAST SURREY)

The Mansion, Church St, Leatherhead, Surrey KT22 8LL; Tel 01372 363655
Team Manager Toby Wells
(based at Woking),

YOUTH OFFENDING TEAM (WEST SURREY)

Churchill Hse, Mayford Grn, Woking, Surrey GU22 0PW; Tel 01483 723922; Fax 01483 771786

FAMILY PLACEMENT SERVICES

Family Finding Team Runnymede Centre, Chertsey Rd, Addlestone, Surrey KT15 2EP; Tel 01932 565999; Fax 01932 565878
Team Manager Linda King
Family Placement Team Beaufort Hse, Mayford Grn, Woking, Surrey GU22 0PG; Tel 01483 728022
Manager (Family Placement Services) Sheila Smith
Fostering Team (West) Heritage Hse, 93 Eastworth Rd, Chertsey, Surrey KT16 9DY
Team Manager Alison Benjamin; Tel 01932 794444
Fostering Team (East) Children's Services, Fostering Team East, South East Area Office, Omnibus, Lesbourne Rd, Reigate, Surrey RH2 7JA; Tel 01737 737867
Team Manager Cea Francis,
Permanency Team Belair Hse, Chertsey Blvd, Hanworth La, Chertsey, Surrey KT16 9JX; Tel 01932 566272; Fax 01932 565878
Team Manager Mary Davidson

FAMILY CENTRES

North Surrey Family Centre Stanwell Rd, Ashford, Greater London TW15 3DU; Tel 01784 241556; Fax 01784 241560
Service Manager Angela Louis (Based at Ashford)
Mid Surrey Family Centre
Service Manager Molly Ward
St. Faith's Family Centre Cleeve Rd, Leatherhead, Surrey KT22 7NF; Tel 01372 363190
East Surrey Family Centre
Service Manager Jim Horn
The Bridge Family Centre 132–138 Station Rd, Redhill, Surrey RH1 1ET; Tel 01737 762661
West Surrey Family Centre
Service Manager Vacancy
Shaw Family Centre Chobham Rd, Woking, Surrey GU21 4AS; Tel 01483 761195; Fax 01483 715026
South West Surrey Family Centre
Service Manager Vacancy (based at Farnham)

COMMUNITY HOMES

Burbank Community Home Wych Hill, St. John's, Woking, Surrey GU22 0EX; Tel 01483 724837
Team Manager Sharon Newton
Faircroft Community Home 73 Between Streets, Cobham, Surrey KT11 1AA; Tel 01932 866566; 01932 866567
Team Manager Terry Brooks
Highfield Community Home Cheyne Wlk, Horley, Surrey RH6 7ND; Tel 01293 412002
Team Manager Gordon Chinchen
Karibu Community Home Mayford Grn, Woking, Surrey GU22 0PG; Tel 01483 730729
Team Manager Carol Cammiss
Libertas Community Home 84 Epsom Rd, Guildford, Surrey GU1 2BX; Tel 01483 766059
Team Manager Darryl Freeman
Meadowview Community Home Mayford Grn, Woking, Surrey GU22 0PG; Tel 01483 764399
Team Manager Amanda Carpenter

COMMUNITY HOMES FOR CHILDREN WITH DISABILITIES

Squirrel Lodge Children's Community Home 47 Mount Hermon Rd, Woking, Surrey GU22 7UN; Tel 01483 760515
Team Manager Amanda Harvey
Wells House Children's Community Home Spa Dr, Epsom, Surrey KT18 7LR; Tel 01372 720839
Team Manager Frances Corbishley

RESETTLEMENT TEAM

23 Mallow Cres, Burpham, Guildford, Surrey GU4 7BU; Tel 01483 454311; Fax 01483 561396
County Resettlement Co-ordinator Kieth Sparks

Adult Services

COMMUNITY TEAMS FOR PEOPLE WITH LEARNING DISABILITIES

The abbreviation CTPLD is used in the following section for Community Teams People with Learning Difficulties
Dorking CTPLD The Comfrey Centre, Clarendon Hse, Dorking, Surrey RH4 1UJ; Tel 01306 502401
Redhill and Reigate CTPLD Kingsfield Centre, Philanthrope Rd, Redhill, Surrey RH1 4DP; Tel 01737 382387
Team Manager Vivienne Gilby
Tanbridge CTPLD Brackets Resource Centre, 116 Station Road East, Oxted, Surrey RH8 0QA; Tel 01883 382387
Team Manager Dennis Ellis

Mid-Surrey CTPLD Old Town Hall, The Parade, Epsom, Surrey KT18 5EY; Tel 01372 204090
Team Manager Vacancy

West Surrey CTPLD Heritage Hse, 93 Eastworth Rd, Chertsey, Surrey KT6 8DY; Tel 01932 564445

Spelthorne CTPLD Fairmead, 1a Worple Rd, Staines, Greater London; Tel 01784 465128

RESIDENTIAL ESTABLISHMENTS FOR PEOPLE WITH LEARNING DISABILITIES

Arundel Hostel 34 Garratts La, Banstead, Surrey SM7 2EB; Tel 01737 361076
Team Manager Corin Brown

Badgers Wood Slade Rd, Ottershaw, Surrey KT16 0JN; Tel 01932 872593
Team Manager Keely Glithero

Coveham Home Anyards Rd, Cobham, Surrey KT11 2LJ; Tel 01932 864115
Team Manager Michael Rogan

Hillside Home Portesbury Rd, Camberley, Surrey GU15 3SZ; Tel 01276 27720
Team Manager Marylin Woolger

Langdown Home Off Yeend Cl, High St, West Molesey, Surrey KT8 2NA; Tel 020 8979 4561
Team Manager Carole Gardner

Rodney House Rodney Rd, Walton-on-Thames, Surrey KT12 3LE; Tel 01932 241219
Team Manager Sally Reardon

Mallow Crescent Home 29 Mallow Crescent, Guildford, Surrey GU4 7BU; Tel 01483 455879
Team Manager Mary Mahoney

DAY SERVICES

Service Manager Colin Lineham (Based at Colebrook)

Bentley Day Service The Horseshoe, Bolters La, Banstead, Surrey SM7 2BG; Tel 01737 357901
Team Manager Kris Meyers

The Bridge Clare Cres, Leatherhead, Surrey KT22 7RB
Team Manager Alastair Jack (Based at Bentley)

Colebrook Greensand Rd, off Noke Dr, Redhill, Surrey RH1 1PT; Tel 01737 769231
Team Manager Martin Weston (Acting)

Cranstock Hermitage Rd, St. John's, Woking, Surrey GU11 1UA; Tel 01483 769676
Team Manager Mary Hendrick

Fairways Knowle Grn, Staines, Greater London TW18 1AJ; Tel 01784 450211
Team Manager Carol Newnham

Fernleigh Hersham Rd, Walton-on-Thames, Surrey KT12 1RZ; Tel 01932 241335
Team Manager Carol Daines

The Harbour Oxted Grn, Milford, Guildford, Surrey GU8 5DG; Tel 01483 415393
Team Manager Gerald Picozzi

Lockwood 9–13 Westfield Rd, Slyfield Ind Est, Slyfield Grn, Guildford, Surrey GU1 1RR; Tel 01483 532502
Team Manager Vacancy

Physical and Sensory Disability Services

DAY CENTRES

Service Manager (Physical and Sensory Disabilities) Hilary Thomas
Rentwood Resource Centre, School La, Fetcham, Leatherhead, Surrey KT22 9JX; Tel 01372 360614

Frenches Lodge Centre 171 Frenches Rd, Redhill, Surrey RH1 2HZ; Tel 01737 761024
Assistant Team Manager Pat Donachie

Nexus Day Centre Green St, Sunbury on Thames, Greater London TW16 7QB; Tel 01932 785962
Assistant Team Manager Tony Scott

Rentwood Day Centre School La, Fetcham, Leatherhead, Surrey KT22 9JX; Tel 01372 378269
Assistant Team Manager Jackie Steele

St. Peters Day Centre Old School Pl, Westfield, Woking, Surrey GU22 9LY; Tel 01483 768814
Team Manager Chris Hadfield

Deaf Services Rentwood Resource Centre, School La, Leatherhead, Surrey KT22 9JX; Tel 01372 376558
Service Manager Vacancy

Surrey Voluntary Association for the Blind Rentwood Resource Centre, School La, Leatherhead, Surrey KT22 9JX; Tel 01372 377701
Chief Executive Lance Clarke

RESIDENTIAL HOME FOR PEOPLE WITH PHYSICAL DISABILITIES

The Summers Residential Home High St, West Molesey, Surrey KT8 0NA; Tel 020 8979 4689
Team Manager Liz Paoli

MENTAL HEALTH SERVICES

East Surrey Mental Health Service Area Kingsburgh, 5 Linkfield La, Redhill, Surrey RH1 1SX; Tel 01737 766578; Fax 01737 789021
Area Manager Sarah Cook
Area Manager Betty Loveland

Mid Surrey Mental Health Service Area The Brickfield Centre, Portland Pl, Epsom, Surrey KT17 1DL; Tel 01372 749916; Fax 01372 724767
Area Manager Sarah Cook
Area Manager Betty Loveland

North Surrey Mental Health Service Area Bridgewell Hse, 29 Claremont Ave, Woking, Surrey GU22 7SF; Tel 01932 850970; Fax 01932 851983
Area Manager Donal Hegarty

West Surrey Mental Health Service Area 14 Jenner Rd, Guildford, Surrey GU1 3PL; Tel 01483 453283; Fax 01483 451236
Area Manager Eric McMaster

RESIDENTIAL CARE FOR OLDER PEOPLE

Manager (Adult Services) Maureen Eales
There are 16 local authority residential homes.

DOMICILIARY CARE SERVICES

East Alma Hse, Alma Rd, Reigate, Surrey RH2 0AZ; Tel 01737 246240
Service Manager Therese Ross

West Alexander Hse, 55a–61a Commercial Way, Woking, Surrey GU21 1HN; Tel 01483 768903
Service Manager Di Stevens

INSPECTION AND REGISTRATION

Astolat, Coniers Way, Guildford, Surrey GU4 7HL; Tel 01483 579808; Fax 01483 536150
Head (Inspection and Registration) Heather Wing
Principal Inspection and Registration Officer Sue O'Leary

GUARDIAN AD LITEM AND REPORTING OFFICERS

Astolat, Coniers Way, Guildford, Surrey GU4 7HL; Tel 01483 455268; Fax 01483 574528
Panel Manager Tess Duncan (Based at Guildford)

COMMISSION FOR SERVICE USERS AND CARERS (SURREY)

Astolat, Coniers Way, Burpham, Guildford, Surrey GU4 7HL
Contact Peter Bolt (based at Guildford); Tel 01483 531308; Fax 01483 301072

6

Education Department

County Hall, Kingston upon Thames, Surrey KT1 2DJ;
URL www.surreycc.gov.uk/education; Tel 020 8541
8800; Fax 020 8541 9503
Director (Education) Dr Paul Gray
Deputy Director (Education) and Head (School's Branch)
Steve Clarke
Head (Quality and Performance) Frank Offer (Acting)
Head (Education Children's Services) Ashley Ayre
Head (School Effectiveness) Judith Johnson
Head (Community Services) Kevin Crompton
Head (Student Support Service) David Line
Head (Psychology Service) Dr Roger Booker
Head (Education Welfare Service) Gail Calkley
Head (Financial Services) Alan Docksey
Head (Behaviour and Pupil Support Service) Pauline Bye
Head (Special Needs Administration) Sylvina Mellor
Head (Education Children's Services Development)
Paul Foster
Head (Planning and Development) Simon Shepard
Head (Governor Services) Jill Marsden
Head (Service Development) Frank Offer
Head (Strategic Planning) Clive Webster
Head (Business Process Review) Dave Hanly
Head (Curriculum and Management Consultancy) Viv King
Runnymede Centre, Chertsey Rd, Addlestone, Surrey
KT15 2EP; Tel 01932 569663
Head (Personnel Service) John White
Mid Surrey Area Office, Bay Tree Ave, Kingston Rd,
Leatherhead, Surrey KT22 7SY; Tel 020 8541 7800
Head (Technology Support for Learning) Tony Humphries
Glyn Hse, Church St, Ewell, Surrey KT17 2AR; Tel 020 8393
0208
Head (County Arts Unit) Keith Willis
County Music Centre, Westfield Primary School, Woking,
Surrey GU22 9PR; Tel 01483 728711
Head (Youth Strategy Development) Angela Palmer
Runnymede Centre, Chertsey Rd, Addlestone, Surrey
KT15 2EP; Tel 01932 570329
*County Co-ordinator (Inter-Cultural and English Language
Service)* Chris Rush
SW Local Education Office, Andrews Hse, College Rd,
Guildford, Surrey GU1 4QF; Tel 01483 455253
*Deputy County Co-ordinator and Head (English Language
Service)* Anthony Sanderson
Local Education Office, 123 Blackborough Rd, Reigate,
Surrey RH2 7DD; Tel 01737 272137
County Co-ordinator (Sensory Support Service – Hearing)
Pauline Hughes
The Lodge, Glyn Hse, Church St, Ewell, Surrey KT17 2AP;
Tel 020 8393 2872
Deputy County Co-ordinator (Sensory Support Service – Vision)
Eirwen Grinter
Junior Hse, 6 Gosden Hse, Bramley, Guildford, Surrey
GU5 0AD; Tel 01483 898822
*County Co-ordinator (The Portage Early Education Support
Service)* Sue Weston
Local Education Office, 123 Blackborough Rd, Reigate,
Surrey RH2 7DD; Tel 01737 272140
County Co-ordinator (Learning and Language Support Service)
John Belfield
Local Education Office, 123 Blackborough Rd, Reigate,
Surrey RH1 7DD; Tel 01737 272166
*Deputy County Co-ordinator (Learning and Language Support
Service)* Joan Robson
Bisley Centre, Guildford Rd, Woking, Surrey GU24 9EP;
Tel 01483 474893
*Local Education Officer (Elmbridge, Runnymede, Spelthorne,
Surrey Heath)* John Ambrose
Local Education Office, NW Alexander Hse, 35a–61a
Commercial Way, Woking, Surrey GU21 1HN; Tel 01483
744006
*Local Education Officer (Epsom and Ewell, Mole Valley, Reigate
and Banstead, Tandridge)* John Quigley
Local Education Office (SE) 123 Blackborough Rd, Reigate,
Surrey RH2 7DD; Tel 01737 272135

Local Education Officer (Guildford, Waverley, Woking)
Ian Skelton
Local Education Office (SW), Andrews Hse, College Rd,
Guildford, Surrey GU1 4QF; Tel 01483 484800
Officer (Strategic Partnership Development) David Hall

LEARNING DIFFICULTIES

Day Schools

The Abbey (Community) School Menin Way, Farnham,
Surrey GU9 8DY; Tel 01252 725059; Fax 01252 737300
Headteacher Ms A. Scott
8–16

Carwarden House (Community) School 118 Upper
Chobham Rd, Camberley, Surrey GU15 1EJ; Tel 01276
709080; Fax 01276 709081
Headteacher J.G. Cope
8–19

The Park (Community) School Onslow Cres, Woking,
Surrey GU22 7AT; Tel 01483 772057; Fax 01483 740976
Headteacher J.A Lonsdale
8–16

Philip Southcote (Community) School Addlestonemoor,
Addlestone, Surrey KT15 2QH; Tel 01932 562326; Fax 01932
567092
Headteacher G.L. Rogers
8–16

West Hill (Community) School Kingston Rd, Leatherhead,
Surrey KT22 7PW; Tel 01372 814714; Fax 01372 814710
Headteacher M. Goldie
8–16

Woodfield (Community) School Sunstone Gr, Merstham,
Redhill, Surrey RH1 3PR; Tel 01737 642623; Fax 01737
642775
Headteacher S.M. Plant
8–16

RESIDENTIAL SCHOOLS

With Day Places

Gosden House (Community) School Horsham Rd, Bramley,
Guildford, Surrey GU5 0AH; Tel 01483 892008; Fax 01483
894057
Headteacher J. David
5–16

St. Nicholas (Community) School Taynton Dr, Merstham,
Redhill, Surrey RH1 3PU; Tel 01737 215488; Fax 01737
646173
Headteacher J.D. Walker, MA
10–16

CHILDREN WITH SEVERE LEARNING DIFFICULTIES

Day Schools

Clifton Hill (Community) School Chaldon Rd, Caterham,
Surrey CR3 5PH; Tel 01883 347740; Fax 01883 349617
Headteacher M. Unsworth
9–19

Manor Mead (Community) School Laleham Rd,
Shepperton, Surrey TW17 8EL; Tel 01932 241834; Fax 01932
248927
Headteacher Mrs F. Neal
2–12

Pond Meadow (Community) School Pond Meadow, Park
Barn Est, Guildford, Surrey GU2 8YG; Tel 01483 532239;
Fax 01483 537049
Headteacher D.J. Monk
2–19

Portesbury (Community) School Portesbury Rd, Camberley,
Surrey GU15 3SZ; Tel 01276 63078; Fax 01276 29234
Headteacher J. Nuthall
2–19

The Ridgeway (Community) School 14 Frensham Rd, Farnham, Surrey GU9 8HB; Tel 01252 724562; Fax 01252 737247
Headteacher M.A. Hattey
2–19

Walton Leigh (Community) School Queen's Rd, Walton-on-Thames, Surrey KT12 5AB; Tel 01932 223243; Fax 01932 254320
Headteacher L. Curtis
11–19

Woodlands (Community) School Fortyfoot Rd, Leatherhead, Surrey KT22 8RY; Tel 01372 377922; Fax 01372 376434
Headteacher H.D.J. Taylor
2–19

HEARING IMPAIRED CHILDREN (DAY UNITS)

The Bishop David Brown (Community) School Albert Dr, Sheerwater, Woking, Surrey GU21 5RF; Tel 01932 349696; Fax 01932 349175
Headteacher D.M. Coppard

Epsom and Ewell High (Foundation) School Ruxley La, West Ewell, Epsom, Surrey KT19 9JW; Tel 020 8397 0671; Fax 020 8397 0724
Headteacher P. Hutchinson
11–18

CHILDREN WITH VISUAL IMPAIRMENT (DAY UNITS)

George Abbot (Community) School Woodruff Ave, Burpham, Guildford, Surrey GU1 1XX; Tel 01483 888000; Fax 01483 888001
Headteacher D.C. Moloney
11–18

Oxted (Community) School Bluehouse La, Oxted, Surrey RH8 0AB; Tel 01883 712425; Fax 01883 723973
Headteacher Mrs M. Hawley
11–18

CHILDREN WITH PHYSICAL DISABILITIES (DAY UNIT)

Kings College for the Arts and Technology Southway, Guildford, Surrey GU2 8DU; Tel 01483 458956; Fax 01483 458957
Headteacher D. Crossley
11–18

CHILDREN WITH LANGUAGE DIFFICULTIES (DAY UNITS)

Therfield (Community) School Dilston Rd, Leatherhead, Surrey; Tel 01372 818123; Fax 01372 818124
Headteacher G. Tuck
11–18

CHILDREN WITH EMOTIONAL AND LEARNING DIFFICULTIES (RESIDENTIAL SCHOOLS)

Limpsfield Grange (Community) School 89 Bluehouse La, Oxted, Surrey RH8 0RZ; Tel 01883 713928; Fax 01883 730578
Headteacher J.A. Humphreys
11–16

Sunnydown (Community) School Portley Hse, 152 Whyteleafe Rd, Caterham, Surrey CR3 5ED; Tel 01883 342281; 01883 346502; Fax 01883 341342
Headteacher T.M. Armstrong
11–16

PUPIL REFERRAL UNITS

North East Area Pupil Referral Unit
Hersham Teaching Centre 174 Molesey Rd, Hersham, Surrey KT12 4QY; Tel 01932 229369; Fax 01932 229369
Contact P. Dobbs
11–16

Sycamore Centre 14 West Hill, Epsom, Surrey KT19 8HR; Tel (admin Tue and Thur only) 01372 722939; Fax 01372 748713
Contact Mrs A. Homer
11–16

North West Area Pupil Referral Unit
Pyrford Centre Engliff La, Pyrford, Woking, Surrey GU22 8SU; Tel 01932 342451; Fax 01932 336517
Head of Centre E.M. Webb
4–16

Woking Pupil Referral Unit 45 Kingsway, Woking, Surrey GU22 7LK; Tel 01483 728474; Fax 01483 757410
Contact Mrs A. Goebel

The Camberley Centre Old Dean Youth Centre, Kingston Rd, Camberley, Surrey GU15 4AF; Tel 01276 66225
Contact A. Goebel

South East Area Pupil Referral Unit
South East Surrey Allingham Rd, South Pk, Reigate, Surrey RH2 8HU; Tel 01737 243806; Fax 01737 240322
Contact Mrs G. Allen
11–16

The Lodge Teaching Centre The Mansion, Church St, Leatherhead, Surrey KT22 8DP; Tel 01372 373311
Contact G. Allen

Sidlow Bridge Centre Ironsbottom La, Sidlow Bridge, Reigate, Surrey RH2 8PP; Tel 01737 249079; Fax 01737 226520
Contact Mrs H. Taylor
14–16

South West Area Pupil Referral Unit
Guildford Pupil Referral SW Surrey Staff Development Centre, Pewley Hill, Guildford, Surrey GU1 3SQ; Tel 01483 452352; Fax 01483 579275
Contact P. Morris

RESIDENTIAL SCHOOLS

Starhurst (Community) School Chart La South, Dorking, Surrey RH5 4DB; Tel 01306 883763; 01306 885951; Fax 01306 889819
Headteacher H.J. Kiernan
Some day places.
11–16

Thornchace (Community) School Grove Rd, Merrow, Guildford, Surrey GU1 2HL; Tel 01483 888690; Fax 01483 888691
Headteacher C.D. Lodge
Some day places.
11–16

Wishmore Cross (Community) School Alpha Rd, Chobham, Surrey GU24 8NE; Tel 01276 857555; Fax 01276 855420
Headteacher Ms A. Close
10–16

CHILDREN WITH EMOTIONAL AND COMMUNICATION DIFFICULTIES

Freemantles (Community) School Pyrcroft Rd, Chertsey, Surrey KT16 9ER; Tel 01932 563460; Fax 01932 569679
Headteacher R. Buchan
4–11

Linden Bridge (Community) School Grafton Rd, Worcester Pk, Surrey KT4 7JW; Tel 020 8330 3009; Fax 020 8330 6811
Headteacher R. Smith
5–17

Epsom and Ewell High School Ruxley La, West Ewell, Epsom, Surrey KT19 9JW; Tel 020 8397 0671; Fax 020 8397 0724
Headteacher P. Hutchinson

6

SWINDON BOROUGH COUNCIL
www.swindon.gov.uk

Population 182 600
Political Composition: Con: 29, Lab: 22, LD: 8
Civic Offices, Euclid St, Swindon SN1 2JH;
  URL www.swindon.gov.uk;
  E-mail swindon-council@swindon.gov.uk; Tel 01793
  463000; Fax 01793 463930
Chief Executive Simon Birch
Director (Finance) Paul Blacker (Acting)
Director (Swindon Services) John Short
Head (Information and Communications Technology) Mike Lay
Head (Policy and Performance) Cliff Garland
Director (Environment and Property) Graeme Bell (Acting)
Director (Housing) Bernie Brannan (Acting)
Director (Law and Corporate Governance) Stephen Taylor

Social Services

Civic Offices, Swindon SN1 2JH; Tel 01793 463000;
  Fax 01793 490420; Minicom 01793 436659
Director (Social Services) Keith Skerman
Assistant Director (Children and Family Services)
  Jean Polland; Tel 01793 463418
Assistant Director (Adult Services) Graham Pearson;
  Tel 01793 465852
Head (Support Services) Jerry Oliver; Tel 01793 463609
Manager (Adult Commissioning) Peter Starr; Tel 01793
  463973
Contracts Manager (Children and Family Services) Janet
  Janeway; Tel 01793 465854
Planning Officer (Children and Family Services) Sue Wald;
  Tel 01793 465847

EMERGENCY DUTY SERVICE (OUT OF HOURS)

Manager Tony Hoskin

TEAM FOR PEOPLE WITH LEARNING DISABILITIES

Clarence Hse, Civic Offices, Euclid St, Swindon SN1 2JH;
  Tel 01793 466900
Manager Larry Grady

TEAM FOR ADULTS WITH DISABILITIES

Civic Offices, Swindon SN1 2JH; Tel 01793 465856
Service Manager (Disabilities) John Hughes

HOME CARE TEAM

Civic Offices, Swindon SN1 2JH; Tel 01793 465820
Manager (Home Care Service) Jeanette Fisher

TEAM FOR ELDERLY PERSONS

Civic Offices, Swindon SN1 2JH; Tel 01793 465856
Service Manager (Elderly) John Hughes

Education Services

Sanford Hse, Sanford St, Swindon SN1 1QH;
  URL www.swindon.gov.uk;
  E-mail hpitts@swindon.gov.uk; Tel 01793 463068;
  Fax 01793 488597
Director (Education and Community) Hilary Pitts

SPECIAL SCHOOLS

Brimble Hill School Lyndhurst Cres, Park North, Swindon
SN3 2RW; E-mail head@brimblehill.swindon.sch.uk;
Tel 01793 617426
Headteacher Mr R.K. Walker

The Chalet School Queens Dr, Swindon SN3 1MR;
Tel 01793 534537; Fax 01793 435244
Headteacher Mrs M. Topping

Crowdys Hill School Jefferies Ave, Cricklade Rd, Swindon
SN2 6HJ; E-mail head@crowdyshill.swindon.sch.uk;
Tel 01793 332400; Fax 01793 331860
Headteacher Mr K. Smith

Nyland Special School Nyland Rd, Nythe, Swindon
SN3 3RR; E-mail head@nyland-pri.swindon.sch.uk;
Tel 01793 535023; Fax 01793 535023
Headteacher Mr P. Summers

St. Luke's School Cricklade Rd, Swindon SN2 5AH;
E-mail head@stlukes.swindon.sch.uk; Tel 01793 705566;
Fax 01793 705858
Headteacher Jinna Hale

Uplands School Leigh Rd, Penhill, Swindon SN2 5DE;
E-mail head@uplands.swindon.sch.uk; Tel 01793 724751;
Fax 01793 703396
Headteacher Mary Bishop

TAMESIDE METROPOLITAN BOROUGH COUNCIL
www.tameside.gov.uk

Population 250 000 (Approx)
Political Composition: Lab: 46, Con: 6, Ind: 3, LD: 2
Council Offices, Wellington Rd, Ashton-under-Lyne,
  Tameside OL6 6DL; URL www.tameside.gov.uk;
  E-mail general@mail-tameside.gov.uk; Tel 0161 342 8355;
  Fax 0161 342 3070
Mayor Cllr S. Poole
Mayor's Parlour, Council Offices, Ashton-under-Lyne,
  Tameside OL6 6DL
Chief Executive M.J. Greenwood
Strategic Director (Corporate Services) P. Dowthwaite
Strategic Director (Education and Cultural Services) P. Lawday
Strategic Director (Development and Technical) T. Gilbert
Strategic Director (Social Services) C. McKinless

Social Services Directorate

E-mail social.services@mail.tameside.gov.uk; Tel (Out-of-
  hours (all services)) 0161 342 2222; 0161 342 8355;
  Fax 0161 342 3793; Minicom 0161 342 3351
Strategic Director (Social Services) Colin McKinless
Head (Social Services – Children and Families) A. Dodd
Head (Social Services – Adults) S. Butterworth
Head (Social Services – Strategy, Planning and Performance)
  D. Jones
Housing-related provision
Homes for adults with learning disabilities (1); Homes for
children with learning disabilities (2); Homes for people
with physical disabilities (3); Children's residential
resource centres (3).
Staff Development and Training Unit
Responsible for training professional and support staff in
the department.
Denton Town Hall, Market Street, Denton, Tameside
  ME34 2AP; Tel 0161 342 3491; Fax 0161 342 3600
Training Manager K. Schofield

Children and Families Division

ASSESSMENT AND CARE MANAGEMENT UNIT

56 Warrington St, Ashton-under-Lyne, Tameside OL7 7JX;
  Tel 0161 342 4004; Fax 0161 342 4123; Minicom 0161 343
  5474
Unit Business Manager D. Crank

Referral and Information Team (Children Customer Services)
Team Manager Y. Starkey
Acts as the focal point for all enquiries and referrals concerning children and young people of any age.

Adoption and Permanency Team
Team Manager J. Carey
Specialises in planning for and meeting the needs of children who require to be cared for either permanently or on a long term basis outside of their natural families, through substitute care arrangements or by adoption.

Duty and Assessment Team
Team Manager Y. Starkey
Team Manager K. Scragg
The Duty and Assessment Team responds to referrals, working on a multi-agency basis to secure services for children to promote their welfare and development. When protective action is indicated, the team takes required steps with agreed timescales.

Assessment and Care Managment Team
Team Manager P. Ratican
Team Manager G. Bold
Offer a care co-ordination service to children needing longer term involvement from the department.

Family First Team Newton Family Centre, Victoria St, Newton, Hyde, Tameside SK14 4AA; Tel 0161 368 3192; Fax 0161 368 3215
Team Manager J. Whiteside
Aims to assist parents and young people of secondary school age who are presenting care and control difficulties.

QUALITY ASSURANCE UNIT (CONFERENCE AND REVIEW)

Union St, Hyde, Tameside SK14 1ND; Tel 0161 342 4343; Fax 0161 368 8612
Unit Business Manager A. Stott (Acting)
Undertakes Child Protection Conferences and Looked After Children Reviews. It also holds the Child Protection Register. The Register is available at the above address during office hours and with the Out Of Hours Team at all other times.
Information available: The Child Protection Conference, a guide for children and young people; The Child Protection Conference, a guide for parents; The Child Protection Conference, a guide for workers; Looked After Children Reviews, a guide for children and young people; Looked After Children Reviews, a guide for parents; Appeals against Child Protection Conference Decisions.

Child and Family Social Work and Consultation Team
Staveleigh Clinic, Stamford St, Stalybridge, Tameside SK15 1JT; Tel 0161 303 8121; Fax 0161 303 9582
Team Manager S. Shaw
This service provides a range of diagnostic and therapeutic responses to children below the age of 16 years who may be experiencing behavioural, emotional or psychological difficulties.

FAMILY SUPPORT UNIT

Union St, Hyde, Tameside SK14 1ND; Tel 0161 368 8563; Fax 0161 368 8630
Unit Business Manager J. McDonough
The unit comprises family centres which provide a range of family support sercies both centre-based an on an outreach basis. family support teams provide support to children in need and parents or carers in their homes, and operate 0800–2000 seven days per week. The provider development team pursues a commissioning strategy that will enable social services to procure provision of day/sesssional and out-of-school care that promotes the welfare of children in need.

Children with Disabilities Jubilee Gdns, Garden Ave, Droylesden, Tameside M43 7XA; Tel 0161 371 2060; Fax 0161 371 2061
Team Manager S. Wooding

Provides an assessment and case management service to families and children with permanent and substantial disabilities.

Provider Development Team Union St, Hyde, Tameside SK14 1ND; Tel 0161 342 4330; Fax 0161 368 8630
Team Manager G. Casey

Birch Lane Family Centre Birch La, Dukinfield, Tameside SK16 5AU; Tel 0161 339 3996; Fax 0161 339 9350
Family Support Manager W. Acton

Newton Family Centre Victoria St, Newton, Hyde, Tameside SK14 4AA; Tel 0161 368 3192; Fax 0161 368 3215
Family Support Manager J. Cooper

Ridge Hill Family Centre Ambleside, Stalybridge, Tameside SK15 1EF; Tel 0161 338 8297; Fax 0161 303 0264
Family Support Manager S. Garnett

Russell Scott Family Centre Linden Rd, Denton, Tameside M34 6EF; Tel 0161 336 2143; Fax 0161 320 9244
Family Support Manager E. Cooper

West End Family Centre Katherine St, Ashton-under-Lyne, Tameside OL7 0AG; Tel 0161 330 1354; Fax 0161 339 9271
Family Support Manager C. Redmond

LOOKED AFTER CHILDREN UNIT

Union St, Hyde, Tameside SK14 1ND; Tel 0161 342 4300; Fax 0161 368 8642
Unit Business Manager B. Connolly

Education Resource Team 56 Warrington St, Ashton-under-Lyne, Tameside OL6 7JX; Tel 0161 342 4150; Fax 0161 342 4123

LEAVING CARE SUPPORT TEAM

Tel 0161 366 5181; Fax 0161 366 5195; Minicom 0161 342 5474
Team Manager C. Gerrard
Provides advice and information to young people who have been in care after the age of 16 years.

Fostering Team Tel 0161 342 4300; Fax 0161 368 8642
Team Manager J. Dunbavin
The Fostering Team recruits, assesses and supports foster carers for children that need accommodation or respite care.

Boyds Walk Children's Unit 109–111 Boyds Wlk, Dukinfield, Tameside SK16 4AX; Tel 0161 344 2508; Fax 0161 339 6780
Team Manager C. Eddy

Chester Avenue Children's Unit 64 Chester Ave, Dukinfield, Tameside SK16 5BW; Tel 0161 338 5671; Fax 0161 304 9710
Team Manager C. Eddy

Chester Avenue Children's Home 66 Chester Ave, Dukinfield, Tameside SK16 5BW; Tel 0161 303 2534; Fax 0161 303 2831
Team Manager C. Wilde

Older People Assessment

Service Unit Manager M. Garnett

OLDER PEOPLE ASSESSMENT UNIT

Stalybridge Resource Centre, Waterloo Rd, Stalybridge, SK15 2AU; Tel 0161 342 2400; Fax 0161 342 2460
Unit Business Manager D. Walton

Reception and Initial Assessment Team
Acts as the front line for all enquiries and referrals concerning adults and people with disabillities.
Team Manager D. Fryers

Transfer Service Social work Dept, Community Liaison Bldg, Tameside General Hospital, Fountain St, Ashton-under-Lyne, OL6 9RP; Tel 0161 331 5173; Fax 0161 331 5187
Team Leader S. Metcalfe
Provides a service to hospital in-patients, assessing the needs of the individual and planning care needed on discharge.

6

ASSESSMENT AND CARE MANAGEMENT TEAM

Team Manager P. Rae

Older People Provision

ADULT PROVIDER UNIT

Hyde Town Hall, Market St, Hyde, Tameside SK14 1NN;
Tel 0161 342 3491; Fax 0161 368 2673
Unit Business Manager T. Flanagan

Adult Placement Team Acorn Hse, Albert St, Droylsden,
Ashton-under-Lyne, Tameside M43 7BA; Tel 0161 371 5622;
Fax 0161 371 9303
Team Manager P. Dulson
Manages long- and short-term residential placements for
service users living with carers in the community.

JobMatch Employment Team Broadoak and Smallshaw
Community Centre, Broadoak Rd, Ashton-under-Lyne,
Tameside OL6 8QG; Tel 0161 339 9829; Fax 0161 339
9541
Team Manager C. Craig

Community Alarm Service Acorn Hse, Albert St,
Droylsden, Ashton-under-Lyne, Tameside M43 7BA;
Tel (Freephone) 0161 371 9310; Fax 0161 371 7965
Team Manager C. Craig
Offers 24-hour support to people in their homes, provided
by control operators and mobile wardens.

LEARNING DISABILITY RESIDENTIAL SERVICES UNIT

4 Crowthorn Rd, Ashton-under-Lyne, Tameside OL7 0DH;
Tel 0161 330 5892; Fax 0161 339 1438; Minicom 0161 330
5892
Unit Business Manager M. Whitehead

Provider Teams – Homemaker Service
Team Manager J. Moore
Team Manager S. Lawton
The Homemaker Service is a community-based service that
provides 24-hour support to service users in their own
home.

Staley House Lakes Rd, Stalybridge, Tameside SK15 1JE;
Tel 0161 338 4898; Fax 0161 338 4898
Team Manager S. Lawton

LEARNING DISABILITY DAY SERVICES UNIT

4 Crowthorn Rd, Ashton-under-Lyne, Tameside OL7 0DH;
Tel 0161 330 5892; Fax 0161 339 1438
Unit Business Manager J. Winfield
Team Manager (Copley) J. Hill
Team Manager (Werneth Grange) G. Kelly

Broadoak Centre Broadoak Rd, Ashton-under-Lyne,
Tameside; Tel 0161 339 4146; Fax 0161 339 4146
Team Manager G. Surico

Denton Resource Centre Mill La, Denton, Tameside
M34 1RF; Tel 0161 336 5363; Fax 0161 320 4041
Assistant Team Manager Vacancy

Droylsden Resource Centre Ash Rd, Droylsden, Tameside
M43 6QU; Tel 0161 371 1721; Fax 0161 371 1215
Assistant Team Manager J. Lomas

Hurst Resource Centre Carr St, Hurst Cross, Ashton-under-
Lyne, Tameside OL6 8ES; Tel 0161 330 3720; Fax 0161 343
2385
Assistant Team Manager G. Surico

Top Notch Garden Service Unit 6, Bayley St, Stalybridge,
Tameside SK15 1PU; Tel 0161 338 6346; Fax 0161 338
6346
Assistant Team Manager C. Potts

Werneth Grange Day Centre Grange Rd South, Hyde,
Tameside SK14 5NJ; Tel 0161 368 1730; Fax 0161 368
1730
Assistant Team Manager D. Buckley

Adults Assessment and Commissioning Service

Stalybridge Resource Centre, Waterloo Rd, Stalybridge,
Tameside SK15 2AU; Tel 0161 342 2400; Fax 0161 342
2460; Minicom 0161 342 2577
Manager S. Wills
Administration Officer J. Maher

PHYSICAL DISABILITIES UNIT

Stalybridge Resource Centre, Waterloo Rd, Stalybridge,
SK15 2AU; Tel 0161 342 2400; Fax 0161 342 2460
Unit Business Manager S. Blezard

Direct Payments
Assistant Team Manager B. Kay

Sensory Impairment Team
Team Manager J. Stokes
Provides a service to adults who are experiencing sensory
disabilities such as hearing and visual impairment.
Includes occupational therapy service.

Katherine House Bentinck St, Ashton-under-Lyne,
Tameside OL6 7HY; Tel 0161 339 9455; Fax 0161 330 0085
Senior Team Leader J. Richards

Loxley House Birch La, Dukinfield, Tameside SK16 5AU;
Tel 0161 366 9746; Fax 0161 366 7996
Senior Day Care Officer J. Higgins

MENTAL HEALTH SERVICES UNIT

4 Crowthorn Rd, Ashton-under-Lyne, Tameside OL7 0DH;
Tel 0161 343 7852; Fax 0161 330 9674
Unit Business Manager T. Tench

Community Dementia Team and Mental Health – Over 65s
1st Fl, Hyde Hospital, Grange Road South, Hyde, Tameside
SK14 5NY; Tel 0161 368 4157; Fax 0161 351 4987
Team Manager (Over 65s) J. George
Team Manager (Dementia) D. Thompson

Community Mental Health Teams Haughton Hse, 67
Stamford Street East, Ashton-under-Lyne, Tameside
OL6 6QQ; Tel 0161 339 2627; Fax 0161 339 0266
Service Manager R. Wolfenden

Employment Team (Head Start) Brindle Hse, 34 Church St,
Hyde, Tameside SK14 1JJ; Tel 0161 366 8040; Fax 0161 368
0612
Team Manager M. Haurigan

Substance Misuse Team Lees St, Ashton-under-Lyne,
Tameside O16 0NG; Tel 0161 339 4141; Fax 0161 339 8644
Team Manager M. Hopper

West Villa West St, Dukinfield, Tameside SK16 4PL;
Tel 0161 339 2985; Fax 0161 339 6266

LEARNING DISABILITY ASSESSMENT AND COMMISSIONING UNIT

4 Crowthorn Rd, Ashton-under-Lyne, Tameside OL7 0DH;
Tel 0161 330 5892; Fax 0161 339 1438
Unit Business Manager L. Knight

Community Assessment Teams Ryecroft Hall, Manchester
Rd, Audenshaw, Tameside M34 5GJ; Tel 0161 371 5623;
Fax 0161 371 2000
Team Manager M. Lee

Monitoring and Review Team
Team Manager S. Parsons

Education and Cultural Services

Council Offices, Wellington Rd, Ashton-under-Lyne,
Tameside OL6 6DL; Tel 0161 342 8355; Fax 0161 342 3744
Strategic Director (Education and Cultural Services)
P.P. Lawday, BEd(Hons), MSc, MBA
Head (Sport) John Knighton
Head (Human Resources) J. White
Head (Financial Resources) Elaine Todd
Head (Youth) Sue Nathan

Chief Education Officer   Ian Smith
Manager (School Organisation and Social Inclusion)
   L.K. Davies
Manager (Buildings and Finance)   E. Todd
Education Officer (Human Resources)   T. Brennand
Education Officer (School Organisation)   J. Fludder
Education Officer (Capital)   R. Muller
Principal Educational Psychologist   Nick Caws
Assistant Education Officer (Building Unit)   R. Higson
Principal Education Welfare Officer   C. Platt
Principal Educational Psychologist   Nick Caws
General Adviser (Governor and Management Support)
   A. Bailey

CHILD GUIDANCE CLINIC

Staveley Clinic Health Centre, Stamford St, Stalybridge,
Greater Manchester SK15 1JT; Tel 0161 338 2278
Contact   Dr Davenport
Contact   Dr Bowers

SPECIAL SCHOOLS

Cromwell School Yew Tree La, Dukinfield, Greater
Manchester SK16 5BJ;
E-mail admin@cromwell.tameside.sch.uk; Tel 0161 338
9730
   SLD

Dale Grove Secondary Centre Wilshaw La, Ashton-under-
Lyne, Tameside OL7 9RF;
E-mail admin@dalegrove.tameside.sch.uk; Tel 0161 330
7595
   EBD (32)

Hawthorns Community School Corporation Rd,
Audenshaw, Tameside M34 5LZ;
E-mail admin@hawthorns.tameside.sch.uk; Tel 0161 336
3389
   MLD

Oakdale School Cheetham Hill Rd, Dukinfield, Tameside
SK16 5LD; E-mail admin@oakdale.tameside.sch.uk;
Tel 0161 367 9299
   SLD

Samuel Laycock School Mereside, Stalybridge, Greater
Manchester SK15 1JF;
E-mail admin@samuellaycock.tameside.sch.uk; Tel 0161
303 1321
Secondary
   MLD (118)

Tameside Hospital School Boiler Hse Cottage, General
Hospital, Ashton-under-Lyne, Tameside OL6 9RW; Tel 0161
331 6772
Incorporating home tuition service.

TUTORIAL CENTRE

Dale Grove Primary Centre Grange Rd, Hyde, Tameside
SK14 5NU; Tel 0161 368 1718
   EBD (17)

UNIT

Hyde Technology High and Hearing Impaired Unit Old
Road, Hyde, Tameside SK14 4SP; Tel 0161 368 1353
   Secondary

HEARING IMPAIRED SERVICE

Education Development Centre Lakes Rd, Dukinfield,
Tameside SK16 4TR; Tel 0161 330 1375

SPECIFIC LEARNING DIFFICULTIES RESOURCE CENTRE

c/o Two Trees High Two Trees La, Denton, Tameside;
Tel 0161 320 7729

Telford and Wrekin Council is a unitary authority. In March
1999 the Council transferred its housing stock to The
Wrekin Housing Trust Ltd and consequently it no longer
has a landlord function. However, the Council continues to
be proactive in housing matters through its strategic and
enabling housing role and related functions.
Political Composition: Lab: 24, Con: 12, Ind: 6, LD: 6
Darby Hse, PO Box 214, Telford, Wrekin TF3 4LE;
   URL www.telford.gov.uk;
   E-mail contact@telford.gov.uk; Tel 01952 202100
Head (Housing and Consumer Services)   Mike Atherton
Chief Executive   Michael Frater

Social Care

Tel 01952 202100; Fax 01952 201490
Corporate Director   John Coughlan
Executive Member (Social Care)   Roy Sloan
Head (Social Services – Children and Families)
   Barbara Evans

Children and Families Services

SOCIAL WORK TEAMS

North Wrekin Social Work Team Highfield Hse, Wrekin Rd,
Telford, Shropshire; Tel 01952 246810

South Wrekin Social Work Team Castle Lodge, Attwood
Terr, Telford, Shropshire; Tel 01952 506000

ADOPTION SERVICE

Observer House Shire Bus Pk, Hollywell St, Shrewsbury,
Shropshire; Tel 01743 241915

RESOURCE CENTRES (FOSTERING AND FAMILY SUPPORT)

30 West Rd, Wellington, Shropshire; Tel 01952 222971
North Wrekin Resource Centre Highfield Hse, Wrekin Rd,
Wellington, Shropshire; Tel 01952 246810
South Wrekin Resource Centre Castle Lodge, Attwood Terr,
Telford, Shropshire; Tel 01952 506000

COMMUNITY HOMES FOR CHILDREN

Burford Children's Community Home 123 Burford,
Brookside, Telford, Shropshire; Tel 01952 660243
Church Street Children's Community Home 2 Church St,
Oakengates, Telford, Shropshire; Tel 01952 619396
Dodmoor Grange Children's Community Home Randlay,
Telford, Shropshire; Tel 01952 593412

CHILD AND FAMILY SERVICE (BEHAVIOURAL ISSUES)

Wrekin Hospital Holyhead Rd, Wellington, Telford,
Shropshire; Tel 01952 244667

DISABILITY SERVICES

HIV and AIDS Information 77 Severn Wlk, Sutton Hill,
Telford, Shropshire; Tel 01952 680064
Loan Equipment Store Horton Wood, Telford, Shropshire;
Tel 01952 242664

6

Parville House Respite Care Crescent Rd, Wellington, Telford, Shropshire; Tel 01952 225702

Sensory Impairment Team 77 Severn Wlk, Sutton Hill, Telford, Shropshire; Tel 01952 588413; Minicom 01952 588430

Social Work and Occupational Therapy Team 77 Severn Wlk, Sutton Hill, Telford, Shropshire; Tel 01952 680064

Stirchley Day Centre Telford, Shropshire TF3 1DY; Tel 01952 595543

CHILDREN WITH DISABILITIES

Highfield House Wrekin Rd, Wellington, Telford, Shropshire; Tel 01952 246819

YOUTH JUSTICE TEAM

Dawley Road Youth Justice Team 1 Dawley Rd, Wellington, Telford, Shropshire; Tel 01952 247477

Older People

SOCIAL WORK TEAMS OLDER PEOPLE

Princess Royal Hospital Apley Castle, Telford, Shropshire; Tel 01952 641222

Severn Walk Social Work Team Sutton Hill, Telford, Shropshire; Tel 01952 680052

Tan Bank Social Work Team Wellington, Telford, Shropshire; Tel 01952 254371

ADULTS WITH LEARNING DISABILITIES

Carwood Residential Home 16 Carwood, Stirchley, Telford, Shropshire; Tel 01952 592436
(26)

Downing House Dee Cl, Telford, Shropshire TF1 3JU; Tel 01952 244180
Contact P. Styles
(30)

Community Support and Day Care Halesfield 22, Heslop, Telford, Shropshire TF7 4EW; Tel 01952 684998
(96)

Newhall Road Centre Employment Support, Telford, Shropshire TF1 1JR; Tel 01952 251416
(48)

Employment Services and Day Service John Rose Bldg, Coalport, Telford, Shropshire; Tel 01952 588835

Social Education Centre TCAT Haybridge Rd, Wellington, Telford, Shropshire; Tel 01952 242768

Leisure Services Dothill Centre, Severn Dr, Telford, Shropshire; Tel 01952 244960

Mental Impairment Service Ringway Hse, Bridge Rd, Telford, Shropshire; Tel 01952 588835

Social Work Team Ringway Hse, Bridge Rd, Telford, Shropshire; Tel 01952 222031

OTHER SERVICES

Bennett House Residential Home Park La, Woodside, Telford, Shropshire; Tel 01952 582588

Cartlidge House Residential Home Charlton St, Oakengates, Telford, Shropshire; Tel 01952 618293

Home Care Service Tan Bank, Telford, Shropshire; Tel 01952 222898

Millbrook EMI Day Centre Barclay Lodge, Donnington, Telford, Shropshire; Tel 01952 670349

Mental Health Services

COMMUNITY MENTAL HEALTH TEAM

Community Mental Health Team (Central) Grosvenor Hse, Telford, Shropshire; Tel 01952 293366

Community Mental Health Team (North Wrekin) Bridge Rd, Wellington, Telford, Shropshire; Tel 01952 222725

Community Mental Health Team (South Wrekin) Church St, Madeley, Telford, Shropshire; Tel 01952 680104

MENTAL HEALTH DAY CENTRES

North Wrekin Mental Health Day Centre Wrekin Rd, Wellington, Telford, Shropshire; Tel 01952 251521

South Wrekin Metal Health Day Centre High St, Dawley, Telford, Shropshire; Tel 01952 502117

SUBSTANCE MISUSE SERVICES AND DRUG HELP

Portico House Wellington, Telford, Shropshire; Tel 01952 222229

REGULATION AND REVIEW

Darby Hse, PO Box 214, Telford, Shropshire TF3 4LE; Tel 01952 202284

GALRO AND COMPLAINTS

Darby Hse, PO Box 214, Telford, Shropshire TF3 4LE; Tel 01952 202254

Education and Culture

Civic Offices, PO Box 440, Telford, Wrekin TF3 4WF; URL www.telford.gov.uk; E-mail education@wrekin.gov.uk; Tel 01952 202121
Director (Education and Culture) Christine Davies; Tel 01952 202335; Fax 01952 293946

SPECIAL SCHOOLS

The Bridge School Stirchley Site, Grange Ave, Telford, Shropshire TF3 1UP; Tel 01952 417020
Headteacher Mrs U. Vandenberg
Mixed SLD

Haughton School Queen St, Madeley, Telford, Shropshire TF7 4BW; Tel 01952 684995; Fax 01952 583616
Headteacher B. Logan (Acting)
Mixed MLD

Mount Gilbert School Hinkshay Rd, Dawley, Telford, Shropshire TF3 1DG; Tel 01952 272473
Headteacher A. Valentini
EBD (25)

Southall School off Rowan Ave, Dawley, Telford, Shropshire TF4 3PN; Tel 01952 592485; Fax 01952 591207
Headteacher A.J. Day
Mixed MLD

THURROCK BOROUGH COUNCIL
www.thurrock.gov.uk

In April 1998 both Thurrock and Southend became unitary authorities. The rest of Essex retains its two-tier structure and is listed alphabetically within this chapter.
Population 134 806 (1999)
Political Composition: Lab: 37, Con: 9, Ind: 2, LD: 1
Civic Offices, New Rd, Grays, Thurrock RM17 6SL; URL www.thurrock.gov.uk; Tel 01375 652390
Managing Director David White

Directorate of Housing and Social Care

PO Box 140, Civic Offices, New Rd, Grays, Thurrock
RM17 6TJ; Tel 01375 652675; Fax 01375 652798
Director (Housing and Social Care)   Christine Paley
Head (Social Care and Health)   Zena Deayton
Head (Children and Families)   Mark Gurrey
Head (Business Support)   Tim Madden
Mental Health Commissioner   Kevin Dowling
Service Manager (Community Care – Older People)
   Liz Biebuyck
Service Manager (Community Care – Disabilities)
   Eileen McCabe
*Service Manager (Children and Families – Children Looked
   After)*   Jean Imray
*Service Manager (Children and Families – Assessment and
   Family Support)*   Jill Forrest
Service Manager (Young People's Services)   Chris Dove
Manager (Quality and Performance)   Chris Miller
Manager (Human Resources)   Ade Fadare
Manager (Principal Finance)   Pauline Piper
Manager (Training and Staff Develpoment)
   Fran Leddra-Chapman
Contracts Manager   Carole Rainbird

Cabinet

Portfolio Member (Health and Social Services)   D. Hooper

Social Work Office

The Civic Offices, PO Box 140, New Rd, Grays, Thurrock
RM17 6TJ; Tel (Emergency) 01375 372468; 01375 652675;
01375 652769

Services to Children and Families

ASSESSMENT TEAM

PO Box 140, The Civic Offices, New Rd, Grays, Thurrock
RM17 6TJ; Tel 01375 652657; 01375 652634; Fax 01375
652768

CONTINUING CARE

PO Box 140, Civic Offices, New Rd, Grays, Thurrock
RM17 6TJ; Tel 01375 652743; 01375 652744; 01375 652745;
01375 652747; 01375 652749; Fax 01375 652768

YOUTH OFFENDER TEAM

Five Wells, West St, Grays, Thurrock RM17 6XR; Tel 01375
414900; Fax 01375 414901

SUPPORTING ADOLESCENTS IN LIFE (SAIL) TEAM

PO Box 140, Civic Offices, New Rd, Grays, Thurrock
RM17 6TJ; Tel 01375 413711

UNACCOMPANIED ADOLESCENT ASYLUM SEEKERS (UAAS) TEAM

PO Box 140, Civic Offices, New Rd, Grays, Thurrock
RM17 6TJ; Tel 01375 413710

FAMILY SUPPORT TEAM

PO Box 140, Civic Offices, New Rd, Grays, Thurrock
RM17 6TJ; Tel 01375 652749; Fax 01375 652768

CHILD AND FAMILY CONSULTATION SERVICE

62 Maidstone Rd, Grays, Thurrock RM17 5PD; Tel 01375
816900; Fax 01375 816913

FAMILY PLACEMENTS

Thurrock Council Social Services, PO Box 140, Civic
Offices, New Rd, Grays, Thurrock RM17 6TJ; Tel 01375
652617; Fax 01375 652798

TEAM FOR DISABLED CHILDREN

Thurrock Council Social Services, PO Box 140, Civic
Offices, New Rd, Grays, Thurrock RM17 6TJ; Tel 01375
652633; Fax 01375 652798

RESIDENTIAL CARE ESTABLISHMENTS AND HOMES FOR CHILDREN

Corve Lane Community Home 11a Corve La, South
Ockendon, Thurrock RM15 6BA; Tel 01708 857525;
Fax 01708 857979

FAMILY CENTRES

Bluebell Family Centre Garron La, South Ockendon,
Thurrock RM15 5JQ; Tel 01708 856352; Fax 01708 852465

Oaktree Family Centre 62–64 Hogg La, Grays, Thurrock
RM17 5QS; Tel 01375 391127; Fax 01375 392460

DAY ACTIVITIES FOR DISABLED PEOPLE

Community Services Centre 13–15 Clarence Rd, Grays,
Thurrock; Tel 01375 413700; Fax 01375 413708

Dilkeswood Resource Centre Darenth La, South Ockendon,
Thurrock RM15 5RS; Tel 01708 856055

FACILITIES FOR CARERS

Thurrock Carers Centre Cromwell Hse, Cromwell Rd,
Grays, Thurrock RM17 5HQ; Tel 01375 390973

Services for Older People

Community Mental Health Resource Centre for Older People
51 Orsett Rd, Grays, Thurrock RM17 5DF; Tel 01375
413912

HOME CARE BUSINESS UNIT

PO Box 140, Civic Offices, New Rd, Grays, Thurrock
RM17 6TJ; Tel 01375 652849; 01375 652860; Fax 01375
652798

OLDER PEOPLE'S ASSESSMENT AND CARE MANAGEMENT TEAM

PO Box 140, Civic Offices, New Rd, Grays, Thurrock
RM17 6TJ; Tel 01375 652859; 01375 652868; Fax 01375
652798

SERVICES FOR DISABLED PEOPLE

Community Support Team (Learning Disability) Thurrock
Council Social Services, PO Box 140, Civic Offices, New Rd,
Grays, Thurrock RM17 6TJ; Tel 01375 652607; Fax 01375
652798

Disability Team: Physical and Sensory Impairment
Thurrock Council Social Services, PO Box 140, Civic
Offices, New Rd, Grays, Thurrock RM17 6TJ; Tel 01375
652648; Fax 01375 652799

MENTAL HEALTH SERVICES

East and West Community Mental Health Teams Grays
Hall, Orsett Rd, Grays, Thurrock; Tel 01375 402276;
Fax 01375 402274

OCCUPATIONAL THERAPY SERVICES

Thurrock Council Social Services PO Box 140, Civic Offices,
New Rd, Grays, Thurrock RM17 6TJ; Tel 01375 652873;
Fax 01375 652798

RESIDENTIAL CARE FOR OLDER PEOPLE

There are two residential homes for older people.

6

Education Department

PO Box 118, New Rd, Grays, Thurrock RM17 6GF;
E-mail education@thurrock.gov.uk; Tel 01375 652652;
Fax 01375 652792; Minicom 01375 652516
Director (Education)   Steve Beynon
Head (School Effectiveness and Children's Services)
Ann Lewin
Co-ordinator (Special Needs)   Vacancy

SPECIAL SCHOOLS

Knightsmead School   Fortin Cl, South Ockendon, Thurrock
RM15 5NH; Tel 01708 852956; Fax 01708 851741
Headteacher   Ms J. Thomas

Treetops School   Dell Rd, Grays, Thurrock RM17 5LH;
Tel 01375 372723; Fax 01375 390784
Headteacher   P. Smith

Woodacre School   Erriff Dr, South Ockendon, Thurrock
RM15 5AY; Tel 01708 852006; Fax 01708 851679
Headteacher   J. Stringer

TORBAY COUNCIL

www.torbay.gov.uk

In April 1998 both Plymouth and Torbay became unitary
authorities. The rest of Devon retains its two-tier structure
and is listed alphabetically within this chapter.
Political Composition: LD: 27, Con: 9
Town Hall, Torquay, Torbay TQ1 3DR;
URL www.torbay.gov.uk;
E-mail webmaster@torbay.gov.uk; Tel 01803 201201
Managing Director   Richard Painter
Leader of Council   Eileen Salloway
Deputy Leader of Council   Ron Morris

Social Services Directorate

Oldway Mansion, Torquay Rd, Paignton, Devon TQ3 2TS;
URL www.torbay.gov.uk; Tel 01803 201201
Director (Social Services)   Jain Wood
Executive Officer (Social Services)   Steve Honeywill
Assistant Director (Adult Services)   Philippa Scott (Acting)
Assistant Director (Childrens Services)   Vince Clark
Assistant Director (Policy and Performance)   Sue Lewis
Assistant Director (Housing and Health Services)   Vacancy
Manager (Learning Disabilities Partnership)
Helen Toker-Lester
Manager (Housing Services)   Simon Sherbersky
Manager (Directorate Support)   Steve Keir
Manager (Information for Social Care)   Paul Whitcomb
Training   Kings Ash Hse, Kings Ash Rd, Paignton, Devon
TQ3 3TT; Tel 01803 402848
Manager (Training)   Phil Reid
The Council
LD: 26, Con: 9
Leader of the Council   Cllr C. Harris

Services to Adults and Older People

3rd Fl, Union Hse, Union St, Torquay, Devon TQ1 3YA;
Tel 01803 208500
Operations Manager (Contact and Assessment)
Tim Gainsford
Operations Manager (Commissioning)   Ray Hodgson
Service Manager (Emergency Duty Service)   David White;
Tel 01803 292166
Service Manager (Contracts Team)   Susan Anderson-Carr
18 Palace Ave, Paignton, Devon TQ3 3HS; Tel 01803 208462
Service Manager (Dual Sensory Loss Team)   Katie Heard

Service Manager (Mental Health Team – Older Adults)
Cheryl Mears
Oldway Mansion, Torquay Rd, Paignton, Devon TQ3 2TS;
Tel 01803 208462
Service Manager (Assessment Team)   Adele Tithecott
Service Manager (Assessment Team)   Gordon Batten
Service Manager (Assessment Team)   Barry Smith
Service Manager (Review Team)   Pat Sooben
Service Manager (Review Team)   Mark Kozak
Service Manager (Review Team)   Richard Harris
Service Manager (Information and Contact Team)   Sharon Gray
Service Manager (Information and Contact Team)
Brian Perriam

Hospital Adults Team   Belmont Crt, 124 Newton Rd,
Torquay, Devon TQ2 7AD; Tel 01803 654727
Service Manager   Mike Waldron
Service Manager   Alison Newall

**Crisis Assessment Rapid Reenablement Intervention for the
Elderly Team (CARRIE)**
Service Manager   Nicky Nendick; Tel 01803 292618

Dunboyne Community Care and Support Centre   172 St.
Marychurch Rd, Torquay, Torbay TQ1 3JT; Tel 01803 326592
Service Manager   Bob Hayden

Fernham Day Care Centre   Manor Cres, Paignton, Devon
TQ3 2TW; Tel 01803 550449

St. Edmund Community Care and Support Centre   Victoria
Park Rd, Torquay, Torbay TQ1 3QH; Tel 01803 324595
Service Manager   Linda Bryant

St. Kilda Residential Home and Day Centre   15 Drew St,
Brixham, Devon TQ5 9JU; Tel 01803 853249
Service Manager   Margaret Gibbings

Domiciliary Care and Crisis Response Team   Kings Ash
Hse, Kings Ash Rd, Paignton, Devon TQ3 3TT; Tel 01803
402820
Service Manager   Sylvia Ball

Community Alarms   Brookfield Cl, Paignton, Devon
TQ3 2JE; Tel 01803 324595
Service Manager   Peter Winsor

Learning Disabilities

Team Manager (Community Learning Disability)
Stuart Robinson
Castle Circus Health Centre, Abbey Rd, Torquay, Devon
TQ2 5YH; Tel 01803 291321
Learning Disability Development Officer   Jane Goodwill;
Tel 01803 201201

Baytree House Respite and Assessment Unit   Croft Rd,
Torquay, Torbay TQ2 5UD; Tel 01803 211300
Service Manager   Diane Graham

Fairwinds Special Development Day Centre   Preston Down
Rd, Paignton, Devon TQ3 1RN; Tel 01803 529939
Service Manager   Emelyn Jeffries

Hollacombe Community Resource Centre   386 Torquay Rd,
Paignton, Devon TQ3 2DJ; Tel 01803 523711
Service Manager   David Horsburgh

Torquay Community Resource Centre   Lincombe Crt,
Lincombe Hill Rd, Torquay, Torbay TQ1 2HN; Tel 01803
215531
Service Manager   Gisella Parkes

Services for Children

1st and 2nd Fl, Union Hse, Union St, Torquay, Devon
TQ1 3YA; Tel 01803 208500
Operations Manager (Permanency Planning Service)
Joy Howick
Operations Manager (Children In Need Service)   Lindy Brown
Service Manager (Permanency Planning Team)   Jan Branton
Service Manager (Permanency Planning Team)   Brian Hunt
Service Manager (Intake Team)   Vashti Hawkins
Service Manager (Intake Team)   Jan Budden
Service Manager (Children In Need Team)   Jenni Skilton

Service Manager (Children's Disability Team) Jan Colley;
Tel 01803 402781
Service Manager (Children's Disability Team)
Claire Harding; Tel 01803 402781
Service Manager (Contact, Intervention and Assessment Team)
Carol Griffiths
Hillside Family Centre, South Parks Rd, Torquay, Devon
TQ2 8JE; Tel 01803 208462
Service Manager (LAC Review Service and Child Protection)
John Edwards; Tel 01803 208559
Manager (Youth Offending Service and Link Youth Support)
Fred Pethard
3rd Fl, Commerce Hse, 97–101 Abbey Rd, Torquay, Devon
TQ2 5PJ; Tel 01803 201655
Manager (Link Youth Support) Dominique Slaney
Units 4–5 South Quay, Paignton Harbour, Paignton, Devon
TQ4 6DT; Tel 01803 557870
Manager (Adoption Service) Rhona Lewis
Oldway Mansion, Torquay Rd, Paignton, Devon TQ3 2TS;
Tel 01803 201201
Manager (Fostering Services) Georgina Dunk; Tel 01803
402781
Manager (Care to Community Team) Derek King
Old Town Hall, New St, Paignton, Devon TQ3 3HL;
Tel 01803 208345
Manager (Residential Services) Kim Merriot
Broadhaven, 5 Broadsands Rd, Paignton, Devon TQ4 6JX;
Tel 01803 842460
Contracts and Development Officer Peter Taylor
Independent Co-ordinator (Family Group Conferences)
Nick Thayre
1st Fl, 56 Palace Ave, Paignton, Devon TQ3 3HZ; Tel 01803
402802

Haswell House Family Centre 53 Totnes Rd, Paignton,
Devon TQ4 5LE; Tel 01803 522052
*Service Manager (Contact, Intervention, Assessment and Group
Work Team)* Ali Matthews

Torbay Children's Special Needs and Disability Partnership
Parkfield Hse, 38 Esplanade Rd, Paignton, Devon
TQ3 2NH; Tel 01803 402781
Manager (Project and Service Development) Jim Skilton

Learning and Cultural Services Directorate

Oldway Mansion, Torquay Rd, Paignton, Devon TQ3 2TE;
URL www.torbay.gov.uk;
E-mail education.reception@torbay.gov.uk
Executive Director (Learning and Cultural Services)
Tony Smith (Acting)
Assistant Director (Personal and Community Services)
Frances Billinge
Assistant Director (Strategy and Resources) Terry Connolly
(Acting)
Assistant Director (School Standards) Vacancy

SPECIAL SCHOOLS

Combe Pafford School Steps La, Watcombe, Torquay,
Torbay TQ2 8NL;
E-mail admin@combepafford-special.torbay.sch.uk;
Tel 01803 327902; Fax 01803 327902
Headteacher M.E. Lock, BEd
7–16 MLD, Autism and Physical Difficulties

Mayfield School Moor La, Watcombe, Torquay, Torbay
TQ2 8NU; E-mail admin@mayfield-special.torbay.sch.uk;
Tel 01803 328375; Fax 01803 326761
Headteacher Mrs J. Palmer
Mixed SLD, PMLD, Autism and Physical Difficulties

Torbay School 170b Torquay Rd, Paignton, Devon
TP3 2AL; E-mail admin@torbay.school.sch.uk; Tel 01803
665522; Fax 01803 668320
Headteacher Mr W. Hug
9–16 Emotional and Behavioural Difficulties

Population 228 000
Political Composition: Lab: 31, Con: 29, LD: 3
Trafford Town Hall, Talbot Rd, Stretford, Manchester
M32 0YT; URL www.trafford.gov.uk; Tel 0161 912 1212;
Fax 0161 912 4184
Chief Executive Carole Hassan
Head (Legal Services) Beverley Dunn
Trafford Town Hall, Talbot Rd, Stretford, Manchester
M32 0YU

Department of Social Services and Housing Strategy

Social Services Committee
Cabinet Spokesperson Cllr D. Quayle
Opposition Spokesperson Cllr Mrs D. Lynch

TRAINING
Responsible for training professional and support staff in
the department.
Trafford Town Hall, Talbot Rd, Stretford, Manchester
M33 0JH; Tel 0161 912 5199; Fax 0161 912 4184
Employee Development Officer (Elderly) Mike Day; Tel 0161
912 4208
*Employee Development Officer (Health, Disability and Learning
Disability)* M. Gibney; Tel 0161 912 4466
Employee Development Officer (Mental Health) Vacancy;
Tel 0161 912 1010

AREA OFFICES

North Area Office
Stretford Public Hall, Chester Rd, Stretford, Greater
Manchester M32 0LG; URL www.trafford.gov.uk;
E-mail cat@trafford.gov.uk; Tel 0161 912 5199; Fax 0161
912 5127 0161 912 5128

South Area Office
Town Hall, Market St, Altrincham, Greater Manchester
WA14 1PG; URL www.trafford.gov.uk;
E-mail cat@trafford.gov.uk; Tel 0161 912 5199; Fax 0161
912 5127 0161 912 5128

West Area Office
Council Offices, Crofts Bank Rd, Urmston, Greater
Manchester M31 1UD; URL www.trafford.gov.uk;
E-mail cat@trafford.gov.uk; Tel 0161 912 5199; Fax 0161
912 5127 0161 912 5128

HOSPITAL SOCIAL WORKERS
Trafford General Hospital, Moorside Rd, Davyhulme,
Greater Manchester M41 5SL; Tel 0161 746 2420;
Fax 0161 746 2404
Social Worker C. Lomas

Altrincham General Hospital Market St, Altrincham,
Greater Manchester WA14 1PE; Tel 0161 928 6111
Social Worker J. Byrne

Moorside Unit (Mental Health) Trafford General Hospital,
Moorside Rd, Davyhulme, Greater Manchester M31 3SL;
Tel 0161 746 2679

QUALITY PROTECTS – CHILDREN'S SERVICES

Trafford Town Hall, Talbot Rd, Stretford, Greater
  Manchester M32 0TH;
  E-mail matthew.brazier@trafford.gov.uk; Tel 0161 912
  5199
Manager   Matthew Brazier
Wythenshaw Hospital 2nd Fl, Tower Block, Southmoor Rd,
Manchester M23 9LT

ADOPTION AND PERMANANCY TEAM

Stretford Public Hall, Chester Rd, Stretford, Greater
  Manchester M32 0LG;
  E-mail arthur.taylor@trafford.gov.uk; Tel 0161 912 5001
Team Manager   Arthur Taylor

CHILD PROTECTION CO-ORDINATOR

Stretford Public Hall, Chester Rd, Stretford, Greater
  Manchester M32 0LG;
  E-mail catherine.fleming@trafford.gov.uk; Tel 0161 912
  5008
Catherine Fleming

FAMILY PLACEMENT TEAM

Stretford Public Hall, Chester Rd, Stretford, Greater
  Manchester M32 OLG; Tel 0161 912 5039
Team Manager   Eileen McGlone;
  E-mail eileen.mcglone@trafford.gov.uk

FAMILY CENTRES

Atkinson Road Family Centre Atkinson Rd, Sale, Greater
Manchester M33 9FZ; Tel 0161 969 4686
Manager   Lynn Richards
  (49)
Central Road Family Centre Central Rd, Partington,
Cheshire M31 4EL; Tel 0161 775 5120
Manager   T. Burns
  (40)
Hayeswater Road Family Centre Hayeswater Rd,
Davyhulme, Greater Manchester M41 7BR; Tel 0161 748
3676
Manager   Lynn Wilson
  (49)
Poplar Road Family Centre Poplar Rd, Stretford, Greater
Manchester M32 9AN; Tel 0161 865 6863
Manager   P. Lavin
  (49)

CHILDREN AND YOUNG PERSONS' RESOURCE CENTRES

Flixton Road Resource Centre 190–192 Flixton Rd, Flixton,
Greater Manchester; Tel 0161 748 6003
Centre Manager   Steve Lowry
Kingsway Park Resource Centre 363 Kingsway Pk,
Davyhulme, Greater Manchester M41 7FE; Tel 0161 747
7205
Manager   Sally Rimmer
  (9)
Marple Grove Resource Centre 12–16 Marple Gr, Stretford,
Greater Manchester M32 0BD; Tel 0161 865 6114
Centre Manager   Tony Ridgeway
  (11)
Northenden Road Resource Centre 71 Northendon Rd, Sale,
Greater Manchester M33 2DG; Tel 0161 912 3521; Fax 0161
912 3522
Centre Manager   Alicia Cooper
  (25)
Old Hall Road Resource Centre Stretford, Greater
Manchester M32 9TL; Tel 0161 747 2052
Manager   Kath Delenda

CHILD AND FAMILY CENTRE

70 Chapel Rd, Sale, Greater Manchester M33 1EG; Tel 0161
  969 3026
Psychiatrist   Dr A. Bagadi

ADOLESCENT RESOURCE CENTRE

71a Northenden Rd, Sale, Greater Manchester M33 2DG;
  E-mail dermot.murphy@trafford.gov.uk; Tel 0161 912
  3503; Fax 0161 969 2036
Manager (Childrens Service)   Dermot Murphy

YOUTH OFFENDING TEAM

Team Manager   Helen McFarlane;
  E-mail helen.mcfarlane@trafford.gov.uk; Tel 0161 912
  3424; Fax 0161 912 3429

EQUIPMENT FOR PEOPLE WITH A PHYSICAL DISABILITY

One Stop Resource Centre (Disabilities) Dane Rd Ind Est,
Dane Rd, Sale, Greater Manchester M33 7BH; Tel 0161 283
4614
Centre Manager   Ms P. Roberts
St. Giles Lodge Resource Centre Atkinson Rd, Sale,
Greater Manchester M33 6FZ; Tel 0161 969 9711

DAY CENTRES FOR PEOPLE WITH A LEARNING DISABILITY

Future Visions (Learning Disability Empowerment Group)
Co-ordinator   Linda Humphrey; Tel 07966 474607
Albert Place Day Centre Altrincham, Greater Manchester
WA14 4NT; Tel 0161 928 6755
Manager   J. McCulloch
Meadowside Day Centre Torbay Rd, Urmston, Greater
Manchester M41 9LH; Tel 0161 748 4432
Manager   L. Merry

RESIDENTIAL HOME FOR PEOPLE WITH LEARNING DISABILITIES

Shawe Road Residential Home 10 Shawe Rd, Flixton,
Manchester M41 5DV; Tel 0161 747 0924
Manager   A. Sleeman (Acting)

COMMUNITY RESOURCE DAY CENTRE – MENTAL HEALTH

Cedar Road Resource Day Centre 20 Cedar Rd, Partington,
Cheshire M31 4LY; Tel 0161 777 6007
Chapel Road Resource Day Centre 70a–71b Chapel Rd,
Sale, Greater Manchester M33 1EG; Tel 0161 962 3070
Manager   C. Anderson
Day resources, staffed accommodation and crisis beds.

DAY CARE FOR THE ELDERLY

Northlea Resource Centre Gratrix La, Sale, Greater
Manchester M33 2SA; Tel 0161 962 2077
Manager   Joyce Hughes
The North Trafford Combined Care Centre 226 Seymour Gr,
Old Trafford, Manchester M16 0DU; Tel 0161 860 2702
Manager   John Ginty
Princess Centre Princess Rd, Flixton, Greater Manchester
M41 7FS; Tel 0161 747 1172
Manager   L. Corbett
  (30)
Pownall Road Altrincham, Greater Manchester; Tel 0161
912 5960; 0161 912 5961; 0161 912 5962
Manager   A. Beattie
  (50)
Intermediate Care – Sale (Older People Services) Northlea
Resource Centre, Gratrix La, Sale, Greater Manchester M33
Centre Manager   Julie Derbyshire; Tel 0161 976 1880;
  Fax 0161 976 1972

ACCOMMODATION FOR OLDER PEOPLE

There are nine local authority homes for elderly people offering a total of 375 places.
Manager Mark Grimes; Tel 0161 912 1585; Fax 0161 860 2702

Education, Art and Leisure Department

PO Box 40, Trafford Town Hall, Talbot Rd, Stretford, Greater Manchester M32 0EL; Tel 0161 912 1212; Fax 0161 912 4184
Executive Director (Children and Young People's Services) C. Pratt
Head of Service (Learner Support) R. Menmuir, BA
Deputy Head of Service A. Reynolds
Head (Sensory Impairment) B. Crossthwaite
Senior Educational Psychologist H. Madden, BSc, DipEdPsych
Assistant Education Officer (Special Needs) S.M.E. Roberts

SPECIAL SCHOOLS

Brentwood School Brentwood Ave, Timperley, Altrincham, Greater Manchester WA14 1SR; Tel 0161 928 8109
Headteacher B. Kostick

Delamere School Irlam Rd, Flixton, Stretford, Greater Manchester M41 6AP; Tel 0161 747 5893
Headteacher S. Huddart

Egerton School Kingsway Pk, Davyhulme, Greater Manchester M41 7FF; Tel 0161 749 7096
Headteacher E. Scroggi

Longford Park School Longford Pk, Stretford, Greater Manchester; Tel 0161 881 2341
Headteacher M. Coxe, DipE(Special)

Manor High School Manor Ave, Sale, Greater Manchester M33 5JX; Tel 0161 976 1553
Headteacher N. Eltringham (Acting)

Pictor School Harboro Rd, Sale, Greater Manchester M33 5AH; Tel 0161 962 5432
Headteacher J. Spruce

TYNE AND WEAR METROPOLITAN AREA

The following Metropolitan Councils comprise the Tyne and Wear Metropolitan Area and may be found in alphabetical order within this chapter: Gateshead, Newcastle upon Tyne, North Tyneside, South Tyneside, Sunderland.

WAKEFIELD METROPOLITAN DISTRICT COUNCIL
www.wakefield.gov.uk

Population 317 533
Town Hall, Wood St, Wakefield, West Yorkshire WF1 2HQ; URL www.wakefield.gov.uk; E-mail thereception@wakefield.gov.uk; Tel 01924 306090
Mayor Cllr R. Mitchell
Chief Executive John Foster
Chief Officer (Regeneration) A. Kerr

Housing and Social Care

8 St. John's North, Wakefield, West Yorkshire WF1 3QA; Tel 01924 307700; Fax 01924 307792; Minicom 01924 307701
Chief Officer (Housing and Social Care) Elaine McHale; Tel 01924 307725
Head (Commissioning Social Care) M. Grady; Tel 01924 307779
Head (Community Care) Richard Slade; Tel 01924 307737
Head (Children's Services) B. Toward; Tel 01924 307734
Manager (Community Care Services) I. Smith; Tel 01924 306239
Manager (Children's Services) J. Donaldson; Tel 01924 306291
Manager (Children's Services) G. Allin; Tel 01924 306211
Manager (Commissioning and Central Support Services) I.D. Campbell; Tel 01924 307738
Manager (Community Care Services) J. Farrar; Tel 01924 306202
Manager (Personnel) R. Rowe; Tel 01924 307799
Manager (Personnel and Training) M. Grinstead; Tel 01924 307704
Manager (Regulations and Complaints Services – R and I Unit F. O'Hanlon; Tel 01924 303451
Management Information Officer Helen Murray; Tel 01924 307790
Manager (Management Support Service) Julie Osborne; Tel 01924 307711
Manager (Finance) Caroline Briggs; Tel 01924 307787
Personnel Officer L. Webster; Tel 01924 307799
Communications Officer Adrian Johnson; Tel 01924 307765
Contact (Family Placements Scheme) D.J. Haughton; Tel 01924 302167

TRAINING

Responsible for training professsional and support staff in the department.
Staff Development John Ryden
Study Centre, 6 Springfield Grange, Wakefield, West Yorkshire WF2 9QP; Tel 01924 302137; Fax 01924 302152

Social Care Committee

Lab: 27, Con: 1
Cabinet Member (Social Care) A. Dean (Lab)
2 Highfield Rd, Pontefract, West Yorkshire WF8 3QA
Deputy Spokesperson (Health) G. Burton (Lab)
110 Arncliffe Dr, Ferrybridge, Knottingley, West Yorkshire WF11 8SS

HOSPITAL SOCIAL WORKERS

Pinderfields General and Fieldhead Hospitals
Hospital Social Services Officer Judith Sewell
Pontefract Hospitals
Hospital Social Services Officer Trish Edwards

COMMUNITY TEAM OFFICES

Featherstone North and South Teams Town Hall, Ackworth Rd, Featherstone, West Yorkshire WF7 5LX; Tel 01977 722640
Contact G. Rainey

Flanshaw and Wrenthorpe Team 2–4 Springfield Grange, Flanshaw, Wakefield, West Yorkshire WF2 9QA; Tel 01924 302195
Contact Derek Eastham

Hemsworth, Fitzwilliam, Ackworth and Ryhill Teams
Whitehall, Wakefield Rd, Hemsworth, West Yorkshire WF9 4AA; Tel 01977 722305
Contact Lyn Jones

Horbury Team Horbury Community Centre, Cluntergate, Horbury, West Yorkshire WF4 5DH; Tel 01924 302915

6

Ossett Team Ossett Town Hall, Ossett, West Yorkshire WF5 8BE; Tel 01924 303000
Contact Ruth Love

CHILDREN'S SPECIALIST CENTRES

Flanshaw Children's Centre 6 Springfield Grange, Flanshaw, West Yorkshire; Tel 01924 302110
Manager J. Barrett

Youth Justice 51 West Mead, Airedale, Castleford, West Yorkshire WF10 3AF; Tel 01977 722010
Team Manager S. Crofts
Operations Manager R. Rose

COMMUNITY HOMES

ABC Unit Flanshaw Children's Centre, 6 Springfield Grange, Wakefield, West Yorkshire WF2 9QP; Tel 01924 302144
Manager (ABC Unit) J. Barnes

Dacre Avenue Community Home 9 Dacre Ave, Lupset, Wakefield, West Yorkshire WF2 8AH; Tel 01924 302685; 01924 302686
Manager G.L. Smith
  (11)

Ings Road Community Home 2 Ings Rd, Kinsley, Pontefract, West Yorkshire WF9 5EW; Tel 01977 723125
Officer-in-Charge D. Hassan
  (11)

Marton Avenue Community Home 13a Marton Ave, Hemsworth, Pontefract, West Yorkshire WF9 4EZ; Tel 01977 723105; 01977 723106
Manager S. Richardson
  (11)

York Villas Community Home off Church La, Normanton, Wakefield, West Yorkshire WF6 1HA; Tel 01924 302595
Contact J. Williams

FAMILY CENTRES

Airedale Family Centre The Mount, Airedale, Castleford, West Yorkshire WF10 3JN; Tel 01977 722145
Unit Manager C.M. Riley

Langthwaite Family Centre Lidgate Cres, Langthwaite Grange Ind Est, Pontefract, West Yorkshire WF9 3NR; Tel 01977 722965
Unit Manager E. Taylor

Snapethorpe Family Centre Snapethorpe Gate, off Broadway, Wakefield, West Yorkshire WF2 8YU; Tel 01924 302710
Unit Manager J. Eccles

SIGNPOST

Flanshaw Children's Centre 6 Springfield Grange, Flanshaw, Wakefield, West Yorkshire WF2 9QP; Tel 01924 302105

TRAINING CENTRES FOR ADULTS WITH LEARNING DISABILITIES

Hemsworth Centre Holly St, Hemsworth, West Yorkshire WF9 4AD; Tel 01977 722250
Contact D. Wood
  Mixed

Pontefract Centre Knottingley Rd, Pontefract, West Yorkshire WF8 2JQ; Tel 01977 722695
Contact D. Hinchliffe
  (140)

Wakefield Centre Lawefield La, Wakefield, West Yorkshire WF2 8SX; Tel 01924 302295
Contact J.S. Smith
  (145)

RESPITE UNIT AND TEAM BASE FOR SUPPORTED LIVING SERVICE FOR PEOPLE WITH LEARNING DISABILITIES

Batley Road Centre 82 Batley Rd, Wakefield, West Yorkshire; Tel 01924 302680
Manager (Respite Unit) D. Woolley
Manager (Supported Living Services) J. Barlow
Manager (Supported Living Services) C. Jackson
Operations Manager (Supported Living Services) L. Reed
  SLS (50) Respite (36)

Carlton Close Centre 18 Carlton Cl, Hemsworth, West Yorkshire; Tel 01977 723116
Contact J. McIntosh
  Children (11)

Wasdale Road Centre 70 Wasdale Rd, Flanshaw, Wakefield, West Yorkshire WF2 9EX; Tel 01924 303420; 01924 303421

COMMUNITY LEARNING DISABILITIES TEAM

Beancroft Road Castleford, West Yorkshire; Tel 01977 465735

ASSESSMENT AND SUPPORT FOR PEOPLE WITH MENTAL HEALTH PROBLEMS

Mental Health Teams
There are community mental health teams based throughout the district.
Management Officer (Mental Health) S. Jarvis Municipal Offices; Tel 01977 727613

ACCOMMODATION FOR PEOPLE WITH MENTAL HEALTH PROBLEMS

Warren Crt, Park Lodge La, Wakefield, West Yorkshire WF1 4XA; Tel 01924 303415
Contact R. Logush
  (17)

DAY CENTRE FOR MENTALLY ILL

Garden Street Day Centre Garden St, Wakefield, West Yorkshire WF1 1DX; Tel 01924 327670; Fax 01924 327670
Centre Co-ordinator K. Barden

DAY CENTRES FOR ELDERLY PEOPLE

Grange View Day Centre Grange View, Outwood, Wakefield, West Yorkshire
Contact G.B. Parkinson

Horbury Community Centre Cluntergate, Horbury, West Yorkshire WF4 5PD; Tel 01924 276336

Lock Lane Day Centre Castleford, West Yorkshire; Tel 01977 722965
Contact D.M. Knight

Lupset Jubilee Hall Day Centre Townley/Haselden Rd, Lupset, Wakefield, West Yorkshire WF2 8NS; Tel 01924 366158
Contact J. Ward

AGED PERSONS' HOMES

There are nine local authority homes for elderly people offering a total of 275 places and three resource centres.

Education and Cultural Services

County Hall, Wakefield, West Yorkshire WF1 2QL; URL www.wakefield.gov.uk; Tel 01924 306090; Fax 01924 305632
Corporate Director (Education) J. McLeod, MA
Assistant Chief Education Officer (Resources and Performance) K. Jones, BSc, IPFA
Assistant Chief Education Officer (School Improvement and Cultural Services) J. Storey

Assistant Chief Education Officer (Inclusion and Lifelong Learning) J. Winter, BA
Head (School Governance and Organisation) D. Bowen, MA
Head (Early Years) A. Farrell
Head (Planning and Development) P. Mosby, LLB, ACIS
Head (ICT and Data Management) K. Watson, ACIS
Head (Education Personnel) I. Metcalfe
Head (Lifelong Learning) P. Elliot
Head (Research and Information Services) J. Potts, MA
Head (Young People's Service) L. Baynes
Head (Young People's Service) J. Price, BEd
Head (SEN Inclusion) S. Coleman
Senior Adviser (Transforming Primary Education) M. Gallagher
Education Officer (Special Projects) J. Lindley, BA, MEd
Senior Adviser (Transforming Secondary Education) J. Edwards
Senior Adviser/Service Manager (Secondary) S. Macleod
Senior Adviser/Service Manager (Training and Professional Development) J. Smith
Principal Adult Education Officer S. Dodderidge (Acting)
Principal Youth Officer L. Baynes
Principal Education Welfare Officer J. Price, BEd

HOSPITAL SPECIAL SCHOOL

Pinderfields and Pontefract Hospital School Aberford Rd, Wakefield, West Yorkshire WF1 4DG; E-mail headteacher@hospitalschools.wakefield.sch.uk; Tel 01924 303695
Headteacher H.M. Ferguson

SPECIAL DAY SCHOOLS

Highfield School Gawthorpe La, Gawthorpe, Ossett, West Yorkshire WF5 9BS; E-mail headteacher@highfield.wakefield.sch.uk; Tel 01924 302980
Headteacher A. Spalding
Kingsland Primary School Aberford Rd, Stanley, Wakefield, West Yorkshire WF3 4BA; Tel 01924 303100
Headteacher Mrs N. Wainwright
Oakfield Park School Barnsley Rd, Ackworth, Pontefract, West Yorkshire WF7 7DT; Tel 01977 723145
Headteacher Ms W.E. Fereday
Wakefield Pathways School, Castleford Poplar Ave, Townville, Castleford, West Yorkshire WF10 3QJ; E-mail headteacher@pathways.wakefield.sch.uk; Tel 01977 723085
Headteacher Y. Limb

SPECIAL BOARDING SCHOOL

The Felkirk School High Well Hill La, South Hiendley, Barnsley, South Yorkshire S72 9DF; E-mail headteacher@felkirk.wakefield.sch.uk; Tel 01226 718613
Joint Headteacher L. Halsey
Joint Headteacher J. McPhail
  Boys

WALSALL METROPOLITAN BOROUGH COUNCIL
www.walsall.gov.uk

Population 261 599
Civic Centre, Darwall St, Walsall, West Midlands WS1 1TS; URL www.walsall.gov.uk; Tel 01922 650000; Fax 01922 720885
Head (Personnel) Deb Clarke

Mayor Cllr E.W. Newman
Chief Executive Hardial Bhogal
Director (Education) Chris Green
Director (Housing and Central Services) Joanne Tyzzer
Director (Health and Regeneration) Valerie Little

Social Services

The Civic Centre, Darwall St, Walsall, West Midlands WS1 1RG; Tel 01922 652700; Fax 01922 646350; Minicom 01922 652715
Director (Health and Social Affairs) David Martin (Acting)
Divisional Social Work Manager (Adults) Norman Pitcher; Tel 01922 652790
General Manager (Adult Services) Joan Bramall; Tel 01922 652702
General Manager (Children's Services) Pauline Pilkington; Tel 01922 652756
General Manager (Business and Support Services) Kelvin Dawson; Tel 01922 652701
Head (Learning Disability Services) Kathleen McAteer; Tel 01922 658218
Service Manager (Learning Disabilities – Social Care) Ann Middlemiss; Tel 01922 652796
Service Manager (Learning Disabilities – Health and Theraputic Services) Jon Wright; Tel 0121 480 5945
Service Manager (Children's Resources) David Bottomley; Tel 01922 652783
Manager (Planning and Contracting) William Henwood; Tel 01922 652770
Service Manager (Elderly) Lloyd Brodrick (Acting); Tel 01922 652794
Consumer Relations Officer Tony Hyland; Tel 01922 652766

STAFF DEVELOPMENT AND TRAINING SECTION

Responsible for training professional and support staff in the department.
Mossley Centre, 1 Roche Rd, Walsall, West Midlands WS3 2QT; Tel 01922 713500
Manager Julian Mellor

Supported Living, Housing and Neighbourhood Services and Community Safety Overview and Scrutiny Committee

Lab: 5, Con: 4, LD: 1
Chair Cllr V.G. Woodruff (LD)
14 Darvel Rd, Willenhall, West Midlands WV12 4TR
Vice-Chair Cllr T.S. Oliver (Lab)
54 Delves Cres, Walsall, West Midlands WS5 4LR
Members of the Committee
Lab: J.M. Barton, I.C. Robertson, W. Saleem, R.V. Worrall.
Con: Mrs J. Beilby, A.J. Paul, W.T. Tweddle, M. Yasin.

YOUTH OFFENDING TEAM

104 Essington Rd, New Invention, Willenhall, West Midlands WV12 5DT; Tel 01922 493006
Team Manager Gerard Campion

REVIEW, PERFORMANCE AND CHILD PROTECTION UNIT

1st Fl, Core 2, Civic Centre, Darwall St, Walsall, West Midlands WS1 1RG; Tel 01922 652705
Principal Officer Kay Child

EMERGENCY DUTY TEAM

Windsor Ward, Goscote Hospital, Goscote La, Walsall, West Midlands WS3 1SJ; Tel 01922 653555
Team Manager Blasinder Jaspall-Mander

LOCAL AREA OFFICES

Manor Hospital Area Office

Moat Rd, Walsall, West Midlands WS2 9PY; Tel 01922 721172
Team Manager (Adults) Jayne Ptolomey (Acting)

Walsall East Area Office (Aldridge, Shelfield and Brownhills)

Walsall Wood, Rushall, Shelfield, Pelsall, Brownhills, Hatherton, Aldridge, Pheasey, Streetly.
158a Lichfield Rd, Shelfield, West Midlands WS4 1PW; Tel 01922 685811
Green La, Shelfield, West Midlands WS4 1RN; Tel (Adults) 01922 694993
Baytree Hse, Erdington Rd, Aldridge, West Midlands WS9 8HU; Tel (Adults) 01922 743337
Area Manager (Children's Assessment and Inclusion) Carol Boughton
Area Manager (Walsall East – Adults) Carol Grice (based at Walsall South); Tel 01922 658904

Walsall North (Bloxwich)

Mossley, Dudley Fields, Bloxwich Central, Beechdale, Ryecroft, Leamore, Bloxwich North, Goscote, Harden
Mossley Centre, 1 Roche Rd, Walsall, West Midlands WS3 2QT; Tel 01922 710001
Area Manager (Children's Assessment and Inclusion Services) Carol Boughton
Area Manager (Walsall North – Adults) John O'Meara

Walsall South Area Office

North Walsall, Chuckery, Paddock, Caldmore, Delves, Alumwell, Pleck, Birchills
Area Manager (Walsall South – Adults) Carol Grice
9th Fl, Townend Hse, Townend Sq, Walsall, West Midlands; Tel 01922 658900
Manager (Children's Services – Initial Response) Ann Thompson
The Quest, 139–143 Lichfield St, Walsall, West Midlands; Tel 01922 658170
Manager (Children's Service – Initial Response) Lesley Walker

Walsall West Area Office (Darlaston)

Darlaston, Moxley, Bentley
Town Hall, Victoria Rd, Darlaston, West Midlands WS10 8AA; Tel 0121 568 6611
Manager (Looked After Children's Team) Robert Heighway

Walsall West Area Office (Willenhall)

New Invention, Short Heath, Willenhall
108 Essington Rd, New Invention, Willenhall, West Midlands WV12 5EX; Tel 01922 710533
Area Manager (Walsall West – Adult Services) John O'Meara

Mental Health and Learning Disability

Broadway North Centre, Broadway North, Walsall, West Midlands WS1 2QA; Tel 01922 643650; 01922 649088
Operational Manager (Mental Health Crisis) Jim Warburton
Team Manager Robert Brown
Joint Team Development Manager (Learning Disabilities) Paul Stanley

MENTAL HEALTH TEAM (EAST WALSALL)

Anchor Meadow Health Centre, Aldridge, Walsall, West Midlands WS9 8AJ
Team Manager Pam Bevan (Acting) (based at South Walsall)

MENTAL HEALTH TEAM (SOUTH WALSALL)

Brace St Health Centre, 63 Brace St, Walsall, West Midlands WS1 3PS; Tel 01922 858928
Team Manager Pam Bevan

MENTAL HEALTH TEAM (NORTH WALSALL)

Bloxwich Hospital, Reeves St, Bloxwich, West Midlands WS3 2JJ; Tel 01922 858670
Team Manager Stephen Nash

MENTAL HEALTH TEAM (WEST WALSALL)

Conway Villa, The Cres, Darlaston, West Midlands; Tel 0121 526 5663
Team Manager Stephen Nash (based at North Walsall)

FAMILY CENTRES

Dale Street Family Centre Dale St, Walsall, West Midlands WS1 2AH; Tel 01922 721464
Centre Manager Barbara Richardson

Stroud Avenue Family Centre Stroud Ave, Lodge Farm Est, Willenhall, West Midlands WV12 4EG; Tel 01902 366733
Centre Manager Janet Murray

Teddesley Street Family Centre Teddesley St, Walsall, West Midlands WS4 2AH; Tel 01922 720747
Centre Manager Lynda Mayo

CHILDREN'S RESIDENTIAL ESTABLISHMENTS

Castleview Children's Centre Castleview Cl, Moxley, West Midlands WS10 8SE; Tel 01902 409402
Manager Chris Collis

Hilton Road Children's Home 43a–4a Hilton Rd, Willenhall, West Midlands; Tel 01922 710110; 01922 711775
Manager Janet Brien (Acting)

Lichfield Road Children's Home 57 Lichfield Rd, Walsall, West Midlands WS4 2HU; Tel 01922 627161
Manager Hayley Mason

Stroud Avenue Children's Home Lodge Farm Est, 248 Stroud Ave, Willenhall, West Midlands WV12 4EG; Tel 01902 366813
Manager Alison Blackwood

RESIDENTIAL ACCOMMODATION FOR CHILDREN WITH DISABILITIES – SHORT TERM BREAKS

Eldon Home Eldon St, Walsall, West Midlands WS1 2JS; Tel 01922 721332
Manager June Johnson

DISABLED LIVING CENTRE

The Priory, Odell Rd, Leamore, Walsall, West Midlands WS3 2ED; Tel 01922 402520
Manager (Specialist Teams) Cally Lock
Team Manager (Deaf and Hearing Impaired People) Vacancy

RESIDENTIAL ESTABLISHMENTS FOR PEOPLE WITH LEARNING DIFFICULTIES

Beacon View Home 20 Little Aston Rd, Aldridge, Walsall, West Midlands WS9 0NN; Tel 01922 743712
Assistant Resource Manager Elaine Delaney

Fallings Heath House Walsall Rd, Darlaston, West Midlands WS10 9SH; Tel 0121 568 6297
Resource Centre Manager Carole Curtis

Narrow Lane Home Narrow La, Pleck, Walsall, West Midlands WS2 9QP; Tel 01922 720705
Assistant Resource Manager Elaine Delaney

Rivers House Slacky La, Goscote, Walsall, West Midlands WS3 1NN; Tel 01922 710480
Resource Centre Manager Lynn Susan Jones

RESIDENTIAL AND DAY CARE FOR PEOPLE WITH MENTAL HEALTH PROBLEMS

Broadway North Centre Broadway North, Walsall, West Midlands WS1 2QA; Tel (Daycare) 01922 648019; (Residential) 01922 649640
Resource Centre Manager Michael Hicklin

DAY CENTRES FOR PEOPLE WITH LEARNING DISABILITIES

Brewer Street Adult Training Centre Brewer St, Walsall, West Midlands WS2 8BA; Tel 01922 720690
Assistant Resource Centre Manager Jan Robinson

Goscote Adult Training Centre Goscote La, Goscote, Walsall, West Midlands WS3 1SJ; Tel 01922 710312
Assistant Resource Centre Manager Jackie Wilmot

Northgate Adult Training Centre Northgate, Aldridge, Walsall, West Midlands WS9 8JT; Tel 01922 743909
Assistant Resource Centre Manager Jan Robinson

Shepwell Green Adult Training Centre Bilston La, Willenhall, West Midlands WV13 2QJ; Tel 01902 366772
Resource Centre Manager Richard Devlin

DAY CARE CENTRES FOR PEOPLE WITH A PHYSICAL DISABILITY

Darlaston Day Centre – Multipurpose Centre Old School, Victoria Rd, Darlaston, West Midlands WS10 8AS; Tel 0121 568 6267
Resource Centre Manager Sue Lloyd (based at Hollybank House)

Pinfold Centre Field Cl, Bloxwich, West Midlands; Tel 01922 710747
Resource Centre Manager Martin Hall

RESIDENTIAL ESTABLISHMENT FOR PEOPLE WITH A PHYSICAL DISABILITY

Hollybank House Coltham Rd, Short Heath, Willenhall, West Midlands WV12 5QB; Tel 01922 710524
Home Manager David Boyes

RESOURCE CENTRES

Baytree House Erdington Rd, Aldridge, Walsall, West Midlands WS9 8UH; Tel (Daycare) 01922 453204; (Residential) 01922 743606
Resource Centre Manager Denise Clift

Bentley Home Wilkes Ave, Bentley, Walsall, West Midlands WS2 0JT; Tel (Daycare) 01922 643611; (Residential) 01922 721250
Resource Centre Manager Debbie Wright

Delves Home Brockhurst Cres, Walsall, West Midlands WS5 4PW; Tel (Daycare) 01922 621903; (Residential) 01922 721033
Resource Centre Manager Gloria John

Rushall Mews Rehabilitation Centre New St, Rushall, Walsall, West Midlands; Tel 01922 720300
Officer-in-Charge Peter Blackburn

Sanstone House Sanstone Rd, Bloxwich, West Midlands WS3 8SJ; Tel (Daycare) 01922 406700; (Residential) 01922 710572
Resource Centre Manager Graham Sharples

Short Heath House Sandbeds Rd, Willenhall, West Midlands WV12 4EX; Tel (Daycare) 01902 366612; (Residential) 01902 366969
Resource Centre Manager Vacancy

St. James Home Short St, Brownhills, West Midlands WS8 6AD; Tel (Daycare) 01543 452007; (Residential) 01543 452572; (Meals service) 01543 452626
Resource Centre Manager Brian Taylor

RESIDENTIAL ESTABLISHMENTS FOR THE ELDERLY

There are three homes for the elderly.

Education Walsall

From 1st December 2002, Education Walsall took control of the majority of outsourced LEA functions.
Education Development Centre, Pelsall La, Rushall, Walsall, West Midlands WS4 1NG; Tel 01922 686200; Fax 01922 682621
Managing Director Elaine Simpson; Tel 01922 686277
Director (Learning – SEN and Inclusion) Helen Denton; Tel 01922 686213
Director (Commercial) Keith Thompson; Tel 01922 686206
Director (Learning – School Improvement) Tony Stainer; Tel 01922 686201
Director (Projects) Trevor Edinborough (Acting); Tel 01922 686211
Manager (PR and Communications) Amanda Best; Tel 01922 686279

EDUCATION PSYCHOLOGICAL SERVICE

Lime Hse, Little Street West, Walsall, West Midlands; Tel 01992 721551
Principal Educational Psychologist Frank Barnes

INCLUSION SUPPORT SERVICE

Inclusion Support Centre Field Rd, Bloxwich, Walsall, West Midlands; Tel 01922 711931
Contact Linda Adey
Includes vision and hearing impairment teams. Learning support and early years SEN. For details of other specialist units and special schools in Walsall please call 01922 686200.

WARRINGTON BOROUGH COUNCIL
www.warrington.gov.uk

In April 1998 both Warrington and Halton Councils became unitary authorities. The rest of Cheshire retains a two-tier structure and is listed alphabetically within this chapter.
Population 193 000
Political Composition: Lab: 42, LD: 13, Con: 4
Town Hall, Sankey St, Warrington WA1 1UH; URL www.warrington.gov.uk; Tel 01925 444400; Fax 01925 442138
Chief Executive Steven Broomhead
Leader of the Council John Gartside
Director (Finance) Peter Carey
Director (Direct Services and Housing) Peter Connell
Director (Environment and Regeneration) Alan Stephenson
Director (Housing) Tom Roberts
Director (Environmental Services) Keith Millington

Social Services Department

Warrington Borough Council, Bewsey Old School, Lockton La, Bewsey, Warrington WA5 0BF; E-mail socialservices@warrington.gov.uk; Tel 01925 444400; Fax 01925 444002
Director (Social Services) David Whitehead
Assistant Director (Policy and Performance) David Whyte
Assistant Director (Older People and Physical Disability) Pam Smith
Assistant Director (Mental Health and Learning Disability) Helen Sumner
Assistant Director (Children and Families) John Dunkerley
Social services for children, people with learning disabilities and mental health problems and older people.

Social Services Committee

Lab: 11, LD: 3, Con: 1

DIVISIONAL OFFICE

Service Reception Team

Social Services Office, 57 Winmarleigh St, Warrington
WA1 1LE; E-mail servicereception@warrington.gov.uk;
Tel (Direct) 01925 444239; (Switchboard) 01925 444400;
Fax 01925 444201; 01925 444207

Children and Families

The Children's Centre 71–75 St. Katherine's Way,
Warrington WA1 2EP; Tel 01925 414385

Orford Lane Family Centre Orford La, Warrington
WA2 7AF; Tel 01925 632486; Fax 01925 244053

Ross Close Short Break Centre 27–28 Ross Cl, Old Hall,
Warrington WA5 5PW; Tel 01925 651381

Severe Learning Disabilities

Gorse Covert Day Centre 22 Adlington Crt, off Risley Rd,
Birchwood, Warrington WA3 6PL; Tel 01925 824764

James Phoenix House Hilden Rd, Padgate, Warrington
WA2 0JP; Tel 01925 815586

Orford Day Centre Festival Ave, Orford, Warrington
WA2 9EP; Tel 01925 637134

Penketh Day Centre Meeting La, Penketh, Warrington
WA5 2BG; Tel 01925 791259

West and East Network 2 Brookside Crt, off Hilden Rd,
Padgate, Warrington WA2 0JP; Tel 01925 815586; Fax 01925
826387

Physical Disabilities

**Warrington Disability Partnership, Centre for Independent
Living** Beaufort St, Warrington WA5 1BA; Tel 01925
240064

Dallam Centre Back Dallam La, Warrington WA2 7NG;
Tel 01925 632105

Mental Health

Community Outreach Team Harrison Centre, Boutling Ave,
Warrington WA5 2EP; Tel 01925 416560

Community Mental Health Team – West Harrison Centre,
Boulting Ave, Warrington WA5 2EP; Tel 01925 573489

Older People's Services

Chestnut House Community Support Centre Bridge La,
Appleton, Warrington WA4 3AH; Tel 01925 266571

Houghton Day Centre Greenwood Cres, Orford, Warrington
WA2 0EA; Tel 01925 821077

Mosslands, Housing with Care and Support Aldewood Cl,
Gorse Covert, Warrington WA3 6UW; Tel 01925 814556

Padgate House Residential Centre Vulcan Cl, Padgate,
Warrington WA2 0HL; Tel 01925 821639

Woodleigh Community Resource Centre Callands Rd,
Callands, Warrington WA5 9RJ; Tel 01925 235237

Education and Lifelong Learning Department

New Town Hse, Buttermarket St, Warrington WA1 2NJ;
Tel 01925 442971; Fax 01925 442969
Strategic Director (Education and Lifelong Learning)
Malcolm Roxburgh
Special Schools
2 Day; 1 Special Residential

SPECIAL SCHOOLS

Fox Wood School Chatfield Dr, Birchwood, Warrington
WA3 6QW; Tel 01925 851393
Headteacher Mrs Lesley Roberts
Mixed SLD

Grappenhall Hall Residential School Church La,
Grappenhall, Warrington WA4 3EU; Tel 01925 263895;
Fax 01925 860487
Headteacher Angela Findlay
Boys EBD Residential (55) Day (39) (117)

Green Lane School Green La, Padgate, Warrington
WA1 4JL; Tel 01925 480128; Fax 01925 480127
Headteacher Paul King
Mixed MLD (118)

WARWICKSHIRE COUNTY COUNCIL
www.warwickshire.gov.uk

Population 493 654
Political Composition: Lab: 28, Con: 20, LD: 13, Other: 1
Shire Hall, Warwick, Warwickshire CV34 4RR;
URL www.warwickshire.gov.uk; Tel 01926 410410
Chair of the Council Jill Dill-Russell
Chief Executive I.G. Caulfield, CBE, BA, DipTP
County Treasurer Dave Clarke
County Officer (Libraries, Heritage and Trading Standards)
N.C. Hunter, FITSA, FRSA
Old Budbrooke Rd, Warwick, Warwickshire CV35 7DP;
Tel 01926 414040
Director (Property Services) P.H. Ridley, BSc(Hons), FRICS,
MCIOB
Director (Planning, Transport and Economic Strategy)
John Deegan, BA, MSc, DipTP, MRTPI, MCIT

Social Services Department

PO Box 48, Shire Hall, Warwick, Warwickshire CV34 4RD;
Tel 01926 410410; Fax 01926 412799
Director (Social Care and Health) Marion Davis
Head (Adult Services) John Bull
Head (Children's Services) Simon Lord
Head (Resources Management) Andy Burns
Head (Organisational Development) Linda Holland
Principal Press Officer Anne Goodey

Social Services Committee

Lab: 12, Con: 9, LD: 3

MANAGEMENT SERVICES

Central Charging Team

Warwick Hse, Wheat St, Nuneaton, Warwickshire
CV11 4AJ; Tel 01926 412533

Children's Planning Team

Regency Arcade, 152 The Pde, Leamington Spa,
Warwickshire CV32 4BQ; Tel 01926 418280

Customer Relations Team

Old Clink, Warwick, Warwickshire CV34 4SJ; Tel 01926
414119

Fostering and Adoption Services

Faraday Hall, Lower Hillmorton Rd, Rugby, Warwickshire
CV21 3TU; Tel 01788 541333

Human Resources

8–16 Russell St, Leamington Spa, Warwickshire; Tel 01926 451911

Information Strategy

Myton Pk, off Myton La, Warwick, Warwickshire CV34 6PX; Tel 01926 414878

Interpreting and Translation

PO Box 48, Shire Hall, Warwick, Warwickshire CV34 4RD; Tel 01926 412532

Residential Administration Team

Warwick Hse, Wheat St, Nuneaton, Warwickshire CV11 4AJ; Tel 01926 413114

Services to Deaf People

Warwick Hse, Wheat St, Nuneaton, Warwickshire CV11 4AQ; Tel 01926 413043

SIBS (Sexualised Inappropriate Behaviours)

District Council Offices, The Grange, Southam, Warwickshire CV33 8BD; Tel 01926 813110

Staff Development Commissioning Unit

PO Box 48, Shire Hall, Warwick, Warwickshire CV34 4RD; Tel 01926 410410

Youth Offending Team (North)

Newton Hall, Lower Hillmorton Rd, Rugby, Warwickshire CV21 3TU; Tel 01788 331256

Youth Offending Team (South)

Sterling Hse, 12 Hamilton Terr, Leamington Spa, Warwickshire CV32 4LY; Tel 01926 736200

DISTRICT OFFICES

North Warwickshire District Office Warwick Hse, Ratcliffe St, Atherstone, Warwickshire CV9 1JP; Tel (Intake and Duty Team) 01827 720800

Nuneaton and Bedworth District Office Vicarage St, Nuneaton, Warwickshire CV11 4AU; Tel 024 7634 7383

Rugby District Office Faraday Hall, Lower Hillmorton Rd, Rugby, Warwickshire CV21 3TU; Tel 01788 541333

Stratford District Office Arden Hse, Masons Rd, Stratford-upon-Avon, Warwickshire CV37 9NW; Tel 01789 269391

Warwick District Office Regency Arcade, 152 The Pde, Leamington Spa, Warwickshire CV32 4BQ; Tel 01926 451911

ADULT TEAMS

Bedworth Newtown Rd, Bedworth, Warwickshire CV12 8QB; Tel 024 7664 3838

Kenilworth and Warwick 39–41 Warwick Rd, Kenilworth, Warwickshire CV8 1HN; Tel 01926 859221

Leamington 56–58 Holly Wlk, Leamington Spa, Warwickshire CV32 4JE; Tel 01926 334111

North Warwickshire Warwick Hse, Ratcliffe St, Atherstone, Warwickshire CV9 4JP; Tel 01827 714861

Nuneaton Warwick Hse, Wheat St, Nuneaton, Warwickshire CV11 4AJ; Tel 024 7634 1234

Rugby Oakfield Pk, 32 Bilton Rd, Rugby, Warwickshire CV22 7AL; Tel 01788 541333

Shipston Ellen Badger Hospital, Stratford Rd, Shipston on Stour, Warwickshire CV36 4AX; Tel 01608 661090

Stratford Grove Hse, Gunnings Rd, Alcester, Warwickshire B49 6AB; Tel 01789 762219

CHILDREN AND FAMILY SERVICES

North Warwickshire Children and Family Services

Arden Hill 55 South St, Atherstone, Warwickshire CV9 1DZ; Tel 01827 716956

Nuneaton and Bedworth Children's Teams

Newtown Road Bedworth, Warwickshire; Tel 024 7664 3838

Warwick House Wheat St, Nuneaton, Warwickshire CV11 4AJ; Tel 024 7635 1234

District Children's Services Team

Henry Street Centre, 23 Henry St, Nuneaton, Warwickshire CV11 5SQ; Tel 024 7638 7363

Rugby Short-Term and Community Needs Unit

Intensive Support and Assessment The Bridge, 55 Clifton Rd, Rugby, Warwickshire CV21 3QE; Tel 01788 543886

Long-Term Team Fawsley Hse, 25 Hillmorton Rd, Rugby, Warwickshire CV22 5BX; Tel 01788 562045

Oakfield Park 32 Bilton Rd, Rugby, Warwickshire CV22 7AL; Tel 01788 541333

Warwick Long-Term Team

16 Old Sq, Warwick, Warwickshire CV34 4RA; Tel 01926 410410

District Assessment Team 56–58 Holly Wlk, Leamington Spa, Warwickshire CV32 4JE; Tel 01926 334111

Leamington Long-Term Team Myton Pk, Myton La, Warwick, Warwickshire CV34 6PX; Tel 01926 492431

Stratford and Alcester Children's Team

8 Rother St, Stratford-upon-Avon, Warwickshire CV37 6LU; Tel 01789 269391

Southam and Shipston Children's Team

District Council Offices, The Grange, Southam, Warwickshire CV33 8BD; Tel 01926 813110

Stratford Family Support Team

Drayton Avenue Centre, 185 Drayton Ave, Stratford-upon-Avon, Warwickshire CV37 9PS; Tel 01789 414774

STRATFORD FAMILY CENTRE

Alcester Rd, Stratford-upon-Avon, Warwickshire CV37 9DD; Tel 01789 298652

COMMUNITY MENTAL HEALTH TEAMS AND CENTRES

Bedworth 9a Bulkington Rd, Bedworth, Warwickshire CV12 9DG; Tel 024 7631 0037

Coleshill Water Orton Clinic, 112a Coleshill Rd, Water Orton, West Midlands B46 1QE; Tel 0121 747 2080

Kenilworth 95 Abbey End, Kenilworth, Warwickshire CV8 1LS; Tel 01926 851285

Leamington St. Mary's Lodge, 12 St. Mary's Rd, Leamington Spa, Warwickshire CV31 1JN; Tel 01926 339261

North Warwickshire 10 Friary Rd, Atherstone, Warwickshire CV9 3AG; Tel 01827 714069

6

Nuneaton Riversley Park Resource Centre, Riversley Pk, Nuneaton, Warwickshire CV11 5TY; Tel 024 7637 3806

Rugby 34 Clifton Rd, Rugby, Warwickshire CV21 3QF; Tel 01788 562472

Stratford Stratford Hospital, Arden St, Stratford-upon-Avon, Warwickshire CV37 6NX; Tel 01789 415440

COMMUNITY MENTAL HEALTH TEAMS (ELDERLY)

Kingsbury Health Centre Coventry Rd, Kingsbury, Tamworth, Warwickshire; Tel 01827 874873

Manor Court Community Mental Health Team 6 Manor Crt, Nuneaton, Warwickshire; Tel 024 7632 0912

COMMUNITY PLACEMENT UNITS

Rugby 84 Bromwich Rd, Rugby, Warwickshire CV21 4HZ; Tel 01788 537582

Warwick and Leamington Emscote Centre, Nelson La, Warwick, Warwickshire CV34 5NP; Tel 01926 419471; 01926 419472; 01926 419473

Bedworth 1–3 Hurst Rd, Bedworth, Warwickshire CV12 8AD; Tel 024 7664 3443

CORE TEAMS FOR PEOPLE WITH LEARNING DISABILITIES

North Warwickshire Polesworth Health Clinic, High St, Polesworth, Warwickshire; Tel 01827 898884

Nuneaton and Bedworth 136 Manor Court Rd, Nuneaton, Warwickshire CV11 5HQ; Tel 024 7634 3773

HEALTH TEAMS (ADULT AND CHILDREN)

George Eliot Hospital College St, Nuneaton, Warwickshire CV10 7DJ; Tel 024 7635 1351

Hospital of St. Cross Barby Rd, Rugby, Warwickshire CV22 5PX; Tel 01788 572831

Warwick Hospital Lakin Rd, Warwick, Warwickshire CV34 5BW; Tel 01926 495321

HOMECARE UNITS

Bedworth Newtown Rd, Bedworth, Warwickshire; Tel 024 7664 3838

Kenilworth, Warwick and Leamington Myton Pk, Myton La, off Myton Rd, Warwick, Warwickshire CV34 6BR; Tel 01926 492481

North Warwickshire Warwick Hse, Ratcliffe St, Atherstone, Warwickshire CV9 1AU; Tel 01827 714862

Nuneaton Vicarage St, Nuneaton, Warwickshire; Tel 024 7635 1234

Rugby Oakfield Pk, 32 Bilton Rd, Rugby, Warwickshire CV22 7AL; Tel 01788 541333

Stratford

The Bungalow rear of Low Furlong HEP, Darlingscote Rd, Shipston on Stour, Warwickshire CV36 4DY; Tel 01608 663522

Drayton Avenue Home Care Unit 187 Drayton Ave, Stratford-upon-Avon, Warwickshire; Tel 01789 269391

HOMES FOR ELDERLY PEOPLE

There are nine local authority homes for elderly people.

RESOURCE CENTRES

Ramsden Centre School Wlk, off Highfield Rd, Nuneaton, Warwickshire CV11 4PJ; Tel 024 7637 1737

Rowan Organisation North St, Atherstone, Warwickshire CV9 1JN; Tel 01827 718972

Saltway Centre Alcester Rd, Stratford-upon-Avon, Warwickshire; Tel 01789 298823

SOCIAL EDUCATION CENTRES

Alnebank Centre Cunnings Rd, Alcester, Warwickshire B49 6AB; Tel 01789 765309

Avonbank Centre Block C, Stratford College, The Willows North, Stratford-on-Avon, Warwickshire; Tel 01789 269178

Bloxham Centre Somers Rd, Rugby, Warwickshire CV22 7DE; Tel 01788 565556

Bridgeway Centre Coalpits Fields Rd, Bedworth, Warwickshire CV12 9HU; Tel 024 7631 6075

Brookbank Alcester Rd, Stratford-upon-Avon, Warwickshire CV37 9DG; Tel 01926 736580

Emscote Centre Nelson La, Warwick, Warwickshire CV34 5JB; Tel 01926 492100

Freeway Centre Park Ave, Nuneaton, Warwickshire CV11 4GP; Tel 02476 382126

Newbold Centre Leicester St, Leamington Spa, Warwickshire CV32 4TE; Tel 01926 334973

Seeswood Centre Hilary Rd, Nuneaton, Warwickshire CV10 9AD; Tel 024 7638 2126

Shortwoods Centre Dordon, Tamworth, Staffordshire B78 1TP; Tel 01827 895747

Education Department

22 Northgate St, Warwick, Warwickshire CV34 4SP; E-mail edcomms@warwickshire.gov.uk; Tel 01926 410410; Fax 01926 412746
County Education Officer Eric Wood, MSc
Assistant County Education Officer (Community Division) Jim Fitzgibbon
Assistant County Education Officer (Strategy Division) Mark Gore
Director (Resources) Jeff Mann
Director (Warwickshire Education Services – WES) John Fletcher
Manager (Finance) John Betts
Assistant County Education Officer (SEN) Beryl Lockwood
Chief Inspector Stella Blackmore
Principal Educational Psychologist Ros Sinclair
Principal Education Social Worker J. Sullivan

Central Area School Team

Education Office, 22 Northgate St, Warwick, Warwickshire CV34 4SP; Tel 01926 410410
Area Education Officer Tim Howram

DAY SPECIAL SCHOOLS

The Ridgeway School Montague Rd, Warwick, Warwickshire CV34 5LW; Tel 01926 491987; Fax 01926 407317
Headteacher Mrs P.A. Flynn
SLD (91)

The Round Oak School and Support Service Pound La, Lillington, Leamington Spa, Warwickshire CV32 7RT; Tel 01926 335566; Fax 01926 886163
Headteacher Ms P. Pocock
MLD (87)

Southern Area School Team

Area Education Officer Mr C. Larvin
Education Office, 22 Northgate St, Warwick, Warwickshire CV34 4SP
Number of Schools
9 Secondary; 2 Day Special.

DAY SPECIAL SCHOOLS

River House School Stratford Rd, Henley in Arden, Solihull, West Midlands B95 6AD; Tel 01564 792514; Fax 01564 792179
Headteacher Mr M. Turner

The Welcombe Hills School Blue Cap Rd, Stratford-upon-Avon, Warwickshire CV37 6TQ; Tel 01789 266845; Fax 01789 204121
Headteacher Mrs J. Clark

Eastern Area School Team

Education Office, 22 Northgate St, Warwick, Warwickshire CV34 4SP
Area Education Officer Peter Thompson

DAY SPECIAL SCHOOL

Brooke School Merttens Dr, Rugby, Warwickshire CV22 7AE; Tel 01788 576145; Fax 01788 541207
Headteacher Mrs S. Cowen

North Warwickshire Area School Team

Education Office, 22 Northgate St, Warwick, Warwickshire CV34 4SP
Area Education Officer Mr D. Potter

DAY SPECIAL SCHOOLS

Blythe School Packington La, Coleshill, Birmingham, West Midlands B46 3JE; E-mail blythe@ermplc.co.uk; Tel 01675 463590; Fax 01675 463584
Headteacher Mrs G. Simpson

Sparrowdale School Spon La, Grendon, Atherstone, Warwickshire CV9 2PD; Tel 01827 713436; Fax 01827 720472
Headteacher Mrs M. Pomfrett

Nuneaton and Bedworth Area School Team

Education Office, 22 Northgate St, Warwick, Warwickshire CV34 4SP
Area Education Officer Nigel Mills

SPECIAL SCHOOLS

Exhall Grange School Wheelwright La, Ash Grn, Coventry, West Midlands CV7 9HP; Tel 0247 636 4200; Fax 0247 664 5055
Headteacher Mr R.G. Bignall
PS/PH (230)

The Griff School Coventry Rd, Nuneaton, Warwickshire CV10 7AX; Tel 0247 638 3315; Fax 0247 637 1768
Headteacher Mrs R.M. Scott (Acting)
MLD (113)

Leyland School Leyland Rd, Nuneaton, Warwickshire CV11 4RP; Tel 0247 638 5313; Fax 0247 635 0042
Headteacher Mrs L. Bush
SLD (94)

WEST BERKSHIRE COUNCIL
www.westberks.gov.uk

In April 1998 Berkshire County Council was replaced by Bracknell Forest, Reading, Slough, West Berkshire, Windsor and Maidenhead and Wokingham, all responsible for local government services within their area. They are listed alphabetically within this chapter.
Political Composition: LD: 26, Con: 26
Council Offices, Market St, Newbury, West Berkshire RG14 5LD; URL www.westberks.gov.uk; Tel 01635 42400; Fax 01635 519431

Chief Executive Jim Graham
Corporate Director (Environment and Public Protection)
John Ashworth
Corporate Director (Community Care and Housing)
Margaret Goldie
Corporate Director (Strategy and Commissioning)
Nick Carter
Corporate Director (Children and Young People)
Richard Hubbard

Social Services

Avonbank Hse, West St, Newbury, West Berkshire RG14 1BZ; URL www.westberks.gov.uk; E-mail mgoldie@westberks.gov.uk; Tel 01635 519730; (Emergency) 01344 786543; Fax 01635 519939
Corporate Director (Community Care and Housing)
Margaret Goldie
Head (Older People's Services) Jan Evans
Head (Children's Services) Andy Couldrick
Head (Community Care and Housing Services) Bev Searle
Head (Quality, Partnerships and Performance) Teresa Bell
Service Manager (Strategy and Effectiveness – Children's Services) Paul Nixon
Service Manager (Care Management and Commissioning (Elderly and Physical Disabilities)) Trish Robertson
Services Manager (Care Management and Commissioning (Mental Health and Learning Disabilities)) Mary Bennett
Service Manager (Direct Provision) Vacancy
Service Manager (Learning Disability) Helen Jermy
Service Manager (Quality Protects) Sue Adamantos
Manager (Quality and Performance) Vacancy

Executive

Leader Dr Royce Longton
Deputy Leader Owen Jeffery
Members of the Executive
Mollie Lock, Phil Barnett, John Farrin, Sally Hannon, Trevor Banning, James Mole.

NATIONAL CARE STANDARDS COMMISSION

1015 Arlington Bus Pk, Theale, West Berkshire RG7 4SA; Tel 0118 903 3230; Fax 0118 903 3276
Manager Richard Hayes

AREA OFFICES

Newbury Area Office Pelican Hse, 9–15 West St, Newbury, West Berkshire RG14 1PL; Tel 01635 46545; Fax 01635 516789
Children's services Access Point and Adults Main Team West.

Theale Area Office Units 11–12 Coopers Hse, Brewery Crt, off High St, Theale, West Berkshire RG7 5AJ; E-mail ccenquiries@westberks.gov.uk; Tel (Enquiry Centre) 0845 601 4726; 0118 930 2777; Fax 0118 930 5272

ADOLESCENT TEAM

The Priory Church La, Thatcham, West Berkshire RG19 3JL; Tel 01635 862060; Fax 01635 863267
Adolescent Team Manager Collette Hanson

FAMILY RESOURCE CENTRE

York House 50 Andover Rd, Newbury, West Berkshire RG14 6TW; Tel 01635 43639; Fax 01635 522682
Manager Robert Bradshaw

RESPITE FOR YOUNG PEOPLE WITH LEARNING DISABILITIES

Castlecroft Love La, Donnington, Newbury, West Berkshire RG14 2JG; Tel 01635 43778
Manager Rachel Palin
Six beds per night.

6

DAY CARE ESTABLISHMENTS FOR ELDERLY PEOPLE

Downland Day Centre Burrell Rd, Newbury, West Berkshire
RG20 6NP; Tel 01635 578580
Manager Caroline Dibley; Tel 0118 945 4744
12 places (Mon, Wed and Fri)
  (24)

Highview Day Centre Highview Rd, Calcot, Reading
RG31 4XD; Tel 0118 945 4744
Manager Caroline Dibley
24 (Mon, Wed and Fri)

Hungerford Day Centre Ramsbury Dr, Hungerford, West
Berkshire RG17 0EE; Tel 01488 682601
Manager Richard Horton
25 places (Mon–Fri)

Shaw Day Centre Hutton Cl, Newbury, West Berkshire
RG14 1HJ; Tel 01635 551045
Manager Caroline Dibley; Tel 0118 945 4744
12 places (Mon, Wed and Fri)

Walnut Close Day Centre Brownsfield Rd, Thatcham, West
Berkshire RG18 3GF; Tel 01635 868550
Manager Anne Moffat
26 places (Tues–Fri).

Windmill Court Day Centre Windmill Rd, Mortimer,
Reading RG7 3RJ; Tel 0118 933 2468
Manager Caroline Dibley; Tel 0118 945 4744
12 places (Mon, Tue, Wed and Fri)

HOME CARE TEAM

Avonbank Hse, West St, Newbury, West Berkshire
  RG14 1BZ; Tel 01635 519756; Fax 01634 519740
Home Care Manager Pat Seeley

RESIDENTIAL CARE ESTABLISHMENTS FOR ELDERLY PEOPLE

There are four local authority homes for older people.

COMMUNITY TEAM FOR PEOPLE WITH LEARNING DISABILITIES

**Newbury Community Team for People with Learning
Disabilities** 1st Fl, Newbury Day Centre, Newbury,
West Berkshire RG14 7EB; Tel 01635 520120; Fax 01635
520122
Manager Val Burge

DAY CENTRES FOR ADULTS WITH LEARNING DISABILITIES

Greenfield Hse Calcot Centre, off Highview Rd, Calcot,
Reading RG31 4XD; Tel 01189 419181
Manager Cliff Haynes
  (40)

Newbury Day Centre Newtown Rd, Newbury, West
Berkshire RG14 7EB; Tel 01635 43886; Fax 01635 552022
Manager John Lynch
  (100)

DAY FACILITIES FOR PEOPLE WITH MENTAL HEALTH NEEDS

Cornwell Day Centre Home Croft, Clements Mead,
Tilehurst, West Berkshire RG31 5WJ; Tel 0118 945 2761
Manager Pam Bonding
15 places (Wed only)

Hilltop Day Centre George Hse, Pelican La, Newbury, West
Berkshire RG14 1NP; Tel 01635 31031
Manager Pam Bonding
20 places (Mon–Fri)

DAY CENTRE FOR ADULTS WITH A PHYSICAL DISABILITY

Ormonde Centre Newbury College of Further Education,
Monks La, Newbury, West Berkshire RG14 7TD;
URL www.westberks.gov.uk; Tel 01635 42374
Manager David Tait
  100 over a week.

COMMUNITY MENTAL HEALTH TEAM

Newbury Community Mental Health Team Pelican La,
Newbury, West Berkshire RG14 1NP; Tel 01635 40558;
Fax 01635 522948
Manager Vacancy

Education Department

Avonbank Hse, West St, Newbury, West Berkshire
  RG14 1BZ; URL www.westberks.gov.uk/westberkshire/
  education.nsf; Tel 01635 519716; Fax 01635 519725
Corporate Director (Children and Young People)
  Richard Hubbard

EDUCATION WELFARE AND PSYCHOLOGY

Avonbank Hse, West St, Newbury, West Berkshire
  RG14 1BZ; Tel 01635 519785
Principal Education Welfare Officer Karen Bartholomew
Principal Educational Psychologist Robin Bartlett

SPECIAL CLASSES AND RESOURCES

Denefield Special Resource (Hearing Impairment)
Denefield School (Secondary), Long La, Tilehurst, Reading
RG31 6XY; URL www.denefield.org.uk;
E-mail office.denefield@westberks.org; Tel 0118 941 3458;
Fax 0118 945 2847
Headteacher Mr E. Joint
  Hearing impairment

Kennet Special Resource (Physical Disability) Kennet
School (Secondary), Stoney La, Thatcham, West Berkshire
RG19 4LL; E-mail office.kennet@westberks.org; Tel 01635
862121; Fax 01635 871814
Headteacher Mr P. Dick
  Physical disability

**Lambourn Special Resource (Moderate Learning
Difficulties)** Lambourn Primary School, Greenways,
Lambourn, Hungerford, West Berkshire RG17 7LJ;
E-mail office.lambourn@westberks.org; Tel 01488 71479;
Fax 01488 73723
Headteacher Mrs M. Appleton

Park House Special Resource (Hearing Impairment) Park
House School (Secondary), Andover Rd, Newbury, West
Berkshire RG14 6NQ; URL www.parkhouse.westberks.org;
E-mail office.parkhouse@westberks.org; Tel 01635 573911;
Fax 01635 528884
Headteacher Mr D. Peaple
  Hearing impairment

Robert Sandilands Special Resource (Assessment) Digby
Rd, Speen, Newbury, West Berkshire RG14 1TS;
E-mail office.sandilands@westberks.org; Tel 01635 40318;
Fax 01635 580948
Headteacher Mr R. Blofeld

Speenhamland Special Resource (Physical Disability)
Speenhamland Primary School, Pelican La, Newbury, West
Berkshire RG14 1NU;
E-mail office.speenhamland@westberks.org; Tel 01635
41077; Fax 01635 551239
Headteacher Mrs E. Brooks
  Physical disability

Theale Language and Literacy Centre Theale CE Primary
School, Church St, Theale, Reading RG7 5BZ;
E-mail office.theale@westberks.org; Tel 0118 930 2239;
Fax 0118 930 4232
Headteacher Mrs K. Williams

Trinity Special Resource (Specific Learning Difficulties)
Trinity School (Secondary), Church Rd, Newbury, West
Berkshire RG14 2DU; E-mail office.trinity@westberks.org;
Tel 01635 510500; Fax 01635 510510
Headteacher Ms D. Forster
  Special Learning Difficulties

Westwood Farm Special Resource Infant (Hearing Impairment) Westwood Farm Infant School, Fullbrook Cres, Tilehurst, Reading RG31 6RY; E-mail office.wwi@westberks.org; Tel 0118 942 6113
Headteacher Mrs E. Loveridge (Acting)

Westwood Farm Special Resource Junior (Hearing Impairment) Westwood Farm Junior School, Fullbrook Cres, Tilehurst, Reading RG31 6RY; E-mail office.wwj@westberks.org; Tel 0118 942 5182; Fax 0118 945 4498
Headteacher Mr P.M. Booth

Winchcombe Language and Literacy Centre Winchcombe Junior School, Maple Cres, Newbury, West Berkshire RG14 1LN; E-mail office.winjun@westberks.org; Tel 01635 41767; Fax 01635 41767
Headteacher Mr M.G. Fowler

Winchcombe Special Resource (Speech and Language Difficulties) Winchcombe Infant School, Maple Cres, Newbury, West Berkshire RG14 1LN; E-mail office.wininf@westberks.org; Tel 01635 40923
Headteacher Mrs J. Tyas

SPECIAL SCHOOLS

Brookfields School Sage Rd, Tilehurst, Reading RG31 6SW; E-mail office.brookfields@westberks.org; Tel 0118 924 1382
Headteacher Mr J.C. Byrne

The Castle School Prince Rupert Hse, Love La, Donnington, Newbury, West Berkshire RG14 2JG; E-mail office.castle@westberks.org; Tel 01635 42976; Fax 01635 551725
Headteacher Mrs K. Gray

PUPIL REFERRAL UNITS

Badgers Hill Pupil Referral Unit 22 Highview, Calcot, Reading RG31 4XD; E-mail office.badgers@westberks.org; Tel 0118 941 6636
Teacher-in-Charge Ms D. McDonnell

Bridgeway Pupil Referral Unit Newtown Rd, Newbury, West Berkshire RG14 7BQ; E-mail office.bridgeway@westberks.org; Tel 01635 49397
Teacher-in-Charge Mrs J. Davies

Newbury Primary Day Unit 88 Newtown Rd, Newbury, West Berkshire RG14 7BT; E-mail office.newburypdu@westberks.org; Tel 01635 43794
Teacher-in-Charge Miss F. Holland

Priory Pupil Referral Unit Church La, Thatcham, West Berkshire RG19 3JL; E-mail office.priory@westberks.org; Tel 01635 861019
Teacher-in-Charge Mrs J. Reid

The Quay Pupil Referral Unit Riverside Community Centre, Rosemoor Gdns, Newbury, West Berkshire RG14 2FG; E-mail thequay@westberks.gov.uk; Tel 01635 279709
Teacher-in-Charge Ms S. Williams

WEST MIDLANDS METROPOLITAN AREA

The following Metropolitan Councils comprise the West Midlands Metropolitan Area and may be found in alphabetical order within this chapter: Birmingham, Coventry, Dudley, Sandwell, Solihull, Walsall, Wolverhampton.

JOINT COMMITTEE

The Joint Committee undertakes the co-ordination of services mentioned in the Local Government Act 1985, which were formerly carried out by the West Midlands County Council. It also co-ordinates action on important issues affecting the West Midlands Metropolitan area, and is the vehicle for communicating these actions, and the area's needs, to government and to other influential bodies.
Birmingham City Council, Council Hse, Birmingham, West Midlands B1 1BB; E-mail paul_smith@birmingham.gov.uk; Tel 0121 303 2077; Fax 0121 303 1372
Chair Cllr W.H. Thomas Sandwell MBC

WEST SUSSEX COUNTY COUNCIL
www.westsussex.gov.uk

Population 750 000
Political Composition: Con: 41, LD: 19, Lab: 9.
County Hall, Chichester, West Sussex PO19 1RQ; URL www.westsussex.gov.uk; E-mail webmaster@westsussex.gov.uk; Tel 01243 777100; Fax 01243 777952
Chair of the Council Mrs M.D. Johnson
Chief Executive D.P. Rigg, CPFA
County Secretary M.P. Kendall, MA
County Treasurer Mrs H. Kilpatrick, MA, CPFA
Deputy County Treasurer B. Robinson, BA, LPA, IPFA

Social and Caring Services

URL www.westsussex.gov.uk; E-mail social.services@westsussex.gov.uk; Tel (Emergency) 01903 694422; (Main Switchboard) 01243 777100; Fax 01243 777324
Strategic Director (Social and Caring Services) John Dixon
Deputy Director (Social and Caring Services) John D. Leaver
Head (Resources) Richard Perry
Head (Adult Services) Mary Downes
Head (Strategic Commissioning and Performance Development) Anna Coss
Head (Families and Schools Support) Sue Berelowitz

Social and Caring Services

LD: 18, Con: 42, Lab: 10, Lab: and Co-operative: 1
Cabinet Member for Social and Caring Services Mark Dunn (Con)
Chair Mrs M. Millson (LD)
Vice-Chair R. Brown (Con)

OFFICES

Adur Office Glebelands, Middle Rd, Shoreham by Sea, West Sussex BN43 6GA; Tel 01273 268800; Fax 01273 268801
Area Manager (Adult Social Care – Coastal) Catherine Sweeney
Group Manager (Children's Services) Nick Longdon

Arun Office Elizabeth Hse, 83 Victoria Dr, Bognor Regis, West Sussex PO21 2TB; Tel 01243 852800; Fax 01243 852865
Area Manager (Adult Social Care – Western) David Underwood
Group Manager (Children's Services) Nick Longdon
High Street Office 44–48 High St, Littlehampton, West Sussex BN17 5ED; Tel 01903 738900; Fax 01903 738989

Chichester Office 1a East Row, Chichester, West Sussex PO19 1PD; Tel 01243 752999; Fax 01243 752644
Area Manager (Adult Social Care – Western) David Underwood
Group Manager (Children's Services) Nick Longdon
Midhurst Whiphill Farm Hse, Lamberts La, Midhurst, West Sussex GU29 9DZ; Tel 01243 752999; Fax 01243 752644

Crawley Office Centenary Hse, County Bldg, Crawley, West Sussex RH10 8GN; Tel 01293 895100; Fax 01293 895114
Area Manager (Adult Social Care – Crawley) Chris Scanes
Group Manager (Children's Services) Margo McIntosh

6

Horsham Office Talbot Hse, 20–22 East St, Horsham, West Sussex RH12 1HL; Tel 01403 213100; Fax 01403 213125
24–26 West St, Storrington, West Sussex RH20 4EE; Tel 01403 213100; Fax 01403 213125
Area Manager (Adult Social Care – Horsham)
Gary Bowman
Group Manager (Children's Services) Margo McIntosh

Mid Sussex Office 4 Orchard Way, East Grinstead, West Sussex RH19 1AS; Tel 01444 446100; Fax 01444 446568
Area Manager (Adult Social Care – Mid Sussex) Jim Pillow
Group Manager (Children's Services) Margo McIntosh

Worthing Office Centenary Hse, Durrington, Worthing, West Sussex BN13 2QB; Tel 01903 839100; Fax 01903 839248
Area Manager (Adult Social Care – Coastal)
Catherine Sweeney
Group Manager (Children's Services) Nick Longdon

Education Department

County Hall, West St, Chichester, West Sussex PO19 1RF; Tel 01243 777100; Fax 01243 777229
Director (Education and the Arts) R. Back
County Youth and Community Officer T. Caley

LOCAL OFFICES

Education Office (North)

Centenary Hse, County Bldgs, Crawley, West Sussex RH10 2GP
Special Schools
6

SPECIAL SCHOOLS

Abbotsford Community School Cuckfield Rd, Burgess Hill, West Sussex RH15 8RE; Tel 01444 235848; Fax 01444 241786
Headteacher D. Muchmore (Acting)
(Day, Boarders)
Boys 7–16 Social, emotional and behavioural difficulties (68)

Catherington School Martyrs Ave, Langley Grn, Crawley, West Sussex RH11 7SF; Tel 01293 526873; Fax 01293 510363
Headteacher D. Reid
(Day)
Mixed 2–19 SLD

Colwood and Larchwood Hospitals School Hurstwood La, Haywards Heath, West Sussex RH17 7SH; Tel 01444 456427; Fax 01444 412327
Headteacher Dr A. Harvey
(Day)
Mixed 5–18 Psychologically disturbed children resident in the hospitals. (30)

Court Meadow School Hanlye La, Cuckfield, Haywards Heath, West Sussex RH17 5HN; Tel 01444 454535; Fax 01444 412289
Headteacher Mrs J. Hedges
(Day)
Mixed 2–19 SLD

Deerswood School Ifield Grn, Ifield, Crawley, West Sussex RH11 0HG; Tel 01293 520351; Fax 01293 510559
Headteacher M.R. Turney
(Day)
Mixed 4–16 MLD (including classes for children with communication disorders).

Newick House School Birchwood Grove Rd, Burgess Hill, West Sussex RH15 0DP; Tel 01444 233550; Fax 01444 870043
Headteacher Ms G. Perry
(Day)
Mixed 4–16 MLD (including classes for children with communication disorders)

Queen Elizabeth II Silver Jubilee School Comptons La, Horsham, West Sussex RH13 5NW; Tel 01403 266215; Fax 01403 270109
Headteacher Mrs L.K. Dyer
(Day)
Mixed 2–19 SLD

SPECIAL SUPPORT FACILITIES/UNITS/SERVICES

Support Team for Ethnic Minority Pupils Kendre, Langley Green Middle School, Crawley, West Sussex RH11 7PF; Tel 01293 548184; Fax 01293 550313
Team Leader Hazel Squire

Crawley Special Support Facilities for Hearing-Impaired Children Northgate First School, Green La, Crawley, West Sussex RH10 2DX; Tel 01293 526729; 01293 614878
Headteacher Mrs S.E. Carter
Teacher-in-Charge Mrs A. Caton
Day
Mixed 4–11

Crawley Primary Special Support Facilities for Children with Severe Specific Learning Difficulties Ifield Middle School, Ifield Dr, Crawley, West Sussex RH11 0EL; Tel 01293 525320
Headteacher Mrs J. Lewis
Teacher-in-Charge Mrs C. Hiley
Day
Mixed 8–12

Crawley Portage Service c/o Old Robert May Bldgs, Furnace Dr, Crawley, West Sussex RH10 6JB; Tel 01293 615325
Supervisor N. Blackwell
Portage Co-ordinator J. Parry

Crawley Secondary Special Support Facility for Children with Severe Specific Learning Difficulties Ifield Community College, Lady Margaret Rd, Crawley, West Sussex RH11 0DB; Tel 01293 420500
Headteacher Dr W. Lind
Teacher-in-Charge Mrs J. Elcombe
(Day)
Mixed 12–18

Crawley Special Support Facilities for Speech and Language-Impaired Children Three Bridges First School, Gales Pl, Crawley, West Sussex RH10 1QG; Tel 01293 524076; (Unit) 01293 615807
Headteacher Mrs J.A. Parsons
Teacher-in-Charge Mrs J. Triggs
Day
Mixed 4–8

Crawley Support Facilities for Speech and Language-Impaired Children Three Bridges M School, Gales Dr, Crawley, West Sussex RH10 1PD; Tel 01293 526888; (Unit) 01293 615864
Headteacher S. Mines
Teacher-in-Charge Mrs S. Harman
Day
Mixed 8–12

Horsham and Mid-Sussex Portage Service c/o Mid Sussex Area Professional Centre, Clarence Rd, Horsham, West Sussex RH13 5SQ; Tel 01403 264763; Fax 01403 249583
Supervisor Mrs S. Hall
Co-ordinator Mrs S. Maskell
Horsham and Mid-Sussex Portage Service (Annexe) Room 27, Manor Field CP, Burgess Hill, West Sussex RH15 0PZ; Tel 01444 243150; Fax 01444 232012
Supervisor Mrs S. Hall
Co-ordinator Mrs S. Maskell

Mid-Sussex Primary Special Support Facility for Children with Severe Specific Learning Difficulties Blackthorns Community Primary School, Blackthorns Cl, Haywards Heath, West Sussex RH16 2AY; Tel 01444 454866
Headteacher Miss R. Boulton
Teacher-in-Charge Mrs P. Ellis
Mixed (Day)

Mid-Sussex Secondary Special Support Facility for Children with Severe Specific Learning Difficulties Warden Pk School, Broad St, Haywards Heath, West Sussex; Tel 01444 457881
Headteacher S. Johnson
Teacher-in-Charge Mrs A. McQueen
Mixed (Day)

Mid-Sussex Special Support Facility for Speech- and Language-Impaired Children London Meed Community Primary School, Chanctonbury Rd, Burgess Hill, West Sussex RH15 9YQ; Tel 01444 232336
Headteacher D.V. Hughes
Teacher-in-Charge (Infants) Mrs A. Holgate
Teacher-in-Charge (Juniors) Mrs T. Bates
Mixed (Day)

North Pupil Referral Unit (Burgess Hill) Marle Pl, Leylands Rd, Burgess Hill, West Sussex RH15 8JD; Tel 01444 232771; Fax 01444 870229
Head (Pupil Referral Units – North) R. Gasson
Mixed (Day)

North Pupil Referral Unit (Crawley) Worth Annex, Turners Hill Rd, Crawley, West Sussex RH10 7RN; Tel 01293 883209
Teacher-in-Charge N. Urwin
Mixed (Day)

Crawley Physically Disabled Special Support Facility Southgate Middle School, Barrington Rd, Crawley, West Sussex RH10 6DG; Tel 01293 525372
Headteacher Mrs K. Sibley
Teacher-in-Charge Mrs J. Tomkinson
Mixed 4–12 (Day)

Queen Victoria Hospital Holtye Rd, East Grinstead, West Sussex RH19 3DZ; Tel 01342 410210
Teacher-in-Charge Mrs R. Cartwright

Thomas Bennett Special Support Facility for Hearing-Impaired Children Thomas Bennett Community College, Ashdown Dr, Crawley, West Sussex RH10 5AD; Tel 01293 526255; (Unit) 01293 539310
Headteacher Ms Y. Maskatiya
Teacher-in-Charge Mrs J. Newton

Education Office (South)

Centenary Hse, Durnington La, Worthing, West Sussex BN13 2QB

SPECIAL SCHOOLS

Cornfield School Cornfield Cl, Littlehampton, West Sussex BN17 6HY; Tel 01903 731277; Fax 01903 731288
Headteacher Mrs S. Roberts
(Day)
Mixed 11–16 EBD

Fordwater School Summersdale Rd, Chichester, West Sussex PO19 4PL; Tel 01243 782475; Fax 01243 539210
Headteacher R. Rendall
Bursar Mrs J. Bunyan
(Day)
Mixed 2–19 SLD

Littlegreen School Compton, Chichester, West Sussex PO18 9NW; Tel 023 9263 1259; Fax 023 9263 1740
Headteacher Vacancy
Bursar Mrs S. Richardson
Boys 7–14 Social, emotional and behavioural difficulties (Boarders) (41)

Herons Dale School Hawkins Cres, Shoreham by Sea, West Sussex BN43 6TN; Tel 01273 596904; 01273 596967; Fax 01273 591126
Headteacher Mrs S.A. Pritchard
(Day)
Mixed 4–16 MLD (including class for children with communication disorders)

Highdown School Durrington La, Worthing, West Sussex BN13 2QQ; Tel 01903 249611; Fax 01903 700817
Headteacher G.R. Elliker
Mixed 2–19 SLD (Day)

Palatine School Palatine Rd, Worthing, West Sussex BN12 6JP; Tel 01903 242835; Fax 01903 700264
Headteacher J.D. Clough
Mixed 4–16 MLD (including classes for children with communication disorders) (Day)

St. Anthony's School Woodlands La, off St. Paul's Rd, Chichester, West Sussex PO19 3PA; Tel 01243 785965; Fax 01243 530206
Headteacher T. Salt
Bursar Mrs F. Fisher
(Day)
Mixed 4–16 MLD (including classes for children with communication disorders)

St. Cuthman's School Stedham, Midhurst, West Sussex GU29 0QJ; Tel 01730 812331; 01730 812332; Fax 01730 812335
Headteacher H.L. Rooks
Bursar Mrs A. Hanlon
Mixed 7–16 MLD (Day, Boarders)

SPECIAL SUPPORT FACILITIES/UNITS/SERVICES

Angmering the Lavina Norfolk Centre for Physically Disabled and Hearing Impaired Children The Angmering School, Station Rd, Littlehampton, West Sussex BN16 4HH; Tel 01903 772351; (Unit) 01903 773146
Headteacher D. Brixey (Acting)
Teacher-in-Charge S. Richards (Acting)
(Day)
Mixed 11–18

Barnham Special Support Facility for Physically Disabled Children Barnham Primary School, Elm Gr, Barnham, West Sussex PO22 0HW; Tel 01243 552197
Headteacher Ms J. Hodgson
Teacher-in-Charge Mrs J. Currie
Mixed

Behaviour Support Team Education Office South, Centenary Hse, Durnington La, Worthing, West Sussex BN13 2QB; Tel 01903 839222
Head of Team Ms F. Gray

Chichester Portage Service Orchard St Annexe, Orchard St, Chichester, West Sussex PO19 1DQ; Tel 01243 536182
Supervisor Mrs L. Woodhouse
Portage Co-ordinator Mrs S. Webb

Chichester Primary Special Support Facility for Children with Severe Specific Learning Difficulties Parklands Community School, Durnford Cl, Chichester, West Sussex PO19 3AG; Tel 01243 788630
Headteacher Mrs L. Brown
Teacher-in-Charge Mrs R. Percival
Mixed

Chichester Special Support Facility for Speech and Language Impaired Children Portfield Community Primary School, St. James' Rd, Chichester, West Sussex PO19 4HR; Tel 01243 783939; Fax 01243 781256
Headteacher Mrs K. Williams
Mixed

Littlehampton Special Support Facility for Hearing Impaired Pupils (Junior) Connaught Junior School, York Rd, Littlehampton, West Sussex BN17 6EW; Tel 01903 715575; 01903 721677
Headteacher Mrs M. Chapman
Teacher-in-Charge Mrs J. Small
Mixed

South Pupil Referral Unit (Chichester) Fletcher Pl Bldg, North Mundham, Chichester, West Sussex PO20 6JR; Tel 01243 788044
Teacher-in-Charge R. Stepien
Mixed (Day)

6

South Pupil Referral Unit (Worthing) 37 Richmond Rd, Worthing, West Sussex BN11 1PW; Tel 01903 211855; Fax 01903 216998
Head (South Pupil Referral Units) Ms E. Conway
Teacher-in-Charge P. Hughes
Mixed (Day)

Steyning Primary Special Support Facility for Children with Severe Specific Learning Difficulties St. Andrew's CE Primary School, Shooting Field, Steyning, West Sussex BN44 3RX; Tel 01903 879200; Fax 01903 813420
Headteacher J. Luckin
Teacher-in-Charge Mrs L. Latham
Mixed

Steyning Secondary Special Support Facility for Children with Severe Specific Learning Difficulties Steyning Grammar School, Shooting Field, Steyning, West Sussex BN44 3RX; Tel 01903 814555; 01903 814786
Headteacher P. Senior
Teacher-in-Charge Mrs J. Thomas
11–18 (Day)

Western Area Secondary Special Support Facility for Children with Severe Specific Learning Difficulties Bognor Regis Community College, Westloats La, Bognor Regis, West Sussex PO21 5LH; Tel (Lower Unit) 01243 841746; (Upper Unit) 01243 842313
Headteacher L. Savins
Teacher-in-Charge Mrs P. Clough
Mixed 11–18 (Day)

Worthing Primary Special Support Facility Class for Children with Severe Specific Learning Difficulties and Physical Disabilities West Park CE First and Middle School, Marlborough Rd, Worthing, West Sussex BN12 4HD; Tel 01903 243099; 01903 506278
Headteacher J. Hofton
Teacher-in-Charge (SSLD) Mrs F. Goodward
Teacher-in-Charge (PD) Mrs P. Dockree

Worthing Portage Service School Hse, Littlehampton Rd, Worthing, West Sussex BN13 1SB; Tel 01903 242558; Fax 01903 242337
Supervisor M.S.C. Montgomery
Co-ordinator Mrs B. Miles

Worthing Secondary Special Support Facility for Children with Severe Specific Learning Difficulties Worthing High School, South Farm Rd, Worthing, West Sussex BN14 7AR; Tel 01903 237864
Headteacher Mrs A. Beer
Teacher-in-Charge Mrs S. Lamba
Mixed (Day)

Worthing Special Support Facility for Children with Social Communication Language Difficulties Lyndhurst First School, Lyndhurst Rd, Worthing, West Sussex BN11 2DG; Tel 01903 235390
Headteacher Mrs A. Lawrenson
Teacher-in-Charge Mrs J. Blewitt
Mixed

Worthing Special Support Facility for Speech and Language Impaired Children Field PL First School, Nelson Rd, Worthing, West Sussex BN12 6EN; Tel (Unit) 01903 242611; (School) 01903 700234
Headteacher Mrs F. Dunkin
Teacher-in-Charge Mrs G. Desilva

WEST YORKSHIRE METROPOLITAN AREA

The following Metropolitan Councils comprise the West Yorkshire Metropolitan Area and may be found in alphabetical order within this chapter: Bradford, Calderdale, Kirklees, Leeds, Wakefield.

WIGAN METROPOLITAN BOROUGH COUNCIL

www.wiganmbc.gov.uk

Population 310 000
Political Composition: Lab: 60, LD: 4, Con: 3, Community Action: 5
Town Hall, Library St, Wigan, Greater Manchester WN1 1YN; URL www.wiganmbc.gov.uk; Tel 01942 244991; Fax 01942 827451
Chief Executive S.M. Jones, BA
Chief Executive (Wigan and Leigh Housing Company Ltd) P. Gee, FIH
50 Millgate, Wigan, Greater Manchester WN1 1AF
Director (Finance and IT) Dr David Smith, PhD
Civic Centre, Millgate, Wigan, Greater Manchester WN1 1YD

Social Services Department

Civic Centre, Millgate, Wigan, Greater Manchester WN1 1AZ; Tel 01942 244991; (Emergency) 0161 834 2436
Director (Social Services) B.A. Walker
Deputy Director (Social Services) Gerald Meehan
Assistant Director (Children and Family Services) Kath Nelson; Tel 01942 827799
Assistant Director (Commissioning) Louise Sutton; Tel 01942 827798
Assistant Director (Provision) J. Blott; Tel 01942 827800
Communications Officer John Roughley
Borough Director (Mental Health) Trish Anderson
Mental Health Block, Leigh Infirmary, The Ave, Leigh, Greater Manchester WN7 1HS; Tel 01942 264334

Health and Social Services Panel

Cabinet Member (Health and Social Services) Cllr Brian J. Strett (Lab)
Link Member Cllr D. Kelly (Lab)
Members of the Health and Social Services Panel
Lab: K.R. Baldwin, M.M. Coghlin, R. Holmes, D. Kelly, P.M. Kelly, Mrs E. Smethurst, G.R. Walsh , F.B. Walker.
Community Action K.V. Williams.
LD: R.T. Splaine.

TRAINING

Responsible for training professional and support staff in the department.
Service Manager (Staff Development and Training) Vacancy
Staff Development and Training Centre, Social Services, Haigh Hall, Haigh, Wigan, Greater Manchester WN2 1PE; Tel 01942 833484

AREA OFFICES

Golborne Area Office 32 High St, Golborne, Warrington; Tel 01942 728603
Service Manager G. Frost

Ince Area Office Town Hall, Ince Gren La, Wigan, Greater Manchester; Tel 01942 44991

Leigh Area Office Town Hall, Market St, Leigh, Greater Manchester; Tel 01942 604611; 01942 672421
Service Manager B. Bates

Standish Area Office Aspull Distirct Office, Holly Rd, Aspull, Greater Manchester; Tel 01942 832592
Service Manager J.A. Sutton

Tyldesley Area Office Town Hall, Tyldesley, Manchester; Tel 01942 883635

Wigan Area Office Flats 20–28 Plane Ave, Worsley Hall, Wigan, Greater Manchester; Tel 01942 828202
Service Manager B. Hollingsworth

HOSPITAL SOCIAL WORKERS

Wigan Area Team Flats 20–28 Plane Ave, Worsley Hall, Wigan, Greater Manchester; Tel 01942 244991
Service Manager B. Hollingsworth

CENTRAL DUTY TEAM

Hyndelle Lodge, King St, Wigan, Greater Manchester WN2 3AW; Tel 01942 828777; 01942 828787
Team Manager John Siddall

CHILDREN'S HOMES

Green Lane Children's Home 1 Green La, Standish, Wigan, Greater Manchester WN6 0TS; Tel 01257 472331
Manager A. Young
(8)

Gregory Avenue Children's Home 26 Gregory Ave, Atherton, Manchester; Tel 01942 891380
Manager Vacancy
(8)

Maxwell House Children's Home Gidlow La, Wigan, Greater Manchester; Tel 01942 241986
Manager Jean Glass
(8)

Princess Street Children's Home 1 Princess St, Hindley, Wigan, Greater Manchester WN2 3HJ; Tel 01942 255960
Manager D. Jeffs
(8)

HOMES FOR CHILDREN WITH LEARNING DIFFICULTIES

Children and Parents Support Service (CAPSS) Outreach Service, 9 Wensleydale Rd, Leigh, Greater Manchester WN7 2HX; Tel 01942 603796
Manager C. Harding

Ladies Lane Children's Home 98 Ladies La, Hindley, Wigan, Greater Manchester; Tel 01942 222918
Manager J. Hurst
(8)

Tanfield Overnight Stay Unit Borsdane Ave, Hindley, Wigan, Greater Manchester; Tel 01942 255682
Headteacher E. Edge
(8)

Two Porches Overnight Stay Unit Gloucester St, Atherton, Manchester; Tel 01942 882012
Headteacher L.A. Roberts
(8)

HOME AND CENTRE FOR THE YOUNGER PHYSICALLY HANDICAPPED (22–35)

Fourways Cleworth Hall La, off Manchester Rd, Manchester; Tel 01942 870841; 01942 870842
Principal Officer C. Pilling
(22)

JUVENILE TREATMENT CENTRE

Youth Offending Team
Resource Manager J. Postlethwaite

COMMUNITY TEAM FOR PERSONS WITH LEARNING DISABILITIES

Learning Disabilities Team 196a Newton Rd, Lowton, Warrington; Tel 01942 515093

DAY CENTRES FOR PEOPLE WITH LEARNING DISABILITIES

Amberswood Day Centre King St, Hindley, Wigan, Greater Manchester; Tel 01942 255514
(81)

Broadmead Day Centre Golborne Rd, Lowton, Greater Manchester; Tel 01942 276056
(60)

Hunters Lodge Day Centre Hunter Rd, Marsh Grn, Wigan, Greater Manchester WN5 0QD; Tel 01942 222291
Manager (Day Service) Vacancy
(60)

Mayfield Day Centre Mayfield Rd, Orrell, Wigan, Greater Manchester; Tel 01942 222948
Manager (Day Service) J. Godsil
(60 and 15 special care)

The Orchards Day Centre Chatham St, off Leigh Rd, Leigh, Greater Manchester; Tel 01942 671045
Locality Manager Vacancy
(50)

HOSTELS FOR ADULTS WITH LEARNING DISABILITIES

The Pines Mayfield Rd, Orrell, Greater Manchester; Tel 01942 223563
Assistant Manager (Accommodation) Vacancy
(25)

Ullswater Court Ullswater Rd, Golborne, Warrington; Tel 01942 715781
Assistant Manager (Accommodation) Vacancy
(25)

DAY CENTRES

Central Day Centre Sullivan Way, Wigan, Greater Manchester; Tel 01942 826303
Manager Y. Brockley
(40)

Crompton Street Day Centre Crompton St, Wigan, Greater Manchester; Tel 01942 243800
(20)

Etherstone Day Centre Etherstone St, Leigh, Greater Manchester; Tel 01942 601458
Manager S. Crompton
(40)

Golborne Day Centre Queen St, Golborne, Greater Manchester; Tel 01942 718898
Manager M. Mercer
(40)

Heath Road Day Centre Heath Rd, Ashton in Makerfield, Wigan, Greater Manchester; Tel 01942 767086
Manager J. Wadcock
(33)

Hindley Day Centre First Ave, Wigan, Greater Manchester; Tel 01942 521927
Manager Vacancy
(40)

Laburnum Road Day Centre Laburnum Rd, Lowton, Warrington; Tel 01942 601180
Manager Vacancy
(20)

Larch Avenue Day Centre Pemberton, Wigan, Greater Manchester; Tel 01942 215219
Manager Vacancy
(45)

Lindale Hall Day Centre Lindale Rd, Mosley Common, Manchester; Tel 0161 790 1223
Caretaker Vacancy

New Lodge Day Centre Mealhouse La, Atherton, Manchester; Tel 01942 873932
Manager S.M. Mortimer
(50)

6

Priory Road Day Centre Priory Rd, Ashton in Makerfield, Wigan, Greater Manchester; Tel 01942 727108
Caretaker C. Collier
(25)

Tunstall Lane Day Centre Pemberton, Wigan, Greater Manchester; Tel 01942 214468
Assistant Principal Officer B. Johnson
(24)

ACCOMMODATION FOR PEOPLE WITH MENTAL HEALTH PROBLEMS

Brookfield Home Scot La, Wigan, Greater Manchester; Tel 01942 215850
Principal Officer Vacancy
(15)

SHELTERED EMPLOYMENT

Metrolite Industries (Workshops for the Blind and Handicapped) 60 Warrington Rd, Wigan, Greater Manchester; Tel 01942 497861
General Manager Vacancy

HOME FOR ELDERLY MENTALLY INFIRM

Heathside, Plank La, Leigh, Greater Manchester WN7 4UD; Tel 01942 724910
Manager (Day Services) J. Wadcock
Manager (Residential Services) A. Feeney

Education Department

Gateway Hse, Standishgate, Wigan, Greater Manchester WN1 1AE; URL www.wiganmbc.gov.uk; E-mail education@wiganmbc.gov.uk; Tel 01942 244991 01942 828881; Fax 01942 828811
Chief Executive ('Positive Futures') Deborah Brownlee
Education Business Partnership, Investment Centre, Wigan, Greater Manchester WN3 5BA; Tel 01942 705391; Fax 01942 705488
Director (Education) R.J. Clark, MA, CBE
Deputy Director (Social and Community Inclusion) J.E. Cowen
Assistant Director (Management and Development) Avril V. Walton
Assistant Director (School Effectiveness) G. Williams
Assistant Director (School Inclusion) Janette M. Gilbourne
Head (Educational Placements) L. Mappin
Head (SEN Assessment) Cath Hitchen
Head (Services for Young People) D. Hill
Head (Education Welfare Services) D. Greenhalgh
Manager (Education Development) D.J. Davies
Strategic Manager (Development and Premises) Lynne Cottrell
Strategic Manager (Behaviour Support) Avril Brown
Strategic Manager (Educational Psychological Service) Simon Jenner; Tel 01942 828815
Development Officer (Early Years) Dominique Wright
Senior Educational Psychologist Steve Clarke
Senior Educational Psychologist Vacancy
Team Leader (Behaviour Support) Maggie Biddlestone
Co-ordinator (Alternative/Complementary Provision) Nick Manning

SPECIAL DAY SCHOOLS

Atherton Two Porches School Gloucester St, Atherton, Greater Manchester M46 0HX; Tel 01942 882012; Fax 01942 889650
Headteacher Mrs L.A. Roberts
SLD

Brookfield High School Park Rd, Hindley, Wigan, Greater Manchester WN2 3RY; Tel 01942 776142; Fax 01942 776143
Headteacher J. Young
MLD

Green Hall Primary School Green Hall Cl, Atherton, Greater Manchester M46 9HP; Tel 01942 883928; Fax 01942 870069
Headteacher I.A. Triska, BEd
MLD

Hindley Tanfield School Borsdane Ave, Hindley, Wigan, Greater Manchester WN2 3QB; Tel 01942 255682; Fax 01942 514239
Headteacher E.M. Edge
SLD

Montrose School Montrose Ave, Pemberton, Wigan, Greater Manchester WN5 9XN; Tel 01942 223431; Fax 01942 225911
Headteacher A. Farmer
MLD

Standish Mere Oaks School Boars Head, Standish, Wigan, Greater Manchester WN1 2RF; Tel 01942 243481; 01942 243482; Fax 01942 231121
Headteacher J. Leach
PH

Wigan Hope School Kelvin Gr, Marus Bridge, Wigan, Greater Manchester WN3 6SP; Tel 01942 824150; Fax 01942 230361
Headteacher J.P.R. Dahlstrom, MEd
SLD

Willow Grove Primary School Willow Gr, Ashton-in-Makerfield, Wigan, Greater Manchester WN4 8XF; Tel 01942 727717; Fax 01942 271627
Headteacher V. Pearson
EBD

SPECIAL RESIDENTIAL SCHOOLS

Highlea Secondary School 294 Mosely Common Rd, Boothstown, Greater Manchester M28 1DA; Tel 0161 790 2698; 0161 790 8424; Fax 0161 703 8724
Headteacher J. McManus, OBE
EBD

Kingshill School Elliott St, Tyldesley, Greater Manchester M29 8JE; Tel 01942 892104; Fax 01942 892113
Headteacher M. Myerscough
EBD

EDUCATION WELFARE OFFICE

Argyle St, Hindley, Wigan, Greater Manchester WN2 3PN; Tel 01942 749910

WILTSHIRE COUNTY COUNCIL
www.wiltshire.gov.uk

The County Council retains its two-tier structure. However on 1st April 1997 Swindon became a separate unitary authority and is responsible for its local government services – Swindon is listed alphabetically in this chapter.
Population 325 548 (2003)
Political Composition: Con: 27, LD: 13, Lab: 3, Ind: 4
County Hall, Bythesea Rd, Trowbridge, Wiltshire BA14 8JN; URL www.wiltshire.gov.uk; E-mail keithrobinson@wiltshire.gov.uk; Tel 01225 713000; Fax 01225 713999
Chair of the County Council Mr D.J. Willmott, CBE, QFSM
Chief Executive Dr Keith Robinson
Director (Corporate Services) P. Smith
Director (Environmental Services) G. Batten
County Treasurer M. Prince

Adult and Community Services Department

E-mail socialservices@wiltshire.gov.uk; Tel (Emergency) 0845 607 0888; Fax (Emergency Duty Team, Out of hours) 01380 724008; Textphone 01380 728585
Director (Adult and Community Services) Dr Ray Jones
Assistant Director (Older People and Physical Impairment) Jeanette Longhurst
Assistant Director (Older People and Physical Impairment) Maggie Durnell
Assistant Director (Mental Health and Learning Disabilities) Chris Chorley
Manager (Training) Kim Holmes

Social Services Advisory Panel

Con: 8, LD: 3, Lab: 1, Ind: 1, Co-opted members: 5.
Chair Cllr Judith Seager (Con)
Ashley Lodge, Ashley Box, Corsham, Wiltshire SN14 9AN
Vice-Chair Cllr Anthony Moore, (Con)
Oakfield, 37 Westwood Rd, Trowbridge, Wiltshire BA14 9BR
Members of the Advisory Panel
Con: Bill Braid, Anthony Molland, Anthony Moore, Allan Peach, Colin Read, Pat Rugg.
Co-opted: Richard Allen, Ann Dunham, Hilary Fairfield, John Nicholas.
LD: Grace Hill, Jeff Osborn, Sandie Webb.

LOCALITY OFFICES

Adult Team

Salisbury District Hospital, Social Work Department, Salisbury, Wiltshire SP2 8BJ; Tel 01722 336262 ext 2400; Fax 01722 410939
Team Manager Valerie Sonnenberg

Bath Hospitals Social Work Team

Wiltshire Social Services Department, Royal United Hospital (North), Bath, Bath and North East Somerset BA1 3NG; Tel 01225 824342; Fax 01225 825470
Manager (Hospital Team) Gregg Hardstaff

Bradford-on-Avon Adult Care Team

The Health Centre, Bradford on Avon, Wiltshire BA15 1DQ; Tel 01225 867795; Fax 01225 868621
Team Leader Debbie Elliott

Chippenham Adult Care Team

34 Marshfield Rd, Chippenham, Wiltshire SN15 1JT; Tel 01249 444747; Fax 01249 443071; Textphone 01249 444747
Team Leader Sue Reynolds

City and South Locality Team

Salt La, Salisbury, Wiltshire SP1 1DU; Tel 01722 411322; Fax 01722 413509; Textphone 01722 411322
Team Leader Barbara Criddle
Team Leader Andrew Stag

Calne Adult Care Team

Family Health Centre, Broken Cross, Calne, Wiltshire SN11 8BN; Tel 01249 810040; Fax 01249 810049
Team Leader Wendy Barker

Community Based Support Services

Marlborough Resource Centre, Cherry Orchard, Marlborough, Wiltshire SN8 4AR; Tel 01672 515045; Fax 01672 612872
Manager Heather Rhodes

Community Safety Team

Court Mills, Polebarn Rd, Trowbridge, Wiltshire BA14 7EG; Tel 01225 776773; 01225 776890; Fax 01225 774883
Manager (Community Safety) Lynn Gaskin

Community Team for People with Learning Disabilities (Chippenham Area)

3–4 Burlands Rd, Chippenham, Wiltshire SN5 3DF; Tel 01249 659197; Fax 01249 446937
Area Manager (Learning Disability) Phil Stevenson

Community Team for People with Learning Disability (Kennet Area)

Salisbury Rd, Marlborough, Wiltshire SN8 4AR; Tel 01672 515637; Fax 01672 515008
Team Leader Andrew Lane

Community Team for People with Learning Disability (Salisbury Area)

44–48 Bedwin St, Salisbury, Wiltshire SP2 3UW; Tel 01722 410814; Fax 01722 339581
Team Leader Heather Rhodes,

Community Team for People with Learning Disability (Trowbridge Area)

Andil Hse, Crt St, Trowbridge, Wiltshire BA14 8BR; Tel 01225 760106; Fax 01225 775278
Team Leader Alan Mogg

Corsham and Box Adult Care Team

Family Health Centre, Beechfield Rd, Corsham, Wiltshire SN13 9DN; Tel 01249 716582; Fax 01249 712652
Team Leader Sue Grier

Devizes Adult Team

The Cedars, Browfort, Devizes, Wiltshire SN10 2AP; Tel 01380 730055; Fax 01380 723190; Textphone 01380 730055
Team Leader Dee Robinson

Drug Action Team

Court Mills, Polebarn Rd, Trowbridge, Wiltshire BA14 7EG; Tel 01225 776773; 01225 776890; Fax 01225 774883
Co-ordinator (Drug Action Team) Ben Hughes

Financial Assessments Benefit Team

B7 Tyak Est, Vincent Rd, Bumpers Farm Ind Est, Chippenham, Wiltshire SN14 6NQ; Tel 01249 706910; Fax 01249 446025
Team Manager Clare Bassett

Ludgershall/Tidworth/Pewsey

The Castle Practice, Central St, Ludgershall, Wiltshire SP11 9RA; Tel 01264 793917; Fax 01264 791539
Team Manager Lynn Franklin

Malmesbury and Sherston Adult Care Team

Family Health Centre, Malmesbury, Wiltshire SN16 9AT; Tel 01666 826186; Fax 01666 826016
Team Leader Kim Chick

Marlborough Adult Team

Merriman Ward, Savernake Hospital, Marlborough, Wiltshire SN8 3HL; Tel 01672 511950; Fax 01672 516696
Team Leader Larraine Kelly

Melksham Adult Care Team

Melksham Hospital, Spa Rd, Melksham, Wiltshire
SN12 7NZ; Tel 01225 701036; 01225 701037; Fax 01225
701035
Team Leader Richard Warren

North and West Locality Team

Redworth Hse, Flower La, Amesbury, Wiltshire SP4 7HG;
Tel 01980 623256; Fax 01980 625682; Textphone 01980
623256
Team Leader Heather Ludlow
Team Leader Barbara Criddle

Trowbridge Adult Care Team (1)

Social Services Department, County Hall (East),
Trowbridge, Wiltshire BA14 8JQ; Tel 01225 773500;
Fax 01225 773535; Textphone 01225 773500
Team Leader Louise Bryce
(Lovemead and Widbrook)

Trowbridge Adult Care Team (2)

Social Serivces Department, County Hall (East),
Trowbridge, Wiltshire BA14 8JQ; Tel 01225 773500;
Fax 01225 773535; Textphone 01225 773500
Team Leader Barbara Hearn
(Bradford Rd and Adcroft)

Warminster Adult Care Team

Social Services Department, Beckford Centre, Warminster,
Wiltshire BA12 9LR; Tel 01985 218021; Fax 01985
846069
Team Leader Marguerite Mussell

Westbury Adult Care Team

Community Hospital, Hospital Rd, Westbury, Wiltshire
BA13 3EQ; Tel 01373 858998; Fax 01373 827414
Team Leader Dave Streeter

Wootton Bassett Adult Care Team

The Manor Hse, Lime Kiln, Wootton Bassett, Wiltshire
SN4 7HB; Tel 01793 853434; Fax 01793 849103
Team Leader Martin Brown

HEARING AND VISION TEAM

The House Southfield, Victoria Rd, Devizes, Wiltshire
SN10 1EY; Answerphone 01380 729002; Textphone 01380
725201
Team Leader Vacancy

ADULT PLACEMENT SCHEME

County Hall, Bythesea Rd, Trowbridge, Wiltshire
BA14 8LE; Tel 01225 713000; Fax 01225 719396;
Textphone 01225 719396
Manager (Adult Placement) Ronni Hedge
Bedwin Street Adult Placement Scheme 50 Bedwin St,
Salisbury, Wiltshire SP1 3UW; Tel 01722 415225
Adult Placement Officer Christopher Lyne

HOSTELS FOR ADULTS WITH LEARNING DISABILITIES

Rutland House Rutland Cres, Trowbridge, Wiltshire
BA14 0NY; Tel 01225 754066
Manager Roger Mouncher
(17)

Sarum House Beehive Corner, Old Sarum, Salisbury,
Wiltshire SP4 6BL; Tel 01722 335283
Manager Malcolm Wilson
(20)

Waverley House Semington Rd, Melksham, Wiltshire
SN12 6QF; Tel 01225 703572
Contact Jo Whyman
(23)

RESPITE CARE UNITS FOR ADULTS WITH LEARNING DISABILITIES

Crowhill Respite Care Unit Thicketts Rd, Mildenhall,
Marlborough, Wiltshire SN8 2ND; Tel 01672 513748
Manager Lorraine Walters
(5)

Derriads Respite Care Unit 70 Derriads La, Frogwell,
Chippenham, Wiltshire SN14 0QL; Tel 01249 652814
Manager Barbara Pollard
(4)

Meadow Lodge Respite Care Unit Sadlers Mead, Monkton
Pk, Chippenham, Wiltshire SN14 3PE; Tel 01249 656136
Manager Barbara Pollard
(4)

Sonas House Respite Care Unit 4a Horse Rd, Hilperton,
Trowbridge, Wiltshire BA14 7PE; Tel 01225 764625
Manager Roger Mouncher
(5)

RESOURCE CENTRES FOR ADULTS WITH LEARNING DISABILITIES (INCLUDES SPECIAL NEEDS UNITS)

Ashton Street Resource Centre (with Special Needs Unit)
Ashton St, Trowbridge, Wiltshire BA14 7EU; Tel 01225
753780
Manager Anna Stasyshyn
(114)

Marlborough Resource Centre Cherry Orchard,
Marlborough, Wiltshire SN8 4AR; Tel 01672 512865
Manager Helen Judge
(75)

Middlefield Resource Centre (with Special Needs Unit)
Hungerdown La, Chippenham, Wiltshire SN14 0JP;
Tel 01249 652212
Manager Russell Sargent
Manager Steve Southern
(114)

Sarum Resource Centre (with Special Needs Unit) Beehive
Corner, Old Sarum, Salisbury, Wiltshire SP4 6EU; Tel 01722
335234
Manager Sue Hiscock
(118)

Trowbridge Adult Resource Centre Trowbridge Hospital,
Adcroft St, Trowbridge, Wiltshire BA14 8PH; Tel 01225
767991
Manager Susan Verity

DAY CENTRE FOR OLDER PEOPLE

Coombe End House London Rd, Marlborough, Wiltshire
SN8 2AP; Tel 01672 512075
Manager Anna Lovesey
(27)

RESIDENTIAL HOMES FOR OLDER PEOPLE

There is one local authority home for older people.

DAY CENTRES AND ACTIVITY CENTRES FOR ADULTS

Amesbury Activity Centre Holders Rd, Amesbury,
Salisbury, Wiltshire SP4 7ND; Tel 01980 625235
Manager Diane Jenkins

Beckford Activity Centre Gipsy La, Warminster, Wiltshire
BA12 9LR; Tel 01985 219663
Manager Sharon Burns

Devizes Activity Centre Escourt Cres, Devizes, Wiltshire
SN10 1LR; Tel 01380 720471
Manager Wendy Joslin

West Wiltshire Community Care Centre United Reform
Church, Church St, Trowbridge, Wiltshire BA14 8DY
Contact (Older People Day Centre) Brenda Rowe; Tel 01225
764435
Contact (Disabilities Unit) Jayne Norman; Tel 01225 764201

Department for Children, Education and Libraries

County Hall, Bythesea Rd, Trowbridge, Wiltshire BA14 8JB;
URL www.wiltshire.gov.uk; Tel 01225 713000
Director (Children, Education and Libraries) Bob Wolfson
Assistant Director (Children and Families) Ruth Vincent

Children, Education and Libraries Advisory Panel

Chair Mr W.A.B. Snow (Con)
128 Bouverie Ave, Salisbury, Wiltshire SP2 8EA

CHILDREN AND FAMILIES DIVISION

County Hall, Bythesea Rd, Trowbridge, Wiltshire; Tel 01225
713000; Fax 01225 713983; Textphone 01225 713936
Assistant Director (Children and Families) Annie Hudson
Head (Safer Care) Vacancy
Head (Area Services) Liz Jones
Manager (Training) Ben Ruddock

North and West Area

County Hall (East Wing), Bythesea Rd, Trowbridge,
Wiltshire BA14 8JQ; Tel 01225 713000; Fax 01225 713983
Area Services Manager (West Wiltshire) Nigel Harrison
Area Services Manager (North Wiltshire and Kennet) Vacancy
Contracts Manager (Children and Families) Nick Norris

TEAM FIELDWORK MANAGERS

Bradford and Melksham Team County Hall (East Wing),
Bythesea Rd, Trowbridge, Wiltshire BA14 8JQ; Tel 01225
773500; Fax 01225 773535
Team Leader Jackie Turner

Chippenham Team 357 Hungerdown La, Chippenham,
Wiltshire SN14 0UY; Tel 01249 444321
Team Leader John Alcock

Corsham and Calne Team 357 Hungerdown La,
Chippenham, Wiltshire SN14 0UY; Tel 01249 444321
Team Leader Rebecca Barson

Trowbridge Team County Hall (East Wing), Bythesea Rd,
Trowbridge, Wiltshire BA14 8JQ; Tel 01225 773500;
Fax 01225 773535
Team Leader Linda Hallowell

Warminster and Westbury Team The Beckford Centre, 6
Gipsy La, Warminster, Wiltshire BA14 9LR; Tel 01985 218021
Team Leader Neil Preston

Wootton Bassett Team The Manor Hse, Lime Kiln,
Swindon SN4 7HB; Tel 01793 853434
Team Leader Jackie Chipping

CHILD HEALTH

Lowbourne House Lowbourne, Melksham, Wiltshire
SN12 7DX; Tel 01225 709777
Manager Mark Green

Royal United Hospital (North) Combe Pk, Bath, Bath and
North East Somerset BA1 3NG; Tel 01225 824342
Manager Mark Green

CHILDREN'S RESOURCE CENTRES

Chippenham Resource Centre 357 Hungerdown La,
Chippenham, Wiltshire SN14 0UY; Tel 01249 460222
Manager Shannon Clarke

'Home from Home' Team Trowbridge Resource Centre, 53
Rutland Cres, Trowbridge, Wiltshire BA14 0NY; Tel 01225
752198
Team Leader Phil Egan

Trowbridge Resource Centre 53 Rutland Cres, Trowbridge,
Wiltshire BA14 0NY; Tel 01225 752198
Manager Shannon Clarke

CHILDREN'S HOMES

Orchard House Children's Home Stratford-sub-Castle,
Salisbury, Wiltshire SP1 3LG; Tel 01722 327769
Manager Chris Hiett

Towpath Road Children's Home 46 Towpath Rd,
Trowbridge, Wiltshire BA14 7QD; Tel 01225 719284
Manager Graham Pepper

HOME FOR CHILDREN WITH LEARNING DISABILITIES

Canon's House Children's Home Belle Vue Rd, Devizes,
Wiltshire SN10 2AJ; Tel 01380 722359
Manager Alison Mulley
(10)

South Wiltshire Area

(Children and Families Area Reception), Salt La, Salisbury,
Wiltshire SP1 1DU; Fax 01722 330957; Textphone 01722
327551
Area Services Manager (Children and Families)
John Stoddart
Contracts Manager (Children and Families) Nick Norris

TEAM FIELDWORK MANAGERS (CHILDREN AND FAMILIES)

Amesbury and West Team Redworth Hse, Flower La,
Salisbury, Wiltshire SP4 7HG; Tel 01980 623256
Team Leader Pier Pritchard

Kennet Team The Cedars, Browfort, Devizes, Wiltshire
SN10 2AP; Tel 01380 730055
Team Leader Eleanor Ward

Salisbury East Team Salt La, Salisbury, Wiltshire SP1 1DU;
Tel 01722 327551
Team Leader John Pook

Salisbury West Team Salt La, Salisbury, Wiltshire SP1 1DU;
Tel 01722 327551
Team Leader Sue Phillips

CHILD HEALTH

Kennet The Cedars, Browfort, Devizes, Wiltshire
SN10 2AP; Tel 01380 730055
Manager Barbara Laws

Salisbury Salt La, Salisbury, Wiltshire SP1 1DU; Tel 01722
411322
Manager Barbara Laws

CHILDREN'S RESOURCE CENTRE

Riverside Resource Centre 29 Churchfields, Salisbury,
Wiltshire SP2 7NH; Tel 01722 333552
Manager Shannon Clarke

SPECIAL SCHOOLS

Downland School Downlands Rd, Devizes, Wiltshire
SN10 5EF; E-mail admin@downland.wilts.sch.uk; Tel 01380
724193; Fax 01380 728441
Headteacher G. Hiscocks

Exeter House Special School Somerset Rd, Salisbury,
Wiltshire SP1 3BL; E-mail admin@exeterhouse.wilts.sch.uk;
Tel 01722 334168; Fax 01722 334168
Headteacher G.M. Heather

6

Larkrise School Ashton St, Trowbridge, Wiltshire
BA14 7EB; E-mail admin@larkrise.wilts.sch.uk; Tel 01225
761434; Fax 01225 774585
Headteacher C. Goodwin

Rowdeford School Rowde, Devizes, Wiltshire SN10 2QQ;
E-mail admin@rowdeford.wilts.sch.uk; Tel 01380 850309;
Fax 01380 859708
Headteacher G.R. Darnell

Springfields School Curzon St, Calne, Wiltshire SN11 0DS;
E-mail admin@springfields.wilts.sch.uk; Tel 01249 814125;
Fax 01249 811907
Headteacher G. Templeman

St. Nicholas School Malmesbury Rd, Chippenham,
Wiltshire SN15 1QF;
E-mail admin@st-nicholas.wilts.sch.uk; Tel 01249 650435;
Fax 01249 447033
Headteacher J. Dyer

ROYAL BOROUGH OF WINDSOR AND MAIDENHEAD

www.rbwm.gov.uk

In April 1998 Berkshire County Council was replaced by
Bracknell Forest, Reading, Slough, West Berkshire, Windsor
and Maidenhead, Wokingham – all responsible for local
government services in their areas. They are listed
alphabetically within this chapter.
Population 136 455
Political Composition: LD: 21, Con: 29, Ind: 7, Lab: 1
Town Hall, St. Ives Rd, Maidenhead, Berkshire SL6 1RF;
URL www.rbwm.gov.uk; E-mail info@rbwm.gov.uk;
Tel 01628 798888; Fax 01628 796408; Minicom 01628
796056
Chief Executive David Lunn, LLB
Borough Secretary Diana Hills, MA
Director (Planning and Environment) Michael Coughlin
Director (Leisure, Cultural and Property Services)
David Oram
Head (Finance) John Taylor
Head (Personnel) Vacancy

Social Services Directorate

URL www.rbwm.gov.uk;
E-mail morna.sloan@rbwm.gov.uk; Tel (Emergency
Duty Team) 01344 786543; 01628 798888; Fax 01628
796672
Director (Social Services and Housing) Jim Gould
Head (Strategy Support and Performance)
Andy Sedgwick
Head (Organisational Development) David Horler
Head (Children and Families Services) Heather Andrews
Head (Housing Policy) Chris Thomas

Social Services Lead Members

Cabinet Lead Member Cllr Pam Proctor
Scrutiny Panel Chair Cllr Bruce Adams

Local Social Services Offices

Maidenhead Social Services 4 Marlow Rd,
Maidenhead, Berkshire SL6 7YR; Tel 01628 798888;
Fax 01628 683100

Windsor Social Services York Hse, Sheet St, Windsor,
Berkshire SL4 1DD; Tel 01753 810525; Fax 01853
683700

TRAINING AND STAFF DEVELOPMENT AGENCY (SERVING BERKSHIRE UNITARY AUTHORITIES)

TaSDA, Royal Borough of Windsor and Maidenhead Town
Hall, St. Ives Rd, Maidenhead, Berkshire SL6 1RF; Tel 01628
798888
Manager D. Horler

ADOPTION ADVISORY SERVICE (SERVING BERKSHIRE UNITARY AUTHORITIES)

**Adoption Advisory Service, Royal Borough of Windsor and
Maidenhead** York Hse, Sheet St, Windsor, Berkshire
SL4 1DD; Tel 01753 810525
Senior Adoption Consultant Alyson Graham

HOSPITAL SOCIAL WORK TEAMS

Heatherwood Hospital Social Services Centre London Rd,
Ascot, Berkshire SL5 8AA; Tel 01344 877601

RESIDENTIAL ESTABLISHMENT FOR CHILDREN

Kennel Ride Home 100a Kennel Ride, Ascot, Berkshire
SL5 7NW; Tel 01344 882888
Manager B. Fitzsimmons
(6)

YOUTH OFFENDING TEAM

Windsor and Maidenhead Youth Resources Team, Reform
Rd, Maidenhead, Berkshire SL6 8BY; Tel 01628 683295
Manager Trevor Lowe

FAMILY PLACEMENT SERVICE (FOSTERING AND ADOPTION)

Windsor and Maidenhead Fostering and Adoption Team
Social Services, 4 Marlow Rd, Maidenhead, Berkshire
SL6 7YR; Tel 01628 798888
Manager Ros Whittaker

CHILD PROTECTION CO-ORDINATOR

Social Services 4 Marlow Rd, Maidenhead, Berkshire
SL6 7YR; Tel 01628 798888
Co-ordinator Sheila Caie

HOME CARE

Windsor and Maidenhead Social Services Home Care 4
Marlow Rd, Maidenhead, Berkshire SL6 7YR; Tel 01628
798888
Manager H. Latter

RESIDENTIAL ESTABLISHMENTS FOR ELDERLY PEOPLE

There are two local authority residential homes for older
people.

COMMUNITY TEAM FOR PEOPLE WITH LEARNING DISABILITIES

Windsor and Maidenhead 3 Abell Gdns, Maidenhead,
Berkshire SL6 6PS; Tel 01628 670117
Joint Manager (Learning Disabilities Services) Louise Kerfoot

**DAY CENTRES FOR ADULTS WITH LEARNING DISABILITIES AND
SPECIAL NEEDS UNITS FOR ADULTS WITH LEARNING DISABILITIES
(ATTACHED TO DAY CENTRES)**

Brunel Centre (and Brunel Horticultural Project) Brunel Rd,
Maidenhead, Berkshire SL6 2RT; Tel 01628 626397
Manager Cindy Blackman

Oakbridge Day Centre Imperial Rd, Windsor, Berkshire
SL4 3RU; Tel 01753 833654
Manager C. Blackman

COMMUNITY MENTAL HEALTH TEAM

Windsor and Maidenhead Community Mental Health Team
Reform Rd, Maidenhead, Berkshire SL6 8BY
Joint Manager (Mental Health Services) Garry Nixon

DAY FACILITIES FOR PEOPLE WITH MENTAL HEALTH NEEDS

Forest Lodge Day Unit Kings Ride, Ascot, Berkshire
SL5 8AA; Tel 01344 21336
Manager Vacancy

Education Directorate

Town Hall, St. Ives Rd, Maidenhead, Berkshire SL6 1RF;
Tel 01628 798888; Fax 01628 796256
Director (Education) Malcolm Peckham, JP, BA (Hons)
CEd, Dip EdAdmin, FRSA
Unit Manager (Pupil and Student Services) Anna Crispin;
Tel 01628 796756
Education Officer (Special Educational Needs) Rhidian Jones;
Tel 01628 796776
Special Schools
1

SPECIAL SCHOOL (BOARDING AND DAY)

Holyport Manor School Ascot Rd, Holyport, Maidenhead,
Berkshire SL6 3LE; Tel 01628 623196; Fax 01628 623608
This school can provide for children with complex, severe
and profound learning difficulties; moderate learning
difficulties; challenging or autistic behaviour and children
with sensory impairment.
Headteacher P. Donkersloot
Campus School and Hostel

RESOURCE UNIT FOR CHILDREN WITH A PHYSICAL DISABILITY

Charters Secondary School Sunningdale, Ascot, Berkshire
SL5 9QY; Tel 01344 624826
Headteacher Mrs M.A. Twelftree

**AURAL AND ORAL RESOURCE UNITS FOR CHILDREN WITH HEARING
IMPAIRMENT**

Wessex Infant and Nursery School St. Adrian's Cl, Cox
Grn, Maidenhead, Berkshire SL6 3AT; Tel 01628 629607
Headteacher Mrs G. Sillitto

Wessex Junior School St. Adrian's Cl, Cox Grn,
Maidenhead, Berkshire SL6 3AT; Tel 01628 626724
Headteacher V. Preece

**RESOURCE UNIT FOR CHILDREN WITH MODERATE LEARNING
DIFFICULTIES**

St. Edward's Royal Free Special Resource St. Edwards
Royal Free Ecumenical Middle School, Parsonage La,
Windsor, Berkshire SL4 5EN; Tel 01753 867809
Headteacher Miss W.F. Merwood

**RESOURCE UNIT FOR CHIDREN WITH SPECIFIC LEARNING
DIFFICULTIES**

Dedworth Special Resource Dedworth Middle School,
Smith's La, Windsor, Berkshire SL4 5PE; Tel 01753
860561
Headteacher Mrs K. Bolton

SPEECH AND LANGUAGE RESOURCE UNIT

Altwood Special Resource Altwood CE Secondary School,
Altwood Rd, Maidenhead, Berkshire SL6 4PU; Tel 01628
622236 01628 785417
Headteacher Miss K. Higgins

OTHER ESTABLISHMENTS

Specialist Inclusion Services St. Edmunds Hse, Ray Mill
Road West, Maidenhead, Berkshire SL6 8SB; Tel 01628
670816
Head (Specialist Inclusion Services) S. Brown
This service is made up of the following teams: Pre-School
Teacher Counsellors, Learning Support Teachers, Education
Otherwise than at School, Behaviour Support Team.

Brocket Pupil Referral Unit 15 Boyn Hill Ave, Maidenhead,
Berkshire SL6 4EY; Tel 01628 631624; Fax 01628 631624
Co-ordinator Ms S. Snape

**Sensory Consortium (Hearing, Visual or Multi-Sensory
Difficulties)** Town Hall, St. Ives Rd, Maidenhead, Berkshire
SL6 1RF; Tel 01628 796787
Head (Sensory Consortium Service) Gillian Coles

Educational Psychological Service Brocket, 15 Boyn Hill
Ave, Maidenhead, Berkshire SL6 4EY; Tel 01628 624408;
Fax 01628 635022
Principal Educational Psychologist Mrs H Green

Child and Family Consultation Service Brocket, 15 Boyn
Hill Ave, Maidenhead, Berkshire SL6 4EY; Tel 01628 624408
Co-ordinator Helen Hay

Education Welfare Service Marlow Rd, Maidenhead,
Berkshire SL6 7YR; Tel 01628 683174
Principal Education Welfare Officer Mrs M. Hayter

6

METROPOLITAN BOROUGH OF WIRRAL

www.wirral.gov.uk

Population 312 289
Political Composition: Lab: 26, Con: 23, LD: 16, Ind: 1
Town Hall, Brighton St, Wallasey, Wirral CH44 8ED;
URL www.wirral.gov.uk; Tel 0151 638 7070
Chief Executive Steve Maddox;
E-mail stephenmaddox@wirral.gov.uk
Director (Property Services) David Norton
South Annexe, Brighton St, Wallasey, Wirral CH44 8ED;
E-mail davidnorton@wirral.gov.uk; Tel 0151 691 8407
*Deputy Chief Executive and Director (Planning and Economic
Development)* Jim Wilkie
North Annexe, Brighton St, Wallasey, Wirral;
E-mail jimwilkie@wirral.gov.uk; Tel 0151 691 8183
Director (Highway and Engineering Services) David Green
Town Hall, Civic Way, Bebington, Wirral CH63 7PT;
E-mail davidgreen@wirral.gov.uk; Tel 0151 643 7104
Director (Finance) Ian Coleman
Treasury Bldgs, PO Box No 2, Cleveland St, Birkenhead,
Wirral CH41 6BU; E-mail iancoleman@wirral.gov.uk;
Tel 0151 666 3056
Director (Housing and Environmental Protection)
Alan Stennard
Westminster Hse, Hamilton St, Birkenhead, Wirral
CH41 5FN; E-mail alanstennard@wirral.gov.uk; Tel 0151
666 4955
Director (Personnel and Policy) Bob Williams
Town Hall, Brighton St, Wallasey, Wirral CH44 8ED;
E-mail bobwilliams@wirrall.gov.uk; Tel 0151 691 8590
Borough Solicitor and Secretary J. Miller;
E-mail jomiller@wirral.gov.uk; Tel 0151 691 8498

Social Services Department

Social Services Headquarters, Westminster Hse, Hamilton
St, Birkenhead, Merseyside CH41 5FN; Tel 0151 666 3650
Director (Social Services) K. Miller
Assistant Director (Special Needs) Maura Noone
Assistant Director (Child and Family Services) Julia Hassall

Assistant Director (Older People's Services) Jenny Ricketts
Assistant Director (Finance) Mark Fowler (Acting)
Manager (Youth Offending Team) Steve Pimblett

TRAINING

The following has responsibility for training professional and support staff in the department.
Service Manager (Staff Development) S. Wright
76 Hamilton St, Birkenhead, Merseyside; Tel 0151 647 7000; Fax 0151 666 5196

Social Services Committee

Lab: 7, Con: 4, LD: 1
Chair A.P. Witter (Lab)
Vice-Chair Mclaughlan (Lab)
Members of the Committee
Lab: Davis, Day, Dowe, Green, Groves, Williams.
LD: Bridson, Lindsey.
Con: Price, Stedman, Jones.

AREA OFFICES

Bebington Area Office Civic Centre, Civic Way, Bebington, Merseyside CH63 7SF; Tel 0151 643 9000; Fax 0151 643 7018
Manager (Support Services) Chris Boyle
Manager (Adult Services) Bill Lea
Manager (Adult Services) H. Chambers

Birkenhead North Area Office Conway Bldg, Burlington St, Birkenhead, Merseyside CH41 4FD; Tel 0151 666 4697; Fax 0151 666 4651
Manager (Support Services) Linda King
Manager (Learning Disabilities) Jenny McGovern
Manager (Learning Disabilities) P. Timson
Manager (Children) Tony Burscough

Birkenhead South Area Office 2a Meadow La, Rock Ferry, Birkenhead, Merseyside CH46 8TN; Tel 0151 643 8223; Fax 0151 643 8183

Central Wirral Area Office Municipal Office, Knutsford Rd, Moreton, Wirral CH46 8TN; Tel 0151 677 0481; Fax 0151 604 1841
Manager (Support Services) J. Wharton
Manager (Children's Services) Russ Tattersall

West Wirral Area Office 2a Bridge Rd, West Kirby, Wirral CH48 5JT; Tel 0151 625 0045; Fax 0151 625 0047
Manager (Support Services) Norma Jones
Manager (Physical Disabilities) K. Roberts

Wallasey Area Office Municipal Offices, 52 Seaview Rd, Wallasey, Wirral CH45 5FY; Tel 0151 630 6196; Fax 0151 631 3319
Manager (Support Services) Stella Joseph
Manager (Adult Services) Russ Tattersall

HOSPITAL SOCIAL WORKERS

Arrowe Park Hospital Arrowe Park Rd, Upton, Birkenhead, Merseyside; Tel 0151 678 5111; Fax 0151 604 0848

Ashton House 26 Village Rd, Oxton, Birkenhead, Merseyside; Tel 0151 652 3143

Clatterbridge Hospital Bebington, Wirral; Tel 0151 334 4000; Fax 0151 343 1598

St. Catherine's Hospital Church Rd, Birkenhead, Merseyside; Tel 0151 678 5111

Victoria Central Hospital Medical Unit, Mill La, Wallasey, Wirral; Tel 0151 678 5111

Victoria Central Hospital Geriatric Day Hospital, Mill La, Wallasey, Wirral; Tel 0151 678 5111

CHILDREN'S CENTRES FOR UNDER FIVES

Beckwith Street Family Centre Beckwith St, Birkenhead, Merseyside; Tel (Fax linked to telephone) 0151 653 6293
(30)

Bromborough Family Centre Gratrix Rd, Bromborough, Merseyside; Tel 0151 334 1381; Fax 0151 334 1381
(25)

Moreton Family Centre Pasture Rd, Moreton, Wirral; Tel (Fax linked to telephone) 0151 678 8338
(30)

Under Fives Centre St. Pauls Rd, Wallasey, Wirral; Tel 0151 630 1845; Fax 0151 630 4445
(50)

Wirral Social Care Assessment Centre Kennett Cl, Bebington, Wirral; Tel 0151 608 8188; Fax 0151 609 1079
(25)

Woodchurch Family Support Project c/o Fender Primary School, New Hey Rd, Woodchurch, Merseyside; Tel 0151 606 0800
(30)

RESIDENTIAL ESTABLISHMENTS FOR CHILDREN

Fernleigh Home Twickenham Dr, Leasowe, Wirral; Tel 0151 638 5602; Fax 0151 638 9962

The Lodge Noctorum La, Birkenhead, Merseyside CH43 7QG; Tel 0151 652 2001; Fax 0151 653 6389

Meadowcroft Home Spital Rd, Bebington, Wirral; Tel 0151 334 6325

Mendell Lodge New Chester Rd, Bromborough, Merseyside; Tel 0151 334 3601; Fax 0151 334 3601

Newholme Home Berrylands Rd, Moreton, Wirral; Tel 0151 677 6557; Fax 0151 677 6557

Pensall House Fairview Way, Pensby, Merseyside; Tel 0151 342 2771; Fax 0151 342 2771

Poolwood Road Home 33–35 Poolwood Rd, Woodchurch, Merseyside; Tel 0151 677 1182
Long stay boys and girls (12)

Poulton House Winterhey Ave, Seacombe, Merseyside; Tel 0151 639 8844; Fax 0151 639 8844

Rosclare House Rosclare Cl, Noctorum, Merseyside; Tel 0151 677 7789; Fax 0151 677 7789
Mentally handicapped long stay. (10)

Willow Tree Resource Centre Stavordale Rd, Moreton, Wirral; Tel 0151 522 0710; Fax 0151 522 0717
Rotating care (children with special needs) (26)

Wimbrick Hey Home Burnley Rd, Moreton, Wirral; Tel 0151 677 9431
Observation and assessment (29)

HOME FOR YOUNGER PEOPLE WITH PHYSICAL DISABILITIES

Girtrell Court Girtrell Rd, Saughall Massie, Liverpool, Merseyside L12 0NY; Tel 0151 678 5056; Fax 0151 604 0256
(20)

CENTRES FOR ADULTS WITH LEARNING DIFFICULTIES

Dale Farm Oldfield Rd, Heswall, Merseyside; Tel 0151 342 7819
(16)

Eastham Centre Eastham Rake, Wirral; Tel 0151 327 4348; Fax 0151 327 4348
(75)

Heswall Centre Telegraph Rd, Heswall, Merseyside; Tel 0151 342 6402; Fax 0151 342 6402
(135)

Moreton Centre Pasture Rd, Moreton, Wirral; Tel 0151 677 6169; Fax 0151 677 6169
(186)

Pensby Wood Centre Somerset Rd, Pensby, Merseyside; Tel 0151 648 7313; Fax 0151 648 7313

Riverside Centre Pensby St, Birkenhead, Merseyside; Tel 0151 652 5252; Fax 0151 652 5252
(150)

ESTABLISHMENTS FOR ADULTS WITH LEARNING DIFFICULTIES (GROUP LIVING)

Balls Road Centre 27 Balls Rd, Birkenhead, Merseyside; Tel 0151 653 6108; Fax 0151 663 6108
(8)

Balls Road Centre 70 Balls Rd, Birkenhead, Merseyside; Tel 0151 653 6108

Fellowship House Hoylake, Merseyside; Tel 0151 632 4603
(12)

Manor Road Centre 96 Manor Rd, Wallasey, Wirral; Tel 0151 639 0401; Fax 0151 639 0401

ESTABLISHMENTS FOR ADULTS WITH LEARNING DIFFICULTIES

The Carriage Lamp Centre St. James' Rd, New Brighton, Merseyside; Tel 0151 639 2598
(16)

Lamorna Hamilton Rd, New Brighton, Merseyside; Tel 0151 639 5190
(12)

Sylvandale Centre 191 Spital Rd, Bromborough, Merseyside; Tel 0151 334 0142; Fax 0151 334 0510
(24)

Waverley Centre Vittoria St, Birkenhead, Merseyside; Tel 0151 647 6582
(24)

DAY CENTRES FOR PEOPLE WITH MENTAL HEALTH PROBLEMS

Prenton Day Care Centre 227 Prenton Hall Rd, Birkenhead, Merseyside; Tel 0151 608 0422; Fax 0151 609 1062
(30)

Roscoe Court Day Centre Old Chester Rd, Birkenhead, Merseyside; Tel 0151 647 5981; Fax 1051 650 1312
(40)

Union Street Centre 78 Union St, Wallasey, Wirral; Tel 0151 639 1761; Fax 0151 639 1761
(30)

ACCOMMODATION FOR PEOPLE WITH MENTAL HEALTH PROBLEMS

Manor Grange Seabank Rd, New Brighton, Merseyside; Tel 0151 630 4929
(12)

RESIDENTIAL SUPPORT UNIT

7 St. Andrew's Rd, Birkenhead, Merseyside; Tel 0151 652 2461

SHELTERED HOUSING

Attached to residential homes for senior citizens.

DAY CENTRES – ADULTS WITH A PHYSICAL DISABILITY

Bebington Day Centre 'Highcroft', Heath Rd, Bebington, Wirral; Tel 0151 643 7240; Fax 0151 643 7241
(35)

Cambridge Road Day Centre Cambridge Rd, New Brighton, Wallasey, Merseyside; Tel 0151 638 9237; Fax 0151 638 2184
(35)

Girtrell Court Day Centre Woodpecker Cl, Saughall Massie, Liverpool, Merseyside L12 0NY; Tel 0151 678 5056
(30)

DAY CENTRE FOR SENIOR CITIZENS

Seacombe House Day Centre Demesne St, Wallasey, Wirral; Tel 0151 638 6637; Fax 0151 638 6637

RESIDENTIAL HOMES FOR SENIOR CITIZENS

There are 20 local authority homes for elderly people offering a total of 570 places.

MEALS ON WHEELS SERVICE

Principal Officer Tel 0151 647 7000

SERVICES FOR THE BLIND

Team Manager (Rehabilitation) Frances Tordoff
Rehabilitation Officer Patricia McSorley
Rehabilitation Officer Belinda Thompson

LEARNING DISABILITIES (RESPITE) RESIDENTIAL

Mapleholme 98 Bidston Rd, Birkenhead, Wirral L43 6TW; Tel 0151 653 8735; Fax 0151 652 6162
Learning disabilities (respite). Residential

RESOURCE CENTRE AND RESIDENTIAL RESPITE FOR PEOPLE WITH MENTAL HEALTH PROBLEMS

Rosewarne 74 Bidston Rd, Bidston, Wirral CH43 6TN; Tel 0151 670 0861; Fax 0151 670 0860
Resource centre and residential respite for people with mental health problems.

Education and Cultural Services Department

Hamilton Bldg, Conway St, Birkenhead, Merseyside CH41 4FD; Tel 0151 666 2121
Director (Education and Cultural Services)
Howard Cooper
Deputy Director L. Maxim
Senior Inspector (Pupil and Student Services) D.W. Griffith
General Inspector (Pupil Services Primary) C. Royle
Head (Education Social Welfare Service) Jill Bennett
Solar Campus, Leasowe Rd, Leasowe, Wirral, Merseyside; Tel 0151 637 6060
Principal Educational Psychologist (Special Education Support Service) S. Willan
Solar Campus, 235 Leasowe Rd, Leasowe, Wirral, Merseyside; Tel 0151 637 6090

SPECIAL SCHOOLS AND UNITS

Clare Mount School Fender La, Moreton, Wirral CH46 9PA; Tel 0151 606 9440
Headteacher L.C. Clare, MEd
12–19

Foxfield School 100 Douglas Dr, Moreton, Wirral; Tel 0151 677 8555; Fax 0151 678 5480
Headteacher A. Baird
11–19 SLD

Kilgarth School Cavendish St, Birkenhead, Wirral CH41 8DU; Tel 0151 652 8071
Headteacher J.M. Dawson, BEd
11–16 EH (51)

The Link Centre Solar Campus, 235 Leasowe Rd, Wallasey, Wirral CH45 8LW; Tel 0151 638 8399
Headteacher C. Royle

Meadowside School Pool La, Woodchurch, Birkenhead, Wirral CH49 5LR; Tel 0151 678 7711; Fax 0151 678 9155
Headteacher L. Kane
13–19 PH

6

Wirral Hospital School The Solar Campus, 235 Leasowe Rd, Wallasey, Wirral CH45 8LW; Tel 0151 638 8599; Fax 0151 638 8640
Headteacher I.D. Price
2–19

SPECIAL AND REMEDIAL UNITS

Sanderling Ravenswood Unit Rock Ferry High School, Ravenswood Ave, Birkenhead, Wirral CH42 4NY; Tel 0151 644 6670
Head of Unit R. Rogers

Wimbrick Hey Teaching Support Service for Social Services 61 Burnley Rd, Moreton, Wirral CH46 9QE; Tel 0151 606 0826
Head of Service R. Taylor

EDUCATION SOCIAL WELFARE SERVICE AND OFFICERS

Education Offices Solar Campus, 235 Leasowe Rd, Wallasey, Wirral CH49 8LW; Tel 0151 638 7659; Fax 0151 639 3581
Head of Service J. Innes

Liscard Municipal Offices 52 Seaview Rd, Wallasey, Wirral CH45 4FY; Tel 0151 639 7869 ext 331
North Team Leader J. Bennet
South Team Leader Mike Clarke

SPECIAL EDUCATION SUPPORT SERVICES

The Solar Campus, 235 Leasowe Rd, Wallasey, Wirral; Tel 0151 637 6090
Head S. Willan

HEARING IMPAIRED SERVICE

The Solar Campus, 235 Leasowe Rd, Wallasey, Wirral; Tel 0151 637 6115
Head C. Peake

VISUALLY IMPAIRED SERVICE

The Solar Campus, 235 Leasowe Rd, Wallasey, Wirral; Tel 0151 637 6104
Head W. Kearns, MEd

WOKINGHAM DISTRICT COUNCIL
www.wokingham.gov.uk

In April 1998 Berkshire County Council was replaced by Bracknell Forest, Reading, Slough, West Berkshire, Windsor and Maidenhead and Wokingham – all responsible for local government services within their area. They are listed alphabetically within this chapter.
Population 150 000
Political Composition: Con: 33, LD: 20, Lab: 1
Civic Offices, Shute End, Wokingham RG40 1WN;
URL www.wokingham.gov.uk; Tel 0118 974 6000;
Fax 0118 978 9078
Chief Executive Doug Patterson
Council Leader Alan Spratling (LD)
Council Leader Frank Browne (Con)
Head (Policy Unit) Paul Turrell

Community Services Department

Chief Officer (Social Services and Housing) Sue Richards; Tel 0118 974 6750; Fax 0118 974 6770
Assistant Chief Officer (Adult Services) Pat Brecknock; Tel 0118 974 6762; Fax 0118 974 6770

Assistant Chief Officer (Performance Development) Keith Burns (Acting); Tel 0118 974 6875; Fax 0118 974 6770
Head (Children's Services) Mark Molloy (Acting); Tel 0118 974 6775; Fax 0118 974 6770
Head (Housing) Howard Squires; Tel 0118 974 3760; Fax 0118 974 3788
Head Member (Social Services) Pauline Helliar-Symons
Head (Mental Health Services) Pat Jones; Tel 0118 989 0707; Fax 0118 979 5561
Head (Learning Disability Service) Stuart Rowbotham; Tel 0118 974 6800
Manager (Children's Services – Fieldwork) Jeremy Curtis (Acting); Tel 0118 944 5350; Fax 0118 944 8003
Manager (Care Services (Adults)) Alain Wilkes; Tel 0118 974 6810; Fax 0118 974 6940
Manager (Adult Services) Harvey Campbell; Tel 0118 974 6841; Fax 0118 974 6927
Manager (Children's Services) Lynne Pitt; Tel 0118 974 6880; Fax 0118 974 6940
Manager (Children's Development) Tina Gayle; Tel 0118 974 6768; Fax 0118 974 6770

Housing Services

Waterford Hse, Erftstadt Crt, Wokingham RG40 2YF; Tel 0118 974 3770; Fax 0118 974 3788

Area Teams (Children and Adults)

WOKINGHAM

Wellington Hse, Wellington Rd, Wokingham RG40 2QB; Tel 0118 974 6800; Fax 0118 978 9261

WOODLEY

Lytham Crt, Lytham Rd, Woodley, Wokingham RG5 3PQ; Tel 0118 944 5300; Fax 0118 944 3003

CHILDREN'S RIGHTS SERVICE

46 Church Rd, Woodley, Reading; Tel 0118 927 2000; Fax 0118 969 6863

RESOURCE CENTRE

Bridges Resource Centre 109 Colmansmoor Rd, Woodley, Reading RG5 4DA; Tel 0118 969 5977; Fax 0118 969 2920

FAMILY CENTRES

Woodley Family Centre 46 Church Rd, Woodley, Wokingham RG5 4QJ; Tel 0118 969 0624
Wokingham Family Centre The Oaks, 83–85 Finchampstead Rd, Wokingham RG41 2PE; Tel 0118 977 5611

YOUTH OFFENDING TEAM (READING AND WOKINGHAM)

34–36 Crown St, Reading RG1 2SE; Tel 0118 939 0420; Fax 0118 939 0935

FAMILY PLACEMENT SERVICE (FOSTERING AND ADOPTION)

Lytham Court Lytham Rd, Woodley, Wokingham RG5 3PQ; Tel 0118 944 5300; Fax 0118 944 8003

LEAVING CARE TEAM

6 Langborough Rd, Wokingham RG40 2BT; Tel 0118 979 3008

OUTREACH TEAM

6 Langborough Rd, Wokingham RG40 2BT; Tel 0118 979 3008

PARENTING PROGRAMMES

Wokingham Social Services North, Lytham Crt, Lytham Rd, Woodley, Wokingham RG5 3PQ; Tel 0118 944 5300

SHELTERED ACCOMODATION AND DAY CENTRES

Arnett Avenue 109 Arnett Ave, Wokingham RG40 4EE; Tel 0118 973 0545; Fax 0118 973 4789

Fosters Fosters La, Woodley, Reading RG5 4HH; Tel 0118 969 0630; Fax 0118 969 5113

Suffolk Lodge 18 Rectory Rd, Wokingham RG40 1DH; Tel 0118 979 3202; Fax 0118 977 6446

DAY CENTRE FOR PEOPLE WITH A PHYSICAL DISABILITY

Westmead Centre Rances La, Wokingham RG40 2LH; Tel 0118 989 4032; Fax 0118 989 4036

DAY CENTRE FOR PEOPLE WITH A LEARNING DISABILITY

Wokingham Resource and Opportunity Centre 56–58 Woosehill La, Wokingham RG41 2TS; Tel 0118 979 2588; Fax 0118 977 0259

SUPPORTED HOUSING FOR ADULTS WITH LEARNING DISABILITIES

1 Oakfield Crt, Barkham Rd, Wokingham RG41 2SW

ADULT PLACEMENT AND RESPITE SERVICE FOR ADULTS WITH A LEARNING DISABILITY

Wellington Hse, Wellington Rd, Wokingham RG40 2AG; Tel 0118 974 6832; Fax 0118 977 6244

DAY CARE FOR PEOPLE WITH MENTAL HEALTH PROBLEMS

Resource Centre 48 Reading Rd, Wokingham RG41 1EH; Tel 0118 989 0365

COMMUNITY TEAM FOR PEOPLE WITH LEARNING DISABILITIES

Wellington House Wellington Rd, Wokingham RG40 2AG; Tel 0118 974 6832; Fax 0118 974 6244

COMMUNITY MENTAL HEALTH TEAM

Wallis House 27 Broad St, Wokingham RG40 1AU; Tel 0118 989 0707; Fax 0118 979 5561

DOMICILIARY CARE SERVICES

Wellington Hse, Wellington Rd, Wokingham RG40 2QB; Tel 0118 974 6923; Fax 0118 974 6914

SENSORY NEEDS SERVICES

Lytham Crt, Lytham Rd, Woodley, Wokingham RG5 3PQ; Tel 0118 944 5420; Fax 0118 927 2223; Minicom 0118 927 2202

SUPPORTING PEOPLE PROJECT

Community Services Department, Shute End, Wokingham RG40 1WN; Tel 0118 974 6778; 0118 974 6781

WAYS INTO WORK

Community Services Department, Shute End, Wokingham RG40 1BN; Tel 0118 974 6291; Fax 0118 974 6770

Education and Cultural Services Department

PO Box 156, Council Offices, Shute End, Wokingham RG40 1WN; Tel 0118 974 6105; Fax 0118 974 6135
Assistant Director Judith Pettersen

WOLVERHAMPTON CITY COUNCIL
www.wolverhampton.gov.uk

Population 236 582
Political Composition: Lab: 34, Con: 21, LD: 5
Civic Centre, St. Peters Sq, Wolverhampton, West Midlands WV1 1SH; URL www.wolverhampton.gov.uk; E-mail wolverhampton.ocepc@dial.pipex.com (Chief Executive's Department only); Tel 01902 556556; Fax (Chief Executive's Department only) 01902 554030
Leader of the Council Cllr Roger Lawrence
Chief Executive and Policy Co-ordinator D.B. Anderson, CBE, BSc(Hons), MA, MILAM; Tel 01902 554000; Fax 01902 554030
Chief Human Resources Officer Anne Dokov; Tel 01902 554050; Fax 01902 554030
Assistant Chief Executive C. Raine, MSc; Tel 01902 554020; Fax 01902 554030
Co-ordinating Director (Finance and Physical Resources) Brian Bailey, BSc, IPFA; Tel 01902 554500; Fax 01902 554406
Co-ordinating Director (Law and Resources) R. Roberts, LLB, MBA; Tel 01902 554900; Fax 01902 554970
Co-ordinating Director (Lifelong Learning) M.S. Rowley, BSc, MCIEH; Tel 01902 554304; Fax 01902 554300
Co-ordinating Director (Social Care and Housing) Jeff Webster, DMA; Tel 01902 554700; Fax 01902 555387
Director (Housing) R.J. Borrowman; E-mail wmbc.hsginfo@dial.pipex.com; Tel 01902 554799; Fax 01902 555300
Director (Public Health) A. Phillips
Wolverhampton Health Authority, Coniston Hse, Chapel Ash, Wolverhampton, West Midlands WV3 0XE; Tel 01902 444888
Director (Direct Services) M.S. Rowley, BSc, MCIEH; Tel 01902 554300; Fax 01902 554304
Director (Leisure Services) Sue Nixon; Tel 01902 555100; Fax 01902 555138

6

Social Care and Housing

Tel (Out-of-office hours) 01902 552999; 01902 556556
Chair (Social Services Committee) Cllr P. Byrne
c/o Members' Rooms, Civic Centre, Wolverhampton, West Midlands; Tel 01902 556556
Vice-Chair Cllr G. Foster
c/o Members' Rooms, Civic Centre, Wolverhampton, West Midlands; Tel 01902 555300; Fax 01902 555387
Co-ordinating Director (Social Care and Housing) Jeff Webster

Social Care, Housing and Health Cabinet Team

Members of the Team
Lab: Cllr Bilson, Cllr Byrne, Cllr Foster, Cllr Johnson.
Con: Cllr G.J. Patten, Cllr Thompson.

CHILDREN'S SERVICES DIVISION

Assistant Director Vacancy

Chief Children's Services Officer

66 Mount Pleasant, Bilston, Wolverhampton, West Midlands WV14 7PR; Tel 01902 553033
Contact Ms S. Lane

FAMILY PLACEMENTS

66 Mount Pleasant, Bilston, Wolverhampton, West Midlands WV14 7PR; Tel 01902 553070

YOUTH OFFENDING TEAM

Beckminster Hse, Birches Barn Rd, Wolverhampton, West Midlands WV3 7BJ; Tel 01902 553722

CHILD PROTECTION TEAM

St. Peter's Sq, Wolverhampton, West Midlands WV1 1RT; Tel 01902 556573

ENQUIRY AND REFERRAL SERVICE

Civic Centre, St. Peter's Sq, Wolverhampton, West Midlands; Tel 01902 555392

FAMILY SUPPORT SERVICE EAST

Chervil Rise, Heath Town, Wolverhampton, West Midlands; Tel 01902 553166

FAMILY SUPPORT SERVICE WEST

Ryefield, Pendeford, Wolverhampton, West Midlands; Tel 01902 553100

LOOKED AFTER CHILDREN TEAM

66 Mount Pleasant, Bilston, Wolverhampton, West Midlands; Tel 01902 553001

DAY CENTRES FOR CHILDREN

Barnhurst Day Centre Grangefield Cl, Pendeford, Wolverhampton, West Midlands; Tel 01902 553282

Bilston Day Centre Prouds La, Bilston, Wolverhampton, West Midlands; Tel 01902 553278

Blakenhall Family Resource Centre Derry St, Wolverhampton, West Midlands; Tel 01902 553261

Fallings Park Day Centre Helenny Cl, Wolverhampton, West Midlands; Tel 01902 553285

Stowheath House Respite Home 21 Stowheath La, Wolverhampton, West Midlands; Tel 01902 553344

Windmill Lane Respite Home 54 Windmill La, Wolverhampton, West Midlands; Tel 01902 553290

RESOURCE CENTRES FOR CHILDREN

Bramerton Resource Centre 17 Bramerton Cl, Wolverhampton, West Midlands WV11 1RT; Tel 01902 553239

Danescourt Resource Centre Danescourt Rd, Tettenhall, Wolverhampton, West Midlands; Tel 01902 553180

ADULT SERVICES DIVISION

Chief Officer (Adult Services) Vacancy

Divisional Headquarters

St. Jude's Rd, Wolverhampton, West Midlands; Tel 01902 553300

DELIVERED MEALS SERVICE

Unit 4, Kennedy Rd, Wolverhampton, West Midlands WV10 0LL; Tel 01902 556677

TRANSPORT SECTION

Kennedy Rd, Wolverhampton, West Midlands; Tel 01902 554883

HOME SUPPORT SERVICE

South East Home Support Tel 01902 553543

South West Home Support Tel 01902 553419

North East Home Support and North West Home Support
Tel 01902 553494

DISABILITY RESOURCE CENTRE

Craddock St, Wolverhampton, West Midlands; Tel 01902 553580

DAY CENTRES – DISABILITIES AND OLDER PEOPLE

Bradley Day Centre Wilkinson Ave, Bradley, Wolverhampton, West Midlands; Tel 01902 553448

Ekta Day Centre Mander St, off Penn Rd, Wolverhampton, West Midlands; Tel 01902 553554

Linthouse Day Centre Griffiths Dr, Wednesfield, Wolverhampton, West Midlands; Tel 01902 553550

Maltings Day Centre Herbert St, Wolverhampton, West Midlands; Tel 01902 553558

COMMUNITY RESOURCE CENTRES

Blakenhall House Community Resource Centre Haggar St, Blakenhall, Wolverhampton, West Midlands; Tel 01902 553547

Bradley Community Resource Centre Lord St, Bradley, Wolverhampton, West Midlands; Tel 01902 553447

Warstones Community Resource Centre Warstones Dr, Wolverhampton, West Midlands; Tel 01902 553425

Woden Community Resource Centre Vicarage Rd, Wednesfield, Wolverhampton, West Midlands; Tel 01902 443500

RESIDENTIAL HOMES – DISABILITIES AND OLDER PEOPLE

Dale House Showell Circus, Low Hill, Wolverhampton, West Midlands; Tel 01902 553440

Merry Hill House Langley Rd, Merry Hill, Wolverhampton, West Midlands; Tel 01902 553397

Nelson Mandela House Whitburn Cl, Pendeford, Wolverhampton, West Midlands; Tel 01902 553462

OMI Unit Nelson Mandela Hse, Whitburn Cl, Wolverhampton, West Midlands; Tel 01902 553466

Underhill House Underhill La, Wolverhampton, West Midlands; Tel 01902 553431

LEARNING DISABILITIES AND MENTAL HEALTH – GENERAL

Adult Placement Team Oxley Moor Hse, Probert Rd, Wolverhampton, West Midlands; Tel 01902 553323

Corner House Day Centre 200 Dunstall Rd, Wolverhampton, West Midlands; Tel 01902 553382

The Croft Resource Centre 87 Greencroft, Bilston, Wolverhampton, West Midlands; Tel 01902 553823

Employment Team 16 Darlington St, Wolverhampton, West Midlands WV1 4HW; Tel 01902 553371

Old Tree Nursery Pendeford Hall La, Pendeford, Wolverhampton, West Midlands; Tel 01902 786042

DAY TRAINING CENTRES – LEARNING DISABILITIES

Albert Road Day Centre Albert Rd, Wolverhampton, West Midlands; Tel 01902 553354

Oxley Day Centre Probert Rd, Wolverhampton, West Midlands; Tel 01902 553341

Stowheath Day Centre Stowheath La, Wolverhampton, West Midlands; Tel 01902 553346

OUTREACH SERVICES – LEARNING DISABILITIES

North West Outreach Oxley Moor Hse, Probert Rd, Wolverhampton, West Midlands; Tel 01902 553335

St. Aidan's Outreach Muchall Gr, Wolverhampton, West Midlands; Tel 01902 553381

South East Outreach 2 Cullwick St, Wolverhampton, West Midlands; Tel 01902 839839

South West Outreach Flat 1, Merry Hill Hse, Langley Rd, Wolverhampton, West Midlands; Tel 01902 553381

OUTREACH SERVICES – MENTAL HEALTH

Corner House 300 Dunstall Rd, Wolverhampton, West Midlands WV6 0NZ; Tel 01902 553382

RESIDENTIAL HOMES – LEARNING DISABILITIES

Holloway House Residential Home Holloway St, Bilston, Wolverhampton, West Midlands; Tel 01902 553362

Muchall Green Residential Home Muchall Rd, Penn, Wolverhampton, West Midlands; Tel 01902 553369

RESIDENTIAL HOME – MENTAL HEALTH

Blakeley Green House Green La, Aldersley, Wolverhampton, West Midlands; Tel 01902 553388

COMMUNITY CARE COMMISSIONING

Assistant Director B. O'Leary

Chief Community Care Commissioning Officer

Civic Centre, St. Peter's Sq, Wolverhampton, West Midlands WV1 1RT; Tel 01902 556556

ADULT ASSESSMENT (SOCIAL WORK) TEAMS

Disabilities Team Neville Garratt Centre, Bell St, Wolverhampton, West Midlands; Tel 01902 553666

Health Team New Cross Hospital, Wolverhampton, West Midlands; Tel 01902 307999

North East Adults Team Alfred Squire Rd, Wednesfield, Wolverhampton, West Midlands; Tel 01902 553600

North West Adults Team Showell Circus, Low Hill, Wolverhampton, West Midlands; Tel 01902 553777

South East Adults Team Dudley Road Schools, Blakenhall, Wolverhampton, West Midlands; Tel 01902 553635

South West Adults Team Beckminster Hse, Birches Barn Rd, Pennfields, Wolverhampton, West Midlands; Tel 01902 553700

PERFORMANCE REVIEW AND SYSTEM SUPPORT

Assistant Director Vacancy

Chief Performance Review and System Support Officer

Civic Centre, St. Peter's Sq, Wolverhampton, West Midlands WV1 1RT; Tel 01902 556556
Contact Mr I. Coleman

COMPLAINTS AND CLIENT RELATIONS

Danescourt Rd, Tettenhall, Wolverhampton, West Midlands; Tel 01902 553203

EUROPEAN BLUE BADGES

Civic Centre, St. Peter's Sq, Wolverhampton, West Midlands; Tel 01902 555309

TRAINING AND STAFF DEVELOPMENT

Beckminster Hse, Birches Barn Rd, Wolverhampton, West Midlands WV3 7BJ; Tel 01902 553750

Education Services

St. Peter's Sq, Wolverhampton, West Midlands WV1 1RR; E-mail educ.mail@wolverhampton.gov.uk; Tel 01902 556556; Fax 01902 554218
Co-ordinating Director (Lifelong Learning) R. Lockwood, BA
Principal Assistant Director D. Rawlinson, MA
Chief Officer (Access and Inclusion) B.A. Keil, MA, MEd
Jennie Lee Professional Centre, Lichfield Rd, Wolverhampton, West Midlands WV11 3HT; Tel 01902 555900; Fax 01902 555290

SPECIAL SCHOOLS AND RESOURCE AREAS

Braybrook Centre (Key Stage 3 Pupil Referral Unit) Bellamy La, Wednesfield, Wolverhampton, West Midlands WV11 1NN; Tel 01902 558144; Fax 01902 558144
Headteacher T. Ray

Castlecroft Resource Area for Visual Handicap Castlecroft (J and I School), Windmill Cres, Wolverhampton, West Midlands WV3 8HS; E-mail schooloffice@castlecroft.biblio.net; Tel 01902 556606; Fax 01902 556608
Headteacher Mrs P.J. Keech

Colton Hills Resource Area for Physical Handicap Jeremy Rd, Goldthorn Pk, Wolverhampton, West Midlands WV4 5DG; E-mail kbyatt@coltonhills.wolverhampton.sch.uk; Tel 01902 558420; Fax 01902 558421
Headteacher K.J. Byatt

Coppice Performing Arts School and Resource Area for Mild Learning Difficulties Ecclestone Rd, Wednesfield, Wolverhampton, West Midlands WV11 2QE; E-mail headteacher@coppice.biblio.net; Tel 01902 558500; Fax 01902 558501
Headteacher R. Rossides

Danesmore Park Resource Area for Mild Learning Difficulties Russell Cl, Wednesfield, Wolverhampton, West Midlands WV11 2LA; Tel 01902 558551; Fax 01902 558554
Headteacher E.G. Wheeler

Deansfield Resource Area for Hearing Impaired Deans Rd, Wolverhampton, West Midlands WV1 2BH; E-mail indesk@deansfield.biblio.net; Tel 01902 556400; Fax 01902 556401
Headteacher S. Hawke

East Park Resource Area for Hearing Impaired Hollington Rd, Wolverhampton, West Midlands WV1 2DS; E-mail eastparkjuniorschool@wolverhampton.gov.uk; Tel 01902 558735; Fax 01902 558738
Headteacher D. Gill

Green Park School Green Pk Ave, Bilston, West Midlands WV14 6EH; Tel 01902 556429; 01902 556430; Fax 01902 556431
Headteacher M.H. Partington

Heath Park High Resource Area for MLD Prestwood Rd, Wolverhampton, West Midlands WV11 1RD; E-mail info@heathpark.net; Tel 01902 556360; Fax 01902 556361
Headteacher D. Selkirk

Kingston Centre (Primary Pupil Referral Unit) Valley Park Campus, Cromer Gdns, Wolverhampton, West Midlands WV6 0TD; E-mail administrator@kingston.biblio.net; Tel 01902 558149; Fax 01902 558149
Headteacher Mrs G. Phillip

Midpoint (Key Stage 4 Pupil Referral Unit) Valley Park Campus, Cromer Gdns, Wolverhampton, West Midlands WV6 0UA; E-mail midpoint.school@wolverhampton.gov.uk; Tel 01902 551695; Fax 01902 556924
Headteacher Miss D. McIlmurray

Moreton Community School Resource Area for EBD/MLD Old Fallings La, Wolverhampton, West Midlands WV10 8BY; E-mail moreton@moreton.biblio.net; Tel 01902 558310; Fax 01902 558306
Headteacher T. Leach

6

New Park School Cromer Gdns, Wolverhampton, West Midlands WV6 0UB; Tel 01902 551642
Headteacher N. Smith

The Orchard Centre (Home and Hospital Pupil Referral Unit) Great Brick Kiln, Cromer Gdns, Wolverhampton, West Midlands WV3 0PR; Tel 01902 555947; Fax 01902 555965
Headteacher S. Humphreyson

Our Lady and St. Chad RC Resource Area for MLD Old Fallings La, Wolverhampton, West Midlands WV10 8BL; E-mail info@olsc.biblio.net; Tel 01902 558250; Fax 01902 558251
Headteacher Miss M.C. Keelan

Palmers Cross Resource Area for Language and Communication Windermere Rd, Tettenhall, Wolverhampton, West Midlands WV6 9DF; E-mail ncope@palmerscross.biblio.net; Tel 01902 558322; Fax 01902 558322
Headteacher N. Cope

Parkfield High Resource Area for MLD Wolverhampton Rd East, Wolverhampton, West Midlands WV4 6AP; E-mail admin@parkfieldhighschool.co.uk; Tel 01902 558660; Fax 01902 558661
Headteacher A.I. Thompson

Pendeford High Resource Area for MLD/EBD Marsh La, Fordhouses, Wolverhampton, West Midlands WV10 6SE; E-mail phs@pendeford.biblio.net; Tel 01902 551551; Fax 01902 551550
Headteacher A. Harrison (Acting)

Penn Fields School Birches Barn Rd, Penn Fields, Wolverhampton, West Midlands WV3 7BJ; E-mail school@pennfields.biblio.net; Tel 01902 339786; 01902 558640; Fax 01902 558641
Headteacher B. Brigginshaw

Penn Hall School Vicarage Rd, Penn, Wolverhampton, West Midlands WV4 5HP; E-mail admin@pennhall.biblio.net; Tel 01902 558355; Fax 01902 558363
Headteacher A.J. Stoll

Smestow Resource Area for Visual Handicap Windmill Cres, Castlecroft, Wolverhampton, West Midlands WV3 8HU; E-mail office@smestow.biblio.net; Tel 01902 558585; Fax 01902 558586
Headteacher D. Ennis

Special Needs Early Years Team Wood End Primary School, Wood End Rd, Wolverhampton, West Midlands WV11 1YQ; Tel 01902 558406; Fax 01902 558406
Headteacher J. Wellings

Tettenhall Wood School School Rd, Tettenhall Wood, Wolverhampton, West Midlands WV6 8EJ; E-mail tettenhallwoodspecial@wolverhampton.gov.uk; Tel 01902 556519; Fax 01902 556520
Headteacher M. Mahoney

Westcroft School and Sports College Greenacres Ave, Underhill, Wolverhampton, West Midlands WV10 8NZ; E-mail scockhill@westcroft.biblio.net; Tel 01902 558350; Fax 01902 558342
Headteacher D. Alexander (Acting)

WORCESTERSHIRE COUNTY COUNCIL
www.worcestershire.gov.uk

In April 1998 Hereford and Worcester split to form one unitary authority (Herefordshire Council) and one two-tier authority (Worcestershire County Council) – each listed alphabetically in this chapter.
Political Composition: Con: 26, Lab: 14, LD: 8, Ind: 1, Other: 8

County Hall, Spetchley Rd, Worcester, Worcestershire WR5 2NP; URL www.worcestershire.gov.uk; Tel 01905 763763; Minicom 01905 766399
Chief Executive R.H Sykes
Director (Corporate Services) T. Norton
Director (Environmental Services) R. Wigginton
Director (Financial Services) M. Weaver
Chair (County Council) P.H. Fallows
Leader of the County Council G. Lord
Head (Cultural Services) Tim Porter

Social Services Department

Tel 01905 766912; Fax 01905 766982
Director (Social Services) Jennie Bashforth
Head (Adult Services) Eddie Clarke
Head (Children's Services) Anne Binney

Social Services Scrutiny Panel

Lab: 9, Con: 9, LD,: 2 Ind: 1
Members of the Committee
Lab: C.R. Beardwood, J.L. Gordon, E.A. Holmes, N. Knowles, P.A. Mould, B. Passingham, P.J. Pinfield, L.W. Thomas, M.C.G. Wills.
Con: P.E. Davey, R.J. Farmer, M.G.N. Fordyce, D. Inight, J.A.H. Longmuir, K.J. Peers, H. Purcell, E.J. Sheldon, D. Woodward-Sheath.
LD: J.M. Davey, B.A. Watton.
Ind: M.M.G. Oborski.

RESIDENTIAL HOMES FOR ELDERLY PEOPLE

There are three homes for elderly people.

HOSTEL FOR PEOPLE WITH PHYSICAL DISABILITIES

Freda Eddy Court Orchard St, Kidderminster, Worcestershire DY10 2JA; Tel 01562 823656
Officer-in-Charge Elizabeth Best

DAY CENTRES FOR PEOPLE WITH PHYSICAL DISABILITIES

Sandalwood Day Centre Comberton Rd, Kidderminster, Worcestershire DY10 3DH; Tel 01562 820891
Manager Lyn Archer

Unity House Day Centre Stanley Rd, Worcester, Worcestershire WR5 1BE; Tel 01905 355009
Manager Tony Urosevic

MULTI-PURPOSE DAY CENTRES

Halcyon Day Centre Easemore Rd, Redditch, Worcestershire B98 8HA; Tel 01527 66505
Manager Sue Merrick

Three Springs Day Centre Abbots Grange, off Springs Rd, Pershore, Worcestershire WR10 1HR; Tel 01386 553889
Manager Tony Mann

Wendron Day Services Chapel St, Bromsgrove, Worcestershire B60 2BQ; Tel 01527 832032
Manager Mick Drage

MENTAL HEALTH HOSTELS

Franche Road Hostel 134 Franche Rd, Kidderminster, Worcestershire DY11 5BE; Tel 01562 69731
Officer-in-Charge Angela Buckley

Stanley Road Hostel 2 Stanley Rd, Worcester, Worcestershire WR5 1DU; Tel 01905 356479
Officer-in-Charge Garry Hobbs

MENTAL HEALTH RESOURCE CENTRES

Bromsgrove Mental Health Resource Centre Rivendell Hse, Windsor St, Bromsgrove, Worcestershire B60 2BL; Tel 01527 488440
Manager Steve Perry

Covercroft Mental Health Resource Centre Colman Rd, Droitwich, Worcestershire WR9 8QU; Tel 01905 778118
Manager Martin Leeder

Edward Parry Centre Coventry St, Kidderminster, Worcestershire DY10 2BP; Tel 01562 743436
Manager Simon Cox

Orchard Place Mental Health Resource Centre Orchard St, Redditch, Worcestershire B98 7PF; Tel 01527 488714
Manager Margaret Buxton

Studdert Kennedy Centre Spring Gdns, Worcester, Worcestershire WR1 2AE; Tel 01905 22185
Manager Hugh Thomas

Touchstone Mental Health Resource Centre 41 Geraldine Rd, Malvern, Worcestershire WR14 3PQ; Tel 01684 565471
Manager Marian Bailey

HOSTELS FOR PEOPLE WITH LEARNING DISABILITIES

Ashorne Close Hostel 17–18 Ashhorne Cl, Matchborough, Redditch, Worcestershire B98 0EY; Tel 01527 523301
Contact Michaela Beckley

Consterdyne 6 Mason Rd, Kidderminster, Worcestershire DY11 6AF; Tel 01562 69525
Contact Linda Harradine

Crofters Close Hostel 81–83 Crofters Cl, Droitwich, Worcestershire WR9 9HT; Tel 01905 773993
Contact Val Goode

1, 3 and 5 Exmoor Drive Bromsgrove, Worcestershire B61 0TW; Tel 01527 576591
Contact Gary Smith

Hughenden 23 and 26 Players Ave, Malvern Link, Worcestershire WR14 1DU; Tel 01684 892239
Contact Sue Cox

Pershore Short Breaks Service 48 Station Rd, Pershore, Worcestershire WR10 1PD; Tel 01386 556898
Manager Simon Edwards

Worth Crescent Hostel 35 Worth Cres, Stourport on Severn, Worcestershire DY13 8RR; Tel 01299 822515
Contact Donette Shaw

DAY OPPORTUNITIES

WYRE FOREST

Chester Road Day Centre 238 Chester Road North, Kidderminster, Worcestershire DY10 1TE; Tel 01562 69168
Contact Nicky Hyams

Wesley Place 8b Parkes Passage, Stourport on Severn, Worcestershire DY13 9EA; Tel 01299 879904
Contact Sandra Hill

The Elms SEC Habberley Rd, Kidderminster, Worcestershire DY11 6AB; Tel 01562 68773
Manager Ron Atherton

BROMSGROVE

Greenscope Stourbridge Rd, Bromsgrove, Worcestershire B61 0AH; Tel 01527 871186
Contact Chris Harper

Padstone Day Services Recreation Rd, Bromsgrove, Worcestershire B61 8DT; Tel 01527 576550
Manager Sandra Hill

Padstone Industries Unit 3, 37 Sherwood Rd, Bromsgrove, Worcestershire B60 3DR; Tel 01527 835385
Contact John Hamilton

REDDITCH

Millfields SEC Middlehouse La, Redditch, Worcestershire B97 6RG; Tel 01527 65470
Manager Shirley Howson

Social Recreation Group (Halcyon Centre) Easemore Rd, Redditch, Worcestershire B98 8HA; Tel 01527 66505
Manager Lyn Archer

DROITWICH

Kingsfield SEC 39a and 39b Ledwych Rd, Droitwich, Worcestershire WR9 9LA; Tel 01905 778271
Manager Sandra Hibbert

WORCESTER

Checketts Lane Unit 6a Ind Est, Checketts La, Worcester, Worcestershire; Tel 01905 756245
Contact Jackie Bostan

Cherry Orchard Centre Orchard St, Worcester, Worcestershire WR5 3DY; Tel 01905 764700
Manager Alison Stone

Perryfields Centre Midland Rd, Worcester, Worcestershire WR5 1DU; Tel 01905 355529
Contact Alison Stone

Open View (Satellite Unit to Perryfield,) The Citadel, The Trinity, Worcester, Worcestershire WR1 2PN; Tel 01905 20695

Other Voices Theatre Company Angel Centre, Angel Pl, Worcester, Worcestershire WR1 3QN; Tel 01905 724801

MALVERN

Malvern SEC Geraldine Rd, Malvern, Worcestershire WR14 3NT; Tel 01684 560234
Manager Ken Instan

VALE OF EVESHAM

Evesham Day Centre Davies Rd, Evesham, Worcestershire WR11 6XJ; Tel 01386 47591
Manager Tony Mann

Pershore Care Centre 48 Station Rd, Pershore, Worcestershire WR10 1PD; Tel 01386 556989
Manager Tony Mann

Three Springs Day Centre Abbots Grange, 3 Springs Rd, Pershore, Worcestershire WR10 1HR; Tel 01386 553889
Manager Karina Palmer

SUPPORTED EMPLOYMENT (BROMSGROVE AND REDDITCH ONLY)

Modus, 9 Stourbridge Rd, Bromsgrove, Worcestershire B61 0AE; Tel 01527 570199
Manager Sue Keating

CHILDREN'S HOMES

Malvern Children's Home 126 Barnards Green Rd, Malvern, Worcestershire WR14 3NA; Tel 01684 560830
Due to reopen Dec 2003.
Manager Vacancy

Rea Way Children's Home Worcester, Worcestershire WR2 5HA; Tel 01905 748528
Manager Yaf Yafai

Shap Drive Children's Home 4–6 Shap Dr, Worcester, Worcestershire WR4 9NY; Tel 01905 452141
Manager Vacancy

Walton Close Children's Home 71 Walton Cl, Winyates, Redditch, Worcestershire B98 0NS; Tel 01527 501394
Manager Leo Maturi

CHILDREN'S CENTRE

Redditch Immediate Response Unit 45 Downsell Rd, Webheath, Redditch, Worcestershire B97 5RJ; Tel 01527 543135
Manager Simon Streather

6

CHILDREN'S SHORT BREAKS UNITS

Bromsgrove Children's Short Breaks Unit 48–50 Providence Rd, Bromsgrove, Worcestershire B61 8EF; Tel 01527 575710
Manager Bev Harris

Wyre Forest Children's Breaks Unit 1 Moule Cl, Habberley Rd, Kidderminster, Worcestershire DY11 6AB; Tel 01562 823653
Manager Gail Williams

FAMILY SUPPORT UNIT (CHILDREN WITH SPECIAL NEEDS)

Hansel and Gretel Family Support Unit Radford Ave, Kidderminster, Worcestershire DY10 2ES; Tel 01562 68295
Manager Sue Hunter

FAMILY SUPPORT CENTRES

The Birches Family Support Centre 98 New Rd, Bromsgrove, Worcestershire B60 2LN; Tel 01527 579824
Manager Sam Slater

Bromsgrove Family Support Centre Churchfields, Bromsgrove, Worcestershire B61 8DX; Tel 01527 575997
Contact Sam Slater

Evesham Family Centre 103/105 Cheltenham Rd, Evesham, Worcestershire WR11 6LE; Tel 01386 49836
Manager Joan Woodley

Hillborough Family Centre Stanley Rd, Worcester, Worcestershire WR5 1BD; Tel 01905 360444
Manager Claire Locker

Kornerstone Family Centre off Geraldine Rd, Barnards Grn, Malvern, Worcestershire WR14 3PQ; Tel 01684 577427
Manager Joan Woodley

Park Street Family Support Centre Park St, Kidderminster, Worcestershire DY11 6TW; Tel 01562 747564
Manager Jackie Miller

The Pines Family Support Centre Bilford Rd, Worcester, Worcestershire WR3 8PU; Tel 01905 752800
Manager Peter Holland

Redditch Family Resource Centre Friends Meeting Hse, Matchborough, Redditch, Worcestershire B98 0ER; Tel 01527 520084
Manager Heather Coughlin

Redditch Family Support Centre West Ave, Redditch, Worcestershire B98 7DQ; Tel 01527 584699

Education Offices

County Hall, Spetchley Rd, Worcester, Worcestershire WR5 2NP; URL www.worcestershire.gov.uk; Tel 01905 763763; Fax 01905 766860
Director (Educational Services) Julien Kramer

SPECIAL SCHOOLS

Alexander Patterson School Park Gate Rd, Wolverley, Kidderminster, Worcestershire DY10 3PU; URL www.alexpatt.worcs.sch.uk; E-mail head@alexpatt.worcs.sch.uk; Tel 01562 851396; Fax 01562 851192
Headteacher M.E. Calvert
Mixed MLD/SLD (110)

Blakebrook School Bewdley Rd, Kidderminster, Worcestershire DY11 6RL; URL www.blakebrookschool.co.uk; E-mail mrussell@blackbrook.worcs.sch.uk; Tel 01562 753066; Fax 01562 824533
Headteacher M.D.G. Russell
Mixed SLD

Chadsgrove School Meadow Rd, Catshill, Bromsgrove, Worcestershire B61 0JW; E-mail richardaust@chadsgrove.worcs.sch.uk; Tel (Physiotherapy) 01527 578216; 01527 871511; Fax 01527 579341
Headteacher R.H. Aust
Mixed PH

Cliffey House School Rhydd, Hanley Castle, Worcestershire WR8 0AD; Tel 01684 310336; Fax 01684 310076
Headteacher Ann Starr
Mixed MLD + unit for autistic children (75)

Manor Park School Turnpike Cl, Oldbury Rd, Worcester, Worcestershire WR2 6AB; E-mail mps@manorparkschool.demon.co.uk; Tel 01905 423403; Fax 01905 748338
Headteacher D.C. Palmer
Mixed SLD

Pitcheroak School Willow Way, Redditch, Worcestershire B97 6PQ; E-mail jayne@pitchbrook.worcs.sch.uk; Tel 01527 65576; Fax 01527 67845
Headteacher K.M. Earle
Mixed MLD/SLD (185)

Redgrove School (Lower School Site) Prophet's Cl, Batchley, Redditch, Worcestershire B97 4SD; Tel 01527 63577
Headteacher S. Nash
Mixed

Redgrove School Shaw La, Stoke Prior, Bromsgrove, Worcestershire B60 4EL; Tel 01527 878888; Fax 01527 875314
Headteacher L. Albert
Mixed

Rigby Hall School Rigby La, Bromsgrove, Worcestershire B60 2EP; E-mail enquires@rigbyhall.worcs.sch.uk; Tel 01527 875475; Fax 01527 870211
Headteacher P.A. Griffiths
Mixed MLD/SLD (110)

Riversides School Thorneloe Rd, Worcester, Worcestershire WR1 3HZ; E-mail head@riverside.worcs.sch.uk; Tel 01905 21261; Fax 01905 22247
Headteacher B. Scott

Rose Hill School Windermere Dr, Warndon, Worcestershire WR4 9JL; URL www.rosehill.worcs.sch.uk; E-mail admin@rosehill.worcs.sch.uk; Tel 01905 454828; Fax 01905 453695
Headteacher F.W. Steel
Mixed PH

Stourminster School Comberton Rd, Kidderminster, Worcestershire DY10 3DX; E-mail mail@stourminster.worcs.sch.uk; Tel 01562 747183; 01562 823156; Fax 01562 824552
Headteacher I.D. Hardicker
Mixed MLD

Thornton House School Wylds La, Worcester, Worcestershire WR5 1DR; E-mail hugh@thorntonhouse.worcs.sch.uk; Tel (Nursery Unit) 01905 355191; 01905 355525; Fax 01905 358867
Headteacher H.B. Thomas
Mixed MLD + unit for autistic children (125) Nursery unit (30)

The Vale of Evesham School Four Pools La, Evesham, Worcestershire WR11 6DH; E-mail office@valeofevesham.worcs.sch.uk; Tel 01386 443367; Fax 01386 765787
Headteacher E.P. Matthews
Mixed MLD/SLD (small unit for autistic children) (125)

AUDIOLOGY CENTRES

The Clinic 1 Moor St, Worcester, Worcestershire WR1 3BD; Tel 01905 24952

Nelson Street Hereford, Herefordshire; Tel 01432 274549

SERVICE FOR CHILDREN WITH SENSORY IMPAIRMENTS

Castle Street Service for Children 17 Castle St, Worcester, Worcestershire WR1 3AD; Tel 01905 765629
Head R. Broadbent

CITY OF YORK COUNCIL
www.york.gov.uk

Population 178 000
Political Composition: Lab: 25, LD: 24, Con: 3, Ind: 1
Guildhall, York YO1 9QN; URL www.york.gov.uk;
Tel 01904 613161
Chief Executive   David Atkinson
Director (Commercial Services)   D. Finnegan
Director (Environment and Development Services)
R. Templeman
Director (Resources)   Vacancy
Director (Education)   J. Winter (Acting)
Director (Community Services)   Jim Crook
Head (York Leisure Office)   C. Croft

Community Services Department

Customer Advice Centre, PO Box 402, George Hudson St,
York YO1 6ZE; Tel 01904 613161; Fax 01904 554017
Director   Jim Crook
Senior Assistant Director   B. Hodson
Assistant Director (Housing Services)   Steve Waddington
Assistant Director (Adult Services)   R. Hurren
Assistant Director (Children's Services)   P. Dwyer
Manager (Customer Advice)   Lesley Healey
Manager (Finance)   Ruth Brigham

Social Services Committee

LD: 29, Lab: 15, Green: 2, Other: 1.
Chair   Sue Galloway
Vice-Chair   M. Lancelott
Members of the Committee
LD: Keith Aspden, M. Kirk, M. Lancelott, G. Nimmo.
Lab: S. Fraser, V. Kind.
Ind: J. Hopton.

CHILDREN'S SERVICES

Ashbank 1 Shipton Rd, York YO30 5RE; Tel 01904 613161;
Fax 01904 555602
Group Manager (0–10 and Special Needs)   Ken Exton
Service Manager (Health and Disabilities)   Marg McDonald
Service Manager (Referral and Assessment (0–18)
Lyn Clarkson
Service Manager (0–10 West)   John Corden
Service Manager (0–10 East)   Malcolm Wright

Customer Advice Centre PO Box 402, George Hudson St,
York YO1 6ZE; Tel 01904 613161
Assistant Director (Children)   P. Dwyer
Manager (Quality Assurance)   J. Kent

Hollycroft Wenlock Terr, Fulford Rd, York YO10 4DU;
Tel 01904 613161; Fax 01904 555305
Group Manager (Resources/Health and Disabilities)
Howard Lovelady
Service Manager (11+ West)   Richard Hunt
Manager (Family Placement Team)   Mary McKelvey
Service Manager (11+ East)   Michelle Carlisle
Service Manager (Pathway Team)   John Roughton
Group Manager (West and East Pathway Team)   Ruth Love

COMMUNITY SERVICES

Huntington Road Day Centre Huntington Rd, York
YO3 9BN; Tel 01904 613161; Fax 01904 555121
Service Manager (Sheltered Housing and Residential Homes)
M. Little
Assistant Director (Adult Services)   Rob Hurren
*Service Mangaer (Residential and Day Service for Learning
Disabilities)*   Daryoush Haj-Najafi

York Road Centre 50 York Rd, Acomb, York YO24 4LZ;
Tel 01904 613161; Fax 01904 555209
Service Manager (Community and Residential Care)
M. Browne

CUSTOMER SERVICES

Customer Advice Centre PO Box 402, George Hudson St,
York YO1 6ZE; Tel 01904 613161; Fax 01904 554017
Assistant Director (Adult Services)   R. Hurren
Group Manager (Access and Support)   L. Healey
Manager (Advice)   Becky Ward
Customer Services Manager (Health and Disabilities)
Vacancy
Manager (Customer Services – Disability Support Services)
S. Prentice
Manager (Grants and Adaptations)   Vacancy

PO Box 403 George Hudson St, York YO1 6ZE; Tel 01904
613161; Fax 01904 554017
Manager (Allocations)   Judi Dove

20 George Hudson Street York; Tel 01904 613161
Manager (Customer Services)   C. Gajewicz

St. Anthony's House Brook St, York; Tel 01904 613161;
Fax 01904 555209
Manager (Adult Services)   S. Diggle

HOUSING SERVICES

Community Services Acomb Office 50 York Rd,
Acomb, York YO2 4LZ; Tel 01904 613161; Fax 01902
788318
Manager (Housing Services)   Paul Morrison

FAMILY CENTRES

Clifton Family Centre 249 Kingsway North, Clifton, York
YO30 6JE; Tel 01904 622123
Manager   Juliet Burton

Heworth Family Centre Sixth Ave, Heworth, York
YO31 0TT; Tel 01904 424305
Service Manager (0–10 East)   Malc Wright
Manager   Jeannie Freeman

Holgate Family Centre 6 Nursery Dr, Acomb, York
YO24 4PE; Tel 01904 798761
Manager   L. Malkinson

DAY SERVICES

The Customer Advice Centre, PO Box 402, York YO1 6ZE;
Tel 01902 613161; Fax 01904 554119

Education and Leisure

Mill Hse, North St, York YO1 6JD; Tel 01904 613161;
Fax 01904 554293
Director (Education and Leisure)   Patrick Scott

SPECIAL SCHOOLS

Fulford Cross School Fulford Rd, York YO10 4PB; Tel 01904
653219; Fax 01904 622935
Headteacher   J. Lock, BA

Galtres School Bad Bargain La, York YO31 0LW; Tel 01904
415924; Fax 01904 431281
Headteacher   C. Rutherford (Acting)

Lidgett Grove School Wheatlands Gr, Acomb, York
YO26 5NH; Tel 01904 791437; Fax 01904 795640
Headteacher   S. Williams (Acting)

Northfield School Beckfield La, Acomb, York YO26 5RQ;
Tel 01904 791315; Fax 01904 789207
Headteacher   W.J.W. Ford, MA

6

Local Government London

- **Main Council Information**
- **Social Services Department**
  including all related services and key personnel
- **Education Department**
  including Special Needs Education

Key

(110)	Number of pupils
Mixed	Takes boys and girls
Boys	Takes boys only
Girls	Takes girls only
11–18	Age range of pupils

Abbreviations

ADHD	Attention Deficit Hyperactivity Disorder
ASD	Autism Spectrum Disorder
EBD	Emotional Behavioural Difficulties
LD	Learning Difficulties
LI	Language Impairment
MH	Mentally Handicapped
MLD	Moderate Learning Difficulties
PH	Physically Handicapped
PHAB	Physically Handicapped and Able-Bodied
PMLD	Profound and Multiple Learning Difficulties
PS	Partially Sighted
PtHg	Partially Hearing
SCU	Special Care Unit
SEBD	Severe Emotional Behaviour Difficulties
SEN	Special Educational Needs
SLD	Severe Learning Difficulties
SLDD	Students with Learning Difficulties and Disabilities
SMH	Severely Mentally Handicapped

Local Government London

BARKING AND DAGENHAM LONDON BOROUGH COUNCIL

www.barking-dagenham.gov.uk

Population 156 962
Political Composition: Lab: 42, Ind: 4, LD: 3, Con: 2
Civic Centre, Dagenham, Essex RM10 7BN;
    URL www.barking-dagenham.gov.uk;
    E-mail enquiries@barking-dagenham.gov.uk; Tel 020
    8592 4500; Fax 020 8227 2806
Leader of the Council   Cllr C.J. Fairbrass
Chief Executive   G. Farrant
Borough Finance Officer   W.B. Pummell, IPFA
Director (Leisure and Environmental Services)
    D.J. Knowles
Town Hall, Barking, Essex; Tel 020 8592 4500
Director (Housing and Health)   D.W. Woods, DMS, MRSH
Roycraft Hse, 15 Linton Rd, Barking, Essex IG11 8HE

Social Services Department

Fax 020 8227 2241
Director (Social Services)   Julia Ross
Head (Older Peoples' Division)   Cathy Mitchell
Head (Adult Services)   Bruce Morris
Head (Children and Families)   B. Kedward

Initial Contact Service

Civic Centre, Dagenham, Essex; Tel 020 8227 2195

Social Services Committee

Members of the Executive
Alexander, Fairbrass (Leader), Geddes (Deputy Leader),
Jeyes, Osborne, Shaw, Wade, Worby.

SERVICE TEAMS

Head (Human Resources)   Vacancy
General Manager (Localities)   J. Hutton
General Manager (Provider Services)   Vacancy
Manager (Placements)   K. Morgan
Manager (Day Care and Family Support)   P. Segurola
Manager (Commissioning)   Vacancy
Manager (Residential and Day Care)   Vacancy
Manager (Finance)   S. Whitelock
Manager (Training)   T. McCarthy
Manager (Mental Health Borough)   T. Drew
Manager (Disability Services)   Vacancy
Co-ordinator (Child Protection)   Teresa Walsh-Jones

Children and Families Social Work Teams (Barking Area)

Ripple Road Municipal Services, 127 Ripple Rd, Barking,
    Essex; Tel 020 8592 4500; Fax 020 8507 0680

Physical and Sensory Disabilities Team

St. George's Road Centre, St. George's Rd, Dagenham,
    Essex; Tel 020 8227 5447

Learning Disabilities Team

Woodward Road Resource Centre, 27 Woodward Rd,
    Dagenham, Essex; Tel 020 8270 6234
Issuing of all adaptations and equipment.

Community Mental Health Team (Barking)

Hedgecock Centre, Upney La, Barking, Essex IG11 7LX;
    Tel 020 8276 7880

Community Mental Health Team (Dagenham)

Hedgecock Centre, Upney La, Barking, Essex IG11 7LX;
    Tel 020 8276 7870

Child and Family Consultation Service

Child and Family Centre, 31 Woodward Rd, Dagenham,
    Essex; Tel 020 8592 4445; 020 8592 4446

DAY NURSERIES

Annie Prendergast Day Nursery Ashton Gdns, Romford,
Essex RM6 6RT; Tel 020 8270 6419
Team Leader   J. Halliday
    (50)

Eastbury Day Nursery Blake Ave, Barking, Essex IG11 9SQ;
Tel 020 8270 6425
Team Leader   D. Mills
    (50)

Ford Road Day Nursery Dagenham, Essex; Tel 0208 592
0765
Team Leader   A. Meredith
    (45)

Gascoigne Day Nursery 140 St. Ann's, Barking, Essex
IG11 7AD; Tel 020 8507 3695
Team Leader   D. McEwan

Kingsley Hall Day Nursery Parsloes Ave, Dagenham, Essex
RM9 5NH; Tel 020 8270 6544
Team Leader   L. Greenwood

MOTHER AND BABY HOME

Spot purchased.

CHILDREN'S HOME

Woodlands Resource Centre Rainham Road North, Dagenham, Essex RM10 7EJ; Tel 020 8270 6513
Manager S. Marler
(12)

HOMES FOR PERSONS WITH LEARNING DISABILITIES

Tudor House 212 Becontree Ave, Dagenham, Essex RM8 2TR; Tel 020 8270 6712
Officer-in-Charge S. Hindley
(25)

York House Frizlands La, Dagenham, Essex RM10 7YD; Tel 020 8270 6499
Officer-in-Charge Linda Neaves

MENTAL HEALTH SERVICE

Porters Avenue Day Centre, Porters Ave, Dagenham, Essex RM8 2AW; Tel 020 8270 6411
Officer-in-Charge B. Doran
(50)

DAY CENTRES FOR PEOPLE WITH LEARNING DISABILITIES

Gascoigne Centre 80 Gascoigne Rd, Barking, Essex; Tel 020 8270 6675
Centre Manager A. Caulfield-Ross
Heathlands Day Centre Heathway, Dagenham, Essex; Tel 020 8270 5921
Manager P. O'Dwyer
(60)

RESIDENTIAL HOMES FOR THE ELDERLY

There are eight local authority homes for older people.

DISABLEMENT ASSOCIATION OF BARKING AND DAGENHAM

Pembroke Gdns, Dagenham, Essex; Tel 020 8592 8603
Co-ordinator L. Hawes

LUNCHEON CLUBS

Age Concern, Barking, Essex; Tel 020 8227 2891
Manager P. Reed

Education, Arts and Libraries Department

Town Hall, Barking, Essex IG11 7LU;
URL www.barking-dagenham.gov.uk;
E-mail sthomson@barking-dagenham.gov.uk; Tel 020 8227 3022; Fax 020 8227 3471
Director (Education, Arts and Libraries) R. Luxton, OBE
Head (Lifelong Learning and Inclusion) J. Donovan
Head (Social Inclusion) Ms A. Harskemp

EDUCATIONAL PSYCHOLOGY SERVICE

Seabrook House 22 Shipton Cl, Bennetts Castle La, Dagenham, Essex RM8 3DR;
E-mail bdavis@barking-dagenham.gov.uk; Tel 020 8593 7577; Fax 020 8592 9002
Deputy Principal Educational Psychologist and Service Manager B. Davis

SPECIAL SCHOOL

Trinity School Heathway Site, Heathway, Dagenham, Essex RM10 7SJ; Tel 020 8270 1601; Fax 020 8270 4969
Headteacher Ms H. Hardie

INSPECTION AND ADVISORY SERVICE

Westbury Centre, Ripple Rd, Barking, Essex IG11 7PT; E-mail lesjen@bardaglea.org.uk; Tel 020 8270 4800; Fax 020 8270 4811

BARNET LONDON BOROUGH COUNCIL
www.barnet.gov.uk

Population 339 853
Political Composition: Con: 28, Lab: 26, LD: 6
The Town Hall, The Burroughs, Hendon, London NW4 4BG; URL www.barnet.gov.uk; Tel 020 8359 2000; Fax 020 8359 3057
Leader of the Council Cllr A. Williams; Tel 020 8359 2000; Fax 020 8359 2762
Chief Executive Leo Boland; Tel 020 8359 2000; Fax 020 8359 2480
Head (Law and Probity) Vacancy; Tel 020 8359 2000; Fax 020 8359 2680
Head (Personnel) Christine Bennett
Ravensfield Hse, The Boroughs, Hendon, London NW4 4BE; Tel 020 8359 2000; Fax 020 8359 2675
Strategic Director (Resources) J. Jaroszek, MA, MSc, IPFA, IRRV; Tel 020 8359 2000; Fax 020 8359 2561
Strategic Director (Environment) Anne Lippitt, BSc, DipT, MRTPI; Tel 020 8359 2000; Fax 020 8359 4455
Strategic Director (Social Affairs) Brian Reynolds; Tel 020 8359 2000; Fax 020 8359 2284
Borough Treasurer Clive Medan; Tel 020 8359 2000; Fax 020 8359 2561
Head (Design and Build Service) G. Beattie, BSc, MPhil, DMS, CEng, MICE, MBIM
Barnet Hse, 1255 High Rd, London N20 0EJ; Tel 020 8359 2000; Fax 020 8359 4455

Social Services Department

Barnet Hse, 1255 High Rd, Whetstone, London N20 0EJ; URL www.barnet.gov.uk; Tel 020 8359 2000; Fax 020 8359 4887
Director (Social Services) and Head (Children's Services) Paul Fallon; Tel 020 8359 5799; Fax 020 8359 4819
Head (Community Care) Ian Banner; Tel 020 8359 4210
Divisional Manager (Looked After Children) Marion Ingram
Divisional Manager (Family Support) Gaynor Hudson
Divisional Manager (Physical Disabilities) Paul Edwards; Tel 020 8359 2000; Fax 020 8359 4212
Divisional Manager (Listening to Children) Bridget Griffin
Divisional Manager (Listening to Children) Phil Morris
Divisional Manager (Information and Service Improvement) Tony Nakhimoff; Tel 020 8359 2000; Fax 020 8359 4819
Partnership Manager (Learning Disabilities) Denny Cruickshant
313 Ballads La, London N12 8LY
Assistant Chief Education Officer (Early Years, Families and Play) David Canney; Tel 020 8359 7592

Cabinet Committee

Chair Victor Lyon (Con)
Members Room, Hendon Town Hall, Hendon, London NW4 4BS; Tel 020 8202 8282
Members of the Committee
Maureen Braun, Brian Coleman, Katia David, Peter Davis, Anthony Finn, Mike Freer, Lynne Hillan, Kanti Patel, Brian Salinger.

AREA OFFICES

East Area Office

The Town Hall, The Burroughs, Hendon, Greater London
NW4 4BG; Tel 020 8359 4000
Divisional Manager (Adults)   Jackie Mayer

West Area Office

The Town Hall, The Burroughs, Hendon, Greater London
NW4 4BG; Tel 020 8359 3522
Contact   Chana Unadkat
Care Group Manager (Older Adults)   Glynnis Joffee; Tel 020
8359 4290

HOSPITAL OFFICES

Barnet General Hospital Social Work Team, Wellhouse La,
Barnet, London EN5 3DJ; Tel 020 8275 5397 Ext 4302
Principal Team Manager   Baldish McCurrin

Barnet Healthcare Trust Hospitals
Principal Team Manager   J. Meyer

PSYCHIATRIC SOCIAL WORK SERVICES

Colindale Hospital Silkstream Unit, Colindale Ave, London
NW9; Tel 020 8952 2381 ext 3781
Team Manager   John Hawting

Community Support Team BPU, Barnet Hospital, Wellhouse
La, Barnet, Hertfordshire EN5 3DJ; Tel 020 8364 8636
Service Manager   Emily Newman

East Team (Barnet/Finchley) Barnet General Hospital,
Psychiatric Unit, Barnet, Hertfordshire EN5 3DJ; Tel 020
8216 4400
Care Manager   Marian Tobin
Care Manager   V. Uttarkar

West Team (Edgware/Hendon) Premier Hse, 112 Station Rd,
Edgware, Greater London HA8 7AB
Care Manager   Phil Byrne

CHILD GUIDANCE SERVICE

Burnt Oak Child Guidance Centre Child Guidance Centre,
East Rd, Edgware, Greater London HA8 0BT; Tel 020 8951
1044

Vale Drive Child Guidance Centre c/o Vale Drive Clinic,
Vale Dr, Barnet, Hertfordshire EN5 2ED; Tel 020 8440 8668

CHILDREN AND FAMILY CENTRES

Curtis Family Centre Coppies Gr, New Southgate, London
N11 1NT; Tel 020 8368 0260
Contact   G. Bennett
   (27)

Fairway Early Years Centre 1 The Fairway, London
NW7 3HS; Tel 020 8959 5776
Contact   M. King
   (40)

Lakeview Children and Family Centre Tyrrel Way, West
Hendon, London NW9 7DX; Tel 020 8202 7960
Contact   H. McCarthy
   (60)

Meadway Children and Family Centre 110 Meadway,
Barnet, Hertfordshire EN5 5JX; Tel 020 8447 0343
Contact   D. Dearman

Newstead Children and Family Centre 1 Fallows Cl,
London N2 8LG; Tel 020 8346 0420
Contact   S. Sharma

Wingfield Children and Family Centre The Concourse,
Grahame Pk, London NW9 5UX; Tel 020 8205 6175
Contact   Morag Manson
   (50)

RESIDENTIAL CENTRE

New Park House Residential Centre 25 Parkhurst Rd,
London N11 3EN; Tel 020 8368 9191
Contact   S. Hadi

HOSTEL FOR YOUNG ADULTS WITH LEARNING DIFFICULTIES

Harwood Hostel 55 Christchurch Ave, Finchley, London
N12 0DG; Tel 020 8445 8034
Contact   Paul Chamberlain
   (11)

ADOLESCENT UNIT

Meadow Close Adolescent Unit 68a Meadow Cl, Barnet,
Hertfordshire EN5 2UF; Tel 020 8440 8943
Contact   I. Anderson
   (8)

ADOLESCENT RESOURCE TEAM

34 Woodhouse Rd, North Finchley, London N12 0RG;
   Tel 020 8359 6243
Contact   W. Ingles

Leaving Care Team 34 Woodhouse Rd, North Finchley,
London N12 0RG; Tel 020 8359 6205; 020 8359 6206
Contact   Lyn Owen

HOMES FOR ADULTS WITH LEARNING DISABILITIES

Fieldways Residential Dollis Valley Way, Barnet, London
EN5 2AE; Tel 020 8440 3498
Contact   Kim Beavis (Acting)

The Leys Barnet La, Elstree, Hertfordshire HA8 8FR;
Tel 020 8207 0122
   (23)

DAY CENTRE FOR PEOPLE WITH MENTAL HEALTH PROBLEMS

Station Road Day Centre 154 Station Rd, Hendon, London;
Tel 020 8202 2916/7
Contact   J. McCraig
Contact   S. Ploumati

DAY CENTRE FOR PEOPLE WITH PHYSICAL DISABILITIES

Flightways Day Centre The Concourse, Graham Pk,
London NW9 5UX; Tel 020 8205 5803
Manager   J. Richardson
   (90)

DAY CENTRE FOR OLDER PEOPLE

Springwood Resource Centre Springwood Cres, Edgware,
London HA8 9EO; Tel 020 8958 8123
Contact   J. Calcagni

MEALS ON WHEELS/SHOPPING SERVICE

Manager   R. Hyland
Barnet Hse, 1225 High Rd, Whetstone, London N20 0EJ

Information Offices

Information Centre, The Town Hall, Hendon, London
   NW4 4BG; Tel 020 8359 2277

Education Department

Bldg 4, North London Bus Pk, Oakleigh Road South,
   London N11 1NP; URL www.barnet.gov.uk;
   E-mail education.info@barnet.gov.uk; Tel 020 8359 3136;
   Fax 020 8359 3057
Director (Education and Children)   J. Stansfield
Chief Education Officer   Gillian Palmer

Chief Children's Officer and Director (Social Services)
P. Fallon
Assistant Chief Education Officer (Early Years, Families and Play) D. Canney
Assistant Chief Education Officer (Standards and Inclusion) G. Durham
Co-ordinator (Parent Partnership) D. Smith
Principal Education Welfare Worker A. Corcoran
Principal Youth Officer D. Patel
Co-ordinator (Drugs and Alcohol) Vacancy
Co-ordinator (Health Promoting Schools) L. Kelly
Manager (Inclusive Education Advisory Team) Elaine Crawford, BEd, DipTH, AdvDipinSEN, RSADipSpLD
Principal Educational Psychologist A. Fuller

BEDSIDE TUITION

Barnet General Hospital Sunshine Ward, Wellhouse La, Barnet, London; Tel 020 8359 3220

Edgware Hospital Ward C3, Edgware, Greater London; Tel 020 8359 3220

SPECIAL SCHOOLS

Mapledown School Claremont Rd, London NW2 1TR; E-mail info@mapledown.barnet.gov.uk; Tel 020 8455 4111; Fax 020 8455 4895
Headteacher John Feltham, BEd
12–16+ SLD (52)

Northway School The Fairway, Mill Hill, London NW7 3HS; E-mail northwayschool@netscapeonline.co.uk; Tel 020 8959 4232; Fax 020 8959 6436
Headteacher Lesley Burgess
5–11 MLD 3–11 Autistic Unit (79)

Oak Lodge School Heath View, off East End Rd, London N2 0QY; E-mail oaklodge@aol.com; Tel 020 8444 6711; Fax 020 8444 6468
Headteacher Lynda Walker, MA
11–18 MLD Autistic Unit

Oakleigh School Oakleigh Road North, Whetstone, London N20 0DH; Tel 020 8368 5336; Fax 020 8361 6922
Headteacher Jenny Gridley

MINORITIES ACHIEVEMENT PROJECT (MAP)

Professional Development Centre 451 High Rd, Finchley, London N12 0AS; Tel 020 8359 3891
Head of Service M. Kenny, BA(Econ)

PUPIL REFERRAL UNIT (SECONDARY)

Pavilion Study Centre 58b Chandos Ave, Whetstone, London N20 9DX; Tel 020 8446 4085; Fax 020 8445 8548
Headteacher Shelley Dannell

PUPIL REFERRAL UNIT (PRIMARY)

The Park Referral Unit Silkstream Rd, Edgware, Greater London HA8 0DA; Tel 020 8952 0900; Fax 020 8952 0310
Headteacher Mary Helmore

BEXLEY COUNCIL
www.bexley.gov.uk

Population 217 006
Political Composition: Lab: 32, Con: 30, LD: 1
Bexley Civic Offices, Broadway, Bexleyheath, Kent DA6 7LB; URL www.bexley.gov.uk; E-mail customer.services@bexley.gov.uk; Tel 020 8303 7777; Fax 020 8301 2661
Chief Social Services Officer Simon Leftley
Hill View, Hill View Dr, Welling, Kent DA16 3RY; Fax 020 8308 4996

Council

Cabinet Member (Social Care and Health) Cllr Donna Briant
101 Penhill Rd, Bexley, Kent DA5 3ER
Cabinet Member (Social Inclusion, Community Cohesion and Housing) Cllr Manny Blake
19 Willersley Ave, Sidcup, Kent DA15 9EJ

AREA OFFICES

North Area Office Howbury Centre, Slade Green Rd, Erith, Kent DA8 2HX; Tel 020 8303 7777 ex 3876

South Area Office 8 Brampton Rd, Bexleyheath, Kent DA7 4HB; Tel 020 8303 7777 3420

CIVIC OFFICES

Broadway, Bexleyheath, Kent DA6 7LB; Tel 020 8303 7777

HOSPITAL SOCIAL WORKERS

Queen Mary's Hospital Frognal Ave, Sidcup, Kent DA14 6LT; Tel 020 8302 2678
Team Leader Vacancy

SERVICES FOR CHILDREN AND FAMILIES

Child and Adolescent Mental Health Team 4 Emerton Cl, Bexleyheath, Kent DA6 8DQ; Tel 020 8301 9400
Senior Social Worker Vacancy

East Child Care Unit Civic Offices, Broadway, Bexleyheath, Kent DA6 7LB; Tel 020 8303 7777
Team Leader M. Newell

Family Centre Wilkinson Hse, Powys Close, Bexleyheath, Kent DA7 5RS; Tel 020 8310 8055
Team Leader A. Lambird

West Child Care Unit Yarnton Way, Thamesmead, London DA18 4DR; Tel 020 8310 0566
Team Leader I. Aubery

DAY NURSERY

Belvedere Day Resources Centre 1 Station Rd, Belvedere, Kent DA17 6JJ; Tel 020 8311 7508
Manager N. Reynolds
(45)

HOSTEL FOR CHILDREN WITH LEARNING DISABILITIES

Falconwood Resource Centre 33–37 The Green, Welling, Kent DA16 2PA; Tel 020 8303 7995
Manager J. Cox
(10)

CHILDREN'S SERVICES

Leaving Care Team Howbury Centre, Slade Green Rd, Erith, Kent DA8 2HX; Tel 020 8303 7777
Team Leader M. August

LEARNING DISABILITY TEAM

Erith Centre Park Cres, Erith, Kent DA8 3EE; Tel 01322 356165
Team Leader Vacancy

COMMUNITY MENTAL HEALTH TEAMS

Bexleyheath Centre 4 Emerton Cl, Bexleyheath, Kent DA6 8DQ; Tel 020 8301 9400
Community Manager J. Yan

Erith Centre Park Cres, Erith, Kent DA8 3EE; Tel 01322 356161
Community Manager J. Frain

DAY CENTRE FOR PEOPLE WITH MENTAL HEALTH PROBLEMS

Crayford Centre 4–6 London Rd, Crayford, Kent DA1 4BH; Tel 01322 521162
Manager G. Norris
(27)

ACCOMMODATION FOR PEOPLE WITH MENTAL HEALTH PROBLEMS

Chapel Hill Hostel Chapel Hill, Crayford, Kent DA1 4BY; Tel 01322 553201
Manager P. Swaffer
(25)

EMPLOYMENT PROJECT FOR PEOPLE WITH MENTAL HEALTH PROBLEMS

Feathers Unit N14, Europa Trading Est, Erith, Kent DA8 1QL
Manager J. Waters

Reinstate West St, Erith, Kent DA8 1AN; Tel 01322 438155
Manager R. Carder

ADULT TRAINING CENTRES FOR PEOPLE WITH LEARNING DISABILITIES

Carlton Resource Centre Carlton Rd, Sidcup, Kent DA14 6AH; Tel 020 8302 4619
Manager G. Wooder
(130)

Smerdon Resource Centre 19 Lumley Cl, Belvedere, Kent DA17 6NR; Tel 01322 432212
Manager A. Glyde
(120)

DAY CENTRE FOR PHYSICALLY-DISABLED PEOPLE

Whitehall Day Centre 20 Whitehall La, Erith, Kent DA8 2DH; Tel 01322 341638
Manager D. Page
(60)

DAY CENTRES FOR ELDERLY PEOPLE

Bexleyheath Day Centre Danson Youth Centre, Brampton Rd, Bexleyheath, Kent DA7 4EZ; Tel 020 8303 0701
Senior Officer Gloria Fuller

Hadlow Road Day Centre 7 Hadlow Rd, Sidcup, Kent DA14 4AA; Tel 020 8300 0907

Northern Day Centre c/o 35–37 Lesley Park Rd, Erith, Kent; Tel 01322 338570

Directorate of Education and Community Services

Hill View, Hill View Dr, Welling, Kent DA16 3RY; Tel 020 8303 7777
Director (Education and Community Services) Nick Johnson, MA
Assistant Director (Planning and Resources) John Bamfield, MA, MSc
Assistant Director (Children and Student Services) Paul Knight, MA
Head (SEN and Support Services) Christine Salter, BSc, PGCE, CertPsych
Head (Social Inclusion) Vacancy
Team Leader (Teaching Team) Schools Effectiveness and Lifelong Learning Dylis Oliver
Team Leader (English Language) Brenda Boyce

SPECIAL SCHOOLS

Marlborough Community Special School Marlborough Park Ave, Sidcup, Kent DA15 9DP; Tel 020 8300 6896
Headteacher Audrey Chamberlain, BEd
11–19+

Oakwood Community Special School Woodside Rd, Crayford, Kent DA7 6LB
Headteacher Rachel Warner
(41)

Shenstone Community Special School Old Rd, Crayford, Kent DA1 4DZ; Tel 01322 524145
Headteacher Linda Aldcroft, BEd, MA(Ed)
2–11

Westbrooke Community Special School South Gipsy Rd, Welling, Kent DA16 1JB; Tel 020 8304 1320
Headteacher Carol Hance
4–10

Woodside Community Special School Halt Robin Hood, Belvedere, Kent DA17 6DW; Tel 01322 433494; Fax 01322 433442
Headteacher Linda Crooks, CertEd
5–16+ (206)

PUPIL REFERRAL UNITS

Pupil Referral Unit (Secondary) Howbury Grange Centre, Slade Green Rd, Erith, Kent DA8 2HX; Tel 020 8303 7777
Head Jenny Spittles (Acting)
11–16

BRENT LONDON BOROUGH COUNCIL
www.brent.gov.uk

Population 263 463
Political Composition: Lab: 35, Con: 19, LD: 9
Brent Town Hall, Forty La, Wembley, Greater London HA9 9HD; URL www.brent.gov.uk;
E-mail chief.executive@brent.gov.uk;
E-mail cit@brent.gov.uk; Tel 020 8937 1234; Fax 020 8937 1444

Brent Social Services

Tel 020 8937 1234; Fax 020 8937 4065
Director (Social Services) Jenny Goodall
Assistant Director (Children's Services) Mimi Konigsberg; Tel 020 8937 4091; Fax 020 8937 4036
Assistant Director (Quality and Support) Janet Palmer; Tel 020 8937 4048; Fax 020 8937 4194
Assistant Director (Community Care Services) Christabel Shawcross; Tel 020 8937 4230; Fax 020 8937 4065
Head (Finance) Charles Hampshire; Tel 020 8937 3249; Fax 020 8937 4194
Head (Youth Offending Service) Peter Sutlieff
1 Craven Pk, London NW10 8SX; Tel 020 8965 6020
Head (Brent Mental Health Services) Diana Warren
36 London Rd, Wembley, Greater London HA9 7SS; Tel 020 8937 4284
Service Unit Manager (Emergency Duty Team) Marlies McDougall; Tel 020 8937 4057
Service Unit Manager (Children's Services – East) John McNally
Brent Hse Annexe, 349–357 High Rd, Wembley, Greater London HA9 6BX; Tel 020 8937 4382
Service Unit Manager (Children's Services – West) Yashi Shah; Tel 020 8937 4382
Service Unit Manager (Children's Services – Resources) Christine Bridgett
1st Fl Barnhill Nursery, Barnhill Rd, Wembley, Greater London HA9 9YP; Tel 020 8904 8291
Service Unit Manager (Children's Services – Placements) Jan Fishwick
Triangle Hse, 328–330 High Rd, Wembley, Greater London HA9 6AZ; Tel 020 8937 4558

Service Unit Manager (Community Care Services – Adult Physical Disability) Diane Brown
36 London Rd, Wembley, Greater London HA89 7SS; Tel 020 8937 4625
Service Unit Manager (Brent Learning Disability Services) Kofi Nyero
Stonebridge Centre, Twybridge Way, London NW10 0SL; Tel 020 8961 4489
Service Unit Manager (Community Care Services – Older People's Services) Ros Howard
13–15 Brondesbury Rd, London NW6 6BX; Tel 020 8937 4869

Lead Member (Health and Social Care)

Lead Member (Health and Social Care) Ralph Fox

CUSTOMER SERVICE POINTS

Referrals to Social Services are taken through Brent's six borough-wide One-stop shops or over the telephone on the central One-stop shop line 020 8937 1200.

Education, Arts and Libraries

Education Offices, Chesterfield Hse, 9 Park La, Wembley, Greater London HA9 7RW; Tel 020 8937 3000; Fax 020 8937 3010
Director (Education) John Christie

BRENT EDUCATION PSYCHOLOGY AND LEARNING SUPPORT SERVICE

The Education Dept, Chesterfield Hse, 9 Park La, Wembley, Greater London HA9 7RW; Tel 020 8937 3202
Principal Officer M. Hymans

SPECIAL SCHOOLS

Grove Park School Grove Pk, Kingsbury, London NW9 0JY; Tel 020 8204 3293
Headteacher Miss J.F. Edwards

Hay Lane School Grove Pk, Kingsbury, London NW9 0JY; Tel 020 8204 5396
Contact P.M. Theuma

Manor School Chamberlayne Rd, London NW10 3NT; Tel 020 8968 3160
Headteacher Mrs Drake, MA, BEd

Vernon House School Drury Way, London, Greater London NW10 0NQ; Tel 020 8451 6961
Headteacher Mr G.S. Davidson

Woodfield School Glenwood Ave, Kingsbury, London NW9 7LY; Tel 020 8205 1977
Headteacher Ms D. Collins

LANGUAGE UNIT

Mitchell Brook School Bridge Rd, London NW10 9BX; Tel 020 8459 5681
Headteacher Mrs Mathison

SENSORY IMPAIRMENT UNITS

Kingsbury Green School Old Kenton La, Kingsbury, London NW9 9ND; Tel 020 8204 6423
Headteacher Mr A. Vaughan

Kingsbury High School (Grant Maintained) Princes Ave, Kingsbury, London NW9 9JR; Tel 020 8204 9814
Headteacher Mr C. Chung

PUPIL REFERRAL UNIT

364a Stag La, London NW9 9AG; Tel 020 8937 3193
Head of Service Paul Roper

BROMLEY LONDON BOROUGH COUNCIL
www.bromley.gov.uk

Population 295 530
Political Composition: Con: 41, LD: 13, Lab: 6
Civic Centre, Stockwell Cl, Bromley, Kent BR1 3UH; URL www.bromley.gov.uk; Tel 020 8464 3333; Fax 020 8313 4620
Mayor Cllr Carole Hubbard
Chief Executive D. Bartlett, IPFA
Borough Treasurer Paul Dale
Borough Secretary W. Million
Director (Environmental Services) G. Hayward, CEng, BSc, MICE, MIR, MIStructIE

Social Services and Housing Department

URL www.bromley.gov.uk; Tel 020 8464 3333; (Out of hours) 020 8464 4848
Director (Social Services and Housing) Terry Rich
Assistant Director (Strategy, Development and Performance) David Vowles
Assistant Director (Older People's Division) David Roberts
Assistant Director (Adults Services Division) Margaret Howard
Assistant Director (Children and Families Division) Rory Patterson
Assistant Director (Housing Division) David Gibson
Manager (Contracts) Vacancy
Manager (Planning and Development) Anne Watts
Manager (Planning and Development) Terri Walters
Manager (Partnership Development) Judy Wolfram
Manager (Care Management) Joy Smith
Manager (Hospital Teams and Building Care Capacity) Sheila Porter
Manager (Transport) Bryan Curle
Manager (Direct Services) Richard Haines
Manager (Learning Disabilities) Heather Hughes
Manager (Physical Disabilities) Andy Crawford
Manager (Physical Disabilities) Rosemary Plumb
Manager (Mental Health Commissioning) David Halliwell
Manager (Joint Mental Health Community Services) Kay Beaumont
Manager (Assessment and Family Support) Merlin Joseph
Manager (Specialist Family Support) Sally Moran
Manager (Care and Resources) David Bradley
Manager (Quality Assurance) Julie Daly
Principal Manager (Housing) Vacancy
Manager (Development and Strategy) Vacancy
Manager (Supporting People) Wendy Norman
Manager (Asylum Team) John McBrearty

Education Offices

Civic Centre, Stockwell Cl, Bromley, Kent BR1 3UH; Tel 020 8464 3333; Fax 020 8313 4049
Director (Education) K. Davis, MA, BEd, FIMgt
Assistant Director (Pupil and Student Services) G.L. Pearson, MEd
Assistant Director (Standards and Effectiveness Services) G.W. Searle, BSc(Hons), PhD, MRSC, CCChem, DMS
Head (Planning, Research and Communication Unit) J. Miller
Manager (Education Welfare) J. Gunning

INFORMATION OFFICE

Staff at these offices will answer as far as possible questions relating to any of the Council's services.

Press and Public Relations Office Civic Centre, Stockwell Cl, Bromley, Kent BR1 3UH; Tel 020 8313 4392

General Enquiry Desk Civic Centre, Stockwell Cl, Bromley, Kent BR1 3UH
In addition to the Central Library, there are 14 branches where the public may seek answers to their enquiries on a more limited scale. Addresses can be given if required.

SPECIAL SCHOOL (PRE-SCHOOL ASSESSMENT CENTRE)

Phoenix Centre Phoenix Pre-School Centre, 40 Masons Hill, Bromley, Kent BR2 9JG; Tel 020 8466 8811; Fax 020 8466 8855
Head (Pre-School Services) D. O'Kane

LONDON BOROUGH OF CAMDEN
www.camden.gov.uk

Population 193 800
Political Composition: Lab: 35, Con: 11, LD: 8.
Town Hall, Judd St, London WC1H 9JE;
 URL www.camden.gov.uk; Tel 020 7974 4444
Chief Executive Moira Gibb; Tel 020 7974 5686; Fax 020 7974 5998
Director (Housing) Neil Litherland
Bidborough Hse, Bidborough St, London WC1H 9BF;
 Tel 020 7974 5800; Fax 020 7974 5558
Director (Environment) Peter Bishop
Town Hall Extension, Argyle St, London WC1 8EQ; Tel 020 7974 5621; Fax 020 7974 5556
Director (Leisure and Community Services) Ian McNicol
Crowndale Centre, 218–220 Eversholt St, London NW1 1BD; Tel 020 7974 1606; Fax 020 7974 1587

Social Services Department

79 Camden Rd, London NW1 9ES; Tel 020 7278 4444;
 (Direct Information Line) 020 7974 6666; Fax 020 7974 6704
Chair (Social Services Executive) Penny Abraham
Town Hall, Euston Rd, London WC1H 9JE
Director (Social Services) Jane Held
Assistant Director (Resource and Customer Services) Joy Harris
Assistant Director (Children and Families) Catherine Doran
Assistant Director (Strategy, Partnerships and Performance) Charlotte Pomery
Assistant Director (Community Care – Commissioning) and Deputy Director (Social Services) Vacancy

Social Services Executive

Lab: 12, Con: 2, LD: 1
Chair Penny Abraham
Minority Party Spokespeople
LD:Martin Davies, Andrew Marshall, Jane Schopflin, Heather Thompson.

HOSPITAL-BASED SOCIAL WORK DEPARTMENTS

Royal Free Hospital Pond St, London NW3 2QG
Team Manager (Adults) Pam Mossman; Tel 020 7830 2100
Team Manager (Children and Families) Christine Allen; Tel 020 7830 2103

St. Pancras Hospital Social Work Department, 4 St. Pancras Way, London NW1 0PE; Tel 020 7380 9813
Team Manager (Adults) Louise Cornforth

University College Hospital Gower St, London WC1 6AU
Team Manager (Adults) Louise Cornforth; Tel 020 7380 9813
Team Manager (Children and Families) Clive Preece; Tel 020 7380 9592

HEALTH CENTRE/CLINIC-BASED SOCIAL WORK DEPARTMENTS

Crowndale Health Centre 59 Crowndale Rd, London NW1 1TU; Tel 020 7530 3878; Fax 020 7530 3879

Gospel Oak Health Centre Lismore Circus, London NW5 4QF; Tel 020 7530 4654; Fax 020 7530 4652

Hunter Street Health Centre Hunter St, London WC1E 6AE; Tel 020 7530 4386; Fax 020 7530 4321

Kentish Town Health Centre 2 Bartholomew Rd, London NW5 2AJ

Solent Road Health Centre 9 Solent Rd, London NW6 1TP; Tel 020 7530 2597; Fax 020 7530 2577

SPECIALIST HEALTH AUTHORITIES

Great Ormond Street Hospital for Sick Children Great Ormond St, London WC1 3JH; Tel 020 7829 8896 ext 5324; Fax 020 7829 8847
Principal Officer Anne Elton

National Hospital for Neurology and Neurosurgery Queen's Sq, London WC1 3BG; Tel 020 7380 9812; Fax 020 7829 8720
Team Manager Chris Garlick

Children and Families Division

Assistant Director Catherine Doran; Tel 020 7974 6641
Co-ordinator (Children Protection Unit) Bodil Mlynarska; Tel 020 7974 6999
Principal Officer (Policy and Staff Development Unit – Service Development) Vacancy; Tel 020 7974 1400
Manager (Division Administration) Brenda Tredgold; Tel 020 7974 6643

EMERGENCY DUTY TEAM

A generic, borough-wide service is provided Mon–Fri (1700–0900) weekends and Bank holidays (24 hours).

YOUTH OFFENDING TEAM

115 Wellesley Rd, London NW5 4PA; Tel 020 7974 6181
Team Manager Peggy Schaffter; Tel 020 7974 6762

SOCIAL SERVICES CENTRES

Crowndale Centre 218 Eversholt St, London NW1 1BD; Tel 020 7974 1640; Fax 020 7974 1638
Principal Officer (Children in Need–South) Ila Modi; Tel 020 7974 1502
Manager (Section Administration) Maria Jones; Tel 020 7974 1503

Gospel Oak Centre Gospel Oak, 115 Wellesley Rd, London NW5 4PA; Tel 020 7974 6789; Fax 020 7974 6799
Principal Officer (Children Looked After by the Department (incl family placements, residential care, respite care and juvenile justice team)) Anne Turner; Tel 020 7974 6166
Manager (Section Administration) Janice Walls; Tel 020 7974 6795

West End Lane Centre 156 West End La, London NW6 1SD; Tel 020 7974 6600; Fax 020 7974 6611
Principal Officer (Children in Need–North) Meryl Phillpot; Tel 020 7974 6628
Manager (Section Administration) Bernadette Sweeney; Tel 020 7974 6627

Primary Care Division

Principal Officer (Assessment and Care Management) Lesley Parker; Tel 020 7974 6092; Fax 020 7974 6089
Head (Community Commissioning) Margaret Jones
Head (Camden Learning Disabilities Service) Jean Hanson
Bedford Hse, 1st Fl, London NW1 7JR; Tel 020 7974 3746
Head (Physical Disability Service) Caroline Penfold; Tel 020 7974 6713

7

Manager (Section Administration – Social Work for Older People and People with Physical Disabilities and Sensory Impairment) Vacancy; Tel 020 7974 6093
Manager (Section Administration – Brokerage) Reshma Upadhyaya
Principal Officer (Brokerage and Procurement) Lorraine Colledge; Tel 020 7974 2827

SUPPORTED LIVING PRIMARY CARE

Dartmouth Park Avenue 6 Dartmouth Park Ave, London NW5 1JN; Tel 020 7485 5384
  Residential

Ebbsfleet Road Home 15 Ebbsfleet Rd, Cricklewood, London NW2 3NB; Tel 020 8452 1811
Organiser Vacancy
  Residential

Kentish Town Project 93 Mayford Sq, Oakley, London NW1 1NY; Tel 020 7267 7914
Organiser Jeff Wallace
  Day care

Lothos Road Home Flat 1, Juniper Hse, 52 Lithos Rd, London NW3 6EY; Tel 020 7433 1938
Team Leader Vacancy

Mayford Day Care 93 Mayford, Oakley Sq, London NW1 1NY; Tel 020 7387 9589
Day Centre Manager Kishor Darji
  Day care

Prince of Wales Road 174 Prince of Wales Rd, London NW5 3QB; Tel 020 7485 5606
Manager Carmen Warner
  Respite care

Shoot-up-Hill Home 96–98 Shoot-up-Hill, London NW2 3XJ; Tel 0208 452 6091
Organiser Pat Copley
  Day care

Warden Road Home 78 Warden Rd, London NW5 4NR; Tel 0207 284 2958
Team Leader Martin Payne
  Residential

MENTAL HEALTH RESOURCES

Bridge Project Peckwater Centre, 6 Peckwater St, London NW5 2TX; Tel 020 7530 6445
Organiser Charlene Edwards
  Day care

Highgate 19–37 Highgate Rd, London NW5 1JY; Tel 020 7485 5783
Organiser Tony Creedon

Netherwood Centre 5 Netherwood St, London NW6 2QU; Tel 020 7372 0750
Organiser Ros Stewart

New Routes 50 Parliament Hill, East Hampstead, London NW3 2TL; Tel 020 7328 3540
Organiser Lone Tonsgaard

Raglan Centre 1 Raglan St, London NW5 3BD; Tel 020 7916 6588
Contact Helena King

ELDERLY PERSONS DAY CARE

Bramhurst Project 10 Bolton Rd, London NW8 0AX; Tel 020 7624 8824
Team Leader Julie Sikod

Minster Road Project 37 Minster Rd, London NW2; Tel 020 7794 0670
Group Leader Ian Kahn

Warden Road Project 80 Warden Rd, London NW5; Tel 020 7284 4801
Group Leader Betty Berry

SUPPORTED LIVING SCHEME

The Supported Living Scheme offers a range of supported living options for adults with mental health problems, learning difficulties, physical disabilities, and for elderly people. This includes Adult Carers who provide board, lodging and special projects which are tailor-made to suit each user.

HIV/AIDS SERVICES

115 Wellesley Rd, London NW5 4PA; Tel 020 7974 6777
Team Manager Peter Barber

ELDERLY PERSONS' HOMES

There are four local authority elderly persons' homes.

SUSTAINED CARE

10 Rochester Pl, London NW1; Tel 020 7974 6684; Fax 020 7267 6849
Service Manager Robert Donald

HOME SUPPORT

Service Manager Marcia Thompson; Tel 020 7974 1550

SERVICE SUPPORT

Co-ordinator (Service Support) Jill Crawley; Tel 020 7413 6686
Manager (Section Administration) Vacancy; Tel 020 7413 6695

Resources and Customer Services

Assistant Director Joy Harris; Tel 020 7974 6719
Head (Human Resource Group) Vacancy; Tel 020 7974 1367; Fax 020 7974 6638
Head (Business and Financial Services) Stephanie Mitchener; Tel 020 7974 6705; Fax 020 7974 6098
Information Points for Customer Enquiries Tel 020 7974 6666
Customer Services and Complaints Phill Sowter; Tel 020 7974 6673; (Freephone) 0800 393 561; Fax 020 7974 1439

ASYLUM SEEKERS SERVICE

Manager Glenda Gallacher; Tel 020 7974 1428

Education Department

Crowndale Centre, 218–220 Eversholt St, London NW1 1BD; Tel 020 7974 1525; Fax 020 7974 1536
Director (Education) R. Litchfield

UNDER FIVES CENTRES

Acol Under 5s Centre 16 Acol Rd, London NW6 3AG; Tel 020 7624 2937
Head of Centre Carol Lyness

Fitzrovia Under 5s Centre 52 Whitfield St, London W1T 4ER; Tel 020 7436 2293
Head of Centre Zakia Mir

Gospel Oak Under 5s Centre Lismore Circus, London NW5 3LE; Tel 020 7267 4517
Head of Centre Sue Rushton (34)

Hampden Under 5s Centre 80 Polygon Rd, London NW1 1HQ; Tel 020 7387 1822
Head of Centre Lydia McEwan (34)

Konstam Centre 75 Chester Rd, London N19 5DH; Tel 020 7272 3594
Head of Centre Trish Franks (32)

Langtry Under 5s Centre Langtry Rd, London NW8 0AJ; Tel 020 7624 0963
Head of Centre Yvette Tyrell
(34)

Lyndhurst Under 5s Centre Lyndhurst Hall, Athlone St, London NW5 4RE; Tel 020 7485 4823
Head of Centre Janine Sukkar
Holiday schemes, including one for handicapped children, are also provided: Tel 020 7278 4444.
(60)

Regents Park Under 5s Centre Augustus St, London NW1 3TJ; Tel 020 7387 2382
Head of Centre Sue Williamson
(30)

HOSPITAL SCHOOLS

Children's Hospital School Great Ormond St, London WC1N 3JH; Tel 020 7813 8269
Headteacher Y. Hill

Royal Free Hospital School 6th Fl, Royal Free Hospital, Pond St, London NW3 2QG; Tel 020 7472 6298
Headteacher M. Beste

SPECIAL SCHOOLS

Chalcot School Harmood St, London NW1 8DP; Tel 020 7485 2147
Headteacher M. Cresswell
EBD

Frank Barnes Primary School Harley Rd, London NW3 3BN; Tel 020 7586 4665
Headteacher K. Simpson
Hearing impaired

Jack Taylor School Ainsworth Way, off Boundary Rd, London NW8 0SR; Tel 020 7328 6731
Headteacher S. Quilter
SLD

Swiss Cottage School Avenue Rd, London NW3 3HF; Tel 020 7681 8080
Headteacher Kay Bedford
MLD

Community Services Committee

Chair Christopher R. Mitchell
Deputy Chair Richard D. Regan
Members of the Committee
Wilfred W. Archibald, Kenneth E. Ayres, Stephen L. Barter, William Ian Baverstock Brooks, Joseph C.F. Byllam Byllam-Barnes, Daniel Caspi, Benson F. Catt, William H. Dove , Martin C. Farr, Gavyn Farr Arthur, Rodney C.A. FitzGerald, Stuart J. Fraser, George M.F. Gillon, Dr Peter Bernard Hardwick, Dr Richard L. Harris-Jones, Elizabeth H.L. Holliday, Peter Leck, Vivienne Littlechild, Christine Mackenzie Cohen, Sir Clive Martin, Wendy Mead, Hugh B.G. Montgomery, Brian D.F. Mooney , Anthony D. Moss, Dorothy C. Robinson, Stephen Salinger, Iris Samuel, John G.S. Scott, Richard G. Scriven.

SOCIAL WORK GROUPS

Community PO Box 270, Guildhall, London EC2P 2EJ; E-mail ann.saunders@corpoflondon.gov.uk; Tel 020 7332 1218
Head (Community Care Services) Ann Saunders

Psychiatric Dept of Psychological Medicine, St. Bartholomew's Hospital, London EC1A 7BE; E-mail tony.seigal@corporation.gov.uk; Tel 020 7601 8888
Senior Social Worker Tony Seigal

Hospital Social Work St. Bartholomew's Hospital, West Smithfield, London EC1A 7BE; E-mail bob.crosbie@corpoflondon.gov.uk; Tel 020 7601 8718
Head (Health and Partnerships) R.J. Crosbie
Access Officer (People with Disabilities) J. Fleck
Access Office, 6th Fl, Guildhall, London EC2P 2EJ; Tel 020 7332 1995

Education Service

Corporation of London, PO Box 270, London EC2P 2EJ; E-mail education@corpoflondon.gov.uk; Tel 020 7332 1750; Fax 020 7332 1621
City Education Officer Ian Comfort
Executive Officer (Services – London Region – FELORS) J. Wise, PhD, MA, MBA

CORPORATION OF LONDON
www.cityoflondon.gov.uk

Population 7100 Residential; 357 000 Daytime
Non Political Body
PO Box 270, Guildhall, London EC2P 2EJ;
URL www.cityoflondon.gov.uk;
E-mail education@corporation.gov.uk; Tel 020 7332 1750;
Fax 020 7332 1621
Town Clerk Chris Duffield
Chamberlain P. Derrick, BA, CIPFA
Comptroller and City Solicitor A.J. Colvin, LLM
City Surveyor E.T. Hartill, BSc, FRICS, FRSA
Director (Technical Services) Philip Everett, Esc, CEng, MICE
City Planning Officer P.W. Rees, BSc, BArch, BTP, RIBA, FRTPI, FRSA
Director (Community Services Department) T. Rogers, FCIH, FRSH, FRSA, JP

Social Services Department

PO Box 270, Guildhall, London EC2P 2EJ;
E-mail community.services@corpoflondon.gov.uk;
Tel 020 7332 1224; Fax 020 7588 1573
Head (Children and Families Services) Elaine Peace

LONDON BOROUGH OF CROYDON
www.croydon.gov.uk

Population 339 875
Political Composition: Lab: 37, Con: 32, LD: 1
Taberner Hse, Park La, Croydon, Surrey CR9 2BA;
URL www.croydon.gov.uk; Tel 020 8686 4433
Chief Executive David Wechsler, BA
Director (Corporate Services) Miles Smith
Director (Finance and IT) Jan Willis
Director (Housing) Mike Davies
Director (Planning and Transportation) Phillip Goodwin
Director (Environmental, Cultural and Sports Services) Steve Halsey
1st Fl, Crosfield Hse, Mint Wk, Croydon, Surrey CR9 1BS;
Tel 020 8407 1325; Fax 020 8686 1231
Head (Property Services) Tony Middleton
Head (Policy and Executive Office) Will Tuckley

Social Services Department

Taberner Hse, 2–4 Park La, Croydon, Surrey CR9 2BA;
URL croydon.gov.uk/socialservices;
E-mail social_services@croydon.gov.uk; Tel 020 8686 4433; Fax 020 8686 1251
Director (Social Services) Hannah Miller

Divisional Director (Older People and Physical Disability Division)   M.T. Phung
Divisional Director (Children's Services)   Steve Liddicott
Divisional Director (Adult Services)   Jane Doyle
Divisional Director (Change Management)   John Duggleby
Divisional Director (Policy and Performance)   Jonathan Swain
Divisional Director (Finance)   Paul Heynes

Social Services Member

Cabinet Member for Social Services   Cllr Paula Shaw (Lab)
Shadow Cabinet Member for Social Services   Cllr Margaret Mead (Con)

DISTRICT OFFICES

Addington District Office

Addington, Forestdale, Monks Hill, New Addington
Central Pde, New Addington, Croydon, Surrey CR0 0JB;
   Tel 01689 841020; Fax 01689 41020
Manager (Childcare Services)   Steve Hall

Purley District Office

Sanderstead, Selsdon, Purley, Coulsdon, Kenley
Venture Hse, 15 High St, Purley, Surrey CR2 2AF; Tel 020
   8686 4433

Rees District Office

Covers Addiscombe, East Croydon, Shirley, Upper
Norwood, South Norwood, Woodside.
Rees Hse, 2–4 Morland Rd, Croydon, Surrey CRO 6NA;
   Tel 020 8654 8100; Fax 020 8655 1875
Contact   Ian Davidson
Contact   Steve Hall

Strand District Office

Covers Norbury, Thornton Heath
Strand Hse, Zion Rd, Thornton Heath, Surrey CR7 8RG;
   Tel 020 8689 1544; Fax 020 8665 6390
Manager (Children's Services)   Steve Hall
Rees Hse, 2–4 Morland Rd, Croydon, Surrey CR0 6NA

Taberner District Office

Covers Central Croydon, Broad Green, Selhurst, Waddon
Taberner Hse, Park La, Croydon, Surrey CR9 2BA; Tel 020
   8686 4433

OUTREACH PROJECT

Oak Avenue   167 Oak Ave, Shirley, Croydon, Surrey
CR0 8ER; Tel 020 8777 3658
Contact   S. Dent (Acting)
   9–12

Children and Family Services

DAY CARE CENTRE (FOR CHILDREN UNDER 5)

New Addington Day Care Centre   Kennelwood Cres, New
Addington, Croydon, Surrey; Tel 01689 846323
Contact   S. Parmenter

CHILDREN'S RESIDENTIAL HOMES AND SHORT STAY UNITS

Calleydown Crescent   New Addington, Croydon, Surrey
CR0 0EP; Tel 01689 842464
Unit Manager   Geoff Corbishley
   2–10 (8)

Mickleham Way   New Addington, Croydon, Surrey
CR0 0PN; Tel 01689 842466
Unit Manager   G. Hughes

Kempfield   1 Reedham Park Ave, Purley, Surrey CR2 4BQ;
Tel 020 8660 4234
Unit Manager   J. Rainford

Kingsdown   112 Orchard Rd, South Croydon, Surrey
CR2 9LQ; Tel 020 8651 5611
Unit Manager   D. Macfarlane

Northwood   21 Alverston Gdns, South Norwood, London
SE25 6LR; Tel 020 8771 1820
Unit Manager   L. Pratt

CHILDREN WITH DISABILITY

3rd Fl, Fell Rd, Croydon, Surrey CR9 2BA
Contact   Terry Palmer

RESPITE AND SHORT-TERM CARE FOR CHILDREN WITH MENTAL AND PHYSICAL DISABILITIES

Calley Down, 47a Calley Down Cres, Croydon, Surrey
   CR0 0EP; Tel 01689 842464
Unit Manager   Geoff Corbishley

CHILDREN AND FAMILIES RESOURCE TEAM (ASSESSMENT AND THERAPEUTIC SERVICE)

112 Orchard Rd, Sanderstead, Surrey CR2 9LQ; Tel 020 8651
   5611
Team Manager   C. Esposito

FOSTERING AND ADOPTION

Room 4.06, Fell Rd, Croydon, Surrey CR9 2BA; Tel 020 8686
   4433
Contact   S. Forbes

LEAVING CARE AND INDEPENDENCE SERVICE

28 Wellesley Rd, Croydon, Surrey CR0 2AD; Tel 020 8239
   4290
Contact   E. Harkness

YOUTH JUSTICE CENTRE

14 Whitehorse Rd, Croydon, Surrey CR0 2JA; Tel 020 8665
   5588; Fax 020 8404 5810
Youth Offending Team Manager   Ramos Maguire

Adult Services

Provides a wide range of services from domiciliary, through
to residential for people with learning and physical
disabilities, mental health problems and for older people.
On any one day approximately 6552 people in Croydon out
of a total population of 325 000 are receiving social services
from the Department. This represents 2% of the people of
Croydon. Before receiving a service, a person is assessed
against the Department's eligibility criteria for the service.
Each Local Authority draws up and agrees its own eligiblity
criteria for services, and these are up-dated and amended
from time to time by the Social Services Committee.

Sheltered Housing Services

This service manages 1044 flats in 25 sheltered housing
blocks. It ensures that tenants have a point of contact
24 hours a day for assistance in emergencies, or when
difficulties are experienced, and enables tenants, if they
wish, to take part in social community activities. There are
also six special sheltered housing blocks supporting 259
flats to ensure that tenants have a daily point of contact and
receive social and practical assistance plus five midday
meals where necessary. The service enables tenants, if they
wish, to take part in communal social activities. Blocks are
staffed 24 hours a day.

RESIDENTIAL CARE FOR THE PHYSICALLY DISABLED

Frederick Gardens Home   1–3 Frederick Gdns, Thornton
Heath, Croydon, Surrey CR0 2PP
   Young disabled men and women.

DAY CARE FOR THE PHYSICALLY DISABLED

Waylands Day Centre 487 Purley Way, Croydon, Surrey CR0 4RG; Tel 020 8686 6776
PD (50)

RESIDENTIAL SERVICES

The service manages six residential care homes and three satellite units providing 78 beds for people assessed as vulnerable because of physical or learning disability or mental illness. The primary aim of the service is to promote the independence and social integration of service users, and to support carers through the provision of respite care.

DAY CARE FOR LEARNING DISABLED

There are five day centres providing 487 places daily for people with either a physical disability, learning disability or a mental health problem and a Transport Service undertaking duties across the Department, with the capacity to carry 270 passengers daily.

Cherry Orchard 171 St. James Rd, Croydon, Surrey; Tel 020 8689 2625
(110)

Heavers Farm 122–124 Selhurst Rd, South Norwood, London SE25 6LI; Tel 020 8771 1321

Waylands Day Centre 487 Purley Way, Croydon, Surrey CR0 4RG; Tel 020 8686 6776

RESPITE CARE SERVICES (LEARNING DISABILITY)

Craignish Norbury Ave, Norbury, Croydon, Surrey

Heatherway 11 Monks Hill Est, Selsdon, Croydon, Surrey

SUPPORTED LIVING SERVICE

10–12 Heathfield Rd, South Croydon, Surrey CR0 1ES

MENTAL HEALTH, PHYSICAL DISABILITY AND ADULT PLACEMENT SCHEME – RESIDENTIAL AND DAY CARE

Ashburton Road 58 Ashburton Rd, Addiscombe, Surrey CR0 6AN; Tel 020 8654 4301
24 hour emergency crisis unit for mental health.

Glazier House 53 Birdhurst Rd, South Croydon, Surrey CR2 7EF; Tel 020 8681 0048
Adult placement, mental health unit (unstaffed). Rehabilitation (7)

Lennard Assessment Unit 28 Lennard Rd, Croydon, Surrey CR0 2UL; Tel 020 8686 8324
16 Wellington Rd, Croydon, Surrey
Assessment for (15) homeless persons with mental health problems.

DAY SERVICES FOR PEOPLE WITH MENTAL HEALTH PROBLEMS

Bensham Day Centre Queens Resource Centre, 66a Queens Rd, Croydon, Surrey CR9 2PQ; Tel 020 8683 2335
30 places daily for people aged 55 and over.

Lantern Hall Day Centre 190 Church Rd, Croydon, Surrey CR0 1SE; Tel 020 8680 1373
65 places daily for people aged 18–65.

ADULT PLACEMENT SUPPORT AND DEVELOPMENT UNIT

4th Fl, Ellis Hse, Katherine St, Croydon, Surrey CR0 1NX
Postal address
c/o Social Services, Taberner Hse, Park La, Croydon, Surrey CR9 2BA; Tel 020 8686 4433 ext 63516
The Unit recruits, trains and supports carers and works with colleagues from the client side and the National Care Standards Commission (NCSC). Care is provided in family homes to vulnerable adults who have a learning disability, suffer from mental health problems or are disadvantaged by physical disabilities or advancing years. Where personal care is required/available carers are registered with the NCSC. The option of 'supportive lodgings' is available to service users who can live more independently. Currently the Scheme has 140 places.

PHYSICAL DISABILITY AND SENSORY IMPAIRMENT

14th Fl, Taberner Hse, Croydon, Surrey CR9 2BA; Tel 020 8686 4433
Provides services to enable people, including children, with disabilities and/or sensory impairment to live as independently as possible within their own home. SCS receives approximately 1000 new referrals each year. This service maintains the statutory registers, provides specialist equipment, skills training and support, and arranges for minor and major adaptations to Service Users properties. SCS manages a joint user Equipment Store with Croydon Community Health Trust. An interpreting service for deaf people is also provided.

HOME CARE SERVICES

The Home Care Service provides support to people in their homes with many tasks. These range from intensive personal care tasks, washing, assistance with dressing and also includes assistance with shopping and laundry. The service aims to promote independence and work closely with other agencies such as the NHS. The service users come from all adult client groups, although the majority are elderly.

Addington Heights Croydon, Surrey; Tel 01689 689 1544

Strand House Croydon, Surrey; Tel 020 8689 1544

DIVISIONAL SUPPORT SERVICES

Manages central, division wide support for the eight operational services in the areas of Personnel, Training, Income Management and Administrative Assistance. This service makes the necessary arrangements to cover the Council's statutory obligation for funerals.

MEALS SERVICES

Social Services Meals Services Catering Dept, Town Hall Room 12, Croydon, Surrey CR9 2BA; Tel 020 8760 5607
Catering Manager Jean Naish

Croydon Voluntary Action 97 High St, Thornton Heath, Surrey CR7 8RY; Tel 020 8684 3862

Women's Royal Voluntary Services 68 Park La, Croydon, Surrey; Tel 020 8686 6996

Education Department

Taberner Hse, Park La, Croydon, Surrey CR9 1TP; Tel 020 8686 4433; Fax 020 8760 5603
Director (Education) Peter Wylie
Group Director (Student Services) Alan Malarkey, CertEd, BA, MBA, FRSA
Group Director (Quality Development) R.A. Ellis, MA(Ed)
Group Director (Information and Management Services) A. Parkin, BSc(Hons), CPFA, DMS
Manager (Personnel) K. Brady (Acting)
Assistant Education Officer (Special Needs) M. McCormack, MA
Chief Educational Psychologist A. Moore
Court Liaison Officer J. Walsh

SPECIAL SCHOOLS

Beckmead School Monks Orchard Rd, Beckenham, Kent BR3 3BZ; E-mail office@beckmead.croydon.sch.uk; Tel 020 8777 9311; 020 8777 9312; Fax 020 8777 6550
Headteacher K. Johnson
EBD

Bensham Manor School Ecclesbourne Rd, Thornton Heath, Surrey CR7 7BR; Tel 020 8684 0116; Fax 020 8683 1301
Headteacher J. Green
Secondary, MLD, Autism

7

Red Gates School 489 Purley Way, Croydon, Surrey
CR0 4RG; E-mail head@redgates.croydon.sch.uk; Tel 020
8681 8910; 020 8688 1761; Fax 020 8680 2167
Headteacher   S. Beaman
   SLD, Autism

Priory School Tennison Rd, London SE25 5RR;
E-mail secretary@priory.croydon.sch.uk; Tel 020 8653 7879;
020 8653 8222; Fax 020 8771 6761
Headteacher   G. Thomas
   SLD, Autism

St. Giles' School Pampisford Rd, Croydon, Surrey
CR2 6DF; E-mail stgiles1@global.net.co.uk; Tel 020 8680
1536; 020 8680 2141; Fax 020 8681 6359
Headteacher   J. Thomas
   PH

St. Nicholas School Old Lodge La, Purley, Surrey
CR8 4DN; E-mail sue@st-nicholas.croydon.sch.uk; Tel 020
8660 4861; 020 8660 4862; Fax 020 8660 8119
Headteacher   J. Melton
   MLD, Autism

Bridge To School Pupil Referral Unit Samuel Coleridge
Taylor, 194 Selhurst Rd, South Norwood, London
SE25 6XX; Tel 020 8771 8256; Fax 028 8768 2789
Head   John Gregory
   (46)

Coningsby Centre Pupil Referral Unit 45 Coombe Rd,
Croydon, Surrey CR0 1BQ;
E-mail administrator@coningsby.croydon.sch.uk; Tel 020
8680 0949; Fax 020 8680 5497
Headteacher   Sue Podd
   (131)

Moving On Pupil Referral Unit Suite 402, Park Hse, 4th Fl,
22 Park St, Croydon, Surrey CR0 1YE; Tel 020 8604 1414;
Fax 020 8604 1295
Headteacher   Sue Welling
   (42)

Phil Edwards Centre Pupil Referral Unit 17 Syluan Rd,
South Norwood, London SE19 2RU;
E-mail office@philedwards.croydon.sch.uk; Tel 020 8771
5603; Fax 020 8771 5650
Headteacher   J. Oliver
   (80)

Victoria House Pupil Referral Unit Southbridge Pl,
Croydon, Surrey CR0 4HA;
E-mail helen_logan@croydon.gov.uk; Tel 020 8686 0393;
Fax 020 8680 0890
Headteacher   Helen Logan
   (44)

EALING LONDON BOROUGH COUNCIL
www.ealing.gov.uk

Population 301 600
Political Composition: Lab: 48, Con: 17, LD: 4
Town Hall, New Broadway, Ealing, London W5 2BY;
   URL www.ealing.gov.uk;
   E-mail webmaster@ealing.gov.uk; Tel 020 8825 5000
Executive Director (Corporate Resources)   S. Lawes
Town Hall Annexe, New Broadway, Ealing, London
   W5 2BY
Director (Environment)   J. Birch
Perceval Hse, 14–16 Uxbridge Rd, Ealing, London W5 2HL;
   Tel 020 8579 2424

Housing and Social Services Department

Perceval Hse, 14–16 Uxbridge Rd, London W5 2HL;
   URL www.ealing.gov.uk;
   E-mail socialservices@ealing.gov.uk; Tel 020 8825 5000

Executive Director   Norman Tutt
Director (Strategy and Resources – Older People)
   Stephanie Finch
Director (Adults Services)   Catharine Roff
Director (Finance)   Zena Cooke
Director (Children's Services)   Judith Finlay
Director (Strategy and Resources)   John Anderson
Training   Ian Aitken
Information Services   David Commerford
Youth Offending Service   Ed Shaylor
Customer Care   Carole Bonifas
Human Resources   Jean Atkinson

COMMISSIONING AREA TEAMS

Acton Acton Town Hall, Winchester St, Acton, London W3;
Tel 020 8825 5000

Ealing and Hanwell Perceval Hse, 14–16 Uxbridge Rd,
Ealing, London W5 2HL; Tel 020 8825 5000

Greenford, Northolt, and Southall 301 Ruislip Rd,
Greenford, London; Tel 020 8825 5000

HOSPITAL AND PRINCIPAL SOCIAL WORKERS

Ealing Hospital St. Bernard's Wing, Uxbridge Rd, Southall,
Greater London; Tel 020 8574 2444
Head of Commissioning (Mental Health)   Bridget Ledbury

CHILDREN'S HOMES

Florence Road Children's Home 15 Florence Rd, Ealing,
London W9 3TU; Tel 020 8579 6351
Manager   Verity Lloyd

Uxbridge Road Children's Home 376 Uxbridge Rd, Ealing,
London; Tel 020 8992 2774 ext 42686
Manager   Maria Miguens-Souto

RESIDENTIAL UNIT FOR CHILDREN WITH DISABILITIES

Heller House 124 Norwood Rd, Southall, Greater London;
Tel 020 8574 5835
Manager   Rose Baldwin
   (12)

FAMILY RESOURCE CENTRE

1st Response and Family Centre 91 Cowings Mead,
Northolt, London; Tel 020 8841 5046
Manager   Paul Crouch

YOUTH OFFENDING TEAM

2b Cheltenham Pl, Acton, London W3 8JS; Tel 020 8752
2152
Team Leader   Ed Shaylor

DAY CENTRES

Carlton Centre 8–10 Carlton Rd, Chiswick, London
W4 5DY; Tel 020 3742 3134
Manager   N. Suriakamur

David Cousins Centre 131 Windmill La, Greenford,
London; Tel 020 8575 5550
Manager   T. Linnane
   (50)

RESIDENTIAL UNIT FOR ADULTS WITH A MENTAL HANDICAP

Cowgate Community Unit 14–16 Cowgate Rd, Greenford,
London UB6 8HQ; Tel 020 8575 9100
Manager   Clare Carpenter
   (12)

COMMUNITY MENTAL HEALTH RESOURCE CENTRES

Avenue House Resource Centre 43–47 Avenue Rd, Acton, London W3 8NJ; Tel 020 8993 7781; Fax 020 8896 2914

Cherington House Resource Centre Cherington Rd, Hanwell, London W7 3HL; Tel 020 8566 2777; Fax 020 8840 8526

Manor Gate Resource Centre 1a Manor Gate, Northolt, Greater London UB5 5TG; Tel 020 8841 5271; Fax 020 8845 5086

Southall and Norwood Resource Centre The Green, Southall, Greater London UB2 4BH; Tel 020 8571 6110; Fax 020 8574 6099

Walpole House Resource Centre 13 Mattock La, Ealing, London W5 3BG; Tel 020 8840 6900; Fax 020 8567 7736

ACCOMMODATION FOR PEOPLE WITH MENTAL HEALTH PROBLEMS

Bowmans Close Home 58 Bowmans Cl, West Ealing, London W13; Tel 020 8567 1394
Manager Mike Foley
(24)

Community Road Home 50 Community Rd, Greenford, London UB6 8XF; Tel 020 8575 2684
Manager Peter Barr
(20)

SERVICES FOR THE BLIND

Rehabilitation Officer for the Blind Philip Sharpe; Tel 020 8579 2424
Rehabilitation Officer for the Blind A. McGeoghegan; Tel 020 8579 2424

DAY CENTRES FOR THE ELDERLY

Acton Adult Training Centre Stirling Rd, Acton, London W3; Tel 020 8993 6283
Manager Noreen Meredith
(165)

Albert Dane Centre 19–21 Western Rd, Southall, Greater London UB2 5UA; Tel 020 8574 5074
(50)

Cowgate Community Unit 18 Cowgate Rd, Greenford, Greater London UB6 8HQ; Tel 020 8575 9100
Manager Clare Carpenter

Learning Curve Roslin Rd, Acton, London W3 8AH; Tel 020 8752 1907
Manager Sharon Lander
(85)

Michael Flanders Centre Church Rd, Acton, London W3 8PP; Tel 020 8993 5805
Manager M. Hall
(75)

ACCOMMODATION FOR THE ELDERLY

There are three Local Authority Homes under the 1948 National Assistance Act with a total of 185 places. There are 11 voluntary homes for older people with 335 places; two voluntary homes for alcoholics with 48 places; five voluntary homes providing mental health care with 48 places; nine voluntary homes for people with learning disabilities with 82 places; six private homes for older people with 99 places and three private homes for people with a learning disability with 36 places under the Registered Homes Act 1984.

MOBILE MEALS SERVICE

Distributed by 13 vans during the week and ten vans serving the weekend.

Education Department

Perceval Hse, 14–16 Uxbridge Rd, Ealing, London W5 2HL; E-mail education@ealing.gov.uk; Tel 020 8825 5000; Fax 020 8825 5995
Executive Director (Learning and Ambition) Dr C. Whalley
Director (Education Access and Inclusion) H. McCafferty
Director (Schools and Achievements) J. Morning
Director (Education Resources) D. Gallie
Head (School Effectiveness) B. Anderson, BSc, MSc, CertEd
Service Head (Educational and Social Work) T. Galvin
Service Head (Planning, Research and IT) G. Redhead
Service Head (Special Education) John Keever
Service Head (Community Learning) S. Jones
Service Head Tracey McNeil (Acting)
Service Head (Pupil Support and Contract Services) E. Lustig
Service Head (Library and Information Service) J. Battye
Service Head (Youth Services) C. Grant (Acting)
Service Head (Early Years, Childcare and Play) C. Barnard
Service Head (Special Educational Needs Support Service) R. MacConville
Principal Inspector Mike Doran
Deputy Principal Educational Psychologist B. King
Deputy Principal Educational Psychologist S. Nath
Senior Personnel Officer Mark Nelson
Principal Officer (Arts and Museums) Neena Sohal
Group Accountant Dave Jefferis

EDUCATIONAL PSYCHOLOGISTS AND SOCIAL WORKERS

Perceval Hse, 14–16 Uxbridge Rd, Ealing, London W5 2HL; Tel 020 8825 5000; Fax 020 8825 5353

SPECIAL DAY SCHOOLS

Belvue School Rowdell Rd, Northolt, Greater London UB5 6AG; Tel 020 8845 5766; Fax 020 8841 4409
Headteacher S. O'Shea
MLD

Castlebar School Hathaway Gdns, Ealing, London W13 0DH; Tel 020 8998 3135; Fax 020 8810 7597
Headteacher D.J. Perkins
MLD

John Chilton School Compton Cres, Northolt, Greater London UB5 5LD; Tel 020 8842 1329; Fax 020 8841 1328
Headteacher S. Rosenberg
PD

Mandeville School Eastcote La, Northolt, Greater London UB5 4HW; Tel 020 8864 0911; 020 8864 4921; Fax 020 8423 1096
Headteacher Christine Marks
SLD

St. Ann's School Springfield Rd, Hanwell, London W7 3JP; Tel 020 8567 6291; Fax 020 8840 4664
Headteacher G. Carver
SLD

Springhallow School Compton Cl, off Cavendish Ave, Ealing, London W13 0JG; Tel 020 8998 2700; Fax 020 8810 7610
Headteacher J. Birch
(52)

THE STUDY CENTRE

Longfield Site Study Centre (KS3) Compton Cl, Ealing, London W13 0JG; Tel 020 8991 9590; Fax 020 8566 8538
Head (Longfield) T. McNeil

Boston Site Study Centre 42 Lower Boston Rd, Hanwell, London W7 2NR; Tel 020 8840 4484; Fax 020 8579 0934
Joint Head (Boston) Mrs B. Raymond
Joint Head (Boston) V. Griffin

Park Site Study Centre 9 Longfield Rd, Ealing, London W5 2DH; Tel 020 8998 6583; Fax 020 8571 2507
Head (Park) M. Hofmeister

7

ENFIELD LONDON BOROUGH COUNCIL
www.enfield.gov.uk

Population 262 600
Political Composition: Con: 39, Lab: 24
Civic Centre, PO Box 61, Enfield, Greater London EN1 3XY;
  URL www.enfield.gov.uk; Tel 020 8379 1000
Leader of the Council   Mike Rye
Director (Resources)   Mark McLaughlin
Director (Housing Services)   Donald Graham
Director (Environmental Services)   J. Pryor
Assistant Director (Planning and Transport)
  Stephen Tapper
Assistant Director (Operational Services)   P. Gardner, CEng,
  FICE, MIHT, MBIM
Head (Property Services)   David Tullis

Social Services Group

PO Box 59, Civic Centre, Enfield, Greater London EN1 3XL;
  E-mail socialservices@enfield.gov.uk; Tel 020 8379 3333;
  Fax 020 8379 5076; Textphone (Social Services access to
  Specialist Teams) 020 8379 5048
Director (Community and Social Services)   Donal Graham
  Eastman

Social Services Scrutiny Panel

Con 5, Lab 3
Cabinet Member   Alan Barker (Con)
Deputy Cabinet Member   Vacancy
Labour Lead Member (Social Services)   Chris Cole

Strategy and Policy Division

Assistant Director   Lance Douglas;
  E-mail lance.douglas@enfield.gov.uk; Tel 020 8379 3993;
  Fax 020 8379 3674
Head (Strategy and Performance)   Janice Lucas;
  E-mail janice.lucas@enfield.gov.uk; Tel 020 8379 3917;
  Fax 020 8379 3928
Head (Access and Modern Working)   Joyce Webster;
  E-mail joyce.webster@enfield.gov.uk; Tel 020 8379 3940;
  Fax 020 8379 3884
*Manager (Equalities, Diversity and BME Community
  Development)*   Meeta Jhala
1st Fl, St. Andrew's Crt, 1–4 River Front, Enfield, Greater
  London EN13SY; E-mail meeta.jhala@enfield.gov.uk;
  Tel 020 8379 1508; Fax 020 8379 5057

Adults Division

Assistant Director (Adults Division)   Penny Butler;
  E-mail penny.butler@enfield.gov.uk; Tel 020 8379 4160;
  Fax 020 8379 4274

Adults of Working Age

2nd Fl, St. Andrew's Crt, 1–4 River Front, Enfield,
  Greater London EN1 3SY; Tel 020 8379 3713; Fax 020
  8379 5040
Head (Services for Adults of Working Age)   Lorraine Davies;
  E-mail lorraine.davies@enfield.gov.uk
Service Manager (Physical Disabilities)   Niel Niehorster;
  Tel 020 8379 8114; Fax 020 8379 8080
Service Manager (Learning Difficulties)   Vicky Main; Tel 020
  8379 3309
Service Manager (Occupational Therapy)   Bernadette
  Simpson; Tel 020 8379 5914; Fax 020 8379 5935

Commissioning and Strategic Development

Swan Annexe, 221 High St, Enfield, Greater London
  EN3 4DX; E-mail ray.james@enfield.gov.uk; Tel 020 8379
  8009; Fax 020 8379 8080
Head   Ray James
Manager (Strategic Development – Drug Action Support Team)
  Lindsey Daley
Manager (Procurement)   Kim Sandford
Project Manager (Supporting People)   Pauline Kettless
Principal Officer (Housing Options)   Sharon Strutt
Welfare Rights Adviser   Carmel Walker

Finance and Performance

Swan Annexe, 221 High St, Enfield, Greater London
  EN3 4DX; E-mail carol.dalman@enfield.gov.uk; Tel 020
  8379 8159; Fax 020 8379 8080
Head   Carol Dalman
Contact (Finance and Office Services)   Wendy Shirley
Manager (Income Team)   Pamela Odumody (Acting)
Manager (Performance Team)   Eric Hill (Acting)

Mental Health Services

305–309 Fore St, Edmondon, London N9 0PD;
  E-mail frank.harrington@beh-mht.nhs.uk; Tel 020 8887
  0606; Fax 020 8345 6947
Head (Forensic Social Work)   Julian Haines (Acting)
Manager (Operations)   Frank Harrington
Manager (North Enfield CMHT)   Leigh Saunders
Manager (North Southgate CMHT)   Paul McKevitt
Manager (South Southgate CMHT)   Cathy Newcombe
Manager (Edmonton CMHT)   Peter Tapang
Manager (Enfield Community drug and Alcohol Service)
  Andrew Akers (Acting)

Older People Services

221 High St, Enfield, Greater London EN3 4DX;
  E-mail steve.tall@enfield.gov.uk; Tel 020 8379 8031;
  Fax 020 8379 8080
Head   Steve Tall
Service Manager (Assessment and Care Management)
  Vacancy
Service Manager (Integrated Care)   Brigitte Shallow
Service Manager (Re-enablement)   Sue Collingridge
Manager (Purchasing, Monitoring and Review Team)
  Bernie Pizzaro
Southgate Town Hall, Green Lnes, Palmers Grn, London
  N13 4XD; E-mail bernie.pizzaro@enfield.gov.uk; Tel 020
  8319 2825; Fax 020 8379 2810
Manager (Health)   Anita Shepherd
Chase Farm Hospital, The Ridgeway, Enfield, Greater
  London EN2 8JL; E-mail anita.shepherd@enfield.gov.uk;
  Tel 020 8366 9131; Fax 020 8366 9130
Team Leader (Home Care)   Jenny Murtagh (Acting)
Pine Lodge, St. Michael's Site, Gater Dr, Enfield, Greater
  London EN1 3XL; E-mail jenny.murtagh@enfield.gov.uk;
  Tel 020 8350 1113; Fax 020 8350 1112

Children and Families Division

Assistant Director (Children and Families)   Andrew Fraser;
  E-mail andrew.fraser@enfield.gov.uk; Tel 020 8379 4541;
  Fax 020 8379 4274

Asylum Team Southgate Town Hall, Green Lnes, Palmers
Grn, London N13 4XD;
E-mail judith.aklama@enfield.gov.uk; Tel 020 8379 2861;
Fax 020 8379 2807
Manager (Asylum Team)   Judith Aklama

Children In Need Services Edmonton Centre, 36–44 South
Mall, Edmonton, London N9 0TN;
E-mail julian.edwards@enfield.gov.uk; Tel 020 8379 2593;
Fax 020 8379 2595
Head   Julian Edwards

Children's Hospital Social Work Team
Team Manager   Dermot Kelly
North Middlesex Hospital, Sterling Way, Edmonton,
    London N18 1QX; E-mail dermot.kelly@enfield.gov.uk;
    Tel 020 8887 2759; Fax 020 8887 2766
Deputy Manager   Andrea Collins
Chase Farm Hospital, The Ridgeway, Enfield, Greater
    London EN2 8JL;
    E-mail andrea.collins@enfield.gov.uk; Tel 020 8366 6000
    Ext 6446; Fax 020 8366 9130

Commissioning Performance and Development   PO Box 59,
Civic Centre, Silver St, Enfield, Greater London EN1 3XL;
E-mail tony.theodoulou@enfield.gov.uk; Tel 020 8379 3950;
Fax 020 8379 4274
Head   Tony Theodoulou
Senior Manager (Child Protection and Review)   Carla Acket
Manager (Support and Divisional Performance Information)
    Ann Clifton
Senior Policy, Planning and Development Officer
    Pauline Parish

Looked After Children Services   Southgate Town Hall,
Green Lnes, Palmers Grn, London N13 4XD;
E-mail liz.hill@enfield.gov.uk; Tel 020 8379 2885; Fax 020
8379 2699
Head   Liz Hill
Senior Manager (Leaving Care)   Jonathan Mason
Team Manager (Adoption and Permanence)   Ingrid Perkins
Team Manager (Fostering)   Janice Darling
Team Manager (Looked After Children Team A)
    Julian Green
Team Manager (Looked After Children Team B)
    Anja Chawhan (Acting)

Youth Offending and Outreach   2nd Fl, St. Georges
Chambers, 23 South Mall, Edmonton, Greater London
N9 0TS; E-mail keith.napthine@enfield.gov.uk; Tel 020 8345
5557; Fax 020 8345 6954
Service Centre Manager   Keith Napthine
Operations Manager   Liz Davies
Operations Manager (Post-sentence)   Carol Maxwell

RESIDENTIAL AND DAY CARE ESTABLISHMENTS

Swan Annexe, 219 High St, Enfield, Greater London
    EN3 4DX; Tel 020 8379 8100
Team Leader (Day Care and Outreach)   Bryan Collins

Disability

Park Avenue Disability Resource Centre   Ground Fl, 65c Pk
Ave, Enfield, Greater London EN1 2HH; Tel 020 8360 1195;
Fax 020 8360 7586
Manager (Independent Living)   Vacancy
Day care.

Learning Difficulties

Carterhatch Supported Tenancy Project   104 Linwood Cres,
Enfield, Greater London EN1 4UR; Tel 020 8292 7977;
Fax 020 8292 7865
Manager   Marion Friskin (Acting)
Residential.

Formont Centre   Waverly Rd, Enfield, Greater London
EN2 7BP; Tel 020 8363 6388; Fax 020 8366 3576
Manager   Sarah Carney (Acting)
Manager   Barbara Hope (Acting)
Day care.

Edmonton Community Link   Portacabin, Knights La, London
N9 0PG; E-mail martin.wright@enfield.gov.uk; Tel 020 8807
7817; Fax 020 8887 9149
Team Leader   Martin Wright

Enfield Community Link   84 Silver St, Enfield, London
EN1 3EP; E-mail anne.duffy@enfield.gov.uk; Tel 020 8367
9129; Fax 020 8367 9125
Manager   Anne Duffy (Acting)

New Options   12 North Way, Claverings Ind Est, Montagu
Rd, Edmonton, London N9 0AD;
E-mail denise.bunyan@enfield.gov.uk; Tel 020 8887 0766;
Fax 020 8807 9828
Manager   Denise Bunyan

Mental Health

Park Avenue Mental Health Resource Centre (Day Care)   1st
Fl, 65c Park Ave, Enfield, Greater London EN1 2HH;
E-mail james.armstrong@enfield.gov.uk; Tel 020 8364 1855;
Fax 020 8364 3934
Manager   James Armstrong (Acting)
Day care.

Older People

Elizabeth House   1 Old Rd, Enfield, Greater London
EN3 5XX; Tel 020 8379 5754; Fax 020 8443 1841
Manager (Residential)   Joyce Hintzen
Supervisor (Day Care)   Mary Savas
Residential and day care.

Reardon Court   26 Cosgrove Cl, London N21 3BH; Tel 020
8447 9980; Fax 020 8350 4802
Manager (Day Care)   John Rixon
Manager (Residential)   Mark Whitbread
Residential, day care and Greek/Cypriot luncheon club.

Rose Taylor Day Centre   55b The Sunny Rd, Enfield,
Greater London EN3 5EF;
E-mail shelly.king@enfield.gov.uk; Tel 020 8804 1168;
Fax 020 8805 2857
Manager   Shelly King
Day care.

Ruth Winston House   190 Green Lanes, Palmers Grn,
London N13 5UE; E-mail val.gudge@enfield.gov.uk; Tel 020
8886 5346; Fax 020 8350 9909
Manager   Val Gudge
Day centre and luncheon club.

William Preye Centre   Houndsfield Rd, London N9 7RA;
E-mail shelly.king@enfield.gov.uk; Tel 020 8805 2164;
Fax 020 8805 9230
Manager   Shelly King (Acting)
Day care.

Children and Young People

Arnos Family Centre   321a Bowes Rd, London N11 1BA;
E-mail david.phillips@enfield.gov.uk; Tel 020 8368 9465;
Fax 020 8368 4467
Manager   David Phillips
Day care.

Cheviots Children's Centre   81 Cheviot Cl, Enfield,
Greater London EN1 3UZ; Tel 020 8363 4047; Fax 020 8366
2561
Manager   Sue Roberts
Manager   Janet Leach
Day care.

Edmonton Family Centre   5 Lacey Cl, London N9 7SA;
E-mail cynthia.maragna@enfield.gov.uk; Tel 020 8379 1703;
020 8884 2464; Fax 020 8887 0028
Manager   Cynthia Maragna
Day care.

Moorfield Family Centre   2 Moorfield Rd, Enfield,
Greater London EN1 5TU; Tel 020 8805 6313; Fax 020 8804
1897
Day care.
Manager   David Phillips

Young People's Resource Centre   265 Church St, Edmonton,
London N9 9JA; E-mail joe.blatter@enfield.gov.uk; Tel 020
8360 9102; Fax 020 8360 0473
Manager   Joe Blatter
Contact (Residential Unit)   Maria Shenton

7

Education Department

PO Box 56, Civic Centre, Silver St, Enfield, Greater London
EN1 3XQ; Tel 020 8366 6565; Fax 020 8379 3243;
Minicom 020 8367 8701; Tel exDX 90615 ENFIELD
Director (Education) L. Graham, MA
Head (Resources and Asset Management) J. Hill
Head (Strategy Planning and Performance Management)
A. Pennell
Head (Children's Services) K. Fletcher-Wright (Acting)
Head (Schools and Community) N. Rousell
Senior Development Officer (Special) K. Fletcher-Wright
Principal Officer (Education Psychology Service) D. Grant

SPECIAL SCHOOLS

Aylands School Keswick Dr, Enfield, Greater London
EN3 6NY; Tel 01992 761229
Headteacher D. Feeley
(Day)
Mixed 7–16 EBD

Durants School 4 Pitfield Way, Enfield, Greater London
EN3 5BY; Tel 020 8804 1980
Headteacher K. Bovair
(Day)
Mixed 5–16 MLD

Oaktree School Chase Side, Southgate, London N14 4HN;
Tel 020 8440 3100
Headteacher J. Harrison
Mixed 5–16 MLD (Day)

Russet House School 11 Autumn Cl, Enfield, Greater
London EN1 4JA; Tel 020 8350 0650
Contact J. Foster

Waverley School 105 The Ride, Enfield, Greater London
EN3 7DL; Tel 020 8805 1858
Headteacher L.C. Gibbs
(Day)
Mixed 3–18 SLD

West Lea School Haselbury Rd, Edmonston, London
N9 9TU; Tel 020 8807 2656
Headteacher A. Fox

SPECIAL CENTRES

In-School Support Service Addison Hse, Addison Ave,
London N14 4AE; Tel 020 8441 7300
Headteacher G. Currie

Children and Family Service 8 Bycullah Ave, Enfield,
Greater London; Tel 020 8367 8844

Educational Psychology Service Garvary, 8 Dryden Rd,
Enfield, Greater London EN1 2PP; Tel 020 8360 6771

Enfield Secondary Tuition Centre Eldon Rd, London
N9 8LG; Tel 020 8345 6648
Manager O. Flavin

Enfield Secondary Tuition Centre Bury St, Edmonton,
London N9 7JR; Tel 020 8804 6344

Language and Curriculum Access Centre Tile Kiln La,
London N13 6BY; Tel 020 8803 4460
Manager N. Parr, BA

LONDON BOROUGH OF GREENWICH

Population 215 238
Political Composition: Lab: 38, Con: 9, LD: 4
Leader of the Council Cllr Chris Roberts
Director (Finance) Chris Perry
45–53 Wellington St, London SE18 6RA
Director (Housing Services) Richard Thompson
Peggy Middleton Hse, 50 Woolwich New Rd, London
SE18 6HQ

Greenwich Planning Steve Merryfield
Peggy Middleton Hse, 50 Woolwich New Rd, London
SE18 6HQ; Tel 020 8854 8888
Greenwich Engineering David Jessup
Peggy Middleton Hse, 50 Woolwich New Rd, London
SE18 6HQ; Tel 020 8854 8888
Property Management Laurence Smith
Peggy Middleton Hse, 50 Woolwich New Rd, London
SE18 6HQ
Head (Legal Services) Russell Power
29–37 Wellington St, London SE18 6RA

Social Services Department

Nelson Hse, Wellington St, London SE18 6PY;
Tel (Emergency Tel) 020 8854 8888
Cabinet Member Cllr David Grant
Director (Social Services) David Behan
Director (Mental Health Services) Fenella Trevillion
Head (Children and Families Resource) Barbara Peacock
Head (Social Work and Assessment) A. O'Sullivan
Head (Elderly and Disabled Services) M. Marriott
Head (Financial Services) R. Mellors
Head (Learning Disability Services) D. Cox
Head (Support Services) B. Young
Head (Training and Staff Development) Trish Letchfield
Manager (Planning and Commissioning – Equalities)
M. Lone
Manager (Business Support) Marilyn Pearson

DISTRICT OFFICES

East District Nelson Hse, 50 Wellington St, Woolwich,
London SE18 1JN; Tel 020 8921 3173; 020 8921 3183; Fax 020
8312 5197; Minicom 020 8312 7989

FAMILY RESOURCE CENTRES

Ezra Family Resource Centre 17 Leslie Smith Sq,
Woolwich Common, London SE10 4DW; Tel 020 8316
0951

Jumoke Family Resource Centre 47 Abbey Gr, Abbey
Wood, London SE2 9EU; Tel 020 8310 9659

Prospects Family Resource Centre 360 Middle Park Ave,
Eltham, London SE9 6HQ; Tel 020 8859 4449

CHILDREN'S HOMES

Broad Walk Children's Home 125a Broad Walk, London
SE3 8NF; Tel 020 8856 5031
(8)

Erwood Road Children's Home 17 Erwood Rd, London
SE7 8DR; Tel 020 8855 6471
Girls (12)

HOME FOR CHILDREN WITH LEARNING DISABILITY

Eastcombe Avenue Children's Home 79 Eastcombe Ave,
London SE7 7LL; Tel 020 8858 2178

ADULT TRAINING CENTRES FOR THOSE WITH LEARNING DISABILITY

Ashley Adult Training Centre Parry Pl, London SE18 6AS;
Tel 020 8854 2141
(90)

Sherard Road Centre Tattersall Cl, Eltham, London
SE9 6ET; Tel 020 8859 7607
(80)

Woolwich Dockyard Training Centre 88 Antelope Rd,
London SE18 5QG; Tel 020 8317 8338

HOSTEL FOR ADULTS WITH LEARNING DISABILITY

Hervey Road Hostel 28 Hervey Rd, London SE3 8BS;
Tel 020 8856 4656
(20)

COMBINED DAY CENTRE (MENTAL HEALTH AND PHYSICAL DISABILITY)

Greenwich Disability Resource Centre Sandpit Pl, London
SE7 8HE; Tel 020 8317 8393
(75)

COMMUNITY REHABILITATION TEAM

50 Abbey Wood Rd, London SE2; Tel 020 8310 3943

GROUP HOMES PROJECT TEAM

Abbey Wood Road Project Team 50 Abbey Wood Rd,
London SE2 9NW; Tel 020 8311 6388
Hervey Road Project Team 24a Hervey Rd, London
SE3 8BF; Tel 020 8319 8864

STAFF GROUP HOME

69 Coleraine Rd, London SE3

DAY CLUBS FOR THE ELDERLY

Elford Close Lunch and Day Club Elford Cl, London
SE3 7EF; Tel 020 8856 8669
(20)

Elmgrove Day Centre Elmgrove, 78 Walmer Terr, London
SE18 7EF; Tel 020 8854 2775
(12)

Indian Cultural Society Old Town Hall, Calderwood St,
London SE18; Tel 020 8317 9345
(16)

Tegal Lunch and Day Club 11 Simnel Rd, London SE12 9BG;
Tel 020 8857 2005
(16)

MEALS SERVICES

Mobile meals and lunch clubs provided by the local
authority.

Education Department

Riverside Hse, Woolwich High St, Woolwich, London
SE18 6DF; URL www.greenwich.gov.uk; Tel 020 8921
8038; Fax 020 8921 8228
Director (Education) P. Burnet
Deputy Director Chris Wells
Assistant Director (Pupil and Student Support) Vacancy
Assistant Director (Effectiveness and Improvement)
P. Reynolds
Head (Policy) Mike Hickie
Head (Administration and Communications) Maggie King
Head (Personnel) Alain Audibert
Head (Education Finance) S. Peach
Ethnic Minorities Achievement Service John Clay
Policy Officer (Primary) Phil Jones
Policy Officer (Secondary and Post 16) Dean Waller
Policy Officer (Adult and Community Education)
Chris Banda
Policy Officer (Social Inclusion and Equalities) Vacancy
Principal (Attendance and Advisory Service)
Denice Sealy
Principal Educational Psychologist Kath Fingleton
Principal Psychiatric Social Worker (Child Guidance Service)
Linda Devlin

SPECIAL SCHOOLS

Churchfield School Church Manorway, London SE2 0HY;
E-mail headteacher.churchfield.greenwich@lgft.net; Tel 020
8854 3739
Headteacher P. Shippey
Secondary MLD

Moatbridge School Eltham Palace Rd, Middle Park Ave,
London SE9 5LX;
E-mail headteacher.moatbridge.greenwich@lgft.net; Tel 020
8850 8081
Headteacher M. Byron
EBD

Willow Dene School Swingate La, London SE18 2JD;
E-mail headteacher.willowdene.greenwich@lgft.net; Tel 020
8854 9841; Fax 020 8854 9846
Headteacher Ms P. Hardaker
PM and assessment Nursery MLD, SLD, PMLD, ASD

HACKNEY LONDON BOROUGH COUNCIL
www.hackney.gov.uk

Population 192 492
Political Composition: Lab: 29, LD: 17, Con: 11, Ind: 1.
Hackney Town Hall, Mare St, London E8 1EA;
URL www.hackney.gov.uk; Tel 020 8356 5000
Mayor Joe Lobenstein, MBE
Managing Director Max Caller
Director (Education) Elizabeth Reid
Director (Elderly Services) Fran Stewart
Director (Regulatory Services) Robert Biggs
Director (Adult Community Services) Fran Stewart (Acting)
Director (Customer and Advice Services) Ann Malloy
Director (Learning and Leisure Service) Vacancy
Director (Estate Management and Development Service)
David Thompson
Head (Children and Families Service) Josephine Kwhali

Social Services Department

205 Morning La, London E9 6JX; Tel 020 8356 5000; Fax 020
8986 0593
Director (Social Services) Mary Richardson
Head (Children and Families) Josephine Kwhali
Head (Community Care) Steve Goodman
Head (Strategy and Resources) Bob Morgan

Cabinet

Cabinet Member (Social Services) Cllr Frances Pearson (Lab)
Hackney Town Hall, Mare St, London E8 1EA
Leader Jules Pipe
Hackney Town Hall, Mare St, London E8 1EA
Deputy Leader Jessica Crowe,
Hackney Town Hall, Mare St, London E8 1EA
Members of the Cabinet
J. Carswell, F. Khan, S. Lloyd, G. Nicholson, J. Nkafu,
I. Peacock, F. Pearson, V. Stops.

AREA OFFICES

North East

30 Clapton Sq, London E5 8HZ; Tel 020 8356 6800

North West

17 Manor Rd, London N16 5PE; Tel 020 8356 6200

East Office (Children and Families)

185–203 Morning La, London E9 6JX; Tel 020 8356 5200

West Office (Children and Families)

81 Downham Rd, London N1; Tel 020 8356 5500

CHILDREN'S SPECIALIST SERVICES

(Learning Difficulties, Disabilities, Sensory Impairment, Occupational Therapy/Hospital Social Work Service). 7 Marcon Pl, London E8 1LP; Tel 020 8356 4200

HIV/AIDS/ALCOHOL/DRUGS SERVICE

205 Morning La, London E9 6JX; Tel (Call centre) 020 8356 6262

FOSTERING/ADOPTION

205 Morning La, London E9 6JX; Tel 020 8356 5000

YOUNG OFFENDERS, INTERMEDIATE TREATMENT AND BAIL SUPPORT TEAM

55 Daubeney Rd, London E5; Tel 020 8533 7070; Fax 020 8986 7446

LOCALITY MENTAL HEALTH TEAMS

North East

176–178 Clapton Common, London E5 9AG; Tel 020 8919 8999

North West

Anita Hse, Wilmer Pl, London N16 0LN; Tel 020 7923 0257

South East

26 Shore Rd, London E9 7TA; Tel 020 8533 6116

South West

100 Shepherdness Walk, London N1 7JM; Tel 020 7445 7900

Education Services

Edith Cavell Bldg, Enfield Rd, London N1 5BA; Tel 020 8356 8436; Fax 020 8356 7345
Director (Education)   Alan Wood; Tel 020 8356 8413

SPECIAL SCHOOLS

Crusoe House School Nile St, London N1 9EX; Tel 020 7251 3932; Fax 020 7250 0740
Headteacher   Irene Flynn
  EBD

Downsview School Downs Rd, Tiger Way, London E5 8QP; Tel 020 8985 6833; Fax 020 8985 4020
Headteacher   Bill Bulman
  MLD

Horizon School Wordsworth Rd, London N16 8DA; Tel 020 7254 8096; Fax 020 7923 3665
Headteacher   Anne Uhart
  MLD

Ickburgh School Ickburgh Rd, London E5 8AD; Tel 020 8806 4638; Fax 020 8806 4638
Headteacher   Phil Goss
  SLD

Stormont House School Downs Park Rd, London E5 8NP; Tel 020 8985 4245; Fax 020 8985 6886
Headteacher   Angela Murphy

Population 166 000
Political Composition: Lab: 29, Con: 17.
Town Hall, King St, Hammersmith, London W6 9JU;
  URL www.lbhf.gov.uk; Tel 020 8753 2001
Director (Policy and Administration)   Henry Peterson, MA
Director (Finance)   Jane West
Director (Housing Services)   Elaine Elkington
Hammersmith Housing Centre, Riverview Hse, London
  W6 9AR; Tel 020 8753 4000

Social Services Department

145 King St, Hammersmith, London W6 9XY;
  URL www.lbhf.gov.uk; E-mail james.reilly@lbhf.gov.uk;
  Tel 020 8753 5000; Fax 020 8753 5739
Deputy (Social Inclusion)   Cllr T. Stanley c/o Members
  office, Hammersmith Town Hall
Assistant Deputy (Social Inclusion)   Cllr R. McLaughlin c/o
  Members' Office, Hammersmith Town Hall
Director (Social Services)   James A. Reilly
Assistant Director (Social Services (Community Care Services)
  J. Reilly
Assistant Director (Social Services – Children's Services)
  A. Christie
*Assistant Director (Social Services – Strategy and Resource
  Management)*   Heather Schroeder
Head (Strategic Commissioning)   S. Rafferty
Head (Human Resources Strategy and Resource Management)
  D. Shoesmith
Head (IT)   Tony Ellis
*Divisional Manager (Resources for Older People – Community
  Care Services)*   D. Williams
*Divisional Manager (Community Care Services – Residential
  Care Services for Older People)*   K. Levey
*Divisional Manager (Children's Services – Children's Resources
  and Asylum Services)*   P. Houghton
*Divisional Manager (Older People Social Work – Community
  Care)*   Alan Tyrer
*Divisional Manager (Children's Services – Children's
  Placements)*   S. Miley
Divisonal Manager (Resources and Support Services – SRM)
  S. Beresford
*Service Manager (Learning Disability Provider Service –
  Community Care)*   Philip Hutchings
*Service Development Manager (Contract Manager – Best Value
  (SRM))*   K. Fisher
*Manager (Disability Support Services – Community Care
  Services)*   M. Turner
Manager (Service Development – Residential and Day Care)
  M. De Silva
Project Manager (Better Government for Older People)
  Beverly Hone
*Principal Officer (Children's Services – Review and Quality
  Assurance Unit)*   J. Crowther
*Principal Officer (Children's Services – Review and Quality
  Assurance Unit)*   Terry Downe

Social Services Committee

Lab: 4, Con: 2.
Deputy (Social Inclusion)   Tim Stanley (Lab)
Assistant Deputy (Social Inclusion)   R. McLaughlin (Lab)

AREA TEAMS

Child Care Services North Sawley Rd, London W12 0NZ;
Tel 020 8749 3331
Divisional Manager   Leroy Harry

Child Care Services South Barclay Hse, Effie Rd, London SW6; Tel 020 8753 5512
Divisional Manager L. Harry

ADULT SERVICES (MENTAL HEALTH AND HIV, AIDS, DRUGS AND ALCOHOL)

Charring Cross Hospital, 3 North, Pulham Palace Rd, London W6 8RF; Tel 020 8846 1514
Head (Mental Health Services) Trevor Farmer

ADULT SERVICES (PEOPLE WITH LEARNING DIFFICULTIES AND PHYSICAL DISABILITIES)

145 King St, London W6 9XY
Divisional Manager S. McClinton

ASYLUM SEEKERS TEAM

164 King St, London W6; Tel 020 8576 5327

DAY NURSERY

Brook Green Day Nursery 49 Brook Grn, London W6 7BJ; E-mail prerna.patalia@lbhf.gov.uk; Tel 020 7603 5915
Manager Perna Patalia
(50)

CHILDREN'S COMMUNITY HOMES

Askham Family Centre 1 Askham Rd, London W12 0NW; E-mail steve.gordon@lbhf.gov.uk; Tel 020 8749 6936
Manager Steve Gordon

Grove House Family Centre
(NSPCC)
Bagleys La, London SW6 2QB; Tel 020 7731 1987
Manager Laura McFarlane

The Haven Children's Community Home
(NCH Action for Children)
1 Ollgar Cl, London W12 0NT; Tel 020 8749 7211
Manager Angie Moore

North Eyot Gardens Children's Community Home 52 North Eyot Gdns, London W6 9NL;
E-mail lloyd.scott@lbhf.gov.uk; Tel 020 8741 1319
Contact Lloyd Scott

Respite Care Unit 57 Finlay St, London SW6 6HF;
E-mail mandy.lawson@lbhf.gov.uk; Tel 020 7371 5762
Manager Mandy Lawson

White City Close Children's Community Home 120 Dalling Rd, London W6 0JE; Tel 020 8749 7286
Contact Delroy Lewis (Acting)

SECURE UNIT

Stamford Hse, 25 Cathnor Rd, London W12;
E-mail tony.goring@lbhf.gov.uk; Tel 020 8746 0050
Divisional Manager (Secure Care) Tony Goring
(130)

ADOLESCENT SERVICES

Youth Offending Team Sawley Rd, London W12 0NZ; Tel 020 8753 6200
Manager L. Wright

Young Adults Service 145 Hammersmith Rd, London W6 7JP; Tel 020 7348 3370
Contact Maria Gallagher

Maya Project 5 New King's Rd, London SW6 4SD; Tel 020 7736 0688
Manager J. Baker

DAY SERVICES FOR PEOPLE WITH LEARNING DISABILITIES

North Day Centre 280 Goldhawk Rd, London W12 9PF; Tel 020 8749 9602
Manager Vacancy

HOUSES FOR PEOPLE WITH LEARNING DIFFICULTIES

Coverdale Road Centre 2 Coverdale Rd, London W12 8JJ; Tel 020 8749 9559
Manager S. Green

Goldhawk Road Centre 235 Goldhawk Rd, London W12 8EJ
Manager A. Yeorghaki

Goldhawk Road Centre 117 Goldhawk Rd, London W12 8EJ; Tel 020 8749 3334
Manager M. Knibbs

Park Court Day Centre 61 and 62 Park Crt, Ravenscourt Pk, London W6; Tel 020 8846 9513
Manager A. Yeorghaki

Starfield Road Centre 29 Starfield Rd, London W12 9SW; Tel 020 8740 5013
Manager A. Yeorghaki

DAY CENTRE FOR PEOPLE WITH MENTAL HEALTH PROBLEMS

Erconwald Street Day Centre 45 Erconwald St, London W12 0BP; Tel 020 8740 6352
Manager A. Sutton (Acting)

MENTAL HEALTH RESIDENTIAL SERVICES

Mental Health Resource Centre Tamworth Project, 11 Farm La, London SW6 1PU; Tel 020 7386 5699
Manager P. McCarthy (Acting)
(8)

Wood Lane Resource Centre 59 Wood La, London W12 7DP; Tel 020 8749 6878
Manager C. Ali (Acting)
(14)

EMPLOYMENT PROJECT

Blakes Link Project 677a Fulham Rd, London SW6 5PZ; Tel 020 7371 7338
Manager M. Neville
Learning Difficulties and Mental Health.

DAY SERVICES FOR ELDERLY PEOPLE AND PEOPLE WITH DISABILITIES

Sunberry South Centre 147 Stevenage Rd, London SW6 6PB; Tel 020 7386 8255
Assistant Manager P. Arnell
People with Learning Difficulties.

Sunberry Centre (North) 147 Stevenage Rd, London SW6 6PB; Tel 020 7381 5304
Manager P. Cooper
Physically Disabled People.

Sunberry Day Centre (Bathing Service) 147 Stevenage Rd, London SW6 6PB; Tel 020 7381 5304
Manager (Sunberry Centre) P. Cooper
People with Physical Disabilities and Elderly People.

DOMICILIARY CARE SERVICES (NORTH)

Home Help North, 6th Fl, Town Hall Extension, King St, London W6 9JU; Tel 020 8748 5879
Manager V. Huggins

DOMICILIARY CARE SERVICES (SOUTH)

Home Help South, 6th Fl, Town Hall Extension, King St, London W6 9JU; Tel 020 7385 9548; 020 7385 9549
Manager L. Nolan

ACCOMMODATION FOR ELDERLY PEOPLE

There are four local authority, two private and two voluntary residential homes for older people.

7

MEALS SERVICE

London Borough of Hammersmith and Fulham, 25 Bagleys La, London SW6; Tel 020 8576 5020
Contact L. Rhodes

Education Department

Town Hall, King St, Hammersmith, London W6 9JU;
URL www.lbhf.gov.uk; E-mail enquiries@hafed.org.uk;
Tel 020 8753 3625; Fax 020 8753 3614
Director (Education) Sandy Adamson
Deputy Director (Resources and Lifelong Learning)
G. Brookbank
Deputy Director (School Improvement and Pupil Inclusion)
G. Last
Head (Planning and Development) T. Coventry
Head (Access and Inclusion) M. McCarthy
Head (Individual Progress) B. Pountney
Principal Education Social Worker L. Spearman
Principal Educational Psychologist B. Clarke
Manager (Pupil Referral Service) Karen Anderson

SPECIAL SCHOOLS

Cambridge School Cambridge Gr, London W6 0LB;
E-mail admin@cambridge.lbhf.sch.uk; Tel 020 8748 7585;
Fax 020 8741 9375
Headteacher J. Barton
MLD

Gibbs Green School Mund St, London W14 9LY;
E-mail gibbsgreen.lbhf@lgfl.net; Tel 020 7385 3908; Fax 020 7610 3565
Headteacher Roderick Davies
EBD

Jack Tizard School Finlay St, London SW6 6HB;
E-mail jacktizard@btconnect.com; Tel 020 7736 7949;
Fax 020 7384 2790
Headteacher T. Baker
SLD

Queensmill School Clancarty Rd, London SW6 3AA;
E-mail queensmill.lbhf@lgfl.net; Tel 020 7384 2330; Fax 020 7384 2750
Headteacher J. Page
Complex Needs

Woodlane School Du Cane Rd, London W12 0TN;
E-mail admin@woodlane.lbhf.sch.uk; Tel 020 8743 5668;
Fax 020 8743 9138
Headteacher N. Holt

HARINGEY LONDON BOROUGH COUNCIL
www.haringey.gov.uk

Population 216 100
Political Composition: Lab: 42, LD: 15
Civic Centre, High Rd, London N22 8LE;
URL www.haringey.gov.uk
Director (Environmental Services) P. Norton
Tottenham Town Hall, London N15 4RY; Tel 020 8489 4537
Chief Executive D. Warwick
Civic Centre, Haringey, London N22 4LE

Social Services Department

Lead Member (Social Services) Cllr Taki Sulaiman
Deputy Lead Member (Social Services) Cllr Gina Adamou
Chair (Social Services Scrutiny Panel) Cllr Maureen Dewar
40 Cumberland Rd, London N22 7SG; Tel 020 8489 5914

Director (Social Services) Anne Bristow
40 Cumberland Rd, London N22 7SG; Tel 020 8489 5919
Assistant Director (Adults) Tony Creisson
Apex Hse, 820 Seven Sisters Rd, London N15 5PQ; Tel 020 8949 4260
Assistant Director (Children's Services) David Derbyshire
40 Cumberland Rd, London N22 7SG; Tel 020 8949 5913
Assistant Director (Older People) Alastair Gibbons
Job-share; Tel 020 8489 2326
Assistant Director (Asylum Seekers) Ben Brown Job-share;
Tel 020 8489 4948
Assistant Director (Finance) Monique Hanjaree (Acting)
40 Cumberland Rd, London N22 4SG; Tel 020 8949 3732
Commissioning Manager (Asylum Seekers' Services)
Zaya Yeebo
35 Station Rd, Wood Green, London N22 4TR; Tel 020 8949 3180

ACCESS POINTS

Hornsey One Stop Shop Duke Hse, Crouch Hall Rd,
Hornsey, London N8 8HE; Tel 020 8489 1887
Senior Information Officer Chelin Ahmet

Seven Sisters One Stop Shop 768–772 Tottenham High Rd,
Tottenham, London N17 0BU; Tel 020 8489 4318
Senior Information Officer Donna Pauell

Wood Green One Stop Shop Safeway Arcade, The
Broadway, Wood Green, London N22; Tel 020 8489 3254
Senior Information Officer Neba Adani

CHILDREN'S SERVICES

Commissioning Manager (Children's Services) Joe Heatley;
Tel 020 8489 3919
Service Manager (Children's Protection, Quality and Review)
Ann Graham; Tel 020 8489 1177
Service Manager (Looked After Children's Service)
Rachel Oakley; Tel 020 8489 1124
Service Manager (Leaving Care) Vacancy; Tel 020 8489 0000
Service Manager (Finance and Performance Unit)
Michael Jury (Acting); Tel 020 8489 3416
Service Manager (Finance and Performance Unit)
Mcena Kishinani (Acting); Tel 020 8489 3416
*Service Manager (Family Support Services including Children
and Disabilities)* Luciana Frederick; Tel 020 8489 3644
Manager (Youth Offending Team) Jean Croot; Tel 020 8489 1146

UNDER FIVES CENTRE

Rowland Hill Centre for Childhood White Hart La,
Tottenham, London N17 7LT; Tel 020 8808 6089
Headteacher Julie Vaggers

DAY NURSERIES AND FAMILY CENTRES

Red Gable Family Centre 113 Crouch Hill, Hornsey,
London N8 9QN; Tel 020 8489 8001
Contact Carol Scorey
(40)

Stroud Green Pre-School Centre Ennis Rd, London
N4 3HD; Tel 020 7263 9574
Contact S. Cripps

Woodlands Park and Nursery Centre Woodlands Park Rd,
London N15; Tel 020 8802 0041
Contact Carol Worden

CHILDREN'S HOMES

Haringey Park Children's Home 32 Haringey Pk, Crouch
End, London; Tel 020 8341 9183
Officer-in-Charge N. Harriett

Muswell House Children's Home 9–11 Coppetts Rd,
Muswell Hill, London N10 1HR; Tel 020 8802 7157
Contact M. Nelson-Cole
(12)

COMMUNITY CARE SERVICES – ADULTS

Service Manager (Learning Difficulties) Gary Jefferson;
Tel 020 8489 1127
Service Manager (Mental Health Difficulties) Gillian Lacey;
Tel 020 8489 1128
Service Manager (Substance Misuse) Bernard Lanigan
(Acting); Tel 020 8489 2338
Service Manager (Physical Disabilities and HIV)
Lisa Redfern (Acting); Tel 020 8489 5922
Service Manager (Finance and Performance Unit)
Toyin Bamidele (Acting); Tel 020 8489 4790

DAY CENTRES – LEARNING DIFFICULTIES

Ermine Road Centre Ermine Rd, London N15 6DB; Tel 020
8802 5642
Contact Beverley Tarka

Gordon Road Service Gordon Rd, Bounds Green, London
N11 3HD; Tel 020 8888 3425
Contact Mikkel Sims

Green Pepper Care – Training Project 118 Philip La,
London N15 4JL; Tel 020 8801 3927; Fax 020 8801 3922

Keston Road Centre Keston Rd, London N17 6PW; Tel 020
8880 3515
Contact Chole Rawlingson

DAY CENTRES – MENTAL HEALTH

Clarendon Day Centre Clarendon Rd, London N8 0DJ;
Tel 020 8489 4871
Contact Gavin Eastley

Tottenham Drop-In Centre United Reformed Church,
Colsterworth Rd, London N15 4BJ; Tel 020 8885 4468
Contact Sheri Rostron

RESIDENTIAL CARE – MENTAL HEALTH

Alexandra Road Crisis Unit 32 Alexandra Rd, Hornsey,
London N8 0PP; Tel 020 8365 7287
Contact Eiji Sinitalo

RESIDENTIAL CARE – LEARNING DIFFICULTIES

Talbot Road Respite and Emergency Residential Service 8
Talbot Rd, Tottenham, London N15 4DH; Tel 020 8808 8758
Contact Antoinette Reese

DAY CENTRE – PHYSICAL DISABILITIES

Winkfield Road Resource Centre 33 Winkfield Rd, London
N22 5RP; Tel 020 8889 0396
Contact Patrick O'Neil

COMMUNITY CARE SERVICES OLDER PEOPLE

Commissioning Manager (Older People) Lisa Redfern
(Acting); Tel 020 8489 5922
Service Manager (Home Care) Peter Mason
The Grange 32–34a White Hart La, Tottenham, London
N17 8PD; Tel 020 8489 4823
*Service Manager (Residential and Day Care and Supported
Housing)* Len Weir; Tel 020 8489 2338
Service Manager (Finance and Performance Unit) Chris Cava
(Acting); Tel 020 8489 2339

DAY CENTRES FOR OLDER PEOPLE

The Grange Day Centre 32–33a White Hart La, London
N17 8DP; Tel 020 8489 4818
Contact Sonia Gardner

The Haven Day Centre 20a Waltheof Gdns, Tottenham,
London N17 7DN; Tel 020 8885 5199
Contact Diane Cousins

Winkfield Resource Centre 33 Winkfield Rd, London
N22 5RP; Tel 020 8885 5199
Contact Patrick O'Neill

RESIDENTIAL SERVICES FOR OLDER PEOPLE

There are two local authority residential homes for older
people.

LUNCHEON CLUBS FOR OLDER PEOPLE

Haringey Irish Community Centre Pretoria Rd, Tottenham,
London N17 8DX; Tel 020 8801 6398
Contact Mary O'Brien

Osborne Grove Luncheon Club 18 Upper Tollington Pk,
London N4 3EL; Tel 020 7263 2538
Supervisor Patricia Capon

Willoughby Road Willoughby Rd, London N8 0HR; Tel 020
8340 2277
Contact Tina Shotton

Woodside House Luncheon Club Woodside Pk, 284 High
Rd, London; Tel 020 8888 4002
Contact Pat Donnellan

ASYLUM SEEKERS

Service Manager (Advice and Support) Vacancy; Tel 020 8489
0000
Manager (Finance and Performance Unit) Sarah Barter;
Tel 020 8489 4947
Service Manager (Social Care) Vacancy; Tel 020 8489 0000

Education Services

48 Station Rd, Wood Green, London N22 4TY; Tel 020 8489
0000; Fax 020 8489 3864
Director (Education Services) Sharon Shoesmith
Principal Educational Psychologist Christa Rippon
Head (Children and Young People's Service)
Theresa Shortland

SPECIAL SCHOOLS (2½–19)

Blanche Nevile School Burlington Rd, London N10 1NJ;
E-mail blancheneville.school@haringey.gov.uk; Tel 020 8442
2750
Headteacher Margaret Sumner (Acting)
(Day)
3–16 Phg

Greenfields School Coppetts Rd, Muswell Hill, London
N10 1JP; Tel 020 8444 5366
Headteacher Sally Wood
(Day)
5–16 EBD

Moselle School Adams Rd, London N17 6HW;
E-mail mosellespecial.school@haringey.gov.uk; Tel 020 8808
8869
Headteacher Martin Doyle (Acting)
MLD (Day)

The Vale School Resource Base, Northumberland Park
School, Trulock Rd, London N17 OPG; Tel 020 8801 6111
Headteacher Gerald Hill
2-19 PH

William C. Harvey School Adams Rd, London N17 6HW;
E-mail williamharvey.school@haringey.gov.uk; Tel 020 8808
7120
Headteacher Margaret Sumner
(Day)
3–19 SLD

Advice Centres

HORNSEY ADVICE BUREAU

7 Hatherley Gdns, London N8 9JH; Tel 020 8528 0250;
Fax 020 8528 0250

TOTTENHAM ADVICE BUREAU

Tottenham Town Hall, Town Hall Approach Rd, London N15 4RY; Tel 020 8808 6555

TURNPIKE LANE ADVICE BUREAU

16 Turnpike La, London N8 0PT; Tel 020 8888 4233

HARROW LONDON BOROUGH COUNCIL
www.harrow.gov.uk

Population 215 000
Political Composition: Lab: 31, Con: 29, LD: 3
Civic Centre, Station Rd, Harrow, Greater London
HA1 2XF; URL www.harrow.gov.uk;
E-mail info@harrow.gov.uk; Tel 020 8863 5611
Mayor Cllr Mano Dharmarajah

People First Directorate

This new directorate brings together health, social and learning services (largely comprising the former education services and social services departments)
General Enquiries, Former Social Services, PO Box 7, Civic Centre, Harrow, Greater London HA1 2UL;
URL www.harrow.gov.uk; E-mail info@harrow.gov.uk;
Tel (Emergency) 020 8424 0999; (General Enquiries) 020 8424 1352; Fax 020 8863 0236; Minicom 020 8424 7526
Chair (Health and Social Care Scrutiny Sub-committee)
Cllr Marie-Louise Nolan
15 Dauphine Crt, Spencer Rd, Wealdstone, Harrow, Greater London HA3 7AS; Tel 020 8861 2521
Vice-Chair Cllr Eric Silver
8 Grantham Cl, Edgware, Greater London HA8 8DL;
Tel 07812 405560
Executive Director (People First) Paul Osburn
Area Director (People First) Michael Hart
Director (Strategy) Geoff Wingrove
Director (Children's Services) Paul Clark
Director (Learning and Community Development)
Javed Khan
Head (Community Care) Nick Georgiou
Head (Planning and Performance Management) M. Ellis
Head (Finance and Contracting) A. Rush
Head (Human Resources) L. Freshwater (Acting)
Head (Management Information Services) M. Jeeves
Head (Provided Services) C. Eckersley
Head (Care Management PSD and Elders) C. Melly
Head (Care Management LD and MH) D. van Brummen
Group Manager (Provided Services) G. Lambrick
Manager (Equalities) V. Malik
Manager (Planning and Research) R. Finer
Manager (Planning and Research) M. Jalali
Manager (Pan London Contacts Team) B. Flight
Manager (Complaints and Consultation) V. Enos
Manager (CwD Project) B. Houston
Manager (Children and Families IT Development) G. Maguire
Contracts Manager (Elderly, Physical and Learning Disability, and Asylum Seekers) R. Pettitt
Contracts Manager (Children, Mental Health, Drugs and Alcohol, HIV and AIDs) D. South

CHILDREN'S QUALITY, PERFORMANCE AND REVIEW GROUP

Civic Centre, PO Box 7, Station Rd, Harrow, Greater London HA1 2UL; Tel 020 8424 1341; Fax 020 8424 1012
Manager (Quality and Performance) A. Twynam
Senior Co-ordinator (Child Protection) S. Spurr

Co-ordinator (ACPC Policy and Performance) B. Lynch
Co-ordinator (Commissioning and Strategy) R. Vaughan
Manager (IRT Paroject) J. Noble
Manager (CQIT – Children's Quality and Information Team)
M. Stevens

FIELDWORK OFFICES

HOSPITAL SOCIAL WORKERS

Northwick Park Hospital Watford Rd, Harrow, Greater London HA1 3UJ; Tel (Main switchboard) 020 8864 3232
Children and Families Social Work Team at Northwick Park Hospital
Tel 020 8869 2401; Fax 020 8869 2397
Practice Leader Kea Byer

Disability and Elderly Social Work Team at Northwick Park Hospital
Tel 020 8869 2594; Fax 020 8869 2598
Team Leader Ninette Fernandes

CHILDREN AND FAMILIES SERVICES

429–433 Pinner Rd, North Harrow, Harrow, Greater London HA1 4HN; Tel 020 8863 5544; Fax 020 8424 8045
Head (Children's Provided Services) M. Henley
Manager (Operational Services) T. Ganly
Manager (Gatsby Project) G. Dermody
Manager (Duty Team and NPH Services) B. Kirwan
Manager (Children in Need and Leaving Care Services)
J. Batra
Manager (Children in Need Service) A. Bridgewater

Leaving Care Team 267 Alexandra Ave, South Harrow, Harrow, Greater London HA2 9DX; Tel 020 8423 9183;
Fax 020 8423 6306
Manager J. Batra

CHILDREN'S RESIDENTIAL CARE ESTABLISHMENTS

Haslam House Crisis Intervention Unit 304 Honeypot La, Stanmore, Greater London HA7 1DY; Tel 020 8204 4222;
Fax 020 8206 0769
Manager T. Darien

Silverdale 1 Silverdale Cl, Northolt, Greater London UB5 4BL; Tel 020 8422 8550; Fax 020 8864 4645
Manager J,. Roach

CHILD AND FAMILY CENTRE

Gayton Child and Family Service 80 Gayton Rd, Harrow, Greater London HA1 2LS; Tel 020 8427 9192; Fax 020 8863 9360
Business Manager Sarah Mansurelli

FAMILY CENTRE

Alexandra Avenue Family Centre 267 Alexandra Ave, Harrow, Greater London HA2 9DX; Tel 020 8426 8029;
Fax 020 8426 5468
Manager L. Brown

HARROW YOUTH OFFENDING TEAM

Mental Health Resource Centre
13 St. John's Rd, Harrow, Greater London HA1 2EE; Tel 020 8901 4455; Fax 020 8901 4466
Head (Youth Offending Service) R. Segalov

SERVICES FOR PEOPLE WITH LEARNING DISABILITIES

Harrow Learning Disability Team Civic Centre, PO Box 161, Harrow, Greater London HA1 2AY; Tel 020 8424 1019;
Fax 020 8420 9674
Area Manager H. Keeble

ESTABLISHMENTS FOR PEOPLE WITH LEARNING DISABILITIES

Bedford House James Bedford Cl, Pinner, Greater London HA5 3TD; Tel 020 8866 5696; Fax 020 8866 0160
Manager C. Bozier

Bessborough Road 79 Bessborough Rd, Harrow, Greater London HA1 3DB; Tel 020 8422 0606; Fax 020 8422 1720
Manager V. Adebiyi (Acting)

Brember Centre Brember Rd, Harrow, Greater London HA2 8BE; Tel 020 8422 5516; Fax 020 8422 3524
Manager B. Cox

The Firs 229 The Heights, Northolt, Greater London UB5 4BY; Tel 020 8422 5156; Fax 020 8422 1715
Manager Nicky Gold

Gordon Avenue Centre 4 Gordon Ave, Stanmore, Greater London HA7 3QD; Tel 020 8954 8866; Fax 020 8954 2543
Manager J. Croft

Roxborough Park 62 Roxborough Pk, Harrow, Greater London HA1 3AY; Tel 020 8423 5603; Fax 020 8423 7519
Manager D. O'Connell

Southdown 1 Southdown Cres, Harrow, Greater London HA2 0QT; Tel 020 8423 0078; Fax 020 8537 2815
Manager A. Manser

Vaughan Centre Wilson Gdns, Harrow, Greater London HA1 4EA; Tel 020 8864 8034; Fax 020 8423 4942
Manager C. Lloyd-Hallett
Manager J. Chillingworth

Woodlands 64 and 66 Woodlands Dr, Stanmore, Greater London HA7 3PA; Tel 020 8954 2348 (64); Fax 020 8954 2692 (64); 020 8954 2692 (66)
Manager R. Beale

HARROW UNIFIED MENTAL HEALTH SERVICES (HUMHS)

Mental Health Resource Centre

Atkins House 19 Marshall Cl, Harrow, Greater London HA1 4DH; Tel 020 8422 9443; Fax 020 8422 2890
Manager (South Sector) M. Hall-Pearson

Community Mental Health Team (East)

Honeypot Lane Centre 839 Honeypot La, Stanmore, Greater London HA7 1AT; Tel 020 8951 3770; Fax 020 8951 0756
Manager (East Sector) C. Harrison-Read

Mental Health Specialist Services Tenby Road Clinic, Tenby Rd, Edgeware, Greater London HA8 6DP; Tel 020 8731 5140; Fax 020 8952 1724
Manager (Administrative Service) A. Joseph
Manager (Administrative Service) R. Bungaroo

DAY CENTRES FOR PEOPLE WITH MENTAL HEALTH PROBLEMS

The Bridge Day Centre Christchurch Ave (opp Harrow Leisure Centre), Wealdstone, Greater London HA3 5BD; Tel 020 8861 6390; Fax 020 8861 6394
Manager M. Stead

Wiseworks Day Centre 74a Marlborough Hill, Harrow, Greater London HA1 1TY; Tel 020 8863 8704; Fax 020 8861 2740
Manager G. Smith

RESIDENTIAL CARE FOR PEOPLE WITH MENTAL HEALTH PROBLEMS

Kenton Road Home 7 Kenton Rd, Harrow, Greater London HA1 2BW; Tel 020 8423 0765; Fax 020 8423 2533
Manager G. Fan (Acting)

Kenton Road Home 14–15 Kenton Rd, Harrow, Greater London HA1 2BW; Tel 020 8423 7484; Fax 020 8423 7389
Manager E. Harandy

HARROW COMMUNITY DRUG AND ALCOHOL SERVICE

Bessborough Road Centre 44 Bessborough Rd, Harrow, Greater London HA1 3DJ; Tel 020 8423 7423; 020 8864 9622; Fax 020 8423 6814
Manager J. Kennedy

PHYSICAL DISABILITY AND SENSORY IMPAIRMENT CARE MANAGEMENT SERVICE

Youngmans 1 Building Civic Centre, PO Box 167, Harrow, Greater London HA1 2FR; Tel 020 8424 1694; Fax 020 8427 7154; Minicom 020 8424 2902
Area Manager D. Sheridan

HIV TEAM

Exchequer Building Civic Centre, PO Box 7, Rm 61, Harrow, Greater London HA1 2UL; Tel 020 8424 1252; Fax 020 8863 0236
Manager A. Jonston-Sterry

DAY CENTRE FOR PEOPLE WITH PHYSICAL DISABILITIES

Bentley Day Centre 94 Uxbridge Rd, Harrow Weald, Greater London HA3 6DH; Tel 020 8954 0979; Fax 020 8954 1322
Manager M. Miles

OLDER PEOPLE SERVICES (EAST)

19 Buckingham Rd, Edgware, Greater London HA8 6LY; Tel 020 8951 3811; Fax 020 8951 3723
Area Manager (Elderly Care Management) L. Charles

OLDER PEOPLE SERVICES (WEST)

Talbot Hse, 204–226 Imperial Dr, Rayners La, Harrow, Greater London HA2 7DW; Tel 020 8429 4488; Fax 020 8429 3138
Area Manager (Elderly Care Management) J. Shaw

RESIDENTIAL AND DAY CARE SERVICES FOR ELDERS

Anmer Lodge Day Centre Coverdale Cl, Stanmore, Greater London HA7 3DH; Tel 020 8954 1311; Fax 020 8954 0460
Manager A. O'Donnell

Milmans Resource Centre Grove Ave, Pinner, Greater London HA5 5PF; Tel 020 8868 2449; Fax 020 8866 2545
Manager M. Murphy
Officer (Milmans) A. Sayer
Officer (Pinner Hil) D. Leandre

OTHER SERVICES

Asylum Seekers Team Civic Centre, PO Box 7, Station Rd, Harrow, Greater London HA1 2UL; Tel 020 8863 5611 ext 3067; Fax 020 8420 9641
Team Leader T. Fernand

Harrow Adult Placement Scheme (HAPS) Atkins Hse, 19 Marshall Cl, Harrow, Greater London HA1 4DH; Tel 020 8422 9443; Fax 020 8422 2890
Manager H. Wicker (Acting)

Harrow Casual Workline Talbot Hse, 204–226 Imperial Dr, Harrow, Greater London HA2 7DW; Tel 020 8429 0763; Fax 020 8866 0383
Manager J. Terry

Helpline Emergency Alarm Centre 60 Elmgrove Rd, Harrow, Greater London HA1 2QH; Tel 020 8861 3242; Fax 020 8861 6200
Manager M. Biddle

Meals on Wheels Service Tel 020 8421 6064; Fax 020 8861 6200

Education Enquiries

PO Box 22, Civic Centre, Harrow, Greater London HA1 2UW; URL www.harrow.gov.uk; E-mail education.department@harrow.gov.uk; Tel 020 8863 5611; Fax 020 8427 0810
Principal Education Social Worker John Kennedy
Manager (Children's Services)/Principal Educational Psychologist Roger Rickman
Manager (Assessment and Provision SEN) Michael Bateman
Manager (Early Years and Childcare Services) Wendy Beeton

7

HARROW PSYCHOLOGY SERVICE

Civic Centre, Harrow, Greater London HA1 1FE; Tel 020 8424 1635
Deputy Principal Education Psychologist Gladys de Groot

SPECIAL SCHOOLS

Alexandra School Alexandra Ave, South Harrow, Greater London HA2 9DX; E-mail alexandra.sch@harrow.gov.uk; Tel 020 8864 2739; Fax 020 8864 9336
Headteacher Dennis Goldthorpe
  Learning difficulties with associated behavioural problems.
Kingsley High School Whittlesea Rd, Harrow Weald, Greater London HA3 6ND;
E-mail kingsley.high.sch@harrow.gov.uk; Tel 020 8421 3676; Fax 020 8421 7597
Headteacher Kay Johnson
  SLD
Shaftesbury High School Headstone La, Harrow, Greater London HA3 6LE;
E-mail adminoffice@shaftesbury.harrow.sch.uk; Tel 020 8428 2482; Fax 020 8420 2361
Headteacher Paul Williams
  Learning difficulties with associated behavioural problems.
Woodlands First and Middle School Whittlesea Rd, Harrow Weald, Greater London HA3 6ND;
E-mail woodlands.sch@harrow.gov.uk; Tel 020 8421 3637; Fax 020 8421 7597
Headteacher John Feltham
  SLD

HAVERING LONDON BOROUGH COUNCIL
www.havering.gov.uk

Population 229 492
Political Composition: Lab: 30, Resident's Group: 16, Con: 13, LD: 3
Town Hall, Main Rd, Romford, Essex RM1 3BD;
  URL www.havering.gov.uk; Tel 01708 434343
Executive Director (Resources) Mark Gaynor
Executive Director (Community Services)
  Anthony Douglas
Executive Director (Environment and Enterprise)
  Heather Barfield

Directorate of Social Services

Tel 01708 434343; Fax 01708 433010
Head (Children and Families) Ruth Jenkins
Head (Strategy and Commissioning) Bob Page
Head (Health and Social Care) Peter Brennan
Service Manager (Children and Families Assessment and Care)
  Carol Caruthers
Service Manager (Children and Families Resources)
  Stephen Richards
Service Manager (Assessment and Care Management)
  Helen Allum (Acting)
Service Manager (Learning Disabilities) Annette Froud
Service Manager (Mental Health – Adults)
  Stephanie Dawe
Manager (Finance) Spencer Dainton
Manager (Quality Assurance – Children and Families)
  Nick Nicholas (Acting)
Co-ordinator (Statutory Case – Children and Families)
  Eileen Collier

Social Care and Health Overview and Scrutiny Committee

Chair Cllr Graham Price (Con)
Vice-Chair Pat Mylod

SOCIAL WORK OFFICES

Havering Community Learning Disability Team The Hermitage, Billet La, Hornchurch, Essex RM1 1BR; Tel 01708 433446; Fax 01708 437923
Upminster Locality Team Chippenham Rd, Harold Hill, Essex RM3 8YF; Tel 01708 433554; 01708 433562; Fax 01708 344497
Children and Families Services Assessment Services, 16 Marks Rd, Romford, Essex; Tel 01708 433359; Fax 01708 755296
Hornchurch Locality Team The Broadway, Rainham, Essex RM13 9HB; Tel 01708 433500; Fax 01708 521865

SERVICES TO CHILDREN AND FAMILIES

Family Placement Service and Leaving Care Service Midland Hse, 109–113 Victoria Rd, Romford, Essex RM1 2LX; Tel 01708 434576
Children with Disabilities Team Mawney Centre, Mawney Rd, Romford, Essex RM7 8DP; Tel 01708 433651; Fax 01708 434327
Children in Need Teams 16 Marks Rd, Romford, Essex RM7 7AB; Tel 01708 433284; 01708 433370; Fax 01708 755296
Looked After Children Team Mawney Centre, Mawney Rd, Romford, Essex RM7 8DP; Tel 01708 433535; Fax 01708 434327

EARLY YEARS CENTRES

Clockhouse Lane Early Years Centre Collier Row, Romford, Essex RM5 3QJ; Tel 01708 765430
  (50)
Elm Park Early Years Centre Diban Ave, Hornchurch, Essex RM12 4YH; Tel 01708 451110
  (50)
St. Kilda Early Years Centre 90 Eastern Rd, Romford, Essex RM1 3QA; Tel 01708 743135
  (55)

YOUTH OFFENDING TEAM

Portman Hse, 16–20 Victoria Rd, Romford, Essex; Tel 01708 436220

DAY CENTRES FOR PEOPLE WITH LEARNING DISABILITIES

Nason-Waters Day Centre 100 Avelon Rd, Rainham, Essex RM13 7DH; Tel 01708 522469; Fax 01708 526436
  (70)
St. Bernards Day Centre Peel Way, Harold Wood, Essex RM3 0PD; Tel 01708 377829
  SLD (30)

DAY SERVICES FOR PEOPLE WITH LEARNING DISABILITIES

Clubhouse 62–64 Western Rd, Romford, Essex; Tel 01708 724929
Community College Support Centre Broxhill Centre, Broxhill Rd, Harold Hill, Essex RM4 1XN; Tel 01708 433975
Jacksons Café 47 High St, Romford, Essex; Tel 01708 723636
MCCH Independence Project, Kingswood Lodge, Romford, Essex; Tel 01708 769470
Melville Court Spilsby Rd, Romford, Essex; Tel 01708 370987

RESIDENTIAL ACCOMMODATION FOR PEOPLE WITH A LEARNING DISABILITY

Fountains 12 Theydon Gdns, Rainham, Essex RM13 7TU; Tel 01708 553183
(25)

COMMUNITY MENTAL HEALTH TEAMS (CMHT)

Romford Community Mental Health Team Victoria Centre, Petits La, Romford, Essex RM1 4HL; Tel 01708 796868; Fax 01708 761893

Upminster Community Mental Health Team Oasis Hse, 28–30 Gubbins La, Harold Wood, Essex; Tel 01708 796330

Assessment and Crisis Team Harrow Lodge Hse, Hornchurch Rd, Hornchurch, Essex RM11 1JU; Tel 01708 796000

Hornchurch Community Mental Health Team Suttons La, St. George's Hospital, Hornchurch, Essex RM12 6RS; Tel 01708 465034

DAY CARE FOR PEOPLE WITH MENTAL HEALTH PROBLEMS

Harold Centre Project St. George's Church, Chippenham Rd, Harold Hill, Essex RM3 9HX; Tel 01708 377007

Romford Centre Project St. Andrews Parish Centre, 4 St. Andrews Rd, Romford, Essex RM7 9AT; Tel 01708 739489

Small Works Project 45 Heather Ave, Collier Row, Romford, Essex RM1 4SU; Tel 01708 725798

PHYSICAL AND SENSORY DISABILITY SERVICE

Yew Tree Lodge Day Service, 24 Yew Tree Gdns, Romford, Essex RM7 9AA; Tel 01708 434566
(150)

PHYSICAL AND SENSORY DISABILITY RESPITE SERVICES

Yew Tree Lodge 24 Yew Tree Gdns, Romford, Essex RM7 9AA; Tel 01708 434555; 01708 434556; Fax 01708 434565
Short stay (24)

DAY CARE – OLDER PEOPLE

Elmhurst Lodge 9 Torrance Cl, Hornchurch, Essex RM11 1JT; Tel 01708 442739; Fax 01708 476675

The Grange Learning Disability Service Faringdon Ave, Harold Hill, Essex RM3 8SJ; Tel 01708 344014
Special Care (85)

Hampden Lodge Clockhouse La, Collier Row, Essex RM5 3QJ; Tel 01708 764786; (Day Care Services) 01708 764055

Winifred Whittingham House Brook Way, Rainham, Essex RM13 9JE; Tel (Day Service) 01708 522314; (Residential) 01708 559083

RESIDENTIAL CARE HOMES – OLDER PEOPLE

There are four homes for older people.

Education

The Broxhill Centre, Broxhill Rd, Harold Hill, Romford, Essex RM4 1XN; Tel 01708 434343; Fax 01708 433837
Executive Director (Education – CEO) David MacLean (Acting)

SPECIAL SCHOOLS

Corbets Tey School Harwood Hall La, Upminster, Essex RM14 2YQ; E-mail sue.young@corbetsteyschool.org; Tel 01708 225888
Headteacher Colin Arthey, BEd, MA

Dycorts School Settle Rd, Harold Hill, Romford, Essex RM3 9YA; Tel 01708 343649
Headteacher G.S. Wroe, BA, MSc

Ravensbourne School Neave Cres, Faringdon Ave, Romford, Essex RM3 0AB; E-mail admin@ravensbourne.havering.sch.uk; Tel 01708 341800
Headteacher Mrs M. Cameron, BEd, BA

LONDON BOROUGH OF HILLINGDON
www.hillingdon.gov.uk

Population 243 000
Political Composition: Con: 31, Lab: 27, LD: 7
Civic Centre, High St, Uxbridge, Greater London UB8 1UW; URL www.hillingdon.gov.uk
Leader of the Administration (Conservative Group) Cllr R. Puddifoot
Borough Treasurer J. Maule
Corporate Director (Housing Services) Pam Lockley

Social Services Department

Director Hugh Dunnachie
Head (Community Care Services) Jeremy Ambache (Acting)
Head (Commissioning and Performance Management) John Doran
Manager (Early Years Team) Katrina Jacobs
Manager (Youth Offending Team) Lynn Hawes

Cabinet

Leader Ray Puddifoot
Deputy Leader (Social Services and Health) David Simmonds
Environment Jim O'Neill
Housing Philip Corthorne
Education, Youth and Leisure Solveig Stone
Finance and Corporate Services Jonathan Bianco
Performance, Partnerships and Regeneration Douglas Mills
Planning and Transportation Mike Heywood

Hospital Social Work Teams

Hillingdon Hospital Social Work Team Hillingdon Hospital, Pield Heath Rd, Hillingdon, Greater London UB8 3NN; Tel 01895 279306; Fax 01895 279306

Mount Vernon Social Work Team Rickmansworth Rd, Northwood, Greater London HA6 2RN; Tel 01923 826111

Emergency Duty Team 4S-06 Civic Centre, Uxbridge, Greater London UB8 1UW; Tel 01895 205111; Fax 01895 250875

Children's Services

Head (Children and Families) Kamini Rambellas
Service Manager (Child Protection and Young People's Justice Team) Cathy Bambrough
Service Manager (East Team and 16+ Team) Chris Hogan
Service Manager (West Team and Children's Asylum Team) Ros Morris
Service Manager (Fostering and Adoption Team, and Children with Disabilities Team) Marion Robin; Tel 01895 277850

West Team Mezzanine Offices, Civic Centre, Uxbridge, Greater London UB8 1UW; Tel 01895 250111 ext 3752; Fax 01895 250752

East Team Barra Hall, Wood End Green Rd, Hayes, Greater London UB3 2SA; Tel 01895 250211 ext 3174; Fax 01895 277131

CHILDREN WITH DISABILITIES

855 Uxbridge Rd, Hayes, Greater London UB4 8HZ;
Tel 01895 277880; Fax 01895 277881

YOUNG OFFENDING TEAM

Darren Hse, 65 High St, Uxbridge, Greater London
UBB 1JP; Tel 01895 812279; Fax 01895 812281

16+ TEAM

Barra Hall Wood End Grn Rd, Hayes, Greater London
UB3 2SA; Tel 01895 250111 ext 7066/7067; Fax 01895 277066

ADOPTION AND FOSTERING

855 Uxbridge Rd, Hayes, Greater London UB4 8HZ;
Tel 01895 277850; Fax 01895 277851

SHORT STAY RESOURCES

Colham Road 3 Colham Rd, Hillingdon, Greater London
UB8 3RD; Tel 01895 271245
PLD

Copperfield 21 Copperfield Ave, Hillingdon, Uxbridge,
Greater London UB8 3NU; Tel 01895 274015

Howletts Lane 54 Howletts La, Ruislip, Greater London
HA4 7RZ; Tel 01895 621268

Merrimans Hostel 3 Merrimans, West Drayton Rd,
Hillingdon, Greater London UB8 3JZ; Tel 01895 234039
PLD/PD

RESOURCE AND DAY CENTRES

Barnhill Independence Centre Acol Cres, South Ruislip,
Ruislip, Greater London HA4 6QP; Tel 020 8842 1255

Hayes Early Years Centre Nestles Ave, Hayes, Greater
London UB3 4QA; Tel 020 8573 0229
Under 5s

South Ruislip Early Years Centre Station Approach, South
Ruislip, Ruislip, Greater London HA4 6QP; Tel 020 8845
6669
Under 5s

Uxbridge Early Years Centre Park Rd, Uxbridge, Greater
London UB8 1NN; Tel 01895 232539
Under 5s

Adult Services

Older People's Services (Home Care) Nick Ellender
Disability Services, HIV Services Family Care Scheme,
Equipment Loan Service, Mental Health Services,
Community Team, Racial Harassment, Domestic Violence and
Equalities Frank Toner

Uxbridge

2W06 Civic Centre Uxbridge, Greater London UB8 1UW;
Tel 01895 250738; Fax 01895 277024

Ruislip

High Street Centre 130 High St, Ruislip, Greater London
HA4 8LP; Tel 01895 250111 ext 3100; Fax 01895 250100

Hayes

Library Centre 1st Floor, Yiewsley Library, 192 High St,
Yiewsley, Greater London UB7 7BE; Tel 01895 445544;
Fax 01895 436626

RESIDENTIAL HOMES

Bedwell Gardens Residential Home 62 Bedwell Gdns,
Hayes, Greater London UB3 4EQ; Tel 020 8573 0481
Young men

Charville Lane Residential Home Hayes, Greater London
UB4 8PD; Tel 020 8841 1445; 020 8841 6169
Young refugees

Mulberry Parade Residential Home 15 Mulberry Pde, West
Drayton, Greater London UB7 9AE; Tel 01895 442775
Young women

MENTAL HEALTH NORTH

Pembroke Centre 90 Pembroke Rd, Ruislip, Greater
London HA4 8NQ; Tel 01895 622424; Fax 01895 621992

MENTAL HEALTH SOUTH EAST

Mead House Hayes End Rd, Hayes End, Hayes, Greater
London UB4 8UW; Tel 020 8561 6676; Fax 020 8573 0046

PEOPLE WITH DISABILITIES TEAM

2S/01 Civic Centre Uxbridge, Greater London UB8 1UW;
Tel 01895 250111 ext 3959; Fax 01895 250959

RESIDENTIAL HOMES FOR PEOPLE WITH A LEARNING DISABILITY

The Beeches Residential Home High St, Cowley, Greater
London UB8 2AW; Tel 01895 271071; 01895 271773

Bourne Lodge Residential Home Station Approach, South
Ruislip, Greater London HA4 6SW; Tel 020 8845 1080

Charles Curran House Residential Home 36 Boniface Rd,
Ickenham, Greater London UB10 8BU; Tel 01895 674935

Goshawk Gardens Residential Home 74 Goshawk Gdns,
Hayes, Greater London; Tel 020 8841 3188
Minimal Staffing

Hatton Grove Residential Home 4 Hatton Gr, West Drayton,
Greater London UB7 7AU; Tel 01895 441349

Hobart Lane Residential Home 120 Hobart La, Hayes,
Greater London UB4 6NB; Tel 020 8841 2446

Merchiston House Residential Home Colham Rd,
Hillingdon, Greater London UB8 3RD; Tel 01895 235920

Standale Grove Residential Home 1–3 Standale Gr, Ruislip,
Greater London HA4 7UA; Tel 01895 639354

Swakeleys Road Residential Home 236 Swakeleys Rd,
Ickenham, Greater London UB10 8AU; Tel 01895 254761

RESIDENTIAL HOMES – MENTAL HEALTH

Colham Road Residential Home 3 Colham Rd, Hillingdon,
Greater London UB8 3RD; Tel 01895 271245

Hayes Park House Residential Home Hayes End Rd, Hayes
End, Greater London UB4 9LS; Tel 020 8573 8900

Tasman House Residential Home 111 Maple Rd, Hayes,
Greater London UB4 9LS; Tel 020 8845 6645

RESOURCE AND DAY CENTRE FOR PEOPLE WITH A LEARNING DISABILITY

Coaxden Day Centre 102 Park Rd, Uxbridge, Greater
London UB8 1JQ; Tel 01892 238800

Grassy Meadow Grange Rd, Hayes, Greater London
UB3 2UF; Tel 020 8561 4228; 020 8573 2120

Honeycroft Honeycroft Hill, Uxbridge, Greater London
UB10 9NH; Tel 01895 238193

Maple Road Employment Service 151b Maple Rd, Hayes,
Greater London UB4 9NQ; Tel 020 8845 0802

Parkview Stockley Rd, Hillingdon, Greater London
UB8 3HB; Tel 01895 436695

Rural Activities Centre West Drayton Rd, Hillingdon,
Greater London UB8 3JZ; Tel 01895 270160

Southbourne Employment Services 161 Elliott Ave, Ruislip,
Greater London HA4 9UA; Tel 020 8426 1340

Woodside 401 Uxbridge Rd, Hayes, Greater London UB4 0RE; Tel 020 8561 8180

RESOURCE AND DAY CENTRES FOR PEOPLE WITH PHYSICAL OR SENSORY DISABILITIES

Grassy Meadow Grange Rd, Hayes, Greater London UB3 2UF; Tel 020 8561 4228; 020 8573 2120

RESOURCE/DAY CENTRES – MENTAL HEALTH

Mead House Hayes End Rd, Hayes End, Hayes, Greater London UB4 8EN; Tel 020 8561 6676

Pembroke Centre 80 Pembroke Rd, Ruislip, Greater London HA4 8NQ; Tel 01895 622424

RESOURCE/DAY CENTRES FOR OLDER PEOPLE

Eastbury Road 24 Eastbury Rd, Northwood, Greater London HA6 3AL; Tel 01923 821676

Grassy Meadow Grange Rd, Hayes, Greater London UB3 2UF; Tel 020 8561 4228; 020 8573 2120

Poplar Farm Day Centre 151a Maple Rd, Hayes, Greater London UB4 9NQ; Tel 020 8845 8584; 020 8845 8909

Community Care Provider Services

Asha Day Centre Townfield Site, Central Ave, Hayes, Greater London UB3 9NQ; Tel 020 8569 2792

Community Drugs Team Old Bank Hse, 64 High St, Uxbridge, Greater London UB8 1JP; Tel 01895 207777; Fax 01895 207733

Adult Care Scheme 130 High St, Ruislip, Greater London HA4 8LP; Tel 01895 250111 ext 7026; Fax 01895 277027

HIV Prevention Team Barra Hall, Wood End Green Rd, Hayes, Greater London UB3 2SA; Tel 01895 250111 ext 3165; Fax 01895 250180

Home Care Barra Hall, Wood End Green Rd, Hayes, Greater London UB3 2SA; Tel 01895 250111 ext 3194

Meals Service 2S02 Civic Centre, Uxbridge, Greater London UB8 1UW; Tel 01895 250496

One Stop – Hayes 49–51 Station Rd, Hayes, Greater London UB3 4BE; Tel 020 8606 2900; Fax 020 8606 2909

Education, Youth and Leisure Services Group

Civic Centre, High St, Uxbridge, Greater London UB8 1UW; Tel 01895 250111
Corporate Director (Education, Youth and Leisure Services) P. O'Hear

EDUCATIONAL PSYCHOLOGY SERVICE

The Lancaster Centre 26 Bennetts Yd, off Lancaster Rd, Uxbridge, Greater London UB8 1BN; Tel 01895 256524
Principal Educational Psychologist C. Sullivan

SPECIAL SCHOOLS

Meadow High School Royal La, Hillingdon, Uxbridge, Greater London UB8 3QU; E-mail meadow@lbhill.gov.uk; Tel 01895 443310
Headteacher R. Payne, BA, AdvDipEd(Man)
(Day)
    11–18 MLD

Moorcroft School Bramble Cl, Hillingdon, Uxbridge, Greater London UB8 3BF; E-mail moorcrof@lbhill.gov.uk; Tel 01895 437799
Headteacher M.J. Geddes, BA(Hons)
(Day)
    11–19 SLD

HOUSING ADVICE CENTRE

Advice Centre, Civic Centre, Greater London UB8 1UW; Tel 01895 250111

INFORMATION CENTRE

Central Library 14–15 High St, Uxbridge, Greater London UB8 1HD; Tel (Borough and Tourist Information) 01895 250600

HOUNSLOW LONDON BOROUGH COUNCIL
www.hounslow.gov.uk

Population 212 344
Political Composition: Lab: 36, Con: 15, LD: 5; Isleworth Community Group: 3; A Bee C: 1
Civic Centre, Lampton Rd, Hounslow, Greater London TW3 4DN; URL www.hounslow.gov.uk; E-mail information.ced@hounslow.gov.uk; Tel 020 8583 2000
Borough Treasurer Alan Steele
Borough Solicitor Mike Smith, Sol, DMA
Director (Hounslow Homes) Chris Langstaff
Director (Street Management and Public Protection) Suresh Kamath

ADVICE CENTRES

Rent Officer Service Candy Hse, 3rd Fl, 21 The Mall, Ealing, London W5 2QZ; Tel 020 8280 2760

RECEPTION AND INFORMATION

Civic Centre, Lampton Rd, Hounslow, Greater London URL www.hounslow.gov.uk; E-mail information.ced@hounslow.gov.uk; Tel 020 8583 2599

Social Services Department

Fax 020 8583 3071
Director (Social Services) Susanna White
Assistant Director (Children and Families) Cecile Hitchen
Assistant Director (Community Care) Sue Spurlock
Head (Finance and Business) Shelma Amirthanayagam
Head (Human Resources) Christine Beran (Acting)
Head (Mental Health Services) J. Scott
Manager (Standards and Quality Assurance) K. Kaur
Manager (Administration) C. Pierre
Commissioning Manager (Older People) M. Fyfe
Service Manager Provider (Older People) G. Calen
Service Manager Provider (Older People) B. Turnbull
Service Manager (Child Protection) Sally Phillips
Service Manager (Learning Disability) Melvyn Simmons
Group Manager (Children and Families) Vacancy
Group Manager (Children and Families) Vacancy
Accountant D. Cameron

LOCAL OFFICES

Chiswick Local Office Ashburnham Hse, Horticultural Pl, Chiswick, London W4 4BY; Tel 020 8862 6560

Feltham Local Office 13 Hanworth Rd, Feltham, Greater London TW13 5AF; Tel 020 8862 6398

Heston Local Office 41 New Heston Rd, Heston, Greater London TW5 0LW; Tel 020 8862 6789

Hounslow Local Office Civic Centre, Lampton Rd, Greater London TW3 4DN; Tel 020 8862 6103; 020 8862 6104

7

HOSPITAL SOCIAL WORKERS

West Middlesex Hospital, London Rd, Greater London TW7 6AF; Tel 020 8565 5609; 020 8565 5610
Team Manager P. Hemsworth

UNDER EIGHTS CENTRES

Brentford Child and Family Centre Brentford Portsdown Hse, 1 The Butts, Brentford, Greater London TW8 8BJ; Tel 020 8560 8041
Manager A. Bamber
Mixed

Feltham Child and Family Centre Danesbury Rd, Feltham, Greater London TW13 5AL; Tel 020 8890 3816
Manager C. Womersley
Mixed

Hounslow Child and Family Centre Nantley Hse, 33 Lampton Rd, Hounslow, Greater London TW3 1JG; Tel 020 8570 4378
Manager Lisa Jeary
Mixed 52 + 9 in PH Unit

RESIDENTIAL CHILDREN'S HOMES/HOSTELS

Staines Road Adolescent Resource Centre 537a Staines Rd, Feltham, Greater London TW14 8BP; Tel 020 8890 1920
Mixed (12)

The Ride Resource Centre 7–9 The Ride, Brentford, Greater London TW8 9LB; Tel 020 8560 8805
Manager Vacancy
Mixed (6)

RESIDENTIAL HOME FOR CHILDREN WITH A LEARNING DIFFICULTY

Westbrook Children's Home 55 New Heston Rd, Heston, Greater London TW5 0LW; Tel 020 8572 1884
Mixed

DAY SERVICE FOR ADULTS WITH A LEARNING DISABILITY

Brentford Adult Training Centre 84 London Rd, Brentford, Greater London TW8 8JJ; Tel 020 8560 7579
Manager S. O'Sullivan
Mixed MH (140)

Two Bridges 2a Marriott Cl, Feltham, Greater London; Tel 020 8890 3480
Manager Dianne Martin
Mixed MH (24)

The Triangle Whitton Rd, Hounslow, Greater London; Tel 020 8572 0937
Manager M. Blake

HOME FOR PEOPLE WITH A PHYSICAL DISABILITY

Eldridge Hse, Hounslow Rd, Feltham, Greater London TW14 0BD; Tel 020 8890 3832
Manager P. Brooke
Mixed Short stay 41

WORK CENTRE FOR THE PHYSICALLY DISABLED

Heston Work Centre New Heston Rd, Heston, Greater London TW5 0LW; Tel 020 8570 6585
Mixed

DAY CARE CENTRES FOR ELDERLY PEOPLE

Bedfort Day Care Centre Southville Rd, Feltham, Greater London TW14 8AP; Tel 020 8890 8587
Manager L. McKenna
Mixed (38)

Chiswick Day Care Centre Bridge St, Chiswick, London W4 5UF; Tel 020 8995 6664
Manager C. Page
Mixed

Heston Day Care Centre 36 Springwell Rd, Heston, Greater London TW5 9EJ; Tel 020 8572 0229
Manager M. Doyle
Mixed

RESIDENTIAL HOMES FOR THE ELDERLY

There are four local authority homes for older people with approx 200 places.

VERY SHELTERED HOUSING

Dashwood Court 40 Livingstone Rd, Hounslow, Greater London TW3 1XX; Tel 020 8570 6775
Manager M. Seechurn
(38)

Lavender Court Becketts Cl, Harlington Road West, Feltham, Greater London TW14 0BP; Tel 020 8890 7158
Manager L. McKenna

SPECIAL SERVICES

Social Services Incontinent Laundry Service
Personal laundry service for housebound or handicapped elderly.

Equipment Store and Workshop Brentford Baths Annexe, Clifden Rd, Brentford, Greater London; Tel 020 8560 4683
Equipment and minor adaptations under the CSPDP Act 1970.

Lifelong Learning, Leisure and Cultural Services

The Civic Centre, Lampton Rd, Hounslow, Greater London TW3 4DN; Tel 020 8583 2600; Fax 020 8583 2613
Corporate Director (LLLCS) R. Garnett
Assistant Director (LLLCS, SEN and Community Learning) J. Clarke
Head (Education Welfare and School Attendance) I. Whittaker
Education Officer (Special Needs) M. Abbott
Principal Educational Psychologist N. D'Aeth
Deputy Principal Educational Psychologist Vacancy
Senior Educational Psychologist K. Duggan

TEACHING SUPPORT SERVICE

Head J. Capstick

SPECIAL SCHOOLS

The Lindon-Bennett School Main St, Hanworth, Greater London TW13 6ST; Tel 020 8898 0479
Headteacher S. Line

The Marjory Kinnon School Hatton Rd, Feltham, Greater London TW14 9QZ; Tel 020 8890 2032
Headteacher D.J. Harris, BA, MEd

Syon Park School Twickenham Rd, Isleworth, Greater London TW7 6AU; Tel 020 8560 4300
Headteacher K. Nowabilski

LONDON BOROUGH OF ISLINGTON
www.islington.gov.uk

Population 177 754
Political Composition: LD: 38, Lab: 10.
Town Hall, Upper St, London N1 2UD;
URL www.islington.gov.uk; Tel 020 7527 2000
Leader of the Council Cllr Steve Hitchins
Chief Executive Helen Bailey
Assistant Chief Executive Nick Sharman

Assistant Chief Executive and Director (Education)
    Jonathan Slater
Director (Social Services)   Paul Curran
Highbury Hse, Highbury Cres, London N5 1RN; Tel 020
    7527 4293
Head (Corporate Strategy)   Damien Roberts; Tel 020 7527
    3122

Social Services

Highbury Hse, 5 Highbury Cres, London N5 1RN;
    E-mail info.socialservices@islington.gov.uk; Tel 020 7527
    4072; Fax 020 7527 4118
Lead Executive Member   Meral Ece
Director (Social Services)   Paul Curran
Assistant Director (Children and Families)   David Worlock
Assistant Director (Community Care and Commissioning)
    Gwen Ovshinsky
Assistant Director (Adult Resources)   Neal Murtagh
Assistant Director (Finance and Support)   Katherine Tyrrell
IT Systems and Support   Ken Middleton
Manager (Information Services)   Michael Woolcott
Islington Town Hall, Upper St, London N1 2UD; Tel 020
    7527 3489; Fax 020 7527 3475

Social Services Committee

Chair   Cllr Douglas Taylor LD
c/o Town Hall, Upper St, London N1 2UD; Tel 020 7527
    4120; Fax 020 7527 4241
Vice-Chair   Cllr Doreen Scott, LD
Members of the Committee
Lab: P. Haynes, R. Perry, J. Rathbone.
LD: J. Coupland.
Substitute Members Lab: R. Blackmore, J. Burgess, M. Leigh.
LD: I. Cox, L. Willoughby, R. Wooding.

Children and Families Division

Assistant Director (Children and Families)   David Worlock;
    Tel 020 7527 4397

AREA OFFICES

Children and Families Child Care Service 292 Essex Rd,
London N1 3AZ; Tel 020 7527 1742
Manager   James Hood
Children and Families Assessment Service 292 Essex Rd,
London N1 3AZ; Tel 020 7527 1597
Contact   Catherine Dockrell
Hospital Team Children and Families Whittington Hospital,
Highgate Hill, London N19 5NF; Tel 020 7288 5260
Contact   Annie Souter

SPECIALIST CHILDREN'S SERVICES

14a Conewood St, London N5 1EB; Tel 020 7354 9370
Manager   Eleni Dialkou
Youth Offending Team Dingley Centre, 27 Dingley Pl,
London EC1V 8BR; Tel 020 7527 7060
16+ Service 29 Highbury New Pk, London N5 2EN; Tel 020
7527 8585
Disabled Children's Team 166 Upper St, London N1 1XU;
Tel 020 7527 3394

CHILDREN'S RESOURCES

5 Highbury Cres, London N5 1RN; Tel 020 7527 4073
Manager   James Dougan

RESIDENTIAL CHILDREN'S HOMES

Colgrain Children's Home 1 Dukes Ave, London N10 2PS;
Tel 020 8883 8191

Grosvenor Avenue Children's Home 114 Grosvenor Ave,
London N5 2NY; Tel 020 7359 2945
Highbury New Park Children's Home 80 Highbury New Pk,
London N5 2DC; Tel 020 7359 3814

RESPITE CARE UNIT

61–71 Lough Rd, London N7 8RH; Tel 020 7700 6769
Manager   Roy Figes

DISABLED CHILDREN'S OUTREACH SERVICE

47 Leigh Rd, London N5 1AH; Tel 020 7359 7469

THE CHILDREN'S TASK-CENTRED TEAM

11–12 Highbury Cres, London N5 1RN; Tel 020 7527 4432

FAMILY SUPPORT TEAM

11–12 Highbury Cres, London N5 1RN; Tel 020 7527 4130

NEW HORIZONS ACCOMMODATION UNIT

26–28 Northampton Pk, London N1 2PJ; Tel 020 7704 1580

CHILD PROTECTION AND REVIEWS

3 Elwood St, London N5 1EB; Tel 020 7704 2754
Manager   Jo Olsson
Child Protection and Reviewing Co-ordination Team 3
Elwood St, London N5 1EB; Tel 020 7704 2856
Elwood Family Centre 3 Elwood St, London N5 1EB; Tel 020
7704 2754

Community Care Division

Assistant Director (Community Care and Commissioning)
    Gwen Ovshinsky; Tel 020 7527 4093

COMMUNITY CARE CENTRES

Archway Community Care Centre 4 Vorley Rd, London
N19 5JH; Tel 020 7527 7500
Calshot Community Care Centre 57 Calshot St, London
N1 9XH; Tel 020 7527 6400
Canonbury Community Care Centre 68 Halliford St, London
N1 3RH; Tel 020 7527 8200
Drayton Community Care Centre 52d Drayton Pk, London
N5 1NS; Tel 020 7527 8800
Mental Health Team Elthorne 17–23 Beaumont Rise,
London N19 3AX; Tel 020 7527 8800
Islington Learning Disabilities Partnership 1 Lowther Rd,
London N7 8SL; Tel 020 7527 6600
Whittington Hospital Highgate Hill, London N19 5NF;
Tel 020 7272 3070; 020 7288 5260
Manager   M. Cook
Occupational Therapy 1a Church Cottages, Pemberton
Gdns, London N19 5RR; Tel 020 7527 5200
Team Leader   Debbie Levy

Adult Resources Division

Assistant Director (Adult Resources)   Neal Murtagh; Tel 020
    7527 4212

LEARNING DISABILITY RESOURCES

5 Highbury Cres, London N5 1RN; Tel 020 7527 4298
Group Manager   Naomi Cox

RESIDENTIAL HOMES FOR PEOPLE WITH LEARNING DISABILITY

Arlington Project Residential Home 13–14a Arlington Sq,
London N1 7DR; Tel 020 7359 2617

7

Ashley Road Residential Home 43 Ashley Rd, London N19 3AG; Tel 020 7281 3613

Highbury Resource Centre 14 Highbury Gr, London N5 2EA; Tel 020 7704 7470

Leigh Road Residential Home 53 Leigh Rd, London N5 1AH; Tel 020 7359 7460

Orchard Close Residential Home 4 Orchard Cl, Morton Rd, London N1 3SA; Tel 020 7354 9436

Wray Court Residential Home 3 Wray Crt, Tollington Pl, London N4 3QS; Tel 020 7281 4464

MENTAL HEALTH RESOURCES AND OLDER PEOPLE

5 Highbury Cres, London N5 1RN; Tel 020 7527 4270
Service Manager Peter Cartlidge

RESIDENTIAL (MENTAL HEALTH)

Clerkenwell Project, 7 Cumberland Gdns, London WC1X 1AG; Tel 020 7278 4421

ISLEDON ROAD RESOURCE CENTRE

76–80 Isledon Rd, London N7; Tel 020 7700 7458

DAY CENTRES (MENTAL HEALTH)

Lambo African and Caribbean Day Centre 48 Despard Rd, London N19 5NW; Tel 020 7263 3046

Pine Street Day Centre 13–15 Pine St, London EC1R 0JH; Tel 020 7837 6736

PHYSICAL DISABILITIES

5 Highbury Cres, London N5 1RN; Tel 020 7527 4270
Group Manager Martin Elliot

DAY CENTRE (PHYSICAL DISABILITIES)

St. John's Day Centre, 133 St. John's Way, London N19 3RQ; Tel 020 7263 3537

RESIDENTIAL UNIT FOR PEOPLE WITH PHYSICAL DISABILITY (RESPITE AVAILABLE)

28 King Henry's Wlk, London N1 4PB; Tel 020 7272 6419

RESIDENTIAL HOMES

There are three local authority residential homes for older people.

RESIDENTIAL AND RESPITE (OLDER PEOPLE)

Lennox Hse, Durham Rd, London N7; Tel 020 7272 9517

Highbury New Park Centre 127 Highbury New Pk, London N5 2DS; Tel 020 7226 9678

RESOURCE CENTRES (OLDER PEOPLE)

Highbury New Park Resource Centre 127 Highbury New Pk, London N5 2DS; Tel 020 7359 3797

Preedy Resource Centre 37 Muriel St, London N1 0TH; Tel 020 7833 5991

DAY CENTRES (OLDER PEOPLE)

Alsen Day Centre 71 Durham Rd, London N7 7DS; Tel 020 7263 0676

New Park Day Centre 19 Highbury New Pk, London N5; Tel 020 7354 2493

EXTRA CARE SHELTERED HOUSING

Belmore Extra-Care Housing, 245 Camden Rd, Hilldrop Cres, London N7 0HL; Tel 020 7609 0492

HOME CARE SERVICES

5 Highbury Cres, London N5 1RN; Tel 020 7527 4435

CEA @ Islington

Laycock St, London N1 1TH; Tel 020 7527 5800; Fax 020 7527 5903
Director (School's Service) Bill Clark
Assistant Director Thanos Morphitis
Assistant Director Lela Kogbara
Assistant Director Kirit Modi

SPECIAL SCHOOLS

Harborough School Elthorne Rd, Holloway Rd, London N19 4AB; Tel 020 7272 5739
Headteacher Jim Wolger
Autistic

Richard Cloudesley School Golden La, London EC1Y 0TJ; Tel 020 7251 1161
Headteacher A. Corbett
PH

Rosemary School 75 Prebend St, London N1 8PW; Tel 020 7226 8223
Headteacher David Dewhurst
Upper School, Sans Wk, London EC1; Tel (Primary Department) 020 7226 8223; (Secondary Department) 020 7253 6893
SLD

Samuel Rhodes School Dowrey St, Richmond Ave, London N1 0HR; Tel 020 7837 9075
Headteacher J. Blount
MLD

EARLY YEARS CENTRES

Andover Centre 49 Corker Wlk, London N7 7RY; Tel 020 7263 6995
Head of Centre Ann McTagart

Archway Centre Vorley Rd, London N19 5HE; Tel 020 7272 3350
Head of Centre Nasso Christou

Bemerton Centre 1a Coatbridge Hse, Carnoustie Dr, London N1 0DX; Tel 020 7607 7743
Head of Centre Janet Morris

Fortune Park Centre 86 Golden La, London EC1Y 0QT; Tel 020 7638 1272
Head of Centre Helen James

Gillespie Centre Gillespie Primary School, Gillespie Rd, London N5 1LH; Tel 020 7354 5567
Teacher-in-Charge Hilary Randall

Goodinge Centre 7 Corporation St, London N7 9EH; Tel 020 7607 5850
Head of Centre Nancy Young

New River Green Centre Marquess Road North, London N1 2PY; Tel 020 7226 7725
Head of Centre Anita Mohindra

Rosedale Centre 12 Lough Rd, London N7 5RR; Tel 020 7609 2344
Head of Centre Sylvia Clack

Springdale Centre 15a Springdale Rd, London N16 9NS; Tel 020 7275 9393
Head of Centre Maggie Ross

Willow Centre Holbrooke Crt, 23 Tufnell Park Rd, London N7 0PG; Tel 020 7607 3985
Head of Centre Venti Costantini

KENSINGTON AND CHELSEA
www.rbkc.gov.uk

Population 170 000
Political Composition: Con: 42, Lab: 12
The Town Hall, Hornton St, Kensington, London W8 7NX;
URL www.rbkc.gov.uk;
E-mail information.services@rbkc.gov.uk; Tel 020 7937
5464; Fax 020 7938 1445
Chief Executive and Town Clerk   Derek Myers, BA, LLB
Director (Legal Services)   Gifty Edila, MA, LLB

Social Services Department

Tel 020 7361 2563; Fax 020 7361 2148
Executive Director (Housing and Social Services)   Moira Gibb,
MA, CQSW; Tel 020 7361 2563 ex 2400
Head (Community Care Services)   Peter West; Tel 020 7361
2563 ext 2398
Head (Children and Families Services)   Alastair Pettigrew;
Tel 020 7361 2563 ext 2354
Service Manager (Older People's Commissioning)
George Marshman; Tel 020 7361 2563 ext 3081
Service Manager (Mental Health and Substance Use)
Vacancy; Tel 020 7361 2563 ext 2517
Service Manager (Disability and HIV/AIDS Services)
Hector Medora; Tel 020 7361 2563 ext 2408
Service Manager (Older People)   Jo Tumelty; Tel 020 7361
2563 ext 8101
Service Manager (Older People's Provision)   Janet Palmer;
Tel 020 7361 2563 ext 4626
Service Manager (Care Resources)   Alan Jones; Tel 020 7361
2563 ext 3086
Service Manager (Under Eight's)   Liz Sharpe; Tel 020 7361
2563 ext 2726
Service Manager (Support Services)   Trevor Pratt
Service Manager (Children's Services – North)   Mike Brace;
Tel 020 7361 2563 ext 4453
Service Manager (Children's Services – Central and South Area)
Malcolm Mackenzie; Tel 020 7361 2563 ext 3013
Commissioning Manager (Children and Families)
Jennifer Didsdall; Tel 020 7361 2563 ext 5832
Support Services Manager   Trevor Pratt; Tel 020 7361 2563
ext 2088
Manager (Homelessness Social Work Team)   Alison Brown
Manager (Asylum Team)   Jackie Harrison
Manager (Unaccompanied Minors Team)   Harry Cole
Manager (Emergency Duty Team)   Alison Brown; Tel 020
7373 2227
Principal Family Support and Child Protection Adviser
Mary Gillingham
Manager (Assessment and Social Work Team)
Alan Frampton
Manager (Sensory Impairment Social Work Team)
Trish Welton
Manager (CSDP Services)   Theresa McShane
Commissioning Manager (HIV Services)   Sue Allen
Manager (Learning Disability Social Work Team)
Robert Templeton
Senior Practical Care Assessor (Central Practical Care Team)
Adrie Davies

Social Services Committee

Chair   Cllr John Corbet-Singleton, CBE (Con)
3 Carlyle Sq, London SW3 6EX; Tel 020 7352 1892
Vice-Chair   Cllr Nicholas Paget-Brown (Con)
Flat 4, 35 Hollywood Rd, London SW10 9HT; Tel 020 7352
1650
Members of the Committee
J.M. Blakeman, Prof Sir Anthony Coates, Timothy
Coleridge, Robert J. Freeman, Bridget Hoier, Pat Healy,
Shireen Ritchie, Dr Charles Tannock.

HEALTH SERVICE SOCIAL WORK

Barlby Road Clinic   81 Barlby Rd, London W10 6AZ; Tel 020
8968 2084
Manager   Carole Jarvis (Acting)
Chelsea and Westminster Hospital   369 Fulham Rd, London
SW10 9NH; Tel 020 8746 8779; 020 8746 8788
Manager (Hospital Social Work Team)   Vivienne Broadhurst
Manager (Hospital Social Work Team)   Val Moeri
Manager (HIV Team)   Penny Cave
Courtfield Community Mental Health Team   23a Courtfield
Gdns, London SW5 0PF; Tel 020 7598 4555
Manager   Steve Chamberlain
Royal Brompton NHS Hospital   Sydney St, London
SW3 6NP; Tel 020 7351 8060
Senior Social Worker   Jennifer Iliffe
Royal Marsden Hospital   Fulham Rd, London SW3 6JJ;
Tel 020 7808 2481
Senior Social Worker   Alison Higgs (Acting)
St. Charles Hospital   Exmoor St, London W10 6DA; Tel 020
8962 4180
Manager (Community Mental Health Team A)   Sian Thomas
Manager (Community Mental Health Team B)
Joe Mensah-Tandoh
Manager (Social Work Team)   Nick Murray (Acting)
St. Mary's Hospital   Praed St, London W2 1NY; Tel 020 7886
6533
Team Manager   Nick Murray (Acting)
South Kensington and Chelsea Mental Health Unit   1
Nightingale Pl, London SW10 9NG; Tel 020 8237 2700
Manager (South Community Mental Health Team)
Aurelie Freeman

Children and Families Services

Chelsea Old Town Hall   King's Rd, London SW3 5EE;
Tel 020 7352 8101
Manager   Liz Sidley
Manager (Home Care – South)   Audrey Murphy
Manager (Social Work and Assessment Team)   Serena Nuttall
Manager (Social Work and Assessment Team)   Alan Frampton
Manager (Occupational Therapy Team)   Sue Smith
Senior Practical Care Assessor (South Practical Care Team)
Maria White
Children's Resource Team   2a Wallingford Ave, London
W10 6QB; Tel 020 7854 5880
Manager   John Page
Collingham Gardens Child and Family Psychiatry Unit   5
Collingham Gdns, London SW5 0HR; Tel 020 8846 6644
Manager   Liz Sidley
Earls Court Neighbourhood Office   282 Earls Court Rd,
London SW5 9AS; Tel 020 7598 4950
Manager (Social Work and Assessment Team)   Alan Watkins
Manager (Central and South Occupational Therapy Team)
Sue Smith
Family Partnership Team   Emperor's Gate Centre for
Health, 49 Emperors Gate, London SW7 4HJ; Tel 020 8237
5319
Co-ordinator   Audrey Lewis
Independence Support Team   Westway EPICS, 2-4 Malton
St, London W10 5UP; Tel 020 7598 4660
Manager   Sheila Simpson
Kensal Neighbourhood Team   175 Kensal Rd, London
W10 5BX; Tel 020 8960 4337
Manager   Rupinder Virdee
Lancaster West Estate   1st Fl, Grenfell Tower, Grenfell Rd,
London W11 1TG; Tel 020 7792 8170
Manager (Lancaster West Estate Team)   Chris Luke
Manager (Ladbroke South Team)   Patricia Butler
Westway Information and Aid Centre   Westway Information
and Aid Centre, 140 Ladbroke Grn, London W10 5ND;
Tel 020 7598 4444

7

Manager (Ladbroke North Team) Melanie Davies
Manager (Portobello North Team) Anne Edwards
Manager (Portobello South Team) Jim Cope
Manager (Family Placement Unit) Jan Fishwick
Manager (Family Placement Unit) Morelda Powell
Manager (Social Work and Assessment Team) Ruth Garry
Manager (Substance Use Team) Gaynor Driscoll
Manager (Physical Disability Team) Jane Hill
Manager (HIV Team – North) Penny Cave
Senior Practical Care Assessor (North Practical Care Team)
    James Bryne
Team Leader (Occupational Therapy Team – North)
    Allison Pinder
Family Support and Child Protection Adviser (North)
    Isabel Friedlander

Worlds End Neighbourhood Office 1–3 Greaves Tower,
Worlds End Est, London SW10 0EA; Tel 020 7351 3992
Manager Imelda Murphy
*Family Support and Child Protection Adviser (Central and
    South)* Peter Robinson
Senior Social Worker Lorna Cornett

CHILDREN'S DISABILITY TEAM

34b Oxford Gardens London W10 5UQ; Tel 020 7598 4646
Manager Tim O'Neill

UNDER EIGHTS DAY CARE SERVICES

Cheyne Family Centre 10 Thorndike Cl, London SW10 0ST;
Tel 020 7352 5473
Contact Jan Keen
    (56)
Clare Gardens Family Centre 349 Westbourne Park Rd,
London W11 1EG; Tel 020 7727 2725
Manager Kathy Baine
    (50)
Ladbroke 34 Ladbroke Gr, London W11 3TG; Tel 020 7727
4807
Manager Vanessa Hamilton-Bailey
    (60)
Latymer Family Centre Freston Rd, London W10 6TT;
Tel 020 8969 9327
Manager Elaine Steel
    (46)
St. Quintin's Family Centre 90 Highlever Rd, London
W10 6PN; Tel 020 8969 0826
Manager Cheryl Hill
    (80)
Violet Melchett Family Centre 30 Flood Wlk, London
SW3 5RR; Tel 020 7352 1512
Manager Laura Coletti
Senior Social Worker (Child and Family Consultation Service)
    Alan Hudson; Tel 020 8237 2837
    (60)

CHILDREN'S RESIDENTIAL ESTABLISHMENTS

Creswick Road Home 7 Creswick Rd, London; Tel 020 8992
9352
Manager Joan Miller
    (5)
The Little House 36 Oxford Gdns, London W10 5UQ;
Tel 020 7598 4717
Manager Margaret Jack
St. Mark's Close 3 St. Marks Cl, London W11 1TZ; Tel 020
7221 4298
Manager Terry Windsor
    (12)
Whistler Walk 28 Whistler Wlk, London SW10 0EP; Tel 020
7352 4707
Manager Patrick O'Leary
    (12)

YOUTH OFFENDING TEAM

34 Oxford Gdns, London W10 5UQ; Tel 020 7598 4700
Manager Brendan O'Keefe

Community Care Services

DAY CENTRE FOR PEOPLE WITH LEARNING DIFFICULTIES

Scope 1–9 St Mark's Rd, London W11 1RG; Tel 020 7727
4765
Manager (Community Resources) Steven Porter
    MH (42)

ACCOMMODATION FOR PEOPLE WITH LEARNING DISABILITIES

Piper Hse, 2b St Marks Rd, London W11 1RQ; Tel 020 7229
7623
Manager Michael Downey
    (24)

DAY CENTRES FOR PEOPLE WITH MENTAL HEALTH PROBLEMS

Denbigh Centre 1 Elkstone Rd, London W10 5NT; Tel 020
8968 5569
Centre Manager Jolanta Lis
    (12)
Oremi – African-Carribean Mental Health Resource Centre
The Harvey Centre, Unit 3 Trelick Tower, 5 Golborne Rd,
London W10 5NX; Tel 020 8964 0033
Team Manager Cashain David
Pembroke Centre 74 Pembroke Rd, London W8 6NX;
Tel 020 7603 0722
Head of Centre Orla Forde (Acting)
St. Mark's Centre 1–9 St. Mark's Rd, London W11 1RG;
Tel 020 7727 6210
Centre Manager Jolanta Lis
    (20)

ACCOMMODATION FOR PEOPLE WITH MENTAL HEALTH PROBLEMS

One Local Authority Home offering 16 places plus six
places in group homes.
Tavistock Hostel 91 Tavistock Cres, London W11 1AZ;
Tel 020 7727 4346
Manager Mark Boyles
    (16)

DAY CENTRES FOR OLDER PEOPLE

Edenham Day Centre 1 Elkstone Rd, London W10 5NT;
Tel 020 8960 1301
Manager H. Chamchoun
    (20)
Gertrude Street Day Centre 15 Gertrude St, London; Tel 020
7352 1041
Manager Ann McAdam
    PH and Elderly (45)
Westway Centre EPICS 2–4 Malton St, London W10 5UP;
Tel 020 7598 4600
Manager Carol Orgell Rosen
Manager (Home Care Team – North) Victoria Hartland
Manager (Dementia Development Team) Sue Heiser

ACCOMMODATION FOR THE ELDERLY

There are four local authority homes for elderly people
offering 241 places; one Sheltered Housing scheme offering
34 places.

JOINT HOMELESSNESS TEAM

Pembroke Centre, 84 Pembroke Rd, London W8 6NX;
    Tel 020 7603 1443
Manager Liz Bruce

BEATRICE PLACE

2 Beatrice Pl, London W8 5LP; Tel 020 7937 1611
Co-ordinator (Community Support Services)
Paul Featherstone
Co-ordinator (Kensington Recruitment) Peter Murphy

Education Department

The Town Hall, Hornton St, London W8 7NX;
URL www.rbkc.gov.uk; E-mail eduadmin@rbkc.gov.uk;
Tel 020 7361 3334; Fax 020 7361 2078
Executive Director (Education, Libraries and Arts) J. Griffin
Director (Schools) Vacancy
Director (Community Education) I. Comfort
Head (SEN and Additional Needs) D. Dyer
Head (Access and Inclusion) R. Sachie
Principal Education Welfare Officer H. Shaw
Principal Educational Psychologist P. Wagner

SPECIAL SCHOOL

Parkwood Hall School Beechenlea La, Swanley, Kent BR8
8DR; URL www.parkwoodhall.kensington-chelsea.sch.uk;
E-mail info@parkwoodhall.kensington-chelsea.sch.uk;
Tel 01322 664441; Fax 01322 613163
Headteacher H. Dando
MLD

KINGSTON UPON THAMES

www.kingston.gov.uk

Population 147 273
Political Composition: LD: 30, Con: 15, Lab: 3
Guildhall, Kingston upon Thames, Surrey KT1 1EU;
URL www.kingston.gov.uk; Tel 020 8546 2121
Director (Community Services) Roy Taylor, CBE; Tel 020
8547 6000; Fax 020 8547 6086
Director (Finance) Tony Knight; Tel 020 8547 5570; Fax 020
8547 5925
Director (Environmental Services) Devendra Saksena;
Tel 020 8547 5320; Fax 020 8547 5363
Head (Legal Services) Nick Bishop; Tel 020 8547 5110;
Fax 020 8547 5127
Head (Democratic Services and Partnership)
Andrew Bessant; Tel 020 8547 4628; Fax 020 8547 5032
Head (Housing) Michael England; Tel 020 8547 5430;
Fax 020 8547 6003
Borough Environmental Health Officer Bob Smart; Tel 020
8547 5530; Fax 020 8547 5568
Borough Valuer John Barlow; Tel 020 8547 5670; Fax 020
8547 5925

Community Services Directorate

Tel 020 8547 6000; Fax 020 8547 6086
Director (Community Services) R. Taylor, CBE, MA, CQSW
Head (Community Care Services) J. Webb
Head (Children and Family Services) M. Rooke
Head (Accountancy) L. Wishart
Head (Strategy and Performance Division) C. Fitzgerald
Principal Manager (Looked After and Leaving Care)
G. Snelling
Principal Manager (Performance and Development) D. Webb
Principal Manager (Quality Assurance and Development)
Sarah Tapp
Principal Manager (Health, Disability and OT Services)
Vacancy
Principal Manager (Home Care Services) S. Todd
Principal Manager (Workforce Development and Training)
K. Meyers

Principal Manager (Resource Centres for Older People)
Fiona Connolly
Principal Manager (Placements) S. Cole
Principal Manager (Older People and Hospital Services)
J. Bearman
Manager (Customer Services) L. Phillips
Manager (Support Services) C. Atkins
Manager (Quality and Performance) S. Daly
Manager (Directorate IT Development) Chris Stottor
Manager (Welfare Benefits) Vacancy
Manager (Strategic Commissioning and Learning Disabilities)
Vacancy
Finance Manager (Community Care) A. Bowen
Principal Service Co-ordinator (Disabled Children) P. Jefferies
Borough Commissioner (Mental Health and Substance Misuse)
V. Boswell

ASSESSMENT AND CARE MANAGEMENT TEAMS

Health and Disability Team
Team Manager S. Hart

Children and Family Services
Team Manager (North/East) Lesley Rabbatts
Team Manager (North/East) Joyce Ranger
Team Manager (Looked After and Leaving Care) J. Budden
Manager (Disabled Children's Care Planning Team)
L. Hopkins
Manager (Disabled Children's Specialists Services Team)
C. Nelson
Principal Service Co-ordinator (Services for Disabled Children)
P. Jefferies

Child Protection Services
*Principal Manager (Child and Family Protection Support
Service)* Eoin Rush

Family Placement Team
Team Manager Jenny Rigby

Services for Older People (Care Management Teams)
Team Manager (North/East) A. Filkin
Team Manager (South) D. Luchowa
Deputy Manager (North/East) Shah Ali

Kingston and Tolworth Hospital Teams
Manager E. Moyo

Learning Disabilities (Adults)
Team Manager (CLDT) L. Kingston-Smith

EARLY YEARS RESOURCE CENTRE

132 Kingston Rd, New Malden, Surrey KT3 3ND; Tel 020
8547 6575
Head (Early Years Education and Childcare)
Christine Halstead
(40)

COMMUNITY HOMES

Berradene Community Home 2 Berrylands Rd, Surbiton,
Surrey KT5 8RA; Tel 020 8399 7834
Home Manager L. Roberts
(6)

Beverley House Community Home 140–142 Dukes Ave,
New Malden, Surrey KT3 4HR; Tel 020 8942 2090
Manager Helen Davis

FAMILY CENTRE

Beaconsfield Children's Resource Centre 17 Beaconsfield
Rd, New Malden, Surrey KT3 3HY; Tel 020 8547 6591
Premises Manager Lesley Yexley

RESIDENTIAL CARE FOR ADULTS WITH LEARNING DISABILITIES

Fairlawn Warren Rd, Kingston Hill, Kingston, Surrey;
Tel 020 8541 1061
Manager J. Wells
(8)

7

Woodbury 8 Kingsdowne Rd, Surbiton, Surrey KT6 6JA;
Tel 020 8390 9441
Manager J. Wells

COMMUNITY MENTAL HEALTH TEAMS

Community Mental Health Team (Kingston)
Manager D. Emmett (Acting)
Community Mental Health Team (New Malden)
Shirley Martin
Community Mental Team (Surbiton) Sheila McGlashen
(Acting)
Community Mental Health Team (Chessington) J. Carmody
Mental Health Team for Older People
Manager Rita Seewooruttun

DAY CENTRE FOR PEOPLE WITH MENTAL HEALTH PROBLEMS

Sherwood Centre Warren Rd, Kingston Hill, Kingston,
Surrey KT2 7HY; Tel 020 8546 6360
Manager Ed Brennan
(30)

SOCIAL EDUCATION CENTRE

The Causeway Centre Cocks Cres, Blagdon Rd, New
Malden, Surrey KT3 4TA; Tel 020 8949 0631
Manager Marie Jukes
(100)

DAY CENTRE FOR PEOPLE WITH DISABILITIES

Crescent Resource Centre Cocks Cres, Blagdon Rd, New
Malden, Surrey KT3 4TA; Tel 020 8949 1955
Manager G. Tong
(55)

RESOURCE CENTRES FOR OLDER PEOPLE (DAY AND RESIDENTIAL CARE)

Hobkirk House Resource Centre 109 Blagdon Rd, New
Malden, Surrey KT3 4DB; Tel 020 8949 3377
Manager Lorna Vanson
(50)

Murray House Resource Centre Acre Rd, Kingston, Surrey
KT2 4EE; Tel 020 8549 3272
Manager Nicky Axon
(50)

Newent House Resource Centre 8–10 Browns Rd, Surbiton,
Surrey KT5 8SP; Tel 020 8547 6311
Manager M. Twigg
(50)

RESOURCE CENTRE FOR OLDER PEOPLE WITH MENTAL HEALTH PROBLEMS (DAY AND RESIDENTIAL CARE)

Amy Woodgate House Resource Centre Warren Rd,
Kingston Hill, Kingston, Surrey KT2 7HY; Tel 020 8549
2614
Manager Hannah Doody
Day Centre: 40
Residential: 28 + 4 respite

SHELTERED HOUSING SCHEMES

There are 18 sheltered housing schemes, 21 estate groups
administered by the Housing Department – Information
available from Housing Department.

HOME CARE AND MOBILE SERVICE

Murray House Acre Rd, Kingston, Surrey KT2 4EE; Tel 020
8549 3272
Newent House 8–10 Browns Rd, Surbiton, Surrey KT5 8SP;
Tel 020 8390 0285

Education and Leisure Services

Guildhall 2, Kingston upon Thames, Surrey KT1 1EU;
Tel 020 8546 2121; Fax 020 8547 5296
Director (Education and Leisure) Patrick Leeson

EDUCATIONAL PSYCHOLOGY SERVICE

Dukes Centre Dukes Ave, Kingston upon Thames, Surrey
KT2 5QY; Tel 020 8547 6699; Fax 020 8547 6669

SPECIAL DAY SCHOOLS

Bedelsford (Foundation) School Grange Rd, Kingston upon
Thames, Surrey KT1 2QZ;
URL www.bedelsford.kingston.sch.uk;
E-mail bds@rbksch.org; Tel 020 8546 9838; Fax 020 8296
9238
Headteacher J. Murfitt
PH

Dysart (Community) School 190 Ewell Rd, Surbiton, Surrey
KT6 6HL; E-mail dys@rbksch.org; Tel 020 8412 2600;
Fax 020 8412 2700
Headteacher S. James
SLD

St. Philip's (Community) School Harrow Cl, Leatherhead
Rd, Chessington, Surrey KT9 2HP; E-mail phs@rbksch.org;
Tel 020 8397 2672; Fax 020 8391 5431
Headteacher H.J. Goodall
MLD

LONDON BOROUGH OF LAMBETH
www.lambeth.gov.uk

Population 275 800
Political Composition: Lab: 28, LD: 28, Con: 7
Town Hall, Brixton Hill, Lambeth, London SW2 1RW;
URL www.lambeth.gov.uk; Tel 020 7926 1000
Chief Executive Faith Boardman
Director (Finance Services) Michael Crich
International Hse, Canterbury Cres, London SW9 7BE;
Tel 020 7926 1000
Director (Legal Services) Jed Curran
Lambeth Town Hall, Brixton Hill, London SW2 1RN;
Tel 020 7926 1000
Director (Housing Services) John Broomfield
Hambrook Hse, Porden Rd, London SW2; Tel 020 7926
1000
Director (Team Lambeth) Paul Nolan
Serviceteam Hse, 185–205 Shakespeare Rd, London
SE24 9BN; Tel 020 7346 0500

Directorate of Social Services

Mary Seacole Hse, 91 Clapham High St, Lambeth, London
SW4 7TF; Tel 020 7926 4539; (Emergency) 020 7926 1000
Executive Member Cllr Judith Brodie
c/o Lambeth Town Hall, Brixton Hill, Brixton, London
SW2 1RW
Executive Member Cllr Ty Goddard
c/o Lambeth Town Hall, Brixton Hill, Brixton, London
SW2 1RW
Executive Director (Social Services and Health Improvement)
Andrew Webster; E-mail awebster@lambeth.gov.uk
Assistant Director (Social Services – Adults) Steve Cody
Assistant Director (Social Services – Children and Families)
Marion Wheeler
Assistant Director (Performance Management)
Doreen Redwood
Assistant Director (Business Support) Joy Harris

AREA OFFICES

North District Area Office 44–46 Offley Rd, London SW9 0LS; Tel 020 7926 5400

Central District Area Office 35 Clapham Park Rd, London SW4 7DQ; Tel 020 7926 5600

South District Area Office 225a Hopton Hse, Streatham High Rd, London SW16 6EY; Tel 020 7926 6500

CHILDREN AND FAMILIES DISTRICT OFFICES

North District 44–46 Offley Rd, Stockwell, London SW9 0LS; Tel 020 7926 5400

Central District 35 Clapham Pk Rd, Clapham, London SW4 7DQ; Tel 020 7926 5600

South District Hopton Hse, 243a Streatham High Rd, London SW16 6EY; Tel 020 7926 6500

ADOLESCENTS SERVICE

Youth Justice Service 1–9 Acre La, Brixton, London SE11 5DX; Tel 020 7926 2644

Young Adults Service 190 Kennington La, Kennington, London SE11 5DX; Tel 020 7926 6300

ADOPTION AND FOSTERING

Family Finders 392–394 Brixton Rd, Stockwell, London SW9 7AW; Tel 020 7926 8500

ACCOMMODATION FOR FAMILIES

All enquiries to the Director of Housing and Property Services.

DAY CENTRES FOR ADULTS WITH LEARNING DIFFICULTIES

Brixton Social Education Centre 2 Somerleyton Rd, London SW9 8ND; Tel 020 7733 3248

Lambeth Walk Day Centre 109 Lambeth Wlk, London SE11 6EE

Southwood Day Centre 154 Chalfont Rd, London SE25 9OD; Tel 020 8771 7969

ACCOMMODATION FOR PEOPLE WITH LEARNING DIFFICULTIES

Southwood STCU and ISU Chalfont Rd, London SE25 9OD

Stockwell Park Crescent 11–15 Stockwell Park Cres, London SW9 0DQ

25 Warham Road South Croydon, Surrey

DAY CENTRES FOR PEOPLE WITH MENTAL HEALTH PROBLEMS

Effra Day Centre 65 Effra Rd, London SW2 1BZ; Tel 020 7274 3714

Kennington Day Centre 1 Othello Cl, Kennington Park Rd, London SE11 4RE

Norwood Day Centre 1 Parkhall Rd, London SE21 8EH

Stockwell Day Centre 190 Stockwell Park Rd, London SW9 0DW

DAY CENTRE FOR ADULTS WITH DISABILITIES

Norwood Centre 1 Park Hall Rd, West Norwood, London SE21 8EH; Tel 020 7926 8077

DAY CENTRES FOR THE ELDERLY

Central Hill Day Centre Lunham Rd, London; Tel 020 8670 2767

Kennington Park Day Centre Othello Cl, London; Tel 020 7582 9471

ACCOMMODATION FOR THE ELDERLY

There are three local authority old peoples' homes; eight voluntary old peoples' homes administered by Director of Social Services; 15 sheltered housing schemes, administered by the Director of Housing and Property Services.

SOCIAL REHABILITATION CENTRE

Norwood Centre 1 Parkhill Rd, London; Tel 020 8761 1235

MEALS SERVICE FOR THE ELDERLY

Contracts Monitoring, Mary Seacole Hse, London SW4 7TF; Tel 020 7926 4586

INSPECTION AND REGISTRATION UNIT

Mary Seacole Hse, 91 Clapham High St, London SW4 7TF; Tel 020 7926 4597

COMMENTS, COMPLIMENTS AND COMPLAINTS

Mary Seacole Hse, 91 Clapham High St, London SW4 7TF; Tel 020 7926 4840

PLANNING AND COMMISSIONING UNIT

Mary Seacole Hse, 91 Clapham High St, London SW4 7TF; Tel (Information and Publicity) 020 7926 4682; (Joint Planning and Commissioning) 020 7926 4809; (Voluntary Sector Commissioning) 020 7926 4897

7

Education Directorate

International Hse, Canterbury Cres, London SW9 7QE; Tel 020 7926 1000
Executive Director (Education) Michael Peters; Tel 020 7926 9760
Deputy Director Alan Wood; Tel 020 7926 9771
Head (Pupil and Student Services) Dorothy Worsford (Acting)
International Hse, Canterbury Cres, London SW9 7QE; Tel 020 7926 9377
Head (Educational Psychology Service) Julia Hardy; Tel 020 7926 9641
Head (Support for Pupils and Schools) Sandra Morrison (Acting)

SPECIAL SCHOOLS

Clapham Park School 127 Park Hill, London SW4 9PA; Tel 020 8674 5639; Fax 020 8674 5639
Headteacher David Prothero (Acting)
Visual impairment

Elm Court School Elmcourt Rd, London SE27 9BZ; Tel 020 8670 6577; Fax 020 8766 0309
Headteacher Bill Hutcheson
MLD

Grove House School Elmcourt Rd, London SE27 2DA; Tel 020 8670 9429; Fax 020 8655 7313
Headteacher Pam Odlin
Hearing Impairment

Lansdowne School Argyll Cl, Dalyell Rd, London SW9 9QL; Tel 020 7737 3713; Fax 020 7738 6877
Headteacher Ginni Bealing
MLD

Mortimer School Dingley La, Woodfield Ave, London SW16 1AU; Tel 020 8677 7521; Fax 020 8769 7199
Headteacher Marie Stern
MLD

Shelley School Oakden St, London SE11 4UG; Tel 020 7735 9081; Fax 020 7735 9082
Headteacher Maria Lozano-Luoma
SLD

Thurlow Park School Elmcourt Rd, London SE27 9DA; Tel 020 8670 3975; Fax 020 8761 8922
Headteacher John Barrow
2–16

Turney School Turney Rd, West Dulwich, West Dulwich, London SE21 8LX; Tel 020 8670 7220; Fax 020 8766 7588
Headteacher Jenny Davis
5–16

Willowfield School Heron Rd, Herne Hill, London SE24 0HY; Tel 020 7274 4372; Fax 020 7737 7511
Headteacher Josie Loy
11–16 EBD

Windmill School Mandrell Rd, London SW2 5DW; Tel 020 7733 0681; Fax 020 7733 7154
Headteacher Heather Parker
SLD

LEWISHAM LONDON BOROUGH COUNCIL
www.lewisham.gov.uk

Population 240 353
Lewisham Town Hall, Catford Rd, London SE6 4RU; URL www.lewisham.gov.uk; Tel 020 8314 6000; Fax 020 8314 3000
Director (Resources) Rob Whiteman; Tel 020 8314 8013; Fax 020 8314 3046
Manager (Design Services) Ralph Harris
Wearside Road Service Centre, Wearside Rd, London SE13 7EZ; E-mail ralph.harris@lewisham.gov.uk; Tel 020 8314 2585; Fax 020 8469 2715
Director (Regeneration) Patrick Hayes
5th Fl, Laurence Hse, 1 Catford Rd, London SE6 4RU; E-mail patrick.hayes@lewisham.gov.uk; Tel 020 8314 8502; Fax 020 8314 3642

Social Care and Health

Laurence Hse, 1 Catford Rd, London SE6 4RU; Tel 020 8314 8674; Fax 020 8314 6000
Executive Director (Social Care and Health) Chris Hume
Head (Elderly Peoples Homes) James Parnell
Head (Care, Commissioning and Health Partnerships) Kathryn Hudson
Head (Care Services) Frank Lowe (Acting)
Head (Resources) Chris Pottinger

Social Services Committee

Lab: 9, LD: 1, Con: 1
Chair N.G. Merling (Lab)
c/o Members' Services, Town Hall, Catford, London SE6 4RU
Vice-Chair K. Donnelly (Lab)
c/o Members' Services, Town Hall, Catford, London SE6 4RU
Members of the Committee
Ng, Anderson, Curran, Donnelly, Fallon, Gordon, Long, Moore, Sullivan, Wilson.

LOCAL OFFICES
Adult Services

Social Work Team Lewisham Hospital, Lewisham High St, Lewisham, London SE13 6LH; Tel 020 8333 3000

Louise House Dartmouth Rd, Forest Hill, London SE23 3HZ; Tel 020 8314 7755

8–12 Eltham Road Lee, London SE12 8TF; Tel 020 8314 8866

John Henry Neighbourhood Office 299 Verdant La, London SE6 1TP; Tel 020 8314 7766

St. Paul's House 125 Deptford High St, Deptford, London SE8 4NS; Tel 020 8314 6094; Fax 020 8314 9091

Children and Families Services

1 Eros House Brownhill Rd, Catford, London SE6 2EG; Tel 020 8314 6677

8–12 Eltham Road Lee, London SE12 8TF; Tel 020 8314 7419

Kingswear Dartmouth Rd, Forest Hill, London SE23 3YE; Tel 020 8314 8877

St. Paul's House 125 Deptford High St, Deptford, London SE8 4NS; Tel 020 8314 7308; Fax 020 8314 9004

Sensory Services Team

Duke House Service Team 3rd Fl, Duke Hse, 84–86 Rushey Grn, Catford, London SE6 4SW; Tel 020 8314 7777 (Hearing Impairment); (Visual Impairment) 020 8314 7777; Minicom 020 8314 3309
Manager (Service Unit) Sue Whitehorn

HOSPITAL SOCIAL WORK

1st Fl, Nursery Block, Lewisham Hospital, Lewisham High St, London SE13 6LH; Tel 020 8333 3000
Manager (Service Unit) Tony Lawpor

OTHER ENQUIRIES

Communications and PR, Social Services, Catford, London SE6 4RU; Tel 020 8314 8544
Manager (Service Unit) Vacancy

FAMILY ASSESSMENT CENTRE

Family Assessment Centre 33 Wickham Rd, Brockley, London SE4 1PW; Tel 020 8691 9422
Manager (Service Unit) Ronike van der Cungel

DAY CENTRES FOR ADULTS WITH LEARNING DISABILITIES

Lifestyles Centre 29–39 Clarendon Rise, London SE13 5ES; Tel 020 8852 9302
Manager Carole Britton
(152)

Mulberry Education Centre 15 Amersham Vale, London SE14 6LE; Tel 020 8691 4515
Manager V. Warren
(140)

RESIDENTIAL ACCOMMODATION FOR PEOPLE WITH LEARNING DIFFICULTIES

Clarendon Rise 43 Slaithwaite Rd, London SE13 6DJ; Tel 020 8852 4545
Manager Vacancy
(24)

Community Support Team Ballantyne, Lushington Rd, Bellingham, London SE6 3RJ; Tel 020 8695 9538
Manager Andio Oliver

DAY CENTRES FOR PEOPLE WITH MENTAL HEALTH PROBLEMS

Compass Day Centre 34 Watson St, Deptford, London SE8 4AU; Tel 020 8694 6519
Manager (Service Unit) R. Lilley

Independents Centre Independents Rd, London SE3; Tel 020 8852 7489
Manager (Service Unit) R. Lilley

Kirkdale Resource Centre 200 Kirkdale, Sydenham, London SE26 4ML; Tel 020 8676 0441
Manager H. Harries

Northover Support Centre 102 Northover Downham, Bromley, Kent BR1 5JX; Tel 020 8695 8891
Manager (Service Unit)   R. Lilley

ACCOMMODATION FOR PEOPLE WITH MENTAL HEALTH PROBLEMS

Honor Lea 103–117 Brockley Rise, London SE23 1LN; Tel 020 8699 5181
Manager (Service Unit)   A. Humphrey

DAY CENTRE FOR PEOPLE WITH DISABILITIES

Ladywell Centre 148 Dressington Ave, London SE4 1JJ; Tel 020 8690 8140
Centre Manager   Bob Shaw

DAY CENTRES FOR ELDERLY PEOPLE

Calabash Centre 24–26 George La, London SE13 6HH; Tel 020 8461 3420
Manager   Obashie Obeng
   (100)

Mental Health in the Elderly Resource Centre Laurelbrook MHE Resource Centre, Waters Rd, London SE6 1UG; Tel (Day Care) 020 8695 6802; (Residential) 020 8698 6843
Manager (Day Care)   Patrick Umeran
Manager (Residential Care)   Amaechi Nyaenic

Obelisk Riverdale, The Lewisham Centre, London SE13; Tel 020 8318 4487

St. Laurence 37 Bromley Rd, London SE6 2TS

Saville including the Vietnamese Elderly Club 436 Lewisham High St, London SE13

DAY CENTRE

Woodpecker 100 Woodpecker Rd, London SE14 6EU; Tel 020 8692 8025
Centre Manager   J. Angell
   Elderly PH

LEWISHAM LINKLINE

A 24-hour central alarm system for elderly people and younger physically disabled people living in Community Housing Schemes and elderly tenants in other council and private properties.
Manager   L. Sanford
Flat 17, Roseview, London SE13 7AF; Tel 020 8690 0440

MEALS SERVICES

Meals-on-wheels provided by the Council seven days a week. This service is available through Local Social Services Offices.

EMERGENCY DUTY TEAM

Flat 17, Roseview, London SE13 7AF; Tel 020 8690 0440
Manager   D. Owen (Acting)

Education and Culture

Lewisham Education, London Borough of Lewisham, 3rd Fl, Laurence Hse, 1 Catford Rd, London SE6 4RU; Tel 020 8314 6200; Fax 020 8314 3039
Head (Pupil Services)   Christine Grice
Service Unit Manager (SEN)   D. Delve
Principal Educational Psychologist   Vacancy

Educational Psychology and Learning Support Service

New Woodlands Centre, 49 Shroffold Rd, Bromley, Kent BR1 5PD; Tel 020 8314 7041
Head of Service   Vacancy

SPECIAL SCHOOLS

Anerley School Versailles Rd, London SE20 8AX; Tel 020 8402 2929
Headteacher   E. Milner
   EBD

Brent Knoll School Mayow Rd, London SE23 2XH; Tel 020 8699 1047
Headteacher   Jon Sharpe

Greenvale School 69 Perry Rise, London SE23 2QU; Tel 020 8699 6515
Headteacher   P.A. Munro
   SLD

Meadowgate School Revelon Rd, Brockley, London SE4 2PR; Tel 020 7635 9022
Headteacher   R. Leszczynski
   MLD

New Woodlands School 49 Shroffold Rd, Downham, Bromley, Kent BR1 5PD; Tel 020 8314 9911
Headteacher   D. Harper
   EBD

Pendragon School 59 Pendragon Rd, Bromley, Kent BR1 5LD; Tel 020 8698 9738
Headteacher   P. Martinez
   MLD

Sedghill Partial Hearing Unit Sedgehill Rd, London SE6 3QW
Head (Hearing Unit)   M. Jefferson

Watergate School 12 Church Grn, London SE13 7UU; Tel 020 8314 1751
Headteacher   A. Youd
   SLD

EARLY YEARS CENTRES

Amersham Road Early Years Centre Amersham Rd, New Cross, London SE14 6QH;
E-mail amersham.eyc@leys.org.uk; Tel 020 8691 1114
Head of Centre   Yvonne Ellis

Clyde Early Childhood Centre Alverton St, London SE8 5LW; E-mail clyde.eyc@leys.org.uk; Tel 020 8692 3899
Head (Childcare)   Tracey Hill

Grove Street Early Years Centre 231 Grove St, London SE8 3PZ; E-mail grovestreet.eyc@leys.org.uk; Tel 020 8692 2297
Head of Centre   Helen Rooney

Heathside Early Years Centre 31 Melville Hse, Sparta St, London SE10 8DP; E-mail heathside.eyc@leys.org.uk; Tel 020 8691 7929
Head of Centre   Janet Brannan

Honor Oak Early Years Centre Brockley Way, London SE4 2LW; E-mail honoroak.eyc@leys.org.uk; Tel 020 7639 1802
Head of Centre   Daphne Holland

Ladywell Early Years Centre 30 Rushey Mead, London SE4 1JJ; E-mail ladywell.eyc@leys.org.uk; Tel 020 8690 9845
Head of Centre   Claire Gurbett

Louise House Early Years Centre Louise Hse, Dartmouth Rd, London SE23 3HZ;
E-mail louise.house.eyc@leys.org.uk; Tel 020 8291 5771
Head of Centre   Sylvia Maguire

Rushey Green Early Years Centre 41 Rushey Grn, Catford, London SE6 4AS; E-mail rushey.green.eyc@leys.org.uk; Tel 020 8698 1608
Head of Centre   Joanne Sharpe

Woodpecker Early Years Centre 20 Woodpecker Rd, Forest Hill, London SE14 6EU;
E-mail woodpecker.eyc@leys.org.uk; Tel 020 8694 9557
Head of Centre   Denise Goodyal

7

Borough Information and Advice Centres

LEWISHAM INFORMATION OFFICE

Lewisham Library, Lewisham High St, London SE13 6LG;
Tel 020 8314 6374; Fax 020 8297 9241

LAURENCE HOUSE

1 Catford Rd, London SE6 4RU; Tel 020 8314 8757; Fax 020
8314 1992

GIFFIN STREET NEIGHBOURHOOD OFFICE

5 Giffin St, London SE8 4RJ; Tel 020 8314 6388; Fax 020 8691
9285

MERTON LONDON BOROUGH COUNCIL

www.merton.gov.uk

Population 190 000
Merton Civic Centre, London Rd, Morden, Surrey
SM4 5DX; URL www.merton.gov.uk;
E-mail postroom@merton.gov.uk; Tel 020 8274 4901
Mayor Cllr Edith Macauley
Chief Executive Vacancy
Director (Financial Services) Mike Parsons
Director (Environmental Services) Richard Rawes

Housing and Social Services Department

Tel 020 8543 2222
Director (Housing and Social Services) Rea Mattocks; Tel 020
8545 3711
Head (Community Care, Purchasing and Commissioning)
Simon Williams; Tel ext 3681
Head (Children's Services) Helen Lincoln; Tel ext 3631
Head (Housing Services) P. Ryrie; Tel ext 3683
Head (Housing Policy and Consultation) Peter Mulloy;
Tel ext 3940
Head (Information and Business Support) Jo Williams;
Tel ext 3792
Departmental Manager (Human Resources) Erica Burke;
Tel ext 3613
Manager (Housing Strategy and Development) K. Bucknill;
Tel 020 8545 3684
Manager (Performance Review and Contracts) C. Willard;
Tel 020 8545 4002
Manager (Research and Service Planning) D. Wright; Tel 020
8545 3710
Manager (Statutory Cases) M. Hurrell; Tel ext 3633

Cabinet Members

Cabinet Member for Care Services Cllr Peter McCabe (Lab)
London Borough of Merton, London Rd, Morden, Surrey
SM4 5DX; Tel 020 8545 3494
Cabinet Member for Primary Education and Children's Services
Maxi Martin (Lab)
London Borough of Merton, London Rd, Morden, Surrey
SM4 5DX

DIVISIONAL OFFICES

Children's Services Division

Worsfold Hse, Church Rd, Mitcham, Surrey CR4 3BE;
Tel 020 8545 4201
Manager (Fieldwork Services) Vacancy; Tel 020 8545 4201
ext 4224

Community Care Provider Service Division

Adjacent to Chaucer Centre, Canterbury Rd, Morden,
Surrey SM4 6PX; Tel 020 8543 6103
Manager (Direct Provision) Pat Nethergate; Tel 020 8288
6465

Community Care Purchasing and Commissioning (Older People Services)

Gifford Hse, 67c St. Helier Ave, Morden, Surrey; Tel 020
8545 4360
Service Manager (Older People and Home Care) Cindy Baker;
Tel 020 8545 4364

Community Care Purchasing and Commissioning (Adult Services)

42 Russell Rd, Wimbledon, London SW19 1QL; Tel 020 8545
4490; Fax 020 8543 4555; Minicom 020 8543 3212
Community Care Manager (Disability Services) N. Adamson;
Tel 020 8545 4490 ext 4498
*Community Care Manager (Mental Health and Substance
Misuse)* Craig Chalmers; Tel 020 8545 4490 ext 4499
Manager (Direct Provision) Andy Ottaway (Acting); Tel 020
8545 4490 ext 4500
Including Borough-wide services for adults with learning
disabilities.

DAY NURSERIES

Bond Road Day Nursery 55 Bond Rd, Mitcham, Surrey;
Tel 020 8640 3258
Officer-in-Charge S. Doyle
(50)

Leyton Road Family Centre 21 Leyton Rd, Wimbledon,
London SW19 1LY; Tel 020 8542 3989
Project Manager Jacqueline Georglou
(50)

RESPITE CARE HOUSE FOR CHILDREN WITH DISABILITIES

Brightwell, Bordesley Rd, Morden, Surrey; Tel 020 8646
6055
Officer-in-Charge John Deegan

DAY CENTRES FOR PEOPLE WITH LEARNING DISABILITIES

**Employment Assessment Centre for People with Learning
Disabilities** Weir Rd, Wimbledon, London SW19 8UG;
Tel 020 8879 3606
Assistant Manager Sarah Lilley

High Path Day Centre 61 High Path, London SW19 2JY;
Tel 020 8241 2233
Manager Vaughan Charlton

Jan Malinowski Social Education Centre Wandle Way,
Willow La, Mitcham, Surrey; Tel 020 8646 8300
Manager Jo McDonald
(130)

DAY CENTRE FOR THE YOUNG PHYSICALLY HANDICAPPED

All Saints Centre All Saints Rd, Wimbledon, London
SW19 1BX; Tel 020 8542 9587
Manager J. Carroll

RESIDENTIAL UNIT FOR PEOPLE WITH LEARNING DISABILITIES

15 Haslemere Ave, London; Tel 020 8947 6673
Contact J. Beavis

GROUP HOMES FOR PEOPLE WITH LEARNING DISABILITIES

There are 13 group homes for people with learning
disabilities.

DAY CENTRE FOR PEOPLE WITH MENTAL HEALTH PROBLEMS

Chapel Orchard Church Rd, Mitcham, Surrey; Tel 020 8545 4848
Contact Anne Marie Harrison

ACCOMMODATION FOR PEOPLE WITH MENTAL HEALTH PROBLEMS

There is one group home for people with mental health problems.

DAY CENTRES FOR OLDER PEOPLE

Eastway Day Centre 44 Eastway, Morden, Surrey; Tel 020 8542 7599
Manager Patrick Finn
(30)
Pollards Hill Day Centre and Luncheon Club South Lodge Ave, Mitcham, Surrey; Tel 020 8679 0305
Manager Y. Lowe
(20)

RESIDENTIAL HOMES FOR OLDER PEOPLE

There are eight voluntary homes for the elderly.

Education, Leisure and Libraries Department

Merton Civic Centre, London Rd, Morden, Surrey SM4 5DX; Tel 020 8543 2222
Director (Education, Leisure and Libraries) Sue Evans
Team Leader (SEN Group) Debbie West
Case Worker (SEN Group) Diane O'Calloghan
Case Worker (SEN Group) Wendy Bolsover
Case Worker (SEN Group) R. Macmullen
Senior Education Social Worker Ian Hogg

CHILD GUIDANCE CLINIC

Worsfold House Chapel Orchard, Church Rd, Mitcham, Surrey CR4 3BE; Tel 020 8648 4066

SPECIAL SCHOOLS

Cricket Green School Lower Green West, Surrey CR4 3AF; Tel 020 8640 1177
Headteacher Celia Dawson
MLD
Melrose School Church Rd, Mitcham, Surrey CR4 3BE; Tel 020 8646 2620
Headteacher D. Eglin
Secondary EBD (47)
St. Ann's School Bordesley Rd, Morden, Surrey SM4 5LT; Tel 020 8648 9737
Headteacher T. Harvey
SLD

EDUCATIONAL PSYCHOLOGY SERVICE

Merton Civic Centre London Rd, Morden, Surrey SM4 5DX; Tel 020 8545 3268

OTHER UNITS

Assessment Unit c/o Merton Abbey First School, High Path, Merton, London SW19 2JY; Tel 020 8542 7129
Language Development Unit c/o Singlegate Primary School, South Gdns, London SW19 2NT; Tel 020 8542 6503
Learning Support Service Canterbury Bldg, Canterbury Rd, Morden, Surrey; Tel 020 8646 6279

Housing Advice

Civic Centre, London Rd, Surrey SM4 5DX; Tel 020 8545 3734

NEWHAM LONDON BOROUGH COUNCIL

www.newham.gov.uk

Population 230 000
Town Hall, Barking Rd, London E6 2RP;
URL www.newham.gov.uk; Tel 020 8430 2000
Chief Executive Dave Burbage
Chief Finance Officer Bob Heaton
Director (Housing) Chris Wood
Bridge Hse, 320 High St, Stratford, London E15
Director (Environment) Malcolm Smith

Social Services Department

Broadway Hse, 322 High St, Stratford, London E15 1AJ;
URL www.newham.gov.uk; Tel 020 8430 2000;
(Emergency) 020 8983 8000; Fax 020 8557 8827
Director (Social Services) Kathryn Hudson
Assistant Director (Adults) Edward Roberts
Assistant Director (Children and Families) Jenny Dibsdall
Assistant Director (Strategy and Performance) David Cubey
Head (Integrated Commissioning – Adults) Roger Harris
Head (Children's Service Planning and Review) Jackie Cook
Head (Human Resources) Beverley Williams
Head (Administration) Michelle Mills
Head (Policy and Performance) Althea Wilkinson
Head (Finance) Hitesha Jolapara
Head (Quality) Bronwen Williams
Head (Adult Community and Mental Health)
Caroline Godleman
Head (Project and Partnerships) Pratima Solanki
Senior Commissioning Manager (Children) Robert Maragh
Service Manager (Assessment and Care of Older People)
Charmaine Wiggins
Service Manager (Adult Learning Disabilities) Ruth Darling
Service Manager (Children in Need) Sue Williams
Service Manager (Continuing Care) Eulyn Joseph
Service Manager (Placement Services) Jenny Elliott
Service Manager (Domestic Violence and Welfare Rights)
Frances Martineau
Service Manager (Adult Disability Services) Pat Lion
Service Manager (Home Support Services) Avril Frankish
Service Manager (Residential and Day Services – Older People)
Ian Kennedy
Team Manager (Asylum) Claudia Shrimplin

Key Councillors for Newham Social Services

Mayoral Adviser (Social Services and Health) Quintin Peppiatt
Mayoral Adviser (Equalities and Social Inclusion) Neil Wilson
Cabinet Member (Education) Graham Lane

LOCAL SERVICE CENTRES

Beckton 1 Kingsford Way, Beckton, London E6 3JQ; Tel 020 8430 2000
Canning Town 3 Beckton Rd, London E16 4DE
ICS Manager P. Uddin
Docklands 4 Pier Pde, North Woolwich, London E16 2LJ; Tel 020 8430 2000
East Ham Town Hall Annexe, 330–354 Barking Rd, East Ham, London E6 2RT
ICS Manager M. Fuller

Forest Gate 4–20 Woodgrange Rd, Forest Gate, London E7 0QH; Tel 020 8430 2000

Manor Park 685–689 Romford Rd, Manor Park, London E12 5AD; Tel 020 8430 2003
Team Manager (Learning Difficulties) Howard Masters

Stratford 112–118 The Grove, Stratford, London E15 1NS
ICS Manager M. Wenham

SOCIAL SERVICES OFFICES

Canning Town Office 5 Beckton Rd, Canning Town, London E16 4ED; Tel 020 7474 7070

East Ham Office High Street South, East Ham, London E6 2RP; Tel 020 8472 1430

Stratford Office Unit 10, Stratford Office Village, London E15 4EA; Tel 020 8519 5454

SOCIAL WORK IN HOSPITALS

Newham General Hospital Glen Rd, Plaistow, London E13 8SI; Tel 020 7476 4000
Team Manager S. Jones

Sickle Cell and Thalassaemia Unit Plaistow Hospital, Samson St, London E13 9EH; Tel 020 8586 6386
Senior Practioner L. Geddes

St. Andrew's Hospital Derons Rd, Bow, London E3 3NT; Tel 020 7476 4000
Team Manager A. Zaidi

DAY SERVICES

Arragon Road Day Centre 95 Arragon Rd, London E6 1QN; Tel 020 8472 2633; Fax 020 8552 5322
Manager Marianne Bond
Elderly (65)

Cumberland Road Centre 192 Cumberland Rd, Plaistow, London E13 8IT; Tel 020 7474 4814; 020 7474 4922; Fax 020 7476 1364
Manager Gill Teamer
(52)

Mariner Road Day Centre 1 Mariner Rd, Manor Park, London E12 5RX; Tel 020 8514 5621; Fax 020 8478 6334
Manager Marianne Bond

Samuel Boyce Day Centre 192 Cumberland Rd, Plaistow, London E13 8IT; Tel 020 7474 4814; 020 7474 4922; Fax 020 7476 1334
Contact Gill Teather

Education Department

Broadway Hse, 322 High St, Stratford, London E15 1AJ; URL www.newham.gov.uk; Tel 020 8430 2000; Fax 020 8503 0014
Director (Education) P. Maddison
Divisional Director (School Management, Advice and Support Services) A. Panton
Divisional Director (School Improvement Support) A. Drizi
Divisional Director (Social Inclusion and Special Needs Support) C. Kiernan
Principal Educational Psychologist I. Millward

SPECIAL SCHOOLS

Eleanor Smith School North St, Plaistow, London E13 9HN; Tel 020 8471 0018
Headteacher L. Haddock (Acting)
EBD (primary)

John F. Kennedy School Pitchford St, Stratford, London E15 4RZ; Tel 020 8534 8544
Headteacher G. Goldsmith
SLD

INFORMATION AND ADVICE CENTRES

Town Hall East Ham, London URL www.newham.gov.uk; Tel 020 8430 2000

REDBRIDGE LONDON BOROUGH COUNCIL
www.redbridge.gov.uk

Population 238 634
Political Composition: Con: 33, Lab: 20, LD: 9
Town Hall, 128–142 High Rd, Ilford, Essex IG1 1DD;
    URL www.redbridge.gov.uk;
    E-mail customer.cc@redbridge.gov.uk; Tel 020 8554 5000
Chief Executive Roger Hampson;
    E-mail delia.stott@redbridge.gov.uk; Tel 020 8708 2100;
    Fax 020 8478 2356
Chief Finance Officer Geoff Pearce
Lynton Hse, 255–259 High Rd, Ilford, Essex IG1 1NY;
    Tel 020 8708 3588; Fax 020 8708 3185
Chief Officer (Engineering and Building Services)
    Dave Renvoize
Lynton Hse, 255–259 High Rd, Ilford, Essex IG1 1NY;
    Tel 020 8708 3410; Fax 020 8708 3970
Chief Legal Officer and Council Solicitor Heidi Chottin;
    Tel 020 8708 2201; Fax 020 8708 2981

Social Services

Social Services comprises three separate departments – Community Care, Children and Families and Housing, each headed by a Chief Officer answerable to the Director of Social Services and Social Inclusion.
Ley Street Hse, 497–499 Ley St, Ilford, Essex IG2 7QX;
    E-mail john.drew@redbridge.gov.uk; Tel 020 8478 3020;
    (Children and Families Services) 020 8478 9535; Fax 020 8478 9523 (Community Care Services)
Director (Social Services and Social Inclusion) John Drew
Chief Community Care Officer John Powell
Chief Housing Officer Vacancy

Cabinet Member for Social Services and Health

Secretariat A.T. Hughes (Con)
c/o Members' Secretariat, Town Hall, Ilford, Essex

Social Services and Housing Scrutiny Committee

Con: 6, Lab: 4, Co-opted: 4, LD 1
Chair R. Cole (Con)
c/o Members Secretariat, Town Hall, Ilford, Essex
Vice-Chair A. Powell (Con)
c/o Members Secretariat, Town Hall, Ilford, Essex
Members of the Committee
Lab: S. Green, R. Mahal, F. Maravala, K. Turner.
Con: C. Cummins, C. Elliman, H. Moth, L. Sladden.
LD: J. Tyne.
Co-opted: Mrs Gregory, J. Hogben, Mr Khushnood-Rauf, A. Knight.

Children and Families Services

Ley Street Hse, 497–499 Ley St, Ilford, Essex IG2 7QX;
    Tel 020 8708 5752; Fax 020 8708 5403
Chief Children and Families Officer Patrick Power;
    E-mail patrick.power@redbridge.gov.uk

CHILDREN'S HOMES

Bathurst Road Children's Home 2–4 Bathurst Rd, Ilford, Essex IG1 4LA; Tel 020 8518 0262; Fax 020 8518 0228

Station Road Children's Home Barkingside, Ilford, Essex IG6 1NB; Tel 020 8708 7542; Fax 020 8708 7454

COMMISSIONING AND QUALITY

Ley Street Hse, 497–499 Ley St, Ilford, Essex IG2 7QX; Tel 020 8708 5043; Fax 020 8708 5557
Principal Officer Roger Carruthers;
  E-mail roger.carruthers@redbridge.gov.uk

QUALITY PROTECTS

Ley Street Hse, 497–499 Ley St, Ilford, Essex IG2 7QX; Tel 020 8708 5236; Fax 020 8708 5408
Principal Officer Susanna Shouls;
  E-mail susanna.shouls@redbridge.gov.uk

FAMILY CENTRES AND DISABILITY SERVICES

Station Rd, Barkingside, Ilford, Essex IG6 1NB; Tel 020 8708 7533; Fax 020 8708 7458
Principal Officer Caroline Cutts;
  E-mail caroline.cutts@redbridge.gov.uk

FAMILY DAY CENTRES

Albert Road Family Day Centre 53 Albert Rd, Ilford, Essex; Tel 020 8553 3083; Fax 020 8514 1733

Woodford Family Day Centre Liston Way, Woodford Green, Essex IG8 7BL; Tel 020 8708 7646; Fax 020 8514 9144

Thackeray Drive Family Day Centre and Residential Assessment Unit Thackeray Dr, Chadwell Heath, Romford, Essex RM6 4RE; Tel 020 8708 7778; Fax 020 8597 7339

RESPITE AND DAY CARE CENTRE

13 Granville Rd, Ilford, Essex IG1 4RU; Tel 020 8708 2408; Fax 020 8518 5829

FOSTERING AND ADOPTION SERVICE

235 Grove Rd, Chadwell Heath, Romford, Essex RM6 4XD; Tel 020 8708 7760; Fax 020 8503 8072
Principal Officer Ruth Holmes;
  E-mail ruth.holmes@redbridge.gov.uk

SOCIAL WORK SERVICES

Ley Street Hse, 497–499 Ley St, Ilford, Essex IG2 7QX; Tel 020 8708 5152; Fax 020 8708 5979
Principal Officer Paul McCarthy;
  E-mail paul.mccarthy@redbridge.gov.uk

ADOLESCENT SERVICES

Adolescent Resource Centre Station Rd, Barkingside, Ilford, Essex IG6 1NB; Tel 020 8708 7540; Fax 020 8708 7454
Principal Officer Martin Halsey;
  E-mail martin.halsey@redbridge.gov.uk

Youth Offending Team Fencepiece Rd, Barkingside, Ilford, Essex IG6 2JS; Tel 020 8708 9303; Fax 020 8708 9302
Manager Kathy Nixon;
  E-mail kathy.nixon@redbridge.gov.uk

ASYLUM SEEKERS SERVICE

Ilford Chambers, Ilford, Essex IG1 2AF; Tel 020 8708 6606; Fax 020 8708 6658
Principal Officer Carole Brown

Community Care Service

Ley Street Hse, 497–499 Ley St, Ilford, Essex IG2 7QX; Tel 020 8708 5595; Fax 020 8708 5332
Chief Community Care Officer John Powell;
  E-mail john.powell@redbridge.gov.uk

COMMUNITY CARE ADVICE CENTRE

Aldborough Rd North, Newbury Pk, Ilford, Essex IG2 7BR; Tel 020 8503 8833; Fax 020 8503 8198

ASSESSMENT AND DISABILITY

Ley Street Hse, 497–499 Ley St, Ilford, Essex IG2 7QX; Tel 020 8708 5169; Fax 020 8708 5586
Principal Officer Pauline Brown;
  E-mail pauline.brown@redbridge.gov.uk

DAY CENTRE

Link Place Development Centre Bramston Cl, Hainault, Ilford, Essex IG6 3DU; Tel 020 8501 2220; Fax 020 8500 0309

LEARNING DISABILITY

852 Cranbrook Rd, Barkingside, Ilford, Essex IG6 1HZ; Tel 020 8708 7046; Fax 020 8708 7022
Principal Officer Mark Humble;
  E-mail mark.humble@redbridge.gov.uk

DAY CENTRES

Chadwell Centre 161 Gresham Dr, Chadwell Heath, Romford, Essex RM6 4TR; Tel 020 8599 7401; Fax 020 8599 1010

Mulberry Lodge Day Centre 47–50 Mulberry Way, Barkingside, Ilford, Essex IG6 1EU; Tel 020 8551 4719; Fax 020 8551 7415

Woodbine Club 25 Woodbine Pl, Wanstead, London E11 2RH; Tel 020 8708 7403; Fax 020 8708 7404

MENTAL HEALTH

Ley Street Hse, 497–499 Ley St, Ilford, Essex IG2 7QX; Tel 020 8708 5424; Fax 020 8708 5586
Principal Officer Peter Spelman;
  E-mail peter.spelman@redbridge.co.uk

DAY CENTRE

Ley Street Day Centre 497–499 Ley St, Ilford, Essex IG2 7QX; Tel 020 8708 5112; Fax 020 8708 5977

RESIDENTIAL ACCOMMODATION FOR PEOPLE WITH MENTAL HEALTH PROBLEMS

Abury House 485 Aldborough Road North, Newbury Pk, Ilford, Essex IG2 7SY; Tel 020 8599 7755; Fax 020 8599 9153

OLDER PEOPLE

Ley Street House 497–499 Ley St, Ilford, Essex IG2 7QX; Tel 020 8708 5613; Fax 020 8708 5586
Principal Officer Bryn Williams;
  E-mail bryn.williams@redbridge.gov.uk

DAY CENTRES FOR OLDER PEOPLE

Elderberries Day Centre Broadmead Rd, Woodford Grn, Ilford, Essex IG8 0AD; Tel 020 8708 7641; Fax 020 8505 3977

Fullwell Cross Day Centre Fencepiece Rd, Barkingside, Ilford, Essex IG6 2JS; Tel 020 8500 3606; Fax 020 8500 1202

Kielder Close Day Centre 3 Kielder Cl, Hainault, Ilford, Essex IG6 3ER; Tel 020 8500 8304; Fax 020 8500 1355

Mildmay House Day Centre 69 Albert Rd, Ilford, Essex IG1 1HP; Tel 020 8553 3616; Fax 020 8514 1225

Oakfield Day Centre Oakfield Lodge, Albert Rd, Ilford, Essex IG1 1HJ; Tel 020 8514 4766; Fax 020 8553 9034

ACCOMMODATION FOR THE ELDERLY

There is one residential care home for the elderly.

7

COMMISSIONING AND QUALITY

Ley Street Hse, 497–499 Ley St, Ilford, Essex IG2 7QX;
    Tel 020 8708 5153; Fax 020 8708 5336
Principal Officer   Vacancy

Housing Services

17–23 Clements Rd, Ilford, Essex IG1 1AG; Tel 020 8708
    4156; Fax 020 8708 4119
Chief Housing Officer   Vacancy

Education Service

Lynton Hse, 255–259 High Rd, Ilford, Essex IG1 1NN;
    Tel 020 8708 3839; Fax 020 8708 3894
Director (Education and Lifelong Learning)   Edwina Grant,
    MA, MBA
Head (Pupil Support, Access and Inclusion)   Colin Moore
Principal Educational Welfare Officer   Stephen Clarke

EDUCATIONAL PSYCHOLOGY SERVICE

852 Cranbrook Rd, Barkingside, Ilford, Essex IG6 1HZ;
    Tel 020 8478 3020 ext 87071 / 87023; Fax 020 8708
    7037
Principal Educational Psychologist   David Townley

SPECIAL SCHOOLS

Ethel Davis School   258 Barley La, Goodmayes, Ilford, Essex
IG3 8XS; Tel 020 8599 1768
Headteacher   P. Bouldstridge
(Day)
    2–17 PH

Hatton School   Roding Lane South, Woodford Grn, Essex
IG8 8EU; Tel 020 8551 4131
Headteacher   Miss L. Richardson

Hyleford School   200 Loxford La, Ilford, Essex IG3 9AR;
Tel 020 8590 7272
Headteacher   G.D. Morgan
(Day)
    3–19 SLD

Little Heath Foundation School   Hainault Rd, Little Heath,
Romford, Essex RM6 5RX; Tel 020 8599 4864
Headteacher   P. Johnson
    11–16 (145)

New Rush Hall School   Fencepiece Rd, Hainault, Ilford,
Essex IG6 2LJ; Tel 020 8501 3951
Headteacher   J.V. d'Abbro, BEd(Hons)
    (30)

First Stop Shop

Lynton Hse, Ilford, Essex IG1 1NN; Tel 020 8554 8000;
    Fax 020 8708 3984

ADVICE CENTRES

Housing Advice Centre Duty Desk   17–23 Clements Rd,
Ilford, Essex IG1 1AG; Tel 020 8708 4002 84034; Fax 020
8708 4172
Manager   A. Baldock

Children and Families Advice Centre   Ley Street Hse,
497–499 Ley St, Ilford, Essex IG2 7QX; Tel 020 8708 5657;
Fax 020 8708 5352
Team Manager   Caroline Cutts

Community Services Functional Unit   4th Fl, Ley Street Hse,
Ley St, Ilford, Essex IG2 7QX;
E-mail nicola.parry@redbridge.gov.uk; Tel 020 8708 5445;
Fax 020 8708 5170
Principal Officer   Nicola Parry

RICHMOND UPON THAMES
LONDON BOROUGH COUNCIL
www.richmond.gov.uk

Population 183 500
Political Composition: Con: 39, LD: 15
Civic Centre, 44 York St, Twickenham, Greater London
    TW1 3BZ; URL www.richmond.gov.uk; Tel 020 8891
    1411
Assistant Director (Housing Services)   R. Birtles
Civic Centre, 44 York St, Twickenham, Greater London
    TW1 3BZ; Tel 020 8891 7881; Fax 020 8891 7482
Assistant Director (Housing Services)   B. Castle
Civic Centre, 44 York St, Twickenham, Greater London
    TW1 3BZ; Tel 020 8891 7881; Fax 020 8891 7482
Chief Executive   Joan Mager
Richmond and Twickenham NHS Primary Care, Thames
    Hse, 180 High St, Teddington, Greater London
    TW11 8HU; Tel 020 8973 3000; Fax 020 8973 3001
Head (Construction and Property)   W. Dyke, MBEng; Tel 020
    8891 7393; Fax 020 8891 7702

Social Services and Housing Directorate

42 York St, Twickenham, Greater London TW1 3BW;
    URL www.rich.gov.uk; Tel 020 8891 7600; Fax 020 8891
    7719
Assistant Director (Services for Children and Families)
    B. Murray
Assistant Director (Services for Adults)   J. Rogan
Assistant Director (Strategy and Resources)   C. Brewin
Assistant Director (Housing)   B. Castle
Assistant Director (Housing)   R. Birtles
Director (Social Services and Housing)   Jeff Jerome

Mortlake Family Support Centre   The Old Court Hse, Sheen
La, Mortlake, London SW14 8LP; Tel 020 8876 7294
Manager   A. Carroll

Twickenham Family Support Centre   Gifford Lodge, 27
Popes Ave, Twickenham, Greater London TW2 5TR; Tel 020
8894 5046

Children Looked After Team   91 Queen's Rd, Twickenham,
Greater London TW1 4EU; Tel 020 8891 7607
Manager   Paul Walsh

COMMUNITY HOME

Teddington Park Community Home   40 Teddington Pk,
Teddington, Greater London; Tel 020 8977 1683
Contact   Alma Noveal

INTERMEDIATE TREATMENT CENTRE

Strathmore Centre   Strathmore Rd, Teddington, Greater
London TW11 8UH; Tel 020 8943 1691
Contact   Julie Martin

YOUTH OFFENDING TEAM

Strathmore Centre
Contact   Robert Henderson

COMMUNITY TEAMS

Community Support Service   1a Grove Rd, Richmond,
Surrey TW10 6HN; Tel 020 8948 8863
Contact   E. Hillier

Community Team (Learning Difficulties – Richmond)   Old
Court Hse, Sheen La, London SW14 8LP; Tel 020 8392 1088

Community Team (Learning Difficulties – Twickenham)
Teddington Centre, 18 Queen's Rd, Teddington, Greater
London TW11 0LR; Tel 020 8977 6881

Community Team (Mental Health – Hampton) The Maddison Centre, 140 Church Rd, Teddington, Greater London; Tel 020 8977 3156

Community Team (Mental Health – Richmond) Richmond Royal, Kew Foot Rd, Richmond, Surrey TW9 2TE; Tel 020 8940 3331
Contact (East Team) Vivienne Williamson
Contact (West Team) Damien Bregnnan

Community Team (Mental Health – Twickenham) Richmond Hamlet, Kenfoot Rd, Richmond, Surrey TW9 2TE; Tel 020 8355 1967

Community Drug and Alcohol Team Richmond Royal, Kew Foot Rd, Richmond, Surrey TW9 2TE; Tel 020 8940 3331

DAY CENTRES FOR PEOPLE WITH LEARNING DIFFICULTIES

The Avenue Centre 1 Normansfield Ave, Teddington, Greater London TW11 9RP; Tel 020 8977 4343
Contact S.P. Bailey

Mortlake Bakery and Training Development Unit Lower Richmond Rd, Mortlake, London SW14 7HJ; Tel 020 8392 9370
Contact R. Taylor

HOMES FOR PEOPLE WITH LEARNING DIFFICULTIES

Cambridge Park Home 40 Cambridge Pk, Twickenham, Greater London; Tel 020 8892 6375
Contact M. Wood

Crane Way Home 36 Crane Way, Whitton, Greater London TW2 7NJ; Tel 020 8894 5742
Manager V. Hamilton

Cross Street Home 26 Cross St, Hampton Hill, Greater London; Tel 020 8783 0973
Contact J. King

Munster Road Home 11 Munster Rd, Teddington, Greater London; Tel 020 8943 9690
Manager K. Sharpe

Princes Road Home 46 Princes Rd, Teddington, Greater London; Tel 020 8614 8090
Contact C. Gregg

Respite Service 26 Egerton Rd, Twickenham, Greater London; Tel 020 8891 6308
Manager V. Steven

Tudor Avenue Home 3 Tudor Ave, Hampton, Greater London; Tel 020 8979 2696
Contact P. McBride

DAY CENTRES FOR PEOPLE WITH MENTAL HEALTH NEEDS

The Level Crossing Day Centre 27 Sheen La, Mortlake, London SW14 8HY; Tel 020 8876 4017
Contact V. Ritchie

Mereway Centre Mereway Rd, Twickenham, Greater London TW2 6RF; Tel 020 8898 6880
Contact J. Bell

Twining Employment Resource Centre Grimwood Rd, Twickenham, Greater London TW1 1BY; Tel 020 8892 6786
Contact C. Llorente

ACCOMMODATION FOR PEOPLE WITH MENTAL HEALTH NEEDS

Kingston Lane Home 21 Kingston La, Teddington, Greater London; Tel 020 8977 8996
Contact K. O'Pray

DAY CENTRE FOR PEOPLE WITH PHYSICAL DISABILITIES

Whitton Day Centre Access Project 111a Knellger Rd, Whitton, Greater London; Tel 020 8898 3858
Contact C. Downs

DAY CENTRES FOR OLDER PEOPLE

Barnes Green Day Centre Church Rd, Barnes, London SW13 9HE; Tel 020 8876 2377
Manager Ferry Senevirante

Ham Day Centre Woodville Rd, Ham, Richmond, Surrey TW10 7QW; Tel 020 8948 0911
Contact P. Garner

Sheen Lane Day Centre 74 Sheen La, London SW14 8LP; Tel 020 8876 1706
Contact N. Galvin

Twickenham Day Centre Arragon Rd, Twickenham, Greater London TW1 3NH; Tel 020 8891 1252
Contact S. Walsh

DAY CENTRE FOR OLDER PEOPLE SUFFERING FROM DEMENTIA

Tangley Hall Day Centre 1 Bramble La, Hampton, Greater London TW12 3XB; Tel 020 8783 1976
Contact Jenny Bailey

MEALS ON WHEELS SERVICE

Administered by the Social Services Department

Education, Arts and Leisure Department

7

Director (Education and Leisure Service) Anji Phillips
Assistant Director (Planning and Resources) Jessica Saraga
Assistant Director (Lifelong Learning) Philip J. Lomax
Head (School Improvement) N. Empringham
Head (Community Health Services) Dr J.D. Williamson
Senior Inspector (SEN) L. Rhead
SEN Officer Monica Quinn
Manager (Youth Service) A. Hopgood

SPECIAL SCHOOLS AND UNITS

Buckingham Assessment Unit Buckingham Rd, Hampton, Greater London TW12 3LT; Tel 020 8941 2548; Fax 020 8783 1579

Cassel Hospital Unit Cassel Hospital, Ham Common, Greater London TW10 7JF; Tel 020 8940 8181; Fax 020 8237 2996

Clarendon School Hanworth Rd, Hampton, Greater London TW12 3DH;
E-mail info@clarendon.richmond.sch.uk; Tel 020 8979 1165; Fax 020 8941 3069
    All-age

Darell Unit Darell Rd, Richmond, Surrey TW9 4LQ; Tel 020 8876 6721; Fax 020 8876 3895
    4–8

Heathfield Infant Language Unit Cobbett Rd, Twickenham, Greater London TW2 6EN; Tel 020 8894 4074; Fax 020 8893 3419
    3–8

Heathfield Junior Language Unit Cobbett Rd, Twickenham, Greater London TW2 6EN; Tel 020 8894 3525; Fax 020 8893 4073

Jigsaw ASD Unit Windham Rd, Richmond, Surrey TW9 2HP

Oldfield House Unit Oldfield Rd, Hampton, Greater London TW12 2HP; Tel 020 8979 5102; Fax 020 8941 8605
    7–11

Richmond House Buckingham Rd, Hampton, Greater London TW12 3LT; Tel 020 8941 2623; Fax 020 8783 0086
    11–16

The Russell Unit Petersham Rd, Richmond, Surrey TW10 7AH; Tel 020 8940 1446; Fax 020 8332 0985

Stanley Infant Unit Strathmore Rd, Teddington, Greater London TW11 8UE; Tel 020 8977 4793; Fax 020 8943 5579

Strathmore School Meadlands Dr, Petersham, Richmond, Surrey TW10 7ED; E-mail info@strathmore.richmond.sch.uk; Tel 020 8948 0047; Fax 020 8948 0047
All-age

Pupil Referral Service (Strathmore Centre) Strathmore Rd, Teddington, Greater London; Tel 020 8943 1691; Fax 020 8977 9558
11–16

Pupil Referral Service (Oldfield House Centre) Oldfield Rd, Hampton, Greater London TW12 2HP; Tel 020 8979 5102; Fax 020 8979 5102

SCHOOL PSYCHOLOGICAL SERVICE

58 Hampton Road Twickenham, Greater London TW2 5QB; Tel 020 8894 1288; Fax 020 8894 4292

EDUCATION WELFARE SERVICE

Hampton Road 58 Hampton Rd, Twickenham, Mitcham, Greater London; Tel 020 8893 3923; Fax 020 8894 4292

Information Centres

DEPARTMENT OF SOCIAL SERVICES

42 York St, Twickenham, Greater London TW1 3BW; Tel 020 8891 7719; Fax 020 8940 6899
All district and branch libraries, contact Department of Leisure Services; Tel 020 7940 0031.

Housing Needs

Department of Housing, London; Tel 020 8891 1411

LONDON BOROUGH OF SOUTHWARK
www.southwark.gov.uk

Political Composition: Lab: 28, LD: 30, Con: 5
Southwark Town Hall, London SE5 8UB;
   URL www.southwark.gov.uk; Tel 020 7525 5000; Fax 020 7525 5200
Director (Housing)   K. Broxup
Municipal Bldgs, Larcom St, London SE17 1EX; Tel 020 7525 5000
Director (Regeneration)   P. Evans
Chiltern Hse, Portland St, London SE17 2ES; Tel 020 7525 5000
Director (Environment)   G. Davis
Chiltern Hse, Portland St, London SE17 2ES; Tel 020 7525 5000

Social Services Department

Headquarters, Mabel Goldwin Hse, 49 Grange Wk, London SE1 3DY; Tel 020 7525 3838; (Emergency) 020 7525 5000
Executive Member (Health and Social Care)
   Cllr Catriona Moore
Strategic Director (Social Services) and Chief Executive of Southwark PCT   C. Bull
Deputy Director and Head (Children's Division)   R. Bowen
Business Development Manager (Community Care)
   C. Dorey
Manager (Adult Provider)   D. Addo
Public Relations and Communications   K. Basra
Departmental Training Officer (Children)   K. Bootle
Departmental Training Officer (Community Care)
   D. Young

DISTRICT OFFICES

Children's District North 23 Harper Rd, London SE1 6AW; Tel 020 7525 1925
Business Manager   T. Heyda

Children's Direct Services 47b East Dulwich Rd, London SE22 9BZ; Tel 020 7525 4409
Business Manager   J. O'Hagan

Children's District South Sumner Hse, Sumner Rd, London SE15 5QS; Tel 020 7525 1049
Business Manager   T. Heyda

MENTAL HEALTH SERVICES

Community Mental Health Team (North West) 27–29 Camberwell Rd, London SE5 0EZ; Tel 020 7525 2751
Locality Manager   M. Rix

Community Mental Health Team (North East) The Chaucer Resource Centre, 13 Ann Moss Way, London SE16 2TH; Tel 020 7231 4578
Locality Manager   Chris McCree

Community Mental Health Team (South) 300 Ivydale Rd, London SE15 3DG; Tel 020 7301 8000
Locality Manager   A. Witham

CHILDREN'S SERVICES

Fostering and Adoption Section 47b East Dulwich Rd, London SE22 9BZ; Tel 020 7525 4409
Manager (Residential)   J. Hughes
Manager (Adoption and Fostering)   S. Sinclair

CHILDREN'S HOMES

Abbey Street Children's Home 70 Abbey St, London; Tel 020 7231 7854

Regional Resource Centre Orchard Lodge, William Booth Rd, London SE20 8BE; Tel 020 8402 9696

St. Mary's Road Children's Home 38 St. Mary's Rd, London; Tel 020 7639 7494

Talfourd Place Children's Home 7 Talfourd Pl, London; Tel 020 7708 4680

SOUTHWARK FAMILY COURT ASSESSMENT CENTRE

Sumner House Centre Sumner Rd, London SE15 5QS; Tel 020 7525 7975

HOMELESS FAMILIES

Accommodation for homeless families is the responsibility of the Housing Department.

DAY CENTRES FOR PEOPLE WITH LEARNING DIFFICULTIES

Grange Project 12–13 Grange Rd, London SE1 3BG; Tel 020 7237 9518

Queens Road Day Centre 133–137 Queens Rd, London SE15 2ND; Tel 020 7252 8276

HOMES FOR PEOPLE WITH LEARNING DIFFICULTIES

Dover Lodge Home 41 Wood Vale, London SE23 3DS; Tel 020 8693 5460

Friern Road Home 114 Friern Rd, London SE22 0AZ; Tel 020 8299 9860
Children

Gibson House 12 The Grange, London SE1 3AG; Tel 020 7252 3762

Grosvenor Terrace Home 52–60 and 100 Grosvenor Terr, London SE5 0NP; Tel 020 7277 1619

Mount Adon Park Home 49 Mount Adon Pk, London; Tel 020 8299 0305

Orient Street Home 19 Orient St, London SE11 4SR; Tel 020 7582 5907

Therapia Road Home 26 Therapia Rd, London SE22 0SE; Tel 020 8693 3822

DAY CENTRE FOR PEOPLE WITH MENTAL HEALTH PROBLEMS

Castle Day Centre Hampton St, London SE1 6SN; Tel 020 7703 4596

Disabilities Services 151 Walworth Rd, London SE17 1RY; Tel 020 7525 2139
Principal Care Manager (Learning Disabilities) R. Young
Principal Care Manager (Physical Disabilities) J. Emery

Occupational Therapy Woodmill Offices, Neckinger, London SE16 3QN; Tel 020 7525 3959
Principal Care Manager C. Purdie

DAY CENTRES FOR THE ELDERLY

Fred Francis Day Centre 269–281 Lordship La, London SE22 8JG; Tel 020 7525 2980

Southwark Park Road Day Centre 345 Southwark Park Rd, London SE16 2JN; Tel 020 7237 0732

DAY CENTRES FOR ELDERLY PEOPLE WITH MENTAL HEALTH PROBLEMS

Evelyn Coyle Day Centre 49a Grange Wlk, London SE1 3DY; Tel 020 7525 3821

Holmhurst Day Centre 46 Half Moon La, London SE24 9JX; Tel 020 7274 6552

DAY CENTRE FOR PEOPLE WITH PHYSICAL DISABILITIES

Aylesbury Day Centre 2 Bradenham Cl, Boyson Rd, London SE17 2QB; Tel 020 7525 5216

MEALS SERVICES

For details Contact Social Services Department Tel 020 7525 3627.

Southwark Education Services

John Smith Hse, 144-152 Walworth Rd, London SE17 1JL; URL www.southwark.lgfl.net; Tel 020 7525 5001; (Information) 020 7525 5050; Fax 020 7525 5200
Director (Education and Culture Department) Dr R. Smith
Director (Schools Services) S. Jenkin

DAY NURSERIES

Ann Bernadt Day Nursery Chandler Way, London SE15 6DY; Tel 020 7703 6577

Aylesbury Day Nursery Taplow, Dawes St, London SE17 2EB; Tel 020 7703 6440

Bishops House Day Nursery 5 Kennington Park Pl, London SE11 4AS; Tel 020 7735 3215

Camberwell Grove Day Nursery 195e Camberwell Gr, London SE5 8JU; Tel 020 7274 7245

Lympstone Day Nursery Lympstone Gdns, London SE15 1AZ; Tel 020 7639 4568

Merryfield Day Nursery Sultan St, London SE5 0XG; Tel 020 7703 3260

Nunhead Green Day Nursery 5 Nunhead Grn, London SE15 3QQ; Tel 020 7639 5552

Tenda Road Day Nursery Tenda Rd, Bermondsey, London SE16 3PN; Tel 020 7237 0616

Whitstable Day Nursery Stevens St, London SE1 3BX; Tel 020 7525 9067

SPECIAL SCHOOLS

Beormund School Crosby Row, Long La, London SE1 3PS; Tel 020 7525 9027; Fax 020 7525 9026
Headteacher Sharon Gray
5–11 EBD

Bredinghurst School Stuart Rd, London SE15 3AZ; Tel 020 7639 2541; Fax 020 7732 5502
Headteacher J. Anderson
11–16 EBD Boarding

Cherry Garden School Macks Rd, London SE16 3XU; Tel 020 7237 4050; Fax 020 7237 7513
Headteacher T. Neary
2–19 SLD

Haymerle School Haymerle Rd, London SE15 6SY; Tel 020 7639 6080; Fax 020 7277 9906
Headteacher C. Wood
5–11 Mixed Special Needs

Highshore School Bellenden Rd, London SE15 5BB; Tel 020 7639 7211; Fax 020 7252 9024
Headteacher Y.A. Conlon
11–16 Mixed Special Needs

Maudsley and Bethlem Hospital School Monks Orchard Rd, Beckenham, Kent BR3 3BX; Tel 020 8777 1897; Fax 020 8777 1239
Headteacher J. Ivens

Spa School Monnow Rd, London SE1 5RN; Tel 020 7237 3714; Fax 020 7237 6601
Headteacher J. Ragan
11–16 Mixed Special Needs

Tuke School Woods Rd, London SE15 2PX; Tel 020 7639 5584; Fax 020 7635 8937
Headteacher H. Tully
2–19 SLD

WELFARE RIGHTS UNIT

221 Lordship La, East Dulwich, London SE22; Tel 020 8299 1515/1516

SOUTHWARK CHILD AND FAMILY SERVICE

Lister Primary Care Centre, 101 Peckham Rd, London SE15 5LJ; Tel 020 7701 7371; Fax 020 7701 8697
Manager Teresa Bailey

SUTTON LONDON BOROUGH COUNCIL

www.sutton.gov.uk

Population 178 737
Civic Offices, St. Nicholas Way, Sutton, Surrey SM1 1EA; URL www.sutton.gov.uk; Tel 020 8770 5000; Fax 020 8770 5404
Mayor Cllr Robert Landeryou
Strategic Director (Finance and Information) Sue Higgins
Strategic Director (Environment and Leisure) Tom Jeffrey
Strategic Director (Community Services) Eleanor Brazil
Chief Executive Joanna Simons

Community Services

Fax 020 8770 5665
Chair (Social Services Committee) Cllr Mike Cooper
Vice-Chair Cllr Leslie O'Connell
Executive Head of Service (Housing and Regeneration) P. Dolan
Strategic Director (Community Services) E. Brazil

Executive Head of Service (Community Living)   S. Latham
Executive Head of Service (Children and Families)   D. Warlock
Executive Head of Service (Community Care)   E. Morris
Head (Finance)   W. Sagar (Acting)
Head (Personnel Staff Development and Training)   M. Hope
Quality and Performance Manager (Child Protection and Looked After Children)   P. Sharma

Strategy Committee

Chair   Cllr Mike Cooper (LD)
Vice-Chair   Cllr Leslie O'Connell (LD)
Members of the Committee
LD: Richard Bailey, Angela Boughan, Don Brims, Colin Hall, C. Saunders, Graham Tope.
Lab: Charlie Mansell.
Con: Edward Trevor.

DISTRICT OFFICES

Carshalton District Office

Carshalton District Office, Honeywood Wlk, Carshalton, Surrey SM5 3PB; Tel 020 8770 4337

Cheam District Office

Cheam District Office, 314 Malden Rd, Surrey SM3 8EP; Tel 020 8770 4337

Wallington District Office

Mint Hse, Stanley Park Rd, Wallington, Surrey SM6 0EH; Tel 020 8770 4337

HOSPITAL SOCIAL WORKERS

Queen Mary's Hospital for Children Carshalton, Surrey; Tel 020 8644 4343

St. Ebba's Hospital Hook Rd, Epsom, Surrey; Tel 22212

St. Helier Hospital Carshalton, Surrey; Tel 020 8644 4343

Sutton Hospital Chiltern Wing, Cotswold Rd, Sutton, Surrey; Tel 020 8644 4343

FAMILY CENTRES

London Road Family Centre 717 London Rd, North Cheam, Sutton, Surrey SM3 9DL; Tel 020 8337 0095
Manager   Vacancy

Sutton Family Centre Robin Hood La, Sutton, Surrey; Tel 020 8643 5418
Service Manager   T. Price

CENTRE FOR THE DISABLED

Hallmead Day Centre Anton Cres, Collingwood Rd, Sutton, Surrey SM1 2NT; Tel 020 8644 3949

DAY CENTRES FOR THE ELDERLY

Centre for the Disabled Hallmead Day Centre, Anton Cres, Sutton, Surrey SM1 2NT; Tel 020 8644 3949

Gaynesford Lodge Day Centre Blake Cl, off Wellbeck Rd, Carshalton, Surrey SM5 1LG; Tel 020 8646 6543

Ludlow Lodge Alcester Rd, Wallington, Surrey SM6 8BB; Tel 020 8669 7170

HOMES FOR PEOPLE WITH A LEARNING DISABILITY

Abbotts Lodge 56 Abbotts Rd, Cheam, Surrey SM3 9TA; Tel 020 8395 9052

Albion Road Home 44 Albion Rd, Sutton, Surrey SM2 5TF; Tel 020 8642 2092

Clifton Manor Home 67 Manor Rd, Wallington, Surrey SM6 0DE; Tel 020 8669 5305

HOMES FOR PEOPLE WITH LEARNING DISABILITY

101 Cheam Rd, Sutton, Surrey SM1 2BE; Tel 020 8642 0307

The Green Home 3 The Green, Sutton, Surrey SM1 1QT; Tel 020 8641 9348
(8)

London Road Home 418 London Rd, Cheam, Surrey SM3 8JF; Tel 020 8641 5173
(6)

Lourdes House Home 19 Stanley Park Rd, Wallington, Surrey SM6 0HL; Tel 020 8647 2824
Manager   Ms Wallace
(11)

Plough Lane Home Purley, Surrey CR2 3QJ; Tel 020 8660 2234
Manager   Mrs Marsden
(16)

HOMES FOR OLDER ADULTS WITH LEARNING DISABILITY

Cottisbraine House 36 Sandy La South, Wallington, Surrey SM6 9QZ; Tel 020 8647 7981
Manager   Mr Brand
(11)

Woodcote House 167 Sandy La South, Wallington, Surrey SM6 9NP; Tel 020 8395 4010
Manager   Mr Physentzides
(11)

HOMES FOR PEOPLE WITH MENTAL HEALTH PROBLEMS

Bridge House 1 The Ridgeway, Sutton, Surrey SM2 5JX; Tel 020 8643 5453
(11)

Linda Lodge 91 Worcester Rd, Sutton, Surrey SM2 6QZ; Tel 020 8642 0343
(24)

RESIDENTIAL CARE HOMES FOR ELDERLY PEOPLE

There are 16 homes for the elderly.

HOMES FOR ELDERLY PEOPLE WITH MENTAL ILL HEALTH

Grange Cottage Home 6 Grange Rd, Sutton, Surrey SM2 6RT; Tel 020 8642 2721
Manager   Mr Read
(11)

Heatherside Home 129 Burdon La, Cheam, Surrey SM2 7DB; Tel 020 8661 7904
(11)

Montclair Home 216 Banstead Rd, Banstead, Surrey SM7 1QE; Tel 020 8393 7433
(10)

Rutland House Home 67 All Saints Rd, Sutton, Surrey SM1 3DQ; Tel 020 8644 5699
(20)

Sandilands Lodge Home 228 Carshalton Rd, Sutton, Surrey SM1 4SA; Tel 020 8643 6291
(15)

Wendover Home 7 Hall Rd, Wallington, Surrey SM6 0RT; Tel 020 8773 3699
(14)

MEALS ON WHEELS SERVICE

Civic Offices, St. Nicholas Way, Sutton, Surrey; Tel 0208 770 4539

Learning for Life

The Grove, Carshalton, Surrey SM5 3AL; Tel 020 8770 6568
Strategic Director I. Birnbaum, MA(Cantab), PhD; Tel 020 8770 6500
Executive Head (Parent, Pupil and Student Services) M. McIntosh; Tel 020 8770 6650; Fax 020 8770 6532
Executive Head (Foundation and Lifetime Learning) D. Anderson, BA(Hons), MBA; Tel 020 8770 6534; Fax 020 8770 6660
Executive Head (Core and Support Services) S. Ingram; Tel 020 8770 6684; Fax 020 8770 6636
Head (Sutton Youth Music Service) Nigel Hiscock
Sutton Youth Music Service, c/o Wandle Valley School, Welbeck Rd, Carshalton, Surrey SM5 1LW; Tel 020 8640 8781
Head (Play, Youth and Community Service) J. Hurst; Tel 020 8770 6648; Fax 020 8770 6655
Manager (Play Service) S. Boeje; Tel 020 8405 3503; Fax 020 8404 0017
Manager (Play Centre) S. Corbett
Tweeddale Play Centre, Tweeddale Rd, Carshalton, Surrey; Tel 020 8644 6924
Manager (Play Centre) S. Jordan-Passmore
Lindbergh Play Centre, Lindbergh Rd, Roundshaw, Wallington, Surrey SM6 9HB; Tel 020 8669 6658
Manager (Play Centre) J. Kelly
The Grange Play Centre, Beddington Pk, London Rd, Wallington, Surrey SM6 7BT; Tel 020 8669 1802
Principal Educational Psychologist B. Tubbs; Tel 020 8770 6780; Fax 020 8770 6532
Chief Education Welfare Officer E. Arnold; Tel 020 8770 6606; Fax 020 8770 6545

CHILD AND FAMILY CLINIC

Robin Hood Lane Health Centre 3 Robin Hood La, Sutton, Surrey SM1 2RJ; Tel 020 8642 3848
Contact Dr S. Dinnick, MB, BS, MRCPsych

NURSERY SCHOOLS

Spencer Nursery Spencer Rd, Mitcham Junction, Surrey CR4 4JP; Tel 020 8648 4126
Headteacher F. Downing

Thomas Wall Nursery Robin Hood La, Sutton, Surrey SM1 2SF; Tel 020 8642 5666
Headteacher M.R. Ross-Harper
Deputy Headteacher F.E. McGregor

SPECIAL SCHOOLS

Carew Manor School Church Rd, Wallington, Surrey SM6 7NH; Tel 020 8647 8349
Headteacher M. Midgley, DipSpEd, AdvDipEd(M)
    Mixed

Sherwood Park School Streeters La, Wallington, Surrey SM6 7NP; Tel 020 8773 9930
Headteacher R.A. Bezant, BEd(Hons)
    Mixed SLD

Unit for Hearing-Impaired Children (Primary) Rushy Meadow Primary School, Fellowes Rd, Carshalton, Surrey SM5 2SG; Tel 020 8669 7588
Contact Miss J. Herbert
Joint Co-ordinator (Hearing Impaired Unit) Miss Jacqueline Herbert

Wandle Valley School Welbeck Rd, Carshalton, Surrey SM5 1LP; Tel 020 8648 1365
Headteacher D.L. Bone, BA, MEd, DipSpEd
    EBD

Unit for Children with Communications Difficulties Foresters Primary School, Redford Ave, Wallington, Surrey SM6 9DP; Tel 020 8669 6910
(on the autistic spectrum)
Headteacher G. Hutton, BEd

Unit for Children with Moderate Learning Difficulties Amy Johnson Primary School, Mollison Dr, Wallington, Surrey SM6 9JN; Tel 020 8669 3978
Headteacher M. Kaye, MA(Ed), MA(PE), DPSE, CertEd
Teacher-in-Charge B. Kaye

Unit for Children with Physical Disabilities Culvers Hse Primary School, Orchard Ave, Mitcham, Surrey CR4 4JH; Tel 020 8255 6199
Headteacher S. Jackson, CertEd
Teacher-in-Charge Ms Judith Garland

Unit for Children with Specific Learning Difficulties Abbey Primary School, Glastonbury Rd, Morden, Surrey SM4 6NZ; Tel 020 8770 6770
Headteacher L. Tunstall, BEd(Hons)

Unit for Children with Specific Speech and Language Difficulties Muschamp Primary School, Muschamp Rd, Carshalton, Surrey SM5 2SE; Tel 020 8669 2514
Teacher-in-Charge H. Westley

Unit for Hearing Impaired Children (Secondary) Overton Grange School, Stanley Rd, Sutton, Surrey SM2 6TQ; Tel 020 8239 2383
Head of Unit J. Herbert (Acting)

TOWER HAMLETS LONDON BOROUGH COUNCIL

www.towerhamlets.gov.uk

7

Population 196 630
Political Composition: Lab: 36, LD: 15
Mulberry Pl, 5 Clove Cres, London E14 2BG;
    URL www.towerhamlets.gov.uk; Tel 020 7364 5000
Leader of the Council Cllr Helal Abbas
Chief Executive Christine Gilbert
Head (Community Partnership) A. King (Acting)
Head (Regeneration and Tourism) T. Chudleigh
Head (Media Relations) S. Crozier
Head (Corporate Services) D. Kingdon

Education Directorate

Corporate Director (Education) Stephen Grix

SPECIAL SCHOOLS

Beatrice Tate School Beatrice Tate, St. Jude's Rd, London E2 9RW; Tel 020 7739 6249
Headteacher Alan Black
    SLD/PMLD Secondary

Bowden House School (Residential) Firle Rd, Seaford, East Sussex BN25 2JB; Tel 01323 893138
Headteacher Mr Asif Arif

Bromley Hall School Bromley Hall Rd, London E14 0LF; Tel 020 7987 2563
Headteacher J. Earnshaw
    PD Secondary and JMI

Cherry Tree School 68 Campbell Rd, London E3 4EA; Tel 020 8983 4344
Headteacher Alan Fletcher
    EBD

Harpley School Globe Rd, London E1 4DZ; Tel 020 7790 5170
Headteacher Mr Tony Crisp (Acting)
    SNC Secondary

Ian Mikardo High School 60 William Guy Gdns, Talwin St, London E3 3LF; Tel 020 8981 2413
Headteacher Clare Lillis
    EBD, Secondary

Phoenix School 49 Bow Rd, London E3 2AD; Tel 020 7980 4740
Headteacher Stewart Harris
SNC Primary/Secondary

Stephen Hawking School Brunton Pl, London E14 7LL; Tel 020 7423 9848
Headteacher Christine Sibley

Information

Tower Hamlets Information Centre, 18 Lamb St, London E1 6EA; Tel 020 7364 4970; 020 7364 4971; Fax 020 7375 2539

Homeless Persons Unit

Block B, Millharbour, London E14 9XP; Tel 020 7364 5000; Fax 020 7364 7167

WALTHAM FOREST LONDON BOROUGH COUNCIL
www.lbwf.gov.uk

Population 220 900
Political Composition: Lab: 28, Con: 18, LD: 14
Town Hall, Forest Rd, Walthamstow, London E17 4JF;
URL www.lbwf.gov.uk;
E-mail simon.white@ce.lbwf.gov.uk; Tel 020 8496 3000;
Fax 020 8527 8313
The Mayor Cllr M. Nasim
Executive Director (Corporate Services) Chan Badrinath
Room 233, Town Hall, London E17 4JF
Executive Director (Community Services) and Director (Social Services) Ron Wallace
Executive Director (Environmental Services) Len Norton
Sycamore Hse, Town Hall Complex, London E17 4SY
Head (Legal Services) Philip Jackson
Sycamore Hse, Town Hall Complex, Forest Rd, London E17 4UL
Head (Portfolio Management Services) Linda Woods (Acting)
Municipal Offices, The Ridgeway, Chingford, London E4 6PS
Head (Community Protection) Linda Wacey
Cherry Tree Hse, Town Hall Complex, Forest Rd, London E17 4JF
Head (Financial Services) Ron Cooke
Head (Housing) James Wintour
Willow Hse, 869 Forest Rd, Walthamstow, London E17 4UH
Head (Leisure and Recreation) Vacancy
Sycamore Hse, Town Hall Complex, Forest Rd, London E17 4UL
Head (Planning and Development) Bob Bennett
Municipal Offices, The Ridgeway, Chingford, London E4 6PS
Head (Building Services) Tony Barrett
Municipal Offices, The Ridgeway, Chingford, London E4 6PS
Head (Libraries and Cultural Services) Colin Richardson
Central Library, High St, Walthamstow, London E17 7JN
Chief Education Officer Vacancy
Municipal Offices, High Rd, Leyton, London E10 5QJ

Community Services

Social Services Division, Municipal Offices, High Rd, Leyton, London E10 5QJ; URL www.lbwf.gov.uk;
E-mail carol.wilson@soc.lbwf.gov.uk; Tel 020 8496 3000; Fax 020 8558 7162
Executive Director (Community Services) Ron Wallace; Tel 020 8496 4502

Head (Social Services) Carol Wilson; Tel 020 8496 5142
Head (Adults Services) Lesley Bell;
E-mail lesley.bell@soc.lbwf.gov.uk; Tel 020 8496 5113

Social Services and Health Scrutiny

Lab: 4, Con: 3, LD: 2
Chair L. Braham
Members Office, Town Hall, Forest Rd, Walthamstow, London E17 4JF
Vice-Chair A. Bean (Lab)
Members' Office, Town Hall, Forest Rd, Walthamstow, London E17 4JF
Members of the Committee
Lab: S.K.A. Highfield, I. Leslie, R. Sweden.
Con: D. Divine, M.J. Fitzgerald.
LD: E. Phillips, J. Sullivan.

STRATEGY AND RESOURCES DIVISION

Municipal Offices, High Rd, Leyton, London E10 5QJ;
URL www.lbwf.gov.uk; Tel 020 8496 3000; Fax 020 8558 7162
Head (Strategy and Resources Unit) Deborah Hindson;
E-mail deborah.hindson@soc.lbwf.gov.uk; Tel 020 8496 5142
Head (Community Development and Grant Aid Services) Sharon Hanoomansingh; Tel 020 8496 5162
Manager (Human Resources) Keith Golding; Tel 020 8496 5210
Manager (Business Administration) Sue Mills; Tel 020 8496 5281
Manager (Finance) Maqsood Sheik (Acting); Tel 020 8496 5308
Manage (Contracts) Michael Jupe; Tel 020 8496 5336
Manager (Principal Planning and Service Development) Peter Boon; Tel 020 8496 1948

OPERATIONAL DIVISIONS

Services for Older People

313 Billet Rd, Walthamstow, London E17 6PX;
E-mail john.wiltshire@soc.lbwf.gov.uk; Tel 020 8496 3000; Fax 020 8496 1960
Head (Services for Older People) John Wiltshire; Tel 020 8496 1942
Group Manager Brenda Jarvis; Tel 020 8496 2054
Group Manager (Mental Health; HIV, Drugs and Alcohol) Nuzhat Anjum; Tel 020 8496 1950
Group Manager Peter Illes; Tel 020 8496 1944
Group Manager Steve Codling; Tel 020 8496 2055
Group Manager John McGinley; Tel 020 8496 2053
Group Support Manager Jayne Sillitoe; Tel 020 8496 1946
Group Support Manager Tracey Culling; Tel 020 8496 1943

LOCAL OFFICES

Chingford Local Office 2b Hatch La, Chingford, London E4 6NG; Tel 020 8496 1680; Fax 020 8496 1677
Assessments; Family Support; Home Care; Occupational Therapy

Leyton and Leytonstone Local Office 1 Russell Rd, Leyton, London E10 7ES; Tel 020 8496 1321; Fax 020 8496 1320
Assessments; Family Support; Home Care; Occupational Therapy

Walthamstow Local Office 47 Gainsford Rd, Walthamstow, London E17 6QB; Tel 020 8496 1817; Fax 020 8496 1864
Assessments; Family Support; Home Care; Occupational Therapy

HOSPITAL SOCIAL WORKERS

Whipps Cross Hospital Whipps Cross Rd, Leytonstone, London E11 1NR; Tel 020 8539 5522 Ext 5291

Children and Families Unit

604 High Rd, Leyton, London E10 6RN;
E-mail hugh.valentine@soc.lbwf.gov.uk; Tel 020 8496 2121; Fax 020 8496 2123
Head (Children and Families)   Hugh Valentine
Municipal Offices, High Rd, Leyton, London E10 5QJ;
Tel 020 8496 5113
Group Manager (Youth Offending Services)   Ronke Martins;
Tel 020 8496 2151
Group Manager (Plans, Quality and Protection)
Tolis Vouyioukas; Tel 020 8496 2140
Group Manager (Assessment – Children and Families)
Ade Adetosoye (Acting)
14 Prospect Hill, Walthamstow, London E17 3EL; Tel 020 8496 2848
Group Manager (Business Support)   Chirs Ugorji; Tel 020 8496 2136
Group Manager (Asylum Seekers)   Theresa Moore; Tel 020 8496 2135

ASIAN FAMILY RESOURCE CENTRE

Truro Rd, Walthamstow, London E17 7BY; Tel 020 8521 7831
Co-ordinator   S. Masood

CHILDREN WITH DISABILITIES TEAM

92 Leyton Green Rd, Leyton, London E10 6DA; Tel 020 8496 2439; Fax 020 8496 2437
Principal Officer (Special Needs)   Richard Paton (Acting)

RESPITE CARE CENTRE FOR CHILDREN WITH A LEARNING DIFFICULTY

92 Leyton Green Rd, Leyton, London E10 6DA; Tel 020 8496 1428; Fax 020 8496 1429
Unit Manager   Jo Siney
(12)

CHILD AND FAMILY CONSULTATION SERVICE

Thorpe Coombe Hospital, Shernhall St, London E17 3EA;
Tel 020 8509 0424
Team Manager   Rosemary Arnold

CHILDREN'S PLACEMENT UNIT

1c The Drive, Walthamstow, London E17 3BN; Tel 020 8496 2419; Fax 020 8496 2439
Group Manager (Family Support)   Neena Khosla; Tel 020 8496 2438

CHILDREN PROTECTION, REVIEWS AND SAFEGUARDS

17 Orford Rd, Walthamstow, London E17 9LP; Tel 020 8520 0914; Fax 020 8520 3491
Principal Officer   Lucy Erber

16+ SERVICES

14 Prospect Hill, Walthamstow, London E17 3EL; Tel 020 8496 2848; Fax 020 8520 6662
Principal Officer (16+ Services)   Ade Adetosoye

SERVICES FOR PEOPLE WITH MENTAL HEALTH PROBLEMS

Ferguson Centre, (Mental Health Resource Centre) Low Hall La, Walthamstow, London E17 8BE; Tel 020 8521 5223
Principal Manager   Nuzhat Anjum
Greenthorne 1 Merriam Cl, Chingford, London E4 9JQ;
Tel 020 8523 0799
Over 65s
North Adult Locality Team Larkswood Centre, Thorpe Coombe Hospital, Walthamstow, London E17 3HP; Tel 020 8535 6848
18–65 years

Red Oak Lodge 17 Thorne Cl, Leytonstone, London E11 4HU; Tel 020 8535 6476
Over 65s
South Adult Locality Team 21 Thorpe Cl, Leytonstone, London E11 4HU; Tel 020 8535 6480

DAY FACILITY FOR PHYSICAL AND SENSORY DISABILITY

Wyemead Centre 5 Oaks Gr, Friday Hill, London E4 6EY;
Tel 020 8529 9791
Group Manager   Rohini Widyaratna

DISABILITY SERVICES ADMINISTRATION

154 Blackhorse Rd, London E17 6NW; Tel 020 8496 4744
Manager (Administration Team)   Ken Faulkner; Tel 020 8496 4755

ACCOMMODATION FOR OLDER PEOPLE

There are four local authority old peoples homes and 15 local authority sheltered housing schemes giving over 400 places in warden-supervised flatlets.

Education Department

Town Hall, Forest Rd, London E17 4JF; Tel 020 8496 3000;
Fax 020 8527 8313
Executive Director (Lifelong Learning Services)   Stephen Hay
Head of Service   V. Cotton
Chief Education Welfare Officer   L. Cowen
Assistant Education Officer (Special Needs)   Christine Air

SPECIAL SCHOOLS

Belmont Park Leyton Green Rd, Leyton, London E10 6DB;
Tel 020 8556 0006; 020 8556 0007; Fax 020 8556 5680
Headteacher   M. Loizou
Brookfield House School Alders Ave, Woodford Green, Essex IG8 9PY; Tel 020 8527 8328; Fax 020 8527 2464
Headteacher   H. Clasper
Hawkswood School Antlers Hill, Chingford, London E4 7RS; Tel 020 8529 2561; Fax 020 8524 8230
Headteacher   K. Khan
The Joseph Clarke School Vincent Rd, London E4 9PP;
Tel 020 8523 4833; Fax 020 8523 5003
Headteacher   F.J. Smith
William Morris School Folly La, Walthamstow, London E17 5NT; Tel 020 8503 2225; Fax 020 8503 2227
Headteacher   I. Johnston

Aid and Advice Centre

807 High Rd, Leyton, London E10; Tel 020 8558 0033

WANDSWORTH LONDON BOROUGH COUNCIL

www.wandsworth.gov.uk

Population 273 400 (2001 estimate)
Wandsworth Town Hall, Wandsworth High St, London SW18 2PU; URL www.wandsworth.gov.uk; Tel 020 8871 6000
Chief Executive and Director (Administration)   G.K. Jones, MA, MTech
Deputy Chief Executive and Director (Finance)
H.J.S. Heywood
Director (Housing)   C.J. Buss, BA, CPFA
Director (Technical Services)   W.G. Myers, OBE
Director (Leisure and Amenity Services)   P.G. Brennan

7

Social Services Department

Director (Social Services) P. West; Tel 020 8871 6291; Fax 020 8871 7995

Assistant Director (Planning and Support Services) K. Jane; Tel 020 8871 6216

Assistant Director (Children and Families) J. Wooster; Tel 020 8871 8177

Assistant Director (Community Care) H. Dobson; Tel 020 8871 6215

Head (Physical and Learning Disabilities – Community Care) M. Abel; Tel 020 8871 8900

Sector Manager (Older People, Physical Disability – Community Care Division) J. Green; Tel 020 8871 6989

Sector Manager (Support Services – Community Care Division) P. French; Tel 020 8871 6212

Service Manager (Physical Disability – Community Care Division) S. Sinclair (Acting); Tel 020 8871 6211

Sector Manager (Resources – Children and Families Division) J. Royle; Tel 020 8871 6916

Sector Manager (Social Work Services – Children and Families Division) V. Rogers; Tel 020 8871 7547

Social Work Manager (Children in Need – Children and Families Division) L. Williams; Tel 020 8871 6326

Manager (Assessment, Referral and Child Protection – Children and Families Division) P. Secker; Tel 020 8871 6998

Manager (Permanency and Under 8's – Children and Families Division) E. Carr; Tel 020 8871 7252

Manager (Youth Offending Team – Children and Families Division) Sean Dunkling; Tel 020 8871 6209

Manager (Specialist Services – Children and Families Division) N. Greenbank; Tel 020 8871 6283

Manager (Sector Administration (Resources – Children and Families Division) E. Cloke; Tel 020 8871 7243

Manager (Residential, Fostering and Placements – Children and Families Division) D. Brooks; Tel 020 8871 6260

Manager (Sector Administration (Social Work – Children and Families Division) D. Green; Tel 020 8871 7216

Social Work Manager (Older People – Community Care Division) Vincent Kelly; Tel 020 8871 7020

Social Work Manager (Hospital and Disability – Community Care) R. Khan; Tel 020 8871 7108

Social Work Manager (Children Looked After – Children and Families Division) P. McCarthy; Tel 020 8871 6259

Care Services Overview and Scrutiny Committee

Con: 8, Lab: 2
Cabinet Member: Care Services Cllr V. Graham (Con)
Chair Cllr P. Ellis (Con)
Deputy Chair Cllr K. Lindsay (Con)
Members of the Committee
Con: Finn, Hallmark, Hope, Robson, Walker, Zahawi.
Lab: Joshi, Tatlow.

WANDSWORTH HOME CARE SERVICE

Tel 020 8871 7154
Manager (Home Care) Noel Mulvihill (Acting)

HOSPITAL SOCIAL WORK DEPARTMENTS

Atkinson Morley Atkinson Morley Wing, St. George's Hospital, Blackshaw Rd, London SW17 0QT; Tel 020 8725 4676

Barnes Hospital South Worple Way, London SW14 8SU; Tel 020 8878 4981

Bolingbroke Hospital Wakehurst Rd, London SW11 6HN; Tel 020 7223 7411

Queen Mary's Hospital Roehampton La, London SW15 5PN; Tel 020 8789 6611

St. George's Hospital Blackshaw Rd, London SW17 0QT; Tel 020 8672 1255

Springfield Hospital 61 Glenburnie Rd, London SW17 7DJ; Tel 020 8767 3411

Children and Families Division

Early Years Centre 1 Siward Rd, London SW17 0LA; Tel 020 8946 0900

Respite Home for Children and Young People 5 North Dr, London SW16 1RN; Tel 020 8769 5747

Special Education Unit 5 Westdean Cl, London SW18 2JX; Tel 020 8874 8251

CHILDREN'S CENTRES

Roehampton Children's Centre Jamieson Bldg, Downshire College Est, Roehampton La, London SW15 4MR; Tel 020 8785 9363

Battersea Park Road Children's Centre 259 Battersea Park Rd, London SW11 4LF; Tel 020 7720 0753

Longley Road Children's Centre 48 Longley Rd, London SW17 9 LL; Tel 020 8672 3506

Oldridge Road Children's Centre 60 Oldridge Rd, London SW12 8PW; Tel 020 8673 4945

Victoria Drive Children's Centre 78 Victoria Dr, London SW19 6HR; Tel 020 8789 2397

Waverton Road Children's Centre 1 Waverton Rd, London SW18 3BY; Tel 020 8870 6869

Wynter Street Children's Centre 65 Wynter St, London SW11 2TU; Tel 020 7223 5569

YOUTH OFFENDING TEAM

177 Blackshaw Rd, London SW17 0DJ; Tel 020 8672 7074

SERVICES TO YOUNG PEOPLE

Wayside, 28 West Hill, London SW18 1SB; Tel 020 8874 5127

ADOPTION AND FOSTERING UNIT

Welbeck Hse, Wandsworth High St, London SW18 2PS; Tel 020 8871 7261; Fax 020 8871 8550

FAMILY RESOURCE CENTRES

Bridge House Resource Centre 1a Larch Cl, London SW12 9SU; Tel 020 8673 6156

Falcon Grove Resource Centre 10 Falcon Gr, London SW11 2ST; Tel 020 7228 0836

Wilna Road Resource Centre 80 Wilna Rd, London SW18 3BA; Tel 020 8874 8751

Community Care Division

SPECIALIST DAY CENTRES FOR PEOPLE WITH LEARNING DISABILITIES

Battersea SEC 50 Thessally Rd, London SW8 4XS; Tel 020 7622 4577

Burntwood SEC Springfield Hospital, 61 Glenburnie Rd, London SW17 7DJ; Tel 020 8767 1850

HOSTELS FOR PEOPLE WITH LEARNING DISABILITIES

Hartfield House 170 Roehampton La, London SW15 4EU; Tel 020 8780 0408; 020 8871 7689

Roehampton 230 Roehampton La, London SW15 4LE; Tel 020 8789 0740

COMBINED CENTRE

Atheldene Centre 305 Garratt La, London SW18 4EQ; Tel 020 8871 6344

HOSTELS FOR PEOPLE WITH MENTAL HEALTH PROBLEMS

Chellowdene Hostel 76 Putney Hill, London SW15 6RB; Tel 020 8788 2652
Staffed hostel plus unstaffed bedsits.

Inner Park Road Hostel 27 Inner Park Rd, London SW19 6DF; Tel 020 8789 7957
Staffed hostel plus semi-independent living accommodation.

Thurleigh Road Hostel 86 Thurleigh Rd, London SW12 8UD; Tel 020 8675 2076
Staffed hostel.

West Drive Hostel 3–4 West Dr, London SW16 1RP; Tel 020 8769 3352
Staffed hostel plus independent living scheme.

PLANNING AND SUPPORT SERVICES DIVISION

Chief Administration Manager P. Mills; Tel 020 8871 6208
Manager (Personnel) C. Parsons; Tel 020 8871 6228
Manager (IT) C. Northfield; Tel 020 8871 6237
Manager (IT) J. Trimnell; Tel 020 8871 6237
Manager (Planning and Quality) A. Young; Tel 020 8871 7579
Manager (Business Support) S. Armstrong; Tel 020 8871 6856

Education Department

Wandsworth Town Hall, Wandsworth High St, Wandsworth, London SW18 2PU;
E-mail eddirectors@wandsworth.gov.uk; Tel 020 8871 8013
Director (Education) Paul Robinson
Deputy Director Mary Evans
Chief Education Inspector Peter Dougill
Assistant Director (Education) Adrian Butler

SPECIAL SCHOOLS

Bradstow School Dumpton Park Dr, Broadstairs, Kent CT10 1RG;
E-mail info@bradstow.wandsworth.sch.uk; Tel 01843 862123; Fax 01843 866648
Headteacher Albert Furze
SLD (Boarders)

Chartfield School St. Margaret's Cres, Roehampton, London SW15 6HL;
E-mail info@chartfield.wandsworth.sch.uk; Tel 020 8788 7471; Fax 020 8788 8081
Headteacher Anne Doyle (Acting)

Elsley School 31 Elsley Rd, Battersea, London SW11 5TZ;
E-mail admin@elsley.wandsworth.sch.uk; Tel 020 7738 2968; Fax 020 7738 9119
Headteacher Margaret Fisher
EBD

Garratt Park School Waldron Rd, Garratt La, London SW18 3TB; E-mail info@garrattpark.wandsworth.sch.uk; Tel 020 8946 5769; Fax 020 8947 5605
Headteacher Jennifer Price
MLD

Greenmead School St. Margaret's Cres, London SW15 6HL;
E-mail admin@greenmead.wandsworth.sch.uk; Tel 020 8789 1466; Fax 020 8788 5945
Headteacher Angela Laxton
Primary PD

Linden Lodge School 61 Princes Way, London SW19 6JB;
E-mail info@lindenlodge.wandsworth.sch.uk; Tel 020 8788 0107; Fax 020 8780 2712
Headteacher Roger Legate
Blind and partially sighted.

Nightingale School Beechcroft Rd, London SW17 7DF;
E-mail info@nightingale.wandsworth.sch.uk; Tel 020 8874 9096; Fax 020 8877 3724
Headteacher John Murphy
EBD (Day, Boarders)

Oak Lodge School 101 Nightingale La, London SW12 8NA;
E-mail info@oaklodge.wandsworth.sch.uk; Tel 020 8673 3453; Fax 020 8673 9397
Headteacher Peter Merrifield
Deaf SM Day and Boarding Hostel.

Paddock School Priory La, London SW15 5RT;
E-mail admin@paddock.wandsworth.sch.uk; Tel 020 8878 1521; Fax 020 8392 9735
Headteacher Linda Charman
SLD

The Vines School Forthbridge Rd, London SW11 5NX;
E-mail sao@admin.vines.wandsworth.sch.uk; Tel 020 7228 0602; Fax 020 7978 7954
Headteacher Kevin Anscomb (Acting)
MLD

WESTMINSTER CITY COUNCIL
www.westminster.gov.uk

7

Population 181 700
Political Composition: Con: 48, Lab: 12
Westminster City Hall, Victoria St, London SW1E 6QP;
URL www.westminster.gov.uk; Tel (Switchboard) 020 7641 6000
Chief Executive Peter Rogers
Director (Legal Services) Colin Wilson
Director (Housing) Julie Jones
Director (Planning and Transportation) Carl Powell

Social and Community Services Department

Director (Social and Community Services) Julie Jones; Tel 020 7641 6000; Fax 020 7641 2246
Deputy Director Vivienne Lukey; Tel 020 7641 1964
Assistant Director (Children and Families) Michael O'Connor; Tel 020 7641 2253; Fax 020 7641 2246
Assistant Director (Strategy and Performance) Sean Rafferty; Tel 020 7641 2273
Assistant Director (Finance and Business Services) Caroline Holland; Tel 020 7641 2297
Assistant Director (Older People, Disability and Health) Marian Harrington; Tel 020 7641 1940
Chief Housing Officer Frances Mapstone; Tel 020 7641 2576

Training

Responsible for training professional and support staff in the department.
Head (Training and Staff Development) Phillip Berechree; Tel 020 7641 2048

Health and Community Services Overview and Scrutiny Committee

Nominated Chair Cllr Tim Mitchell (Con)
PO Box 240 City Hall, 64 Victoria St, London SW1E 6QP
Nominated Vice-Chair Cllr Barrie Taylor (Lab)
Members of the Committee
Con: Melvin Caplan, Andrew Havery, Louise Hyams, Gwyneth Hampson, Barbara Schmeling, John Wyatt.
Lab: Sharon Tabari.

Children and Young People Overview and Scrutiny Committee

Nominated Chair Cllr Carolyn Keen (Con)
PO Box 240, City Hall, 64 Victoria St, London SW1E 6QP
Nominated Vice-Chair Cllr Paul Dimoldenberg (Lab)
Nominated Vice-Chair Barbara Schmeling (Con)
Members of the Committee
Con: Cathy Longworth, Gwyneth Hampson,
Anne Mallinson, Dominic Schofield, Frixos Tombolis,
Michael Vearncombe.
Lab: Josephine Ohene-Djan.
Co-opted voting representatives: Raymond Armstrong (Parent Governor), Gabrielle Barry (Roman Catholic Diocesan Board), Rev Richard Burt (Church of England Diocese), Michael Beckett.
Co-opted non-voting representatives: Jo White (Headteacher, Mary Paterson Nursery School), Elizabeth Phillips (Headteacher, St. Marylebone CE School).

CHILDREN AND FAMILIES COMMISSIONING

Assistant Director Michael O'Connor

LOOKED AFTER CHILDREN

7th Fl, City Hall, Westminster, London SW1E 6QP
Head of Commissioning (Looked After Children)
Geoff Skinner

Youth Justice and Leaving Care

Youth Offending Team
6a Crompton St, London W2 1ND; Tel 020 7641 5307;
Fax 020 7641 5311

Westminster Accommodation and Leaving Care Team (WALC) 33 Tachbrook St, London SW1V 2JR; Tel 020 7641 3130; 020 7641 3146; Fax 020 7641 3094

ASSESSMENT AND FAMILY SUPPORT

4 Frampton St, London; Tel 020 7641 1600; Fax 020 7641 1608
Head of Commissioning (Assessment and Family Support)
Trevor Moores

ASSESSMENT TEAM

4 Frampton St, London NW8 8LF; Tel 020 7641 7498; 020 7641 7535; Fax 020 7641 7507

FAMILY PLACEMENTS SERVICE

33 Tachbrook St, London SW1V 2JR; Tel 020 7641 2175; Fax 020 7641 2527

CHILD PROTECTION (CITYWIDE)

4 Frampton St, London NW8 8LF; Tel 020 7641 7665; Fax 020 7641 7672
Head of Commissioning (Child Protection and Quality)
Sally Trench

ELDERLY PERSONS' RESOURCE CENTRES

Carlton Dene Elderly Resource Centre 45 Kilburn Park Rd, London NW6 5XD; E-mail anwaenie@westminster.gov.uk; Tel 020 7641 4890; 020 7641 4891; Fax 020 7641 5439
Registered Manager Amaechi Nwaenie

Charlwood House Centre Lillington Gardens Est, Vauxhall Bridge Rd, London SW1V 2SY;
E-mail acheang@westminster.gov.uk; Tel 020 7641 6368; Fax 020 7641 6326
Registered Manager Alice Cheang

Westmead Elderly Resource Centre 4 Tavistock Rd, London W11 1BA; E-mail araykidger@westminster.gov.uk; Tel 020 7641 4595; Fax 020 7641 5781
Registered Manager Anna Ray-Kidger

ELDERLY PERSONS' DAY CARE SERVICES

Carlton Dene Day Care 45 Kilburn Park Rd, London NW6 5XD; E-mail imunday@westminster.gov.uk; Tel 020 7641 4890; 020 7641 4891
Manager Ian Munday

Learning Disability Day and Employment Services DSO (Learning Disabilities)

Manager (DSO) Helen Banham
Lisson Gr, London NW8 8LW;
E-mail hbanham@westminster.gov.uk; Tel 020 7641 4196; Fax 020 7641 1386

CENTRES

Autism Service 131 Droop St, London W10 3DB; Tel 020 7641 5851; Fax 020 7641 5857
Manager Tom Moore

Community Support Team 215 Lisson Gr, London NW8 8LW; Tel 020 7641 1536; Fax 020 7641 4148
Manager Gill Whyte

Complex Support Service 131 Droop St, London W10 3DB; Tel 020 7641 4589; Fax 020 7641 5821
Manager Gloria Reid

Complex Support Service 4 Lilestone St, London NW8 8SU; E-mail broberts@westminster.gov.uk; Tel 020 7641 5499; Fax 020 7641 5440
Manager Bronwyn Roberts

Westminster Employment Service 215 Lisson Gr, London NW8 8LW; E-mail dward@westminster.gov.uk; Tel 020 7641 1500; Fax 020 7641 1587
Service Manager Tanja Tinari

Assessment and Care Management Services (Elderly and Disability)

Assistant Director (Older People, Disability and Health)
Marian Harrington
7th Fl, City Hall, London SW1E 6QP;
E-mail mharrington@westminster.gov.uk; Tel 020 7641 1940

ELDERLY (NORTH LOCALITY)

Service Manager Bill Davis
4 Frampton St, London NW8 8LW; Tel 020 7641 1123; 020 7641 1628

ST. MARYS HOSPITAL TEAM

Service Manager David Newbery
St. Mary's Hospital Care Management Team, St. Mary's Hospital, London W2 1MY; Tel 020 7886 6576

ELDERLY (SOUTH LOCALITY)

Service Manager Karen Clark
7th Fl, City Hall, London SW1 6QP; Tel 020 7641 3952

DISABILITY CARE MANAGEMENT

4 Frampton St, London NW8 8LW; Tel 020 7641 1123
Service Manager Hugh Cole

Learning Disabilities Assessment and Care Management Team (City Wide)

Service Manager (Care Management Team) Janet Lang
4 Frampton St, London NW8 8LW; Tel 020 7641 7400

Mental Health Commissioning

Head (Commissioning – Mental Health) Stella Baillie
7th Fl, City Hall, Victoria St, London SW1E 6QP; Tel 020 7641 2430

Mental Health Teams

South Locality
Team Manager   George Nazer; Tel 020 8237 2040
North Locality   Tel 020 7266 6000
Team Manager   Colin Constantine

SUBSTANCE MISUSE TEAM

4 Frampton St, London NW8 8LW; Tel 020 7641
   7468
Manager   Catherine Fairbairn

JOINT HOMELESSNESS TEAM

Manager   Sue Lipscombe
Soho Centre for Health and Care, 1 Frith St, Soho, London;
   Tel 020 7534 6711

Education Department

13th Fl, Westminster City Hall, 64 Victoria St, London
   SW1E 6QP; URL www.westminster.gov.uk; Tel 020 7641
   6000
Director (Education)   Phyl Crawford
Head (Early Childhood Services)   Jennifer Greenwood
Head (Special Education and Additional Needs)   June Simson

SPECIAL SCHOOLS

College Park School   Garway Rd, London W2 4PH; Tel 020
7641 4460; Fax 020 7641 5731
Community
Headteacher   Frances Crockwell
Queen Elizabeth II School   Kennet Rd, London W9 3LG;
Tel 020 7641 5825; Fax 020 7641 5823
Community
Headteacher   M. Loughnan

7

Local Government Wales

8

- **Main Council Information**
- **Social Services Department**
  Including all social services provision
- **Education Department**
  Including special needs provision

Key

(110)	Number of pupils
Mixed	Takes boys and girls
Boys	Takes boys only
Girls	Takes girls only
11–18	Age range of pupils

Abbreviations

ADHD	Attention Deficit Hyperactivity Disorder
ASD	Autism Spectrum Disorder
EBD	Emotional Behavioural Difficulties
LD	Learning Difficulties
LI	Language Impairment
MH	Mentally Handicapped
MLD	Moderate Learning Difficulties
PH	Physically Handicapped
PHAB	Physically Handicapped and Able-Bodied
PMLD	Profound and Multiple Learning Difficulties
PS	Partially Sighted
PtHg	Partially Hearing
SCU	Special Care Unit
SEBD	Severe Emotional Behaviour Difficulties
SEN	Special Educational Needs
SLD	Severe Learning Difficulties
SLDD	Students with Learning Difficulties and Disabilities
SMH	Severely Mentally Handicapped

Local Government Wales

ISLE OF ANGLESEY COUNTY COUNCIL
www.anglesey.gov.uk

Population 66 828
Political Composition: New Coalition Group: 20, Ind: 15, Plaid Cymru: 3, Unaffiliated: 1, Vacant seat: 1.
Swyddfa'r Sir, Llangefni, Isle of Anglesey LL77 7TW;
  URL www.anglesey.gov.uk;
  E-mail gjxce@anglesey.gov.uk; Tel 01248 750057;
  Fax 01248 750839
Managing Director Geraint F. Edwards, BSc, DipTP, MBA, MRTPI; Tel 01248 752102; Fax 01248 750839
Corporate Director (Finance) D.G. Elis-Williams, MA, MSc, CStat, IPFA; Tel 01248 752601; Fax 01248 752696
Head of Service (Leisure and Community) G. Aled Roberts; Tel 01248 752912; Fax 01248 752999

Social Services Department

Corporate Director (Housing and Social Services)
  B. Williams, BSc, CQSW, BASW; Tel 01248 752703;
  Fax 01248 752705

Social Inclusion Committee

New Coalition Group: 6, Independent: 4, Plaid Cymru: 1.
Chair John Rowlands (NCG)
Vice-Chair Gwyn Roberts (NCG)

HOSPITAL SOCIAL WORKERS

Ysbyty Gwynedd
Team Leader Ann Lloyd Williams; Tel 01248 384968
Social workers in attendance at: Ysbyty Gwynedd Hospital (District General Hospital), Bangor; Tel: 01248 384384, Cefni Hospital, Llangefni 01248 750117, Penrhos Stanley Hospital, Holyhead 01407 765000.

CHILDREN'S COMMUNITY HOME

Queen's Park Close Community Home 5 Queen's Park Cl, Holyhead, Ynys Môn, Isle of Anglesey LL65 1PU; Tel 01407 762678
Officer-in-Charge Lynda Evans

CHILD AND ADOLESCENT MENTAL HEALTH SERVICE

Talarfon Holyhead Rd, Bangor, Gwynedd; Tel 01248 353825
Social Worker April Cummings

ADULT TRAINING CENTRE

Canolfan Mona Ind Est, Llangefni, Isle of Anglesey LL77 7JA; E-mail raxsa@anglesey.gov.uk; Tel 01248 722965
Manager R. Astley

CASE MANAGEMENT TEAM (LEARNING DISABILITY)

Council Offices Swyddfa'r Sir, Llangefni, Isle of Anglesey LL77 7TW
Team Leader Kevin Thomas

RESOURCE CENTRE FOR PEOPLE WITH MENTAL HEALTH PROBLEMS

Priory Richmond Hill, Holyhead, Isle of Anglesey LL65 2HH; Tel 01407 761611
Manager Lorna Thomas

DAY CARE CENTRES FOR THE ELDERLY

Afallon Day Centre Holyhead, Isle of Anglesey LL65 2EY; Tel 01407 763603

Beaumaris Day Centre Beaumaris, Isle of Anglesey LL58 8EU; Tel 01248 810633

Hafan Day Centre Bryngwran, Isle of Anglesey LL65 3RA; Tel 01407 720949

ACCOMMODATION FOR THE ELDERLY

Tel 01248 752791
There are six elderly people's homes.

SHELTERED WORKSHOP

Gweithdy Mona Ind Est, Llangefni, Isle of Anglesey LL77 7JA; Tel 01248 722990
Manager Iwan Williams

Education and Leisure Department

Park Mount, Ffordd Glanhwfa Rd, Llangefni, Isle of Anglesey L77 7EY; Tel 01248 752900; Fax 01248 752999
Vice-Chair Cllr H.M. Morgan, MBE
County Treasurer D.G. Ellis-Williams, MA, MSc, CStat, IPFA
Director (Education and Leisure) R. Parry Jones, MA

SPECIAL SCHOOL

Ysgol y Bont Llangefni, Isle of Anglesey LL77 7JA
Headteacher D. Hughes, BEd

SPECIAL EDUCATIONAL NEEDS JOINT-COMMITTEE

Joint arrangement with Gwynedd Council.
Plas Llanwnda, Caernarfon, Isle of Anglesey LL55 1SH;
  Tel 01286 672255

8

Principal Educational Psychologist   R. Coupe; Tel 01248 752951
Senior Educational Psychologist   R.E. Owen; Tel 01286 679178
Advisory Teacher (Vision Impairment/Physically Handicapped) S. Thomas; Tel 01286 679295
Advisory Teacher (Pre-School Sector)   L. Williams
Statementing Officer   Gwen Lloyd Williams; Tel 01286 679180

BLAENAU GWENT COUNTY BOROUGH COUNCIL
www.blaenau-gwent.gov.uk

Political Composition: Lab: 32, Ind: 2, Ratepayers: 3, LD: 4, Independent Labour: 2.
Municipal Offices, Civic Centre, Ebbw Vale, Blaenau Gwent NP23 6XB; URL www.blaenau-gwent.gov.uk; Tel 01495 350555; Fax 01495 301225
Chief Executive   Robin Morrison

Social Services Department

URL www.blaenau-gwent.gov.uk;
   E-mail judith.cosgrove@blaenau-gwent.gov.uk;
   Tel 01495 350555; Fax 01495 355285
Director (Social Services)   Roger K. Bone
Head (Quality, Planning and Commissioning)   Mike Murphy
Head (Provider Services)   Angela Penwill
Head (Adult Social Work Services)   Jan Scrivens

Executive

Executive Member (Social Services)   Cllr Karen Williams (Lab)

Health and Social Care Scrutiny Committee

Lab: 11, Ind: 2, LD: 2
Chair   Cllr D.C. Edwards (Lab)
Vice-Chair   Cllr A. Morgan (Lab)
Members of the Committee
Lab: Brian Clements, Malcolm Dally, Des Davies, W.H. Davies, D.I. Morris, J.T. Rogers, G. Smith, S.C. Thomas, D.H. Wilkshire.
Ind: T. Edwards, D. Hancock.
LD: S. Bard, C. Morgan.

LOCAL OFFICES

Community Care Team (Elderly and Disabled) Abertillery Social Services, The Bridge Centre, Foundry Bridge, Abertillery, Blaenau Gwent NP13 1BQ; Tel 01495 322770; Fax 01495 322790

Community Care Team (Elderly and Disabled) Tredegar Social Services, The Grove, Church St, Tredegar, Blaenau Gwent NP22 3DS; Tel 01495 722457; 01495 722697; Fax 01495 722437

Community Care Team (Learning Disability) Abertillery Social Services, The Bridge Centre, Foundry Bridge, Abertillery, Blaenau Gwent NP13 1BQ; Tel 01495 322660; Fax 01495 322790

Community Care Team (Mental Health – Adult Services) Lyndhurst, Eureka Pl, Ebbw Vale, Blaenau Gwent NP23 6PN; Tel 01495 353700; Fax 01495 353737

Child and Family Team Ebbw Vale Social Services, 7 Bridge St, Ebbw Vale, Blaenau Gwent NP23 6EY; Tel 01495 350555; Fax 01495 350719
Head (Children's Social Work Services)   Kay Owen

Youth Offending Team Libanus Hse, 260 High St, Blackwood, Blaenau Gwent NP12 1YT; Tel 01495 235623; Fax 01495 235620

Home Finding Team Ebbw Vale Social Services, 7 Bridge St, Ebbw Vale, Blaenau Gwent NP23 6EY; Tel 01495 350555; Fax 01495 350719

HOMES FOR THE ELDERLY

There are five homes for the elderly.

HOME FOR PEOPLE WITH A LEARNING DISABILITY

Greenacre Hostel St. Luke's Rd, Nantybwch, Tredegar, Blaenau Gwent NP22 4XF; Tel 01495 723007

RESPITE CARE HOME FOR PEOPLE WITH A LEARNING DISABILITY

Augusta House Augusta Pk, Victoria, Ebbw Vale, Blaenau Gwent NP23 8DN; Tel 01495 305805; Fax 01495 308833

DAY CENTRES

Arosfa Day Centre for the Promotion of Mental Health High St, Blaina, Blaenau Gwent NP13 3AN; Tel 01495 290273; Fax 01495 292392

Bert Denning Centre Warwick Rd, Brynmawr, Blaenau Gwent NP23 4AR; Tel 01495 315278; Fax 01495 313148

Multipurpose Day Centre Joint Day Care Unit, c/o Ebbw Vale Hospital, Hillside, Ebbw Vale, Blaenau Gwent NP23 5WA; Tel 01495 356921; 01495 356922; Fax 01495 307906

COMMUNITY SUPPORT

Ashville Products and Training c/o Bert Denning Centre, Warwick Rd, Brynmawr, Blaenau Gwent NP23 4AR; Tel 01495 315278; Fax 01495 313148
   LD

Welfare Rights Team Brynmawr Social Services, 107–110 Worcester St, Brynmawr, Blaenau Gwent NP23 4JP; Tel 01495 313803; Fax 01495 310285

Education Department

Festival Hse, Victoria Bus Pk, Ebbw Vale, Blaenau Gwent NP23 8ER;
   E-mail education.department@blaenau-gwent.gov.uk;
   Tel 01495 355337
Director (Lifelong Learning)   John Pearce
Chief Education Officer   Dr Brett Pugh
   Development, finance, pupil and student services and management support services.
Principal Educational Psychologist   T. Dyson
   Also responsible for the service for pupils with specific learning difficulties.
Head (School Services)   J. Howells
   Includes responsibility for out-of-school hours child care, nursery education development, building development, Governor support, school admissions, home/school transport and pupil/ student grants.
Divisional Head (School Support)   Hannah Mayrick
   Includes responsibility for LMS, personnel support to schools and special needs administration.
Divisional Head (Children and Young People's Services) S. Annett
   Includes responsibility for children and young people's services.

SPECIAL SCHOOL

Penycwm School Beaufort Hill, Ebbw Vale, Blaenau Gwent NP23 5QG; Tel 01495 304031

PUPIL REFERRAL UNIT

Thomas Richards Centre Sirhowy, Tredegar, Blaenau Gwent NP22 4PY; Tel 01495 724980

BRIDGEND COUNTY BOROUGH COUNCIL
www.bridgend.gov.uk

Political Composition: Lab: 40, LD: 6, Ind: 4, Con: 1, Plaid Cymru: 1, Ind Lab: 1, Ind Wales: 1
Civic Offices, Angel St, Bridgend CF31 4WB;
    URL www.bridgend.gov.uk;
    E-mail talktous@bridgend.gov.uk; Tel 01656 643643;
    Fax 01656 668126
Chief Executive Keri Lewis;
    E-mail lewisik@bridgend.gov.uk; Tel 01656 643227;
    Fax 01656 767152
Director (Corporate Services) Lyn James;
    E-mail jameslm@bridgend.gov.uk; Tel 01656 643301;
    Fax 01656 663632
Director (Environmental and Planning Services)
    Malcolm E. Thomas;
    E-mail thomame2@bridgend.gov.uk; Tel 01656 643401;
    Fax 01656 668249
Director (Personal Services) Tony Garthwaite;
    E-mail gartht@bridgend.gov.uk; Tel 01656 642211;
    Fax 01656 766162

Social Services Department

Council Offices, Sunnyside, Bridgend CF31 4AR;
    URL www.bridgend.gov.uk; Tel 01656 642200
Director (Personal Services – Social Services and Housing)
    Tony Garthwaite
Assistant Director (Children's Services) Barbara Street
Assistant Director (Resources Management) Dave McGregor
Head (Learning Disability, Mental Health and Substance Misuse Service) Sue Cooper
Head (Elderly and Disability Service) Gordon Jones

Social Services and Housing Scrutiny Committee
Members
R.W. Bowser, B. Davies, C.G. Evans, W.B. Evans, E.F. Foley, R. Hughes, D. John, L. Phillips, R.D. Power, M.L. Simmons, R.H. Thomas, G. Walters.

COMMUNITY HOMES

Cartrefle Community Home Merthyr Mawr Rd, Bridgend CF31 3NS; Tel 01656 652257
    (8)

Maesteg Road Community Home 21 Brookfield Rd, Garth, Maesteg, Bridgend CF34 0NJ; Tel 01656 733466
    (7)

Pant Morfa Community Home 31 Pant Morfa, Porthcawl, Bridgend CF36 5EN; Tel 01656 782914
    (10)

DAY CARE

Day Care is provided at nine Centres throughout the County Borough.

Services for People with a Learning Disability

DAY SERVICES

Bridgend Day Centre Cowbridge Rd, Bridgend; Tel 01656 766242

Persondy Day Centre Heol Persondy, Aberkenfig, Bridgend; Tel 01656 720249

Wood B Unit 50, Tondu Enterprise Pk, Bryn Rd, Tondu, Bridgend; Tel 01656 722675

ACCOMMODATION SERVICES

Bryneithin Resource Centre Crown Rd, Maesteg, Bridgend; Tel 01656 734350
    (33)

Maesglas Resource Centre 64 Mount Earl, Bridgend; Tel 01656 653447; 01656 648389
    (22)

STAFFED HOUSES

Abbey Road Houses 14–16 Abbey Rd, Kenfig Hill, Bridgend; Tel 01656 744017
Care providers.
    (5)

Heol Llansantffraid House 1 Heol Llansantffraid, Sarn, Bridgend; Tel 01656 720019
    (5)

Heol y Mynydd Houses 19–21 Heol y Mynydd, Bryncethin, Bridgend; Tel 01656 725115
Care providers.
    (5)

Heol y Nant House 7 Heol y Nant, Garth, Maesteg, Bridgend; Tel 01656 739306
Care providers.

RESPITE CARE FOR ADULTS

Wimbourne Road Centre 9 Wimbourne Rd, Pencoed, Bridgend; Tel 01656 864804

RESPITE CARE FOR CHILDREN

Bakers Way Centre 2a Bakers Way, Bryncethin, Bridgend; Tel 01656 720509

Mental Health Services

DAY SERVICES

Ty'r Ardd Day Centre Sunnyside, Bridgend; Tel 01656 766250

ACCOMMODATION SERVICES

Glyn Cynffig Hostel School Rd, Kenfig Hill, Bridgend; Tel 01656 742700
    (16)

GROUP HOMES

There are four Group Homes in the County Borough.

DAY SERVICES FOR THE ELDERLY

Maesteg Day Centre Castle St, Maesteg, Bridgend; Tel 01656 733539

Minerva Street Day Centre Minerva St, Bridgend; Tel 01656 661572

The Vernon Hart Centre Coegnant Rd, Maesteg, Bridgend; Tel 01656 730296

RESIDENTIAL HOMES FOR ELDERLY PEOPLE

There are five homes for the elderly.

8

Education, Leisure and Community Services

Education Office, Sunnyside, Bridgend CF31 4AR;
   URL www.bridgend.gov.uk;
   E-mail sutton@bridgend.gov.uk; Tel 01656 642610;
   Fax 01656 642675
Director (Education, Leisure and Community Services)
   David Matthews
Assistant Director (Special Needs Services)   Dr G. Price

EDUCATIONAL PSYCHOLOGY SERVICE

Ty Morfa Psychological Centre Hafan Deg, Aberkenfig,
Bridgend CF32 9AW; URL ww.bridgend.gov.uk;
E-mail davier2@bridgend.gov.uk; Tel 01656 729319;
Fax 01656 725806
Principal Educational Psychologist   R. Davies

SPECIAL SCHOOLS

Ysgol Bryn Castell Llangewydd Rd, Cefn Glas, Bridgend
CF31 4JP; Tel 01656 767517
Headteacher   G.E. Le Page
   (180)

Heronsbridge School Ewenny Rd, Bridgend CF31 3HT;
Tel 01656 653974
(Also residential)
Headteacher   C.D. Major
   (165)

CAERPHILLY COUNTY BOROUGH COUNCIL
www.caerphilly.gov.uk

Population 171 000
Tredomen, Ystrad Mynach, Hengoed, Caerphilly
   CF82 7WF; URL www.caerphilly.gov.uk;
   E-mail info@caerphilly.gov.uk; Tel 01443 815588;
   Fax 01443 864211
Leader of Council   Cllr L. Whittle
Chair   Cllr M. Parker
Chief Executive   Malgwyn Davies

Directorate of Social Services

Headquarters, Hawtin Pk, Blackwood, Caerphilly
   NP12 2PZ; URL caerphilly.gov.uk;
   E-mail caerphilly.gov.uk; Tel 01443 864639; Fax 01443
   864523
Director (Social Services)   Joe Howsam
Assistant Director (Resourcing and Performance)
   Nigel Barnett
Assistant Director (Children's Services)
   Derek Millington
Assistant Director (Adult Services)   Margaret Ellis
Service Manager (Resourcing)   Satya Schofield
Service Manager (Financial Services)   John Hold
Service Manager (Children's Services)   Gareth Waters
Service Manager (Performance Management)   Dave Pettit
Service Manager (Learning Disability/Mental Health)
   Sue Wright
Service Manager (Elderly/Disability)   Adrian Read
Service Manager (Elderly/Disability)   Liz Majer
Service Manager (Planning Adults)   Bill Garnett
Service Manager Locality (Children's Services)
   Lyn Richards
Service Manager County (Children's Services)   Jane Moore

Social Services Committee
Lab: 28, Plaid Cymru: 39, Ind: 3, LD: 3

CHILDREN'S SERVICES OFFICES

BARGOED CHILDREN'S SERVICES AREA TEAM

Northern Locality Office, William St, Gilfach, Bargoed,
   Caerphilly CF81 8ND; Tel 01443 873561
Team Manager   Chris Thomas

BLACKWOOD CHILDREN'S SERVICES AREA TEAM

Hawtin Pk, Gellihaf, Pontllanfraith, Blackwood, Caerphilly
   NP12 2PZ; Tel 01443 864558
Team Manager   Chris Nicholls

CAERPHILLY CHILDREN'S SERVICES AREA TEAM (TWO TEAMS)

Cwm Ifor, Caledfryn Way, Penyrheol, Caerphilly CF83 2XZ;
   Tel 029 2085 4818
Team Manager   Tina Blake
Team Manager   Moray Grant

RISCA CHILDREN'S SERVICES AREA TEAM

Hawtin Pk, Gellihaf, Pontllanfraith, Blackwood, Caerphilly
   NP12 2PZ; Tel 01443 864558
Team Manager   Barbara Jones

RHYMNEY CHILDREN'S SERVICES AREA TEAM

Trigfan, 11 The Terr, Rhymney, Caerphilly NP12 5LY;
   Tel 01685 844295
Team Manager   Alison Parker

INTAKE AND ASSESSMENT 1

Northern Locality Office, 42 Williams St, Gilfach, Bargoed,
   Caerphilly CF81 8ND; Tel 01443 873502
Team Manager   Kay Jenkins

INTAKE AND ASSESSMENT 2

Northern Locality Office, 42 Williams St, Gilfach, Bargoed,
   Caerphilly CF81 8ND; Tel 01443 873568
Team Manager   Julie Downs

CHILDREN WITH DISABILITIES TEAM

Northern Locality Office, 42 Williams St, Gilfach, Bargoed,
   Caerphilly CF81 8ND; Tel 01443 873518
Team Manager   Glenice Robinson

LEAVING CARE TEAM AND RESIDENTIAL SERVICES

Heol Aneurin (Res. Team), 24 Heol Aneurin, Caerphilly
   CF83 2PB; Tel 029 2085 2547
Team Manager   Mike Sira-Parfitt

FAMILY PLACEMENT TEAM

Avenue Hse, King Edward Ave, Caerphilly CF1 1PC;
   Tel 029 2088 0090
Team Manager (Fostering)   Caroline Borley Mitchell
Team Manager (Adoption)   Rob Pook

DAY CARE AND FAMILY SERVICE TEAM

Cwm Ifor, Caledfryn Way, Penyrheol, Caerphilly CF83 2XZ;
   Tel 029 2085 4800
Team Manager   Vacancy

YOUTH OFFENDING TEAM

Libanus Hse, Libanus Rd, Blackwood, Caerphilly; Tel 01495
   235623
Service Manager   Gillian O'Donovan

PLAYGROUP

Fochriw Playgroup Fochriw Community Centre, Fochriw, Rhymney, Caerphilly; Tel 01685 840635
Manager Jenny Lewis

FAMILY CENTRES

Risca Family Centre Brooklands Rd, Risca, Caerphilly NP11 6BU; Tel 01633 615859
Manager Pam Tart

Variety Club Family Centre Caledfryn Way, Penyrheol, Caerphilly CF83 1UZ; Tel 029 2085 2550
Manager Cath Morris

CHILDREN'S RESIDENTIAL HOME

Heol Aneurin 24 Heol Aneurin, Penyrheol, Caerphilly CF83 2PD; Tel 029 2085 2547
Manager Mike Sira-Parfitt

ADULT SERVICES OFFICES

BLACKWOOD

Blackwood Elderly/Disabled Adult Area Team Hawtin Pk, Gellihaf, Pontllanfraith, Blackwood, Caerphilly NP12 2PZ; Tel 01443 864720
Team Manager Tony Crawford

Blackwood Home Care Team Hawtin Pk, Gellihaf, Pontllanfraith, Blackwood, Caerphilly NP12 2PZ; Tel 01443 864509
Home Care Manager Barbara Smith

RHYMNEY

Rhymney Elderly/Disabled Adult Area Team The Chapel, Ramsden St, Rhymney, Caerphilly NP12 5NS; Tel 01685 847100
Team Manager Ralph Angel

Rhymney Home Care Team The Chapel, Ramsden St, Rhymney, Caerphilly NP12 5NS; Tel 01685 847108
Home Care Manager Sandra Davies

RISCA

Risca Elderly/Disabled Adult Area Team Hawtin Pk, Gellihaf, Pontllanfraith, Blackwood, Caerphilly NP12 2PZ; Tel 01443 864721
Team Manager Tony Crawford

Risca Home Care Team Hawtin Pk, Gellihaf, Pontllanfraith, Blackwood, Caerphilly NP12 2PZ; Tel 01443 864519
Home Care Manager Barbara Smith

BARGOED

Bargoed Elderly/Disabled Adult Area Team Northern Locality Office, William St, Gilfach, Bargoed, Caerphilly CF81 8ND; Tel 01443 873518
Team Manager Stephen Howells

Bargoed Home Care Team Northern Locality Office, William St, Gilfach, Bargoed, Caerphilly CF81 8ND; Tel 01443 873597
Home Care Manager Sandra Davies

CAERPHILLY

Caerphilly Elderly/Disabled Adult Area Team Mill Rd, Caerphilly CF83 3FD; Tel 029 2085 5000
Team Manager Gareth Powell

Caerphilly Home Care Team Mill Rd, Caerphilly CF83 3FD; Tel 029 2085 5038
Home Care Manager Ann Gray

RESIDENTIAL CARE TEAM

Hawtin Pk, Gellihaf, Pontllanfraith, Blackwood, Caerphilly NP12 2PZ; Tel 01443 864522
Team Manager Jonathan Griffiths

HOME CARE TEAM

Hawtin Pk, Gellihaf, Pontllanfraith, Blackwood, Caerphilly NP12 2PZ; Tel 01443 864712
Team Manager Anne Potter

LEARNING DISABILITY TEAM

Suflex Bldgs, Newport Rd, Pontymister, Risca, Caerphilly; Tel 01633 612123
Team Manager Karen Rowley

MENTAL HEALTH TEAM

Mill Rd, Caerphilly CF83 3FD; Tel 029 2085 5000
Team Manager Peter Evans

MENTAL HEALTH PROVIDER TEAM

The Chapel, Ramsden St, Rhymney, Caerphilly NP12 5NS; Tel 01685 847100
Team Manager Chris Walsh

ADULT ACCOMMODATION PROVIDER TEAM

Suflex Bldgs, Newport Rd, Pontymister, Risca, Caerphilly; Tel 01633 618103
Team Manager Janet Jones

COMMUNITY SUPPORT SERVICES PROVIDER TEAM

Suflex Bldgs, Newport Rd, Pontymister, Risca, Caerphilly; Tel 01633 618103
Team Manager Linda Williams

OCCUPATIONAL THERAPY

Northern Locality Office, William St, Gilfach, Bargoed, Caerphilly CF81 8ND; Tel 01443 873518
Team Manager Jo Williams

DAY CENTRES – MULTIPURPOSE

Brondeg Day Centre Bloomfield Rd, Blackwood, Caerphilly NP12 1QB; Tel 01495 226542
Manager Sandra Forbes

Caerphilly Day Centre Station Terr, Caerphilly CF83 1HD; Tel 029 2085 2558
Manager Susan Jones

Rhymney Day Centre Oakland Terr, Rhymney, Caerphilly NP22 5EP; Tel 01685 840666
Manager Laura Williams

Twyncarn Day Centre Twyncarn Hse, Cwmcarn, Caerphilly NP11 7LY; Tel 01495 270164
Manager Pam Adams

DAY CENTRES – LEARNING DISABILITIES

Clos Tyr y Pwll 6 Clos Tyr Y Pwll, Pantside Est, Newbridge, Caerphilly NP11 5GE; Tel 01495 244917
Manager Dave Watkins

Markham Resource Centre Pantycefn Rd, Markham, Caerphilly NP12 0RX; Tel 01495 229879
Manager Rod Berry

Ystrad Mynach Day Centre Caerphilly Rd, Ystrad, Mynach Hengoed, Caerphilly CF83 7PI; Tel 01443 862160
Manager Aileen Carey

DAY CENTRES – MENTAL HEALTH

Hafod Deg Day Centre High St, Rhymney, Caerphilly NP22 5EP; Tel 01685 840905
Manager Diane Carole

8

Pentrebane Street Day Centre Pentrebane St, Caerphilly; Tel 029 2086 1771
Manager Janet Thomas

SHORT BREAK SERVICE

Montclaire Short Break Service (Learning Disability) 65 Montclaire Ave, Blackwood, Caerphilly NP12 1EF; Tel 01495 220248
Manager Lynne Price

Ty Gwilyn Short Break Service Court Rd, Energlyn, Caerphilly CG83 2LU; Tel 029 2086 8398
Manager Alison Moss

RESIDENTIAL SERVICES – LEARNING DISABILITY

Craig Road Group Home 14 Craig Rd, Hengoed, Caerphilly; Tel 01443 862024
Manager Diane Maddocks

Hengoed Hall Close Group Home 18 Hengoed Hall Cl, Hengoed, Caerphilly CF83 7JH; Tel 01443 815889
Manager Diane Maddocks

Hill View Group Home 6 Hill View, Maes-y-cymmer, Hengoed, Caerphilly; Tel 01443 814349
Manager Diane Maddocks

Tair Erw Residential Home Nelson Rd, Ystrad Mynach, Hengoed, Caerphilly CF83 7EG; Tel 01443 812198
Manager Julie Jones

Waunfach Street Group Home 14–16 Waunfach St, Caerphilly CF83 3HL; Tel 029 2085 2557
Manager Diane Maddocks

RESIDENTIAL SERVICES – PHYSICAL DISABILITY

Independent Living House – Disability Action Team 22 The Crescent, Trecenydd, Caerphilly; Tel 029 2086 2728
Disability Action Team Wally Haines

RETIREMENT PROJECT (ELDERLY)

St. John's Ambulance Hall, Bryncenydd, Caerphilly CF83 2PB; Tel 029 2086 0146
Manager Anthony Thomas

ADULT TRAINING CENTRES

Brooklands Adult Training Centre Brooklands Rd, Risca, Caerphilly NP11 6BU; Tel 01633 615338
Manager Jacqui Phillips

Coed Duon 14 Coed Duon View, Pentwynmawr, Newbridge, Caerphilly; Tel 01495 270164
Manager Stish Piekarski c/o Twyncarn Day Centre

Directorate of Education and Leisure

Council Offices, Caerphilly Rd, Hengoed, Caerphilly CF82 7EP; URL www.caerphilly.gov.uk; E-mail hopkid@caerphilly.gov.uk; Tel 01443 864956; Fax 01443 864869
Director (Education and Leisure) David Hopkins
Head (School Effectiveness) Bob Howells
Head (Planning and Strategy) Bleddyn Hopkins
Head (Lifelong Learning) Peter Gomer
Head (Inclusion Services) Robin Brown
Principal Officer (Learning Support) Dinnella Shelton
Principal Educational Psychologist Jackie Garland
Principal Officer (SIMS Support and IT Development) Stuart Lawton
Principal Officer (Community Education) Huw Jones
Adviser (Teaching and Learning, Secondary) June Davies
Adviser (Teaching and Learning – Primary and Secondary) Ken Cole
Adviser (Teaching and Learning – Primary) Bev Jenkins

SPECIAL SCHOOL

Trinity Fields School and Resource Centre Caerphilly Rd, Ystrad Mynach, Hengoed, Caerphilly CF82 7DT; Tel 01443 866000
Headteacher D.M. Hughes
(120)

CARDIFF COUNTY COUNCIL
www.cardiff.gov.uk

Political Composition: Lab: 49, LD: 17, Con: 5, Ind: 2, Plaid: 1, Vacancy: 1
County Hall, Atlantic Wharf, Cardiff CF10 4UW; URL www.cardiff.gov.uk; Tel 029 2087 2000
Chief Executive B. Davies; Tel 029 2087 2401

Social Services Department

County Hall, Atlantic Wharf, Cardiff CF10 4UW; Tel (Connect 2 Cardiff) 029 2087 2087; (Emergency (Out-of-office hours)) 029 2039 6873; Fax 029 2055 4958; 029 2087 2086
Director (Social Services) C. Davies

INSPECTION UNIT

West Hse, Stanwell Rd, Penarth, Cardiff; Tel 029 2071 2722; Fax 029 2071 1498
Head (Inspection) Lee Davis

CHILDREN'S SERVICES

Canton Family Centre Romilly Rd, Cardiff; Tel 029 2023 9826; Fax 029 2064 4992
Principal Officer (Social Services) P. Humphreys

Deane House Family Centre 168 Newport Rd, Cardiff; Tel 029 2046 0601; Fax 029 2045 1838
Team Manager (Fieldwork) C. Beardsley
Team Manager (Fieldwork) N. Bryning
Team Manager (Fieldwork) L. Willingham

Ely Family Centre Grand Ave, Ely, Cardiff; Tel 029 2057 8918; Fax 029 2057 6132
Principal Officer (Social Services) R. Mecklenburgh
Team Manager (Fieldwork) K. Bayes
Team Manager (Fieldwork) M. Watt
Team Manager (Fieldwork) P. Gray

Llanedeyrn Family Centre Roundwood, Llanedeyrn, Cardiff; Tel 029 2054 1401; Fax 029 2054 1729
Principal Officer (Social Services) P. Jones

Splott Family Centre Loudown Hse, 272 Loudoun Sq, Butetown, Cardiff CF1 4JT; Tel 029 2046 3848; Fax 029 2045 1839
Principal Officer (Social Services) I. Stokes

St. Mellons Family Centre Heol Maes Eirwg, St. Mellows, Cardiff; Tel 029 2036 9700; Fax 029 2036 9998
Principal Officer (Social Services) T. Bloore

CHILDREN'S SERVICES (FOSTERING AND ADOPTION)

Trowbridge Centre Greenway Rd, Cardiff CF3 8QS; Tel 029 2077 4600; Fax 029 2079 1791
Contact R. Rees

CHILD PROTECTION

Trowbridge Centre, Greenway Rd, Cardiff CF3 8QS; Tel 029 2077 4600; Fax 029 2079 1791
Principal Officer (Social Services) C. Manser

DAY INSPECTION AND REGISTRATION (UNDER EIGHTS)

Trowbridge Centre, Greenway Rd, Cardiff CF3 8QS; Tel 029 2077 4600; Fax 029 2079 1791
Senior Practitioner (Social Work)   K. Powell

FAMILY CENTRES WITH DAY CARE

Canton Family Centre Romilly Rd, Canton, Cardiff CF5 1FH; Tel 029 2022 5948
   (20)

Ely Family Centre Grand Ave, Ely, Cardiff CF5 4LE; Tel 029 2057 8918

Trowbridge Day Care Unit Greenway Rd, Trowbridge, Cardiff; Tel 029 2077 7383

Splott Family Centre 69b Splott Rd, Splott, Cardiff; Tel 029 2046 3848

RESIDENTIAL CARE

Abergele Road Home 29 Abergele Rd, Trowbridge, Cardiff CF3 8RS; Tel 029 2077 8930; Fax 029 2077 8930
Unit Manager   Sandra Herbert

Beechley Drive Home 52 Beechley Dr, Pentrebane, Cardiff CF4 3SN; Tel 029 2057 7020; Fax 029 2057 5016
Principal Officer (Social Services)   Bob Garner

Crosslands 318 Cowbridge Road West, Cardiff CF5 5TD; Tel 029 2059 1392; Fax 029 2059 8556
Unit Manager   Debbie Martin-Jones

Gorse Place Home 38 Gorse Pl, Fairwater, Cardiff CF5 1FH; Tel 029 2056 4765; Fax 029 2057 7050
Unit Manager   Mike Paton

Gwbert Close Home 18 Gwbert Cl, Trowbridge, Cardiff CF3 8QY; Tel 029 2077 8737; Fax 029 2077 8737
Unit Manager   Sandra Soares

John Kane Centre Thornhill Rd, Cardiff SF4 5UA; Tel 029 2061 9661; Fax 029 2052 2425
Unit Manager   Bob Mathews

Walker House Fidlas Rd, Llanishen, Cardiff CF4 5LZ; Tel 029 2075 5069; Fax 029 2076 1641
Unit Manager   Maria Bowles

YOUNG PEOPLE'S SERVICES

After Care Young People's Service 69b Splott Rd, Splott, Cardiff CF2 2BW; Tel 029 2048 6894; Fax 029 2047 0809
PSSO   M. Cove (Acting)

Youth Justice Penhill Centre, The Rise, Cardiff CF2 9PR; Tel 029 2056 0839; Fax 029 2057 8746
PSSO   P. Dinham

SERVICES FOR PERSONS WITH LEARNING DISABILITY/MENTAL HEALTH/EMI

Community Team (Cardiff East) 35 Ty Gwyn Rd, Penylan, Cardiff CF1 5JG; Tel 029 2045 0222; Fax 029 2046 4328
Principal Officer (Social Services)   G. Bowden
   (Acting)

Accommodation and Day Services (Cardiff East) 30 Richmond Rd, Roath, Cardiff CF2 3AS; Tel 029 2046 2466; Fax 029 2047 0690
Principal Officer (Social Services)   K. Barker (Acting)

Community Team (Cardiff West) 30 Riverside Terr, Cardiff; Tel 029 2055 1184; Fax 029 2057 5810
Principal Officer (Social Services)   C. Horrocks

Accommodation and Day Services (Cardiff West) 10 Penlline Rd, Whitchurch, Cardiff CF4 2AD; Tel 029 2061 0711; Fax 029 2062 4374
Principal Officer (Social Services)   J. Noble (Acting)

MENTAL HEALTH SERVICES

Cardiff North Community Mental Health Service Pentwyn Health Centre, Brynheulog, Pentwyn, Cardiff CF2 7JD; Tel 029 2073 1466; Fax 029 2054 9212
Principal Officer (Social Services)   K. Morgan
Cardiff North East Team Pentwyn Health Centre, Brynheulog, Pentwyn, Cardiff CF2 7JD; Tel 029 2073 1466; Fax 029 2054 9212
Cardiff North West Team Gabalfa Clinic, 213 North Rd, Gabalfa, Cardiff CF4 3AG; Tel 029 2069 3941; Fax 029 2062 7954
Cardiff South East Team The Links Centre, 60 Newport Rd, Cardiff CF2 1DF; Tel 029 2045 1144; Fax 029 2045 1742
Cardiff South Community Mental Health Service The Pendine Centre, 124–126 Cowbridge Rd, Ely, Cardiff CF5 5BT; Tel 029 2057 8778; Fax 029 2057 8450
Principal Officer (Social Services)   M. Wiltshire
Cardiff South West Team Riverside Health Centre, Wellington St, Canton, Cardiff CF1 9SH; Tel 029 2023 3533; Fax 029 2023 2945
Cardiff West Team The Pendine Centre, 124–126 Cowbridge Rd, Cardiff CF5 5BT; Tel 029 2057 8778; Fax 029 2057 8450

ELDERLY MENTALLY INFIRM

Cardiff North and West Heol Don Centre, Heol Don, Whitchurch, Cardiff CF4 2XG; Tel 029 2052 1860; Fax 029 2062 8917
Principal Officer (Social Services)   B. Jones

Cardiff South Royal Hamadryad, Hunter St, Cardiff CF1 6VQ; Tel 029 2045 0250; Fax 029 2045 8253
Principal Officer (Social Services)   I. Cutler

8

ELDERLY AND PHYSICALLY DISABLED – COMMISSIONING SERVICES

Canton and Riverside Centre Market Rd, Canton, Cardiff CF5 1QE; Tel 029 2038 3555; Fax 029 2064 5743
Principal Officer (Social Services)   G. McQuade

Centre for the Visually Impaired 125 Cathedral Rd, Cardiff CF1 9PH; Tel 029 2022 5810; Fax 029 2066 6304

Community Care Support Unit Shand Hse, Fitzalan Pl, Cardiff CF2 1BD; Tel 029 2049 4676; Fax 029 2049 6337
Principal Officer (Social Services)   P. Lawrence (Acting)

Cord House 2 Finchley Rd, Fairwater, Cardiff CF5 3AX; Tel 029 2057 5570; Fax 029 2057 5496
Principal Officer (Social Services)   I. Bull

Heol Don Centre Heol Don, Whitchurch, Cardiff CF4 2XG; Tel 029 2052 1855; Fax 029 2052 9437
Principal Officer (Social Services)   M. James

Highfields Centre Allensbank Rd, Heath, Cardiff CF4 3RB; Tel 029 2076 6531; Fax 029 2076 2295
Principal Officer (Social Services)   H. Teague

The Parade Centre 34 The Pde, Roath, Cardiff CF2 3AR; Tel 029 2045 6525; Fax 029 2045 5308
Principal Officer (Social Services)   K. Griffiths

Social Workers for the Deaf
based at the following three centres:
Canton and Riverside Centre Market Rd, Canton, Cardiff CF5 1QE; Tel 029 2038 3555; Fax 029 2038 3555
Highfields Centre Allensbank Rd, Heath, Cardiff CF4 3RB; Tel 029 2076 6531; Fax 029 2076 2295
The Parade Centre 34 The Parade, Roath, Cardiff CF2 3AR; Tel 029 2045 6525; Fax 029 2045 6525

Social Workers for the Blind 125 Cathedral Rd, Cardiff CF1 9PH; Tel 029 2022 5810; Fax 029 2066 6304
based at the Centre for the Visually Impaired.

Social Work Support to the Acute Hospital and Health Services
Social workers are based in hospitals and in some instances general practitioners' practices.
Principal Officer (Social Services)   P. Akande; Tel 029 2074 7747
Principal Officer (Social Services)   M. James; Tel 029 2056 6281

Cardiff Royal Infirmary (West Wing) Newport Rd, Cardiff CF2 1SZ; Tel 029 2033 5703; Fax 029 2045 7034
Rookwood Hospital Fairwater Rd, Cardiff CF5 2YN; Tel 029 2056 6281; Fax 029 2057 5220
University Hospital of Wales Heath Pk, Cardiff CF4 4XW; Tel 029 2074 7747; Fax 029 2074 4868
Velindre Hospital Velindre Rd, Whitchurch, Cardiff CF4 7XL; Tel 029 2061 5888; Fax 029 2061 9189

Woodcroft Centre Glan-y-Mor Rd, Trowbridge, Cardiff CF3 8RP; Tel 029 2077 0212; Fax 029 2077 0217
Principal Officer (Social Services) R. Davies

ELDERLY AND PHYSICALLY DISABLED – DIRECT SERVICES

Gabalfa Avenue Day Centre Gabalfa Ave, Cardiff CF4 2HU
Manager (Day Service) D. Houlihan; Tel 029 2061 3341
Grand Avenue Day Centre 89–91 Grand Ave, Ely, Cardiff CF5 4LF; Tel 029 2056 5806; Fax 029 2057 5024
Manager (Day Service) D. Mitchell
Principal Officer (Social Services) J. Pianowski
Plasmawr Road Day Centre Fairwater, Cardiff CF5 3JU
Manager (Day Service) G. Emes; Tel 029 2056 6528

Market Road Day Centre
Manager (Day Service) P. Csaszar; Tel 029 2038 3555

Meals in the Home
Plasmawr Road Fairwater, Cardiff CF5 3JU
Organiser A. Bines; Tel 029 2056 6533

DAY SERVICES FOR OLDER PEOPLE

Llanedeyrn Day Centre The Maelfa, Llanedeyrn, Cardiff CF3 7BL
Manager (Day Care) J. Jarman; Tel 029 2073 2533
Oldwell Court Day Centre Ty Gwyn Rd, Roath, Cardiff CF2 5DA
Manager (Day Care) J. Jarman; Tel 029 2047 0022
Dalton Street Day Centre Dalton St, Cardiff CF2 4HB
Manager (Day Service) D. Brown; Tel 029 2022 0675
Highfields Day Centre for People with a Physical Disability Allensbank Rd, Heath, Cardiff CF4 3RB
Manager (Day Service) K. Wilkin; Tel 029 2075 0315; Fax 029 2076 2285

RESIDENTIAL SERVICES FOR OLDER PEOPLE

Moorland Road Centre Moorland Rd, Splott, Cardiff CF2 2LG
Manager (Day Service) C. McMullen; Tel 029 2046 2594; Fax 029 2046 2439
Llanrumney Day Centre Minehead Rd, Cardiff CF3 9TH
Manager (Day Service) M. Troake; Tel 029 2079 7454; Fax 029 2079 7545
Clydach Street Day Centre Clydach St, Cardiff CF1 7AE; Tel 029 2037 7627; Fax 029 2037 7627
Manager (Day Service) D. Jones
Centre for the Deaf 163 Newport Rd, Cardiff CF2 1AG; Tel 029 2049 3144

MEALS IN THE HOME

Moorlands Road Splott, Cardiff CF2 2LG
Organiser C. McMullen; Tel 029 2046 2439

RESIDENTIAL SERVICES FOR OLDER PEOPLE

Cae Glas Home Beaumaris Rd, Rumney, Cardiff CF3 8LD; Tel 029 2077 8193; Fax 029 2036 2078
Residential Manager P. Gardner
Rothesay House Loundoun Sq, Docks, Cardiff CF1 5JN
Residential Manager J. O'Keefe; Tel 029 2048 1558; Fax 029 2047 0443

Tymawr Home Southminster Rd, Roath, Cardiff CF2 5AT
Residential Manager M. MacNeil; Tel 029 2049 8921; Fax 029 2045 6202
Principal Officer (Social Services) G. Sherlock; Tel 029 2046 2717; Fax 029 2045 6202

ETHNIC MINORITY SERVICES

Children's Services for the Asian Community
Splott Family Centre Loudoun Hse, 272 Loudoun Sq, Butetown, Cardiff CF1 4JT; Tel 029 2046 3848
Contact C. Pant; Tel 029 2046 3848
Dean House Family Centre 168 Newport Rd, Cardiff CF2 1DL
Contact N. Kumar; Tel 029 2046 0601
Children's Services for the Chinese Community
Canton Family Centre Romilly Rd, Canton, Cardiff CF5 1FH
Services for the Somali Community
Splott Family Centre Loudoun Hse, Loudoun Sq, Butetown, Cardiff CF1 4JT; Tel 029 2046 3848
Contact L. Saeed
Contact B. Elmi
Somali Services for Physically Disabled 34 The Parade, Roath, Cardiff CF2 3AR
Contact A. Ali; Tel 029 2045 6525
Somali Community Development City Centre Team, Marland Hse, Cardiff CF1 1ED; Tel 029 2087 1792
Contact H. Noar
Services to Ethnic Minority People with Learning Disabilities
Health/Social Care Advocates
For the Bangladeshi Community M. Sengupta; Tel 029 2023 2565
For the Chinese Community C. Wong; Tel 029 2064 4255
For the Greek Community M. Polycarpou; Tel 029 2022 4206

WELFARE RIGHTS TEAM

Services for People with a Learning Disability Shand Hse, Fitzalan Pl, Cardiff CF2 1BD
Team Manager G. Parsons; Tel 029 2043 5765; Fax 029 2045 4284

Schools Service

County Hall, Atlantic Wharf, Cardiff CF10 4UW; E-mail h.knight@cardiff.gov.uk; Tel 029 2087 2000; Fax 029 2087 2777
Chief Schools Officer Hugh Knight
Manager (Pupil Services) Celia Butler
Manager (Standards and School Effectiveness) Robert Hopkins
Officer (SEN) Glynnis Withrington

SPECIAL SCHOOLS

The Court School 96a Station Rd, Llanishen, Cardiff CF14 5UX; E-mail headteacher@thecourtsp.cardiff.sch.uk; Tel 029 2075 2713; Fax 029 2076 3895
Headteacher Gill Unwin, BEd(Hons), DipSpEd
Greenhill School Heol Brynglas, Rhiwbina, Cardiff CF14 6UJ; E-mail schooladmin@greenhillsp.cardiff.sch.uk; Tel 029 2069 3786; Fax 029 2062 1991
Headteacher A.R. Lewis, BA, DipSpecEd
The Hollies School Pentwyn Dr, Pentwyn, Cardiff CF23 7XG; E-mail headteacher@theholliessp.cardiff.sch.uk; Tel 029 2073 4411; Fax 029 2054 0239
Headteacher Mrs C. Matthews, BEd(Spec), AdvDip(SLD)
Meadowbank School Colwill Rd, Gabalfa, Cardiff CF14 2QQ; E-mail headteacher@meadowbanksp.cardiff.sch.uk; Tel 029 2061 0501; 029 2061 6018; Fax 029 2061 0118
Headteacher Mrs C. Arthurs

Riverbank School Vincent Rd, Ely, Cardiff CF5 5AQ;
E-mail headteacher@riverbanksp.cardiff.sch.uk; Tel 029
2056 3860; Fax 029 2056 8398
Headteacher Mrs A. Smith, BEd, DipSEN

Ty Gwyn School Ty Gwyn Rd, Penylan, Cardiff CF23 5JG;
E-mail headteacher@tygwynsp.cardiff.sch.uk; Tel 029 2048
5570; Fax 029 2045 3922
Headteacher D.W. Dwyer, BEd, DipTHC

Woodlands High School Vincent Rd, Ely, Cardiff CF5 5AQ;
E-mail headteacher@woodlandshigh.cardiff.sch.uk; Tel 029
2056 1279; Fax 029 205 76185
Headteacher Mrs A. Dunne, BEd(Hons)

CARMARTHENSHIRE COUNTY COUNCIL

www.carmarthenshire.gov.uk

Political Composition: Lab: 28, Ind: 27, Plaid Cymru: 16,
Ind Lab: 2, Unaffiliated: 1
County Hall, Carmarthen, Carmarthenshire SA31 1JP;
  URL www.carmarthenshire.gov.uk;
  E-mail information@carmarthenshire.gov.uk; Tel 01267
  234567
Chief Executive Mark James

Social Care and Housing Department

3 Spilman St, Carmarthen, Carmarthenshire SA31 1LE;
  E-mail bmclernon@carmarthenshire.gov.uk; Tel 01267
  234567; Fax 01267 221616
Director Bruce McLernon; Tel 01267 228701; Fax 01267
  221616
Executive Board Member Cllr P.J. Edwards (LD)
Head (Policy and Finance) Maggie Bell; Tel 01267 228701;
  Fax 01267 221616
Head (Children and Families) Ann Williams; Tel 01267
  228903; Fax 01267 228908
Head (Adult Services) Bill Collins; Tel 01267 228900;
  Fax 01267 228908
Senior Principal Officer (Physical Disabilities) Mr C. Allen;
  Tel 01267 228917; Fax 01267 228908
Senior Principal Officer (Elderly) J. Philpin; Tel 01267
  228918; Fax 01267 228908
Senior Principal Officer (Mental Health) M.P. Evans
Lime Gr Hse, Lime Gr Ave, Carmarthen, Carmarthenshire
  SA31 1SW; Tel 01267 224291; Fax 01267 224259
Senior Principal Officer (Learning Disabilities) R. Moulster;
  Tel 01267 224268; Fax 01267 224259
Senior Principal Officer (Children's Services) A. Maynard;
  Tel 01267 228905; Fax 01267 228908
Senior Principal Officer (Children's Services) S. Smith;
  Tel 01267 228914; Fax 01267 228908
Senior Principal Officer (Children's Services) A. Williams;
  Tel 01267 228913; Fax 01267 228908
Senior Principal Officer (Direct Services Best Value)
  M. Winnicott
Lime Gr Hse, Lime Gr Ave, Carmarthen, Carmarthenshire
  SA31 1SW; Tel 01267 224216; Fax 01267 224259
Head (Support Services) G. John; Tel 01267 228849;
  Fax 01267 221616
Senior Principal Officer (Service Strategy) M. Catling;
  Tel 01267 228789; Fax 01267 221616

Social Work Teams

LLANELLI EAST CHILD CARE TEAM

Ty Elwyn, Llanelli, Carmarthenshire SA15 3AH; Tel 01554
  742227; Fax 01554 774972
Manager Vacancy

LLANELLI WEST CHILD CARE TEAM

Ty Elwyn, Llanelli, Carmarthenshire SA15 3AH; Tel 01554
  742318; Fax 01554 774972
Manager J. Griffiths

Assessment Team Ty Elwyn, Llanelli, Carmarthenshire
SA15 3AH; Tel 01554 742124; Fax 01554 742176
Team Leader G. Tuckey

Assessment Team The Old Library, 15 Cennan Rd,
Ammanford, Carmarthenshire SA18 3BD; Tel 01558 825475;
Fax 01558 825482
Team Leader A. Grace

Carmarthen Child Care Team Cambrian Pl, Carmarthen,
Carmarthenshire SA31 1QG; Tel 01267 224403; Fax 01267
223950
Team Leader N. Hutchison

Dinefwr Child Care Team The Old Library, 15 Cennan Rd,
Ammanford, Carmarthenshire SA18 3BD; Tel 01558 825414;
Fax 01558 825414
Team Leader P. Pike

Youth Offending Team 1 West End, Llanelli, Carmarthenshire
SA15 3AH; Tel 01554 740120; Fax 01554 740122
Team Leader R. Summers

FAMILY PLACEMENT AND LEAVING CARE TEAM

Ty Elwyn, Llanelli, Carmarthenshire SA15 3AH; Tel 01554
  772262; Fax 01554 742312
Team Leader J. Sloane

Carmarthen Adult Team Cambrian Pl, Carmarthen,
Carmarthenshire SA31 1QG; Tel 01267 224401; Fax 01267
223950
Senior Manager (Care) B. Lewis

Dinefwr Adult Team Cartref, Tirydail, Ammanford,
Carmarthenshire SA18 3AS; Tel 01558 825431; Fax 01269
594677
Senior Manager C. Wilkes

Family and Community Team 24 Station Rd, Llanelli,
Carmarthenshire; Tel 01554 776323
Team Manager M. Shamte

LLANELLI EAST AND WEST ADULT TEAMS

3 Crown Precinct, Llanelli, Carmarthenshire SA15 3UT;
  Tel 01554 774951; Fax 01554 749382
Senior Manager (Care) Vacancy

Community Team (Learning Disabilites) 5–6 Queen St,
Carmarthen, Carmarthenshire SA31 1JR; Tel 01267 236899;
Fax 01267 222849
Principal Officer N. Edwards

Community Team (Learning Disabilities) 12 Bay View,
Capel Rd, Llanelli, Carmarthenshire SA14 8SN; Tel 01554
775916; Fax 01554 770489
Principal Officer M. Jones

AREA MENTAL HEALTH TEAM

13 Goring Rd, Llanelli, Carmarthenshire SA15 3HH;
  Tel 01554 775299; Fax 01554 770489
Co-ordinator M. Evans

AREA MENTAL HEALTH TEAM

Wellfield Resource Centre, 22 Wellfield Rd, Carmarthen,
  Carmarthenshire; Tel 01267 236017; Fax 01267 238506
Co-ordinator T. Price

Hospital Social Work Team West Wales General Hospital,
Carmarthen, Carmarthenshire SA31 2PP; Tel 01267 227559;
Fax 01267 238572
Social Worker J. Rimell

Hospital Social Work Team Prince Phillip Hospital,
Bryngwyn Mawr, Llanelli, Carmarthenshire SA14 8QF;
Tel 01554 756567; Fax 01554 746500
Co-ordinator A. Thomas

8

CHILDREN

There are two respite homes and two family centres for children.

LEARNING DISABILITIES

There is one residential home, two respite homes and three social activity centres for people with learning disabilities.

PHYSICAL DISABILITIES

There is one residential home and one day centre for people with physical disabilities.

MENTAL ILLNESS

There is one day centre for people with a mental illness.

ELDERLY

There are 14 residential homes and 12 day centres for the elderly.

Lifelong Learning and Leisure

Pibwrlwyd, Carmarthen, Carmarthenshire SA31 2NH; Tel 01267 224532; Fax 01267 221692
Director (Lifelong Learning and Leisure)   A.G. Davies
Head (Policy and Performance)   R.D. Blewitt
Head (Education Standards and Lifelong Learning)
   T.W. Williams
Head (Schools Support Services)   B. Stephens
Head (Recreation and Leisure)   C.D. James
Head (Facilities Management)   E. Cullen
Manager (Inclusion)   M. Provis
Manager (Support Unit)   W. Edwards
Senior Officer (Education Welfare)   A. Jones

PROFESSIONAL SERVICES

Griffith Jones Centre St. Clears, Carmarthen, Carmarthenshire SA33 4BT; Tel 01994 231866; Fax 01994 231255
Principal Adviser   P. Richardson
Principal Educational Psychologist   R. White
Principal Educational Psychologist   A. Davies
Senior Educational Psychologist   S. Spare
Senior Educational Psychologist   S. Corrall

SPECIAL SCHOOLS

Heol Goffa School Heol Goffa, Llanelli, Carmarthenshire SA15 3LS; Tel 01554 759465
Headteacher   Mr P. Newell
   (76)

Ysgol Rhyd-y-gors Johnstown, Carmarthen, Carmarthenshire SA31 3QU; Tel 01267 231171
Headteacher   S.C. Saunders, BEd, MEd

CEREDIGION COUNTY COUNCIL
www.ceredigion.gov.uk

Population 75 384
Political Composition: Ind: 22, Plaid Cymru: 12, LD: 8, Lab: 1, Ind Un-grouped: 1
Neuadd Cyngor Ceredigion, Penmorfa, Aberaeron, Ceredigion SA46 0PA; URL www.ceredigion.gov.uk; E-mail info@ceredigion.gov.uk; Tel 01545 570881; Fax 01545 572009
Chief Executive Officer   O. Watkin

Social Services Department

Headquarters, Min-Aeron, Aberaeron, Ceredigion
   SA46 0DY; E-mail socservs@ceredigion.gov.uk; Tel 01545
   570881; Fax 01545 572619
Director (Social Services)   Vacancy
Assistant Director (Children Services)   G.H Davies
Assistant Director (Adult Services)   D.W. Harries
Chief Administrative Officer   M. Pickering
Manager (Direct Service)   G. Maddox
Principal Officer (Child Care)   E. Howells
Principal Officer (Adult)   C. Allen

Social Services Committee

Members of the Committee
Ind: W.G. Bennett, B.L. Davies, J.E. Davies, Ll. G. Edwards, G. Ellis, D.J. Evans, S.G. Hopley, J.G. Jenkins, L.Ll. Jones, T.J. Jones, T.H. Lewis, S.M. Morris, W.T.K. Raw-Rees, J.D. Thomas, R.E. Thomas, S.M. Thomas, T.A. Thomas, W.J.G. Varney, H.T. Jones, J.I. Williams.
LD: W.R. Edwards, P.W. Eklund, E.J. Griffiths, J.D.R. Jones, E.C. Williams, F. Williams.
Plaid Cymru: T.J. Adams-Lewis, E.ap Gwynn, E.W. Davies, J.T.O. Davies, H.G. Evans, T.T. Griffiths, G.H. Gruffydd, D.M. James, W.P. James, C. Llwyd, S.H. Richards, Ll. Roberts-Young, S. Thomas.
Lab: R.G. Harris.

TEAM OFFICES

Aberystwyth

BURTON CHAMBERS

29–31 Terr Rd, Aberystwyth, Ceredigion SY23 2AE
Team Manager (North Ceredigion Family Support Team)
   A. Jones; Tel 01970 626137
Team Manager (North Ceredigion Adult)   Tel 01970 627830

COUNTY OFFICES

Campws Felinfach, Felinfach, Lampeter, Ceredigion
   SA48 8AF; Tel 01545 572745; Fax 01545 572745
Team Manager (Community Team Learning Disabilities)   P. Sani

DAY CENTRE

Aberystwyth Day Centre Park Ave, Aberystwyth, Ceredigion SY23 1PB; Tel 01970 615502

GORWELION

Llanbadarn Rd, Aberystwyth, Ceredigion SY23 1HB;
   Tel 01970 615448
Team Manager (Community Mental Health Team)   J. Scullard
Bronglais Hospital Social Work Department, Aberystwyth, Ceredigion; Tel 01970 635818

SOCIAL ACTIVITY CENTRE

Aberystwyth Social Activity Centre Llanbadarn Fawr, Aberystwyth, Ceredigion SY23 3QP; Tel 01970 624907

Aberteifi/Cardigan

CARNINGLI

Priory St, Aberteifi, Cardigan, Ceredigion SA43 1BT;
   Tel 01239 614121
Team Manager (South Ceredigion Adult Team)   A. Tidball

Lampeter

FAMILY AND CHILD SUPPORT TEAM (SPECIAL NEEDS)

Pant y Fedwen, 9 Market St, Aberystwyth, Ceredigion
   SY23 1DL; Tel 01970 627016; Fax 01970 627801
Team Manager   Eryl Bray

GOVERNMENT BUILDINGS

Pontfaen Rd, Llanbedr Pont Steffan, Lampeter, Ceredigion
SA48 7BN; Tel 01570 423660
Team Manager (South Ceredigion Family Support)   A.F. Aynsley

HOMES FOR OLDER PEOPLE

There are seven homes for the elderly.

SOCIAL ACTIVITY CENTRE

Bronaeron Social Activity Centre Felinfach, Llanbedr Pont
Steffan, Lampeter, Ceredigion SA48 8AF; Tel 01570 470874

TRANSPORT AND EQUIPMENT STORE

Campws Felinfach Felinfach, Llanbedr Pont Steffan,
Lampeter, Ceredigion SA48 8AF; Tel 01545 572706;
Fax 01545 572704

Education Department

County Offices, Marine Terr, Aberystwyth, Ceredigion
SY23 2DE; E-mail lisw@ceredigion.gov.uk; Tel 01970
633655; 01920 633656; Fax 01970 633663
Director (Education and Community Services)
Roger J. Williams
Assistant Director (Professional Services)   M. Fowler
Assistant Director (Management Services)   D.G. Hughes
Assistant Director (Cultural Services)   G. Lewis
Advisory Teacher (SEN)   E. Owen
Education Officer (SEN)   C.E.S. Leishman
Link Officer   A. Evans
Senior Education Psychologist   L. Roberts
Senior Officer (Education Welfare)   P. Lee Jones
Education Psychologist   B. Roberts
Education Welfare Officer   E.D. Jones
Education Welfare Officer   D.W. Jones

CONWY COUNTY BOROUGH COUNCIL
www.conwy.gov.uk

Political Composition: Lab: 19, Ind: 15, LD: 13, Con: 5,
Plaid Cymru: 7
Bodlondeb, Conwy LL32 8DU; URL www.conwy.gov.uk;
E-mail gwe.web@conwy.gov.uk; Tel 01492 574000;
Fax 01492 592114
Chief Executive   C.D. Barker

Directorate of Social Care and Health

Builder St, Llandudno, Conwy LL30 1DA; Tel 01492 574065;
Fax 01492 874739

HOSPITAL SOCIAL WORK

Llandudno General Hospital, Hospital Rd, Llandudno,
Conwy L30 1LB; Tel 01492 862367

WELFARE RIGHTS TEAM

Social Services, Argyll Rd, Llandudno, Conwy; Tel 01492
871444

AREA-BASED TEAMS

Services for Older People, Physically Handicapped, Sensory Impaired

CONWY ROAD CENTRE

94 Conwy Rd, Colwyn Bay, Conwy; Tel 01495 575600

DAY CARE CENTRES FOR OLDER PEOPLE

Bryn Castell Day Care Centre Aber Rd, Llanfairfechan,
Conwy LL33 0NR; Tel 01248 681285
Derwen Deg Day Care Centre Blodwel Annexe, Llandudno
Junction, Conwy LL31 9HL; Tel 01492 582909

HOMES FOR OLDER PEOPLE

There are seven residential homes for older people.

HOME FOR THE PHYSICALLY HANDICAPPED

Plas Tre Marl Broad St, Llandudno Junction, Conwy
LL31 9HL; Tel 01492 583696

Services for People with a Learning Disability

DAY TRAINING CENTRES FOR LEARNING DISABLED

Canolfan yr Orsedd Ffordd yr Orsedd, Llandudno, Conwy
LL30 1LA; Tel 01492 878041
Provider Unit Bron y Nant, Dinerth Rd, Colwyn Bay,
Conwy LL28 4YN; Tel 01492 544277

CASE MANAGEMENT TEAM

74 Conwy Rd, Colwyn Bay, Conwy; Tel 01492 531332

Services for the Mentally Ill

COMMUNITY MENTAL HEALTH TEAM

Community Mental Health Team, Nant y Gamar Rd,
Llandudno, Conwy; Tel 01492 860926

RESOURCE CENTRE

Nant y Glyn Rd, Colwyn Bay, Conwy; Tel 01492 532164

RESIDENTIAL HOME FOR THE MENTALLY ILL

Bron Haul Residential Home Fernbrook Rd,
Penmaenmawr, Conwy LL34 6DE; Tel 01492 622727

Children and Families Services

FAMILY PLACEMENT TEAM

Civic Centre Annexe, Colwyn Bay, Conwy LL29 8AR;
Tel 01492 514871

CHILDREN WITH DISABILITIES TEAM

Civic Centre Annexe, Colwyn Bay, Conwy LL29 8AR;
Tel 01492 514871

CHILD CARE TEAM

Civic Centre Annexe, Colwyn Bay, Conwy LL29 8AR;
Tel 01492 514871

YOUTH OFFENDER TEAM

68 Conwy Rd, Colwyn Bay, Conwy; Tel 01492 523500

Education Department

Government Bldgs, Dinerth Rd, Rhos on Sea, Colwyn
Bay, Conwy LL28 4UL; Tel 01492 575001; Fax 01492
575017
Director (Education)   R. Elwyn Williams
Senior Officer (SEN)   A. Wilson
County Psychologist   Richard Ellis Owen
Service Manager (Education Social Worker)   S. Davies

8

SPECIAL SCHOOLS

Cedar Court Residential School/Clinic 65 Victoria Pk, Bae Colwyn, Conwy LL29 7AJ; Tel (Clinic) 01492 532458; (School) 01492 533199
Headteacher Val Roberts

Ysgol y Gogarth Nant-y-Gamar Rd, Llandudno, Conwy LL30 1YF; E-mail pennaeth@gogarth.conwy.sch.uk; Tel 01492 860077
Headteacher Dr J. Hewitt, PhD

DENBIGHSHIRE COUNTY COUNCIL
www.denbighshire.gov.uk

Political Composition: Ind: 17, Lab: 11, Plaid Cymru: 9, Dem All of Wales: 3, Non-aligned: 4, Con: 2, LD: 1
Council Offices, Wynnstay Rd, Ruthin, Denbighshire LL15 1AT; URL www.denbighshire.gov.uk; E-mail enquiries@denbighshire.gov.uk; Tel 01824 706000; Fax 01824 707446
Chief Executive Ian Miller
Corporate Director (Environment) Iwan Prys Jones
Corporate Director (Resources) Alan Evans
Corporate Director (Lifelong-Learning) Sioned Bowen
Corporate Director (Personal Services) Sally Ellis

Social Services Headquarters

Ty Nant, Nant Hall Rd, Prestatyn, Denbighshire LL19 9LG; Tel 01824 706655; Fax 01824 706660
Director (Social Services) Sally Ellis; E-mail sally-ellis@denbighshire.gov.uk
Head (Adult Services) Neil Ayling; E-mail neil.ayling@denbighshire.gov.uk; Tel 01824 706655
Head (Children and Families) Nicola Francis; E-mail nicola.francis@denbighshire.gov.uk; Tel 01824 706651
Manager (Adult Services – Intake and Assessment)/Care Manager (South) Yvonne Hughes; E-mail yvonne.hughes@denbighshire.gov.uk
Manager (Children Services) Gwynfor Griffiths; E-mail gwynfor.griffiths@denbighshire.gov.uk
Manager (Adult Services – Intake and Assessment)/Care Manager (North) Peter Fowler; E-mail peter.fowler@denbighshire.gov.uk
Manager (Adult Services – Provider) Helena Thomas; E-mail helena.thomas@denbighshire.gov.uk
Manager (Quality Assurance) Jackie Maelor; E-mail jackiemaelor@denbighshire.gov.uk
Manager (Business Support and Development) Roberta Hayes; E-mail roberta.hayes@denbighshire.gov.uk
Manager (Staffing/Personnel) Kerry Evans; E-mail kerry.evans@denbighshire.gov.uk

Personal Services Policy Review and Scrutiny Committee

Ind: 2, Lab: 2, Plaid Cymru: 1, Democratic Alliance of Wales: 1, LD: 1
Members of the Committee
Ind: S. Thomas, A.J. Tobin.
Lab: J. Butterfield, P.M. Jones.
Plaid Cymru: N.J. Hughes.
Democratic Alliance of Wales J.R. Hughes.
LD: R.J.R. Jones.

Staff Development and Training

Henllan Centre, Henllan, Denbighshire LL16 5YA; E-mail dcc_socialservices@denbighshire.gov.uk; Tel 01745 813871

AREA OFFICES

Cefndy Resources Centre Cefndy Rd, Rhyl, Denbighshire; E-mail dcc_socialservices@denbighshire.gov.uk; Tel 01745 332468

Hospital Social Work Team Ysbyty Glan Clwyd, Bodelwyddan, Denbighshire; E-mail glanclwyd.socialworkers@denbighshire.gov.uk; Tel 01745 534144
Contact Stephen Meadows

Morfa Hall Rhyl, Denbighshire; E-mail dcc_socialservices@denbighshire.gov.uk; Tel 01824 708300

Ruthin Local Office Station Rd, Ruthin, Denbighshire; E-mail dcc_socialservices@denbighshire.gov.uk; Tel 01824 703551

Children's Services

LOOKED AFTER CHILDREN FAMILY PLACEMENT

Cefndy Resources Centre Cefndy Rd, Rhyl, Denbighshire; E-mail dcc_socialservices@denbighshire.gov.uk; Tel 01745 332468

YOUTH OFFENDING TEAM

66 Conwy Rd, Colwyn Bay, Conwy LL29 7LD; E-mail dcc_socialservices@denbighshire.gov.uk; Tel 01492 532500

CHILD DEVELOPMENT

Rhuddlan Children's Centre Vicarage La, Rhuddlan, Denbighshire; E-mail dcc_socialservices@denbighshire.gov.uk; Tel 01745 591415
Manager Glenys Parfitt

SHELTERED WORKSHOP

Cefndy Enterprises Cefndy Rd, Rhyl, Denbighshire; E-mail dcc_socialservices@denbighshire.gov.uk; Tel 01745 343877

HOSPITALS (EMI)

Llangollen Hospital Llangollen, Wrexham; E-mail dcc_socialservices@denbighshire.gov.uk; Tel 01978 869045
Manager Claire Taylor

Royal Alexandra Hospital (EMI) Glantraeth Ward, Marine Rd, Rhyl, Denbighshire; E-mail dcc_socialservices@denbighshire.gov.uk; Tel 01745 343188

Adult Services

COMMUNITY MENTAL HEALTH TEAM

Clwyd (EMI) Community Mental Health Team Middle La, Denbigh, Denbighshire; E-mail dcc_socialservices@denbighshire.gov.uk; Tel 01745 813138
Team Leader Tim Dyffryn

Hafod (EMI) Community Mental Health Team Beechwood Rd, Rhyl, Denbighshire; E-mail dcc_socialservices@denbighshire.gov.uk; Tel 01745 351505

Lawnside Community Mental Health Team Olinda St, Rhyl, Denbighshire; E-mail dcc_socialservices@denbighshire.gov.uk; Tel 01745 330881

Oakleigh Community Mental Health Team Abbey Rd, Llangollen, Denbighshire;
E-mail dcc_socialservices@denbighshire.gov.uk; Tel 01978 860707

COMMUNITY LIVING SERVICES

Social Services Department Station Rd, Ruthin, Denbighshire;
E-mail dcc_socialservices@denbighshire.gov.uk; Tel 01824 706246

Cefndy Resource Centre Cefndy Rd, Rhyl, Denbighshire;
E-mail dcc_socialservices@denbighshire.gov.uk; Tel 01745 330365

WORK OPPORTUNITIES SERVICE

Henllan Centre Henllan, Denbighshire LL16 5YA;
E-mail dcc_socialservices@denbighshire.gov.uk; Tel 01745 816426

Work Opportunities Service Co-options Ltd, Victoria Ave, Prestatyn, Denbighshire;
E-mail dcc_socialservices@denbighshire.gov.uk; Tel 01745 851454

REGISTRATION AND INSPECTION UNIT

Inspection Unit Bron Coed Hse, Bron Coed Bus Pk, Wrexham Rd, Mold, Flintshire CH7 1HP; Tel 01352 756961

RECEIVERSHIP OFFICER

Ty Nant Nant Hall Rd, Prestatyn, Denbighshire LL19 9LG; Tel 01352 702640

DISABILITY EQUIPMENT SERVICE

Stores Department C1 Pinfold Est, Ffordd Derwen, Rhyl, Denbighshire;
E-mail disability.equipmentstores@denbighshire.gov.uk; Tel 01745 344675

DAY CENTRES FOR OLDER PEOPLE

Awelon Day Centre School Rd, Ruthin, Denbighshire LL15 1YL; E-mail awelon.home@denbighshire.gov.uk; Tel 01824 702018

Dolwen Day Centre Ruthin Rd, Denbigh, Denbighshire LL15 3ER; E-mail dolwen.daycare@denbighshire.gov.uk; Tel 01745 814135

Hafan Deg Day Centre Grange Rd, Rhyl, Denbighshire LL18 4AD; E-mail hafan.deg@denbighshire.gov.uk; Tel 01745 339588

Llys Nant Day Centre Marine Rd, Prestatyn, Denbighshire; E-mail ilysnant@denbighshire.gov.uk; Tel 01745 854844

St. Winifred's (Mental Illness) Brighton Rd, Rhyl, Denbighshire LL18 3HM;
E-mail swinifre@denbighshire.gov.uk; Tel 01745 336363

ACCOMMODATION FOR THE ELDERLY

There are four elderly people's homes.

HOME CARE SERVICES

Hafan Deg War Memorial Crt, Grange Rd, Rhyl, Denbighshire;
E-mail dcc_socialservices@denbighshire.gov.uk; Tel 01745 343877

Home Care Awelon School Rd, Ruthin, Denbighshire LL15 1YL; E-mail dcc_socialservices@denbighshire.gov.uk; Tel 01824 707535

Home Care Dolwen Ruthin Rd, Denbigh, Denbighshire LL15 3ER; E-mail dcc_socialservices@denbighshire.gov.uk; Tel 01745 814135

Home Care Llys Nant Marine Rd, Prestatyn, Denbighshire; Tel 01745 859159

Directorate of Education, Culture and Information

Denbighshire County Council, c/o Phase IV, Mold, Flintshire CH7 6GR; Tel 01824 706777; Fax 01824 706780
Director (Education, Culture and Information)
    Edgar O. Lewis, BA(Hons), FRSA
Head (Resource and Management Services) G.E. Brooks, BA(Hons)
Head (Curricular Services) I.L. Roberts, BA
Head (Cultural Services) W.G. Williams, HonFLA, MinstAM, FRSA
Head (IT/Information System) Dylan Roberts

SPECIAL SCHOOLS

Ysgol Plas Brondyffryn Ffordd Ystrad, Denbigh, Denbighshire LL16 4RH; Tel 01745 813841
Contact Dr M.J. Toman
    (55)

Ysgol Tir Morfa Ffordd Derwen, Rhyl, Denbighshire LL18 2RN; Tel 01745 350388; 01745 590242
Contact S. Murphy

FLINTSHIRE COUNTY COUNCIL **8**
www.flintshire.gov.uk

Political Composition: Lab: 42, Alliance: 15, LD: 7, Plaid Cymru: 2, Non-aligned Group: 2, Non-aligned: 1; Non-aligned Green: 1
County Hall, Mold, Flintshire CH7 6NB;
    URL www.flintshire.gov.uk;
    E-mail communication@flintshire.gov.uk; Tel 01352 752121; Fax 01352 758240

Directorate of Adult Social Care

County Hall, Mold, Flintshire CH7 6NN;
    URL www.flintshire.gov.uk;
    E-mail social@flintshire.gov.uk; Tel 01352 702642;
    Fax 01352 701499

SERVICES TO OLDER PEOPLE

Croes Ati Prince of Wales Ave, Flint, Flintshire CH6 5JU; Tel 01352 733598

Hafan Glyd Shotton La, Shotton, Deeside, Flintshire CH5 1EK; Tel 01244 812059

Llys Gwenffrwd Brynford St, Holywell, Flintshire CH8 7RO; Tel 01352 713338

Marleyfield House Nant Mawr Rd, Buckley, Flintshire CH7 1RA; Tel 01244 543957

MULTIPURPOSE CENTRE

Melrose Melrose Ave, Shotton, Deeside, Flintshire CH5 1NG; Tel 01244 830723

SERVICES TO PEOPLE WITH MENTAL ILLNESS

Community Mental Health Team (Deeside) 82b High St, Connah's Quay, Deeside, Flintshire CH5 4DD; Tel 01244 836220

Community Mental Health Team (Flint/Holywell) Ty Celyn, Unit 1, Flint, Flintshire CH6 5YN; Tel 01352 731293

Community Mental Health Team (Mold/Buckley) Pwll Glas Centre, Pwll Glas, Mold, Flintshire CH7 1RA; Tel 01352 750252

Department of Education and Children's Services and Recreation

County Hall, Mold, Flintshire CH7 6ND; Tel 01352 704010
Director (Education and Children's Services and Recreation)
    John R. Clutton, BA(Hons), MSc(EdMan)
Assistant Director and Head (Schools Services)   Vacancy
Assistant Director and Head (Development Resources)
    H. Loveridge, BA(Hons), MSc, DMS
Assistant Director/Head (Libraries, Culture and Heritage)
    L. Rawsthorne, MLib, ALA, MIMGT
Assistant Director/Head (Children's Services)   K. Reilly,
    CQSW, CertMan(OU), DipMan(OU), MBA

SPECIAL SCHOOLS

Ysgol Belmont Windmill Rd, Buckley, Flintshire CH7 3HA; Tel 01244 543971
Headteacher   D.G. Jones, BEd
    MLD (155)
Ysgol Delyn Alexandra Rd, Mold, Flintshire CH7 1HJ; Tel 01352 755701
Headteacher   Mr Ceris Owen
    SLD (50)
Ysgol-y-Bryn King George St, Shotton, Flintshire CH5 2EQ; Tel 01244 830281
Headteacher   J. Kelly, MEd, DipEd
    (43)

GWYNEDD COUNCIL
www.gwynedd.gov.uk

Population 120 000
County Offices, Shirehall St, Caernarfon, Gwynedd
    LL55 1SH; URL www.gwynedd.gov.uk;
    E-mail enquiries@gwynedd.gov.uk; Tel 01286 672255;
    Fax 01286 673993
Council Treasurer   Harry Thomas
Secretary and Solicitor   A.E. Roberts
Director (Planning and Economic Development)   H. Roberts
Director (Highways and Municipal)   R.B. Daimond
Director (Personnel)   B. Davies

Social Services Department

Tel 01286 679227; Fax 01286 677486
Director (Social Services)   Vacancy
Service Leader (Welfare and Social Services)   Cllr P.G. Larsen
Assistant Service Leader (Welfare and Social Services)
    Cllr M. Williams
Manager (Financial Services)   J.T. Williams
Assistant Director (Planning and Commissioning)
    Glyn Hughes

AREA OFFICES

Arfon Office
Assistant Director (Operational (Children's Services))
    C. Williams
Dwyfor Office
Assistant Director (Operational (Adult Services))   B. Griffith
Meirionnydd Office
Assistant Director (Departmental Provider Units)   D. Poole

Department of Education, Culture and Leisure

County Offices, Shirehall St, Caernarfon, Gwynedd
    LL55 1SH; E-mail addysg@gwynedd.gov.uk; Tel 01286
    672255; Fax 01286 677347
Director (Education, Culture and Leisure)   D. Whittall, BA
Assistant Director (Quality)   R.W. Parri, BSc, MEd
Assistant Director (Resources)   I. Roberts, BSc, MEd
Assistant Director (Culture)   G.H. Williams, MA, JP, DAA
Assistant Director (Leisure)   Marianne Jackson, BA(Hons),
    ILAM(Cert)

SPECIAL SCHOOLS

Ysgol Hafod Lon Y Ffor, Pwllheli, Gwynedd; Tel 01766 810626
Headteacher   R. Davies, CertEd

Ysgol Pendalar Caernarfon, Gwynedd; Tel 01286 672141
Headteacher   E. Jones, MEd

Ysgol Coed Menai Bangor, Gwynedd LL57 2RX; Tel 01248 353527
Headteacher   J. Grisdale, BSc

SPECIAL EDUCATIONAL NEEDS JOINT COMMITTEE

Joint arrangement with Isle of Anglesey County Council.
Chief Educational Psychologist   R. Coupe
Senior Educational Psychologist   R. Ellis Owen
Advisory Teacher (Hearing Impairment)   G. Roberts
Advisory Teacher (Vision Impairment/Physically Handicapped)
    Vacancy
Advisory Teacher (Pre-School)   Vacancy

MERTHYR TYDFIL COUNTY BOROUGH COUNCIL
www.merthyr.gov.uk

Population 59 300
Ty Keir Hardie, Riverside Crt, Avenue de Clichy, Merthyr
    Tydfil CF47 8XD; URL www.merthyr.gov.uk;
    E-mail socialservices@merthyr.gov.uk; Tel 01685 724600;
    Fax 01685 721965

Social Services Department

Ty Keir Hardie, Riverside Crt, Avenue de Clichy, Merthyr
    Tydfil CF47 8XE; E-mail socialservices@merthyr.gov.uk;
    Tel 01685 725000; Fax 01685 384868
Social Services Portfolio Member   Cllr Helen Thomas
Social Services Portfolio Member   Cllr Len Goodwin
Director (Social Services)   John Wreford
Head (Adults and Social Care)   Giovanni Isingrini
Manager (Children's Services)   Leighton Rees

TRAINING

Training Officer (Adult Services)   Lynette Warrilow
Training Officer (Children's Services)   Trevor Evans

SOCIAL CENTRE

Ty Gwyn Day Centre Church St, Merthyr Tydfil; Tel 01685 721766

DAY CENTRE FOR PEOPLE WITH LEARNING DIFFICULTIES

Sandbrook Day Centre Queen's Rd, Merthyr Tydfil; Tel 01685 721763

HOSTEL FOR PEOPLE WITH LEARNING DISABILITIES AND WITH MENTAL HEALTH PROBLEMS

Thomastown House Queens Rd, Merthyr Tydfil; Tel 01685 721767
(16)

STAFFED HOUSES FOR PEOPLE WITH LEARNING DIFFICULTIES

Glendere Drovers La, Cefn Coed, Merthyr Tydfil
(5)

Llysfaen Fach Llysfaen, Cefn Coed, Merthyr Tydfil
(4)

Llysfaen Respite Centre Cefn Coed, Merthyr Tydfil

DAY CENTRE FOR PEOPLE WITH MENTAL HEALTH PROBLEMS

Gwaelodygarth Day Care Centre Gwaelodygarth La, Merthyr Tydfil; Tel 01685 721671

ACCOMMODATION FOR THE ELDERLY

There are four homes for the elderly.

Education Department

Ty Keir Hardie, Riverside Crt, Avenue de Clichy, Merthyr Tydfil CF47 8XD; URL www.mnet2000.org.uk; E-mail education@merthyr.gov.uk; Tel 01685 724600; Fax 01685 721965
Corporate Chief Officer (Education) Vernon Morgan

SPECIAL EDUCATIONAL NEEDS SERVICE

Ty Keir Hardie, Riverside Crt, Merthyr Tydfil CF47 8XD; E-mail education@merthyr.gov.uk; Tel 01685 724642

PUPIL REFERRAL UNIT

Tram Rd La, Alexandra Ave, Penydarren, Merthyr Tydfil CF47 9AF; E-mail pru@mtcbc.fsbusiness.co.uk; Tel 01685 721733

SPECIAL SCHOOL

Greenfield School Duffryn Rd, Pentrebach, Merthyr Tydfil CF48 4BJ; E-mail headmaster@greenfield.biblio.net; Tel 01443 690468; Fax 01443 692010
Headteacher A. Blake
(136)

MONMOUTHSHIRE COUNTY COUNCIL
www.monmouthshire.gov.uk

Population 86 248
Political Composition: Lab: 18, Con: 19, Ind: 3, LD: 1; No Party: 1
County Hall, Cwmbran, Monmouthshire NP44 2XH; URL www.monmouthshire.gov.uk; Tel 01633 644644; Fax 01633 644666
Chair of Council Donald Spencer
Chief Executive Elizabeth Raikes

Social and Housing Services

County Hall, Cwmbran, Monmouthshire NP44 2XH; Tel 01633 644644; Fax 01633 644577
Cabinet Member (Social Services) Cllr Verona Nalmes
Cabinet Member (Housing) Cllr R.J. Higginson

Director Colin Berg
Head (Children's Services) John Waters
Head (Community Care) Moyna Wilkinson
Head (Housing) Richard Moses

Social and Housing Committee
Members of the Committee
Lab: A.J. Arkell, V. Bamford, H. Bennett, P. Birchall, G. Eburne, W.E. Edwards, Mrs O.G. Evans, R.A. Griffiths, J. Harvey, R.J. Higginson, G. Howard, G.J. Jenkins, V.M.R. Nelmes, G. Powell, Mrs M. Roach, M.R. Smith, M.L. Thomas, D.F. Waring, G. Williams.
Con: A.W. Breeze, R. Le Gros Cass, P.R. Clarke, W.A.L. Crump, J.P. Foulser, T. Dorel, G.L. Down, P.A. Fox, E.J. Harrhy, B.R. Hood, J. Major, C. Meredith, W.E. Price, V.E. Smith, H.D. Spencer, C.P.W. White, A.M. Wintle, C.D. Woodhouse.
LD: D.J. Anstey, S.E. Heighton.
Ind: G.P. Robbins, A.W. Thomas, R.J.B. Wilcox.

AREA OFFICE

Newbridge Hse, Baker St, Abergavenny, Monmouthshire NP7 5HU; Tel 01873 735900; Fax 01873 735957
Group Manager (Direct Care) Beverly Moore

SOCIAL WORK TEAMS

Coed Glas Firs Rd, Abergavenny, Monmouthshire NP7 5LE; Tel 01873 735455; Fax 01873 735467
Learning Disabilities Team.

Dixton Road Health Clinic Dixton Rd, Monmouth, Monmouthshire NP5 3PL; Tel 01600 775100; Fax 01600 775108
Community Care Team (Monmouth).

Newbridge House Baker St, Abergavenny, Monmouthshire NP7 5HU; Tel 01873 735900; Fax 01873 735957
Community Care Team (Abergavenny); Children's Services Team (North); Children Services Resource Team; Domiciliary Care Service.

Hanbury House Welsh St, Chepstow, Monmouthshire NP16 5LL; Tel 01291 635666; Fax 01291 635650
Children's Services Team (South); Community Care Team (Chepstow).

HOSPITAL TEAM

Nevill Hall Hospital Bron Haul, Abergavenny, Monmouthshire NP7 7EG; Tel 01873 732526; Fax 01873 732532

DAY SERVICES

Monmouth Resource Unit Monmouth, Monmouthshire; Tel 01600 715638

Monnow Court Day Centre Monmouth Crt, Monmouth, Monmouthshire; Tel 01600 712224

Severn View Day Centre Chepstow, Monmouthshire; Tel 01291 638925

Tudor Day Centre Abergavenny, Monmouthshire; Tel 01873 853645

Ty'r Fenni Day Centre Abergavenny, Monmouthshire; Tel 01873 735415

RESPITE CARE SERVICE – LEARNING DISABILITIES

Budden Cres, Caldicot, Monmouthshire; Tel 01291 425121

RESIDENTIAL HOME FOR PHYSICALLY DISABLED PEOPLE

Monnow Court Residential Home Drybridge Pk, Monmouth, Monmouthshire NP25 3BL; Tel 01600 712224
Team Manager (Disability Services) A. Kalawsky

8

RESIDENTIAL HOMES FOR THE ELDERLY
There are two homes for the elderly.

Lifelong Learning and Leisure Directorate

County Hall, Cwmbran, Monmouthshire NP44 2XH;
URL www.monmouthshire.gov.uk;
E-mail philcooke@monmouthshire.gov.uk; Tel 01633
644487; Fax 01633 644488
Corporate Director (Lifelong Learning and Leisure) P. Cooke
Head (Resources and Performance Management) P. Ham
Head (School Improvement Service) Malcolm Morris
Head (Libraries and Leisure) P. Ellis

SPECIAL SCHOOL

Mounton House School Chepstow, Monmouthshire
NP16 6LA; Tel 01291 635642
Headteacher M.L. Munting

NEATH PORT TALBOT COUNTY BOROUGH COUNCIL

www.neath-porttalbot.gov.uk

Political Composition: Lab: 40, Plaid Cymru: 10,
Ratepayers: 5, Ind: 3, Social Dem: 3, LD: 2, Other: 1.
Civic Centre, Port Talbot, Neath Port Talbot SA13 1PJ;
URL www.neath-porttalbot.gov.uk; Tel 01639 763333;
Fax 01639 899930
Chief Executive K. Sawyers

Social Services and Housing Department

E-mail social.services@neath-porttalbot.gov.uk; Tel 01639
763333; Fax 01639 763286
Director (Social Services and Housing) Colin Preece
Head of Service (Children's Service) R. Ciborowski
Head of Service (Community Care) A. Clements
*Head of Service (Strategic Co-ordinator – Business and Support
Services)* K. Jones
Head of Service (Housing) R. Rees
Principal Officer (Family Support and Child Care Disability)
T. Roberts
Principal Officer (Business and Performance Management Unit)
D. Rees
Principal Officer (Accommodation) P. Grinter
Principal Officer (Child and Family Social Work Services)
R. Williams
Principal Officer (Personnel) G. Cox
Principal Officer (Finance) H. Tyler
Principal Officer (Mental Health and Learning Disability)
I. Maunder
*Principal Officer (Care Management Elderly and Disability
Services)* J. Hawkridge
*Principal Officer (Residential, Day and Specialist Services –
Elderly and Disability)* S. Calder
Principal Officer (Domiciliary Care) M. Davies
Principal Officer (Child Protection Co-ordinator) L. Pearce
Manager (Secure Unit) C. Davies
Strategic Manager (Older Disabled People) S. Roberts

Social Services and Housing Cabinet Committee

Health, Community Care and Housing Building Services
C. Owen (Lab)
*Commissioner (Children, Young People and Families,
Communities and Social Inclusion)* Mrs O. Jones (Lab)

Overview and Scrutiny Committee

Chair M.I. Jones (Lab)
Vice-Chair Mrs L.H. James (Ind)

AREA OFFICES

Port Talbot (Area 1 Office) 12 Talbot Rd, Port Talbot, Neath
Port Talbot SA13 1HN; Tel 01639 765500

Neath (Area 2 Office) 8 Wind St, Neath, Neath Port Talbot
SA11 3EG; Tel 01639 765300

Pontardawe (Area 3 Office) Old Cwmtawe School, Upper
Heathfield Rd, Pontardawe, Neath Port Talbot SA8 4LQ;
Tel 01792 510700

HOSPITAL SOCIAL WORKERS

Neath Hospital
Team Leader D. Cosedge-White
Tonna Hospital
Team Leader D. Cosedge-White

Children's Services

RESIDENTIAL

Fairways Children's Centre 137 Fairways, Sandfields,
Neath Port Talbot; Tel 01639 883791

SECURE UNIT

Hillside Secure Unit Off Burnside, Cimla, Neath, Neath
Port Talbot; Tel 01639 641648

FAMILY CENTRE

Sandfields Family Centre Pendarvis Terr, Port Talbot,
Neath Port Talbot

PLAYGROUPS

Managed by NCH.
Blaengwynfi Playgroup Jersey Rd, Blaengwynfi, Neath Port
Talbot
Cymmer Playgroup Glamorgan Hse, Cymer, Neath Port
Talbot
Glyncorrwg Playgroup Glyncorrwg Community Centre,
Glyncorrwg, Neath Port Talbot

Services to Elderly and Physically Disabled People

RESIDENTIAL CARE

Arwelfa Eastern Ave, Croeserw, Neath Port Talbot;
Tel 01639 850461
Number of beds/places, 35
Caewern Dwryfelin Rd, Neath, Neath Port Talbot;
Tel 01639 636115
Number of beds/places, 32
Danybryn Brecon Rd, Pontardawe, Neath Port Talbot;
Tel 01792 869729
Number of beds/places, 40
Glyndulais Mary St, Crynant, Neath Port Talbot; Tel 01639
750663
Number of beds/places, 38
Gorffwysfa Llys Gwynfryn, Bryncoch, Neath Port Talbot;
Tel 01639 643125
Number of beds/places, 30
Hafod Wenham Pl, Neath, Neath Port Talbot; Tel 01639
634291
Number of beds/places, 37

Min yr Afon London Row, Cwmavon, Neath Port Talbot;
Tel 01639 896455
Number of beds/places, 40

Morfa Afan Dalton Rd, Sandfields, Neath Port Talbot;
Tel 01639 884488
Number of beds/places, 42

Tremyglyn off Parc Ave, Glyn-Neath, Neath Port Talbot;
Tel 01639 720786
Number of beds/places, 40

Ty Bryncoch Heol Illtyd, Neath, Neath Port Talbot;
Tel 01639 637259
Number of beds/places, 29

DAY CARE

Arwelfa Eastern Ave, Croeserw, Neath Port Talbot;
Tel 01639 852246
Number of beds/places, 100 per week

Gelligron Gelligron Rd, Pontardawe, Swansea; Tel 01792 830488
Number of beds/places, 175 per week

Hafod Wenham Pl, Neath, Neath Port Talbot; Tel 01639 634291
Number of beds/places, 100 per week

Morfa Afan Dalton Rd, Sandfields, Neath Port Talbot;
Tel 01639 890905
Number of beds/places, 150 per week

Tremyglyn off Parc Ave, Neath, Neath Port Talbot;
Tel 01639 722764
Number of beds/places, 100 per week

SOCIAL CENTRES

Briton Ferry Centre Ty Llansawel Flats, Briton Ferry, Neath Port Talbot

Croeserw Community Centre Sunnybank Cres, Croeserw, Neath Port Talbot

Gelligron Gelligron Rd, Pontardawe, Neath Port Talbot

Neath Community Centre Neath, Neath Port Talbot

Resolven St. David's Hall, Resolven, Neath Port Talbot

Canolfan Community Centre Seven Sisters, Neath Port Talbot

Taibach Community Centre Margam Rd, Taibach, Neath Port Talbot

Services to People with Learning Disabilities

RESIDENTIAL RESPITE

Rhodes House CSU Rhodes Ave, Sandfields, Neath Port Talbot; Tel 01639 895754
Number of beds/places, 12 users

DAY SERVICES

Bronleigh Day Centre Cadoxton Rd, Cadoxton, Neath Port Talbot
Number of beds/places, 170 per week

Local DS
Port Talbot 48 Pen y Cae Rd, Port Talbot, Neath Port Talbot
Number of beds/places, 100 per week
Swansea Valley 102 Herbert St, Pontardawe, Neath Port Talbot
Number of beds/places, 100 per week
Upper Afan Valley Glyncorrwg Ponds, Glyncorrwg, Neath Port Talbot
Number of beds/places, 50 per week

Day Service
Vocational Skills Centre Monastery Rd, Neath Abbey, Neath Port Talbot
Number of beds/places, 380 per week

Special Needs Day Services
Cadoxton 91 Bryn Catwg, Cadoxton, Neath Port Talbot
Number of beds/places, 70 per week.
Abbey View Day Service Unit 15, Neath Ind Est, Neath, Neath Port Talbot
Number of beds/places, 100 per week.
Neath Unit 15, Neath Abbey Ind Est, Neath, Neath Port Talbot
Number of beds/places, 100 per week.

Day Services Beacons View, Neath Abbey, Neath, Neath Port Talbot

Services to People with a Mental Illness

UNIT HOMES

Baglan Sycamore Cres, Baglan, Neath Port Talbot
Number of beds/places, 3

Fairyland Fairylands, Neath, Neath Port Talbot
Number of beds/places, 3

Morfa Afan Dalton Rd, Port Talbot, Neath Port Talbot
Number of beds/places, 3

DAY CARE SERVICE

Ty Croeso Victoria Gdns, Neath, Neath Port Talbot
Number of beds/places, 170 per week.

Education, Leisure and Lifelong Learning Directorate

Civic Centre, Port Talbot, Neath Port Talbot SA13 1PJ;
Tel 01639 763298
Corporate Director (Education, Leisure and Lifelong Learning)
K. Napieralla
Head (Access and Support Services) S.G. Evans
Head (Schools, Achievement and SEN) Mrs K. Boyce
Head (Lifelong Learning, Culture and Leisure) R. Ward
Co-ordinator (Personnel and Professional Services)
Mrs L. Preece
Co-ordinator (Access and Support Services) D.R Sutherland
Co-ordinator (Lifelong Learning) Mrs M. Dawson
Co-ordinator (Education Development Services) A. Richards
Co-ordinator (Cultural Services) J.L. Ellis
Co-ordinator (SEN and Pupil Inclusion) Mrs H. Reid
West Glamorgan Music Service P.H. Emanuel

SPECIAL SCHOOLS

Briton Ferry School Ynysmaerdy Rd, Briton Ferry, Neath Port Talbot SA11 2TL; Tel 01639 813100
Headteacher M. Scales

Ysgol Hendre Main Rd, Bryncoch, Neath, Neath Port Talbot SA10 7TY; Tel 01639 642786
Headteacher P. Smith
(Boarders)

NEWPORT CITY COUNCIL
www.newport.gov.uk

Population 138 500
Political Composition: Lab: 38, Con: 5, Ind: 2, LD: 1, Plaid Cymru: 1
Civic Centre, Newport NP20 4UR;
URL www.newport.gov.uk; Tel 01633 244491
Managing Director Chris Freegard
Strategic Director (Environment and the Economy) Carol Leslie
Strategic Director (Social Wellbeing and Housing)
Graham Bingham

Social Wellbeing and Housing

Tel 01633 233104
Cabinet Member (Young People's Services)
Cllr J.J. Pembridge
Cabinet Member (Adult and Housing) Cllr E.M. Burke
Head (Resource and Strategy) and Director (Social Services)
Ellis Williams
Head (Children and Families) Jan Leightley
Head (Community Care and Adults) Peter Cozens
Head (Housing and Area Regeneration) Robert Lynbeck

AREA OFFICES

Home Care Royal Chambers, High St, Newport NP20 1FY;
Tel 01633 246260; 01633 246724
Child Protection Unit Royal Chambers, High St, Newport
NP20 1FR
Community Care Services The Corn Exchange, High St,
Newport NP20 1RG
Children and Families Services The Corn Exchange, High
St, Newport NP20 1RN

Under Fives

NURSERIES

Alway Henry Wood Cl, Newport NP19 9SY; Tel 01633
290326
Bettws Don Cl, Newport NP20 6RT; Tel 01633 821608

Children with Learning Disabilities

RESPITE

Oaklands 12 St. James Cres, Rogerstone, Newport
NP10 9EY; Tel 01633 892196

Children and Young People

RESIDENTIAL

Cambridge House 1 Stow Park Ave, Newport NP20 4FH;
Tel 01633 246541
Forest Lodge Maescoed Wood, Rogerstone, Newport
NP1 9GP; Tel 01633 891465
Monnow Way Home 152 Monnow Way, Bettws, Newport
NP20 6UF; Tel 01633 821504

YOUTH OFFENDING TEAM

Halyg Centre, Ringland Centre, Newport NP19 9PJ;
Tel 01633 292900

People with a Learning Disability

RESPITE

The New Willows 9 Tennyson Ave, Llanwern, Newport
NP18 2DY; Tel 01633 413948

RESIDENTIAL

Crouch Close Home 1 Crouch Cl, Bettws, Newport
NP20 6RW; Tel 01633 821184
(7)
Welland Crescent Home 96–98 Welland Cres, Bettws,
Newport NP20 6BH; Tel 01633 855817
Manager G. Davies

ADULT TRAINING CENTRE

Brynglas Centre Brynglas Rd, Newport NP20 5QU;
Tel 01633 821377

COMMUNITY SUPPORT

Ringwood House Dents Hill, Newport NP19 9ED; Tel 01633
279813

Adults/Elderly

DAY SERVICE

Ladyhill Day Centre Aberthaw Rd, Newport NP19 9QS;
Tel 01633 290452

MENTAL HEALTH

Kensington Day Centre Oaklands Rd, Maindee, Newport
NP19 8GQ; Tel 01633 290330

RESIDENTIAL

Blaen-y-Pant House Blaen-y-Pant Cres, Malpas, Newport
NP20 7PX; Tel 01633 855548
Parklands Blackett Ave, Malpas, Newport NP20 6NH;
Tel 01633 821249

RESIDENTIAL AND EMI

Usk View Beaufort Rd, Newport NP19 7NP; Tel 01633
246963

RESIDENTIAL AND DAY SERVICE

Hillside Resource Centre Gaer Park Rd, Newport
NP20 3GX; Tel 01633 246994

RESIDENTIAL, EMI AND DAY SERVICE

Spring Gardens Resource Centre Courtabella Terr,
Newport NP20 2LD; Tel 01633 222768

Education Department

Civic Centre, Newport NP20 4UR;
URL www.newport.gov.uk; Tel 01633 244491; Fax 01633
233376
Strategic Director (Lifelong Learning and Leisure)
Carol Leslie
Head (School Improvement) David Norbury
*Head (Resourcing, Support and Coordination) and Chief
Education Officer* David Griffiths
Head (Education Inclusion) Alan Stubbersfield

SPECIAL UNITS

Pollards Well Education Unit St. Cadoc's Hospital,
Caerleon, Newport NP18 1XQ; Tel 01633 430147
Head (Unit) D. Hobbs
Queens Hill Education Unit Queens Hill, Newport;
Tel 01633 262564
Head (Unit) P. Fields
Royal Gwent Education Unit Children's Ward, Royal Gwent
Hospital, Newport; Tel 01633 234900
Head (Unit) M. Park

PEMBROKESHIRE COUNTY COUNCIL
www.pembrokeshire.gov.uk

Population 113 700
Political Composition: Ind: 41, Lab: 13, LD: 3, Con: 1,
Plaid Cymru: 2
County Hall, Haverfordwest, Pembrokeshire SA61 1TP;
URL www.pembrokeshire.gov.uk; Tel 01437 764551

Chief Executive   B. Parry-Jones
Director (Support Services and Cultural Services)   H. James
Director (Finance and Leisure)   M. Lewis
Director (Development)   R. Barrett-Evans
Director (Housing and Regulatory Services)   D. Seal
Director (Transportation and Technical Services)   H. Roberts

Social Care and Housing

County Hall, Haverfordwest, Pembrokeshire SA61 1PX;
   URL www.pembrokeshire.gov.uk; Tel 01437 764551;
   Fax 01437 776492
Director (Social Care and Housing)   J. Skone
Head (Community Care Commissioning)   A. Bell
Head (Child Care Commissioning)   D. Halse
*Customer Services Manager (Assessment and Care Management
   – Adults)*   J. Bolt
Customer Services Manager (Care Management – Children)
   J. Clark
Customer Services Manager (Quality Projects)   M. Brown
Customer Services Manager (Assessment – Children)
   A. Lloyd
Manager (Direct Services)   S. Thompson
Manager (Youth Offending Team)   P. Brecknall

MENTAL HEALTH TEAM MANAGER

Bro Cerwyn Day Hospital, Fishguard Rd, Haverfordwest,
   Pembrokeshire SA61 2PZ; Tel 01437 773296
Manager (Mental Health Team)   D. Jenkins

COMMUNITY TEAM (LEARNING DISABILITIES)

Meadow Pk, Haverfordwest, Pembrokeshire SA61 2RB;
   Tel 01437 776090
Customer Services Manager (Learning Disabilities)   P. Bee

DISABILITIES TEAM

Meadow Park Resource Centre, Stokes Ave, Haverfordwest,
   Pembrokeshire SA61 2RB; Tel 01437 776070
Customer Services Manager (Disability)   J. Price

HOSPITAL SOCIAL WORK TEAM

Social Work Dept, Withybush General Hospital,
   Haverfordwest, Pembrokeshire SA61 2PZ; Tel 01437
   764545
Assessor/Care Manager   Sue Zatac

HOMES FOR ELDERLY PEOPLE

There are six homes for the elderly.

FAMILY CENTRES

There are seven Family Centres.
Howarth Close Family Centre   Milford Haven,
Pembrokeshire; Tel 01646 693724
Contact   S. Bartlett
Larch Road Family Centre   Mount Estate, Milford Haven,
Pembrokeshire; Tel 01646 698562
Contact   R. Rowlands
Milford Haven Family Centre   Trafalgar Rd, Milford Haven,
Pembrokeshire; Tel 01646 690043
Contact   E. Penny
Monkton Family Centre   16 Colley Crt, Monkton, Pembroke
Dock, Pembrokeshire; Tel 01646 621728
Contact   G. Jones
Pennar Family Centre   Pennar Old School, Pembroke Dock,
Pembroke, Pembrokeshire; Tel 01646 684447
Contact   M. Thorne
Trafalgar Road Family Centre   515 Hywel Rd,
Haverfordwest, Pembrokeshire; Tel 01437 760464
Contact   M. Thorne

YoYo Family Resource Centre   24–26 Hamilton Crt,
Pembroke Dock, Pembrokeshire SA72 6LT; Tel 01646
695768
Contact   J. Coban

ACCOMMODATION FOR PEOPLE WITH MENTAL HEALTH PROBLEMS

Milford House   Dartmouth St, Milford Haven,
Pembrokeshire; Tel 01646 698197
Contact   J. Anderson

DAY CENTRES

Hamilton House Day Centre   Hamilton Terr, Milford Haven,
Pembrokeshire; Tel 01646 695923
Contact   M. Parkes
Hawkstone Road Day Centre
Contact   P. Townsend
Meadowpark Day Centre   Stokes Ave, Haverfordwest,
Pembrokeshire; Tel 01437 764307
Contact   M. Parkes
Narberth Day Centre   Bloomfield Hse, Northfield Rd,
Narberth, Pembrokeshire; Tel 01834 861386
Contact   V. Leggett
Neyland Day Centre   Brunel Hse, Charles St, Neyland,
Pembrokeshire; Tel 01646 600066
Contact   G. Cook
Wintern Day Centre   High St, Fishguard, Pembrokeshire;
Tel 01348 873904
Contact   L. Thomas

SHELTERED HOUSING SCHEMES

There are a number of schemes which have Warden
Services.

SOCIAL ACTIVITY CENTRES

The Anchorage Social Activity Centre   Commercial Row,
Pembroke Dock, Pembrokeshire; Tel 01646 686177
Contact   M. Bulley
Portfield Social Activity Centre
Manager   S. Coldwell
Tenby Social Activity Centre   Greenhill Ave, Tenby,
Pembrokeshire; Tel 01834 842224
Manager   G. Hesbrook

CARE STANDARDS INSPECTORATE

Meyler Hse, St. Thomas Grn, Haverfordwest,
   Pembrokeshire; Tel 01437 769111; Fax 01437 768388

FAMILY PLACEMENT TEAM

The Elms, Golden Hill, Pembroke, Pembrokeshire;
   Tel 01646 683747
Customer Services Manager   J. Dowdall

Education Department

County Hall, Haverfordwest, Pembrokeshire SA61 1TP;
   Tel 01437 775861; Fax 01437 775838
Director (Education and Community Services)   G.W. Davies
Head (Lifelong Learning and Development)   J.A. Wakefield
Head (School Improvement and Inclusion)   G. Longster
Head (Pupil Support)   Michelle Rees
Senior Educational Psychologist   T.C.H. Thomas
Youth Services Officer (Community Education)   Eirian Evans
Adult Services Officer (Community Education)   D. Davies
Principal Officer (SEN Services to Children)   Mr J. Benbow

PUPIL REFERRAL UNIT

Head of Service   Mrs J.A. Jones

8

The Pembroke Centre Pupil Referral Service, The Old College, Neyland, Pembrokeshire; Tel 01646 602473
Head (Centre) J.A. Jones

Portfield School off Portfield Ave, Haverfordwest, Pembrokeshire SA61 1BS; Tel 01437 762701
Headteacher Mrs S. Painter

PROFESSIONAL EDUCATION CENTRE

Pembrokeshire Professional Education Centre St. Clement's Rd, Neyland, Pembroke, Pembrokeshire SA73 1SH; Tel 01646 890069; Fax 01646 602154

POWYS COUNTY COUNCIL

www.powys.gov.uk

Population 123 600
County Hall, Llandrindod Wells, Powys LD1 5LG;
    URL www.powys.gov.uk;
    E-mail webmaster@powys.gov.uk; Tel 01597 826000;
    Fax 01597 826230
Chief Executive Jacky Tonge

Social Care Services

Library Headquarters, Cefnllys La, Llandrindod Wells, Powys LD1 5DP; Tel 01597 826808; Fax 01597 826856
Director (Social Services)/Head (Social Care) Philip Robson
Head (Children's Services) Neil Dunn
Principal Service Manager (Older and Disabled People) Cath Simmonds
Principal Service Manager (Learning Disabilities) Susan O'Grady
Portfolio Member (Social Care Services) Cllr Chris Mann
Portfolio Member (Children's Services) Cllr Gillian Thomas

AREA OFFICES

Montgomeryshire

Bryntirion, Salop Rd, Welshpool, Powys SY21 7YA; Tel 01938 552017
Senior Social Care Manager Mike Gregory

Brecknockshire and Radnorshire

Gwalia, Ithon Rd, Llandrindod Wells, Powys LD1 6AA; Tel 01597 827102
Manager (Child Protection) Clive Bartley

Brecknockshire and Radnorshire

Watton Mount, Brecon, Powys LD3 7HR; Tel 01874 623741
Principal Service Manager (Provider Services) Ros Thomas
Principal Service Manager (Mental Health and Substance Misuse) Penny Vaughn
Principal Services Manager (Business Support) Donna Wilson
Hendre, Ladus, Ystradgynlais, Powys; Tel 01639 844595

RESIDENTIAL AND DAY CARE ESTABLISHMENTS

Brecknockshire

DAY SERVICES (LEARNING DISABILITY)

Candles Workshop 88 The Watton, Brecon, Powys; Tel 01874 611333
Manager Andy Kaye

Cyffwdd Brecon Leisure Centre, Brecon, Powys
Manager Linda Watts

Ennig Stores High St, Talgarth, Powys; Tel 01874 712281
Manager Andy Kaye

Hay/Talgarth Project Great Barn Hse, Talgarth, Powys; Tel 01874 712030
Manager Andy Kaye

Honddu Wholefoods Shop 1, Cwmlais, Rich Way, Brecon, Powys; Tel 01874 610598
Manager Jackie Davies

The Rhyd Canal Rd, Brecon, Powys; Tel 01874 622119
Manager Jackie Davies

Y Gegin Fach Market Arcade, Brecon, Powys; Tel 01874 622102
Manager Jackie Davies

Ystradgynlais Day Service Hendre Ladus, Ystradgynlais, Powys; Tel 01639 849025
Manager Jackie Davies

DAY CENTRES

Arosfa Day Centre Camden Rd, Brecon, Powys; Tel 01874 624666
Manager Barbara Bufton

Canolfan Day Centre Derwen Rd, Ystradgynlais, Powys SA9 1HL; Tel 01639 842212
Manager Debbie Evans

Maes y Ffynon Day Centre Beaufort St, Crickhowell, Brecon, Powys; Tel 01873 811717
Manager Dilwyn Powell

CHILDREN'S HOME (RESPITE CARE)

Ty Canol Children's Home Ger y Tarrell, Llanfaes, Brecon, Powys; Tel 01874 624707
Manager Hazel Aulsebrook

Montgomeryshire

DAY SERVICES (LEARNING DISABILITY)

Leignton Day Services Base Coed Isaf, Leighton, Welshpools, Powys; Tel 01938 556052
Manager Gary Roberts

Colourshop Day Services Enterprise Centre, Salop Rd, Welshpool, Powys; Tel 01938 55623
Manager Paul Medland

Cyfle Newydd Day Services Base Forge Rd, Machynlleth, Powys; Tel 01654 703463
Manager Ann Mills

Oakleaf Crafts Great Oak St, Llanidloes, Powys; Tel 01686 622726
Manager Caroline Rutter

Station Day Services Base Old Station, Unit L, Llanidloes, Powys; Tel 01686 411077
Manager Caroline Rutter

Ty Rowan Rowan Hse, Trehafren, Newtown, Powys SY16 1EN; Tel 01691 626056
Manager Nat Warne

Sylfaen Day Services Base Llanidloes Day Services, Llangurig Rd, Llanidloes, Powys SY18 6ES; Tel 01686 413969
Manager Alison Taylor

DAY CENTRES

Maes Y Wennol Day Centre Llangurig Rd, Llanidloes, Powys; Tel 01686 413738
Manager Carole Rees

Park Day Centre Park St, Newtown, Powys; Tel 01686 628192
Manager Megan Beddoes

Westwood Day Centre Salop Rd, Welshpool, Powys;
Tel 01938 554458
Manager Maureen Watkins

HOME FOR PEOPLE WITH LEARNING DIFFICULTIES

Milford House Trehafren, Newtown, Powys; Tel 01686
627021
Manager Les Clarke
(24)

Radnorshire

DAY CENTRE

Arlais Day Centre Beaufort Rd, Llandrindod Wells, Powys;
Tel 01597 823905
Manager Hilary Jones
(50)

Children, Families and Lifelong Learning

Powys County Hall, Llandrindod Wells, Powys LD1 5LG;
URL www.education.powys.gov.uk;
E-mail cfll@powys.gov.uk; Tel 01597 826422; Fax 01597
826475
Group Director (Children, Families and Lifelong Learning)
Michael R.J Barker, BSc
Principal Educational Psychologist Alun Flynn
Chief Officer (Education Welfare) D. Walsh

South Powys

SPECIAL SCHOOL

Ysgol Penmaes Canal Rd, Brecon, Powys LD3 7HL;
E-mail admin@penmaes.powys.sch.uk; Tel 01874 623508;
Fax 01874 625197
Headteacher I. Elliot
Mixed

North Powys

SPECIAL SCHOOLS

Brynllywarch School Kerry, Newtown, Powys SY16 4PB;
E-mail admin@brynllywarch.powys.sch.uk; Tel 01686
670276; Fax 01686 670894
Headteacher D.C. Williams
Mixed Residential (46)

Ysgol Cedewain Maesyrhandir, Newtown, Powys
SY16 1LH; E-mail admin@cedewain.powys.sch.uk;
Tel 01686 627454; Fax 01686 621867
Headteacher P.A. Tudor

Ysgol Cedewain Senior Unit, Garth Owen, Newtown,
Powys SY16 1LH; E-mail admin@cedewain.powys.sch.uk;
Tel 01686 626640
Headteacher P.A. Tudor

RHONDDA CYNON TAFF COUNTY BOROUGH COUNCIL

www.rhondda-cynon-taff.gov.uk

Population 232 581
Ty Trevithick, Abercynon, Mountain Ash, Rhondda, Cynon,
Taff CF45 4UQ; URL www.rhondda-cynon-taff.gov.uk;
Tel 01443 424000; Fax 01443 424024

Group Director (Education and Children's Services) Mr Dewi
Jones; E-mail kim.ryley@rhondda-cynon-taff.gov.uk
County Borough Officer (Human Resources) A.R.J. Wilkins
County Borough Officer (Legal and Democratic Services)
P.J. Lucas

Social Services Department

The Pavilions, Cambrian Pk, Clydach Vale, Tonypandy,
Rhondda, Cynon, Taff CF40 2XX;
E-mail john.wrangham@rhondda-cynon-taff.gov.uk;
Tel 01443 424000; (Emergency Duty Team) 01443 204010;
Fax (Direct Line) 01443 424027; (Emergency Duty Team)
01443 217198
Director (Social Services) John Wrangham
Divisional Director (Children and Young People) S. Halls
Divisional Director (Community Care) B. Gatis (Acting)
Cabinet Committee Member for Better Health Layton Jones

Education and Children's Services

Ty Trevithick, Abercynon, Mountain Ash, Rhondda, Cynon,
Taff CF45 4UQ; URL www.rctednet.net; Tel 01443
744000; Fax 01443 744024
Group Director (Education and Children's Services) D. Jones,
BA, MSc, DipEd, MIMgt
Divisional Director (Children and Young People)
Sally Halls
Divisional Director (School Support and Improvement)
M. Keating
Divisional Director (Resources and Performance Management)
David Brown
Divisional Director (Lifelong Learning) G. Newton
Head (Development and Planning) G. Kiss
Head (Access and Inclusion) Barbara Brown (Acting)
Head (Liaison Services) N. Stead
*Principal Educational Psychologist (School Psychological
Service)* V.E. Board
Senior Educational Psychologist Paul Rees

Pupil Referral Unit

TAI EDUCATION CENTRE

Grovefield Terr, Penygraig, Tonypandy, Rhondda,
Cynon, Taff CF40 1HL; Tel 01443 422666; Fax 01443
436487
Headteacher Ann Jones

SPECIAL DAY SCHOOLS

Park Lane Special School Park La, Trecynon, Aberdare,
Rhondda, Cynon, Taff CF44 8HN; Tel 01685 874489
Headteacher C. Jones (Acting)
(47)

Rhondda Special School Brithweunydd Rd, Trealaw,
Tonypandy, Rhondda, Cynon, Taff CF40 2UH;
E-mail rhondda.special@rhonddaspe.rctednet.net; Tel 01443
433046; Fax 01443 440034
Headteacher A. Henderson

Maesgwyn Special School Cwmdare Rd, Cwmdare,
Aberdare, Rhondda, Cynon, Taff CF44 8RE;
E-mail maesgwyn.special@maesgwynspe.rctednet.net;
Tel 01685 873933; Fax 01685 873933
Headteacher V. Jones

SPECIAL RESIDENTIAL SCHOOL

Ysgol Ty Coch Lansdale Dr, Tonteg, Pontypridd, Rhondda,
Cynon, Taff CF38 1PG; Tel 01443 203471; Fax 01443
206828
Headteacher Heather Hodges
(95)

8

CITY AND COUNTY OF SWANSEA
www.swansea.gov.uk

Population 230 600
Political Composition: Lab: 47, Ind: 8, LD: 10, Con: 4,
Plaid Cymru: 2
County Hall, Swansea SA1 3SN;
   URL www.swansea.gov.uk; Tel 01792 636000; Fax 01792
   636700
Lord Mayor   R.F. Davies
Chief Executive   Vivienne Sugar
Head (Legal and Committee Services)   J. James
Director (Finance)   R.F. Carter
Director (Housing)   A. Phillips
Director (Technical Services)   P. Thomas
Director (Culture and Recreation)   D. Evans
Director (Environment and Health)   J. Spence
Director (Development)   C. Anderson
Assistant Director (Management Services)   C.J. Williams
   (Acting)

Social Services Department

E-mail social.services@swansea.gov.uk; Tel 01792 636000;
   Fax 01792 636807
Director (Social Services)   Hugh Gardner
*Assistant Director (Mental Health and Learning Disability
   Services)*   Chris Maggs
Assistant Director (Child and Family Services)
   Mark Roszkowski
Assistant Director (Elderly and Disability Services)
   Pat Dalzell
Head (Registration and Inspection Unit)   Jackie Evans
Principal Officer (Care Management)   Vacancy
Principal Officer (Service Provision)   Pam Williams
Principal Officer (Mental Health)   David Hughes
Principal Officer (Youth Justice)   Neville Morris
Principal Officer (Family Support)   Sian Hughes
Principal Officer (Accommodation/Adoption)
   Andrew Vipond
Principal Officer (Residential and Day Care Services)
   John Jenkins
Principal Officer (Domiciliary Support)   Roberta McAvoy
Principal Officer (Planning and Contracting)   Richard Leggett
Divisional Manager (Care Management – South)
   Martin Davies
Divisional Manager (Care Management – North)
   Sheila Ludman

Policy Development Team Members for Social Services

Lab: V. Alexander, D. James, R. Thomas, G. Williams.
LD: M. Jones.
Ind: M. Smith.

Scrutiny Members for Social Services

Lab: M. Child, D. Cox, J. Evans, D. Hopkins, D. Jones,
D. Lawlor, V. Lloyd, C. Thomas.
LD: M. Day, J. Stanton.
Ind: K. Marsh.

TRAINING

Staff Development Officer   Sue Rawson; Tel 01792 543890

WELFARE RIGHTS

Swansea Welfare Rights Unit PO Box 35, Swansea
SA1 5YT; Tel 01792 533500; Fax 01792 533501
Manager   Clive Oliver

TRANSPORT

Transport Unit The Kingsway, Fforestfach Ind Est, Swansea;
Tel 01792 522970
Manager   C. Jones

CHILD AND FAMILY SERVICES

Child Care Area Teams

AREA 1

Hafan Plentyn Guildhall Road South, Swansea; Tel 01792
635522

AREA 2

Hafan Plentyn Guildhall Road South, Swansea; Tel 01792
635855

AREA 3

West Street Gorseinon, Swansea; Tel 01792 533200

AREA 4

Morfydd House Morriston, Swansea; Tel 01792 775416

CHILD PROTECTION (SOUTH)

Hafan Plentyn Guildhall Road South, Swansea; Tel 01792
635835

CHILD PROTECTION (NORTH)

West Street Gorseinon, Swansea; Tel 01792 533200

YOUTH JUSTICE

Llwyncelyn Campus Cockett, Swansea; Tel 01792 522800

CHILD DISABILITIES AND FAMILY SUPPORT

Unit B1 and B2 Lakeside Technology Pk, Llansamlet,
Swansea; Tel 01792 522900

COMMUNITY PLACEMENTS/ADOPTION

Cockett House Cockett, Swansea; Tel 01792 584622

COMMUNITY HOMES

Cockett Houses Cockett Rd, Swansea; Tel 01792 522851
West Cross Children's Home West Cross La, Swansea;
Tel 01792 405230; 01792 405231

SHORT-TERM CARE FOR CHILDREN WITH LEARNING DISABILITIES

Gwerneinon Derwen Fawr Rd, Swansea; Tel 01792 204752

FAMILY CENTRE

Mayhill Family Centre Mayhill Rd, Mayhill, Swansea;
Tel 01792 468584

LEARNING DISABILITY SERVICES

Community Support Teams

SOUTH

Cefn Coed Hospital Cockett, Swansea; Tel 01792 587749
Team Leader   S. Harper

NORTH

Llwyneryr Hospital 151 Clasemont Rd, Morriston, Swansea; Tel 01792 701343

DAY SERVICES FOR ADULTS WITH LEARNING DIFFICULTIES

The Beeches Alternative Day Centre 116 Eaton Cres, Upland, Swansea; Tel 01792 455569

Fforestfach Adult Training Centre Fforestfach Ind Est, Fforestfach, Swansea; Tel 01792 588614

Flexible Day Service 2 Whitethorne Pl, Sketty, Swansea; Tel 01792 790062

Glandwr Day Service 225 Neath Rd, Landore, Swansea; Tel 01792 650350

Gorseinon Alternative Day Centre Former Library, West St, Swansea; Tel 01792 897646

West Cross Local Day Service Tircoed, Fairwood Rd, Swansea; Tel 01792 405629

Special Needs Day Service 985 Llangyfelach Rd, Swansea; Tel 01792 792160

Special Needs Day Service 31 Lon Gwesyn, Birchgrove, Swansea; Tel 01792 321522

Special Needs Day Service 49 Parkway, Sketty Pk, Swansea; Tel 01702 207005

Special Needs Day Service Maesglas Rd, Swansea; Tel 01792 585546

RESIDENTIAL SERVICES FOR ADULTS

Maesglas Community Unit Maesglas Hse, Maesglas Rd, Swansea; Tel 01792 586173

RESPITE SERVICES

Acacia Road Centre 21 Acacia Rd, West Cross, Swansea; Tel 01792 401669

Alexandra Road Centre 70–72 Gorseinon, Gorseinon, Swansea; Tel 01792 893426

Glanyrafon Gardens Centre 2a Glanyrafon Gdns, Sketty, Swansea; Tel 01792 280745

MENTAL HEALTH SERVICES

Community Mental Health Teams

AREA 1

Tredillion House 26 Uplands Cres, Swansea; Tel 01792 469700

AREA 2

Central Clinic 21 Orchard St, Swansea; Tel 01792 517853

AREA 3

Ty Einon Princess St, Gorseinon, Swansea; Tel 01792 899909

AREA 4

Gelligron Gelligron Rd, Pontardawe, Swansea; Tel 01792 865696

DAY SERVICE

Cwmbwrla Day Centre Cwmbwrla Sq, Swansea; Tel 01792 652101

RESIDENTIAL SERVICE

Llanfair House Norton Ave, Norton, Swansea; Tel 01792 404756

SERVICES TO ELDERLY AND DISABLED PEOPLE

Area Offices

AREAS 1/2

County Hall Swansea SA1 3SN; Tel 01792 636000

AREA 3

West Street Gorseinon, Swansea; Tel 01792 533200

AREA 4

Morfydd Street Morriston, Swansea; Tel 01792 775416

HOSPITAL SOCIAL WORKERS

Singleton Hospital Sketty La, Swansea; Tel 01792 285255

DAY CARE UNIT FOR PHYSICALLY DISABLED

Residential Unit for Physically Disabled Ty Cila, Wimmerfield Rd, Killay, Swansea; Tel 01792 516360

SWANSEA DISABLED LIVING CENTRE

Brondeg House St. John's Rd, Manselton, Swansea; Tel 01792 580161

HOME CARE RESOURCE CENTRES

Meals on Wheels Beaufort Works, Morriston, Swansea; Tel 01792 795072

Parkway Sketty Pk, Swansea; Tel 01792 280564

Plasmelyn 2 Y Plas, St Cenydd Rd, Swansea; Tel 01792 582053

COMMUNITY ALARM SERVICE

Central Control Pentrepoeth School Rd, Morriston, Swansea; Tel 01792 791771

RESIDENTIAL CARE FOR ELDERLY PEOPLE

There are seven homes for the elderly.

SHORT-TERM CARE

Earlsmoor Bryn Rd, Brynmill, Swansea; Tel 01792 466012

DAY CENTRES

Hollies Day Centre Cae Cerrig Rd, Pontarddulais, Swansea; Tel 01792 885183

Norton Day Centre Norton Rd, Norton, Swansea; Tel 01792 405384

Rose Cross Day Centre Brenig Rd, Penlan, Swansea; Tel 01792 586499

St. John's Day Centre Cae Rowland Rd, Cwmbwrla, Swansea; Tel 01792 456593

Ty Waunarlwydd Swansea Rd, Waunarlwydd, Swansea; Tel 01792 872255

Education Department

County Hall, Oystermouth Rd, Swansea SA1 3SN;
URL www.swansea.gov.uk;
E-mail education.department@swansea.gov.uk;
Tel 01792 636560; Fax 01792 636642
Director (Education) R. Parry
Assistant Director (Improving Access to Learning)
Ms M.A. Bullen

8

Assistant Director (School Improvement)   F. Jones
Executive Manager   Mrs H. Davies
Manager (Access to Learning)   Mrs S. Davies
Manager (Employment Training)   S. Harris
Community Education Manager (Lifelong Learning)
   M. Hughes

SPECIAL SCHOOLS

Pen-y-bryn School Glasbury Rd, Morriston, Swansea
SA6 7PA; E-mail pen-y-bryn.school@swansea.gov.uk;
Tel 01792 799064; Fax 01792 781311
Headteacher   A.G. Williams

Ysgol Crug Glas Croft St, Swansea SA1 1QA;
E-mail crug.glasspecial@swansea.gov.uk; Tel 01792 652388;
Fax 01792 457774
Headteacher   P. Martin

TORFAEN COUNTY BOROUGH COUNCIL
www.torfaen.gov.uk

Population 90 400
Civic Centre, Pontypool, Torfaen NP4 6YB;
   URL www.torfaen.gov.uk;
   E-mail your.call@torfaen.gov.uk; Tel 01495 762200;
   Fax 01495 755513
Chief Executive   Peter Durkin (Acting)
Director (Education)   M. de Val, BA, MEd
Director (Social Services)   G. Birch

Social Services Department

Tel 01495 762200; Fax 01633 648794
Director (Social Services)   Gary Birch, CMA, DMS, MBA
Assistant Director (Performance and Partnership)
   Stewart Greenwell
Assistant Director (Children's Services)   P. Meredith
Assistant Director (Community Care)   E. Law
Group Manager (Children's Services)   K. Rutherford
Group Manager (Performance and Partnerships)
   S. Gillingham
Group Manager (Community Care)   A. Thompson
Principal Officer (Protect and Review)   P. Langley
Principal Officer (Looked After Children)   L. Wright

Social Services Committee

Executive Member   Gwiliam Evans

CUSTOMER SERVICES

DAY NURSERY

Cwmbran Family Centre Wesley St, Cwmbran, Torfaen
NP44 3LZ; Tel 01633 838758

DAY CENTRES

Cwmbran Day Centre Five Locks Rd, Pontnewydd,
Cwmbran, Torfaen NP44 1AP; Tel 01633 838070
Ty Nant Ddu Resource Centre Hospital Rd, Pontnewynydd,
Pontypool, Torfaen NP4 8LE; Tel 01495 767937

ADULT TRAINING CENTRE FOR PEOPLE WITH LEARNING DISABILITIES

The Highway Croesyceiliog, Cwmbran, Torfaen NP44 2HF;
Tel 01633 838474

RESIDENTIAL HOMES FOR PEOPLE WITH LEARNING DISABILITIES

Cresswell Walk Residential Home 49 Cresswell Wlk, St.
Dials, Cwmbran, NP44 4RG
Plas-y-Garn Bungalow Residential Home Lower Park
Gdns, Penygarn, Pontypool, Torfaen NP4 8DB; Tel 01495
758921

Education Offices

County Hall, Cwmbran, Torfaen NP44 2WN; Tel 01633
   648610; Fax 01633 648164
Director (Education)   M. de Val

SPECIAL SCHOOL

Crownbridge School Greenhill Rd, Sebastapol, Pontypool,
Torfaen NP4 5YW; Tel 01495 758739
Headteacher   L. Bush

VALE OF GLAMORGAN COUNCIL
www.valeofglamorgan.gov.uk

Political Composition: Lab: 18, Con: 22, Plaid Cymru: 6,
LD: 1
Civic Offices, Holton Rd, Barry, Vale of Glamorgan
   CF63 4RU; URL www.valeofglamorgan.gov.uk;
   E-mail webmaster@valeofglamorgan.gov.uk;
   Tel 01446 709202; (Switchboard) 01446 700111; Fax 01446
   745566
Chief Executive   J. Maitland Evans; Tel 01446 709303;
   Fax 01446 421479

Community Services

The Dock Office, Subway Rd, Barry, Vale of Glamorgan
   CF63 4RT; Tel 01446 700111; (Out of hours) 029 2039
   6873
Director   James Cawley; Tel 01446 704676
Head of Service (Community Care and Health)
   D. McDonald
Head (Children's Services)   A. Young
Head (Strategy, Performance Management and Commissioning)
   Carys Lord; Tel 01446 704606
Group Accountant   S. Keen

Cabinet Members

Social and Care Services   Cllr Clive Williams
Housing and Community Safety   Cllr J. Thomas

TRAINING

Training and Development Officer   H. Lloyd
Training and Development Officer   Z. McBreen

HOSPITAL SOCIAL WORKERS

Llandough Hospital Penlan Rd, Penarth, Vale of
Glamorgan; Tel 029 2071 1711

Children's Services

RESOURCE CENTRE

Barry Childcare Team Haydock Hse, Holton Rd, Barry, Vale
of Glamorgan; Tel 01446 725202

SUPPORT SERVICES FOR CHILDREN

Looked After Services for Children (Fostering and Adoption and Day Care) Haydock Hse, Holton Rd, Barry, Vale of Glamorgan; Tel 01446 725202

RESIDENTIAL UNITS

Barry Hostel Gladstone Rd, Barry, Vale of Glamorgan; Tel 01446 733952

Bryneithin St. Andrew's Rd, Dinas Powys, Vale of Glamorgan; Tel 029 2051 2218

Cartref Porthceri Salisbury Rd, Barry, Vale of Glamorgan; Tel 01446 739438

Southway Town Mill Rd, Cowbridge, Vale of Glamorgan; Tel 01446 772265

Adult Services

RESOURCE CENTRES

Elderly Mentally Infirm Persons Bryneithin, St. Andrew's Rd, Dinas, Powys, Vale of Glamorgan; Tel 029 2051 5326

Elderly Persons Rondel Hse, Maes-y-Cwm St, Barry, Vale of Glamorgan; Tel 01446 745922

Elderly Persons Gardenhurst, Holmesdale Pl, Penarth, Vale of Glamorgan; Tel 029 2071 1555

People with Learning Difficulties Woodlands Centre, Woodlands Rd, Barry, Vale of Glamorgan; Tel 01446 732158

People with Learning Difficulties Ty Jenner, Gladstone Rd, Barry, Vale of Glamorgan CF63 4RT; Tel 01446 725100

People with Mental Health Problems Amy Evans Centre, Holton Rd, Barry, Vale of Glamorgan; Tel 01446 733331

Physically Handicapped Persons/Elderly Persons Hen Goleg, College Fields Cl, Barry, Vale of Glamorgan; Tel 01446 730402

Learning and Development

Civic Offices, Holton Road, Barry, Vale of Glamorgan CF63 4RU; Tel 01446 700111; Fax 01446 701820
Director (Learning and Development) B. Jeffreys
Head (School Improvement Service) S. Aspinall

SPECIAL SCHOOLS

Ashgrove School Sully Rd, Penarth, Vale of Glamorgan CF64 2TP; E-mail ashgroves@valeofglamorgan.gov.uk; Tel 029 2070 4212
Headteacher B.M. Brayford, BEd, DipSpEd, DipTDeaf
Autism and associated difficulties (Residential).

Ysgol Erw'r Delyn St. Cyres Rd, Penarth, Vale of Glamorgan CF64 2WR;
E-mail yerwrdelen@valeofglamorgan.gov.uk; Tel 029 2070 7225
Headteacher M. Farrell, BEd(SpEd), BA, MEd
PH (Residential); PMLD.

Ysgol Maes Dyfan Gibbonsdown Rise, Barry, Vale of Glamorgan CF63 1DT;
E-mail ymaesdyfan@valeofglamorgan.gov.uk; Tel 01446 732112
Headteacher Mrs I. Aubrey, BEd

SPECIAL EDUCATIONAL NEEDS

Pupil Support Service, Directorate of Learning and Development, Barry, Vale of Glamorgan;
E-mail bgrover@valeofglamorgan.gov.uk; Tel 01446 709184; Fax 01446 701821

WREXHAM COUNTY BOROUGH COUNCIL
www.wrexham.gov.uk

Population 128 500
Political Composition: Lab: 24, Radical: 10, Ind: 11, Con: 4, Non-aligned: 3.
PO Box 1284, Guildhall, Wrexham LL11 1WF;
URL www.wrexham.gov.uk;
E-mail webmaster@wrexham.gov.uk; Tel 01978 292000;
Fax 01978 292106
Chief Executive Isobel Garner
Director (Corporate Services) B. Goodall
Director (Finance and Information Services) M. Scholes
Director (Development Services) Paul Roberts
Director (Environmental Services) P. Walton
Chief Housing Officer P. Calland

Directorate of Personal Services

PO Box 1286, Wrexham LL11 1WG; Tel 01978 292901;
Fax 01978 292903
Director (Personal Services) Malcolm Russell
Chief Officer (Social Services) Andrew Figiel
Social Services Department, 2nd Fl, Crown Bldgs, Chester St, Wrexham LL13 8ZE;
E-mail andrewfigiel@wrexham.gov.uk; Tel 01978 298010;
Fax 01978 298029
Assistant Chief Officer (Children and Families)
Bob MacLaren
Assistant Chief Officer (Adult Services)
Sheila Wentworth
Senior Manager (Support Services) Jim Duffy
Manager (Finance) A. Green
Manager (Performance) Rob Gifford
Human Resources Manager (Training and Personnel)
D.B. Palmer
Manager (Welfare Rights) Damian Keogh
Representation and Complaints Officer Jane Roberts

HOSPITAL SOCIAL WORKERS

Maelor Hospital Croesnewydd Rd, Wrexham; Tel 01978 291100
Team Manager (Child Health and Disability) Kevin Fryer
Team Manager (Adults) V. Burrows

CHILD PROTECTION CO-ORDINATOR

Kelso Hse, 13 Grosvenor Rd, Wrexham LL13 82E; Tel 01978 267092
Co-ordinator (Child Protection) Lynette Evans

CHILDREN'S RESOURCE CENTRE

7 Tan y Dre, Holt Rd, Wrexham LL13 9AU; Tel 01978 261863

CHILDREN'S HOME

Cherry Hill 91 Borras Park Rd, Wrexham LL12 7TF; Tel 01978 263284

FAMILY CENTRES

Caia Park Family Centre Prince Charles Rd, Wrexham; Tel 01978 355900

8

Dean Road Family Centre Dean Rd, Rhosnesni, Wrexham; Tel 01978 352249

Idwal Family Centre Plas Madoc, Wrexham; Tel 01978 824342

DAY CENTRE FOR PEOPLE WITH MENTAL HEALTH PROBLEMS

Centre 67 Cunliffe Hse, Wrexham LL11 1EB; Tel 01978 264344

DAY CENTRE FOR PEOPLE WITH PHYSICAL DISABILITY/SENSORY IMPAIRMENT

Cunliffe Day Centre Rhosddu Rd, Wrexham LL11 2NW; Tel 01978 352588; (Cunliffe Information Centre Disability Helpline) 01978 261436; (Q-DOS Business and Training Services) 01978 354441

GATE (Greystones Achievement Through Endeavour – Respite Care/Rehabilitative Care/Independent Living for People with Physical Disability/Sensory Impairment) 82 Rhossddu Rd, Wrexham LL11 2NP; Tel 01978 261572

COMMUNITY MENTAL HEALTH TEAM FOR OLDER PEOPLE

Wrexham Maelor Hospital (formerly Psychological Therapies Bldg), Croesnewydd Rd, Wrexham LL13 7TD; Tel 01978 291100

COMMUNITY DRUGS TEAM

Pru Stothard Wrexham Community Drugs Team, Swn-y-coed, Grove Rd, Wrexham; Tel 01978 261125; (Standby Duty Service) 01978 264358

Department of Education and Leisure Services

Ty Henblas, Queens Sq, Wrexham LL13 8AZ;
  URL www.wrexham.gov.uk;
  E-mail terry.garner@wrexham.gov.uk; Tel 01978 297400
Director (Education and Leisure Services)   Terry Garner
Chief Officer (Leisure, Libraries and Culture)   A. Watkin
Chief Officer (Education)   M. Lloyd Jones
Chief Officer (Strategic Services)   W. Thomas
Special Officer (Secondary)   John Roberts
Special Officer (Primary)   G. Morris
Head (Learning Support Services)   Graham Edwards

SPECIAL SCHOOL

St. Christopher's School Stockwell Gr, Wrexham LL13 7RW; Tel 01978 346910
Headteacher   M. Grant
  (219)

Ymlaen Dodd's La, Gwersyllt, Wrexham LL11 4PA; Tel 01978 753103
Manager (Behavioural Support)   Alison Peddie

Local Government Scotland

9

- **Main Council Information**
- **Social Work Department**
  Including all social services provision
- **Education Department**
  Including special needs provision

Key

(110)	Number of pupils
Mixed	Takes boys and girls
Boys	Takes boys only
Girls	Takes girls only
11–18	Age range of pupils

Abbreviations

ADHD	Attention Deficit Hyperactivity Disorder
ASD	Autism Spectrum Disorder
EBD	Emotional Behavioural Difficulties
LD	Learning Difficulties
LI	Language Impairment
MH	Mentally Handicapped
MLD	Moderate Learning Difficulties
PH	Physically Handicapped
PHAB	Physically Handicapped and Able-Bodied
PMLD	Profound and Multiple Learning Difficulties
PS	Partially Sighted
PtHg	Partially Hearing
SCU	Special Care Unit
SEBD	Severe Emotional Behaviour Difficulties
SEN	Special Educational Needs
SLD	Severe Learning Difficulties
SLDD	Students with Learning Difficulties and Disabilities
SMH	Severely Mentally Handicapped

Local Government Scotland

ABERDEENSHIRE COUNCIL
www.aberdeenshire.gov.uk

Woodhill Hse, Westburn Rd, Aberdeen AB16 5GB;
   URL www.aberdeenshire.gov.uk; Tel 01467 620981;
   Fax 01224 665444
Chief Executive   Alan G. Campbell, CBE;
   E-mail alan.g.campbell@aberdeenshire.gov.uk

Housing and Social Work

Woodhill Hse, Westburn Rd, Aberdeen, Aberdeenshire
   AB16 5GB
Director (Housing and Social Work)   Colin Mackenzie;
   E-mail colin.mackenzie@aberdeenshire.gov.uk
Strategic Development Manager (Child Care)
   Linda Morrison
Strategic Development Manager (Community Care)
   Anne Sutherland

Social Work and Housing Committee

Chair   Cllr E.A. Robertson
'Struan', School Rd, Turriff, Aberdeenshire AB53 8QE
Vice-Chair   Cllr S. Thomson
47 Hillside Terr, Portlethen, Aberdeenshire AB12 4QG
Members of the Committee
W. Agnew, R. Bisset, S. Coull, J. Cox, J. Duncan,
T. Flemming, A.M. Fowler, Dr H.M. Fowler, A. Howie,
S.M. Lonchay, J. Loveday, J. Mair, S.B. Mair, N. Makin,
J. Morrison, C.H. Nelson , A. Ritchie, Dr G.S. Saluja,
D. Smith, A. Strachan, N.E. Thomson, B.A. Topping,
A. Wallace.

NORTH

Seafield Hse, 37 Castle St, Banff, Aberdeenshire AB45 1FQ;
   Tel 01261 812001; Fax 01261 818244
*Head (Social Work – Mental Health, Learning Disabilities, Youth
   and Criminal Justice)*   Vacancy
Social Work Manager (Community Support)
   K. Theodoreson
Social Work Manager (Community Care Services)
   F. Lloyd Watt
Social Work Manager (Care in the Community)   J. Ledger
Social Work Manager (Criminal Justice)   P. English
Joint Commissioning Manager   Linda Reid
Manager (Child Protection)   S. Campbell
Senior Social Worker (Community Support)   M. Miller
Senior Social Worker (Criminal Justice)   J. Munro
Senior Social Worker (Adoption and Fostering)   S. Hough
Senior Social Worker (Social Work, HM Prison Peterhead)
   A. Shirran; Tel 01779 473315
Senior Social Worker (Youth Strategy)   A. Strachan

Senior Social Worker (Sex Offenders)   S. Watson
Senior Social Worker (Addictions)   S. Dickson
Senior Care Manager   J. Bown
Senior Occupational Therapist   M. Wilson
Senior Support Services Officer   A. MacLean

CHILDREN'S HOME

Scalloway Park Children's Home 11a Scalloway Pk,
Fraserburgh, Aberdeenshire AB43 5FB; Tel 01346
516608
Officer-In-Charge   J. Ral
   (10)

FAMILY CENTRES

Banff Family Centre Academy Dr, Banff, Aberdeenshire
AB45 1BL; Tel 01261 813180
Manager   F. Macdonald

Fraserburgh Family Centre 2 Bervie Rd, Fraserburgh,
Aberdeenshire AB43 5UY; Tel 01346 515187
Manager   D. O'Neill

Peterhead Family Centre 53a Windmill St, Peterhead,
Aberdeenshire AB42 6UE; Tel 01779 473368
Manager (Family Centre)   M. Strachan

DAY CENTRES FOR PEOPLE WITH DISABILITIES

Banff Day Services Colleonard Rd, Banff, Aberdeenshire
AB45 1DZ; Tel 01261 818281
Manager   M. McDermott

Boyndie Day Centre Boyndie, Banff, Aberdeenshire
AB45 2JT; Tel 01261 843249
Manager   Vacancy
   (75)

Robertson Road Centre Robertson Rd, Fraserburgh,
Aberdeenshire AB43 9BF; Tel 01346 515292
Manager   C. Gibbs
   (75)

Willowbank Centre Glendaveny, Peterhead, Aberdeenshire
AB42 7DT; Tel 01779 838301
Manager   M. Mackie
   (75)

HOSTELS FOR PEOPLE WITH DISABILITIES

Anderson House 44–46 Ardanes Brae, Banff, Aberdeenshire
AB45 1FG; Tel 01261 815911
Manager   Vacancy
   (11)

Willowbank Centre Glendavney, Peterhead, Aberdeenshire
AB42 7DT; Tel 01779 838301
Manager   M. Florence
   (16)

9

RESPITE CARE SERVICES

Fraserburgh Respite Care Robertson Road Centre, Robertson Rd, Fraserburgh, Aberdeenshire AB43 5BF; Tel 01346 515292

DAY CENTRES FOR THE ELDERLY

Burnside Court Day Care Centre Burnside Crt, Portsoy, Banff, Aberdeenshire AB42 8FP; Tel 01771 623166
Manager S. Duck

Dawson Court Day Centre Victoria Terr, Turriff, Aberdeenshire AB53 7FP; Tel 01888 568925
Manager Vacancy
(30)

Doo-cot View Day Centre St. Combs Crt, Banff, Aberdeenshire AB45 1GA; Tel 01261 815946
Manager S. Tran

Kinbroom House Day Centre Blackford Ave, Rothienorman, Aberdeenshire AB51 8YG; Tel 01651 821510
Warden E. McHattie
(15)

Roanheads Day Centre Roanheads Sheltered Housing Complex, Peterhead, Aberdeenshire; Tel 01779 477601
Manager H. Noble

Robertson Road Resource Centre Robertson Rd, Fraserburgh, Aberdeenshire AB43 5BF; Tel 01346 515292
Manager Vacancy
(18)

Ugievale Day Centre c/o Zion Tabernacle, Hope St, Peterhead, Aberdeenshire AB42 6FB; Tel 01779 479899
Manager J. Barber
(15)

CENTRAL

Gordon Hse, Blackhall Rd, Inverurie, Aberdeenshire AB51 3WA; Tel 01467 620981; Fax 01467 624277
Head (Social Work) D. Boynton
Manager (Social Work – Elderly and Home Care) C. Valentine
Manager (Social Work – Community Support) R. Driscoll
Manager (Social Work – Community Care) S. Watts
Senior Support Services Officer P. Grant

CHILDREN AND FAMILIES SUPPORT SERVICES

Inverurie Day Centre Port Rd, Inverurie, Aberdeenshire AB51 3SP; Tel 01467 629046; Fax 01467 629047
Team Manager Aileen Clark

CHILDREN'S HOME

Coblehaugh Children's Home Port Elphinstone, Inverurie, Aberdeenshire AB51 3XD; Tel 01467 621233; Fax 01467 625345
Officer-in-Charge W. Stickle
(10) (2 emergency)

DAY CENTRES FOR PEOPLE WITH LEARNING DISABILITIES

Ellon Resource Centre 29 Station Rd, Ellon, Aberdeenshire AB41 9AE; Tel 01358 720066
Manager D. Miller

Harlaw Centre Harlaw Rd, Inverurie, Aberdeenshire AB51 4TE; Tel 01467 621885
Manager A. Dobson
(107)

DAY CARE CENTRES FOR THE ELDERLY

Alford Day Care Centre Alford Community Centre, Alford Academy, Murray Terr, Alford, Aberdeenshire AB33 8PY; Tel 01975 562922
Day Care Organiser G. Maclean

Huntly Day Care Centre Huntly Business Centre, Unit 26–27, Gordon St, Huntly, Aberdeenshire; Tel 01466 795302; Fax 01466 794488
Day Care Organiser A. Barclay

Insch Day Care Centre Insch Church Hall, Western Rd, Insch, Aberdeenshire AB52 6JR; Tel 01464 821385
Manager A. Barclay

Inverurie Day Centre Port Rd, Inverurie, Aberdeenshire AB51 3SP; Tel 01467 629046; Fax 01467 629047
Team Manager A. Clark

John Wilson Day Centre Garlogie, Skene, Aberdeenshire AB32 6SA; Tel 01224 743653; 01224 744234
Manager Vacancy

Kemnay Day Care Centre Village Hall, Kemnay, Inverurie, Aberdeenshire; Tel 01467 629046; 01467 643571
Day Care Organiser N. Jamieson
Day Care Organiser I. Tewnion

St. Mary's on the Rock South Rd, Ellon, Aberdeenshire AB41 9NP; Tel 01358 720033
Day Care Organiser L. Bowie

ACCOMMODATION FOR THE ELDERLY

There are three residential homes for the elderly.

SOUTH

Carlton Hse, Arduthie Rd, Stonehaven, Aberdeenshire AB39 2DL; Tel 01569 763800; Fax 01569 768450
Head (Social Work) C. Booth
Manager (Social Work) L. Valentine
Manager (Home Care) P. Bradley
Manager (Residential Care) J. Carr
Team Manager (Looked After Children's Review) S. Cooper
Team Manager (Children and Families) Margaret Bruce
Team Manager (Portlethen) N. Barnett
Team Manager (Upper and Lower Deeside) M. Sutherland
Team Manager (Kincardine South) S. Brunton
Senior Care Manager J. Bond
Senior Support Services Officer R. O'Connor
Senior Social Worker (Criminal Justice) Fiona Westland
56 Cameron St, Stonehaven, Aberdeenshire AB39 2HE; Tel 01569 767553
Senior Occupational Therapist W. Cormack

DAY CENTRES FOR PEOPLE WITH LEARNING DISABILITIES

Forest View Day Centre Woodview Pl, Stonehaven, Aberdeenshire AB39 2TD; Tel 01569 765765
Manager P. Binns
(66)

The Scolty Centre Arbeadie Rd, Banchory, Aberdeenshire AB31 4EH; Tel 01330 823046
Manager A. Thomson

RESIDENTIAL AND DAY CARE ESTABLISHMENTS FOR THE ELDERLY

Allachburn Low Rd, Aboyne, Aberdeenshire AB34 5HX; Tel 01339 886888
Manager C. Hatton
(30 plus 4 day care)

Edenholme 66 Arduthie Rd, Stonehaven, Aberdeenshire AB39 2EH; Tel 01569 762325
Manager R. Hulme
(30 plus 2 day care)

Invercarron Resource Centre Low Wood Rd, Stonehaven, Aberdeenshire AB39 2LJ; Tel 01569 766622
Manager Grace Ferguson
(Day)

Aberdeenshire Education and Recreation

Woodhill House Annexe, Westburn Rd, Aberdeen
AB16 5GJ; URL www.aberdeenshire.gov.uk; Tel 01224
664630; Fax 01224 664615
Director (Education and Recreation) Hamish Vernal
Head of Service (Community Inclusion) Jim Banks

BUCHAN AREA AND BANFF AND BUCHAN AREA

Banff and Buchan Education Office

2nd Fl, St. Leonard's, Banff, Aberdeenshire AB45 1BH;
Tel 01261 813340; Fax 01261 813396

EDUCATIONAL PSYCHOLOGY SERVICE

Old Infant School, Prince St, Peterhead, Aberdeenshire
AB42 6PL;
E-mail peterheadpsych.er@aberdeenshire.gov.uk;
Tel 01779 470411; 01779 473269; Fax 01779 470390

SPECIAL SCHOOLS

Anna Ritchie School Grange Gdns, Peterhead,
Aberdeenshire AB42 2AP;
E-mail annaritchie.sch@aberdeenshire.gov.uk; Tel 01779
473293; Fax 01779 491063
Headteacher Ishbel Cruickshank

Westfield School Argyll Rd, Fraserburgh, Aberdeenshire
AB43 9BL; E-mail westfield.sch@aberdeenshire.gov.uk;
Tel 01346 518699; Fax 01346 512540; 01346 516633
Headteacher Gordon Davidson

FORMARTINE AREA AND GARIOCH AREA

Garioch Education Office

Gordon Hse, Blackhall Rd, Inverurie, Aberdeenshire
AB51 3WB; Tel 01467 620981; Fax 01467 622254

EDUCATIONAL PSYCHOLOGY SERVICE

The Portacabin, Victoria St, Inverurie, Aberdeenshire
AB51 3QS;
E-mail inveruriepsych.er@aberdeenshire.gov.uk;
Tel 01467 625464; Fax 01467 625806

SPECIAL SCHOOLS

Ellon Academy SEN Base Schoolhill, Ellon, Aberdeenshire
AB41 9AX; E-mail ellon.aca@aberdeenshire.gov.uk;
Tel 01358 720715; Fax 01358 723758
Headteacher Dr Brian Wilkins

Ellon Primary SEN Base Modley Pl, Ellon, Aberdeenshire
AB41 9BB; E-mail ellon.sch@aberdeenshire.gov.uk;
Tel 01358 720692; Fax 01358 724297
Headteacher James S. Stott

The Gordon Schools Special Unit Huntly, Aberdeenshire;
Tel 01466 792181; Fax 01466 794715
Teacher-in-Charge Valerie Hutcheon

St. Andrew's Special School St. Andrew's Gdns, Inverurie,
Aberdeenshire AB51 3XT;
E-mail standdrewsinv.sch@aberdeenshire.gov.uk; Tel 01467
621215; Fax 01467 621954
Headteacher Jacqueline Burnett

KINCARDINE AND MEARNS AREA AND MARR AREA

Kincardine and Mearns/Marr Education Office

Queens Rd, Stonehaven, Aberdeenshire AB39 2HQ;
Tel 01569 766960; Fax 01569 768489

EDUCATIONAL PSYCHOLOGY SERVICES CENTRE

52 Cameron St, Stonehaven, Aberdeenshire AB39 2HE;
E-mail stonehavenpsych.er@aberdeenshire.gov.uk;
Tel 01569 764110; Fax 01569 764133

SPECIAL SCHOOLS

Aboyne Academy SEN Base Bridgeview Rd, Aboyne,
Aberdeenshire AB34 5JN;
E-mail aboyne.aca@aberdeenshire.gov.uk; Tel 013398 86222;
Fax 013398 86922
Headteacher Charlie Wood

Aboyne Primary SEN Base Aboyne, Aberdeenshire
AB34 5JN; E-mail aboyne.sch@aberdeenshire.gov.uk;
Tel 013398 86638; Fax 013398 87408
Headteacher Margaret McKenna

Carronhill School Mill of Forest Rd, Stonehaven, Aberdeen-
shire AB39 2GZ; E-mail carronhill.sch@aberdeenshire.gov.uk;
Tel 01569 763886; Fax 01569 762332
Headteacher Lesley Hawksfield

ABERDEEN CITY COUNCIL
www.aberdeencity.gov.uk

Population 210 000
Town Hse, Broad St, Aberdeen AB10 1FY;
URL www.aberdeencity.gov.uk; Tel 01224 522500;
Fax 01224 644346
Chief Executive D. Paterson

9

Social Work Service

St. Nicholas Hse, Broad St, Aberdeen AB10 1BY; Tel 01224
522000; (Duty Team) 01224 522939; (Out of hours) 01224
693936; Fax 01224 633324
Director (Social Work) John Tomlinson
Assistant Director (Children and Families and Criminal Justice)
A. Dawson
Assistant Director (Community Care and Adult Services)
A. Pilkington
Assistant Director (Support Services) T. Simpson
*Assistant Director (Quality Assurance, Planning and Service
Development)* D. Tumelty
Assistant Director (Policy Development and Implementation)
S. Smith
Head (Quality Assurance) A. MacDonald
Social Work Manager (Research and Development) A. Baird
Head (Registration and Inspection) C. Stadames
Manager (Facilities) N. Jaffray
Social Work Manager (Training Team) J. Loder
Social Work Manager (Services for Older People) G. Smith
Principal Officer (Personnel) and Manager (Admin) W. Taylor
Social Work Manager (Children's Resources) M. Stephenson
Social Work Manager (Disability Services) H. McNeill
Social Work Manager (Children's Services) Vacancy
Social Work Manager (Adult Care) F. Palin
Social Work Manager (Criminal Justice) J. Bew
Principal Accountant J. Belford

Community Services Committee

Convener Cllr J. Lamond (Lab)
15 Belvidere St, Aberdeen AB25 2QS
Vice-Convener Cllr D. Maitland (Lab)
8 Concraig Pl, Kingswells, Aberdeen AB15 8LH
Vice-Convener M.E. Smith
Members of the Committee
G. Adam, J. Anderson, I. Cormack, S. Gordon, G. Graham,
G. Leslie, P. McDonald, A. McLean, A. Milne, R. Milne,
K. Stewart, W. Traynor, R. Webster.

PRE FIVE SECTION

Ashgrove Centre Gillespie Pl, Aberdeen; Tel 01224 482293
Senior Support Worker S. Stewart
Senior Support Worker L. Mann

Deeside Family Centre Girdleness Rd, Aberdeen; Tel 01224 248389
Senior Support Worker M. Gibson
Senior Support Worker A. McQueen

Quarry Family Centre Cummings Park Cres, Aberdeen; Tel 01224 691800
Senior Support Worker M. McDermid
Senior Support Worker M. Stanley

Seaton Family Centre School Rd, Seaton, Aberdeen; Tel 01224 494067
Senior Support Worker A. Dalgarno

Tillydrone Family Centre Pennan Rd, Tillydrone, Aberdeen; Tel 01224 495683
Senior Support Worker J. Richie
Senior Support Worker D. Duffus

Williamson Family Centre Mastrick Cl, off Mastrick Dr, Aberdeen; Tel 01224 692428
Senior Support Worker M. Rennie

YOUNG PEOPLE'S UNIT

Airyhall The Lane, Northcote Cres, Aberdeen; Tel 01224 867631
Contact J. Millar
(12)

CHILDREN'S HOMES

Gilbert Road Children's Home 2 Gilbert Rd, Bucksburn, Aberdeen AB2 9AJ; Tel 01224 714067
Contact D. Barclay

Kincorth Children's Home 41 Faulds Gate, Aberdeen; Tel 01224 872743
Contact A. Nicholson

Netherhills Children's Home 26 Netherhills Ave, Bucksburn, Aberdeen; Tel 01224 716510
Contact E. Leith

CENTRES FOR ADULTS WITH LEARNING DISABILITIES

Garden Craft Products Units 3 and 4, Farburn Ind Est, Aberdeen AB21 0HT; Tel 01224 725479
Contact S. Scott

Park House 120 Westburn Rd, Aberdeen; Tel 01224 645822
Contact Campbell Majoribanks

Pitfodels Day Care Unit North Deeside Rd, Aberdeen AB1 9PN; Tel 01224 861483
Manager A. Adams

Rosehill House 202 Ashgrove Road West, Aberdeen; Tel 01224 681732
Contact I. Stoddart

HOSTELS FOR ADULTS WITH LEARNING DISABILITIES

Back Hilton Road Hostel 8 Back Hilton Rd, Aberdeen; Tel 01224 492625
Contact M. Manojlovic

Dominies Road Hostel 3 Dominies Rd, Aberdeen; Tel 01224 484874
Contact C. Hadden

Pitfodels Aberdeen; Tel 01224 868956
Contact A. Adams

Stocket Parade 16b Stocket Pde, Aberdeen; Tel 01224 693649
Contact L. Brown

CENTRES FOR PEOPLE WITH PHYSICAL DISABILITIES

Burnside Mastrick Dr, Aberdeen; Tel 01224 692638
Centre Manager C. Traill

Community Special Needs Unit Airyhall Hse, Aberdeen; Tel 01224 868473
Contact E. Scott

Horizons Rehabilitation Resource Centre 2 Eday Wlk, Aberdeen; Tel 01224 403040
Centre Manager B. Thomson

Westburn Resource Centre 'Choices' 116 Westburn Rd, Aberdeen; Tel 01224 636475
Contact I. Gorner
(50)

DAY CENTRES FOR OLDER PEOPLE

Balnagask Day Centre Provost Hogg Crt, Victoria Rd, Aberdeen; Tel 01224 879198
Contact M. Findlay
(45)

Craigton Road Day Centre Craigielea Gdns, Craigton Rd, Aberdeen; Tel 01224 208579
Contact S. Cassie

Quarry Centre Cummings Park Cres, Aberdeen; Tel 01224 692990
Supervisor D. Homer

COMMUNITY SERVICE

11 Willowdale Pl, Aberdeen; Tel 01224 624317
Manager J. Murray

CRIMINAL JUSTICE TEAMS

Exchequer House 3 Exchequer Row, Aberdeen AB11 5BW; Tel 01224 405800
Contact J. Bew

Criminal Justice Services

PROBATION HOSTEL

St. Fittick's House Probation Hostel 36 Crombie Rd, Torry, Aberdeen AB1 3QQ; Tel 01224 877910
Officer-in-Charge S. Dickson

Education Department

Summerhill Centre, Stronsay Dr, Aberdeen AB15 6JA; E-mail furen@education.aberdeen.net.uk; Tel 01224 346060; 01224 522000; Fax 01224 346061
Corporate Director (Learning and Leisure) J. Stodter, BA, BA(Hons), PGCE
Head of Service (Quality of Life, Culture and Learning – Neighbourhood Central) Graham Wark
Head (Quality of Life, Culture and Learning – Neighbourhood North) Charles Muir, MA(Hons)
Head (Quality of Life, Culture and Learning – Neighbourhood South) Ann Landels, MA(Hons), MEd
Head (School Planning and Improvement) Alex Hunter
Education Officer Jan Roy
Education Officer Pete Hamilton
Principal Educational Psychologist Helen K. Carmichael

Central Neighbourhood

SPECIAL SCHOOLS

Beechwood School Raeden Park Rd, Aberdeen AB15 5PD; E-mail enquiries@beechwood.aberdeen.sch.uk; Tel 01224 323405; Fax 01224 311192
Headteacher A. Young, BSc, MEd

Donbank School SEN Base Dill Rd, Tillydrone, Aberdeen AB24 2XL; E-mail enquiries@donbank.aberdeen.sch.uk; Tel 01224 483217; Fax 01224 488690
Headteacher Margaret Bolton

English as an Additional Language Service St. Machar Primary School, Harris Dr, Tillydrone, Aberdeen AB24 2TF; E-mail ealservice@rmplc.co.uk; Tel 01224 494272; Fax 01224 494272
Head of Service Maeve McDowall

Gilcomstoun School SEN Base Skene St, Aberdeen AB10 1PG; E-mail enquiries@gilcomstoun.aberdeen.sch.uk; Tel 01224 642722; Fax 01224 620784
Headteacher Stewart Duncan

Harlaw Academy SEN Base 18–20 Albyn Pl, Aberdeen AB10 1RG; E-mail accharlaw@rmplc.co.uk; Tel 01224 589251; Fax 01224 227494
Headteacher John Murray

Raeden Centre Nursery School Mid Stocket Rd, Aberdeen AB15 5PD; E-mail raeden@rmplc.co.uk; Tel 01224 321381; Fax 01224 311109
Headteacher Kathleen Threadgold

St. Machar Academy SEN Base St. Machar Dr, Aberdeen AB24 3YZ; URL www.rsc.co.uk/stmachar; E-mail enquiries@stmacharacademy.aberdeen.sch.uk; Tel 01224 492855; Fax 01224 276112
Headteacher Leonard Taylor

St. Machar School SEN Base Harris Dr, Tillydrone, Aberdeen AB24 2TF; E-mail enquiries@st-machar.aberdeen.sch.uk; Tel 01224 484254; Fax 01224 484565
Headteacher Louise McIntosh

Seaton School SEN Base Seaton Place East, Aberdeen AB24 1XE; E-mail enquiries@seaton.aberdeen.sch.uk; Tel 01224 483414; Fax 01224 480539
Headteacher Charlotte Harkess

Sunnybank Primary School (Language Unit) Sunnybank Rd, Aberdeen AB24 3NJ; E-mail enquiries@sunnybank.aberdeen.sch.uk; Tel 01224 633363; Fax 01224 621174
Headteacher Caroline Johnstone

Sunnybank Primary School (Partially Hearing Unit) Sunnybank Rd, Aberdeen AB24 3NJ; E-mail enquiries@sunnybank.aberdeen.sch.uk; Tel 01224 633363; Fax 01224 621174
Headteacher Caroline Johnstone

North Neighbourhood

SPECIAL SCHOOLS

Cordyce Residential School Riverview Dr, Dyce, Aberdeen AB21 7NF; E-mail cordyce@rmplc.co.uk; Tel 01224 724215; Fax 01224 772738
Headteacher Neil C. Brown, BEd(Hon), MEd(SEN)

Dyce Academy MICAS Base Riverview Dr, Dyce, Aberdeen AB21 7NF; E-mail mparker.micas@dyceacademy.aberdeen.sch.uk; Tel 01224 725118; Fax 01224 772571
Headteacher Michael Taylor

Dyce School Language Unit Gordon Terr, Dyce, Aberdeen AB21 7BD; E-mail enquiries@dyce.aberdeen.sch.uk; Tel 01224 772220; Fax 01224 772033
Headteacher Joan E. Fenton

Holy Family R.C. School SEN Base Summerhill Terr, Aberdeen AB15 6HE; E-mail enquiries@holyfamilyrc.aberdeen.sch.uk; Tel 01224 316446; Fax 01224 326294
Headteacher Graeme McKnight

Hospital and Home Tuition Service Lowit Unit RACH, Cornhill Rd, Aberdeen AB25 2ZG; E-mail lowitunit@rmplc.co.uk; Tel 01224 554699; Fax 01224 554699
Head of Service Patricia Calder

Marlpool School Cloverfield Gdns, Bucksburn, Aberdeen AB21 9QN; E-mail enquiries@marlpool.aberdeen.sch.uk; Tel 01224 712735; Fax 01224 712524
Headteacher Hilary Gordon

Muirfield School SEN Base Mastrick Dr, Aberdeen AB16 6UE; E-mail enquiries@muirfield.aberdeen.sch.uk; Tel 01224 694958; Fax 01224 696671
Headteacher Annie Sleven

Northfield Academy SEN Base Granitehill Pl, Aberdeen AB16 7AU; URL www.northfield.aberdeen.sch.uk; E-mail accnorth@rmplc.co.uk; Tel 01224 699715; Fax 01224 685239
Headteacher Susan Muncer

Oldmachar Academy Provision for SPLD Jesmond Dr, Bridge of Don, Aberdeen AB22 8UR; URL www.oldmachar.aberdeen.sch.uk/; E-mail enquiries@oldmachar.aberdeen.sch.uk; Tel 01224 820887; Fax 01224 823850
Headteacher Joseph Leiper

Scotstown School SEN Base Scotstown Rd, Bridge of Don, Aberdeen AB22 8HH; URL www.scotstown.aberdeen.sch.uk; E-mail enquiries@scotstown.aberdeen.sch.uk; Tel 01224 703331; Fax 01224 820289
Headteacher Caroline Bain

Smithfield School SEN Base Clarke St, Aberdeen AB16 7XJ; E-mail enquiries@smithfield.aberdeen.sch.uk; Tel 01224 696952; Fax 01224 682106
Headteacher Dorothea Adams

Visual Impairment Service Newhills School, Wagley Pde, Bucksburn, Aberdeen AB21 9UB; E-mail enquiries@vip-newhills.aberdeen.sch.uk; Tel 01224 715648; Fax 01224 714957
Head of Service Pat Dowds

South Neighbourhood

SPECIAL SCHOOLS

Bridge of Don Academy SEN Base Braehead Way, Bridge of Don, Aberdeen AB22 8RR; E-mail accboda@rmplc.co.uk; Tel 01224 707583; Fax 01224 706910
Headteacher Robert McClymont

Bucksburn School SEN Base Inverurie Rd, Bucksburn, Aberdeen AB21 9LL; E-mail enquiries@bucksburn.aberdeen.sch.uk; Tel 01224 712862; Fax 01224 716522
Headteacher Michael Robertson

Cults School SEN Base Earlswells Rd, Cults, Aberdeen AB15 9RG; E-mail enquiries@cultsprimary.aberdeen.sch.uk; Tel 01224 869221; Fax 01224 869372
Headteacher Iain Smithers

Fernielea School SEN Base Stronsay Pl, Aberdeen AB15 6HD; E-mail enquiries@fernielea.aberdeen.sch.uk; Tel 01224 318533; Fax 01224 326952
Headteacher Sarah Webb

Hazlewood School Fernielea Rd, Aberdeen AB15 6GU; E-mail r.jarvis@hazlewood.aberdeen.sch.uk; Tel 01224 321363; Fax 01224 311162
Headteacher Rhona Jarvis

Hazlehead Academy SEN Base Groat's Rd, Aberdeen AB15 8BE; E-mail enquiries@hazleheadacy.aberdeen.sch.uk; Tel 01224 310184; Fax 01224 208434
Headteacher Brian J. Wood

Kaimhill School SEN Base Pitmedden Terr, Aberdeen AB10 7HR; URL www.kaimhill.aberdeen.sch.uk; E-mail enquiries@kaimhill.aberdeen.sch.uk; Tel 01224 316356; Fax 01224 208369
Headteacher Nancy E. Davidson

9

Kincorth Academy SEN Base Kincorth Circle, Aberdeen AB12 5NL; E-mail kinacad@rmplc.co.uk; Tel 01224 872881; Fax 01224 878958
Headteacher Hugh Bryce

Kirkhill School SEN Base Cairngorm Gdns, Aberdeen AB12 5BS; E-mail headteacher@kirkhill.aberdeen.sch.uk; Tel 01224 874439; Fax 01224 877885
Headteacher Lorraine Brodie

Loirston School, SEN Base Loirston Ave, Cove Bay, Aberdeen AB12 3HE; URL www.loirston.aberdeen.sch.uk; E-mail enquiries@loirston.aberdeen.sch.uk; Tel 01224 897686; Fax 01224 896967
Headteacher Morag Thom

Torry Academy SEN Base Tullos Circle, Aberdeen AB11 8HD; URL www.torry.aberdeen.sch.uk; E-mail sen.base@torry.aberdeen.sch.uk; Tel 01224 876733; Fax 01224 249597
Headteacher Robert T. Skene

Tullos School SEN Base Girdleness Rd, Aberdeen AB11 8FJ; URL www.tullosprimary.aberdeen.sch.uk; E-mail enquiries@tullosprimary.aberdeen.sch.uk; Tel 01224 876621; Fax 01224 899415
Headteacher Ellen Smith

Walker Road SEN Base Walker Rd, Aberdeen AB11 8DL; E-mail headteacher@walkerroad.aberdeen.sch.uk; Tel 01224 879720; Fax 01224 873158
Headteacher Maureen Robertson

Woodlands School Craigton Rd, Cults, Aberdeen AB15 9PR; E-mail woodlands.s@rmplc.co.uk; Tel 01224 868814; Fax 01224 868501
Headteacher Malcolm Johnston

ANGUS COUNCIL
www.angus.gov.uk

Political Composition: SNP: 17, Ind: 6, LD: 3, Con: 2, Lab: 1
The Cross, Forfar, Angus DD8 1BX;
   URL www.angus.gov.uk;
   E-mail chiefexec@angus.gov.uk; Tel 01307 461460;
   Fax 01307 461874
Chief Executive Alexander B. Watson

Social Work Department

County Bldgs, Market St, Forfar, Angus DD8 3WS;
   E-mail socialwork@angus.gov.uk; Tel 01307 461460
Director (Social Work and Health Liaison) R. Peat
Head (Strategic Planning and Commissioning, and Adult Care Services) T. Armstrong (Acting)
Head (Older People's Services) L. Young
Head (Operations – Children and Families) G. McIntosh
Head (Finance, Human Resources and IT) L. Hutchinson
Head (Criminal Justice Services) G. McIntosh

Social Work and Health Committee
Convener G. Middleton (SNP)
Vice-Convener W. Roberton (SNP)

SERVICE CENTRES

Academy Lane Service Centre Academy La, Arbroath, Angus DD11 1EJ; Tel 01241 878585

Camus House Service Centre West Path, Carnoustie, Angus DD7 7DB; Tel 01241 857201

Dundee Street Service Centre 41 Dundee St, Carnoustie, Angus DD7 7PG; Tel 01241 859884

John Street Service Centre 51 John St, Montrose, Angus DD10 8LZ; Tel 01674 672702

Kirriemuir Sub Office Kirkton Hill, Kirriemuir, Angus DD8 4JT; Tel 01575 572958

Monifieth Office Library, High St, Monifieth, Angus DD5 4AE; Tel 01382 534244

Panmure Street Service Centre 28 Panmure St, Brechin, Angus DD9 6AP; Tel 01356 624771

Ravenswood Service Centre New Rd, Forfar, Angus DD8 2AF; Tel 01307 462405

Strang Street Service Centre 2 Strang St, Forfar, Angus DD8 2HR; Tel 01307 465143

HOSPITAL SOCIAL WORK

Stracathro Hospital School Edzell, by Brechin, Angus DD9 7QA; Tel 01356 647291

Sunnyside Royal Hospital Montrose, Angus; Tel 01674 830361 ext 238/267

CHILD AND FAMILY CENTRE

Arbroath East Mary St, Arbroath, Angus; Tel 01241 870163

RESOURCE CENTRES (YOUNG PEOPLE)

Broomfield Road Resource Centre Montrose, Angus DD10 8SY; Tel 01674 678509

Catherine Street Resource Centre 3–5 Catherine St, Arbroath, Angus DD11 1RL; Tel 01241 874241

Dunnichen Road Resource Centre Kingsmuir, Forfar, Angus DD8 2RQ; Tel 01307 468084

YOUNG PEOPLE'S RESIDENTIAL UNIT

Kinnaird Street Residential Unit 39–41 Residential Unit, Arbroath, Angus DD11 4EF; Tel 01241 875207

CENTRES FOR PEOPLE WITH LEARNING DIFFICULTIES

Arbroath Lochlands Resource Centre, 2 Cairnie Rd, Arbroath, Angus DD11 3DY; Tel 01241 430027

Lilybank Arbroath Rd, Forfar, Angus DD8 2JJ; Tel 01307 466788

Montrose Forties Rd, Montrose, Angus DD10 9ET; Tel 01674 673313

HOSTELS FOR PEOPLE WITH LEARNING DIFFICULTIES

The Gables Arbroath Rd, Forfar, Angus DD8 2JL; Tel 01307 462020

Wirren House Northesk Rd, Montrose, Angus DD10 8TG; Tel 01674 672390

COMMUNITY SERVICE OFFICE

9 Fergus Sq, Arbroath, Angus DD11 3DG; Tel 01241 871161

ACCOMMODATION FOR OLDER PEOPLE

There are four homes for older people in the area.

Education Department

County Bldgs, Market St, Forfar, Angus DD8 3WE;
   E-mail education@angus.gov.uk; Tel 01307 461460;
   Fax 01307 461848
Director (Education) Jim Anderson, MA, MEd, MBA, DipEd
Head (Educational Services – School and Community Support) N. Logue, MA(Hons)

Head (Educational Services – Pupil and Parent Support)
J. Nowak, DCE
Head (Educational Services – Finance, Property and IT Support)
C. Clement, BA, CPFA
Principal Psychologist   R. Flavahan
Principal Community Education Worker   S. Maxwell
Senior School and Family Support Worker   G. Strachan

ARGYLL AND BUTE COUNCIL
www.argyll-bute.gov.uk

Kilmory, Lochgilphead, Argyll and Bute PA31 8RT;
URL www.argyll-bute.gov.uk;
E-mail enquiries@argyll-bute.gov.uk; Tel 01546 602127;
Fax 01546 604138

Community Services

Dalriada Hse, 3–5 Lochnell St, Lochgilphead, Argyll and
Bute PA31 8ST; Tel 01546 602127; Fax 01546 604533
Director (Community Services)   Douglas Hendry; Tel 01546
604537
Head (Commuity Support)   S. Greer
Head (Children, Young People and Families including Criminal
Justice)   D. Dunlop

Strategic Committee

Spokesperson (SPC Policy – Housing)   George Freeman
Spokesperson (Social Work and Health)   Alan Macaskill

COMMUNITY CARE

Service Officer (Sensory Impairment)   S. McHugh
Service Officer (Elderly)   M. Brodie
Service Officer (Health)   M. Beaton
Service Officer (Quality Assurance)   Anne Marie Waltham
Manager (Supporting People)   I. McFadyen

CHILDREN, YOUNG PEOPLE AND FAMILIES
(INCORPORATING CRIMINAL JUSTICE)

Service Officer (Looked After Children)   D. Bannon
Service Officer (Child Protection)   Liz Strang
Service Officer (Groupwork)   H. Kidd
Service Officer (Community Work)   P. Keenan
Manager (Criminal Justice)   A. Filshie

DIRECTORATE

Service Officer (Information Technology and Administration)
E. Brown
Service Officer (Personnel)   R. Dalgleish
Training Officer   L. MacCallum
Manager (Accounting Services)   Margaret Moncur

QUALITY ASSURANCE UNIT

45 West Princes St, Scott Crt Hse, Helensburgh, Argyll and
Bute; Tel 01436 658801
Manager (Quality Assurance)   E. Docherty

SERVICE CENTRES

Bute and Cowal Service Centre Ellis Lodge, Argyll Rd,
Dunoon, Argyll and Bute PA23 8ES; Tel 01369 707300
Service Manager   Colin Elliot

Helensburgh and Lomond Service Centre Lomond Hse, 29
Lomond St, Helensburgh, Argyll and Bute; Tel 01436
658750
Service Manager   Vacancy

Mid-Argyll Service Centre Kintyre and Islay, Old Quay
Head, Campbeltown, Argyll and Bute PA28 6BA; Tel 01586
552659
Service Manager   A. Smith

Oban Service Centre Lorn and the Isles, Soroba Rd, Oban,
Argyll and Bute PA34 4JA; Tel 01631 563068
Service Manager   A. Taylor

CHILDREN'S HOMES

Dunclutha Children's Home Kirn, Dunoon, Argyll and Bute
PA23 8HH; Tel 01369 704245

East King Street Home 50 East King St, Helensburgh,
Argyll and Bute; Tel 01436 670385

Shellach View Children's Home Soroba Rd, Oban, Argyll
and Bute PA34 4JA; Tel 01631 563806

RESOURCE CENTRES

Cowal Centre Bullwood Rd, Dunoon, Argyll and Bute;
Tel 01369 703003

Lochgilphead Centre Kilmory Rd, Lochgilphead, Argyll
and Bute PA31 8SY; Tel 01546 603744

Lorn Centre Soroba Rd, Oban, Argyll and Bute PA34 4HY;
Tel 01631 562725

Mull Centre Old Salen Rd, Salen, Isle of Mull, Argyll and
Bute; Tel 01680 300515

Rothesay Centre 35 Union St, Rothesay, Isle of Bute
PA20 0HD; Tel 01700 504402

Woodlands Centre Woodlands Dr, Campbeltown, Argyll
and Bute PA28 6JW; Tel 01586 553226

HOSTELS FOR PEOPLE WITH DISABILITIES

Greenwood Woodlands Dr, Campbeltown, Argyll and Bute
PA28 6JW; Tel 01586 552515

Willowview Hostel Soroba Rd, Oban, Argyll and Bute
PA34 4JA; Tel 01631 566053

DAY CENTRE FOR ELDERLY

Oban Day Centre North Pier, Oban, Argyll and Bute
PA34 4PP; Tel 01631 563012

CRIMINAL JUSTICE OFFICE

27 King St, Dunoon, Argyll and Bute; Tel 01389 707829

Dalriada House Lochnell St, Lochgilphead, Argyll and Bute
PA31 8ST; Tel 01546 602177

HOMES FOR ELDERLY PEOPLE

There are seven homes for elderly people in the area.

Education Office

Argyll Hse, Alexandra Pde, Dunoon, Argyll, Argyll and
Bute PA23 8AJ; URL www.argyll-bute.gov.uk;
E-mail suzanne.kerr@argyll-bute.gov.uk; Tel 01369
704000
Head (Secondary Education)   Ronnie Gould
Head (Primary Education)   Carol Walker
Head (Planning and Performance)
Malcolm MacFadyen
Manager (Quality Standards)   Christopher Shirley
Principal Educational Psychologist   Ted Jeffries
Principal Officer (Community Education)
Jim McCrossan
Principal Officer (Early Years)   M. Lauder
Head (Community Regeneration)   Donald MacVicar

9

SPECIAL SCHOOLS

Drummore Learning Centre Soroba Rd, Oban, Argyll, Argyll and Bute PA34 4SB;
E-mail enquiries@drummore.argyll-bute.sch.uk; Tel 01631 5464811
Headteacher L. MacAllister
(Day)
  Mixed 5–16 MH, SMH, PMH 14 roll, 7 shared placements.

Parklands School 27 Charlotte St, Helensburgh, Argyll and Bute G84 7EZ;
E-mail enquiries@parklands.argyll-bute.sch.uk; Tel 01436 673714
Headteacher L.R. Downie
  Mixed 5–16 24 roll, 3 shared placements.

White Gates Learning Centre Lochgilphead, Argyll and Bute PA31 8SY;
E-mail enquiries@whitegates.argyll-bute.sch.uk; Tel 01546 602583
Headteacher E. Mackenzie
(Day)
  Mixed 5–16 MH, SMH, PMH 5 roll, 10 shared placements.

CLACKMANNANSHIRE COUNCIL
www.clacksweb.org.uk

Political Composition: Lab: 10, SNP: 6, Con: 1, Ind: 1
Greenfield, Alloa, Clackmannanshire FK10 2AD;
  URL www.clacksweb.org.uk; Tel 01259 450000;
  Fax 01259 452230
Chief Executive K. Bloomer

Services to People (Social Services, Housing, Education)

Lime Tree Hse, Castle St, Alloa, Clackmannanshire
  FK10 1EX; Tel 01259 452373; Fax 01259 452440
Director David Jones
Head (Adult Care) and Chief Social Work Officer D. Cilliers
Head (Child Care Pre-5's and Criminal Justice Services)
  G. McGeoch
Officer (Performance and Monitoring) I. Shovlin

Housing, Health and Social Services Committee

SNP: 10, Lab: 7, Con: 1
Spokesperson Sam Ovens (Lab)
Depute Spokesperson Kenneth Earle (Lab)

AREA OFFICES

ALLOA Centre 8 Hillcrest Dr, Alloa, Clackmannanshire;
Tel 01259 225000

Whins Road Alloa, Clackmannanshire; Tel 01259 727010

RESIDENTIAL CHILD CARE

Woodside Home 18 Woodside Terr, Clackmannan, Clackmannanshire FK10 2SD; Tel 01259 213401

ADULT DAY CARE

ALLOA Centre 8 Hillcrest Dr, Alloa, Clackmannanshire;
Tel 01259 225001

Whins Resource Centre Whins Rd, Alloa, Clackmannanshire FK10 3FA; Tel 01259 226800

RESIDENTIAL ELDERLY

There are two residential homes for older people.

Services To People (Education)

Lime Tree Hse, Alloa, Clackmannanshire FK10 1EX;
  URL www.clacksweb.org.uk; Tel 01259 452374;
  Fax 01259 452440
Head (Education and Lifelong Learning) S. Wilson
Head (Policy, Planning and SEN) Elaine McPherson

PSYCHOLOGICAL SERVICES

Headquarters 15 Mar St, Alloa, Clackmannanshire
FK10 1HR; E-mail swilkinson@clacks.gov.uk

SPECIAL NEEDS

Fairfield School Pompee Rd, Sauchie, Alloa, Clackmannanshire FK10 3BX
Headteacher A. Morgan

Lochies School Gartmorn Rd, Sauchie, Alloa, Clackmannanshire FK10 3BX; Tel 01259 216928
Headteacher A. Morgan
  5–12 MH

Secondary Schools Support Service Bedford Pl, Alloa, Clackmannanshire FK10 1LJ

DUMFRIES AND GALLOWAY COUNCIL
www.dumgal.gov.uk

Population 147 780
Political Composition: Scottish Lab: 14, Ind: 12, Con: 11, LD: 5, SNP: 5
Council Offices, English St, Dumfries, Dumfries and Galloway DG1 2DD; URL www.dumgal.gov.uk;
  Tel 01387 260000; Fax 01387 260034

Social Services Headquarters

Grierson Hse, The Crichton, Dumfries, Dumfries and Galloway DG1 4ZH; URL www.dumgal.gov.uk;
  E-mail emma@dumgal.gov.uk; Tel 01387 260928;
  Fax 01387 260924
Director (Social Services) Keith Makin
Head (Children's Services) Gerry Brown
Commissioning Manager (Adult Services)
  Rosemary Flexney

OPERATIONAL AREAS

Annandale and Eskdale

Main Office, 2 Bank St, Annan, Dumfries and Galloway DG12 6AA; Tel 01461 203411

AREA OFFICES

Town Hall Area Office Annan Council Offices, High St, Annan, Dumfries and Galloway; Tel 01461 207025
Team Manager (Adult Services – Over 65s) B. Hickie
Occupational Therapy L. Priestley

Dryfe Road Area Office Lockerbie, Dumfries and Galloway;
Tel 01576 205072
Manager (Assessment and Planning – Child Care)
  M. Briggs
Inspection and Registration Officer E. Moffat

HOSPITAL TEAM

DGRI Bankend Road Dumfries, Dumfries and Galloway;
Tel 01387 241595
Team Manager (Adult Services) S. Welsh

Galloway (Stewartry and Wigtown)

Stewartry Office
1 Academy St, Castle Douglas, Dumfries and Galloway
DG7 1AP; Tel 01556 504101

Nithsdale

5 and 8 Gordon St, Dumfries, Dumfries and Galloway
DG1 1EG; Tel 01387 260875
Team Manager (65+ Services) G. Wright
Team Manager (Youth and Families Services) G. Dean
Occupational Therapy M.I. Hutchings

AREA OFFICES

Criminal Justice Services 79 Buccleuch St, Dumfries,
Dumfries and Galloway DG1 2AB; Tel 01387 262409

Kirkconnel Main St, Kirkconnel, Dumfries and Galloway
DG4 6LU; Tel 01659 67601
Team Leader (65+) S. Welsh

Sensory Support Services 24 Catherine St, Dumfries,
Dumfries and Galloway DG1 1HZ; Tel 01387 253927
Senior Practitioner (Hearing Impairment) M. McGroarty
Senior Practitioner (Visual Impairment) D. Large

Wigtown (Stranraer and Newton Stewart)

Stranraer Offices, 72–74 George St, Stranraer, Dumfries and
Galloway DG9 7JS; Tel 01776 707272

39 Lewis Street Stranraer, Dumfries and Galloway
DG9 7AD; Tel 01776 706167
Team Leader (Criminal Justice) A. Monteforte

Newton Stewart Office 23 King St, Newtown Stewart,
Dumfries and Galloway DG8 6DQ; Tel 01671 403933
Team Manager (Over 65's) A. Cook

YOUNG PERSONS' RESIDENTIAL UNITS

CRISP Craig's Rd, Dumfries, Dumfries and Galloway
DG1 4EX; Tel 01387 249880
Unit Manager Paul Sinclair

Milton House Residential Unit 9 London Rd, Stranraer,
Dumfries and Galloway DG9 8AF; Tel 01776 707231
Unit Manager I. Lamb

FAMILY SUPPORT

Annan 29 Bank St, Annan, Dumfries and Galloway
DG12 6AA; Tel 01461 204927
Stranraer 39 Lewis St, Stranraer, Dumfries and Galloway
DG9 7AD; Tel 01776 703148
Senior Family Support Worker A. Connor

LEARNING DISABILITY

Tel 01387 260000

ACTIVITY AND RESOURCES CENTRES

Annan Activity Resources Centre Ednam St, Annan,
Dumfries and Galloway DG12 6EF; Tel 01461 204576
Unit Manager A. Thomson

Castle Douglas Activity and Resources Centre Carlingwark,
Castle Douglas, Dumfries and Galloway DG7 1TH;
Tel 01556 504019
Unit Manager C. Jones

Dumfries Activity and Resources Centre Burns St,
Dumfries, Dumfries and Galloway DG1 2PS; Tel 01387
255754
Unit Manager R. Burns
Kirkconnel Activities and Resources Centre Main St,
Kirkconnel, Dumfries and Galloway DG4 6NE
Unit Manager J. Murdoch
Newton Stewart Activities and Resources Centre King St,
Newton Stewart, Dumfries and Galloway DG8 6DQ;
Tel 01671 403483
Unit Manager B. Bleasdale
Stranraer Activities and Resources Centre Sun St, Stranraer,
Dumfries and Galloway DG9 7JH; Tel 01776 704525
Unit Manager K. Ferguson

RESIDENTIAL HOSTEL

Dunmuir Park Residential Hostel Dunmuir Rd, Castle
Douglas, Dumfries and Galloway DG7 1LD; Tel 01556
503326
Unit Manager H. McKie

Education and Community Services

Woodbank, 30 Edinburgh Rd, Dumfries, Dumfries and
Galloway DG1 1NW; URL dumgal.gov.uk;
E-mail frasers@dumgal.gov.uk; Tel 01387 260427
Corporate Director (Education and Community Services)
F. Sanderson
Group Manager (Schools Services) C. Dignan
Group Manager (Children's Services) S.H. Beck
Operations Manager (Secondary) C. Brett
Operations Manager (Pre-School/Primary) K. Best
Group Business Manager C. Taylor

SPECIAL SCHOOLS

Elmbank Special School Lovers Wlk, Dumfries, Dumfries
and Galloway DG1 1DD; Tel 01387 25448; Fax 01387 248259
Headteacher (Part-time) W. Maxwell

Langlands School Loreburn Pk, Dumfries, Dumfries and
Galloway DG1 1LS; Tel 01387 267834
Headteacher Mrs M. Rinaldi
Mixed

LEARNING CENTRES

Annan Academy St. John's Rd, Annan, Dumfries and
Galloway DG12 6AP; Tel 01461 202954; 01461 202955
Headteacher J. Leggat

Calside Learning Centre Calside Primary School, Dumfries,
Dumfries and Galloway DG1 4HB; Tel 01387 268567;
Fax 01387 248154
Headteacher Mr D. McDowall

Castle Douglas High School Dunmuir Rd, Castle Douglas,
Dumfries and Galloway DG7 1LQ; Tel 01556 502821; 01556
502822
Headteacher I. Proudfoot

Castle Douglas Primary School Castle Douglas, Dumfries
and Galloway DG7 1JA; Tel 01556 502516; Fax 01556 504778
Headteacher J. Niven

Douglas Ewart High School Corsbie Rd, Newton Stewart,
Dumfries and Galloway DG8 6JQ; Tel 01671 403773;
Fax 01671 402807
Headteacher J. Judge

Dumfries Academy Academy St, Dumfries, Dumfries and
Galloway DG1 1DD; Tel 01387 252846; Fax 01387 252846
Headteacher C. McAteer
Dumfries also has a learning centre.

Dumfries High School Marchmount, Dumfries, Dumfries
and Galloway DG1 1PX; Tel 01387 263061; Fax 01387 268951
Headteacher C. Mitchell

9

Kelloholm Primary School Kelloholm, Sanquhar,
Dumfries and Galloway DG4 6QJ; Tel 01659 67228;
Fax 01659 67582
Headteacher W. McLarty

Kirkolm Primary School Kirkcolm, Stranraer, Dumfries and
Galloway DG9 0NS; Tel 01776 853232
Headteacher Mr H. McCracken

Lincluden Primary School Lincluden, Dumfries, Dumfries
and Galloway DG2 0PU; Tel 01387 252028
Headteacher Mrs J. Forest

Lochans Primary School Lochans, Stranraer, Dumfries
and Galloway DG9 9AW; Tel 01776 820289; Fax 01776
820289
Headteacher Miss A. Clanachan

Lochmaben Primary School Lochmaben, Lockerbie,
Dumfries and Galloway DG11 1NR; Tel 01387 810208;
Fax 01387 810352
Headteacher Mrs A. Simpson

Lochside Primary Learning Centre Lochside Rd, Dumfries,
Dumfries and Galloway DG2 0NF; Tel 01387 720318;
Fax 01387 720450
Headteacher Mrs M. Farrell

Lockerbie Academy Dryfe Rd, Lockerbie, Dumfries and
Galloway DG11 2AL; Tel 01576 202626; Fax 01576 202189;
01576 203032
Headteacher Mr G. Herbert

Lockerbie Primary Learning Centre King Edward Pk,
Lockerbie, Dumfries and Galloway DG11 2PQ; Tel 01576
203361; Fax 01576 202956
Headteacher Mrs B. Doogan

Maxwelltown High School Lochside Rd, Dumfries,
Dumfries and Galloway DG2 0EL; Tel 01387 720458;
Fax 01387 721544
Headteacher Mr T. Pierce

Newington Primary School Hospital Rd, Annan, Dumfries
and Galloway DG12 6LA; Tel 01461 202459
Headteacher I. Torbett

Noblehill Primary School Annan Rd, Dumfries, Dumfries
and Galloway DG1 3HB; Tel 01387 252167
Headteacher Mrs D. Logan

Penninghame Primary School Auchendon Rd, Newton
Stewart, Dumfries and Galloway DG8 6HD; Tel 01671
402386
Headteacher Mr D. Tyson

St. Joseph's College Craigs Rd, Dumfries, Dumfries and
Galloway DG1 4UU; Tel 01387 244320
Headteacher J.M. Chezeaud

Sanquhar Academy Broomfield, Sanquhar, Dumfries and
Galloway DG4 6JN; Tel 01659 50208
Headteacher J. Nicholson

Stranraer Academy McMaster's Rd, Stranraer,
Dumfries and Galloway DG9 8BY; Tel 01776 706484;
01776 706486
Contact J. Higgins

Wallace Hall Academy Thornhill, Dumfries and Galloway
DG3 5DS; Tel 01848 330294; Fax 01848 330294
Contact A. Douglas

REGIONAL PSYCHOLOGICAL SERVICES

Aird Education Centre Cairnport Rd, Stranraer, Dumfries
and Galloway DG9 8BQ; Tel 01776 706161; Fax 01776
889693

Brewery House 23 King St, Newton Stewart, Dumfries
and Galloway DG8 6DQ; Tel 01671 403455; Fax 01671
402915

Dryfe Road Lockerbie, Dumfries and Galloway DG11 2AP;
Tel 01576 205000; Fax 01576 204455

St. Teresa's Primary School Lochside Rd, Dumfries,
Dumfries and Galloway DG2 0DY; Tel 01387 267350

DUNDEE CITY COUNCIL
www.dundeecity.gov.uk

Population 146 690.
City Chambers, City Sq, Dundee DD1 3BY;
  URL www.dundeecity.gov.uk;
  E-mail alex.stephen@dundeecity.gov.uk; Tel 01382
  434000; Fax 01382 434104
Leader of the Administration Cllr Julie Sturrock
Chief Executive Alex Stephen, FCCA
Director (Education) Anne Wilson
Director (Finance) D. Dorward
Director (Corporate Planning) C. Ward
Director (Housing) E. Zwirlein

Social Work Department

Tayside Hse, Fl 7, 28 Crichton St, Dundee DD1 3RN;
  URL www.dundeecity.gov.uk;
  E-mail socialwork@dundeecity.gov.uk; Tel 01382 433712;
  Fax 01382 433012
Convener (Social Work) Baillie Helen Wright
Director (Social Work) A.G. Baird
Manager (Child Care) G.S. Oliver
Manager (Community Care) L. Bannerman
Manager (Criminal Justice Services) M. Anderson
Manager (Finance and Support Services) A. Mackay

Social Work Committee

Lab: 13, Con: 4, SNP: 11, Ind Lab: 1
Members of the Committee
Lab: C.D.P. Farquhar JP, G. de Gernier, N. Glen, F.M. Grant
JP, J.R. Letford JP, I.M. Luke JP, R. Presswood, G. Regan,
M.J. Rolfe JP, I. Shimi JP, J.M. Sturrock, B. Ward,
H.W. Wright JP.
Con: B. Mackie OBE JP, Nic Powrie, D.J. Scott, R.J. Wallace.
SNP: J. Barrie, D. Beattie, R. Beattie, D. Bows, J. Corrigan,
A. Dawson, J. Fitzpatrick, E. Fordyce, K.N. Guild JP,
A. Petrie, W.W. Sawers.
Ind Lab: I. Borthwick JP.

HOSPITAL SOCIAL WORKERS

Ashludie Hospital Victoria St, Monifieth, Angus DD5 4HQ;
Tel 01382 532101

General Hospital Team Ninewells Hospital, Dundee
DD1 9SY; E-mail reception.ninewells@dundeecity.gov.uk;
Tel 01382 632650

Psychiatric Hospital Team Royal Dundee Liff Hospital,
Dundee DD2 5NF; E-mail liff.sw@dundeecity.gov.uk;
Tel 01382 423100

Royal Victoria Hospital Jedburgh Rd, Dundee DD2 1SQ;
Tel 01382 666959

COMMUNITY CARE

Balmerino Road Dundee DD4 8RW;
E-mail reception.balmerino@dundeecity.gov.uk; Tel 01382
438300

Social Work Access Team Unit 7, Nethergate Business
Centre, Nethergate, Dundee DD1 4ER;
E-mail admin.accessteam@dundeecity.gov.uk; Tel 01382
435265

CHILDREN'S SERVICES

Balmerino Road Dundee DD4 8RW;
E-mail reception.balmerino@dundeecity.gov.uk; Tel 01382
438300

Lochee Children's Centre 74a High St, Lochee, Dundee DD2 3BG; E-mail sw.lochee@dundeecity.gov.uk; Tel 01382 436661

Kirkton Road Centre 6 Kirkton Rd, Dundee DD3 0BZ; E-mail reception.kirkton@dundeecity.gov.uk; Tel 01382 436000

Seymour Lodge 259 Perth Rd, Dundee DD2 1JP; E-mail seymourlodge.reception@dundeecity.gov.uk; Tel 01382 667360; 01382 668538

Whitfield Lothian Cres, Dundee DD4 DHU; E-mail reception.whitfield:dundeecity.gov.uk; Tel 01382 438260

CHILD AND FAMILY CENTRES

Bruce Street Child and Family Centres 36a Bruce St, Dundee DD3 6RG; E-mail brucestreet.cfc@dundeecity.gov.uk; Tel 01382 436515

Douglas Child and Family Centre Balmerino Rd, Dundee DD4 8RW; E-mail douglas.cfc@dundeecity.gov.uk; Tel 01382 438445

Happyhillock Child and Family Centre 29 Happyhillock Rd, Dundee DD4 8LT; E-mail happyhillock.cfc@dundeecity.gov.uk; Tel 01382 438661

Kirkton Child and Family Centre Kirkton Rd, Dundee; Tel 01382 436412

Linlathan Child and Family Centre 1 Rowantree Cres, Dundee DD4 8EY; Tel 01382 438654

Lochee Child and Family Centre 5 Peel St, Dundee DD2 3TS; E-mail lochee.cfc@dundeecity.gov.uk; Tel 01382 436725

Pootler Children's Centre Turnberry Ave, Dundee DD2 3UA; Tel 01382 436399

Whitfield Child and Family Centre Lothian Cres, Dundee DD4 0HU; E-mail whitfield.cfc@dundeecity.gov.uk; Tel 01382 438280

Woodlea Children's Centre 45 Harefield Rd, Dundee DD2 3JY; E-mail beechwood.cfc@dundeecity.gov.uk; Tel 01382 436712

YOUNG PEOPLES' RESIDENTIAL UNITS

Balgowan Avenue Residential Unit 57–59 Balgowan Ave, Dundee DD3 0HB; E-mail balgowanavenue.ypl@dundeecity.gov.uk; Tel 01382 436557

Duncan Place Residential Unit 7 Duncan Pl, Dundee DD3 0JT; E-mail duncanplace.ypu@dundeecity.gov.uk; Tel 01382 436565

Fairbairn Street Residential Unit Dundee DD3 7JH; E-mail fairbairn.ypu@dundeecity.gov.uk; Tel 01382 436563

Strathcarron Place Residential Unit 20 Strathcarron Pl, Dundee DD2 4BB; E-mail strathcarron.ypu@dundeecity.gov.uk; Tel 01382 435994

CENTRES FOR PEOPLE WITH LEARNING DIFFICULTITES

Dudhope Gardens 30 Dudhope Terr, Dundee DD3 6TD; E-mail dudhope.arc@dundeecity.gov.uk; Tel 01382 435324

Kemback Street Centre 10 Kemback St, Dundee DD4 6PQ; E-mail kemback.arc@dundeecity.gov.uk; Tel 01382 438811

HOSTELS FOR PEOPLE WITH LEARNING DIFFICULTIES

Elmgrove House 315 South Rd, Lochee, Dundee DD2 2RT; E-mail elmgrove.house@dundeecity.gov.uk; Tel 01382 436720

Maryfield House 20 Mains Loan, Dundee DD4 7AA; E-mail maryfield.house@dundeecity.gov.uk; Tel 01382 438797

White Top Centre Westfield Ave, Dundee DD1 4JT; E-mail reception.whitetop@dundeecity.gov.uk; Tel 01382 435198

COMMUNITY SERVICE OFFICES

Friarfield House Barrack St, Dundee DD1 1PQ; E-mail criminal.justice@dundeecity.gov.uk; Tel 01382 435001

DAY CARE AND RESIDENTIAL CARE FOR PHYSICALLY HANDICAPPED

Mackinnon Centre 491 Brook St, Broughty Ferry, Dundee DD5 2PZ; E-mail mackinnon.centre@dundeecity.gov.uk; Tel 01382 436840

DAY CARE FOR THE ELDERLY

Menzieshill House Dickson Ave, Dundee DD2 4UY; E-mail daycentre.menzieshill@dundeecity.gov.uk; Tel 01382 435877

Wellgate Ladywell Ave, Dundee DD1 2LA; E-mail daycentre.wellgate@dundeecity.gov.uk; Tel 01382 435336

ACCOMMODATION FOR THE ELDERLY

There are four homes for the elderly.

Education Department

Fls 8–9, Tayside Hse, 28 Crichton St, Dundee DD1 3RJ; Tel 01382 434000; Fax 01382 433080; 01382 433804
Director (Education) Anne Wilson
Convener F. Macpherson
Manager (Education Services – Dundee West) L. Waghorn
Manager (Education Services – Dundee East) G. Taylor
Manager (Education Services – Dundee Central) J. Collins
Manager (Education Resources) S. Weston
Principal Educational Psychologist L.C. Meade
Principal Officer (Support Services) S.M. Faichney

EDUCATIONAL PSYCHOLOGY CENTRE

Dochart Terrace Dundee DD2 4HB; E-mail dundee.eps@dundeecity.gov.uk; Tel 01382 435780

EDUCATION DEVELOPMENT SERVICE

Principal Psychologist L. Meade

SPECIAL SCHOOLS

Frances Wright Pre-School Centre Caird Ave, Dundee DD3 8AR; E-mail headteacher@fwright.dundeecity.sch.uk; Tel 01382 436406
Headteacher L. Hutt (Acting)

Kingspark School Gillburn Rd, Dundee DD3 0AB; E-mail kingspart@dundeecity.gov.uk; Tel 01382 436284
Headteacher S. Johnston
4–16 MH, PH

EAST AYRSHIRE COUNCIL

www.east-ayrshire.gov.uk

Population 124 000
Council Headquarters, London Rd, Kilmarnock, East Ayrshire KA3 7BU; URL www.east-ayrshire.gov.uk; E-mail the.council@east-ayrshire.gov.uk
Chief Executive David Montgomery

Department of Educational and Social Services

E-mail education@east-ayrshire.gov.uk; Tel 01563 576000; Fax 01567 576500

Director (Education and Social Services) John Mulgrew; Tel 01563 576017; Fax 01563 576210

Head (Social Work) Stephen Moore; Tel 01563 576729; Fax 01563 576920

Principal Officer (Children and Families; Criminal Justice) Bill Eadie; Tel 01563 576845; Fax 01563 576654

Principal Officer (Community Care) Jackie Donnelly; Tel 01563 576931; Fax 01563 576924

Principal Officer (Quality and Planning) John Alexander; Tel 01563 576978; Fax 01563 576729

Head (Community Support) Kay Gilmour; Tel 01563 576104; Fax 01563 576210

Head (Schools) Graham Short; Tel 01563 576089; Fax 01563 576210

Head (Resource Support) Vacancy; Tel 01563 576090; Fax 01563 576123

Social Work Committee

Lab: 11, SNP: 8, Con: 1
Chair Cllr Darnbrough (Lab)
Vice-Chair Cllr Walsh (Lab)
Members of the Committee
Lab: Cllrs Carmichael, Farrell, Jackson, Kelly, Macrae, McIntyre, Menzies, Raymond, Taylor.
SNP: D. Coffey, Faulds, Hall, Linton, F. MacLean, L. MacLean, Reid, Weir.
Con: Young.

TRAINING SECTION

Flat 1a, Cressnock Gdns, Hurlford, East Ayrshire KA1 5DB; E-mail training_flat_hurl@lineone.net; Tel 01563 573190
Training Manager Karen McLaughlan

SOCIAL WORK OFFICES

Dalmellington Sub-Office 33 Main St, Dalmellington, East Ayrshire KA6 7SJ; Tel 01292 552900

Galston Sub-Office Cross St, Galston, East Ayrshire; Tel 01563 820876

Kilmarnock Social Work Office

Balmoral Rd, Kilmarnock, East Ayrshire; Tel 01563 528011; Fax 01563 573798

CRIMINAL JUSTICE SUB TEAM

43–49 John Finnie St, Kilmarnock, East Ayrshire; Tel 01563 539888

SOCIAL WORK SERVICES – HOSPITAL

Social Work Office Crosshouse Hospital, 23 Lister St, Kilmarnock, East Ayrshire; Tel 01563 577570

STEWARTON SUB-OFFICE

24 High St, Stewarton, East Ayrshire; Tel 01560 483167

SUB-OFFICE (SUPPORT TO COMMUNITIES, MONEY ADVICE AND CYS TEAM)

49–55 Campbeltown Dr, Longpark, Kilmarnock, East Ayrshire; Tel 01563 572757

PSYCHOLOGICAL SERVICES

Woodstock Centre, Woodstock St, Kilmarnock, East Ayrshire KA1 2BE; URL www.east-ayrshire.gov.uk; E-mail education@east-ayrshire.gov.uk; Tel 01563 555640; Fax 01563 574079
Principal Psychologist Tom Williams

Ayrshire Technicians Support Service St. Joseph's Academy, A Block, Grassyards Rd, Kilmarnock, East Ayrshire KA3 7SL; Tel 01563 544550; Fax 01563 571278
Contact Brian Richmond

Hearing Impairment Peripatetic Service Crosshouse Education Centre, Playingfield Rd, Crosshouse, East Ayrshire KA2 0JJ; Tel 01563 551219
Contact Anne Cowgill

Home Visiting Service Woodstock Centre, Woodstock St, Kilmarnock, East Ayrshire KA1 2BE; Tel 01563 555650; Fax 01563 574079
Contact Isobel Wilson

Instrumental Service James Hamilton Academy, Sutherland Dr, Kilmarnock, East Ayrshire KA1 3BS; Tel 01563 543591; Fax 01563 534370
Contact Andrew Keachie, MBE

Language and Communication Unit Westpark Base, Playingfield Rd, Crosshouse, East Ayrshire KA2 0JJ; Tel 01563 551624; Fax 01563 551624
Contact Anne Basford

Network Support Base (North) Playingfield Rd, Crosshouse, East Ayrshire KA2 0JJ; Tel 01563 551624; Fax 01563 551624
Co-ordinator (Network Support) Anne Basford
Early Intervention Project (North Base) Margaret Addison; Tel 01563 570739; Fax 01563 570739

Network Support Base (South) St. John's Primary School, John Weir Ave, Cumnock, East Ayrshire KA18 1NJ; URL www.east-ayrshire.gov.uk; E-mail education@east-ayrshire.gov.uk; Tel 01290 426137; Fax 01290 426137
Co-ordinator (Network Support) Anne Basford
Early Intervention Project (South Base) Lesley Martin; Tel 01290 422867; Fax 01290 426137

New Community Schools c/o Hillhead Primary School, 2 Kilmaurs Rd, Kilmarnock, East Ayrshire; Tel 01563 549280; Fax 01563 543018
Contact Hugh Carswell

Outdoor Education Service St. Joseph's Academy, Block A, Grassyards Rd, Kilmarnock, East Ayrshire KA3 8SL; Tel 01563 551457; Fax 01563 571278
Contact Mike Howes

Pre-School Community Organisers Woodstock Centre, Woodstock St, Kilmarnock, East Ayrshire KA1 2BE; Tel 01563 555650; Fax 01563 574079
Contact Val Walker

Quality Development Team Woodstock Centre, Woodstock St, Kilmarnock, East Ayrshire KA1 2BE; E-mail kenneth.mckinlay@east-ayrshire.gov.uk; Tel 01563 555650; Fax 01563 574079
Principal (Quality Development) Kenneth McKinlay

Barshare Unit Barshare Primary School, Dalgleish Ave, Cumnock, East Ayrshire KA18 1QG; URL www.east-ayrshire.gov.uk; E-mail lorraine.facchini@east-ayrshire.gov.uk; Tel 01290 422212
Headteacher Lorraine Facchini

Bilingual Support Service St. Columba's Primary School, Elmbank Dr, Kilmarnock, East Ayrshire; URL www.east-ayrshire.gov.uk; E-mail education@east-ayrshire.gov.uk; Tel 01563 573658
Contact Ann Stevens

Cumnock Unit Cumnock Academy, Ayr Rd, Cumnock, East Ayrshire KA18 1EH; URL www.east-ayrshire.gov.uk; E-mail gordon.bell@east-ayrshire.gov.uk; Tel 01290 425940; Fax 01290 425812
Headteacher Gordon Bell

Crosshouse Communications Unit Crosshouse Primary School, Gatehead Rd, Crosshouse, East Ayrshire URL www.east-ayrshire.gov.uk; E-mail raymond.finlayson@east-ayrshire.gov.uk; Tel 01563 521459
Headteacher Raymond Finlayson

Early Intervention Project Woodstock Centre, Woodstock St, Kilmarnock, East Ayrshire KA1 2BE; URL www.east-ayrshire.gov.uk; E-mail education@east-ayrshire.gov.uk; Tel 01563 555650; Fax 01563 574079
Co-ordinator Hilary MacGillivray

Grange Hearing Impaired Unit Grange Academy, Beech Ave, Kilmarnock, East Ayrshire KA1 2EW; URL www.east-ayrshire.gov.uk; E-mail education@east-ayrshire.gov.uk; Tel 01563 543050; Fax 01563 542648
Contact Anne Barnaby

Hearing Impairment Peripatetic Service St. Columbia's Primary School, Elmbank Dr, Kilmarnock, East Ayrshire URL www.east-ayrshire.gov.uk; E-mail education@east-ayrshire.gov.uk; Tel 01563 551219
Contact Marion McFarlane

Hospital Education Service Ward 1a, Room 54, Kilmarnock, East Ayrshire KA2 0BE; URL www.east-ayrshire.gov.uk; E-mail education@east-ayrshire.gov.uk; Tel 01563 521133 ext 2818; Fax 01563 534370
Contact Carol Kerr

Patna Supported Learning Centre Patna Primary School, Carnshalloch Ave, Patna, East Ayrshire URL www.east-ayrshire.gov.uk; E-mail marion.mclean@east-ayrshire.gov.uk; Tel 01292 531271; Fax 01292 532301
Headteacher Marion McLean

Post 16+ Unit James Hamilton Academy, Sutherland Dr, Kilmarnock, East Ayrshire KA3 7DF; URL www.east-ayrshire.gov.uk; E-mail education@east-ayrshire.gov.uk; Tel 01563 421721; Fax 01563 534370
Contact Ewan Macleod

Youth Strategy Project (Base) – Kilmarnock Kilmarnock Academy, Elmbank Dr, Kilmarnock, East Ayrshire KA1 3BS; URL www.east-ayrshire.gov.uk; E-mail education@east-ayrshire.gov.uk; Tel 01563 525509; Fax 01563 542683
Contact Marion McFarlane

Youth Strategy Project (Base) – Auchinleck Auchinleck Academy, Sorn Rd, Auchinleck, East Ayrshire URL www.east-ayrshire.gov.uk; E-mail education@east-ayrshire.gov.uk; Tel 01290 421721; Fax 01290 425811
Contact Margaret Devlin

Youth Strategy Project (Base) – Shortlees Shortlees Primary School, Knockmarloch Dr, Kilmarnock, East Ayrshire URL www.east-ayrshire.gov.uk; E-mail education@east-ayrshire.gov.uk; Tel 01563 572715; Fax 01563 550047
Manager (Youth Strategy) Maggie Fallon

Ayrshire Audiologist Westpark Base, Playingfield Rd, Crosshouse, East Ayrshire KA2 0JJ; URL www.east-ayrshire.gov.uk; E-mail education@east-ayrshire.gov.uk; Tel 01563 536296
Contact Carol Clark

Visual Impairment Service c/o Grange Academy, Beech Ave, Kilmarnock, East Ayrshire URL www.east-ayrshire.gov.uk; E-mail education@east-ayrshire.gov.uk; Tel 01563 521969; Fax 01563 542648
Contact Anne Basford

SPECIAL SCHOOLS

Hillside School Dalgleish Ave, Cumnock, East Ayrshire KA18 1QQ; URL www.east-ayrshire.gov.uk; Tel 01290 423239; Fax 01290 425870
Headteacher Jim McCaffrey

Park School Grassyards Rd, Kilmarnock, East Ayrshire KA3 7BB; URL www.east-ayrshire.gov.uk; E-mail anne.wilson@east-ayrshire.gov.uk; Tel 01563 525316; Fax 01563 525465
Headteacher Anne Wilson
Mixed 5–16 MH, PH (130)

Witchhill School Witch Rd, Kilmarnock, East Ayrshire KA3 1JF; URL www.east-ayrshire.gov.uk; E-mail nana.laughlan@east-ayrshire.gov.uk; Tel 01563 533863; Fax 01563 574517
Headteacher Nana Lauchlan
MH Profound

Woodstock School 30 North Hamilton St, Kilmarnock, East Ayrshire KA1 2QJ; URL www.east-ayrshire.gov.uk; E-mail linda.macphee@east-ayrshire.gov.uk; Tel 01563 533550; Fax 01563 573808
Headteacher Linda Macphee
Mixed 5–16 MH Severe (60)

RESIDENTIAL HOMES FOR CHILDREN

Bellsford House Children's Unit
Service Unit Manager (Children and Families Services) Lesley Gibson; Tel 01563 576901

Kilmaurs Children's Unit
Service Unit Manager (Children and Families Services) Lesley Gibson; Tel 01563 576901

CENTRES (LEARNING DISABILITY)

Service Unit Manager (Learning Disability Services) Alison Findlay; Tel 01563 576935

Gilliesknowe Centre High Main St, Dalmellington, East Ayrshire; Tel 01292 550104

Hurlford Centre Cessnock Rd, Hurlford, East Ayrshire; Tel 01563 533933

Riverside Centre Ayr Rd, Cumnock, East Ayrshire; Tel 01290 424446

RESIDENTIAL ACCOMMODATION (LEARNING DISABILITY)

Service Unit Manager (Learning Disability Services) Alison Findlay; Tel 01563 576935

Carrick View Residential Unit Judge Ave, Auchinleck, East Ayrshire; Tel 01290 423382

Kerrmuir 7–9 Kerrmuir Ave, Hurlford, East Ayrshire; Tel 01563 527018

RESIDENTIAL ACCOMMODATION FOR OLDER PEOPLE

Service Unit Manager (Older Peoples' Services) Martin Clark; Tel 01563 576927
There are four homes for older people.

EAST DUNBARTONSHIRE COUNCIL
WWW.EASTDUNBARTON.GOV.UK

Population 110 000
Council Headquarters, Tom Johnston Hse, Civic Way, Kirkintilloch, East Dunbartonshire G66 4TJ; URL www.eastdunbarton.gov.uk; Tel 0141 578 8000; Fax 0141 777 8576
Chief Executive Dr Vicki Nash

9

Strategic Directorate (Community Social Work and Joint Ventures)

2–4 West High St, Kirkintilloch, East Dunbartonshire
    G66 1AD; Tel 0141 775 9000; Fax 0141 777 6203
Head (Social Work and Joint Ventures)   Tony Keogh
    (Acting)

Social Services Committee

LD: 12, Lab: 9, Con: 3.
Members of the Committee
Lab: M. O'Donnell, J. Dempsey, R. Geekie, A. Hannah,
C. Kennedy, E. McGaughrin, A. Moir, T. Smith, J. Young.
LD: Vice-Convener Fiona Callison, D. Cummings,
R. Duncan, E. Gotts, C. McInnes, M. McNaughton,
K. Moody, V. Moody, J. Morrison, Convener Fiona Risk,
J. Southcott, P. Steel, G. Macdonald.
Con: A. Brown, B. Hendry, A. Jarvis.

FIELDWORK OFFICES

Bearsden and Milngavie

Stewart Street Office 38 Stewart St, Milngavie, East
Dunbartonshire G62 2BW; Tel 0141 570 2400

Bishopbriggs

Balmuildy Road Office 1 Balmuildy Rd, Bishopriggs, East
Dunbartonshire G64 3BS; Tel 0141 772 6384

Kirkintilloch

Luggiebank Road Office 2 Luggiebank Rd, Kirkintilloch,
East Dunbartonshire G66 1LR; Tel 0141 775 2110

Advice and Response

Cowgate Office 126 Cowgate, Kirkintilloch, East
Dunbartonshire G66 1HF; Tel 0141 775 1311

RESIDENTIAL UNITS FOR CHILD CARE

Auchinloch Road Residential Unit 31 Auchinloch Rd,
Lenzie, East Dunbartonshire G66 5EU; Tel 0141 775
9098
Heatherbank Residential Unit 102 Milngavie Rd, Bearsden,
East Dunbartonshire G61 2TP; Tel 0141 942 4096
Kenmure Children's Unit St. Mary's Rd, Bishopbriggs, East
Dunbartonshire G63 2EH; Tel 0141 586 1200

ADULT DAY CENTRE

Kelvinbank Resource Centre Kilsyth Rd, Kirkintilloch, East
Dunbartonshire G66 1RP; Tel 0141 776 7107

MENTAL HEALTH

Larkfield Resource Centre Garngaber Ave, Lenzie, East
Dunbartonshire G66 3UG; Tel 0141 232 8200

RESIDENTIAL UNIT FOR ADULTS

John Street House Residential Unit 38 John St,
Kirkintilloch, East Dunbartonshire G66 1JU; Tel 0141 777
7708

COMMUNITY CARE SERVICES

Southbank House 1 Strathkelvin Pl, Kirkintilloch, East
Dunbartonshire G66 1XQ; Tel 0141 578 2100

COMMUNITY CARE ALARM SYSTEM

Hourcare 24 Southbank Hse, 1 Strathkelvin Pl,
Kirkintilloch, East Dunbartonshire G66 1XQ; Tel 0141 942
2424

WELFARE RIGHTS

Unit 1 Whitegates, Kirkintilloch, East Dunbartonshire
G66 3BL; Tel 0141 777 0520; 0141 777 6339

COMMUNITY CARE HEADQUARTERS

Unit 1 Whitegates Lenzie Rd, Kirkintilloch, East
Dunbartonshire G66 3BL; Tel 0141 777 6090

CRIMINAL JUSTICE

Fraser House Unit 23, Whitegates, Kirkintilloch, East
Dunbartonshire G66 3BL; Tel 0141 578 0100

Department of Community (Education Service)

Boclair Hse, 100 Milngavie Rd, Bearsden, Glasgow
    G61 2TQ; URL www.eastdunbarton.gov.uk;
    E-mail john.simmons@eastdunbarton.gov.uk; Tel 0141
    578 8000; Fax 0141 578 8653
Strategic Director (Community)   Sue Bruce
Convener   Cllr E. Gotts
Vice-Convener   Cllr P. Steel
Head (Performance and Development)   Gordon Smith
Head (Social Inclusion and Community Development)
    David Anderson
Head (Education)   John Simmons
Head (Operational Support)   Sandy McGarvey

EDUCATIONAL PSYCHOLOGY SERVICE

Gartconner Primary School Gartshore Rd, Kirkintilloch,
East Dunbartonshire G66 3TH;
E-mail psychserviceoffice@gartconner.e-dunbarton.sch.uk

SCHOOLS FOR PUPILS WITH SPECIAL EDUCATIONAL NEEDS

Campsie View School Boghead Rd, Lenzie, East
Dunbartonshire G66 4DP;
E-mail office@campsieview.e-dunbarton.gov.uk; Tel 0141
777 6269; Fax 0141 775 3551
    SLD/CLD
Merkland School Langmuir Rd, Kirkintilloch, East
Dunbartonshire G66 2QF;
E-mail office@merkland.e-dunbarton.gov.uk; Tel 0141 578
0177; Fax 0141 777 8139
    MLD/PH

EAST LOTHIAN COUNCIL
www.eastlothian.gov.uk

Political Composition: Scottish Lab: 17, Scottish Con: 4,
SNP: 1, LD: 1
John Muir Hse, Haddington, East Lothian EH41 3HA;
    URL www.eastlothian.gov.uk; Tel 01620 827827;
    Fax 01620 827888
Director (Education and Community Services)   A. Blackie
Chief Executive   J. Lindsay;
    E-mail jlindsay@eastlothian.gov.uk

Department of Social Work and Housing

9–11 Lodge St, Haddington, East Lothian EH41 3DX;
  Tel 01620 826600; Fax 01620 824295
Director (Social Work and Housing)   B. Walker
Chief Officer (Socal Work and Housing)   Vacancy
Head (Children and Families; Criminal Justice)   A. Ross
Head (Community Care)   P. Alexander

Social Work and Housing Committee

Lab: 7, Con: 3
Convener   W. Innes (Lab)
Vice-Convener   A. McCarthy (Lab)
Members of the Committee
Lab: D. Grant, K. Jarvie, J. McNeill, P. O'Donnell.
Con: F. Crawford, P. Ford.

SOCIAL WORK CENTRES

Haddington Social Work Centre 6–8 Lodge St, Haddington,
East Lothian EH41 3DX; Tel 01620 826600; Fax 01620 826202
Musselburgh Social Work Centre Brunton Hall, Ladywell
Way, Musselburgh, East Lothian EH21 6AF; Tel 0131 665
3711; Fax 0131 653 2122

CHILDREN AND YOUNG PEOPLE'S RESIDENTIAL CENTRE

Lothian Villa Residential Centre 40 Ravensheugh Rd,
Musselburgh, East Lothian EH21 7QB; Tel 0131 653 6909
Pathway Residential Centre Meadowmill, Tranent, East
Lothian; Tel 01875 610794; Fax 01875 610833

ADULT TRAINING/RESOURCES CENTRES

Mansfield Road Musselburgh, East Lothian; Tel 0131 665
9309; Fax 0131 665 0835
Port Seton South Seton Pk, Port Seton, Prestonpans, East
Lothian EH32 0BQ; Tel 01875 815220; Fax 01875 815239
Tynebank 16 Kirkview, Haddington, East Lothian
EH41 4AP; Tel 0162 082 4415

DAY CENTRE FOR ADULTS WITH A PHYSICAL DISABILITY

Prestonpans Day Centre 1 Preston Rd, Prestonpans, East
Lothian EH32 9EL; Tel 01875 812747; Fax 01875 811134

HOMES FOR OLDER PEOPLE

There are three local authority homes for older people.

Department of Education and Community Services

John Muir Hse, Haddington, East Lothian EH41 3HA;
  Tel 01620 827631; Fax 01620 827291
Director (Education and Community Services)
  Alan J. Blackie, BA, DipYCS
Head (Education)   Vacancy
Head (Community Services)   Tom Shearer

PSYCHOLOGICAL SERVICE

East Lothian Psychological Service John Muir Hse,
Haddington, East Lothian EH41 3HA
Principal Psychologist   Nancy Allsop

PUPIL SUPPORT

Outreach Service John Muir Hse, Haddington, East
Lothian EH41 3HA
Principal Officer (Inclusion)   Veronica McCall

COMMUNITY EDUCATION

Bridge Community Education Centre Poldrate Mill,
Haddington, East Lothian EH41 4DA; Tel 01620 823137
Community Development Officer   Gordon Horsburgh
Continuing Education Unit Court St, Haddington, East
Lothian EH41 3HA; Tel 01620 827606
Principal Community Development (Community Education)
  Myra Galloway
Countess Youth and Community Centre Bleachingfield,
Dunbar, East Lothian EH42 1DX; Tel 01368 863484
Community Development Officer   Jo McNamara
Fisherrow Community Centre South St, Musselburgh, East
Lothian EH21 6AT; Tel 0131 665 7590
Community Development Officer   Drew Easton
Longniddry Community Centre Seton Rd, Longniddry, East
Lothian EH32 0LW; Tel 01875 852933
Community Development Officer   Donna Strachan
Musselburgh Area CD Office c/o Musselburgh Sports
Centre, Newbigging, Musselburgh, East Lothian EH21 7AS;
Tel 0131 653 3003
Team Leader (West Area)   Mike Rodger
North Berwick Area CD Office Quality St, North Berwick,
East Lothian; Tel 01620 895593
Team Leader (East Area)   Colin Forbes
North Berwick Community Centre Law Rd, North Berwick,
East Lothian EH39 4PN; Tel 01620 893056
Community Development Officer   Heather Gardner
Port Seton Community Centre South Seton Pk, Port Seton,
Prestonpans, East Lothian EH32 0BQ; Tel 01875 815815;
Fax 01875 81517
Centre Head   Moira Robertson
Prestonpans Community Centre Preston Rd, Prestonpans,
East Lothian EH32 9EL; Tel 01875 813349
Community Development Officer   Elizabeth White
Red School Youth Centre Kirk St, Prestonpans, East Lothian
EH32 9DY; Tel 01875 812474
Community Development Officer   Louis Isbrand
Tranent Under 12s Centre Alexander St, Tranent, East
Lothian EH33 1QA; Tel 01875 614164
Community Development Officer   Helen Harper
Wallyford Community Centre Albert Pl, Wallyford, East
Lothian EH21 8LB; Tel 0131 653 2804
Community Development Officer   Iain Twaddle
Whitecraig Community Centre 44a Whitecraig Cres,
Musselburgh, East Lothian EH21 8NG; Tel 0131 653 2227
Community Development Officer   Margaret Macdonald

9

EAST RENFREWSHIRE COUNCIL
www.eastrenfrewshire.gov.uk

Council Headquarters, Eastwood Pk, Rouken Glen Rd,
  Giffnock, East Renfrewshire G46 6UG;
  URL www.eastrenfrewshire.gov.uk; Tel 0141 577 3000;
  Fax 0141 620 0884
Chief Executive   P. Daniels, MA
Director (Social Work)   Dr S. Ross, MA, MSc, CQSW, PhD

Social Work Department

Tel 0141 577 3840; Fax 0141 577 3846
Director   George Hunter
Head of Service (Operations)   Safaa Baxter-Ameen
Head (Strategy and Development)   Julie Murray
For details of Social Services provision, please contact the
council headquarters above.

RESIDENTIAL HOME FOR OLDER PEOPLE

There is one home for the elderly.

Education Department

East Renfrewshire Council, Council Offices, Eastwood Pk, Rouken Glen Rd, Giffnock, East Renfrewshire G46 6UG; URL www.eastrenfrewshire.gov.uk; E-mail john.wilson@eastrenfrewshire.gov.uk; Tel 0141 577 3430; Fax 0141 577 3405
Director (Education) John Wilson, BSc(Hons)
Head of Education Services (Children and Young People) I. Fraser, MA

SPECIAL SCHOOL

The Isobel Mair School Drumby Cres, Clarkston, East Renfrewshire G76 7HN; Tel 0141 577 4546
Mixed 5–18 (40)

THE CITY OF EDINBURGH COUNCIL
www.edinburgh.gov.uk

Political Composition: Lab: 31, Con: 13, Scottish LD: 13, SNP: 1
City Chambers, High St, Edinburgh EH1 1YJ; URL www.edinburgh.gov.uk; Tel 0131 200 2000; Fax 0131 469 3010
Chief Executive Tom Aitchison

Social Work Department

Shrubhill Hse, 7 Shrub Pl, Edinburgh EH7 4PD; Tel (Emergency Duty Team) 0131 554 4301; (Freephone) 0800 731 6969; Fax 0131 554 5775
Director (Social Work) Vacancy
Head (Operations) D. MacAulay
Head (Planning and Commissioning) S. Brace
Head (Business Services) M. Boyle
Officer (Client Services and Complaints) L. Allen

Executive Committee

Leader Cllr Anderson (Lab)
Deputy Leader Cllr Perry (Lab)
Communication and Business Management Cllr Wilson
Corporate Resources Cllr Russell
Economic Development Cllr Cameron
Education Cllr Aitken
Environment Cllr Fallon
Equalities Cllr Kennedy
Finance Cllr Child
Housing Cllr Gilmore
Social Work Cllr Thomas
Transport Cllr Burns

CENTRAL CRIMINAL JUSTICE SERVICES

21 Market St, Edinburgh EH11 1BL; Tel 0131 469 3408; Fax 0131 469 3410

CHILDREN'S RESIDENTIAL/SECURE/CLOSE SUPPORT UNITS

Howdenhall 39 Howdenhall Rd, Edinburgh EH16 6PJ; Tel 0131 664 8488; Fax 0131 664 3549

Pentland View Close Support Unit 83 Pentland View, Edinburgh EH10 4TR; Tel 0131 445 4024; Fax 0131 445 5929

St. Katharine's 29b Balmwell Terr, Edinburgh EH16 6PS; Tel 0131 672 1109; Fax 0131 666 2979

Wellington Peebles Rd, Penicuik, Edinburgh EH26 8PT; Tel 01968 672515; Fax 01968 675812

RESPITE RESIDENTIAL CARE FACILITY FOR CHILDREN WITH DISABILITIES

Seaview, 52 Seaview Cres, Edinburgh EH15 2LT; Tel 0131 669 7490; Fax 0131 657 2723

BLINDCRAFT EDINBURGH

Craigmillar Works, 2 Peffer Pl, Edinburgh EH16 4BB; Tel 0131 661 1205; Fax 0131 652 2095

WORKING TOGETHER

North Edinburgh Youth Strategy Team 163 Leith Wlk, Edinburgh EH6 8HR; Tel 0131 555 0791; Fax 0131 554 6118

Panmure House Lochend Cl, Canongate, Edinburgh EH8 8BP; Tel 0131 556 8833; Fax 0131 557 5658

TRANSPORT SECTION

Cleekim Depot Dunningston Rd, Edinburgh EH7 6UL; Tel 0131 553 2421; Fax 0131 555 4737

WELFARE RIGHTS TEAMS

South Bridge Welfare Rights Team 85–87 South Bridge, Edinburgh EH1 1HN; Tel 0131 225 1255; Fax 0131 225 6171

Niddrie Mains Road Welfare Rights Team 94 Niddrie Mains Rd, Edinburgh; Tel 0131 659 6528; Fax 0131 661 7918

North East Edinburgh

SOCIAL WORK CENTRES

Craigentinny Social Work Centre Loaning Rd, Edinburgh EH7 6JE; Tel 0131 661 8291; Fax 0131 652 0984

Giles Street Social Work Centre 9–11 Giles St, Edinburgh EH6 6DJ; Tel 0131 553 3835; Fax 0131 553 6540

Leith Social Work Centre St. John's Hse, 71 Constitution St, Edinburgh EH6 7AF; Tel 0131 553 2121; Fax 0131 555 0842

HOSPITAL SOCIAL WORK UNIT

Royal Hospital for Sick Children 3 Rillbank Terr, Edinburgh EH9 1LL; Tel 0131 536 0501; Fax 0131 536 0186

CHILD AND FAMILY CENTRES

Pilrig 102 Pilrig St, Edinburgh EH6 5AY; Tel 0131 554 3040

Victoria Park 159 Newhaven Rd, Edinburgh EH6 4QA; Tel 0131 554 4077

CHILDREN AND YOUNG PEOPLE'S RESIDENTIAL CENTRES

Moredun 15 Moredun Park Crt, Edinburgh EH17 7EY; Tel 0131 664 5297

Northfield 34 Northfield Dr, Edinburgh EH8 7RP; Tel 0131 661 3076

ADULT TRAINING/RESOURCE CENTRES

Bonnington Bonnington Rd, Edinburgh EH6 5NL; Tel 0131 555 0920

Hawkhill 17 Hawkhill Ave, Edinburgh EH7 6BU; Tel 0131 652 1859

DAY CENTRE FOR ADULTS WITH A PHYSICAL DISABILITY

Craighall Day Centre 210 Ferry Rd, Edinburgh EH6 4RB; Tel 0131 551 2194

DAY CENTRES FOR OLDER PEOPLE

Ferrylee Day Centre 33 North Junction St, Edinburgh EH6 6HR; Tel 0131 553 7329

Parkview Day Centre 64 Peffermill Rd, Edinburgh EH16 5LP; Tel 0131 668 4234

Porthaven Day Centre 14 Wellington Pl, Edinburgh EH6 7EQ; Tel 0131 554 2271

HOMES FOR OLDER PEOPLE

There are four local authority homes for older people.

North West Edinburgh

SOCIAL WORK CENTRES

Muirhouse Crescent Social Work Centre 34 Muirhouse Cres, Edinburgh EH4 4QL; Tel 0131 343 1991; Fax 0131 315 2172

Westfield House Social Work Centre 5 Kirk Loan, Edinburgh EH12 7HD; Tel 0131 334 9933; Fax 0131 316 4095

West Pilton Gardens Social Work Centre 8 West Pilton Gdns, Edinburgh EH4 4DP; Tel 0131 529 5400; Fax 0131 529 5429

HOSPITAL SOCIAL WORK UNITS

Royal Victoria Hospital 13 Craigleith Rd, Edinburgh EH4 2DN; Tel 0131 537 5000

Western General Hospital Crewe Rd, Edinburgh EH4 2XU; Tel 0131 537 1000

CHILD AND FAMILY CENTRES

Granton Child and Family Centre 10 Wardieburn Rd, Edinburgh EH5 1LY; Tel 0131 552 4808

Parkway Child and Family Centre 8 Muirhouse Parkway, Edinburgh EH4 5EU; Tel 0131 332 1949

West Pilton Child and Family Centre 33 Ferry Road Dr, Edinburgh EH4 4DB; Tel 0131 332 3855

CHILDREN'S AND YOUNG PEOPLE'S RESIDENTIAL CENTRE

Drylaw Residential Centre 135 Easter Drylaw Dr, Edinburgh EH4 2RX; Tel 0131 332 0381

HOSTELS FOR PEOPLE WITH LEARNING DISABILITIES

Ravensglass 432 Lanark Rd, Edinburgh EH13 0NJ; Tel 0131 441 2397

South Gyle (Respite) 2a South Gyle Gdns, Edinburgh EH12 7RZ; Tel 0131 538 7256

ACCOMMODATION FOR PEOPLE WITH MENTAL HEALTH PROBLEMS

Northumberland Street 65 Northumberland St, Edinburgh EH3 6JQ; Tel 0131 556 5753

ADULT TRAINING AND RESOURCE CENTRES

Grindlay Court Grindlay St, Edinburgh EH3 9AR; Tel 0131 229 7941

St. Helen's 7 West Coates, Edinburgh EH12 5JG; Tel 0131 337 2108

DAY CENTRES FOR OLDER PEOPLE

Clermiston Day Centre 93 Parkgrove Terr, Edinburgh EH4 7RD; Tel 0131 336 1181

Granton Day Centre 15 Wardieburn St West, Edinburgh EH5 1DN; Tel 0131 552 8647

Silverlea Day Centre 14 Muirhouse Parkway, Edinburgh EH4 5EU; Tel 0131 336 4495

The Tower Day Centre 18 Murrayfield Dr, Edinburgh EH12 6EB; Tel 0131 337 9344

HOMES FOR OLDER PEOPLE

There are three local authority homes for older people.

South East Edinburgh

SOCIAL WORK CENTRES

Captains Road Social Work Centre 40 Captains Rd, Edinburgh EH17 8QF; Tel 0131 529 5300; Fax 0131 529 5384

Craigmillar Social Work Centre 111 Peffer Rd, Edinburgh EH16 4AL; Tel 0131 656 9800; Fax 0131 652 2749

Victoria Street Social Work Centre 11 Victoria St, Edinburgh EH1 2HE; Tel 0131 226 6731; Fax 0131 220 4883

HOSPITAL SOCIAL WORK UNITS

Astley Ainslie Hospital 133 Grange Loan, Edinburgh EH9 2HL; Tel 0131 537 9161

Liberton Hospital 113 Lasswade Rd, Edinburgh EH16 6UB; Tel 0131 536 7800

Royal Infirmary of Edinburgh 51 Littlefrance Cres, Edinburgh EH16 4SA; Tel 0131 242 7850

CHILD AND FAMILY CENTRES

Craigmillar Child and Family Centre 8 Craigmillar Castle Gdns, Edinburgh EH16 4AD; Tel 0131 661 3126

Gilmerton Child and Family Centre 66 Gilmerton Dykes St, Edinburgh EH17 8PL; Tel 0131 664 1202

Greendykes Child and Family Centre 205 Craigmillar Castle Ave, Edinburgh EH16 4DZ; Tel 0131 661 3109

CHILDREN AND YOUNG PEOPLE'S RESIDENTIAL CENTRES

Ferniehill Residential Centre 2 Ferniehill St, Edinburgh EH17 7BB; Tel 0131 664 1939

Greendykes Residential Centre 10 Greendykes Rd, Edinburgh EH16 4JW; Tel 0131 661 4801

Niddrie Family Resource Centre 33 Niddrie Marischal Dr, Edinburgh EH16 4ER; Tel 0131 669 9865

ADULT TRAINING AND RESOURCE CENTRES

Deanbank 35–37 Canaan La, Edinburgh EH10 4SG; Tel 0131 447 7688

Pefferbank 157 Duddington Rd West, Edinburgh EH16 4UY; Tel 0131 652 1986

HOSTELS FOR PEOPLE WITH LEARNING DISABILITIES

Glenallan (Respite) 142 Glenallan Dr, Edinburgh EH16 5RE; Tel 0131 666 2858

Greenhill Gardens 38 Greenhill Gdns, Edinburgh EH10 4BJ; Tel 0131 447 7041

DAY CENTRES FOR OLDER PEOPLE

Liberton Gardens Day Centre 57 Liberton Gdns, Edinburgh EH16 6TE; Tel 0131 664 5828

Oaklands Day Centre 35 Canaan La, Edinburgh EH10 4SG; Tel 0131 447 0770

HOMES FOR OLDER PEOPLE

There are four local authority homes for older people.

9

South West Edinburgh

SOCIAL WORK CENTRES

Murrayburn Gate Social Work Centre 5 Murrayburn Gate, Edinburgh EH14 2SS; Tel 0131 442 4131; Fax 0131 442 4842

Oxgangs Path Social Work Centre 4 Oxgangs Path, Edinburgh EH13 9LX; Tel 0131 445 4451; Fax 0131 445 5501

Springwell House Social Work Centre 1 Gorgie Rd, Edinburgh EH11 2LA; Tel 0131 313 3366; Fax 0131 346 7768

HOSPITAL SOCIAL WORK UNIT

Royal Edinburgh Hospital 51 Morningside Pl, Edinburgh EH10 5HF; Tel 0131 537 6000; Fax 0131 537 6113

CHILD AND FAMILY CENTRES

Hailesland Child and Family Centre 23 Hailesland Pl, Edinburgh EH14 2SL; Tel 0131 442 2163

Sighthill Child and Family Centre 12 Calder Gdns, Edinburgh EH11 4JD; Tel 0131 442 2018

Stenhouse Child and Family Centre 43 Fords Rd, Edinburgh EH11 3HS; Tel 0131 443 1207

Viewforth Child and Family Centre 18 Viewforth Terr, Edinburgh EH10 4LH; Tel 0131 229 6667

CHILDREN'S AND YOUNG PEOPLE'S RESIDENTIAL CENTRES

Oxgangs Residential Centre 54 Oxgangs Ave, Edinburgh EH13 9JP; Tel 0131 447 7971

Southhouse Residential Centre 13 Southouse Gr, Edinburgh EH17 8EH; Tel 0131 664 1355

ADULT TRAINING/RESOURCE CENTRES

Longstone Centre 62 Longstone St, Edinburgh EH14 2DA; Tel 0131 443 3837

McLeod Street Centre 13 McLeod St, Edinburgh EH11 2NJ; Tel 0131 337 3353

HOSTEL FOR PEOPLE WITH LEARNING DISABILITIES

Currie Hostel 100 Forthview Cres, Edinburgh EH14 5QR; Tel 0131 449 2318

OTHER ADULT HOSTELS

Albrae Hostel 24 Broughton Pl, Edinburgh EH1 3RT; Tel 0131 556 9969

Colinton Mains Hostel 12 Firrhill Cres, Edinburgh EH13 9EL; Tel 0131 441 2719

DAY CENTRE FOR ADULTS WITH A PHYSICAL DISABILITY

Firrhill Day Centre 257 Colinton Rd, Edinburgh EH14 1DW; Tel 0131 441 7162

DAY CENTRES FOR OLDER PEOPLE

Fords Road Day Centre 4 Fords Rd, Edinburgh EH11 2HP; Tel 0131 443 0662

Sighthill Day Centre 12 Calder Gdns, Edinburgh EH11 4JD; Tel 0131 453 2418

HOMES FOR OLDER PEOPLE

There are three local authority homes for older people.

Education Department

10 Waterloo Pl, Edinburgh EH1 3EG; Tel 0131 469 3000; Fax 0131 469 3141
Director (Education) Roy Jobson

Education Support Services Group

Head (Education Support Services) C. Dalrymple

Community Education Group

Head (Community Education) M. Rosendale
Senior Community Education Worker (Youth and Children) R. Byfield

Policy Planning and Communications Group

Head (Policy Planning and Communications) David Fenton

Pupil Support Services Group

Head (Pupil Support Services) Ian Glen

Quality Services Group

Head (Quality Services) F.P. McLeod
Adviser (Learning Support and SEN) M. Brice

REGIONAL PSYCHOLOGICAL SERVICE

Edinburgh (East) 7 Merchiston Pk, Edinburgh EH10 4PR; Tel 0131 229 4223; 0131 229 4224
Principal Psychologist Anna Boni
Principal Psychologist Janice Duguid

Edinburgh (West) Easter Drylaw Dr, Edinburgh EH4 2RY; Tel 0131 343 6181
Principal Psychologist John Young
Principal Psychologist Greg McMillan

SPECIAL EDUCATION

Cairnpark School Redhall House Dr, Edinburgh EH14 1JA; Tel 0131 443 0903
Headteacher J. McClintock

Canonmills School Rodney St, Edinburgh EH7 4EL; Tel 0131 556 6000
Headteacher M. Wilson

Graysmill School 1 Redhall House Dr, Edinburgh EH14 1JE; Tel 0131 443 8096
Headteacher I.H. Elfick

Howdenhall Children's Unit 39 Howdenhall Rd, Edinburgh EH16 6PG; Tel 0131 664 8488
Headteacher A. Marjoribanks

Kaimes School 140 Lasswade Rd, Edinburgh EH16 6RT; Tel 0131 664 8241
Headteacher C. Mumford

Kingsinch School 233 Gilmerton Rd, Edinburgh EH16 5UD; Tel 0131 664 1911
Headteacher J. Eales

Oaklands School Broomhouse Cres, Edinburgh EH11 3UB; Tel 0131 467 7867
Headteacher S. Harland

Pilrig Park School Balfour Pl, Edinburgh EH6 5DW; Tel 0131 467 7960
Headteacher J.H. Mudie

Prospect Bank School 81 Restalrig Rd, Edinburgh EH6 8BQ; Tel 0131 553 2239
Headteacher M.E. Donaldson

Rowanfield School 167a Groathill Rd North, Edinburgh EH4 2RY; Tel 0131 343 6116
Headteacher F. Dickens

St. Crispin's School Watertoun Rd, Edinburgh EH9 3HZ; Tel 0131 667 4831
Headteacher E. Murray

St. Katharine's School 29 Balmwell Terr, Edinburgh EH16 6PG; Tel 0131 672 1109
Headteacher A. Marjoribanks

St. Nicholas' School Gorgie Rd, Edinburgh EH11 2RG; Tel 0131 337 6077
Headteacher C. McLaren

Willowpark School Gorgie Rd, Edinburgh EH11 2BG; Tel 0131 337 1622
Headteacher Arlene Mooney

FALKIRK COUNCIL
www.falkirk.gov.uk

Population 143 370
Municipal Bldgs, Falkirk FK1 5RS;
    URL www.falkirk.gov.uk; Tel 01324 506070; Fax 01324 506071
Chief Executive M. Pitcaithly

Social Work Services

Brockville, Hope St, Falkirk FK1 5RW;
    URL www.falkirk.gov.uk; Tel 01324 506400;
    (Emergency) 01786 470500; Fax 01324 506401
Director Janet Birks
Convenor Cllr P. McCafferty
Vice-Convenor Cllr J. Wilson
Head of Service A. Boyd
Head of Service B. Kerr

HOSPITAL TEAMS

Dementia Projects Dollar Pk, Camelon Rd, Falkirk FK1 5RY; E-mail james.kilgour@virgin.net; Tel 01324 501730
Project Co-ordinator J. Kilgour

Falkirk Royal Infirmary Falkirk FK1 5QE; E-mail gina.anderson@falkirk.gov.uk; Tel 01324 616039; Fax 01324 616074
Team Manager Gina Anderson

AREA OFFICES

Bo'ness Office

14–16 Corbiehall, Bo'ness, Falkirk EH51 0AP; Tel 01506 778668; Fax 01506 778669

Denny Office

Carronbank Hse, Carronbank Cres, Denny, Falkirk FK6 6GA; Tel 01324 504160; Fax 01324 504161

Grahamston Office

155 Grahamston Rd, Falkirk FK2 7BQ; Tel 01324 506595; Fax 01324 506596

Grangemouth Office

Oxgang Rd, Grangemouth, Falkirk FK3 9EF; Tel 01324 504343; Fax 01324 504344

Meadowbank Office

1 Salmon Inn Rd, Polmont, Falkirk FK2 0XF; Tel 01324 503883; Fax 01324 503884

Stenhousemuir Office

130 King St, Stenhousemuir, Larbert, Falkirk FK5 4HS; Tel 01324 503503; Fax 01324 503504

DAY CENTRES FOR PEOPLE WITH LEARNING DISABILITIES

Bainsford Day Centre Waverley St, Bainsford, Falkirk FK2 7LU; Tel 01324 501630
Manager R. Paul
    MH (80)

Camelon Day Centre 108b Glasgow Rd, Camelon, Falkirk FK1 4HS; Tel 01324 501600; Fax 01324 501601
    MH (80)

Grangemouth Day Centre 46 Oswald Ave, Grangemouth, Falkirk FK3 9AX; Tel 01324 501380
Manager R. Paul
    MH (80) PH (15)

DAY CENTRE FOR PEOPLE WITH PHYSICAL DISABILITY

Dundas Resource Centre Oxgang Rd, Grangemouth, Falkirk FK3 9EF; Tel 01324 504311; Fax 01324 504312
Manager P. Finlay

MENTAL HEALTH SERVICES

Antonine Enterprises 17–19 Tamfourhill Ind Est, Tamfourhill, Camelon, Falkirk FK1 4RT; Tel 01324 501622; Fax 01324 501621

Caledonia House Etna Rd, Falkirk FK2 9EG; Tel 01324 501720; Fax 01324 501721

Cluaran Project Watling Lodge, Tamfourhill Rd, Falkirk FK1 4RE; Tel 01324 632903

Dunrowan Mental Health Resource Centre Maggiewoods Loan, Falkirk FK1 5EH; Tel 01324 630154; Fax 01324 626238

Falkirk West Team 108b Glasgow Rd, Camelon, Falkirk FK1 4HS; Tel 01324 501200; Fax 01324 501201

FIND (Falkirk into New Directions) Morar, Royal Scottish National Hospital, Old Denny Rd, Larbert, Falkirk FK5 4SD; Tel 01324 404432

Joint Loan Equipment Scheme Unit 9, West Main Ind Est, Grangemouth, Falkirk FK3 8YE; Tel 01324 508762; Fax 01324 508761

HOMES FOR OLDER PEOPLE

There are six local authority homes for older people.

Education Services

McLaren Hse, Marchmont Ave, Polmont, Falkirk FK2 0NZ;
    URL www.falkirk.gov.uk;
    E-mail director.educ@falkirk.gov.uk; Tel 01324 506600; Fax 01324 506601
Director (Education) Dr G. Young
Head (Educational Provision) James McKinstry
Head (Educational Support) A. Carnachan
Head (Policy, Quality and Resources) N. Fletcher
Principal Psychologist Charles Gibb
Moray Pl, Grangemouth, Falkirk FK3 9DL

SPECIAL CLASSES

Dundas Unit c/o Moray Primary School, Moray Pl, Grangemouth, Falkirk FK3 9DL; Tel 01324 501311; Fax 01324 501311
Headteacher Tom Begen

Education Assessment Unit Weedingshall, Polmont, Falkirk FK2 0XS; Tel 01324 506770; Fax 01324 506770
Headteacher M. Kydd

Falkirk Day Unit Camelon Education Centre, Abercrombie St, Camelon, Falkirk FK1 4HA; Tel 01324 501650; Fax 01324 503719
Headteacher G. Bell

9

SPECIAL SCHOOLS

Carrongrange School Carrongrange Ave, Stenhousemuir, Falkirk FK5 3BH;
E-mail carrongrangeschool@falkirk.gov.uk; Tel 01324 555266; Fax 01324 503555
Headteacher K. O'Hagan
6–16 MH, PH, PS

Torwood School Stirling Rd, Torwood, Larbert, Falkirk FK5 4SR; Tel 01324 503470; Fax 01324 503471
Headteacher Dorothy Hill (Acting)
6–16 SMH

Windsor Park School Bantaskine Rd, Falkirk FK1 5HT; Tel 01324 508640; Fax 01324 508647
Headteacher C. Finestone
4–16 Partially deaf/sensory service

FIFE COUNCIL
www.fife.gov.uk

Population 351 200
Political Composition: Lab: 36, LD: 23, SNP: 11, Ind: 4, Left Alliance: 2, Con: 2.
Fife Hse, North St, Glenrothes, Fife KY7 5LT;
URL www.fife.gov.uk; Tel 01592 414141; Fax 01592 414142
Convener J. Simpson
Chief Executive Douglas Sinclair
Strategic Manager (Children and Adult Services) E. Byers
Strategic Manager (Support Services) D. Martin
Head (Community Services) D. Somerville
Head (Information Technology) E. Brewster
Head (Law and Administration) H.B. Tait

Social Work Services

URL www.fifedirect.org.uk; Tel 01592 414141; Fax 01592 413320
Head S. Moore
Senior Manager (Support Services) J. Easson
Senior Manager (Community Development) J. McDonald
Senior Manager (Adults) I. Tate
Senior Manager (Child Care) J. Pease
Senior Manager (Older People) P. McCaw

Social Work Offices

CENTRAL AREA

Glenrothes Social Work Office 390 South St, Glenrothes, Fife KY7 5NL; Tel 01592 415252; Fax 01592 415278

Kirkcaldy Social Work Office 16 East Fergus Pl, Kirkcaldy, Fife KY1 1XT; Tel 01592 412424; Fax 01592 412321

Leven Social Work Office 12 Station Rd, Leven, Fife KY8 4QU; Tel 01333 592222; Fax 01333 592229

Out of Hours Service 2 Rimbleton Pk, Rimbleton, Glenrothes, Fife KY6 2BZ; Tel (Emergency) 01592 415000; Fax 01592 415483

EAST AREA

Cupar Social Work Office 7 Castlehill, Cupar, Fife KY15 4HA; Tel 01334 412121; Fax 01334 412131

WEST AREA

Cowdenbeath Social Work Office 70 Stenhouse St, Cowdenbeath, Fife KY4 9DD; Tel 01383 313233; Fax 01383 313293

Dunfermline Social Work Office Ling Hse, 29 Canmore St, Dunfermline, Fife KY12 7NU; Tel 01383 312100; Fax 01383 312109

Rosyth Social Work Office Park Rd, Rosyth, Fife KY11 2JL; Tel 01383 313333; Fax 01383 313340

CHILDREN AND FAMILIES

Child Protection Unit (Dunfermline) Dunfermline Police Station, 2 Holyrood Pl, Dunfermline, Fife KY12 7RA; Tel 01383 312910; Fax 01383 312909

Child Protection Unit (Kirkcaldy) Broomlea, 1 Swan Rd, Kirkcaldy, Fife KY1 1UZ; Tel 01592 412970

CRIMINAL JUSTICE SERVICES

Criminal Justice Service 96–98 Wellesley Rd, Buckhaven, Leven, Fife KY8 1HT; Tel 01592 414488

Criminal Justice Services 21 St. Catherine St, Cupar, Fife KY15 4LS; Tel 01334 412015; Fax 01334 412034

Criminal Justice Services Rannoch Hse, Comely Pk, Dunfermline, Fife KY12 7HU; Tel 01383 312131; Fax 01383 312131

Education Service

Rothesay Hse, Rothesay Pl, Glenrothes, Fife KY7 5PQ;
E-mail margaret.johnston@fife.gov.uk; Tel 01592 414141; Fax 01592 416411
Head (Education) Roger Stewart
Senior Manager (East/Levenmouth) James Bellshaw
Senior Manager (Glenrothes/Cowdenbeath/Lochgelly) Garry Crosbie
Senior Manager (Kirkcaldy) B. Kirkaldy
Senior Manager (Dunfermline/Inverkeithing) Kenneth Greer
Senior Manager (Resources) Ian Robertson
Education Officer (East/Levenmouth) Belinda Asmar
Education Officer (Glenrothes/Cowdenbeath/Lochgelly) Les Fargie
Education Officer (Kirkcaldy) Yvonne Carling
Principal Psychologist Hamish MacPhee
Education Officer (Dunfermline/Inverkeithing) Nora Conlin
Education Officer (Dunfermline/Inverkeithing) Heather Hamilton

SPECIAL DAY CLASSES FOR PUPILS WITH MODERATE LEARNING DIFFICULTIES

Balwearie High School Balwearie Gdns, Kirkcaldy, Fife KY2 5LY; Tel 01592 412262
Headteacher G.D. Mackenzie

Bell-Baxter High School Carslogie Rd, Cupar, Fife KY15 4HY; Tel 01334 412300
Headteacher D. Campbell

Benarty Primary School 67–69 Lochleven Rd, Lochore, Lochgelly, Fife KY5 8HU; Tel 01592 414375
Headteacher A.D. Pritchard

Buckhaven High School Methilhaven Rd, Buckhaven, Fife KY8 1HL; Tel 01592 414400
Headteacher J. Lusby

Buckhaven Primary School College St, Buckhaven, Leven, Fife KY8 1JZ; Tel 01592 414555
Headteacher Y. Menzies

Castlehill Primary School Ceres Rd, Cupar, Fife KY15 5JT; Tel 01334 412470
Headteacher A.D. Kilgariff

Langlands Primary School Kilrymont Rd, St. Andrews, Fife KY16 8DF; Tel 01334 412600
Headteacher J. Cunningham

Lochgelly High School Station Rd, Lochgelly, Fife KY5 8LZ; Tel 01592 418000
Headteacher B.W. Blanchflower

Madras College South St, St. Andrews, Fife KY16 9EJ; Tel 01334 412500
Headteacher L. Matheson

Pitreavie Primary School Pitcorthie Dr, Dunfermline, Fife KY11 5AB; Tel 01383 312990
Headteacher S. Martin (Acting)

Rimbleton Primary School Bilsand Rd, Glenrothes, Fife KY6 2DZ; Tel 01592 415383
Headteacher S. Forbes (Acting)

Valley Primary School Valley Gdns, Kirkaldy, Fife KY2 6BL; Tel 01592 412531
Headteacher S. Carrie

Woodmill High School Shields Rd, Dunfermline, Fife KY11 4ER; Tel 01383 312505
Headteacher M. Gilmour

SPECIAL SCHOOLS FOR PUPILS WITH SEVERE/PROFOUND LEARNING DIFFICULTIES

Headwell School Headwell Ave, Dunfermline, Fife KY12 0JU; Tel 01383 721589
Headteacher J. Lopez

Hyndhead School Barncraig St, Buckhaven, Fife KY8 1JE; Tel 01592 414499
Headteacher R. Gourlay (Acting)

John Fergus School Erskine Pl, Glenrothes, Fife KY7 4JB; Tel 01592 415335
Headteacher M. Sankey

Kilmaron School Balgarvie Rd, Cupar, Fife KY15 4PE; Tel 01334 653125
Headteacher W.E. Lawson

Lochgelly North School 6 McGregor Ave, Lochgelly, Fife KY5 9PE; Tel 01592 418110
Headteacher M. Sparling (Acting)

Robert Henryson School Linburn Rd, Dunfermline, Fife KY11 4LD; Tel 01383 312027
Headteacher M. Lorimer

Rosslyn School Viewforth Terr, Kirkcaldy, Fife KY1 3BP; Tel 01592 415930
Headteacher G. MacFarlane

GLASGOW CITY COUNCIL
www.glasgow.gov.uk

City Chambers, George Sq, Glasgow G2 1DU;
URL www.glasgow.gov.uk; E-mail pr@glasgow.gov.uk;
Tel 0141 287 2000; Fax 0141 287 5666
Director (Building Services) Stewart Fallis
Director (Direct and Care Services) Fergus Chambers
Director (Cultural and Leisure Services) Bridget McConnell
Director (Education Services) Ken Corsar
Director (Land Services) Alastair Young
Director (Environmental Protection Services) Brian Kelly
Director (Personnel and Administration Services)
Hogan Burke
Director (Development and Regeneration Services)
Rodger McConnell
Director (Social Work Services) David Comley (Acting)
Director (Financial Services) George Black
Director (Housing Services) David Comley
Head (Public Relations and Marketing) John Brown

Social Work Services

Nye Bevan Hse, 20 India St, Glasgow G2 4PF;
URL www.glasgow.gov.uk/socialwork;
E-mail social@glasgow.gov.uk; Tel 0141 287 8700; (Out of hours service) 0800 0811505; Fax 0141 287 8855

Director (Social Work Services) David Comley
Depute Director (Community Care) Rab Murray
Depute Director (Resources) Keith Moore
Head (Children and Family and Criminal Justice) Joan Elliot
Head (Performance, Standards and Strategic Management)
John Legg
Head (Personnel and Administration, Training)
Graham Lindsay
Head (Finance and Information Technology) Neil Copland
Head (Community Care – Older People) Peter McLaren
Head (Community Care – Adults) George Smith
Joint General Manager (Learning Disabilities)
Mark Feinmann
Head (Children and Family and Criminal Justice)
Christopher Holmes

Social Work Committee

Convener John McKenzie
Members of the Committee
Bashir Ahmad, Keith Baldassara, Mary Beckett,
Shaukat Butt, Elizabeth Cameron, Paul Carey,
James Coleman, Malcolm Cunning, Stephan Curran,
Christine Devine, Josephine Dodds, John Flanagan,
Charles Gordon, Gary Gray, John Gray, Ellen Hurcombe,
Gordon Macdiarmid, Jim Mackechnie, Hugh Macrae,
Hanzala Malik, Haleema Malik, John Mason,
Dr Christopher Mason, James Matter, Margaret McCafferty,
Elaine McDougal, Mary Paris, George Ryan,
Margaret Sinclair, Alan Stewart, Robert Winter.

AREA SERVICE TEAMS

West

Area Services Manager Gerry Breslin
Anniesland 1660–1670 Great Western Rd, Glasgow G13 1HH; Tel 0141 276 2420; Fax 0141 276 2530
Drumchapel Mercat Hse, 31 Hecla Sq, Glasgow G15 8NN; Tel 0141 274 4300; Fax 0141 944 6931

North West

Area Services Manager David Moffat
Maryhill The Quadrangle, 59 Ruchill St, Unit 8b, Glasgow G20 9PY; Tel 0141 287 6300; Fax 0141 287 6267
Partick 35 Church St, Partick, Glasgow G11 5JT; Tel 0141 276 3100; Fax 0141 276 3194

North

Area Services Manager Martin Kettle
Possil 7 Closeburn St, Possilpark, Glasgow G22 5JZ; Tel 0141 276 4570; Fax 0141 276 4555
Springburn 94 Red Rd, Glasgow G21 4PH; Tel 0845 330 3595; Fax 0141 557 0310

East

Area Services Manager Ann Marie Rafferty
Bridgeton Anson Hse, 582–588 London Rd, Glasgow G40 1DZ; Tel 0141 551 5000; Fax 0141 551 5010
Parkhead The Newlands Centre, 871 Springfield Rd, Glasgow G31 4HZ; Tel 0141 565 0100; Fax 0141 565 0112

North East

Area Services Manager Linda Connolly
Baillieston 6 Buchanan St, Glasgow G69 6DY; Tel 0141 773 0001; Fax 0141 771 2584
Easterhouse Westwood Hse, 1250 Westerhouse Rd, Glasgow G34 9AE; Tel 0141 276 3410; Fax 0141 276 3432
Ruchazie 1 Ruchazie Pl, Cranhill, Glasgow G33 3HA; Tel 0141 770 8531; Fax 0141 770 5058

9

South East

Area Services Manager   Jim Cameron

Castlemilk 10 Ardencraig Pl, Castlemilk, Glasgow
G45 9US; Tel 0141 287 6100; Fax 0141 287 6127

South

Area Services Manager   Sheena Morrison

Gorbals and Govanhill 187 Old Rutherglen Rd, Gorbals,
Glasgow G5 0RE; Tel 0141 420 8000; Fax 0141 420 8004

Pollokshields East Pollokshields Project, 100 McCulloch St,
Glasgow G41 1NX; Tel 0141 429 6301

Greater Pollok

Area Services Manager   Raymond Bell

Pollok 130 Langton St, Glasgow G53 5DP; Tel 0141 276
2900; Fax 0141 276 2914

Pollokshaws 24–34 Shawbridge Arcade, Glasgow G43 1RT;
Tel 0141 287 1601; Fax 0141 287 1602

South West

Area Services Manager   John Owens

Govan 1 Merryland St, Glasgow G51 2QG; Tel 0141 445
3178; Fax 0141 425 1062

SOUTH WEST RECEIVING SERVICES

West Drumoyne Partnership Office, 299–301 Shieldhall Rd,
Glasgow G51 4HB; Tel 0141 880 9936; Fax 0141 882 3717

HOMELESS TEAM

118 Osborne St, Glasgow G1 5QH; Tel 0141 552 7991;
Fax 0141 552 5460
Manager   Jim Littlejohn

STANDBY

35 Church St, Glasgow G11 5JT; Tel 0141 305 6970; 0800
811505; Fax 0141 334 8577
Contact   Jim Lativy

CHILDREN AND FAMILY SERVICES

Castlemilk Family Care Project 10 Ardencraig Pl, Glasgow
G45 9US; Tel 0141 287 6182; Fax 0141 287 6127

Castlemilk Young Persons Befriending Project 10
Ardencraig Pl, Glasgow G45 9US; Tel 0141 287 6181;
Fax 0141 287 6127

Children and Families Counselling Project 11 Ladyloan
Ave, Glasgow G15 8LE; Tel 0141 944 4025

Children's Health and Disability Team Centenary Hse, 100
Morrison St, Glasgow G5 8LN; Tel 0141 420 5514; 0141 420
5849; Fax 0141 420 5516

Families for Children Centenary Hse, 100 Morrison St,
Glasgow G5 8LN; Tel 0141 420 5555; Fax 0141 420 5528

Family Resource Unit 436a Kinfauns Dr, Glasgow
G15 7NE; Tel 0141 944 4007; Fax 0141 944 3161

Greater Easterhouse Family Support Project 36
Westerhouse Rd, Glasgow G34 9PD; Tel 0141 771 8481

Halt Project 196 Bath St, Glasgow G2 4HH; Tel 0141 287
2470; Fax 0141 287 2471

Isolated Parents Project 7 Closeburn St, Glasgow G22 5JZ;
Tel 0141 276 4570; Fax 0141 336 4778

Launchpad Project 48 Albion St, 5th Fl, Glasgow G1 1LH;
Tel 0141 287 5476; Fax 0141 287 5477

Leaving Care Services 115 Wellington St, Glasgow G2 2XT;
Tel 0141 302 2673; Fax 0141 302 2626

Outdoor Resource Centre 3 Martha St, Glasgow G1 1JN;
Tel 0141 287 4508; Fax 0141 287 0157

Through School Care Project St. Margaret Mary's
Secondary School, 65 Dougrie Rd, Glasgow G45 9NJ;
Tel 0141 630 1868; Fax 0141 630 1796

LOCAL AUTHORITY RESIDENTIAL CARE FOR CHILDREN

Social Work Services manages a range of residential care
units for children. Any enquiries in respect of these should
be addressed to the Head of Children and Family Services
or the Principal Officer (Residential), Children and Family
Service on Tel 0141 420 5500.

REGISTRATION AND INSPECTION UNIT

117 Brook St, Glasgow G40 3AP; Tel 0141 550 7700; Fax 0141
550 7707

DAY CARE FOR ADULTS WITH LEARNING DISABILITIES

ACCORD Centre 35 Springfield Rd, Glasgow G40 3EL;
Tel 0141 556 3391; Fax 0141 556 6734

Berryknowes 14 Hallrule Dr, Glasgow G52 2HH; Tel 0141
883 9181; Fax 0141 883 6729

Carlton 1–7 Coburg St, Glasgow G5 9JF; Tel 0141 429 7975

Elmvale Elmvale St, Glasgow G21 1LR; Tel 0141 557 3578;
Fax 0141 557 3510

Gold Project Flat 1–3, 10 Petershill Crt, Glasgow G45 9UE;
Tel 0141 558 1191; Fax 0141 557 3248

Hinshaw Street 13–20 Hinshaw St, Glasgow G20 7BY;
Tel 0141 946 1799

Killearn 29 Shakespeare St, Glasgow G20 8TH; Tel 0141 276
3600

PICAS (Partners in Care and Support) Berryknowes Centre,
14 Hallrule Dr, Glasgow G52 2HH; Tel 0141 882 6068

PPAS 8 Boon Dr, Glasgow G15 6AT; Tel 0141 944 4330;
Fax 0141 944 7119

Priesthill 300 Nitshill Rd, Glasgow G53 7BT; Tel 0141 880
5262

Renfield Services 24 Newton Pl, Glasgow G3 7PY; Tel 0141
353 0085; Fax 0141 353 0086

Riddrie Centre 2 Riddrievale Crt, Glasgow G33 3RN;
Tel 0141 770 9106

Southbrae Resource Centre 190 Southbrae Dr, Glasgow
G13 1TX; Tel 0141 954 2011; Fax 0141 435 4983

Summerston 1 Glenbervie Pl, Glasgow G23 5QF; Tel 0141
945 3565; Fax 0141 945 1580

Tollcross 1196 Tollcross Rd, Glasgow G32 8HQ; Tel 0141
763 1214

Toryglen Resource Centre 179 Prospecthill Circus, Glasgow
G42 0LA; Tel 0141 613 1576; Fax 0141 613 0144

Whiteinch 25 Inchlee St, Glasgow G14 9QH; Tel 0141 959
3448

DAY CARE FOR ADULTS WITH PHYSICAL DISABILITES

Disability Resource Centre 130 Langton Rd, Glasgow
G53 5DP; Tel 0141 882 5632; Fax 0141 883 1442

Fernan Street Day Services 30 Fernan St, Shettleston,
Glasgow G32 7HF; Tel 0141 778 9553; Fax 0141 778 5369

St. Ninians Rehabilitation Centre 26 Moraine Ave, Glasgow
G15 6EU; Tel 0141 944 1179; Fax 0141 944 8373

Springbank Centre for Independent Living 41 Doncaster St,
Maryhill, Glasgow G20 7DQ; Tel 0141 945 5662; Fax 0141
945 1529

RESIDENTIAL CARE FOR ADULTS WITH LEARNING DISABILITIES

Brighton Place Hostel 8–12 Brighton Pl, Glasgow G51 2RP;
Tel 0141 445 1850; Fax 0141 440 1695

Downcraig Respite 1 Downcraig Terr, Castlemilk, Glasgow G45 9PA; Tel 0141 634 1074; Fax 0141 634 8896

Riddrie Hostel 2 Riddrievale Crt, Glasgow G33 2RN; Tel 0141 770 4635; Fax 0141 770 4643

RESIDENTIAL CARE FOR ADULTS WITH PHYSICAL DISABILITIES

Fernan Street Hostel 30 Fernan St, Shettleston, Glasgow G32 0BS; Tel 0141 778 4501; Fax 0141 778 5369

DISABLED PEOPLE – OTHER SERVICES

Centre for Sensory Impaired People 17 Gullane St, Partick, Glasgow G11 6AH; Tel 0141 334 5530; Fax 0141 334 5530

Disability Information Service 30 Fernan St, Glasgow G32 7HF; Tel 0141 778 5147; Fax 0141 778 5369

Growning Concern Westwood Business Centre, 69 Aberdalgie Rd, Glasgow G34 9HJ; Tel 0141 771 8887; Fax 0141 771 8754

Job Coaching Service Nye Bevan Hse, 20 India St, Glasgow G2 4PF; Tel 0141 287 9222; 0141 287 9233; Fax 0141 287 8855

Point Project 11 Foundry St, Atlas Ind Est, Glasgow G21 4PR; Tel 0141 557 0981; 0141 557 1433; Fax 0141 558 7106

Sign Language Interpreting Service c/o Centre for Sensory Impaired People, 17 Gullane St, Glasgow G11 6AH; Tel 0141 334 5530; Fax 0141 334 5530; Textphone 0141 341 0825

LOCAL AUTHORITY DAY CARE FOR OLDER PEOPLE

Anderston Mel Milaap 134 Berkeley St, Anderston, Glasgow G3 7HY; Tel 0141 222 2287; Fax 0141 248 1535

Bannerman Day Care Centre Community Wing, Bannerman High School, Glasgow Rd, Baillieston, Glasgow G69 7NS; Tel 0141 771 9397

Battlefield Court Day Centre 17 Cathkin View Pl, Mt Florida, Glasgow G42 9ER; Tel 0141 636 6797

Burnbank House 25 Burnbank Gdns, Glasgow G20 6HD; Tel 0141 332 0952

Cardonald and Penilee Core and Cluster Project Flat 0–1, 11 Tinwald Path, Cardonald, Glasgow G52 2PX; Tel 0141 810 1823

Crossmyloof Resource Centre 80 Titwood Rd, Glasgow G41 2DD; Tel 0141 636 5595; Fax 0141 632 4776

Davislea 100 Mallaig Rd, Glasgow G51 4PE; Tel 0141 445 4397; Fax 0141 445 4531

Dixon Day Centre 656 Cathcart Rd, Glasgow G42 8AA; Tel 0141 423 2481; Fax 0141 423 5361

Drumry House 40 Kinfauns Dr, Glasgow G15 7TS; Tel 0141 944 1146; Fax 0141 944 3596

Elmvale Day Care Centre Elmvale St, Glasgow G21 1LR; Tel 0141 558 6362

Eskdale 163 Wardie Rd, Glasgow G34 9EG; Tel 0141 773 1246; Fax 0141 771 4210

Focal Point 73 Hecla Ave, Drumchapel, Glasgow G15 8LX; Tel 0141 944 8805

Forfar Ave 60 Farfar Ave, Glasgow G52 3JF; Tel 0141 810 4344

Garthamlock Day Centre c/o Cheviot, 151 Mossdale Rd, Glasgow G33 5PT; Tel 0141 774 6108; Fax 0141 774 6108

Gatehouse Spencer St, Glasgow G13 1EA; Tel 0141 950 1771; Fax 0141 950 1698

Govan Day Centre St. Gerards School, 80 Vicarfield St, Glasgow G51 2DJ; Tel 0141 445 6103

Hamiltonhill Day Centre Milton Community Education Centre, 424 Liddesdale Rd, Glasgow G22 7BY; Tel 0141 347 1534

Helenvale Day Centre Calton and Parkhead Parish Church, 142 Helenvale St, Glasgow G31 4NA; Tel 0141 554 5143; Fax 0141 554 5143

Loancroft 101 Muirhead Rd, Glasgow G69 7HB; Tel 0141 771 1562; Fax 0141 771 1562

Merrylee Lodge 55 Muirskeith Rd, Glasgow G43 2JX; Tel 0141 632 1993; Fax 0141 636 0540

Mobile Day Care Flat 22a, 100 Hawthorn St, Glasgow G22 6RG; Tel 0141 336 5783; Fax 0141 336 8073

Newlands Day Centre c/o Braidfauld Hse, 80 Dalness St, Tollcross, Glasgow G32 7RF; Tel 0141 778 9646

Oran Street 45 Oran St, Maryhill, Glasgow G20 8LY; Tel 0141 946 5659

Peter McEachran House 12 Kennyhill Sq, Glasgow G31 1LW; Tel 0141 556 6646

Pinkston Community Care Resource Centre 3–5 Pinkston Dr, Glasgow G21 1PG; Tel 0141 558 4056

Purdon Street Day Care Centre 18 Purdon St, Glasgow G11 6AJ; Tel 0141 338 6126

Ravelston 994 Great Western Rd, Glasgow G12 0NS; Tel 0141 357 3765

Scope c/o Glenwood, 160 Castlemilk Dr, Glasgow G45 9UE; Tel 0141 630 1116; Fax 0141 630 3751

Shanti Bhavan 1 La Belle Pl, Charing Cross, Glasgow G3 7LH; Tel 0141 332 2412; Fax 0141 332 2412

Springburn Centre 62 Broomfield Rd, Glasgow G21 3UB; Tel 0141 558 6464; Fax 0141 558 9640

OLDER PEOPLE – OTHER SERVICES

Burnbank House (Respite Team) 25 Burnbank Gdns, Glasgow G20 6HD; Tel 0141 332 0952

Elderly Resource Team Elmvale Centre, Elmvale St, Glasgow G21 1LR; Tel 0141 557 1010; 0141 557 1020; Fax 0141 558 6362

Merrylee Lodge Resource Unit (Respite) 55 Muirskeith Rd, Glasgow G43 2JX; Tel 0141 632 1993; Fax 0141 636 0540

LOCAL AUTHORITY RESIDENTIAL CARE FOR OLDER PEOPLE

There are 24 residential care homes for people in the area.

CAREERS PROJECT

Carer Support Team 94 Red Rd, Glasgow G21 4PH; Tel 0141 558 6296; Fax 0141 557 0310

Carer's Support Project 29 Shakespeare St, Glasgow G20 8TH; Tel 0141 946 5612; Fax 0141 945 4532

HIV AND AIDS SERVICES

Counselling and Support Team Gartnavel General Hospital, Brownlee Centre, 1053 Gt Western Rd, Glasgow G12 0YN; Tel 0141 211 1090; Fax 0141 211 1097

Positive Accommodation Team Fl 2, Granite Hse, 31 Stockwell St, Glasgow G1 4RZ; Tel 0141 552 4488; Fax 0141 552 2760

HOSPITAL SOCIAL WORK SERVICES

Counselling and Support Team Gartnavel General Hospital, Brownlee Centre, 1053 Gt Western Rd, Glasgow G12 0YN; Tel 0141 211 1090; Fax 0141 211 1097

Drumchapel Hospital Social Work Unit, 129 Drumchapel Rd, Glasgow G15 6PX; Tel 0141 211 6000; Fax 0141 211 6067

Gartnavel General Hospital Social Work Unit, 1053 Gt Western Rd, Glasgow G12 0YN; Tel 0141 211 3102; Fax 0141 211 3486

Glasgow Royal Infirmary Social Work Unit, Cuthbertson Bldg, Fl 5, 91 Wishart St, Glasgow G31 2ER; Tel 0141 211 4787; 0141 211 4788; 0141 211 4791; Fax 0141 552 6189

9

Glasgow Royal Maternity Social Work Unit, Rottenrow, Glasgow G4 0NA; Tel 0141 211 4000; Fax 0141 552 6189

Lennox Castle Hospital Social Work Unit, Lennoxtown, Glasgow G65 7LB; Tel 01360 329200; Fax 01360 329366

Queen Mother's Hospital Social Work Unit, Dalnair St, Glasgow G3 8SJ; Tel 0141 201 0577; Fax 0141 357 4307

Royal Hospital for Sick Children Social Work Unit, Dalnair St, Glasgow G3 8SJ; Tel 0141 201 0057; 0141 201 0058; Fax 0141 357 4307

Southern General Hospital Social Work Unit, 1345 Govan Rd, Glasgow G51 4TF; Tel 0141 201 1446; 0141 201 1447; 0141 201 1448; Fax 0141 201 1148

Stobhill Hospital Social Work Unit, Treasury Bldg, 133 Balornock Rd, Glasgow G21 3UW; Tel 0141 201 3743; Fax 0141 558 7074

Western Infirmary Social Work Unit, Dumbarton Rd, Glasgow G11 6NT; Tel 0141 211 2630; Fax 0141 211 2820

MENTAL HEALTH PROJECTS

Anvil Centre Community Mental Health Team, 81 Salamanca St, Glasgow G31 5BA; Tel 0141 211 8414; Fax 0141 211 8474

Arran Centre 10–18 Redan St, Glasgow G40 2QA; Tel 0141 550 3324; Fax 0141 554 6802

Auchinlea House Community Mental Health Team, Auchinlea Rd, Glasgow G34 9PA; Tel 0141 781 4847; 0141 781 4849; Fax 0141 781 0328

Douglas Inch Clinic 2 Woodside Terr, Glasgow G3 7UY; Tel 0141 211 8000

G15 Mental Health Support Project Social Work Services, 236 Kinfauns Dr, Glasgow G15 7AH; Tel 0141 944 0551; Fax 0141 944 6931

Govan Community Mental Health Project 10 Summertown Rd, Glasgow G51 2LY; Tel 0141 445 1022

Greater Easterhouse Mental Health Project 34 Blythe Rd, Glasgow G33 4QS; Tel 0141 771 8362

Shawpark Resource Centre 41 Shawpark St, Glasgow G20 9DR; Tel 0141 531 8770; Fax 0141 531 8778

Springpark Centre Community Mental Health Team, 101 Denmark St, Glasgow G22 5EU; Tel 0141 531 9300; Fax 0141 531 9304

Education Department

Nye Bevan Hse, 20 India St, Glasgow G2 4PF; Tel 0141 287 6710; Fax 0141 287 6892
Director (Education) Ronnie O'Connor, BA(Hons), DipEd
Depute Director (Planning and Performance) Richard Barron, MA, MEd
Depute Director (Personnel and Finance) G.R. Gardner, BSc
Head (Special Educational Needs) M. Orr, MA

PSYCHOLOGICAL SERVICES

North East Area Office 48 Gourlay St, Glasgow G21 1AE; Tel 0141 558 5303

North West Area Office c/o St. Gregory's Primary School, Glenfinnon Dr, Glasgow G20 8HF; Tel 0141 946 0655

South East Area Office 106 Allan St, Glasgow G40 4TD; Tel 0141 556 1141

South West Area Office c/o Battlefield Primary, Carmichael Pl, Glasgow G42 9SY; Tel 0141 632 0638

SCHOOLS FOR PUPILS WITH SPECIAL EDUCATIONAL NEEDS (DAY)

Abercorn School 195 Garscube Rd, Glasgow G4 9QH; Tel 0141 332 6212
Headteacher P. Smith, DipSpecEduc
   12–16 Mixed MH (135)

Ashcraig School 100 Avenue End Rd, Glasgow G33 3SW; Tel 0141 774 3428
Headteacher M. McGeever
   Mixed 12–16+ PH, PS (136)

Broomlea School 168 Broomhill Dr, Glasgow G11 7NH; Tel 0141 339 6494
Headteacher E. Rankin
   Mixed Nursery 16 MH profound (37)

Carnbooth Residential School 80 Busby Rd, Carmunnock, Glasgow G76 9EG; Tel 0141 644 2773
Headteacher C. Clark

Cartvale School 80 Vicarfield St, Glasgow G51 2DF; Tel 0141 445 5272
Headteacher M. Castle
   Mixed 12–16 (28)

Croftcroighn School 180 Findochty St, Glasgow G33 5EP; Tel 0141 774 7777
Headteacher W. Craig, DCE, DipSpEd
   Mixed Nursery–16 MH Profound (61)

Drummore School 129 Drummore Rd, Glasgow G15 7NH; Tel 0141 944 1323
Headteacher M. Wallace
   Mixed 5–13 MH (65)

Eastmuir School 211 Hallhill Rd, Glasgow G33 4QL; Tel 0141 771 3464
Headteacher Lorraine Inglis
   Mixed 5–13 MH (78)

Gadburn School 70 Rockfield Rd, Glasgow G21 3DZ; Tel 0141 558 5373
Headteacher G. Hercus, BA, DipSpEd, DCE
   Mixed 5–13 MH (48)

Greenview School Buckley St, Glasgow G22 6DJ; Tel 0141 336 8391
Headteacher Mary Ferguson
   Mixed 5–13 (33)

Hampden School 80 Ardnahoe Ave, Glasgow G42 0DL; Tel 0141 647 7720
Headteacher M. Cloughley
   Mixed 5–16 MH severe (42)

Hollybrook School 135 Hollybrook St, Glasgow G42 7HU; Tel 0141 423 5937
Headteacher Lillian Orsi (Acting)
   Mixed 12–16 MH (127)

Howford School 487 Crookston Rd, Glasgow G53 7TX; Tel 0141 882 2605
Headteacher M. Barwell
   Mixed 5–13 MH (77)

Kelbourne School 109 Hotspur St, Glasgow G20 8LH; Tel 0141 946 1405
Headteacher M. McIntosh
   Mixed 3–16

Kelvin School 69 Nairn St, Glasgow G3 8SE; Tel 0141 339 5835
Headteacher Sr Patricia Gribben
   Mixed 5–16 Blind and partially sighted (37)

Kennyhill School 375 Cumbernauld Rd, Glasgow G31 3LP; Tel 0141 554 2765
Headteacher I. Orr
   Mixed 12–16 MH (120)

Kirkriggs School 500 Croftfoot Rd, Glasgow G45 0NJ; Tel 0141 634 7158
Headteacher Elena Convery
   Mixed 5–13 MH (59)

Ladywell School 12a Victoria Park Drive South, Glasgow G14 9RU; Tel 0141 959 6665
Headteacher A. Bombelli
   Mixed 12–16 (30)

Langlands School 100 Mallaig Rd, Glasgow G51 4PE; Tel 0141 445 1132
Headteacher W. Crawford
   Mixed Nursery–16 MH profound (54)

Linburn School 77 Linburn Rd, Glasgow G52 4EX; Tel 0141 883 2082
Headteacher Janette Stewart
    Mixed 5–16 MH severe (46)

Middlefield School 26 Partickhill Rd, Glasgow G11 5BP; Tel 0141 334 0159
Headteacher Liz McKenna (Acting)
    Mixed

Milton School 6 Liddesdale Terr, Glasgow G22 7HL; Tel 0141 762 2102
Headteacher E.J. McCallum
    Mixed 5–16 MH severe (49)

Newhills School Newhills Rd, Glasgow G33 4HJ; Tel 0141 773 1296
Headteacher Mary Mimnagh, BA
    Mixed 5–16 MH severe (47)

Rosshall Visually Impaired Unit c/o Rosshall Academy, 131 Crookston Rd, Glasgow G52 3QF; Tel 0141 582 0200
Unit Co-ordinator Jan Leeming

Richmond Park School 30 Logan St, Glasgow G5 0HP; Tel 0141 429 6095
Headteacher Daniel Grorry
    Mixed 5–13 PH

Rosevale School 48 Scalpay St, Glasgow G22 7DD; Tel 0141 772 1756
Headteacher C. Fraser
    Mixed 5–13 (36)

St. Aidan's School 255 Rigby St, Glasgow G32 6DJ; Tel 0141 556 6276
Headteacher Gerard McDonald
    Mixed 12–16 MH (97)

St. Joan of Arc School 722 Balmore Rd, Glasgow G22 6QS; Tel 0141 336 6885
Headteacher M. McCusker, BA
    Mixed 12–16 MH (102)

St. Kevin's School 25 Fountainwell Rd, Glasgow G21 1TN; Tel 0141 557 3722
Headteacher Mary Gallagher
    Mixed 5–13

St. Oswald's School 83 Brunton St, Glasgow G44 3NF; Tel 0141 637 3952
Headteacher G. McDonnell
    Mixed 12-16 MH (137)

St. Raymond's School 384 Drakemire Dr, Glasgow G45 9SR; Tel 0141 634 1551
Headteacher E.M. Muchan, BA
    Mixed 5–13 MH (42)

St. Roch's Hearing Impaired Unit c/o St. Roch's Secondary, 40 Royston Rd, Glasgow G21 2NF; Tel 0141 582 0273
Unit Co-ordinator Elizabeth Orr

St. Vincent's (Tollcross) School 30 Fullarton Ave, Glasgow G32 8NJ; Tel 0141 778 2254
Headteacher A. Crilly
    Mixed 2–18 Blind, deaf + deaf/blind partially hearing (80)

SCHOOL FOR PUPILS WITH SPECIAL EDUCATIONAL NEEDS (RESIDENTIAL)

Nerston Residential School Nerston Village, East Kilbride, Glasgow G74 4PD; Tel 01355 279 242
Headteacher Ian Smith
    Mixed 5–12 (25)

SCHOOLS FOR PUPILS WITH COMMUNICATION DIFFICULTIES

Bannerman Communication Disorder Unit c/o Bannerman High School, Glasgow Rd, Glasgow G69 7NS; Tel 0141 771 8770
Principal Teacher Elizabeth A. Houston

Caledonia Speech and Language Unit c/o Caledonia Primary School, Calderwood Dr, Baillieston, Glasgow G69 7DJ; Tel 0141 781 4239
Unit Co-ordinator J. Ferguson

Crookston Speech and Language Unit c/o St. Monica's Primary School, 30 Kempsthorn Rd, Glasgow G53 5SR; Tel 0141 892 0813
Unit Co-ordinator R. Garside

Darnley Visual Impairment Unit c/o Darnley Primary School, 169 Glen Morriston Rd, Glasgow G53 7HT; Tel 0141 621 2919
Headteacher Monica McGeever

Hillpark Communication Disorder Unit c/o Hillpark Secondary School, 36 Cairngorm Rd, Glasgow G43 2XB; Tel 0141 582 0112
Headteacher Nadine Barber

Royston Speech and Language Unit c/o Royston Primary School, 102 Royston Rd, Glasgow G21 2NU; Tel 0141 552 1673
Unit Co-ordinator M. McArthur

Ruchill Communication Disorder Unit c/o Ruchill Primary School, 29 Brassey St, Glasgow G20 9HW; Tel 0141 948 0073
Headteacher Helen Barr

St. Charles' Speech and Language Unit c/o St. Charles' Primary School, 13 Kelvinside Gdns, Glasgow G20 6BG; Tel 0141 945 2121
Unit Co-ordinator J. Ross

St. Joseph's Hearing Impaired Unit c/o St. Joseph's Primary School, 39 Raglan St, Glasgow G4 9QX; Tel 0141 353 6136
Headteacher Veronica O'Hagan

St. Thomas Aquinas Language Unit c/o St. Thomas Aquinas Secondary, 147 Berkeley St, Glasgow G3; Tel 0141 221 9558
Head of Unit Ruth Hamilton (Acting)

St. Vincent's Communication Disorder Unit c/o St. Vincent's Primary School, 40 Crebar St, Glasgow; Tel 0141 621 1968
Headteacher Isobel McAllister

Toryglen Communication Disorder Unit c/o Toryglen Primary School, 6 Drumreoch Pl, Glasgow G42 0ER; Tel 0141 613 3840
Unit Co-ordinator Rosemary Russell

9

THE HIGHLAND COUNCIL
www.highland.gov.uk

Headquarters, Glenurquhart Rd, Inverness, Highland IV3 5NX; URL www.highland.gov.uk; E-mail webmaster@highland.gov.uk; Tel 01463 702000; Fax 01463 702111
Chief Executive Arthur D. McCourt

Social Work Services

Kinmylies Bldg, Leachkin Rd, Inverness, Highland IV3 8NN; E-mail social.work@highland.gov.uk; Tel 01463 703456; Fax 01463 713237
Chair (Social Work Services) Cllr Garry Coutts
Vice-Chair Cllr D. Fraser
Vice-Chair Cllr O. MacDonald
Vice-Chair Cllr M. Davidson
Director (Social Work Services) H. Dempster
Head (Client Services) A. Riddell
Head (Criminal Justice Services) George Gray (Acting)
Head (Support Services) G. Gray

Housing and Social Work Committee

Chair (Housing) G.J. Coutts (Ind)
Vice-Chair (Social Justice) Mrs O.J. Macdonald (Ind)
Depute Chair (Community Care) and Chair of Joint Committee
D.C.M. Flear
Depute Chair (Children's Services) and Chair of Joint Committee
Mrs M.C. Davidson

AREA OFFICES

Aviemore Area Office

115 Grampian Rd, Aviemore, Highland PH22 1RH;
Tel 01479 810251; Fax 01479 811502
Area Manager (Social Services) John Richards
Senior Social Worker M. Stewart

Caithness Area Office

125–127 High St, Wick, Highland KW1 4LR; Tel 01955
605040; Fax 01955 605488
Area Manager (Social Work Services) R.L. Silverwood
Assistant Area Manager (Social Work) Dawn Grant

Thurso Area Team

High St, Thurso, Highland KW14 8AG; Tel 01847 893835;
Fax 01847 896309
Area Team Manager I. McElroy

Dingwall Area Office

Council Offices, High St, Dingwall, Highland IV15 9QN;
Tel 01349 868567; Fax 01349 868574
Area Manager (Social Work Services) J. King
Assistant Area Manager (Social Work (Community Care))
Sue Owen
Assistant Area Manager (Social Work) Ian McMurtre
Children and Families Team South Slioch, Castle St,
Dingwall, Highland IV15 9BU; Tel 01349 865262; Fax 01349
864438
Area Team Manager (Children and Families Team)
Shelagh Newton
Senior Social Worker (Care Management) John Mackennan
Children and Young People's Team Conon Family Resource
Centre, Sellar Pl, Inverness, Highland; Tel 01349 861508;
Fax 01349 866899
Manager (Children and Young People's Services Team)
H. Gillan
North East Ross Children and Families Team Suie Hse,
Bridgend, Alness, Highland IV17 0UD; Tel 01349 882609;
Fax 01349 883687
Area Team Manager Robert Gibson
Wester Ross Social Work Services Team Service Point, 29
Market St, Ullapool, Highland; Tel 01854 613307
Senior Social Worker J. MacLennan

Inverness Area Office

The Town Hse, Inverness, Highland IV1 1JJ; Tel 01463
724220; Fax 01463 724291
Area Manager (Social Work Services) S. Campbell
Assistant Area Manager (Social Work) R. Taylor
Assistant Area Manager (Social Work) D. Stallard
Community Care Team Suites 7, 8 and 9, Culloden
Shopping Centre, Tappock Rd, Culloden, Inverness,
Highland; Tel 01463 798337; Fax 01463 798092
Area Team Manager M. Dolan
West Team, Children and Families Carsegate Hse, 18
Glendoe Terr, Inverness, Highland; Tel 01463 724040;
Fax 01463 724000
Area Team Manager M. Morrison
East Team, Children and Families Keppoch Rd, Culloden,
by-Inverness, Highland; Tel 01463 791338; Fax 01463 793229
Manager (East Team) Wendy Allman (Acting)

Lochaber

Tweedale, High St, Fort William, Highland; Tel 01397
703397; Fax 01397 706175
Area Manager (Social Work) Stephen Mackay
Assistant Area Manager (Social Work) P. McClelland
Resource Manager (Community Care Services) T. James
Resource Manager (Disabilities) M. Laird
Manager (Residential Service) M. MacLeod
Senior Social Worker (West Lochaber Team) D. Main-Fraser
Fulton Hse, Gordon Sq, Fort William, Highland; Tel 01397
707025; Fax 01397 707047
Senior Social Worker (East Lochaber Team) D. Main-Fraser
Fulton Hse, Gordon Sq, Fort William, Highland; Tel 01397
703263; Fax 01397 705408
Senior Social Worker (Children's Resources) Armrget Kaur
An Drochaid, Claggan Rd, Claggan, Fort William,
Highland; Tel 01397 703263

Nairn

Corsee, Victoria Rd, Nairn, Highland; Tel 01667 453951
Manager (Area Social Work Services) J. Dunlop
60 King St, Nairn, Highland; Tel 01667 453746; Fax 01667
453217
Senior Social Worker A. Dallas

Skye

Bridge St, Portree, Isle of Skye, Highland; Tel 01478 612943;
Fax 01478 613213
Area Team Manager (Social Work Services) K. McAvoy
Team Manager Helen Fontaine

Sutherland

Council Offices, Main St, Golspie, Highland; Tel 01408
635200; Fax 01408 633120
Assistant Area Manager (Social Work Services) J. Airth
Golspie Area Team Leader I. Mitchell
Olsen Hse, Main St, Golspie, Highland; Tel 01408 634040;
Fax 01408 633034

SPECIALIST SERVICES

Community Disabilities Support Team Isobel Rhind Centre,
Tomich Rd, Invergordon, Highland; Tel 01349 854154;
Fax 01349 852013
Manager Lindsey Tennent
Community Mental Health Team – Caithness Bank Head
Rd, Wick, Highland; Tel 01955 606915; Fax 01955 606916
Team Manager M. MacLeod
Community Mental Health Team – Inverness Kinmylies
Bldg, Leachkin Rd, Inverness, Highland; Tel 01463 703411
Team Manager Ken Bolger
Community Mental Health Team – Lochaber Fulton Hse,
Gordon Sq, Fort William, Highland; Tel 01397 707026
Team Manager D. O'Hara
Community Mental Health Team – Ross and Cromarty
County Hospital, Saltburn Rd, Invergordon, Highland;
Tel 01349 853633
Team Manager Lesley Fraser (Acting)
New Craigs Leachkin Rd, Inverness, Highland; Tel 01463
704666; Fax 01463 712260
Senior Social Worker Ken Bolger
Deaf Services and Hearing Support Team Slioch, Castle St,
Dingwall, Highland; Tel 01349 865418; Fax 01349 864438
Team Manager Helen Farrelly
Learning Disabilities Support Team Coronation Pk,
Inverness, Highland; Tel 01463 729282; Fax 01463
715993
Team Manager P. Cooper (Acting)
Raigmore Hospital Inverness, Highland; Tel 01463 704205;
Fax 01463 711003
Team Manager M. Scott

CRIMINAL JUSTICE SERVICES

Carsegate House Glendoe Terr, Inverness, Highland;
Tel 01463 724022; Fax 01463 724000
Team Leader (Inverness and Dingwall) W. Rainnie
Calendonian Hse, High St, Dingwell, Highland; Tel 01349
865600

Kinmylies Building Leachkin Rd, Inverness, Highland;
Tel 01463 703456; Fax 01463 713237
Development Manager J. Paulin; Tel 01463 703407

Porterfield Prison
Social Worker B. Barr

RESIDENTIAL PROVISION FOR CHILDREN

Coulpark Children's Centre Coulpark, Alness, Highland;
Tel 01349 882472; Fax 01349 883834
Manager C. Williams
(8)

The Orchard Broom Dr, Inverness, Highland; Tel 01463
714165; Fax 01463 716032
Manager Neil Campbell

Wick Children's Centre Northcote St, Wick, Highland;
Tel 01955 604279; Fax 01955 605019
Manager Hilary Woodward
(5)

FAMILY RESOURCE CENTRE

Inverness Family Resource Centre Limetree Ave,
Inverness, Highland; Tel 01463 234120; Fax 01463
715984
Manager Carolyn Blackett

RESOURCE CENTRES (LEARNING DISABILITIES)

Beachview Day Centre Muirfield, Brora, Highland;
Tel 01408 622312; Fax 01408 622314
Manager Gareth Evans

Isobel Rhind Centre Tomich Rd, Invergordon, Highland;
Tel 01349 854154; Fax 01349 852012
Manager Lindsey Tennant

Lochaber Resource Centre Angus Cres, Upper Achintore,
Fort William, Highland; Tel 01397 705427; Fax 01397
700677
Senior Day Centre Officer K. Watson
Senior Day Centre Officer J. MacPherson

Wellington Centre Airport Ind Est, Wick, Highland;
Tel 01955 603744; Fax 01955 605581
Manager Ms I. Doyle

SERVICES TO THE HANDICAPPED

Corbett Centre Coronation Pk, Inverness, Highland;
Tel 01463 729282; Fax 01463 715993
Manager Vacancy

Thor House Provost Smith Dr, Thurso, Highland; Tel 01847
896448; Fax 01847 896943
Manager Pat Boyle

Tigh-na-Drochaid Bridge Rd, Portree, Isle of Skye,
Highland; Tel 01478 613113; Fax 01478 613707
Manager Vacancy

HOSTELS

Assynt Road Hostel 4 Assynt Rd, Inverness, Highland;
Tel 01463 236262

Beachview Resource Centre Muirfield, Brora, Highland;
Tel 01408 622004; Fax 01408 621077
Manager G. Evans

Grant Street Hostel Wick, Highland; Tel 01955 603737

DAY CARE FOR ADULTS WITH PHYSICAL DISABILITIES

Isobel Rhind Centre Tomich Rd, Invergordon, Highland;
Tel 01349 854154; Fax 01349 852013
Manager Lindsey Tennent

Kilmallie Centre Kilmallie Hall, Corpach, Highland;
Tel 01397 772858

DAY CENTRES FOR THE ELDERLY

Acharacle Day Centre Acharacle Centre, Morrison Pl,
Acharacle, Highland; Tel 01967 431323
Manager A. MacPherson

Assynt Centre Lochinver, Highland; Tel 01571 844465;
Fax 01571 844596
Manager R. Pirie

Caol Day Centre Caol, Fort William, Highland; Tel 01397
704259

Eigg Day Centre Eigg Day Centre, Isle of Eigg, Highland;
Tel 01687 482479
Senior Day Care Officer S. Keane

MacKenzie Centre Culduthel Rd, Inverness, Highland;
Tel 01463 231488; Fax 01463 715991
Manager C. Taylor

Tigh-na-Drochaid Bridge Rd, Portree, Isle of Skye,
Highland; Tel 01478 613113; Fax 01478 613213
Manager D. Morton

RESOURCE CENTRES FOR THE ELDERLY

Ach-an-Eas Resource Centre Inverness, Highland;
Tel 01463 710890; Fax 01463 715198
Manager M. Nicholson

Bayview House Resource Centre Thurso, Highland;
Tel 01847 892314; Fax 01847 893470
Manager G. MacLeod

Burnside Home Resource Centre Inverness, Highland;
Tel 01463 233167; Fax 01463 715197
Manager M. Nicolson

Corsee Home Resource Centre Nairn, Highland; Tel 01667
453951; Fax 01667 456202
Manager D. Dolan

Dail Mhor House Resource Centre Strontian, Argyll, Argyll
and Bute; Tel 01967 402481; Fax 01967 402036
Manager Jane Ellis (Acting)

Duthac House Resource Centre Tain, Highland; Tel 01862
894064; Fax 01862 892941
Manager J. Goodfellow

Graham House Resource Centre Dornie, Highland;
Tel 01599 555313; Fax 01599 555419
Manager C. MacLeod (Acting)

Grant House Resource Centre Castle Rd, Grantown-on-
Spey, Highland; Tel 01479 872333; Fax 01479 873476
Manager A. Rainy-Brown

Invernevis House Resource Centre Fort William, Highland;
Tel 01397 702939; Fax 01397 700206
Manager Joanna Hynd

Pulteney House Resource Centre Wick, Highland; Tel 01995
602844; Fax 01995 605371
Manager E. McAllan

Seaforth House Resource Centre Golspie, Highland;
Tel 01408 633730; Fax 01408 633327
Manager F. Thompson

Strathburn Home Resource Centre Gairloch, Highland;
Tel 01445 712493; Fax 01445 712196
Manager J. Hodges

Urray House Resource Centre Muir-of-Ord, Highland;
Tel 01463 870516; Fax 01463 871295
Manager G. MacKinnon

9

COMMUNITY CARE UNITS (ELDERLY)

An Acarsaid Community Care Unit Broadford, Highland; Tel 01471 822670; Fax 01471 822021
Manager M. Noble
(25 day care, 9 residents)

Lochbroom House Community Care Unit Ullapool, Highland; Tel 01854 612705; Fax 01854 612604
Manager Vacancy
(25 day care, 9 residents)

Melvich Centre Portskerra, Melvich, Highland; Tel 01641 531210; Fax 01641 531293
Manager Margaret Dempsey

The Telford Centre Fort Augustus, Highland; Tel 01320 366511; Fax 01320 366583
Manager Tim Blackie
(25 day care, 9 residents)

The Wade Centre Kingussie, Highland; Tel 01540 661863; Fax 01540 661159
Manager S. McCorquodale
(25 day care, 9 residents)

Education, Culture and Sport Service

Glenurquhart Rd, Inverness, Highland IV3 5NX;
URL www.highland.gov.uk/cduc/default.htm;
E-mail ecs@highland.gov.uk; Tel 01463 702806; Fax 01463 702828
Director (Education, Culture and Sport) Bruce Robertson, MA
Head (Community and Leisure) Ian Murray
Head (Support Services) Hugh Fraser
Head (Education Services) D.R.J. MacDonald, BSc
Manager (Community Learning) W.F. MacPherson

PSYCHOLOGICAL SERVICE

11–13 Culcabock Ave, Inverness, Highland IV2 3RG;
Tel 01463 233494; Fax 01463 713775
Principal Psychologist S. Iliffe, BA, MEd

SPECIAL SCHOOLS

Drummond School Drummond Rd, Inverness, Highland IV2 4NZ; Tel 01463 233091; Fax 01463 713106

St. Clement's School Old Academy, Dingwall, Highland IV15 9JZ; Tel 01349 863284

St. Duthus School Academy St, Tain, Highland IV19 1ED; Tel 01862 894407

INVERCLYDE COUNCIL
www.inverclyde.gov.uk

Population 89 990
Municipal Bldgs, Greenock, Inverclyde PA15 1LZ;
URL www.inverclyde.gov.uk; Tel 01475 724400;
Fax 01475 712010
Chief Executive Robert Cleary

Social Work Services

Dalrymple Hse, 195 Dalrymple St, Greenock, Inverclyde PA15 1UN; Tel 01475 714000; Fax 01475 714060
Director (Social Work and Housing Services) Tom Keenan
Head (Social Work Services) Robert Murphy
Head (Community Care and Strategic Services) Barbara Billings
Head (Finance and Administration) Colin Struthers

CHILDREN'S AND YOUNG PEOPLE'S RESIDENTIAL HOMES

Crosshill Residential Home 1 Crosshill Pl, Port Glasgow, Inverclyde; Tel 01475 715634; Fax 01475 715638
(16)

Neil Street Residential Unit 41 Neil St, Greenock, Inverclyde PA16 9JA; Tel 01475 715809; Fax 01475 715811
(14)

Redholm Residential Unit Alderwood Rd, Port Glasgow, Inverclyde; Tel 01475 715789; Fax 01475 715790

DAY CARE AND ADULT TRAINING CENTRES (LOCAL AUTHORITY)

Devol Centre Auchinleck La, Port Glasgow, Inverclyde; Tel 01475 715786; Fax 01475 715788
LD

Fitzgerald Centre 110 Lyndoch St, Greenock, Inverclyde PA15 4AH; Tel 01475 715800; Fax 01475 715803
LD (80)

McPherson Centre McPherson Dr, Gourock, Inverclyde; Tel 01475 659136; Fax 01475 659114
LD

Outreach Project Fitzgerald Centre, 110 Lynedoch St, Greenock, Inverclyde; Tel 01475 715804
LD

RESIDENTIAL CARE AND ACCOMMODATION

Bank Street Hostel Bank St, Greenock, Inverclyde; Tel 01475 729415
LD

Finnart Hostel 68–70 Finnart St, Greenock, Inverclyde; Tel 01475 715782
LD

Jericho House 5 Bank St, Greenock, Inverclyde; Tel 01475 783063
Homelessness and alcoholism

Lynedoch House Lower Lynedoch St, Greenock, Inverclyde; Tel 01475 729196
Contact Mrs McGill
Mental illness (14)

Oronsay Hostel 106 Oronsay Ave, Port Glasgow, Inverclyde; Tel 01475 715784; Fax 01475 715785
LD

Salvation Army Hostel Terrace Rd, Greenock, Inverclyde; Tel 01475 721572
Homelessness and alcoholism

DAY CARE CENTRES FOR THE ELDERLY

Alzheimers Day Centres William St, Greenock, Inverclyde; Tel 01475 728215

Inverclyde Day Centre Barlas Centre, 195 Dalrymple St, Greenock, Inverclyde; Tel 01475 714151
(incorporating Meadowlark and Octavia Centres)
Elderly

Muirsheil Centre The Factory, Ind Est, Port Glasgow, Inverclyde; Tel 01475 745115

SMALL GROUP DAY CARE (LOCAL AUTHORITY)

195 Dalrymple St, Greenock, Inverclyde
(Provision of day care in an informal setting for the vulnerable elderly and/or those suffering from dementia).

RESIDENTIAL HOMES FOR THE ELDERLY (LOCAL AUTHORITY)

(including day care in a residential setting).

Hillend Home for the Elderly East Crawford St, Greenock, Inverclyde; Tel 01475 715795; Fax 01475 715796

Kempock Home for the Elderly Kirn Dr, Gourock, Inverclyde; Tel 01475 631175; Fax 01475 634834

VOLUNTARY AND PRIVATE HOMES FOR THE ELDERLY

There are 16 voluntary and private homes for the elderly.

INTERMEDIATE TREATMENT CENTRES

Mearns Centre Mearns St, Greenock, Inverclyde; Tel 01475 715805; Fax 01475 715808

SUPPORTED LIVING TEAM

36 Lynedoch St, Greenock, Inverclyde PA16 4HE; Tel 01475 715816
Supported accommodation schemes are operated for a range of client groups.

Education Services

Inverclyde Council, 105 Dalrymple St, Greenock, Inverclyde PA15 1HT; Tel 01475 712824; Fax 01475 712875
Director B. McLeary
Head (Support for Learning) A. MacDonald
Head (Planning and Resources) J. Sutherland
Head (SEN and ICT) Albert Henderson
Head (Pre-5 and Children's Services) E. Henderson
Manager (SEN Service) Maureen Irving

SPECIAL SCHOOLS

Garvel School Chester Rd, Greenock, Inverclyde PA16 0TT; Tel 01475 635477
Mixed 5–18 Deaf and partially deaf (15)

Glenburn School Inverkip Rd, Greenock, Inverclyde PA16 0QG; Tel 01475 715400
Headteacher Eileen McGeer
Mixed 5–18 MH, PH, PS (275)

Lilybank School Birkmyre Ave, Port Glasgow, Inverclyde PA14 5AN; Tel 01475 715703
Headteacher Eileen Stewart
Mixed 5–18 MH severe and profound unit (60)

PSYCHOLOGICAL SERVICE

Highholm Centre Highholm Ave, Port Glasgow, Inverclyde PA14 5JN; Tel 01475 715430
Principal E. Hart

SEN NETWORKS

Glenburn Communication Disorder Unit Glenburn School, Inverkip Rd, Greenock, Inverclyde PA16 0QG
Headteacher Eileen McGeer
Secondary Communication and Language Disorders (6)

Network 1 St. Mungo's Primary School, Grosvenor Rd, Greenock, Inverclyde PA15 2DP; Tel 01475 715732
Co-ordinator J. Buchta

Network 2 Larkfield Primary School, Chester Rd, Greenock, Inverclyde PA16 0TT; Tel 01475 715677
Co-ordinator Wendy Patrick

Primary Support Unit Boglestone Primary School, Bridgend Ave, Port Glasgow, Inverclyde PA15 5SU
Headteacher Lilian Hasson
Social, emotional and behavioural difficulties (6)

St. Mungo's Language and Communication Base St. Mungo's Primary School, Grosvenor Rd, Greenock, Inverclyde PA15 2DP
Headteacher Anne Marie McLeary (Acting)
Communication and Language Disorders (Primary) (6)

Population 82 200
Fairfield Hse, 8 Lothian Rd, Dalkeith, Midlothian EH22 1DJ; URL www.midlothian.gov.uk; E-mail enquiries@midlothian.gov.uk; Tel 0131 270 7500; Fax 0131 271 3050
Chief Social Work Manager Malcolm McEwan

Social Work, Executive Services

Fairfield Hse, 8 Lothian Rd, Dalkeith, Midlothian EH22 3ZH; E-mail malcolm.mcewan@midlothian.gov.uk; Tel 0131 271 3605
Chief Social Work Officer Malcolm McEwan

Cabinet

Spokesperson (Social Work, Housing and Health) Cllr D. Molloy

Housing Unit

Manager (Housing) J. Burgoyne

Social Work HQ

Fairfield Hse, 8 Lothian Rd, Dalkeith, Midlothian EH22 3ZH; Tel 0131 271 3605; Fax 0131 271 3624
Manager (Children and Families and Criminal Justice) N. Glennie
Manager (Community Care) J. Cochran
Manager (Business Services) R. Ross

Social Work Centres

DALKEITH SOCIAL WORK CENTRE

11 St. Andrew St, Dalkeith, Midlothian EH22 1AL; Tel 0131 271 3860; Fax 0131 663 2826
Practice Manager (Children and Families Team) E. Pinnons
Service Manager (Assessment and Care) B. Taylor
Service Manager (Criminal Justice Team) I. Neil
Manager (Resources) J. Fairnie

LOANHEAD SOCIAL WORK CENTRE

4 Clerk St, Loanhead, Midlothian EH20 9DR; Tel 0131 271 3900; Fax 0131 448 2151
Divisional Mental Health Officer R. Buchanan
Resource Manager (Children and Families) A. Martin
Service Manager (Community Care Team) N. Lomes

Day Establishments

JOHN CHANT CENTRE

Eastfield Farm Rd, Penicuik, Midlothian EH26 8EZ; Tel 01968 678346

ADULT TRAINING/RESOURCE CENTRE

Cherry Road Centre 8 Cherry Rd, Bonnyrigg, Midlothian EH19 3ED; Tel 0131 663 2239

CHILDREN'S CENTRE

Hawthorn Children's Centre 2f Bogwood Rd, Mayfield, Dalkeith, Midlothian EH22 5DQ; Tel 0131 660 1938

9

DAY CENTRE FOR OLDER PEOPLE

Highbank Day Centre 9 Bonnyrigg Rd, Eskbank, Midlothian EH22 3EY; Tel 0131 663 3155

Residential Establishments

CHILDREN AND YOUNG PEOPLE'S CENTRES

Gorebridge CSU 23 Ladybrae, Gorebridge, Midlothian EH23 4HT; Tel 01875 820307

Midfield House Hawthornden Rd, Lasswade, Midlothian EH18 1ED; Tel 0131 663 1112; Fax 0131 660 3090

HOMES FOR OLDER PEOPLE

There are three residential homes for older people.

Education Division

Fairfield Hse, 8 Lothian Rd, Dalkeith, Midlothian
    EH22 3ZG; URL www.midlothian.gov.uk;
    E-mail education@midlothian.gov.uk; Tel 0131 271 3718;
    Fax 0131 271 3751
Director (Education)   D.S. MacKay
Head (Schools and Community Education)   F. Mitchell
Head (Support Services)   J.M. Clarke
Education Officer (Nursery, Primary, Special)   M. Barclay
Education Officer (Nursery, Primary, Special)   J. Thayers
Education Officer (Curriculum Development)   W. Whitelaw
Education Officer (Staff Development)   H. Wylie
Education Officer (Technical and Curriculum Support)
    T. Lawson
Education Officer (Administration)   P. Brown
Education Officer (Special Needs – Pupil Support)   C. Knight
Education Officer (Community Education)   G. Clayton

PUPIL SUPPORT SERVICES

Greenhall Centre Gowkshill, Gorebridge, Midlothian EH23 4PE; Tel 01875 823699; Fax 01875 823603
Principal Psychologist   Alan Haughey

SCHOOL FOR PUPILS WITH SPECIAL EDUCATIONAL NEEDS

Saltersgate School Lugton Brae, Dalkeith, Midlothian EH22 1JX; Tel 0131 663 7146
Headteacher   J. Loughlin

MORAY COUNCIL
www.moray.org

Population 87 000
Council Office, High St, Elgin, Moray IV30 1BX;
    URL www.moray.org; E-mail hotline@moray.gov.uk;
    Tel 01343 543451; Fax 01343 540183
Convener   Eddie Aldridge
Chief Executive   Alastair Keddie

Community Services Department

Tel 01343 563530; Fax 01343 563521
Director (Community Services)   M. Martin

Social Work Division – Children and Families and Criminal Justice

Head (Children, Families and Criminal Justice)   J. Sullivan
Social Work Manager (Children and Families)   J. Carney
Social Work Manager (Criminal Justice Services)   B. Dempsie

Community Care Division

Head (Community Care)   S. Chisholm

COMMUNITY SERVICES COMMITTEE

Chair   Percy Watt (Ind)
Auchoynanie, Keith, Moray AB55 5AW
Vice-Chair   Jennifer Shaw (Ind)
Sherrifston, Elgin, Moray IV30 8LA
Members of the Committee
Lab: A. Burgess, J. Divers, M. Ettles, J. Leslie.
Scottish Conservative and Unionist Party: I. Young.
SNP: P. Paul.
Ind. Nationalist: W. Jappy, S. Longmore.
Scottish Lib Dem: L. Gorn.

Local Offices

Anchernack Local Office High St, Forres, Moray; Tel 01309 694031
Senior Social Worker   M. Cotter

Cluny Square Local Office 13 Cluny Sq, Buckie, Aberdeenshire; Tel 01542 837200
Senior Social Worker   P. Hall

Mid Street Local Office 26 Mid St, Keith, Aberdeenshire; Tel 01542 882281
Senior Social Worker   P. Hall

Moss Street Local Office Moss St, Elgin, Moray
Senior Area Manager (Community Care)   J. Tidey
Manager (Planning and Commissioning)   M. Christie
Manager (Home Care)   S. Anderson
Manager (Residential and Leaving Care Services)   J. Brewer
Senior Social Worker (Children's Services)   G. Sinclair
Senior Social Worker (Resources for Children)   D. Cameron
Senior Occupational Therapist   A. Clark

North Guildry Street Local Office 9 North Guildry St, Elgin, Moray; Tel 01343 541111
Senior Social Worker (Criminal Justice)   B. Dempsie
Senior Social Worker (Learning Disability)   Anne Slee

Post Office Building Local Office 252 High St, Elgin, Moray; Tel 01343 552211
Senior Social Worker (Addictions)   Blair Dempsie

South Street Local Office 78 South St, Elgin, Moray; Tel 01343 552699
Senior Social Worker   Graeme Rizza
Senior Social Worker   G. Harkins
Senior Social Worker   Blair Dempsie

DAY CARE CENTRES FOR ELDERLY PEOPLE

Bellie Church Hall Day Centre The Square, Fochabers, Moray; Tel 01343 821420
Contact   F. Stephen
    (6)

Bishopmill House Day Centre 2 Lossiemouth Rd, Elgin, Moray; Tel 01343 542544
Contact   Fiona Stephen

Castlehill Day Centre Tomnabat Crt, Tomintoul, Moray; Tel 01807 580326
Contact   Anne Kennaugh

Clydeville Bungalow Day Centre Queen St, Buckie, Aberdeenshire; Tel 01542 835388
Contact   F. Stephen

Glenview Day Centre Louise St, Dufftown, Moray; Tel 01340 20966
Contact   Anne Kennaugh
    (10)

New Elgin Day Centre New Elgin Hall, Land St, New Elgin, Moray; Tel 01343 551626

Rothes Day Centre Linnburn, High St, Rothes, Highland; Tel 01340 831794
Contact   Anne Kennaugh

SERVICES FOR PEOPLE WITH A LEARNING DIFFICULTY

Cedarwood Edgar Row, Elgin, Moray; Tel 01343 542023
Manager A. MacDonald
(77)

Clydeville Training Centre 9 Queen St, Buckie, Aberdeenshire; Tel 01542 832272
Manager J. Wilson
(30)

Moray Respite Unit 11 Logie Ave, Cullen, Moray; Tel 01542 841341
Manager P. Bulmer

CENTRES FOR PEOPLE WITH A DISABILITY

Keith Resource Centre 26 Mid St, Keith, Aberdeenshire; Tel 01542 882281
Manager A. Benvie

Moray Resource Centre Maisondieu Rd, Elgin, Moray; Tel 01343 551339
Manager Mike Gray
(15)

HOME FOR ELDERLY PEOPLE

There is one residential home for older people.

Educational Services

The Moray Council, High St, Elgin, Moray IV30 1BX;
URL www.moray.org;
E-mail donna.brown@moray.gov.uk; Tel 01343 563267;
Fax 01343 563478
Director (Educational Services) Donald M. Duncan

SCHOOLS WITH SEN BASES

Applegrove Primary School SEN Base Orchard Rd, Forres, Moray IV36 1PJ;
E-mail admin.applegrovep@moray-edunet.gov.uk;
Tel 01309 672367; Fax 01309 674978
Headteacher Mrs A.R. Maclennan

Aberlour Primary School SEN Base Mary Ave, Aberlour, Moray AB38 9PN;
E-mail admin.aberlourp@moray.edunet.gov.uk; Tel 01340 871255; Fax 01340 871076
Headteacher Chris Burns

Beechbrae Education Centre Duffus Rd, Elgin, Moray IV30 4NP; E-mail douglas.wilson@moray.gov.uk; Tel 01343 557900; Fax 01343 557935
Manager (Inclusion and Support) Douglas Wilson

Buckie Community High School SEN Base West Cathcart St, Buckie, Moray AB56 1QB;
E-mail admin.buckiehigh@moray-edunet.gov.uk; Tel 01542 832605; Fax 01542 835758
Headteacher Chris Sugden

Elgin Academy SEN Base Morriston Rd, Elgin, Moray IV30 4ND; E-mail admin.elginacad@moray-edunet.go.uk;
Tel 01343 543485; Fax 01343 540893
Headteacher Alistair Brown

Elgin High SEN Base – Kestrel House High School Dr, New Elgin, Moray IV30 6UD;
E-mail admin.elginhigh@moray-edunet.gov.uk; Tel 01343 545181; Fax 01343 540892
Headteacher Andrew Simpson

English as an Additional Language Central Support Service, Beechbrae Education Centre, Duffus Rd, Elgin, Moray IV30 4NP; E-mail kim.stokes@moray.gov.uk; Tel 01343 557921

Forres Academy SEN Base Burdsyard Rd, Forres, Moray IV36 IFG; E-mail admin.forresacad@moray-edunet.gov.uk; Tel 01309 672271; Fax 01309 676745
Headteacher Fiona Hewitt

Greenwards Primary School SEN Base Edgar Rd, New Elgin, Elgin, Moray IV30 6UQ;
E-mail admin.greenwardsp@moray-edunet.gov.uk;
Tel 01343 541661; Fax 01343 550656
Headteacher G. Richard Donald

Hearing-Impaired and Visual-Impaired Service Central Support Services, Beechbrae Education Centre, Duffus Rd, Elgin, Moray IV30 4NP; E-mail kim.stokes@moray.gov.uk; Tel 01343 557921

Hythehill Primary School SEN Base Lossiemouth, Moray IV31 6RF; E-mail admin.hythehillp@moray-edunet.gov.uk; Tel 01343 812014; Fax 01343 815467
Headteacher Hazel McPherson

Keith Grammar School SEN Base School Rd, Keith, Moray AB55 5ES;
E-mail admin.keithgrammar@moray-edunet.gov.uk;
Tel 01542 882461; Fax 01542 886032
Headteacher John Aitken

Keith Primary School SEN Base School Rd, Keith, Moray AB55 5ES; E-mail admin.keithp@moray-edunet.gov.uk; Tel 01542 882802; Fax 01542 886916
Headteacher Helen Kirkwood

Kinloss Primary School SEN Base Burghead Rd, Kinloss, Moray IV36 3SX;
E-mail admin.kinlossp@moray-edunet.gov.uk; Tel 01309 690376; Fax 01309 691548
Headteacher Ian Brodie

Language Support and Early Years Team Central Support Services, Beechbrae Education Centre, Duffus Rd, Elgin, Moray IV30 4NP; E-mail kim.stokes@moray.gov.uk; Tel 01343 557921

Lhanbryde Primary School SEN Base Garmouth Rd, Lhanbryde, Moray IV30 8PD;
E-mail admin.lhanbrydep@moray-edunet.gov.uk; Tel 01343 842649; Fax 01343 843285
Headteacher Alison Underwood

Lossiemouth High School SEN Base Coulardbank Rd, Lossiemouth, Moray IV31 6JU;
E-mail admin.lossiehigh@moray-edunet.gov.uk; Tel 01343 812047; Fax 01343 814343
Headteacher Lachlan MacPherson

Millbank Primary School SEN Base McWilliam Cres, Buckie, Moray AB56 1LU;
E-mail admin.millbankp@moray-edunet.gov.uk; Tel 01542 831113; Fax 01542 831935
Headteacher John Trodden

Milne's High School SEN Base West St, Fochabers, Moray IV32 7DJ; E-mail admin.milneshigh@moray-edunet.gov.uk; Tel 01343 820611; Fax 01343 820306
Headteacher W. Gordon McPherson

Pinefield Project, Assessment and Resource Centre No. 1 Perimeter Rd, Pinefield Ind Est, Elgin, Moray IV30 6AQ; Tel 01343 545260

Speyside High School SEN Base Mary Ave, Aberlour, Moray AB38 9PN;
E-mail admin.speysidehigh@moray-edunet.gov.uk; Tel 01340 871522; Fax 01340 871098
Headteacher David Tierney

9

NORTH AYRSHIRE COUNCIL

www.north-ayrshire.gov.uk

Population 135 817
Political Composition: Lab: 21, Con: 4, SNP: 3, Ind: 2
Cunningham Hse, Irvine, North Ayrshire KA12 8EE;
URL www.north-ayrshire.gov.uk;
E-mail info@north-ayrshire.gov.uk; Tel 01294 324100;
Fax 01294 324144
Chief Executive Bernard Devine

Social Services

Headquarters, Elliott Hse, Redburn Ind Est, Irvine, North Ayrshire KA12 8TB; URL www.north-ayrshire.gov.uk; Tel 01294 317700; (Emergency) 0800 811505; Fax 01294 317701
Corporate Director (Social Services) Bernadette M. Docherty

Social Work Committee

Lab: 15, Con: 1, SNP: 1
Chair A. Munro Lab
Vice-Chair J. Donn Lab
Vice-Chair M. McDougall Lab
Members of the Committee
Lab: J. Carson, I. Clarkson, S. Dewar, D. Duncan, D. Gallagher, J. Gorman, J. Moffat, M. Munn, D. O'Neill, R. Reilly, S. Taylor.
Con: E. Marshall.
SNP: A. Hill.

Headquarters

Head (Community Care) L. Skehal
Principal Officer (Adult Services) S. Gault
Principal Officer (Resources) B. Burns
Principal Officer (Children and Families Services) A. Beattie
Principal Officer (Criminal Justice Services) W.R. McLean

Direct Service Units

Head of Service (Children and Families; Criminal Justice) S. Paterson
Principal Officer (Children and Families Fieldwork) D. MacRitchie
Principal Officer (Community Care) C. Hamilton
Assistant Principal Officer (Welfare Rights) Isobel Kelly

AREA HEADQUARTERS

Irvine Bridgegate Hse, Irvine, North Ayrshire; Tel 01294 324800; Fax 01294 324844

Kilbirnie, Largs and Arran Craigton Rd, Kilbirnie, North Ayrshire; Tel 01505 684551; Fax 01505 685598

Three Towns 17 Vernon St, Saltcoats, North Ayrshire; Tel 01294 605261; Fax 01294 610794

TEAM OFFICES

Ardrossan Office Aitken Pl, Ardrossan, North Ayrshire; Tel 01294 468213

Arran Office Council Offices, Shore Rd, Lamash, Isle of Arran, North Ayrshire; Tel 01770 600742

Dreghorn Office 23 Main St, Dreghorn, North Ayrshire; Tel 01294 218407

Irvine Office Bridgegate Hse, North Ayrshire; Tel 01294 324800

Kilbirnie Office Craigton Rd, Kilbirnie, North Ayrshire; Tel 01505 684551; Fax 01505 685598

Kilwinning Office 17 Byres Rd, North Ayrshire; Tel 01294 559820

Largs Office 32–34 Boyd St, North Ayrshire; Tel 01475 674585

Saltcoats Office 17 Vernon St, Saltcoats, North Ayrshire; Tel 01294 605261

Stevenston Office 17 Vernon St, Saltcoats, North Ayrshire; Tel 01294 605261

ADDICTION CENTRES

Townhead Centre Townhead, Irvine, North Ayrshire; Tel 01294 275631

Vernon Centre Vernon St, Saltcoats, North Ayrshire; Tel 01294 461731

CHILDREN'S UNITS

Dalrymple Place Children's Unit Irvine, North Ayrshire; Tel 01294 276994

Dreghorn Hostel 108 Main St, Dreghorn, North Ayrshire; Tel 01294 213451

Harley Place Children's Unit 16 Harley Pl, Saltcoats, North Ayrshire; Tel 01294 466497

McKellar Avenue Children's Unit 25 McKellar Ave, Ardrossan, North Ayrshire; Tel 01294 603813

Seaton Terrace Children's Unit 59a–c Seaton Terr, Irvine, North Ayrshire; Tel 01294 276001

COMMUNITY RESOURCE CENTRE

Throughcare Team 41 Kinnier Rd, Saltcoats, North Ayrshire; Tel 01294 602527

CRIMINAL JUSTICE SERVICES

Criminal Justice Service Team 60 Bank St, Irvine, North Ayrshire; Tel 01294 273110

Criminal Justice Service Team 157 New St, Stevenston, North Ayrshire; Tel 01294 463924

Community Service Order Office Unit 13, Ashgrove Rd, Kilwinning, North Ayrshire; Tel 01294 550353

DISABILITY RESOURCE CENTRE

Pavilion 9, Ayrshire Central Hospital, Irvine, North Ayrshire; Tel 01294 323209

HOMES FOR THE ELDERLY

There are six homes for the elderly.

HOSPITAL SOCIAL WORK

Ayrshire Central Hospital Kilwinning Rd, Irvine, North Ayrshire
General Social Work Team Tel 01294 323092
Home from Hospital Project Tel 01294 323091

RESOURCE CENTRES AND HOSTELS (LEARNING DISABLED)

Fergushill Resource Centre Fergushill Rd, Kilwinning, North Ayrshire; Tel 01294 551899

Hawthorn Court Hostel Kilwinning, North Ayrshire; Tel 01294 521180

Hazeldene Resource Centre Blair Rd, Kilwinning, North Ayrshire; Tel 01294 558201

Mount Pleasant Group Tenancy Unit Stevenston, North Ayrshire; Tel 01294 601865

SPECIAL PROJECTS

Hazeldene Employment Development Initiative Hazeldene Work Centre, Blair Rd, Kilwinning, North Ayrshire; Tel 01294 557561

Irvine Community Befriend A Child Scheme 17 Byres Rd, Kilwinning, North Ayrshire; Tel 01294 559820

Irvine Kids and Carers Project 17 Byres Rd, Kilwinning, North Ayrshire; Tel 01294 559820

Educational Services

Cunninghame Hse, Irvine, North Ayrshire KA12 8EE; URL www.north-ayrshire.gov.uk; E-mail education@north-ayrshire.gov.uk; Tel 01294 324400; Fax 01294 324443

Corporate Director John Travers
Head (Educational Resources) Brian Gardner
Head (Education Services) James Leckie
Head (Education Services) Lesley Owens
Head (Education Services) James Tulips
Head (Education Services) Jan Ward

PSYCHOLOGICAL SERVICE

Montgomerie Crescent Saltcoats, North Ayrshire
KA21 5BX ; Tel 01294 463495; Fax 01294 470060

SPECIAL SCHOOLS (DAY)

Haysholm School Bank St, Irvine, North Ayrshire
KA12 0NE; E-mail haysholmss@aol.com; Tel 01294 272481;
Fax 01294 276673
    5–18 Severe learning difficulties.

James McFarlane School Dalry Rd, Ardrossan, North
Ayrshire KA22 7DQ; E-mail jamesmcf@aol.com; Tel 01294
461370; Fax 01294 470225
    5–18 Multiple and complex learning difficulties.

James Reid School Primrose Pl, Saltcoats, North Ayrshire
KA21 6LH; E-mail jreidss@aol.com; Tel 01294 467105;
Fax 01294 470702
    5–18 Learning difficulties

Stanecastle School Burns Cres, Girdle Toll, Irvine, North
Ayrshire KA11 1AQ; E-mail staneteach@aol.com; Tel 01294
211914; Fax 01294 211792
    5–18 Learning difficulties

NORTH LANARKSHIRE COUNCIL
www.northlan.gov.uk

PO Box 14, Civic Centre, Motherwell, North Lanarkshire
ML1 1TW; URL www.northlan.gov.uk; Tel 01698 302222;
Fax 01698 275125
Chief Executive Gavin Whitefield; Tel 01698 302452;
Fax 01698 230265

Social Work Department

73–77 Merry St, Motherwell, North Lanarkshire ML1 1JE;
URL www.northlan.gov.uk;
    E-mail socialwork@northlan.gov.uk; Tel 01698 332000
Director Jim Dickie

SOCIAL WORK AREA TEAM OFFICES

Airdrie Area Office Coats Hse, Gartlea Rd, Airdrie, North
Lanarkshire ML1 9LJ; Tel 01236 757000

Bellshill Area Office 303 Main St, Bellshill, North
Lanarkshire ML4 1AW; Tel 01698 346666

Coatbridge Area Office 122 Bank St, Coatbridge, North
Lanarkshire ML5 1ET; Tel 01236 622100

Chryston Sub-Office 3 Lindsaybeg Rd, Chryston, North
Lanarkshire; Tel 0141 779 2291

Cumbernauld Area Office Carron Hse, Town Centre,
Cumbernauld, North Lanarkshire G67 1DP; Tel 01236
784000

Motherwell Area Office Scott Hse, Merry St, Motherwell,
North Lanarkshire ML1 1JE; Tel 01698 332100

Shotts Sub-Office 169 Station Rd, Shotts, North
Lanarkshire ML7 4BQ; Tel 01501 824700

Wishaw Area Office Kings Bldg, King St, Wishaw, North
Lanarkshire; Tel 01698 348200

RESIDENTIAL CARE HOMES

Bellhaven Dryburgh Rd, Wishaw, North Lanarkshire
ML2 7JA; Tel 01698 374850

Chilterns 2 Park Rd, Chryston, North Lanarkshire; Tel 0141
779 3723

Herbison House Manse Rd, Shotts, North Lanarkshire;
Tel 01501 822683

Leslie House Merry St, Motherwell, North Lanarkshire;
Tel 01698 267195
    Elderly

Lochview House Tay St, Coatbridge, North Lanarkshire;
Tel 01236 421774

Meadowside Forrest St, Airdrie, North Lanarkshire ML1;
Tel 01236 762461

Monklands 1 Stanrigg Pl, Plains, Airdrie, North
Lanarkshire ML6 9LA; Tel 01236 842648

Muirpark 78 Laburnum Rd, Viewpark, Uddingston, North
Lanarkshire; Tel 01698 816368
    Elderly

Ochilview 5 Hume Rd, Cumbernauld, North Lanarkshire;
Tel 01236 727752

DAY CENTRES

Contact local Social Work Area Office, to access these
facilities.

Education Department

Municipal Bldgs, Kildonan St, Coatbridge, North
    Lanarkshire ML5 3BT; URL www.northlan.gov.uk;
    E-mail education@northlan.gov.uk; Tel 01236 812222;
    Fax 01236 812247
Director (Education) Michael O'Neill
Depute Director Christine Pollock
Head (Educational Provision) Murdo MacIver
Head (Quality and Support Service) John O'Keane

PSYCHOLOGICAL SERVICES

Main Office Kyle Rd, Kildrum, Cumbernauld, North
Lanarkshire G67 2DN; Tel 01236 731041

Monklands Area St. Aloysius Primary School, Main St,
Airdrie, North Lanarkshire ML6 8SF; Tel 01236 764135

Motherwell Area St. Brendan's Primary School, 45 Barons
Rd, Motherwell, North Lanarkshire ML1 2NB; Tel 01698
262840

SPECIAL SCHOOLS (DAY)

Bothwellpark School Annan St, Motherwell, South
Lanarkshire ML1 2DL;
E-mail ht@bothwellpark.n-lanark.sch.uk; Tel 01698 230700
    Mixed 14–16+ MH severe (25)

Clyde View School Magna St, Motherwell, North
Lanarkshire ML1 3QZ;
E-mail ht@clydeview.n-lanark.sch.uk; Tel 01698 264843
    Mixed 5–16 MH severe (30)

Drumpark School Coatbridge Rd, Bargeddie, Balieston,
Glasgow G69 7TW; E-mail ht@drumpark.n-lanark.sch.uk;
Tel 01236 423955
    Mixed 5–16 MH, PH (260)

Fallside Secondary School Sanderson Ave, Bothwell Pk,
Uddingston, North Lanarkshire G71 6JZ;
E-mail ht@fallride.n-lanark.sch.uk

Firpark School Firpark St, Motherwell, North Lanarkshire
ML1 2PR; E-mail ht@firpark.n-lanark.sch.uk; Tel 01698
251313
    Mixed 5–16 MH, PH

9

Glencryan School Greenfaulds Rd, Cumbernauld, North Lanarkshire G67 2XJ; E-mail ht@glencryan.n-lanark.sch.uk; Tel 01236 724125
Mixed 5–16 MH, PH (40)

Mavisbank School Mitchell St, Airdrie, North Lanarkshire ML6 0EB; E-mail ht@mavisbank.n-lanark.sch.uk; Tel 01236 752725
Mixed 5–16 MH, profound (40)

Pentland School Tay St, Coatbridge, North Lanarkshire G69 9DL; E-mail ht@pentland.n-lanark.sch.uk; Tel 01236 420471

Portland High School 31–33 Kildonan St, Coatbridge, North Lanarkshire ML5 3BT; E-mail ht@portland.n-lanark.sch.uk; Tel 01236 440634

Redburn School Mossknowe Bldgs, Kildrum, Cumbernauld, North Lanarkshire G72 2EG; E-mail ht@redburn.n-lanark.sch.uk; Tel 01236 736904
Mixed 5–16 PMH

Willowbank School 299 Bank St, Coatbridge, North Lanarkshire ML5 1EG; E-mail ht@willowbank.n-lanark.sch.uk; Tel 01236 421911

ORKNEY ISLANDS COUNCIL
www.orkney.gov.uk

Population 19 480
Council Offices, School Pl, Kirkwall, Orkney Islands KW15 1NY; URL www.orkney.gov.uk; Tel 01856 873535; Fax 01856 874615
Convener of the Council Stephen Hagan
Chief Executive Alistair Buchan, MA, MCIPD
Assistant Chief Executive Malcolm Burr
Director (Development and Protective Services) J. Baster
Director (Technical Services) B. Thomson
Principal Legal Officer David Thompson

Community Social Services Department

Tel 01856 873535; Fax 01856 876159
Director (Community Social Services) Harry Garland
Assistant Director (Children and Families and Criminal Justice) Adrian Williams
Assistant Director (Community Care) Sandra McKinlay
Head (Strategic Services) Gillian Morrison

TRAINING

Responsible for training professional and support staff in the department.
Training Officer Gill Shee; Tel 01856 878617

COMMUNITY CARE SERVICES

Queen St, Kirkwall, Orkney Islands KW15 1NW; Tel 01856 871784

CHILDREN'S RESOURCE CENTRE

Camoran Resource Centre Holm Rd, Kirkwall, Orkney Islands KW15 1RT; Tel 01856 873135

CHILDREN AND FAMILIES SERVICES

Laing St, Kirkwall, Orkney Islands KW15 1NW; Tel 01856 870193

CENTRE FOR ADULTS WITH LEARNING DIFFICULTIES

St. Colm's Centre Muddisdale Loan, Kirkwall, Orkney Islands KW15 1RP; Tel 01856 873217

DAY CENTRE FOR PEOPLE WITH COMPLEX NEEDS

Keelylang Day Centre Muddisdale Loan, Kirkwall, Orkney Islands KW15 1RP; Tel 01856 871430

DAY CENTRES FOR ELDERLY PEOPLE

Gilbertson Day Centre Kirkwall, Orkney Islands KW15 1BB; Tel 01856 872122
West Mainland Day Centre Stenness, Orkney Islands KW16 3LB; Tel 01856 851435

ACCOMMODATION FOR THE ELDERLY

There are two residential homes for older people.

CRIMINAL JUSTICE

The Strynd, Kirkwall, Orkney Islands; E-mail jon.humphreys@orkney.gov.uk; Tel 01856 875733

Education and Recreation Services Department

Council Offices, School Pl, Kirkwall, Orkney Islands KW15 1NY; Tel 01856 873535; Fax 01856 870302
Director (Education and Recreation Services) W.L. Manson, MA
Principal Educational Psychologist P.J. Shearer, MA; Tel 01856 874779; Fax 01856 876049
Co-ordinator (Adult Education) M. Graves, BSc, PhD

SPECIAL EDUCATION

Glaitness Aurrida School Kirkwall, Orkney Islands; Tel 01856 870330
Mixed MH various (22)

PERTH AND KINROSS COUNCIL
www.pkc.gov.uk

Population 134 949
Political Composition: SNP: 15, Con: 10, Scottish LD: 9, Lab: 5, Ind: 2
2 High St, Perth, Perth and Kinross PH1 5PH; URL www.pkc.gov.uk; E-mail enquiries@pkc.gov.uk; Tel 01738 475000; Fax 01738 475710
Chief Executive Bernadette Malone
Director (Education and Children's Services) Bill Frew
General Manager (Care Together) Ian Manson

Education and Children's Services

Pullar Hse, 35 Kinnoull St, Perth, Perth and Kinross PH1 5GD; URL www.pkc.gov.uk; E-mail gwaddell@pkc.gov.uk; Tel 01738 476200; Fax 01738 476210
Executive Director (Education and Children's Services) George Waddell; E-mail gwaddell@pkc.gov.uk
Spokesperson Cllr M. Lennie
Depute Director Len McConnell; E-mail lmcconnell@pkc.gov.uk
Lead Officer (Children's Services and Criminal Justice) Joyce Clark; E-mail jclark@pkc.gov.uk
Lead Officer (Cultural and Community Services) Maria Walker; E-mail mwalker@pkc.gov.uk
Lead Officer (Finance/Resource Services) Alan Taylor; E-mail amtaylor@pkc.gov.uk
Lead Officer (School Improvement Services) Cecilia Flanigan; E-mail cflanigan@pkc.gov.uk

Lead Officer (Staffing Services) Ian Mason;
E-mail imason@pkc.gov.uk
Lead Officer (Strategic Business Services) Barbara Renton;
E-mail brenton@pkc.gov.uk
Lead Officer (Support Services) Peter McAvoy;
E-mail pmcavoy@pkc.gov.uk

SUB OFFICES

Blairgowrie Sub Office 2 Balmoral Rd, Rattray, Blairgowrie, Perth and Kinross PH10 7AB; Tel 01250 872255; Fax 01250 876421

Crieff Sub Office 32 James Sq, Crieff, Perth and Kinross PH7 3EY; Tel 01764 657510; Fax 01764 657539

HOSPITAL SOCIAL WORKERS

Murray Royal Hospital Muirhall Rd, Perth, Perth and Kinross PH2 7BH; Tel 01738 621151; Fax 01738 625477

Perth Royal Infirmary 8 Western Ave, Perth, Perth and Kinross PH1 1NY; Tel 01738 623311

CHILD AND FAMILY CENTRE

Gowans Terrace Child and Family Centre Gowans Terr, Perth, Perth and Kinross PH1 2TG; Tel 01738 442174

RESOURCE CENTRES (CHILDREN AND FAMILIES AND YOUNG PEOPLE)

Colonsay Resource Centre 37–39 Colonsay St, Perth, Perth and Kinross PH1 3TU; Tel 01738 626940; Fax 01738 440765

Nimmo Place Resource Centre 22 Nimmo Pl, Perth, Perth and Kinross; Tel 01738 643066; Fax 01738 622240

YOUNG PEOPLE'S RESIDENTIAL UNITS

Almondbank Cottage A Residential Unit Lewis Pl, Perth, Perth and Kinross PH1 3BD; Tel 01738 633115

Wellbank House 41 Dundee Rd, Perth, Perth and Kinross PH2 7AQ; Tel 01738 580850; Fax 01738 580090

Woodside Crescent Residential Unit 36 Woodside Cres, Perth, Perth and Kinross; Tel 01738 630732

RESOURCE CENTRES FOR PEOPLE WITH LEARNING DISABILITIES

Blairgowrie ARC Jessie St, Blairgowrie, Perth and Kinross PH10 6BT; Tel 01250 875658

Gleneagles ARC Gleneagles Rd, Perth, Perth and Kinross PH2 0AW; Tel 01738 639719

Kinnoull ARC Annexe Kinnoull Hse, Isla Rd, Perth, Perth and Kinross PH2 7HQ; Tel 01738 621833

Kinnoull ARC Shuna Crt, Perth, Perth and Kinross PH1 3DN; Tel 01738 634174

HOMES FOR PEOPLE WITH LEARNING DISABILITIES

Almondbank House Lewis Pl, Perth, Perth and Kinross PH1 3BD; Tel 01738 628099

Birchwood Birch Avenue Centre, Birch Ave, Scone, Perth, Perth and Kinross PH2 6LE; Tel 01738 553500; Fax 01738 553053

DAY CARE FOR OLDER PEOPLE

Lewis Place Resource Centre Lewis Pl, Perth, Perth and Kinross PH1 3BD; Tel 01738 622993

HOMES FOR OLDER PEOPLE

There are three homes for the elderly.

MEALS SERVICE

Social Work Department in conjunction with WRVS, Salvation Army, British Red Cross Society (Scottish Branch) and OPWC.

CRIMINAL JUSTICE SERVICES

High Street Offices 3–5 High St, Perth, Perth and Kinross PH1 5JS; Tel 01738 476915; Fax 01738 476347

Whitfriar Street Offices 22 Whitefriar St, Perth, Perth and Kinross; Tel 01738 444244; Fax 01738 444250

PROJECTS

Early Years Resource Team 2a Angus Crt, Fairfield, Perth, Perth and Kinross PH1 2TQ

Family Change Project Strathmoor, Harley Pl, Perth, Perth and Kinross PH1 5DP; Tel 01738 447479; Fax 01738 622883

Go Project 1st Fl, 25 Scott St, Perth, Perth and Kinross PH1 5EN; Tel 01738 639138; Fax 01738 639092

New Community Schools, Goodlyburn Primary School Crieff Rd, Perth, Perth and Kinross PH1 2NT; Tel 01738 632841; Fax 01738 634772

Perth Connect 34 Watergate, Perth, Perth and Kinross PH1 5TF; Tel 01738 580336; Fax 01738 580339

Reintegration Project George Inn La, Perth, Perth and Kinross PH1 5LG; Tel 01738 477970; Fax 01738 477980

RENFREWSHIRE COUNCIL
www.renfrewshire.gov.uk

9

Population 172 867
Political Composition: Lab: 21, SNP: 15, LD: 3, Con: 1
Council Headquarters, Cotton St, Paisley, Renfrewshire PA1 1BU; URL www.renfrewshire.gov.uk; Tel 0141 842 5000; Fax 0141 840 3212
Chief Executive Thomas Scholes

Social Work Headquarters

North Bldg, 4th Fl, Cotton St, Paisley, Renfrewshire PA1 1TZ; URL www.renfrewshire.gov.uk;
E-mail sw@renfrewshire.gov.uk; Tel 0141 842 5957; (Emergency) 0800 811505; Fax 0141 842 5144
Director (Social Work) D. Crawford
Head (Strategic Development) B. Gorman
Head (Resources and Support Services) L. Friel
Head (Operations) P. McLeod
Principal Officer (Resources and Support Services) F. McFetridge
Principal Officer (Community Care – Adults) J. Smith
Principal Officer (Planning and Social Inclusion) L. Monteith
Principal Officer (Registration, Inspection and Complaints) J. Lafferty
Principal Officer (Child Care) I. Beattie
Principal Officer (Criminal Justice) D. Bowie
Principal Officer (Community Care – Older People) P. McCulloch
Principal Officer (Commissioning) P. Maclachlan

AREA OFFICES

Ferguslie Park Area Centre 32 Falcon Cres, Paisley, Renfrewshire PA3 1NS; Tel 0141 840 2100
Unit Head K. Leinster

Johnstone Area Office Floorsburn Hse, Floors St, Johnstone, Renfrewshire PA5 8TL; Tel 01505 342300
Unit Head P. McLeod

Paisley Area Office Kelvin Hse, River Court Wlk, Paisley, Renfrewshire PA1 1YS; Tel 0141 842 5151
Unit Head K. Leinster

Renfrew Area Office 6–8 Manse St, Renfrew, Renfrewshire PA4 8QH; Tel 0141 886 5784
Unit Head J. Torrens

WELFARE RIGHTS AND ADVICE WORKS

High Street 42 High St, Paisley, Renfrewshire; Tel 0141 887 7632
Unit Head A. McAllister

HOSPITAL SOCIAL WORK TEAMS

Child and Family Centre Hawkhead Hospital, Paisley, Renfrewshire; Tel 0141 889 8151
Unit Head P. O'Grady

Dykebar Social Work Team Grahamston Rd, Paisley, Renfrewshire PA2 7DA; Tel 0141 884 5122
Unit Head P. O'Grady

Merchiston Hospital Resettlement Team Brookfield, Johnstone, Renfrewshire PA5 8TY; Tel 01505 328261
Unit Head K. Russell

Paisley Maternity Corsebar Rd, Paisley, Renfrewshire PA2 9PJ; Tel 0141 887 9111
Unit Head C. Carmichael

Royal Alexandra Corsebar Rd, Paisley, Renfrewshire PA2 9PJ; Tel 0141 887 9111
Unit Head J. Boddy

Child Care

RESIDENTIAL ACCOMMODATION

Beech Avenue 1–3 Beech Ave, Paisley, Renfrewshire PA2 6ZN; Tel 0141 889 7375
Unit Head J. Hamilton
  (8)

Carsewood House Hillfoot Dr, Howwood, Renfrewshire PA9 1BX; Tel 01505 703363
Unit Head C. Dearie
  (14)

Chapel House 2 Ardgowan St, Paisley, Renfrewshire PA2 65X; Tel 0141 889 2525
Unit Head A. Findlay
  (8)

Longcroft 2 Longcroft Dr, Renfrew, Renfrewshire PA4 8NF; Tel 0141 885 2353
Unit Head M. McGoldrick
  (8)

Roneil 8 Stanely Rd, Paisley, Renfrewshire PA2 6HA; Tel 0141 887 7981
Unit Head S. Thompson
  (10)

Seedhill Road 75 Seedhill Rd, Paisley, Renfrewshire PA1 1QU; Tel 0141 887 7681
Unit Head J. Hamilton
  (3)

RESIDENTIAL RESOURCE CENTRE

Newfield Resource Centre Barochan Rd, Johnstone, Renfrewshire PA5 8TS; Tel 01505 329334
Unit Head C. McCaig

COMMUNITY-BASED SERVICES

Thoroughcare Project and Community Support Project
Craigielea Hse, Blackstonn Rd, Paisley, Renfrewshire PA3 1UB; Tel 0141 581 0500
Unit Head M. Fitzpatrick

Community Care – Adult

DAY SERVICES

Greenside Centre Bredibid Rd, Linwood, Renfrewshire PA3 3RA; Tel 01505 325305
Unit Head C. Lewis

Maxwellton Centre Maxwellton Rd, Paisley, Renfrewshire PA1 2RH; Tel 0141 887 8016
Unit Head A. Murray

RESIDENTIAL ACCOMMODATION – LEARNING DISABILITY

Linwood 18–22 Richmond Dr, Linwood, Renfrewshire PA3 3TQ; Tel 01505 327453
Unit Head S. Kane

Urquhart House Fleming Rd, Houston, Renfrewshire PA6 7EU; Tel 01505 613100
Unit Head H. Lowry

RESIDENTIAL RESPITE ACCOMMODATION

Braeview Respite Unit Moredun Rd, Paisley, Renfrewshire PA2 9LJ; Tel 0141 884 2726

COMMUNITY BASED SERVICES – ADULTS

Anchor Centre 51 Stock St, Paisley, Renfrewshire PA2 6DF; Tel 0141 887 1006
Unit Head E. Fisher

Charleston Centre 49 Neilston Rd, Paisley, Renfrewshire PA2 6LY; Tel 0141 842 3400
Unit Head S. Dowell

Disability Resource Centre 74 Love St, Paisley, Renfrewshire PA5 2EA; Tel 0141 848 1123
Unit Head A. Cassidy

Disability Centre for Independent Living Community Services Centre, Queen St, Paisley, Renfrewshire PA1 2TT; Tel 0141 887 0597
Unit Head G. Dykes

Flexicare 18–20 Barscube Terr, Paisley, Renfrewshire PA2 6XA; Tel 0141 849 1630

Renfrewshire Community Health Initiative Ferguslie Park Area Centre, Falon Cres, Paisley, Renfrewshire PA3 1NS; Tel 0141 887 0646
Social Inclusion Partnership Funded.
Contact Jan Henderson

Substance Abuse Resource Project 20 Backsneddon St, Paisley, Renfrewshire PA3 2DF; Tel 0141 889 1223
Unit Head A. Boyle

Unit for Hearing Impaired 10–12 St. James' St, Paisley, Renfrewshire PA3 2HT; Tel 0141 889 3655
Unit Head L.A. O'Hare

Unit for Visually Impaired 10–12 St. James' St, Paisley, Renfrewshire PA3 2HT; Tel 0141 889 3655
Unit Head S. Metcalfe

CRIMINAL JUSTICE SERVICES

Paisley Sheriff Court 10 St. James St, Paisley, Renfrewshire; Tel 0141 889 0617
Unit Head L. Maloney

Community Alternatives Unit Community Services Centre, Queen St, Paisley, Renfrewshire PA1 2TT; Tel 0141 887 5470
Unit Head G. Aitken

Community Service Orders 62 Espedair St, Paisley, Renfrewshire PA2 6RW; Tel 0141 840 1001
Unit Head K. McCoombes

Community Care – Elderly

DAY CENTRES

Falcon Centre Falcon Cres, Ferguslie Pk, Paisley, Renfrewshire PA3 1NS; Tel 0141 887 6365
Unit Head R. Buchanan

Johnstone Day Centre 21 Walkinshaw St, Johnstone, Renfrewshire PA5; Tel 01505 382227
Unit Head K. Mullen

Linwood Day Centre Unit 31, Ardlamont Sq, Linwood, Renfrewshire PA3; Tel 01505 329167
Unit Head E. Devaney

Lochwinnoch Day Centre McKillop Institute, Main St, Lochwinnoch, Renfrewshire PA12 4AJ; Tel 01505 842841
Unit Head Mrs Kelly

Paisley Augmented Centre Cyril St, Paisley, Renfrewshire PA1 1RW; Tel 0141 887 6125
Unit Head M. Mullin

Ralston Day Centre Community Hall, Allanton Ave, Ralston, Paisley, Renfrewshire PA1 3BL; Tel 0141 882 1132
Unit Head H. McGowan

Rowan Centre (Lochfield) Rowan St, Paisley, Renfrewshire PA2 6RY; Tel 0141 848 7021
Unit Head I. McGuire

Speirsfield House Day Centre Stevenson St, Paisley, Renfrewshire PA2 6BP; Tel 0141 889 2611

Stewart House Day Centre Glendee Rd, Renfrew, Renfrewshire PA4 0AD; Tel 0141 886 7385
Unit Head A. Riddell

SPECIALIST DAY CARE – OLDER PEOPLE

Garthland House Garthland La, Paisley, Renfrewshire PA1 3PY; Tel 0141 889 0478

Speirsfield House Stevenson St, Paisley, Renfrewshire PA2 6BP; Tel 0141 889 2611

RESIDENTIAL ACCOMMODATION

There are six homes for the elderly.

Education and Leisure Services

Cotton St, Paisley, Renfrewshire PA1 1LE;
URL www.renfrewshire.gov.uk;
E-mail els@renfrewshire.gov.uk; Tel 0141 842 5663;
Fax 0141 842 5699
Director (Education and Leisure) S. Rae
Head (Quality and Service Development) S. McKenzie
Head (Lifelong Learning) Sheila Cronin
Head (Resource Services) John McDonald (Acting)
Senior Adviser (Performance) Gordon Morton
Senior Adviser (Curriculum) Liz Jamieson
Senior Adviser (Education Support) Alan Locke
Senior Adviser (Inclusion) Marjorie Munro
Manager (Psychological Services) B. Rutherford
Manager (Early Years) Kathleen McDonagy
Manager (Finance Services) D. Paton
Manager (Property and Support Services) H. Morrison
Manager (Personnel Services) I. Millar
School Support Officer Elaine McKay

SPECIAL SCHOOLS

Clippens School Brediland Rd, Linwood, Paisley, Renfrewshire PA3 3RX; Tel 01505 325333
Headteacher Olwynne Clark
Mixed 5–18 MH Profound (60)

Hunterhill Tutorial Centre Cartha Cres, Paisley, Renfrewshire PA2 7EL; Tel 0141 889 6876
Headteacher Rhona Campbell

Kersland School Ben Nevis Rd, Paisley, Renfrewshire PA2 7BU; Tel 0141 889 8251
Headteacher Carol Jackson
Mixed 5–18 MH Severe (100)

The Mary Russell School Hawkhead Rd, Paisley, Renfrewshire PA2 7BE; Tel 0141 889 7628
Headteacher J. Dorby
Mixed 5–18 MH, PH, PS (390)

SCOTTISH BORDERS COUNCIL
www.scotborders.gov.uk

Political Composition: Ind: 15, Con: 10, LD: 8, SNP: 1
Council Headquarters, Newtown St. Boswells, Melrose, Scottish Borders TD6 0SA;
URL www.scotborders.gov.uk;
E-mail enquiries@scotborders.gov.uk; Tel 01835 824000;
Fax 01835 825001
Chief Executive David Hume

Lifelong Care

Newtown St, Boswells, Melrose, Scottish Borders TD6 0SA; Tel 01835 825080; (Emergency) 01896 752111; Fax 01835 825081
Director (Social Work) Colin Johnson
Head (Families and Criminal Justice) P. Gibson
Head (Community Care) Frances Stuart
Head (Business Management) R. Davies
Manager (Contracts) K. Norman
Group Manager T. Welsh
Group Manager (Children and Families) J. Hawthorn
Group Manager B. Harrison
Group Manager (Criminal Justice) C. Hawkes
Service Manager (Community Care Services) C. Morrison
Service Manager (Community Care Services) C. Fowler

Lifelong Care Portfolio

Ind: 4, LD: 5, SNP: 2, Non Affiliated: 1
Chair Cllr S. Scott
Vice-Chair Cllr C. Riddle-Carr

LOCAL OFFICES

Duns 24 Newtown St, Duns, Scottish Borders; Tel 01361 883050
Locality Manager M. Wilson

Galashiels 4 Abbotsford Rd, Galasheils, Scottish Borders; Tel 01896 755365
Locality Manager Steve Adamson

Hawick 5–7 Lothian St, Hawick, Scottish Borders
Locality Manager Chris Clarke

Kelso Rose La, Kelso, Scottish Borders; Tel 01573 223501
Locality Manager Vacancy

Peebles Chambers Institute, Peebles, Scottish Borders; Tel 01721 722777
Locality Manager Vacancy

Selkirk Chapel St, Selkirk, Scottish Borders; Tel 01750 20738
Locality Manager B. Pavey

HOSPITAL

Borders General Hospital Melrose, Scottish Borders; Tel 01896 826000
Locality Manager G. Forsyth

9

CHILDREN'S HOME

Glen View Children's Home Marigold Dr, Langlee, Galasheils, Scottish Borders TD1 2LP; Tel 01896 752064
Manager H. Fraser

CHILDREN'S SERVICES UNIT

11 Market St, Galasheils, Scottish Borders; Tel 01896 757230
Locality Manager Ann Blackie

FAMILY CENTRES

Contact Local Offices.

ACCOMMODATION FOR ADULTS WITH LEARNING DISABILITIES

Trinity House 44 Weensland Rd, Hawick, Scottish Borders TD9 3HW; Tel 01450 374400
Manager D. Mather

DAY CENTRES FOR ADULTS WITH LEARNING AND PHYSICAL DISABILITIES

The Ability Centre Livingstone Pl, Galasheils, Scottish Borders TD1 1DQ; Tel 01896 751333
Manager B. Pollock
Katharine Elliot Centre Howdenbank, Hawick, Scottish Borders TD9 7JT; Tel 01450 374230
Manager J. Spiteri (Acting)
Lanark Lodge Day Centre Bridgend, Duns, Scottish Borders TD11 3EX; Tel 01361 882540
Manager B. Haines
Victoria Park Day Centre Kingsmeadow Rd, Peebles, Scottish Borders EH45 9BH; Tel 01721 722622
Manager Cliff Carrie

DAY CENTRES FOR PEOPLE WITH MENTAL ILLNESS

Berwickshire Dementia Project The Bungalow, Lanark Lodge, Duns, Scottish Borders TD11 3EX; Tel 01361 883134
Co-ordinator E. Scott (Acting)
Eyemouth Community Support Project Albert Pl, Eyemouth, Scottish Borders; Tel 01890 751543
Support Worker C. Hudson
Support Worker S. Marsh
Parkvilla Day Centre 69 Gala Pk, Galasheils, Scottish Borders TD1 1EZ; Tel 01896 750349

LOCAL AUTHORITY HOMES FOR OLDER PEOPLE

There are six homes for older people.

DAY CENTRES FOR OLDER PEOPLE

There are nine local authority day centres for older people attached to the Residential Homes. Contact Local Offices or Residential Homes for further information.

COMMUNITY ALARM SYSTEM

Bordercare Community Alarm System Albert Pl, Galasheils, Scottish Borders TD1 3LD; Tel 01896 752111
Co-ordinator G. Gowans

HOME CARE MANAGERS

Contact Local Offices.

MEALS ON WHEELS

Contact Local Offices.

Lifelong Learning

Scottish Borders Council, Council Headquarters, Newtown St, Boswells, Melrose, Scottish Borders TD6 0SA; Tel 01835 824000; Fax 01835 825091
Director (Lifelong Learning) John Christie, MTheol, DipEd
Assistant Director (Continuing Education) G. Donald, DPE, DMS
Assistant Director (Services to Young People) K.N. Paterson, BSc, MEd
Assistant Director (Educational Development) D. Mallen, MA, DipEd, MEd
Assistant Director (Finance and Administration) Vacancy
Senior Education Officer (SEN) Maria Lucia MacConnachie, MA
Senior Education Officer R. MacLeod, BA
Senior Education Officer S. Richmond, MA, BA(Hons)
Senior Education Officer Helen Cotton, BEd

HOSPITAL CLASS

Children's Ward, Borders General Hospital, Galasheils, Scottish Borders; Tel 01896 4333
Contact E. Moon

ADDITIONALLY RESOURCED PROVISION FOR SEN (PRIMARY)

Chirnside Primary School Chirnside, Duns, Scottish Borders TD11 3HX; Tel 01890 817002
Headteacher Jenny Prince
Langlee Primary School Langlee Dr, Galasheils, Scottish Borders TD1 2EB; Tel 01896 757892; Fax 01896 759316
Headteacher Margaret Darling
Wilton School Wellfield Rd, Hawick, Scottish Borders TD9 7EN; Tel 01450 372075; Fax 01450 370538
Headteacher Linda Turnbull

ADDITIONALLY RESOURCED PROVISION FOR SEN (SECONDARY)

Berwickshire High School Duns, Scottish Borders TD11 3QQ; Tel 01361 883710; Fax 01361 883018
Headteacher R. Kelly
Galashiels Academy Elm Row, Galashiels, Scottish Borders TD1 3HU; Tel 01896 754788; Fax 01896 755652
Contact B. Keenan
Hawick High School Buccleuch St, Hawick, Scottish Borders TD9 0EG; Tel 01450 372429; Fax 01450 377830
Headteacher N. Horne
Jedburgh Grammar School Jedburgh, Scottish Borders TD8 6DQ; Tel 01835 863273; Fax 01835 863993
Headteacher H. Watt
Kelso High School Bowmont St, Kelso, Scottish Borders TD5 7EG; Tel 01573 224444; Fax 01573 223862
Headteacher C. Robertson
Peebles High School Peebles, Scottish Borders EM45 8HB; Tel 01721 720291; Fax 01721 722563
Headteacher Dr R. Kerr

SPECIAL EDUCATIONAL NEEDS

Contact Professional and Administrative Headquarters Council Headquarters, Newtown St. Boswells, Scottish Borders; Tel 01835 824000

SPECIALIST RESOURCE – LANGUAGE RESOURCE

Coldstream Primary School Coldstream, Scottish Borders; Tel 01890 882189
Headteacher Heather Waldron
Philiphaugh Community School Selkirk, Scottish Borders; Tel 01750 721774
Headteacher Margaret Mason

SPECIALIST RESOURCE – HEARING IMPAIRMENT AND VISUAL IMPAIRMENT

Earlston Primary School Earlston, Scottish Borders TD4 6ED; Tel 01896 848977; Fax 01896 848180
Contact Fiona Dove, DipEd

SPECIALIST RESOURCE – SEBD

Burnfoot Community School Kenilworth Ave, Hawick, Scottish Borders TD9 7SW; Tel 01450 378478; Fax 01450 372026
Contact Evelyn Craig

Coldstream Primary School Coldstream, Scottish Borders TD11 3SJ; Tel 01890 882189; Fax 01890 883066
Contact Heather Waldron
    Sp/Lang

Denholm Primary School Denholm, Hawick, Scottish Borders TD9 8LZ; Tel 01450 870619; Fax 01450 870254
Contact Sarah Fitch
    Autism

Philiphaugh Community School 2 Linglie Rd, Selkirk, Scottish Borders TD7 5LT; Tel 01750 721774; Fax 01750 721896
Contact Margaret Mason
    Sp/Lang

Wilton Centre Princes St, Hawick, Scottish Borders TD9 7AY; Tel 01450 378644; Fax 01450 370538
Contact Moira Buckle
    Secondary

SPECIALIST RESOURCE – SEVERE/COMPLEX DIFFICULTIES (POST-16)

Howdenburn School House Lothian Rd, Jedburgh, Scottish Borders TD8 6LA; Tel 01835 864577
Contact K. Keenan, MA

SHETLAND ISLANDS COUNCIL
www.shetland.gov.uk

Population 22 910
Political Composition: Ind: 13, LD: 8, Ind Lib Dem: 1
Town Hall, Lerwick, Shetland Isles ZE1 0HB;
    URL www.shetland.gov.uk;
    E-mail sic@sic.shetland.gov.uk; Tel 01595 744504;
    Fax 01595 744509
Convenor of the Council T. Stove
Chief Executive Morgan H. Goodlad
Executive Director (Corporate Services) A. Matthews
Brewick Hse, South Rd, Lerwick, Shetland Isles
Executive Director (Infrastructure Services) G. Spall
Toll Clock Centre, Lerwick, Shetland Isles
Executive Director (Community Services) J. Watt
Hayfield Hse, Hayfield La, Lerwick, Shetland Isles

Community Services Department, Social Care Services

Hayfield Hse, Lerwick, Shetland Isles ZE1 0QD; Tel 01595 744444; Fax 01595 744460

TRAINING AND STAFF DEVELOPMENT

Manager (Training) Jean Aaron-Walker
91–93 St. Olaf St, Lerwick, Shetland Isles ZE1 0ES; Tel 01595 744420; Fax 01595 744460

Services Committee

Chair Florence Grains
Town Hall, Lerwick, Shetland Isles
Vice-Chair William Stove
Town Hall, Lerwick, Shetland Isles
Members of the Committee
Leslie Angus, Barbara Cheyne, Alexander J. Cluness,
Cecil B. Eunson, R. Geoff Feather, Brian P. Gregson,
Leonard G. Groat, Iris J. Hawkins, James H. Henry,
J. Alistair Inkster, James C. Irvine, Edward J. Knight,
William H. Manson, Gordon G. Mitchell, John P. Nicholson,
William A. Ratter, Frank A. Robertson, Josie Simpson,
Thomas W. Stove, William Tait.

RESIDENTIAL SERVICES FOR CHILDREN AND YOUNG PEOPLE

Leog Children's Centre Leog La, Lerwick, Shetland Isles ZE1 0AP; Tel 01595 692740
Unit Manager Martha Nicolson
Residential unit for children and young people.

Laburnum House 15 Burgh Rd, Lerwick, Shetland Isles ZE1 0LA; Tel 01595 694063
Unit Manager Peter Goodlad
Residential respite and day care for children and young adults with special needs.

SPECIALIST CHILDCARE STAFF

Service Manager (Looked After Children) Kate Gabb
Social Care Service, 91–93 St. Olaf St, Lerwick, Shetland Isles
Intensive one to one help for young people at risk; full time foster placements. Family support services.

MENTAL HEALTH RESOURCE CENTRE

Annsbrae House Lerwick, Shetland Isles; Tel 01595 694787
Senior Social Care Worker Sandra Gair

RESPITE PROVISION FOR ADULTS WITH LEARNING DISABILITIES

Craigielea Hostel St. Olaf St, Lerwick, Shetland Isles ZE1 0DA; Tel 01595 695145
Project Manager Max Barnett

EDUCATION, TRAINING AND DAY CARE FOR ADULTS WITH LEARNING DISABILITIES

Eric Gray Resource Centre Kantersted Rd, Lerwick, Shetland Isles ZE1 0RJ; Tel 01595 694647
Unit Manager Ingrid Webb
Unit Manager Connie Russell

DAY CENTRE FOR OLDER PEOPLE

Freefield Centre Lerwick, Shetland Isles; Tel 01595 692127

RESIDENTIAL ACCOMMODATION FOR OLDER PEOPLE

There are three homes for older people.

Community Services Department, Education Service

Hayfield Hse, Hayfield La, Lerwick, Shetland Isles ZE1 0QD; Tel 01595 744000; Fax 01595 692810
Head A. Jamieson
Principal Psychologist Anne Bain

SPECIAL CLASS

Class attached to Bell's Brae Primary School Lerwick, Shetland Isles; Tel 01595 692973; Fax 01595 693860
Assistant Headteacher Mrs S. Linklater
(Day)
    Mixed (22)

9

SOUTH AYRSHIRE COUNCIL
www.south-ayrshire.gov.uk

Political Composition: Lab: 17, Con: 13
County Bldgs, Wellington Sq, Ayr, South Ayrshire
  KA7 1DR; URL www.south-ayrshire.gov.uk; Tel 01292
  612000; Fax 01292 612143
Chief Executive   G. Thorley

Social Work, Housing and Health Department

Tel 01292 612419; Fax 01292 612481
Director   Elaine Noad
Head (Social Work)   J. Thompson
Head (Housing Services)   P. Whyte
Holmston Hse, 3 Holmston Rd, Ayr, South Ayrshire
  KA7 3BA; Tel 01292 612010; Fax 01292 288244
Head (Social Justice)   K. Hamilton
Manager (Quality and Assurance)   W. Docherty

Community Services Committee

Lab: 7, Con: 6, Ind: 1
Convener   R. Miller (Lab)
Vice-Convener   L. McNicol (Lab)
Vice-Convener   A. Cairns Lab
Members of the Committee
J. Baillie, S. Bowie, A. Cairns, B. Campbell, J. Cree,
D. Duncan, H. Hunter, M. Kilpatrick, B. McIntosh,
B. McNally, L. McNicol, R. Miller, W. Sloan, I. Stewart,
P. Torrance, C. Young.

Inspection Advisory Committee

Contact   Cllr R. Miller

AREA OFFICES

Ayr North Area Office

Whitletts Road Area Office   181 Whiletts Rd, Ayr, South
Ayrshire; Tel 01292 267675; Fax 01292 284711

SUB-OFFICES

Main Street Sub Office   12 Main St, Prestwick, South
Ayrshire; Tel 01292 470099; Fax 01292 671572
Municipal Buildings Sub Office   Troon, South Ayrshire;
Tel 01292 316666; Fax 01292 314124

Ayr South Area

Kyle Street Area Office   67 Kyle St, Ayr, South Ayrshire;
Tel 01292 281993; Fax 01292 285595

SUB-OFFICES

Knockcushan Street Sub Office   17–19 Knockcushan St,
Girvan, South Ayrshire; Tel 01465 712299; Fax 01465 716101
Whitehall Sub Office   12 Whitehall, Maybole, South
Ayrshire; Tel 01655 883293; Fax 01655 882488

Department of Education, Culture and Lifelong Learning

County Bldgs, Wellington Sq, Ayr, South Ayrshire
  KA7 1DR; E-mail mike.mccabe@south-ayrshire.gov.uk;
  Tel 01292 612201; Fax 01292 612258

Director (Education, Culture and Lifelong Learning)
  Michael McCabe
Head (Resource, Planning and Support)   C. Scalpello;
  Tel 01292 612202
Head (Lifelong Learning)   N. Larkin
Head (Educational Attainment)   A. Noble; Tel 01292 612234

NETWORK SUPPORT TEAMS

Queen Margaret Academy   Dalmellington Rd, Ayr, South
Ayrshire; E-mail isobel.mackenzie@south-ayrshire.gov.uk;
Tel 01292 611489; 01292 612378
Official-in-Charge   Isobel MacKenzie
Regional Psychology Service   St. John's Bldg, Whitletts Rd,
Ayr, South Ayrshire; Tel 01292 261738; Fax 01292 263571
Official-in-Charge   D. Stewart

SPECIAL SCHOOLS

Craigpark School   Belmont Ave, Ayr, South Ayrshire
KA8 0QP; Tel 01292 288982; Fax 01292 618765
Headteacher   Miss L. Stoddart
  Mixed 3–16 MH Profound (12)
Invergarven School   15 Henrietta St, Girvan, South Ayrshire
KA26 9EJ; Tel 01465 712035; Fax 01465 712035
Headteacher   Mrs K. Faulder-Branson
  Mixed 5–16 MH Profound (12)
Mainholm Academy Centre for Support for Learning
Mainholm Rd, Ayr, South Ayrshire; Tel 01292 267300;
Fax 01292 287990
Contact   M. Muir
Rosebank School   Belmont Ave, Ayr, South Ayrshire
KA7 2NA; Tel 01292 269422; Fax 01292 618271
Headteacher   M. Muir
  Mixed 5–16 MH, PH
South Park School   Belmont Ave, Ayr, South Ayrshire
KA7 2PS; Tel 01292 282259; Fax 01292 618310
Headteacher   Mrs S. McLachlan
  Mixed 5–16 (30)

SOUTH LANARKSHIRE COUNCIL
www.southlanarkshire.gov.uk

Headquarters, Almada St, Hamilton, South Lanarkshire
  ML3 0AA; URL www.southlanarkshire.gov.uk; Tel 01698
  454444; Fax 01698 454275
Chief Executive   Michael Docherty

Social Work Resources

South Lanarkshire Council, Almada St, Council Offices,
  Hamilton, South Lanarkshire ML3 0AA;
  E-mail social.work.slc@cableol.co.uk; Tel 01698 454444
Executive Director (Social Work Resources)   Sandy Cameron,
  CBE; E-mail sandy.cameron@southlanarkshire.gov.uk;
  Tel 01698 453700; Fax 01698 453784
Head (Support Services)   Tom Barrie;
  E-mail tom.barrie@southlanarkshire.gov.uk; Tel 01698
  453704; Fax 01698 453784
Social Work Resources are structured on specialist client
group lines. Each client group is represented on the social
work directorate and the head for each client group is listed
above. For specific service information or referral reference
should be made to the relevant sections in this directory.

Social Work Committee

Lab: 53, SNP: 11, Con: 2
Chair   J. Handibode Lab
Chair   J. Molloy
Deputy Chair   Jackie Burns

Members of the Committee

Lab: M. Ahmad, C. Condie, L. Craw, J. Daisley, J. Docherty, M. Duffy, H. Dunsmuir (Senior Deputy Chair), A. Falconer, R. Ferguson, J. Lowe, E. McAvoy, M. McGlynn, J. McGuinness, A. McInnes, B. McKenna, D. McLaughlin, M. McNeill, P. Morgan, I. Roberts, W. Ross, M. Smith, M. Smith, P. Smith.

SNP: J. Young, Rev B. Gauld, R. Murray.

LD: G. Ross.

Con: B. Forrest.

LOCAL OFFICES

Blantyre Local Office

Social Work Resources, 45 John St, Blantyre, Glasgow G72 0JG; Tel 01698 417400; Fax 01698 417428

Clydesdale Local Office

Social Work Resources, South Vennel, Lanark, South Lanarkshire ML11 7NE; Tel 01555 673000

East Kilbride Local Office

Social Work Resources, 1st Fl, Civic Centre, Andrew St, East Kilbride, South Lanarkshire G74 1AB; Tel 01355 807000; Fax 01355 264458

Hamilton Local Office

Social Work Resources, Brandongate, Leechlee Rd, South Lanarkshire ML3 0XB; Tel 01698 286900; Fax 01698 283257

Larkhall Local Office

Social Work Resources, Claude St, Larkhall, South Lanarkshire ML9 1DR; Tel 01698 884656; Fax 01698 307504

Rutherglen and Cambuslang Local Office

Social Work Resources, 380 King St, Rutherglen, South Lanarkshire G73 1DQ; URL www.southlanarkshire.gov.uk; Tel 0141 647 9977; Fax 0141 613 5075

HOSPITAL SOCIAL WORK UNITS

Carstairs State Hospital Hospital Social Work Manager, Carstairs Junction, Lanark, South Lanarkshire ML11 8RP; Tel 01555 840923

Hairmyres Hospital Psychiatric Unit Eaglesham Rd, East Kilbride, South Lanarkshire G75 8RG; Tel 01355 572615

Hairmyres Hospital (Social Work Resource Unit) Eaglesham Rd, East Kilbride, South Lanarkshire G75 8RG; Tel 01355 572588

Kirklands Hospital Fallside Rd, Bothwell, South Lanarkshire G71 8BB; Tel 01698 852508

Udston Hospital Farm Rd, Burnbank, Hamilton, North Lanarkshire ML3 9JA; Tel 01698 823255

CHILD AND FAMILY SERVICES

Blantyre Area 45 John St, Blantyre, Glasgow G72 0LG; E-mail billy.armstrong@southlanarkshire.gov.uk; Tel 01698 417407

Team Leader Billy Armstrong

Clydesdale Area South Vennel, Lanark, South Lanarkshire ML11 7NE; E-mail heston.johnstone@southlanarkshire.gov.uk; Tel 01555 673416

Team Leader Heston Johnstone

Council Offices Almada St, Hamilton, South Lanarkshire ML3 0AA; URL www.southlanarkshire.gov.uk; E-mail brenda.doyle@southlanarkshire.gov.uk; Tel 01698 454887; Fax 01698 453950

Head (Child and Family Services) Brenda Doyle
Fieldwork Manager Jackie Kerr
Fieldwork Manager Anne Marie Stewart

Manager (Child Care Services) Liz Lafferty
Manager (Family Support Services) Mary Gallagher
Manager (Child and Family Services) Andrew Girvan

East Kilbride Area Civic Centre, Andrew St, East Kilbride, South Lanarkshire G74 1AB; E-mail lesley.gray@southlanarkshire.gov.uk; Tel 01355 807000

Team Leader Lesley Gray

Hamilton Area Brandongate, Leechlee Rd, Hamilton, South Lanarkshire ML3 0XB; E-mail paul.begley@southlanarkshire.gov.uk; Tel 01698 455449

Team Leader Paul Begley

Larkhall Area 18 Claude St, Larkhall, South Lanarkshire ML9 1DR; URL www.southlanarkshire.gov.uk; E-mail duncan.turner@southlanarkshire.gov.uk; Tel 01698 884656

Team Leader Duncan Turner

Rutherglen/Cambuslang Area 380 King St, Rutherglen, South Lanarkshire G73 1DQ; E-mail rena.mccarry@southlanarkshire.gov.uk; Tel 0141 647 9977

Team Leader Rena McCarry

Strategic Services Section Council Offices, Almada St, Hamilton, South Lanarkshire ML3 0AA; Tel 01698 453724; 01698 453751

Children's Rights Officer Allison Shearer
Children's Rights Officer Sarie Young
Children's Rights Officer Lynn McGilp

CHILDREN'S UNITS

Bankhead Children's Unit 10 Wattlow Ave, Bankhead, Rutherglen, South Lanarkshire G73 2TP; Tel 0141 643 0097

Calder House (Alternative to Care Project) Calder Hse, Bardykes Rd, Blantyre, Glasgow G72 9UJ; Tel 01698 527200

Calder House (Short Term Children's Unit) Calder Hse, Bardykes Rd, Blantyre, Glasgow G72 9UJ; Tel 01698 827834

Carluke Children's Unit 39 Station Rd, Carluke, South Lanarkshire ML8 5AD; Tel 01555 771996

Church Street Unit 7 Church St, Uddingston, South Lanarkshire G71 7PT; Tel 01698 815221

Glenavon Children's Unit 78 Commercial Rd, Strathaven, South Lanarkshire ML10 6JJ; Tel 01357 521977

Rosslyn Children's Unit 17 Rosslyn Ave, East Kilbride, South Lanarkshire G74 4BP; Tel 01355 226749

Whitehill Family Centre 10 Hunter Rd, Whitehill, Hamilton, South Lanarkshire ML3 0LH; Tel 01698 458832

ADULT SERVICES

Anford Place 30 Anford Pl, Blantyre, Glasgow G72 0NR; Tel 01698 827592

Auchentibber Resource Centre East Ave, Main St, High Blantyre, South Lanarkshire G72 0JB; Tel 01698 824445

Cambuslang Addiction Project 13 Main St, Cambuslang, South Lanarkshire; Tel 0141 641 7038

Cathkin Resource Centre Langlea Rd, Cambuslang, South Lanarkshire G72 8HG; Tel 0141 634 3077

Community Mental Health Team 9 High Patrick St, Hamilton, South Lanarkshire ML3 7ES; Tel 01698 455546

Council Offices Almada St, Hamilton, South Lanarkshire ML3 0AA; Tel 01698 453753; Fax 01698 453910

Head (Adults' Services) Alex Davidson
Team Leader (Mental Health) Annie McGeenie
Team Leader (Physical Disability) Nadia Ait-Hocine
Team Leader (Addiction) Isobel McCarthy
Manager (Reception Services) Brian Moore
Manager (Residential and Day Care) Rhoda MacLeod
Manager (Adults Services) Brian Moore

Dale Centre (Day Centre) Yvetot Ave, Lanark, South Lanarkshire ML11 7BW; Tel 01555 664419

9

Dale House Yvetot Ave, Lanark, South Lanarkshire ML11 7BW; Tel 01555 664410

Faichney Field Day Centre 96 Main St, East Kilbride, South Lanarkshire G74 4JY; Tel 01355 234986

Joint Community Team Tel 01698 417400

Laburnum 2 Laburnum Ave, Greenhills, East Kilbride, South Lanarkshire G75 9EU; Tel 01355 241908

Larkhall Resource Centre Strutherhill Ind Est, Carlisle Rd, Larkhall, South Lanarkshire ML9 2PJ; Tel 01698 886699

Network Project 96 Main St, The Village, East Kilbride, South Lanarkshire; Tel 01355 223778

Richmond Court 2 Richmond Pl, East Main St, Rutherglen, South Lanarkshire G73 3BF; Tel 0141 647 9166

Robert Owen Centre Tel 01698 459245

OLDER PEOPLE'S SERVICES

ALERT 24 Control Centre, Pollock Avenue Business Unit, Hamilton, South Lanarkshire ML3; Tel 01698 897700
Manager Jane Swanson

Blantyre Area 45 John St, Blantyre, Glasgow; E-mail helen.jeffrey@southlanarkshire.gov.uk; Tel 01698 417400
Team Leader Helen Jeffrey

Clydesdale Area South Vennel, Lanark, South Lanarkshire; E-mail jessica.craig@southlanarkshire.gov.uk; Tel 01555 661681
Team Leader Jessica Craig

Council Offices Almada St, Hamilton, South Lanarkshire ML3 0AA; Tel 01698 453701
Head (Older People's Services) Jim I. Wilson
Manager (Assessment and Care) Sandra Sage
Manager (Residential and Day Care) Caroline Deerin
Manager (Home Care and ALERT) Malcolm McAuley
Manager (Older People's Services) Jim I. Wilson

East Kilbride Area Civic Centre, Andrew St, East Kilbride, South Lanarkshire; E-mail jim.odonnell@southlanarkshire.gov.uk; Tel 01355 807000
Team Leader Jim O'Donnell

Hamilton Area Brandongate, Leechlee Rd, Hamilton, South Lanarkshire ML3 0XB; E-mail susan.gallagher@southlanarkshire.gov.uk; Tel 01698 455400
Team Leader Susan Gallagher

Larkhall Area 18 Claude St, Larkhall, South Lanarkshire; E-mail sharron.archibald@southlanarkshire.gov.uk; Tel 01698 884656
Senior Social Worker Sharron Archibald

Rutherglen/Cambuslang Area 380 King St, Rutherglen, Glasgow; E-mail moira.mccafferty@southlanarkshire.gov.uk; Tel 0141 647 9977
Team Leader Moira McCafferty

DAY CARE CENTRES FOR OLDER PEOPLE

Belmont Day Centre Westwood, East Kilbride, South Lanarkshire G75 8HG; Tel 01355 239305

Blantyre (PHEC) Blantyre, Glasgow; Tel 01698 820654

Cambuslang Day Care Centre Cambuslang, Glasgow G72 8AR; Tel 0141 641 9751

Candor Avon (Day Care) Stonehouse, Larkhall, South Lanarkshire ML9 3EF; URL www.southlanarkshire.gov.uk; Tel 01698 793454

Claremont Day Care St. Leonards, East Kilbride, South Lanarkshire G74 2AU; Tel 01355 246809

David Walker House Day Care 329a Main St, Rutherglen, South Lanarkshire G73 3AQ; Tel 0141 643 1404

Elderly Activities Day Care 126 Fleming Way, Hamilton, South Lanarkshire ML3 9QN; Tel 01698 825359

Lesmahagow Day Care Glebe Gdns, Lesmahagow, South Lanarkshire; Tel 01555 895643

McClymont House (Day Care) Lanark, South Lanarkshire ML11 7NE; Tel 01555 665953

McWhirters Day Care Larkhall, South Lanarkshire ML9 3EF; Tel 01698 883137

Old Coach Road Centre The Village, East Kilbride, South Lanarkshire G74 4DR; Tel 01355 224110

Parker Place Day Care Larkhall, South Lanarkshire; Tel 01698 884523

Red Deer Centre Westwood, East Kilbride, South Lanarkshire G75 8NH; Tel 01355 244254

The Share Project for Older People Brandongate, Leechlee Rd, Hamilton, South Lanarkshire ML3 0XB; Tel 01698 455400

Simpson Court Day Centre 2 Simpson St, Uddingston, South Lanarkshire; Tel 01698 814600

Strathaven Day Centre Strathaven, South Lanarkshire ML10 6NH; Tel 01357 522496

HOMES FOR OLDER PEOPLE

There are eight residential homes run by South Lanarkshire Council for older people.

CRIMINAL JUSTICE SERVICES

Social Work Resources Headquarters, Council Offices, Almada St, Hamilton, South Lanarkshire ML3 0AA; E-mail mairi.brackenridge@southlanarkshire.gov.uk; Tel 01698 453715
Head (Criminal Justice Services) Mairi Brackenridge
Manager (Criminal Justice Services) Hugh McGregor
Team Leader (Clydesdale; Larkhall; Hamilton; Blantyre) Hazel Johnson
Team Leader (Hamilton Sheriff Court; Rutherglen; Cambuslang; East Kilbride) Hilary Finnegan

Alternative to Custody Project Calder Hse, Bardykes Rd, Blantyre, Glasgow G72 9U3; Tel 01698 527200

Community Service Office Unit 2–3a Third Rd, Blantyre Ind Est, Blantyre, Glasgow G72 0UX; Tel 01698 829509

Court Social Work Unit 101 Almada St, Hamilton, South Lanarkshire ML3 0EX; Tel 01698 282044

Lanark Sheriff Court Social Work Unit 24 Hope St, Lanark, South Lanarkshire ML11 7NQ; Tel 01555 661531

STRATEGIC SERVICES

Council Offices, Almada St, Hamilton, South Lanarkshire ML3 0AA; Tel 01698 453703; Fax 01698 453784
Head (Strategic Services) Harry Stevenson;
E-mail harry.stevenson@southlanarkshire.gov.uk; Tel 01698 453703
Manager (Planning and Information) Marie Valente;
E-mail marie.valente@southlanarkshire.gov.uk; Tel 01698 453722
Manager (Strategy and Contracting) Mary O'Toole;
E-mail mary.otoole@southlanarkshire.gov.uk; Tel 01698 453781

SUPPORT SERVICES

Council Offices, Almada St, Hamilton, South Lanarkshire ML3 0AA; Tel 01698 453704; Fax 01698 453784
Head (Support Services) Tom Barrie;
E-mail tom.barrie@southlanarkshire.gov.uk; Tel 01698 453704
Manager (Personnel Services) Brenda Hutchinson;
E-mail brenda.hutchinson@southlanarkshire.gov.uk; Tel 01698 453774
Manager (Training) Willie McAllan
45 John St, Blantyre, Glasgow G72 0JG;
E-mail willie.mcallan@southlanarkshire.gov.uk; Tel 01698 417470

Manager (Business Systems)   Martin Low;
E-mail martin.low@southlanarkshire.gov.uk; Tel 01698 453912
Finance Manager (Children and Families Services)
Kathleen Gowrie;
E-mail kathleen.gowrie@southlanarkshire.gov.uk;
Tel 01698 454873
Finance Manager (Older People's Services)   Jennifer Berry;
E-mail jennifer.berry@southlanarkshire.gov.uk; Tel 01698 453866
Finance Manager (Adult Services)   Pat McCormack;
E-mail pat.mccormack@southlanarkshire.gov.uk;
Tel 01698 453708

Education Resources

Council Offices, Almada St, Hamilton, South Lanarkshire
ML3 0AE; E-mail education@southlanarkshire.gov.uk;
Tel 01698 454379; (Education Resources Helpline) 01698
454545; Fax 01698 454465
Executive Director (Education Resources)   Maggi Allan
Head (Specialist Services)   Ken Arthur
Head (Integrated Lifelong Learning)   Andrea Batchelor
Head (School Development)   Jim Duffin
Manager (SEN)   Anne Rooney
Manager (Integrated Children's Services)   Isobel MacDougal;
Tel 01698 455617
Manager (Psychological Services)   Vacancy
Station Rd, Blantyre, Glasgow G72 6YJ; Tel 01698 710568

SPECIAL EDUCATIONAL NEEDS ESTABLISHMENTS

Craighead School   Whistleberry Rd, Hamilton, South
Lanarkshire ML3 0EG; Tel 01698 285678
Headteacher   John Mcenaney

Greenburn School   Maxwellton Ave, East Kilbride, South
Lanarkshire G74 3DU; Tel 01355 237278
Headteacher   Adelaide Duffy

Hamilton School for the Deaf   c/o Earnock High School,
Wellhall Rd, Hamilton, South Lanarkshire ML3 9UE;
Tel 01698 286618
Headteacher   Jean Gorman

Kittoch School   Livingstone Dr, Murray, East Kilbride,
South Lanarkshire G75 0AB; Tel 01355 244348; 01355 244349
Headteacher   James W. Hughes

Ridgepark School   Mousebank Rd, Lanark, South
Lanarkshire ML11 7RA; Tel 01555 662151; 01555 662152
Headteacher   Miller W. Thomson

Rutherglen High School   Reid Street, Rutherglen, South
Lanarkshire G73 3DF; Tel 0141 647 4230; Fax 0141 647 0680
Headteacher   Mr Pat McGovern

Sanderson High School   High Common Rd, St. Leonards,
East Kilbride, South Lanarkshire G74 2LX; Tel 01355 249073
Headteacher   Morag McLullich

Victoria Park School   Market Rd, Carluke, South
Lanarkshire ML8 4BE; Tel 01555 750591
Headteacher   Margaret Constable

West Mains School   Logie Pk, East Kilbride, South
Lanarkshire G74 4BU; Tel 01355 249938
Headteacher   May Campbell

STIRLING COUNCIL
www.stirling.gov.uk

Political Composition: Lab: 11, Con: 9, SNP: 2
Viewforth, Stirling URL www.stirling.gov.uk; Tel 01786
443322; Fax 01786 443078
Chief Executive   K. Yates

Community Services

Tel 01786 443084; Fax 01786 443410
Director (Community Services)   Helen Munro
Head (Strategic Support Services)   H. McMorrow
Head (Community Care Services)   I. Cavanagh
Head (Criminal Justice Services)   A. Pinkman
Criminal Justice Services, Wolfcraig Bldgs, Dumbarton Rd,
Stirling; Tel 01786 443852
Executive Manager   L. McAlpine
Manager (Service Design)   C. McMillan
Manager (Business Systems)   M. Meiklejohn
Manager (Advice Services)   G. Alexander
Manager (Information Services)   D. Whyte
Manager (Accounting)   G. Morrison
Chief Social Work Officer   Irene Cavanagh
Personnel Officer   A. Smith

LOCAL OFFICES FOR SOCIAL WORK SERVICES

Stirling

Drummond House   Wellgreen Pl, Stirling; Tel 01786 471177
Development Manager (Assessment and Care Management)
M. Mackay
Area Manager (Services)   R. Cameron
Manager (Mental Health Services)   D. Armstrong

STIRLING ROYAL INFIRMARY

Stirling; Tel 01786 434093
Community Care Senior   R. Cranfield

DAY CENTRE FOR PEOPLE WITH DISABILITIES

Streets Ahead   2nd Fl, Wolfcraig Bldg, Dumbarton Rd,
Stirling; Tel 01786 849001
Riverbank Centre, Forthview, Riverside, Stirling FK8 1TZ;
Tel 01786 470852
Manager   D. Harrison
Manager   M. McAughtrie

RESIDENTIAL CARE FOR PEOPLE WITH A LEARNING DISABILITY

Torbrex House   St. Ninians, Stirling; Tel 01786 470832
Unit Manager   J. Wilson

RESIDENTIAL CARE FOR THE ELDERLY

*Development Manager (Residential Respite and Day Care
Services)*   H. Fulton
There are four homes for the elderly.

Children's Services

Viewforth, Stirling FK8 2ET; URL www.stirling.gov.uk;
Tel 0845 277 7000; Fax 01786 442782
Director (Children's Services)   G. Jeyes
Head of Schools   M. Doran
Head (Early Childhood Play and Out of School Care)
L. Kinney
Head (Planning and Resources – Children's Services)
R. Maxwell
Head (Social Work – Children's Services)   F. McBride
Number of Schools
Seven Secondary
Special Schools
Three Special Schools; Specialist provision in all
secondaries and two primaries; Two Pupil Support Services
(one covers 3–9 years, one covers 10–18 years).

PSYCHOLOGICAL SERVICE

Langgarth   Stirling FK8 2HA; E-mail liddlei@stirling.gov.uk;
Tel 01786 442553; Fax 01786 442946
Principal Psychologist   Ian Liddle

9

SPECIAL SCHOOLS (DAY)

Charles M. Brown School c/o Fallin Primary School, Fallin, Stirling FK7 7EJ; E-mail charlsunit@stirling.gov.uk
Headteacher   Joan Smith; Tel 01786 816756

Kildean School Stirling FK8 1RW;
E-mail kildeans@stirling.gov.uk; Tel 01786 473985
Headteacher   Maureen Howie
   3–16 SMH

Whins of Milton School Fairhill Rd, Whins of Milton, Stirling FK7 0LL; E-mail wofmps@stirling.gov.uk; Tel 01786 812667
Headteacher   Maureen Howie

PRIMARY PUPIL SUPPORT SERVICE

St. Mary's, Kildean, Stirling FK8 1RR;
   E-mail ppsupser@stirling.gov.uk; Tel 01786 463248
Headteacher   Cathy Mills

SECONDARY STUDENT SUPPORT SERVICE

Edward Rd, Riverside, Stirling FK8 1UP;
   E-mail secsser@stirling.gov.uk; Tel 01786 464641
Co-ordinator   Margaret Gibson

MAINSTREAM SECONDARY SCHOOLS WITH EXTENDED PROVISION

Balfron High School Roman Rd, Balfron, Glasgow G63 0PW; E-mail balfronhs@stirling.gov.uk; Tel 01360 440469; Fax 01360 440260
Headteacher   Val Corry
   (887)

Bannockburn High School Bannockburn Rd, Broomridge, Stirling FK7 0HG; E-mail bannockburnhs@stirling.gov.uk; Tel 01786 813519; Fax 01786 818040
Headteacher   Jim McAlpine
   12–16 (MH)

Dunblane High School Highfields, Dunblane, Stirling FK15 9DR; E-mail dunblanehs@stirling.gov.uk; Tel 01786 823823; Fax 01786 824462
Headteacher   David McKenzie
   (802)

McLaren High School Mollands Rd, Callander, Stirling FK17 8JH; E-mail mclarenhs@stirling.gov.uk; Tel 01877 330156; Fax 01877 331601
Headteacher   May Sweeney
   (672)

St. Modan's High School Barnsdale Rd, Stirling FK7 0PU; E-mail stmodanshs@stirling.gov.uk; Tel 01786 470962; Fax 01786 447117
Headteacher   Frank Lennon
   (848)

Stirling High School Ogilvie Rd, Stirling FK8 2PA; E-mail stirlinghs@stirling.gov.uk; Tel 01786 472451; Fax 01786 447127
Headteacher   Greig Ingram
   Mixed

Wallace High School Othyl Hse, Dumyat Rd, Stirling FK9 5HW; E-mail wallacehs@stirling.gov.uk; Tel 01786 449571; Fax 01786 447134
Headteacher   Linda Horsburgh

MAINSTREAM PRIMARY SCHOOLS WITH EXTENDED PROVISION

Callander Primary School Bridgend, Callander, Stirling FK17 8AG; E-mail callaps@stirling.gov.uk; Tel 01877 331576
Headteacher   Ann Genese

Dunblane Primary School Doune Rd, Dunblane, Stirling FK15 9AU; E-mail dunbps@stirling.gov.uk; Tel 01786 822351
Headteacher   Joy Macfarlane

Riverside Primary School Forrest Rd, Stirling FK8 1UJ; E-mail rvrsdeps@stirling.gov.uk; Tel 01786 474128
Headteacher   Eleanor Jess

WEST DUNBARTONSHIRE COUNCIL
www.west-dunbarton.gov.uk

Council Offices, Garshake Rd, Dumbarton, West Dunbartonshire G82 3PU;
   URL www.west-dunbarton.gov.uk; Tel 01389 737000; Fax 01389 737700
Chief Executive   Tim Huntingford

Department of Social Work and Housing Services

Director (Social Work and Housing Services)   Alexis Jay
Head (Social Work Operations)   A. Ritchie
Head (Strategy)   B. Clark
Head (Housing)   Cy Neil
Manager (Resources)   Jim Pow
Principal Officer (Community Care)   D. Doherty
Principal Officer (Child Care)   J. Watson

AREA TEAMS

Bowling, Milton and Dumbarton

Social Work Department Glencairn Hse, 95 High St, Dumbarton, West Dunbartonshire G82 1LF; Tel 01389 608118
Area Manager   J. Dean

Alexandria, Renton, Balloch and Bonhill

Social Work Department 4 Church St, Alexandria, West Dunbartonshire G82 0NP; Tel 01389 608080; Fax 01389 608088
Area Manager   J. Dean

Clydebank, Dalmuir, Drumry, Old Kilpatrick, Linnvale, Parkhall and Whitecrook

Social Work Department Council Offices, Rosebery Pl, Clydebank, West Dunbartonshire G81 1TG; Tel 0141 952 8800; Fax 0141 562 8899
Area Manager   Anne-Marie McDonald

HOSPITAL, HEALTH CENTRES AND CLINICS

Social Work Department Lomond Health Care Trust, North Main St, Alexandria, West Dunbartonshire G83 0AW; Tel 01389 754121; Fax 01389 755948
Senior Social Worker   M. Logan

HOMES FOR YOUNG PEOPLE

The Bungalow Blairvadach, Rhu, Helensburgh, West Dunbartonshire G84 8NN; Tel 01436 820279
Unit Manager   Jean Cockburn

Burnside 13 Davidson Rd, Jamestown, Alexandria, West Dunbartonshire G83 8AY; Tel 01389 753910
Contact   M. Buchanan

Craigellachie 16 Cochno St, Clydebank, West Dunbartonshire G81 1QX; Tel 0141 952 4637
Contact   Alice King

Hillpark Independent Living Unit 62 Stewart Dr, Hardgate, Clydebank, West Dunbartonshire G81 6AG; Tel 01389 872200
Contact   R. Walsh

Ramsay House Risk St, Dalmuir, Clydebank, West Dunbartonshire G81 3LW; Tel 0141 952 6121
Contact   C. Watt

COMMUNITY CENTRES AND UNITS

Haldane Community Flat 2 Carmona Dr, Haldane, Balloch, West Dunbartonshire G83 ; Tel 01389 608444
Contact E. Young

Linnvale Community Work Unit Jowitt Ave, Clydebank, West Dunbartonshire G81 2RL; Tel 0141 952 6088
Senior Community Worker Eric Young

SHELTERED HOUSING

Gray Street Alexandria, West Dunbartonshire; Tel 01389 753826
Contact I. Phillips
Contact Edna Bryan

Hogan Court Dalgleish Ave, Duntocher, West Dunbartonshire; Tel 01389 873228
Contact M. Paul

Manse Gardens Balloch, West Dunbartonshire G83 8BU; Tel 01389 756037
Contact J. Miller

Melfort Avenue 51 Melfort Ave, Clydebank, West Dunbartonshire G81; Tel 0141 952 2792
Contact J. McQuillan

Mill Road 205–7 Mill Rd, Clydebank, West Dunbartonshire; Tel 0141 952 6320
Contact A. Ronald
Contact A. McBride

Second Avenue Second Ave, Clydebank, West Dunbartonshire G81; Tel 0141 952 9716
Contact I. Stevenson

Westbridgend 1 and 2 Leven Crt, Westbridgend, Dumbarton, West Dunbartonshire G82; Tel 01389 608196
Contact M. Russell
Contact C. Stevenson

Young Street Young St, Clydebank, West Dunbartonshire G81; Tel 0141 952 7502
Contact P. Smith

RESIDENTIAL UNIT FOR ADULTS WITH LEARNING DISABILITY

Marelen 57 Drumry Rd, Clydebank, West Dunbartonshire G82 2LI; Tel 0141 941 1670
Contact A.M. Crassey

DAY CENTRES FOR ELDERLY

Dalreoch Day Centre Westbridgend, Dumbarton, West Dunbartonshire G82 4AD; Tel 01389 732725
Contact P. Flaherty

Faifley Regeneration Centre 31 Lennox Dr, Faifley, Clydebank, West Dunbartonshire G81 5JX; Tel 0141 952 5814
Contact E. Mathews

Frank Downie Day Centre Ottowa Cres, Dalmuir, Clydebank, West Dunbartonshire G81 4LB; Tel 0141 952 0650
Contact A. Shaw

Langcraigs Day Centre 2 Gooseholm Rd, Dumbarton, West Dunbartonshire G82 2AY; Tel 01389 608158
Contact C. McWatt

Queen Mary Day Centre 35 Queen Mary Ave, Clydebank, West Dunbartonshire G81 2LS; Tel 0141 952 3372
Contact C. McGuire

Satellite Day Care Centre c/o Gray Street Sheltered Housing Complex, Gray St, Alexandria, West Dunbartonshire; Tel 01389 753826
Contact M.M. McQuade

HOMES FOR ELDERLY PEOPLE

There are seven homes for the elderly.

WELFARE RIGHTS OFFICERS

Mansefield House Stathleven Pl, Dumbarton, West Dunbartonshire G82 1BA; Tel 01389 608348; Fax 01389 608055
Welfare Rights Development Officer J. Hepburn

RESOURCE CENTRES FOR ADULTS WITH LEARNING DISABILITY

Auchentoshan Centre Auchentoshan Est, Dalmuir, Clydebank, West Dunbartonshire G81 4SN; Tel 01389 872566
Contact A. Anderson

Dumbarton Centre 3 Bruce St, Dumbarton, West Dunbartonshire G82 1HY; Tel 01389 730823
Contact J. McCann

ADDICTION SERVICES

Social Work Department Glencairn Hse, 95 High St, Dumbarton, West Dunbartonshire G82 1LF; Tel 01389 608467; Fax 01389 608122
Assistant District Officer (Addiction) B. Rogerson

SERVICES FOR VISUALLY IMPAIRED

Department of Social Work and Housing Council Offices, Roseberry Pl, Clydebank, West Dunbartonshire G82 1PY; Tel 0141 562 8800; Fax 0141 562 8899

CRIMINAL JUSTICE UNIT

Principal Officer (Offenders) R. McQuillan
Municipal Bldgs, Station Rd, Church St, Dumbarton, West Dunbartonshire G82 1QA; Tel 01389 738484

Community Service Orders Unit Municipal Bldgs, Station Rd, Dumbarton, West Dunbartonshire G82 1QA; Tel 01389 738484
CSO Philip L. Dady

Department of Education and Cultural Services

West Dunbartonshire Council, Garshake Rd, Dumbarton, West Dunbartonshire G82 3PU;
E-mail ian.mcmurdo@west-dunbarton.gov.uk; Tel 01389 737301; Fax 01389 737348
Director (Education and Cultural Services) I. McMurdo

PSYCHOLOGICAL SERVICE

c/o Aitkenbar Primary School, Whiteford Ave, Dumbarton, West Dunbartonshire G82 3JZ; Tel 01389 763279; Fax 01389 734728
Principal Educational Psychologist Margaret Connolly (Acting)

SPECIAL SCHOOLS

Cunard School Cochno St, Clydebank, West Dunbartonshire G81 1RQ; Tel 0141 952 6614; Fax 0141 952 6463
Headteacher Angela McHardy
Mixed EBD

Kilpatrick School Mountblow Rd, Dalmuir, Clydebank, West Dunbartonshire G81 4SW; Tel 01389 872168; 01389 872171; Fax 01389 875646
Headteacher Michele Newall
Mixed 5–16 MH, PH, LD

Renton Language Unit Renton Primary School, Main St, Renton, Alexandria, West Dunbartonshire G82 4NA; Tel 01389 754042; Fax 01389 757675
Headteacher Mary Wheeler
Mixed 5-11

9

Special Educational Needs Support Service (Sensory Impaired–Visual Impairment) Sensory Impairment Base, c/o Dumbarton Academy, Dumbarton, West Dunbartonshire G82 2AJ; Tel 01389 761048; Fax 01389 739004
VI Co-ordinator Vacancy

Special Educational Needs Support Service (Sensory Impaired–Hearing Impairment) Sensory Impairment Base, c/o Braehead Primary School, Dumbarton, West Dunbartonshire G82 2BL; Tel 01389 762166; Fax 01389 761934
Headteacher (HI Service) Vacancy
  Mixed 5–16 Partially deaf (20)

WEST LOTHIAN COUNCIL
www.westlothian.gov.uk

Population 156 000
West Lothian Hse, Almondvale Blvd, Livingston, West Lothian EH54 6QG; URL www.westlothian.gov.uk; Tel 01506 777141; Fax 01506 777102
Chief Executive A. Linkston
Director (Community and Support Services) D. Kelly

Social Work Services

Tel 01506 777333; Fax 01506 777256
Head (Social Policy) Grahame Blair
Senior Manager (Older People) Vacancy
Senior Manager (Children and Families) B. Atkinson
Senior Manager (Adults) Jan Quigley
Senior Manager (Health and Planning) Ann Gee

SOCIAL WORK TEAMS

St. John's Hospital Older People's Team Howden West, Livingston, West Lothian EH54 6PP; Tel 01506 419666; Fax 01506 416614

CHILDREN AND FAMILIES COMMUNITY CARE

Bathgate Children and Families; Older People 69 Whitburn Rd, Bathgate, West Lothian EH48 1HE; Tel 01506 776700; Fax 01506 776735

Broxburn Adults; Children and Families; Older People Strathbrock Partnership Centre, Strathbrock, West Lothian EH52 5HN; Tel 01506 775666; Fax 01506 775667

Livingston Adults; Children and Families Cheviot Hse, Owen Sq, Livingston, West Lothian EH54 6PW; Tel 01506 777777; Fax 01506 777711

CHILDREN AND FAMILIES RESOURCE TEAM, SUPPORTED ACCOMMODATION TEAM (ADULTS) AND SUPPORTED ACCOMMODATION TEAM (YOUNG PEOPLE)

Lomond House Beveridge Sq, Livingston, West Lothian EH54 6QF; Tel 01506 775960; Fax 01506 775925

CRIMINAL JUSTICE SERVICES

West Lothian Lomond Hse, Beveridge Sq, Livingston, West Lothian EH54 6QF; Tel 01506 775900; Fax 01506 775925

FAMILY CENTRE

Livingston Family Centre Jackson Pl, Eliburn, Livingston, West Lothian EH54 6RH; Tel 01506 416555
  (50)

CHILDREN AND YOUNG PEOPLE'S CENTRES

Bathgate 24 Race Rd, Bathgate, West Lothian EH48 2AU; Tel 01506 632059
  (6)

Uphall 132 Forrest Wlk, Uphall, West Lothian EH52 5PW; Tel 01506 855416
  (6)

YOUTH STRATEGY

North Bridge Street 25 North Bridge St, Bathgate, West Lothian; Tel 01506 776929; Fax 01506 776930

DAY CENTRES FOR PEOPLE WITH LEARNING DISABILITIES

Blackburn Day Centre 31 East Main St, Blackburn, West Lothian EH47 7QR; Tel 01506 653081
  (80)

Clarendon Day Centre 30 Manse Rd, Linlithgow, West Lothian EH54 8HL; Tel 01506 670818
  (30)

Eliburn Day Centre Jackson Pl, Eliburn, Livingston, West Lothian EH54 6RH; Tel 01506 420320
  (106)

Riddochhill Workshop Unit 4, Pottishaw Pl, Bathgate, West Lothian; Tel 01506 631351
  (10)

DAY CENTRE FOR ADULTS WITH PHYSICAL DISABILITIES

Ability Centre Carmondean, Livingston, West Lothian
  (40)

HOSTEL FOR PEOPLE WITH LEARNING DISABILITIES

Deans House Broomieknowe Dr, Livingston, West Lothian EH54 8DQ; Tel 01506 411907
  (12)

RESIDENTIAL HOMES FOR OLDER PEOPLE

There are four homes for the elderly with a total of 210 places.

Education Services

West Lothian Hse, Almondvale Blvd, Livingston, West Lothian EH54 6QG; Tel 01506 777414; Fax 01506 777029
Director (Education and Cultural Services) Vacancy

Primary and Planning

Head (Education Services – Primary and Planning) M. Niven

Education Development and Quality Assurance

Head (Education Development and Quality Assurance) K. Reid
Manager (Pupil Support) J. Stark
Principal Psychologist Laura Ann Currie
Manager (Support for Learning) J. Henderson
Senior Educational Welfare Officer J. McDonald

Culture, Leisure and Performance Management

Manager (Culture, Leisure and Performance Management) G. Fitzpatrick

PSYCHOLOGICAL SERVICE

West Lothian Cedarbank Centre, Ladywell East, Livingston, West Lothian EH54 6DR; Tel 01506 775801; Fax 01506 775805
Principal Psychologist Laura Ann Currie

SPECIAL EDUCATION

Beatlie School Campus The Mall, Livingston, West Lothian EH54 5EJ; Tel 01506 777598
Headteacher K.E. White, DipCE
(36)

Burnhouse School The Ave, Whitburn, West Lothian EH47 0BX; Tel 01501 678100; Fax 01501 678108
Headteacher Kate McHairney (Acting)

Cedarbank School Cedarbank, Ladywell East, Livingston, West Lothian EH54 6DR; Tel 01506 442172
Headteacher D. McPhail, DipCE, MEd

Pinewood School Elm Gr, Blackburn, Bathgate, West Lothian EH47 7OX; Tel 01506 656374
Headteacher Mary O'Brien

Willowgrove House School 1–6 Willowgrove, Craigshill, Livingston, West Lothian EH54 5LU; Tel 01506 434274
Headteacher Kate McNairney (Acting)

WESTERN ISLES (COMHAIRLE NAN EILEAN)

www.w-isles.gov.uk

Population 26 502
Council Offices, Sandwick Rd, Stornoway, Western Isles HS1 2BW; URL www.w-isles.gov.uk; E-mail cne.siar.gov.uk; Tel 01851 703773; Fax 01851 705349
Convener of the Council Alexander A. MacDonald; Fax 01851 706022
Chief Executive Bill Howat; Fax 01851 706022
Director (Corporate Services) David O'Loan
Director (Technical Services) M. Murray
Director (Social Work) Malcolm Smith

Social Work Department

Fax 01851 709532
Chair (Social Work Committee) Murdo MacLeod
Vice-Chair R. Morrison
Director (Social Work) Malcolm Smith; E-mail msmith@cne-siar.gov.uk
Depute Director (Social Work) I. Macaulay
Organiser (Home Help) M. Macaulay
Organiser (Home Help) M.A. Maciver
Administration D. Finlayson

TRAINING

Responsible for training professional and support staff in the department.
Principal Officer/Development Manager (Joint Future) M. Mackay
Social Work Department, Comhairle Naneilean Siar, Stornoway, Isle of Lewis; Tel 01851 709335; Fax 01851 709532

AREA OFFICES

Castlebay Area Office

Barra, Isle of Barra; Tel 01871 810311
Social Worker and Housing Officer I. Anderson

Tarbert Area Office

Harris, Isle of Lewis; Tel 01859 502367
Team Leader J. Edward
Social Worker M. Griffin

Uists and Barra Area Office

Balivanich, Benbecula, Western Isles; Tel 01870 602425
Social Worker Andrew Walker
Home Help Organiser C. Laing

CHILDREN'S HOMES

NCH Action for Children Hillcrest Goathill Rd, Stornoway, Isle of Lewis; Tel 01851 703963
Officer-in-Charge Sheila Erskine

TEMPORARY ACCOMMODATION

Various local arrangements.

HOSTEL FOR THE MENTALLY HANDICAPPED

Ardseileach Stornoway, Isle of Lewis; Tel 01851 704365
Officer-in-Charge A. Monks

DAY CENTRES FOR THE HANDICAPPED

Ardseileach Centre Stornoway, Isle of Lewis; Tel 01851 704342
Contact A. Monks

Bragar Day Centre Western Isles; Tel 01851 710250
Manager F. Macleod

Craigaird Day Centre Lochmaddy, North Uist, Western Isles; Tel 01876 500375
Contact M. Keltie

Grianan Day Centre Stornoway, Isle of Lewis; Tel 01851 703443
Unit Manager A. Monks

Uist Resource Centre Daliburgh, South Uist, Western Isles; Tel 01878 700216
Contact V. Dix

ADULT TRAINING CENTRE FOR THE HANDICAPPED

Ardseileach Adult Training Centre Willowglen Rd, Stornoway, Isle of Lewis; Tel 01851 704342
Manager A. Monks

ACCOMMODATION FOR THE ELDERLY

There are six local authority homes for elderly people.

SHELTERED HOUSING

There are 21 sheltered housing schemes.

MEALS SERVICES

No Meals on Wheels service in the Western Isles.

Education Department

Council Offices, Sandwick Rd, Stornoway, Isle of Lewis HS1 2BW; URL www.cne-siar.gov.uk; Tel 01851 703773; Fax 01851 705796
Director (Education) Murdo Macleod, MA
Assistant Director (Support Services) Malcolm Hunter, MA
Head (Secondary Education and Human Resources) Catriona Dunn
Head (Inclusion and Early Education) Bernard Chisholm
Head (Quality Improvement) Iain A. Mackinnon
Head (Educational Resources) Jennet Gordon

9

Local Government
Channel Islands,
Isle of Man, Isles of Scilly

10

- ■ **Main Council Information**
- ■ **Social Services Department**
  Including all social services provision
- ■ **Education Department**
  Including all special needs provision

Key

(110)	Number of pupils
Mixed	Takes boys and girls
Boys	Takes boys only
Girls	Takes girls only
11–18	Age range of pupils

Abbreviations

ADHD	Attention Deficit Hyperactivity Disorder
ASD	Autism Spectrum Disorder
EBD	Emotional Behavioural Difficulties
LD	Learning Difficulties
LI	Language Impairment
MH	Mentally Handicapped
MLD	Moderate Learning Difficulties
PH	Physically Handicapped
PHAB	Physically Handicapped and Able-Bodied
PMLD	Profound and Multiple Learning Difficulties
PS	Partially Sighted
PtHg	Partially Hearing
SCU	Special Care Unit
SEBD	Severe Emotional Behaviour Difficulties
SEN	Special Educational Needs
SLD	Severe Learning Difficulties
SLDD	Students with Learning Difficulties and Disabilities
SMH	Severely Mentally Handicapped

Local Government
Channel Islands, Isle of Man, Isles of Scilly

GUERNSEY
www.gov.gg

Population 58 681
Sir Charles Frossard Hse, PO Box 43, St. Peter Port,
Guernsey GY1 1FH; URL www.gov.gg;
E-mail adv.fin@gov.gg; Tel 01481 717000; Fax 01481
713787
States Supervisor and Chief Executive   K. Mann
States Treasurer   D.M. Clark

Social Security Authority

Edward T. Wheadon Hse, Le Truchot, St. Peter Port,
Guernsey GY1 3WH; Tel 01481 732581; Fax 01481 732501
President   Deputy O.D. Le Tissier
Administrator   M. Nutley

States of Guernsey Housing Authority

Sir Charles Frossard Hse, La Charroterie, St. Peter Port,
Guernsey GY1 1FH; URL www.gov.gg / housing;
Tel 01481 717000; Fax 01481 713976
Director (States Houses)   K. Mann
Chief Executive   S.R. Langford

RESIDENTIAL HOMES FOR THE ELDERLY

There are two residential homes with a total of 111
residents in one and two bedrooms. Two sheltered housing
schemes comprising 20 flatlets, 16 bedsitter units and one
bedroom unit with attendant wardens.

Children Board

The Children Board exists to promote the welfare of
children and young people in partnership with families
and other agencies, and to provide a service within a legal
framework which will protect them.
Perruque Hse, Rue de la Perruque, Castel, Guernsey
GY5 7NT; Tel 01481 253266
Director (Child Care Services)   Mrs J.E. Gaggs
Deputy Director (Accommodation Services)   J. Wolfe
Assistant Director (Community Services)   R. Jones

States of Guernsey Education Council

Education Dept, The Grange, St. Peter Port, Guernsey
GY1 1RQ; E-mail enquiries@education.gov.gg; Tel 01481
710821; Fax 01481 714475
President   Deputy M.A. Ozanne

Vice-President   Deputy J. Pritchard
Director (Education)   D.T. Neale, BA, MA(Ed)
Deputy Director (Education)   S. Ryde, BSc, MPhil
Assistant Director (Education – Resources)   F. Flynn, Cert PA,
Dip PA, ACMA
Assistant Director (Education – Education Services)   G. Root,
MEd
Manager (Lifelong Learning)   A. Williams, BA, DipCG, MEd
Manager (Pupil Services)   S. Isbister, DipEd, BA,
MScEdPsych
Youth Services Officer   Vacancy
Principal Educational Psychologist   S.M. Hayward, BA, MSc,
EdPsych, ACP, ABPsS(Principal)
Senior Education Social Worker   A. Herve
Service for the Partially Hearing   M. Herquin, CertEd,
DipAdEdSt(DEd)
Service for Visually Impaired Children   S.A. Miller, CertEd,
DipSpEd, MEd, AdDipSpEd

SPECIAL SCHOOLS

Mont Varouf School   Le Neuf Chemin, St. Saviour, Guernsey
GY7 9FG; E-mail office@montverouf.sch.gg; Tel 01481
263135; Fax 01481 266635
Headteacher   J. Stephens, MEd, CertEd, DipEd(SEN)

Oakvale School   Collings Rd, St. Peter Port, Guernsey
GY1 1FW; E-mail office@oakvale.sch.gg; Tel 01481 723045;
Fax 01481 701071
Headteacher   A.T. Brown, BSc(Hons), PGCE

ASSESSMENT UNIT

Longfield Centre   Maurepas Rd, St. Peter Port, Guernsey
GY1 2DS; Tel 01481 722339; Fax 01481 728941
Headteacher   V. Guilbert, CertEd) (Acting

JERSEY
www.jersey.gov.uk

Population 87 186
States Greffe, Morier Hse, St. Helier, Jersey JE1 1DD;
URL www.jersey.gov.uk; E-mail m.delahaye@gov.je;
Tel 01534 502020; Fax 01534 502098
President of the States   Bailiff Sir Philip Bailhache Bailiff's
Chambers; Tel 01534 502102; Fax 01534 502137
States' Greffe (Greffier of the States)   Mr M.N. de la Haye;
Tel 01534 502013; Fax 01534 502098
States Treasurer   Ian Black, BSc(Econ), CPFA
States Treasury, Cyril Le Marquand Hse, St. Helier, Jersey;
Tel 01534 603215; Fax 01534 789901
Chief Executive Officer (Housing)   E.H. Le Ruez
Housing Department, PO Box 587, Jubilee Wharf, 24 The
Esplanade, St. Helier, Jersey JE4 8XT; Tel 01534 884422;
Fax 01534 884488

10

Chief Executive J.H. Young
Environment and Public Services Committee, South Hill, St. Helier, Jersey; Tel 01534 725511 ext 400; Fax 01534 768952

Chief Executive John D. Richardson
Public Services, South Hill, St. Helier, Jersey; Tel 01534 601690; Fax 01534 768950

Chief Executive Mr W.D. Ogley
Policy and Resources Department, PO Box 140, St. Helier, Jersey JE4 8QT; Tel 01534 603445; Fax 01534 603644

Chief Executive Anton Skinner (Acting)
Health and Social Services, 4th Fl, St. Helier, Jersey JE2 3QS; Tel 01534 622285; Fax 01534 622887

Director (Education) T.W. McKeon
PO Box 142, St. Helier, Jersey JE4 8QJ; Tel 01534 509500; Fax 01534 509343

Chief Officer (States of Jersey Police) G. Power, Esq
PO Box 789, St. Helier, Jersey JE4 8ZD; Tel 01534 612502; Fax 01534 612503

Chief Probation Officer B. Heath
13–15 Don St, St. Helier, Jersey JE4 8YZ; Tel 01534 833933; Fax 01534 833944

Medical Officer (Health) Dr J. Harvey
Public Health Services, Le Bas Centre, St. Helier, Jersey JE1 4HR; Tel 01534 623780; Fax 01534 623720

Controller (Employment and Social Security) Mrs A.E. Esterson
Department of Employment and Social Security, St. Helier, Jersey JE4 8PE; Tel 01534 280000; Fax 01534 280209

Judicial Greffier M. Wilkins
Judicial Greffe, Morier Hse, St. Helier, Jersey JE1 1DD; Tel 01534 502303; Fax 01534 502399

EMPLOYMENT AND SOCIAL SECURITY COMMITTEE

President Senator P.F. Routier
Vice-President Deputy P.N. Troy
Members of the Committee
Deputy J.L. Dorey, Deputy S.C. Ferguson, Constable M.J. Touzel of St. John.

SOCIAL SERVICES

Maison Le Pape, The Parade, St. Helier, Jersey JE3 3PU; Tel 01534 623500; Fax 01534 623598
Director (Community and Social Services) A. Skinner
Manager (Children and Adult Social Services) Ms M. Baudains
Manager (Children's Service) P. Dennett
Manager (Adult Services) Vacancy
Manager (Special Needs) Vacancy

CHILD AND ADOLESCENT MENTAL HEALTH

Royde Hse, Midvale Rd, St. Helier, Jersey JE2 3YR; E-mail family@super.ent.uk; Tel 01534 789861; Fax 01534 280079
Lead Clinician (Child and Adolescent) Dr Carolyn Coverley
Team Manager John Gordon

RESIDENTIAL, RESPITE CARE AND SUPPORTED ACCOMMODATION

Aviemore Children's Respite Home St. Martin, Jersey; Tel 01534 856484
Officer-in-Charge C. Ludlow

Heathfield Children's Centre Bagatelle La, St. Saviour, Jersey; Tel 01534 758204
Contact L. McLennan

Hostel for Homeless Teenagers 24 St. Mark's Rd, St. Helier, Jersey; Tel 01534 725297
Officer-in-Charge C. Baldwin

La Chasse Centre
Supported Family Accommodation
La Chasse, St. Helier, Jersey; Tel 01534 23727
Officer-in-Charge M. Finn

La Preference St. Martin, Jersey; Tel 01534 854453
Officer-in-Charge K. Sedeghat

Oakwell Children's Respite Home and Hospice Park Est, St. Brelade, Jersey; Tel 01534 745205
Officer-in-Charge C. Ludlow

RESIDENTIAL CARE, LEARNING DISABILITIES AND PHYSICALLY DISABLED

Adult Special Needs Services Maison Le Pape, The Parade, St. Helier, Jersey JE3 3PU

RESIDENTIAL HOME FOR ADULTS WITH LEARNING DIFFICULTIES

Les Amis Incorporated Five Oaks, St. Saviour, Jersey JE2 7JA; URL www.lesamis.org.je; E-mail info@lesamis.org.je; Tel 01534 519955; Fax 01534 519956

HOUSING DEPARTMENT

PO Box 587, Jubilee Wharf, The Esplanade, St. Helier, Jersey JE4 8XT; Tel 01534 884422; Fax 01534 884488
Chief Executive Officer E. Le Ruez

MEDICAL OFFICER OF HEALTH

Public Health Services, Le Bas Centre, St. Saviour's Rd, St. Helier, Jersey JE2 4HR; Tel 01534 623780; Fax 01534 623720
Director (Public Health Services) Dr John Harvey

COMMUNITY NETWORK TEAM

Maison Le Pape, The Parade, St. Helier, Jersey JE2 3PU; Tel 01534 623520
Senior Social Worker L. Blade
Manager (Operations) B. Flett

PROBATION

PO Box 656, 13–15 Don St, St. Helier, Jersey JE4 8YT; E-mail probation@gov.je; Tel 01534 833933; Fax 01534 833944
Chief Probation Officer B.A. Heath

PSYCHIATRIC SOCIAL WORK

Psychiatric Depatment, General Hospital, St. Helier, Jersey JE2 3QS; Tel 01534 622000
Team Leader A. Holt

EMPLOYMENT AND SOCIAL SECURITY DEPARTMENT

PO Box 55, La Motte St, St. Helier, Jersey JE4 8PE; URL www.ess.gov.je; E-mail a.esterson@gov.je; Tel 01534 280000; Fax 01534 280209
Chief Executive Officer (Employment and Social Security) Ann Esterson

TRAINING CENTRE

Le Geyt Centre, Five Oaks, St. Saviour, Jersey JE2 7JA; Tel 01534 888300
Manager D. Hart

ADULT SOCIAL WORK TEAM

Social Services Department, Maison Le Pape, St. Helier, Jersey JE2 3PU; Tel 01534 623535
Team Manager Julie Shaw

Public Health Services

Le Bas Centre, St. Saviours Rd, St. Helier, Jersey JE1 4HR; Tel 01534 789933; Fax 01534 623720

States of Jersey Education, Sport and Culture

PO Box 142, St. Helier, Jersey JE4 8QJ;
URL www.esc.gov.je; E-mail esc@gov.je; Tel 01534 509500

SPECIAL SCHOOLS SEVERE HANDICAP

D'Hautree House School (Secondary) St. Saviour's Hill, St. Saviour, Jersey JE2 7LF; Tel 01534 618042
Headteacher Mr R. Matthews
EBD

Mont a l'Abbe School St. Helier, Jersey JE2 3FN; Tel 01534 875801
Headteacher Mrs S. Eddie
MLD/SLD

St. James' School Le Breton La, St. Helier, Jersey JE2 4QN; Tel 01534 33801
Headteacher Mr C. Rogers
EBD

RESIDENTIAL SPECIAL SCHOOL

Greenfields Centre, Five Oaks, St. Saviour, Jersey JE2 7GS; Tel 01534 872940
Headteacher K. Mansell

PHYSICALLY HANDICAPPED FACILITIES

Bel Royal School (Primary) Bel Royal, St. Lawrence, Jersey JE3 1JQ; Tel 01534 37193
Headteacher Mrs S. Burton
Teacher-in-Charge Mrs D. Marsay
Education Department PO Box 142, St. Helier, Jersey JE4 8QJ; E-mail w.hurford@gov.je
Manager (Support Services) Mrs W. Hurford; Tel 01534 509500

Les Quennevais School (Secondary) St. Brelade, Jersey JE3 8GH; Tel 01534 43171
Headteacher Mr J. Thorp
Teacher-in-Charge Mr S. Pearson

ISLE OF MAN
www.gov.im

Population 76 315
Murray Hse, Mount Havelock, Douglas, Isle of Man IM1 2SF; URL www.gov.im; E-mail ceo@dlge.gov.im; Tel 01624 685859; Fax 01624 685943

Department of Health and Social Security

Hillary Hse, Prospect Hill, Douglas, Isle of Man IM1 1EQ; URL www.gov.im/depindex/lgovfo.asp; Tel 01624 686179; Fax 01624 686198
Minister Hon C. Christian, MLC
Member (Social Services) Mrs H. Hannan, MHK
Member (Health Services) D. Anderson, MHK
Member (Social Security) P. Gawne, MHK
Chief Executive D. Killip
The Department, on behalf of central government, provides a range of services through its three Divisions: Health, Social Security and Social Services. The Social Services Division functions as both provider and co-ordinator of services.

Social Services Division

Hilary Hse, Prospect Hill, Douglas, Isle of Man IM1 2EQ; E-mail dutysocialworker@socialservices.dhss.gov.im; Tel 01624 686179; Fax 01624 686198
Director (Social Services) D. Cooke
Deputy Director D. Gibson
Assistant Director (Adult Services) M. Crossley
Assistant Director (Children and Families) T. Noden
Manager (Administration) G.F. Tuck
Team Manager (Children and Families, Referral and Assessment Team) A. Merchant
Team Manager (Children and Families, Care Management Team) J. Gilbert
Contracts Manager (Children and Families) E. Coates
Principal Social Worker (Elderly and Mental Health) M. Lannen
Principal Social Worker (Disabilities) P. Cartmel
Quality Assurance G. Duff

HOME REGISTRATION

Registration Officer S. Wadsworth

NURSERIES AND CHILDMINDERS

Registration Officer R. Moore
Registration Officer E. Payne

RESIDENTIAL CARE (CHILDREN)

Residential assessment services are provided by two voluntary agencies on a contractual basis:

Knottfield (Isle Of Man Children's Centre) Woodbourne Rd, Douglas, Isle of Man; Tel 01624 67076
Officer-in-Charge J. Knight
(1) Residential care; (2) Day care; (3) Therapeutic care; (4) Juvenille Justice unit.

Priory House Tromode, Douglas, Isle of Man; Tel 01624 611424
Project Leader T. Lee (1) Therapeutic care (2) juvenile justice unit.

DISABILITY EMPLOYMENT SERVICE

Disability Employment Adviser S. Crossley

RESIDENTIAL AND DAYCARE (LEARNING DISABILITIES)

There are 22 community houses.
Manager (Residential Services) J. Carey

Eastcliffe Resource Centre Victoria Rd, Douglas, Isle of Man; Tel 01624 624305
Manager J. Duncalf

MENTAL HEALTH SERVICES

The Lodge, Braddan, Isle of Man; Tel 01624 642642
Assistant Director I. Wadsworth

SERVICES FOR BLIND

Manx Blind Welfare, RNIB, Douglas, Isle of Man; Tel 01624 674727
Rehabilitation Officer (RNIB) J. Yeardsley
Manager (Resource Centre) Vacancy
(1) Daycare and library; (2) Counselling

PHYSICALLY DISABLED

Crossroads Caring for Carers (IOM) Ltd 19 Drinkwater St, Douglas, Isle of Man; Tel 01624 673103
Co-ordinator R. Robinson

10

Manx Foundation for Physically Disabled Masham Crt, Victoria Rd, Douglas, Isle of Man; Tel 01624 628926
Principal Officer R. Fowler
(1) Day centre; (2) counselling and support

RESIDENTIAL CARE ELDERLY

Also six registered homes managed by voluntary agencies; 18 registered homes privately owned.

Cummal Mooar Promenade, Ramsey, Isle of Man; Tel 01624 814167
Manager (Resource Centre) P. Beattie

Glenside Victoria Rd, Douglas, Isle of Man; Tel 01624 623266
Manager (Resource Centre) P. Beattie

Rearyt ny Baie Albert Terr, Douglas, Isle of Man; Tel 01624 662499
Manager (Resource Centre) J. Bairstow

Southlands Church Rd, Port St. Mary, Isle of Man; Tel 01624 831831
Manager (Resource Centre) J. Bairstow

Social Security Division

Markwell Hse, Market St, Douglas, Isle of Man; Tel 01624 685685
Administrator G. Hull

Health Services Division

Crookall Hse, Demesne Rd, Douglas, Isle of Man; Tel 01624 642642
Head (Administration) J. Wilson

HOSPITALS

Nobles Hospital (Acute, General and Maternity)
Westmoreland Rd, Douglas, Isle of Man; Tel 01624 642642
Secretary F. Inman

Ramsey Cottage Hospital, (General, Acute and Geriatric)
Ramsey, Isle of Man; Tel 01624 811811
Secretary C. Wilson

Education Department

St. George's Crt, Upper Church St, Douglas, Isle of Man IMI 2SG; URL www.gov.im; Tel 01624 685820; Fax 01624 685834
Director (Education) J.R. Cain, MEd

SPECIAL NEEDS SUPPORT SERVICE

St. George's Crt, Upper Church St, Douglas, Isle of Man IM1 2AG; Isle of Man; URL www.gov.im; E-mail j.kermode@doe.gov.im; Tel 01624 686084
Assistant Education Officer (Special Needs) J.C. Kermode

COUNCIL OF THE ISLES OF SCILLY
www.scilly.gov.uk

Population 2000 (including off islands)
Town Hall, St. Mary's, Isles of Scilly TR21 0LW; URL www.scilly.gov.uk; Tel 01720 422537; Fax 01720 422202
Chair of the Council Cllr D. Mumford
Clerk/Chief Executive P.S. Hygate, BA, FRSA
Treasurer B. Archer
Medical Officer (Health) Dr T. Dalton, Health Centre St. Mary's; Tel 01720 422628

Social Services Department

Park Hse, The Parade, St. Mary's, Isles of Scilly TR21 0LP; E-mail iossocsevv@unisonfree.net; Tel 01720 422148; Fax 01720 422148
Director (Social Services) A. Lejk
Assistant Director (Social Services) J. Clark
Assistant Director (Social Services) H. Charnock
Medical Officer (Health) Dr D. MilesSt. Austell, Cornwall

TRAINING

Responsible for training professional and support staff in the department.
Training Officer J. Clark
Netherfield, Skyburriowe Mill, Helston, Cornwall TR12 0LP

Housing and Social Services Committee

Chair F. Ticehurst
Vice-Chair C.S. Savill
Members of the Council
K.M. Bennett, G.R. Lucas, A.L. Oyler, E.M. Peacock, M. Smith, F.J. Ticehurst, S.J. Whomersley.

ACCOMMODATION FOR THE ELDERLY

There is one local authority old people's home catering for 11 persons. Also limited daycare and respite care available. There is one private registered old people's home catering for 16 persons.
Meals on wheels and home care assistance are provided when required on each island.

Education Department

Town Hall, St. Mary's, Isles of Scilly TR21 0LW; Tel 01720 422537; Fax 01720 422202
Secretary for Education P.S. Hygate, BA, FRSA
Special Advisor (Education) Peter Clifton, BSc, CertEd, DipEd

Local Government Northern Ireland

- **Main Council Information**
- **Social Services Board**
  Including all social services provision

Key

(110)	Number of pupils
Mixed	Takes boys and girls
Boys	Takes boys only
Girls	Takes girls only
11–18	Age range of pupils

Abbreviations

ADHD	Attention Deficit Hyperactivity Disorder
ASD	Autism Spectrum Disorder
EBD	Emotional Behavioural Difficulties
LD	Learning Difficulties
LI	Language Impairment
MH	Mentally Handicapped
MLD	Moderate Learning Difficulties
PH	Physically Handicapped
PHAB	Physically Handicapped and Able-Bodied
PMLD	Profound and Multiple Learning Difficulties
PS	Partially Sighted
PtHg	Partially Hearing
SCU	Special Care Unit
SEBD	Severe Emotional Behaviour Difficulties
SEN	Special Educational Needs
SLD	Severe Learning Difficulties
SLDD	Students with Learning Difficulties and Disabilities
SMH	Severely Mentally Handicapped

Local Government
Northern Ireland

HEALTH AND SOCIAL SERVICES BOARDS NORTHERN IRELAND

Central Services Agency

25–27 Adelaide St, Belfast BT2 8FH; Tel 028 9032 4431;
 Fax 028 9023 2304
Chief Executive   S.J. Hodkinson, BSc(Econ), MSc, FHSM
Director (Finance and Administration)   P. Gick
Director (General Dental Services)   I. McCappin
Director (Legal Services)   A. Maginness
Director (Regional Supplies)   T. Molloy
Director (Nicare)   Dr C. Sullivan
Director (Family Practitioner Services)   P. Sheils
Director (Human Resources)   H. McPoland
Head (Professional and Pharmacy Services)   Kathryn Turner
Head (Counter Fraud Unit)   N. Jones
Dental Officer   P. Waters
Dental Officer   Vacancy
Adviser (Catering)   Vacancy
Adviser (Domestic Services)   F. Campbell
Adviser (Laundry)   A.W.G. Campbell

Eastern Health and Social Services Board
www.ehssb.n-i.nhs.uk

Champion Hse, 12–22 Linenhall St, Belfast BT2 8BS;
 URL www.ehssb.n-i.nhs.uk;
 E-mail enquiry@ehssb.n-i.nhs.uk; Tel 028 9032 1313;
 Fax 028 9055 3681
Chair   David Russell
Chief Executive   Dr Paula Kilbane, CBE, MB, MSc, FRCP, FFPHM
Director (Public Health)   Dr David Stewart, MB, BCH, BAO(QUB), MFCH, FFPHM, FRCP
Director (Nursing)   Mary Waddell, RN, RM, RCNT
Director (Social Services)   Hugh Connor
Director (Pharmaceutical Services)   Andree McCollum, BSc, MSc, MPSNI
Director (Dental Services)   Will Maxwell, BDS
Director (Planning and Contracting)   Anne Lynch, BSc, MPhil
Director (Finance)   Angela Paisley, BA(Hons), FCA
Medical Director (Primary Care)   Dr Stanton Adair, FRCGP
Head (Contracts)   Colm McConville, BSc, MPhil
Head (Corporate Services)   Stephen Adams, BSc(Econ)

HSS TRUSTS

All Community Units now have Trust Status.

North and West Belfast HSS Trust

Glendinning Hse, 6 Murray St, Belfast BT1 6DP;
 URL www.nwbt.org.uk;
 E-mail crowhurstm@nwb.n-i.nhs.uk; Tel 028 9032 7156;
 Fax 028 9082 1284
Chair   P.A. McCartan
Chief Executive   R.G. Black, CSW, MHSM
Director (Finance)   P.S. Harvey, BSc(Econ), IPFA, DipMS
Director (Operations and Community Care)   Vacancy
Director (Nursing)   B. Connolly
Director (Medical Services (Hospital))   Dr C. Marriott
Director (Medical Services (Community))   Dr R. McKee
Director (Planning, Contracts and Information) Deputy Chief Executive   P.M. Ryan, BA, MSc, DipSS, DipMS
Director (Hospital Services)   Miriam Somerville, MA, LCST
Director (Human Resource and Corporate Affairs)   E. Molloy

SOCIAL SERVICES OFFICES

North Belfast   449 Antrim Rd, Belfast BT13 2LJ; Tel 028 9050 8100; Fax 028 9050 8101
Family and Child Care Teams.

West Belfast   Lawther Bldgs, 16 Cupar St, Belfast BT13 2LJ; Tel 028 9032 0840; Fax 028 9024 0358
Family and Child Care Teams.

Andersonstown   21 Andersontown Rd, Belfast BT11 9AF; Tel 028 9030 1434; Fax 028 9043 1610
Elderly/Learning Disability Teams.

North Belfast Elderly   The Everton Complex, 2 Ardyone Rd, Belfast BT14 6DT; Tel 028 9056 6000; Fax 028 9056 6166
Elderly Teams.

Shankill Centre   151 Shankill Rd, Belfast BT13 1FD; Tel 028 9031 5005; Fax 028 9031 5178
Elderly Teams; Family and Child Care Team.

Everton Complex   Crumlin Rd, Belfast BT14 7GB; Tel 028 9056 6000; Fax 028 9056 6060; (Estate Dept) 028 9056 6010
Physical Health and Disability Teams; Community Mental Health and Mental Handicap Managers; Estate Service Department.

Social Services Department   Level 5, Royal Victoria Hospital, Belfast BT12 6BA; Tel 028 9024 0503; Fax 028 9024 5280
Hospital Social Work Team.

Social Services Department   Mater Infirmorum Hospital, Crumlin Rd, Belfast BT14 6AB; Tel 028 9074 1211; Fax 028 9074 5434
Hospital Social Work Team.

Transport Department   Northern Ireland Carrriers, Grosvenor Rd, Belfast BT12 5AX; Tel 028 9023 0557
Domestic Services Department/Transport.

11

Hotel Services Department Iveagh Bldgs, Broadway, Belfast BT12 6HF; Tel 028 9024 7821; Fax 028 9024 7610

PRE-SCHOOL PLAYGROUP

Whiterock Pre-School Playgroup 6 Whiterock Gr, Belfast BT12 7RQ; Tel 028 9032 3153; Fax 028 9043 8112

CHILDREN'S HOME

Somerton 57 Somerton Rd, Belfast BT15 4DD; Tel 028 9037 0701; Fax 028 9077 0633

FAMILY CENTRES

Falls Family and Education Centre 1st Fl, Falls Library, Belfast BT12; Tel 028 9032 6574

North Belfast Family Centre 21 Victoria Pde, Belfast BT15 2EN; Tel 028 9024 7580

Whiterock Family Centre 6 Whiterock Gr, Belfast BT12 7RQ; Tel 028 9032 3153

DAY CENTRES

Ballyowen Day Centre 179 Andersonstown Rd, Belfast BT11 9EA; Tel 028 9030 1034
Elderly (40)

Beech Hall Day Centre 21a Andersonstown Rd, Belfast BT11 9AF; Tel 028 9062 2939
Physically disabled. (40)

Carlisle Terrace Day Centre 2 Carlisle Terr, Belfast BT13 2PR; Tel 028 9023 1135

Glencairn Day Centre 98 Forthriver Rd, Belfast BT13 3SL; Tel 028 9039 1468

North Belfast Day Centre 585–587 Crumlin Rd, Belfast BT14 7GB; Tel 028 9056 6000; Fax 028 9056 6066
Mental health (50)

Parkmount Day Centre 704 Shore Rd, Belfast BT15 4HJ; Tel 028 9077 2413
Elderly (45)

Shankill Day Centre 135 Shankill Pde, Belfast BT13 1SD; Tel 028 9032 7518

Whiterock Day Centre 6 Whiterock Gr, Belfast BT12 7RQ; Tel 028 9032 3153

Woodlands Day Centre 9 Woodland Ave, Belfast BT14 6BY; Tel 028 9075 1215; Fax 028 9074 3502

HOSTELS FOR PEOPLE WITH LEARNING DISABILITY

Greystone 200 Donore Cres, Antrim, County Antrim BT41 1JB; Tel 028 9442 8852

Hanna Street Hostel 8 Hanna St, Belfast BT15 1GQ; Tel 028 9035 1314

Rigby Close Hostel 8 Rigby Cl, Cayehill Rd, Belfast BT15 5JF; Tel 028 9037 0832

Shaws Road Core and Cluster Hostel 1–3 Shaws Ave, Belfast BT11 9QF; Tel 028 9061 6661
(6)

DAY CARE FACILITIES

Everton Centre 589–593 Crumlin Rd, Belfast BT14 7GB; Tel 028 9039 1172; Fax 028 9071 5087

Fortwilliam Centre 17–19 Alexandra Gdns, Belfast BT15 3JL; Tel 028 9037 0530; Fax 028 9077 6091

Mica Centre 1 Mica Dr, Belfast BT12 7BQ; Tel 028 9024 1727

Muckamore Adult Training Centre Abbey Rd, Antrim, County Antrim BT41 4SH; Tel 028 9446 3333

Suffolk Centre 88 Stewartstown Rd, Belfast BT11 9JP; Tel 028 9030 1811
Learning disability (95)

RESIDENTIAL HOMES FOR THE ELDERLY

There are six homes for the elderly.

HEALTH CENTRES

Albert Street Health Centre 21 Ross Rd, Belfast BT12 4AT; Tel 028 9024 2816; Fax 028 9023 9580

Ballyowen Health Centre 179 Andersonstown Rd, Belfast BT11 9EA; Tel 028 9061 0611; Fax 028 9060 8600

Crumlin Road Health Centre 130–132 Crumlin Rd, Belfast BT14 6AP; Tel 028 9074 1188; Fax 028 9074 7158

Shankill Health Centre 135 Shankill Pde, Belfast BT13 1DY; Tel 028 9024 7181; Fax 028 9032 7198

Skegoneill Health Centre 195 Skegoneill Ave, Belfast BT15 3LL; Tel 028 9077 2471; Fax 028 9077 2449

Whiterock Health Centre 6 Whiterock Gr, Belfast BT12 7FW; Tel 028 9032 3153; Fax 028 9043 8112

HEALTH CLINICS

Cupar Street Clinic 91 Cupar St, Belfast BT13 2LJ; Tel 028 9032 7613; Fax 028 9024 0362
Chiropody, cytology, dental, family planning, infant health, occupational therapy, ophthalmic services, school health services and speech therapy.

Lincoln Avenue Clinic 5–13 Lincoln Ave, Belfast BT14 6AZ; Tel 028 9074 8363; Fax 028 9074 3364
Chiropody, cytology, dental, family planning, infant health, ophthalmic services, school health, dietetics and speech therapy.

Parkmount Clinic 704 Shore Rd, Belfast BT15 4HJ; Tel 028 9077 2413
Chiropody, dental, family planning, infant health and school services.

HOSPITAL

Muckamore Abbey Hospital 1 Abbey Rd, Muckamore, Belfast BT41 4SH; Tel 028 9446 3333; Fax 028 9446 7730
Provides a specialist service for people with learning disability from the Eastern and Northern Health and Social Services Board areas and offers core specialisms on a regional basis to all four Boards. Specialist psychiatric outpatient clinics on an outreach basis.

TRUST HEADQUARTERS

Glendinning Hse, Murray St, Belfast BT1 6DP; Tel 028 9032 7156; Fax 028 9082 1284

FORTWILLIAM RESOURCE CENTRE

2nd Fl, 17–19 Alexandra Gdns, Belfast BT15 3LJ; Tel 028 9037 0393; Fax 028 9077 6091

FINANCE DEPARTMENT

16 College St, Belfast BT1 6BT; Tel 028 9032 1313; Fax 028 9033 3701

LCID PROJECT

16 College St, Belfast BT15 6BT; Tel 028 9032 1313; Fax 028 9077 6091

South and East Belfast HSS Trust

Trust Headquarters, Knockbracken Healthcare Pk, Saintfield Rd, Belfast BT8 8BH; Tel 028 9056 5656; Fax 028 9056 5813
Chair B. McLaughlin
Chief Executive Patricia Gordon
Executive Director (Finance) N. Carson
Executive Director (Medical) Dr P. Bell
Executive Director (Nursing) R. McGee
Executive Director (Social Services) H. Connor

HOSPITALS

Albertbridge Road Day Hospital 225 Albertbridge Rd, Belfast BT5 4PX; Tel 028 9045 6007

Knockbracken Mental Health Services Knockbracken Healthcare Pk, Saintfield Rd, Belfast BT8 8DH; Tel 028 9056 5656

SOCIAL SERVICES OFFICES

Derryvolgie Avenue Office 11 Derryvolgie Ave, Belfast BT9 6FL; Tel 028 9068 1735; Fax 028 9066 5488

Gilnahirk Rise Office Belfast BT5 7DT; Tel 028 9079 7383; Fax 028 9040 2079

Lower Crescent Office 14 Lower Cres, Belfast BT7 1NR; Tel 028 9024 4061; Fax 028 9033 0965

Ormeau Road Office 414 Ormeau Rd, Belfast BT7 3HY; Tel 028 9064 2905; Fax 028 9064 2805

Strand House Office 102 Hollywood Rd, Belfast BT4 1NU; Tel 028 9067 2319; Fax 028 9056 3456

Templemore Avenue Office 195 Templemore Ave, Belfast BT5 4FR; Tel 028 9045 4638; Fax 028 9045 2635

University Street Office 92 University St, Belfast BT7 1HE; Tel 028 9024 0255; Fax 028 9031 2313

Wellington Park Office 33 Wellington Pk, Belfast BT9 6DL; Tel 028 9068 3101; Fax 028 9066 4091

Woodstock Link Office 1–15 Woodstock Link, Belfast BT6 8EA; Tel 028 9045 0997; Fax 028 9073 8266

CHILDREN'S HOMES

Bawnmore Children's Home 70 Bawnmore Rd, Belfast BT9 6LD; Tel 028 9066 8553

College Park Avenue Adolescent Unit 57a College Park Ave, Belfast BT7 1LR; Tel 028 9020 4888

North Road Children's Home 60 North Rd, Belfast BT5 5NH; Tel 028 9065 8656

SPECIALIST CENTRE

Family Trauma Centre 1 Wellington Pk, Belfast BT9 6DJ; Tel 02890 20 4700

DAY CARE CENTRES

The Beersbridge Family Centre 216 Woodstock Rd, Belfast BT6 8PQ; Tel 028 9045 4291

Child Care Centre 87 Lisburn Rd, Belfast BT9 7AE; Tel 028 9024 4903; Fax 028 9031 3768

City Way Day Centre 2a Boyne Crt, Belfast BT12 5BL; Tel 028 9024 3000; Fax 028 9031 1777

Edgcumbe Day Centre 8–10 Edgcumbe Gdns, Belfast BT4 2EG; Tel 028 9065 7028; Fax 028 9047 1591

The Island Resource Centre Cuba Wlk, Newtownards Rd, Belfast BT4 1EQ; Tel 028 9045 4400; Fax 028 9046 0068

Millar's Lane Day Centre Millar's La, Dundonald, Belfast BT16 0DA; Tel 028 9048 4974; Fax 028 9041 0896

Mount Oriel Day Centre 53–57 Saintfield Rd, Belfast BT8 4HL; Tel 028 9079 0284; Fax 028 9040 3364

Sandown Road Day Centre 57 Sandown Rd, Belfast BT5 6GT; Tel 028 9065 5502

Orchardville Social Education 10 Orchardville Ave, Finaghy, Belfast BT10 0JM; Tel 028 9062 7455; Fax 028 9061 0813

Young People's Centre 10 College Gdns, Belfast BT9 6BQ; Tel 028 9066 1825; Fax 028 9066 6792

REHABILITATION CENTRES

Beechbank House-Rehabilitation Centre for Blind and Deaf 11 Derryvolgie Ave, Belfast BT9 6FL; Tel 028 9068 1735; Fax 028 9066 5488

Edgcumbe Training Resource Centre Edgcumbe Gdns, Belfast BT4 2EG; Tel 028 9067 2290; Fax 028 9047 2075

Ravenhill Road Adult Centre 318–322 Ravenhill Rd, Belfast BT6 8GL; Tel 028 9073 1528; Fax 028 9045 7133

Victoria Day Centre 25a Tamar St, Belfast BT4 1HS; Tel 028 9045 6251; Fax 028 9046 0760

RESIDENTIAL HOMES FOR PEOPLE WITH LEARNING DISABILITY

Mertoun Park Complex 17 Mertoun Pk, Knocknagoney Rd, Belfast BT18 9QE; Tel 028 9076 1324

Red Hall 109 Circular Rd, Belfast BT4 2FE; Tel 028 9076 0088

RESIDENTIAL ACCOMMODATION FOR PEOPLE WITH A LEARNING DISABILITY OR MENTAL ILLNESS

Belvoir Park Hostel 12–14 Castlerobin Rd, Belfast BT8 4DW; Tel 028 9049 1809

Malone Road Home 80 Malone Rd, Belfast; Tel 028 9068 1428

Myrtlefield Home 77 Myrtlefield Pk, Belfast BT4 6NG; Tel 028 9038 1933

Ormeau Road Home 342 Ormeau Rd, Belfast; Tel 028 9049 3524

Ormeau Road Home 611 Ormeau Rd, Belfast BT7 3GY; Tel 028 9064 0816

HEALTH CENTRES AND CLINICS

Belvoir Clinic 52 Drumart Sq, Belvoir Pk, Belfast BT8 4DL; Tel 028 9049 1126

Braniel Clinic 16 Glen Rd, Belfast BT5 7DH; Tel 028 9040 1153

Carryduff Clinic Church Rd, Carryduff, Belfast BT8 8DT; Tel 028 9081 4334

Cherryvalley Health Centre 17 King's Sq, Belfast BT5 7BP; Tel 028 9079 9321; Fax 028 9040 2069

Cherryville Clinic 2a Cherryville St, Belfast BT6 8BJ; Tel 028 9045 0887; Fax 028 9045 1161

Cregagh Clinic 331 Cregagh Rd, Belfast BT6 0LG; Tel 028 9079 3918; Fax 028 9070 2874

Dundonald Clinic 16 Church Rd, Dundonald, Belfast BT16 0LN; Tel 028 9048 2991

Dunluce Health Centre 1–2 Dunluce Ave, Belfast BT9 7AW; Tel 028 9024 0884; Fax 028 9020 4330

Finaghy Health Centre 13–25 Finaghy Road South, Belfast BT10 0BW; Tel 028 9062 8211; Fax 028 9061 2210

Holywood Arches Health Centre 1 Westminster Avenue North, Belfast BT4 1NS; Tel 028 9056 3200; Fax 028 9056 3327

Malone Place Clinic 31 Malone Pl, Belfast BT12 5FD; Tel 028 9024 2521; Fax 028 9032 9844

Mount Oriel Clinic 4 Mount Oriel, Belfast BT8 4HL; Tel 028 9070 1845

Ormeau Road Health Centre 137–41 Ormeau Rd, Belfast BT7 1SL; Tel 028 9032 0437; Fax 028 9031 1679

Templemore Avenue Health Centre 98a Templemore Ave, Belfast BT5 4FW; Tel 028 9045 4321; Fax 028 9045 2640

ELDERLY PERSONS' HOMES

There are six homes for the elderly.

11

Ulster, Community and Hospitals HSS Trust

The Health and Care Centre, 39 Regent St, Newtownards,
County Down BT23 4AD; Tel 028 9181 6666; Fax 028
9151 2131; 028 9182 0140
Chief Executive   Jim McCall

SOCIAL SERVICES SUB-OFFICES

BANGOR ADMINISTRATION BUILDING

Newtownards Rd, Bangor, County Down BT20 4LB; Tel 028
9146 8521

ACCOMMODATION FOR CHILDREN

Tel 028 9182 3783
There are three homes providing eight long term places
each. One unit provides eight short term assessment places.
One home provides places and respite for children with
special needs.

COMMUNITY CARE DEPARTMENT

10 Church St, Newtownards, County Down BT23 4AL;
Tel 028 9151 0000

SERVICES FOR PEOPLE WITH A LEARNING DISABILITY

Tel 028 9147 9657
There is one home providing 14 places, 11 supervised
dwellings providing 26 places, and there are three adult
training centres providing 198 places.

DAY CARE IN BANGOR AND NEWTOWNARDS

Tel 028 9146 2690
There are two day centres providing 500 places weekly.

RESIDENTIAL ACCOMMODATION FOR THE ELDERLY

Tel 028 9146 2690
There are five homes providing 189 places.

COMMUNITY MENTAL HEALTH TEAM

3 Church St,; Tel 028 9182 0355

Down Lisburn HSS Trust

Trust Headquarters, Lisburn Health Centre, Linenhall St,
Lisburn, County Antrim BT28 1LU;
URL www.n-i.nhs.uk;
E-mail enquiries@dltrust.n-i.nhs.uk; Tel 028 9266 5181;
Fax 028 9266 5179
Chief Executive   John Compton, MSc, BA, DipSocAdmin
Director (Social Work and Primary Care Services)
Kate Thompson, MA, CQSW
Director (Planning and Performance)   John Simpson,
BSc(Hons), DipAss, CQSW, CASW(Man)
Director (Nursing and Acute Services)   Alan Finn, RGN,
RMN
Director (Human Resources)   Alan Best, MIPD
Director (Corporate Affairs)   Paul McBrearty, BA, MBA
Director (Finance)   Paul Simpson, IPFA, FCIS
Director (Disability, Mental Health and Support Services)
Sean O'Rourke, BA, CQSW, IPM

BALLYNAHINCH PATCH

Ballynahinch Community Services Office 45–47 Main St,
Ballynahinch, County Down BT24 8DN; Tel 028 9756 5456
Manager (Community Services)   Clive Wallington

DOWNPATRICK PATCH

Downpatrick Clinic 12–14 Pound La, Downpatrick, County
Down BT30 6HY; Tel 028 4461 3811
Manager (Community Services)   Laurence Clarke
Manager (Primary Care)   Anne Kerr

Market Street Children's Centre 81 Market St, Downpatrick,
County Down BT30 6LZ; Tel 028 4461 3511
Manager (Child Care)   Paul McConville
Manager   Angela Connor (Acting)

DUNMURRY PATCH

Dunmurry Clinic 19–21 Upper Dunmurry La, Dunmurry,
Belfast BT17 0AA; Tel 028 9030 1029
Manager (Community Services)   Marion Robertson

Stewartstown Road Health Centre 212 Stewartstown Rd,
Dunmurry, Belfast BT17 0FB; Tel 028 9060 2705
Community Services Manager (Children)   John Toner

HILLSBOROUGH PATCH

Hillsborough Health Centre 29 Ballnahinch St,
Hillsborough, County Down BT26 6AW; Tel 028 9268 3609
Manager (Community Services)   Lynda Campbell
Manager (Primary Care)   Harry McManus

LISBURN PATCH

Lisburn Health Centre 25 Linenhall St, Lisburn, County
Antrim BT28 1LU; Tel 028 9266 5181
Community Services Manager (Primary Care)
Janice Colligan

NEWCASTLE PATCH

Newcastle Community Services Office 20–22 Park Ave,
Newcastle, County Down BT33 0DY; Tel 028 4472 3346
Manager (Community Services)   Kathleen Weir

HOSPITAL SOCIAL SERVICES DEPARTMENTS

Downe Hospital 9a Pound La, Downpatrick, County Down
BT30 6JA; Tel 028 4461 3311
Principa Nurse Manager (Operations)   Frances Donovan

Downshire Hospital Ardglass Rd, Downpatrick, County
Down BT30 6RA; Tel 028 4461 3311
Senior Social Worker   J. Smyth
Principal Nurse and Manager (Mental Health Services)
Arthur Dick

Lagan Valley Hospital 39 Hillsborough Rd, Lisburn,
County Antrim BT28 1JP; Tel 028 9266 5141
Community Services Manager (Primary Care)
Janice Colligan

ELDERLY PERSONS' RESOURCE CENTRES/RESIDENTIAL HOMES

Ardview House 18 The Ward, Ardglass, Downpatrick,
County Down BT30 7UP; Tel 028 4484 1093
Manager (Resource Centre)   Therese O'Higgins

Drumlough House 3–19 Moira Rd, Lisburn, County Antrim
BT28 1RB; Tel 028 9260 1228
Manager (Resource Centre)   Michele Barton

Grove House 76 Antrim Rd, Ballynahinch, County Down
BT24 8BA; Tel 028 9756 2720; 028 9756 5631
Manager (Resource Centre)   Angela Cartwright

Laurelhill House 1a Ballymacash Pk, Lisburn, County
Antrim BT28 3EX; Tel 028 9260 2116
Manager (Resource Centre)   Eugene Lynch

St. John's 3 Pound La, Downpatrick, County Down
BT30 6HY; Tel 028 4461 2754
Manager (Resource Centre)   Sharon McKnight

Seymour House 1 Laurel Way, Seymour Hill, Dunmurry,
Belfast BT17 9PX; Tel 028 9030 1829
Manager (Resource Centre)   Geraldine Howe

CHILDREN'S HOMES

Appletree House Children's Home 100a Bridge St,
Downpatrick, County Down BT30 6HD; Tel 028 4461 3363
Senior Social Worker   Nuala Maguire

Flaxfield Children's Home 39a Hillsborough Rd, Lisburn, County Antrim BT28 1JP; Tel 028 9250 1242; (via Logan Valley) 028 9266 5141 ext 2326
Manager Steve Mack

Glenmore House Children's Home 1a Glenmore Pk, Hilden, Lisburn, County Antrim BT27 4RT; Tel 028 9266 2081
Senior Social Worker Vacancy

FAMILY AND CHILDREN'S CENTRES

Colin Family Centre Pembroke Loop Rd, Poleglass, Dunmurry, Belfast BT17 0PH; Tel 028 9030 1828
Senior Social Worker Maria McCluskey
Senior Social Worker Donna Marks

Knocknashinna Family Centre 37 Knocknashinna Rd, Downpatrick, County Down BT30 6RE; Tel 028 4461 5208
Senior Social Worker Marie McCluskey

Warren House Children's Centre 61 Woodland Pk, Lisburn, County Antrim BT28 1LQ; Tel 028 9260 7528
Manager (Child Care – Fostering and Adoption)
   Marian Hall
Manager (Child Care – Child, Adolescent and Family Consultation Team) Kate Anderson
Manager (Disability Services) Edna McConville

RESOURCE CENTRES – DISABILITY SERVICES

Market Street 81 Market St, Downpatrick, County Down BT30 6LZ; Tel 028 4461 3511
Manager Angela Connor (Acting)

Rowan Centre 52 Wallace Ave, Lisburn, County Antrim BT27 4AG; Tel 028 9262 8523
Manager (Day Centre) Lynda Eagleson
Manager (Disability Services) Margaret O'Kane

RESIDENTIAL AND RESPITE FACILITY – DISABILITY SERVICES

Thompson House Hospital 19–21 Magheralave Rd, Lisburn, County Antrim BT28 3BP; Tel 028 9266 5646
Manager Garry Hyde

RESIDENTIAL HOMES FOR PEOPLE WITH A LEARNING DISABILITY

Glenwood Residential Care Services 1 Glenwood Grn, Dunmurry, Poleglass, Belfast BT17 0QX; Tel 028 9030 1595
Manager Colette Jordan

Hillhall Home 11–19 Hillhall Gdns, Lisburn, County Antrim BT27 5DD; Tel 028 9267 9364
Manager Raphael Kearns

Lindsay House Children's Home Laurel Way, Seymour Hill, Belfast BT17 9PR; Tel 028 9043 1072
Manager Shane McIlvenny

Struell Lodge Residential and Resource Centre 2 Ardglass Rd, Downpatrick, County Down BT30 6JG; Tel 028 4451 3850
Manager Marian Fitzsimons (Acting)

RESOURCE CENTRES FOR PEOPLE WITH A LEARNING DISABILITY

Lisburn Assessment and Resource Centre 58 Wallace Ave, Lisburn, County Antrim BT27 4AE; Tel 028 9267 8111
Manager Elizabeth McAlister

Mountview Assessment and Resource Centre Flying Horse Rd, Downpatrick, County Down BT30 6QP; Tel 028 4451 3818
Manager Seamus Laird

COMMUNITY SERVICES – DISABILITY

Adult Disability Services (Down) Downshire Hospital, Ardglass Rd, Downpatrick, County Down BT30 6RA; Tel 028 4461 6915
Manager (Disability Services) Sheila Simons

Adult Disability Services (Lisburn) Rowan Centre, 52 Wallace Ave, Lisburn, County Antrim BT27 4AG; Tel 028 9260 4031
Manager (Disability Services) Elizabeth McAllister

Children's Disability Services (Down) Cherryvalley Downshire Hospital, Downpatrick, County Down BT30 6RA; Tel 028 4451 3830
Community Services Manager (Children) Brian Mongan

Adult Disability Services (Lisburn) Cherryvalley Downshire Hospital, Downpatrick, County Down BT30 6RA; Tel 028 4451 3830
Sector Manager (Down) Edna McConville

Sensory Impaired Services Cherryvalley Downshire Hospital, Ardglass Rd, Downpatrick, County Down BT30 6RA; Tel 028 4451 3830
Manager (Operations) Edna McConville

RESIDENTIAL HOMES – MENTAL HEALTH SERVICES

Ballymacoss Hostel 4–14 Mourneview Pk, Brokerstown Rd, 9 Ballymacoss, Lisburn, County Antrim BT27 2UQ; Tel 028 9267 6277
Manager (Clinical Services) Fintan McGreevy

Inch/Meadowlands Residential Complex c/o Downshire Hospital, Ardglass Rd, Downpatrick, County Down BT30 6RA; Tel 028 4461 3311
Manager (Residential Services) Janet Clarke

COMMUNITY SERVICES – MENTAL HEALTH

Community Mental Health Services (Lisburn) Lisburn Health Centre, 25 Linenhall St, Lisburn, County Antrim BT28 1LU; Tel 028 9266 5181
Community Services Manager (Primary Care)
   Janice Colligan

Community Mental Health Services (Down) Downshire Hospital, Ardglass Rd, Downpatrick, County Down BT30 6RA; Tel 028 4461 3311
Manager (Mental Health Services) Fintan McGreevy

COMMUNITY SERVICES OFFICES

Lisburn Health Centre, Linenhall St, Lisburn, County Antrim BT28 1LU; Tel 028 9266 5181

DOWNPATRICK CHILDREN'S AND DISABILITY SERVICES

81 Market St, Downpatrick, County Down BT30 6LZ; Tel 028 4461 3511

11

Northern Health and Social Services Board

www.nhssb.n-i.nhs.uk

County Hall, 182 Galgorm Rd, Ballymena, County Antrim BT42 1QB; URL www.nhssb.n-i.nhs.uk; E-mail chiefexecutive@nhssb.n-i.nhs.uk; Tel 028 2565 3333; Fax 028 2566 2311
Chair M. Wood
County Hall, 182 Galgorm Rd, Ballymena, County Antrim BT42 1AB

Social Services Department

NHSSB, County Hall, Ballymena, County Antrim BT42 1QB; E-mail firstname.surname@nhssb.ni.nhs.uk; Tel 028 2566 62218; 01266 663 333; Fax 028 2566 62311
Director (Social Services) Mary Wilmont, CQSW
Assistant Director (Social Services-Child Care)
   Margaret Black, DipSW, CQSW

*Assistant Director (Social Services-Training and Staff
Development)* Janeen Maconachie, BSocStud(Hons),
DipSWork, CQSW, PQS (Ed/Training
Holywell Hospital, 60 Steeple Rd, Antrim, County Antrim
BT41 2RJ; Tel 028 9441 3393; Fax 028 9448 7655
Assistant Director (Social Services-Adult Services)
Kevin Keenan, BA, MA, MPhil, CQSW
Principal Social Worker (Child Care) John Fenton,
BA(Hons), CQSW
Principal Social Worker (Adult Services) Seamus Logan,
BA(Hons), MSW, CQSW, DEM
Project Manager (Children Services Planning) Vacancy

HSS Trusts

Homefirst Community Trust

Trust Headquarters, The Cottage, 5 Greenmount Ave,
Ballymena, County Antrim BT43 6DA;
E-mail chief.executive@homefirst.n-i.nhs.uk; Tel 028
2563 3700; Fax 028 2563 3733
Chair W. Boyd
Chief Executive Mr Christie Colhoun
Executive Director (Finance) Harold Sharp
Executive Director (Nursing, Dental and Governance)
Hazel Baird
Executive Director (Child Health Services and Allied Health)
Joan Stephenson (Acting)
Executive Director (Medical) Dr Michael Mannion
Director (Social Care and Disability) Rosemary Simpson
Director (Personnel) William Day
Director (Planning and Information) Martin Sloan
Director (Mental Health) Mr Glenn Houston
Director (Social Work and Child Care) Brenda Smyth

SOCIAL SERVICES ADMINISTRATION

Children's Services Pinewood Offices, 101 Frys Rd,
Ballymena, County Antrim BT43 7EN; Tel 028 2563 8662;
Fax 028 2565 2512

Social Care Spruce Hse, Braid Valley Site, Cushendall Rd,
Ballymena, County Antrim BT43 6HL; Tel 028 2563 6500;
Fax 028 2564 4221

SOCIAL SERVICES OFFICES

Antrim 30 Station Rd, Antrim, County Antrim BT41 4AB;
Tel 028 9446 4031; Fax 028 9446 5663

Ballyclare The Beeches Resource Centre, 76 Avondale Dr,
Ballyclare, County Antrim BT39 9DB; Tel 028 9334 9797;
Fax 028 9335 4024

Ballymena – Salisbury House Queen St, Ballymena,
County Antrim BT42 1DB; Tel 028 2565 6447; Fax 028 2565
2275

Ballymena – Slemish Community Services Centre Braid
Valley Site, Cushendall Rd, Ballymena, County Antrim
BT43 6HR; Tel 028 2563 5640; Fax 028 2563 5617

Carrickfergus – Ellis Street Carrickfergus, County Antrim
BT38 8AZ; Tel (Adult Learning Disability) 028 9331 5100;
(Early Years) 028 9331 5112; (Family and Child Care;
Children's Disability) 028 9331 5114; Fax 028 9331 5120

Carrickfergus – Taylor's Avenue Carrickfergus, County
Antrim BT38 7HF; Tel 028 9331 5850; Fax 028 9336 0586

Cookstown Community Services Centre 52 Orritor Rd,
Cookstown, County Tyrone BT80 8BN; Tel 028 8672 3800;
Fax 028 8672 3818

Glengormley Community Services Centre 40 Carnmoney
Rd, Glengormley, Newtownabbey, County Antrim
BT36 6HP; Tel 028 9084 9142; Fax 028 9083 8944

Larne Community Services Centre Gloucester Ave, Larne,
County Antrim BT40 1RP; Tel 028 2827 5427; Fax 028 2827
9578

Magherafelt (Adult Services) 55 Hospital Rd, Magherafelt,
County Londonderry BT45 5EG; Tel 028 7930 1700; Fax 028
7930 1446

Magherafelt (Children's Services) Sperrin Hse, Queens
Ave, Magherafelt, County Londonderry; Tel 01645 301700;
Fax 01645 301446

Rathcoole 57 Rosslea Way, Newtownabbey, County Antrim
BT37 9BZ; Tel 028 9086 7111; Fax 028 9036 4035

Learning Disability Team Pennybridge Resource Centre,
Pennybridge Ind Est, Larne Rd, Ballymena, County Antrim
BT42 3HB; Tel 028 2564 6849; Fax 028 2563 9320

Physical Disability Team Wilson Hse Resource Centre, 17
Raceview Rd, Ballymena, County Antrim BT42 4JL; Tel 028
2586 2774; Fax 028 2586 2420

HOSPITALS

Holywell Hospital 60 Steeple Rd, Antrim, County Antrim
BT41 2RJ; Tel 028 9446 5211; Fax 028 9441 3190

Whiteabbey Hospital Psychiatric Unit, Doagh Rd,
Newtownabbey, County Antrim BT37 9RH; Tel 028 9086
5181; Fax 028 9036 9581

HOSPITAL SOCIAL WORK TEAMS

Antrim Antrim Hospital, Bush Hse, Bush Rd, Antrim,
County Antrim BT41 2QB; Tel 028 9442 4841; Fax 028 9442
4042

Magherafelt Mid Ulster Hospital, Hospital Rd,
Magherafelt, County Londonderry BT45 5EG; Tel 028 7963
1031; Fax 028 7963 3050

Newtownabbey Whiteabbey Hospital, Doagh Rd,
Newtownabbey, County Antrim BT37 9RH; Tel 028 9055
2569; Fax 028 9036 4015

DAY CENTRES

Antrim 32a Station Rd, Antrim, County Antrim BT41 4AB;
Tel 028 9442 8551

Carrickfergus Taylor's Ave, Carrickfergus, County Antrim
BT38 7HF; Tel 028 9336 5855; Fax 028 9336 0586

Cookstown 2 Westland Rd, Cookstown, County Tyrone
BT80 8BX; Tel 028 8676 3800; Fax 028 8676 6988

Gloucester Park Larne, County Antrim BT40 1PD; Tel 028
2827 4311; Fax 028 2827 3496

Inniscoole 57 Rosslea Way, Rathcoole, Newtownabbey,
County Antrim BT37 9EZ; Tel 028 9085 4333; Fax 028 9036
4035

Maghera 24 Coleraine Rd, Maghera, County Down
BT46 5BN; Tel 028 7964 3360; Fax 028 7954 9858

Magherafelt 57 Hospital Rd, Magherafelt, County
Londonderry BT45 5EG; Tel 028 7936 5075; Fax 028 7936
5076

Wilson House 17 Raceview Rd, Ballymena, County Antrim
BT42 4JL; Tel 028 2586 1228; Fax 028 2586 2420

ADULT CENTRES

Antrim 32c Station Rd, Antrim, County Antrim BT41 4AB;
Tel 028 9448 7992; Fax 028 9446 4129

Cookstown 2 Westlands Rd, Cookstown, County Tyrone
BT80 8BX; Tel 028 8672 3911; Fax 028 8672 3959

Drumross O'Neill Rd, Newtownabbey, County Antrim
BT36 6BZ; Tel 028 9084 9632; 028 9084 9635; Fax 028 9083
0929

George Sloane Centre Unit 35, Pennybridge Ind Est, Larne
Rd, Ballymena, County Antrim BT42 3HB; Tel 028 2564
6266; Fax 028 2563 1832

Hawthorns Ellis St, Carrickfergus, County Antrim
BT38 8AZ; Tel 028 9331 5110; Fax 028 9331 5120

Larne 72 Ballymena Rd, Ballyloran, Larne, County Antrim BT40 2AD; Tel 028 2827 0950; Fax 028 2827 0891

Magherafelt 55 Hospital Rd, Magherafelt, County Londonderry BT45 5EG; Tel 028 7936 5060

WORKSHOPS

Broadway Workshops Abbotts Rd, Newtownabbey, County Antrim BT37 9RB; Tel 028 9086 2122; Fax 028 7936 5060

HOMES FOR THE ELDERLY

Contact Tracy McCartney

Clonmore House 22–28 Crossreagh Dr, Rathcoole, Newtonabbey, BT37 9DY; Tel 028 9085 1153

Ferrard House 32 Station Rd, Antrim, BT41 4AB; Tel 028 9441 5508; Fax 028 9441 6508

Greenisland House 91 Shore Rd, Greenisland, Carrickfergus, BT38 8TZ; Tel 028 9086 5344; Fax 028 9086 7472

Joymount House Joymount Crt, Carrickfergus, BT38 7DN; Tel 028 9336 3904; Fax 028 9336 9982

Lis-garel Home Gloucester Pk, Larne, BT40 1PD; Tel 028 2827 4833; Fax 028 2827 3496

Moylinney Home Ballyalton Pk, Monkstown, Newtownabbey, BT37 0ET; Tel 028 9086 1861; Fax 028 9085 9763

Pinewood Home 101 Frys Rd, Ballymena, BT43 7EN; Tel 028 2563 8664; Fax 028 2563 7923

Rosedale Home 101 Killgreel Rd, Antrim, BT41 1EH; Tel 028 9442 9402

Westlands Home 2 Westland Rd, Cookstown, BT80 8BX; Tel 028 8672 3922; Fax 028 8676 6988

CHILDREN'S HOMES

Ardrath Children's Home 52 Hospital Rd, Magherafelt, BT45 5EG; Tel 028 7936 5093; Fax 028 7936 5050

Carnview 41 Knockenagh Ave, Rathfern, Newtownabbey, County Antrim BT36 6AQ; Tel 028 9036 5688; 028 9036 5733; Fax 028 9085 3913

Princes Gardens 4 Princes Gdns, Larne, County Antrim BT40 1RQ; Tel 028 2827 8802; Fax 028 2827 8802

Whitehaven Respite Unit 17 Edward Rd, Whitehead, Carrickfergus, County Antrim BT38 9RU; Tel 028 9335 3367; Fax 028 9337 3691

FAMILY CENTRES

Antrim 411 Firmount Dr, Greystone Rd, Antrim, County Antrim BT41 1JL; Tel 028 9442 8715; Fax 028 9446 0295

Cookstown Westland Rd, Cookstown, County Tyrone BT80 8BX; Tel 028 8672 3933

Magherafelt 62 Hospital Rd, Magherafelt, County Londonderry BT45 5EG; Tel 028 7963 5097; Fax 028 7936 5098

Newtownabbey Family Centre Innis Ave, Rathcoole, Newtownabbey, County Antrim BT37 9NA; Tel 028 9085 5960; Fax 028 9036 9855

HOMES FOR PEOPLE WITH LEARNING DISABILITIES

Clogrennan 12 Andrew Ave, Larne, County Antrim BT40 1EB; Tel 028 2827 2428

Ellis Court Ellis St, Carrickfergus, County Antrim BT38 8AZ; Tel 028 9331 5113; Fax (Social Services Office) 028 9331 5113

Hollybank 13 Union Rd, Magherafelt, County Londonderry BT45 5DF; Tel 028 7963 3369; Fax 028 7963 2537

Lynwood 1–11 Ballyfore Pk, Ballyduff, Newtownabbey, County Antrim BT36 6XU; Tel 028 9036 5856

ADOLESCENT UNIT

Ballee 5a Hollybank Pk, Ballee, Ballymena, County Antrim BT42 2HJ; Tel 028 2564 4220; Fax 028 2563 2012

FAMILY PLACEMENT TEAM

Audley Centre 27 Ballymoney Rd, Ballymena, County Antrim BT43 5BS; Tel 028 2564 1207; Fax 028 2563 0620

Ellis Street Carrickfergus, County Antrim BT38 8AZ; Tel 028 9331 5111; Fax 028 9336 7347

MENTAL HEALTH HOSTELS

Kintyre Park 47 Kintyre Pk, Ballykeel 1, Ballymena, County Antrim BT42 4AN; Tel 028 2565 3755; Fax 028 2563 2863

Norfolk Court 4 Rathenraw, Antrim, County Antrim BT41 2SF; Tel 028 9442 8089
Warden R. McCabe

COMMUNITY MENTAL HEALTH TEAMS

Audley Terrace 27 Ballymoney Rd, Ballymena, County Antrim BT43 5BS; Tel 028 2564 7766; Fax 028 2564 3955

Cookstown Community Services Centre 52 Orritor Rd, Cookstown, County Tyrone BT80 8BN; Tel 028 8672 3847; Fax 028 8672 3818

Glenview House Whiteabbey Hospital, Doagh Rd, Newtownabbey, County Antrim BT37 9RH; Tel 028 9086 5181; Fax 028 9055 2280

Holywell House Holywell Hospital, 60 Steeple Rd, Antrim, County Antrim BT41 2RJ; Tel 028 9446 5211; Fax 028 9441 3655

Loughview Resource Centre 2–4 Ballyronan Rd, Magherafelt, County Londonderry BT45 6BP; Tel 028 7963 2885

Crisis Response Team Greystone Offices, Unit 1, Rathenraw Ind Est, 56 Greystone Rd, Antrim, BT41 2SJ; Tel 028 9442 7900; Fax 028 9442 7902

Community Outrach Team Greystone Offices, Unit 1, Rathenraw Ind Est, 56 Greystone Rd, Antrim, BT41 2SJ; Tel 028 9442 7920; Fax 028 9442 7904

SOCIAL SERVICES TRAINING CENTRES

Holywell Hospital 60 Steeple Rd, Antrim, County Antrim BT41 1RJ; Tel 028 9441 3393; Fax 028 9448 7655

Station Road Antrim, County Antrim BT41 4AB; Tel 028 9446 4695; Fax 028 9446 5505

Joymount Joymount Crt, Carrickfergus, County Antrim BT38 7DN; Tel 028 9336 9868; Fax 028 9336 9982

WARDEN SCHEMES

Glenvarna Drive 29 Glenvarna Dr, Ballyhenry Rd, Glengormley, Newtownabbey, County Antrim BT36 5JB; Tel 028 9083 7127

Rathcoole Close 7a Rathcoole Cl, Rathcoole, Newtownabbey, County Antrim BT37 9QQ; Tel 028 9086 9164

Woodland Crescent 21 Woodland Cres, Rush Pk, Newtownabbey, County Antrim BT37 9AP; Tel 028 9086 4016

OTHER OFFICES

Child, Adolescent and Family Consultation Centre Station Rd, Antrim, County Antrim BT41 4BS; Tel 028 9441 5700; Fax 028 9442 4360

Community Addictions Team 1 Parkmore Dr, Cullybackey Rd, Ballymena, County Antrim BT43 5DT; Tel 028 2565 8462; Fax 028 2563 1252

11

Brain Injury Clinic Cedar Foundation, Galgorm, Ballymena, County Antrim BT42 1AQ; Tel 028 2563 2035; Fax 028 2564 6344

Causeway Health and Social Services Trust

8e Coleraine Rd, Ballymoney, County Antrim BT53 6BP; E-mail norma.evans@chsst.n-i.nhs.uk; Tel 028 2766 6600; Fax 028 2766 1201
Chief Executive Norma Evans
Director (Child and Community Care Services) J. Loughrey, MA, MSc, HDipEd, DipYouthWork, CQSW

BALLYMONEY COMMUNITY OFFICES

Armour Day Centre

6 Newal Rd, Ballymoney, County Antrim BT53 6HD; E-mail armour@chsst.n-i.nhs.uk; Tel 028 2766 4101

Ballycastle Social Services (Elderly Care Team)

1a Coleraine Rd, Ballycastle, County Antrim BT54 6EY; Tel 028 2076 2651

Physical Disability Team

Brookgreen Resource Centre, Brook St, Coleraine, County Londonderry BT51 1QG; Tel 028 7035 5112

Mental Health Resource Centre

Castlerock Rd, Coleraine, County Londonderry BT51 3HP; E-mail clare.armour@chsst.n-i.nhs.uk; Tel 028 7034 2721

Community Child Care Offices

Family Support Project, Castlerock Rd, Coleraine, County Londonderry BT51 3HP; E-mail martysteele@chsst.n-i.nhs.uk; Tel 028 7035 2221

Learning Disability Team

Mountfern Hse, 10 Rugby Ave, Coleraine, County Londonderry; Tel 028 7034 4700

Hospital Social Work Team

Causeway Hospital, 4 Newbridge Rd, Coleraine, County Londonderry BT52 1TP; Tel 028 7032 7032

Adult Services (Finance and Administration)

6 Newall Rd, Ballymoney, County Antrim BT53 6HD; Tel 028 2766 4101

SOCIAL WORK TEAMS

Reception Team and Children in Need Team Child Care Office, 7a Castlerock Rd, Coleraine, County Londonderry BT51 3HP; Tel 028 7035 2221

Ballymoney and Moyle Family and Child Care Team Armour, Newal Rd, Ballymoney, County Antrim BT53 6HD; Tel 028 2766 4101

Family Placements Riverside Hse, 28 Portstewart Rd, Coleraine, County Londonderry BT52 1RN; Tel 028 7035 8158

Early Years Team Riverside Hse, 28 Portstewart Rd, Coleraine, County Londonderry BT52 1RN; Tel 028 7035 8158

HOSPITALS

Causeway Hospital 4 Newbridge Rd, Coleraine, County Londonderry BT52 1TP; Tel 028 7032 7032

Dalriada Hospital and MS Centre 1a Coleraine Rd, Ballycastle, County Antrim BT54 6EY; Tel 028 2076 2666

Robinson Memorial Hospital 23 Newal Rd, Ballymoney, County Antrim BT53 6HB; Tel 028 2766 0322

Ross Thomson Unit Causeway Hospital, 4 Newbridge Rd, Coleraine, County Antrim BT52 1TP; Tel 028 7032 7032

FAMILY CENTRE

Brookgreen Family Centre 12 Brookgreen, Coleraine, County Londonderry BT52 1QG; Tel 028 7034 3921

ADULT CENTRES

Millbrook Resource Centre 49a Ballymena Rd, Ballymoney, County Antrim BT53 7EZ; Tel 028 2766 6889

Mountfern Centre 6 Rugby Ave, Mountsandel Rd, Coleraine, County Londonderry; Tel 028 7035 1995

DAY CENTRES

Armour Day Centre 6 Newal Rd, Ballymoney, County Antrim BT53 6HD; Tel 028 2766 4101

Brookgreen Day Centre Pavestone Project, 11 Brook St, Coleraine, County Londonderry BT52 1QG; Tel 028 7035 5112

Glenmona Resource Centre 10 Glendun Rd, Cushenden, Ballymena, County Antrim BT44 0PX; Tel 028 2176 1218

Rathmoyle Day Centre 6 Mary St, Ballycastle, County Antrim BT54 6QH; Tel 028 2076 2713

Southern Health and Social Services Board

www.shssb.org

Tower Hill, Armagh, County Armagh BT61 9DR; URL www.shssb.org; Tel 028 3741 0041; Fax 028 3741 4550
Chair W.F. Gillespie
Chief Executive B.P. Cunningham
Director (Social Services) B. Dornan
Assistant Director (Social Services) T. Smith
Assistant Director (Social Services) T. Rodgers
Assistant Director (Social Services) Mrs F. McAndrew

HSS Trusts

Craigavon and Banbridge Community Health and Social Services Trust

Bannvale Hse, 10 Moyallan Rd, Gilford, Craigavon, County Down BT63 5JX; Tel 028 3883 1983; Fax 028 3883 2690
Chair D.S. Cook
Chief Executive W.D. Preston
Director (Child and Family Care) L.F. Boyle, BSc, DSS, MSc, CQSW; Tel 028 3883 1983; Fax 028 3883 2690
Director (Elderly and Primary Care) R. Burns, RGN, HV, HEdCert
Director (Finance) W.R. Crozier, BSc(Econ), FICAI
Director (Human Resources) K. Donaghy, BA, HND, GIPM, MIPM
Director (Business and Planning) C. Donaghy
Director (Mental Health and Disability) R. Moore
Manager (Business and Planning – Information) M. Atkinson
Manager (Business and Planning – Contracts) L. Skelly

ADMINISTRATION OFFICES

Finance Department 100 Sloan St, Lurgan, Craigavon, County Down BT66 8NT; Tel 028 3832 3262; Fax 028 3832 9483
Director (Finance) W.R. Crozier

Headquarters Bannvale Hse, 10 Moyallan Rd, Gilford, Craigavon, County Down BT63 5JY; Tel 028 3883 1983; Fax 028 3883 1993

Personnel Department Lurgon HSS Centre, 100 Sloan St, Lurgan, Craigavon, County Armagh
Personnel Manager M. Burns
Personnel Manager L. Gordon

Transport Department 68 Lurgan Rd, Portadown, Craigavon, County Armagh BT63 5QQ; Tel 028 3833 4444
Assistant Manager (Operational Services) C. Jefferies

Bocombra Children's Centre 2 Old Lurgan Rd, Portadown, Craigavon, County Armagh BT63 5SG; Tel 028 3833 2479
Contact M. White
   Assessment and Residential Child Care Unit (10)

CARE OF THE MENTALLY ILL

The Beeches Russell Dr, Lurgan, Craigavon, County Armagh BT66 8HD; Tel 028 3834 7537; Fax 028 3834 7949
Manager Vacancy

Hoophill Day Centre Connolly Pl, Trasna Way, Lurgan, Craigavon, County Armagh; Tel 028 3832 8436
   Day centre; elderly mentally infirm. (15)

Hoophill House Connolly Pl, Trasna Way, Lurgan, Craigavon, County Armagh; Tel 028 3832 2556

Psychiatric Unit 68 Lurgan Rd, Portadown, Craigavon, County Armagh BT63 5QQ; Tel 028 3833 4444; Fax 028 3835 1179
   Acute services; mental health (80) Day care services; mental health (40)

Russell Drive Day Centre Russell Dr, Lurgan, Craigavon, County Armagh BT66 8HD; Tel 028 3834 7537; Fax 028 3834 7949
   Day care; mental health (15)

CARE OF OLDER PERSONS

Crozier House Meeting Hse Rd, Banbridge, County Down BT32 3ER; Tel 028 4066 2734
Manager Hilda McDowell
   Residential: care of older people, four respite (35)

Dollingstown Social Centre Alfred Terr, Dollingstown, Lurgan, Craigavon, County Armagh BT66 7JX; Tel 028 3832 3680
   Social centre; care of older persons (30)

CARE OF PERSONS WITH SPECIAL LEARNING NEEDS

Edenvale 16–18 Windsor Ave, Lurgan, Craigavon, County Armagh BT67 9BG; Tel 028 3832 4207
Contact H. McMullan

Riverside 10 Moyallan Rd, Gilford, Craigavon, County Down BT63 5JY; Tel 028 3883 2094
Contact A. Martin

Windsor Gate Lodge Windsor Ave, Lurgan, Craigavon, County Armagh; Tel 028 3832 9652
Contact H. McMullan; Tel 028 3832 4207

CHILD AND FAMILY CARE

Child and Family Care Office 2 Old Lurgan Rd, Portadown, Craigavon, County Armagh BT63 5SG; Tel 028 3833 3747; Fax 028 3833 5528
Manager (Child and Family Care) P. Morgan
Manager (Child and Family Care) V. O'Rourke

Child Protection Centre (NSPCC Joint Centre) The Children's Centre, Moyraverty Centre, Craigavon, County Armagh BT65 5HX; Tel 028 3834 3620; Fax 028 3834 3143

Edenvilla 6 Edenderry Rd, Banbridge, County Down BT32 3AF; Tel 028 4066 2614

Fostering Resource Centre 2 Old Lurgan Rd, Portadown, Craigavon, County Armagh BT63 5SG; Tel 028 3833 7181

DAY CARE CENTRES

Banbridge Social Education Centre Meeting House Rd, Banbridge, County Down BT32 3ER; Tel 028 4062 6773
Manager Dessie Cunningham

Bannvale Social Education Centre 10 Moyallan Rd, Gilford, Craigavon, County Down BT63 5JY; Tel 028 3883 1545
Contact L. Knox
   Day care; learning disability (100)

The Beeches Russell Dr, Lurgan, Craigavon, County Armagh BT66 8HD; Tel 028 3834 7537; Fax 028 3834 7949
Manager Vacancy

Copperfields Meeting House Rd, Banbridge, County Down BT32 3ER; Tel 028 4066 2349
Manager D. Cunningham
   Day care; physical disability and mental handicap (30)

Psychiatric Day Hospital 68 Lurgan Rd, Portadown, Craigavon, County Armagh BT63 5QQ; Tel 028 3833 4444; Fax 028 3835 1179

Eden Social Education Centre 293 Bridge St, Portadown, Craigavon, County Armagh BT63 5BJ; Tel 028 3833 3589
Contact D. Cunningham

Manor Centre Manor Dr, Lurgan, Craigavon, County Armagh BT66 8QD; Tel 028 3832 6525; 028 3832 8896
Contact D. Cunningham
   Day care; physical disability and mental health (80)

The Meadows Day Centre 293 Bridge St, Portadown, Craigavon, County Armagh BT63 5BJ; Tel 028 3833 8145
Contact D. Kelly

Skeagh House 15 Banbridge Rd, Dromore, County Down BT25 1NB; Tel 028 9269 2999
Contact I. Cromie
   Residential: care of older persons, four respite (34)

HEALTH CENTRES/CLINICS AND HEALTH AND SOCIAL SERVICES CENTRES

Banbridge HSS Centre Scarva St, Banbridge, County Down BT32 3AD; Tel 028 4066 2866; Fax 028 4062 6059
   Primary care and social services

Brownlow HSS Centre 1 Legahory Centre, Legahory, Craigavon, County Armagh BT65 5BE; Tel 028 3834 1431; 028 3834 3011; 028 3834 4973; Fax 028 3834 5983
Contact A. McVeigh; Tel 028 3832 7824
   Primary care services.

Dromore Clinic 18 Banbridge Rd, Dromore, County Down BT25 1NB; Tel 028 9269 2461
Contact A. McVeigh; Tel 028 4066 2866
   Primary care services

Gilford Health Centre Castleview, Gilford, Craigavon, County Down BT63 6JS; Tel 028 3883 1225; 028 3883 1701; 028 3883 2091; 028 3883 2270; Fax 028 3883 1318
Contact A. McVeigh; Tel 028 4066 2866
   Primary care services

Lurgan HSS Centre 100 Sloan St, Lurgan, Craigavon, County Armagh BT66 8NT; Tel 028 3832 7824; Fax 028 3832 9353
Contact A. McVeigh
   Primary care and social services

Portadown HSS Centre Tavanagh Ave, Portadown, Craigavon, County Armagh BT62 3BU; Tel 028 3833 4400; 028 3833 5117; Fax 028 3835 1246
Contact A. McVeigh; Tel 028 3839 1212
   Primary care and social services

RESOURCE CENTRES

Cherrytrees Resource Centre 1a Edenderry Gdns, Portadown, Craigavon, County Armagh BT63 5EA; Tel 028 3839 4088; Fax 028 3839 4095
Contact S. Robinson; Tel 028 3839 1212
Contact P. McCann

11

Community Mental Handicap Resource Centre Moylinn Resource Centre, Legahory, Craigavon, County Armagh; Tel 028 3834 8811
Contact N. Mangan

Community Mental Health Resource Centre Russell Dr, Lurgan, Craigavon, County Armagh BT66 8HD; Tel 028 3834 7537; Fax 028 3834 7949

SPECIALISED DEPARTMENTS

Occupational Therapy Department 68 Lurgan Rd, Portadown, Craigavon, County Armagh BT63 5QQ; Tel 028 3833 4444; Fax 028 3835 0068
Contact C. Cranston

Speech Therapy Department 68 Lurgan Rd, Portadown, Craigavon, County Armagh BT63 5QQ; Tel 028 3833 4444; Fax 028 3835 0068
Contact R. Nesbitt

Newry and Mourne HSS Trust

5 Downshire Pl, Downshire Rd, Newry, County Down BT34 1DZ; Tel 028 3026 0505; Fax 028 3026 9064
Chair Sean Hogan
Chief Executive Eric Bowyer
Director (Social Services) Jim Flynn
Director (Professions Allied to Medicine) E. Cavan
Director (Finance and Planning) M.J. Dillon
Daisy Hill Hospital,
Director (Nursing and Community Health) Joan O'Hagan
Director (Acute Services) Dr P. Loughran
Daisy Hill Hospital,
Director (Administrative and Support Services) Anita Carroll
Advisor (General Medical Services) Dr A. Mulholland
Health Centre, Newtownhamilton, Newry, County Down BT35
Consultant Community Paediatrician Dr M. Hollinger

HOSPITALS

Daisy Hill Hospital 5 Hospital Rd, Newry, County Down BT35 8DR; Tel 028 3083 5000
Mourne Hospital Newry St, Kilkeel, Newry, County Down BT34 4DN; Tel 028 4176 2235

FIELDWORK SERVICES – CHILD CARE

Butterfield House 24 Monaghan St, Newry, County Down BT35 6AA; Tel 028 3025 0808

CHILDREN'S RESIDENTIAL HOME

Cedar Grove Centre 3 Windsor Ave, Newry, County Down BT34 1EG; Tel 028 3026 8025

IVYBROOK SOCIAL SERVICES

Dromalane Rd, Newry, County Down BT35 8AP; Tel 028 3026 6026

PROVIDER UNIT

Dromalane Hse, Newry, County Down BT35 8AP; Tel 028 3026 6026

FIELDWORK SERVICES – HEALTH AND DISABILITY

Study Centre Dromalane Rd, Newry, County Down BT35 8AP; Tel 028 3026 3755

RESIDENTIAL AND DAY CARE SERVICES – LEARNING DISABILITY PROGRAMME

Crossmaglen Day Centre Rathkeel Hse, Castleblayney Rd, Crossmaglen, Newry, County Down; Tel 028 3086 8622

Horticultural Centre (Daycare) Rathfriland Hill Rd, Newry, County Down BT34 1JN; Tel 028 3026 2543
The Laurels (Daycare) Dromalane Rd, Newry, County Down BT35 8AP; Tel 028 3026 1570
Needham House Kiln St, Newry, County Down BT35 8EQ; Tel 028 3026 1300
Social Education Centre (Daycare) Rathfriland Rd, Newry, County Down BT34 1HU; Tel 028 3026 1951

SENSORY IMPAIRMENT CENTRE

The Conifers Dromalane, Newry, County Down BT35 8DR; Tel 028 3025 0800

RESIDENTIAL AND DAY CARE SERVICES – OLDER PEOPLE PROGRAMME OF CARE

Cloughreagh House (Residential) Cloughreagh, Bessbrook, Newry, County Down BT35 7EH; Tel 028 3083 0520
The Orchard Centre (Day Centre) Dromalane Rd, Newry, County Down BT35 8AT; Tel 028 3026 6374
Slieve Roe House (Residential) Manse Rd, Kilkeel, Newry, County Down BT34 4BN; Tel 028 4176 3760

DEMENTIA CARE UNIT

Bramblewood Dromalane Rd, Newry, County Down BT35 8AP; Tel 028 3026 0477

DAY CARE – HEALTH AND DISABILITY PROGRAMME OF CARE

Binnian Lodge Manase Rd, Kilkeel, Newry, County Down BT34 4BN; Tel 028 4176 5473
Donard Day Centre Manse Rd, Kilkeel, Newry, County Down BT34 4BN; Tel 028 4176 4096
Millview Centre Millvale Rd, Bessbrook, Newry, County Down BT35 7DA; Tel 028 3083 0347

CORE AND CLUSTERS

Oakdale House Newry and Mourne Health and Social Services, Social Services Department, Dromdane Rd, Newry, County Down BT35 8AP; Tel 028 3082 5000; Fax 028 3082 5151
Shanlieve House Randall Heights, Kilkeel, Newry, County Down BT34 4XU; Tel 028 4176 4890
Teach Sona 5 Mullanstown, Maphoner Rd, Mullaghbawn, Newry, County Down BT35 9EX; Tel 028 3088 8866

Armagh and Dungannon HSS Trust

St. Luke's Hospital, Loughgall Rd, Armagh, County Armagh BT61 7NQ; E-mail chiefexec@adhsst.n-i.nhs.uk; Tel 028 3752 2381
Chief Executive Miss P. Stanley
Director (Social Services) R.E. Hamilton; Tel 028 3752 2381; Fax 028 3741 2536
Trust Director Eric Hamilton
Assistant Director – Disability Services (Physical Disability) Mrs K. Courtenay
Assistant Director – Disability Services (Learning Disability) M. Sweeney
Assistant Director (Mental Health) C. McPhillips
Principal Social Worker and Manager (Child and Family Care Services) L.V. Johnston
Assistant Principal Social Worker (Elderly Services and Healthcare) Mrs M.O. McGeary
Assistant Principal Social Worker (Child and Family Care Services) Mrs M. McIntosh
Assistant Principal Social Worker (Training and Staff Development) J.E. Turkington
Senior Social Worker (Community Work) Mrs M. Patterson
Gosford Pl, The Mall, Armagh, County Armagh BT61 9AR

SUB OFFICES

Armagh Gosford Pl, The Mall, Armagh, County Armagh
BT61 9AR; Tel 028 3752 2262
Senior Social Worker (Elderly/Health Care Team) S. Kingsmill
Senior Social Worker (Child and Family Care Team) M. Miller
Senior Social Worker (Child and Family Care Team)
Mrs S. Johnston
Senior Social Worker (Child Protection Team) Mrs G. Harvey
Senior Social Worker (Early Years Team) Mrs J. McDaid
Senior Social Worker (Early Years Team) Mrs J. Riddall

Dungannon County Bldgs, Thomas St, Dungannon, County
Tyrone BT70 1HS; Tel 028 8772 3101
Senior Social Worker (Elderly/Health Care Team)
Mrs M. Madden
Senior Social Worker (Child and Family Care Team)
Mrs M. Logan
Senior Social Worker (Sensory Impaired Team)
Mrs V. McDonagh (Acting)
Resource Centre, Dungannon Rd, Moy, County Tyrone
Senior Social Worker (Learning Disability) Ms M. Lavelle
10 Victoria St, Armagh, County Armagh BT61 9DT
Senior Social Worker (Family Placement Team)
Mrs G. Mulholland
Resource Centre, Drumglass Bungalow, Dungannon,
County Tyrone
Senior Social Worker (Physical Disability) Mrs D. Curley
10 Victoria St, Armagh, County Armagh BT61 4DT
Senior Social Worker (Mental Health) Mrs M. Murphy
The Mews, The Mall, Armagh, County Armagh BT61 9BH
Senior Social Worker (Mental Health) Mrs M. O'Maolain
St. Luke's Hospital, Armagh, County Armagh BT61 7NQ
Senior Social Worker (Children with Disability) Mrs B. Curley

CHILDREN'S HOME

Drumglass Lodge and Woodside Adolescent Centre
Coalisland Rd, Dungannon, County Tyrone; Tel 028 8772
2234; 028 8772 6065
Team Leader Miss E. Coburn
Team Leader R. Patton

SOCIAL EDUCATION CENTRES

Appleby Social Education Centre Ballinahonemore,
Armagh, County Armagh BT61 1JD
Manager Mrs C. McGrath

Oakridge Social Education Centre Coalsend, Dungannon,
County Tyrone BT71 6LA
Manager J. Hunter

DAY CENTRES AND SOCIAL CENTRES FOR THE ELDERLY

The Community Centre Dobbin St, Armagh, County
Armagh BT61 7QQ

Clogher Resource Centre 8 Tullybroom Rd, Clogher,
County Tyrone BT76 0UW

STATION ROAD RESOURCE CENTRE

Station Rd, Armagh, County Armagh BT61 7NP
Manager Mrs M. Murphy

Western Health and Social Services Board

15 Gransha Pk, Clooney Rd, Londonderry, County
Londonderry BT47 6FN;
E-mail mgormley@cwhssb.n-i.nhs.uk; Tel 028 7186 0086;
Fax 028 7186 0311
Chair Karen Meeham
Chief Executive S. Lindsay
Director (Public Health) Dr W.W.M. McConnell, MFCM,
MRCGP (I)
Director (Finance and Information) P. McLaughlin

Director (Social Care) D. Burke, CQSW, MBA
Director (Dental Health) J. McGaffin
Chief Nursing Adviser and Director (Health Care)
Margaret Kelly
Assistant Director (Finance) B. Baker
*Assistant Director (Social Services) and Service Planner
(Childcare)* C. Rooney
*Assistant Director (Social Services)/Service Planner (Elderly and
Physically Disabled)* Vacancy
*Assistant Director Social Services and Service Planner (Mentally
Ill and Learning Disability)* J. Simpson
Manager (Information Services) Liam Hegarty
Area Clinical Representative (Community) Dr P. Cosgrove
Area Clinical Representative (Hospitals) Dr J.A.F. Beirne
Chief Internal Auditor S. Wade
Consultant Public Health Medicine Dr C. Hamilton
Consultant Communicable Disease Control Dr R. Smithson
G.P. Adviser Dr M. Brown

Bureau Services

Lime Villa, 12c Gransha Pk, Londonderry, County
Londonderry BT47 1FJ; Tel 028 7186 0616; Fax 028 7186
0468
Director (Estate Services) W. Doran
Assistant Director (Finance) J. Wilson
Assistant Director (Finance) C. McCauley
General Manager Will Doran
Area Manager (Health Promotion) Paula O'Boyle
Manager (Personnel Services) M. Neely
Manager (Management Development) A. McConnell
Area Supplies Officer Eamon Lynch
Chief Ambulance Officer D. Armstrong
Chief Librarian F. O'Deorain
Assistant Principal Social Work (Training) J. Ross

UNITS OF MANAGEMENT

Foyle HSS Trust

Riverview Hse, Abercorn Rd, Londonderry, County
Londonderry BT48 6SB; URL www.foyletrust.org;
Tel 028 7126 6111; Fax 028 7126 0806
Chief Executive Elaine Way, MHSM, DiPHSM
Director (Health Care) Phil Mahon, SRN, SCM, HV
Director (Business Services) Joe Lusby
Director (Social Care) John Doherty, MSc, CQSW, DMS
Director (Finance) Lesley Mitchell
Director (Personnel) Nuala Sheerin
Medical Director Dr Artie O'Hara
Programme Manager (Family and Care) Tom Cassidy
Programme Manager (Older People) Bridget Bergin
Programme Manager (Community Health Care)
Sara Croogan
Programme Manager (Learning Disability) Trevor Millar
Programme Manager (Mental Health) Bernard McAnaney

SOCIAL SERVICES OFFICES

Limavady Social Services Limavdy Health Centre, Scroggy
Rd, , Limavady, County Londonderry; Tel 028 7776 6110
Social Work Manager Siobhen Campbell
Manager (Community Services) Robin Kennedy

Riverview House Abercorn Rd, Londonderry, County
Londonderry BT48 6SB; Tel 028 7126 6111; Fax 028 7126
0806
Service Manager (Looked After Services) Ann McDuff
Manager (Community Services) Fionnuala Griffiths

Shantallow Social Services Shantallow Health Centre,
Racecourse Rd, Londonderry, County Londonderry
BT48 8HJ; Tel 028 7135 1350
Service Manager (Family Intervention – West Bank) Robert
Niven, CQSW, CASW

Strabane Social Services County Bldgs, Barrack St,
Strabane, County Tyrone; Tel 028 7138 1600
Manager (Community Services – Older People) Billy Page
Social Work Manager Lorraine Doyle

11

Waterside Social Services Rossdowney Hse, Glendermott Rd, Waterside, Londonderry, County Londonderry BT47 1BH; Tel 028 7131 4200
Service Manager (Family Internvention – East Bank)
    John Meehan (Acting)
Manager (Community Services) Catriona Stone

CHILDREN'S HOMES

Chapel Road Children's Home 103 Chapel Rd, Waterside, Londonderry, County Londonderry; Tel 028 7131 3381
Social Work Manager Marjorie Lesley

Chapel Road Children's Home 84 Chapel Rd, Waterside, Londonderry, County Londonderry
Social Work Manager Clare McCallion

Harberton House Children's Home (Assessment Centre) 106 Irish St, Londonderry, County Londonderry BT47 2ND; Tel 028 7134 2587; 028 7134 8490
Social Work Manager Charlie Hasson

Racecourse Road Children's Home 23 Racecourse Rd, Londonderry, County Londonderry BT48 8HJ; Tel 028 7136 1224
Social Work Manager John Gillespie

Scroggy Road Children's Home 23d Scroggy Rd, Limavady, County Londonderry; Tel 028 7776 1950
Social Work Manager Lesley Badell

Upper Galliagh Road Children's Home 5 Upper Galliagh Rd, Londonderry, County Londonderry BT48 8LW; Tel 028 7127 6680
Social Work Manager Sandra McDevitt

FAMILY CENTRE

Shantallow Family Centre Racecourse Rd, Londonderry, County Londonderry; Tel 028 7135 1350

ADULT TRAINING CENTRES FOR PEOPLE WITH LEARNING DISABILITIES

Benbradagh Resource Centre Scroggy Rd, Limavady, Limavady, County Londonderry; Tel 028 7777 68720
Manager Fidelma Armstrong

Glenside Adult Training Centre 45a Derry Rd, Strabane, County Tyrone; Tel 028 7138 2950
    (65)

Maybrook Adult Training Centre Racecourse Rd, Londonderry, County Londonderry; Tel 028 7135 3754
    (124)

DAY CENTRES

Creggan Day Centre Central Dr, Londonderry, County Londonderry; Tel 028 7126 9082
Social Work Manager Martin McCafferty

Foyle Disability Resource Centre Glen Rd, Londonderry, County Londonderry; Tel 028 7126 6593
Manager Cathal McElhatton
    (74)

Melrose Day Centre Rossdowney Hse, Glendermott Rd, Waterside, Londonderry, County Londonderry BT47 1BH; Tel 028 7131 1603
Manager Cathy O'Neill

Strabane Day Centre County Bldgs, Bannock St, Strabane, County Tyrone; Tel 028 7188 5681
Manager Michelle McMackin
    (103)

HEALTH CENTRES

Claudy Health Centre 38a Irwin Cres, Claudy, Londonderry, County Londonderry BT47 4AB; Tel 028 7133 8371; Fax 028 7133 7230
Supervisor Denise McCloskey

Dungiven Health Centre 1 Chapel Rd, Dungiven, Londonderry, County Londonderry BT47 4RS; Tel 028 7774 3000; Fax 028 7774 3017
Supervisor Tanya Hutchinson
Supervisor Teresa Taggart

Great James Street Health Centre 51–61 Gt James St, County Londonderry BT48 7DF; Tel 028 7136 5177; Fax 028 7137 8520
Supervisor Agnes Watts

Limavady Health Centre Scroggy Rd, Limavady, County Londonderry BT49 0NA; Tel 028 7776 1100; Fax 028 7776 1106
Supervisor Tanya Hutchinson
Supervisor Teresa Taggart

Shantallow Health Centre Racecourse Rd, Londonderry, County Londonderry BT48 8NL; Tel 028 7135 1350; Fax 028 7135 5015
Supervisor Gary Gallagher

Strabane Health Centre Upper Main St, Strabane, County Tyrone BT82 8AR; Tel 028 7138 4114; Fax 028 7138 4115
Supervisor Margaret Gallagher

Waterside Health Centre Glendermott Rd, Waterside, County Londonderry BT47 1BH; Tel 028 7132 0100; Fax 028 7134 9323
Supervisor Roland Helps

HOSPITALS

Gransha Hospital Gransha Pk, Clooney Rd, Londonderry, County Londonderry; Tel 028 7186 0261
Consultant Dr O'Hara

Stradreagh Hospital (includes Derg House) Gransha Pk, Clooney Rd, Londonderry, County Londonderry; Tel 028 7186 0261; Fax 028 7186 0356
Consultant Dr David Eyre
Consultant Dr Michael Curran
Assistant Programme Manager Mary Ralphs

ALCOHOL AND DRUG SERVICE

Woodlea House Gransha Pk, Clooney Rd, Londonderry, County Londonderry; Tel 028 7186 5237

RESPITE CARE COTTAGES

The Cottages Shepherds Way, Rossdowney Rd, Londonderry, County Londonderry; Tel 028 7134 4484
Contact Yvonne Gallagher

CHILD DEVELOPMENT CENTRE

Little Acorn Centre, 12c Gransha Pk, Clooney Rd, Londonderry, County Londonderry; Tel 028 7186 0056
Consultant Community Paediatrician Dr Hutton

CHILD HEALTH AND INFORMATION AND RECORDS FACILITY

Bridgeview Hse, 12c Gransha Pk, Clooney Rd, Londonderry, County Londonderry; Tel 028 7186 5105; 028 7186 5107; Fax 028 7186 5103
Manager (Information Services) Theresa Conaghan

COMMUNITY MENTAL HEALTH TEAMS

Child and Family Team Woodlea Hse, Gransha Pk, Clooney Rd, Londonderry, County Londonderry; Tel 028 7186 5238
Contact Dr A. Murray

Cityside Community Mental Health Team 22 Crawford Sq, Londonderry, County Londonderry BT48 7HT; Tel 028 7137 2230
Contact Dr I.D. Robertson

Community Mental Health Team for Older People Fold Housing with Care Project, Sevenoaks, Crescent Link, Londonderry, County Londonderry BT47 1AL; Tel 028 7131 4270
Contact Dr S.M. Rea

Limavady Community Mental Health Team Roe Valley Hospital, 24d Benevengh Dr, Limavady, County Londonderry BT49 0AQ; Tel 028 7772 2123
Contact Dr C.M. McDonnell

Strabane Community Mental Health Team 5a Railway Rd, Strabane, County Tyrone BT82 8EG; Tel 028 7138 2963
Contact Dr Hussein (Locum)

Shantallow Community Mental Health Team Slievemore Hse, Glengalliagh, Londonderry, County Londonderry BT48 8FA; Tel 028 7135 0063
Contact Dr McGlennon

Waterside Community Mental Health Team Rossdowney Hse, Glendermott Rd, Londonderry, County Londonderry BT47 1BH; Tel 028 7131 4200
Contact Dr M. Ghannam (Locum)

ACCOMMODATION FOR THE ELDERLY

There are six homes for elderly people provided by the Foyle HSS Trust offering a total of 179 places.

Altnagelvin Hospitals HSS Trust

Altnagelvin Area Hospital, Glenshane Rd, Londonderry, County Londonderry BT47 6SB; Tel 028 7134 5171; Fax 028 7161 1222
Chief Executive S. Burnside, BPhil, RGN, RMN, RNT, MHSM
Director (Business Services) R. McCartney
Director (Nursing) Ms I. Duddy
Director (Finance) N.J. Smyth
Director (Personnel) M. Doherty
Medical Director Dr G. Nesbitt
Clinical Director (Medical Services and Ambulatory Care Directorate) Dr K. Moles
Clinical Director (Surgery and Critical Care Directorate) P. Bateson
Clinical Director (Women and Children's Services Directorate) Dr M. Parker
Clinical Director (Critical Care, Surgery and Critical Care Directorate) Dr G. Furness
Clinical Director (Specialist Surgery, Surgery and Critical Care Directorate) Mr. N. Sharma
Clinical Director (Pathology Services) Dr M. O' Kane
Clinical Director (Imaging Services) Dr M. Reilly
Clinical Director (Pharmacy Services) Mrs S. O'Kane
Clinical Services Manager (Pathology Services) Mr K. Garrett
Clinical Services Manager (Imaging Services) I. Craig
Clinical Services Manager (Women and Children's Services Directorate) Mrs M. Doherty
Clinical Services Manager (Medical and Ambulatory Care Directorate) Ms. D. Brennan
Clinical Services Manager (Surgery and Critical Care Directorate) Mrs S. Allen-Hamilton (Acting)

Sperrin Lakeland Health and Social Care Trust

Trust Headquarters, Strathdene Hse, Omagh, County Tyrone BT79 0NS
Chair R. Scott
Chief Executive H.S. Mills, BSc(Hon)Econ, MSc(Policy Analysis)
Director (Human Resources and Operational Services) G. McLaughlin, MIPM
Director (Acute Hospital Services) E. Fee
Director (Finance) M. MacCrossan
Director (Community Care) D. Bolton, BA(Hons), CQSW, DMS(Hons)
Director (Corporate Affairs) B. O'Rawe
Director (Mental Health and Elderly Services) G. Carey
Director (Planning, Contracting and Information) V. Ryan
Medical Director Dr Jim Kelly

COMMUNITY SERVICES DEPARTMENT

Omagh Sector Tyrone and Fermanagh Hospital, Omagh, County Tyrone; Tel 028 8224 5211; Fax 028 8224 9982
Manager (Community Services (Family and Child Care) G. Young
Manager (Community Services – Elderly) J. Clements

Fermanagh Sector 2 Coleshill Rd, Enniskillen, County Fermanagh; Tel 028 6634 4000
Community Services Manager (Family and Child Care) C. Rooney
Community Services Manager (Elderly) Teresa Burns

PRE-SCHOOL PLAYGROUP

Elliott Place, Enniskillen, County Fermanagh; Tel 028 6634 4000

CHILDREN'S HOME

Coneywarren Hse, Derry Rd, Omagh, County Tyrone; Tel 028 8224 7847

FAMILY CENTRE

Erne Family Centre, 15 Elliott Pl, Enniskillen, County Fermanagh; Tel 028 6632 5632

SOCIAL EDUCATION CENTRE FOR THE LEARNING DISABLED

Omagh Centre, Deverney Rd, Omagh, County Tyrone; Tel 028 8224 4001

Omagh Sector

Contact J. Clements
Gortmore Day Centre, Omagh, County Tyrone; Tel 028 8224 4134

DAY CENTRES

Beragh Day Centre 34 Main St, Sixmilecross, Omagh, County Tyrone BT79 0TA; Tel 028 8075 7058

Dromore Day Centre 34 St. Dympna's Rd, Dromore, County Tyrone BT78 3DJ; Tel 028 8289 8914

Gortin Day Centre 62 Main St, Gortin, Omagh, County Tyrone BT79 8NH; Tel 028 8164 8988

Newtownstewart Day Centre Ardstraw and Baronscourt Hall, 55 Dublin St, Newtownstewart, County Tyrone BT78 4AQ; Tel 028 8166 2045

Strathroy Day Centre Strathroy Community Centre, Drumlea Cres, Omagh, County Tyrone BT79 7XE; Tel 028 8225 0457

Fermanagh Sector

Contact Mrs. T. Burns (Acting); Tel 028 6634 4000

SENIOR CITIZENS CLUBS

Age Concern Irvinestown, Eniskillen, County Fermanagh

55 Alive Club Belcoo, County Fermanagh

The Young at Heart Club Bellek, Eniskillen, County Fermanagh

REGISTRATION AND INSPECTION UNIT

Hilltop, Tyrone and Fermanagh Hospital Site
Manager R. Logue
Inspector Brendan Duffy

11

NHS Trusts, Care Trusts, Health Authorities and Health Councils

12

- ■ **England**
  - Strategic Health Authorities
  - NHS Trusts
  - Care Trusts
  - Primary Care Trusts
  - Special Health Authorities
- ■ **Wales**
  - NHS Trusts
  - Local Health Boards
  - Community Health Councils and Associations
- ■ **Scotland**
  - NHS Trusts
  - Health Boards
  - Health Councils and Associations
  - Agency
- ■ **Northern Ireland**
  - HSS Trusts
  - Health Boards
  - Health and Social Services Councils
  - Agencies

NHS Trusts, Care Trusts, Health Authorities and Health Councils

ENGLAND

Strategic Health Authorities

Avon, Gloucestershire and Wiltshire

Jenner Hse, Langley Pk, Chippenham, Wiltshire SN15 1GG;
Tel 01249 858500; Fax 01249 858501
Chair Anthea Millett
Chief Executive Geoff Scaife

Bedfordshire and Hertfordshire

63–77 Victoria St, St. Albans, Hertfordshire AL1 3LR;
Tel 01727 812929
Chair Ian White
Chief Executive Jane Herbert

Birmingham and the Black Country

St. Chads Court, 213 Hagley Rd, Edgbaston, West Midlands
B16 9RG; Tel 0121 6952222
Chair Elisabeth Buggins
Chief Executive Geoff Scaife

Cheshire and Merseyside

930–932 Birchwood Blvd, Millenium Pk, Birchwood,
Warrington WA3 7QN; Tel 01925 704000
Chair Judith Greensmith, DL
Chief Executive Christine Hannah

County Durham and Tees Valley

Teesdale Hse, Westpoint Rd, Thornaby, Stockton-on-Tees,
TS17 6BL; URL www.countydurhamandteesvalley.nhs.uk;
Tel 01642 666700
Chair Tony Waites
Chief Executive Ken Jarrold

Cumbria and Lancashire

Preston Business Centre, Watling Street Rd, Fulwood,
Preston, Lancashire PR2 8DY; Tel 01772 647190
Chair Kath Reade
Chief Executive Pearse Butler

Dorset and Somerset

Charter Hse, Bartec 4, Watercombe La, Lynx West Trading
Est, Yeovil, Somerset BA20 2SU; Tel 01935 384000;
Fax 01935 384079
Chief Executive Sir Ian Carruthers, OBE;
E-mail ian.carruthers@dsha.nhs.uk
Chair Jane Barrie

Essex

8 Collingwood Rd, Witham, Essex CM8 2TT; Tel 01376
302100
Chief Executive Mr Terry Hanafin
Chair Michael Brookes

Hampshire and the Isle of Wight

Oakley Rd, Southampton, Hampshire SO16 4GX; Tel 02380
725000
Chief Executive Gareth Cruddace
Chair Peter Bingham

Kent and Medway

Preston Hall, Royal British Legion Village, Aylesford, Kent
ME20 7NJ; Tel 01622 710161
Chief Executive Candy Morris
Chair Kate Lampard

Leicestershire, Northamptonshire and Rutland

Lakeside Hse, 4 Smith Way, Grove Pk, Leicester,
Leicestershire LE19 1SS; URL www.lnrsha.nhs.uk;
Tel 0116 295 7000
Chief Executive David Sissling
Chair Sir Richard Tilt

Greater Manchester

Gateway Hse, Piccadily South, Manchester M60 7LP;
Tel 0161 236 9456
Chief Executive Neil Goodwin
Chair Philip Smith

London (North West)

Victory Hse, 170 Tottenham Court Rd, London W1T 7HA;
Tel 020 7756 2500
Chief Executive Prof Ron De Witt
Chair Jane Kelly

Norfolk, Suffolk and Cambridgeshire

Capital Pk, Fulbourn, Cambridge, Cambridgeshire
CB1 5XB; URL www.nscstha.nhs.uk; Tel 01223 597500;
Fax 01223 597555
Chief Executive Peter Houghton
Chair Stewart Francis

London (South West)

Wilson Hospital, Cranmer Rd, Mitcham, Surrey CR4 4TP;
Tel 020 8648 3021
Chief Executive Julie Dent
Chair James Cochrane

London (South East)

1 Lower Marsh, London SE1 7NT;
  URL www.selondon.nhs.uk;
  E-mail <firstname>.<lastname>@selondon.nhs.uk;
  Tel 020 7716 7000
Chief Executive Duncan Selbie
Chair Linda Smith

North and East Yorkshire, and Northern Lincolnshire

The Innovation Centre, York Science Pk, University Rd,
  Heslington, York, North Yorkshire YO10 5DG; Tel 01904
  435331
Chief Executive David Johnson
Chair Prof David Johns, CBE

Northumberland, Tyne and Wear

Newcastle General Hospital, Westgate Rd, Newcastle upon
  Tyne, NE4 6BE; URL www.ntwha.nhs.uk; Tel 0191 256
  3100; Fax 0191 256 3099
Chief Executive David Flory
Chair Peter Carr, CBE DL

London (North Central)

Victory Hse, 170 Tottenham Court Rd, London W1T 7HA;
  Tel 020 7725 5300
Chief Executive Christine Outram
Chair Marcia Saunders

London (North East)

Aneurin Bevan Hse, 81 Commercial Rd, London E1 1RD;
  URL www.nelondon.nhs.uk;
  E-mail <firstname>.<lastname>@nelondon.nhs.uk;
  Tel 020 7655 6600
Chief Executive Carolyn Regan
Chair Prof Elaine Murphy

Shropshire and Staffordshire

Mellor Hse, Corporation St, Stafford, ST16 3SR;
  URL www.sasha.nhs.uk; Tel 01785 252233; Fax 01785
  254640
Chief Executive Prof Bernard Crump
Chair Michael Brereton

South West Peninsula

John Keay Hse, Tregonissey Rd, St. Austell, Cornwall
  PL25 4NQ; Tel 01726 77777
Chief Executive Thelma Holland
Chair Judith Leverton

South Yorkshire

5 Old Fulwood Rd, Sheffield, South Yorkshire S10 3TG;
  Tel 0114 271 1100
Chief Executive Mike Farrar
Chair Kathryn Riddle

Surrey and Sussex

36–38 Friars Wlk, Lewes, East Sussex
Chief Executive Simon Robbins
Chair Terese Hawksworth

Thames Valley

Jubilee Hse, 5510 John Smith Dr, Oxford Bus Pk, South
  Cowley, OX4 2LH; Tel 01865 337000
Chief Executive Nick Relph
Chair Jane Betts

Trent

1 Standard Crt, Park Row, Nottingham, Nottinghamshire
  NG1 6GN; URL www.trent-sha.nhs.uk; Tel 0115 912 3302
Chief Executive Alan Burns
Chair Arthur Sandford

West Midlands South Strategic Health Authority

(Coventry, Warwickshire, Herefordshire and
  Worcestershire)
Albert St, Prospect Hill, Redditch, Worcestershire B97 4DE;
  Tel 01527 587500
Chair Charles Goody
Chief Executive Mike Marchment

West Yorkshire

Blenheim Hse, Duncombe St, Leeds, West Yorkshire
  LS1 4PL; Tel 0113 2952000; Fax 0113 2952222
Chair Sir Alistair Graham
Chief Executive Richard Jeavons

NHS Trusts

Addenbrooke's NHS Trust

Hills Rd, Cambridge, Cambridgeshire CB2 2QQ;
  URL www.addenbrookes.org.uk;
  E-mail webmaster@addenbrookes.anglox.nhs.uk;
  Tel 01223 245151; Fax 01223 216520
Chair Dr Mary Archer
Chief Executive Malcolm Stamp
Director (Administrative) K. Day;
  E-mail keith.day@addenbrookes.nhs.uk
Director (Human Resources) A. Huxham
Director (Operations) R. Sunley
Director (Finance) R. Swain
*Associate Director (Operations – Women and Children's
  Services)* K. Haynes
Associate Director (Operations – Medical Services)
  Ross McEwan
Associate Director (Operations – Oncology and Surgery)
  D. Baker
Associate Director (Operations – Perioperative Care)
  C. McFarlane
Chief Nurse M. Berry
Operations Manager (Neuroscience and Transplant)
  Kathy Haynes

HOSPITALS

Addenbrooke's Hospital Hills Rd, Cambridge,
Cambridgeshire CB2 2QQ;
URL www.addenbrookes.org.uk;
E-mail webmaster@addenbrookes.nhs.uk

Rosie Hospital Robinson Way, Cambridge, Cambridgeshire
CB2 2SW; URL www.addenbrookes.org.uk;
E-mail yvonne.ewers@addenbrookes.nhs.uk; Tel 01223
217619
Refer to Homerton College of Nursing Studies.
  Specialism: Maternity.

Aintree Hospitals NHS Trust

Aintree Hse, University Hospital Aintree, Longmoor La,
  Liverpool, Merseyside L9 7AL; Tel 0151 525 3622;
  Fax 0151 525 6086
Chair J. Dray
Chief Executive J.R. Birrell
Medical Director E.M. Preston
Chief Nurse and Director (Operations) C.L. Pearce
Director (Finance) N.A. Heery
Director (Information and Risk Management) C.S. Smith
Annual budget
£146 million

University Hospital Aintree Longmoor La, Liverpool,
Merseyside L9 7AL; Tel 0151 525 5980
  Specialism: Acute. Total number of beds:
  (896) residential plus 20 day.

Walton Hospital Rice La, Liverpool, Merseyside L9 1AE;
Tel 0151 525 3611
  Specialism: Acute. Total number of beds: (48)

Airedale NHS Trust

Airedale General Hospital, Skipton Rd, Steeton, Keighley,
  West Yorkshire BD20 6TD; URL www.airedale-
  trust.nhs.uk; Tel 01535 652511; Fax 01535 655129
Chair Prof Brian R. Jewell
Chief Executive Robert E. Allen
Deputy Chief Executive and Director (Finance and Information)
  Janet A. Crouch
Medical Director Dr Paul G.R. Godwin
Director (Nursing and Quality) Susan A. Franks
Director (Planning and Performance) Doug Farrow

HOSPITALS

Airedale General Hospital Skipton Rd, Steeton, Keighley,
West Yorkshire BD20 6TD; Tel 01535 652511; Fax 01535
655129
  Specialism: Acute. Total number of beds: (549)

Bingley Hospital Fernbank Dr, Bingley, West Yorkshire
BD16 4HD; Tel 01274 563438; 01274 563439; Fax 01274
510565
  Specialism: Geriatric.

Castleberg Hospital Raines Rd, Giggleswick, Settle, North
Yorkshire BD24 0BN; Tel 01729 823515; Fax 01729 823082
  Specialism: Geriatric. Total number of beds: (15)

Coronation Hospital Springs La, Ilkley, West Yorkshire
LS29 8TG; Tel 01943 609666; Fax 01943 816129
  Specialism: Outpatient.

Skipton General Hospital Keighley Rd, Skipton, North
Yorkshire BD23 2RJ; Tel 01756 792233; Fax 01756 700485
  Specialism: Elderly; young disabled. Total number of
  beds: (9)

HEALTH CENTRES

Bentham Grasmere Dr, Bentham, Lancaster, Lancashire
LA2 7JP

Bingley Myrtle Pl, Bingley, West Yorkshire BD16 2TL

Ilkley Springs La, Ilkley, West Yorkshire LS29 8TQ

Keighley Oakworth Rd, Keighley, West Yorkshire
BD21 1SA

Settle Townhead, Settle, North Yorkshire BD24 9HZ

Silsden Elliott St, Silsden, Keighley, West Yorkshire
BD20 0DG

Steeton Chapel Rd, Steeton, Keighley, West Yorkshire
BD20 6NU

Wilsden Townfield, Wilsden, Bradford, West Yorkshire
BD15 0HT

Allington NHS Trust

The Allington NHS Trust has merged with Mid Anglia
NHS Trust to become Local Health Partnerships NHS
Trust, which is listed alphabetically in this section.

Ashford and St. Peter's Hospitals NHS Trust

St. Peter's Hospital, Guildford Rd, Chertsey, Surrey
  KT16 0PZ; URL www.ashfordstpeters.nhs.uk; Tel 01932
  872000; Fax 01932 872951
Chair Clive Thompson

Chief Executive Glenn Douglas
Medical Director Mike Baxter
Director (Corporate Services) and Director (Ashford Hospital)
  Mark Jennings
Director (Nursing Services) and Director (St. Peter's Hospital)
  Joyce Winson-Smith
Director (Financial) Keith Mansfield
Director (Human Resources) Sian Thomas

HOSPITALS

Ashford Hospital London Rd, Ashford, Greater London
TW15 3AA; Tel 01784 884488; Fax 01784 884881
Annual budget
£91 million

St. Peter's Hospital Guildford Rd, Chertsey, Surrey
KT16 0PZ; Tel 01932 872000; Fax 01932 874757

Avon Ambulance Service NHS Trust

Ambulance Service Headquarters, Marybush La, Tower
  Hill, Bristol BS2 0AT; URL www.avonambulance.org.uk;
  E-mail post@avonambulance.nhs.uk; Tel 0117 927 7046;
  Fax 0117 925 1419
Chair D. Giles
Chief Executive Kevin Hogarty
Director (Finance) J. Parkinson
Director (Operations) T. Hayward
Director (Corporate Services) E. Scott
Annual budget
£10 million

Avon and Wiltshire Mental Health Partnership NHS Trust

Bath NHS Hse, Newbridge Hill, Bath, Somerset BA1 3QE;
  Tel 01225 731731; Fax 01225 731732
Chair Christine Reid
Chief Executive Roger Pedley
Director (Medical) Dr Susan O'Connor
Director (Nursing) Patrick McKee (Acting)
Director (Finance) Charlotte Moar
Director (Human Resources) Liz Nicholson
Director (Swindon and Wiltshire) Tony Gardner
Director (Development and Research) Richard Vellerman
Programme Director (Avon) Fred Inman

MAIN HOSPITALS AND UNITS

Barrow Hospital Barrow Gurney, Bristol BS19 3SG;
Tel 01275 392811; Fax 01275 394277

Blackberry Hill Hospital (parts of) Manor Rd, Fishponds,
Bristol BS16 2EW; Tel 0117 965 6061

Green Lane Hospital Devizes, Wiltshire SN10 5DS;
Tel 01380 731200

Grove Road Day Hospital (Bristol) 12 Grove Rd, Redland,
Bristol BS6 6JJ; Tel 0117 973 0225

Old Manor Hospital Wilton Rd, Salisbury, Wiltshire
SP2 7EP; Tel 01225 460694

Sandalwood Court Highworth Rd, Stratton St. Margaret,
Swindon SN3 4WF; Tel 01761 417755

Victoria Hospital Okus Rd, Swindon, Wiltshire SN1 4HZ;
Tel 01793 481182

Barking, Havering and Redbridge Hospitals NHS Trust

Harold Wood Hospital, Gubbins La, Harold Wood, Essex
  RM3 0BE; URL www.bhrhospitals.nhs.uk;
  E-mail teresa.rogers@bhrhospitals.nhs.uk; Tel 01708
  345533; Fax 01708 708465
Chair Ian Kirkpatrick
Chief Executive Mark Rees

12

HOSPITALS

Barking Hospital Upney La, Barking, Essex IG11 9LX; URL www.bhrhospitals.nhs.uk; Tel 020 8983 8000; Fax 020 8924 6199

Harold Wood Hospital Gubbins La, Harold Wood, Romford, Essex RM3 0BE; URL www.bhrhospitals.nhs.uk; Tel 01708 345533; Fax 01708 708099

King George Hospital Barley La, Goodmayes, Ilford, Essex IG3 8YB; URL www.bhrhospitals.nhs.uk; Tel 020 8983 8000; Fax 020 8970 8001

Oldchurch Hospital Oldchurch Rd, Romford, Essex RM7 0BE; URL www.bhrhospitals.nhs.uk; Tel 01708 746090; Fax 01708 708137

Barnet and Chase Farm Hospitals NHS Trust

The Ridgeway, Enfield, Greater London EN2 8JL; Tel 020 8366 6600; Fax 020 8366 1361
Chair Peter Brokenshire
Chief Executive Paul O'Connor
Medical Director Michael Ward
Director (Operations) Russell Emery
Director (Finance) Alan Levett
Director (Nursing) Juliet Beal
Annual budget
£170 million

HOSPITALS

Barnet General Hospital Wellhouse La, Barnet, Greater London EN2 8JL

Chase Farm Hospital 127 The Ridgeway, Enfield, Greater London EN2 8JL

Edgeware General Hospital Edgeware, Greater London HA8 0AD

Barnet Healthcare NHS Trust

Barnet Healthcare NHS Trust has been dissolved and its services are now covered by Barnet, Enfield and Haringey Mental Health NHS Trust, Barnet Primary Care Trust and Hertsmere Primary Care Trust, which are listed alphabetically under the appropriate headings in this chapter.

Barnet, Enfield and Haringey Mental Health NHS Trust

Avon Villa, Chase Farm Hospital, The Ridgeway, Enfield, Greater London EN2 8JL;
URL www.beh.nhs.uk/mentalhealth;
E-mail clare.callard@enfieldcc-tr.nthames.nhs.uk; Tel 020 8366 9167; Fax 020 8366 9166
Chief Executive John Newbury-Helps

HOSPITAL

Colindale Hospital Colindale Ave, London NW9 5HG; Tel 020 8952 2381

Barnsley Community and Priority Services NHS Trust

Barnsley Community and Priority Services NHS Trust has now become Barnsley Primary Care Trust, which is listed alphabetically under the Primary Care Trust section in this chapter.

Barnsley District General Hospital NHS Trust

Barnsley District General Hospital, Gawber Rd, Barnsley, South Yorkshire S75 2EP; Tel 01226 730000; Fax 01226 202859

Chair G.E. Firth
Chief Executive Mr Jan Sobieraj
Medical Director D. Hicks
Director (Nursing and Midwifery) Mrs S. Hinchliffe
Director (Clinical Services) D.W. Peverelle
Director (Finance) J. Loeb
Director (Strategy and Service Improvement) Ms S. Light
Director (Information) I. Atkinson
Director (Human Resources) Mr S. Ned
Annual budget
£83 million

HOSPITAL

Barnsley District General Hospital Gawber Rd, Barnsley, South Yorkshire S75 2EP

HEALTH CENTRES

Athersley Laithes La, Athersley, Barnsley, South Yorkshire S71 3AG

Cudworth Rose Tree Ave, Barnsley, South Yorkshire S72 8UA

Darfield Church St, Darfield, Barnsley, South Yorkshire S73 9LG

Hoyland Duke St, Hoyland, Barnsley, South Yorkshire S70 1NJ

Lunwood Pontefract Rd, Lunwood, Barnsley, South Yorkshire S71 5HR

New Street Upper New St, Barnsley, South Yorkshire S70 1LP

Worsborough Oakdale, Worsborough Dale, Barnsley, South Yorkshire S70 5EG

Barts and the London NHS Trust

Alexandra Hse, Royal London Hospital, Whitechapel, London E1 1BB; Tel 020 7377 7000; Fax 020 7377 7666
Chair John Ashworth
Chief Executive Paul White
Medical Director Charles Gutteridge
Chief Nurse and Director (Quality Assurance) Jonathan Asbridge
Director (Finance) John Goulston
Director (Human Resources) Ann MacIntyre
Director (Service Transformation) Merav Dover
Director (Capital and Facilities) Steve Saunders
Director (Performance Management and Planning) Gail Beer
Director (Communications) Susan Cunnington-King
Trust Secretary Ian Walker
Annual income
£320.5 million approx.

HOSPITALS

The London Chest Hospital Bonner Rd, London E2 9JX; Tel 020 7377 7000
    Specialism: Respiratory medicine; cardiac services. Total number of beds: (111)

The Royal London Hospital, Mile End 275 Bancroft Rd, London E1 4DG; Tel 020 7377 7000
    Specialism: Orthopaedics; rheumatology. Total number of beds: (226)

The Royal London Hospital, Whitechapel Whitechapel Rd, London E1 1BB; Tel 020 7377 7000
    Specialism: Acute; accident and emergency. Total number of beds: (590)

St. Bartholomew's Hospital West Smithfield, London EC1A 7BE; Tel 020 7377 7000
    Specialism: Acute. Total number of beds: (393)

Basildon and Thurrock University Hospitals NHS Trust

Basildon Hospital, Nethermayne, Basildon, Essex
SS16 5NL; E-mail enquiries@btuh.nhs.uk; Tel 01268
533911
Chair David Hooper
Chief Executive Sue Jennings, CBE
Chief Operating Officer Alan Whittle
Medical Director Dr Gill Jenner
Director (Nursing) Maggi Rogers
Director (Finance) Trevor Smith
Director (Planning and Service Development) Mark Magrath
Director (Projects and Facilities) Jenny Galpin
Annual budget
£120 million

HOSPITALS

Basildon Hospital Nethermayne, Basildon, Essex SS16 5NL;
URL www.basildonandthurrock.nhs.uk; Tel 01268 533911
Specialism: Acute. Total number of beds: (650)

Orsett Hospital Rowley Rd, Orsett, Grays, Essex
RM16 3EU; Tel 01268 533911
Specialism: Day surgery, outpatient, minor injuries unit.

Bedford Hospitals NHS Trust

Kempston Rd, Bedford, Bedfordshire MK42 9DJ; Tel 01234
355122; Fax 01234 218106
Chair Helen Nellis
Chief Executive Andrew Reed
Medical Director Donald Parsons
Director (Nursing and Patient Services) Julie Halliday
Director (Finance and Performance) Alan Warren
Director (Clinical Operations) Ian Campbell
Annual budget
£88 million

HOSPITAL

Bedford Hospital Kempston Rd, Bedford, Bedfordshire
URL www.bedfordhospital.org.uk;
E-mail chiefexecoffice@bedhos.anglpx.nhs.uk; Tel 01234
355122
Specialism: Acute; maternity; geriatric; other.
Total number of beds: (497)

Bedfordshire and Hertfordshire Ambulance and Paramedic Service NHS Trust

Ambulance Headquarters, Hammond Rd, Bedford,
Bedfordshire MK41 0RG; URL www.bhamb.nhs.uk;
E-mail info@bhamb.nhs.uk; Tel 01234 408999; Fax 01234
270480
Chair Ms Maria Ball
Chief Executive Mrs Anne Walker
Director (Clinical Services) Jill Moseley
Director (Performance Management) Oskan Edwardson
Director (Finance and Facilities) William Hancock
Annual budget
£27 million

Bedfordshire and Luton Community NHS Trust

Trust Headquarters, Charter Hse, Luton, Bedfordshire
LU1 2PL; Tel 01582 700151; Fax 01582 700171
Chair Alison Davis
Chief Executive Paul Mullin
Medical Director Dr Hameen Markar
Weller Wing, Bedford Hospital, Kempton Rd, Bedford,
Bedfordshire MK42 9DT
Director (Nursing) Margaret Thornley
Director (Finance) Gerry Nolan
Director (Shared Services) Nigel Deacon
Project Manager Debbie Dunning

HOSPITALS

Biggleswade Hospital Potton Rd, Biggleswade,
Bedfordshire SG18 0EL; Tel 01767 312925; Fax 01767 318641
Specialism: Continuing care; respite care; terminal and
pallative care. Total number of beds: (28)

Steppingley Hospital Nr Ampthill, Bedford, Bedfordshire
MK45 1AB; Tel 01525 713152; Fax 01525 720065
Specialism: Continuing care. Total number of beds: 32

MENTAL HEALTH

Associate Director (Mental Health) Tom Downie (based at
Charter House); Tel 01582 700157
Consultant Psychiatrist Dr Balasubramaniam (based at
Weller Wing); Tel 01234 355122 ext 2717
Consultant Psychiatrist Dr Patel; Tel 01234 355122 ext 2749;
Fax 01234 310155

Day Resource Centre Flo Ball Hse, North Wing Reception,
Bedford, Bedfordshire; Tel 01234 310044

Health Link 26–28 Bromham Rd, Bedford, Bedfordshire
MK40 2QD; Tel 01234 270123
Manager Sharon Walsh
Specialism: Drug and alcohol advisory service.

The Lawns Mental Health Resource Centre The Lawns, The
Baulk, Biggleswade, Bedfordshire; Tel 01767 601735

Twinwoods Health Resource Centre Admin Bldg, Bedford,
Bedfordshire MK41 6AT; Tel 01234 310529
Associate Director (Learning Disability Services)
Tony Broughton; Tel 01234 310527
Clinical Director Dr M. O'Rourke; Tel 01234 310582
Specialism: Learning disabilities.

Pathfinder Team 5–7 Rush Crt, Grove Pl, Bedford,
Bedfordshire; Tel 01234 350663
Community Psychiatric Nurses and Social Workers to
provide community psychiatric support.

Weller Wing Ampthill Rd, Bedford, Bedfordshire
MK42 9DT; Tel 01234 267444
Specialism: Acute mental health.

CHILDREN'S SERVICES

Associate Director Christine Cole; Tel 01234 310226;
Fax 01234 310222
Clinical Director Dr Elliman; Tel 01582 700300
Consultant Paediatrician Dr P. Hey; Tel 01582 700146

Child Development Centre Hill Rise, Kempston, Bedford,
Bedfordshire; Tel 01234 310278

Child and Family Consultation Clinic Union St Clinic,
Bedford, Bedfordshire MK40 2SH; Tel 01234 310700

COMMUNITY DENTAL SERVICES

Associate Director (Community Dental Services)
Michael Cranfield; Tel 01234 310061

Berkshire Healthcare NHS Trust

Church Hill Hse, 51–52 Turing Dr, Crowthorne Rd,
Bracknell, Berkshire RG12 7FR;
URL www.berkshire.nhs.uk; Tel 01344 422722; Fax 01344
867990
Chair Lorna Roberts
Chief Executive Philippa Slinger
Medical Director Dr P. Sudbury
Director (Operations – West) Barry Day
Director (Nursing and Human Resources) L. O'Byrne
Director (Finance) Vacancy
Director (Modernisation and Performance) Kevin Lewis

HOSPITALS

Church Hill House 51–52 Turing Dr, Bracknell, Berkshire
RG12 7FR; Tel 01344 422722
Specialism: Learning disabilities and mental health.

12

Prospect Park Hospital Howey End La, Tilehurst, Reading RG30 4EJ; Tel 0118 960 5000; Fax 0118 960 5304

Birmingham and Solihull Mental Health NHS Trust

Trust Offices, Uffculme Centre, 52 Queensbridge Rd, Moseley, Birmingham, B13 8QY; Tel 0121 678 2757; Fax 0121 678 2756
Chair Jonathan Shapiro
Chief Executive Sue Turner
Medical Director Prof Mohan George
Director (Nursing) Ros Alstead

HOSPITALS

Devon House Uffculme Psychotherapy Service, Mindelsohn Way, Birmingham, West Midlands B15 2QR; Tel 0121 678 5800; Fax 0121 678 5848

Queen Elizabeth Psychiatric Hospital Mindelsohn Way, off Vincent Dr, Birmingham, West Midlands B15 2QZ; Tel 0121 678 2000

Reaside Clinic Bristol Rd South, Rubery, Birmingham, West Midlands B45 9BE; Tel 0121 678 3000; Fax 0121 678 3014

Birmingham Children's Hospital NHS Trust

Steelhouse La, Birmingham, West Midlands B4 6NH; Tel 0121 333 9999; Fax 0121 333 9998
Chief Executive Dr Sandy J. Bradbrook

Birmingham Heartlands and Solihull (Teaching) NHS Trust

Bordesley Green East, Birmingham, West Midlands B9 5SS; Tel 0121 424 2000; Fax 0121 424 2200
Chair P. Castle
Chief Executive Mark Goldman
Medical Director (Medical Services) Dr C. Skinner
Medical Director (Clinical Services) Dr R. Hopkinson
Director (Nursing) J. Ellison
Director (Finance) D. Poynton

HOSPITALS

Birmingham Chest Clinic 151 Great Charles St, Queensway, Birmingham, West Midlands B3 3HX; Tel 0121 233 2235; Fax 0121 236 2796

Solihull Hospital Lode La, Solihull, West Midlands B91 2JL
Hospital Director G. Martin

Birmingham Women's Health Care NHS Trust

Birmingham Women's Hospital, Edgbaston, Birmingham, West Midlands B15 2TG; Tel 0121 427 1377; Fax 0121 627 2602
Chair C. Kenrick
Chief Executive M. Hackett
Medical Director G. Durbin
Medical Director J. Jordan
Director (Finance) J. Summers
Annual budget
£32 million

HOSPITAL

Birmingham Women's Hospital Edgbaston, Birmingham, West Midlands B15 2TG; Tel 0121 472 1377; Fax 0121 627 2602

Black Country Mental Health NHS Trust

Trust Headquarters, 48 Lodge Rd, West Bromwich, West Midlands B70 8NY; Tel 0121 553 7676; Fax 0121 607 3290
Chief Executive K. Dowman

Blackburn, Hyndburn and Ribble Valley Health Care NHS Trust

Queen's Park Hospital, Haslingden Rd, Blackburn, Lancashire BB2 3HH; Tel 01254 263555; Fax 01254 293803
Chair W.I. Woolley, JP, BPharm(Hons), MSc, MRPharmS
Chief Executive J.L. Thomas, BA(Hons), MHSM, DipHSM; Tel 01254 293800; Fax 01254 293803
Medical Director D. Grimes
Director (Nursing and Quality) R. Gildert
Director (Single Site Hospital Development) Simon Neville
Director (Finance) M. Cowen
Director (Human Resources) Elaine Baker
Director (Corporate Development) Robert Bellingham
Director (Operations) J. Dell
Director (Pharmacy) P. Birch
Head (Estates) J. Peers
Manager (Supplies Services) S. Walsh
Manager (Support Services) M. Hall
Annual budget
£92 million

HOSPITALS

Accrington Victoria Community Hospital Haywood Rd, Accrington, Blackburn BB5 6A7; Tel 01254 263555

Blackburn Royal Infirmary Bolton Rd, Blackburn BB2 3LR; Tel 01254 263555

Clitheroe Community Hospital Chatburn Rd, Clitheroe, Blackburn BB7 4JX; Tel 01200 27311

Queen's Park Hospital Haslingden Rd, Blackburn BB2 3HH; Tel 01254 263555

Blackpool Victoria Hospital NHS Trust

Blackpool Victoria Hospital NHS Trust has merged with Blackpool, Wyre and Fylde Community Health Services NHS Trust to become Blackpool, Fylde and Wyre Hospitals NHS Trust , which is listed alphabetically in this section.

Blackpool, Fylde and Wyre Hospitals NHS Trust

Trust Headquarters, Victoria Hospital, Whinney Heys Rd, Blackpool, Lancashire FY3 8NR; URL www.bfwhospitals.nhs.uk; Tel 01253 303254; Fax 01253 303250
Chair Beverly Lester
Chief Executive Roy Male
Medical Director Dr Peter Hayes

HOSPITALS

Blackpool Victoria Hospital Whinney Heys Rd, Blackpool, Lancashire FY3 8NR; Tel 01253 300000; Fax 01253 306873

Clifton Hospital Pershore Rd, off Clifton Drive, Lytham St. Anne's, Lancashire FY8 1PB; Tel 01253 306204; Fax 01253 306214

Devonshire Road Hospital Devonshire Rd, Blackpool, Lancashire FY3 8AZ; Tel 01253 303364; Fax 01253 303386

Fleetwood Hospital Pharos St, Fleetwood, Lancashire FY7 6BE; Tel 01253 306000; Fax 01253 306029

Lytham Hospital Warton St, Lytham St. Anne's, Lancashire FY8 5EE; Tel 01253 303953; Fax 01253 303972

Rossall Hospital (Rehabilitation Unit) West Way, Rossall, Fleetwood, Lancashire FY7 6BE; Tel 01253 655101

South Shore Hospital Stoney Hill Ave, Blackpool, Lancashire FY4 1HX; Tel 01253 306106; Fax 01253 306101

Wesham Hospital (Rehabilitation Unit) Mowbreck La, Wesham, Preston, Lancashire PR4 3AH; Tel 01772 655404

OTHER SERVICES

Blenheim House Child Development Centre Bristol Ave, Bispham, Blackpool, Lancashire FY2 0BF; Tel 01253 306469

National Artificial Eye Centre Newton Dr, Blackpool, Lancashire FY3 8LZ; Tel 01253 397006

Blackpool, Wyre and Fylde Community Health Services NHS Trust

Blackpool, Wyre and Fylde Community Health Services NHS Trust has merged with Blackpool Victoria Hospital NHS Trust to become Blackpool, Fylde and Wyre Hospitals NHS Trust, which is listed alphabetically in this section.

Bolton Hospitals NHS Trust

Royal Bolton Hospital, Minerva Rd, Bolton, Greater Manchester BL4 0JR; Tel 01204 390390; Fax 01204 390794
Chief Executive J.E. Brunt

HOSPITALS

Fall Birch Hospital Lostock, Bolton, Greater Manchester BL6 4LQ; Tel 01204 695714

Hulton Hospital Hulton La, Bolton, Greater Manchester BL3 4JZ; Tel 01204 390390

Royal Bolton Hospital Minerva Rd, Farnworth, Bolton, Greater Manchester BL4 0JR; Tel 01204 390390

Bournewood Community and Mental Health NHS Trust

Bournewood Community and Mental Health NHS Trust has now become North Surrey Primary Care Trust, which is listed alphabetically under the Primary Care Trust section in this chapter.

Bradford District NHS Care Trust

New Mill, Victoria Rd, Saltaire, Shipley, West Yorkshire BD18 3LD; Tel 01274 366007; Fax 01274 366060
Chair Linda Pollard, JP
Chief Executive Con Egan
Medical Director Simon Baugh
Director (Finance) Philip Gutcher
Director (Nursing) Stuart Bootland
Director (Adult Mental Health Services) Chris Bielby
Director (Learning Disabilities) Brian Stanley
Director (Personnel and Development) June Goodson Moore
Director (Healthcare Facilities) Andrew Gunnee
Director (Care Trust Project) Kevin Mitchell
Director (Child and Adolescent Mental Health Services) Lesley Hewson
Director (Mental Health Services for Older People) Stuart Fawcett
Annual budget
£85 million

HOSPITALS

Daisy Bank 109 Duckworth La, Bradford, West Yorkshire BD9 6RL; Tel 01274 494194
Specialism: Mental health; rehabilitation. Total number of beds: (20)

Daisy Hill House Heights La, Bradford, West Yorkshire BD9 6DP; Tel 01274 494194; Fax 01274 363827
Specialism: Elderly mental illness. Total number of beds: (72)

Lynfield Mount Hospital Heights La, Bradford, West Yorkshire BD9 6DP; Tel 01274 494194; Fax 01274 483494
Specialism: Acute psychiatry (84); special care (12); forensic psychiatry (10).

Stoney Ridge Hospital Stoney Ridge Rd, Bingley, West Yorkshire BD16 1UL; Tel (Special care) 01274 322924; (Ward 1) 01274 495737; Fax (Special care) 01274 322925; (Ward 1) 01274 227923
Specialism: Continuing care; frail elderly. Total number of beds: (18)

DAY CENTRES, REHABILITATION CENTRES AND RESOURCE CENTRES

E4 Print Services Unit E4, Enterprise Way, Bradford, West Yorkshire BD10 8EW; Tel 01274 617937
Specialism: Employment; training and print-related.

Listonshiels Centre Bierley La, Bierley, Bradford, West Yorkshire BD4 6QA; Tel 01274 322371
Specialism: Learning disabilities.

Moor Court Resource Centre Fieldway, Ben Rhydding, Ilkley, West Yorkshire LS29 8NA

Moor Lane (Rehabilitation Centre) Moor La, Burley in Wharfedale, West Yorkshire LS29 9AJ; Tel 01943 862031
Specialism: Rehabilitation.

Skipton Road Resource Centre 147 Skipton Rd, Keighley, West Yorkshire BD21 3AU; Tel 01535 607139

Somerset House Mental Health Resource Centre Manor La, Shipley, Bradford, West Yorkshire BD18 3BP; Tel 01274 531536; Fax 01274 770779

Waddiloves Day Centre 44 Queens Rd, Manningham, Bradford, West Yorkshire BD8 7BT; Tel 01274 497121; Fax 01274 771106
Specialism: Learning disabilities.

COMMUNITY MENTAL HEALTH TEAMS (CMHT)

Bingley CMHT for Older People Littlelands Crt, Manor Rd, Cottingley, Bingley, West Yorkshire BD16 1RS; Tel 01274 772304

Bingley North Keighley Area CMHT Bridge Hse, Bailey Hills Rd, Bingley, West Yorkshire BD16 2RS; Tel 01274 772316; 01274 772317

Craven Settle Area CMHT Castleberg Hospital, Raines Rd, Giggleswick, Settle, West Yorkshire BD24 0BN

Craven Skipton Area CMHT 42 Keighley Rd, Skipton, West Yorkshire BD23 2NB; Tel 01756 700688

Keighley Area CMHT 200 South St, Keighley, West Yorkshire BD21 1BB; Tel 01535 665941

Keighley CMHT for Older People Florence Nightingale Hse, Airedale General Hospital, Skipton Rd, Skeetong, Keighley, West Yorkshire BD20 6TD; Tel 01535 292731

Wharfe Valley and Silsden Area CMHT Moor Lane Centre, Moor La, Burley in Wharfedale, West Yorkshire LS29 7AJ; Tel 01943 862031

Wharfe Valley CMHT for Older People Moorcourt Resource Centre, Fieldway, Valley Dr, Ben Rhydding, Ilkley, West Yorkshire LS29 8NA; Tel 01942 609734

LEARNING DISABILITY SUPPORT TEAMS

Holmewood Team 15 Copgrove Rd, Holmewood, Bradford, West Yorkshire BD4 0DJ

Reevy Road Team 60 Reevy Road West, Buttershaw, Bradford, West Yorkshire BD6 3LH

Rix House Team 24 Arncliffe Rd, Keighley, West Yorkshire BD22 6AR

Weaver Court Team Weaver Crt, Moorefield Pl, Idle, Bradford, West Yorkshire BD10 9TL

Whiteoak Team Whiteoak, Foston Cl, Bradford, West Yorkshire BD2 3QF

Bradford Hospitals NHS Trust

Bradford Royal Infirmary, Duckworth La, Bradford, West Yorkshire BD9 6RJ; URL www.bradfordhospitals.nhs.uk; Tel 01274 364787; Fax 01274 364786
Chair J. Ryan
Chief Executive David Jackson
Medical Director Dr M.L. Smith
Director (Hospital Services) R. Stephens
Director (Finance) P. Earp

12

Director (Operations and Clinical Support Services)
Dr I. Hammond
Director (Corporate Affairs) J. Damman
Director (Planning and Performance) M. Poad

HOSPITALS

Bradford Royal Infirmary Duckworth La, Bradford, West
Yorkshire BD9 6RJ; Tel 01274 542200
Specialism: Acute (664); maternity (235).

St. Luke's Hospital Little Horton La, Bradford, West
Yorkshire BD5 0NA; Tel 01274 734744
Specialism: Acute. Total number of beds: (463)

Brighton and Sussex University Hospitals NHS Trust

The Royal Sussex County Hospital, Eastern Rd, Brighton,
Sussex BN2 5BE; Tel 01273 696955
Chair Prof Michael Whiting
Chief Executive Stuart Welling, FCCA, MHSM
Medical Director Dr Charles Turton
Director (Finance) David Dunnigan
Director (Service Improvement) Anne Merricks
Director (Nursing) Karen Parsley, RCN, RSCN, BSc(Hons)
Director (Personnel) Chris Wilson
Director (Facilities and Capital Developments) Lee Soden
Annual budget
£240 million

HOSPITALS

Brighton General Hospital Elm Gr, Brighton, Sussex
BN2 3EW
Specialism: Acute; elderly medicine; respiratory
medicine; HIV and AIDS unit.

The Princess Royal Hospital Lewes Rd, Haywards Heath,
West Sussex RH16 4EX; Tel 01444 441881

The Royal Alexandra Hospital for Sick Children Dyke Rd,
Brighton, Sussex BN1 3JN; Tel 01273 328145
Specialism: Children's acute (102).

The Royal Sussex County Hospital Eastern Rd, Brighton,
Sussex BN2 5BE; Tel 01273 696955
Specialism: Acute; maternity; specialised services.

The Sussex Eye Hospital Eastern Rd, Brighton, Sussex
BN2 5BE; Tel 01273 606126
Specialism: Ophthalmology (22).

Bromley Hospitals NHS Trust

The Princess Royal University Hospital, Farnborough
Common, Orpington, Kent BR6 8ND; Tel 01689 863000
Chair A. Levy
Chief Executive J. Watkinson
Medical Director Dr K. Brown
Director (Nursing) M. Wright
Director (Finance) E. Jakeman
Director (Strategic Development) Ian Burroughs

HOSPITALS

Beckenham Hospital 379 Croydon Rd, Beckenham, Kent
BR3 3QL; Tel 01689 863000
Outpatient services only.

Orpington Hospital Sevenoaks Rd, Orpington, Kent
BR6 9JU; Tel 01689 863000

The Princess Royal University Hospital Farnborough
Common, Orpington, Kent BR6 8ND; Tel 01689 863000

Buckinghamshire Mental Health NHS Trust

Manor Hse, Bierton Rd, Aylesbury, Buckinghamshire
HP20 1EG; Tel 01296 393363; Fax 01296 392606
Chair Shirley Williams

Chief Executive Jill Cox (Acting)
Director (Medical) Robin Philpott (Acting)
Director (Nursing) Alison Livsey
Director (Finance and Performance) Jackie Ross
Director (Strategic Planning) Bob Fitzpatrick
Annual budget
£44 million

HOSPITALS

Aylesbury Vale Manor Hse, Bierton Rd, Aylesbury,
Buckinghamshire HP20 1EG; Tel 01296 393363; Fax 01296
392606

Haleacre Unit Amersham Hospital, Whielden St,
Amersham, Buckingham, Buckinghamshire HP7 0JD;
Tel 01494 734010; Fax 01494 734560

Marlborough House The Hospital Campus, Standing Way,
Eaglestone, Milton Keynes, Bedfordshire MK6 5NG

Tindal Centre Bierton Rd, Aylesbury, Buckinghamshire
HP20 1HU; Tel 01296 393363; Fax 01296 399332
Total number of beds: (45)

Buckinghamshire NHS Trust

Amersham Hospital, Whielden St, Amersham,
Buckinghamshire HP7 0JD; Tel 01494 526161; Fax 01494
734753
Chair Prof David Croisdale-Appleby
Chief Executive Ruth Harrison
Executive Medical Director Dr Andrew Kirk
Executive Director (Nursing) Maureen Davies
Executive Director (Strategy and Communications)
Sheryl Knight
Executive Director (Operations – Wycombe)
Malcolm Newton
Executive Director (Operations – Stoke) John Blakesley
Executive Director (Facilities and Estates – incl PFI)
John Summers
Executive Director (Finance, Performance and Information)
Gordon Greenshields
Executive Director (Human Resources) Sandra Hatton

HOSPITALS

Amersham General Hospital Whielden St, Amersham,
Buckinghamshire HP7 0JD; Tel 01494 526161; Fax 01494
734718
Specialism: Geriatric; dermatology; disability services.
Number of beds: Inpatient (108)

Appleyard Bramble La, Amersham, Buckinghamshire
HP7 9DN; Tel 01494 526161
Number of beds: Respite care for severely disabled (7)

Stoke Mandeville Hospital Mandeville Rd, Aylesbury,
Buckinghamshire HP21 8AL; Tel 01296 315000; Fax 01296
316604

Wycombe General Hospital Queen Alexandra Rd, High
Wycombe, Buckinghamshire HP11 2TT; Tel 01494 526161;
Fax 01494 425339
Number of beds: Acute (354 in-patient plus 28 day care)

Burnley Health Care NHS Trust

Burnley General Hospital, Casterton Ave, Burnley,
Lancashire BB10 2PQ; Tel 01282 425071; Fax 01282
474444
Chair A. Ali
Chief Executive David Chew
Director (Finance) and Deputy Chief Executive D. Meakin
Director (Nursing and Quality) Mrs L. Doherty
Medical Director Dr P. Ehrhardt
Director (Facilities) G.D. Summers
Director (Personnel) M. Bates
Director (Planning) N.A. Matthewman
Total budget
£95 million

HOSPITALS

Burnley General Hospital Casterton Ave, Burnley,
Lancashire BB10 2PQ; Tel 01282 425071; Fax 01282 474444
Specialism: Acute. Total number of beds: (598)

Pendle Community Hospital Leeds Rd, Nelson, Lancashire
BB9 9TF; Tel 01282 474900; Fax 01282 474980
Total number of beds: (72)

Rossendale Hospital Haslingden Rd, Rawtenstall,
Lancashire BB4 6NE; Tel 01706 215151; Fax 01706 233210
Total number of beds: (29)

CLINICAL DIRECTORATES

Burnley General Hospital, Casterton Ave, Burnley,
Lancashire BB10 2PQ
Clinical Director (Accident and Emergency)
Mrs Bhattacharyya
Clinical Director (Anaesthetics) Dr J. Watt
Clinical Director (Child and Adolescent Health) Dr J. Iqbal
Clinical Director (Medical Specialities) Dr M.D. Littley
Clinical Director (Theatres) P.D. Scott
Clinical Director (General Surgery and Urology) E. Gross
Clinical Director (Ophthalmology) A. Vijaykumar
Clincial Director (Oral Surgery and Orthodontics)
A.E. Green
Clinical Director (Trauma and Orthopaedics)
Mr H. Marynissen
Clinical Director (Pathology) Dr J.R. Kendra
Clinical Director (Radiology) Dr P.M. Woodhead
Clinical Director (Women's Health) T.C.M. Inglis

HEALTH CENTRES

Bacup Todmorden Rd, Bacup, Lancashire OL13 9AL

Brierfield Arthur St, Brierfield, Nelson, Lancashire
BB9 5SN

Colne Casterton Ave, Burnley, Lancashire BB10 2PQ

Kiddrow Lane Kiddrow La, Burnley, Lancashire BB12 6LH

Nelson Leeds Rd, Nelson, Lancashire BB9 9TG

Rawtenstall Bacup Rd, Rawtenstall, Lancashire BB4 7PL

St. Nicholas Saunder Bank, Burnley, Lancashire BB11 2EN

Waterfoot Cowpe Rd, Waterfoot, Lancashire BB4 7DN

Burton Hospitals NHS Trust

Queen's Hospital, Belvedere Rd, Burton upon Trent,
Staffordshire DE13 0RB; URL www.burtonhospital.com;
Tel 01283 566333; Fax 01283 593032
Chair T. Tricker
Chief Executive Jo Cubbon
Medical Director Mr H. Gompertz
Director (Nursing and Clinical Services) D.M. Clift
Director (Operations and Performance) Sandra Buckley
Director (Finance and Information) D. Harding
Annual budget
£80 million

HOSPITAL

Queens Hospital Belvedere Rd, Burton upon Trent,
Staffordshire DE13 0RB; Tel 01283 566333; Fax 01283 593032
Specialism: General acute; accident and emergency;
orthopaedic; maternity; geriatric.

Calderdale and Huddersfield NHS Trust

Huddersfield Royal Infirmary, Acre St, Huddersfield, West
Yorkshire HD3 3EA; URL www.huddweb.demon.co.uk;
Tel 01484 342250; Fax 01484 342253
Chair Gordon McLean
Chief Executive Diane Whittingham
Medical Director Mr R.C. Macdonald

Director (Finance) Graham Shipp
Director (Nursing) Helen Thomson
Director (Operational Services) Lynda Hanson
Annual budget
£210 million

HOSPITALS

Calderdale Royal Hospital Salterhebble, Halifax, West
Yorkshire HX3 0PW; Tel 01422 357222
Specialism: Acute.

Calderdale Royal Infirmary Salterhebble, Halifax, West
Yorkshire HX3 0PW; Tel 01422 357171
Specialism: Acute; midwifery; geriatric. Total number of
beds: (394)

Holme Valley Memorial Hospital Holmfirth, Huddersfield,
West Yorkshire HD7 2TS; Tel 01484 422191
Specialism: GP; elderly long stay. Total number of beds:
(44)

Huddersfield Royal Infirmary Acre St, Huddersfield, West
Yorkshire HD3 3EA

St. Luke's Hospital Crosland Moor, Huddersfield, West
Yorkshire HD4 5RQ; Tel 01484 422191
Specialism: Long stay; mental health. Total number of
beds: (186)

Calderstones NHS Trust

Mitton Rd, Whalley, Clitheroe, Lancashire BB7 9PE;
Tel 01254 822121; Fax 01254 823023
Chair G. Parr
Chief Executive T.R. Pearce
Medical Director Dr M.A. Razzaque
Director (Corporate Strategy) G. Jowett
Director (Finance and Information) S. Brookfield
Executive Director (Nursing) C. Whalley

HOSPITAL

Calderstones Hospital Whalley, Clitheroe, Lancashire
BB7 9PE; Tel 01254 822121
Chief Executive T.R. Pearce

Cambridgeshire and Peterborough Mental Health Partnership NHS Trust

Kingfisher Hse, Kingfisher Way, Hinchingbrooke Bus Pk,
Huntingdon, Cambridgeshire PE29 6FH;
URL www.cambsmh.nhs.uk; Tel 01480 398500; Fax 01480
398501
Chair Owen Ingram
Chief Executive Richard Taylor
Medical Director Dr Tom Dening
Director (Nursing and Corporate Development) Tim Bryson
Director (Finance and Performance) Brian Lanman
Director (Partnerships and Service Development)
Geoff Shepherd
Head (Communications) Linda Aschettino
Head (Corporate Services) Jo Prouse

HOSPITALS

Fulbourn Hospital Cambridge Rd, Fulbourn, Cambridge,
Cambridgeshire CB1 5EF

Princess of Wales Hospital Lynn Rd, Ely, Cambridgeshire
CB6 1DN; Tel 01353 652000

COMMUNITY FACILITIES (OUTPATIENT)

Adult Community Mental Health Teams South Community
Mental Health Team, Day Activity Centre, Edith Cavell
Hospital, Bretton Gate, Peterborough

Community Alcohol and Drugs Service 4 Avenue Rd, King's
Lynn, Norfolk PE30 5NU; Tel 01553 761623

12

Community Drugs Team The Pines, Peterborough District Hospital, Thorpe Rd, Peterborough PE3 6DA; Tel 01733 318100

Extended Hours Team Lucille van Geest Centre, Peterborough District Hospital, Thorpe Rd, Peterborough PE3 6DA; Tel 01733 318181
   Specialism: Rehabilitation; psychiatry.

North Community Mental Health Team Little Gables, Peterborough District Hospital, Peterborough; Tel 01733 318171

Older People's Mental Health Service Nursing Team The Pines, Peterborough District Hospital, Thorpe Rd, Peterborough PE3 6AN; Tel 01733 318191

DAY TREATMENT SERVICES

Day Hospital (Adult Mental Health Service) Edith Cavell Hospital, Bretton Gate, Peterborough PE3 6QR; Tel 01733 874000

LEARNING DISABILITIES SERVICES (IN-PATIENT)

Gloucester Centre Morpeth Cl, Orton Longueville, Peterborough PE2 7JU; Tel 01733 363100

Park View Resource Centre 1–4 Birch Tree Cl, King's Lynn, Norfolk PE30 5QD; Tel 01553 766266

LEARNING DISABILITIES (OUT-PATIENT)

Gloucester Centre Morpeth Cl, Orton Longueville, Peterborough PE2 7JU; Tel 01733 363100

Parkview Resource Centre London Rd, King's Lynn, Norfolk PE30 5QD; Tel 01553 766266; Fax 01553 706266

LOCAL COMMUNITY HOSPITAL (IN-PATIENT)

Stamford and Rutland Hospital Ryhall Rd, Stamford, Lincolnshire PE9 1UA; Tel 01780 764151; Fax 01780 63385
   Specialism: Acute; elderly.

MENTAL HEALTH SERVICES (IN-PATIENT)

Acute Mental Illness Wards Edith Cavell Hospital, Bretton Gate, Peterborough PE3 6QR; Tel 01733 330777

Alan Conway Court Doddington Hospital, Cambridgeshire PE15 0UG; Tel 01354 740481
   Specialism: Elderly mental health.

Dove House Gloucester Centre, Morpeth Cl, Peterborough PE2 7JU; Tel 01733 363100
   Specialism: Elderly mental health.

The Gables District General Hospital, Thorpe Rd, Peterborough PE3 6JF; Tel 01733 318181
   Specialism: Adult mental health.

Lucille van Geest Centre Thorpe Rd, Peterborough PE3 6DA; Tel 01733 318181
   Specialism: Mental health; rehabilitation.

Older People's Acute Mental Health Services Edith Cavell Hospital, Bretton Gate, Peterborough PE3 6QR; Tel 01733 330777

MENTAL HEALTH SERVICES (OUT-PATIENT)

The Cedars Peterborough District Hospital, Thorpe Rd, Peterborough PE3 6DA; Tel 01733 874000

Day Activity Centre (Older People's Mental Health Services) Edith Cavell Hospital, Bretton Gate, Peterborough PE3 6QR; Tel 01733 874000

Day Hospital (Older People's Mental Health Services) Alan Conway Crt, Doddington Hospital, March, Cambridgeshire PE15 0UG; Tel 01354 740481

Edward Jenner Day and Out Patient Unit (Child and Adolescent) Peterborough District Hospital, Thorpe Rd, Peterborough PE3 6DA; Tel 01733 874000

Grebe House (Older People's Mental Health Services) Gloucester Centre, Morpeth Cl, Peterborough PE2 7JU; Tel 01733 363100

Camden and Islington Mental Health and Social Care Trust

St. Pancras Hospital, 4 St. Pancras Way, London NW1 0PE;
   Tel 020 7530 3500; Fax 020 7530 3083
Freepost, London NW1 0YR; URL www.candi.nhs.uk
Chair   Prof David Taylor
Chief Executive   Erville Millar
Director (Nursing)   Claire Johnston
Medical Director   Dr Rob Pugh
Director (Finance)   Arnold Palmer
Annual budget
£104 million

HOSPITALS

Camden Mews Day Hospital 5 Camden Mews, London NW1 9DB; Tel 020 7530 4780; Fax 020 7530 4788

Jules Thorn Day Hospital St. Pancras Hospital, 4 St. Pancras Way, London NW1 0PE; Tel 020 7530 3391; Fax 020 7530 3421

Mornington Unit Psychiatric Intensive Care Unit, St. Pancras Hospital, 4 St. Pancras Way, London NW1 0PE; Tel 020 7530 3724; 020 7530 3725; Fax 020 7530 3728

Queen Mary's (Mental Health Unit) 124 Heath St, Hampstead, London NW3 1DU; Tel 020 7431 4111; Fax 020 7431 2724

St. Luke's Hospital Woodside Ave, London N10 3HU; Tel 020 8219 1800; Fax 020 8219 1801

St. Pancras Hospital 4 St. Pancras Way, London NW1 0PE; Tel 020 7530 3500

Waterloo Unit Whittington Hospital, Highgate Hill, London N19 5NX; Tel 020 7530 2200; Fax 020 7530 2276

CLINICS, CARE AND HEALTH CENTRES

Archway Community Care Centre 4 Vorley Rd, London N19 5JH; Tel 020 7527 7500; Fax 020 7527 7507

Bath Street Centre 60 Bath St, London EC1V 9JX; Tel 020 7530 2727; Fax 020 7530 2725

Calshot Community Care Centre 51 Calshot St, London N1 9XH; Tel 020 7527 6400; Fax 020 7527 6407

Canonbury Community Care Centre 68 Halliford St, London N1 3RH; Tel 020 7527 8200; Fax 020 7527 8207

Drayton Community Care Centre 52d Drayton Pk, London N5 1PB; Tel 020 7527 8800; Fax 020 7527 8807

Elthorne Community Care Centre 17–23 Beaumont Rise, London N19 2AX; Tel 020 7527 7300; Fax 020 7527 7307

Hanley Road Day Centre 75 Hanley Rd, London N4 3DY; Tel 020 7281 5796; Fax 020 7281 1757

Hunter Street Health Centre 8 Hunter St, London N19 3YU; Tel 020 7530 4300; Fax 020 7530 4301

Huntley Centre St. Pancras Hospital, 4 St. Pancras Way, London NW1 0PE; Tel 020 7530 3700; Fax 020 7530 3701

Margarete Centre St. James' Hse, 108 Hampstead Rd, London NW1 2LS; Tel 020 7530 3086; Fax 020 7530 3208

North House (Child and Adolescent Mental Health) Cleveland St, London W1N 8AA; Tel 020 7380 9086; Fax 020 7380 9268

Traumatic Stress Clinic 73 Charlotte St, London W1T 4PL; Tel 020 7530 3666; Fax 020 7530 3677

RESOURCE CENTRES

Learning Difficulties Resource Team Bedford Hse, 125–133 Camden High St, London NW1 7JR; Tel 020 7974 3737; Fax 020 7974 3759

Tottenham Mews Resource Centre Tottenham Mews, London W1T 4AA; Tel 020 7530 4400; Fax 020 7530 4447

OTHER SERVICES

Alcohol Advisory Service 309 Gray's Inn Rd, London WC1X 8QF; Tel 020 7530 5900; Fax 020 7530 5901

Assertive Outreach Team 21–28 Well Wlk, Hampstead, London NW3 1LE; Tel 020 7442 5500; Fax 020 7472 5516

Community Support Team (MHCOP) A13, Archway Campus, 1st Fl, Charterhouse Bldg, Whittington Hospital, Highgate Hill, London N19 5NF; Tel 020 7530 2307; Fax 020 7530 2304

Community Support Team (Older People's Services) A13 Archway Campus, 1st Fl, Charterhouse Bldg, Whittington Hospital, London N19 5NF; Tel 020 7530 2307; Fax 020 7530 2304

Cornwallis Project 55 Cornwallis Sq, London NW1 4LZ; Tel 020 7281 2410; Fax 020 7281 2410

Crisis Resolution Team (North Islington) Elthorne Community Care Centre, 17–23 Beaumont Rise, London N19 3AX; Tel 020 7527 7353; Fax 020 7527 7348

Crisis Resolution Team (South Islington) Bath St Centre, 60 Bath St, London EC1V 9JX; Tel 020 7530 2705; Fax 020 7530 2709

Islington Learning Disabilities Partnership 1 Lower Rd, London N7 8SL; Tel 020 7527 6600; Fax 020 7527 6607

North Camden Mental Health Service Royal Free Hospital, Pond St, London NW3 2QG; Tel 020 7794 0500; Fax 020 7830 2468

North Islington Drugs Service 592 Holloway Rd, London N7 6LB; Tel 020 7530 2002; Fax 020 7530 2001

Response Community Drug Services 457 Finchley Rd, London NW3 6HN; Tel 020 7431 1731; Fax 020 7431 0860

Cardiothoracic Centre Liverpool NHS Trust

Thomas Dr, Liverpool, Merseyside L14 3PE; Tel 0151 228 1616; Fax 0151 220 8573
Chair Ken Hoskisson
Chief Executive Mike Bone
Director (Nursing) Sally Ferguson
Director (Finance) Melanie Simmonds

Central and North West London Mental Health NHS Trust

30 Eastbourne Terr, London W2 6LA; URL www.cnwl.org; Tel 020 8237 2000; Fax 020 8746 8978
Chief Executive Peter Carter

HOSPITAL

Gordon Hospital Bloomburg St, London SW1V 2HR; Tel 020 8746 8000

Central Manchester and Manchester Children's University Hospitals NHS Trust

Manchester Royal Infirmary, Oxford Rd, Manchester M13 9WL; URL www.cmmc.nhs.uk; Tel 0161 276 4755; Fax 0161 272 6931
Chief Executive Mike Deegan

HOSPITALS

Manchester Royal Eye Hospital Oxford Rd, Manchester M13 9WH; Tel 0161 276 1234
Specialism: Eye (30).

Manchester Royal Infirmary Oxford Rd, Manchester M13 9WL; Tel 0161 276 1234
Specialism: Acute (835).

St. Mary's Hospital Hathersage Rd, Manchester M13 0JH; Tel 0161 276 1234
Specialism: Acute (293).

University Dental Hospital of Manchester Higher Cambridge St, Manchester M15 6FH; Tel 0161 275 6666

Central Manchester Healthcare Trust

Central Manchester Healthcare Trust is now part of Central Manchester and Manchester Children's University Hospitals NHS Trust, which is listed alphabetically in this section.

Central Sheffield University Hospitals NHS Trust

Central Sheffield University Hospitals NHS Trust is now part of Sheffield Teaching Hospitals NHS Trust, which is listed alphabetically in this section.

Chelsea and Westminster Healthcare NHS Trust

369 Fulham Rd, Chelsea, London SW10 9NH; Tel 020 8746 8000; Fax 020 8846 6539
Chair Juggy Pandit
Chief Executive Heather Lawrence
Medical Director Dr J. Collins
Director (Nursing and Patient Services) T. Davis
Director (Human Resources) K. Ruszkiewlez
Director (Finance and Information) N. Dawe
Director (Strategic and Services Development) C. Dove
Annual budget
£175 million

HOSPITAL

Chelsea and Westminster Hospital 369 Fulham Rd, Chelsea, London SW10 9NH; Tel 0208 746 8000
Specialism: Acute.

Cheshire and Wirral Partnership NHS Trust

Trust Headquarters, West Cheshire Hospital, The Countess of Chester Health Pk, Chester, Cheshire CH2 1UL; URL www.wirralhealth.org.uk; E-mail sarah.jones@cwpnt.nhs.uk; Tel 01244 364368; Fax 01244 364340
Chief Executive Stephen Eames

HOSPITALS

St. Catherine's Hospital Church Rd, Birkenhead, Cheshire CH42 0LQ; Tel 0151 678 5111

West Cheshire Hospital The Countess of Chester Health Pk, Chester, Cheshire CH2 1UL; Tel 01244 364368; Fax 01244 364340

Cheshire Community Healthcare NHS Trust

Cheshire Community Healthcare NHS Trust has now become Central Cheshire Primary Care Trust, which is listed alphabetically under the Primary Care Trust section in this chapter.

Chester and Halton Community NHS Trust

Chester and Halton Community NHS Trust has now become Halton Primary Care Trust, which is listed alphabetically under the Primary Care Trust section in this chapter.

12

Chesterfield and North Derbyshire Royal Hospital NHS Trust

Calow, Chesterfield, Derbyshire S44 5BL;
URL www.chesterfieldroyal.nhs.uk;
E-mail name@cndrh-tr.trent.nhs.uk; Tel 01246 277271;
Fax 01246 276955; Textphone 01246 552611
Chair M. Wall
Chief Executive Eric Morton
Medical Director W.G. Lambert
Director (Finance) Paul Briddock
Director (Personnel and Hospital Services) T. Alty
Director (Nursing and Clinical Development) R. Clarke
Head (Planning and Performance) Nikki Tucker
Annual budget
£99 million

HOSPITAL

Chesterfield and North Derbyshire Royal Hospital
Chesterfield Rd, Calow, Chesterfield, Derbyshire S44 5BL

CLINICS

Edmund Street Clinic Newbold Moor, Chesterfield,
Derbyshire S41 8TD
Marsden Street Clinic Marsden St, Chesterfield, Derbyshire
S40 1JY

Chorley and South Ribble NHS Trust

Chorley and South Ribble NHS Trust has merged with
Preston Acute Hospitals NHS Trust to form Lancashire
Teaching Hospitals NHS Trust, which is listed
alphabetically in this section.

Christie Hospital NHS Trust

Wilmslow Rd, Withington, Manchester M20 4BX; Tel 0161
446 3000; Fax 0161 446 3977
Chair Joan Higgins
Chief Executive Joanna J. Wallace
Executive Director (Nursing) Alison Norman
Medical Director R. Johnson
Director (Paterson Institute) N. Jones
Director (Finance) E. McCarthy
Annual budget
£80 million

HOSPITAL

Christie Hospital Wilmslow Rd, Withington, Manchester
M20 4BX; URL www.christie.nhs.uk

City and Hackney Community Services NHS Trust

City and Hackney Community Services NHS Trust has
now become City and Hackney Primary Care Trust, which
is listed alphabetically under the Primary Care Trust
section in this chapter.

City Hospital NHS Trust

City Hospital NHS Trust is now part of Sandwell and West
Birmingham Hospitals NHS Trust, which is listed
alphabetically in this section.

City Hospitals Sunderland NHS Trust

Trust Headquarters, Kayll Rd, Sunderland, Tyne and Wear
SR4 7TP; E-mail webmaster@phw-tr.northy.nhs.uk;
Tel 0191 565 6256; Fax 0191 514 0220; Minicom 0191
5699610
Chief Executive A. Gibson
Medical Director E.D. Allen

Director (Nursing) C. Ringrow
Director (Strategy and Business Development) I. Tarbit
Director (Finance) and Deputy Chief Executive K. Bremner

HOSPITALS

Ryhope General Hospital Ryhope, Sunderland, Tyne and
Wear SR2 0LY; Tel 0191 521 0541; 0191 521 0561; Fax 0191
521 2243
Sunderland Royal Hospital Kayll Rd, Sunderland, Tyne and
Wear SR4 7TP; Tel 0191 565 6256

OTHER SERVICES

Sunderland Eye Infirmary Queen Alexandra Rd,
Sunderland, Tyne and Wear SR2 9HP; Tel 0191 528 3616
Sunderland Children's Centre Durham Rd, Sunderland,
Tyne and Wear SR3 4AG

Clatterbridge Centre for Oncology NHS Trust

Clatterbridge Rd, Bebington, Wirral, Cheshire CH63 4JY;
Tel 0151 482 7680; Fax 0151 482 7817
Chair A. White
Chief Executive Geoff Greenwood
Medical Director Dr David Husband
Director (Patient Services and Quality) Helen Porter
Director (Research and Development) Dr James Shaw
Director (Finance and Corporate Affairs) Sue Lorimer
Head (Personnel) Kim Doherty
Annual budget
£30 million

SERVICES

Clatterbridge Centre for Oncology Clatterbridge Site,
Clatterbridge Rd, Wirral, Merseyside CH63 4JY

CommuniCare NHS Trust

CommuniCare NHS Trust is now part of Blackburn,
Hyndburn and Ribble Valley Health Care NHS Trust,
which is listed alphabetically in this section.

Community Health Care Service (North Derbyshire) NHS Trust

Community Health Care Service (North Derbyshire) NHS
Trust has now been replaced by the following three
Primary Care Trusts: Chesterfield; North Eastern
Derbyshire; High Peak and Dales, which are listed
alphabetically under the Primary Care Trust section if this
chapter.

Community Health South London NHS Trust

Community Health South London NHS Trust has now
been replaced by the following three Primary Care Trusts:
Lambeth; Lewisham; Southwark, which are listed
alphabetically under the Primary Care Trust section if this
chapter.

Community Healthcare Bolton NHS Trust

Community Healthcare Bolton NHS Trust has now become
Bolton Primary Care Trust, which is listed alphabetically
under the Primary Care Trust section in this chapter.

Cornwall Partnership NHS Trust

Porthpean Rd, St. Austell, Cornwall PL26 6AD; Tel 01726
291000; Fax 01726 291080
Chair Sandra Benjamin
Chief Executive Tony Gardner
Director (Finance) Blaise Mallon

COMMUNITY MENTAL HEALTH TEAM BASES

Caradon Community Mental Health Team Trevillis Hse, Lodge Hill, Liskeard, Cornwall PL14 4EN; Tel 01579 335226

Carrick Community Mental Health Team 57 Pydar St, Truro, Cornwall TR1 2SS; Tel 01872 356000

Kerrier Community Mental Health Team Trengweath Mental Health Unit, Penryn St, Redruth, Cornwall TR15 2SP; Tel 01209 881883

North Cornwall Community Mental Health Team Banham Hse, Bodmin Hospital, Bodmin, Cornwall PL31 2QT; Tel 01208 251304

North Penwith Community Mental Health Team Josiah Thomas Memorial Hall, Trevithick Rd, Camborne, Cornwall TR14 8LQ; Tel 01209 888260; Fax 01209 888259

Restormel Community Mental Health Team Alexandra Hse, 52 Alexandra Rd, St. Austell, Cornwall PL25 4QN; Tel 01726 291212

South Penwith Community Mental Health Team Edward Bolitho Hse, Laregan Hill, Penzance, Cornwall TR18 4NY; Tel 01736 575524

HOSPITALS

Bodmin Hospital Boundary Rd, Bodmin, Cornwall PL31 2QT; Tel 01208 251300; Fax 01208 251512
   Specialism: Adult psychiatric (41); older persons service (25); psychiatric intensive care (16); recover service (15).

Bolitho House (Day Hospital) Laregan Hill, Penzance, Cornwall TR18 4NY; Tel 01736 575555

Longreach House Barncoose Terr, Redruth, Cornwall TR15 3ER; Tel 01209 881900; Fax 01209 881920
   Specialism: Adult psychiatric and older people psychiatric. Total number of beds: Adult (42); Elderly (25)

Lower Cardrew House North St, Redruth, Cornwall TR15 1HJ; Tel 01209 881831; Fax 01209 881838
   Specialism: Psychiatric recovery service. Total number of beds: (10)

Selwood House 60 Alexandra Rd, St. Austell, Cornwall PL25 4QN; Tel 01726 291250
   Specialism: Psychiatric recovery service (10).

Trengweath (Day Hospital) Penryn St, Redruth, Cornwall; Tel 01209 881900; Fax 01209 881920
   Specialism: Psychiatric.

Countess of Chester Hospital NHS Trust

Countess of Chester Hospital, Liverpool Rd, Chester, Cheshire CH2 1UL; URL www.coch.org; Tel 01244 365000; Fax 01244 365292
Chair   Susan Sellers
Chief Executive   Peter Herring
Director (Human Resources)   David Wood
Director (Operations)   Patricia Higgins
Director (Finance and Information)   Louise Shepherd
Director (Nursing and Midwifery)
   Gaynor Tewkesbury (Acting)
Director (Service Development)   Carole Spencer

HOSPITAL

Countess of Chester Hospital Liverpool Rd, Chester, Cheshire CH2 1UL; Tel 01244 365000
   Total number of beds: (600)

County Durham and Darlington Acute Hospitals NHS Trust

Trust Headquarters, University Hospital North Durham, North Rd, County Durham DH1 5TW; Tel 0191 333 2333; Fax 0191 333 2685
Chief Executive   John Saxby

HOSPITALS

Bishop Auckland General Hospital Cockton Hill Rd, Bishop Auckland, County Durham DL14 6AD; Tel 01388 455000; Fax 01388 454127

Chester-le-Street Hospital Front St, Chester-le-Street, County Durham DH3 3AT

Darlington Memorial Hospital Hollyhurst Rd, Darlington, County Durham DL3 6HX; Tel 01325 380100; Fax 01325 743622

Homelands Hospital Helmington Row, Crook, County Durham DL15 0SD

Horn Hall Hospital Stanhope, Bishop Auckland, County Durham DL13 2JR

Richardson Hospital John St, Barnard Castle, County Durham DL12 8ET

Sedgefield Community Hospital Sedgefield, Stockton-on-Tees, County Durham TS21 3EZ

Shotley Bridge Hospital Consett, County Durham DH8 0NB; Tel 0191 333 2333; Fax 0191 333 2685

South Moor Hospital Stanley, County Durham DH9 6AD; Tel 0191 333 6262; Fax 01207 214828

University Hospital North Durham North Rd, Durham, County Durham DH1 5TW; Tel 0191 333 2333; Fax 0191 333 2685

County Durham and Darlington Priority Services NHS Trust

Earls Hse, Lanchester Rd, Durham, County Durham DH1 5RD; Tel 0191 333 6262; Fax 0191 333 6363
Chair   Angela Ballatti
Chief Executive   Sandy Taylor
Director (Finance and Strategic Planning)   Robert Dunning

Coventry Healthcare NHS Trust

Coventry Healthcare NHS Trust has now become Coventry Primary Care Trust, which is listed alphabetically under the Primary Care Trust section in this chapter.

Croydon and Surrey Downs Community NHS Trust

Croydon and Surrey Downs NHS Trust has merged with Croydon Health Authority to become Croydon Primary Care Trust, which is listed alphabetically under the Primary Care Trust section in this chapter.

Cumbria Ambulance Service NHS Trust

Ambulance Headquarters, Salkeld Hall, Infirmary St, Carlisle, Cumbria CA2 7AN; URL www.cas.nhs.uk; Tel 01228 596909; Fax 01228 403027
Chair   J. Brian Clayton, CBE
Chief Executive   Alan Donkersley
Director (Finance and Business Development)   S. Senior
Director (Operations and Training)   N. Smith
Manager (Resources)   J. Pattison
Annual budget
£8 million

Dartford and Gravesham NHS Trust

Darent Valley Hospital, Darenth Wood Rd, Dartford, Kent DA2 8DA; Tel 01322 428100; Fax 01322 428259
Chair   Sarah Dunnett
Chief Executive   Sue Jennings, CBE
Medical Director   Paul Key
Director (Nursing Services)   Jenny Kay
Director (Finance)   Brian Shipley
Director (Personnel Services)   Colin Moore
   Specialism: Acute.

HOSPITAL

Darent Valley Hospital Darenth Wood Rd, Dartford, Kent DA2 8DA; Tel 01322 428100; Fax 01322 428259
Manager (Trust Communications)   Glyn Oakley; Tel 01322 428255; Fax 01322 428259
Specialism: Acute.

Derbyshire Mental Health Services NHS Trust

Bramble Hse, Kingsway Hospital, Derby, Derbyshire DE22 3LZ;
URL www.derbyshirementalhealthservices.nhs.uk; Tel 01332 362221; Fax 01332 331254
Chair   Judith Forrest
Chief Executive   Mike Shewan
Medical Director   Dr John Sykes
Medical Director   Dr Andy Clayton
Director (Human Resources)   Clive Bull
Director (Nursing and Operations)/Assistant Chief Executive/Chief Nurse   David Snowdon
Director (Finance)   Ralph Tingle
Director (Strategic Development)   David Pitt
Associate Director (Public Affairs)   Jackie Dawn

HOSPITALS/UNITS

Ashbourne Health Centre Compton, Ashbourne, Derbyshire DE6 1GN; Tel 01335 343541; Fax 01335 300131

Aston Hall Hospital Weston Rd, Aston, Derbyshire DE72 2AL; Tel 01332 792412; Fax 01332 792039
Specialism: Learning disabilities.

Chesterfield and North Derbyshire Royal Hospital (Hartington Unit) Hartington Unit, Calow, Chesterfield, Derbyshire S44 5BL; Tel 01246 552563; Fax 01246 552612

Child and Adolescent Mental Health Services The Town Hse, 123–125 Green La, Derby DE1 1RZ; Tel 01332 292724; Fax 01332 367582

Child and Adolescent Mental Health Services Century Hse, 100 Nottingham Rd, Long Eaton, Nottinghamshire NG10 2BZ; Tel 01159 946 4568; Fax 01159 946 1967

Child and Adolescent Mental Health Services Rivermead, Goods Rd, Belper, Derbyshire DE56 1UU; Tel 01773 880554; Fax 01773 880921

Child and Adolescent Mental Health Services Ryedale, 10 Rink Dr, Swadlincote, Derbyshire DE11 8JL; Tel 01283 214903; Fax 01283 217432

Child and Adolescent Mental Health Services The Mill, Lodge La, Derby DE1 3HB; Tel 01332 291794; Fax 01332 348519

Derby City General Hospital (Psychiatric Unit) Uttoxeter Rd, Derby DE22 3NE; Tel 01332 346860; Fax 01332 370125

Dovedale Day Hospital London Rd, Derby DE1 1XX; Tel 01332 254886; Fax 01332 254661
Specialism: Elderly care.

The Elms Clinic 65–67 Ashbourne Rd, Derby DE22 3PS; Tel 01332 292416; Fax 01332 739779
Specialism: Substance misuse.

Kingsway Hospital Kingsway, Derby DE22 3LZ; Tel 01332 362221; Fax 01332 331254

Mapleton Day Hospital Derby City General Hospital, Uttoxeter Rd, Derby DE22 3NE; Tel 01332 625570; Fax 01332 625726
Specialism: Elderly care.

Mental Health Resource Centre London Rd, Derby DE1 2QY; Tel 01332 254818; Fax 01332 254936

The Psychiatric Unit (Derby City General Hospital) Uttoxeter Rd, Derby DE22 3NE; Tel 01332 346860; Fax 01332 370125

Psychotherapy Department Temple Hse, Mill Hill La, Derby DE23 6SA; Tel 01332 364512; Fax 01332 293316

Repton Health Centre Askew Gr, Repton, Derbyshire DE65 6SH; Tel 01283 701261; Fax 01283 703616

St. James House Mansfield Rd, Derby DE1 3AD; Tel 01332 547915; Fax 01332 547999

Swadlincote Clinic Community Clinic, Civic Way, Swadlincote, Derbyshire DE11 0AE; Tel 01283 214905; Fax 01283 551958

Wirksworth Health Centre St. John's St, Wirksworth, Derby DE4 4DR; Tel 01629 823721; Fax 01629 826414

Devon Partnership NHS Trust

Headquarters, Wonford House Hospital, Dryden Rd, Exeter, Devon EX2 5AF; Tel 01392 403433
Chair   Keith Portlock
Chief Executive   Valerie Howell

Dewsbury Health Care NHS Trust

Dewsbury Health Care NHS Trust has merged with Pinderfields and Pontefract Hospitals NHS Trust to become part of Mid Yorkshire Hospitals NHS Trust, which is listed alphabetically in this section.

Doncaster and Bassetlaw Hospitals NHS Trust

Armthorpe Rd, Doncaster, South Yorkshire DN2 5LT; URL www.dbh.nhs.uk; Tel 01302 366666; Fax 01302 320098
Chair   Margaret Cox
Chief Executive   N. Clifton
Medical Director   Dr E.W. Jones
Director (Nursing and Service Improvement)   S. Stower
Director (Finance and Commissioning)   D. Goodall
Director (Human Resources)   J. Brayford
Annual budget (2003–04)
£186 million

HOSPITALS

Bassetlaw Hospital Kilton, Worksop, Nottinghamshire S81 0BD; Tel 01909 500990; Fax 01909 502246
Specialism: Acute. Total number of beds: (286)

Doncaster Royal Infirmary Armthorpe Rd, Doncaster, South Yorkshire DN2 5LT; Tel 01302 366666
Specialism: Acute. Total number of beds: (833)

Montagu Hospital Adwick Rd, Mexborough, South Yorkshire S64 0AZ; Tel 01709 585171; Fax 01709 571689
Specialism: Acute. Total number of beds: (160)

Retford Hospital North Rd, Retford, Nottinghamshire DN22 7XF
Specialism: Outpatient services only.

Rotherham District Hospital Moorgate Rd, Rotherham, South Yorkshire S60 2UD
Specialism: Inpatient OMFs/dental only.

Tickhill Road Hospital Tickhill Rd, Doncaster, South Yorkshire DN4 8QL
Specialism: Elderly rehabilitation services only.

Doncaster and South Humber Healthcare NHS Trust

St. Catherines Hse, St. Catherines Hospital, Tickhill Rd, Doncaster, South Yorkshire DN4 8QN;
URL www.dsh-nhs.co.uk; Tel 01302 796400; Fax 01302 796816
Chair   M. Keyworth
Chief Executive   Liam Hayes
Medical Director   D. Goodhead
Deputy Chief Executive   Graham Higgins
Director (Financial)   J. Pressley
Director (Human Resources)   A. Good
Director (Planning)   Richard Banks
Director (Facilities)   Andrew Chatten

Director (Care – Doncaster) Sandra Mitchell
Director (Care – North Lincolnshire) Vacancy
Director (Care – North East Lincolnshire) Kevin Bond
Director (Corporate Affairs) Robert Powell
Annual budget
£81 million

HOSPITALS

Loversall Hospital Western Rd, Balby, Doncaster, South Yorkshire DN4 8NX; Tel 01302 796000
Specialism: Psychiatric. Total number of beds: (129)

Psychiatric Unit, Diana, Princess of Wales Hospital Scartho Rd, Grimsby, North East Lincolnshire DN33 2BA; Tel 01472 874111

Psychiatric Unit, Doncaster Royal Infirmary Armthorpe Rd, Doncaster, South Yorkshire DN2 5LT; Tel 01302 366666

Psychiatric Unit, Scunthorpe General Hospital Cliff Gdns, Scunthorpe, North Lincolnshire DN15 7BH; Tel 01724 282282

St. Catherine's Hospital Tickhill Rd, Doncaster, South Yorkshire DN4 8QN; Tel 01302 796000
Specialism: Learning disabilities. Total number of beds: (102)

St. John's Hospice Weston Rd, Doncaster, South Yorkshire DN4 8JS; Tel 01302 311611; Fax 01302 310954

Swallownest Court Aughton Rd, Swallownest, Sheffield, South Yorkshire S31 0TH; Tel 0114 287 2570; Fax 0114 287 9147

Tickhill Road Hospital Tickhill Rd, Doncaster, South Yorkshire DN4 8QL; Tel 01302 796000
Specialism: Geriatric. Total number of beds: (212)

Dorset Ambulance NHS Trust

Headquarters, Bournemouth Ambulance Station, 42 Portchester Rd, Bournemouth, Dorset BH8 8LE; Tel 01202 438970; Fax 01202 870511
Chair Trevor Jones
Chief Executive J. Cape
Director (Finance) Colin Launchbary
Director (Operations) Roger Ferré
Head (Human Resources and Quality) Chris Thomas
Manager (Information) David Perrett

Dorset Health Care NHS Trust

Trust Headquarters, 11 Shelley Rd, Boscombe, Bournemouth BH1 4JQ; URL www.dorsethealthcare.org; E-mail enquiries@dorsethc-tr.swest.nhs.uk; Tel 01202 303400; Fax 01202 301798
Chair Michael Parkinson
Chief Executive Roger Browning
Medical Director Dr Laurence Mynors-Wallis
Director (Nursing) Paul Lumsdon
Director (Finance and Performance Management) Roy Jackson

ADDICTION SERVICES

Bournemouth Community Drug and Alcohol Team Park Lodge, Gloucester Rd, Boscombe, Bournemouth BH7 6JF; Tel 01202 397003

Dual Diagnosis Project Park Lodge, Gloucester Rd, Bournemouth, Dorset BH7 6JF; Tel 01202 391452; 01202 397003

Flaghead Unit Fairmile Hse, Tasman Cl, Jumpers Rd, Christchurch, Dorset BH23 2JT; Tel 01202 484250

Needle Exchange Park Lodge, Gloucester Rd, Bournemouth, Dorset BH7 6JF; Tel 01202 395768; 01202 397003

Sedman Unit 16–18 Tower Rd, Boscombe, Bournemouth BH1 4LB; Tel 01202 443174

CHILD, ADOLESCENT AND FAMILY MENTAL HEALTH SERVICES

Child Development Centre Longfleet Rd, Poole, Dorset BH15 2JB; Tel 01202 442029

Shelley Clinic 11 Shelley Rd, Boscombe, Bournemouth, Dorset BH1 4JQ; Tel 01202 443011

CLINIC

Poole Community Health Clinic (including Family Planning) Shaftesbury Rd, Poole, Dorset BH15 2NT; Tel 01202 683363

MENTAL HEALTH SERVICES

Alderney Hospital Ringwood Rd, Parkstone, Poole, Dorset BH12 4NB; Tel 01202 735537
Specialism: Elderly mental health; rehabilitation.

Hahnemann House (Rehabilitation) Hahnemann Rd, Westcliff, Bournemouth, Dorset BH2 5JW; Tel 01202 584400
Specialism: Mental health; rehabilitation.

Kings Park Hospital Gloucester Rd, Boscombe, Bournemouth BH7 6JE; Tel 01202 303757
Specialism: Elderly mental health; rehabilitation.

Maple Young People's Service Poole Community Health Clinic, Shaftesbury Rd, Poole, Dorset BH15 2NT; Tel 01202 584600

Nightingale Court and Nightingale House Alumhurst Rd, Westbourne, Bournemouth, Dorset BH4 8EP; Tel 01202 584300
Specialism: Rehabilitation.

Oakley House 15 Oakley La, Canford Magna, Nr Wimborne, Dorset BH21 1SF; Tel 01202 849031
Specialism: Elderly mental health.

St. Ann's Hospital 69 Haven Rd, Canford Cliffs, Poole, Dorset BH13 7LN; Tel 01202 708881

Springbourne House 22 Tower Rd, Boscombe, Bournemouth, Dorset BH1 4LB; Tel 01202 300024
Specialism: Elderly mental health.

HOSPITALS

Alderney Hospital Ringwood Rd, Parkstone, Poole, Dorset BH12 4NB; Tel 01202 735537
Specialism: Elderly mental health; rehabilitation.

Kings Park Hospital Gloucester Rd, Boscombe, Bournemouth BH7 6JE; Tel 01202 303757
Specialism: Elderly mental health; rehabilitation.

St. Ann's Hospital 69 Haven Rd, Canford Cliffs, Poole BH13 7LN; Tel 01202 708881
Specialism: Acute mental health.

EATING DISORDERS

Kimmeridge Court St. Ann's Hospital, 69 Haven Rd, Canford Cliffs, Poole BH13 7LN; Tel 01202 492034

LEARNING DISABILITIES

Addington Clinic Poole La, Kinson, Bournemouth BH11 9DP; Tel 01202 594231
Specialism: Adult learning disabilities.

Albany Close Castletown Way, Sherborne, Dorset DT9 4EA; Tel 01935 817272
Specialism: Adult learning disabilities.

Castle Hill House 65 Bournemouth Rd, Poole BH14 0EN; Tel 01202 584050
Specialism: Children learning disabilities.

The Cedars 37 Recreation Rd, Parkstone, Poole BH12 2EA; Tel 01202 584070
Specialism: Adult learning disabilities.

12

Delphwood Ashdown Cl, Canford Heath, Poole BH17 8WG; Tel 01202 659037
Specialism: Adult learning disabilities.

Douglas House 19 Beaufort Rd, Southbourne, Bournemouth BH6 5AJ; Tel 01202 418312
Specialism: Adult learning disabilities.

Finigan Clinic Herbert Hospital Site, Alumhurst Rd, Bournemouth BH4 8EP; Tel 01202 584322
Specialism: Adult learning disabilities.

Haydon View Coldharbour Rd, Sherborne, Dorset DT9 4JL; Tel 01935 816713
Specialism: Adult learning disabilities.

Hillcrest 31 Slades Farm Rd, Bournemouth BH10 4EU; Tel 01202 858070
Specialism: Adult learning disabilities. Total number of beds: (26)

The Oaks 14–16 Hadow Rd, Bournemouth BH10 5HT; Tel 01202 858050; 01202 858051
Specialism: Adult learning disabilities.

Rawleigh House The Avenue, Sherborne, Dorset DT9 3AJ; Tel 01935 816630
Specialism: Adult learning disabilities.

St. Gabriel's 25 Ringwood Rd, Verwood, Ringwood, Dorset BH31 7AA; Tel 01202 825576
Specialism: Adult learning disabilities. Total number of beds: (10)

Whitehouse Resources Centre Coldharbour Business Pk, Coldharbour, Sherborne, Dorset DT9 4JW; Tel 01935 816782
Specialism: Adult learning disabilities.

OCCUPATIONAL THERAPY ADVISOR

St. Ann's Hospital 69 Haven Rd, Canford Cliffs, Poole, Dorset BH13 7LN; Tel 01202 492103

PSYCHOLOGY AND COUNSELLING

Bournemouth Adult Mental Health Psychology Team 18 Tower Rd, Boscombe, Bournemouth, Dorset BH1 4LB; Tel 01202 304634

Department of Psychological Therapies St. Ann's Crt, St. Ann's Hospital, 69 Haven Rd, Canford Cliffs, Poole BH13 7LN; Tel 01202 492129

Intensive Psychological Therapies Service Branksome Clinic, 51a Layton Rd, Parkstone, Poole BH12 2BJ; Tel 01202 584120

Poole Adult Mental Health Psychology Team The Chines, Nightingale Hse, Alumhurst Rd, Bournemouth BH4 8EW; Tel 01202 766422

VOLUNTEERS SERVICES

Shelley Road 11 Shelley Rd, Bournemouth BH1 4JQ; Tel 01202 443044

The Dudley Group of Hospitals NHS Trust

Wordsley Hospital, Stourbridge, West Midlands DY8 5QX; Tel 01384 456111; Fax 01384 244395
Chair Peter Suddock
Chief Executive Paul Farenden
Medical Director Richard Blunt
Director (Finance) Peter Sawyer
Director (Nursing) Ann Close

HOSPITALS

Corbett Hospital Stourbridge, West Midlands DY8 4JB; Tel 01384 456111
Specialism: Mainly acute. Total number of beds: (150)

The Guest Hospital Dudley, West Midlands DY1 4SE; Tel 01384 456111
Specialism: Outpatients; rehabilitation.

Russells Hall Hospital Dudley, West Midlands DY1 2HQ; Tel 01384 456111; Fax 01384 244051
Specialism: Acute. Total number of beds: (440)

Wordsley Hospital Stream Rd, Stourbridge, West Midlands DY8 5QX; Tel 01384 456111; Fax 01384 244395
Specialism: Acute. Total number of beds: (370)

Dudley Priority Health NHS Trust

Dudley Priority Health NHS Trust has now become Dudley, Beacon and Castle Primary Care Trust, which is listed alphabetically under the Primary Care Trust section in this chapter.

Ealing Hospital NHS Trust

Uxbridge Rd, Southall, Greater London UB1 3HW; Tel 020 8967 5000; Fax 020 8967 5630
Chair J. Jarvie
Chief Executive L. Clifton
Director (Finance) A. Williams
Director (Human Resources) Aurea Jones
Annual budget
£61 million

HOSPITAL

Ealing Hospital Uxbridge Rd, Southall, Greater London UB1 3HW

Ealing, Hammersmith and Fulham Mental Health Trust

Ealing, Hammersmith and Fulham Mental Health NHS Trust is now part of West London Mental Health NHS Trust, which is listed alphabetically in this section.

East and North Hertfordshire NHS Trust

Lister Hospital, Coreys Mill La, Stevenage, Hertfordshire SG1 4AB; Tel 01438 314333
Chair Prof Roy Swanston
Chief Executive Maggie Donovan
Medical Director Dr Colin Pendergast
Director (Nursing Practice) Debra Otte
Director (Finance) Nicholas Gerrard
Director (Assets and Facilities) Richard Harman
Director (Planning and Performance) Simon Meddick
Director (Human Resources and Corporate Affairs) Mark Gammage

HOSPITALS

Danesbury Home School La, Welwyn, Hertfordshire AL6 3PW
Total number of beds: (30)

Hertford County Hospital North Rd, Hertford, Hertfordshire; Tel 01707 328111

Hitchin Hospital Oughtonhead Way, Hitchin, Hertfordshire SG5 2LH; Tel 01462 422444
Specialism: Geriatric. Total number of beds: (136)

Lister Hospital Coreys Mill La, Stevenage, Hertfordshire SG1 4AB; Tel 01438 314333
Specialism: Acute.

Queen Elizabeth II Hospital Howlands, Welwyn Garden City, Hertfordshire AL7 4HQ; Tel 01707 328111
Specialism: Acute. Total number of beds: (520)

Queen Victoria Memorial Hospital School La, Welwyn, Hertfordshire AL6 3PW; Tel 01438 714488
Specialism: Respite; pre-discharge; stroke rehabilitation. Total number of beds: (39)

Royston and District Hospital London Rd, Royston, Hertfordshire SG8 9EN; Tel 01763 242134
Specialism: Geriatric. Total number of beds: (24)

Western House Hospital Collett Rd, Ware, Hertfordshire SG12 7LZ; Tel 01920 468954
Specialism: Geriatric. Total number of beds: (48)

East Anglian Ambulance NHS Trust

Ambulance Headquarters, Hospital La, Norwich, Norfolk NR6 5NA; Tel 01603 424255; Fax 01603 402372
Chair Andrew Egerton-Smith
Chief Executive Dr Chris Carney
Director (Operational Services) Paul Sutton
Director (Human Resources) Seamus Elliott
Director (Finance and Business) Anna Bennett
Clinical Director Dr John Scott
Annual budget
£42 million

East Berkshire Community Health NHS Trust

East Berkshire Community Health NHS Trust has now become Windsor, Ascot and Maidenhead Primary Care Trust, which is listed alphabetically under the Primary Care Trust section in this chapter.

East Cheshire NHS Trust

Victoria Rd, Macclesfield, Cheshire SK10 3BL; Tel 01625 421000; Fax 01625 661644
Chair Mrs K. Cowell
Chief Executive C. Povah
Medical Director Dr A.R. Wills
Director (Nursing Quality) M.A. O'Boyle
Director (Finance) J. Wilbraham
Director (Operations and Support Services – Estates)
D.J. Straker
Director (Human Resources) M. Blackwell
Chief Pharmacist Dr Justine Scanlan
Supplies Manager K. Ashford
Annual budget
£68.85 million

HOSPITALS

Congleton War Memorial Hospital Canal Rd, Congleton, Cheshire CW12 3AR; Tel 01260 294800
Total number of beds: (63)

Knutsford and District Community Hospital Bexton Rd, Knutsford, Cheshire WA16 0ED; Tel 01565 757220
Total number of beds: (52)

Macclesfield District General Hospital Victoria Rd, Macclesfield, Cheshire SK10 3BL; Tel 01625 421000
Consultant Paediatrician Dr J.R. Owens

East Gloucestershire NHS Trust

East Gloucestershire NHS Trust has merged with Gloucestershire Royal NHS Trust to become Gloucestershire Hospitals NHS Trust, which is listed alphabetically in this section.

East Hertfordshire NHS Trust

East Hertfordshire NHS Trust is now part of East and North Hertfordshire NHS Trust, which is listed alphabetically in this section.

East Kent Community NHS Trust

Trust Headquarters, Littlebourne Rd, Canterbury, Kent CT1 1AZ; Tel 01227 459371; Fax 01227 812268
Chair Mary Crittenden
Chief Executive David Parr
Medical Director Dr S. Wood
Director E. O'Connor
Director (Finance) B. Allpress
Director (Human Resources) Deborah Moon

Director (Information Services) Jan Howarth
Deputy Director (Finance) Ada Foreman
Director (Modernisation and Partnerships) Pat Campbell
Director (Corporate Strategy and Business Planning)
P. Walker

HOSPITALS

Arundel Unit William Harvey Hospital, Kennington Rd, Ashford, Kent TN24 0LZ; Tel 01233 633331
Specialism: Acute; mental health.

Lanthorne Court Lanthorne Rd, Broadstairs, Kent CT10 3ND; Tel 01843 602725

Orchard House Family Mental Health Centre, 17 Church St, Broadstairs, Kent CT10 2TT; Tel 01843 604777

St. Martin's Hospital Littlebourne Rd, Canterbury, Kent CT1 1TD; Tel 01227 459371

Thanet Mental Health Unit 164 Ramsgate Rd, Margate, Kent CT9 4BF; Tel 01843 225544

Western Avenue Day Hospital Western Ave, Ashford, Kent TN23 1LX; Tel 01233 204026
Mental health day service.

Winslow Day Hospital Arundel Unit, William Harvey Hospital, Ashford, Kent TN24 0LZ; Tel 01233 633331
Specialism: Mental Health Day Centre

MENTAL HEALTH COMMUNITY SERVICES

Mental Health Team (Canterbury and Faversham) Laurel Hse, 41 Old Dover Rd, Canterbury, Kent CT1 3HH; Tel 01227 597111

Mental Health Team (Herne Bay and Whitstable) Durham Hse, 69 Canterbury Rd, Herne Bay, Kent CT6 5SA; Tel 01227 594888

Mental Health Team (Thanet South and North) Westbrook Centre, 150 Canterbury Rd, Margate, Kent CT9 5DD; Tel 01843 224541

Alcohol Treatment Unit Mount Zeehan, St. Martin's Hospital, Canterbury, Kent CT1 1TD; Tel 01227 761310

Ashford Mental Health Centre 1 Elwick Rd, Ashford, Kent TN23 1PD; Tel 01233 204150

Dover Mental Health Centre Coleman Hse, Brookfield Ave, Dover, Kent CT16 2AH

Shepway Mental Health Centre 2–6 Radnor Park Ave, Folkestone, Kent CT19 5HZ

East Kent Hospitals NHS Trust

Kent and Canterbury Hospital, Ethelbert Rd, Canterbury, Kent CT1 3NG; URL www.kentandmedway.nhs.uk; Tel 01227 766877; Fax 01227 864120
Chief Executive David Astley
Chair Peter Hermitage
Director (Nursing and Quality) Elaine Strachan-Hall
Director (Facilities) Howard Jones
Director (Finance) Rupert Egginton
Director (Operations) Kim Hodgson
Director (Human Resources) Peter Murphy (Acting)
Medical Director (Cancer Services) Dr Anne Greenhalgh
Medical Director Dr Noel Padley
Deputy Medical Director Malcolm Stewart
Clinical Director (Accident and Emergency) Dr Marie Beckett
Clinical Director (Anaesthetics) Barclay Tofte
Clinical Director (Medicine) Dr Ian Sturgess
Clinical Director (Head and Neck) Norman Bradley
Clinical Director (Medicine – Speciality) Dr Phillip Bull
Clinical Director (Women's Health) John Seaton
Clinical Director (Child's Health) Dr Neil Martin
Clinical Director (Pathology) Ruth Lapworth
Clinical Director (Radiology) Vacancy
Clinical Director (Surgery) Robert Insall
Clinical Director (Trauma and Orthopaedics) Vacancy

12

Trust Secretary Michael Lucas
Manager (Communications) James Murray
There is a general email address:
<firstname>.<surname>@ekht.nhs.uk

HOSPITALS

Buckland Hospital Coombe Valley Rd, Buckland, Dover, Kent CT17 0HD; Tel 01304 201624; Fax 01304 208189
Specialism: Acute. Total number of beds: (276)

George Turle House 54 London Rd, Canterbury, Kent CT2 8JY; Tel 01227 597055

Kent and Canterbury Hospital Ethelbert Rd, Canterbury, Kent CT1 3NG; Tel 01227 766877; Fax 01227 864120

Queen Elizabeth The Queen Mother Hospital St. Peters Rd, Margate, Kent CT9 4AN; Tel 01843 225544; Fax 01843 220048

Royal Victoria Hospital Radnor Park Ave, Folkestone, Kent CT19 5AN; Tel 01303 850202; Fax 01303 854433
Specialism: Acute; GP; geriatric. Total number of beds: (96)

William Harvey Hospital Kennington Rd, Willesborough, Ashford, Kent TN24 0LZ; Tel 01233 633331; Fax 01233 616008
Specialism: Acute. Total number of beds: (465)

East London and The City Mental Health NHS Trust

St. Clements Hospital, 2a Bow Rd, London E3 4LL; URL www.elcmht.nhs.uk; Tel 020 8880 6296; Fax 020 8880 6250
Chief Executive Sheila Foley

East Midlands Ambulance Service NHS Trust

Beechdale Rd, Nottingham, Nottinghamshire NG8 3LL; Tel 0115 929 6151; Fax 0115 962 7727
Chair Bob Waterton
Chief Executive Adrian Chubb

East Somerset NHS Trust

Yeovil District Hospital, Higher Kingston, Yeovil, Somerset BA21 4AT; URL www.somerset-health.org.uk; E-mail ask@est.nhs.uk; Tel 01935 475122; Fax 01935 426850
Chair A. Dupont
Chief Executive J. Scott
Medical Director J. Sheffield
Director (Nursing and Clinical Governance) E. Robb
Director (Human Resources) J. Ward
Director (Finance) C. Phillips (Acting)
Community service provision is handled by South Somerset Primary Care Trust which is listed alphabetically under the Primary Care Trust section in this chapter.
Annual budget
£52 million

HOSPITALS

Women's Hospital Higher Kingston, Yeovil, Somerset BA21 4AT; Tel 01935 475122
Specialism: Maternity. Number of beds: (49)

Yeovil District Hospital Higher Kingston, Yeovil, Somerset BA21 4AT; URL www.somerset-health.org.uk; E-mail ask@est.nhs.uk; Tel 01935 475122; Fax 01935 426850
Specialism: Acute. Number of beds: (253)

East Sussex County Healthcare NHS Trust

Headquarters, Bowhill, Hailsham, East Sussex BN27 4EP; Tel 01323 440022; Fax 01323 842868
Chair G. Williams
Chief Executive S. Parkes-Crick

Medical Director Dr B. Heap
Director (Community Health Services) P. Rothwell
Director (Mental Health Services) Dr S. Jones
Director (Finance and Support Services) B. Bailey
Annual budget
£41 million

HOSPITALS

Crowborough War Memorial South View Rd, Crowborough, East Sussex TN6 1HB; Tel 01892 652284
Number of beds: (38)

Uckfield Community Hospital Framfield Rd, Uckfield, East Sussex TN22 5AW; Tel 01825 769999
Number of beds: (50)

East Sussex Hospitals NHS Trust

St. Annes Hse, 729 The Ridge, St. Leonards on Sea, East Sussex TN37 7PT; URL www.esh.nhs.uk; Tel 01424 754488; Fax 01424 754263
Chair John Lewis
Chief Executive Annette Sergeant
Medical Director (Strategy) Dr Hugh McIntyre
Medical Director (Risk Management and Clinical Governance) Dr David Scott

HOSPITALS

All Saints' Hospital King Edwards Pde, Eastbourne, East Sussex BN20 7XA; Tel 01323 417400

Bexhill Hospital Holliers Hill, Bexhill on Sea, East Sussex TN40 2DZ; Tel 01424 755255

Conquest Hospital The Ridge, St. Leonards on Sea, East Sussex TN37 7RD; Tel 01424 755255

District General Hospital Kings Dr, Eastbourne, East Sussex BN21 2UD; Tel 01323 417400

East Wiltshire Health Care NHS Trust

East Wiltshire Healthcare NHS Trust has now become part of Kennet and North Wiltshire Primary Care Trust, which is listed alphabetically under the Primary Care Trust section in this chapter.

East Yorkshire Community Healthcare NHS Trust

East Yorkshire Community Healthcare NHS Trust has merged with Hull and Holderness Community Health NHS Trust to become Hull and East Riding Community Health NHS Trust, which is listed alphabetically in this section.

Eastbourne Hospitals NHS Trust

Eastbourne Hospitals NHS Trust has merged with Hastings and Rother NHS Trust to become East Sussex Hospitals NHS Trust, which is listed alphabetically in this section.

Enfield Community Care NHS Trust

Enfield Community Care NHS Trust has been dissolved and its services have been split between Barnet and Chase Farm Hospitals NHS Trust; Barnet, Enfield and Haringey Mental Health NHS Trust; and Enfield Primary Care Trust, which are listed alphabetically in the appropriate sections of this chapter.

Epsom and St. Helier NHS Trust

St. Helier Hospital, Wrythe La, Carshalton, Surrey SM5 1AA; Tel 020 8296 2000; Fax 020 8641 9391
Chair Jennifer Denning
Chief Executive Dr Nigel Sewell
Medical Director Dr C.M. Steven

Director (Nursing) Mrs R. Robinson
Director (Facilities) C. Bell
Director (Clinical Operations) M. Wells
Director (Finance and Human Resources) D. Bell
Director (Strategic Development) N. Gorvett
Annual budget
£162 million

HOSPITALS

Cobham Cottage Hospital (Community) Portsmouth Rd, Cobham, Surrey KT11 1HT; Tel 01932 584200; Fax 01932 584201
Specialism: Medicine and post-operative care.

Epsom General Hospital Dorking Rd, Epsom, Surrey KT18 7FG; Tel 01372 735735; Fax 01372 735310
Number of beds: (434) including (44) beds on Northey (private wing) and (18) on day case unit.

Leatherhead Hospital (Community) Poplar Rd, Leatherhead, Surrey KT22 8SD; Tel 01372 384384; Fax 01372 384360
Specialism: GP, Elderly care

Nelson Hospital Kingston Rd, Merton, London SW20 8DB; Tel 020 8296 2000; Fax 020 8543 3612
Specialism: Elderly care, day surgery, outpatient.

The New Epsom and Ewell Cottage Hospital (Community) Horton La, Epsom, Surrey KT19 8PB; Tel 01372 734734; Fax 01372 729641
Specialism: GP

Queen Mary's Hospital for Children Wrythe La, Carshalton, Surrey SM5 1AA; Tel 020 8296 2000
Specialism: Paediatrics; surgery.

St. Helier Hospital Wrythe La, Carshalton, Surrey SM5 1AA; Tel 020 8296 2000; Fax 020 8641 9391
Specialism: Acute.

Sutton Hospital Cotswold Rd, Sutton, Surrey SM2 5NF; Tel 020 8296 2000; Fax 020 8770 7051
Specialism: Day surgery; outpatients.

Essex Ambulance Service NHS Trust

Broomfield, Chelmsford, Essex CM1 7WS; URL www.essamb.co.uk; Tel 01245 443344; Fax 01245 442920
Chair B. Goodwin
Chief Executive A. Marsh
Director (Modernisation and Service Delivery) P. Leaman
Director (Finance and Performance Management) K. Wood
Director (Medical) Dr A. Noon
Annual budget
£280 000

Essex Rivers Healthcare NHS Trust

Trust Headquarters, Colchester General Hospital, Colchester, Essex CO4 5JL; Tel 01206 747474; Fax 01206 854877
Chair Prof M. Salmon
Chief Executive Mike Pollard
Medical Director P. Kitchen
Director (Finance and Performance) Vacancy
Director (Service Modernisation) G. Bennett
Director (Nursing and Operations) D. Hagel
Director (Human Resources) J. Kitson
Annual budget
£113 million

HOSPITALS

Colchester General Hospital Turner Rd, Colchester, Essex CO4 5JL; Tel 01206 747474; Fax 01206 742324
Specialism: Acute.

Essex County Hospital Lexden Rd, Colchester, Essex CO3 3NB; Tel 01206 747474; Fax 01206 744512
Specialism: Acute.

Halstead Hospital 78 Hedingham Rd, Halstead, Essex CO9 2DL; Tel 01787 291010; Fax 01787 291023
Specialism: GP; medical.

Exeter Community Health Service NHS Trust

Exeter Community Health Service NHS Trust has been dissolved and its services have been split between: Royal Devon and Exeter Healthcare NHS Trust; East Devon Primary Care Trust; and Exeter Primary Care Trust, which are listed alphabetically under the appropriate headings in this chapter.

5 Boroughs Partnership NHS Trust

Hollins Pk, Hollins La, Winwick, Warrington WA2 8WA; Tel 01925 664000; Fax 01925 664052
Chair John Gartside
Chief Executive Judith Holbrey
Deputy Chief Executive (Borough Services) Alan Slater
Deputy Chief Executive (Corporate Services) Eric Hodgson
Executive Director (Corporate Governance) Christine Hedley
Executive Director (Finance) Jim McKenna
Executive Director (Medical) Dr Geoff Roberts
Director (Facilities Management) Andy Sylvester
Director (Human Resources) Andrew Murawski
Annual budget
£75.4 million

Frimley Park Hospital NHS Trust

Portsmouth Rd, Frimley, Camberley, Surrey GU16 7UJ; URL www.frimleypark.org.uk; Tel 01276 604604; Fax 01276 604148
Chair J. Cooke
Chief Executive A.V. Morris
Medical Director E.L. Palfrey
Director (Nursing, Quality and Patient Services) M. Dunne
Director (Finance, Contracting and Information) D. Crowe
Director (Personnel and Facilities) J. King
Annual budget
£95.5 million

Gateshead Health NHS Trust

Trust Headquarters, Queen Elizabeth Hospital, Gateshead, Tyne and Wear NE9 6SX; Tel 0191 482 0000; Fax 0191 482 6001
Chair P.J. Smith
Chief Executive Mr C. Reed
Medical Director Dr M. Abela
Director (Nursing and Midwifery) S. Richardson
Director (Health Development and Modernisation) A. Lamb
Director (Finance and Information) Mr I. Renwick
Director (Operations) R.A. Smith
Director (Estates and Risk Management) P. Harding

HOSPITALS

Bensham General Hospital Saltwell Rd, Bensham, Gateshead, Tyne and Wear NE8 4YL; Tel 0191 482 0000; Fax 0191 478 3357

Dunston Hill Hospital Whickham Highway, Dunston, Gateshead, Tyne and Wear NE11 9QT; Tel 0191 482 0000; Fax 0191 445 6408

Queen Elizabeth Hospital Sheriff Hill, Gateshead, Tyne and Wear NE9 6SX; Tel 0191 482 0000

The George Eliot Hospital NHS Trust

George Eliot Hospital, College St, Nuneaton, Warwickshire CV10 7DJ; URL www.geh.nhs.uk; E-mail enquiries@geh-tr.wmids.nhs.uk; Tel 024 7635 1351
Chair Cllr F. McCarney
Chief Executive N. Carver

12

The Glenfield Hospital NHS Trust

The Glenfield Hospital NHS Trust has now become part of the University Hospitals of Leicester NHS Trust, which is listed alphabetically in this section.

Gloucestershire Ambulance Service NHS Trust

Gloucestershire TriService Emergency Centre, Waterwells Dr, Waterwells Bus Pk, Quedgeley, Gloucestershire GL2 2BA; URL www.glosamb.org.uk; Tel 01452 753030; Fax 01452 753031
Chair   C. Elwes
Chief Executive   Richard Davis

Gloucestershire Hospitals NHS Trust

Trust Headquarters, 1 College Lawn, Cheltenham, Gloucestershire GL53 7AG; Tel 01452 528555

Gloucestershire Partnership NHS Trust

Rikenel, Montpellier, Gloucestershire GL1 1LY; Tel 01452 891000
Specialism: Mental health; learning disabilities.

HOSPITAL

Wotton Lawn Hospital   Horton La, Gloucester, Gloucestershire GL1 3WL; Tel 01452 891500; Fax 01452 891501

Gloucestershire Royal NHS Trust

Gloucestershire Royal NHS Trust has merged with East Gloucestershire NHS Trust to become Gloucestershire Hospitals NHS Trust, which is listed alphabetically in this section.

Good Hope Hospital NHS Trust

Rectory Rd, Sutton Coldfield, West Midlands B75 7RR; Tel 0121 378 2211; Fax 0121 311 1074
Chair   Sir Bernard Zissman
Chief Executive   J. Chandra
Medical Director   D. Mackay
Nurse Director   J. Nicholson (Acting)
Director (Personnel)   I. Cleminson
Director (Finance)   T. Smythe
Director (Development)   J. Wood
Annual budget
£83 million

HOSPITALS

Good Hope Hospital   Rectory Rd, Sutton Coldfield, Birmingham, West Midlands B75 7RR; Tel 0121 378 2211; Fax 0121 311 1074
Specialism: Acute; obstetrics. Total number of beds: (573)
Northcroft Hospital   Reservoir Rd, Erdington, Birmingham, West Midlands B23 5AX; Tel 0121 378 2211
Specialism: Elderly; rehabilitation.

Great Ormond Street Hospital for Children NHS Trust

Great Ormond St, London WC1N 3JH; URL www.gosh.nhs.uk; Tel 020 7405 9200; Fax 020 7829 8643
Chief Executive   Dr Jane Collins

Greater Manchester Ambulance Service NHS Trust

Ambulance Service Headquarters, Bury Old Rd, Whitefield, Manchester M45 6AQ; Tel 0161 796 7222; Fax 0161 796 0435

Chair   A. Stephenson
Chief Executive   J. Burnside
Director (Operations)   D. Cartwright
Director (Finance)   D. Hardwick
Director (Human Resources)   J. Williams
General Manager (Planning and Corporate Affairs)   T. Butcher
Director (ICT)   D. Jackland
Annual budget
£27 million

The Guild Community Healthcare NHS Trust

Guild Community Healthcare NHS Trust is now part of Lancashire Care NHS Trust, which is listed alphabetically in this section.

Guy's and St. Thomas' Hospital NHS Trust

Guy's Hospital, St. Thomas St, London SE1 9RT; Tel 020 7928 9292; St. Thomas' Hospital, Lambeth Palace Rd, London SE1 7EH; 020 7955 5000
Chair   Patricia Moberly
Chief Executive   Dr Jonathan Michael
Medical Director   Dr Brian Ayres
Director (Personnel)   T. Higginson
Director (Finance and Capital Development)   Martin Shaw
Director (Nursing)   Irene Scott
Director (Facilities)   Mel Rankine
Director (Corporate Development)   Bob O'Leary
Director (Projects)   Graham Burt
Chief Operating Officer   John Pelly
Annual budget
£305 million

HOSPITALS

Guy's Hospital   St. Thomas St, London SE1 9RT; Tel 020 7955 5000

St. Thomas's Hospital (London)   Lambeth Palace Rd, London SE1 7EH; Tel 020 7928 9292
Specialism: Acute Number of beds: (944)

The Hammersmith Hospitals NHS Trust

Hammersmith Hospital, DuCane Rd, London W12 0HS; Tel 020 8383 4002; Fax 020 8740 3169
Chair   Sir Thomas Legg
Chief Executive   D. Smith
Director (Finance and Information)   S. Morris
Director (Nursing)   Dr David Foster (Acting)
Medical Director   Prof Rory Shaw

HOSPITALS

Charing Cross Hospital   116 Fulham Palace Rd, London W6 8RF; Tel 020 8383 0000

Hammersmith Hospital   DuCane Rd, London W12 0HS; Tel 020 8383 1000

Queen Charlotte's and Chelsea Hospital   Hammersmith Hospital, DuCane Rd, London W12 0HS; Tel 020 8383 1000

Hampshire Ambulance Service NHS Trust

Highcroft, Romsey Rd, Winchester, Hampshire SO22 5DH; URL www.hantsam.org.uk; Tel 01962 863511; Fax 01962 842156
Chair   Sarah Murray
Chief Executive   Claire Severgnini (Acting)
Director (Human Resources)   Vacancy
Director (Patient Services)   Mike Cassidy (Acting)
Director (Finance)   Vacancy

Haringey Health Care NHS Trust

Haringey Health Care NHS Trust has now become Haringey Primary Care Trust, which is listed alphabetically under the Primary Care Trust section in this chapter.

Harrogate Health Care NHS Trust

Strayside Wing, Harrogate District Hospital, Harrogate,
North Yorkshire HG2 7SX;
E-mail miles.scott@hhc-tr.northy.nhs.uk; Tel 01423
885959; Fax 01423 555791
Chair   Albert Day
Chief Executive   Miles Scott
Medical Director   Carl Gray
Chief Nurse   Angela Monaghan
Director (Finance)   Jim Fender
Director (Human Resources)   Andrea Hester

HOSPITALS

Harrogate District Hospital   Lancaster Park Rd, Harrogate,
North Yorkshire HG2 7SX; Tel 01423 885959; Fax 01423
555353
Specialism: Acute.

Lascelles   Highgate Pk, Harrogate, North Yorkshire
HG1 4PA; Tel 01423 881977
Specialism: Young disabled people. (12)

Hastings and Rother NHS Trust

Hastings and Rother NHS Trust has merged with
Eastbourne Hospitals NHS Trust to become East Sussex
Hospitals NHS Trust, which is listed alphabetically in this
section.

Heatherwood and Wexham Park Hospitals NHS Trust

Wexham Park Hospital, Wexham, Slough SL2 4HL;
Tel 01753 633000; Fax 01753 634825
Chair   Ruth Watts Davies
Chief Executive   Margaret Edwards
Medical Director   Dr P. Mackie
Nurse Executive Director   Paul Grant
Director (Clinical Services)   Matthew Swindells
Director (Strategic Partnerships)   Colin Hayton
Director (Finance)   J. Graebe
Director (Human Resources)   Ms Liz Frayne

HOSPITALS

Heatherwood Hospital   London Rd, Ascot, Windsor and
Maidenhead SL5 8AA; Tel 01344 623333; Fax 01344 874340
Specialism: Acute Number of beds: (341)

Wexham Park   Wexham St, Slough SL2 4HL; Tel 01753
633008; Fax 01753 634828
Specialism: Acute Number of Beds: (600)

Hereford and Worcester Ambulance Service NHS Trust

Headquarters and Control, Bransford, Worcester,
Worcestershire WR6 5JD; Tel 01886 834200; Fax 01886
834210
Chair   Mrs J. Newton
Chief Executive   Mrs T. Thompson
Director (Operations)   S. McGuiness
Director (Finance and Information)   L. Millinchamp
Director (Clinical Services)   B. Chambers

Hereford Hospitals NHS Trust

County Hospital, Hereford, Herefordshire HR1 2ER;
Tel 01432 355444
Chair   Vacancy
Chief Executive   Mr G. Smith
Director (Planning and Development)   M. Johnson
Director (Nursing and Quality)   Mrs L. Keward (Acting)
Director (Service Delivery)   Mrs S. Beamish
Annual budget
£60 million

HOSPITAL

County Hospital   Hereford, Herefordshire HR1 2ER;
Tel 01432 355444
Specialism: Acute

Hertfordshire Partnership NHS Trust

99 Waverley Rd, St. Albans, Hertfordshire AL3 5TL;
Tel 01727 811888

HOSPITALS

Adolescent Unit   Harperbury Hospital, Harper La, Radlett,
Hertfordshire WD7 9HQ; Tel 01923 427 312

Albany Lodge   Church Cres, St. Albans, Hertfordshire
AL3 5JF; Tel 01727 834330

Community Support Unit   14 Stratford Rd, Watford,
Hertfordshire WD1 3QH; Tel 01923 816686

Lambourn Grove Elderly Assessment Unit   Hixberry La, St.
Albans, Hertfordshire AL4 0TZ; Tel 01727 837155

Lister Hospital Mental Health Unit   Coreys Mill La,
Stevenage, Hertfordshire SG1 4AB

Logandene EMF Unit   Ashley Cl, Bennetts End, Hemel
Hempstead, Hertfordshire HP3 8BL; Tel 01442 215060

The Meadows EMF Unit   Castleford Cl, Allerton Rd,
Borehamwood, Hertfordshire WD6 4AL; Tel 020 8953
4954

Nascot Lawn   92a Langley Rd, Watford, Hertfordshire
WD1 3DJ; Tel 01923 238476

Prospect House EMI Unit   Peace Dr, off Cassiobury Dr,
Watford, Hertfordshire WD1 3XE; Tel 01923 693900

QEII Hospital Mental Health Unit   Howlands, Welwyn
Garden City, Hertfordshire AL7 4HQ

St. Julians Acute Admission Unit   St. Albans City Hospital,
Normandy Rd, St. Albans, Hertfordshire AL3 5TL

Seward Lodge EMI Unit   Stansted Rd, Hertford,
Hertfordshire SG13 7HU

Shrodells Unit   Vicarage Rd, Watford, Hertfordshire
WD1 8HB; Tel 01923 776908

The Stewarts EMF Unit   Carlton Rd, Harpenden,
Hertfordshire; Tel 01582 764081

Hillingdon Hospital NHS Trust

Pield Heath Rd, Hillingdon, Uxbridge, Greater London
UB8 3NN; Tel 01895 238282; Fax 01895 811687
Chief Executive   David McVittie
Medical Director   Mr V.P. Robinson
Director (Nursing)   Sue Greenslade
Director (Human Resources)   D. Shields
Director (Operations)   C. Panniker
Director (Finance)   P. Wratten
Annual budget
£113 million

Hinchingbrooke Health Care NHS Trust

Hinchingbrooke Hospital, Huntingdon, Cambridgeshire
PE29 2BA; URL www.hinchingbrooke.org.uk;
E-mail <firstname>.<surname>@hbhc-tr.anglox.nhs.uk;
Tel 01480 416416; Fax 01480 416434
Chair   Sue Smith
Chief Executive   Douglas Patterson
Medical Director   Declan Flanagan
Director (Nursing, Midwifery and Operations)
Liz Pointing
Director (Finance)   Phil Richards
Director (Human Resources)   Karen Charman
Director (Service Modernisation)   Jenny Sole
Director (Facilities)   Brian Gibbs

12

HOSPITAL

Hinchingbrooke Hospital Hinchingbrooke Hospital, Huntingdon, Cambridgeshire PE29 2BA; Tel 01480 416416

Homerton University Hospital NHS Trust

Trust Management Offices, Homerton Hospital, Homerton Row, Homerton, London E9 6SR; Tel 0208 510 7144; Fax 0208 510 7608
Chief Executive Nancy Hallett

Hull and East Riding Community Health NHS Trust

West Hse, Westwood Hospital, Woodlands, Beverley, North Humberside, East Riding of Yorkshire HU17 8BU; E-mail comms.manager@herch-tr.nhs.uk; Tel 01482 886600; Fax 01482 886541

HOSPITALS

Alfred Bean Hospital Bridlington Rd, Driffield, East Riding of Yorkshire YO25 7JR; Tel 01377 241124

Bridlington and District Hospital Bessingby Rd, Bridlington, East Riding of Yorkshire YO16 5QP; Tel 01262 606666

Hull and East Yorkshire Hospitals NHS Trust

Hull Royal Infirmary, Anlaby Rd, Hull, East Riding of Yorkshire HU3 2JZ; Tel 01482 328541; Fax 01482 674196
Chair I. Blakey
Chief Executive C.P. Appleby
Medical Director Dr J. Dyet
Director (Nursing) Ms J. Brown
Director (Finance and Information) M. Brearley
Director (Operational Services) A. Wardle
Director (Planning) T. Wilders
Director (Facilities) J. Wilkes

HOSPITALS

Castle Hill Hospital Cottingham, East Riding of Yorkshire; Tel 01482 875875
Specialism: ID; chest diseases; geriatric; cardio-thoracic surgery; orthapaedic surgery; obstetrics; gynaecology; younger disabled; general.

Hull and Holderness Community Health NHS Trust

Hull and Holderness Community Health NHS Trust has merged with East Yorkshire Community Healthcare NHS Trust to become Hull and East Riding Community Health NHS Trust, which is listed alphabetically in this section.

Invicta Community Care NHS Trust

Invicta Community Care NHS Trust has now merged with Thames Gateway NHS Trust to become West Kent NHS and Social Care Trust, which is listed alphabetically in this section.

The Ipswich Hospital NHS Trust

Heath Rd, Ipswich, Suffolk IP4 5PD; URL www.ipswichhospital.org.uk; Tel 01473 712233; Fax 01473 703400
Chair Christine Smart
Chief Executive Paul Forden
Medical Director Ian Scott
Deputy Medical Director Gareth Thomas
Director (Nursing) Clare Barlow
Director (Finance) Craig Black (Acting)
Director (Human Resources) Jennifer Jones
Director (Estates and Facilities) Stephen Harrup
Associate Director (Medicine, Child Health and Emergency Care) Vacancy
Associate Director (Surgery and Elective Care) Debbie Oades

Isle of Wight Healthcare NHS Trust

St. Mary's Hospital, Newport, Isle of Wight PO30 5TG; URL www.iwhealthcare.org.uk; Tel 01983 524081; Fax 01983 822569
Chair Rodney Ireland
Chief Executive Graham Elderfield
Deputy Chief Executive/Director (Operations) Jane Wilshaw
Medical Director Dr A. Watson
Director (Human Resources) Terence Hart
Director (Finance and Performance Management) Lynda Eave
Director (Strategic Development) Mark Price
Annual budget
£101 million

James Paget Healthcare NHS Trust

James Paget Hospital, Lowestoft Rd, Gorleston, Great Yarmouth, Norfolk NR31 6LA; E-mail patient.care@jpaget.nhs.uk; Tel 01493 452452; Fax 01493 452078
Chair J.H. Hemming
Chief Executive D.W. Hill
Medical Director W. Slaney
Director (Finance) S. Davis
Director (Human Resources) R. Haynes
Director (Patient Care) N. Coveney
Director (Corporate Services) E. Guest
Director (Pharmaceutical Services) D. Todd
Head (Facilities) A. McHugh
Annual budget
£90 million

HOSPITALS

Lowestoft Hospital Tennyson Rd, Lowestoft, Suffolk NR32 1PT; Tel 01502 587311; Fax 01502 589510
Specialism: Acute; continuing care. Number of beds: (64)

Northgate Hospital Northgate St, Great Yarmouth, Norfolk NR30 1BU; Tel 01493 337600; Fax 01493 852753
Specialism: GP; continuing care. Number of beds: (40)

Kent Ambulance NHS Trust

Heath Rd, Coxheath, Maidstone, Kent ME17 4BG; E-mail jill.good@kentamb.nhs.uk; Tel 01622 747010; Fax 01622 743565
Chair B. Buchanan
Chief Executive H. Newton
Director (Human Resources) J. Brierley
Director (Operations) C. Burgess
Director (Finance) P. Traynor

Kettering General Hospital NHS Trust

Rothwell Rd, Kettering, Northamptonshire NN16 8UZ; Tel 01536 492000; Fax 01536 492599
Chair Dr Brian Silk
Chief Executive G. Martin
Medical Director Dr Ahmed Mukhtar
Director (Nursing and Midwifery) H. Scholefield
Director (Corporate Development) D. Pattisson
Director (Finance) Gill Scoular

King's College Hospital NHS Trust

King's College Hospital, Denmark Hill, London SE5 9RS; URL www.kingshealth.com; Tel 020 7737 4000; Fax 020 7346 3445
Chair M. Doherty
Chief Executive R. De Witt
Medical Director Dr C. Clough
Director (Nursing) J. Docherty
Director (Human Resources) M. Griffin
Director (Finance) P. Forden
Annual budget
£236 million

HOSPITALS

Dulwich Hospital East Dulwich Gr, London SE22 8PT
Specialism: Rehabilitation Number of beds: (181)

King's College Hospital Denmark Hill, London SE5 9RS;
Tel 020 7737 4000
Specialism: Acute Number of beds: (632)

King's Lynn and Wisbech Hospitals NHS Trust

Queen Elizabeth Hospital, Gayton Rd, King's Lynn,
Norfolk PE30 4ET; Tel 01553 613613; Fax 01553 613700
Chair J. Prosser
Chief Executive R. Venning
Deputy Chief Executive and Director (Operations) C. Weston
Medical Director Dr M. Rimmer
Director (Nursing) G. Wilson
Director (Finance) Kevin Walker

HOSPITAL

Queen Elizabeth Hospital Gayton Rd, King's Lynn, Norfolk
PE30 4ET; Tel 01553 613613
Specialism: Acute Number of beds: (562)

Kingston Hospital NHS Trust

Galsworthy Rd, Kingston upon Thames, Surrey KT2 7QB;
URL www.kingstonhospital.nhs.uk;
E-mail enquiries@kingstonhospital.nhs.uk; Tel 020 8546
7711; Fax 020 8547 2182
Chair Mrs C. Swabey
Chief Executive J. Langan
Medical Director A. Winrow
Director (Corporate Services and Developments) A. Pearse
Director (Nursing) J. Shepherd
Director (Finance) C. Leyshon
Annual budget
£113 million

Lancashire Ambulance Service NHS Trust

Ambulance Service Headquarters, Broughton Hse, 449–451
Garstang Rd, Preston, Lancashire PR3 5LN;
URL www.lancashireambulance.com; Tel 01772 862666;
Fax 01772 861003
Chair R.R. Winterbottom
Chief Executive D.W. Hill
Director (Finance and Information) A. Jude
Director (Accident and Emergency Operations) S. Watt
Director (Human Resources) P. Cooney
Director (Patient Transport Services) D. Laird

Lancashire Care NHS Trust

Sceptre Point, Sceptre Way, Walton Summit, Bamber
Bridge, Preston, Lancashire PR5 6AW;
URL www.lancashirecare.nhs.uk; Tel 01772 695300;
Fax 01772 227080
Chair Vourneen Darbyshire
Chief Executive Finlay Robertson
Medical Director Prof Max Marshall
Director (Strategic Development) Dr Barbara Green
Director (Clinical Services) Karen Wilson
Director (Human Resources) Maggie Stainton
Director (Finance, Information and Estates) Dave Tomlinson

MENTAL HEALTH SERVICE REGIONS

Central Lancashire Moor Park Hse, 1 Moor Park Ave,
Preston, Lancashire PR1 6AS; Tel 01772 773600; Fax 01772
257444
Associate Director Mr C. Aspinall

East Lancashire Casterton Ave, Burnley, Lancashire
BB10 2PQ; Tel 01282 474205
Associate Director Mr J. Deegan

Fylde Coast Parkwood, East Park Dr, Blackpool, Lancashire
FY3 8PW; Tel 01253 303695
Associate Director Mr A. Roach

West Lancashire Blundell Hse, Ormskirk and District
Hospital, Wigan Rd, Ormskirk, Lancashire L39 2AZ;
Tel 01695 598141
Associate Director Mr P. Sullivan (Acting)

HOSPITALS

Adelphi House Day Hospital 20 Queen St, Blackpool,
Lancashire FY1 1PD; Tel 01253 751155

Parkwood (Psychiatric Unit) East Park Dr, Blackpool,
Lancashire FY3 8PW; Tel 01253 306980; Fax 01253 306961
Specialism: Mental health.

Ribbleton Hospital Miller Rd, Ribbleton, Preston,
Lancashire PR2 6LS; Tel 01772 401600; Fax 01772 653799
Specialism: Mental health.

MENTAL HEALTH SERVICES

The Avondale Unit Royal Preston Hospital, Sharoe Green
La North, North Preston, Lancashire PR2 9HT; Tel 01772
773400

Clinical Psychology Unit Unit 1, Cable Crt, Pittman Way,
Fulwood, Preston, Lancashire PR2 9ZG; Tel 01772
709362

Department of Psychotherapy 1 Albert Rd, Fulwood,
Preston, Lancashire PR2 8PJ; Tel 01772 406933; Fax 01772
787344

Greenbank Day Centre Ripon St, Preston, Lancashire
PR1 7LY; Tel 01772 401080

Guild Enterprises Maitland Hse, Maitland St, Preston,
Lancashire PR1 5XR; Tel 01172 703169

Guild Lodge Whittingham La, Whittingham, Preston,
Lancashire PR3 2JH; Tel 01772 406600

Oakfield Unit Chorley and South Ribble District General
Hospital, Preston Rd, Chorley, Lancashire PR7 1PP;
Tel 01257 261222

Pendle View Queens Park Hospital, Haslingden Rd,
Blackburn, Lancashire BB2 3HH; Tel 01254 263555

Preston Community Drug Team St. Thomas' Institute,
Appleby St, Preston, Lancashire PR1 1HX; Tel 01772 406923;
Fax 01772 201904

Sion House 52 Sion Cl, Ribbleton, Preston, Lancashire
PR2 6RP; Tel 01772 406930; Fax 01772 406931

Lancashire Teaching Hospitals NHS Trust

Royal Preston Hospital, Sharoe Green La, Fulwood,
Preston, Lancashire PR2 9HT;
URL www.lancsteachinghospitals.nhs.uk; Tel 01772
522565
Chorley and South Ribble Hospital, Preston Rd, Chorley,
Lancashire PR7 1PP; Tel 01257 261222
Chair Brian Booth
Chief Executive Tony Curtis
Medical Director Dr Iain Robertson
Director (Nursing) Sue Reed
Director (Finance) Alan Stuttard
Director (Human Resources) Angela Ruddock
Director (Facilities and Services) Ian Cox

HOSPITALS

Chorley and South Ribble Hospital Preston Rd, Chorley,
Lancashire PR7 1PP; Tel 01257 261222; Fax 01257 245495

Royal Preston Hospital Sharoe Green La North, Fulwood,
Preston, Lancashire PR2 9HT; Tel 01772 522565

Sharoe Green Hospital Shaore Green La South, Fulwood,
Preston, Lancashire PR2 4DU; Tel 01772 522565

12

Leeds Mental Health Teaching NHS Trust

Meanwood Pk, Tongue La, Leeds, West Yorkshire LS6 4QB;
Tel 0113 275 8721; Fax 0113 274 5172
Chair I.E. Hughes
Chief Executive M. Atkin
Medical Director Dr D. Thompson
Director (Nursing and Quality) P.A. McGinnis
Director (Community Services) M. Doyle
Director (Finance) R. North
Director (Corporate Development) J. Walter
Director (Mental Health Services) N. Fenny
Annual budget
£119 million

COMMUNITY AND MENTAL HEALTH SERVICES

Meanwood Pk, Tongue La, Leeds, West Yorkshire LS6 4QB;
E-mail communications@lcmhst-tr.northy.nhs.uk;
Tel 0113 275 8721; Fax 0113 274 5172

Crooked Acres Spen La, Leeds, West Yorkshire LS5 3EJ;
Tel 0113 278 6245
Specialism: Mental handicap Number of beds: (22)

High Royds Hospital Menston, Ilkley, West Yorkshire
LS29 6AQ; Tel 01943 876151
Specialism: Psychiatric Number of beds: (459)

Roundhay Wing St. James's University Hospital, Beckett St,
Leeds, West Yorkshire LS9 7TF; Tel 0113 243 3144
Specialism: Psychiatric. Number of beds: (146)

St. Mary's Hospital Green Hill Rd, Leeds, West Yorkshire
LS12 3QE; Tel 0113 279 0121
Specialism: Geriatric (27) ESMI (30)

Seacroft Hospital York Rd, Leeds, West Yorkshire
LS14 6UH; Tel 0113 264 8164
Specialism: Elderly psychiatric; acute. Number of beds:
(360)

HEALTH CENTRES

Armley Clinic 2 Theaker La, Leeds, West Yorkshire LS12
3NZ; E-mail reception@armleyhc@lcmhst-tr.northy.nhs.uk;
Tel 0113 295 1288; Fax 0113 295 1277

Beeston Community Clinic 123 Cemetary Rd, Beeston,
Leeds, West Yorkshire LS11 8LH;
E-mail reception.beestonclinic@lcmhst-tr.northy.nhs.uk;
Tel 0113 295 4900; Fax 0113 295 4901

Belle Isle Clinic 2 Aberfield Rise, Bramhope, Leeds, West
Yorkshire LS10 3QH; Tel 0113 271 3384; Fax 0113 272 3117

Boston Spa Clinic 1 Lynton Ave, Boston Spa, West
Yorkshire LS23 6BL; Tel 01937 842800; Fax 01937 522801

Bramley Clinic 255 Town St, Bramley, Leeds, West
Yorkshire LS13 3EJ; Tel 0113 295 1550; Fax 0113 295 1551

Burmantofts Health Centre Cromwell Mount, Leeds, West
Yorkshire LS9 7TA; Tel 0113 248 4330

Chapeltown Health Centre Spencer Pl, Leeds, West
Yorkshire LS7 4BB;
E-mail reception.chapeltownhc@lcmhst-tr.northy.nhs.uk;
Tel 0113 295 1000; Fax 0113 295 1001

East Ardsley Health Centre Bradford Rd, East Ardsley,
Wakefield, West Yorkshire WF3 2DN; Tel 0113 253 7627;
Fax 0113 283 3052

East Leeds Clinic Harehills La, Leeds, West Yorkshire
LS9 6NG; Tel 0113 295 1470; Fax 0113 295 1471

Farsley Clinic Farfield Hse, Farfield Ave, Pudsey, West
Yorkshire LS28 5HL; Tel 0113 295 3260; Fax 0113 295 3261

Gasforth Clinic Lidgett La, Garforth, Leeds, West Yorkshire
LS25 1LJ;
E-mail reception.garforthclinic@lcmhst-tr.northy.nhs.uk;
Tel 0113 286 3429; Fax 0113 287 4421

Gildersome Health Centre Finkle La, Gildersome, Leeds,
West Yorkshire LS27 7US; Tel 0113 295 4030; Fax 0113 295
4030

Gipton Clinic 60 Coldcotes Dr, Gipton, Leeds, West
Yorkshire LS9 2PE; Tel 0113 295 3560; Fax 0113 295 3561

Guiseley Clinic Oxford Rd, Guiseley, Leeds, West Yorkshire
LS20 9AT; Tel 01943 870114; Fax 01943 879513

Halton Clinic 2 Primrose La, Halton, Leeds, West Yorkshire
LS15 7HR;
E-mail reception.haltonhc@lcmhst-tr.northy.nhs.uk;
Tel 0113 295 1888; Fax 0113 295 1889

Holt Park Health Centre Holt Rd, Leeds, West Yorkshire
LS16 7QD; Tel 0113 295 1520; Fax 0113 295 1521

Horsforth Clinic Church La, Horsforth, Leeds, West
Yorkshire LS18 5LA;
E-mail reception.horsforthhc@lcmhst-tr.northy.nhs.uk;
Tel 0113 295 3300; Fax 0113 295 3301

Hunslet Health Centre 24 Church St, Hunslet, Leeds, West
Yorkshire LS10 2PT;
E-mail reception.hunslethc@lcmhst-tr.northy.nhs.uk;
Tel 0113 277 1811; Fax 0113 271 9620

Kippax Health Centre Moorgate Dr, Kippax, Leeds, West
Yorkshire LS25 7QT;
E-mail reception.kippaxhc@lcmhst-tr.northy.nhs.uk;
Tel 0113 287 4427; Fax 0113 287 1817

Kirkstall Health Centre 15 Morris La, Kirkstall, Leeds, West
Yorkshire LS5 3DB; Tel 0113 295 1160; Fax 0113 295 1161

Leafield Clinic 107–109 King La, Moortown, Leeds, West
Yorkshire LS17 5BP;
E-mail reception.leafieldclinic@lcmhst-tr.northy.nhs.uk;
Tel 0113 295 1700; Fax 0113 295 1701

Meanwood Health Centre 548 Meanwood Rd, Meanwood,
Leeds, West Yorkshire LS6 4JN;
E-mail reception.meanwoodhc@lcmhst-tr.northy.nhs.uk;
Tel 0113 295 1350; Fax 0113 295 1351

Middleton Clinic Middleton Park Ave, Leeds, West
Yorkshire LS10 4HT; Tel 0113 270 0773; Fax 0113 276 0810

Morley Health Centre Corporation St, Morley, Leeds, West
Yorkshire LS7 9NB;
E-mail reception.morleyhc@lcmhst-tr.northy.nhs.uk;
Tel 0113 252 2051

New Wortley Health Centre 15 Green La, Tong Rd, Leeds,
West Yorkshire LS12 1JE; Tel 0113 295 1933; Fax 0113 295
1944

One Stop Shop 93 Moresdale La, Seacroft, Leeds, West
Yorkshire LS14 6GG; Tel 0113 247 5640; Fax 0113 295 3586

Osmondthorpe Clinic One Stop Shop, Wykebeck Ave,
Leeds, West Yorkshire LS9 0HG; Tel 0113 295 3585; Fax 0113
295 3586

Otley Clinic Manor Sq, Otley, West Yorkshire LS21 3AY;
E-mail reception.otleyclinic@lcmhst-tr.northy.nhs.uk;
Tel 01943 850182; Fax 01943 850646

Oulton Health Centre Quarry Hill, Oulton, West Yorkshire
LS26 8SX; Tel 0113 282 0520; Fax 0113 282 9195

Pudsey Health Centre 18 Mulberry St, Pudsey, West
Yorkshire LS28 7XP; Tel 0113 295 3200; Fax 0113 295 3201

Rothwell Health Centre Stone Brig La, Rothwell, Leeds,
West Yorkshire LS26 0UE; Tel 0113 282 0520; Fax 0113 282
9195

Seacroft Clinic The Green, Seacroft, Leeds, West Yorkshire
LS14 6PF;
E-mail reception.seacrofthc@lcmhst-tr.northy.nhs.uk;
Tel 0113 295 1060; Fax 0113 295 1090

Swillington Clinic Hillcrest Cl, Swillington, Leeds, West
Yorkshire LS26 8DZ; Tel 0113 286 1395; Fax 0113 287 7203

Tyersal Clinic Tyersal Rd, Tyersal, Bradford, West Yorkshire
BD4 8WZ; Tel 01274 664441

Wetherby Health Centre St. James' St, Wetherby, West
Yorkshire LS22 6RS;
E-mail reception.wetherbyhc@lcmhst-tr.northy.nhs.uk;
Tel 01937 522777; Fax 01937 522801

Woodhouse Health Centre off Woodhouse St, Leeds, West Yorkshire LS6 2NS;
E-mail reception.woodhousehc@lcmhst.tr.northy.nhs.uk;
Tel 0113 295 1440; Fax 0113 295 1401

Woodsley Health Centre Woodsley Rd, Leeds, West Yorkshire LS6 1AG; Tel 0113 295 1240; Fax 0113 295 1241

Yeadon Health Centre 17 Southview Rd, Yeadon, Leeds, West Yorkshire LS19 7PS; Tel 0113 295 4280; Fax 0113 295 4281

The Leeds Teaching Hospitals NHS Trust

St. James's University Hospital, Beckett St, Leeds, West Yorkshire LS9 7TF;
URL www.leedsteachinghospitals.com; Tel 0113 243 3144; Fax 0113 242 6496
Chair M. Buckley
Chief Executive N. McKay
Medical Director H. Mascie-Taylor
Chief Nurse M. Naughton
Director (Finance) A.N. Chapman
Director (Personnel) J. McCaffery
Annual budget
£578 million

PROSTHETIC SERVICE AND WHEELCHAIR SERVICE

Chapel Allerton Hospital, Chapeltown Rd, Leeds, West Yorkshire LS7 4SA
Manager (Rehabilitation Services) Nancy Rhodes; Tel 0113 392 4983
Manager (Wheelchairs) Sam Sterling; Tel 0113 392 4984

HOSPITALS

Chapel Allerton Hospital Chapeltown Rd, Leeds, West Yorkshire LS7 4RB; Tel 0113 392 4595
Specialism: Medicine for the elderly; rheumatology; rehabilitation.

Cookridge Hospital Hospital La, Cookridge, Leeds, West Yorkshire; Tel 0113 392 4253
Specialism: Oncology.

The Dental Institute The Worsley Bldg, Clarendon Way, Leeds, West Yorkshire; Tel 0113 233 6202

Leeds General Infirmary Great George St, Leeds, West Yorkshire LS1 3EX; Tel 0113 243 2799
Specialism: Acute; maternity; children; regional cardiothoracic and neurosurgery centre; intensive care; A&E etc.

St. James's Hospital Becket St, Leeds, West Yorkshire LS8 7TF; Tel 0113 243 3144; Fax 0113 242 6496
Specialism: Acute; maternity; children; renal and liver transplantation; intensive care; A and E etc.

Seacroft Hospital York Rd, Leeds, West Yorkshire LS14 6UH; Tel 0113 264 8164
Specialism: Medicine for the elderly.

Wharfedale General Hospital Newall Carr Rd, Otley, West Yorkshire LS21 2LY; Tel 0113 392 2000
Specialism: Minor injuries unit; minor surgery; elderly care.

Leicestershire Partnership NHS Trust

George Hine Hse, Gipsy La, Leicester LE5 0TD;
URL www.leicspt.nhs.uk; Tel 0116 225 6000; Fax 0116 225 3684
Chair Dr Wendy Hickling, OBE
Chief Executive Dr Maggie Cork
Medical Director Dr Jane Hoskyns
Director (Nursing) Noreen Young
Director (Finance, Facilities and Information)
Mike Naylor
Director (Human Resources) David Nance

LEARNING DISABILITIES HOSPITAL

Leicester Frith Hospital Groby Rd, Leicester LE3 9QF;
Tel 0116 225 5200; Fax 0116 225 5202

MENTAL HEALTH UNITS

Beechwood Day Hospital Evington Centre, Gwendolen Rd, Leicester LE5 4QF; Tel 0116 225 1001; Fax 0116 225 1003

Forest Grange Day Unit Groby Rd, Leicester LE3 9DZ; Tel 0116 225 2760; Fax 0116 225 2757

Glenvale Day Hospital Groby Rd, Leicester LE3 9DZ; Tel 0116 225 6180; Fax 0116 225 2770

Bradgate Mental Health Unit Groby Rd, Leicester LE3 9EJ; Tel 0116 225 2650; Fax 0116 225 2651

Brandon Unit Leicester General Hospital, Gwendolen Rd, Leicester LE5 4PW; Tel 0116 225 6180; Fax 0116 225 6228

Evington Centre Gwendolen Rd, Leicester LE5 4QF; Tel 0116 225 1001; Fax 0116 225 1003

Langton Day Hospital Brandon Mental Health Unit, Leicester General Hospital, Gwendolen Rd, Leicester LE5 4PW; Tel 0116 225 6180; Fax 0116 225 6228

Woodlands Unit The Pastures, Narborough, Leicester LE9 5EQ; Tel 0116 225 5850; Fax 0116 225 5770

COMMUNITY MENTAL HEALTH TEAMS (CMHT)

Central City West CMHT 71 St. John's, Narborough, Leicester LE9 5BS; Tel 0116 225 6155; Fax 0116 225 6165
Specialism: Adult.

City East CMHT Old Nurses Home, Towers Hospital, Gipsy La, Leicester LE5 0TD; Tel 0116 225 2861; Fax 0116 225 2852
Specialism: Adult.

Community Rehab Homeless Service Sylvia Reid Hse, Forest Rd, Narborough, Leicester LE9 5ES; Tel 0116 286 7711; Fax 0116 286 1244

Community Rehab Team (East) Swithland Hse, 352 London Rd, Leicester LE9 5ES; Tel 0116 225 5600; Fax 0116 225 5601

Community Rehab Team (West) Sylvia Reid Hse, Forest Rd, Narborough, Leicester LE9 5ES; Tel 0116 286 7711; Fax 0116 286 1244

East Leicestershire CMHT (Melton) St. Mary's Hospital, Thorpe Rd, Melton Mowbray, Leicestershire LE13 1SJ; Tel 01664 854950; Fax 01664 8544959
Specialism: Elderly.

East Leicestershire CMHT (Rutland and Market Harborough) Brooklands, Northampton Rd, Market Harborough, Leicestershire LE16 9HN; Tel 01858 461039; Fax 01858 468252
Specialism: Elderly.

Harborough/Melton CMHT 1st Fl, Old Nurses Home, Towers Hospital, Gipsy La, Leicester LE5 0TD; Tel 0116 225 2861; Fax 0116 225 2852
Specialism: Adult.

North Charnwood CMHT Town Hall Chambers, Town Hall Passage, Market Pl, Loughborough, Leicestershire LE11 3EB; Tel 01509 553901; Fax 01509 553907
Specialism: Elderly; adult.

North East City CMHT Towers Hospital, Gipsy La, Humberstone, Leicester LE5 0TD; Tel 0116 225 3737; Fax 0116 225 5958
Specialism: Elderly.

North West City CMHT St. Paul's Church Rooms, Kirby Rd, Leicester LE3 6BD; Tel 0116 225 5710; Fax 0116 225 5711
Specialism: Elderly.

North West City CMHT Goodacre Hse, Tilling Rd, Beaumont Leys, Leicester LE4 0SY; Tel 0116 225 6820; Fax 0116 225 5711
Specialism: Adult.

12

North West Leicestershire CMHT The Hawthorn Centre, Coalville Community Hospital, Broom Leys Rd, Coalville, Leicestershire LE67 4DE; Tel 01530 453800; Fax 01530 453845
　　Specialism: Elderly; adult.

Rutland CMHT Rutland Volunteer Centre, Rutland College, Barleythorpe Rd, Oakham, Rutland; Tel 01572 756032; Fax 01572 724460
　　Specialism: Adult.

South Charnwood CMHT Bridge Park Plaza, Bridge Park Rd, Thurmaston, Leicester LE5 9PQ; Tel 0116 225 6700; Fax 0116 225 6741
　　Specialism: Elderly; adult.

South East City CMHT Rainham Lodge, Maidstone Centre, Maidstone Rd, Leicester LE2 0TW; Tel 0116 225 5900; Fax 0116 225 5922
　　Specialism: Elderly.

South East City CMHT Maidstone Centre, Maidstone Rd, Leicester LE2 0TW; Tel 0116 225 5888; Fax 0116 225 5899
　　Specialism: Adult.

South Leicestershire CMHT The Cedars Centre, Cedar Ave, Wigston, Leicester LE18 2LA; Tel 0116 225 5700; Fax 0116 225 5650
　　Specialism: Elderly; adult.

South West City CMHT St. Paul's Church Rooms, Kirby Rd, Leicester LE3 6BD; Tel 0116 225 5710; Fax 0116 225 5711
　　Specialism: Elderly.

South West City CMHT Unit 14–16, Cornwall Business Centre, Cornwall Rd, South Wigston, Leicester LE18 4XH; Tel 0116 225 6330; Fax 0116 225 6342
　　Specialism: Adult.

West Leicestershire CMHT The Lawns, Upper Castle St, Hinckley, Leicestershire LE10 1DY; Tel 01455 443600; Fax 01455 443636
　　Specialism: Elderly.

West Leicestershire CMHT Orchard Resource Centre, Hinckley and District Hospital, Hill St, Hinckley, Leicestershire LE10 1DS; Tel 01455 443950; Fax 01455 443944
　　Specialism: Adult.

FACILITIES SERVICES

Bridge Park Plaza Thurmaston, Leicester LE4 8PQ; Tel 0116 225 6622; Fax 0116 225 6675

MENTAL HEALTH REHABILITATION SERVICE

Keyham Upholstery Unit 21, Matrix Hse, 7 Constitution Hill, Leicester LE1 1PL; Tel 0116 251 0362; Fax 0116 251 0362
Linnaeus Nursery Cordelia Cl, off Victoria Park Rd East, Leicester; Tel 0116 276 7906

MENTAL HEALTH SPECIALIST SERVICES

Adolescent Psychiatric Unit Oakham Hse, 17 Herongate Rd, Leicester LE5 0AW; Tel 0116 225 2800; Fax 0116 225 2801
Child and Adolescent Mental Health Service Westcotes Hse, Westcotes Dr, Leicester LE3 0QU; Tel 0116 225 2900; Fax 0116 225 2899
Cognitive Behavioural Therapy Brandon Unit, Leicester General Hospital, Gwendolen Rd, Leicester LE5 4PW; Tel 0116 225 6200; Fax 0116 225 6228
Community Alcohol Team Drury Hse, 50 Leicester Rd, Narborough, Leicester LE9 5DF; Tel 0116 225 6350; Fax 0116 225 6370
Community Drug Team Paget Hse, 2 West St, Leicester LE1 6XP; Tel 0116 225 6400; Fax 0116 247 1600
Dynamic Psychotherapy Service Humberstone Grange Clinic, Thurmaston La, Leicester LE5 0TA; Tel 0116 225 6430; Fax 0116 225 6432

Eating Disorders Brandon Unit, Leicester General Hospital, Gwendolen Rd, Leicester LE5 4PW; Tel 0116 225 6200; Fax 0116 225 6228
Therapeutic Community Francis Dixon Lodge, Gipsy La, Leicester LE5 0TD; Tel 0116 225 6800; Fax 0116 276 1646

The Lewisham Hospital NHS Trust

High St, Lewisham, London SE13 6LH;
　　URL www.uhl.ac.uk; E-mail enquiries@uhl.uk; Tel 020 8333 3000; Fax 020 8333 3333
Chair Steve Bullock
Chief Executive Michael Scott
Medical Director Dr Peter Luce
Director (Nursing and Operations) Vivien Rhodes
Director (Modernisation) Philippa Robinson
Director (Finance) Colin Gentile
Director (Human Resources and Corporate Development) David High
Annual income
£102 million

HOSPITAL

University Hospital Lewisham High St, Lewisham, London SE13 6LH; URL www.uhl.ac.uk; E-mail enquiries@uhl.nhs.uk; Tel 020 8333 3000
　　Specialism: Acute. Number of beds: (650)

Lincoln District Healthcare NHS Trust

The Lincoln District Healthcare NHS Trust has now dissolved and its services have been undertaken by the Lincolnshire Partnership NHS Trust, which is listed alphabetically in this section.

Lincolnshire Ambulance and Health Transport Service NHS Trust

Cross O'Cliff Crt, Bracebridge Heath, Lincoln, Lincolnshire LN4 2HL; Tel 01522 545171; Fax 01522 534611
Chair Mrs Linda Honey
Chief Executive Margaret J. Serna
Director (Finance) D. Atkinson

Lincolnshire Partnership NHS Trust

Cross O'Cliff, Bracebridge Heath, Lincoln, Lincolnshire LN4 2HN

COMMUNITY MENTAL HEALTH TEAMS

Beaconfield Centre Mental Health Resource Centre, Sandon Rd, Grantham, Lincolnshire NG31 9DR; Tel 01476 591233; 01476 591259
Boston CMHT Boston Business Centre, Norfolk St, Boston, Lincolnshire PE21 9HH; Tel 01205 369410
Skegness CMHT 17 Lumley Ave, Skegness, Lincolnshire PE25 2AP; Tel 01754 610509
The Willows Kesteven St, Sleaford, Lincolnshire NG34 7DT; Tel 01529 307733; Fax 01529 307729
Wilson House 64 St. Thomas Rd, Spalding, Lincolnshire PE11 2XT; Tel 01775 760525

HEALTH CENTRES AND OTHER UNITS

Ash Villa Willoughby Rd, South Rauceby, Sleaford, Lincolnshire NE34 8QA; Tel 01529 488061
　　Specialism: Child and adolescent.
Ashley House Beaconfield Site, Beacon La, Grantham, Lincolnshire NE31 9DF; Tel 01476 573985
Beech House Toot La, Fishtoft, Boston, Lincolnshire PE21 0AX; Tel 01205 354988

Boston Health Clinic Lincoln La, Boston, Lincolnshire PE21 8RU; Tel 01205 360880

Bourne Health Centre St. Gilbert's Rd, Bourne, Lincolnshire PE10 9XA; Tel 01778 394185

Children's Services 10–11 Lindum Terr, Lincoln, Lincolnshire LN2 5RT; Tel 01522 513875

Community Mental Health Team Base (East) 2–4 Eastfield Rd, Louth, Lincolnshire LN11 7AN; Tel 01507 607383

Community Mental Health Team Base (North) 10 The Ave, Lincoln, Lincolnshire LN1 1PB; Tel 01522 511800

Community Mental Health Team Base (South) 472 Newark Rd, Lincoln, Lincolnshire LN6 8RZ; Tel 01522 876622

Community Mental Health Team Base and Day Service (East) Homeleigh, Foundry St, Horncastle, Lincolnshire LN9 6AQ; Tel 01507 522470

Department of Psychiatry Pilgrim Hospital Site, 12a–12b Sibsey Rd, Boston, Lincolnshire PE20 9QS; Tel 01205 364801

Elm Lodge Beaconfield Site, Beacon La, Grantham, Lincolnshire NE31 9DF; Tel 01476 573752

ESMI Service Witham Crt, Lincoln, Lincolnshire LN6 8UZ; Tel 01522 500690

ESMI Unit Pilgrim Hospital Site, Sibsey Rd, Boston, Lincolnshire PE20 9QS; Tel 01205 364801 3551

Francis Wilis Unit County Hospital, Lincoln, Lincolnshire LN2 5QY; Tel 01522 573625

Gervas House Long Leys Rd, Lincoln, Lincolnshire LN1 1EJ; Tel 01522 546546

Haven Day Unit Pilgrim Hospital Site, Sibsey Rd, Boston, Lincolnshire PE20 9QS; Tel 01205 364801 Ext 3536

Holly Lodge 9 The Meadows, Lincoln La, Skegness, Lincolnshire PE25 2JA; Tel 01754 766139

Learning Disabilities Service Office Long Leys Crt, Long Leys Rd, Lincoln, Lincolnshire LN2 5RT; Tel 01522 577404

Lough County Hospital Allenby Ward, High Holme Rd, Louth, Lincoln, Lincolnshire LN11 0EU; Tel 01507 600100 ext 1209

The Manthorpe Centre Grantham Hospital Site, 101 Manthorpe Rd, Grantham, Lincolnshire NE31 8DG; Tel 01476 578901

Maple Lodge Toot La, Fishtoft, Boston, Lincolnshire PE21 0AX; Tel 01205 354900

Mental Health Day Unit 40 De Wint Ave, Lincoln, Lincolnshire LN6 7JA; Tel 01522 689652

Peter Hodgkinson Centre County Hospital, Lincoln, Lincolnshire LN2 5QY; Tel 01522 573553

Postgraduate Education and Training Centre South Rauceby, Sleaford, Lincolnshire NG34 8RB; Tel 01529 416036; Fax 01529 416072

Psychotherapy Services 1 St. Anne's Rd, Lincoln, Lincolnshire LN2 5RA; Tel 01522 512000

Skegness Health Clinic Cecil Ave, Skegness, Lincolnshire PE25 2BX; Tel 01754 764636

The Stamford Resource Centre St. George's Ave, Off Rhyhall Rd, Stamford, Lincolnshire; Tel 01780 757142

Sycamore Assessment Unit Beaconfield Site, Beacon La, Grantham, Lincolnshire NE31 9DF; Tel 01476 579707

Welland Hospital Ward One, Roman Bank, Spalding, Lincolnshire PE11 2HN; Tel 01775 766800

Liverpool Women's Hospital NHS Trust

Crown St, Liverpool, Merseyside L8 7SS;
 URL www.lwh.org.uk; Tel 0151 708 9988; Fax 0151 702 4028
Chair R. Cooper
Chief Executive A.M. Marr
Medical Director D. Richmond

Director (Midwifery and Nursing) E. Craig
Director (Finance) D. Young
Director (Personnel) A.M. Stretch
Contact (Estate Management) R. Webster
Contact (Information) D. Young
Contact (Information Technology) Paul Young
Purchasing Officer G. Case
Annual budget
£50 million

Local Health Partnerships NHS Trust

Trust Headquarters, Sampson Hse, Foxhall Rd, Ipswich,
 Suffolk IP3 8BL; URL www.lhp.org.uk;
 E-mail janet.young@centr.lhp.tr.anglox.nhs.uk; Tel 01473 329600; Fax 01473 329019
Chair S. Walmsley
Chief Executive Stuart Hatton
Medical Director Dr J. Darley
Director (Service West) Alan Staff
Director (Finance) M. McCleary
Director (Human Resources) J. Alderton

HOSPITALS AND MENTAL HEALTH

Beccles and District War Memorial Hospital St. Mary's Rd, Beccles, Suffolk NR34 9NQ; Tel 01502 719800; Fax 01502 714696

Child, Adolescent and Family Consultation Service 23 Henley Rd, Ipswich, Suffolk IP1 3TF; Tel 01473 214811; Fax 01473 280809
 Specialism: Child; adolescent and family psychiatry; outpatient services.

Child Health Centre Hospital Rd, Bury St. Edmunds, Suffolk IP33 3NT; Tel 01284 775000

Community Drug Team 37 Berners St, Ipswich, Suffolk; Tel 01473 236069; 01473 280511; Fax 01473 289634

Elm Street Clinic Elm St, Ipswich, Suffolk IP1 1HB; Tel 01473 275200

Mid Suffolk Clubhouse Old Fox Hse, 1 Old Fox Yard, Stowmarket, Suffolk IP14 1AB; Tel 01449 774966; Fax 01449 775018
 Specialism: Rehabilitation; day facilities; adults; short- or long-term mental illness.

Minsmere House Heath Rd, Ipswich, Suffolk IP4 5PD; Tel 01473 712233; Fax 01473 704227
 Specialism: Elderly mental health. (36)

South Suffolk Club House Bridge Hse, 15 Lower Brook St, Ipswich, Suffolk IP4 1AO; Tel 01473 230115; Fax 01473 230523

St. Clement's Hospital Foxhall Rd, Ipswich, Suffolk IP3 8LS; Tel 01473 715111; Fax 01473 276546
 Specialism: Adult psychiatry; elderly mental health. Number of beds: (242)

Violet Hill Day Centre Violet Hill Rd, Stowmarket, Suffolk IP14 1JS; Tel 01449 673872
 Specialism: Psychogeriatric day care.

London Ambulance Service NHS Trust

London Ambulance Service Headquarters, 220 Waterloo Rd, London SE1 8SD;
 URL www.lond-amb.sthames.nhs.uk; Tel 020 7921 5100; Fax 020 7921 5129
Chief Executive Peter Bradley

Luton and Dunstable Hospital NHS Trust

Lewsey Rd, Luton, Bedfordshire LU4 0DZ; Tel 01582 491122; Fax 01582 492130
Chair S. Dhillon
Chief Executive Stephen Ramsden
Medical Director J. Pickles

12

Director (Operations) R. Long
Director (Nursing and Quality) Brigid Stacey
Director (Finance) Andrew Harwood
Annual budget
£72 million

Maidstone and Tunbridge Wells NHS Trust

Pembury Hospital, Tonbridge Rd, Penbury, Tunbridge
 Wells, Kent TN2 4QJ; Tel 01892 823535; Fax 01892
 825468
Chair Miss A. Chapman
Chief Executive S. Collinson
Medical Director Dr C. Unter
Director (Nursing) Dr B. Place
Director (Finance and Information) P. Darling
Director (Operations) Mrs V. Thompson
Director (Human Resources) C. Wilson
Director (Service Development) Mrs L. Clemence
Annual Budget
£166 million

HOSPITALS

Maidstone Hospital (Day Care) Hermitage La, Maidstone,
Kent ME16 9QQ; Tel 01622 729000; Fax 01622 244124

Kent County Ophthalmic and Aural Hospital Church St,
Maidstone, Kent ME14 1DT; Tel 01622 673444; Fax 01622
679979

Kent and Sussex Hospital Mount Ephraim, Tunbridge
Wells, Kent TN4 8AT; Tel 01892 526111; Fax 01892 528381
 Specialism: Acute. Number of beds: (261)

Pembury Hospital Tonbrdige Rd, Tunbridge Wells, Kent
TN2 4QJ; Tel 01892 833535; Fax 01892 824267
 Specialism: Acute. Number of beds: (224)

Preston Hall Hospital Preston Hall, Aylesford, Maidstone,
Kent ME20 7NJ; Tel 01622 710161

Mayday Healthcare NHS Trust

Mayday University Hospital, London Rd, Croydon, Surrey
 CR7 7YE; Tel 020 8401 3000; Fax 020 8665 1974
Medical Director Dr Syamala Thomas
*Director (Nursing and Quality Assurance) and Deputy Chief
 Executive* Frank McGurrin
Director (Finance) Vacancy
Annual budget
£100 million

HOSPITALS

Mayday University Hospital 530 London Rd, Croydon,
Surrey CR7 7YE; Tel 020 8401 3000
 Specialism: Acute.

Purley Memorial Hospital 856 Brighton Rd, Purley, Surrey
CR8 2YL; Tel 020 8401 3000
 Specialism: Geriatric.

The Medway NHS Trust

Medway Maritime Hospital, Windmill Rd, Gillingham,
 Kent ME7 5NY; Tel 01634 830000; Fax 01634 829470
Chair Janardan Sofat
Chief Executive Andy Horne
Medical Director Dr A. Stewart
Director (Nursing) Jacqueline Geoghegan
Director (Human Resources) Ali Mohammed
Director (Finance) Jeremy Moon

Mental Health Services of Salford NHS Trust

Bury New Rd, Prestwich, Manchester M25 3BL; Tel 0161
 773 9121; Fax 0161 772 3639
Chair Hilary Clayton (Acting)
Chief Executive Robert Lee

Medical Director Steve Colgan
Clinical Executive Andy Brogan
Director (Information, Contracting and Finance)
 Carol Warren
Director (Personnel) Margaret Mayor
Service Director (Forensic and High Dependency Services)
 Paul Tarbuck
Service Director (Salford Services) Gary McNamee

Mersey Care NHS Trust

Headquarters, Hamilton Hse, 24 Pall Mall, Liverpool,
 Merseyside L3 6AL; URL www.merseycare.nhs.uk;
 E-mail communications@merseycare.nhs.uk; Tel 0151
 285 2000; Fax 0151 285 2346
Chair Stephen Hawkins
Chief Executive Alan Yates
*Executive Director (Organisational Development and
 Communications)* Kim Crowe
*Executive Director (Finance, Information and Communication
 Technology, and Facilities Management)* John Doyle
Medical Director Dr Cameron Boyd
Director (Nursing, Service and Professional Development)
 Mick Barwood
Director (Service Users and Carers) Lindsey Dyer
Director (Secure Services) and Deputy Chief Executive
 Charles Flynn
Director (Adult Mental Health Services) Emma Foster
Director (Social Care) Tony Oakman
Head (Administration) and Trust Board Secretary
 Derek McAuley
Head (Information Management and Technology)
 Mark Blakeman
Annual Budget
£133 million

HOSPITALS

Ashworth Hospital Parkbourn, Liverpool, Merseyside
L31 1HW

Mossley Hill Hospital Park Ave, Liverpool, Merseyside
L18 8BU; Tel 0151 250 3000
 Specialism: Psychogeriatric

Rathbone Hospital Mill La, Old Swan, Liverpool,
Merseyside L9 7JP

Sir Alfred Jones Memorial Hospital Church Rd, Garston,
Liverpool, Merseyside L19 2LP; Tel 0151 250 3000
 Specialism: Intermediate care (28)

University Hospital Aintree Longmoor La, Liverpool,
Merseyside L9 7AL

HEALTH CENTRE

Hesketh Centre 51–55 Albert Rd, Southport, Merseyside
PR9 0LT

Mersey Regional Ambulance Service NHS Trust

Elm Hse, Blemont Gr, Liverpool, Merseyside L6 4EG;
 URL www.merseyambulance.co.uk; Tel 0151 260 5220;
 Fax 0151 260 7441
Chair B.S. Jeuda
Chief Executive Vacancy
Director (Operations) N. Wylie
Director (Operational Services) M. Jackson
Director (Finance) P. Bradshaw
Associate Director (Human Resources) S. Samuels
Head (Emergency Paramedic Services (Operations))
 P. Mulcahy
Head (Patient Transport Services) A. Hickson
Manager (Estates) C. Baker
Manager (Finance) I. Boyle
Manager (Training and Education) P. Cockayne
Annual budget
£32 million

Mid Anglia NHS Trust

Mid Anglia NHS Trust has merged with Allington NHS Trust to become Local Health Partnerships NHS Trust, which is listed alphabetically in this section.

Mid Cheshire Hospitals NHS Trust

Leighton Hospital, Middlewich Rd, Crewe, Cheshire
CW1 4QJ; Tel 01270 255141; Fax 01270 587696
Chair   Robin L. Farmer
Chief Executive   S. Yates
Director (Medical)   J. Felmingham
Director (Quality Assurance) and Chief Nurse   K. Holbourn
Director (Financial)   D. Goodwin
Annual budget
£56 million

HOSPITALS

Leighton Hospital Middlewich Rd, Crewe, Cheshire
CW1 4QJ; Tel 01270 255141
   Specialism: Acute (673)
Victoria Infirmary Northwich, Cheshire CW8 1AW;
Tel 01606 74331
   Specialism: GP; geriatric.

Mid Essex Hospital Services NHS Trust

Broomfield Crt, Pudding Wood La, Chelmsford, Essex
CM1 7WE; Tel 01245 440761; Fax 01245 514675
Chair   David Bullock
Chief Executive   Andrew Pike
Medical Director   Chris Walker
Director (Nursing and Midwifery and Workforce)
   Sally Gooch
Director (Finance)   Phil Neal
Director (Operations)   Sue Barnett
Director (Estates)   Norman Bruce
Annual budget
£120 million

HOSPITALS

Broomfield Hospital Court Rd, Broomfield, Chelmsford,
Essex CM1 7ET; Tel 01245 440761
   Specialism: Acute; plastic surgery and burns at St.
   Andrew's Centre. Total number of beds: (549)

HOSPITALS

Courtauld (WJ) Hospital London Rd, Braintree, Essex
CM7 2LJ; Tel 01245 440761
   Specialism: GP, maternity (38)
Chelmsford and Essex Centre New London Rd,
Chelmsford, Essex CM1 7LF; Tel 01245 440761
St. John's Hospital Wood St, Chelmsford, Essex CM2 9BG;
Tel 01245 440761
   Specialism: Acute; maternity. Number of beds: (167)

Mid Kent Healthcare NHS Trust

Mid Kent Healthcare NHS Trust has now become part of Maidstone and Tunbridge Wells NHS Trust, which is listed alphabetically in this section.

Mid Staffordshire General Hospitals NHS Trust

Staffordshire General Hospital, Weston Rd, Stafford,
   Staffordshire ST16 3SA; URL www.midstaffs.nhs.uk;
   Tel 01785 257731; Fax 01785 230277
Chair   J. Jessel
Chief Executive   D. O'Neill
Medical Director   Dr J.A. Gibson
Director (Nursing and Quality Assurance)   J. Harry
Director (Finance and Planning)   J. Newsham

Annual budget
£63 million

HOSPITALS

Cannock Chase Hospital Brunswick Rd, Cannock,
Staffordshire WS11 2SY
   Specialism: Acute; geriatric. Number of beds: (224)
Staffordshire General Hospital Weston Rd, Stafford,
Staffordshire ST16 3RS; Tel 01785 257731
   Specialism: Acute. Number of beds: (383)

Mid Yorkshire Hospitals NHS Trust

Pinderfields Hospital, Aberford Rd, Wakefield, West
   Yorkshire WF1 4DG; Tel 01924 213850

HOSPITALS

Castleford, Normanton and District Hospital Lumley St,
Hightown, Castleford, West Yorkshire WF10 5LT; Tel 01977
605500
Clayton Hospital Northgate, Wakefield, West Yorkshire
WF1 3HS; Tel 01924 201688
Dewsbury and District Hospital Halifax Rd, Dewsbury,
West Yorkshire WF13 4HS; Tel 01924 201688
Pinderfields General Hospital Aberford Rd, Wakefield,
West Yorkshire WF1 4DG; Tel 01924 213850
Pontefract General Infirmary Friarwood La, Pontefract, West
Yorkshire WF8 1PL; Tel 01977 600600; Fax 01977 606852

Milton Keynes General NHS Trust

Standing Way, Eaglestone, Milton Keynes,
   Buckinghamshire MK6 5LD; URL www.mkg.org.uk;
   Tel 01908 660033; Fax 01908 669348
Chair   Mike Rowlands
Chief Executive   Jill Rodney
Medical Director   V. Jeevananthan
Medical Director   J. Porter
Director (Nursing Quality and Clinical Support Services)
   R. McMahon
Director (Finance)   Rob Baird
Director (Facilities)   G. Callan
Director (Strategic Planning and Service Development)
   D. Pickard
Director (Human Resources) and Trust Board Secretary
   Tony Capper

Moorfields Eye Hospital NHS Trust

162 City Rd, London EC1V 2PD;
   URL www.moorfields.org.uk; Tel 020 7253 3411; Fax 020
   7253 4696
Chief Executive   I.A.J. Balmer

Morecambe Bay Hospitals NHS Trust

Westmorland General Hospital, Burton Rd, Kendal,
   Cumbria LAG 7RG; Tel 01539 797800; Fax 01539 726687
Annual budget
£200 million

HOSPITALS

Dane Garth Mental Health Unit Furness General Hospital,
Dalton La, Barrow, Lancashire; Tel 01229 870870; Fax 01229
871182
Furness General Hospital Dalton La, Barrow-in-Furness,
Cumbria LA14 4LF; Tel 01229 870870
   Specialism: Acute (373)
Queen Victoria Hospital Thornton Rd, Morecambe,
Lancashire LA4 5NN; Tel 01524 411661
   Specialism: Acute (48)

12

Ridge Lea Hospital Quemmore Rd, Lancaster, Lancashire; Tel 01524 65241; Fax 01524 586201

Royal Lancaster Infirmary Ashton Rd, Lancaster, Lancashire LA1 4RP; Tel 01524 65944
Specialism: Acute; maternity; geriatric. Number of beds: (455) plus 17 day care.

Ulverston Hospital Stanley St, Ulverston, Cumbria LA12 7BT; Tel 01229 583635
Specialism: Geriatric; general medicine

Westmorland General Hospital Burton Rd, Kendal, Cumbria LA9 7RG; Tel 01539 732288
Specialism: Acute (234)

Newcastle upon Tyne Hospitals NHS Trust

Freeman Rd, High Heaton, Newcastle upon Tyne, Tyne and Wear NE7 7DN; Tel 0191 284 3111; Fax 0191 213 1968
Chair Sir Miles Irving
Chief Executive L.R. Fenwick
Medical Director Dr Mike Laker
Director (Business and Development) R. Barker
Director (Finance) R.A. Holmes

HOSPITALS

Dental Hospital Richardson Rd, Newcastle upon Tyne, Tyne and Wear NE2 4BW; Tel 0191 232 5131

Department of Reproductive Medicine Bioscience Centre, International Centre for Life, Times Sq, Newcastle upon Tyne, Tyne and Wear NE1 4EP; Tel 0191 219 4740; Fax 0191 219 4747

Freeman Hospital Freeman Rd, High Heaton, Newcastle upon Tyne, Tyne and Wear NE7 7DN; Tel 0191 284 3111; Fax 0191 213 1968
Specialism: Acute (763)

Institute of Human Genetics International Centre for Life, Central Parkway, Newcastle upon Tyne, Tyne and Wear NE1 3BZ; Tel 0191 241 8600; Fax 0191 241 8799

Newcastle General Hospital Westgate Rd, Newcastle upon Tyne, Tyne and Wear NE4 6BE; Tel 0191 273 8811
Specialism: Acute

Northern Centre for Cancer Treatment Newcastle General Hospital, Westgate Rd, Newcastle upon Tyne, Tyne and Wear
Number of beds: (60 plus 15 hospital beds)

Royal Victoria Infirmary Queen Victoria Rd, Newcastle upon Tyne, Tyne and Wear NE1 4LP; Tel 0191 232 5131
Number of beds: Acute (773)

Walkergate Hospital Benfield Rd, Newcastle upon Tyne, Tyne and Wear NE6 4QD; Tel 0191 265 4521
Specialism: Geriatric; acute; rehabilitation; continuing care. Number of beds: (85)

Newcastle, North Tyneside and Northumberland Mental Health NHS Trust

St. George's Hospital, East Cottingwood, Morpeth, Northumberland NE61 2NU; Tel 01670 512121; Fax 01670 511637

HOSPITAL

St. Georges Hospital East Cottingwood, Morpeth, Northumberland NE61 2NU; Tel 01670 512121; Fax 01670 511637
Specialism: Psychiatric (472)

Newham Healthcare NHS Trust

Executive Offices, Newham General Hospital, Glen Rd, Plaistow, London E13 8SL;
URL www.newham-healthcare.org; Tel 020 7476 4000; Fax 020 7363 8181

Chair Michael Smith
Chief Executive Kathy Watkins
Medical Director Dr Mike Gill
Director (Nursing and Patient Care) Louise Burke
Director (Finance and Resource Management) Ian O'Connor
Director (Human Resources) Brian Neal

HOSPITALS

Newham General Hospital Glen Rd, Plaistow, London E13 8SL; Tel 020 7476 4000
Specialism: Acute; accident and emergency; maternity. Number of beds: (377)

St. Andrew's Bromley-by-Bow Hospital Devas St, Bow, London E3 3NT; Tel 020 7987 2030
Specialism: Acute. Number of beds: (297)

Norfolk and Norwich Health Care NHS Trust

Norfolk and Norwich Health Care NHS Trust is now part of Norfolk and Norwich University Hospital NHS Trust, which is listed alphabetically in this section.

Norfolk and Norwich University Hospital NHS Trust

Norfolk and Norwich University Hospital, Colney La, Norwich, Norfolk NR4 7UY; URL www.nnuh.nhs.uk; E-mail communications.manager@nnuh.nhs.uk; Tel 01603 286286
Chair David Prior
Chief Executive Stephen Day

HOSPITALS

Cromer and District Hospital Mill Rd, Cromer, Norfolk NR27 0BQ

Norfolk and Norwich University Hospital Colney La, Norwich, Norfolk NR4 7UY

Norfolk Mental Health Care NHS Trust

Drayton Old Lodge, 146 Drayton High Rd, Drayton, Norwich, Norfolk NR8 6AN; URL www.nmhct.nhs.uk; Tel 01603 421421; Fax 01603 421118
Chair Lesley Kant
Chief Executive Pat Holman
Medical Director Dr H. Ball
Director (Resources) Mark Taylor
Director (Strategic Development) P. Thain
Director (Estates and Facilities) J. Stewart

HOSPITALS

Carlton Court St. Peter's Rd, Carlton Colville, Lowestoft, Suffolk NR33 8AG; Tel 01502 538008; Fax 01502 538262
Total number of beds: (60)

Hellesdon Hospital Drayton High Rd, Norwich, Norfolk NR6 5BE; Tel 01603 421421
Specialism: Psychiatric. Total number of beds: (179)

The Julian Hospital Bowthorpe Rd, Norwich, Norfolk NR2 3TD; Tel 01603 421421; Fax 01603 421831
Total number of beds: (100)

Northgate Hospital Northgate St, Great Yarmouth, Norfolk NR30 1BU; Tel 01493 337652; Fax 01493 337750
Total number of beds: (95)

Norvic Clinic Thorpe St. Andrews, Norwich, Norfolk NR7 0SS; Tel 01603 439614; Fax 01603 701954
Total number of beds: (38)

North Bristol NHS Trust

Beckspool Rd, Frenchay, Bristol BS16 1ND; URL www.northbristol.nhs.uk; Tel 0117 970 1212; Fax 0117 956 3880

Chair Mr N. Godden
Chief Executive S. Mills
Medical Director Dr M. Morse
Director (Nursing) J. Burgess
Director (Operations) D. Marshall
Director (Finance) S. Webster
Director (Policy and Planning) D. Tappin
Director (Facilities) S. Wood
Head (Human Resources) S. Keith

HOSPITALS

Blackberry Hill Hospital Manor Rd, Fishponds, Bristol
BS16 2EW; Tel 0117 965 6061

Burden Neurological Hospital Beckspool Rd, Stapleton,
Bristol BS16 1QT; Tel 0117 970 1212

Cossham Hospital Lodge Rd, Kingswood, Bristol BS15 1LF;
Tel 0117 967 1661

Frenchay Hospital Frenchay, Park Rd, Bristol BS16 1JE;
Tel 0117 970 1212

Ham Green Hospital (Orchard View) Pill, Bristol BS20 0HH

Southmead Hospital Southmead Rd, Westbury on Trym,
Bristol BS10 5NB; Tel 0117 950 5050; Fax 0117 959 0902

North Cheshire Hospitals NHS Trust

Warrington Hospital, Lovely La, Warrington WA5 1QG;
Tel 01925 635911; Fax 01925 662099
Chair N.L. Banner
Chief Executive Mike Deegan
Medical Director Dr D. Pearson
Director (Finance and Information) B.A. Peacock
Director (Nursing and Operational Services) G. Heaton
Director (Human Resources) A. Nelson
Annual budget
£52 million

HOSPITALS

Halton Hospital Human Resources, Hospital Way, Runcorn,
Warrington WA7 2DA; Tel 01928 753032; Fax 01928 753405

Warrington Hospital Human Resources, Lovely La,
Warrington WA5 1QG; Tel 01925 662253; Fax 01925 662521
Specialism: Acute.

North Cumbria Acute Hospitals NHS Trust

West Cumberland Hospital, Hensingham, Whitehaven,
Cumbria CA28 8JG;
URL www.northcumbriahealth.nhs.uk/acute; Tel 01228
693181; Fax 01228 523513
Chair Barbara Cannon
Chief Executive Nick Wood
Medical Director (Carlisle) W. Reid
Medical Director (Whitehaven) D. Watson, WCH
Director (Patient Access) B. Earley
Director (Corporate Development) Jill Paton
Director (Nursing and Quality) P. Lowes
Director (Finance and Contracting) C. Macklin
Director (Human Resources) K. McIntosh (Acting)
There is a general email format:
<firstname>.<lastname>@ncumbria-acute.nhs.uk

HOSPITALS

Cumberland Infirmary Newton Rd, Carlisle, Cumbria
CA2 7HY; Tel 01228 523444

Penrith Hospital Bridge La, Penrith, Cumbria CA11 8HX
Specialism: Maternity

Ruth Lancaster James Hospital Alston, Cumbria
CA9 3QX

West Cumberland Hospital Hensingham, Whitehaven,
Cumbria CA28 8JQ

North Cumbria Mental Health and Learning Disabilities NHS Trust

The Carleton Clinic, Cumwhinton Dr, Carlisle, Cumbria
CA1 3SX; Tel 01228 602000; Fax 01228 602384
Chair Eric Urquhart
Chief Executive N. Woodcock
Medical Director Carol Harvey; Tel 01228 602377;
Fax 01228 602384
Director (Nursing and Quality) Denise England; Tel 01228
602370; Fax 01228 602384
Director (Finance) Patrick McGohan; Tel 01228 602619;
Fax 01228 602617
Director (Human Resources) Shirley Chipperfield; Tel 01228
602700; Fax 01228 602017
Director (Mental Health and Learning Disabilities)
Phil Robertson; Tel 01228 602552; Fax 01228 602550

COMMUNITY LEARNING DISABILITY TEAM

Central Clinic 50 Victoria Pl, Carlisle, Cumbria CA1 1HN;
Tel 01228 603282; Fax 01228 603201

HOSPITALS

The Carleton Clinic Carlisle, Cumbria CA1 3SX; Tel 01228
602000

West Cumberland Hospital Homewood, Hensingham,
Whitehaven, Cumbria CA28 8JG; Tel 01946 693181;
Fax 01946 523513

Workington Infirmary Infirmary Rd, Workington, Cumbria
CA14 2UN; Tel 01900 602244; Fax 01946 523053

North Durham Health Care NHS Trust

North Durham Healthcare NHS Trust has merged with
South Durham Health Care NHS Trust to become County
Durham and Darlington Acute Hospitals NHS Trust, which
is listed alphabetically in this section.

North East Ambulance Service NHS Trust

Ambulance Headquarters, Scotswood Hse, Amethyst Rd,
Newcastle Bus Pk, Newcastle upon Tyne, Tyne and Wear
NE4 7YL; URL www.neambulance.nhs.uk;
E-mail publicrelations@neas.northy.nhs.uk; Tel 0191 273
1212; Fax 0191 273 7070
Chair Tom Conery (Acting)
Chief Executive Simon Featherstone
Director (Finance) R. French
Director (Corporate Services) R. Alabaster
Director (Clinical Standards and Quality) Colin Cessford
Director (Accident and Emergency Services) Paul Liversidge
Director (Human Resources) Chris Harrison
Director (PTS Services) Arthur Lemin
Annual budget
£48 million

North East London Mental Health NHS Trust

King George Hospital, Barley La, Goodmayes, Ilford, Essex
IG3 8XJ; URL www.nelmht.nhs.uk; Tel 020 8590 6060;
Fax 020 8970 8424
Chair John Garlick
Chief Executive Paul Gocke
Medical Director Dr Annie Lau

HOSPITAL

Thorpe Coombe Hospital 714 Forest Rd, London E17 3HP;
Tel 020 8520 8971; Fax 020 8527 2186

CLINICS AND HEALTH CENTRES

Child and Family Consultation Centre Shernhall St,
Walthamstow, London E17 3EA; Tel 020 8509 0424

12

Havering Child and Family Consultation Service Victoria Centre, Pettits La, Romford, Essex RM1 4HP; Tel 01708 796800

Healthworks Trinity Cl, Leytonstone, London E11 4RP; Tel 020 8558 5606

North Essex Mental Health Partnership NHS Trust

Cuton Hall La, Springfield, Chelmsford, Essex CM2 5PX; URL www.ne-mh.nhs.uk; Tel 01245 318400; Fax 01245 318401
Chair Mary St. Aubyn
Chief Executive Richard Coleman;
E-mail richard.coleman@nemhpt.nhs.uk; Tel 01245 318407
Medical Director Dr Sheila Mann
Director (Nursing) Marion Ravenhill
Director (Finance) Andrew Geldard
Annual budget
£28 million

Adult and Acute Services Area 1

INPATIENT FACILITIES

The Derwent Centre Princess Alexandra Hospital, Hamstel Rd, Harlow, Essex CM20 1RB; Tel 01279 444455; Fax 01279 454018
Wards
Stort Ward, Cam Ward, Avon Ward, Lea Ward.

Herts and Essex Hospital Haymeads La, Bishops Stortford, Hertfordshire CM23 5JH; Tel 01279 655191; Fax 01279 651399
Consultant Psychiatrist (Acute) Dr Omar Daniels
Wards
Chelmsford Ward, Chantry Ward, Barnard Ward.

St. Margarets Hospital The Plain, Epping, Essex CM16 6TN; Tel 01992 561666; Fax 01992 571089
Consultant Psychiatrist Dr Salah Abou el-Fadl
Consultant Psychiatrist Dr Rob Butler
Consultant Psychiatrist Dr Philip Robotis
Consultant Psychiatrist Dr Zuzana Walker
Wards
Chelmer Ward, Roding Ward.

DAY UNITS AND CLINICS

Drug and Alcohol Unit Derwent Centre, Princess Alexandra Hospital, Hamstel Rd, Harlow, Essex CM20 1RB; Tel 01279 444455

Dunmow Clinic – Community Mental Health Team Unit 2, Twyford Crt, High St, Great Dunmow, Essex CM6 1QX; Tel 01371 876551

Epping Forest Day Unit Rectory Lane Health Centre, Rectory La, Loughton, Essex IG10 3RU; Tel 020 8272 4632; Fax 020 8272 4646

Harlow Community Mental Health Team – Elderly Keats Hse, Bush Fair, Harlow, Essex CM18 6LY; Tel 01279 446400; Fax 01279 446488

Harlow Community Mental Health Team – Acute Latton Bush Centre, Southern Way, Harlow, Essex CM18 7BL; Tel 01279 446400; Fax 01279 446488

Harlow Work Skills Development Centre Nettleswell Hall Annexe, Park La, Harlow, Essex CM20 2QH; Tel 01279 421223; Fax 01279 418863

Haymeads Day Hospital Haymeads La, Bishops Stortford, Hertfordshire CM23 5JH; Tel 01279 827242; Fax 01279 827249

Loughton Mental Health Centre 8–10 High Beech Rd, Loughton, Essex IG10 4BL; Tel 020 8271 4000; Fax 020 8271 4006

North Uttlesford Community Mental Health Team Social Services Offices, 37 Fairycroft Rd, Saffron Walden, Essex CM10 1ND; Tel 01799 513132; Fax 01799 525890

Regent Road Centre Regent Rd, Epping, Essex CM16 5DL; Tel 01992 902340; Fax 01992 902340

River Lea House (Community Mental Health Team) St. Margarets Hospital, The Plain, Epping, Essex CM16 6TN; Tel 01992 827332; Fax 01992 571089

Waltham Abbey Mental Health Centre Conquest Hse, Church St, Waltham Abbey, Essex EN9 1DX; Tel 01992 902500; Fax 01992 902505

Adult and Acute Services Area 2

INPATIENT FACILITIES

Drake House Admirals Reach Nursing Home, Ridgewell Ave, Chelmsford, Essex CM7 2GA; Tel 01245 318680; Fax 01245 318681

J6 Ward St. John's Hospital, Wood St, Chelmsford, Essex CM2 9BG; Tel 01245 513116; Fax 01245 513489

The Linden Centre Woodlands Way, Broomfield Hospital, Broomfield Rd, Chelmsford, Essex CM7 5LF; Tel 01245 318800; Fax 01245 318801
Consultant Psychiatrist (Braintree) Dr M. Durrani
Consultant Psychiatrist (Braintree) Dr Klijnsma
Consultant Psychiatrist (Chelmsford South) Dr Chad
Consultant Psychiatrist (Chelmsford North) Dr Flechtner
Consultant Psychiatrist (Chelmsford East) Dr Hamid
Consultant Psychiatrist (Maldon) Dr Cyriac
Consultant Psychiatrist (Witham) Dr Broker
Wards
Cressing Ward, Finchingfield Ward, Galleywood Ward, Tillingham Day Hospital.

DAY UNITS AND CLINICS

Drug and Alcohol Unit Units 4 and 5a, Cornell Estate, Navigation Rd, Chelmsford, Essex CM2 6HE; Fax 01245 318581

C and E Centre New London Rd, Chelmsford, Essex CM2 0QH; Tel 01245 318600; Fax 01245 318601
C & E Day Unit, C & E Spectrum, C & E Cognitive Therapy, C & E Family Therapy, CMHT North, CMHT South

Carmelite Mental Health Team Carmelite Hse, White Horse La, Maldon, Essex CM9 5FU; Tel 01621 854011; Fax 01621 854012

Cherry Trees Day Unit St. Peter's Hospital, Spital Rd, Maldon, Essex CM9 6EG; Tel 01621 727230; Fax 01621 727231

Maldon Community Mental Health Team Villa II, St. Peter's Hospital, Spital Rd, Maldon, Essex CM9 6EG; Tel 01621 727260; Fax 01621 727261

New Ivy Chimneys Hatfield Rd, Witham, Essex CM8 1EN; Tel 01376 302730; Fax 01376 302731

Old Ivy Chimneys Resource Centre, Hatfield Rd, Witham, Essex CM8 1EN; Tel 01376 302700; Fax 01376 302701

Pitfields 3–4 Pitfields, Baddow Rd, Chelmsford, Essex CM2 9QY; Tel 01245 318530; Fax 01245 318531

Redwoods Day Unit St. John's Hospital, Wood St, Chelmsford, Essex CM2 9BG; Tel 01245 318770; Fax 01245 318771

Adult and Acute Services Area 3

Director Carol Edward; Tel 01206 228600
Service Manager Paul Thomasson
2 Boxted Rd, Colchester, Essex CO4 5HG; Tel 01206 228600
Consultant Psychiatrist (Adult Acute) Dr N. Coxhead
Consultant Psychiatrist (Intensive Therapy) Dr P. Read
Consultant Psychiatrist (Substance Abuse)
Dr A. Baldachhino

Consultant Psychiatrist (Rehabilitation)   Dr R.M. Toms
Consultant Psychiatrist (Psychotherapy)   Dr J.W. Walshe
Consultant Psychiatrist   Dr S. Dowse
Consultant Psychiatrist   Dr C.B. Sarathchandra
Service Manager   Sukhi Khaira

INPATIENT FACILITIES

The Lakes Turner Rd, Colchester, Essex CO4 5JL; Tel 01206 228712; Fax 01206 844182

Peter Bruff Unit Tower Rd, Clacton-on-Sea, Essex CO15 1AH; Tel 01255 253620; Fax 01255 222352

DAY HOSPITALS

Abberton Day Hospital The Lakes, Turner Rd, Colchester, Essex CO4 5JL; Tel 01206 228704

Martello Court Day Hospital Clacton Hospital, Freeland Rd, Clacton-on-Sea, Essex CO15 1LH; Tel 01255 253540

COMMUNITY MENTAL HEALTH CENTRES

The Coach House Trinity St, Halstead, Essex CO9 1JD; Tel 01787 291900

The Gables 17 Bocking End, Braintree, Essex CM7 9AE; Tel 01376 555700

The Graylings 188 High St, Dovercourt, Essex CO12 3AP; Tel 01255 207400

Herrick House East Stockwell St, Colchester, Essex CO1 1ST; Tel 01206 287220

Holmer Court Headgate, Colchester, Essex CO3 3BT; Tel 01206 287270

Mayfield Chambers 93 Station Rd, Clacton-on-Sea, Essex CO15 1TN; Tel 01255 207021

Thoroughgood Road 32 Thoroughgood Rd, Clacton-on-Sea, Essex CO15 6DD; Tel 01255 257000

NEEDAS (NORTH EAST ESSEX DRUG AND ALCOHOL SERVICE)

Herrick Hse, 8 St. Helen's La, Colchester, Essex CO1 1ST; Tel 01206 287250 (Community Alcohol Service); 01206 287251 (Community Drugs Service)

Child and Adolescent Division

654 The Cres, Colchester Bus Pk, Colchester, Essex CO4 4YQ; Tel 01206 287500; Fax 01206 287507
Director   Nicola Colston
Service and Business Manager   Vacancy
Consultant Psychiatrist (Colchester)   Dr A. Bashir
Consultant Psychiatrist (Braintree)   Dr A. Anfield
Consultant Psychiatrist (Maldon)   Dr S. Britten
Consultant Psychiatrist (Loughton)   Dr L. Bailly
Consultant Psychiatrist (Longview, Chelmsford)
    Dr N. Hughes
Consultant Psychiatrist (Chelmsford)   Dr I. Lanman
Consultant Psychiatrist (Clacton-on-Sea)   Dr C. North
Consultant Psychiatrist (Harlow)   Prof H. Zeitlin

INPATIENT FACILITIES

Longview Turner Rd, Colchester, Essex CO4 5JP; Tel 01206 228745; Fax 01206 843702

CHILD AND FAMILY CONSULTATION SERVICES

Harkenwell St. Peter's Hospital, Spital Rd, Maldon, Essex CM9 6EG; Tel 01621 722900; Fax 01621 722919

Rannoch Lodge 146 Broomfield Rd, Chelmsford, Essex CM1 1RN; Tel 01245 544869; Fax 01245 544888

Stanwell House Stanwell St, Colchester, Essex CO2 7DL; Tel 01206 287321; Fax 01206 287320

West Avenue 25 West Ave, Clacton-on-Sea, Essex CO15 1JP; Tel 01255 207070; Fax 01255 207088

Whitehills Road Loughton, Essex IG10 1TS; Tel 020 876 4100; Fax 020 8876 4106

White Lodge 21 Coggeshall Rd, Braintree, Essex CM7 6DB; Tel 01376 302800; Fax 01376 302808

Wych Elm House Hamstel Rd, Harlow, Essex; Tel 01279 692300; Fax 01279 692323

DAY HOSPITALS

Defoe Day Hospital The King's Wood Centre, Colchester, Essex; Tel 01206 228928

Freeland Court Day Hospital The Landermere Centre, Clacton-on-Sea, Essex; Tel 01255 253601

Harwich Day Hospital 419 Main Rd, Dovercourt, Harwich, Essex CO12 4EX; Tel 01255 207400

The Mayfield Centre Station Rd, Clacton-on-Sea, Essex CO15 1TN; Tel 01255 207040

The Northgate Centre North Station Rd, Colchester, Essex CO1 1RB; Tel 01206 287340

COMMUNITY MENTAL HEALTH TEAMS

Graylings 190 High St, Dovercourt, Harwich, Essex CO12 3AP; Tel 01255 207400

Mental Health Administration Clacton Hospital, Tower Rd, Clacton-on-Sea, Essex CO15 1LH

The Crescent 654 The Crescent, Colchester Bus Pk, Colchester, Essex CO4 4YQ; Tel 01206 287590; Fax 01206 287599

INPATIENT FACILITIES

Colchester Rehabilitation Centre 439 Ipswich Rd, Colchester, Essex CO4 4HF; Tel 01206 854290

Eaglehurst Assessment Centre 6 Valley Rd, Clacton-on-Sea, Essex CO15 4AR; Tel 01255 257050

1 Glen Avenue Colchester, Essex CO3 3RP; Tel 01206 287360

Severalls House 2 Boxted Rd, Colchester, Essex CO4 5HG; Tel 01206 228630

Willow House 2 Boxted Rd, Colchester, Essex CO4 5HG; Tel 01206 228649; Fax 01206 228644

EMPLOYMENT PROJECT

Work On Units B4 and B7, Cowdray Centre, Colchester, Essex CO1 1BL; Tel 01206 287310; Fax 01206 570036

North Hampshire Hospitals NHS Trust

The North Hampshire Hospital, Aldermaston Rd, Basingstoke, Hampshire RG24 9NA; Tel 01256 473202; Fax 01256 313098
Chair   C. Davies
Chief Executive   M. Davies

HOSPITALS

Lord Mayor Treloar Hospital Chawton Park Rd, Alton, Hampshire GU34 1RJ; Tel 01420 82811
    Specialism: Outpatient

North Hampshire Hospital Basingstoke, Hampshire RG24 9NA; Tel 01256 473202; Fax 01256 313098
    Specialism: Acute (450)

Erdesley House Cliddesden Rd, Basingstoke, Hampshire RG21 3ER; Tel 01256 328864

12

North Hampshire, Lodden Community NHS Trust

North Hampshire, Loddon Community NHS Trust was dissolved in March 2001 and its services split between North Hampshire Hospitals NHS Trust, Surrey Hampshire Borders NHS Trust and North Hampshire Primary Care Trust. All three are listed under the appropriate headings in this chapter.

North Lakeland Healthcare NHS Trust

North Lakeland Healthcare NHS Trust is now part of North Cumbria Mental Health and Learning Disabilities NHS Trust, which is listed alphabetically in this section.

North Manchester Healthcare NHS Trust

North Manchester Healthcare NHS Trust is now part of The Pennine Acute Hospitals NHS Trust, which is listed alphabetically in this section.

North Middlesex University Hospital NHS Trust

Sterling Way, London N18 1QX; Tel 020 8887 2000; Fax 020 8887 4219
Chair C. Lawton
Chief Executive R. Gibb
Medical Director Dr Y. Drabu
Director (Nursing and Patient Services) B. Beal
Director (Operations) D. Hackett
Director (Finance) T. Travers
Head (Human Resources) C. Carvey
Annual budget
£74 million

North Sefton and West Lancashire Community NHS Trust

In March 2002 North Sefton and West Lancashire Community NHS Trust dissolved and its services have now split across into West Lancashire Primary Care Trust, Lancashire Care NHS Trust and Mersey Care NHS Trust which are listed alphabetically in this chapter.

North Staffordshire Combined Healthcare NHS Trust

Bucknall Hospital, Eaves La, Stoke-on-Trent ST2 8LD; URL www.nsch-tr.wmids.nhs.uk; Tel 01782 273510; Fax 01782 275116
Chair Dr E. Slade
Chief Executive Dr C. Buttanshaw
Medical Director Dr R. Bloor
Executive Director (Clinical Governance and Nursing) David Pearson
Director (Operations) Kirk MacKenzie
Director (Finance) D. Edwards

HOSPITALS

Bucknall Hospital Eaves La, Bucknall, Stoke-on-Trent ST2 8LD; Tel 01782 273510
Specialism: Elderly care (96)
City General Hospital 578 Newcastle Rd, Stoke-on-Trent ST4 6RG; Tel 01782 715444
Specialism: Acute; elderly.
Harplands Hospital Hilton Rd, Stoke-on-Trent ST4 6RR; Tel 01782 441600
Specialism: Mental health (306)
Haywood Hospital High La, Burslem, Stoke-on-Trent ST6 7AG; Tel 01782 835721
Specialism: Neuro-behavioural science unit (12)

MENTAL HEALTH SERVICES

Ashcombe Centre 25–26 Wall La Terr, Cheddleton, Staffordshire ST13 7ED; Tel 01538 481200
Brandon Centre Cheadle Hospital, Royal Wlk, Cheadle, Stoke-on-Trent ST10 1NS; Tel 01538 487543
Bennett Centre Richmond Terr, Shelton, Stoke-on-Trent ST1 4ND; Tel 01762 425170
Clydesdale Centre 167 Queens Rd, Penkhull, Stoke-on-Trent ST4 7LF; Tel 01782 427650
Greenfield Centre Furlong Rd, Tunstall, Stoke-on-Trent ST6 5UD; Tel 01782 425740
Lymebrook Centre Bradwell Hospital, Talke Rd, Chesterton, Newcastle-under-Lyme, Staffordshire ST5 7TL; Tel 01782 425350
Sutherland Centre Belgrave Rd, Dresden, Stoke-on-Trent ST3 4PN; Tel 01782 425560

North Staffordshire Hospital NHS Trust

Trust Headquarters, Royal Infirmary, Stoke-on-Trent ST4 7LN; Tel 01782 715444; Fax 01782 555202
Chair C.R. Paton
Chief Executive S. Eames
Medical Director Dr P. Chipping
Director (Nursing Operations) P. Blythin
Director (Corporate Services) A.R. Underwood
Director (Finance) D. Crowley
Annual budget
£200 million

North Tees and Hartlepool NHS Trust

University Hospital of Hartlepool, Holdforth Rd, Hartlepool TS24 9AH; Tel 01429 266654; Fax 01429 235389
Chair Bryan Hanson, OBE, DL
Chief Executive Joan E. Rogers, BA, PhD
Medical Director Dr Peter Royle
Medical Director (North Tees) Dr Andrew Tanner, MD, DM, FRCP
Director (Finance) Stan Irwin, BSc, ACMA
Director (Acute Services, Development and Planning) Julian Hartley
Director (Community Services Development) Aidan Mullan, RGN, MBA, DMS, MHSH
Director (Human Resources and Operational Services) David Allsopp, ACIS, ACMA, MBA
Clinical Director (Accident and Emergency Medicine) Mr D. Emerton
Clinical Director (Obstetrics and Gynaecology – North Tees) Dr E.A. Ryall
Clinical Director (Surgery) Prof McLatchie
Clincial Director (Anaesthetics – North Tees) Dr Peter Broadway
Clinical Director (Medicine and Elderly Care – North Tees) Dr Andrew Tanner
Clinical Director (Children's Services) Dr K. Agrawal
Clinical Director (Orthopaedics) C. Lennox
Clinical Director (Pathology) Dr M. Noone
Clinical Director (Radiology – North Tees) Dr Peter Gill
Annual budget
£128 million

HOSPITALS/UNITS

Peterlee Community Hospital O'Neill Dr, North Blunts, Peterlee, County Durham SR8 5TZ; Tel 0191 586 3474; Fax 0191 586 6562
University Hospital of Hartlepool Holdforth Rd, Hartlepool TS27 9AH; Tel 01429 266654; Fax 01429 235389
University Hospital of North Tees Hardwick, Stockton-on-Tees TS19 8PE; Tel 01642 617617; Fax 01642 623089

North West London Hospitals NHS Trust

Northwick Park Hospital, Watford Rd, Harrow, Greater
London HA1 3UJ; URL www.nwlh.nhs.uk; Tel 020 8864
3232; Fax 020 8869 2009
Chair   Alastair McDonald
Chief Executive   John Pope, CBE
Medical Director   Dr John Riordan, OBE
Director (Nursing)   Sir Graham Morgan
Director (Finance and Information)   Don Richards
Director (Organisational Development)   Helen Rushworth
Director (Corporate and Support Services)   Philip Sutcliffe

HOSPITALS

Central Middlesex Hospital   Acton La, Park Royal, London
NW10 7NS; Tel 020 8965 5733

OTHER CENTRES

The ACAD Centre   Central Middlesex Hospital, Acton La,
Park Royal, London NW10 7NS; Tel 020 8963 8857; Fax 020
8963 8938

Edgeware Urgent Treatment Centre (UTC)   Edgeware
Hospital, Burnt Oak Broadway, Edgeware, London
HA8 0AD; Tel 020 8952 2381; Fax 020 8732 6807

Sickle Central   Brent Sickle Cell and Thalassaenia Centre,
122 High Str, Harlesden, London NW10 4SP;
URL www.sickle-thalassaemia.org; Tel 020 8961 9005;
Fax 020 8453 0681

Wembley Minor Accident Treatment Service (MATS)
Wembley Centre for Health and Care, 116 Chaplin Rd,
Wembley, London HA0 4UX; Tel 020 8903 1323; Fax 020
8962 4051

Willesden Community Hospital   Harlesden Rd, London
NW10 3RY; Tel 020 8451 8017; Fax 020 8451 8030

North West Surrey Mental Health NHS Partnership Trust

Abraham Cowley Unit, Holloway Hill, Lyne, Chertsey,
Surrey KT16 0AE; Tel 01932 872010; Fax 01932 875128
Chief Executive   Lorraine Reid

HOSPITAL

Ashford Hospital   London Rd, Ashford, Surrey TW15 3AA;
Tel 01784 884488; Fax 01784 884017

Northampton General Hospital NHS Trust

Cliftonville, Northampton, Northamptonshire NN1 5BD;
Tel 01604 634700
Chair   Bronwen Curtis
Chief Executive   David Wilson
Medical Director   Dr S. Shribman
Director (Patient, Human Resource and Nursing Services)
J. Rumsey
Director (Finance)   R. Egginton

HOSPITAL

Northampton General Hospital   Cliftonville, Northampton,
Northamptonshire NN1 5BD; Tel 01604 634700
Specialism: Acute. Number of beds: (700)

Northamptonshire Healthcare NHS Trust

Trust Headquarters, York Hse, Isebrook Hospital,
Irthlingborough Rd, Wellingborough, Northamptonshire
NN8 1LP; Tel 01933 440099
Chair   Andrew Scarborough
Vice-Chair   Prof John Knibbs
Chief Executive   Ron Shields
Medical Director   Dr Alex O'Neill-Kerr

Director (Mental Health Services) and Joint Director (Nursing)
Angela Muchatuta
*Director (Learning Disability Services) and Joint Director
(Nursing)*   Greg Steele
Director (Finance)   Bill McFarland
Director (Human Resources)   David Murphy
Clinical Director (Learning Disabilities)   Dr Harnek Masih
Clinical Director (Child and Adolescent Mental Health)
Dr James Pease
Clinical Director (Psychotherapy)   Dr Julie Roberts
Clinical Director (Sexual Health, Drug and Alcohol)
Dr Paul Loo
Clinical Director (Adult Mental Health)   Dr Suheib Abu-
Kmeil
Clinical Director (Elderly Mental Health)   Dr Ram Mudaliar

HOSPITALS

Pendered Centre   Berrywood Rd, Duston,
Northamptonshire; Tel 01604 752323

Princess Marina Hospital   Weedon Rd, Northampton,
Northamptonshire NN5 6UH; Tel 01604 752323

Rushden Hospital   Wymington Rd, Rushden,
Northamptonshire NN10 9JS; Tel 01933 440666

St. Mary's Hospital   London Rd, Kettering,
Northamptonshire NN15 7PW; Tel 01536 410141
Specialism: Elderly; EMI; continuing care; AMI.

Northern Birmingham Mental Health NHS Trust

71 Fentham Rd, Erdington, Birmingham, West Midlands
B23 6AL; Tel 0121 623 5500; Fax 0121 623 5770
Chair   J. Mackay
Chief Executive   J. Mahoney
Medical Director   Prof S. Sashidharan
Director (Finance)   D. Kitchen
Director (Operations)   J. Jenkins
Director (Planning and Service Development)   P. Rooney
Director (Nursing Practice)   E. Mackle

Northern Devon Healthcare NHS Trust

North Devon District Hospital, Raleigh Pk, Litchdon St,
Barnstaple, Devon EX31 4JB; Tel 01271 322577; Fax 01271
311541
Chair   R. Day
Chief Executive   John Rom
Medical Director   E. Claydon
Director (Nursing)   R. Brunt
Munro Hse, North Devon District Hospital, Barnstaple,
Devon EX31 4JB; Tel 01271 311606; Fax 01271 311605
Director (Finance)   M. Sheldon
Director (Personnel)   N. Ring
Head (Facilities)   I. Roy
Annual budget
£59 million

HOSPITALS

Bideford and Torridgeside Hospital   Abbotsham Rd,
Bideford, Devon EX39 3AG; Tel 01237 472692
Specialism: GP; acute; care of elderly; EMI (68)

Holsworthy Community Hospital   Dobles La, Holsworthy,
Devon EX22 6JG; Tel 01409 253424
Specialism: GP; EMI; elderly (28)

Ilfracombe and District Tyrrell Hospital   St Brannock's Pk
Rd, Ilfracombe, Devon EX34 8JP; Tel 01271 863448
Specialism: GP; acute. Number of beds: (14)

Lynton and District Cottage Hospital   Lee Rd, Lynton, Devon
EX33 6BP; Tel 01598 753310
Number of beds: GP; elderly (15)

North Devon District Hospital   Raleigh Pk, Barnstaple,
Devon EX31 4JB; Tel 01271 322577
Specialism: Acute. Number of beds: (445)

12

South Molton Community Hospital Widgery Dr, South Molton, Devon EX36 4DR; Tel 01769 572164
Number of beds: GP; acute; elderly (28)

Torrington Cottage Hospital Calf St, Great Torrington, Devon EX38 7BJ; Tel 01805 622208
Number of beds: GP; acute; elderly (14)

Northern Lincolnshire and Goole Hospitals NHS Trust

Diana Princess of Wales Hospital, Scartho Rd, Grimsby, North East Lincolnshire URL www.nlg.nhs.uk; Tel 01472 874111; Fax 01472 276234
Chair A. Brooks
Chief Executive A.K. North
Medical Director Dr T. Hill
Director (Nursing and Service Development) P. Flood
Director (Information and Patient Services) G. Stonham
Director (Finance and Performance Mangement) K. Turner
Annual budget
£149.9 million

CHILD DEVELOPMENT CENTRE

Diana Princess of Wales Hospital, Scartho Rd, Grimsby, North East Lincolnshire DN33 2BA;
URL www.nlg.nhs.uk; E-mail enquiries@nlg.nhs.uk;
Tel 01472 874111

CHILD ASSESSMENT CENTRE

Handicapped Children's Centre Diana Princess of Wales Hospital, Scartho Rd, Grimsby, North East Lincolnshire DN33 2BA; Tel 01472 874111
Contact Dr B. Reynolds

HOSPITALS

Diana Princess of Wales Hospital Scartho Rd, Grimsby, North East Lincolnshire DN33 2BA; URL www.nlg.nhs.uk; E-mail enquiries@nlg.nhs.uk; Tel 01472 874111
Specialism: Mainly acute (597)

Goole and District Hospital Woodland Ave, Goole, East Riding of Yorkshire BN14 6RX; Tel 01405 720 720

Grimsby Maternity Hospital Grimsby, North East Lincolnshire; Tel 01472 874111
Number of beds: 99 including cots

Scunthorpe General Hospital Cliff Gdns, Scunthorpe, North Lincolnshire DN15 7BH; Tel 01724 282282

Northgate and Prudhoe NHS Trust

Northgate Hospital, Morpeth, Northumberland NE61 3BP; Tel 01670 394000; Fax 01670 394002; (Consultant) 01670 394004; (Secure) 01670 394003
Chair Vacancy
Chief Executive Linda Ions
Medical Director Dr A.F. Perini
Director (Nursing) M. Allen
Director (Finance and Performance Management) J. Duncan
Director (Development) P. Davies

HOSPITAL

Prudhoe Hospital Prudhoe, Northumberland NE42 5NT; Tel 01670 394000; Fax 01670 514590

Northumbria Health Care NHS Trust

North Tyneside General Hospital, Rake La, North Shields, Tyne and Wear NE29 8NH
Chief Executive S. Page
Deputy Chief Executive L. Morgan

Medical Director I. Cobden
Medical Director M. Wearer
Medical Director G. Fraser
Director (Nursing) R. Stephenson
Chief Operating Officer J. Mackey

HOSPITALS

Alnwick Infirmary (including Hillcrest Maternity Unit) Alnwick, Northumberland NE66 2NS; Tel 01665 626700
Number of beds: (68)

Ashington Hospital West View, Ashington, Northumberland NE63 0SA; Tel 01670 521212

Berwick Infirmary (including Berwick Maternity Unit) Berwick-upon-Tweed, Northumberland TD15 1LT; Tel 01289 307484
Number of beds: (86)

Blyth Community Hospital Thoroton St, Blyth, Northumberland NE24 1DX; Tel 01670 396400
Number of beds: (78)

Coquetdale Cottage Hospital Rothbury, Northumberland NE65 7TT; Tel 01669 620555
Number of beds: (17)

Haltwhistle War Memorial Hospital Haltwhistle, Northumberland NE49 9AJ; Tel 01434 320225
Number of beds: (19)

Morpeth Cottage Hospital South Rd, Morpeth, Northumberland NE61 2BT; Tel 01670 395600
Number of beds: (86)

North Tyneside General Hospital Rake La, North Shields, Tyne and Wear NE29 8NH; Tel 0191 259 6660
Number of beds: (450)

Tynemouth Court EMI Nursing Home Hawkey's La, North Shields, Tyne and Wear NE29 0SF; Tel 0191 259 6660
Number of beds: (48)

Wansbeck General Hospital Woodhorn La, Ashington, Northumberland NE63 9JJ; Tel 01670 521212; Fax 01670 529927
Number of beds: (400)

Nottingham City Hospital NHS Trust

Nottingham City Hospital, Hucknall Rd, Nottingham NG5 1PB; Tel 0115 969 1169; Fax 0115 962 7788
Chair Mrs C. Bowering
Chief Executive G. McSorley
Medical Director Dr A. Morgan
Director (Service Improvement, Planning and Nursing) Miss J. Leggott
Director (Human Resources) Mrs G. Hemus
Director (Finance) Mr T. Woods
Director (Facilities and Nutrition) Mrs C. Goldstraw
Director (ICT) Mr A. Fearn

Nottinghamshire Healthcare NHS Trust

Trust Headquarters, Southwell Rd West, Mansfield, Nottinghamshire NG18 4HH; Tel 01623 784821; Fax 01623 784819
Chair Prof Brian Edwards
Chief Executive Jeremy Taylor
Medical Director Dr Richard Turner
Nottinghamshire Area Director (Integrated Services Network) Granville Daniels
Nottingham Area Director (Integrated Servcies Network) Helen Scott
Director (Forensic Services) Dr Mike Harris
Director (Personnel Organisational Learning and Communications) Jacolyn Fergusson
Director (Finance and Performance Review) Kevin Howells
Annual budget
£154 million

HOSPITALS

Forensic Services Rampton Hospital, Retford, Nottinghamshire DN22 0PD; Tel 01777 248321; Fax 01777 248442

Integrated Services Network Area (Nottinghamshire) Forest Hse, Southwell Rd, Mansfield, Nottinghamshire NG18 4HH; Tel 01623 784931; Fax 01623 634126

Integrated Services Network Area (Nottingham) Duncan Macmillan Hse, Porchester Rd, Nottingham, Nottinghamshire NG3 6AA; Tel 0115 969 1300; Fax 0115 952 9479

Queens Medical Centre Nottingham, Nottinghamshire NG7 2UH; Tel 0115 924 9924; Fax 0115 970 9196

Nuffield Orthopaedic Centre NHS Trust

Windmill Rd, Headington, Oxford, Oxfordshire OX3 7LD; Tel 01865 741155; Fax 01865 742348
Chair   Joanna Foster, CBE
Chief Executive   Ed Macalister-Smith
Director   Steve Bolam (Acting)
Director (Medical Affairs)   Prof J. Templeton
Executive Nurse Director   Jan Fowler
Nuffield Professor of Orthopaedic Surgery   Prof A. Carr
Annual budget
£44 million

HOSPITAL

Nuffield Orthopaedic Centre Oxford, Oxfordshire URL www.noc.org.uk; Tel 01865 741155
Number of beds: (170)

Oldham NHS Trust

Oldham NHS Trust is now part of The Pennine Acute Hospitals NHS Trust, which is listed alphabetically in this section.

The Oxford Radcliffe Hospitals NHS Trust

John Radcliffe Hospital, Headley Way, Oxford, Oxfordshire OX3 9DU; Tel 01865 741166; Fax 01865 741408
Chair   Neil Ashley
Chief Executive   David Highton
Medical Director   Dr James Moms
Director (Financial)   Chris Hurst
Chief Nurse   Julie Hartley-Jones

HOSPITALS

The Churchill Headington, Oxford, Oxfordshire OX3 7LD; Tel 01865 741841
Specialism: Acute (368)

Horton Hospital Horton General Hospital, Oxford Rd, Banbury, Oxfordshire OX16 9AL; Tel 01295 275500; (Hospital) 01295 229055

The John Radcliffe Hospital Headley Way, Oxford, Oxfordshire OX3 9DU; Tel 01865 741166
Specialism: Acute; maternity; geriatric. Number of beds: (782)

Oxfordshire Ambulance NHS Trust

Churchill Dr, Old Rd, Oxford, Oxfordshire OX3 7LH; Tel 01865 740100; Fax 01865 741974
Chair   John Goddard
Chief Executive   J. Nichols, BSc, ABPI
Director (Operations)   D. Jolly
Director (Finance)   N. Dolden, BA, IPFA
Director (Personnel and Governance)   Melanie Barber

Oxfordshire Learning Disability NHS Trust

Slade Hse, Horspath Driftway, Headington, Oxfordshire OX3 7JH; URL www.oldt.org.uk; Tel 01865 747455; Fax 01865 228182
Chair   H. Baker
Chief Executive   Y. Cox
Medical Director   Dr J. Morgan
Director (Nursing)   J. Turnbull
Director (Human Resources)   R. Cadvan-Jones
Director (Finance)   J. Derham
Director (Supported Lifestyles)   C. Andrews
Annual budget
£24 million approx.

Oxfordshire Mental Healthcare NHS Trust

The Warneford Hospital, Warneford La, Headington, Oxford, Oxfordshire OX3 7JX; Tel 01865 778911; Fax 01865 226507
Chair   Tony Purkis
Chief Executive   Julie Waldron
Medical Director   Mike Hobbs
Director (Nursing and Practice Development)   Jon Allen
Director (Finance, Information and Facilities)   Duncan Smith
Director (Operations)   Ian Brennan
Service Director (South)   Elizabeth Sheppard
Service Director (North)   Eddie McLaughlin
Service Director (City)   Sam Holmes

HOSPITALS

Abingdon Mental Health Centre Community Hospital Site, Marcham Rd, Abingdon, Oxfordshire OX14 1AG; Tel 01235 555204; Fax 01235 523091
Specialism: Community service; general psychiatry; elderly mental health.

Department of Psychological Medicine (Barnes Unit) John Radcliffe Hospital, Headington, Oxford, Oxfordshire OX3 9DU; Tel 01865 220379; Fax 01865 220373
Specialism: Liaison psychiatry.

Orchard Lodge Orchard Lodge, Warwick Rd, Banbury, Oxfordshire OX16 2AQ; Tel 01295 819020; Fax 01295 819023
Specialism: General psychiatry.

Fiennes Centre Hightown Rd, Banbury, Oxfordshire OX16 9BF; Tel 01295 229301; Fax 01295 229110
Specialism: Community service; elderly mental health.

The Fulbrook Centre Churchill Hospital Site, Old Rd, Oxford, Oxfordshire OX3 7JU; Tel 01865 223800; Fax 01865 223853
Specialism: Elderly mental health.

The Highfield Adolescent Unit The Warneford Hospital, Warneford La, Headington, Oxford, Oxfordshire OX3 7JX; Tel 01865 226280; Fax 08165 226381
Specialism: Adolescent psychiatry.

Littlemore Mental Health Centre Sandford Rd, Littlemore, Oxford, Oxfordshire OX4 4XN; Tel 01865 778911; Fax 01865 223078
Specialism: General psychiatry.

The Manzil Resource Centre Manzil Way, Oxford, Oxfordshire OX1 1XE; Tel 01865 721292; Fax 01865 204370

Moorview 2–8 Moorland Rd, Witney, Oxfordshire OX8 5LF; Tel 01993 773707; Fax 01993 700554
Specialism: Community service; elderly mental health.

Oxford Clinic Littlemore Mental Health Centre, 33 Sandford Rd, Oxford, Oxfordshire OX4 4XN; Tel 01865 778911; Fax 01865 223287
Specialism: Forensic psychiatry

The Park Hospital for Children Old Rd, Headington, Oxford, Oxfordshire OX3 7LQ; Tel 01865 226276; Fax 01865 226351
Specialism: Child psychiatry; childhood epilepsy. Number of beds: (34)

12

The Warneford Hospital Headington, Oxford, Oxfordshire
OX3 7JX; Tel 01865 741717; Fax 01865 226507
    Specialism: General psychiatry; elderly mental health.
    Number of beds: (105)

Oxleas NHS Trust

Pinewood Hse, Old Bexley La, Bexley, Kent DA5 2BF;
    URL www.nhs.uk; Tel 01322 526282; Fax 01322 555491
Chief Executive   Andrew Casey
Provision of mental health and learning disability services.
Staff based at approximately 60 locations throughout
Bexley, Bromley and Greenwich. Forensic mental health
services also provided to Lewisham and North Southwark.

Papworth Hospital NHS Trust

Papworth Everard, Cambridge, Cambridgeshire CB3 8RE;
    URL www.papworth-hospital.org.uk; Tel 01480 830541;
    Fax 01480 831315
Chair   Dr A. Stenner
Chief Executive   S. Bridge
Medical Director   J. Wallwork
Director (Nursing and Quality)   E. Kemp
Director (Corporate Development)   G. Jagger
Director (Transplant Services)   J. Wallwork
Director (Research and Development)   N. Caine
Director (Cardiac Services)   Dr P. Schofield
Director (Thoracic Services)   D. Bilton
Clinical Tutor   Dr J. Kneeshaw
Director (Finance)   S. Donaldson
Annual budget
£47 million

Pennine Acute Hospitals NHS Trust

Headquarters, Westhulme Ave, Oldham, OL1 2PN; Tel 0161
    624 0420; Fax 0161 637 3130
Chair   Steven Price
Chief Executive   Chris Appleby
Medical Director   Dr Roger Glen
Director (Finance)   Bob Chadwick
Director (Nursing)   A. Abbott
Director (Modernisation and Performance)   Karen James
Director (Human Resources)   Roy Tyndall
Director (Facilities)   John Wilkes

HOSPITALS

Pennine Acute (Bury) Fairfeild General Hospital, Rochdale
Old Rd, Bury, Greater Manchester BL9 7TD
Pennine Acute (North Manchester) North Manchester
General Hospital, Delaunays Rd, Manchester M8 5RB
Pennine Acute (Oldham) Royal Oldham Hospital, Rochdale
Rd, Oldham, Greater Manchester OL1 2JH
Pennine Acute (Rochdale) Rochdale Infirmary, Whitehall
St, Rochdale, Greater Manchester OL12 ONB

Pennine Care NHS Trust

Trust Headquarters, Tameside General Hospital, Fountain
    St, Ashton-under-Lyne, Lancashire OL6 9RW;
    E-mail chris.round@penninecare.nhs.uk; Tel 0161 331
    5151; Fax 0161 331 5007
Chief Executive   John Archer

Peterborough Hospitals NHS Trust

Edith Cavell Hospital, Bretton Gate, Peterborough
    PE3 9GZ; Tel 01733 874000; Fax 01733 874001
Chair   C. Morton
Chief Executive   C. Banks
Medical Director   A. Turner
Director (Nursing)   C. Wilkinson
Director (Human Resources)   C. Tolond
Director (Finance)   C. Hall

Director (Organisational Development)   W. Stevenson
Manager (Estates)   G. McIntyre
Chief Pharmacist   V. Shaw
Manager (Supplies)   T. Granger
General Manager (Medical; Woman and Child)   J. Tiplady
General Manager (Surgery)   A. Stone
General Manager (Clinical and Life Support Services Unit)
    D. Sheppard
Annual budget
£78 million

CHILDREN'S SERVICES

Peterborough District Hospital Thorpe Rd, Peterborough
PE3 6DA; Tel 01733 874000
Consultant Paediatrician   Dr S. Tuck

HOSPITALS

Edith Cavell Hospital Bretton Gate, Peterborough PE3 9GZ;
Tel 01733 874000; Fax 01733 874001
    Number of beds: (195)
Peterborough District Hospital Thorpe Rd, Peterborough
PE3 6DA; Tel 01733 874000
    Number of beds: Acute (392)
Peterborough Maternity Unit Alderman's Dr, Peterborough
PE3 6BP; Tel 01733 874000
    Number of beds: (91)

Pinderfields and Pontefract Hospitals NHS Trust

Pinderfields and Pontefract Hospitals NHS Trust has
merged with Dewsbury Health Care NHS Trust to become
part of Mid Yorkshire Hospitals NHS Trust, which is listed
alphabetically in this section.

Plymouth Hospitals NHS Trust

Derriford Hospital, Derriford Rd, Plymouth, Devon
    PL6 8DH; URL www.plymouthhospitals.org.uk;
    E-mail contact@phnt.swent.nhs.uk; Tel 01752 777111;
    Fax 01752 768976
Chair   Prof John Bull, CBE
Chief Executive   P.D. Roberts
Medical Director   T. Lewis
Director (Nursing and Operations)   P. Greenidge
*Manager (Corporate Business)/Head (Patient, Public and
    Corporate Business)* Graham Sykes
Director (Financing and Contracting)   Chris Hoult
Annual budget
£158 million

HOSPITALS

Derriford Hospital Derriford Rd, Crownhill, Plymouth
PL6 8DH; Tel 01752 777111
    Specialism: Acute; geriatric; radiotherapy; cardial
    surgery; renal unit; plastic; neuro surgery (including
    Royal Navy unit). Number of beds: (975)
Mount Gould Hospital Mount Gould Rd, Plymouth
PL4 7QD; Tel 01752 268011
    Specialism: Child and adolescent; psychiatry.
Royal Eye Infirmary Apsley Rd, Plymouth PL4 6PL;
Tel 01752 662078
    Specialism: Ophthalmology Number of beds: (21)
Scott Hospital Beacon Park Rd, Plymouth PL2 2PQ;
Tel 01752 550741
    Specialism: Child development.

Poole Hospitals NHS Trust

Longfleet Rd, Poole, Dorset BH15 2JB;
    URL www.poolehos.org; Tel 01202 665511; Fax 01202
    442562
Chair   P. Harvey

Chief Executive   L. Adams
Medical Director   Dr R. Packham
Director (Nursing)   M. Smits
Director (Finance and Information)   G. Pugh
Director (Human Resources)   C. McCarthy
Director (Service Development)   M. Beswick
Annual budget
£110 million

CHILD DEVELOPMENT CENTRE

Child Development Centre Poole Hospital, Longfleet Rd,
Poole BH15 2JB; Tel 01202 665511
Consultant Paediatrician   Dr M. Black

Portsmouth Hospitals NHS Trust

De La Court Hse, Queen Alexandra Hospital, Southwick
Hill Rd, Cosham, Portsmouth PO6 3LY;
URL www.portshosp.org.uk; Tel 023 9228 6000; Fax 023
9286 6073
Chair   M. Waterland
Chief Executive   A. Bedford
Medical Director   G. Zaki
Director (Nursing)   U. Ward
Director (Planning)   S. Robson
Director (Finance)   W. Shields
Director (Human Resources and Organisational Development)
D. Eccles
Director (Operations)   S. Payler

HOSPITALS

Blackbrook Maternity Home Blackbrook Hse, Fareham,
Hampshire PO14 1PA; Tel 01329 232275
Number of beds: (22)

Blake Maternity Home Elson, Gosport, Hampshire
PO12 4AW; Tel 023 9252 3651
Number of beds: (20)

Queen Alexandra Hospital Cosham, Portsmouth PO6 3LY;
Tel 023 9228 6000
Number of beds: Mainly acute (670)

Royal Hospital Haslar Gosport, Hampshire PO12 2AA;
Tel 02392 584255
Number of beds: (150)

Saint Mary's Hospital Milton Rd, Portsmouth PO3 6AD;
Tel 023 9228 6000
Number of beds: Acute (492)

Preston Acute Hospitals NHS Trust

Preston Acute Hopsitals NHS Trust has now merged with
Chorley and South Ribble NHS Trust to form Lancashire
Teaching Hospitals NHS Trust, which is listed
alphabetically in this section.

The Princess Royal Hospital NHS Trust

The Princess Royal Hospital, Apley Castle, Telford, Wrekin
TF1 6TF; Tel 01952 641222; Fax 01952 242817
Chair   Phil Homer
Chief Executive   Neil Taylor
Medical Director   Dr David Christmas
Director (Nursing)   Trish Mason
Director (Finance)   Peter Jones
Annual budget
£51 million

Queen Elizabeth Hospital NHS Trust

Stadium Rd, Woolwich, London SE18 4QH;
URL www.qehospital.com; Tel 020 8836 6000
Chair   C. Campbell
Chief Executive   A.G. Perkins

HOSPITALS

Queen Elizabeth Hospital Stadium Rd, Woolwich, London
SE18 4QH; URL www.qehospital.com; Tel 020 8836 6000
Specialism: Acute. Number of beds: (477)

Queen Mary's Sidcup NHS Trust

Queen Mary Hospital, Sidcup, Kent DA14 6LT; Tel 020 8302
2678
Chair   Colin Campbell
Chief Executive   Helen Moffatt
Medical Director   Dr David Black
Director (Nursing)   Andrew MacCallum
Director (Personnel)   Mike Sillitoe
Director (Operations)   Jan McColl
Director (Finance and Information)   Sheila Wilkinson
Annual budget (2000/2001)
£63 million

Queen Victoria Hospital NHS Trust

The Queen Victoria Hospital NHS Trust, Holtye Rd, East
Grinstead, West Sussex RH19 3DZ;
URL www.queenvic.demon.co.uk;
E-mail queenvic@queenvic.demon.co.uk; Tel 01342
414000; Fax 01342 414414
Chair   G. Martin
Chief Executive   J.E. Bergman
Medical Director   T. Martin
Director (Finance)   S. Flint

Queen's Medical Centre, Nottingham University Hospital NHS Trust

Nottingham University Hospital, Derby Rd, Nottingham,
Nottinghamshire NG7 2UH; URL www.qmc.nhs.uk;
E-mail kathy.kirkwood@mail.qmcuh-tr.trent.nhs.uk;
Tel 0115 924 9924; Fax 0115 970 9196
Chief Executive   John MacDonald

Sandringham House Castle Crts, Salford, Greater
Manchester; Tel 0161 212 4000

Riverside Community Health Care NHS Trust

Riverside Community Health Care NHS Trust has now
become Hammersmith and Fulham Primary Care Trust,
which is listed alphabetically under the Primary Care Trust
section in this chapter.

Robert Jones and Agnes Hunt Orthopaedic and District Hospital NHS Trust

Oswestry, Shropshire SY10 7AG; Tel 01691 404000;
Fax 01691 404050
Chair   M. Bolderston
Chief Executive   J. Daniel
Medical Director   Dr J. Dixey
Director (Finance)   A. Robinson
Director (Nursing)   S. Byrom

Rochdale Healthcare NHS Trust

Rochdale Healthcare NHS Trust is now part of The Pennine
Acute Hospitals NHS Trust, which is listed alphabetically
in this section.

Rotherham General Hospitals NHS Trust

Moorgate Rd, Rotherham, South Yorkshire S60 2UD;
Tel 01709 820000; Fax 01709 824200
Chair   Margaret Oldfield
Chief Executive   P.E. Nesbitt
Medical Director   Dr W.A. Wali

12

Director (Finance) D. Brown
Director (Nursing) M. Pickup
Director (Corporate Services) J. Wilson
Annual budget
£102 million

HOSPITALS

Barnsley District General Hospital Gawber Rd, Barnsley, South Yorkshire S75 2EP

Rotherham District General Moorgate Rd, Rotherham, South Yorkshire S60 2UD; Tel 01709 820000
Specialism: Acute (850)

Rotherham Priority Health Services NHS Trust

Rotherham Priority Health Services NHS Trust has now become Rotherham Primary Care Trust, which is listed alphabetically under the Primary Care Trust section in this chapter.

Royal Berkshire Ambulance Service NHS Trust

44 Finchampstead Rd, Wokingham RG40 2NN; Tel 0118 936 5500; Fax 0118 977 3923
Chair K. Kerr
Chief Executive K. Nuttall
Director (Human Resources) H. Chapman
Director (Emergency Services) D. Dunning
Director (Finance and Business) J. Cheung
Annual budget
£15.4 million

Royal Berkshire and Battle Hospitals NHS Trust

Royal Berkshire Hospital, London Rd, Reading, Berkshire RG1 5AN; Tel 0118 987 5111; Fax 0118 987 8042
Chair Colin Maclean, OBE
Chief Executive Mark Gritten, MBE
Medical Director Dr Rachel Hall
Director (Nursing Services) Ann Sheen, OBE
Director (Finance) Clive Field (Acting)
Annual budget
£124 million

HOSPITALS

Battle Hospital Oxford Rd, Reading; Tel 0118 987 5111
Specialism: Acute.

Royal Berkshire Hospital London Rd, Reading; Tel 0118 987 5111
Specialism: Acute; maternity.

Townlands Hospital Henley on Thames, Oxfordshire RG9 2EB; Tel 01491 572544

Royal Bournemouth and Christchurch Hospitals NHS Trust

Royal Bournemouth General Hospital, Castle Lane East, Bournemouth, Hampshire BH7 7DW; Tel 01202 303626; Fax (Administration) 01202 704077
Chair S. Collins
Chief Executive T. Spotswood
Medical Director D. Dickson
Director (Nursing) M. Wheatcroft
Director (Finance and IT) C. Perry
Director (Personnel) Vacancy
Income (2001–02)
£102 million approx.

HOSPITALS

Christchurch Hospital Fairmile Rd, Christchurch, Dorset BH23 2JX; Tel 01202 486361
Specialism: Elderly (194)

Royal Bournemouth Hospital Castle Lane East, Bournemouth BH7 7DW; Tel 01202 303626
Specialism: Acute. Number of beds: (674)

Royal Brompton and Harefield NHS Trust

Sydney St, London SW3 6NP;
URL www.rbh.nthames.nhs.uk; Tel 020 7352 8121;
Fax 020 7351 8473
Chief Executive Dr Gareth J. Goodier

Royal Cornwall Hospitals NHS Trust

Royal Cornwall Hospital (Treliske), Bedruthan Hse, Truro, Cornwall TR1 3LJ; Tel 01872 274242; Fax 01872 240574
Chair J.M. Williams
Chief Executive B. Milstead
Medical Director Dr A. Walker
Director (Patient Services) D. Samuels
Director (Personnel) D.R. Maddocks
Director (Finance) P. Madeley
Annual budget
£80 million

CHILD ASSESSMENT CENTRE

Cornwall Counselling and Assessment Unit for Children
Royal Cornwall Hospital, Cornwall TR1 3LJ; Tel 01872 270000
Consultant Paediatrician Dr J. Lewis

Penwith Assessment Unit Nancealverne School, Madron Rd, Penzance, Cornwall; Tel 01736 66611
Consultant Paediatrician Dr J. Lewis

DIRECTORATE OF CHILD HEALTH

Royal Cornwall Hospitals Trust, Treliske, Truro, Cornwall; Tel 01872 270000
Clinical Director Dr N. Gilbertson

HEALTH CENTRES

Chacewater Church Hill, Chacewater, Cornwall; Tel 01872 560073

Falmouth Trevaylor Rd, Falmouth, Cornwall; Tel 01326 211657

Gunnislake Orchard Site, Gunnislake, Cornwall; Tel 01822 833777

Hayle Bodriggy, Hayle, Cornwall; Tel 01736 752056

Helston Trengrouse Way, Helston, Cornwall; Tel 01326 572691

Isles of Scilly St. Mary's Hospital, Hugh Town, Isles of Scilly; Tel 01720 22628

Launceston Church Stile, Launceston, Cornwall; Tel 01566 772296

Liskeard The Health Office, Trewithen Hse, Liskeard, Cornwall; Tel 01579 343014

Redruth Community Health Clinic Forth Noweth, Redruth, Cornwall; Tel 01209 217811

St. Austell The Health Office, Moorland Rd, St. Austell, Cornwall; Tel 01726 72206

St. Just Lafrowdra Cl, St. Just, Cornwall; Tel 01736 788866

St. Keverne Treskewes, St. Keverne, Cornwall; Tel 01326 280767

Saltash Callington Rd, Saltash, Cornwall; Tel 01752 842677

Truro The Health Office, The Leats, Truro, Cornwall; Tel 01872 72202

Wadebridge Brooklyn, Wadebridge, Cornwall; Tel 01208 812225

HOSPITALS

Royal Cornwall Hospital (Treliske) Truro, Cornwall;
Tel 01872 274242
  Specialism: Acute (187)

Royal Devon and Exeter Healthcare NHS Trust

Royal Devon and Exeter Hospital, Barrack Rd, Exeter,
  Devon EX2 5DW; Tel 01392 411611
Chair Prof Ruth Hawker, OBE
Chief Executive A. Pedder
Director (Finance and Information) S. Astbury
Director (Facilities) Linda Hall
Director (Nursing and Service Improvement)
  Marie-Noëlle Orget
Director (Personnel) S. Jupp
Director (Operations) Elaine Hobson
Medical Director Dr Vaughan Pearce
Medical Director Dr Iain Wilson
Clinical Director (Surgery 1) A. Knox
Clinical Director (Specialist Surgery) John Palmer
Clinical Director (Child and Women's Health) Patrick Oades
Clinical Director (Diagnostics) Clive Hamilton-Wood
Clinical Director (Professional Services) Tony Cox
Clincial Director (Trauma and Orthopaedics) Peter Schranz
Clinical Director (Critical Care) Andrew Teasdale
Clinical Director (Medicine) Chris Sheldon
Annual budget (2002–3)
£170 million

HOSPITALS

Princess Elizabeth Orthopaedic Centre Barrack Rd, Exeter,
Devon EX2 5DW; Tel 01392 411611
  Number of beds: (109)

Royal Devon and Exeter Hospital (Heavitree) Gladstone Rd,
Heavitree, Exeter, Devon EX1 2ED; Tel 01392 411611
  Number of beds: (303)

Royal Devon and Exeter Hospital (Wonford) Barrack Rd,
Exeter, Devon EX2 5DW; Tel 01392 411611; Fax 01392
402067
  Number of beds: (505)

UNIT

Honeylands Pinhoe Rd, Exeter, Devon EX4 8AD; Tel 01392
67171
  Specialism: Children's respite care (14) Number of beds:
  Playgroup Placements (18)

Royal Free Hampstead NHS Trust

Royal Free Hospital, Pond St, London NW3 2QG;
  URL www.royalfree.org.uk; Tel 020 7794 0500; Fax 020
  7435 5342
Chair John Carrier; Fax 020 7830 2961
Chief Executive M.T. Else; Fax 020 7830 2961
Medical Director Prof Carol Black
Director (Nursing) Carole Holroyd
Director (Finance) J. Goulston

HOSPITALS

Coppetts Wood Hospital Coppetts Rd, London N10 1JN;
Tel 020 8833 9792
  Specialism: Infectious diseases (72)

Royal National Throat, Nose and Ear Hospital Grays Inn
Rd, London; Tel 020 7915 1300

Royal Liverpool and Broadgreen University Hospitals NHS Trust

Prescot St, Liverpool, Merseyside L7 8XP; Tel 0151 706 2000;
  Fax 0151 706 5806
Chair R. James

Chief Executive M. Boyle
Medical Director Dr F.E. White
Director (Nursing Quality) M. Carroll
Executive Director (Finance) A.J. Wilks
Annual budget
£143 000

HOSPITALS

Liverpool University Dental Hospital Pembroke Pl,
Liverpool, Merseyside L3 5PS; Tel 0151 706 2000
  Number of beds: (147)

Royal Liverpool University Hospital Prescot St, Liverpool,
Merseyside L7 8XP; Tel 0151 706 2000
  Specialism: Acute (836)

Royal Liverpool Children's NHS Trust

Alder Hey Hospital, Eaton Rd, Liverpool, Merseyside
  L12 2AP; Tel 0151 228 4811; Fax 0151 228 0328
Chair Angela Jones
Chief Executive A.P. Bell (Acting)
Medical Director Rick Turnock
Director (Nursing) Rebecca Howard
Director (Finance and Information Services) A. Sharples
Director (Human Resources) T. Harvey

CHILD ASSESSMENT CENTRE

Alder Hey Children's Hospital Eaton Rd, West Derby,
Liverpool, Merseyside L12 2AP; Tel 0151 228 4811
Doctor-in-Charge Dr L. Rosenbloom

HOSPITAL

Alder Hey Children's Hospital Eaton Rd, Liverpool,
Merseyside L12 2AP; Tel 0151 228 4811
  Specialism: Children; acute (382)

The Royal Marsden NHS Trust

Fulham Rd, London SW3 6JJ; URL www.royalmarsden.org;
  Tel 020 7352 8171
Chief Executive Cally Palmer

Sutton Site Downs Rd, Sutton, London SM2 5PT; Tel 020
8642 6011

Royal National Hospital for Rheumatic Diseases NHS Trust

Royal National Hospital for Rheumatic Diseases, Upper
  Borough Walls, Bath, Bath and North East Somerset
  BA1 1RL; E-mail info@rnhrd-tr.swest.nhs.uk; Tel 01225
  465941; Fax 01225 421202
Chair K. Lyon
Chief Executive Nicola Carmichael
Medical Director Dr A.K. Clarke
Director (Nursing and Operations) S. Lynas
Director (Finance) D. Stancliffe
Director (Research and Education) Dr A.K. Bhalla
Annual budget
£10.9 million

Royal National Orthopaedic Hospital NHS Trust

Brockley Hill, Stanmore, Greater London HA7 4LP;
  URL www.rnoh.org.uk; Tel 020 8954 2300;
  Fax 020 8954 6933; 020 8954 9133
Chief Executive Andrew Woodhead
Medical Director T.W.R. Briggs
Director (Nursing) Anthony Palmer
Director (Modernisation and Development) Phyllis Shelton
Director (Finance and Information) Jonathan Tymms
Associate Director (Personnel) Mark Vaughan
Associate Director (Research and Development)
  Martin Ferguson-Pell

12

Associate Director (Estates and Facilities) Eric Fehily
Assistant Director (Performance and Planning)
Tessa Litherland
Manager (Information Technology) Steven Pickup
Manager (Communications) Richard Hudson

Royal Shrewsbury Hospitals NHS Trust

Mytton Oak Rd, Shrewsbury, Shropshire SY3 8XQ;
URL www.rsh.org.uk; Tel 01743 261000; Fax 01743
261006
Chair Tom Caulcott
Chief Executive Neil Taylor
Medical Director Dr Ashley Fraser
Director (Nursing and Operations) Trish Mason
Director (Finance) Peter Jones
Director (Human Resources) W. Lloyd

HOSPITAL

Wrekin Hospital Hollyhead Rd, Wellington, Shropshire
TF1 2ED; Tel 01952 47311

Royal Surrey County Hospital NHS Trust

Royal Surrey County Hospital, Egerton Rd, Guildford,
Surrey GU2 7XX; Tel 01483 571122; Fax 01483 537747
Chair Colston Herbert
Chief Executive Jeff Faulkner

HOSPITAL

Royal Surrey County Hospital Egerton Rd, Guildford,
Surrey GU2 5XX; Tel 01483 571122
Specialism: Acute; radiotherapy (570)

Royal United Hospital Bath NHS Trust

Royal United Hospital, Combe Pk, Bath, Somerset
BA1 3NG; Tel 01225 824022; Fax 01225 824304
Chair Mike Roy
Chief Executive Jenny Barker (Acting)
Medical Director John Waldron
Director (Nursing and Commissioning) Corinne Hall
Director (Finance) Margaret Pratt (Acting)

Royal West Sussex NHS Trust

St. Richard's Hospital, Spitatfield La, Chichester, West
Sussex PO19 6SE; URL www.rwst.org.uk;
E-mail webmaster@rws-tr.nhs.uk; Tel 01243 788122
Chair Lis Spence
Chief Executive Robert Lapraik

The Royal Wolverhampton Hospitals NHS Trust

New Cross Hospital, Wolverhampton Rd, Wolverhampton,
West Midlands WV10 0QP; Tel 01902 307999
Chief Executive M. Hackett

HOSPITALS

New Cross Hospital Wolverhampton, West Midlands
WV10 0QP; Tel 01902 307999
Specialism: Acute. Number of beds: (829)

Wolverhampton and Midland Counties Eye Infirmary
Compton Rd, Wolverhampton, West Midlands WV3 9QB;
Tel 01902 307999
Specialism: Ophthalmology. Number of beds: (23)

Salford Royal Hospitals NHS Trust

Hope Hospital, Stott La, Salford, Greater Manchester
M6 8HD; Tel 0161 789 7373; Fax 0161 787 5974
Chair P.W. Mount
Chief Executive W.H. Sang

Medical Director Dr P.C. Barnes
Business Director Mrs V. Michej
Director (Finance) Mr M. Ogden
Director (Nursing and Human Resource) Mrs C.A. Chisnell

HOSPITALS

Hope Hospital Stott La, Salford, Greater Manchester
M6 8HD; Tel 0161 789 7373

University Department of Dermatology Hope Hospital, Stott
La, Salford, Greater Manchester M6 8HD; Tel 0161 789 7373

Salisbury Health Care NHS Trust

Salisbury District Hospital, Salisbury, Wiltshire SP2 8BJ;
URL www.salisburyhealthcare.org; Tel 01722 336262;
Fax 01722 330221
Chair David S. Noble
Chief Executive Frank Harsent
Director (Medical) E. Waters
Director (Nursing) M. Monnington
Director (Operations) Peter Hill
Director (Finance, Procurement and Information) M. Cassells
Director (Human Resources) A. Denton
Annual budget
£89 million

HOSPITAL

Salisbury District Hospital Salisbury, Wiltshire SP2 8BJ;
Tel 01722 336262; Fax 01722 330221
Specialism: Acute. Number of beds: (569)

Sandwell and West Birmingham Hospitals NHS Trust

Dudley Rd, Birmingham, West Midlands B18 7QH;
URL www.cityhospital.org.uk; Tel 0121 554 3801;
Fax 0121 507 5636
Chair Mrs N. Hafeez
Chief Executive John Adler
Medical Director Mr M. Lee
Medical Director Mr H. Bradby
Director (Finance) Mr P. Assinder
Director (Operations) Vacancy
Director (Nursing Practice) Ms P. Werhun
Director (Human Resources) Mr C. Holden
Director (Planning and Performance) Mr J. Amphlett
Director (Development) Mrs L. Read
Director (I M and T) Mr T. Atack
Director (Facilities) Mr G. Seager

HOSPITALS

Rowley Regis Hospital Moor La, Rowley Regis, West
Midlands B65 8DA

Sandwell Hospital Lyndon, West Bromich, West Midlands
B71 4HJ; Tel 0121 553 1831; Fax 0121 607 3117

OTHER SERVICES

Birmingham and Midland Eye Centre Dudley Rd,
Birmingham, West Midlands B18 7QH; Tel 0121 554 3801

Centre for the Hearing Impaired Western Rd, Birmingham,
West Midlands B18 7QD; Tel 0121 554 3801

Carters Green Medical Centre 396–400 High St, West
Bromwich, West Midlands B70 9LB

Neptune Health Park Sedgeley Rd West, Tipton, West
Midlands DY4 8LT

Oakeswell Health Centre Brunswick Park Rd, Wednesbury,
West Midlands WS10 9HP

Oldbury Health Clinic Albert St, Oldbury, West Midlands
B69 4DE

Victoria Health Centre 5 Suffrage St, Smethwick, West Midlands B66 3PZ

Scarborough and North East Yorkshire Healthcare NHS Trust

Scarborough Hospital, Woodlands Dr, Scarborough, North Yorkshire YO12 6QL; Tel 01723 368111; Fax 01723 377223
Chair The Very Revd J.E. Allen
Chief Executive R. Crawford
Medical Director D. Poole
Director (Nursing Services) D.E. Parker
Director (Finance) G.F. Nolan
General Manager (Acute Hospital Services) C. Long
Director (Planning and Development) M. Hay
Annual budget
£62 million

CHILDREN'S CLINIC

Scarborough Hospital Woodlands Dr, Scarborough, North Yorkshire YO12 6QL; Tel 01723 368111
Manager Dr H.H. Kaye

COMMUNITY RESOURCE TEAM (LEARNING DIFFICULTIES)

Eastfield Clinic Scarborough, North Yorkshire; Tel 01723 581344
Specialism: Learning disabilities.

HOSPITALS

Bridlington Hospital Bessingby Rd, Bridlington, East Riding of Yorkshire YO16 4QP; Tel 01262 606666
Specialism: Acute; maternity. Number of beds: (174)

Kirkbymoorside Clinic North Yorkshire; Tel 01751 31207
Specialism: Orthopaedic outpatients.

Malton, Norton and District Hospital Malton, North Yorkshire; Tel 01653 693041
Specialism: Acute; maternity. Number of beds: (90)

Scarborough Hospital Woodlands Dr, Scarborough, North Yorkshire YO12 6QL; Tel 01723 368111
Specialism: Acute (328)

Whitby Hospital Spring Hill, Whitby, North Yorkshire; Tel 01947 604851
Specialism: Acute; maternity; geriatric. Number of beds: (112)

Severn NHS Trust

Severn NHS Trust has been dissolved and its services are now covered by three NHS Trusts and three Primary Care Trusts. The NHS Trusts are: Gloucestershire Ambulance Service, Gloucestershire Hospitals and Gloucestershire Partnership. The Primary Care Trusts are: Cheltenham and Tewkesbury, Cotswold and Vale, and West Gloucestershire. Each Trust is listed alphabetically under the appropriate headings in this chapter.

Sheffield Care Trust

Fulwood Hse, Old Fulwood Rd, Sheffield, South Yorkshire S10 3TH; URL www.sct.nhs.uk; Tel 0114 271 6310
Chair Prof Alan Walker
Chief Executive Kevan Taylor
Medical Director Dr Tim Kendall
Director (Finance) Mick Rodgers
Director (Human Resources) Rosie McHugh
Non-Executive Director Elizabeth Jones
Non-Executive Director Colin Roth
Non-Executive Director Cllr Marjorie Barker
Non-Executive Director Cllr Mick Rooney
Non-Executive Director Angela Barney
Non-Executive Director Cllr Paul Scriven

HOSPITALS

Beighton Hospital Skelton La, Sheffield, West Yorkshire S19 6FJ

Nether Edge Hospital Osborne Rd, Sheffield, West Yorkshire S11 9EL

Northern General Hospital Herries Rd, Sheffield, West Yorkshire S5 7AU

St. Georges Community Hospital Winter St, Sheffield, West Yorkshire S3 7ND

Sheffield Children's NHS Trust

Western Bank, Sheffield, South Yorkshire S10 2TH; E-mail john.adler@sch.nhs.uk; Tel 0114 271 7000; Fax 0114 272 3418
Chair L. Hagger
Chief Executive J. Adler
Medical Director D. Burke
Director (Finance) Paul Briddock
Chief Nurse Executive H.M. Khatib
Deputy Chief Executive C.T. Sharratt

Weston Park Hospital Whitham Rd, Sheffield, South Yorkshire S10 2SJ; Tel 0114 226 5000; Fax 0114 226 5555
Weston Park Hospital is now an Associate Hospital of the Sheffield Teaching Hospitals NHS Trust.
Chair D. Stone
Chief Executive A. Cash
Medical Director and Hospital Director Dr I.H. Manifold; E-mail ian.manifold@sth.nhs.uk
Head (Nursing and Clinical Services) A. Pulfrey; E-mail anne.pulfrey@sth.nhs.uk
Manager (Finance and Contracts) N. Leek; E-mail nigel.leek@sth.nhs.uk
Head (Clinical Oncology) Prof B.W. Hancock
General Manager P.L. Mackender; E-mail pauline.mackender@sth.nhs.uk
Annual budget
£14 million

Sheffield Teaching Hospitals NHS Trust

Formerly Northern General Hospital NHS Trust.
8 Beech Hill Rd, Sheffield, South Yorkshire S10 2SB; Tel 0114 226 1000; Fax 0114 226 1001
Chair D.R. Stone
Chief Executive A. Cash
Medical Director Prof C.L. Welsh
Chief Nurse H. Drabble
Director (Finance) N. Priestley
Director (Human Resources) J. Watts
Annual budget
£400 million

HOSPITALS

Charles Clifford Dental Hospital 76 Wellesley Rd, Sheffield, South Yorkshire S10 2SZ; Tel 0114 271 7800; Fax 0114 271 7836

Jessop Wing Royal Hallamshire Hospital, Sheffield, South Yorkshire S10 2JF; Tel 0114 271 1900

Northern General Hospital Herries Rd, Sheffield, South Yorkshire S5 7AU; Tel 0114 243 4343

Royal Hallamshire Hospital Glossop Rd, Sheffield, South Yorkshire S10 2JF; Tel 0114 271 1900

Weston Park Hospital Whitham Rd, Sheffield, South Yorkshire S10 2SJ; Tel 0114 226 5000; Fax 0114 226 5555

Sherwood Forest Hospitals NHS Trust

Mansfield Rd, Sutton-in-Ashfield, Nottinghamshire NG17 4JL; URL www.northnotts.nhs.uk; Tel 01623 622515; Fax 01623 621770
Chief Executive Jeffrey Worrall

12

HOSPITALS

Ashfield Community Hospital Portland Hospital, Kirby-in-Ashfield, Nottinghamshire NG17 7AE

The King's Mill Centre Mansfield Rd, Sutton-in-Ashfield, Nottinghamshire NG17 4JL; Tel 01623 622515; Fax 01623 621770

Newark Hospital Boundary Rd, Newark, Nottinghamshire NG24 4DE; Tel 01636 681681; Fax 01636 610177

Shropshire's Community and Mental Health Services NHS Trust

Shropshire's Community and Mental Health Services NHS Trust has now dissolved and its services have been taken over by Telford and Wrekin Primary Care Trust and Shropshire County Primary Care Trust, which are listed alphabetically under the Primary Care section in this chapter.

Solihull Healthcare NHS Trust

Solihull Healthcare NHS Trust has now become Solihull Primary Care Trust, which is listed alphabetically under the Primary Care Trust section in this chapter.

Somerset Partnership NHS and Social Care Trust

Broadway Hse, Broadway Pk, Barclay St, Bridgwater, Somerset TA6 5YA; E-mail ask@sompar.nhs.uk; Tel 01278 446151; Fax 01278 446147
Chair C. Baron
Chief Executive P. Cooney
Medical Director Dr E. Ostler
Director (Nursing) B. Thomas
Director (Social Care) Sue Okell
Director (Finance and Information) Vacancy
Annual budget
£23.5 million

FAMILY AND ADOLESCENT UNIT

Orchard Lodge Young People's Unit Cotford St. Luke, Norton Fitzwarren, Taunton, Somerset TA4 1DB; Tel 01823 432211; Fax 01823 432541
Specialism: Child and adolescent psychiatry. Number of beds: (12)

ADULT SERVICES

Cairnsmoor Numney Rd, Badcox, Frome, Somerset BA11 4LA; Tel 01373 473905; Fax 01373 451912

COMMUNITY MENTAL HEALTH UNITS – ACUTE

Belmont House Technical St, Burnham-on-Sea, Somerset TA8 1PN; Tel 01278 792673; Fax 01278 795212
Number of beds: (10)

Cedar Lodge Summerlands, Preston Rd, Yeovil, Somerset BA20 2BN; Tel 01935 428420; Fax 01935 411612
Specialism: Rehabilitation; day. (29)

East Mendip CMHT Elliott Bldg, Public Offices, Christchurch Street West, Frome, Somerset BA11 1EF; Tel 01373 468060; 01373 468079
Specialism: Acute CMHT

Holly Court Summerlands, Preston Rd, Yeovil, Somerset BA20 2BX; Tel 01935 28420; Fax 01935 411612
Specialism: Adult; CMHT. Number of beds: (22)

Phoenix House Priory Pk, Glastonbury Rd, Wells, Somerset BA5 1TH; Tel 01749 670443; Fax 01749 670575
Specialism: Acute inpatient. Number of beds: (25)

Rosebank Community Mental Health Unit Priory Pk, Glastonbury Rd, Wells, Somerset BA5 1TH; Tel 01749 670445; Fax 01749 679487
Number of beds: (18 day)

Southwood House Community Mental Health Unit Southgate Pk, Taunton Rd, Bridgwater, Somerset TA6 3LS; Tel 01278 456561; Fax 01278 431265
Specialism: Adult

Stonecross House Selbourne Hse, Selbourne Pl, Minehead, Somerset TA24 5TY; Tel 01643 704971; Fax 01643 703024
Specialism: CMHT

COMMUNITY MENTAL HEALTH UNITS – ELDERLY

Barnfield House Selbourne Pl, Minehead, Somerset TA24 5TY; Tel 01643 706999; Fax 01643 707291
Number of places: (16 plus 16 day)

Chantry House Park Rd, Frome, Somerset BA11 1EY; Tel 01373 451223; Fax 01373 451912
Number of places: (22 beds plus 22 day places)

Cranleigh House Broadway Pk, Barclay St, Bridgwater, Somerset TA6 5LY; Tel 01278 446165; Fax 01278 446154
Number of places: (18 plus 18 day)

Ridley Day Hospital Verrington Hospital, Wincanton, Somerset BA9 9DQ; Tel 01963 32006; Fax 01963 31898
Number of places: (12 day)

Little Court 2 Pinnockscroft, Burnham on Sea, Somerset TA8 2NF; Tel 01278 786876; Fax 01278 795290
Number of places: (16 plus 16 day)

Magnolia House 56 Preston Rd, Yeovil, Somerset BA20 2BN; Tel 01935 431725; Fax 01935 411063
Number of places: (28 plus 33 day)

Pyrland House Cheddon Rd, Taunton, Somerset TA2 7AU; Tel 01823 331578; Fax 01823 332058
Number of places: (24 plus 22 day)

St. Andrew's Priory Pk, Glastonbury Rd, Wells, Somerset BA5 1TH; Tel 01749 670448; Fax 01749 679487
Number of places: (26 plus 26 day)

Stratfield House Wellington and District Cottage Hospital, Bulford, Wellington, Somerset TA21 8QQ; Tel 01823 661663; Fax 01823 661626
Number of places: (14 plus 14 day)

COMMUNITY MENTAL HEALTH UNITS – REHABILITATION

The Bridge Community Mental Health Unit Priory Pk, Glastonbury Rd, Wells, Somerset BA5 1TJ; Tel 01749 673456; Fax 01749 679487

Burtons Orchard 9 Wilton St, Taunton, Somerset TA1 3JR; Tel 01823 282349; Fax 01823 332896

College House Broadway Pk, Barclay St, Bridgwater, Somerset TA6 5AY; Tel 01278 446149
Number of places: (32 day)

Eastleigh Court Trinity Rd, Taunton, Somerset TA1 3JL; Tel 01823 351516; Fax 01823 351535
Number of places: (20)

Green Lane Houses Green Lane Cl, Frome, Somerset BA11 4PA; Tel 01373 453005
Number of places: (10)

Keward House Jocelyn Dr, Wells, Somerset BA5 1QH; Tel 01749 676148; Fax 01749 671395
Number of places: (22)

Park Gate House East Reach, Taunton, Somerset TA1 3EX; Tel 01823 330502; Fax 01823 330504
Day CMHT Base

CHILD AND FAMILY THERAPEUTIC SERVICES

Balidon House Preston Rd, Yeovil, Somerset BA20 2BX; Tel 01935 24511; Fax 01935 414060

Park Gate House East Reach, Taunton, Somerset TA1 3EX; Tel 01823 330510; Fax 01823 330504

Petrel House Broadway Pk, Barclay St, Bridgwater, Somerset TA6 5YA; Tel 01278 446909; Fax 01278 446782

St. Aldhelms Green La, Frome, Somerset BA11 LJW; Tel 01373 471220; Fax 01373 452138

South Devon Health Care NHS Trust

Hengrave Hse, Torbay Hospital, Torquay, Devon TQ2 7AA; Tel 01803 614567; Fax 01803 616334
Chair   D.P. Hudson
Chief Executive   A. Parr
Medical Director   Dr S. Smith
Director (Nursing)   E. Childs
Director (Finance and Information)   J. Coatham
Director (Human Resources)   I. Butler
Director (Technical Services)   R. Lomas
Director (Performance and Development)   S. Kerakusevic
Annual budget
£118 million

HOSPITAL

Torbay Hospital Lawes Bridge, Torquay, Torbay TQ2 7AA; Tel 01803 614567
Specialism: Acute. Number of beds: (550)

South Downs Health NHS Trust

Brighton General Hospital, Elm Gr, Brighton, Brighton and Hove BN2 3EW; Tel 01273 696011; Fax 01273 242215
Chair   Q. Barry
Chief Executive   A. Horne
Executive Director   S. Hood
Medical Director   Dr M. Rosenberg
Director (Finance)   J. O'Sullivan
Nurse Executive   L. Rodrigues
Annual budget
£75 million

DEVELOPMENTAL AND LEARNING DISABILITY SERVICE

86 Denmark Villas, Hove, Brighton and Hove BN3 3TY

CHILD DEVELOPMENT UNIT

MacKeith Centre Royal Alexandra Children's Hospital, Dyke Rd, Brighton, Brighton and Hove BN1 3JN

HOSPITALS

Aldrington House Day Support Centre, 35 New Church Rd, Hove, Brighton and Hove BN3 4AG; Tel 01273 778383
Specialism: Psychiatric

Brighton Community Mental Health Centre 76–79 Buckingham Rd, Brighton, Brighton and Hove; Tel 01273 749500

Brighton General Hospital Elm Gr, Brighton, Brighton and Hove BN2 3EW; Tel 01273 696011
Trust Headquarters.
Number of beds: (465)

Chailey Heritage Clinical Services North Chailey, Lewes, East Sussex BN8 4JN; Tel 01825 722112
Number of beds: Rehabilitation and development centre. (142)

Hove Polyclinic Nevill Ave, Hove, Brighton and Hove BN3 7HY; Tel 01273 696011
Specialism: Outpatients

Mill View Hospital Nevill Ave, Hove, Brighton and Hove BN3 7HZ; Tel 01273 696011
Number of beds: Psychiatric (25)

Newhaven Downs House Church Hill, Newhaven, East Sussex BN9 9HH; Tel 01273 513441
Number of beds: Elderly care (65)

Victoria Hospital Nevill Rd, Lewes, East Sussex BN7 1PF; Tel 01273 474153
Number of beds: GP; acute (41)

South Durham Health Care NHS Trust

South Durham Health Care NHS Trust has merged with North Durham Healthcare NHS Trust to become County Durham and Darlington Acute Hospitals NHS Trust, which is listed alphabetically in this section.

South Essex Partnership NHS Trust

Head Office, Runwell Hospital, Runwell Chase, Wickford, Essex SS11 7XX; Tel 01268 366000; Fax 01268 366205
Chair   Jai Tout
Chief Executive   Patrick Geoghegan
Medical Director   Dr Mike Lowe
Director (Personnel)   Karen Hussey
Director (Finance)   Ray Jennings
Director (Mental Health Services)   Eunan MacIntyre
Director (Specialist and Sexual Health Services) and Deputy Chief Executive   Nikki Richardson
Director (Planning and Performance Management)   Peter Wadum-Buhl
Director (Information)   Jan Buck; Tel 01268 366000; Fax 01268 366205
Director (Specialist Services – Sexual Health)   Manfred Hennesey (Acting)
Executive Nurse   Claire Trencher
Annual budget
£60 million

CHILD DEVELOPMENT CENTRES

Children's Centre Basildon Hospital, Nether Mayne, Basildon, Essex SS16 5NL; Tel 01268 533911

Gifford House Thurrock Community Hospital, Long La, Grays, Essex RM16 2PX; Tel 01375 390044

HOSPITALS

Basildon Hospital Nethermaine, Basildon, Essex SS16 5NL; Tel 01268 593000; Fax 01268 593079
Specialism: Mental health.

Heath Close Tye Common Rd, Billericay, Essex CM12 9NR; Tel 01277 631968
Specialism: Learning disabilities (14)

Mayflower House Blunts Wall Rd, Billericay, Essex; Tel 01277 634236

Mental Health Unit Basildon Hospital, Nethermayne, Basildon, Essex SS16 5NL; Tel 01268 533911

Mountnessing Court 230 Mountnessing Rd, Billericay, Essex CM12 0EH; Tel 01277 634596; 01277 634711

Runwell Hospital Runwell Chase, Wickford, Essex SS11 7XX; Tel 01268 366000; Fax 01268 366205

Stroke Unit Lister Ward, Orsett Hospital, Rowley Rd, Grays, Essex RM16 3EU; Tel 01268 592508

Thurrock Community Hospital Long La, Grays, Essex RM16 2PX; Tel 01375 390044
Specialism: Geriatrics; psychogeriatrics; day care; rehabilitation. Number of beds (127)

LEARNING DISABILITIES

Benton's Farm Craft and Horticultural Centre, Mollands La, South Ockendon, Essex RM15 6SB; Tel 01708 851841

Ely House Ely Way, Basildon, Essex SS14 2BQ; Tel 01268 643333

Grays Hall Orsett Rd, Grays, Essex RM17 5TT; Tel 01375 375361

John Tallack Centre Thurrock Community Hospital, Long La, Grays, Essex RM16 2PX; Tel 01375 390044

Pride House Crafts Christy Way, Christy Cl, Laindon, Essex; Tel 01268 410057

12

Sankey House 81 High St, Pitsea, Basildon, Essex SS13 3BB; Tel 01268 583160

South London and Maudsley NHS Trust

Trust Headquarters, 9th Fl, The Tower Bldg, 11 York Rd, London SE1 7NX; Tel 020 7919 2409 210; Fax 020 7919 2362
Chair Madeliene Long
Chief Executive Stuart Bell

HOSPITAL

The Bethlem and Maudsley Hospital Denmark Hill, London SE5 8AZ; Tel 020 7703 6333

South Manchester University Hospitals NHS Trust

!st Fl, Tower Block, Manchester M23 9LT; Tel 0161 998 7070; Fax 0161 291 2037
Chair Prof D.G. Harnden
Chief Executive Mr P. Morris
Medical Director B. Ryan
Director (Human Resources) A.E. Wilding
Director (Finance) A.J. Whitley
Chief Nurse R. Holt

HOSPITAL

Wythenshawe Hospital Southmoor Rd, Wythenshawe, Manchester M23 9LT; Tel 0161 998 7070

South of Tyne and Wearside Mental Health NHS Trust

Cherry Knowle Hospital, Ryhope, Sunderland, Tyne and Wear SR2 0NB; Tel 0191 565 6256; Fax 0191 569 9455
Chair C.W. Rickitt
Chief Executive Alan Hall
Medical Director Dr H. Board
Director (Quality) and Chief Nurse R. Parker
Director (Finance and Corporate Planning) A.A. Hall
Director (Human Resources) J. McDonough

HOSPITALS

Cherry Knowle Hospital Ryhope, Sunderland, Tyne and Wear SR2 0NB; Tel 0191 565 6256; Fax 0191 569 9455
Monkwearmouth Hospital Newcastle Rd, Sunderland, Tyne and Wear SR5 1NB; Tel 0191 565 6256

South Staffordshire Healthcare NHS Trust

Trust Headquarters, St. George's Hospital, Corporation St, Stafford, Staffordshire ST16 3AG; URL www.southstaffshealthcare.nhs.uk; Tel 01785 257888; Fax 01785 258969
Chair Andrew Millward
Chief Executive Mike Cooke
Medical Director Dr Stewart Vaggers
Director (Finance and Information) Jayne Deaville
Director (Human Resources and Oranisational Development) Lesley Francis
Director (Nursing and Operations) Neil Carr
Clinical Director (Mental Health) Dr Abid Khan
Clinical Director (Forensic Mental Health) Dr Nick Griffin
Clinical Director (Learning Disabilities) Judy Morris
Clinical Director (Children's Services) Dr Gunjan Patel

South Tees Hospitals NHS Trust

The James Cook University Hospital, Marton Rd, Middlesbrough TS4 3BW; URL www.southtees.northy.nhs.uk; Tel 01642 850850
Chair John Foster, OBE
Chief Executive Simon Pleydell

Medical Director Dr Paul Lawler
Director (Nursing Development) Brian Footitt, OBE
Director (Facilities and Planning) Jill Moulton
Director (Finance) Steve Anderson

HOSPITALS

The James Cook University Hospital Marton Rd, Middlesbrough TS4 3BW; URL www.southtees.northy.nhs.uk; Tel 01642 850850
Friarage Hospital Northallerton, North Yorkshire DL6 1JS; Tel 01609 779911

South Tyneside Health Care NHS Trust

Harton Wing, South Tyneside District Hospital, South Shields, Tyne and Wear NE34 0PL; URL www.sthct.nhs.uk; Tel 0191 454 8888; Fax 0191 427 9908
Chief Executive L.B. Lambert
Medical Director Dr A. Rodgers
Executive Director (Finance and Corporate Governance) M.P. Robson
Executive Director (Nursing and Clinical Governance) D. Shilton

HOSPITALS

Monkton Hall Monkton La, Jarrow, Tyne and Wear NE32 5NN; Tel 0191 489 4111
Specialism: Learning disabilities; continuing care.
Number of beds: (44)
Palmer Community Hospital Wear St, Jarrow, Tyne and Wear NE32 3UX; Tel 0191 456 6001; Fax 0191 451 6000
Specialism: GP; elderly; dental.
Primrose Community Hospital Primrose Terr, Jarrow, Tyne and Wear NE32 5HA; Tel 0191 428 4601
Specialism: Elderly continuing care.
South Tyneside District Hospital Harton La, South Shields, Tyne and Wear NE34 0PL; Tel 0191 454 8888; Fax 0191 427 9908
Specialism: General (601)

South Warwickshire Combined Care NHS Trust

South Warwickshire Combined Care NHS Trust has now become South Warwickshire Primary Care Trust, which is listed alphabetically under the Primary Care Trust section in this chapter.

South Warwickshire General Hospitals NHS Trust

Lakin Rd, Warwick, Warwickshire CV34 5BW; Tel 01926 495321; Fax 01926 482603
Chair D. Evans
Chief Executive A. Riley
Director (Finance) L. Potts
Medical Director Dr P. Horrocks
Chief Nurse N. Hempstead
Annual budget
£50 million

HOSPITALS

Stratford upon Avon Hospital Arden St, Stratford-upon-Avon, Warwickshire CV37 6NX; Tel 01789 205831
Number of beds: (24)
Warwick Hospital Lakin Rd, Warwick, Warwickshire CV34 5BW; Tel 01926 495321
Number of beds: Acute (409)

South West London and St. George's NHS Trust

Springfield University Hospital, 61 Glenburnie Rd, London SW17 7DJ; Tel 020 8672 9911; Fax 020 8767 7608
Chief Executive Dr Nigel Fisher

HOSPITALS

Barnes Hospital South Worple Way, London SW14 8SU; Tel 020 878 4981

Henderson Hospital 2 Homeland Dr, Sutton, Surrey SM2 5LY; Tel 020 8661 1611

Richmond Royal Hospital Kew Foot Rd, Richmond, Surrey TW9 2TZ; Tel 020 8940 3331

South West London Community Health NHS Trust

South West London Community Health NHS Trust has now become Wandsworth Primary Care Trust, which is listed alphabetically under the Primary Care Trust section of this chapter.

South West Yorkshire Mental Health NHS Trust

Fieldhead, Ouchthorpe La, Wakefield, West Yorkshire WF1 3SP; Tel 01924 327000; Fax 01924 327021
Chair M. Laing
Chief Executive R.A. Wilk
Medical Director Dr R.S. Thiagarajah
Medical Director Dr G. Roney
Director (Human Resources and Facilities) A Davis
Director (Corporate Development and Nursing) H Walshaw
Director (Primary Care and Nursing) A. Hopkins
Director (Finance and Information) A Ramsay
Director (Mental Health) S. Michael

HOSPITALS

Fieldhead Hospital Ouchthorpe La, Wakefield, West Yorkshire; Tel 01924 327000
   Specialism: Mental health; forensic psychiatry; learning disabilities.

Southmoor Hospital Hemsworth, West Yorkshire; Tel 01977 465630
   Specialism: Elderly mental health.

South Yorkshire Ambulance Service NHS Trust

Fairfield, Moorgate Rd, Rotherham, South Yorkshire S60 2BQ; Tel 01709 820520; Fax 01709 827839
Chair S. Hunter
Chief Executive R. Shannon
Director (Patient Transport Services) N. Wade
Director (Finance) T. Waggett
Annual budget
£12 million

Southampton University Hospitals NHS Trust

Southampton University Hospital, Southampton General Hospital, Southampton SO16 6YD;
   URL www.suht.nhs.uk; Tel 023 8077 7222; Fax 023 8079 4153
Chair R.C. Keightley, CB
Chief Executive D. Moss
Medical Director N. Saunders
Director (Nursing and Patient Services) K. Fenton
Director (Human Resources) A. Rayner
Director (Finance) B. Lloyd
Director (Planning and Modernisation) K. Flynn
Annual budget
£298 million

HOSPITALS

Manor House Mansbridge Rd, West End, Southampton SO18 3HW
   Specialism: Convalescent Number of beds: (15)

Countess Mountbatten House Moorgreen Hospital, Botley Rd, Southampton SO30 3JB; Tel 023 8047 7414

The Princess Anne Hospital Coxford Rd, Shirley, Southampton SO16 6YA; Tel 023 8077 7222
   Specialism: Obstetrics and gynaecology Number of beds: (257)

Royal South Hants Hospital Brintons Terr, Southampton SO14 0YG; Tel (including Wessex Radiotherapy Centre) 023 8063 4288
   Specialism: Acute Number of beds: (128)

Southampton General Hospital Tremona Rd, Shirley, Southampton SO16 6YD; Tel 023 8077 7222
   Specialism: Acute

Southend Hospital NHS Trust

Southend Hospital, Prittlewell Chase, Westcliff on Sea, Essex SS0 0RY; URL www.southend-hospital.co.uk; Tel 01702 435555; Fax 01702 221300
Chair J. Bruce
Chief Executive D. Brackenbury
Medical Director Dr G. Tosh
Director (Nursing and Governance) C. Humbles
Director (Finance and Information) A. Morris
Director (Personnel and Communications) S. Buggle
Annual budget
£105 million

HOSPITAL

Southend Hospital Prittlewell Chase, Westcliff on Sea, Southend SS0 0RY; URL www.southend-hospital.co.uk; Tel 01702 435555
   Specialism: Acute; accident and emergency. Number of beds: (800)

Southern Birmingham Community Health NHS Trust

Southern Birmingham Community Health NHS Trust has now become South Birmingham Primary Care Trust, which is listed alphabetically under the Primary Care Trust section of this chapter.

Southern Derbyshire Acute Hospitals NHS Trust

Derby City General Hospital, Uttoxeter Rd, Derby, Derbyshire DE22 3NE; Tel 01332 340131; Fax 01332 290559
Chair J. Forrest
Chief Executive J. Acred
Medical Director H. Jenkins
Assistant Chief Executive B. Ibell
Director (Nursing) M. Dewar
Director (Personnel) Moira Roberts
Director (Service Planning) D. Prescott
Director (Finance) C. Calkin

HOSPITALS

Derby Chest Clinic Green La, Derby DE1 1RX; URL www.sdah-tr.trent.nhs.uk; Tel 01332 340366
   Specialism: Diseases of the chest.

Derby City and Derbyshire Children's Uttoxeter Rd, Derby DE22 3NE; URL www.sdah-tr.trent.nhs.uk; Tel 01332 340131
   Specialism: General acute; obstetrics; gynaecology; SCBU; geriatric; assessment; urology; breast screening unit Number of beds: City beds (498); children's beds (84).

Derbyshire Royal Infirmary London Rd, Derby DE1 2QY; URL www.sdah-tr.trent.nhs.uk; Tel 01332 347141; Fax 01332 254832
   Specialism: Mainly acute; geriatric; accident and emergency; radiotherapy. Number of beds: (599)

12

Nightingale Macmillan Continuing Care Unit London Rd,
Trinity St, Derby DE1 2RA; URL www.sdah-tr.trent.nhs.uk;
Tel 01332 254900
    Number of beds: (15)

Southern Derbyshire Community and Mental Health Services NHS Trust

Southern Derbyshire Community and Mental Health
Services NHS Trust has merged with the Northern
Derbyshire Mental Health Confederation to form the
Derbyshire Mental Health Services NHS Trust, which is
listed alphabetically in this section.

Southport and Ormskirk Hospital NHS Trust

Town La, Kew, Southport, Merseyside PR8 6NJ; Tel 01706
547471; Fax 01704 704541
Chair   Mr A. Johnson
Chief Executive   J. Parry
Deputy Chief Executive   P. Gawthorne
Medical Director   I. Harrison
Director (Nursing Services)   E. Chew
Director (Finance)   C. Bennett
Consultant (Spinal Injuries)   P. Sett
Consultant (General Surgery)   I. Harrison

HOSPITALS

Christiana Hartley Maternity Hospital Town La, Kew,
Southport, Merseyside
    Number of beds: (35)
Ormskirk District General Hospital Wigan Rd, Ormskirk,
Lancashire
    Specialism: Acute
Southport and Formby District General Hospital Town La,
Southport, Merseyside PR8 6NJ; Tel 01704 547471
    Specialism: Acute. Number of beds: Other (35)
Southport General Infirmary Scarisbrick New Rd,
Southport, Merseyside PR8 6PH; Tel 01704 42901
    Specialism: Acute; geriatric. Number of beds: (53)

St. George's Healthcare NHS Trust

Blackshaw Rd, London SW17 0QT;
    URL www.st-georges.org.uk;
    E-mail ian.hamilton@stgeorges.nhs.uk; Tel 020 8672
    1255; Fax 020 8672 5304
Chair   Catherine McLoughlin, CBE
Chief Executive   I. Hamilton
Medical Director   Prof P. Jones
Director (Operations and Nursing)   Marie Grant
Director (Finance)   I. Perkin
Chief Nurse   Sue Cooper
Annual budget
£250 million

HOSPITALS

Atkinson Morley's Hospital Copse Hill, Wimbledon,
London SW20 0NE; Tel 020 8946 7711
    Specialism: Acute; neurosciences.
Bolingbroke Hospital Wandsworth Common, London
SW11 6HN; Tel 020 8223 7411
    Specialism: Geriatric.
St. George's Hospital Blackshaw Rd, London SW17 0QT;
Tel 020 8672 1255
Contact   I. Hamilton
    Specialism: Acute.
Wolfson Medical Rehabilitation Centre Copse Hill, London
SW20 0NQ; Tel 020 8946 7711

St. Helens and Knowsley Community Health NHS Trust

St. Helens and Knowsley Community NHS Trust has been
dissolved and its services are now covered by St. Helens
Primary Care Trust and Knowsley Primary Care Trust,
which are listed alphabetically underneath the Primary
Care Trust section in this chapter.

St. Helens and Knowsley Hospitals NHS Trust

Whiston Hospital, Warrington Rd, Prescot, Merseyside
    L35 5DR; Tel 0151 426 1600; Fax 0151 430 1425
Chair   Mavis Wareham
Chief Executive   Tony Whitfield (Acting)
Medical Director   Dr John Tappin (Acting)
Director (Medical Services)   Steven T. Atherton
Director (Medical Facilities)   Robin Macmillan
Executive Nurse Director   Joyce Wilcock
Director (Finance)   Melanie Simmonas (Acting)
Head (Legal Advice Management)   Carol A. Freeman
Head (Personnel)   J. Dobson
Head (Information Services)   J. Konstankewecz
Head (Service Development and Planning)   S. Holbrook
Annual budget
£100 million

HOSPITALS

Newton Community Hospital Bradleigh Rd, Newton-le-
Willows, Lancashire WA12 8RB; Tel 0192 52 22731
    Specialism: GP; elderly care. Number of beds: (43)
St. Helens Hospital Marshalls Cross Rd, St. Helens,
Merseyside WA9 3EA; Tel 01744 26633
    Specialism: Acute. Number of beds: (324)
Whiston Hospital Whiston, Prescot, Merseyside L35 5DR;
Tel 0151 426 1600
    Specialism: Acute (746)

St. Mary's NHS Trust

Praed St, London W2 1NY; URL www.stmarys.org.uk;
    Tel 020 7886 6666; Fax 020 7886 6200
Chair   Baroness Joan Hanham
Chief Executive   Julian Nettel; Tel 020 7886 1234; Fax 020
    7886 1017
Medical Director   D. Mitchell
Director (Nursing)   S. Osborne
Director (Finance)   J. Armstrong
Business Manager (Chairman and Chief Executive)   J. Seez
Annual budget
£103 million

HOSPITALS

St. Charles's Hospital Exmoor St, London W10 6DZ;
Tel 020 8969 2488
    Specialism: Acute (303)
St. Mary's Hospital Praed St, London W2 1NY; Tel 020 7725
6666
    Specialism: Acute (523)
Western Ophthalmic Hospital Marylebone Rd, London
NW1 5YE; Tel 020 7402 4211
    Specialism: Eye (46)

Staffordshire Ambulance Service NHS Trust

Ambulance Service Headquarters, 70 Stone Rd, Stafford,
    Staffordshire ST16 2TQ; Tel 01785 253521; Fax 01785
    246238
Chair   W. Gourlay
Chief Executive   R. Thayne, OBE
Director (Finance)   P. Brown
Annual budget
£13.8 million

Stockport NHS Trust

Oak Hse, Stepping Hill Hospital, Stockport, Greater
  Manchester SK2 7JE; URL www.stockport.nhs.uk;
  Tel 0161 483 1010
Chair   Mrs Robina Shah
Chief Executive   Dr C.F. Burke
Medical Director   Dr James Catania
Director (Nursing)   Elaine Inglesby
Director (Service Modernisation)   Mr D. Hurrell
Director (Finance)   A. Roberts
Director (Operations)   Ann Barnes
Director (Human Resources)   Nicola Reucroft

HOSPITALS

Cherry Tree Hospital   Cherry Tree La, Great Moor,
Stockport, Greater Manchester SK2 7PZ; Tel 0161 483 1010
St. Thomas' Hospital   Shaw Heath, Stockport, Greater
Manchester SK3 8BL; Tel 0161 483 1010
Stepping Hill Hospital   Stockport, Greater Manchester
SK2 7JE; Tel 0161 483 1010
Consultant Paediatrician   Dr P. Miller
Health Visitor and Specialist Nurse   J. Reid

Stoke Mandeville Hospital NHS Trust

Stoke Mandeville Hospital, Mandeville Rd, Aylesbury,
  Buckinghamshire HP21 8AL; Tel 01296 315000;
  Fax 01296 316208
Chair   Dr A. Woodbrigg
Chief Executive   Mrs F. Wise
Medical Director   Dr A. Tudway
Director (Nursing)   C. McFarlane
Director (Finance and Management Information)
  Mr V. Doherty
Director (Operations)   Mr M. Newton
Director (Personnel)   Rodney Hill

Surrey Ambulance Service NHS Trust

The Horseshoe, Bolters La, Banstead, Surrey SM7 2AS;
  Tel 01737 353333; Fax 01737 370868
Chair   Lady Gardiner
Chief Executive   Alan Kennedy
Director (Operations)   Gary Butson
Director (Finance)   Sue Braysher

The Surrey and Sussex Healthcare NHS Trust

East Surrey Hospital, Canada Ave, Redhill, Surrey
  RH1 5RH; Tel 01737 768511; Fax 01737 231769
Chair   Vivian Hepworth
Chief Executive   Ken Cunningham
Medical Director   Dr Francis Matthey
Director (Nursing and Patient Services)   Nigel Kee
Director (Human Resources)   Ruth McCall
Director (Finance)   Derek Harvey (Acting)
Director (Strategic Development)   Matthew Kershaw
Annual budget
£131 million

HOSPITALS

Caterham Dene Hospital   Church Rd, Caterham, Surrey
CR3 5RA; Tel 01883 349324; Fax 01883 346978
  Specialism: Geriatric, GP.
Crawley Hospital   West Grove Dr, Crawley, West Sussex
RH11 7DH; Tel 01293 600300; Fax 01293 600341
  Specialism: Acute (251)
Dorking Hospital   Horsham Rd, Dorking, Surrey RH4 2AA;
Tel 01737 768511; Fax 01306 742759
  Specialism: Geriatric, GP.
East Surrey Hospital   Canada Ave, Redhill, Surrey
RH1 5RH; Tel 01737 768511
  Specialism: Acute (437)

Harrowlands Rehabilitation Unit   Harrowlands Pk, South
Terr, Dorking, Surrey RH4 2RA; Tel 01306 740449;
Fax 01306 743190
  Specialism: Cognitive or physical disabilities (under
  65s).
Horsham Hospital   Hurst Rd, Horsham, West Sussex
RH12 2DR; Tel 01403 227000; Fax 01403 227030
  Specialism: Community and mental health
Oxted Health Centre   10 Gresham Rd, Oxted, Surrey
RH8 0BG; Tel 01883 832850; Fax 01883 832851

Surrey Hampshire Borders NHS Trust

The Ridgewood Centre, Old Bisley Rd, Frimley, Surrey
  GU16 9QE; Tel 01276 692919; Fax 01276 605599
Chair   Mary Sennett, MBE
Chief Executive   Fiona Green
Medical Director and Joint Director (Clinical Practice)
  Dr Malcolm Hawthorne
*Director (Nursing and Rehabilitation Services) and Joint
  Director (Clinical Practice)*   Norma Jardin
Director (Finance and Facilities)   Gerald Hunt
Director (Operation)   Jo Young
Director (Projects)   Pat Keeling
Head (Human Resources)   Gavin Wright
Head (Performance and Planning)   Julie Gaze
Head (Communications)   Patrick McCullagh

HOSPITALS

Farnham Hospital   Hale Rd, Farnham, Surrey GU9 9QL;
Tel 01483 782000; Fax 01483 782299
  Specialism: Long stay EMI. Number of beds: (145)
Farnham Road Hospital   Farnham Rd, Guildford, Surrey
GU2 7LX; Tel 01483 443535; Fax 01483 443502
Parklands Hospital   Aldermaston Rd, Basingstoke,
Hampshire RG24 9RH; Tel 01252 817718; Fax 01252 37
6408
  Specialism: Mental health; psychogeriatric.
Sherbourne House   Sherbourne Rd, Basingstoke,
Hampshire RG21 2TL
The Ridgewood Centre   Old Bisley Rd, Frimley, Surrey
GU16 9QE; Tel 01276 692919; Fax 01276 605599

Surrey Oaklands NHS Trust

Oaklands Hse, Coulsdon, Caterham, Surrey CR3 5YA;
  URL www.surreyoaklands.nhs.uk; E-mail
  <firstname>.<surname>@surreyoaklands.nhs.uk;
  Tel 01883 383838; Fax 01883 383522
Chair   Cathy Rollinson
Chief Executive   Maggie Somekh

Sussex Ambulance Service NHS Trust

Ambulance Headquarters, 40–42 Friars Wlk, Lewes, East
  Sussex BN7 2XW; E-mail info@sussamb.nhs.uk;
  Tel 01273 489444; Fax 01273 489445
Chief Executive   D. Griffiths

Swindon and Marlborough NHS Trust

The Great Western Hospital, Marlborough Rd, Swindon
  SN3 6BB; URL www.swindon-marlborough.nhs.uk;
  Tel 01793 604020; Fax 01793 604021
Chair   S. Webber
Chief Executive   L. Hill-Tout
Medical Director   J. Henson
Director (Nursing)   E. Strachan-Hall
Director (Operations)   S. Rowley
Director (Finance and Information)   C. Moar
Annual budget
£126 million

12

HOSPITALS

Child and Adolescent Mental Health Unit Okus Rd, Swindon SN1 4JU; Tel 01793 428800

The Great Western Hospital Marlborough Rd, Swindon SN3 6BB; Tel 01793 604020
Specialism: Acute (581)

Savernake Hospital Marlborough, Wiltshire; Tel 01672 514571; Fax 01672 514021
Specialism: Acute, geriatric, day surgery, GP.

Tameside and Glossop Acute Services NHS Trust

Tameside General Hospital, Fountain St, Ashton-under-Lyne, Tameside OL6 9RW; Tel 0161 331 6000; Fax 0161 331 6694
Chair A. Favell
Chief Executive Christine Green
Medical Director Dr A.S. Day
Director (Nursing, Quality and Human Resource) P.A. Ingam
Director (Corporate Development) A.D.L. Barnes
Director (Finance) C.E. Dunn

HOSPITALS

Donneybrook House Clarendon Rd, Hyde, Cheshire SK14 2AH

Hyde Physiotherapy Centre Parsonage St, Hyde, Cheshire

Richmond Group Practice Crickets La, Ashton-under-Lyne, Tameside

Shire Hill Hospital Bute St, Old Glossop, Derbyshire SK13 9PZ

Tameside General Hospital Fountain St, Ashton-under-Lyne, Tameside; Tel 0161 330 8373

Taunton and Somerset NHS Trust

Taunton and Somerset Hospital, Musgrove Pk, Taunton, Somerset TA1 5DA; URL www.somerset.nhs.uk; Tel 01823 333444; Fax 01823 336877
Chair B. Tanner
Chief Executive N. Chapman
Medical Director P. Cavanagh
Director (Patient Care and Nursing Services) L. Redfern
Director (Finance) S. Guy
Director (Planning and Support Services) D. Allwright
Annual budget
£111 million

HOSPITAL

Taunton and Somerset Hospital Musgrove Pk, Taunton, Somerset TA1 5DA; URL www.somerset.nhs.uk; Tel 01823 333444; Fax 01823 336877
Specialism: Acute; geriatric; maternity.

Tavistock and Portman NHS Trust

Tavistock Centre, 120 Belsize La, London NW3 5BA; URL www.tavi-port.org
Chair of Trust Board M. Wakelin-Saint
Chief Executive Dr Nicholas Temple
Director (Finance) Simon Young
Director (Central Services) Pat Key

CLINICS

Portman Clinic 8 Fitzjohns Ave, London NW3 5NA; Tel 020 7794 8262
Specialism: Mental health; psychotherapy; forensic.

Tavistock Clinic 120 Belsize La, London NW3 5BA; Tel 020 7435 7111
Specialism: Mental health; psychotherapy.

Tees and North East Yorkshire NHS Trust

HOSPITALS

Ashwood Mental Health Resource Centre Guisborough General Hospital, Guisborough, North Yorkshire TS14 6HZ; Tel 01287 630932
Specialism: Elderly, GP

East Cleveland Hospital Boulby Suite, Alford Rd, Brotton, Saltburn-by-the-Sea, North Yorkshire TS12 2FF; Tel 01287 676205; Fax 01287 678408
Specialism: Adult Mental Health.

St. Luke's Hospital Marton Rd, Middlesbrough TS4 3AF
Specialism: Adult mental health; special care; adolescent mental health; forensic psychiatry; elderly mental health; forensic learning disabilities. Number of beds: (274)

Stead Memorial Hospital EMI Ward, Kirkleatham St, Redcar, Redcar and Cleveland TS10 1QR; Tel 01642 483251
Specialism: EMI

West Lane Hospital Acklam Rd, Middlesbrough TS5 4EE; Tel 01642 813144; (Newberry Centre) 01642 352112 (Rosewood Centre) 01642 352070; Fax (Newberry Centre) 01642 822717; (Rosewood Centre) 01642 350273
Specialism: Support services.

Tees, East and North Yorkshire Ambulance Service NHS Trust

Fairfields, Shipton Rd, York YO30 1XW; URL www.tenyas.org.uk; E-mail reception@tenyas.nhs.uk; Tel 01904 666000; Fax 01904 666050
Chair Dr Nick Varey
Chief Executive Jayne Barnes, CBE
Director (Operations) Tim Lynch
Director (Finance) P. Holyoake
Director (Personnel and Training) Vacancy

Thames Gateway NHS Trust

Thames Gateway NHS Trust has now merged with Invicta Community Care NHS Trust to become West Kent NHS and Social Care Trust, which is listed alphabetically in this section.

Trafford Healthcare NHS Trust

Trafford General Hospital, Moorside Rd, Urmston, Greater Manchester M41 5SL; URL www.trafford.nhs.uk; E-mail sue.wallis@trafford.nhs.uk; Tel 0161 748 4022; Fax 0161 746 7214
Chief Executive David Cain

HOSPITALS

Altrincham General Hospital Market St, Altrincham, Greater Manchester WA14 1PE; Tel 0161 928 6111

Stretford Memorial Hospital 226 Seymour Gr, Old Trafford, Greater Manchester M16 0DU; Tel 0161 881 5353

St. Anne's Hospital Woodville Rd, Bowdon, Altrincham, Cheshire WA14 2AQ; Tel 0161 928 5851

Trafford General Hospital Moorside Rd, Davyhulme, Greater Manchester M41 5SL; Tel 0161 748 4022; Fax 0161 746 7214

Two Shires Ambulance NHS Trust

The Hunters, Buckingham Rd, Milton Keynes MK19 6HL; Tel 01908 262422; Fax 01908 265014
Chair Ken Cooper
Chief Executive P. Martin

Director (Human Resources)   C. Bailey
Director (Ambulance Services)   David Burk
Director (Finance and Information)   G. Rhodes
Annual budget
£25 million

United Bristol Healthcare NHS Trust

Trust Headquarters, Marlborough St, Bristol BS1 3NU;
URL www.ubht.nhs.uk; Tel 0117 929 0666; Fax 0117 925 6588
Chair   P. Gregory
Chief Executive   Vacancy
Medical Director   Vacancy
Director (Nursing)   L. Scott
Director (Finance)   G. Nix
Director (Personnel)   Ms A. Coults
Director (Service Development and Review)   Vacancy
Annual budget
£178 million

HOSPITALS

Bristol Eye Hospital   Lower Maudlin St, Bristol BS1 2LX;
Tel 0117 923 0060
Specialism: Eye, GP

Bristol General Hospital   Guinea St, Bristol BS1 6SY;
Tel 0117 926 5001
Specialism: Elderly care. (164)

Bristol Haematology and Oncology Centre   Horfield Rd,
Bristol BS2 8ED; Tel 0117 923 0000
Specialism: Radiotherapy; haematology. Number of beds: (55)

Bristol Homeopathic Hospital   Cotham Hill, Cotham, Bristol
BS6 6JU; Tel 0117 973 1231
Specialism: Homeopathic outpatients.

Bristol Royal Hospital for Children   Paul O'Gorman Bldg,
Upper Maudlin St, Bristol BS2 8BJ; Tel 0117 921 5411
Specialism: Paediatrics/BMT.

Bristol Royal Infirmary   Marlborough St, Bristol BS2 8HW;
Tel 0117 923 0000
Specialism: Acute medical (221); acute surgery (229)

Keynsham Hospital   Keynsham, Bristol BS31 1AG; Tel 0117
986 2356
Number of beds: (64)

St. Michael's Hospital   Southwell St, Bristol BS2 8EG;
Tel 0117 921 5411
Specialism: Obstetrics and gynaecology; ENT. Number of beds: (270)

University of Bristol Dental Hospital   Lower Maudlin St,
Bristol BS1 2LY; Tel 0117 923 0050

United Lincolnshire Hospitals NHS Trust

Trust Headquarters, Grantham and District Hospital, 101
Manthorpe Rd, Grantham, Lincolnshire NG31 8DG;
Tel 01476 565232; Fax 01456 567358
Chair   Mrs J. Green
Chief Executive   D. Loasby
Medical Director   Dr Martin Fairman
Director (Nursing)   Sarah W.K. Skelton
Director (Finance)   John A. Smith
Director (Personnel)   A. Avery
Annual budget
£200 million

HOSPITALS

County Hospital Louth   High Holme Rd, Louth, Lincolnshire
LN11 0EU; Tel 01507 600100; Fax 01507 609290
Specialism: Acute

Grantham and District Hospital   101 Manthorpe Rd,
Grantham, Lincolnshire NG31 8DG; Tel 01476 565232;
Fax 01476 590441

John Coupland Hospital   Ropery Rd, Gainsborough,
Lincolnshire DN21 2TJ; Tel 01427 816500; Fax 01427 816517

Johnson Hospital   Priory Rd, Spalding, Lincolnshire
PE11 2XD; Tel 01775 722386; Fax 01775 710038

Lincoln County Hospital   Greetwell Rd, Lincoln,
Lincolnshire LN2 5QY; Tel 01522 512512; Fax 01522 573419

Pilgrim Hospital   Sibsey Rd, Boston, Lincolnshire PE21 9QS;
Tel 01205 364801; Fax 01205 354395

Skegness and District Hospital   Dorothy Ave, Skegness,
Lincolnshire PE25 2BS; Tel 01754 762401; Fax 01754 760132

St. George's Hospital   Long Leys Rd, Lincoln, Lincolnshire
LN1 1EF; Tel 01522 512512
Specialism: Acute

Welland Hospital   Roman Bank, Spalding, Lincolnshire
PE11 2HN; Tel 01775 766800; Fax 01775 768134

University College London Hospitals NHS Trust

John Aster Hse, Foley St, London W2W 6ON;
URL www.uclk.org; Tel 020 7387 9300; Fax 020 7380 9536
Chair   P. Dixon
Chief Executive   R. Naylor
Medical Director   Dr A. Webb
Director (Finance)   H. Chalmers
Director (Human Resources)   H. Gordon
Chief Nurse and Director (Quality)   L. Boden
Annual budget
£240 million

HOSPITALS

The Eastman Dental Hospital   256 Gray's Inn Rd, London
WC1X 8LD; Tel 020 7915 1000

EGA and Obstetric Hospital   Huntley St, London
WC1E 6DY; Tel 020 7387 9300

The Hospital for Tropical Diseases   Mortimer Market,
Capper St, London WC1E 6JB; Tel 020 7387 9300
Specialism: Tropical medicine.

The Middlesex Hospital   Mortimer St, London W1T 3AA;
Tel 020 7636 8333
Specialism: Acute

The National Hospital for Neurology and Neurosurgery
Queen Sq, London WC1N 3BG; Tel 020 7837 3611

University College Hospital   25 Grafton Way, London
WC1E 6DB; Tel 020 7387 9300; Fax 020 7380 9977

University Hospital Birmingham NHS Trust

Trust Headquarters, Queen Elizabeth Medical Centre, Main
Drive, PO Box 9551, Edgbaston, Birmingham, West
Midlands B15 2PR; Tel 0121 627 2800; Fax 0121 627 2938
Chief Executive   Mark Britnell

University Hospitals Coventry and Warwickshire NHS Trust

Walsgrave Hospital, Clifford Bridge Rd, Coventry, West
Midlands CV2 2DX; Tel 024 7660 2020; Fax 024 7662 2197
Chair   Bryan Stoten
Chief Executive   David Roberts
Medical Director   Martin Lee
Medical Director   Prof Janet Powell
Director (Personnel)   Alice Casey
Director (Finance)   Jim Hayburn
Director (Nursing and Quality)   Hilary Scholefield

HOSPITALS

Coventry and Warwickshire Hospital   Stoney Stanton Rd,
Coventry, West Midlands CV1 4FH; Tel 024 7622 4055;
Fax 024 7622 1655

12

Hospital of St. Cross Barby Rd, Rugby, Warwickshire CV22 5PX; Tel 01788 572831; Fax 01788 545151

Walsgrave Hospital Clifford Bridge Rd, Walsgrave, Coventry, West Midlands CV2 2DX; Tel 024 7660 2020
Specialism: Acute Number of beds: (633)

University Hospitals of Leicester NHS Trust

Headquarters, Glenfield Hospital, Groby Rd, Leicester LE3 9QP; URL www.uhl-tr.nhs.uk;
E-mail public.relations@uhl-tr.nhs.uk; Tel 0116 287 1471; Fax 0116 258 3950
Chair P. Hammersley
Chief Executive P. Reading; Tel 0116 256 3188; Fax 0116 256 3187
Medical Director A. Cole
Director (Human Resources) D. Grafton
Director (Finance) S. Hogg
Director (Nursing Services) P. Tagg
Annual budget
£385 million

HOSPITALS

Glenfield Hospital Headquarters, Groby Rd, Leicester, Leicestershire LE3 9QP; URL www.uhl-tr.nhs.uk;
E-mail public.relations@uhl-tr.nhs.uk; Tel 0116 287 1471

Leicester General Hospital Gwendolen Rd, Leicester, Leicestershire LE5 4PW; URL www.uhl-tr.nhs.uk;
E-mail public.relations@uhl-tr.nhs.uk; Tel 0116 249 0490

The Leicester Royal Infirmary Leicester LE1 5WW; URL www.uhl-tr.nhs.uk;
E-mail public.relations@uhl-tr.nhs.uk; Tel 0116 254 1414
Specialism: Acute; obstetrics; neonatal. Number of beds: (1508)

Walsall Community Health NHS Trust

The Walsall Community Health NHS Trust has now become the Walsall Primary Care Trust, which is listed alphabetically under the Primary Care Trust section in this chapter.

Walsall Hospitals NHS Trust

Manor Hospital, Moat Rd, Walsall, West Midlands WS2 9PS; Tel 01922 721172; Fax 01922 656621
Chair Barrie Blower, MBE
Chief Executive Vacancy
Medical Director M. Browne
Deputy Chief Executive and Director (Finance) M. Stevens
Director (Nursing) N. Kee
Director (Support Services and Estates) D. Lawson
Director (Operations) D. Muhl
Director (Organisational Development and Human Resources) Miss S. Wakeman
Annual budget
£107 million

HOSPITALS

Goscote Hospital Goscote La, Walsall, West Midlands WS3 1SJ; Tel 01922 710710
Specialism: Geriatrics.

Manor Hospital Walsall, West Midlands WS2 9PS; Tel 01922 721172
Specialism: Acute (497); maternity (69); elderly care (184).

Walton Centre for Neurology and Neurosurgery NHS Trust

Lower La, Fazakerley, Liverpool, Merseyside L9 7JL; Tel 0151 525 3611; Fax 0151 529 5500
Chair J. Brittain

Chief Executive K. Griffiths (Acting)
Medical Director M.D.M. Shaw
Director (Nursing) J. Holt
Director (Finance and Information) K. Griffiths
Director (Research and Education) P.R. Humphrey
Annual budget
£38 million

Warrington Community Healthcare NHS Trust

Warrington Community Healthcare NHS Trust is now part of 5 Boroughs Partnership NHS Trust, which is listed alphabetically in this section.

Warwickshire Ambulance Service NHS Trust

Dale St, Leamington Spa, Warwickshire CV32 4HY; Tel 01926 881331; Fax 01926 488409
Chair Prof M. Langman, MD, FRCP, FMEDSCI
Chief Executive M.J. Hazell, MBE, MBA
Director (Operations) S. McGuinness
Director (Finance) K. Blower
Director (Human Resources) E. Roughton

The West Dorset General Hospitals NHS Trust

Dorset County Hospital, Williams Ave, Dorchester, Dorset DT1 2JY
Chair R. SeQueira, CBE
Chief Executive Nick Cox
Medical Director Dr D. Cove
Deputy Chief Executive and Director (Service Development) Ms E. Mead
Director (Nursing and Quality Assurance) Mrs E. Maxwell
Director (Finance) P. Turner
Annual budget
£75 million

HOSPITALS

Digby Court Edward Rd, Dorchester, Dorset DT1 2HL
Specialism: Children's learning disabilities.

Dorset County Hospital Williams Ave, Dorchester, Dorset DT1 2JY; Tel 01305 251150
Specialism: Acute Number of beds: (318)

CHILD DEVELOPMENT CENTRE

Children's Centre Damers Rd, Dorchester, Dorset DT1 2LB; Tel 01305 251150

West Hampshire NHS Trust

Maples Bldgs, Tatchbury Mount Hospital, Calmore, Southampton SO40 2RZ; URL www.wht.nhs.uk;
E-mail david.freeman@wht.nhs.uk; Tel 023 8087 4300; Fax 023 8087 4301
Chief Executive Martin Barkley

West Hertfordshire Hospitals NHS

Watford General Hospital, Vicarage Rd, Watford, Hertfordshire WD1 8HB; Tel 01923 244366; Fax 01923 217440
Chair Rosie Sanderson
Chief Executive S. Eames
Medical Director H. Borkett-Jones
Director (Cancer Services) Dr D. Fermont
Director (Finance and Information) Chris Burnside
Director (Personnel) Caroline Corrigan

MOUNT VERNON HOSPITAL – SPECIALIST SERVICES

Rickmansworth Rd, Northwood, Greater London HA6 2RN; Tel 01923 826111; Fax 01923 935803

HOSPITALS

Hemel Hempstead General Hospital Hillfield Rd, Hemel Hempstead, Hertfordshire; Tel 01442 213141

St. Albans City Hospital Normandy Rd, St. Albans, Hertfordshire; Tel 01727 866122

Watford General Hospital Vicarage Rd, Watford, Hertfordshire WD1 8HB; Tel 01923 244366

West Kent NHS and Social Care Trust

35 Kings Hill Ave, West Malling, Kent ME19 4AX; Tel 01732 520400; Fax 01732 520401
Chair Ward Griffiths
Chief Executive Jon Wilkes
Medical Director Dr Sabah Sadik
Director (Nursing) Peter Hasler
Director (Personnel) Louise Norris
Director (Learning Disability Services) Damien Hillen
Director (Corporate Affairs) Dr Claude Pendaries
Director (Specialist Services) Judith Walker
Director (Support Services) Carmel Martin
Director (Facilities) David Vann
Director (Mental Health and Social Care Services) James Sinclair
Director (Mental Health Services East) Kevin Lindsay

HOSPITALS

Archery House Bow Arrow La, Dartford, Kent DA2 6PB; Tel 01322 622222
Specialism: Learning disabilities (80)

Heathside Heath Rd, Coxheath, Maidstone, Kent ME17 4EH; Tel 01622 741855
Mental health services for older people.

Priority House Hermitage La, Maidstone, Kent ME16 9PH; Tel 01622 725000

West London Mental Health NHS Trust

Trust Headquarters, St. Bernard's Hospital, Uxbridge Rd, Southall, Greater London UB1 3EU;
E-mail jacky.vincent@wlmht.nhs.uk

HOSPITALS

Cassell Hospital 1 Ham Common, Richmond, Surrey TW10 7JF

Charing Cross Hospital Fulham Palace Rd, London W6 8RF

John Connolly Wing Uxbridge Rd, Southall, London UB1 3EU; Tel 020 8574 2444; Fax 020 8967 5496

St. Bernard's Wing Uxbridge Rd, Southall, London UB1 3EU; Tel 020 8574 2444; Fax 020 8967 5496

DAY HOSPITALS

Gunnersbury Day Hospital 46 Gunnersbury La, London W3 8EG

Penny Sangam Day Hospital Osterley Park Rd, Southall, Greater London UB2 4EU

MENTAL HEALTH RESOURCE CENTRES

Avenue House 43–47 Avenue Rd, Acton, London W3 8NJ

Cherington House Cherington Rd, London W7 3HL

Manor Gate 1a Manor Gate, Northolt, Greater London UB5 5TG

Southall Norwood The Green, Southall, Greater London UB2 4BH

West Middlesex University Hospital NHS Trust

Twickenham Rd, Isleworth, Greater London TW7 6AF;
URL www.west-middlesex-hospital.org.uk;
E-mail sue.ellen@wmuh-tr.nthames.nhs.uk; Tel 020 8560 2121
Chair Sue Ellen
Chief Executive Gail Wannell

West Midlands Ambulance Service NHS Trust

Millennium Point, Waterfront Bus Pk, Waterfront Way, Brierly Hill, Dudley, West Midlands DY5 1LX;
URL www.wmas.nhs.uk;
E-mail enquiries@wmas-tr.wmids.nhs.uk; Tel 01384 215555; Fax 01384 246316
Chair D.H. Jinks
Chief Executive B.M. Johns
Medical Director Dr I. Robertson-Steel
Director (Operations) R.J. Seaward
Director (Finance) R.W. Hinton
Director (Personnel) Ms J. Howell

West Suffolk Hospitals NHS Trust

Hardwick La, Bury St. Edmunds, Suffolk IP33 2QZ;
URL www.wsufftrust.org.uk; Tel 01284 713000;
Fax 01284 701993
Chair Veronica Worrall
Chief Executive John Parkes
Medical Director and Director (Education) K. Matheson
Director (Nursing and Community Relations) N. Day
Director (Finance and Information) K. Mansfield
Director (Facilities) S. Moore
Director (Modernisation) J. Harper-Smith
Director (Personnel and Corporate Resources) J. Bloomfield
Annual budget
£73 million

HOSPITALS

St. Leonard's Hospital Newton Rd, Sudbury, Suffolk CO10 6RQ; Tel 01787 371341

Walnuttree Hospital Walnuttree La, Sudbury, Suffolk CO10 6BE; Tel 01787 371404
Specialism: Elderly care; rehabilitation.

West Suffolk Hospital Hardwick La, Bury St. Edmunds, Suffolk IP33 2QZ; Tel 01284 713000
Specialism: Acute (575)

West Sussex Health and Social Care NHS Trust

Trust Headquarters, Arundel Rd, Worthing, West Sussex BN13 3EP; URL www.wshsc.nhs.uk; Tel 01903 843000;
Fax 01903 843001
Chair Glynn Jones
Chief Executive Lisa Rodrigues
Medical Director Dr J. McCarthy
Executive Director (Finance and Performance) Spencer Prosser
Executive Director (Nursing) Helen Greatorex
Executive Director (Social Care; Older People and Learning Disability Services) Neil Perkins
Executive Director (Mental Health; Secure and Substance Misuse Service) Sue Morris
Director (Human Resources) Andrew Kelly
Director (Estates and Facilities) Mark Heathcote
Head (Corporate Affairs) Julie Kilner
Head (Communications) Andrew Partington
A specialist mental health and learning disabilities Trust, incorporating substance misuse services.

12

West Yorkshire Metropolitan Ambulance Service NHS Trust

West Yorkshire Metropolitan Ambulance Service, Threelands, Bradford, West Yorkshire BD11 2AH; Tel 01274 707070; Fax 01274 707071
Chair Ralph Berry
Chief Executive Trevor Molton
Director (Corporate Performance) Andrew Cratchley
Director (Finance) Vacancy
Director (Operations) Bob Williams

Westcountry Ambulance Service NHS Trust

Unit 3 Abbey Crt, Eagle Way, Sowton, Exeter, Devon EX2 7HY; URL www.wcas.nhs.uk; E-mail enquiries@wcas-tr.swest.nhs.uk; Tel 01392 261500; Fax 01392 261510
Chair S. Jones
Chief Executive M. Willis

Weston Area Health NHS Trust

Weston General Hospital, Grange Rd, Weston-super-Mare, North Somerset BS23 4TQ; Tel 01934 636363; Fax 01934 647029
Chair Dr J. Post
Chief Executive R. Moyse
Medical Director Dr P. Woodhead
Director (Nursing) C. Becker
Director (Finance and Resources) M. Collins
Annual budget
£45 million

HOSPITALS

Weston General Hospital Grange Rd, Uphill, Weston-super-Mare, North Somerset BS23 4TQ; Tel 01934 636363
Specialism: Acute; geriatric; maternity. Number of beds: (252)

Whipps Cross University Hospital NHS Trust

Management Block, Whipps Cross Hospital, Leytonstone, London E11 1NR; URL www.whippsx.nhs.uk; Tel 020 8539 5522; Fax 020 8558 8115
Chair Stephen Jacobs, OBE
Chief Executive Peter Coles
Medical Director Paul Thomas
Director (Finance) and Deputy Chief Executive Conrad Leslie
Director (Nursing and Quality) Eileen Sills
Director (Human Resources) Frank McKenna

HOSPITAL

Whipps Cross University Hospital Whipps Cross Rd, Leytonstone, London E11 1NR; Tel 020 8539 5522; Fax 020 8558 8115
Specialism: Mainly acute

MEDICAL CENTRES

Forest Medical Centre Old Station Rd, Loughton, Essex IG10 4PE; Tel 020 8508 2288; 020 8532 0880
Silverthorn Medical Centre 2 Friars Cl, Larkshall Rd, Chingford, London E4 6UN; Tel 020 8529 3706; Fax 020 8529 9919

OTHER SITES

Ainslie Rehab Unit 3 Friars Cl, Larkshall Rd, Chingford, London E4 6UW; Tel 020 8529 7141; Fax 020 8535 6470
Specialism: Elderly rehabilitation.
Heronwood and Galleon Unit Makepeace Rd, Hermon Hill, Wanstead, London E11 1UU; Tel 020 8530 5665; Fax 020 8530 5665

Whittington Hospital NHS Trust

Highgate Hill, London N19 5NF; Tel 020 7272 3070; Fax 020 7288 5550
Chair Vacancy
Chief Executive Andrew Riley

HOSPITAL

The Whittington Hospital Highgate Hill, London N19 5NF
Specialism: Acute.

Wiltshire Ambulance Service NHS Trust

Ambulance Headquarters, Greenways Centre, Chippenham, Wiltshire SN15 5LN; E-mail dennis.lauder@wiltsambs-tr.swest.nhs.uk; Tel 01249 443939; Fax 01249 443217
Chair K. Small
Chief Executive D. Lauder

Winchester and Eastleigh Healthcare NHS Trust

Royal Hampshire County Hospital, Romsey Rd, Winchester, Hampshire SO22 5DG; Tel 01962 863535; Fax 01962 824826
Chair D. Livermore
Chief Executive R. Halls
Medical Director H. Sanderson
Director (Nursing and Operations) J. Gillow
Director (Finance) J. Williams
Director (Personnel) V. Fletcher

HOSPITALS

The Mount Hospital Bishopstoke, Eastleigh, Hampshire SO5 6ZB; Tel 023 8061 2335; Fax 023 8065 0954
Specialism: Geriatric (39)
Royal Hampshire County Hospital Romsey Rd, Winchester, Hampshire SO22 5DG; Tel 01962 863535; Fax 01962 824826
Specialism: Acute (530)

Wirral and West Cheshire Community NHS Trust

Wirral and West Cheshire Community NHS Trust has been dissolved and its services are now covered by Wirral Hospital NHS Trust, Cheshire and Wirral Partnership NHS Trust, Clatterbridge Centre for Oncology NHS Trust, Ellesmere Port and Neston Primary Care Trust, Bevington and West Wirral Primary Care Trust, Birkenhead and Wallasey Primary Care Trust and Wirral Primary Care Trust which are listed alphabetically under the appropriate headings in this chapter.

Wirral Hospital NHS Trust

Arrowe Pk Rd, Upton, Wirral CH49 5PE; E-mail wirral.enq@whnt.nhs.uk; Tel 0151 678 5111; Fax 0151 604 7148
Chair E.A. Hoskins
Chief Executive F.G. Burns
Medical Director Dr I.R. Jones
Clinical Director Dr D. King
Director (Operations) and Chief Nurse P.M. Holt
Director (Finance) F.R. Jones
Director (Human Resources) G. Hewitt
Head (IMST) P. Marsh
Director (Facilities) N. Stanier
Chief Pharmacist K. Farrar
Annual budget
£137 million

HOSPITALS

Arrowe Park Hospital Arrowe Park Rd, Upton, Wirral CH49 5PE; Tel 0151 678 5111
Specialism: Acute. Number of beds: (910)

Clatterbridge Hospital Bebington, Wirral CH63 4JY; Tel 0151 334 4000
  Specialism: Acute. Number of beds: (238)

Wolverhampton Health Care NHS Trust

Cleveland and Leasowes, 10–12 Tettenhall Rd, Wolverhampton, West Midlands WV1 4SA; Tel 01902 444203; Fax 01902 444446
Chief Executive M. Pyrah

Worcestershire Acute Hospitals NHS Trust

Worcestershire Royal Hospital, Charles Hastings Way, Worcester, Worcestershire WR5 1DD; Tel 01905 763333; Fax 01905 760555
Chair Michael O'Riordan
Chief Executive John Rostill
Medical Director Dr Charles Ashton
Director (Human Resources) Jeff Crawshaw
Director (Finance and Performance Management)
  James Murray (Acting)
Director (Information) Steve Jarman-Davies
Director (Nursing, Midwifery and Professions Allied to Medicine) Rachel Overfield (Acting)
Annual Budget
£150 million

Worcestershire Mental Health Partnership NHS Trust

Isaac Maddox Hse, Shrub Hill Rd, Worcester, Worcestershire WR4 9RW; Tel 01905 681511; Fax 01905 681515
Chair J. Calvert
Chief Executive Ros Keeton (Acting)
Medical Director Dr Jane Richards
Director (Finance and Informatics) I. McCarley
Director (Clinical Services and Nursing) Colin Vines
Director (Human Resources) C. Nash
Annual budget
£32 million

HOSPITALS

Brook Haven Mental Health Unit Stourbridge Rd, Bromsgrove, Worcestershire B61 0BB; Tel 01527 488279
  Specialism: Psychiatric (133)

Hill Crest Mental Health Unit Quinneys La, Redditch, Worcestershire B98 7WG; Tel 01527 500575

Kidderminster Hospital D Block, Bewdley Rd, Kidderminster, Worcestershire DY11 6RJ; Tel 01562 823424

Lucy Baldwin Hospital Olive Gr, Stourport-on-Severn, Worcestershire DY13 8XY; Tel 01299 827327

Newtown Hospital Newtown Rd, Worcestershire WR5 1JG; Tel 01905 763333

Worthing and Southlands Hospitals NHS Trust

Lyndhurst Rd, Worthing, West Sussex BN11 2DH; Tel 01903 205111; Fax 01903 285045
Chair S. Heatherington
Chief Executive M.B. Smits
Medical Director Dr J. Bull
Director (Nursing and Clinical Services) Ms R. Crannd
Director (Planning) M. Pearson
Director (Finance) S. Cass
Annual budget
£80 million

HOSPITALS

Southlands Hospital Shoreham by Sea, West Sussex BN4 6TQ; Tel 01273 455622
  Specialism: Acute

Worthing Hospital Lyndhurst Rd, Worthing, West Sussex BN11 2DH; Tel 01903 205111
  Specialism: Acute

Wrightington, Wigan and Leigh NHS Trust

NHS Trust Headquarters, Royal Albert Edward Infirmary, Wigan, Greater Manchester WN1 2NN; Tel (Switchboard) 01942 244000; Fax (Trust Headquarters) 01942 822158
Chair Brian Strett; Tel 01942 822196
Chief Executive Mrs S.H. Cumiskey; Tel 01942 822194
Medical Director Dr A.G. Wardman; Tel 01942 822186
Director (Service Improvement) T. Pickering; Tel 01942 822026
Executive Director (Finance and Information) J. Marks
Executive Director (Nursing and Patient Services) M. Pickup
Director (Human Resources) W.L. Livingstone
Wrightington, Wigan and Leigh NHS Trust is an acute trust.
Annual Budget (2002–2003)
£147 million

HOSPITALS

Billinge Hospital Upholland Rd, Billinge, Wigan, Greater Manchester WN6 7ET; Tel 01695 626007; Fax 01695 626113

Leigh Infirmary The Avenue, Leigh, Lancashire WN7 1HS; Tel 01942 264391; Fax 01942 264388

Royal Albert Edward Infirmary Wigan La, Wigan, Greater Manchester WN1 2NN; Tel 01942 244000; Fax 01942 822042
  Specialism: Acute.

Whelley Hospital Bradshaw St, Whelley, Wigan, Greater Manchester WN1 3XD; Tel 01942 822631; Fax 01942 822630

York Health Services NHS Trust

Headquarters, Bootham Pk, York, North Yorkshire YO30 7BY; Tel 01904 725087; Fax 01904 726862
Chair Prof Alan Maynard
Chief Executive Simon Pleydell
Deputy Chief Executive G.T. Wood
Medical Director Dr Michael Porte
Director (Nursing) Mike Proctor
Director (Finance) S.J. Yorston

HOSPITALS

Bootham Park Hospital Bootham, York YO30 7BY; Tel 01904 631313; Fax 01904 726849

Lime Trees Child, Adolescent and Family Unit Shipton Rd, York YO3 6RE; Tel 01904 652908
  Specialism: Child psychiatry

York District Hospital Wigginton Rd, York YO30 7HE; Tel 01904 631313; Fax 01904 726840
  Specialism: Acute (818) Number of beds: Other (795)

12

Care Trusts

The first Care Trust sites were launched on 1 April 2002 in Bradford and Northumberland. They were established with the main aim for closer integration of the services provided by the NHS and local authorities. Care Trusts focus on specific patient groups where needed, such as providing integrated care for those with mental health problems or special services to allow those with physical disabilities to live independent lives. They are established on a voluntary basis where it has been locally agreed that this would be the best model for delivering better health and social care services. Please consult the Department of Health's website (www.doh.gov.uk) for up-to-date additions and contact details.

Bexley Care Trust

221 Erith Rd, Bexleyheath, Kent DA7 6HZ

Bradford District Care Trust

Headquarters, Victoria Rd, Saltaire, Shipley, West Yorkshire
BD18 3LD; Tel 01274 366007; Fax 01274 366060
Chair Linda Pollard, JP
Chief Executive Con Egan
Director (Finance) Philip Gutcher
Director (Medical) Simon Baugh
Director (Nursing) Stuart Bootland
Director (Adult Mental Health Services) Chris Bielby
Director (Learning Disabilities) Brian Stanley
Director (Personnel and Development) June Goodson-Moore
Director (Care Trust Project) Kevin Mitchell
Director (Healthcare Facilities) Andrew Gunnee
Director (Child and Adolescent Mental Health Services)
Lesley Hewson
Director (Older People Mental Health Services)
Stuart Fawcett
Budget
£83 million

Camden and Islington Mental Health and Social Care Trust

St Pancras Hospital, 4 St. Pancras Way, London, NW1 0PE;
URL www.candi.nhs.uk; Tel 020 7530 3000; Fax 020 7530
3735
Chief Executive Erville Millar

Manchester Mental Health and Social Care Trust

Chorlton Hse, 17 Manchester Rd, Chorlton cum Hardy,
Manchester M21 9UN

Northumberland Care Trust

Merley Croft, Loansdean, Morpeth, Northumberland
NE61 2DL; URL www.northumberlandcaretrust.nhs.uk;
Tel 01670 394400; Fax 01670 394501
Chair Prof Ray Cartwright
Chief Executive Linda Ions
Director (Clinical and Care Governance – Medical) Gill Fraser
Director (Public Health) Mike Lavender
Director (Social Care and Planning) David Parkin
Director (Finance) David Reynolds

Sandwell Mental Health NHS and Social Care Trust

48 Lodge Rd, West Bromwich, West Midlands B70 8NY

Sheffield Care Trust

Fulwood Hse, Old Fulwood Rd, Sheffield, S10 3TH;
URL www.sct.nhs.uk; Tel 0114 271 6310; Fax 0114 271
6734

Witham, Braintree and Halstead Care Trust

Market Hse, Market Pl, Braintree, Essex CM7 3HQ;
URL www.braintreecaretrust.nhs.uk;
E-mail becky.osborne@braintreecaretrust.nhs.uk;
Tel 01376 331549; Fax 01376 331556
Chief Executive Paul Zollinger-Read

Primary Care Trusts

Adur, Arun and Worthing Primary Care Trust

The Causeway, Goring by Sea, West Sussex BN12 6BT;
URL www.healthinaaw.nhs.uk;
E-mail chiefexec@aaw.nhs.uk
Chief Executive Steve Phoenix
Chair Margaret Bamford (Acting)

Littlehampton Hospital Fitzalan Rd, Littlehampton, West
Sussex BN17 5EU; Tel 01903 717101
Community

Airedale Primary Care Trust

Airedale Hse, 21a Mornington St, Keighley, West Yorkshire
BD21 2EA; URL www.airedale-pct.nhs.uk;
E-mail rachel.bruniges@bradford.nhs.uk
Chief Executive Kevin Ellis
Chair Elizabeth Wolstenholme

Amber Valley Primary Care Trust

Babington Hospital, Derby Rd, Belper, Derbyshire
DE56 1WH; URL www.ambervalley-pct.nhs.uk;
Tel 01773 525099; Fax 01773 827360
Chief Executive Wendy Lawrence
Chair Adrian Evans

Ashfield Primary Care Trust

Ashfield Business Centre, The Idlewells Precinct, Sutton in
Ashfield, Nottinghamshire NG17 1BP
Chief Executive Clive Brooks
Chair Keith Rees

Ashford Primary Care Trust

3, The Eurogate Bus Pk, Thomson Rd, Ashford, Kent
TN24 8XW
Chief Executive Marion Dinwoodie
Chair Smallridge

HOSPITAL

Westview Hospital Plummers La, Tenterden, Kent
TN30 6TX; Tel 01580 763677

HEALTH CENTRES AND CLINICS

East Cross Clinic Recreation Ground Rd, Tenterden, Kent
TN30 6RA; Tel 01580 262000
Vicarage Lane Clinic Vicarage La, Ashford, Kent TN23 1NJ;
Tel 01233 204100

Ashton, Leigh and Wigan Primary Care Trust

Bryan Hse, 61–69 Standish Gate, Wigan, Lancashire
WN1 1AH
Chief Executive Peter Rowe
Chair Lynne Liptrott

COMMUNITY PREMISES

Ashton Clinic Queen's Rd, Ashton-in-Makerfield, Wigan,
Greater Manchester WN4 8LB; Tel 01942 712551
Aspull Clinic Haigh Rd, Aspull, Wigan, Greater Manchester
WN2 1XH; Tel 01942 831169
Astley Clinic 510 Manchester Rd, Astley, Greater
Manchester M29 7BP; Tel 01942 896040
Atherton Clinic Formby Ave, Atherton, Greater Manchester
M46 0HX; Tel 01942 892166
Beech Hill Health Centre Beech Hall St, Wigan, Greater
Manchester WN6 7XH; Tel 01924 236228
Brown Street Drug Centre 14 Brown St North, Leigh,
Wigan, Greater Manchester WN7 1BU
Child and Family Psychiatry Unit 155–157 Manchester Rd,
Higher Ince, Wigan, Greater Manchester WN2 2JA;
Tel 01942 826063
Children's Hearing Service Park Centre, Park Rd, Hindley,
Wigan, Greater Manchester WN2 3RY; Tel 01942 526311

College Street Health Centre College St, Leigh, Lancashire WN7 2RF; Tel 01942 674431

Golborne Clinic Lowton Rd, Golborne, Warrington WA3 3EG; Tel 01942 711139

Grasmere Street Health Centre Grasmere St, Leigh, Lancashire WN7 1XB; Tel 01942 603311

Hindley Health Centre Liverpool Rd, Hindley, Wigan, Greater Manchester WN2 3HQ; Tel 01942 255291

Ince Clinic and Community Centre Manchester Rd, Ince, Wigan, Greater Manchester WN2 2JA; Tel 01942 493094

Learning Disabilities Service 196 Newton Rd, Lowton, Golborne, Warrington; Tel 01942 513885

Longshoot Health Centre Scholes, Wigan, Greater Manchester WN1 3NH; Tel 01942 248551

Marsh Green Clinic Harrow Rd, Marsh Grn, Wigan, Greater Manchester WN5 0QL; Tel 01942 223462

Marus Bridge Health Centre Highfield Grange Ave, Marus Bridge, Wigan, Greater Manchester WN3 6SU; Tel 01942 236221

Mental Handicap Unit 11 Bridgeman Terr, Wigan, Greater Manchester WN1 1SX

Mere Oaks School Wigan Rd, Standish, Wigan, Greater Manchester WN1 2RF; Tel 01942 243481

Orrell Clinic 299 Orrell Rd, Wigan, Lancashire WN5 8QU; Tel 01695 622892

Pemberton Clinic Portakabins, Kingsdown High School, Montrose Ave, Pemberton, Wigan, Greater Manchester WN5 8QX; Tel 01942 214260

Platt Bridge Clinic Victoria St, Platt Bridge, Wigan, Greater Manchester WN2 5AH; Tel 01942 866445

Psychiatric Drop-In Centre 158–160 Sherwood Dr, Wigan, Greater Manchester WN5 9RS; Tel (Vaccination and Immunisation Section) 01942 216770

Shevington Clinic Miles La, Shevington, Lancashire WN8 8EW; Tel 01257 252666

Standish Clinic 46 High St, Standish, Wigan, Greater Manchester WN6 0HA; Tel 01257 422855

Tyldesley Clinic Poplar St, Tyldesley, Greater Manchester WN5 8QU; Tel 01942 882474

Barking and Dagenham Primary Care Trust

The Clock Hse, East St, Barking, Essex IG11 8EY; Tel 020 8591 9595; Fax 020 8591 9595
Chief Executive Ms Julia Ross
Chair Raymond Parkin

Barnet Primary Care Trust

Hyde Hse, The Hyde, Edgware Rd, London NW9 6QQ
Chief Executive Avaril Dongworth
Chair Peter Hollins

HOSPITALS

Edgware Community Hospital Edgware, Greater London HA8 0AD; Tel 020 8952 2381

Finchley Memorial Hospital Granville Rd, North Finchley, London N12 0JE; Tel 020 8349 3121

Marie Foster Home Wood St, Barnet, London EN5 4BG; Tel 020 8440 5111

Barnsley Primary Care Trust

Hillder Hse, 49–51 Gawer Rd, Barnsley, South Yorkshire S75 2PY; URL www.barnsleypct.nhs.uk
Chief Executive Alisa Claire
Chair Tom Sheard

Basildon Primary Care Trust

Phoenix Crt, Christopher Martin Rd, Basildon, Essex SS14 3GH; URL www.basildon-pct.nhs.uk; E-mail info@basildonpct.nhs.uk; Tel 01268 705000; Fax 01268 705100
Chief Executive Mary-Ann Munford
Chair Alwyn Hollins (Acting)

Bassetlaw Primary Care Trust

Retford Hospital, North Rd, Retford, Nottinghamshire DN22 7XF
Chief Executive Louise Newcombe
Chair John Deakin

Bath and North East Somerset Primary Care Trust

St. Martins Hospital, Midford Rd, Bath, Somerset BA2 5RP; URL www.banes-pct.nhs.uk
Chief Executive Rhona Macdonald
Chair Cllr Hanney, MC

Bebington and West Wirral Primary Care Trust

Admin Block, St. Catherine's Hospital, Church Rd, Birkenhead, Merseyside CH42 0LQ
Chief Executive Cooke
Chair Pursglove

Bedford Primary Care Trust

Gilbert Hitchcock Hse, 21 Kimbolton Rd, Bedford, Bedfordshire MK40 2AW
Chief Executive Margaret Stockham
Chair Alan Loins

Bedfordshire Heartlands Primary Care Trust

1–2 Dolittle Mill, Froghall Rd, Ampthill, Bedfordshire MK45 2NX
Chief Executive John Swain
Chair Robin Younger

HOSPITALS

Biggleswade Hospital Potton Rd, Biggleswade, Bedfordshire SG18 0EL; Tel 01767 224906; Fax 01767 224901

Steppingley Hospital Ampthill Rd, Steppingley, Bedfordshire MK45 1AB; Tel 01525 631185; Fax 01525 631175

Bexhill and Rother Primary Care Trust

Bexhill Hospital, Holliers Hill, Bexhill-on-Sea, East Sussex TN40 2DZ; E-mail stern.rick@bar-pct.sthames.nhs.uk
Chief Executive Rick Stern
Chair Barnes

Bexley Primary Care Trust

Marlowe Hse, 109 Station Rd, Bexely Heath, Sidcup, Kent DA15 7EU
Chief Executive Alwen Williams
Chair Kathleen Balcomb

Billericay, Brentwood and Wickford Primary Care Trust

Trust Headquarters, Highwood Hospital, Ongar Rd, Brentwood, Essex CM15 9DY
Chief Executive Howard Perry
Chair Angela Bloomfield

12

Birkenhead and Wallasey Primary Care Trust

Admin Block, St. Catherine's Hospital, Church Rd,
   Birkenhead, Merseyside CH42 0LQ
Chair Muriel Downs
Head (Corporate Services and Communications) Lin Danher

Blackburn and Darwen Primary Care Trust

Guide Bus Pk, School La, Guide, Blackburn BB1 2HH;
   URL www.bwdpct.org.uk; Tel 01254 267000; Fax 01254
   267009
Chief Executive Vivien Aspey
Chair Pauline Walsh

Blackpool Primary Care Trust

Blackpool Techno Management Centre, Faraday Way,
   Blackpool, Lancashire FY2 0JW
Chief Executive Wendy Potts
Chair Tony Shaw

Blackwater Valley and Hart Primary Care Trust

Winchfield Lodge, Old Potbridge Rd, Winchfield, Hook,
   Hampshire RG27 8BT
Chief Executive Debbie Glenn;
   E-mail debbie.glenn@bvhpct.nhs.uk
Chair John Parker

HOSPITAL

Odiham Cottage Hospital Odiham, Hampshire RG25 1NE;
Tel 01256 393600

Bolton Primary Care Trust

St. Peters Hse, Silverwell St, Bolton, Lancashire BL1 1PP;
   Tel 01204 377000; Fax 01204 377004
Chair Pamela Senior
Chief Executive Dr Kevin Snee
Director (Service Provision) M. Cropper
Director (Service Redesign) A. Gaughan
Director (Resource Allocation) T. Bennett
Director (Personnel and Development) A. Basford
Manager (Estates and Facilities) D. Hunt
Manager (Corporate Affairs) J. Morris
Financial Controller H. Ballantyne
Annual Budget
£23 million

Bournemouth Primary Care Trust

11 Shelly Rd, Boscombe, Bournemouth BH1 4JQ
Chief Executive Debbie Flemmimg
Chair Rex Symons, CBE

Bracknell Forest Primary Care Trust

Church Hill Hse, 51–52 Turing Dr, Bracknell, Berkshire
   RG12 7FR
Chief Executive Diane Hedges;
   E-mail diane.hedges@berks-ha.nhs.uk
Chair Paul Adams

Bradford City Primary Care Trust

Joseph Brennan Hse, Sunbridge Rd, Bradford, West
   Yorkshire BD1 2SY
Chief Executive Lynnette Throp
Chair Mohammed Ajeeb

Bradford South and West Primary Care Trust

Bryan Sutherland Hse, off Dunnock Ave, Bradford, West
   Yorkshire BD6 3XH; URL www.bradfordswpct.co.uk;
   E-mail <firstname>.<surname>@bradford.nhs.uk
Chief Executive Dr Barbara Hakin
Chair Sarah Warner

Brent Primary Care Trust

Wembley Centre for Health and Care, 116 Chaplin Rd,
   Wembley, London HA0 4UZ
Chief Executive Dr Lise Llewellyn
Chair Jean Gaffin

Brighton and Hove City Primary Care Trust

6th Fl, Vantage Point, New England Rd, Brighton, East
   Sussex BN1 4GW;
   URL www.brightonhove.citypct.nhs.uk
Chief Executive Gary Needle
Chair Jean Spray

Bristol North Primary Care Trust

King Square Hse, King Sq, Bristol BS2 8EE
Chief Executive Chris Born
Chair Arthur Keefe

Bristol South and West Primary Care Trust

King Square Hse, King Sq, Bristol BS2 0EE
Chief Executive Deborah Evans
Chair Tom Dowell

Broadland Primary Care Trust

St. Andrews Hse, St. Andrews Bus Pk, Yarmouth Rd,
   Norwich, Norfolk NR7 0HT

Bromley Primary Care Trust

Bassetts Hse, Broadwater Gdns, Farnborough, Orpington,
   Kent BR6 7UA
Chief Executive Bridget Riches
Chair Prof Andrian Eddleston

Broxtowe and Hucknall Primary Care Trust

Trust Headquarters, Priory Crt, Derby Rd, Nottingham,
   Nottinghamshire NG9 2TA;
   URL www.nottingham.nhs.uk; Tel 0115 875 4900;
   Fax 0115 875 4910
Chief Executive Elizabeth McGuirk
Chair Melanie Hatto

Burnley, Pendle and Rossendale Primary Care Trust

31–33 Kenyon Rd, Lomeshaye Est, Nelson, Lancashire
   BB9 5SZ; URL www.bprpct.nhs.uk; Tel 01282 619909;
   Fax 01282 610223
Chief Executive David Peat
Chair James Heyes

Burntwood, Lichfield and Tamworth Primary Care Trust

2nd Fl, Guardian Hse, Rotten Row, Lichfield, Staffordshire
   WS13 6JB
Chief Executive Alan Snuggs
Chair Mrs Durrant

Bury Primary Care Trust

21 Silver St, Bury, Lancashire BL9 0EN
Chief Executive Evan Boucher
Chair Hilda Harvey

Calderdale Primary Care Trust

School Hse, 56 Hopwood La, Halifax, West Yorkshire
   HX1 5ER
Chief Executive Martyn Pritchard
Chair Joyce Catterick

Cambridge City Primary Care Trust

Heron Crt, Ida Darwin Hospital, Fulbourn Rd, Cambridge, Cambridgeshire CB1 5EE
Chief Executive Chris Humphris
Chair Lindy Beveridge

HOSPITALS

Arthur Rank House Brookfields Hospital, Mill Rd, Cambridge, Cambridgeshire CB1 3DF; Tel 01223 723001
Specialism: Palliative care (19)

Brookfields Hospital Mill Rd, Cambridge, Cambridgeshire CB1 3DF; Tel 01223 723001

Ida Darwin Hospital Marlowe Hse, Fulbourn, Cambridge, Cambridgeshire CB1 5EE; Tel 01223 884444

Camden Primary Care Trust

4 St. Pancras Way, London NW1 0PE;
E-mail chief.executive@camdenpct.nhs.uk
Chief Executive Rob Larkman
Chair John Carrier

HEALTH CENTRES

Belsize Priory Health Centre 208 Belsize Rd, London NW6 4DJ; Tel 020 7530 2600; Fax 020 7530 2650

Bloomsbury Day Hospital St. Pancras Hospital, 4 St. Pancras Way, London NW1 0PE; Tel 020 7530 3350; Fax 020 7530 5409

CLASH (Health Promotion) 11 Warwick St, London W1R 5RA; Tel 020 7734 1794; Fax 020 7287 7368

Crowndale Health Centre 59 Crowndale Rd, London NW1 1TU; Tel 020 7530 3800; Fax 020 7530 3856

Daleham Gardens Clinic 5 Daleham Gdns, London NW3 5BY; Tel 020 7530 2500; Fax 020 7530 2524

Gospel Oak Clinic Lismore Circus, London NW5 4QF; Tel 020 7530 4600; Fax 020 7530 4629

Kentish Town Health Centre 2 Bartholomew Rd, London NW1 0PE; Tel 020 7530 4700; Fax 020 7530 4764

King's Cross Primary Care Centre 264 Pentonville Rd, London N1 9JY; Tel 020 7530 5770; Fax 020 7530 5771

Solent Road Health Centre 9 Solent Rd, London NW6 1TP; Tel 020 7530 2550; Fax 020 7530 2552

St. Albans Health Clinic St. Albans Villas, St. Albans Rd, London NW5 1QY; Tel 020 7530 4800; Fax 020 7530 4818

Cannock Chase Primary Care Trust

Block D, Beecroft Crt, off Beecroft Rd, Cannock, Staffordshire WS11 1JP; Tel 01543 465100; Fax 01543 465110
Chief Executive Jean-Pierre Parsons
Chair David Littlemore

Canterbury and Coastal Primary Care Trust

Chestfield Medical Centre, Reeves Way, Chestfield, Whitstable, Kent CT5 3QU
Chief Executive Wilf Williams;
E-mail wilf.williams@ekentha.nhs.uk
Chair John Butler

HOSPITALS

Faversham Cottage Hospital Stone St, Faversham, Kent ME13 8PS; Tel 01795 562066

Queen Victoria Memorial Hospital King Edward Ave, Herne Bay, Kent CT6 6EB; Tel 01227 594700

Whitstable and Tankerton Hospital Northwood Rd, Tankerton, Kent CT5 2HN; Tel 01227 594601

HEALTH CENTRES AND CLINICS

Canterbury Health Centre Old Dover Rd, Canterbury, Kent CT1 3JB; Tel 01227 597000

Faversham Health Centre Bank St, Faversham, Kent ME13 8QR; Tel 01795 562000

Whitstable Health Centre Harbour St, Whitstable, Kent CT5 1BZ; Tel 01227 594400

Carlisle and District Primary Care Trust

The Coppice, Cumwhinton Rd, Carlisle, Cumbria CA1 2SE; Tel 01228 602734; Fax 01228 602766
Chief Executive Graham Ogden
Chair Ruth Popple

HOSPITAL

Wigton Hospital Wigton, Cumbria CA7 9DD; Tel 01697 366600

Castle Point and Rochford Primary Care Trust

12 Castle Rd, Rayleigh, Essex SS6 7QF
Chair Brian Dawbarn

Central Cheshire Primary Care Trust

Barony Hospital, Barony Rd, Nantwich, Cheshire CW5 5QU
Chief Executive Mike Pryah
Chair Prof Pauline Ong

Central Cornwall Primary Care Trust

John Keay Hse, Tregonissey Rd, St. Austell, Cornwall PL25 4NQ
Chief Executive Lynn Manuell
Chair Peter Davies

HOSPITALS

Fowey and District Hospital Green La, Fowey, Cornwall PL23 1EE; Tel 01726 832241; Fax 01726 832775

Newquay and District Hospital St. Thomas' Rd, Newquay, Cornwall; Tel 01637 893600

St. Austell Community Hospital Porthpean Rd, St. Austell, Cornwall PL26 6AA; Tel 01726 291100; Fax 01726 291140

HEALTH CENTRES AND CLINICS

Newquay Health Centre St. Thomas' Rd, Newquay, Cornwall TR7 1RU; Tel 01637 893660

St. Austell Health Centre Moorland Rd, St. Austall, Cornwall PL25 5BS; Tel 01726 291220; Fax 01726 291249

Central Derby Primary Care Trust

Top Fl, Derwent Crt, 1 Stuart St, Derby, Derbyshire DE1 2FZ; Tel 01332 203102; Fax 01332 203206
Chief Executive Graham English
Chair Paul Nathan

Central Liverpool Primary Care Trust

Hartington Road Clinic, Hartington Rd, Toxteth, Liverpool, Merseyside L8 0SQ
Chief Executive Derek Campell
Chair Mr Ben-Tovim

Central Manchester Primary Care Trust

Mauldeth Hse, Mauldeth Road West, Chorlton Cum Hardy, Manchester M21 7RL
Chief Executive Sue Assar
Chair Evelyn Asante Mensah

12

Central Suffolk Primary Care Trust

Stow Lodge Centre, Chilton Way, Stowmarket, Suffolk
IP14 1SZ; URL www.centralsuffolk-pct.nhs.uk
Chair Brian Parrott

HOSPITALS

Hartismere Hospital Eye, Suffolk IP23 7BH; Tel 01379
870543; Fax 01379 870340
Specialism: Care of the elderly; slow stream
rehabilitation Number of beds: (74)
Stow Lodge Centre Chilton Way, Stowmarket, Suffolk
IP14 1SZ; Tel 01449 614024; Fax 01449 615829

Charnwood and North West Leicestershire Primary Care Trust

53 Baxtergate, Loughborough, Leicestershire LE11 1TH
Chief Executive Andrew Clarke
Chair Michael Wells

HOSPITALS

Ashby and District Hospital Ashby-de-la-Zouch,
Leicestershire LE65 1DG; Tel 01530 414222; Fax 01530
566902
Coalville Community Hospital Broom Leys Rd, Coalville,
Leicestershire LE6 3DE; Tel 01530 510510; Fax 01530 835780
Loughborough General Hospital Baxter Gate,
Loughborough, Leicestershire LE11 1TT; Tel 01509 611600;
Fax 01509 219290
Loughborough Hospital Epinal Way, Loughborough,
Leicestershire LE11 5JY; Tel 01509 611600; Fax 01509 219290

HEALTH CENTRES

Barrow Health Centre 27 High St, Barrow upon Soar,
Loughborough, Leicestershire LE12 8PY; Tel 01509 412472;
Fax 01509 620218
Coalville Health Centre Market St, Coalville, Leicestershire
LE6 4DX; Tel 01530 275160; Fax 01530 275160
Shepshed Health Centre Field St, Shepshed, Leicestershire
LE12 9QE; Tel 01509 601201; Fax 01509 651311

Chelmsford Primary Care Trust

Wood Hse, St. John's Hospital, Wood St, Chelmsford, Essex
CM2 9BG;
E-mail <firstname>.<surname>@chelmsford-pct.nhs.uk
Chief Executive Mark Halladay
Chair Pamela Joughlin

Cheltenham and Tewkesbury Primary Care Trust

Unit 43, Central Way, Arle Rd, Cheltenham, Gloucestershire
GL51 8LX
Chief Executive Caroline Fowles
Chair Ruth Fitzjohn

Cherwell Vale Primary Care Trust

Oxford Rd, Banbury, Oxfordshire OX16 9GE;
URL www.cherwellvale-pct.nhs.uk; Tel 01295 819500;
Fax 01295 819555
Chief Executive Barry Thomas;
E-mail barry.thomas@cherwellvale-pct.nhs.uk
Chair Anita Highman, OBE

Cheshire West Primary Care Trust

1829 Bldg, Countess of Chester Health Pk, Liverpool Rd,
Chester, Cheshire CH2 1HJ; URL www.cwpct.nhs.uk
Chief Executive Ged Taylor
Chair Bob Hodson

Chesterfield Primary Care Trust

Headquarters, Scarsdale, Newbold Rd, Chesterfield,
Derbyshire S41 7PF; Tel 01246 231255; Fax 01246 206672
Chief Executive Prem Singh
Chair Patricia Foster

HOSPITAL

Walton Hospital Whitecoates La, Chesterfield, Derbyshire
S40 3HN; Tel 01246 277271

HEALTH SERVICES

Ash Green Ashgate Rd, Chesterfield, Derbyshire S42 7JE
Saltergate Health Centre Chesterfield, Derbyshire S40 1SX

Chiltern and South Buckinghamshire Primary Care Trust

Chiltern District Council Offices, King George V Rd,
Amersham, Buckinghamshire HP6 5AW
Chief Executive Steve Young;
E-mail steve.young@chiltern-pcg.nhs.uk
Chair Richard Worrall

HOSPITALS

The Chalfonts and Gerrards Cross Hospital Hampden Rd,
Chalfont St. Peter, Buckinghamshire SL9 9DR; Tel 01753
883821
Chesham Hospital Hospital Hill, Waterside, Chesham,
Buckinghamshire HP5 1PJ; Tel 01494 783961

Chingford, Wanstead and Woodford Primary Care Trust

Beckett Hse, 2–14 Ilford Hill, Ilford, Essex IG1 2QX
Chief Executive Angela Mcnab
Chair David Kelly

CLINICS AND HEALTH CENTRES

Chingford Health Centre 109 York Rd, Chingford, London
E4 8LF; Tel 020 8529 8655
Handsworth Avenue Health Centre Highams Pk, London
E4 9ED; Tel 020 8527 0021
Highams Court 1 Friars Cl, Larkshall Rd, Chingford,
London E4 6UU; Tel 020 8535 6533; Fax 020 8535 6533
Continuing care unit for elderly people.

Chorley and South Ribble Primary Care Trust

Jubilee Hse, Lancashire Bus Pk, Centurion Way, Leyland,
Lancashire PR26 6TR; URL www.chorley-pct.nhs.uk
Chief Executive Judith Faux
Chair Mr Benson

City and Hackney Primary Care Trust

St. Leonards Hospital, Nuttall St, London N1 5LZ
Chair Jane Winder
Chief Executive Laura Sharpe
Child Development Service Donald Winnicott Centre,
Coate St, London E2 9AG; Tel 020 7599 1000; Fax 020 7599
1010

Colchester Primary Care Trust

Health Offices, Turner Rd, Colchester, Essex CO4 5JR;
URL www.colchester-pct.nhs.uk; Tel 01206 288500;
Fax 01206 288501
Chief Executive Brendan Osborne
Chair Maggie Shakell

Cotswold and Vale Primary Care Trust

Trust HQ, Cirencester Hospital, Tetbury Rd, Cirencester, Gloucestershire GL7 1UY
Chief Executive   Richard James
Chair   Elizabeth Law

HOSPITALS

Berkeley Hospital   Berkeley, Gloucestershire GL13 9BL; Tel 01453 562000

Cirencester Hospital   The Querns, Tetbury Rd, Cirencester, Gloucestershire GL7 1UY; Tel 01285 655711

Stroud General Hospital   Stroud, Gloucestershire GL5 2HY; Tel 01453 562200; Fax 01453 562201

Stroud Maternity Hospital   Stroud, Gloucestershire GL5 2JB; Tel 01453 562140

Coventry Primary Care Trust

Christchurch Hse, Greyfriars La, Coventry, West Midlands CV1 2GQ
Chief Executive   Laurence Tennant
Chair   Alison Gingell

Craven, Harrogate and Rural District Primary Care Trust

50 Lancaster Park Rd, Harrogate, North Yorkshire HG2 7SF
Chief Executive   Penny Jones
Chair   Stuart Wardle

HOSPITALS

Abdale House   49–51 Tewit Well Rd, Harrogate, North Yorkshire HG2 8JJ; Tel 01423 872393
Specialism: Mental illness rehabilitation. Number of beds: (13)

Alexander House, Community Unit for the Elderly   Ash Tree Rd, Knaresborough, North Yorkshire HG5 0UB; Tel 01423 558000

The Briary Wing   Harrogate District Hospital, Lancaster Park Rd, Harrogate, North Yorkshire HG2 7SX; Tel 01423 885959; Fax 01423 553397
Specialism: Psychiatric. (59) Number of beds: (Day) (6)

Darley House   25–27 High St, Starbeck, Harrogate, North Yorkshire HG2 7HX; Tel 01423 886355
Specialism: Special needs unit for people with learning disabilities (8)

The Grove   95 Harrogate Rd, Ripon, North Yorkshire HG4 1SX; Tel 01765 602668
Specialism: Special needs unit for people with learning disabilities (8)

The Orchards Community Unit for the Elderly   Princess Cl, Ripon, North Yorkshire HG4 1HZ; Tel 01765 690751
Specialism: Elderly mentally ill (16)

Ripon Community Hospital   Firby La, Ripon, North Yorkshire HG4 2PR; Tel 01765 602546
Specialism: GP; medicine; care of the elderly.

Crawley Primary Care Trust

Fairfield Annexe, Tern, Crawley, West Sussex RH11 7DH
Chief Executive   Julie Kilner;
E-mail julie.kilner@wsha.nhs.uk
Chair   Dr Robert Ward

Croydon Primary Care Trust

Knollys Hse, 17 Addiscome Rd, Croydon, Surrey CR0 6SR;
URL www.croydon.nhs.uk;
E-mail pals@croydonpct.nhs.uk; Tel 020 8274 6000
Chair   Toni Letts
Chief Executive   Caroline Taylor

Director (Finance and Informatics)   Stephen O'Brien
Director (Human Resources)   Tracey Donnelly
Director (Nursing)   Vacancy
Director (Planning and Corporate Affairs)   Una Dalton
Director (Public Health) and Medical Director
Dr Tim Crayford
Director (North Croydon Locality)   Angela Gibson
Director (Central Croydon Locality)   Sue Arnold
Director (Croydon South Locality)   Stuart Thomson

Dacorum Primary Care Trust

Isbister Centre, Chaulden House Gdns, Off Chaulden La, Hemel Hempstead, Hertfordshire HP1 2BW;
URL www.dacorum-pct.nhs.uk;
E-mail enquiries@dacorum-pct.nhs.uk
Chief Executive   Toni Horn
Chair   Mary Pedlow

Derbyshire Dales and South Derbyshire Primary Care Trust

Repton Health Centre, Askew Rd, Repton, Derby, Derbyshire DE65 6SH
Chief Executive   Nina Ennis
Chair   Peter Purnell

Darlington Primary Care Trust

Valley Hse, Valley Street North, Darlington, County Durham DL1 1TJ
Chief Executive   Colin Morris
Chair   Sandra Pollard

Dartford, Gravesham and Swanley Primary Care Trust

Top Fl, The Livingstone Hospital, East Hill, Dartford, London DA1 1SA
Chief Executive   Stephanie Stanwick;
E-mail stephanie.stanwick@dgs-pct.nhs.uk
Chair   Rev Martin Henwood

Daventry and South Northamptonshire Primary Care Trust

Dantre Hospital, London Rd, Daventry, Northamptonshire NN11 4DY
Chief Executive   Julia Squires
Chair   Simon Schanschieff

HOSPITAL

Danetre Hospital   Daventry, Northamptonshire NN11 5DY; Tel 01327 702113

Derwentside Primary Care Trust

Top Fl, Tower Block, Shotley Bridge Hospital, Consett, County Durham DH8 0NB
Chief Executive   Wynn Griffiths
Chair   Murray Hetherington

Doncaster Central Primary Care Trust

Central Hse, St. Catherine's Hospital, Tickhill Rd, Doncaster, South Yorkshire DN4 8QN
Chief Executive   Mr Morritr
Chair   Sandra Parnham

Doncaster East Primary Care Trust

White Rose Hse, Ten Pound Wlk, Doncaster, South Yorkshire DN4 5DJ
Chief Executive   Jayne Brown
Chair   Roger Greenwood

12

Doncaster West Primary Care Trust

West Lodge, St. Catherine's Hospital, Tickhill Rd,
Doncaster, South Yorkshire DN4 8QN;
URL www.doncasterwestpct.nhs.uk
Chief Executive Michael Potts
Chair Ian Olsson

Dudley Beacon and Castle Primary Care Trust

Russell Hse, 1 The Inhedge, Dudley, West Midlands
DY1 1RR; Tel 01384 366336; Fax 01384 366460
Chief Executive Rob Bacon
Chair Rachel Harris
Medical Director Dr W. Conlon
Director (Finance) N. Nisbet

Dudley South Primary Care Trust

Trust Headquarters, Ridge Hill, Brierley Hill Rd,
Stourbridge, West Midlands DY8 5ST;
E-mail listen@dudley.nhs.uk
Chief Executive Chris Potter
Chair David Ibbs

Durham and Chester-le-Street Primary Care Trust

John Snow Hse, Durham University Science Pk, Durham,
County Durham DH1 3YG;
URL www.durhamclspct.nhs.uk;
E-mail andrew.young@durhamclspct.nhs.uk
Chief Executive Andrew Young
Chair Ann Calman

Durham Dales Primary Care Trust

16 Tenters St, Bishop Aukland, County Durham DL14 7AD;
URL www.durhamdales-pct.co.uk
Chief Executive Andrew Kenworthy
Chair Anne Beeton

Ealing Primary Care Trust

1 Armstrong Way, Southall, Greater London UB2 4SA
Chief Executive Robert Creighton
Chair Marion Saunders

Easington Primary Care Trust

Health Partnership Centre, Fern Crt, Bracken Hill Bus Pk,
Peter Lee, County Durham SR6 2RR
Chief Executive Roger Bolas
Chair Penelope Young

East Cambridgeshire and Fenland Primary Care Trust

Exchange Tower, Alexandra Rd, Wisbech, Cambridgeshire
PE13 1HQ
Chief Executive Audrey Bradford
Chair Rosalind Beveridge

HOSPITAL

North Cambridgeshire Hospital The Park, Wisbech,
Cambridgeshire PE13 3AB; Tel 01945 585781
Specialism: Acute (48), ESMI (21)

East Devon Primary Care Trust

Dean Clarke Hse, Southernhay East, Exeter, Devon
EX1 1PQ
Chief Executive Iain Tulley
Chair Mrs Price

HOSPITALS

Axminster Hospital Chard Rd, Axminster, Devon
EX13 5DU; Tel 01297 32071; Fax 01297 35464

Budleigh Salterton Hospital Budleigh Salterton, Devon
EX9 6HF; Tel 01395 442020

Exmouth Hospital Claremont Gr, Exmouth, Devon EX8 2JN;
Tel 01395 226005; Fax 01395 225453

Honiton Hospital Marlpits Rd, Honiton, Devon EX14 8DD;
Tel 01404 540540; Fax 01404 540550

Ottery St. Mary Hospital Keegan Cl, Ottery St. Mary, Devon
EX11 1DN; Tel 01404 816000; Fax 01404 816030

Seaton and District Community Hospital All Saints Rd,
Sidmouth, Devon EX10 8EN; Tel 01395 512842; Fax 01395
579326

East Elmbridge and Mid Surrey Primary Care Trust

Cedar Crt, Guildford Rd, Fetcham, Leatherhead, Surrey
KT22 9RX; E-mail don.marquis@eeandms-pcg.nhs.uk
Chief Executive Don Marquis
Chair Jackie Bell

HOSPITAL

Molesey Hospital High St, West Molesey, Surrey KT8 0DU;
Tel 020 8979 5060

East Hampshire Primary Care Trust

Raeburn Hse, Hulbert Rd, Waterlooville, Hampshire
PO7 7GP; URL www.easthampshirepct.nhs.uk;
E-mail tony.horne@ports.nhs.uk; Tel 023 9224 8800;
Fax 023 9224 8810
Chief Executive Tony Horne
Chair Margaret Scott

East Kent Coastal Primary Care Trust

Protea Hse, New Bridge, Dover, Kent CT17 9HQ;
E-mail darren.grayson@ekentha.nhs.uk
Chief Executive Darren Grayson
Chair Jan Askew

HOSPITAL

Victoria Hospital London Rd, Deal, Kent CT14 9UA;
Tel 01304 865400

HEALTH CENTRES AND CLINICS

Aylesham Health Centre The Blvd, Aylesham, Kent
CT3 3DY; Tel 01304 867310

Birchington and Westgate Clinic King Ethelbert School,
Canterbury Rd, Birchington, Kent CT7 9BP; Tel 01843
831139

Broadstairs Health Centre The Broadway, Broadstairs, Kent
CT10 2AJ; Tel 01843 255300

College Road Clinic College Rd, Margate, Kent CT9 2RT;
Tel 01843 255175

Crabble Clinic Crabble Rd, Dover, Kent CT1 3JB; Tel 01304
865700

Newington Road Clinic Newington Rd, Ramsgate, Kent
CT11 0QU; Tel 01843 255200

East Lincolnshire Primary Care Trust

c/o Louth County Hospital, High Holme Rd, North
Somercotes, Louth, Lincolnshire LN11 0EU
Chief Executive Jane Elizabeth Froggatt
Chair Vacancy

East Staffordshire Primary Care Trust

The Outwoods Site, Belvedere Rd, Burton on Trent,
   Staffordshire DE13 0QL
Chief Executive   Vacancy
Chair   Alex Fox

East Surrey Primary Care Trust

St. Johns Crt, 51 St. Johns Rd, Redhill, Surrey RH1 6DS
Chief Executive   Jackie Pendleton;
   E-mail jackie.pendleton@eastsurrey-pcg.nhs.uk
Chair   Terry Conaty

East Yorkshire Primary Care Trust

33 Lairgate, Beverley, North Humberside, East Riding of
   Yorkshire HU17 8ET
Chief Executive   Andrew Williams
Chair   Helen Varey

Eastbourne Downs Primary Care Trust

1 St. Anne's Rd, Eastbourne, East Sussex BN21 3UN;
   URL www.eastbournedownspct.nhs.uk;
   E-mail edpct@eastbournedownspct.nhs.uk
Chief Executive   Gina Brocklehurst;
   E-mail gina.brocklehurst@eastbournedownspct.nhs.uk
Chair   Mary Colato

Eastern Birmingham Primary Care Trust

Suite 20, Waterlinks Hse, Richards St, Birmingham, West
   Midlands B7 4AA
Chief Executive   Sofie Christie
Chair   Bishop Aldred

Eastern Hull Primary Care Trust

Netherhall, Wawne Rd, Kingston-upon-Hull, East Riding of
   Yorkshire HU7 4YG
Chief Executive   Iain Mcinnes
Chair   Malcolm Snow

Eastern Leicester Primary Care Trust

3 De Monfort Mews, Leicester, Leicestershire LE1 7FW
Chief Executive   Carolyn Clifton
Chair   Joseph Parkinson

HEALTH CENTRES

Charnwood Health Centre   Mere Rd, Leicester LE5 3GH

Prince Philip House   Malabar Rd, Leicester LE1 2NZ

Rushey Mead Health Centre   Rushey Mead, Leicester LE4 7ZX

Springfield Road Health Centre   Springfield Rd, Leicester
LE2 3BB

St. Peters Health Centre   St. Peters Rd, Highfields, Leicester
LE2 0TA

Uppingham Road Health Centre   Uppingham Rd, Leicester
LE5 4BP

Eastern Wakefield Primary Care Trust

Castleford Normanton and District Hospital, Lumley St,
   Castleford, West Yorkshire WF10 5LT
Chief Executive   Mike Grady
Chair   Roy Widdowson

Eastleigh and Test Valley Primary Care Trust

The Mount Hospital, Church Rd, Eastleigh, Hampshire
   SO50 6ZB
Chief Executive   John Richards;
   E-mail john.richards@eastleighandtvs-pct.nhs.uk
Chair   Lynne Lockyer

Eden Valley Primary Care Trust

8 Tynefield Dr, Penrith, Cumbria CA11 8JA; Tel 01768
   245317; Fax 01768 245318
Chief Executive   Peter Kohn
Chair   Elizabeth Furneaux

Brampton War Memorial Hospital   Brampton, Cumbria
CA8 1TX; Tel 01697 72534

Mary Hewetson Cottage hospital   Keswick, Cumbria
CA12 5PH; Tel 01768 767000

Penrith and Eden Community Hospital   Bridge La, Penrith,
Cumbria CA11 8HX; Tel 01768 245300

Ruth Lancaster James Cottage Hospital   Alston, Cumbria
CA9 3QX; Tel 01434 381218

Ellesmere Port and Neston Primary Care Trust

5 Civic Way, Ellesmere Port, Cheshire CH65 0AX
Chief Executive   Jaqui Harvey
Chair   Michael Darby

HOSPITAL

Ellesmere Port Hospital   Chester Rd, Whitby, Ellesmere
Port, Cheshire CH65 6FG; Tel 0151 355 2345

Enfield Primary Care Trust

Holbrook Hse, Cockfosters Rd, Barnet, Hertfordshire
   EN4 0DR; URL www.beh.nhs.uk/enfieldpct; Tel 020
   8272 5500; Fax 020 8272 5700
Chief Executive   Sally Johnson
Chair   Carolyn Berkeley
Chair (Professional Executive Committee)   Peter Barnes
Director (Nursing)   Bronwen Whittaker
Director (Patient Services) and Director (Edmonton Locality)
   Caroline Tuohy
Director (Organisational Development)   Don Fairley
*Director (Service Development – Internal) and Director
   (Southgate Locality)*   Jo Ohlson
*Director (Service Development – External) and Director (Enfield
   North Locality)*   Liz Wise
Director (Health Improvement)   Peter Sheridan
Director (Finance and Performance)   Richard Martin
Director (Communications and Corporate Affairs)
   Anita Grabarz

HOSPITALS

Chase Farm Hospital   The Ridgeway, Enfield, London
EN2 8JL; Tel 020 8366 6600

North Middlesex University Hospital   Sterling Way,
Edmonton, London N18 1QX; Tel 020 8887 2000

Epping Forest Primary Care Trust

Birchwood Hse, St. Margaret's Hospital, The Plain, Epping,
   Essex CM16 6TN; URL www.efpct.nhs.uk; Tel 01992
   902010; Fax 01992 902012
Chief Executive   Aidan Thomas
Chair   Di Collins

Erewash Primary Care Trust

Ilkeston Medical Centre, South St, Ilkeston, Derbyshire
   DE7 5PZ; Tel 0115 9512300; Fax 0115 9512350
Chief Executive   Paula Clark
Chair   Christine Thompson

Exeter Primary Care Trust

Dean Clarke Hse, Southernhay East, Exeter, Devon
   EX1 1PQ
Chief Executive   Jill Ashton
Chair   Mrs Nisbett

12

Fareham and Gosport Primary Care Trust

Unit 180, 166 Fareham Rd, Gosport, Hampshire
PO13 0FW
Chief Executive Ian Piper
Chair Lucy Doherty

Fylde Primary Care Trust

Ground Fl, 16–18 St. George's Rd, Lytham St. Annes,
Lancashire FY8 2AE
Chief Executive Julie Goulding
Chair Herbert Waddington

Gateshead Primary Care Trust

Team View, 5th Ave Bus Pk, Team Valley Trading Est,
Gateshead, Tyne and Wear NE11 0NB;
URL www.gatesheadpct.nhs.uk
Chief Executive Bob Smith (Acting)
Chair Brian Cusak (Acting)

Gedling Primary Care Trust

Byron Crt, Brookfield Rd, Arnold, Nottingham NG5 7ER;
URL www.nottingham.nhs.uk
Chief Executive Adele Cresswell
Chair Derek Stewart

Great Yarmouth Primary Care Trust

Astley Cooper Hse, Estcourt Rd, Great Yarmouth, Norfolk
NR30 4JH
Chief Executive Michael Stonard
Chair Bernard Williamson

Greater Derby Primary Care Trust

1 Stuart St, Derby, Derbyshire DE1 2FZ; Tel 01332 224000;
Fax 01332 299598
Chief Executive Derek Hathaway
Chair Syed Naqwi

Greenwich Primary Care Trust

1 Hyde Vale, Greenwich, London SE10 8QG
Chief Executive Jane Schofield
Chair Ken May

Guildford and Waverley Primary Care Trust

Broadmede Hse, Farmham Bus Pk, Weydon La, Farnham,
Surrey GU9 8QT; URL www.gwpct.nhs.uk
Chief Executive Liz Slinn
Chair Christopher Grimes

Halton Primary Care Trust

Victoria Hse, The Holloway, Runcorn, Cheshire WA7 4TH;
Tel 01928 593654; Fax 01928 593709
Chair Jim Wilson
Chief Executive Stephen Parry
Director (Human Resources) and Director (Contracts)
Vacancy
Director (Finance) Vacancy
Director (Community and Priority Services) Vacancy
Joint Project Manager Sara Radcliffe
Joint Project Manager John Jones

Hambleton and Richmondshire Primary Care Trust

Station Road Bus Pk, Station Rd, Thirsk, North Yorkshire;
E-mail enquiries@hambrichpct.nhs.uk; Tel 01845 573800;
Fax 01845 573805
Chief Executive Christopher Long
Chair Susan Young

Hammersmith and Fulham Primary Care Trust

Parson's Green Centre, 5–7 Parson's Grn, Bute Gdns,
London SW6 4UL
Chief Executive Sally Hargreaves
Chair Lucinda Bolton

Haringey Teaching Primary Care Trust

St. Ann's General Hospital, St. Ann's Rd, London N15 3TH;
URL www.beh.nhs.uk; Tel 020 8442 6000; Fax 020 8442
6567
Chief Executive David Sloman
Chair Richard Sumray
Medical Director Ann Marie Connolly
Director (Nursing) Helen Hally
Director (Human Resource Management) Clive Martinez
Director (Finance) Geoff Sanford

HOSPITAL

St. Ann's Hospital St. Ann's Rd, South Tottenham, London
N15 3TH;
E-mail <firstname>.<lastname>@haringey.nhs.uk; Tel 020
8442 6000

Harlow Primary Care Trust

16th Fl, Terminus Hse, Terminus St, Harlow, Essex
CM20 1XE; Tel 01279 694713; Fax 01279 694740
Chief Executive Pam Court
Chair Tom Farr

Harrow Primary Care Trust

Kenmore Clinic, Kenmore Rd, Harrow, Greater London
HA3 9EN
Chief Executive Sue McLellen
Chair Geoffrey Rose

Hartlepool Primary Care Trust

Mandale Hse, Harbour Wlk, The Marina, Hartlepool,
Cleveland, North Yorkshire TS24 0UX
Chief Executive Lynn Johnson
Chair Gerald Wistow

Hastings and St. Leonards Primary Care Trust

PO Box 124, St. Leonards on Sea, East Sussex TN38 9WH;
E-mail wilkinson.toni@har-tr.sthames.nhs.uk
Chief Executive Toni Wilkinson
Chair Marie Casey

Havering Primary Care Trust

Trust Headquarters, St. George's Hospital, 117 Suttons La,
Hornchurch, Essex RM12 6RS
Chief Executive Ralph Mccormack
Chair Leonard Smith

Heart of Birmingham Teaching Primary Care Trust

Bartholomew Hse, 142 Hagley Rd, Birmingham, West
Midlands B16 9PA
Chief Executive Anthony Sumara
Chair Ranjit Sonhi

Herefordshire Primary Care Trust

Belmont Abbey, Belmont, Hereford, Herefordshire
HR2 9RP; Tel 01432 344344; Fax 01432 363900
Chief Executive Paul Bates
Chair Ted Willmott
Director (Health Development) Simon Hairsnape

Director (Finance)   Jim Hayburn
Director (Corporate Development)   Julie Thornby
Director (Public Health)   Dr Mike Deakin
General Manager and Head Executive Nurse   Trish Jay
Annual budget
£130 million

HOSPITALS

Bromyard Community Hospital Froome Bank, Bromyard, Herefordshire HR7 4QN; Tel 01885 485700
    Specialism: GP; medical; age care; DMHE.

Kington Cottage Hospital Victoria Rd, Kington, Herefordshire HR5 3BX; Tel 01544 230317

Ledbury Health and Care Centre Market St, Ledbury, Herefordshire HR8 2AQ; Tel 01531 632488
    Specialism: GP; medical.

Leominster Community Hospital South St, Leominster, Herefordshire HR6 8JH; Tel 01568 614211
    Specialism: GP; medical; DMHE.

Ross Community Hospital Alton St, Ross-on-Wye, Herefordshire HR9 5AD; Tel 01989 562100
    Specialism: GP; medical; age care; DMHE.

Stonebow Unit County Hospital, Hereford, Herefordshire HR1 2ER; Tel 01432 355444
    Specialism: Acute psychiatric.

Hertsmere Primary Care Trust

The Elms Clinic, High St, Potters Bar, Hertfordshire EN6 5DA; Tel 01707 647586
Chief Executive   Jacqueline Clark
Chair   Elizabeth Kelly

HOSPITAL

Potters Bar Community Hospital Barnet Rd, Potters Bar, Hertfordshire EN6 2RY; Tel 01707 653286

Heywood and Middleton Primary Care Trust

London Hse, Oldham Rd, Middleton, Greater Manchester M24 1AY
Chief Executive   Keith Surgeon
Chair   Mr Edwards

High Peak and Dales Primary Care Trust

Newholme Hospital, Baslow Rd, Bakewell, Derbyshire DE45 1AD; URL www.highpeakanddalespct.nhs.uk; Tel 01629 812525; Fax 01629 817890
Chief Executive   Neil Swanwick
Chair   Dianne Jeffrey

HOSPITALS

Buxton Hospital London Rd, Buxton, Derbyshire SK17 9NJ; Tel 01298 214000

Cavendish Hospital Manchester Rd, Buxton, Derbyshire SK17 6TE; Tel 01298 212800

Newholme Hospital Baslow Rd, Bakewell, Derbyshire DE45 1AD; Tel 01629 812525

Whitworth Hospital 330 Bakewell Rd, Matlock, Derbyshire DE4 2JD; Tel 01629 580211

HEALTH CENTRES

Buxton Health Centre Bath Rd, Buxton, Derbyshire SK17 6HH

Spring House 26 Market St, Buxton, Derbyshire SK17 6LD

Hillingdon Primary Care Trust

Kirk Hse, 97–109 High St, Yiewsley, West Drayton, Greater London UB7 7HJ; URL www.hillingdon.nhs.uk; Tel 01895 452000; Fax 01895 452108
Chief Executive   Graham Betts
Chair   Sarah Pond

HOSPITAL

Northwood, Pinner and Cottage Hospital Pinner Rd, Northwood, Greater London HA6 1DE; Tel 01923 824182

Hinckley and Bosworth Primary Care Trust

Heath Lane Surgery, Heath La, Earl Shilton, Leicestershire LE9 7PB
Chief Executive   Colin Blackler
Chair   Ernest White

HOSPITALS

Hinckley and District Hospital Mount Rd, Hinckley, Leicestershire LE10 3AG; Tel 01455 441800; Fax 01455 441888

Hinckley Sunnyside Hospital Ashby Rd, Hinckley, Leicestershire LE10 3DA; Tel 01455 441800; Fax 01455 619936

Horsham and Chanctonbury Primary Care Trust

Park Hse, North St, Horsham, West Sussex RH12 1RL; URL www.hcpct.nhs.uk; E-mail angela.ugur@hcpct.nhs.uk
Chief Executive   Angela Ugur
PCT PEC Chair   Dr Jace Clarke

Hounslow Primary Care Trust

Phoenix Crt, 531 Staines Rd, Hounslow, Greater London TW4 5DP; URL www.hounslowpct.nhs.uk; E-mail john.james@hounslowpct.nhs.uk
Chief Executive   John James
Chair   Christine Hay

Huddersfield Central Primary Care Trust

Princess Royal Community Health Centre, Greenhead Rd, Huddersfield, West Yorkshire HD1 4EW
Chief Executive   Vacancy
Chair   Robert Napier

Huntingdonshire Primary Care Trust

The Priory, Priory Rd, St. Ives, Cambridgeshire PE27 5BB
Chief Executive   Vacancy
Chair   Michael Lynch

Hyndburn and Ribble Valley Primary Care Trust

Red Rose Crt, Clayton Bus Pk, Clayton Le Moors, Accrington, Lancashire BB5 5JR
Chief Executive   Leigh Cummins
Chair   Martin Hill

Ipswich Primary Care Trust

Allington Hse, 427 Woodbridge Rd, Ipswich, Suffolk IP4 4ER
Chief Executive
Chair   Lillian Power

NURSING HOME

St. Edmunds Nursing Home Constitution Hill, Ipswich, Suffolk IP1 3RG; Tel 01473 254709; Fax 01473 230414

12

Isle of Wight Primary Care Trust

Whitecroft, Sandy La, Isle of Wight PO30 3ED;
E-mail david.crawley@iwha.swet.nhs.uk; Tel 01983
535455; Fax 01983 822142
Chief Executive David Crawley
Chair Valerie Anderson

Islington Primary Care Trust

110 Hampstead Rd, London NW1 2LJ;
URL www.islingtonpct.nhs.uk
Chief Executive Rachel Tyndall
Chair Paula Khan
There is a general e-mail address:
<firstname>.<surname>@islingtonpct.nhs.uk

HEALTH SERVICES

Child Health Information 580 Holloway Rd, London
N7 6LB; Tel 020 7530 2004; Fax 020 7530 2025
Finsbury Health Centre Pine St, London EC1R 0JH; Tel 020
7530 4200; Fax 020 7530 4219
Goodinge Health Centre Goodinge Cl, London N7 9EW;
Tel 020 7530 4900; Fax 020 7530 4937
Gospel Oak Clinic Lismore Circus, London NW5 4QF
Greenland Road Children's Centre Greenland Rd, London
NW1 0AS; Tel 020 7530 4820; Fax 020 7530 4825
Highbury Grange Health Centre 1–5 Highbury Grange,
London N5 2QB; Tel 020 7530 2888; Fax 020 7530 2884
Hornsey Street Health Centre Hornsey Rise, London
N19 3YU; Tel 020 7530 2400; Fax 020 7530 2466
Northern Health Centre 580 Holloway Rd, London N7 6LB;
Tel 020 7445 8001
River Place Health Centre River Pl, Essex Rd, London
N1 2DE; Tel 020 7530 2900; Fax 020 7830 2468

Kennet and North Wiltshire Primary Care Trust

Trust Headquarters, Southgate Hse, Pans La, Devizes,
Wiltshire SN10 1NR
Chief Executive Barbara Smith
Chair Tim Boucher

COMMUNITY HOSPITALS

Chippenham Community Hospital Rowden Hill,
Chippenham, Wiltshire SN15 2AJ
Devizes Community Hospital Devizes, Wiltshire SN10 1EF;
Tel 01380 723511; Fax 01380 726456
Malmesbury Community Hospital Malmesbury, Wiltshire
SN16 0EQ; Tel 01666 823358

Kensington and Chelsea Primary Care Trust

St. Charles Hospital, Courtfield Hse, Exmoor St, London
W10 6DZ; URL www.kc-pct.nhs.uk
Chief Executive Paul Haigh
Chair Terence Bamford

Kingston Primary Care Trust

22 Hollyfield Rd, Surbiton, Surrey KT5 9AL;
URL www.kingstonpct.nhs.uk; Tel 020 8339 8000;
Fax 020 8339 8101
Chief Executive Chris Butler
Chair Neslyn Watson-Druee
Medical Director Dr Charles Alessi
Director (Operations and Nursing) Jane Willett
Director (Finance and Information) Pamela Farrow
Annual budget
£150 million

HOSPITALS

Surbiton General Hospital Ewell Rd, Surbiton, Surrey
KT6 6EZ; Tel 020 8399 7111; Fax 020 8399 7114
Specialism: GP; geriatric.
Tolworth Hospital Red Lion Rd, Tolworth, Surrey KT6 7QU;
Tel 020 8390 0102
Specialism: Rehab; stroke; mental health.
Western Green Resource Centre Western Green Rd,
Thames Ditton, Surrey KT7 0HY; Tel 020 8398 8019
Specialism: Learning disabilities.

Knowsley Primary Care Trust

Moorgate Rd, Knowsley Ind Pk, Liverpool, Merseyside
L33 7XW
Chair Rosemary Hawley
Project Manager Ian Davis

Lambeth Primary Care Trust

1 Lower Marsh, Waterloo, London SE1 7NT; Tel 020 7716
7100; Fax 020 7716 7103
Chief Executive Kevin Barton
Chair Jane Ramsey

Langbaurgh Primary Care Trust

Langbaurgh Hse, Bow St, Guisborough, Cleveland, North
Yorkshire TS14 7AA
Chief Executive Jon Chadwick
Chair

Leeds East Primary Care Trust

Nurses Home, Seacroft Hospital, York Rd, Leeds, West
Yorkshire LS14 6UH
Chief Executive
Chair Linda Phipps

Leeds North East Primary Care Trust

Sycamore Lodge, 7a Woodhouse Cliff, Leeds, West
Yorkshire LS6 2HF;
E-mail reception@leedsnortheast-pct.nhs.uk
Chief Executive Thea Stein
Chair Brian Marsden

Leeds North West Primary Care Trust

1st Fl, Mill Hse, Troy Rd, Horsforth, Leeds, West Yorkshire
LS18 5TN
Chief Executive Lesley Smith
Chair Martin Drury

Leeds South Primary Care Trust

1st Fl, Navigation Hse, 8 George Mann Rd, Quayside Bus
Pk, Leeds, West Yorkshire LS10 1DJ
Chief Executive Dr George McIntyre
Chair Robert Seymour

Leeds West Primary Care Trust

Armley Park Crt, Stanningley Rd, Leeds, West Yorkshire
LS12 2AE
Chief Executive Chris Reid
Chair Kuldip Bharj

Leicester City West Primary Care Trust

Ground Fl, Mansion Hse, 41 Guildhall La, Leicester,
Leicestershire LE1 5FR
Chief Executive Rob Mcmahon
Chair Bernard Greaves

HEALTH CENTRES

Beaumont Leys Health Centre Tilling Rd, Beaumont Leys, Leicester LE4 0SY

Palsey Road Health Centre Palsey Rd, Leicester LE2 9BU

New Parks Health Centre New Parks, Leicester LE3 6RJ

Westcoates Health Centre Fosse Rd, Westcotes, Leicester LE3 0LP

Winstanley Drive Health Centre Winstanley Dr, Leicester LE3 1PB

SPECIALIST COMMUNITY CHILD HEALTH SERVICES

Bridge Park Plaza Bridge Park Rd, Thurmston, Leicester LE4 8PQ

Lewisham Primary Care Trust

Elizabeth Blackwell Hse, Wardalls Gr, Avonley Rd, London SE14 5ER; URL www.lewishampct.nhs.uk; Tel 020 7635 5555
Chief Executive Lucy Hadfield
Chair Brain Lymbery

Lincolnshire South West Teaching Primary Care Trust

Orchard Hse, South Rauceby, Sleaford, Lincolnshire NG34 8PP; Tel 01529 304438; Fax 01529 307806
Chief Executive Mr Derek Bray
Chair Mr Michael Boddy

Luton Primary Care Trust

Nightingale Hse, 94 Inkerman St, Luton, Bedfordshire LU1 1JD
Chief Executive Regina Shakespeare
Chair Gurch Randhawa

Maidstone Weald Primary Care Trust

Preston Hall, Royal British Legion Village, Preston Hall, Aylesford, Kent ME20 7NJ;
E-mail susan.gibbin@maidstonemalling-pct.nhs.uk
Chief Executive Nigel Howells
Chair Rosanne Corben

Maldon and South Chelmsford Primary Care Trust

Administration Block, St. Peter's Hospital, 32a Spital Rd, Maldon, Essex CM9 6EG; Tel 01621 875336; Fax 01621 875363
Chief Executive Mike Harrison;
E-mail mike.harrison@maldon-pct.nhs.uk
Chair Tony Plumridge

Medway Primary Care Trust

Admirals Office, Historic Dockyard, Chatham, Kent ME4 4TE
Chief Executive Philip Greenhill;
E-mail philip.greenhill@rainhamgillingham-pcg.nhs.uk
Chair Vacancy

Melton, Rutland and Harborough Primary Care Trust

3rd Fl, Pera Innovation Pk, Nottingham Rd, Melton Mowbray, Leicestershire LE13 0RH
Chief Executive Wendy Saviour
Chair John Gant

HOSPITALS

Market Harborough and District Hospital Coventry Rd, Market Harborough, Leicestershire LE16 9BX; Tel 01858 410500

Melton and District War Memorial Hospital Ankle Hill, Melton Mowbray, Leicestershire LE13 0QL; Tel 01664 854800

Rutland Memorial Hospital Cold Overton Rd, Oakham, Rutland LE15 6NT; Tel 01572 722552

St. Lukes Hospital Leicester Rd, Market Harborough, Leicestershire LE16 7BN; Tel 01858 410300

St. Marys Hospital Thorpe Rd, Melton Mowbray, Leicestershire LE16 1SJ; Tel 01664 854800

HEALTH CENTRES

Kibworth Health Centre Kibworth, Leicester LE8 0LG

Syston Health Centre Syston, Leicester LE7 2EQ

Mendip Primary Care Trust

Priory Health Pk, Glastonbury Rd, Wells, BA5 1XL; URL www.mendippct.org.uk
Chief Executive Robin Smith
Chair Mr R.K.S. Ballantine

HOSPITALS

Butleigh Hospital Butleigh, Glastonbury, Somerset BA6 8TF; Tel 01458 850237; Fax 01458 850228

Frome Victoria Hospital Park Rd, Frome, Somerset BA11 1EY; Tel 01373 463591; Fax 01373 456627

Shepton Mallet Community Hospital Old Wells Rd, Shepton Mallet, Somerset BA4 4PG; Tel 01749 342931

Wells and District Hospital Bath Rd, Wells, Somerset BA5 2XL; Tel 01749 683200; Fax 01749 683223

Mid Devon Primary Care Trust

Newcourt Hse, Old Rydon La, Exeter, Devon EX2 7JU
Chief Executive Lesley Dunaway
Chair Mr N. J. Wendover

HOSPITALS

Castle Community Hospital Cavell Rd, Okehampton, Devon EX20 1PN; Tel 01837 658000

Crediton Hospital Western Rd, Crediton, Devon EX17 3NH; Tel 01363 775588

Tiverton and District Hospital Bampton St, Tiverton, Devon EX16 6AN; Tel 01884 253251; Fax 01884 242784

Middlesbrough Primary Care Trust

Riverside Hse, High Force Rd, Riverside Pk, Middlesbrough, North Yorkshire TS2 1RH
Chief Executive Colin McLeod
Chair Ann O'Hanlan

Mid Hampshire Primary Care Trust

Unit 3, Tidbury Farm, Bullington Cross, , Sutton Scotney, Hampshire SO21 3QQ
Chief Executive Chris Evennett;
E-mail chris.evennett@midhampshirepct.nhs.uk; Tel 01962 763940
Chair Bridget Phelps

Mid Sussex Primary Care Trust

Kleinwort, Haywards Heath Hospital, Butlers Green Rd, Haywards Heath, West Sussex RH16 4BE
Chief Executive Mike Wood
Chair Christine Barwell

12

Milton Keynes Primary Care Trust

The Hospital Campus, Standing Way, Eaglestone, Milton
   Keynes MK6 5NG; URL www.mkpct.org.uk;
   E-mail mail@miltonkeynes-pct.nhs.uk; Tel 01908 243124
Chief Executive   Ms Barbara Kennedy;
   E-mail barbara.kennedy@mkpct.nhs.uk
Chair   Malcolm Brighton

Morecambe Bay Primary Care Trust

Tenterfield, Brigsteer Rd, Kendal, Cumbria LA9 5EA;
   URL www.mbpct.nhs.uk;
   E-mail sue.greenwood@mbpct.nhs.uk
Chief Executive   Dr Leigh Griffin
Chair   Dr Robin Talbot

HOSPITALS

Dane Garth Mental Health Unit Furness General Hospital,
Dalton La, Barrow, Lancashire; Tel 01229 870870; Fax 01229
871182
Ridge Lee Hospital Quemmore Rd, Lancaster, Lancashire;
Tel 01524 586200; Fax 01524 586201

New Forest Primary Care Trust

8–9 Sterne Rd, Tatchbury Mount, Calmore, Southampton,
   Hampshire SO4 2RZ; E-mail katy.shaw@nfpct.nhs.uk;
   Tel 023 8087 4270; Fax 023 8087 4275
Chief Executive   Angela Jeffrey;
   E-mail angela.jeffrey@nfpct.nhs.uk
Chair   Dr Anand Chitnis

Newark and Sherwood Primary Care Trust

65 North Gate, Newark, Nottinghamshire NG24 1HD
Chief Executive   Charles Allen
Chair   Bonny Jones

Newbury and Community Primary Care Trust

Newbury Community Hospital, Andover Rd, Newbury,
   Berkshire RG14 6LS;
   URL www.berkshire.nhs.uk/newbury; Tel 01635 32500;
   Fax 01635 580709
Chief Executive   Sheila Hayes
Chair   Mr B. Laurie

Newcastle Primary Care Trust

Benfield Rd, Walkergate, Newcastle upon Tyne, Tyne and
   Wear NE6 4PF; URL www.newcastlepct.nhs.uk; Tel 0191
   219 6000; Fax 0191 219 6066; Minicom 0191 219 6067
Chief Executive   Bob Smith
Chair   Gina Tiller

Newcastle under Lyme Primary Care Trust

Bradwell Hospital, Talke Rd, Chesterton, Newcastle,
   Staffordshire ST5 7NJ; URL www.newcastlepct.co.uk;
   E-mail office@newcastle-ul-pct.nhs.uk
Chief Executive   Ian Rogerson
Chair   Ian Ashbolt

Newham Primary Care Trust

Plaistow Hospital, Samson St, London E13 9EH
Chief Executive   David Stout
Chair   Stephen Jacobs

North and East Cornwall Primary Care Trust

John Keay Hse, Tregonissey Rd, St. Austell, Cornwall
   PL25 4NQ
Chair   Michael Matcham

HOSPITALS

East Cornwall Hospital Rhind St, Bodmin, Cornwall
PL31 2BT; Tel 01208 251557; Fax 01208 251585
Lamellion Hospital Station Rd, Liskeard, Cornwall
PL14 4DG; Tel 01579 335300; Fax 01579 335319
Launceston General Hospital Link Rd, Launceston,
Cornwall PL15 9JD; Tel 01566 756650; Fax 01566 765680
Passmore Edwards Hospital Barras Pl, Liskeard, Cornwall
PL14 6AY; Tel 01579 335277; Fax 01579 335290
St. Barnabas' Hospital Higher Porth View, Saltash,
Cornwall; Tel 01752 857400
Stratton Hospital Hospital Rd, Stratton, Bude, Cornwall
EX23 9BP; Tel 01288 287700

HEALTH CENTRES AND CLINICS

Bodmin Health Centre Dennison Rd, Bodmin, Cornwall
PL31 2LB; Tel 01208 251530
Callington Community Clinic Hayle Rd, Callington,
Cornwall; Tel 01579 384589
Looe Community Clinic Station Rd, East Looe, Pensilva,
Cornwall PL13 1HA; Tel 01503 756969
Tintagel Health Office Fosters La, Tintagel, Cornwall
PL34 0BT; Tel 01840 770794
Torpoint Community Clinic Hooper St, Torpoint, Cornwall
PL11 2AG; Tel 01752 812850

North Birmingham Primary Care Trust

Blakelands Hse, 400 Aldridge Rd, Perry Bar, Birmingham,
   West Midlands B44 8BH
Chief Executive
Chair   Jo Davis

North Bradford Primary Care Trust

New Mill, Victoria Rd, Saltaire, Shipley, West Yorkshire
   BD18 3LD; URL www.northbradford-pct.nhs.uk;
   E-mail nbpct@bradford.nhs.uk
Chief Executive   Dr Ian Rutter
Chair   Norman Roper

North Devon Primary Care Trust

12 Boutport St, Barstaple, Devon EX31 1RW
Chief Executive   Kate Tomkins
Chair   Mr Osbourne

North Dorset Primary Care Trust

Forston Clinic, Charminster, Dorchester, Dorset DT2 9TB;
   Tel 01305 361300; Fax 01305 361330
Chief Executive   Andrew Casey
Chair   Mary Penfold

HEALTH CLINICS

Abbey View Medical Centre (GP owned) Shaftesbury,
Dorset SP7 8DH; Tel 01747 856711; Fax 01747 856701
Blandford Health Clinic Salisbury St, Blandford, Dorset;
Tel 01258 452949
Mental Health Rehabilitation Unit 26 Glendining Ave,
Weymouth, Dorset DT4 9QF; Tel 01305 778465; Fax 01305
778465
   Number of places: (9)
Sturminster Newton Medical Centre (GP owned) Barnes Cl,
Sturminster Newton, Dorset; Tel 01258 473188
Waterloo Lodge Shaftesbury Rd, Motcombe, Shaftesbury,
Dorset SP7 9TT; Tel 01747 824949; Fax 01747 821492
   Number of places: (5)

MENTAL HEALTH UNITS

CADAS (Community Alcohol and Drugs Advisory Service) 28 High West St, Dorchester, Dorset DT1 1UP; Tel 01305 265901; Fax 01305 250285

Community Mental Health Team (Adult) Albert Rd, Dorchester, Dorset DT1 1SF; Tel 01305 251316
    Number of places: (6)

Community Mental Health Team (Adult) Milldown Unit, Blandford, Dorset DT11 7DD; Tel 01258 450610; Fax 01258 454894

Community Mental Health Team (Adult) Ashley Elm Hse, Yeatman Hospital, Sherborne, Dorset DT9 3JU; Tel 01935 816552; Fax 01935 815609

Community Mental Health Team (Elderly) Betty Highwood Unit, Blandford Hospital, Blandford, Dorset DT11 7DD; Tel 01258 456541; Fax 01258 458321

Elderly Mental Health Team Bridport Day Centre, Hospital La, Bridport, Dorset DT6 5DR; Tel 01308 425988; Fax 01308 421864

Forston Clinic Charminster, Dorchester, Dorset DT2 9TB; Tel 01305 361300; Fax 01305 361330

Hughes Unit Community Mental Health Unit (Adult), Bridport Community Hospital, Hospital La, Bridport, Dorset; Tel 01308 421236; Fax 01308 426271

Linden Unit Radipole La, Weymouth, Dorset DT4 0QE; Tel 01305 787274; Fax 01305 787274

HOSPITALS

Blandford Community Hospital Milldown Rd, Blandford Forum, Dorset DT11 7DD; Tel 01258 456541; Fax 01258 450786
    Specialism: Acute; elderly; elderly confused; rehabilitation care; outpatient; x-ray; day hospital; family unit. Number of beds: (66)

Forston Clinic Charminster, Dorchester, Dorset DT2 9TB; Tel 01305 251812
    Specialism: Psychiatric, elderly confused. Number of beds: (38)

Westminster Memorial Hospital Abbey Wlk, Shaftesbury, Dorset SP7 8BD; Tel 01747 851535; Fax 01747 850152

Yeatman Hospital Hospital La, Sherborne, Dorset DT9 3JU; Tel 01935 813991
    Specialism: Acute; elderly and rehabilitation care; outpatient and casualty; x-ray; ESMI. Number of beds: (57)

North Eastern Derbyshire Primary Care Trust

St. Mary's Crt, St. Mary's Gate, Chesterfield, Derbyshire; Tel 01246 551158; Fax 01246 544620
Chief Executive Kevin Holder

North East Lincolnshire Primary Care Trust

Scartho Hall, Scartho Rd, Grimsby, South Humberside, Lincolnshire DN33 2BA; URL www.nelpct.nhs.uk; Tel 01472 875621; Fax 01472 503257
Chief Executive Ms Lewington
Chair Valerie Waterhouse

North East Oxfordshire Primary Care Trust

Montgomery House Surgery, Piggy La, Bicester, Oxfordshire OX6 7HT
Chief Executive Geraint Griffiths;
    E-mail geraint.griffiths@neoxon-pct.nhs.uk
Chair Brigadeer Ian Inshaw

North Hampshire Primary Care Trust

Harness Hse, Aldermaston Rd, Basingstoke, Hampshire RG24 9NB; URL www.northampshire.nhs.uk

Chief Executive Gill Duncan;
    E-mail gill.duncan@nhpct.nhs.uk
Chair Dr Tony Ludlow

HOSPITALS

Alton Community Hospital Alton, Hampshire GU34 1RJ; Tel 01420 82811; Fax 01420 543873

Chase Hospital Conde Way, Whitehill, Hampshire GU34 1RL; Tel 01420 488801

North Hertfordshire and Stevenage Primary Care Trust

Solutions Hse, Dunhams La, Letchworth, Hertfordshire SG6 1BE; Tel 01462 708470; Fax 01462 708472
Chief Executive Jill Peters
Chair Dr Rachel Fox

North Kirklees Primary Care Trust

12 Central Arcade, Cleckheaton, West Yorkshire BD19 5DN
Chair Dr Barry Seal

North Lincolnshire Primary Care Trust

Health Pl, Wrawby Rd, Brigg, North Lincolnshire DN20 8GS; URL www.nlpct.nhs.uk; E-mail cathy.waters@nlpct.nhs.uk; Tel 01652 659659; Fax 01652 601160
Chief Executive Cathy Waters
Chair Sir John Mason, CBE

North Liverpool Primary Care Trust

Cottage No 7, Newhall Campus, Longmoor La, Liverpool, Merseyside L10 1LD
Chief Executive Joanne Forrest
Chair Lily Hopkins

North Manchester Primary Care Trust

2nd Fl, Newton Silk Mill, Holyoak St, Newton Heath, Manchester M40 1HA; URL www.northmanchesterpct.nhs.uk
Chief Executive Laura Roberts
Chair Winifred Dignan

North Norfolk Primary Care Trust

Kelling Hospital, Cromer Rd, Holt, Norfolk NR25 6QA
Chair Lee Muston

North Peterborough Primary Care Trust

St. John's, Thorpe Rd, Peterborough, Cambridgeshire PE3 6JG
Chief Executive Chris Town
Chair Mohammad Choudhary

North Sheffield Primary Care Trust

Firth Park Clinic, North Quadrant, Sheffield, South Yorkshire S5 6NU
Chief Executive Andy Buck
Chair Robert Bailey

North Somerset Primary Care Trust

1st Fl, The Courthouse, 25–27 Old Weston Rd, Flax Bourton, Bristol BS48 1UL; URL www.avon.nhs.uk/nsomerset; Tel 01275 465200; Fax 01275 464995
Chief Executive Julia Sharma
Chair Jane Corke

12

North Stoke Primary Care Trust

Haywood Hospital, High La, Stoke-on-Trent ST6 7AG
Chief Executive   Peter Hammersley
Chair   Brenda McGough

North Surrey Primary Care Trust

Bournewood Hse, Guildford Rd, Fetcham, Chertsey, Surrey
    KT16 0QA; URL www.nsurreypct.nhs.uk;
    E-mail sue.robertson@bcmhs-tr.sthames.nhs.uk;
    Tel 01932 872010; Fax 01932 875346
Chief Executive   Nick Yeo
Chair (Primary Care Trust)   Douglas Robertson
Chair   Dr Elizabeth Lawn
Medical Director (Specialist Services)   Dr Beverly Castleton
Director (Finance)   Vic Jemmett
Director (Human Resources)   Vacancy
Director (Commissioning and Performance Improvement)
    Sue Robertson
Director (Primary Care and Community Services)   Linda Read
Director (Nursing and Clinical Governance)   Celia McGruer
Director (Public Health)   Dr Saroj Auplish
Director (Therapies and Intermediate Care)   Jacqui Smart
Area Director (Surrey Social Services)   Heather Schroeder

HOSPITALS

Walton Community Hospital Sidney Rd, Walton on Thames,
Surrey KT12 3LD; Tel 01932 253674; Fax 01932 253674

Weybridge Community Hospital and Primary Care Centre
Church St, Weybridge, Surrey KT13 8DY; Tel 01932 852931;
Fax 01932 826068

Woking Community Hospital Heathside Rd, Woking, Surrey
GU22 7HS; Tel 01483 715911; Fax 01483 766195

North Tees Teaching Primary Care Trust

Tower Hse, Teesdale South, Thornaby Pl, Thornaby,
    Stockton-on-Tees TS17 6SF
Chief Executive   Chris Willis
Chair   Richard Nicholson

North Tyneside Primary Care Trust

Benfield Rd, Walkergate, Newcastle upon Tyne, Tyne and
    Wear NE6 4PF; URL www.northtynesidepct.nhs.uk;
    Tel 0191 2196000; Fax 0191 2196066; Minicom 0191
    2196067
Chief Executive   Pam McDougal
Chair   David Luke

North Warwickshire Primary Care Trust

139 Earls Rd, Nuneaton, Warwickshire CV11 5HP
Chief Executive   Anne Heckels
Chair   Chris Bain

Northampton Primary Care Trust

Highfield, Cliftonville Rd, Northampton,
    Northamptonshire NN1 5DN
Chair   Dr Tobey

Northamptonshire Heartlands Primary Care Trust

Nene Hse, Isebrook Hospital, Irthlingborough Rd,
    Wellingborough, Northamptonshire NN8 1LP
Chief Executive   Richard Alsop
Chair   Susan Hills

Norwich Primary Care Trust

Little Plumstead Hospital, Hospital Rd, Little Plumstead,
    Norwich, Norfolk NR13 5EW
Chief Executive   Dr Chris Price
Chair   Susan Gale

HOSPITALS

Benjamin Court Cromer, Norfolk NR27 0EU

Beechcroft Hooper La, Sprowston, Norwich, Norfolk
NR3 4ED

Caroline House Colman Hospital, Unthank Rd, Norwich,
Norfolk NR2 2PJ; Tel 01603 286286
    Specialism: Young disabled. Number of beds: (25)

Cranmer House Norwich Rd, Fakenham, Norfolk
NR21 8HR

Dereham Hospital East Dereham, Norfolk; Tel 01362
692391
    Specialism: Rehabilitation. Number of beds: (69)

Kelling Hospital Holt, Norfolk; Tel 01263 713333
    Specialism: Rehabilitation Number of beds: (57)

Little Plumstead Hospital Little Plumstead, Norwich,
Norfolk NR13 5EW; Tel 01603 711227
    Specialism: Learning disabilities. Number of beds: (186)

North Walsham Cottage Hospital
    Specialism: GP referral. Number of beds: (23)

Norwich Community Hospital Bowthorpe Rd, Norwich,
Norfolk NR2 3TU; Tel 01603 776776

Ogden Court Ogden Cl, Wymondham, Norfolk NR18 0PE

Priscilla Bacon Lodge Colman Hospital, Unthank Rd,
Norwich, Norfolk NR2 2PJ; Tel 01603 288950
    Specialism: Palliative care. Number of beds: (25)

St. Michael's Hospital Aylsham, Norfolk; Tel 01263
732341
    Specialism: Rehabilitation Number of beds: (54)

Wayland Hospital Attleborough, Norfolk; Tel 01953 452181
    Specialism: Post-operative rehabilitation; amputee
    service. Number of beds: (60)

Wells Cottage Hospital;
    Specialism: Rehabilitation. Number of beds: (15)

Nottingham City Primary Care Trust

1 Standard Crt, Park Row, Nottingham, Nottinghamshire
    NG1 6GN; Tel 0115 845 4545; Fax 0115 912 3300
Chief Executive   Samantha Milbank
Chair   David Atkinson
Director (Finance)   R. Hawkins
Director (Personnel and Development – Shared Services)
    Ken Hardy

Oldbury and Smethwick Primary Care Trust

Kingston Hse, 438–450 High St, West Bromwich, West
    Midlands B70 9LD
Chair   Richard Nugent

Oldham Primary Care Trust

Westhulme Ave, Oldham, Lancashire OL1 2PL
Chief Executive   Gail Richards
Chair   Riaz Ahmed

Oxford City Primary Care Trust

Richards Bldg, Old Rd, Headington, Oxford, Oxfordshire
    OX3 7LG; URL www.oxfordcity-pct.nhs.uk
Chief Executive   Andrea Young;
    E-mail andrea.young@oxfordcity-pct.nhs.uk
Chair   Malcolm Fearn

Plymouth Primary Care Trust

Building 1, Derriford Bus Pk, Brest Rd, Plymouth PL6 5QZ;
    URL www.plymouth-pct.nhs.uk;
    E-mail enquiries@pct-tr.swest.nhs.uk
Chief Executive   Ann James
Chair   Mr Connelly

Poole Primary Care Trust

Parkstone Health Centre, Mansfield Rd, Poole BH14 0DJ
Chief Executive Andrew Morris
Chair Anne Holland

Portsmouth City Primary Care Trust

Finchdean Hse, Milton Rd, Portsmouth, Hampshire
PO3 6DP
Chief Executive Sheila Clark;
E-mail sheila.clark@portsha.swest.nhs.uk
Chair Zenna Atkins

Preston Primary Care Trust

Sharoe Green Hospital, Sharoe Green La, Fulwood, Preston,
Lancashire PR2 8DU
Chief Executive Jan Hewitt
Chair Wendy Hogg

CLINICS AND HEALTH CENTRES

Ashton Health Centre Peddars La, Ashton, Preston,
Lancashire PR2 1HR

Avenham Health Centre Avenham La, Avenham, Preston,
Lancashire PR1 3RG; Tel 01772 401900

Fulwood Clinic 4 Lytham Rd, Fulwood, Preston, Lancashire
PR2 8JB; Tel 01772 401300; Fax 01772 401334

Geoffrey Street Health Centre Geoffrey St, Preston,
Lancashire PR1 5NE; Tel 01772 401700; Fax 01772 401701

Ingol Health Centre 86 Village Green La, Ingol, Preston,
Lancashire PR2 7DS; Tel 01772 401500; Fax 01772 401504

Ribbleton Clinic Miller Rd, Ribbleton, Preston, Lancashire
PR2 6LS; Tel 01772 401825; Fax 01772 651989

Saulhouse Street Clinic Saulhouse St, Preston, Lancashire
PR1 2QU; Tel 01772 401173; Fax 01772 883502

Willows Child Development Centre Peddars La, Ashton,
Preston, Lancashire PR2 2TR; Tel 01772 401450; Fax 01772
768122

Reading Primary Care Trust

57–59 Bath Rd, Reading, Berkshire RG30 2BA
Chief Executive Janet Fitzgerald
Chair Ms Henrion

Redbridge Primary Care Trust

Becketts Hse, 2–4 Ilford Hill, Ilford, Essex IG1 2QX
Chief Executive Heather O'Meara
Chair Edwin Doyle

Redditch and Bromsgrove Primary Care Trust

Crossgate Hse, Crossgate Rd, Park Farm, Redditch,
Worcestershire B98 7SN
Chief Executive Eamonn Kelly
Chair Graham Vickery

HOSPITAL

Princess of Wales Community Hospital Stourbridge Rd,
Bromsgrove, Worcestershire B61 0BB; Tel 01527 570075

Richmond and Twickenham Primary Care Trust

Thames Hse, 180 High St, Teddington, Greater London
TW11 8HU; E-mail enquiries@rtpct.nhs.uk; Tel 020 8973
8000; Fax 020 8973 8001
Chief Executive Joan Mager
Chair Sîan Bates

Rochdale Primary Care Trust

St. James Pl, 164–166 Yorkshire St, Rochdale, Lancashire
OL16 2DL
Chief Executive Trevor Purt
Chair Debbie Abrahams

Rotherham Primary Care Trust

Bevan Hse, Oakwood Hall Dr, Rotherham, South Yorkshire
S60 3AQ; Tel 01709 302011; Fax 01709 302002
Chief Executive John McIvor
Chair Alan Tolhurst
Director (Public Health and Health Policy) Dr J. Radford
Director (Clinical Services) K. Henderson
Director (Strategic Planning) K.S. Atkinson
Director (Finance and Performance) A. Spring
Annual Budget
£207 million

HOSPITALS

Doncaster Gate Hospital Doncaster Gate, Rotherham,
South Yorkshire S65 1DW; Tel 01709 820000

Maltby Hostel 130 Braithwell Rd, Maltby, Rotherham,
South Yorkshire S66 8JT; Tel 01709 790097

Rotherham District General Hospital (Beechcroft) Moorgate
Rd, Rotherham, South Yorkshire S60 2UD; Tel 01709 824088

Rotherham District General Hospital (Mental Health)
Moorgate Rd, Rotherham, South Yorkshire S60 2UD

Rowely, Regis and Tipton Primary Care Trust

Kingston Hse, 438–450 High St, West Bromwich, West
Midlands B70 9LD
Chief Executive Vacancy
Chair Douglas Round

Royston, Buntingford and Bishop's Stortford Primary Care Trust

Herts and Essex Community Hospital, Haymeads La,
Bishop's Stortford, Hertfordshire CM23 5JH;
URL www.rbbs-pct.nhs.uk
Chief Executive Gareth Jones
Chair Mavis Garner

Rugby Primary Care Trust

Central Surgery, Corporation St, Rugby, Warwickshire
CV21 3SP
Chief Executive Peter Maddock
Chair Ted Pallot

Rushcliffe Primary Care Trust

Barclays Bank Chambers, Tudor Sq, West Bridgford,
Nottingham, Nottinghamshire NG2 6BT;
URL www.nottingham.nhs.uk;
E-mail rpct@rushcliffe-pct.nhs.uk; Tel 0115 956 0305;
Fax 0115 956 0302
Chief Executive Mark Morgan
Chair John Tarrant

Salford Primary Care Trust

Suite 19, 21–23, 5th Fl, St. James Hse, Pendleton Way,
Salford, Greater Manchester M6 5FW
Chief Executive Ms Robinson
Chair Dr Fairhurst

Scarborough, Whitby and Ryedale Primary Care Trust

13 Yorkers Gate, Malton, North Yorkshire YO17 7AA
Chief Executive Michael Whitworth
Chair Colin Morgan Barnes

12

Sedgefield Primary Care Trust

Merrington Hse, Merrington Lane Ind Est, Spennymoor,
County Durham DL16 7UU;
URL www.sedgefield-pct.nhs.uk;
E-mail nigel.porter@sedgefieldpct.nhs.uk
Chief Executive Nigel Porter
Chair Alan Gray

Selby and York Primary Care Trust

Soverign Hse, Kettestring La, Clifton Moor, York, North
Yorkshire YO30 4GQ; URL wypct.com
Chief Executive Dr Susan Ross
Chair Wendy Bundy

Sheffield South West Primary Care Trust

5 Old Fulwood Rd, Sheffield, South Yorkshire S10 3TG;
URL www.sheffield.nhs.uk/southwestpct;
E-mail sswpct@sheffieldsw-pct.nhs.uk
Chief Executive Janet Soo-Chung, CBE
Chair Ann le Sage

Sheffield West Primary Care Trust

Unit 4 Dragoon Crt, Hillsborough Barracks, Penistone Rd,
Sheffield, South Yorkshire S6 2GZ; Tel 0114 2856920;
Fax 0114 2856921
Chief Executive Simon Gilby
Chair Dorothy Dixon-Barrow

Shepway Primary Care Trust

8 Radnor Park Ave, Folkestone, Kent CT19 5BN
Chief Executive Ann Sutton;
E-mail ann.sutton@tgt.sthames.nhs.uk
Chair Andrew Barchi

HEALTH CENTRES AND CLINICS

Folkestone Health Centre 15–25 Dover Rd, Folkestone,
Kent CT20 1JY; Tel 01303 228888

Hythe Clinic 140–144 High St, Hythe, Kent CT21 5JU;
Tel 01303 717070

New Romney Clinic 54 Station Rd, New Romney, Kent
TN28 8LQ; Tel 01797 246600

Shepway Health Centre 2–4 Radnor Park Ave, Folkestone,
Kent CT19 5HN; Tel 01303 222424

Shropshire County Primary Care Trust

Willian Farr Hse, Mytton Oak Rd, Shrewsbury, Shropshire
SY3 8 XL
Chief Executive Julie Grant
Chair Elizabeth Owen

HOSPITALS

Bishop's Castle Community Hospital Union Street Bishop's
Castle, Shropshire SY9 5AJ; Tel 01588 638220; Fax 01588
638756

Bridgnorth Hospital Northgate, Bridgnorth, West Midlands
WV16 4EV; Tel 01746 762641; Fax 01746 766172

Ludlow Hospital Gravel Hill, Ludlow, Shropshire SY8 1QX;
Tel 01584 872201; Fax 01584 877908

Mytton Oak Unit Royal Shrewsbury Hospital, Shrewsbury,
Shropshire SY3 8XQ; Tel 01743 261181; Fax 01743 261446

Shelton Hospital Bicton Health, Shrewsbury, Shropshire
SY3 8DN; Tel 01743 261000; Fax 01743 492054

Whitchurch Hospital Brownlow St, Whitchurch, Shropshire
SY13 1QS; Tel 01948 666292; Fax 01588 638756

Slough Primary Care Trust

Beech Hse, Upton Hospital, Albert St, Slough, Berkshire
SL1 2BJ; URL www.berkshire.nhs.uk/slough;
E-mail mike.attwood@berkshire.nhs.uk; Tel 01753
821441; Fax 01753 635050
Chief Executive Mike Attwood
Chair Geoff Cutting

Solihull Primary Care Trust

20 Union Rd, Solihull, West Midlands B91 3EF;
URL www.solihull.nhs.uk; Tel 0121 711 7171; Fax 0121
711 7212; Minicom 0121 704 2389
Chief Executive Carol Clarke
6th Fl, Mell Hse, 46 Drury La, Solihull, West Midlands
B91 3BU; Tel 0121 712 8312; Fax 0121 712 8301
Chair Anne Dorow
6th Fl, Mell Hse, 46 Drury La, Solihull, West Midlands
B91 3BU; Tel 0121 712 8312; Fax 0121 712 8301
Director (Human Resources and Organisational Development)
N. Gillard
Director (Finance and Contracts) M. Bull

Somerset Coast Primary Care Trust

Riverside Office, Bridgwater Community Hospital, Salmon
Pde, Bridgwater, Somerset TA6 5AH;
URL www.somerset-coast-pct.org.uk;
E-mail somcoast@somcoastpct.nhs.uk
Chief Executive Alan Carpenter
Chair Mrs Dore

HOSPITALS

Bridgwater Community Hospital Salmon Pde, Bridgwater,
Somerset TA6 5AH; Tel 01278 451501; Fax 01278 444896

Burnham on Sea War Memorial Hospital 6 Love La,
Burnham on Sea, Somerset TA8 1ED; Tel 01278 773118;
Fax 01278 793367

Minehead Hospital The Avenue, Minehead, Somerset
TA24 5LY; Tel 01643 707251; Fax 01643 707251

Williton and District Hospital Williton, Somerset TA4 4RA;
Tel 01984 635600; Fax 01984 633026

South and East Dorset Primary Care Trust

Trust Headquarters, Victoria Hse, Princes Rd, Ferndown,
Dorset BH22 9JR
Chief Executive Andrew Cawthron
Chair Mrs Bussey

South Birmingham Primary Care Trust

Moseley Hall Hospital, Alcester Rd, Birmingham, West
Midlands B13 8JL
Chief Executive Cynthia Bower
Chair Prof David Cox

HEALTH CENTRES

Balsall Heath Health Centre Edward Rd, Birmingham, West
Midlands B12 9LB; Tel 0121 446 4858

Bartley Green Health Centre Romsley Rd, Birmingham,
West Midlands B32 3PS; Tel 0121 477 4800

Broadmeadow Health Centre Keynell Covert, Birmingham,
West Midlands B30 3QT; Tel 0121 433 4949

Farm Road Health Centre Sparkbrook, Birmingham, West
Midlands B11 1QS; Tel 0121 772 1395

Greet Centre for Community Care 50 Percy Rd, Greet,
Birmingham, West Midlands B11 1QS; Tel 0121 766 5550

Hawkesley Health Centre 375 Shannon Rd, Birmingham,
West Midlands B38 9NE; Tel 0121 451 3111

Hillmeads Health Centre 57 Hillmeads Rd, Birmingham, West Midlands B38 9NE; Tel 0121 458 3250

Ley Hill Health Centre 165 Holloway, Birmingham, West Midlands B31 1TT; Tel 0121 475 4011

Maypole Health Centre 10 Sladepool Farm Rd, Birmingham, West Midlands B14 5DJ; Tel 0121 430 5353

Northfield Health Centre St Heliers Rd, Birmingham, West Midlands B31 1QT; Tel 0121 478 2000

Quinton Lane Care Centre 27 Quinton La, Birmingham, West Midlands B32 2TR; Tel 0121 427 2511

St. Patrick's Centre for Community Health Highgate St, Birmingham, West Midlands B12 0YA; Tel 0121 446 4747

Selly Oak Health Centre Katie Rd, Birmingham, West Midlands B29 6JG; Tel 0121 627 1627

Shirley Road Health Centre 189 Shirley Rd, Birmingham, West Midlands B27 7NP; Tel 0121 706 7118

Weoley Castle Health Centre 187 Weoley Castle Rd, Birmingham, West Midlands B29 5QH; Tel 0121 427 2160

Woodgate Valley Health Centre Stevens Ave, Birmingham, West Midlands B32 3SD; Tel 0121 427 1344; 0121 427 9818

Yardley Wood Health Centre 401 Highfield Rd, Birmingham, West Midlands B14 4DU; Tel 0121 474 2276

ELDERLY AND REHABILITATION HOSPITAL DIVISION

Moseley Hall Hospital Alcester Rd, Birmingham, West Midlands B13 8JL; Tel 0121 442 4321

The Sheldon Nursing Home Sheldon Dr, Birmingham, West Midlands B31 5EJ; Tel 0121 475 6100

West Heath Day Hospital Rednal Rd, Birmingham, West Midlands B38 8HR; Tel 0121 627 8244

West Heath Hospital Rednal Rd, Birmingham, West Midlands B38 8HR; Tel 0121 627 1627

DENTAL HOSPITAL DIVISION

Dental Hospital St. Chad's Queensway, Birmingham, West Midlands B4 6NN; Tel 0121 236 8611

REHABILITATION DIVISION

Oak Tree Lane Centre Selly Oak, Birmingham, West Midlands B29 6JA; Tel 0121 627 1627; Fax 0121 627 8210

Birmingham Resource Centre for Deafened People Oak Tree Lane Centre, Selly Oak, Birmingham, West Midlands B29 6JA; Tel 0121 627 8930

South Cambridgeshire Primary Care Trust

Block 23, Heron Crt, Ida Darwin, Fulbourn, Cambridge, Cambridgeshire CB1 5EE; URL www.southcambs-pct.nhs.uk
Chair Ruth Rogers
There is a general email address:
<firstname>.<surname>@southcambs-pct.nhs.uk

South East Hertfordshire Primary Care Trust

1–4 Limes Crt, Conduit La, Hoddeson, Hertfordshire EN11 8EP
Chief Executive Vince Mccabe
Chair Lynda Tarpey

South East Oxfordshire Primary Care Trust

Wallingford Community Hospital, Reading Rd, Wallingford, Oxfordshire OX10 9DU
Chief Executive Mary Wicks;
E-mail mary.wicks@seoxon-pct.nhs.uk
Chair Tony Williamson

South East Sheffield Primary Care Trust

9 Orgreave Rd, Sheffield, West Yorkshire S13 9LQ; URL www.se.sheffield.pct.nhs.uk; Tel 0114 226 4050; Fax 0114 226 4051
Chief Executive Helen Fentiman
Chair Adebola Fatogun

South Gloucester Primary Care Trust

Monarch Crt, Emerald Bus Pk, Emerson's Grn, Bristol BS16 7FH; URL www.sqlos-pct.nhs.uk; Tel 0117 330 2400; Fax 0117 330 2401
Chief Executive Jo Whitehead
Chair Mr Goodson

South Hams and West Devon Primary Care Trust

Lescaze Offices, Shinner's Bridge, Dartington, Totnes, Devon TQ9 6JE
Chief Executive Alan Tibbenham
Chair Sally Foxhill

HOSPITAL

Totnes Community Hospital Coronation Rd, Totnes, Devon TQ9 5GH; Tel 01803 862622

South Huddersfield Primary Care Trust

Ward 6, St. Luke's Hospital, Blackmoorfoot Rd, Huddersfield, West Yorkshire HD4 5RQ
Chief Executive Vacancy
Chair John Chiltern

South Leicestershire Primary Care Trust

The Rosings, Forest Rd, Narborough, Leicestershire LE9 5EQ
Chief Executive Julie Wood
Chair Gordon England

HOSPITAL

Fielding Palmer Hospital Gilmorton Rd, Lutterworth, Leicestershire LE17 4DZ; Tel 01455 552150; Fax 01455 558083

HEALTH CENTRES

Lutterworth Health Centre Gilmorton Rd, Lutterworth, Leicestershire LE17 4EB; Tel 01455 553531; Fax 01455 550083

Narborough Health Centre Thornton Dr, Narborough, Leicestershire LE9 5GX; Tel 0116 286 4433; Fax 0116 275 2470

South Wigston Health Centre Blaby Rd, South Wigston, Leicestershire LE18 4SE; Tel 0116 278 5022; Fax 0116 278 4510

South Liverpool Primary Care Trust

Pavilion 6, The Matchworks, 142 Speke Rd, Liverpool, Merseyside L19 2PH
Chief Executive (Acting) Christine Walley
Chair Beatrice Fraenkel

South Manchester Primary Care Trust

Withington Hospital, Nell La, West Didsbury, Manchester M20 2LR
Chief Executive Mr A. Mercer
Chair Michael Green

HOSPITAL

Withington Hospital (including Duchess of York Children's Hospital) Nell La, West Didsbury, Manchester M20 8LR; Tel 0161 445 8111

12

South Peterborough Primary Care Trust

St. Johns, Thorpe Rd, Peterborough, Cambridgeshire
PE3 6JG
Chief Executive   Chris Town
Chair   Marco Cereste

South Sefton Primary Care Trust

Burlington Hse, Crosby Road North, Waterloo, Liverpool,
Merseyside L22 0QB;
E-mail enquiries@southsefton-pct.nhs.uk
Chief Executive   I. Williamson
Chair   Ken Morris

South Somerset Primary Care Trust

South Petherton Hospital, Hospital La, South Petherton,
Somerset TA13 5AR
Chief Executive   Virginia Pearson
Chair   Keith Pearson

HOSPITALS

Chard and District Hospital   Crewkerne Rd, Chard,
Somerset TA20 1NF; Tel 01460 63175; Fax 01460 68172

Crewkerne Hospital   Middle Path, Crewkerne, Somerset
TA18 8BG; Tel 01460 72491; Fax 01460 75423

South Petherton Hospital   South Petherton, Somerset
TA13 5AR; Tel 01460 240333; Fax 01460 242292

Verrington Hospital   Dancing La, Wincanton, Somerset
BA9 9DQ; Tel 01963 32006; Fax 01963 31898

South Stoke Primary Care Trust

Heron Hse, 120 Grove Rd, Fenton, Stoke-on-Trent ST4 4LX;
Tel 01782 298000; Fax 01782 298298
Chief Executive   Tony McGovern
Chair   Michael Tappin

South Tyneside Primary Care Trust

Ingham Hse, Horsely Hill Rd, South Shields, Tyne and
Wear NE33 3DP
Chief Executive   Roy McLachlan
Chair   Stephen Clark

HEALTH CENTRES AND CLINICS

Boker Lane Clinic   Boker La, East Boldon, Tyne and Wear
NE36 0RY; Tel 0191 519 1355

Boldon Lane Clinic   Boldon La, South Shields, Tyne and
Wear NE34 0NB; Tel 0191 456 2845

Flagg Court Health Centre   Flagg Crt, South Shields, Tyne
and Wear NE33 2DW; Tel 0191 456 9222

Hebburn Health Centre   Campbell Park Rd, Hebburn, Tyne
and Wear NE31 2SH; Tel 0191 483 4421

Jarrow ComCare   Glasgow Rd, South Shields, Tyne and
Wear NE32 4AV; Tel 0191 428 1628

Marsden Road Health Centre   Marsden Rd, South Shields,
Tyne and Wear NE34 6RE; Tel 0191 456 7721

Stanhope Parade Health Centre Clinic   Gordon St, South
Shields, Tyne and Wear NE33 4GA; Tel 0191 456 8821

South Warwickshire Primary Care Trust

Governor's Hse, 153 Cape Rd, Warwick, Warwickshire
CV34 5DJ; URL www.swarkpct.nhs.uk; Tel 01926
403403; Fax 01926 409122
Chief Executive   Catherine Griffiths
Chair   Prof David Ashton
Director (Public Health)   Dr S. Munday
Director (Quality and Development)   Vivienne Bennett

Director (Finance and Performance)   Mark Mansfield
Director (Operations)   Shaun Clee
Annual Budget
£160 million

HOSPITALS

Alcester Hospital   Kinwarton Rd, Alcester, Warwickshire
B49 6PX; Tel 01789 762470
Specialism: Geriatric; rehabilitation.

Ellen Badger Hospital   Shipston on Stour, Warwickshire
CV36 4AX; Tel 01608 661410
Number of beds: (35)

The Royal Lemington Spa Rehabilitation Hospital
Heathcote La, Warwick, Warwickshire CV34 6SR; Tel 01926
317700
Specialism: Geriatric rehabilitation; other physical
disability rehabilitation.

St. Michael's Hospital   St. Michael's Rd, Warwick,
Warwickshire CV34 5QW; Tel 01926 496241
Specialism: Psychiatric.

South West Dorset Primary Care Trust

1a Acland Rd, Dorchester, Dorset BH1 1JW;
E-mail marlenebutler@dorsetc-tr.swest.nhs.uk; Tel 01305
259366
Chief Executive   Peter Mankin
Chair   Mr A. S. Thomas

South West Kent Primary Care Trust

Sevenoaks Hospital, Hospital Rd, Sevenoaks, Kent
TN13 3PG; E-mail steve.ford@swkent-pct.nhs.uk
Chief Executive   Steve Ford
Chair   Prof John Smythe

South West Oxfordshire Primary Care Trust

1st Fl, Admin Block, Abingdon Community Hospital,
Marcham Rd, Abingdon, Oxfordshire OX14 1AG;
URL www.swoxon-pct.nhs.uk
Chief Executive   Mary Wicks;
E-mail mary.wicks@swoxon-pct.nhs.uk
Chair   Prof Martin Avis

South West Staffordshire Primary Care Trust

Mellor Hse, Corporation St, Stafford, Staffordshire
ST16 3SR
Chief Executive   William Price
Chair   Jennifer Cornes

South Wiltshire Primary Care Trust

42–44 Chipper La, Salisbury, Wiltshire SP1 1BG
Chief Executive   John Nicholas
Chair   Mr V. M. Prior

South Worcestershire Primary Care Trust

Unit 19, Isaac Maddox Hse, Shrub Hill Ind Est, Worcester,
Worcestershire WR4 9RW;
URL www.worcestershirehealth.nhs.uk;
E-mail janet.ferguson@sworcs-pct.nhs.uk
Chief Executive   Mike Ridley
Chair   David Barlow

HOSPITALS

Evesham Community Hospital   Waterside, Evesham,
Worcestershire WR11 4BS; Tel 01386 502589
Number of beds: (111)

Malvern Community Hospital   Lansdowne Cres, Malvern,
Worcestershire WR14 2AW; Tel 01684 612600

Pershore Cottage Hospital Defford Rd, Pershore, Worcestershire WR10 1HZ; Tel 01386 502070; Fax 01386 502082
Number of beds: (19)

Tenbury and District Hospital Tenbury Wells, Worcester, Worcestershire WR15 8AP; Tel 01584 810643; Fax 01584 819553

Southampton City Primary Care Trust

Central Health Clinic, East Park Terr, Southampton, Hampshire SO14 0YL
Chief Executive Brian Skinner;
E-mail brian.skinner@sehc-pct.nhs.uk
Chair Pauline Quan Arrow

Southend-on-Sea Primary Care Trust

Harcourt Hse, 5–15 Harcourt Ave, Southend-on-Sea, Essex SS2 6HE; URL www.southend-pct.nhs.uk; Tel 01702 224600; Fax 01702 224601
Chief Executive Julie Garbutt
Chair Katherine Kirk

Southern Norfolk Primary Care Trust

St. Andrews Hse, Northside, St. Andrews Bus Pk, Thorpe St. Andrew, Norwich, Norfolk NR7 0HT
Chief Executive Mark Millar
Chair Helen Wilson

Southport and Formby Primary Care Trust

Hesketh Centre, 51–55 Albert Rd, Southport, Merseyside PR9 0LT
Chief Executive Ms J. Beenstock
Chair Mr M. Winstanley

Southwark Primary Care Trust

Mabel Goldwin Hse, 49 Grange Wlk, London SE1 3DY; Tel 020 7525 0400
Chief Executive Chris Bull
Chair Mee Ling Ng

St. Albans and Harpenden Primary Care Trust

99 Waverley Rd, St. Albans, Hertfordshire AL3 5TL
Chief Executive Steve Knighton
Chair John Bennett

St. Helens Primary Care Trust

Cowley Hill La, St. Helens, Merseyside WA10 2AP; URL www.sthkhwealth.nhs.uk
Chief Executive Morag Day
Chair Nora Guibertoni
There is a general e-mail address:
<firstname>.<surname>@sthkhealth.nhs.uk

Staffordshire Moorlands Primary Care Trust

Leek Moorlands Hospital, Ashbourne Rd, Leek, Staffordshire ST13 5BQ
Chief Executive Vacancy
Chair George Wiskin

Stockport Primary Care Trust

Springwood Hse, Poplar Gr, Hazel Gr, Stockport, Cheshire SK7 5BY
Chief Executive Mr R. Popplewell
Chair Prof S. Moore

Suffolk Coastal Primary Care Trust

Bartlet Hospital Annexe, Undercliff Rd East, Felixstowe, Suffolk IP11 7LT; URL www.suffolkcoastal-pct.nhs.uk; E-mail ana.selby@suffolkcoastal-pct.nhs.uk; Tel 01934 458900; Fax 01934 458901
Chief Executive Vacancy
Chair Anthony Robinson

HOSPITALS

Aldeburgh and District Community Hospital Park Rd, Aldeburgh, Suffolk IP15 3ES; Tel 01728 452778; Fax 01728 454056
Specialism: Minor casualty; outpatient; x-ray; GP; frail elderly.

The Bartlet Hospital Undercliff Rd East, Felixstowe, Suffolk IP11 7LT; Tel 01394 458870; Fax 01394 458871
Specialism: Post acute rehabilitation; outpatient physiotherapy. Number of beds: (58)

Felixstowe General Hospital Constable Road, Felixstowe, Suffolk IP11 7HJ; Tel 01394 458820; Fax 01394 458821
Specialism: Minor injuries unit; outpatient clinics; x-ray service; GP.

Suffolk West Primary Care Trust

Thingoe Hse, Cotton La, Bury St. Edmunds, Suffolk IP33 1YJ
Chief Executive Vacancy
Chair Joanna Spicer

HEALTH SERVICES

Blomfield House Health Centre Looms La, Bury St. Edmunds, Suffolk IP33 1HE; Tel 01284 775200

Sunderland Teaching Primary Care Trust

Durham Rd, Sunderland, Cumbria SR3 4AF
Chief Executive Vacancy
Chair David Wardle

Sussex Downs and Weald Primary Care Trust

36–38 Friars Wk, Lewes, East Sussex BN7 2PB
Chief Executive Vacancy
Chair Dr Devada Redman

Sutton and Merton Primary Care Trust

Hamilton Wing, Nelson Hospital, Kingston Rd, London SW20 8DB
Chief Executive Ian Ayres
Chair Kay Sonneborn

HOSPITAL

Carshalton War Memorial Hospital The Park, Carshalton, Surrey SM5 3DB; Tel 020 8647 5534

Swale Primary Care Trust

200 Winch Rd, South Hingbourne Research Centre, South Hingbourne, Kent ME9 8EF
Chief Executive John Mangan;
E-mail john.mangan@swalepct.nhs.uk
Chair John Macrae

Swindon Primary Care Trust

Frankland Rd, Blagrove, Swindon SN5 8YF
Chief Executive Jan Stubbings
Chair Vacancy

12

Tameside and Glossop Primary Care Trust

Century Hse, 107–109 Market St, Hyde, Cheshire
SK11 1HL
Chief Executive   Mike Ditchfield
Chair   Ian Macrae

Taunton Deane Primary Care Trust

Wellsprings Rd, Taunton, Somerset TA2 7PQ;
URL www.tauntondeanepct.nhs.uk
Chief Executive   Edward Colgan
Chair   Alan Hopper

HOSPITALS

Taunton Community Hospital Musgrove Pk, Taunton,
Somerset TA1 5DA; Tel (Community Hospital) 01823
343756; Fax (Outpatient Rehabilitation) 01823 342699

Wellington and District Cottage Council South St,
Wellington, Somerset TA21 8QQ; Tel 01823 662663;
Fax 01823 660179

Teignbridge Primary Care Trust

Bridge Hse, Collett Way, Brunel Ind Est, Newton Abbot,
Devon TQ12 4PH
Chief Executive   Pam Smith
Chair   Mrs C.M. Cribb

HOSPITALS

Ashburton and Buckfastleigh Hospital Ashburton, Devon
TQ13 7AP; Tel 01364 652203

Bovey Tracey Hospital Furzeleigh La, Bovey Tracey, Devon
TQ13 9HJ; Tel 01626 832279

Dawlish Community Hospital Barton Tier, Dawlish, Devon
EX7 9LW; Tel 01626 868500

Newton Abbot Hospital 50 East St, Newton Abbot, Devon
TQ12 4PT; Tel 01626 354321

Teignmouth Hospital Teignmouth, Devon TQ14 4BQ;
Tel 01626 772161

Telford and Wrekin Primary Care Trust

Sommerfeld Hse, Sommerfeld Rd, Trench Lock, Telford,
Shropshire TF1 5RY
Chief Executive   Simon Conolly
Chair   Cllr Susan Davis
There is a general e-mail address:
<firstname>.<surname>@shropshire.wmids.nhs.uk

Tendring Primary Care Trust

Carnavon Hse, Carnavon Rd, Clacton on Sea, Essex
CO15 6QD; URL www.tendringpct.co.uk;
E-mail frances.wolfe@tendring-pct.nhs.uk; Tel 01255
206060; Fax 01255 206061
Chief Executive   Paul Unsworth
Chair   David Rex

Thurrock Primary Care Trust

Civic Offices, PO Box 83, New Rd, Grays, Essex RM17 6FD;
URL www.thurrock-pct.nhs.uk; Tel 01375 406400;
Fax 01375 406401
Chief Executive   Ms V Wagner
Chair   Valerie Liddiard

Torbay Primary Care Trust

Rainbow Hse, Avenue Rd, Torquay, Devon TQ2 5LS
Chief Executive   Simon Warswick
Chair   Michael Wickens

HOSPITALS

Brixham Hospital Greenswood Rd, Brixham, Devon
TQ5 9HW; Tel 01803 882153

Paignton Hospital Church St, Paignton, Devon TQ3 3AG;
Tel 01803 557425

Tower Hamlets Primary Care Trust

Trust Offices, Mile End Hospital, Bancroft Rd, London
E1 4DG; URL www.thpct.nhs.uk;
E-mail sharon.leo@thht.org; Tel 020 8709 5000; Fax 020
8709 5010
Chief Executive   Christine Carter
Chair   Richard Gee
Medical Director   Dr Ruth Caudwell
Director (Primary Care Development and Nursing)
Theresa Berry
Director (Finance)   Alex Johnstone
Director (Specialist Services and Service Development)
Rosie Schaedel
Director (Corporate and Organisational Development)
Martin Cusack
Director (Facilities)   David Butcher
Head (Communications and Corporate Development)
Jeremy Gardner
Manager (Business)   Mark Docherty
Annual budget
£63 million

HOSPITALS

Mile End Hospital Bancroft Rd, London E1 4DG
Specialism: Elderly (171)

Royal London Hospital Whitechapel, London E1 4BB
Specialism: Elderly (61)

Trafford North Primary Care Trust

4th Fl, Peel Hse, Albert St, Eccles, Manchester M30 0NJ
Chief Executive   Mr T. Riley
Chair   Ms Selvin

Trafford South Primary Care Trust

Fl 5b, Peel Hse, Albert St, Eccles, Manchester M30 0NL
Chief Executive   Mr Cubbon
Chair   Prof Norma Raynes

Uttlesford Primary Care Trust

The Old Mill, Haslers La, Great Dunmow, Essex CM6 1XS;
Tel 01371 767007; Fax 01371 767008
Chief Executive   Peta Wilkinson;
E-mail peta.wilkinson@uttlesford-pct.nhs.uk
Chair   David Barron

Vale of Aylesbury Primary Care Trust

Verney Hse, Gatehouse Rd, Aylesbury, Buckinghamshire
HP19 8ET
Chief Executive   Shaun Brogan;
E-mail shaun.brogan@voa-pct.nhs.uk
Chair   Avril Davies

HOSPITAL

Buckingham Hospital High St, Buckingham,
Buckinghamshire MK10 1NU; Tel 01280 813243

Wakefield West Primary Care Trust

White Rose Hse, West Pde, Wakefield, West Yorkshire
WF1 1LT
Chief Executive   Alastair Geldart
Chair   William Barker

Walsall Primary Care Trust

Jubilee Hse, Bloxwich La, Walsall, Staffordshire WS2 7JL;
 Tel 01922 618388; Fax 01922 618360
Chief Executive Alistair Howie
Chair Jindy Khera

HOSPITAL

Dorothy Pattison Hospital Alumwell Cl, Walsall, West
Midlands WS2 9XH; Tel 01922 858 000
 Specialism: Mentally handicapped (74).

Waltham Forest Primary Care Trust

Hurst Road Health Centre, Hurst Rd, Walthamstow,
 London E17 3BL
Chief Executive Sally Gorham
Chair Joan Saddler

Comely Bank Clinic 46 Ravenswood Rd, Walthamstow,
London E17 9LY; Tel 020 8521 8742

Granleigh Road Health Clinic Trinity Cl, Leytonstone,
London E11 4RP; Tel 020 8539 8565

Hurst Road Health Centre 36a Hurst Rd, Walthamstow,
London E17 3BL; Tel 020 8520 8513

Langthorne Health Centre 13 Langthorne Rd, Leytonstone,
London E11 4HX; Tel 020 8558 7821

St. James Health Centre St. James St, Walthamstow,
London E17 7PJ; Tel 020 8520 0921

Wandsworth Primary Care Trust

Teak Tower, Main Bldg, Springfield University Hospital, 61
 Glenburnie Rd, London SW17 7DJ;
 URL www.wandsworth-pct.nhs.uk;
 E-mail comms@swlondon.nhs.uk; Tel 020 8682 6170;
 Fax 020 8682 5846
Chair Melba Wilson
Chief Executive Helen Walley
Deputy Chief Executive Veronica Coterill
Medical Director Dr Andy Neil
Medical Director Dr David Finch
Director (Nursing) Di Caulfield-Stoker
Director (Finance) T. Breen
Director (Integrated Care) John Pullin
Director (Organisational Modernisation) Chris Bulford
This Trust provides some of the services previously
managed by South West London NHS Trust. Other services
have been transferred to Sutton and Merton PCT and
Richmond and Twickenham PCT.

HEALTH CENTRES

Arndale Health Clinic 3a Neville Gill Cl, London SW18 4BS;
Tel 020 8700 0160; Fax 020 8700 0168

Joan Bicknell Centre Burntwood La, Springfield Hospital,
London SW17 7DJ; Tel 020 8700 0450; Fax 020 8700 0480

Balham Health Centre 120 Bedford Hill, London
SW12 9HP; Tel 020 8700 0600; Fax 018 700 0634

St. John's Therapy Centre 162 St. John's Hill, London
SW11 1SP; Tel 020 8700 0180; Fax 020 8700 0203

Bridge Lane Health Centre 20 Bridge La, Home Rd, London
SW11 3AD; Tel 020 7441 0730; Fax 020 7441 0747

Brocklebank Health Centre 249 Garratt La, London
SW18 4DU; Tel 020 8700 0100; Fax 020 8700 0132

Stormont Health Clinic Antrim Hse, 5–11 Stormont Rd,
London SW11 5EG; Tel 020 7441 0700; Fax 020 7441 0710

St. Christopher's Health Clinic Wheeler Crt, Plough Rd,
London SW11 2AY; Tel 020 7441 0770; Fax 020 7441 0784

Doddington Health Clinic 311 Battersea Park Rd, London
SW11 4LU; Tel 020 7441 0900; Fax 020 7441 0926

Tooting Health Clinic 63 Bevill Allen Cl, Amen Corner,
London SW17 8PX; Tel 020 8700 0400; Fax 020 8700 0435

Eileen Lecky Clinic 2 Clarendon Dr, Putney, London
SW15 1AA; Tel 020 8788 2236; Fax 020 8785 1483

Tooting Walk-In Centre Clare Hse, St. Georges Hospital,
Blackshaw Rd, London SW17 0QT

Tudor Lodge Health Centre 8c Victoria Dr, Wimbledon,
London SW19 6AE; Tel 020 8788 1525; Fax 020 8789 1933

Westmoor Community Clinic 248 Roehampton La, London
SW15 4AA; Tel 020 8789 5511; Fax 020 8789 5577

William Harvey Clinic 313–315 Cortis Rd, London
SW15 6XG; Tel 020 8788 0074; Fax 020 8780 3487

HOSPITALS

Putney Hospital Commondale, London SW15 1HW

Queen Mary's Hospital (Roehampton) Roehampton La,
London SW15 5PN; Tel 020 8789 6611

Warrington Primary Care Trust

Millennium Hse, 930–932 Birchwood Blvd, Millennium Pk,
 Birchwood, Warrington WA3 7QN;
 URL www.warrington-health.nhs.uk;
 E-mail hq@warrington-pct.nhs.uk
Manager (Corporate Business) Tim Deeprose
Corporate Support Toni Harper

Watford and Three Rivers Primary Care Trust

1a High St, Rickmansworth, Hertfordshire WD3 1ET
Chief Executive Felicity Cox
Chair Pamela Handley

Waveney Primary Care Trust

6 Regent Rd, Lowestoft, Suffolk NR32 1PA
Chief Executive Mike Stonard
Chair Jane Leighton

Wednesbury and West Bromwich Primary Care Trust

Kingston Hse, 438–450 High St, West Bromwich, West
 Midlands B70 9LD
Chief Executive Graham Wallis
Chair John Crawley

Welwyn Hatfield Primary Care Trust

Charter Hse, Parkway, Welwyn Garden City, Hertfordshire
 AL8 6JL; URL www.welwyn-hatfield-pct.nhs.uk
Chief Executive Peter Horbury;
 E-mail peterhorbury@welhat-pct.nhs.uk
Chair Carol Sherriff

West Cumbria Primary Care Trust

Old Town Hall, Oxford St, Workington, Cumbria CA14 2RS
Chief Executive Nigel Woodcock
Chair Patrick Everingham

West Gloucestershire Primary Care Trust

Units 14 and 15 Highnam Bus Pk, Newent Rd, Highnam,
 Gloucester, Gloucestershire GL2 8DN
Chief Executive Stephen Golledge
Chair Elizabeth Boait

HOSPITALS

Dilke Memorial Hospital Cinderford, Gloucestershire
GL14 3HX; Tel 01594 822372

Lydney District Hospital Gloucestershire GL15 5JF;
Tel 01594 598220; Fax 01594 598221

12

West Hull Primary Care Trust

Brunswick Hse, Strand Cl, Kingston-upon-Hull, East
Riding of Yorkshire HU2 9DB;
E-mail mark.whitaker@whpct.nhs.uk; Tel 01482 606644;
Fax 01482 606627
Chief Executive   Dr Graham Rich
Chair   Kathryn Lavery

West Lancashire Primary Care Trust

Ormskirk and District General Hospital, Wigan Rd,
Ormskirk, Lancashire L39 2JW
Chief Executive   Jane Thompson
Chair   Mr J. Barton

West Lincolnshire Primary Care Trust

Cross O'cliff, Bracebridge Heath, Lincoln, Lincolnshire
LN4 2HN; URL www.westlincspct.co.uk;
E-mail linda.goodman@westlincs-pct.nhs.uk; Tel 01522
546546; Fax 01522 514920
Chief Executive   Vanessa Coomber
Chair   Stanley Keyte

West Norfolk Primary Care Trust

St. James, Extons Rd, Kings Lynn, Norfolk PE30 5NU;
URL www.westnorfolk-pct.nhs.uk;
E-mail enquiries@westnorfolk-pct.nhs.uk; Tel 01553
816200; Fax 01553 761104
Chief Executive   Hilary Daniels
Chair   Sheila Childerhouse

HOSPITAL

Swaffham Community Hospital Sporle Rd, Swaffham,
Norfolk; Tel 01760 721363

West of Cornwall Primary Care Trust

Josiah Thomas Memorial Hall, Trevithick Rd, Cambourne,
Cornwall TR14 8LQ
Chief Executive   Gina Brocklehurst
Chair   Mr E.F.C. Ferrett

West Wiltshire Primary Care Trust

Unit B, Valentines, Epsom Sq, White Horse Bus Pk,
Trowbridge, Wiltshire BA14 0XG
Chief Executive   Donna Stiles
Chair   Mrs A.B. Barker

HOSPITALS

Bradford on Avon Community Hospital Berryfields,
Bradford on Avon, Wiltshire BA15 1TA; Tel 01225 862975;
Fax 01225 867488

Melksham Community Hospital Spa Rd, Melksham,
Wiltshire SN12 7NZ; Tel 01225 703088; (Wheelchair service)
01225 899130; Fax 01225 704904

Trowbridge Community Hospital Adcroft St, Trowbridge,
Wiltshire BA14 8PH; Tel 01225 711300; Fax 01225 764334

Warminster Community Hospital Warminster, Wiltshire
BA12 8QJ; Tel 01985 212076

Westbury Community Hospital Hospital Rd, Westbury,
Wiltshire BA13 3EL; Tel 01373 823616; Fax 01373 827414

Western Sussex Primary Care Trust

1st Fl, Women and Children's Block,, St. Richards Hospital,
Spitalfield La, Chichester, West Sussex PO19 4SE
Chief Executive   Claire Holloway;
E-mail claire.holloway@wsha.nhs.uk
Chair   Susan Pyper

Westminster Primary Care Trust

Trust Headquarters, 50 Eastbourne Terr, London W2 6LX
Chief Executive   Linda Hamlyn
Chair   Diana Scott

Windsor, Ascot and Maidenhead Primary Care Trust

Trust Headquarters, Edward VII Hospital, St. Leonards Rd,
Windsor, Berkshire SL4 3DP; Tel 01753 636801; Fax 01753
636828
Chief Executive   Philip Burgess;
E-mail philipburgess@berkshire.nhs.uk
Chair   John Slater
Director (Finance and Corporate Governance)   Chris Fisher
Director (Nursing and Clinical Services)
Androulla Johnstone
Director (Partnership and Development)   Sharon Collins

HOSPITALS

King Edward VII Hospital St. Leonards Rd, Windsor,
Windsor and Maidenhead SL4 3DP; Tel 01753 860441

St. Marks Hospital St. Marks Rd, Maidenhead, Windsor
and Maidenhead SL6 6DU

Woking Primary Care Trust

Woking Community Hospital, Heathside Rd, Woking,
Surrey GU22 7HS; URL www.woking.nhs.uk
Chief Executive   Jane Dale;
E-mail jane.dale@wokingpct.nhs.uk
Chair   Laurie Doust
There is a general e-mail address:
<firstname>.<surname>@wokingpct.nhs.uk

Wokingham Primary Care Trust

Wokingham Community Hospital, Barkham Rd,
Wokingham, Berkshire RG4 2RE
Chief Executive   Sue Heatherington;
E-mail sue.heatherington@berkshire.nhs.uk
Chair   Dr Alan Penn

HOSPITAL

Wokingham Community Hospital 41 Barkham Rd,
Wokingham RG41 2RE; Tel 0118 949 5000

Wolverhampton City Primary Care Trust

Coniston Hse, Chapel Ash, Wolverhampton, West
Midlands WV3 0XE
Chief Executive   Mr Jon Crockett
Chair   Terence Makriel

Wycombe Primary Care Trust

3rd Fl, Rapid Hse, 40 Oxford Rd, High Wycombe,
Buckinghamshire HP11 2EE
Chief Executive   Tracey Baldwin
Chair   Stewart George

HOSPITAL

Marlow Community Hospital Glade Rd, Marlow,
Buckinghamshire SL7 1DJ; Tel 01628 482292

Wyre Forest Primary Care Trust

7th Fl, Brook Hse, Kidderminster Hospital, Bewdley Rd,
Kidderminster, Worcestershire DY11 6RJ; Tel 01562
826329
Chief Executive   Peter Forrester
Chair   David Priestnall

Wyre Primary Care Trust

Poulton Offices, Furness Dr, Poulton Ind Est, Poulton-le-
Flyde, Lancashire FY6 8JT
Chief Executive Doug Soper
Chair Ray Piggott

Yorkshire Wolds and Coast Primary Care Trust

Health Hse, Grange Park La, Willerby, East Riding of
Yorkshire HU10 6DT; E-mail contactus@ywcpct.nhs.uk;
Tel 01482 672038; Fax 01482 672176
Chief Executive Adrian Smith

Hornsea Cottage Hospital Eastgate, Hornsea, East Riding
of Yorkshire HU18 1PL; Tel 01964 533146; Fax 01964
534273

Withernsea Hospital Queen St, Withernsea, East Riding
of Yorkshire HU19 2PZ; Tel 01964 614666; Fax 01964
615238

Health Councils

In September 2003 the Health Councils in England were
abolished. They have been replaced by the new Patients
Forums, set up in each NHS Trust and Primary Care Trust,
by the Commission for Patient and Public Involvement in
Health, now listed in Chapter 4: Other Government and
Public Offices England.

Special Health Authorities

Family Health Services Appeal Authority (SHA)

30 Victoria Ave, Harrogate, HG1 5PR;
URL www.fhsaa.org.uk; E-mail mail@fhsaa.nhs.uk;
Tel (Appeal Enquiries) 01423 535413; Fax (General
Management Enquiries) 01423 535415
Chief Executive Paul Burns
Appeals Manager Lisa Hughes
The purpose of the FHSAA (SHA) is to improve the
provision of healthcare by efficiently ensuring prompt, fair
and reasoned resolution of disputes within the NHS.

The Health Development Agency

Holborn Gate, 330 High Holborn, London WC1V 7BA;
URL www.hda-online.org.uk;
E-mail communications@hda-online.org.uk; Tel 020 7430
0850; Fax 020 7061 3390
Chair Yve Buckland
The Health Development Agency identifies what works to
improve the health of people in England and to reduce
health inequalities. Working with a range of national and
regional partners, it gathers evidence, advises and supports
policy makers and practitioners, and helps them to get
evidence into practice.

Mental Health Act Commission

Maid Marian Hse, 56 Houndsgate, Nottingham,
Nottinghamshire NG1 6BG;
URL www.mhac.trent.nhs.uk;
E-mail chiefexec@mhac.trent.nhs.uk; Tel 0115 943 7100;
Fax 0115 943 7101
Chief Executive C. Heginbotham
Keeps under review the operation of the Mental Health Act
1983, as it relates to the detention of patients or patients
liable to be detained under the Act and has discretionary
power to investigate complaints from, or made on behalf
of, patients.

National Institute for Clinical Excellence (NICE)

Mid City Place, 71 High Holborn, London WC1V 6NA;
URL www.nice.org.uk; Tel 020 7067 5800; Fax 020 7067
5801
Chief Executive Andrew Dillon
The role of NICE is to provide patients, health professionals
and the public with authoritative, robust and reliable
guidance on current 'best practice'.

National Patient Safety Agency (NPSA)

4–8 Maple St, London W1T 5HD; URL www.npsa.nhs.uk;
Tel 020 7927 9500
Chair Prof Rory Shaw
Joint Chief Executive Sue Osborn
Joint Chief Executive Susan Williams
The aim of the National Patient Safety Agency (NPSA) is to
improve the safety and quality of care through reporting,
analysing and learning from adverse incidents and 'near
misses' involving NHS patients.

National Treatment Agency for Substance Misuse

5th Fl, Hannibal Hse, Elephant and Castle, London
SE1 6TE; URL www.nta.nhs.uk;
E-mail nta.enquiries@nta.nhs.uk; Tel 020 7972 2214;
Fax 020 7972 2248
Chief Executive Paul Hayes
The National Treatment Agency (NTA) was created by the
Government on 1 April 2001 with a remit to increase the
capacity, quality and effectiveness of drug treatment in
England.

WALES

NHS Trusts

Bro Morgannwg NHS Trust

Trust Headquarters, 71 Quarella Rd, Bridgend CF31 1YE;
Tel 01656 752752; Fax 01656 665377
Chief Executive P.M. Williams, OBE, DMS, FIHM, CCMI,
FRSA
Director (Nursing) S. Gregory

COMMUNITY HEALTH OFFICE

Glanrhyd Hospital, Tondu Rd, Bridgend CF31 4LN;
Tel 01656 752752
Senior Clinical Medical Officer (Child Health) Dr J. Crockett
Senior Clinical Medical Officer (Audiology) Dr E. English
Senior Clinical Medical Officer (Family Planning) Dr R. Fox

HOSPITALS

Caswell Clinic Glanrhyd Hospital, Tondu Rd, Bridgend
CF31 4LN; Tel 01656 662179
Specialism: South Wales Forensic Mental Health Services
(33).

Croeso Hospital Highland Crt, Bryncethin, Bridgend
CF32 9YL; Tel (Day Unit) 01656 720371
Specialism: Rehabilitation; respite. Number of beds: (50)

Cimla Hospital Cymla, Neath, Neath Port Talbot SA11 2LH;
Tel 01639 641161
Specialism: Elderly rehabilitation; day care. Number of
beds: (40)

Glanrhyd Hospital Tondu Rd, Bridgend CF31 4LN;
Tel 01656 752752
Specialism: Mental health; elderly mental health.
Number of beds: (143)

12

Groeswen Hospital Margam Rd, Port Talbot, Neath Port Talbot SA4 2LH; Tel 01639 641161
Specialism: Elderly care; respite. Number of beds: (40)

Hensol Hospital Hensol, Pontyclun, Bridgend CF32 8YS; Tel 01443 237373
Specialism: Learning disabilities. Number of beds: (87)

Llwyneryr Unit Clasemont Rd, Morriston, Swansea SA6 6AH; Tel 01792 771262
Specialism: Learning disabilities Number of beds: (26)

Maesteg Community Hospital Neath Rd, Maesteg, Bridgend CF32 9PW; Tel 01656 732732
Specialism: Rehabilitation; GP medical; elderly mental health. Number of beds: (47)

Neath Port Talbot Hospital Baglan Way, Port Talbot, Neath Port Talbot SA12 7BX; Tel 01639 862000
Number of beds: (273)

Princess of Wales Hospital Coity Rd, Bridgend CF31 1RQ; Tel 01656 752752; Fax 01656 665377
Specialism: Acute secondary; acute mental health. Number of beds: (570)

Tonna Hospital Tonna Uchaf, Neath, Neath Port Talbot SA11 3LX; Tel 01639 641161
Specialism: Elderly mental health; acute adult mentally ill day care. Number of beds: (70)

Cardiff and Vale NHS Trust

Heath Pk, Cardiff CF14 4XW
Chair Simon Jones
Chief Executive David Edwards
Executive Director (Medical Services) Ian Lane
Executive Director (Finance) P.G. Davies
Deputy Chief Executive and Director (Operations) J.P. Davies
Executive Director (Nursing, Quality and Risk Management) Sue Hobbs
Annual budget
£260 million

HOSPITALS

The Barry Hospital Colcot Rd, Barry, Vale of Glamorgan CF62 8HE; Tel 01446 704000

Children's Hospital for Wales Heath Pk, Cardiff CF14 4XW; Tel 029 2074 7747

Llandough Hospital Llandough, Penarth, Vale of Glamorgan CF64 2XX; Tel 029 2070 5411

Rookwood Hospital Fairwater Rd, Llandaff, Cardiff CF5 2YN; Tel 029 2056 6281

University Dental Hospital Heath Pk, Cardiff CF14 4XW

St. Davids Hospital Cowbridge Road East, Cardiff CF11 9XB; Tel 029 2053 6666

University Hospital of Wales Heath Pk, Cardiff CF14 4XW

West Wing Cardiff Royal Infirmary, Newport Rd, Cardiff CF2 1S2; Tel 029 2074 7747

Whitchurch Hospital Park Rd, Whitchurch, Cardiff CF14 7XB; Tel 029 2069 3191

Carmarthenshire NHS Trust

Chair Margret Price, OBE
West Wales General Hospital, Carmarthen, Carmarthenshire SA31 2AF
Chief Executive Paul Barnett
West Wales General Hospital, Carmarthen, Carmarthenshire SA31 2AF; Tel 01267 235151; Fax 01267 227715
Deputy Chief Executive Huw Beynon
Prince Philip Hospital, Llanelli, Carmarthenshire SA14 8QF; Tel 01554 756567; Fax 01554 772271
Director (Finance) Denise Llewellyn
Director (Nursing) Denise Llewellyn

West Wales General Hospital, Carmarthen, Carmarthenshire SA31 2AF; Tel 01267 235151; Fax 01267 227715
Director (Medical) Dr Peter Thomas
Prince Phillip Hospital, Llanelli, Carmarthenshire SA14 8QF; Tel 01554 756567; Fax 01554 772271

HOSPITALS

Amman Valley Hospital Folland, Glannaman Rd, Carmarthenshire SA18 2BQ; Tel 01269 822226; Fax 01269 826953
Specialism: Acute.

Bryntirion Hospital Swansea Rd, Llanelli, Carmarthenshire SA15 3DX; Tel 01554 756567
Specialism: Geriatric.

Llandovery Hospital Llandovery, Carmarthenshire; Tel 01550 720322
Specialism: GP.

Mynydd Mawr Hospital Upper Tumble, Llanelli, Carmarthenshire SA14 6BU; Tel 01269 841343; Fax 01269 832913
Specialism: Geriatric.

Prince Philip Hospital Bryngwynmawr Dafen, Llanelli, Carmarthenshire SA14 8QF; Tel 01554 756567; Fax 01554 772271
Specialism: Acute.

West Wales General Hospital Glangwili, Carmarthen, Carmarthenshire SA31 2AF; Tel 01267 235151; Fax 01267 227715
Specialism: Acute.

Ceredigion and Mid Wales NHS Trust

Bronglais General Hospital, Caradog Rd, Aberystwyth, Ceredigion SY23 1ER; Tel 01970 623131; Fax 01970 624930
Chair E. Ebenezer
Chief Executive P. Barnett
Medical Director Dr A. Axford
Director (Nursing and Patient Services) S. Griffiths

HOSPITALS

Aberaeron Hospital Aberaeron, Ceredigion; Tel 01545 570225

Bronglais General Hospital Aberystwyth, Ceredigion; Tel 01970 623131
Specialism: Acute.

Cardigan and District Memorial Hospital Cardigan, Ceredigion; Tel 01239 612214

Tregaron Hospital Tregaron, Ceredigion; Tel 01974 298203

Conwy and Denbighshire NHS Trust

Ysbyty Glan Clwyd, Rhyl, Denbighshire LL18 5UJ; URL www.conwy-denbighshire-nhs.org.uk; E-mail mail@cd-tr.wales.nhs.uk; Tel 01745 583910; Fax 01745 583143
Chair Hilary Stevens
Chief Executive Gren R.D. Kershaw
Executive Director (Operations) Ian Bellingham
Medical Director Dr D. Gozzard
Director (Nursing Services) Bernardine Rees
Director (Finance) Nigel Morris

HOSPITALS

Abergele Hospital Llanfair Rd, Abergele, Conwy, Denbighshire LL22 8DP; Tel 01745 832295
Specialism: Chest; orthopaedic; rheumatology. Number of beds: (77)

Colwyn Bay Community Hospital Hesketh Rd, Colwyn Bay, Clwyd, Conwy LL29 8AY; Tel 01492 515218; Fax 01492 516389
Hospital Manager   Jane Trowman

Conwy Hospital Bangor Rd, Conwy LL32 8EB; Tel 01492 592333; Fax 01492 572903
    Specialism: Elderly (59)

Denbigh Community Hospital Ruthin Rd, Denbigh, Clwyd, Conwy LL16 3ES; Tel 01745 818100; Fax 01745 815851
Hospital Manager   Eva Edwards
    Specialism: GP medical; minor injuries unit; palliative care; post-operative care; respite care; terminal care. Number of beds: (52)

Glan Clwyd Hospital Rhyl, Denbighshire LL18 5UJ; Tel 01745 583910
    Specialism: Acute (546)

HM Stanley Hospital St. Asaph, Clwyd, Conwy LL17 0RS; Tel 01745 583275
    Specialism: Acute; ophthalmology.

Llangollen Community Hospital Abby Rd, Llangollen, Clwyd, Conwy LL20 8SP; Tel 01978 860226; Fax 01978 861047
Hospital Manager   Maureen Whittam
    Specialism: Acute medical; accident and emergency; minor injuries unit; post-operative admissions; palliative care; terminal care; medical respite; rehabilitation.

Prestatyn Community Hospital 49 The Avenue, Woodlands Pk, Clwyd, Conwy LL19 9RD; Tel 01745 853487; Fax 01745 887479
Hospital Manager   Patricia Smith

Royal Alexandra Hospital (Rhyl) Marine Dr, Rhyl, Denbighshire LL18 3AD; Tel 01745 443000; Fax 01745 351460
Hospital Manager   Patricia Smith
    Specialism: Elderly care; GP medical; elderly mental health. Number of beds: (54)

Ruthin Hospital Llanrhydd St, Ruthin, Denbighshire LL15 1PS; Tel 01824 702692; Fax 01824 704719
Hospital Manager   Maureen Whittam
    Specialism: GP medical; minor injuries unit.

DAY HOSPITAL

Glan Traeth Day Hospital Alexandra Rd, Rhyl, Denbighshire LL18 8EA; Tel 01745 443000

HEALTH CENTRES AND CLINICS

Bodnant EMI Unit Maesdu Rd, Llandudno, Gwynedd LL30 1QY; Tel 01492 862347
    Specialism: EMI (16)

Conwy Clinic Murian Bldgs, Rosehill St, Conwy LL32 8LD; Tel 01492 593491

Llanfairfechan Health Centre Village Rd, Llanfairfechan, Gwynedd LL33 0HN; Tel 01248 680537

Llanrwst Health Centre Watling St, Llanrwst, Conwy LL26 0LS; Tel 01492 640345

OTHER SERVICES

Ablett Unit Ablett Psychiatric Unit, Ysbyty Glan Clwyd, Denbighshire LL18 5UT; Tel 01745 583484; Fax 01745 534405
Manager   C. Moor
    Specialism: Acute psychiatric (74)

Bryn Hesketh EMI Unit Hesketh Rd, Colwyn Bay, Clwyd, Conwy LL29 8AT; Tel 01492 807512; Fax 01492 518103
    Specialism: Community psychiatric nursing; occupational therapy; physiotherapy; psychology; social work (32)

Gwent Healthcare NHS Trust

Grange House, Llanfrechfa Grange, Gwmbran, Torfaen NP44 8YN; URL www.gwent-tr.wales.nhs.uk; Tel 01633 623623; Fax 01633 623836
Chief Executive   Martin Turner
Chair   Dr Brian Willott
Medical Director   Dr Stephen Hunter
Director (Personnel)   Tracy Mynill
Director (Finance)   Andrew Cottom
Director (Nursing)   Christine Baxter

HOSPITALS

Aberbargoed Hospital Commercial St, Aberbargoed, Bargoed, Caerphilly CF81 9BU; Tel 01443 821621
    Specialism: Elderly care; GP medical; respite. Number of beds: (28)

Abertillery and District Hospital Pendarren Rd, Aberbeeg, Abertillery, Blaenau Gwent NP3 2XA; Tel 01495 214123; Fax 01495 321082
    Number of beds: (58)

Blaenavon Health Centre Church Rd, Blaenavon, Torfaen NP5 9AF; Tel 01495 790346
    Number of beds: (10)

Blaina and District Hospital Hospital Rd, Nantyglo, Blaenau Gwent NP3 4LY; Tel 01495 290230; Fax 01495 290091
    Number of beds: (47)

Caerphilly District Miners' Hospital St. Martin's Rd, Caerphilly; Tel 029 2085 1811; Fax 029 2085 1666
    Specialism: Integrated medicine; general surgery; obstetrics and gynaecology; orthopaedics; urology. Number of beds: (135)

Chepstow Community Hospital Chepstow, Monmouthshire NP1 5YX; Tel 01291 638800
    Number of beds: (81)

County Hospital Griffithstown, Pontypool, Torfaen NP4 5YA; Tel 01495 768768
    Number of beds: (143)

Ebbw Vale Hospital Hillside, Ebbw Vale, Blaenau Gwent; Tel 01495 302483; Fax 01495 307906
    Number of beds: (27)

Llanfrechfa Grange Hospital Llanfrechfa, Cwmbran, Torfaen NP44 8YN; Tel 01633 623623
    Number of beds: 71

Maindiff Court Hospital Ross Rd, Abergavenny, Monmouthshire NP7 8NF; Tel 01873 735500; Fax 01873 850177
    Number of beds: (66)

Monmouth Hospital 15 Hereford Rd, Monmouth, Monmouthshire NP5 3HG; Tel 01600 713522; Fax 01600 716760
    Number of beds: (25)

Nevill Hall Hospital Brecon Rd, Abergavenny, Monmouthshire NP7 7EG; Tel 01873 852091; Fax 01873 859168
    Number of beds: (414)

Oakdale Hospital Oakdale, Blackwood, Blaenau Gwent NP2 0JH; Tel 01495 225207
    Specialism: Geriatric (20)

Redwood Memorial Hospital The Terr, Rhymney, Blaenau Gwent NP2 5XB; Tel 01685 840314
    Specialism: Elderly care; GP medical.

Royal Gwent Hospital Cardiff Rd, Newport NP9 2UB; Tel 01633 234234
    Specialism: Acute (760)

St. Cadoc's Hospital Lodge Rd, Caerleon, Newport NP6 1XQ; Tel 01633 436700
    Number of beds: (104)

12

St. Woolos Hospital 131 Stow Hill, Newport NP9 4SZ; Tel 01633 234234
  Specialism: Palliative care; adult medicine; ophthalmology. Number of beds: (184)

Tredegar General Hospital Park Row, Tredegar, Blaenau Gwent NP2 3P; Tel 01495 722271
  Number of beds: (58)

Ty Sirhowy Health Centre Cwmgelli, Blackwood, Caerphilly NP2 1YR; Tel 01495 229010
  Number of beds: (19)

Ystrad Mynach Hospital Caerphilly Rd, Ystrad Mynach, Hengoed, Caerphilly CF82 7XD; Tel 01443 812201
  Specialism: Elderly care; elderly mentally infirm. Number of beds: (93)

North East Wales NHS Trust

Trust Headquarters, PO Box 18, Wrexham LL13 7ZH; Tel 01978 291100; Fax 01978 310326
Chair   E.F. Lloyd FitzHugh, OBE, DL
Chief Executive   H.J. Pepler
Medical Director   Dr R.B. Williams
Director (Finance)   W. Harris
Director (Operational Services) and Deputy Chief Executive   Mark Common
Director (Nursing and Planning)   M.E.O. Jones

HOSPITALS

Chirk Community Hospital Chirk, Wrexham LL14 5LN; Tel 01691 772430; Fax 01691 772342
  Specialism: Maternity.

Deeside Community Hospital Plough La, Deeside, Flintshire CH5 1XS; Tel 01244 830461; Fax 01244 836323
  Specialism: Maternity.

Dobshill Hospital Pentrobin, Chester Rd, Buckley, Flintshire CH5 3LZ; Tel 01244 550233; Fax 01244 547872
  Specialism: Geriatric (62)

Flint Community Hospital Cornist Rd, Flint, Flintshire CH6 5HG; Tel 01352 732215; Fax 01352 730494

Holywell Community Hospital Den-y-maes Rd, Holywell, Flintshire CH8 7UH; Tel 01352 713003; Fax 01352 715395

Llwyn Y Groes Psychiatric Unit Ysbyty Manor Hospital, Croesnewydd Rd, Wrexham LL13 7TD; Tel 01978 291100; Fax 01978 321071

Meadowslea Hospital Wrexham Rd, Penyffordd, Flintshire CH4 0EA; Tel 01978 760412; Fax 01978 762871
  Specialism: Geriatric (54)

Mold Community Hospital Ashgrove, Mold, Flintshire CH7 1RH; Tel 01352 750469; Fax 01352 758744
  Specialism: Geriatric (20)

Penley Hospital Whitechurch Rd, Penley, Wrexham LL14 0LH; Tel 01948 74341; Fax 01948 830341
  Specialism: Geriatric (32)

Trevalyn Hospital Manor La, Rossett, Wrexham LL13 7TD; Tel 01244 570446; Fax 01244 571481
  Specialism: Geriatric (34)

North East Wales NHS Trust

Wrexham Maelor Hospital, Croesnewydd Rd, Wrexham LL13 7TD; Tel 01978 291100; Fax 01978 310326
Chair   E.F.L. Fitzhugh, OBE, DL
Chief Executive   Hilary Pepler

North Glamorgan NHS Trust

Prince Charles Hospital, Merthyr Tydfil CF47 9DT; URL www.nglamtr.wales.nhs.uk; Tel 01685 721721 ext 8187; Fax 01685 728429
Chief Executive   J.M. Ludlow (Acting)

North West Wales NHS Trust

Ysbyty Gwynedd, Penrhosgarnedd, Bangor, Gwynedd LL57 2PW; Tel 01248 384384; Fax 01248 370629
Chief Executive   Keith Thomson
Chair   R. Hefin Davies
Executive Director (Finance)   Kate Elis-Williams
Executive Director (Operations and Performance Management)   Martin Jones
Executive Medical Director   Dr David Prichard
Executive Nurse Director   Tony Jones

Pembrokeshire and Derwen NHS Trust

Withybush General Hospital, Fishguard Rd, Haverfordwest, Pembrokeshire SA61 2PZ; Tel 01437 764545; Fax 01437 773353
Chief Executive   Frank O'Sullivan
Chair   Lynette George
Medical Director (Acute and Community)   Dr Peter Jackson
Medical Director (Mental Health)   Dr Matthew Sargeant
Director (Nursing and Community Services)   Mary Hodgeon
Director (Mental Health and Learning Disabilities Service)   Ian McKechnie
Director (Finance)   Keith Jones

COMMUNITY BASES, HEALTH CENTRES AND CLINICS

Afallon Ward and Enlli Ward Bronglais Hospital, Caradog Rd, Aberystwyth, Ceredigion SY23 1ER; Tel (Afallon) 01970 635993; (Enlli) 01970 635839; Fax 01970 635972
  Specialism: Adult mentally ill; elderly assessment.

Assessment Treatment Centre 79 Bro Myrddin, Johnstown, Carmarthen, Carmarthenshire SA31 3HF; Tel 01267 222066; Fax 01267 222066

Brynmair 11 Goring Rd, Llanelli, Carmarthenshire SA15 3HH; Tel 01554 772768; Fax 01554 770489

Cardigan Health Centre Feidre Fair, Cardigan, Ceredigion SA43 1EB; Tel 01239 615460

Community Base, Llandovery Cottage Hospital Llandovery, Carmarthenshire SA20 0HY; Tel 01550 720966

Community Support Team The Old Health Centre, High St, Ammanford, Carmarthenshire SA18 2ND; Tel 01269 597548

Crymych Health Care Centre Crymych, Pembrokeshire SA41 3QF; Tel 01239 831313

Gorwelion Resource Centre Llanbadarn Rd, Aberystwyth, Ceredigion SY23 1HB; Tel 01970 635403; Fax 01970 635424
  Specialism: Mental health.

Hafan Hedd Adpar, Newcastle Emlyn, Ceredigion SA38 9NS; Tel 01239 710454; Fax 01239 711469
  Specialism: Mental health.

Hakin Health Centre Observatory Ave, Hakin, Milford Haven, Pembrokeshire SA73 3EU; Tel 01646 692236

Llys Steffan Temple Terr, Lampeter, Carmarthenshire; Tel 01570 422130; Fax 01570 422698

Milford Haven Health Care Centre York St, Milford Haven, Pembrokeshire SA73 2LL; Tel 01646 697000

Neyland Health Centre Charles St, Neyland, Milford Haven, Pembrokeshire SA73 1SA; Tel 01646 600582

Pembroke Dock Health Care Centre Water St, Pembroke Dock, Pembrokeshire SA72 6DW; Tel 01646 682635

Resource Centre 13 Goring Rd, Llanelli, Carmarthenshire SA15 3HH; Tel 01554 772768; Fax 01554 770489
  Specialism: Mental health.

Resource Centre, Clos Bran Llangadog, Carmarthenshire SA19 7HR; Tel 01550 777771; Fax 01550 777690

Swn Y Gwynt Tir-y-Dail La, Ammanford, Carmarthenshire SA18 3AS; Tel 01269 595473; Fax 01269 597518
  Specialism: Mental health.

Wellfield Resource Centre Wellfield Rd, Carmarthen, Carmarthenshire SA31 1DS; Tel 01267 236017; Fax 01267 238506
> Specialism: Mental health.

CHILD AND FAMILY CONSULTATION UNIT

Mill La, Llanelli, Carmarthenshire SA15 3SE; Tel 01554 772270; Fax 01554 752126

HOSPITALS

Aberaeron Hospital Princes Ave, Aberaeron, Ceredigion SA46 0JJ; Tel 01545 571224
> Specialism: CPN base.

Bryntirion Hospital Swansea Rd, Llanelli, Carmarthenshire SA15 3DX; Tel 01554 756567; Fax 01554 753519
> Specialism: EMI day; EMI assessment.

Canolfan Gwenog West Wales General Hospital, Carmarthen, Carmarthenshire SA31 2AF; Tel 01267 235151; Fax 01267 237662
> Specialism: Adult mentally ill; EMI assessment; EMI day.

St. David's Hospital Jobs Well Rd, Carmarthen, Carmarthenshire SA31 3HB; Tel 01267 237481; Fax 01267 221895
> Specialism: Adult mentally ill; EMI longstay; EMI assessment; rehabilitation.

South Pembrokeshire Hospital Fort Rd, Pembroke Dock, Pembrokeshire; Tel 01646 682114
> Specialism: Partly acute; mentally handicapped.

Tenby Cottage Hospital Trafalgar Rd, Tenby, Pembrokeshire SA70 7EE; Tel 01834 842040
> Specialism: Acute (16)

Withybush General Hospital Fishguard Rd, Haverfordwest, Pembrokeshire SA61 2PZ; Tel 01437 764545
> Specialism: Acute (359)

COMMUNITY LEARNING DISABILITIES TEAMS

Community Team – Learning Disabilities 5–6 Queen St, Carmarthen, Carmarthenshire SA31 1JR; Tel 01267 222456; Fax 01267 222849

Community Team – Learning Disabilities Social Services Department, Ceredigion County Council, Lampeter, Ceredigion SA48 8AF; Tel 01545 572735

Community Team – Learning Disabilities 12 Bay View, Capel Rd, Llanelli, Carmarthenshire SA14 8SN; Tel 01554 775916; Fax 01554 759629

Intensive Support Team, Learning Disabilities South Pembrokeshire Hospital, Fort Rd, Pembroke Dock, Pembrokeshire SA72 6SX; Tel 01646 682114

MENTAL HEALTH SERVICES

Community Base, Adult Mental Health Services (North Pembs) Bro Cerwyn, Fishguard Rd, Haverfordwest, Pembrokeshire; Tel 01437 773157; Fax 01437 773057

Community Base, Adult Mental Health Services (South Pembs) Havenway, Fort Rd, Pembroke Dock, Pembrokeshire; Tel 01437 774042; Fax 01437 774073

Community Base, Older Adults Mental Health Services St. Brynach's, Fishguard Rd, Haverfordwest, Pembrokeshire; Tel 01437 773365; Fax 01437 773820

Myddfai Psychotherapy Centre West Wales General Hospital, Llys Myddfai, Carmarthen, Carmarthenshire; Tel 01267 235151; Fax 01267 220131

St. Caradog Unit, Adult Mental Health Inpatient Services Canolfan Bro Cerwyn Centre, Fishguard Rd, Haverfordwest, Pembrokeshire SA61 2PG; Tel 01437 772850; Fax 01437 772851

St. Non, Psychiatry of Old Age Services Canolfan Bro Cerwyn Centre, Fishguard Rd, Haverfordwest, Pembrokeshire SA61 2PG; Tel 01437 772871; Fax 01437 772872

Community Drugs Teams

Jobswell House Jobswell Rd, Carmarthen, Cardiff SA31 1PH; Tel 01267 223483; Fax 01267 223511

Priory Sreet 2 Priory St, Milford Haven, Pembrokeshire; Tel 01646 690327

Pontypridd and Rhondda NHS Trust

Trust Management Offices, Dewi Sant Hospital, Pontypridd, Rhondda, Cynon, Taff CF37 1LB; Tel 01443 443845; Fax 01443 443842
Chair   I. Kelsall
Chief Executive   M. Foster
Deputy Chief Executive and Director (Planning and Development)   P. Hollard
Medical Director   Dr P.S. Davies
Director (Nursing and Quality)   P.T. Leonard
Director (Finance, Information and Contracting)   David H. Lewis

HOSPITALS

Bwthyn The Common, Pontypridd, Rhondda, Cynon, Taff; Tel 01443 402246; Fax 01443 402694
> Specialism: Palliative medicine; day hospice.

Royal Glamorgan Hospital Ynsmaerdy, Llantrisant, Rhondda, Cynon, Taff CF72 8XR; Tel 01443 443443
> Specialism: Acute (509)

Llwynypia Hospital Llwynypia, Rhondda, Rhondda, Cynon, Taff CF40 2LX; Tel 01443 440440; Fax 01443 431611
> Specialism: Medical; rehabilitation; stroke unit. Number of beds: (140)

Ysbyty George Thomas Treorci, Rhondda, Rhondda, Cynon, Taff CF42 6YD; Tel 01443 440440; Fax 01443 775042
> Specialism: Elderly; mentally infirm. Number of beds: (75)

MENTAL HEALTH UNIT

East Glamorgan General Hospital, Church Village, Pontypridd, Rhondda, Cynon, Taff CF38 1AB; Tel 01443 218218; Fax 01443 218745
> Specialism: Acute psychiatric; elderly mentally infirm; day hospital.

Dewi Sant Hospital Albert Rd, Pontypridd, Rhondda, Cynon, Taff CF37 1LB; Tel 01443 486222; Fax 01443 403268
> Specialism: Medical; rehabilitation. Number of beds: (90)

Powys Healthcare NHS Trust

From April 2003, Powys NHS Trust merged with Powys Local Health Board (please see Powys Local Health Board for new address and contact details).
Bronllys Hospital, Bronllys, Brecon, Powys LD3 0LY
Chair   The Hon A. Lewis
Chief Executive   M. Woodford, BA(Oxon), IPFA
Medical Director   Dr A. Evans
Director (Nursing and Quality)   A. Colben (Acting)
Director (Finance)   Allan Coffey
Director (Human Resources)   Kate Watkins

HEALTH CENTRES

Cemmaes Road Machynlleth, Powys; Tel 01650 12227

Heol Eglwys Colbren, Powys; Tel 01639 700275

12

HOSPITALS

Breconshire War Memorial Hospital Cerrigcochion Rd, Brecon, Powys; Tel 01874 622443; 01874 622445
Specialism: Acute; elderly care; maternity. Number of beds: (70)

Bronllys Hospital Bronllys, Brecon, Powys; Tel 01874 711255
Specialism: Acute; elderly care; learning disabilities.

Bro Ddyfi Community Hospital Machynlleth, Powys; Tel 01654 702266
Specialism: Acute; elderly care; maternity.

Builth Wells Cottage Hospital Builth Wells, Brecon, Powys; Tel 01982 552221; Fax 01982 552398
Specialism: Acute; maternity.

Knighton Hospital Ffrydd Rd, Knighton, Powys; Tel 01547 528633; Fax 01547 520522

Llandrindod Wells War Memorial Hospital Temple St, Llandrindod Wells, Powys; Tel 01597 2951

Llanidloes and District Hospital Llanidloes, Powys; Tel 01686 412121

Montgomery County Infirmary Llanfair Rd, Newtown, Powys; Tel 01686 627722

Victoria Memorial Hospital Salop Rd, Welshpool, Powys; Tel 01938 553133

Ystradgynlais Community Hospital Glanrhyd Rd, Ystradgynlais, Powys SA9 1AU; Tel 01639 844777

Swansea NHS Trust

Central Clinic, 21 Orchard St, Swansea SA1 5AT;
URL www.swanses-tr.wales.nhs.uk; Tel 01792 651501;
Fax 01792 517018
Chief Executive Jane Perrin
Chair D.H. Thomas
Executive Nurse Georgina Gordon
Director (Corporate Development) Andrew J. Bellamy
Director (Finance) Roger Harry

Velindre NHS Trust

2 Charnwood Crt, Heol Billingsley, Parc Nantgarw, Cardiff
CF15 7QZ; URL www.velindre-tr.wales.nhs.uk; Tel 029 2031 6916; Fax 01443 841878
Chief Executive J. Richards
Chair Prof A.J. Hazell
Director (Finance) P. Miller
Director (Nursing and Quality) D. Smith
Medical Director Dr M. Adams
Velindre Hospital, Velindre Rd, Whitchurch, Cardiff
CF14 2TL
From 1 April 2003 Velindre NHS Trust became host to the new National Public Health Service (NPHS) in Wales. The NPHS is led by Regional Directors, based in the regional offices set up by NHS Wales (see Chapter 3, 'NHS Wales' for contact details). The NPHS has a local presence via 22 Local Health Boards.

Welsh Ambulance Services NHS Trust

Trust Headquarters, HM Stanley Hospital, St. Asaph, Denbighshire LL17 0WA; Tel 01745 583106; Fax 01745 584101
Executive Assistant Siobhan Duffy

Health Authorities

From 31 March 2003, the five Health Authorities in Wales were dissolved. Their work has been transferred to a single organisation, the National Public Health Service, which covers the whole of Wales. This organisation is based at Velindre NHS Trust. See Chapter 3 for contact details.

Local Health Boards

Anglesey

17 High St, Llangefni, Ynys Mon, LL77 7LT;
URL www.angleseylhb.wales.nhs.uk; Tel 01248 751229
Chair Dr William Roberts
Chief Executive Lynne Joannou

Blaenau Gwent

Station Hill, Abertillery, Blaenau Gwent NP13 1UJ;
Tel 01495 313838
Chair Marilyn Pitman
Chief Executive Joanne Absalom
Head (Corporate Support and Planning) Richard Bevan

Bridgend

North Court, David St, Bridgend Ind Est, Bridgend, Pembrokeshire CF31 3TP; Tel 01656 766736
Chair Prof Colin Jones
Chief Executive Kay Howells

Caerphilly

Ystrad Mynach Hospital, Caerphilly Rd, Ystrad Mynach, Caerphilly CF82 7XU;
URL www.caerphillylhb.wales.nhs.uk;
E-mail enquiry@caerphillylhb.wales.nhs.uk; Tel 01443 862056
Chair Robert Mitchard
Chief Executive Judith Paget

Cardiff

Trenewydd, Fairwater Rd, Llandaff, Cardiff CF5 2LD;
URL www.cardifflhb.wales.nhs.uk;
E-mail enquiries@cardifflhb.wales.nhs.uk; Tel 029 2055 2212
Chair Dr Robert Jones
Chief Executive Sian Richards

Carmarthenshire

Glanmore Terr, Burry Port, Carmarthenshire SA16 0NE;
Tel 01554 834962
Chair Dr Mark Vaughan
Chief Executive Alan Brace

Ceredigion

The Bryn, North Rd, Lampeter, Ceredigion SA48 7HA;
URL www.ceredigionlhb@wales.nhs.uk;
E-mail general.office@ceredigionlhb.wales.nhs.uk
Chair Mary Griffiths
Chief Executive Derrick Jones

Conwy

Glyn Colwyn, Nant y Glyn Rd, Colwyn Bay, Conwy LL29 7PU; Tel 01492 536586
Chair Allison Cowell

Denbighshire

Ty Livingstone, HM Stanley Hopsital, St. Asaph, Denbighshire LL17 0RS;
URL www.denbighshire.wales.nhs.uk; Tel 01745 589601
Chair Meirion Hughes
Chief Executive Alan Lawrie

Flintshire

Preswylfa, Hendy Rd, Mold, Flintshire CH7 1PZ; Tel 01352
744103
Chair Barry Harrison
Chief Executive Andrew Gunnion

Gwynedd

Eryldon, Ffordd Campbell, Caernarfon, Gwynedd
LL55 1HU; URL www.gwyneddhealth.org;
E-mail gwynedd.lhb@gwyneddlhb.wales.nhs.uk;
Tel 01286 672451
Chair Dr Lyndon Miles
Chief Executive Grace Lewis-Parry

Merthyr Tydfil

Units 2a and 4b Pentrebach, Business Centre, Triangle Bus
Pk, Pentrebach, Merthyr Tydfil CF48 4TQ; Tel 01685
358500
Chair Cllr Raymond Thomas
Chief Executive Ted Wilson

Monmouthshire

Chepstow Community Hospital, Tempest Way, Chepstow,
Monmouthshire NP16 5YX; Tel 01291 636400
Chair Susan Pritchard
Chief Executive Alan Coffey

Neath Port Talbot

Suite A, Britannic Hse, Llandarcy, Neath, Neath Port
Talbot SA10 6JQ;
URL www.neathporttalbotlhb.wales.nhs.uk;
E-mail nptlhb@neathporttalbotlhb.wales.nhs.uk;
Tel 01792 326500
Chair Dr Edward Roberts
Chief Executive Katie Norton

Newport

Wentwood Wards, St. Cadoc's Hospital, Caerleon, Newport
NP18 3XQ; Tel 01633 436200
Chair Sue Kent
Chief Executive Kate Watkins

Pembrokeshire

Unit 5, Merlins Court, Winch La, Haverfordwest,
Pembrokeshire SA61 1SB;
URL www.pembrokeshirelhb.wales.nhs.uk;
E-mail bernardine.rees@pembrokeshirelhb.wales.nhs.uk;
Tel 01437 771220
Chair Chris Martin
Chief Executive Bernardine Rees

Powys

Mansion Hse, Bronllys, Brecon, Powys LD3 0LS;
URL www.powyslhb.wales.nhs.uk; Tel 01874 711661
Chair Chris Mann
Chief Executive Andy Williams

Rhondda Cynon Taff

Unit 16–18 Centre Crt, Treforest Ind Est, Pontypridd, Vale
of Glamorgan CF37 5YR;
URL www.rhonddacynontafflhb.wales.nhs.uk;
E-mail enquiries@rhonddacynontafflhb.wales.nhs.uk;
Tel 01443 824400
Chair Dr Christopher Jones
Chief Executive Mel Evans

Swansea

Kidwelly Hse, Charter Crt, Phoenix Way, Llansamlet,
Swansea SA7 9FS; URL www.swansealhb.wales.nhs.uk;
E-mail info@swansealhb.wales.nhs.uk; Tel 01792 784800
Chair Susan Fox
Chief Executive Jack Straw

Torfaen

Block C, Mamhilad Hse, Mamhilad Park Est, Pontypool,
Monmouthshire NP4 0YP; URL www.wales.nhs.uk/
torfaen; E-mail enquiries@torfaenlhb.wales.nhs.uk;
Tel 01495 745868
Chair Dr Douglas Dare
Chief Executive John Skinner

Wrexham

Ellis Hse, Kingsmills Rd, Wrexham, LL13 8RD
Chair Dr Gwyn Roberts
Chief Executive Geoff Lang

Vale of Glamorgan

2 Stanwell Rd, Penarth, Vale of Glamorgan CF64 2AA;
Tel 029 2035 0600; Fax 029 2035 0601
Chair Dr Michael Robinson
Chief Executive Abigail Harris

Community Health Councils and Associations

ASSOCIATION OF WELSH COMMUNITY HEALTH COUNCILS (AWCHC)

Crickhowell Hse, Capital Waterside, Cardiff CF1 5XT;
E-mail awhc@whcsa.wales.nhs.uk; Tel 029 2050 2366;
Fax 029 2050 2253
Chief Officer Sue Wilshere

Brecknock and Radnor Community Health Council

2nd Fl, 2 The Struet, Brecon, Powys LD3 7LH;
E-mail breckchc@chc.wales.nhs.uk; Tel 01874 624206
Chief Officer Bryn Williams

Bridgend Community Health Council

Suite B, Britannic Hse, Llandarcy, Neath, Neath Port Talbot
SA10 6JQ; E-mail bridgchc@chc.wales.nhs.uk; Tel 01792
324201; Fax 01792 324205
Chief Officer Catherine O'Sullivan

Cardiff Community Health Council

Park Hse, Greyfriars Rd, Cardiff CF10 3AF;
URL www.patienthelp.wales.nhs.uk;
E-mail cardchc@chc.wales.nhs.uk; Tel 029 2037 7407;
Fax 029 2066 5470
Chief Officer Martyn Jenkins

Carmarthen-Dinefwr Community Health Council

103 Lammas St, Carmarthen, Carmarthenshire SA31 3AP;
URL www.patienthelp.wales.nhs.uk;
E-mail carmchc@chc.wales.nhs.uk; Tel 01267 231384;
Fax 01267 221087
Chief Officer Sally Fletcher

Ceredigion Community Health Council

5 Chalybeate St, Aberystwyth, Ceredigion SY23 1HS;
URL www.wales.nhs.uk/chc;
E-mail ceredchc@chc.wales.nhs.uk; Tel 01970 624760;
Fax 01970 627730
Chief Officer Dr M. Williams

12

Clywd Community Health Council

Cartrefle, Cefn Rd, Wrexham LL13 9NH;
E-mail admin@clwydchc.wales.nhs.uk; Tel 01978 356178;
Fax 01978 346870

Conwy Federation of Community Health Councils

4 Trinity Sq, Llandudno, Conwy LL30 2PY;
E-mail conwychc@chc.wales.nhs.uk; Tel 01492 878840
Chief Officer Mrs C. Jones

Gogledd Gwynedd Community Health Council

4 Pepper La, Caernarfon, Gwynedd LL55 1RG;
E-mail gogchc@chc.wales.nhs.uk; Tel 01286 674961;
Fax 01286 672253
Chief Officer David Glanville Owen

Gwent Community Health Council

Mamhilad Hse, Mamhilad Park Est, Pontypool, Gwent,
NP4 0XH; E-mail gwentchc@chc.wales.nhs.uk; Tel 01495
740555; 01495 757600
Chief Officer Colin Hobbs

Llanelli-Dinefwr Community Health Council

103 Lammas St, Carmarthen, Carmarthenshire SA31 3AP;
URL www.wales.nhs.uk/chc;
E-mail llanchc@chc.wales.nhs.uk; Tel 01267 232312;
Fax 01267 230443
Chief Officer Martin Morris

Meirionnydd Community Health Council

Beechwood Hse, Dolgellau, Gwynedd LL40 1AU;
URL www.wales.nhs.uk/chc;
E-mail meirchc@chc.wales.nhs.uk; Tel 01341 422236;
Fax 01341 422897
Chief Officer G. Owen

Merthyr and Cynon Valley Community Health Council

3rd Fl, Hollies Health Centre, Swan St, Merthyr Tydfil
CF47 8ET; E-mail merthyrchc@chc.wales.nhs.uk;
Tel 01685 384023 ext 213; 214
Chief Officer Keith Reynolds

Montgomery Community Health Council

Ladywell Hse, Newtown, Powys SY16 1JB;
E-mail montchc@chc.wales.nhs.uk; Tel 01686 627632;
Fax 01686 629091
Chief Officer J. Howard

Neath and Port Talbot Community Health Council

Suite B, Britannic Hse, Llandarcy, Neath, Neath Port Talbot
SA10 6JQ; Tel 01792 324201; Fax 01792 324205
Chief Officer P.J. Owen

Pembrokeshire Community Health Council

5 Picton Pl, Haverfordwest, Pembrokeshire SA61 2LE;
URL www.patienthelp.wales.nhs.uk;
E-mail pembchc@chc.wales.nhs.uk; Tel 01437 765816;
Fax 01437 765816
Chief Officer Ashley C. Warlow

Pontypridd Rhonnda Community Health Council

13 Gelliwastad Rd, Pontypridd, Rhondda, Cynon, Taff
CF37 2BW; URL www.wales.nhs.uk/chc;
E-mail pontyrhonchc@chc.wales.nhs.uk; Tel 01443
405830
Chief Officer and Secretary Clive Barnby

Swansea Community Health Council

Suite B, Britannic Hse, Llandarcy, Neath, Neath Port Talbot
SA10 6JQ; E-mail swanchc@chc.wales.nhs.uk; Tel 01792
324201; Fax 01792 324205
Chief Officer S. Owen

Vale of Glamorgan Community Health Council

2 Stanwell Rd, Penarth, Vale of Glamorgan CF64 2AA;
URL www.patienthelp.wales.nhs.uk;
E-mail vgch@chc.wales.nhs.uk; Tel 029 2035 0611;
Fax 029 2035 0609
Chief Officer Mr G. Harrop
Personal Assistant Mrs H. Cock

Ynys Mon-Anglesey Community Health Council

8a High St, Llangefni, Ynys Môn, Isle of Anglesey
LL77 7LT; E-mail ymchc@chc.wales.nhs.uk; Tel 01248
723283; Fax 01248 750337
Chief Officer D. Shaw

SCOTLAND

NHS Trusts

Angus NHS Trust

Whitehills Hospital, Forfar, Angus DD8 3DY; Tel 01307
464551; Fax 01307 465129
Chair Major J.S. Ingram, MBE
Chief Executive R. Fletcher, DMS, MHSM, DipHSM, FBIM
Director (Finance and Information Services) R. Oliver, CIPFA
Medical Director A.D. Irving, MBChB, CHM
Stracathro Hospital; Tel 01356 647291
Director (Nursing and Quality Assurance) R. Macleod, BSc,
MSc, RGN
Director (Human Resources) T.S. Johnson, BSc(Hons), DMS,
MHSM

DAY HOSPITAL

Rosemount Day Hospital 14–16 Rosemount Rd, Arbroath,
Angus DD11 2AU; Tel 01241 872584
Specialism: General, geriatric psychiatry.

HEALTH CENTRES

Abbey Health Centre East Abbey St, Arbroath, Angus
DD11 1EN; Tel 01241 430303

Brechin Health Centre Infirmary St, Brechin, Angus
DD9 7AN; Tel 01356 624411

Carnoustie Health Centre Dundee St, Carnoustie, Angus
DD7 7RB; Tel 01241 859888

Friockheim Health Centre Westgate, Friockheim, Angus
D11 4TX; Tel 01241 828444

Kirriemuir Health Centre Tannage Brae, Kirriemuir, Angus
DD8 4DL; Tel 01575 573333

HOSPITALS

Arbroath Infirmary Rosemount Rd, Arbroath, Angus
DD11 2AT; Tel 01241 872584
Specialism: General; maternity; geriatric psychiatry.
Number of beds: (55)

Brechin Infirmary Infirmary St, Brechin, Angus DD9 7AW;
Tel 01356 622291
Specialism: GP; geriatric medicine. Number of beds: (55)

Forfar Infirmary Abroath Rd, Forfar, Angus DD8 2HS; Tel 01307 464551
Specialism: GP; geriatric psychiatry.

Little Cairnie Hospital Arbroath, Angus DD11 2RA; Tel 01241 72584
Specialism: Geriatric long stay (57)

Montrose Royal Infirmary Bridge St, Montrose, Angus DD10 8AJ; Tel 01674 830361
Specialism: GP; geriatric medicine; maternity. Number of beds: (44)

Stracathro Hospital Brechin, Angus DD9 7QA; Tel 01356 647291
Specialism: General (244)

Sunnyside Royal Hospital Sunnyside, Montrose, Angus DD10 9JP; Tel 01674 830361
Specialism: Mental illness (229)

Whitehills Hospital Forfar, Angus DD8 3DY; Tel 01307 464551
Specialism: Geriatric long stay; maternity. Number of beds: (38)

CLINICS

Health Clinic Esk Hse, Melville Gdns, Montrose, Angus DD10 8HG; Tel 01674 675115

Ravenswood Forfar, Angus DD8 2AE; Tel 01307 466281

Ayrshire and Arran Acute Hospitals

Crosshouse Hospital, Ayr, South Ayrshire KA2 0BE; Tel 01563 521133; Fax 01563 577055
Chair Prof Gordon Wilson, MA, PhD, FRSA
Chief Executive Jim Currie
Medical Director Dr R. Masterton
Director (Finance) Stuart Sanderson (Acting)
Director (Nursing) F.M.C. Queen, BA, DMS, MBA, REN
Director (Human Resources) Patricia Leiser
Annual budget
£138 million

HOSPITALS

Ayr Hospital Dalmellington Rd, Ayr, South Ayrshire KA6 6DX; Tel 01292 610555; Fax 01292 288952
Specialism: Acute; general; paediatric and rehabilitation. Number of beds: (350)

Ayrshire Central Hospital Kilwinning Rd, Irvine, South Ayrshire KA12 8SS
Number of beds: (252)

Biggart Hospital Prestwick, South Ayrshire KA9 2HQ; Tel 01292 70611; Fax 01292 79700
Specialism: Care of the elderly; acute rehabilitation and stroke unit. Number of beds: (167)

Crosshouse Hospital Ayr, South Ayrshire KA2 0BE
Number of beds: (562)

Ayrshire and Arran Primary Care NHS Trust

PO Box 13, Eglinton Hse, Ailsa Hospital, Dalmellington Rd, Ayr, South Ayrshire KA6 6AB; Tel 01563 521133; Fax 01563 577055
Chair Sandra Hood, OBE
Chief Executive A. Gunning, PhD, BSc(Hons), CIPFA
Medical Director A. Green
Associate Medical Director (Mental Health) C. Lind
Director (Corporate Services and Information) P. Ardin
Director (Nursing) E. Moore
Director (Finance) D. Yuille
Director (Human Resources) K. Croan
Director (Estates and Facilities) H. Knox

PSYCHIATRIC DAY HOSPITALS

Ayr Community Resource Centre Hartfield Hse, 1 Racecourse View, Ayr, South Ayrshire KA7 2TS; Tel 01292 613777
Specialism: Elderly; adult.

Garnock Day Hospital Ayrshire Central Hospital, Killwinning Rd, Irvine, North Ayrshire KA12 822; Tel 01294 323050; Fax 01294 311747

SECOND LINE DAY HOSPITALS

Brooksby Day Hospital Brisbane Rd, Largs, South Ayrshire KA30 8AA; Tel 01475 676318; Fax 01475 676324

Davidson Day Hospital The Avenue, Girvan, South Ayrshire KA26 9DS; Tel 01465 712571; Fax 01465 714382

Holmhead Day Hospital Cumnock, East Ayrshire KA18 1RR; Tel 01290 422220; Fax 01290 423589

Maybole Day Hospital High St, Maybole, South Ayrshire KA19 7BY; Tel 01655 882211; Fax 01655 889698

HEALTH CENTRES

Ardrossan Health Centre Central Ave, Ardrossan, North Ayrshire KA22 7DX; Tel 01294 603048; Fax 01294 471021

Beith Health Centre Reform St, Beith, North Ayrshire KA15 2AE; Tel 01505 503337; 01505 503338; Fax 01505 504906

Bourtreehill Health Centre Cheviot Way, Bourtreehill, Irvine, North Ayrshire KA11 1JU; Tel 01294 215151; Fax 01294 218461

Dalry Health Centre Vennal St, Dalry, North Ayrshire KA24 4AF; Tel 01294 835605; 01294 835615; Fax 01294 835621

Kilbirnie Health Centre 2 Kirkland Rd, Kilbirnie, North Ayrshire KA25 6UP; Tel 01505 682420; 01505 684978; Fax 01505 685086

Saltcoats Health Centre 17–19 Raise St, Saltcoats, North Ayrshire KA20 5LX; Tel 01294 463456; 01294 605366; Fax 01294 471021

Stevenston Health Centre Main St, Stevenston, North Ayrshire KA20 3BB; Tel 01294 465104; 01294 605166; Fax 01294 462169

EAST AYRSHIRE

Achinleck Health Centre 182 Main St, Auchinleck, East Ayrshire KA18 2AY; Tel 01290 426960; Fax 01290 423991

Cumnock Health Centre 2 The Tanyard, Cumnock, East Ayrshire KA18 1DP; Tel 01290 422214; Fax 01290 425277

Stewarton Health Centre High St, Stewarton, East Ayrshire KA3 5BP; Tel 01560 782423; Fax 01560 482095

SOUTH AYRSHIRE

Dundonald Health Centre Newfield Dr, Dundonald, South Ayrshire KA9 2EW; Tel 01563 850868

Girvan Health Centre 109a Henrietta St, Girvan, South Ayrshire KA26 9AN; Tel 01465 716200; Fax 01465 716244

Maybole Health Centre 6 High St, Maybole, South Ayrshire KA19 7BY; Tel 01655 882211; Fax 01655 882977

North Ayr Health Centre Glenmuir Pl, Ayr, South Ayrshire KA8 9RF; Tel 01292 885500; Fax 01292 885555

HEALTH CLINICS

Eglinton Street Health Clinic GP Surgery, Eglinton St, Irvine, North Ayrshire KA12 8AS; Tel 01294 276008; Fax 01294 313095

12

Lanfine Way Health Clinic The Surgery, Lanfine Way, Irvine, North Ayrshire KA11 1BT; Tel 01294 214974; Fax 01294 211294

Kilwinning Health Clinic Fergushill Rd, Kilwinning, North Ayrshire KA13 7LR; Tel 01294 552212; 01294 552485

Largs Health Clinic Moorburn Rd, Largs, North Ayrshire KA30 9JD; Tel 01475 675370

Townhead Surgery Health Clinic Townhead Surgery, Irvine, North Ayrshire KA12 0AY; Tel 01294 279523; Fax 01294 312832

EAST AYRSHIRE

Catrine Health Clinic Institute Ave, Well Rd, Catrine, East Ayrshire KA5 6RU; Tel 01290 551277; 01290 552019; Fax 01290 552784

Central Clinic Old Irvine Rd, Kilmarnock, East Ayrshire KA1 2BD; Tel 01563 545700; Fax 01563 545710

Crosshouse Health Clinic 14 Gatehead Rd, Crosshouse, East Ayrshire KA2 0HN; Tel 01563 574027

Dalmellington Area Centre Main Street, Dalmellington, East Ayrshire KA6 7QL; Tel 01292 550086; 01292 551044 01292 551189; Fax 01292 551342

Darvel Health Clinic 2a East Donnington St, Darvel, East Ayrshire KA17 0JR; Tel 01560 323910; Fax 01560 323915

Dalrymple Health Clinic 6 Portland Rd, Dalrymple, East Ayrshire KA6 6DN; Tel 01292 560645

Drongan Health Clinic 57 Hannahston Ave, Drongan, East Ayrshire KA6 7AX; Tel 01292 591288; 01292 591577; Fax 01292 590600

Galston Health Clinic 7 Henrietta St, Galston, East Ayrshire KA4 8HN; Tel 01563 822700; 01563 822702; 01563 822706; Fax 01563 822705

Hurlford Health Clinic Union St, Hurlford, East Ayrshire KA1 5BT; Tel 01563 532800; Fax 01563 532805

Kilmaurs Health Clinic East Park Dr, Kilmaurs, East Ayrshire KA3 2QS; Tel 01563 538382

Keep Well Centre 37 Ardbeg Ave, Ardbeg Rd, Kilmarnock, East Ayrshire CA3 2AR; Tel 01563 536402; Fax 01563 573701

Mauchline Health Clinic 1 High St, Mauchline, East Ayrshire KA5 6AN; Tel 01290 552377

Muirkirk Health Clinic Glasgow Rd, Muirkirk, East Ayrshire KA18 3RQ; Tel 01290 661407; Fax 01290 661007

New Cumnock Health Clinic 28a Castle St, New Cumnock, East Ayrshire KA18 4AA; Tel 01290 332073; Fax 01290 338542

Newmilns Health Clinic 79 Loudoun Rd, Newmilns, East Ayrshire KA16 9HQ; Tel 01560 323900; Fax 01560 320041

Ochiltree Health Clinic Gallowlee Ave, Ochiltree, East Ayrshire; Tel 01290 700551

Patna Health Clinic 27 Dalvennan Ave, Patna, East Ayrshire KA6 7NB; Tel 01292 531556; 01292 531706; Fax 01292 531082

Treeswoodhead Clinic Treeswoodhead Rd, Kilmarnock, East Ayrshire KA1 1NX; Tel 01563 525295; 01563 538915

SOUTH AYRSHIRE

Coylton Health Clinic 11 Hole Rd, Coylton, South Ayrshire KA6 6JL; Tel 01292 570322; 01292 571236 01292 571246; Fax 01292 570624

Dailly Health Clinic 9 Hazelwood Ave, Dailly, South Ayrshire KA26 9SU; Tel 01465 811237

Fullarton Street Health Clinic GP Surgery, Fullarton St, Ayr, South Ayrshire; Tel 01292 885528; Fax 01292 283284

Miller Road Health Clinic 32 Miller Rd, Ayr, South Ayrshire KA7 2BN; Tel (Dental) 01292 2932188; (DNS) 01292 293174; (HVS) 01292 293177; (Podiatry) 01292 293180; (School Nurse) 01292 293398; (Speech Therapy) 01292 293339; Fax (OMHT) 01292 289021; (Podiatry) 01292 293185

Prestwick Health Clinic 10 Boyd St, Prestwick, South Ayrshire KA9 1JZ; Tel (Dental) 01292 473910; (HVS) 01292 671492; (Podiatry) 01292 477145; Fax 01292 473915

Racecourse Road Health Clinic GP Surgery, 3 Racecourse Rd, Ayr, South Ayrshire KA7 2DD; Tel 01292 886622; Fax 01292 614303

Tarbolton Health Clinic 36 Montgomerie St, Tarbolton, South Ayrshire KA5 5PZ; Tel 01292 541219

Troon Health Clinic 41 Barassie St, Troon, South Ayrshire KA10 6LX; Tel (DNS) 01292 311089; (HVS) 01292 316585; (Midwives) 01292 312909; (Podiatry) 01292 312353; Fax 01292 318437

Whitletts Health Clinic Glenmuir Pl, Whitletts, Ayr, South Ayrshire KA8 9RF; Tel 01292 885500; Fax 01292 885555

HOSPITALS

Ailsa Hospital Dalmellington Rd, Ayr, South Ayrshire KA6 6AB; Tel 01292 610556; Fax 01292 513027
  Psychiatric (282)

Ayrshire Central Hospital Kilwinning Rd, Irvine, North Ayrshire KA12 8SS; Tel 01294 274191
  Elderly dementia. Number of beds: (42)

Brooksby House Hospital Greenock Rd, Largs, South Ayrshire KA30 8NE; Tel 01475 672285; Fax 01475 672439
  Number of beds: 18
  Continuing care; geriatric.

Crosshouse Hospital Kilmarnock Road, Kilmarnock, East Ayrshire KA2 0BE; Tel 01563 521133
  Psychiatric (58)

Davidson Cottage Hospital The Avenue, Girvan, South Ayrshire KA26 9DS; Tel 01465 712571; Fax 01465 714382
  GP; acute.

East Ayrshire Community Hospital Ayr Rd, Cumnock, East Ayrshire KA18 1EF; Tel 01292 429429; Fax 01290 423589
  Number of beds: (74)

Holmhead Hospital Cumnock, East Ayrshire KA18 1RR; Tel 01290 422220; Fax 01290 423589
  Number of beds: 56
  Continuing care; geriatric.

Kirklandside Hospital Turnford, Kilmarnock, East Ayrshire KA1 5LH; Tel 01563 525172; Fax 01563 575408
  Number of beds: 85
  Continuing care; geriatric.

Lady Margaret Hospital Millport, Isle of Cumbrae, South Ayrshire KA28 0HS; Tel 01475 530307; Fax 01475 530117
  Number of beds: 14
  GP; acute.

RESOURCE CENTRES

Arran War Memorial Resource Centre Lamlash, Isle of Arran KA27 8LF; Tel 01770 600777
  Number of places: (22)

Arrol Park Resource Centre Doonfoot Rd, Ayr, South Ayrshire KA7 4DW; Tel 01292 610558; Fax 01292 614949
  Specialism: People with learning disabilities. Number of places: (67)

Strathlea Resource Centre Holmes Rd, Kilmarnock, East Ayrshire KA1 1TP; Tel 01563 571591; Fax 01563 571247
  Specialism: People with learning disabilities. Number of places: (52)

Three Towns Resource Centre Nelson Rd, Salcoats, North Ayrshire KA21 5RF; Tel 01294 607123; Fax 01294 605012

Borders General Hospital NHS Trust

Melrose, Scottish Borders TD6 9BS;
  URL www.show.scot.nhs.uk/bgh; Tel 01896 826700

COMMUNITY PAEDIATRIC SERVICE

Borders General Hospital, Melrose, Scottish Borders
TD6 9BS; Tel 01896 826682; Fax 01896 826689

Paediatric Department Borders General Hospital, Melrose, Scottish Borders TD6 9BS; Tel 01896 826700
Consultant Paediatrician Dr A. Duncan

HOSPITAL

Borders General Hospital Melrose, Scottish Borders
TD6 9BS; URL www.show.scot.nhs.uk/bgh; Tel 01896
826700
Number of beds: General (416)

Care for the Elderly Unit

Unit Offices, 10 Boydstone Rd, Glasgow G53 6DJ; Tel 0141
211 9200; Fax 0141 211 9229
General Manager Dr P.V. Knight, MB, ChB, FRCP(Edin)
Manager (Support Services and Patient Services) M. Forsyth,
MA, MBA, ACIS
Finance and Information Manager F. Mercer, BA, ACCA
Medical Executive Dr P.V. Knight

Belvidere Hospital 1360–1432 London Rd, Glasgow
G31 4BG; Tel 0141 554 1855

Blawarthill Hospital 129 Holehouse Dr, Knightswood,
Glasgow G13 3TG; Tel 0141 954 9547

Cowglen Hospital 10 Boydstone Rd, Glasgow G53 6XJ;
Tel 0141 211 9200

Duke Street Hospital 253 Duke St, Glasgow G31 1HY;
Tel 0141 556 5222

Knightswood Hospital 125 Knightswood Rd, Glasgow
G13 2XG; Tel 0141 954 9641

Lenzie Hospital Auchinldch Rd, Kirkintilloch, Glasgow
G66 5DF; Tel 0141 776 1208

Mearnskirk Hospital Newton Mearns, Glasgow G77 5RX;
Tel 0141 639 2251

Dumfries and Galloway Acute and Maternity Hospitals NHS Trust

Bankend Rd, Dumfries, Dumfries and Galloway DG1 4AP;
Tel 01387 246246; Fax 01387 241639
Chief Executive John Burns

Dumfries and Galloway Primary Care NHS Trust

Crichton Royal Hospital, Glencaple Rd, Dumfries,
Dumfries and Galloway DG1 4TG;
URL www.show.scot.nhs.uk/dgpct; Tel 01387 244000;
Fax 01387 269696
Chief Executive Dr A. Cameron (Acting);
E-mail acameron@dg.primarycare.scot.nhs.uk

Fife Acute Hospitals NHS Trust

Trust Headquarters, Hayfield Rd, Kirkcaldy, Fife KY2 5AH;
Tel 01592 643355; Fax 01592 648060
Chair David Stewart
Chief Executive John Wilson (Acting)
Medical Director Dr David M. Fraser
Director (Nursing) Caroline Inwood
Director (Finance) Gordon Greenshields
Director (Human Resources) Rona Webster
Head (Operations) Heather Bett (Acting)

HOSPITALS

Forth Park Hospital Bennochy Rd, Kirkcaldy, Fife KY2 5RA;
Tel 01592 643355; Fax 01592 642376
Specialism: Neonatal Unit; Obstetrics; Gynaecology.

Queen Margaret Hospital Whitefield Rd, Dunfermline, Fife
KY12 0SU; Tel 01383 623623

Victoria Hospital Hayfield Rd, Kirkcaldy, Fife KY2 5AH;
Tel 01592 643355; Fax 01592 648062
Specialism: General Surgery; HDU; ENT; Day Surgery
Unit; Infectious Diseases; Paediatrics; Orthopaedics;
A&E; Endoscopy; Dermatology; Gastro-Enterology;
Acute and General Medicine; Orthodontics; Intensive
Care Unit; Radiology; Surgical Appliance; Plaster
Services; Haematology Day Unit; Cardiology; Coronary
Care Unit; Respiratory Medicine; GU Medicine;
Diabetics; Renal Satellite Unit; Hospice.

Fife Primary Care NHS Trust

Cameron Hse, Cameron Bridge, Leven, Fife KY8 5RG;
Tel 01592 712812; Fax 01592 712762
Chief Executive Dr Frances M. Elliot (Acting)

Forth Valley Acute Hospitals NHS Trust

Westburn Ave, Falkirk FK1 5S; Tel 01324 678501; Fax 01324
617421
Chair Graeme Simmers
Chief Executive J. Currie
Medical Director J. Reid, BSc, MB, ChB, FRCP(Edin),
DObst, RCOG
Director (Finance and Information) S. Goldsmith
Director (Human Resources) J. Cameron
Director (Nursing Services) J. Andrews
Director (Planning) B.D. Baillie, AMSM

HOSPITALS

Falkirk and District Royal Infirmary Major's Loan, Falkirk
FK1 5QE; Tel 01324 624000

Stirling Royal Infirmary Livilands, Stirling FK8 2AU;
Tel 01786 434000

Forth Valley Primary Care NHS Trust

Royal Scottish National Hospital, Old Denny Rd, Larbert,
Falkirk FK5 4SD; Tel 01324 570700
Chair Mrs D. Littlejohn
Chief Executive E.A. Hawkins
Medical Director Dr G. Davies
Director (Finance) R. Stewart
Director (Risk Management) P.J. Hastie
Director (Human Resources) H. Kelly
Director (Nursing) G. Melrose

HOSPITALS

Bannockburn Hospital Bannockburn, Stirling FK7 8AH;
Tel 01786 813016
Specialism: Geriatric; psychogeriatric. Number of beds:
(94)

Bellsdyke Hospital Larbert, Stirling FK5 4SF; Tel 01324
570700
Specialism: Psychiatric (102)

Bo'ness Hospital Dean Rd, Bo'ness, Falkirk EH51 0DH;
Tel 01506 829580
Specialism: Geriatric; psychogeriatric (40)

Bonnybridge Hospital Falkirk Rd, Bonnybridge, Falkirk
FK4 1BD; Tel 01324 814685
Specialism: Geriatric; psychogeriatric. Number of beds:
(90)

Clackmannan County Hospital Ashley Terr, Alloa,
Clackmannanshire FK10 2BE; Tel 01259 723840
Specialism: Psychiatric; psychogeriatric. Number of
beds: (35)

Dunrowan Day Hospital 7 Maggie Wood's Loan, Falkirk
FK1 5EH; Tel 01324 639007
Specialism: Psychiatric.

Kildean Hospital Drip Rd, Stirling FK8 1RW; Tel 01786
446615
Specialism: Geriatric (30)

12

Orchard House Day Hospital Union St, Stirling FK8 1PH; Tel 01786 476161
Specialism: Psychogeriatric. Number of beds: (30)

Princes Street Day Hospital 5 Princes St, Stirling FK8 1HQ; Tel 01786 474230
Specialism: Psychiatric. Number of beds: (20)

Royal Scottish National Hospital Old Denny Rd, Larbert, Falkirk FK5 4SD; Tel 01324 570700; Fax 01324 562367
Specialism: Learning disabilities

Sauchie Hospital Parkhead Rd, Sauchie, FK10 3BW; Tel 01259 722060
Specialism: Geriatric (112)

Westbank Day Hospital Westbridge St, Falkirk FK1 5RT; Tel 01324 624111
Specialism: Psychiatric

HEALTH CENTRES

Alva Health Centre West Johnstone St, Alva, Clackmannanshire FK12 5BD; Tel 01259 769471

Balfron Health Centre Buchanan St, Balfron, Clackmannanshire G63 0TS; Tel 01360 440614

Bannockburn Health Centre Firs Entry, Bannockburn, Stirling FK7 0HW; Tel 01786 813262

Bo'ness Health Centre Dean Rd, Bo'ness, Falkirk EH51 0DQ; Tel 01506 827701

Bonnybridge Health Centre Larbert Rd, Bonnybridge, Falkirk FK4 1ED; Tel 01324 815105

Bridge of Allan Health Centre Fountain Rd, Bridge of Allan, Stirling FK9 4EU; Tel 01786 833210

Clackmannan Health Centre Main St, Clackmannan, Clackmannanshire FK10 4JA; Tel 01259 216710

Cowie Health Centre Burns Terr, Cowie, Stirling FK7 7BS; Tel 01786 816424

Denny Health Centre Carronbank Hse, Carronbank Cres, Denny, Falkirk FK6 6GD; Tel 01324 822382

Dollar Health Centre Park Pl, Dollar, Clackmannanshire FK14 7AA; Tel 01254 742120

Doune Health Centre Castlehill, Doune, Stirling FK16 6DR; Tel 01786 841256

Drymen Health Centre 2 Old Gartmoor Rd, Drymen, Stirling G63 0DP; Tel 01360 660239

Dunblane Health Centre Well Pl, Dunblane, Stirling FK15 9BQ; Tel 01786 822595

Grangemouth Health Centre Kersiebank Ave, Grangemouth, Falkirk FK3 9EW; Tel 01324 482653

Killearn Health Centre Balfron Rd, Killearn, Stirling G63 9NA; Tel 01360 550554

Meadowbank Health Centre 3 Salmon Inn Rd, Polmont, Falkirk FK2 0XF; Tel 01324 717920

Orchard House Health Centre Union St, Stirling FK8 1PH; Tel 01786 462992
Specialism: Emergency dental service.

St. Ninian's Health Centre Maryfield St, Stirling FK7 0BS; Tel 01786 479555

Stenhousemuir Health Centre Park Dr, Stenhousemuir, Larbert, Falkirk FK5 3BB; Tel 01324 554231

Tillicoultry Health Centre Ann St, Tillicoultry, Clackmannanshire FK13 6NH; Tel 01259 750531

CLINICS

Airth Clinic 1 Graham Terr, Airth, Falkirk FK2 8LF; Tel 01324 831532

Avonbridge Clinic 57 Main St, Avonbridge, Falkirk FK1 2NG; Tel 01324 861380

Banknock Clinic Community Centre, Kilsyth Rd, Haggs, Falkirk; Tel 01324 840131

Callander Clinic 4 Bracklinn Rd, Callander, Stirling FK17 8EJ; Tel 01877 331000

Camelon Clinic 1 Baird St, Camelon, Falkirk FK1 4PP; Tel 01324 621113

Carronshore Clinic Kincardine Rd, Carronshore, Falkirk FK2 8AE; Tel 01324 553278

Fallin Clinic Stirling Rd, Fallin, Falkirk FK7 7JD; Tel 01786 813315

Lauriston Clinic 1 James St, Laurieston, Falkirk FK2 9PZ; Tel 01324 624300

Plean Clinic Main St, Plean, Stirling FK7 8BU; Tel 01786 812283

Shieldhill Clinic 18 Greenmount Dr, Shieldhill, Falkirk FK1 2EY; Tel 01324 625192

Slamannan Clinic Bank St, Slamannan, Falkirk FK1 3EZ; Tel 01324 851394

Thornhill Health Centre Thornhill, Stirling; Tel 01786 850232

Tullibody Health Clinic Tron St, Tullibody, Stirling FK10 2PS; Tel 01259 722953

Whitecross Clinic 22 Manuel Terr, Whitecross, Falkirk; Tel 01506 845558

SPECIALISED SERVICES

Child and Adolescent Psychiatry and Psychology Falkirk and District Royal Infirmary NHS Trust, The Manor, Brown St, Camelon, Falkirk; Tel 01324 610846

Community Addiction Service Westbank Clinic, West Bridge St, Falkirk; Tel 01324 613012

Community Dental Service St. Ninian's Health Centre, Mayfield St, Stirling; Tel 01786 469181

Community Dental Services Falkirk and District Royal Infirmary NHS Trust, Majors Loan, Falkirk; Tel 01324 616042

Community Psychology Clinic Department of Psychology, University of Stirling, Stirling; Tel 01786 73171

Grampian Healthcare NHS Trust

Westholme, Woodend Hospital, Aberdeen AB15 6LS; E-mail staff@ghc.wintermute.co.uk; Tel 01224 663131; Fax 01224 840790
Chair Dr A.J. Taylor, OBE, FRCCP
Chief Executive J.W.E. Taylor
Medical Director G. Peterkin
Director (Strategic Resources) G. Morrice
Director (Finance and Information) E. Robertson
Director (Planning) Dr P. Williamson
Director (Nursing, Quality Development and Communications) E. Sutherland

HOSPITALS

Aboyne Hospital Aboyne, Aberdeenshire AB34 5HQ; Tel 013398 86433

Campbell Hospital Portsoy, Aberdeenshire AB45 2PP; Tel 01261 842202

Chalmers Hospital Clunie St, Banff, Aberdeenshire AB45 2PS; Tel 01261 812567

City Hospital Urquhart Rd, Aberdeen AB24 5AU; Tel 01224 681818

Dr Gray's Hospital Elgin, Moray IV30 1SN; Tel 01343 543131; Fax 01343 552612

Fleming Hospital Queen's Rd, Aberlour, Moray AB38 9PR; Tel 01340 871464; Fax 01340 871814

Fraserburgh Hospital Lochpots Rd, Fraserburgh, Aberdeenshire AB43 9NF; Tel 01346 573151

Glen O'Dee Hospital Banchory, Grampian, Banchory, Aberdeenshire AB31 5SA; Tel 0133 012 2233

Industrial Therapy Unit 'Unicorn Enterprises' 142 Gt Western Rd, Aberdeen AB10 6QE; Tel 01224 594708

Insch and District War Memorial Hospital Rannes St, Insch, Aberdeenshire AB52 6JJ; Tel 01464 820213

Inverurie Hospital Aberdeenshire AB51 3UL; Tel 01467 620454

Jubilee Hospital Bleachfield St, Huntly, Aberdeenshire AB54 8EX; Tel 01466 792114

Kincardine Community Hospital Arduthie Rd, Stonehaven, Aberdeenshire AB39 2LP; Tel 01569 762137

Kincardine O'Neil War Memorial Hospital St. Marnan Rd, Torphins, Aberdeenshire AB31 4FQ; Tel 0133 98 82302

Ladysbridge Hospital Ladysbridge, Banff, Aberdeenshire AB45 2JS; Tel 01261 861361

Leanchoil Hospital St. Leonard's Rd, Forres, Moray IV36 0RE; Tel 01309 672284; Fax 01309 673935

Maidencraig Unit Woodend Hospital, Eday Rd, Aberdeen AB15 6XS; Tel 01224 663131

Maud Hospital Maud, Aberdeenshire AB42 5NR; Tel 01771 613236

Morningfield Hospital 59 King's Gate, Aberdeen AB15 5EN; Tel 01224 663131

Peterhead Community Hospital Links Terr, Peterhead, Aberdeenshire AB42 2XB; Tel 01779 478234

Rehabilitation Unit 375 Gt Western Rd, Aberdeen AB10 6NU; Tel 01224 316730

Royal Cornhill Hospital Cornhill Rd, Aberdeen AB25 2ZH; Tel 01224 663131

Seafield Hospital Barhill Rd, Buckie, Aberdeenshire AB56 2EJ; Tel 01542 832081; Fax 01542 834254

Spynie Hospital Elgin, Moray IV30 2PW; Tel 01343 543131

Stephen Hospital Stephen Ave, Dufftown, Aberdeenshire AB55 4BH; Tel 01340 820215; Fax 01340 820593

Turner Memorial Hospital Keith, Aberdeenshire AB55 3DJ; Tel 0154 22 882526; Fax 0154 22 882317

Turriff Cottage Hospital Turriff, Aberdeenshire AB53 4DQ; Tel 01888 563292

Ugie Hospital Ugie Rd, Peterhead, Aberdeenshire AB42 1LZ; Tel 01779 472011

Woodend Hospital Eday Rd, Aberdeen AB15 6XS; Tel 01224 663131

Woodlands Hospital Cults Rd, Aberdeen AB15 9PR; Tel 01224 663131

HEALTH CENTRES

Aberlour Health Centre Queens Rd, Aberlour, Moray AB55 9PR; Tel 01340 871210; Fax 01340 871814

Dufftown Health Centre Stephen Hospital, Dufftown, Moray AB55 4BH; Tel 01340 820888; Fax 01340 820593

Elgin Health Centre Maryhill, Elgin, Moray IV30 1AT; Tel 01343 543141; Fax 01343 551604

Forres Health Centre Castlehill, Forres, Moray IV36 0QF; Tel 01309 672233; Fax 01309 673445

Keith Health Centre Turner Hospital, Keith, Moray AB55 3DJ; Tel 015422 882244; Fax 015422 882317

DAY/SPECIAL CENTRES

Airyhall Day Centre Springfield Rd, Aberdeen AB15 7RF; Tel 01224 208134

Balgownie Day Centre Balgownie Rd, Aberdeen AB23 8JP; Tel 01224 703237

Kincorth Day Centre 3 Tollohill Cres, Aberdeen AB12 5DT; Tel 01224 877635

Lochhead Day Centre Royal Cornhill Hospital, Aberdeen AB25 2ZH; Tel 01224 663131

Raeden Centre Midstocket Rd, Aberdeen AB15 5PD; Tel 01224 663131

Grampian University Hospitals NHS Trust

Foresterhill Hse, Ashgrove Rd West, Aberdeen AB25 22B; Tel 01224 681818; Fax 01224 550972
Chair Dr Hance Fullerton
Chief Executive A.J. Cumming
Medical Director Dr D. Ross
Director (Nursing and Quality) David Benton
Director (Human Resources) M. Dowling
Director (Finance) A. Gall
Annual budget
£250 million

HOSPITALS

Aberdeen Royal Infirmary Foresterhill, Aberdeen AB9 2XH; Tel 01224 681818

Aberdeen Royal Infirmary Woolmanhill, Aberdeen AB9 1GS; Tel 01224 681818

Aberdeen Maternity Hospital Cornhill Rd, Aberdeen AB9 2ZA; Tel 01224 681818

Dr Gray's Hospital Pluscardan Rd, Elgin, Moray IV30 1SN; Tel 01343 543131

The Raeden Centre Midstocket Rd, Aberdeen IV30 1AT; Tel 01224 681818

Royal Aberdeen Children's Hospital Cornhill Rd, Aberdeen AB9 2ZA; Tel 01244 681818

Tor-na-Dee Hospital Milltimber, Aberdeen AB1 0HR; Tel 01224 681818

Woodend General Hospital Eday Rd, Aberdeen AB15 6XF; Tel 01224 681818

Greater Glasgow Primary Care NHS Trust

Gartnavel Royal Hospital, 1055 Great Western Rd, Glasgow G12 0XH; Tel 0141 211 3600; Fax 0141 211 0306
Chair Andrew Robertson
Chief Executive Tim Davison
Medical Director Dr Iain Wallace
Director (Nursing) Rosslyn Crocket
Director (Finance) Douglas Griffin
Director (Human Resources) Ian Reid
Director (Estates and Facilitates) George McGregor
Director (Professions Allied to Medicine) Jane Arroll
Divisional General Manager (Primary Care) Terry Findlay
Divisional General Manager (Mental Health)
   Calum MacLeod
Divisional General Manager (Learning Disability)
   Susan Brown
General Manager (Support Services) Alistair Maclean

HOSPITALS

Gartnavel Royal Hospital 1055 Great Western Rd, Glasgow G12 0XH; Tel 0141 211 3600
   Specialism: Psychiatry.

Leverndale Hospital 510 Crookston Rd, Glasgow G53 7TU; Tel 0141 211 6400
   Specialism: Psychiatry.

Parkhead Hospital 81 Salamanca St, Glasgow G31 5BA; Tel 0141 211 8300
   Specialism: Psychiatry.

Ruchill Hospital 520 Bilsland Dr, Glasgow G20 9NB; Tel 0141 946 7120; Fax 0141 946 3230

12

Southern General Hospital Psychiatric Unit, 1345 Govan Rd, Glasgow G51 4TF; Tel 0141 201 1100; Fax 0141 201 1920

Stobhill General Hospital 133 Balornock Rd, Glasgow G21 3UW; Tel (Dept of Psychiatry) 0141 201 3907; Fax 0141 558 1575

Woodilee Hospital Lenzie, Glasgow G66 3UG; Tel 0141 777 8000

Specialism: Psychiatry.

COMMUNITY MENTAL HEALTH RESOURCE CENTRES

Auchinlea House 11 Auchinlea Rd, Easterhouse, Glasgow G34 9QA; Tel 0141 771 3441; Fax 0141 781 0328

The Anvil Centre 81 Salamanca St, Glasgow G31 5BA; Tel 0141 211 8480; Fax 0141 211 8474

The Arran Centre 10–18 Redan St, Glasgow G40 2QA; Tel 0141 550 3324; Fax 0141 554 6802

Brand Street Resource Centre Festival Business Centre, 150 Brand St, Glasgow G51 1DH; Tel 0141 303 8900; Fax 0141 303 8909

Bridgeview Resource Centre Unit 8c, The Quadrangle, Glasgow G20 9PX; Tel 0141 945 3449; Fax 0141 945 4095

Eastvale Resource Centre 130a Stonelaw Rd, Glasgow G73 2PQ; Tel 0141 531 4127; Fax 0141 531 4107

Easwood Resource Centre 38 Seres Rd, Clarkston, Glasgow G76 7QF; Tel 0141 569 1118; Fax 0141 568 7501

Florence Street Resource Centre 26 Florence St, Glasgow G5 0YX; Tel 0141 429 2878; Fax 0141 420 3464

Goldenhill Resource Centre 2 Stewart Dr, Clydebank, Glasgow G81 6AH; Tel 01389 874120; Fax 01389 874120

Govan/Ibrox Resource Centre 10–18 Redan St, Glasgow G40 2QA

Knightswood Clinic 129 Knightswood Rd, Glasgow G13 2XJ; Tel 0141 211 9079

Larkfield Resource Centre Garngaber Ave, Lenzie, Glasgow G66 3UG; Tel 0141 776 7100; Fax 0141 776 7462

Parkview Resource Centre 150 Wellshot Rd, Glasgow G32 7JZ; Tel 0141 303 8800; Fax 0141 303 8811

Riverside Resource Centre 12 Sandy Rd, Patrick, Glasgow G11; Tel 0141 211 1430; 0141 211 1431; Fax 0141 211 1444

Shawmill Resource Centre 35 Wellgreen, Glasgow G43 1RS; Tel 0141 632 6344; Fax 0141 632 2063

Shawpark Resource Centre 41 Shawpark St, Maryhill, Glasgow G20 9DR; Tel 0141 531 8772; Fax 0141 531 8778

Southbank Resource Centre Rooms 5–7, Southbank Hse, Glasgow G66 1XH; Tel 0141 777 7014

Springpark Centre 101 Denmark St, Glasgow G22 0YX; Tel 0141 531 9300; Fax 0141 531 9304

The Woodlands Centre 15–17 Waterloo Cl, Kirkintilloch, Glasgow G66 2HL; Tel 0141 775 3664; Fax 0141 775 0646

COMMUNITY LEARNING DISABILITY TEAMS

North East CLDT Lindsaybeg Rd, Glasgow G69 9DG; Tel 0141 779 2430

North West CLDT Unit 7B, The Quandrangle, Glasgow G20 9PX; Tel 0141 201 6200; Fax 0141 944 2442

South East and South West CLDT 60 Florence St, Gorbals, Glasgow G5 0YX; Tel 0141 429 4409; Fax 0141 429 5913

HEALTH CENTRES

Baillieston Health Centre 20 Muirside Rd, Glasgow G69 7AD; Tel 0141 531 8000; Fax 0141 531 8008

Bridgeton Health Centre 201 Abercrombie St, Glasgow G40 2DA; Tel 0141 531 6500; Fax 0141 531 6505

Castlemilk Health Centre Dougrie Dr, Glasgow G45 9AW; Tel 0141 531 8500; Fax 0141 531 8505

Clydebank Health Centre Kilbowie Rd, Glasgow G81 2TQ; Tel 0141 531 6363; Fax 0141 531 6336

Drumchapel Health Centre 80–90 Kinfauns Dr, Glasgow G15 7TS; Tel 0141 211 6070; Fax 0141 211 6140

Easterhouse Health Centre 9 Auchinlea Rd, Glasgow G34 9QU; Tel 0141 531 8100; Fax 0141 531 8110

Gorbals Health Centre 45 Pine Pl, Glasgow G5 0BQ; Tel 0141 531 8200; Fax 0141 531 8208

Govan Health Centre 5 Drumoyne Rd, Glasgow G51 4BJ; Tel 0141 531 8400; Fax 0141 531 8404

Govanhill Health Centre 233 Calder St, Glasgow G42 7DR; Tel 0141 531 8300; Fax 0141 531 8308

Maryhill Health Centre 41 Shawpark St, Glasgow G20 9DR; Tel 0141 531 8700; Fax 0141 531 8707

Parkhead Health Centre 101 Salamanca St, Glasgow G31 5BA; Tel 0141 531 9000; Fax 0141 531 9009

Pollok Health Centre 21 Cowglen Rd, Glasgow G53 6EQ; Tel 0141 880 8899; Fax 0141 531 6800

Possilpark Health Centre 85 Denmark St, Glasgow G22 5EG; Tel 0141 531 6120; Fax 0141 531 6125

Rutherglen Health Centre 130 Stonelaw Rd, Glasgow G73 2PQ; Tel 0141 531 6000; Fax 0141 531 6206

Shettleston Health Centre 420 Old Shettleston Rd, Glasgow G32 7JZ; Tel 0141 531 6200; Fax 0141 531 6206

Springburn Health Centre 200 Springburn Way, Glasgow G21 1RT; Tel 0141 531 6700; Fax 0141 531 6706

Thornliebank Health Centre 20 Kennishead Rd, Glasgow G46 8NY; Tel 0141 531 6900; Fax 0141 531 6910

Townhead Health Centre 16 Alexandra Pde, Glasgow G31 2ES; Tel 0141 531 8900; Fax 0141 531 8910

Woodside Health Centre Barr St, Glasgow G20 7LR; Tel 0141 332 9977; Fax 0141 353 3055

MENTAL HEALTH DAY HOSPITALS

Acorn Street 23 Acorn St, Glasgow G40 4AA; Tel 0141 556 4789

Fernbank Street 194 Fernbank St, Glasgow G22 6DB; Tel 0141 557 3056; Fax 0141 557 0964

Florence Street 26 Florence St, Gorbals, Glasgow G5 0YX; Tel 0141 429 2878; 0141 429 6700; Fax 0141 420 3464

Hillview Stobhill Hospital, 133 Balornock Rd, Glasgow G21 3UW; Tel 0141 201 3918

Shettleston 152 Wellshot Rd, Glasgow G32 7AX; Tel 0141 778 8381

Whittinghame Gardens 2 Great Western Rd, Glasgow G12 0AA; Tel 0141 211 3616

COMMUNITY HEALTH CLINICS

Anderston 68 St. Vincent Terr, Glasgow G3 8UT; Tel 0141 221 6204

Barlanark 343 Hallhill Rd, Glasgow; Tel 0141 773 0090

Barmulloch Community Centre 46 Wallacewell Quadrant, Glasgow G21 3PX; Tel 0141 558 1772

Bishopbriggs Bishopbriggs High School, South Crosshill Rd, Glasgow G64 2NN; Tel 0141 762 4424 (Chiropody); 0141 772 7673 (Dental)

Callander Street 3 Callander St, Woodside, Glasgow G20 7JZ; Tel 0141 332 3831

Cambuslang Johnson Dr, Cambuslang, Glasgow G72 8JR; Tel 0141 641 2085; Fax 0141 646 1224

Cardonald 74 Berryknowes Rd, Glasgow G52 2TT; Tel 0141 882 4656

Carmyle Gardenside Ave, Glasgow G32 8DR; Tel 0141 641 1524

Carntyne 461 Edinburgh Rd, Glasgow G33 3AL; Tel 0141 770 4266

Cathkin High School Western Rd, Whitlawburn, Glasgow G72 8YS; Tel 0141 641 4331

Clarkston 56 Busby Rd, Glasgow G76 7AT; Tel 0141 638 6484; Fax 0141 638 1303

Courthill 3 Kenilworth Cres, Bearsden, Glasgow G61 4HU; Tel 0141 942 7109

Dalmuir 235 Dumbarton Rd, Glasgow G81 6AA; Tel 0141 941 2091

Elderpark 20 Arklet Rd, Glasgow G51 3XR; Tel 0141 445 1345

Erskine View Erskine View, Old Kilpatrick, Glasgow G60 5JG; Tel 01389 872575

Fairweather Hall Barrhead Rd, Newton Mearns, Glasgow G77 6BB; Tel 0141 639 2081

Fernhill and Cathkin Church 82 Blairbeth Rd, Cambuslang, Glasgow G73 4JA; Tel 0141 531 6000

Glenhead Duntilglennan Rd, Duntocher, Glasgow G81 6HF; Tel 01389 874130

Hillhead Meiklehill Rd, Kirkintilloch, Glasgow G66 2JT; Tel 0141 776 1365

Hinshelwood Hinshelwood Dr, Glasgow G51 2XP; Tel 0141 445 1345 (Elderpark Clinic)

Lennoxtown 103 Main St, Lennoxtown, Glasgow G65 7DB; Tel 01360 310588

Milngavie North Campbell Ave, Glasgow G62 7AA; Tel 0141 956 2212

Milton of Campsie Community Centre, School Rd, Glasgow G65 8DD; Tel 0141 777 8282

Milton 120 Liddesdale Rd, Glasgow G22 7QR; Tel 0141 772 1357

Moodiesburn Glen Manor Ave, Glasgow G69 0BY; Tel 0141 777 8282

Muirhead 192 Cumbernauld Rd, Chryston, Glasgow G69 9NF; Tel 0141 779 1941; Fax 0141 779 2194

Netherton 19 Blackwood St, Glasgow G13 1AL; Tel 0141 959 4748

Plean Street 18 Plean St, Glasgow G14 0YJ; Tel 0141 959 1329

Pollockshields 100 McCulloch St, Glasgow G41 1SU; Tel 0141 429 6301

Pollokshaws 35 Wellgreen, Glasgow G43 1RR; Tel 0141 649 2737; 0141 649 2883; Fax 0141 649 7941

Sandy Road 12 Sandy Rd, Glasgow G11 6HE; Tel 0141 211 1400; Fax 0141 211 1410

South Nitshill 31 Wiltonburn St, Glasgow G53 7JR; Tel 0141 880 7285

Stepps Public Hall, Cardowan Dr, Glasgow G33 6HE; Tel 0141 779 1941

Torrance 51 Main St, Torrance, Glasgow; Tel 01360 620516

Townhead Lenzie Rd, Kirkintilloch, Glasgow G66 3BQ; Tel 0141 777 8282; Fax 0141 775 2958

Twechar Primary School, Main St, Kylsyth, Glasgow G65 9QE; Tel 01236 822280

Woodhall 1 Balmuildy Rd, Bishopbriggs, Glasgow G64 3BS; Tel 0141 772 1567

Highland Acute Hospitals NHS Trust

Raigmore Hospital, Inverness, Highland IV2 3UJ; URL www.show.scot.nhs.uk/haht; Tel 01463 704000; Fax 01463 711322
Chair Mr S.W. Whiteford
Chief Executive Mr R.M. Carey
Medical Director Dr A. Graham

Director (Property and Facilities Management) Mr D.J. Seago
Director (Finance) Mr D.K. McRonald (Acting)
Director (Nursing and Quality) Mr N. Hobson
Director (Human Resources) H.H. Johnston

HOSPITALS

Belford Hospital Fort William, Highland PH33 6BS; Tel 01397 702481; Fax 01397 702772

Caithness General Hospital Bankhead Rd, Wick, Highland KW1 5NS; Tel 01955 605050; Fax 01955 604606

Raigmore Hospital Inverness, Highland IV2 3UJ; Tel 01463 704000; Fax 01463 711322

Highland Primary Care NHS Trust

Inverness Bus and Retail Pk, Inverness, Highland IV2 7GB; Tel 01463 242860; Fax 01463 713844
Chief Executive Paul Martin

HOSPITALS

County Hospital Invergordon, Highland IV18 0JR; Tel 01349 852496; Fax 01349 854328
    Specialism: Geriatric and psychogeriatric. Number of beds: (44)

New Craigs Hospital Inverness, Highland IV3 8NP; Tel 01463 242860; Fax 01463 236154
    Specialism: Mental health (234)

Dunbar Hospital Thurso, Highland KW14 7XE; Tel 01847 893263; Fax 01847 892263
    Specialism: General; care of the elderly. Number of beds: (16)

Gesto Hospital Edinbane, Isle of Skye IV51 9PW; Tel 01470 582262; Fax 01470 582360
    Specialism: Geriatric (16)

Glencoe Hospital Glencoe, Lochaber, Fort William, Highland PA39 4HT; Tel 01855 811254; Fax 01855 811824
    Specialism: Geriatric (25)

Ian Charles' Hospital Grantown-on-Spey, Highland PH26 3HR; Tel 01479 872528; Fax 01479 873503
    Number of beds: General (18)

Lawson Memorial Hospital Golspie, Highland KW10 6SS; Tel 01408 633157; Fax 01408 633947
    Specialism: Elderly care. Number of beds: (45)

Mackinnon Memorial Hospital Broadford, Isle of Skye IV49 9AA; Tel 01471 822491; Fax 01471 822298
    Number of beds: (25)

Migdale Hospital Bonar Bridge, Highland IV24 3AP; Tel 01863 766211; Fax 01863 766623
    Specialism: Care of the elderly; elderly mental ill. Number of beds: (35)

Portree Hospital Portree, Isle of Skye IV51 9BZ; Tel 01478 613200; Fax 01478 613526
    Number of beds: (13)

Ross Memorial Hospital Dingwall, Ross and Cromarty, Highland IV15 3QS; Tel 01349 863313; Fax 01349 865852
    Number of beds: (31)

Royal Northern Infirmary Inverness, Highland IV3 5SS; Tel 01463 242860; Fax 01463 713844
    Specialism: Geriatric (30)

St. Vincent's Hospital Badenoch and Strathspey, Kingussie, Highland PH21 1EX; Tel 01540 661219; Fax 01540 661035
    Specialism: Geriatric; psychogeriatric. Number of beds: (39)

Town and County Hospital Wick, Highland; Tel 01955 605050; Fax 01955 604606
    Specialism: Elderly mental health. Number of beds: (20)

Town and County Hospital Nairn, Highland IV12 5EE; Tel 01667 452101; Fax 01667 454479
    Number of beds: (19)

12

Inverclyde Royal Hospital

Larkfield Rd, Greenock, Inverclyde PA16 0XN; Tel 01475
633777; Fax 01475 636753
Manager Beth Culshaw

Lanarkshire Acute Hospitals NHS Trust

Trust Headquarters, Centrum Pk, Hagmill Rd, Coatbridge,
North Lanarkshire ML5 4TD;
URL www.nhslanarkshire.co.uk; Tel 01236 438100;
Fax 01236 438111
Chair James Dunbar
Chief Executive Joe Owens
Medical Director Dr John Browning
Director (Finance and Information) Iain Crozier
Director (Human Resources) Gordon Walker
Director (Nursing) Paul Wilson
Director (Strategic Planning and Development) Ian Ross
Manager (Press and Communications) Karon Hamilton

HOSPITALS

Hairmyres Hospital Eaglesham Rd, East Kilbride, South
Lanarkshire G75 8RG; Tel 01355 585000; Fax 01355 584473
Specialism: Acute (413); long stay (28)

Monklands District General Hospital Monkscourt Ave,
Airdrie, North Lanarkshire ML6 0JS; Tel 01236 748748;
Fax 01236 760015
Specialism: Acute (479)

Stonehouse Hospital Strathaven Rd, Stonehouse, South
Lanarkshire ML9 3NT; Tel 01698 794000; Fax 01698 794033
Specialism: Geriatric long stay (40)

Strathclyde Outpatient Department Strathclyde Hospital,
Airbles Rd, Motherwell, North Lanarkshire ML1 3BW;
Tel 01698 258781; Fax 01698 267881
Specialism: Outpatient.

Wishaw General Hospital 50 Netherton Road, Wishaw,
South Lanarkshire ML2 0DP; Tel 01698 361100; Fax 01698
376671
Specialism: Acute (416); maternity (79).

Lanarkshire Primary Care NHS Trust

Trust Headquarters, Strathclyde Hospital, Motherwell,
North Lanarkshire ML1 3BW; Tel 01698 245000;
Fax 01698 245009
Chief Executive Martin Hill
Chair Robert S. Thomson, OBE
Medical Director Dr Kathleen Long, MBChB, DRCOG,
LFHom, MPH
Director (Finance and Information) Pamela Ballie
Director (Nursing and Quality) Helen Scott, RGN, HV,
Dir.Nur(London)
Director (Human Resources) Kenneth Small
Director (Mental Health/Learning Disabilities Division)
Dr Steven Novosel
Director (Operations (North Lanarkshire Sector)) Sandy Gray,
RNMH, RGN
Director (Operations (South Lanarkshire Sector))
Richard Burgon, AHSM, MHSM, DipHSM
Director (Facilities) Les Lambert
Director (Planning and Contracts) Roy Watts

North Lanarkshire Sector

Headquarters, Coathill Hospital, Coatbridge, North
Lanarkshire ML5 4DN; Tel 01236 421266; Fax 01236
431252
Director (Operations) Sandy Gray
LHCC General Manager (Cumbernauld and Kilsyth)
Colin Glory
LHCC General Manager (Motherwell) Craig Cunningham
LHCC General Manager (Airdrie) Tom Bryce
Senior Nurse Anne O'Rawe
Manager (Human Resources) Joan Smith

HOSPITALS

Cleland Hospital Bellside Rd, Cleland, North Lanarkshire
ML1 5MR; Tel 01698 860293; Fax 01698 862453
Specialism: Elderly care (60)

Coathill Hospital Hospital St, Coatbridge, North
Lanarkshire ML5 4DN; Tel 01236 421266; Fax 01236
431252
Specialism: Elderly care (63); geriatric assessment (27);
young physically disabled (21).

Kilsyth Victoria Memorial Hospital Glasgow Rd, Kilsyth,
North Lanarkshire G65 9AG; Tel 01236 822172; Fax 01236
825790
Number of beds: (17)

Strathclyde Hospital Airbles Rd, Motherwell, North
Lanarkshire ML1 3BW; Tel 01698 245000
Specialism: Elderly care (76)

Wester Moffat Hospital Towers Rd, Airdrie, North
Lanarkshire ML6 8LW; Tel 01236 763377
Specialism: Elderly care (60)

DAY HOSPITAL

Coathill Day Hospital Hospital St, Coatbridge, North
Lanarkshire ML5 4DN; Tel 01236 421266; Fax 01236 431252
Specialism: Physiotherapy; dentistry; radiography;
speech therapy; podiatry; occupational therapy.
Number of beds: 25

HEALTH CENTRES

Abronhill Health Centre Pine Rd, Cumbernauld, North
Lanarkshire G67 3BE; Tel 01236 731881

Airdrie Health Centre Monkscourt Ave, Airdrie, North
Lanarkshire ML6 0JU; Tel 01236 769388

Adam Avenue Medical Centre South Nimmo St, Airdrie,
North Lanarkshire; Tel 01236 769291

Bellshill Clinic Main St, Bellshill, North Lanarkshire;
Tel 01698 747572

Central Health Centre North Carbrain Rd, Cumbernauld,
North Lanarkshire G67 1EU; Tel 01236 731771

Coatbridge Health Centre 1 Centre Park Crt, Coatbridge,
North Lanarkshire ML5 3AP; Tel 01236 432200

Condorrat Health Centre 16 Airdrie Rd, Condorrat,
Cumbernauld, North Lanarkshire G67 4HS; Tel 01236
723383

Harthill Health Centre Victoria St, Harthill, North
Lanarkshire ML7 5QB; Tel 01501 751795

Kildrum Health Centre Afton Rd, Kildrum, Cumbernauld,
North Lanarkshire G67 2EU; Tel 01236 731711

Kilsyth Health Centre Burngreen Pk, Kilsyth, North
Lanarkshire G65 0HU; Tel 01236 822151

Motherwell Health Centre 138–144 Windmillhill St,
Motherwell, North Lanarkshire ML1 1TB; Tel 01698
254601

Newmains Health Centre 17 Manse Rd, Newmains, North
Lanarkshire ML2 9AY; Tel 01698 381006

Shotts Health Centre 187 Station Rd, Shotts, North
Lanarkshire ML7 4BA; Tel 01501 820519

Wishaw Health Centre Kenilworth Ave, Wishaw, North
Lanarkshire ML2 7BQ; Tel 01698 355511

CLINICS

Croy Clinic McSparran Rd, Croy, North Lanarkshire;
Tel 01698 823305

Fullwood Clinic 120 Stevenston St, New Stevenston, North
Lanarkshire; Tel 01698 733103

Holehills Clinic Thrashbush Rd, Airdrie, North
Lanarkshire; Tel 01236 769229

Kirkwood Clinic Craigend Dr, Coatbridge, North Lanarkshire; Tel 01236 421694

Townhead Clinic Lomond Rd, Coatbridge, North Lanarkshire; Tel 01236 423751

South Lanarkshire Sector

Headquarters, Udston Hospital, Hamilton, North Lanarkshire ML3 9LA; Tel 01698 823255; Fax 01698 710700; 01698 713097
Director (Operations)   Richard Burgon
LHCC General Manager (Clydesdale)   Marilyn Aitken
LHCC General Manager (East Kilbride)   Jim Loudon
LHCC General Manager (Hamilton and Blantyre)   Geoff Sage
Manager (Human Resources)   George Abercrombie
Senior Nurse   Frances Leckie
Senior Nurse   Pat MacDougall

HOSPITALS

Kello Hospital Biggar, North Lanarkshire L12 6AF; Tel 01899 220077
   Number of beds: GP; community (22)

Lady Home Hospital Douglas, Lanark, North Lanarkshire ML11 0RE; Tel 01555 851210
   Number of beds: GP; community (22)

Lockhart Hospital Whitelees Rd, Lanark, North Lanarkshire ML11 7RX; Tel 01555 662496
   Number of beds: GP; community (30)

Roadmeetings Hospital Goremire Rd, Carluke, North Lanarkshire ML8 4PS; Tel 01555 772271; Fax 01555 752328
   Number of beds: Continuing care of the elderly (59)
   Number of beds: Psychogeriatric (24)

Udston Hospital Farm Rd, Burnbank, Hamilton, North Lanarkshire ML3 9LA; Tel 01698 823255; Fax 10698 713097
   Number of beds: Continuing care of the elderly (80)

DAY HOSPITALS

Red Deer Day Hospital Alberta Ave, Westwood, East Kilbride, North Lanarkshire G74 8NB; Tel 01355 244254
   Number of beds: Geriatric assessment (40) Number of beds: Chiropody; physiotherapy; speech therapy; occupational therapy

Udston Hospital Farm Rd, Burnbank, Hamilton, North Lanarkshire ML3 9LA; Tel 01698 823255
   Number of beds: Geriatric assessment (15) Number of beds: Psychogeriatric (15)

HEALTH CENTRES

Alison Lea Medical Centre Calderwood, East Kilbride, North Lanarkshire G74 3BE; Tel 01355 233547

Biggar Health Centre Southcroft Rd, Biggar, North Lanarkshire ML12 6AF; Tel 01899 220383

Blantyre Health Centre Victoria St, Blantyre, Glasgow G72 0BS; Tel 01698 823583

Carluke Health Centre Market Pl, Carluke, North Lanarkshire ML8 4BP; Tel 01555 770635

Carnwath Health Centre Biggar Rd, Carnwath, North Lanarkshire ML11 8HJ; Tel 01555 840775

Greenhills Health Centre 20 Greenhills Sq, East Kilbride, North Lanarkshire G75 8TA; Tel 01355 234325

Hunter Health Centre Andrew St, East Kilbride, North Lanarkshire G74 1AD; Tel 01355 239111

Lanark Health Centre South Vennel, Lanark, North Lanarkshire ML11 7MN; Tel 01555 661534

Strathaven Health Centre The Ward, Strathaven, North Lanarkshire ML10 6AS; Tel 01357 529911

Viewpark Health Centre 119 Burnhead St, Viewpark, Uddington, Glasgow G71 5RR; Tel 01698 810171

CLINICS

Audiology Unit 4b Auchingramont Rd, Hamilton, North Lanarkshire ML3 6JP; Tel 01698 281500

Beckford Lodge Clinic Caird St, Hamilton, North Lanarkshire ML3 9AG; Tel 01698 285828

Central Clinic Orchard St, Hamilton, North Lanarkshire ML3 6PB; Tel 01698 285707

Crawford Clinic The Surgery, 123 Carlisle Rd, Lanark, North Lanarkshire

Forth Clinic Main St, Forth, North Lanarkshire; Tel 01555 811476

Larkhall Health Institute Low Pleasance, Larkhall, North Lanarkshire ML9 2HW; Tel 01698 884731

Medical Rehabilitation Unit 80 Bellshill Rd, Uddingston, North Lanarkshire G71 7NE; Tel 01698 306020

Mental Health and Learning Disabilities Division

Headquarters, Kirklands Hospital, Bothwell, North Lanarkshire G71 8BB; Tel 01698 852508; Fax 01698 852340
Manager (Divisional PAM) and Locality General Manager (Hartwoodhill Hospital)   Fiona Gairns
Manager (Human Resources)   Caroline Hutchinson
Clinical Director   Dr S. Jaigirdar
Clinical Co-ordinator (Motherwell and Clydesdale)   Dr S. Jaigirdar
Clinical Co-ordinator (Monklands and Cumbernauld)   Dr E. Hyland
Clinical Co-ordinator (Child and Family Services)   Dr J. Duncan
Clinical Co-ordinator (Hamilton and East Kilbride)   Dr K. Rohatgi
Clinical Co-ordinator (Learning Disabilities)   Dr C. Mani
Clinical Co-ordinator (Consultant Community Paediatrician)   Dr B. Gallagher

HOSPITALS

Airbles Road Centre Airbles Rd, Motherwell, North Lanarkshire ML1 2TJ; Tel 01698 261331; Fax 01698 258854
   Specialism: Psychogeriatric (20); mental health (17).

Alexander Hospital Blair Rd, Coatbridge, North Lanarkshire ML5 2EP; Tel 01698 422661
   Specialism: Psychogeriatric (20)

Birkwood Hospital Lesmahagow, North Lanarkshire ML1 1JP; Tel 01555 892382; Fax 01555 894860
   Specialism: Learning disabilities (168)

Coathill House Old Monklands Rd, Coatbridge, North Lanarkshire ML5 5EA; Tel 01236 437005
   Specialism: Mental health rehabilitation (10)

Cleland Hospital Bellside Rd, Cleland, North Lanarkshire ML1 5MR; Tel 01698 860293; Fax 01698 862453
   Specialism: Psychogeriatric (112)

Hartwood Hospital Hartwood, Shotts, North Lanarkshire ML7 4LA; Tel 01501 823286; Fax 01501 822272
   Specialism: Mental health (230); psychogeriatric (80).

Kirklands Hospital Fallside Rd, Bothwell, North Lanarkshire G71 8BB; Tel 01698 852508; Fax 01698 852340
   Specialism: Learning disabilities (226)

Roadmeetings Hospital Goremire Rd, Carluke, North Lanarkshire ML8 4PS; Tel 01555 772271; Fax 01555 752328
   Specialism: Psychogeriatric (22)

Udston Hospital Farm Rd, Burnbank, Hamilton, North Lanarkshire ML3 9LA; Tel 01698 823255; Fax 01698 713097
   Specialism: Psychogeriatric (40); psychogeriatric assessment (20).

MENTAL HEALTH DESIGNATED BEDS WITHIN ACUTE HOSPITALS

Hairmyres Hospital Eaglesham Rd, East Kilbride, North Lanarkshire G75 8RG; Tel 01355 220292
   Specialism: Mental health (60)

12

Law Hospital Law, Carluke, North Lanarkshire ML8 5ER; Tel 01698 361100
   Specialism: Psychogeriatric (24)

Monklands Hospital Monkscourt Ave, Airdrie, North Lanarkshire ML6 0JS; Tel 01236 748748; Fax 01236 760015
   Specialism: Mental health (58)

Lothian Primary Care Trust

St. Roque, Astley Ainslie Hospital, 133 Grange Loan, Edinburgh EH9 2HL; URL www.show.scot.nhs.uk/lpct; Tel 0131 537 9525; Fax 0131 537 9500
Chair Garth Morrison
Chief Executive Murray Duncanson
Medical Director Dr Mike Winter
Director (Nursing) Dr Linda Pollock
Director (Finance) Lynne Hollis
Director (Human Resources) Ruth Kelly

HOSPITALS

Astley Ainslie Hospital 133 Grange Loan, Edinburgh EH9 2HL; Tel 0131 537 9500
   Specialism: Medical rehabilitation; geriatric orthopaedics; Scottish Brain Injuries Rehabilitation Service Edinburgh; continuing care of frail elderly. Number of beds: (253)

Belhaven Hospital Beveridge Row, Dunbar, East Lothian EH42 1TR; Tel 01368 62246
   Specialism: Geriatric; long stay; psychogeriatric; GP acute.

Corstorphine Hospital Corstorphine Rd, Edinburgh EH12 6TT; Tel 0131 334 7577; Fax 0131 334 0537
   Specialism: Geriatric; long stay (30)

Edenhall Hospital Pinkieburn, Musselburgh, Midlothian EH21 7TZ; Tel 0131 536 8000
   Specialism: Geriatric; long stay; psychogeriatric. Number of beds: (76)

Edington Cottage Hospital 54 St. Baldreds Rd, North Berwick, East Lothian EH41 4PU; Tel 01620 2878
   Specialism: Acute (9)

Ellens Glen House Carenbee Ave, Edinburgh; Tel 0131 537 6243
   Specialism: Geriatric; psychogeriatric; continuing care. Number of beds: (60)

Ferryfield House Ferry Rd, Edinburgh EH5 3DQ; Tel 0131 536 1000
   Specialism: Continuing care – psychogeriatric and frail elderly.

Findlay House Seafield St, Edinburgh EH6 7LN; Tel 0131 536 7000
   Specialism: Continuing care – psychogeratric and frail elderly (60)

Herdmanflat Hospital Haddington, East Lothian EH41 3BU; Tel 0131 536 8300
   Specialism: Psychiatry; psychogeriatric. Number of beds: (97)

Loanhead Hospital Hunter Ave, Loanhead, Midlothian EH20 9SW; Tel 0131 440 0174
   Specialism: Geriatric long stay. Number of beds: (78)

Roodlands Hospital Haddington, East Ayrshire EH41 3PF; Tel 0131 536 8300
   Specialism: Day surgery; geriatric assessment; outpatient services. Number of beds: (78)

Rosslynlee Hospital Roslin, Midlothian EH25 9QE; Tel 0131 536 7600
   Specialism: Psychiatry, psychogeriatric. Number of beds: (140)

Royal Edinburgh Hospital Morningside Pl, Edinburgh EH10 5HF; Tel 0131 537 6000
   Specialism: Psychiatric; geriatric psychiatry. Number of beds: (705)

The Lothian University Hospitals NHS Trust

51 Little France Cres, Edinburgh EH16 4SA; Tel 0131 536 1000; Fax 0131 536 1001
Chair Prof P. Peattie
Chief Executive Stuart Gray
Medical Director Dr C.P. Swainson
Director (Nursing) I. McCallum
Director (Personnel) F. Sharp
Director (Finance and Performance Review) Aileen Brown

HOSPITALS

Liberton Hospital 113 Lasswade Rd, Edinburgh EH16 6UB; Tel 0131 536 7800
   Specialism: Care of the elderly / stroke assessment. Number of beds: (172)

Princess Alexandra Eye Pavilion Chalmers St, Edinburgh EH3 9HA; Tel 0131 536 1000
   Specialism: Ophthalmology (20)

Royal Hospital for Sick Children 9 Sciennes Rd, Edinburgh EH9 1LF; Tel 0131 536 0000
   Specialism: Paediatrics. Number of beds: (150)

Royal Infirmary of Edinburgh 51 Little France Cres, Edinburgh EH16 4SA; Tel 0131 536 1000
   Specialism: Acute; teaching. Number of beds: (801)

Royal Victoria Hospital 13 Craigleith Rd, Edinburgh EH4 2DN; Tel 0131 537 5000
   Specialism: Elderly care; psychogeriatric; rehabilitation; day places.

Western General Hospital Crewe Rd, Edinburgh EH4 2XU; Tel 0131 537 1000

North Glasgow University Hospitals NHS Trust

Trust Headquarters, 300 Balgrayhill Rd, Glasgow G21 3UR; Tel 0141 201 4200; Fax 0141 201 4201
Chair Ronnie Cleland
Chief Executive Maggie Boyle
Medical Director Dr Bill Anderson
Director (Human Resources) Alan Boyter
Director (Nursing and Quality) Margaret Smith
Director (Finance and Information) Brian Steven

Renfrewshire and Inverclyde Primary Care NHS Trust

Trust Headquarters, Merchiston Hospital, Brookfield, By Johnstone, Renfrewshire PA5 8TY; Tel 01505 384000; Fax 01505 384001
Chair J. Graham Marcus
Chief Executive George S. Buchanan
Medical Director Dr L.J. Jordan
Director (Human Resources) Mr P. O'Hagan
Director (Finance) Mr D. Meikle
Director (Nursing) Mrs L. Smith
Director (Dental Services) Mr A.C. Gerrish
Director (Facilities) Mr D. Cullen
Director (Information Services) Mrs N. Paterson

Royal Alexandra Hospital NHS Trust

Royal Alexandra Hospital, Corsebar Rd, Paisley, Renfrewshire PA2 9PN; Tel 0141 887 9111; Fax 0141 580 4127
Chief Executive M.F. Hill, SNC, MHSM, DipHSM

South Glasgow University Hospitals NHS Trust

Management Bldg, Southern General Hospital, Glasgow G51 4TF; Tel 0141 201 1100; 0141 201 1280; Fax 0141 201 2999
Chair Mrs E. Smith
Chief Executive R. Calderwood, MHSM, DipHSM

Director (Human Resources and Internal Communications)
B. Scully, MIPM, LLB
Director (Finance and Information)   P. Gallagher
Director (Medical Services)   Dr B. Cowan
Director (Nursing and Quality)   M. Henderson, MSc, RGN, RM
General Manager (Planning and Performance)   J.G. Burns, MBA, BA(Hons), MHSM, DipHSM
General Manager (Support Services)   A.S. McIntyre, MHSM, DipHSM

Tayside Primary Care NHS Trust

Ashludie Hospital, Monifieth, Dundee DD3 4HQ;
URL www.show.scot.nhs.uk;
E-mail margaret.moulton@tpct.scot.nhs.uk; Tel 01382 527801; Fax 01382 527891
Chair   M. Petrie, FRICS, IBRV
Chief Executive   W.J. Wells, RMN, RGN, CPN, LHSM
Medical Director   W.J. Mutch, FRCP
Director (Finance)   D. McLaren, MA(Hons), CIPFA
Director (Human Resources)   A.P. Killick, BA(Hons), MA, MIPM
Director (Nursing)   Vacancy

HEALTH CENTRES

Alyth Health Centre New Alyth Rd, Alyth, Perth and Kinross PH11 8EQ; Tel 01828 632931

Broughty Ferry Health Centre Brown St, Broughty Ferry, Dundee DD5 1EP; Tel 01382 737253; Fax 01382 731238

Crieff Health Centre King St, Crieff, Perth and Kinross PH7 3SA; Tel 01764 652456

Drumhar Health Centre North Methven St, Perth, Perth and Kinross PH1 5PD; Tel 01738 621181

Loch Leven Health Centre Lathro, Kinross, Perth and Kinross KY13 7SY; Tel 01577 8621129

Lochee Health Centre 1 Marshall St, Lochee, Dundee DD2 3BR; Tel 01382 610697; Fax 01382 621634

Methven Health Centre The Surgery, Denside, Methven, Perth and Kinross PH1 3PF; Tel 01738 840289

Monifieth Health Centre Victoria St, Monifieth, Dundee DD5 4LX; Tel 01382 534377

Ryehill Health Centre St. Peters St, Dundee DD1 4JH; Tel 01382 669392; Fax 01382 640518

Trades Lane Health Centre Coupar Angus, Perth and Kinross H13 9DP; Tel 01828 628432

Wallacetown Health Centre Lyon St, Dundee DD4 6RB; Tel 01382 459608; Fax 01382 461172

West Gate Health Centre Charleston Dr, Dundee DD2 4AD; Tel 01382 566313; Fax 01382 640519

Whitfield Health Centre 123 Whitfield Dr, Dundee DD4 0PD; Tel 01382 501189; Fax 01382 507453

DAY HOSPITALS

Ashludie Hospital Monifieth, Dundee DD5 4HQ; Tel 01382 423000
Specialism: Psychogeriatric (30)

Birch Avenue Day Hospital 55 Birch Ave, Scone, Perth, Perth and Kinross PH2 6LE; Tel 01738 553500; 01738 553920
Specialism: Mental handicap (18)

Glaxo Day Hospital Ashludie Hospital, Victoria St, Monifieth, Dundee DD5 4HQ; Tel 01382 423000
Specialism: Geriatric assessment (30)

Hawkhill Day Hospital Peddie St, Dundee DD1 5LB; Tel 01382 668300
Specialism: Mental handicap (20)

Macmillan House Isla Rd, Perth, Perth and Kinross PH2 7HQ; Tel 01738 639303

Orleans Day Hospital Orleans Pl, Menzieshill, Dundee DD2 4BH; Tel 01382 667322
Psychogeriatric (20)

Royal Dundee Liff Hospital Dundee DD2 5NF; Tel 01382 423000
Specialism: Mental illness (21)

Royal Victoria Hospital Jedburgh Rd, Dundee; Tel 01382 423000
Geriatric assessment (30)

Strathmartine Hospital Dundee DD3 0PG; Tel 01382 858334
Specialism: Mental handicap (30)

Threshold Day Hospital Dudhope Terr, Dundee DD3 6HG; Tel 01382 322026
Specialism: Mental illness (30)

HOSPITALS

Aberfeldy Cottage Hospital Aberfeldy, Perth and Kinross H15 2DH; Tel 01887 820314
Specialism: Elderly medicine (21)

Ashludie Hospital Monifieth, Dundee DD5 4HQ; Tel 01382 532101; Fax 01382 423000
Specialism: Geriatric assessment; continuing care; geriatric psychiatry. Number of beds: (216)

Blairgowrie Cottage Hospital Blairgowrie, Perth and Kinross H10 6EE; Tel 01250 874466
Specialism: Elderly medicine (56)

Crieff Cottage Hospital King St, Crieff, Perth and Kinross PH7 3HR; Tel 01764 653173
Specialism: Elderly medicine (40)

The Firs Linefield Rd, Carnoustie, Dundee; Tel 01242 856098
Specialism: Mental handicap (4)

Irvine Memorial Hospital Pitlochry, Perth and Kinross H16 5HP; Tel 01796 472052
Specialism: Elderly medicine. (23)

Murray Royal Hospital Muirhall Rd, Perth, Perth and Kinross PH2 7BH; Tel 01738 621151; 01738 621158
Number of beds: Mental health (239)

Royal Dundee Liff Hospital Dundee DD2 5NF; Tel 01382 580441; Fax 01382 423000
Specialism: Mental illness; geriatric psychiatry. Number of beds: (342)

Royal Victoria Hospital Jedburgh Rd, Dundee DD2 1SP; Tel 01382 423000; Fax 01382 667685
Specialism: Geriatric medicine; continuing care; palliative care; young chronic sick. Number of beds: (180)

St. Margaret's Hospital Auchterarder, Perth and Kinross PH3 1JH; Tel 01764 662246
Number of beds: (16)

Windyridge Strathmartine Hospital, Dundee; Tel 01382 858334
Specialism: Mental handicap (7)

COMMUNITY HEALTH CLINICS

Ardler Clinic Turnberry Ave, Dundee DD2 3TP; Tel 01382 825192; Fax 01382 826695

Charleston Clinic Craigowan Rd, Dundee DD2 4NJ; Tel 01382 622169

Douglas Clinic Balmoral Ave, Dundee DD4 8SQ; Tel 01382 78159; Fax 01382 731242

Kirkton Clinic Derwent Ave, Dundee DD3 0BW; Tel 01382 827153

Letham Clinic Marlee Rd, Letham, Perth and Kinross PH1 2HL; Tel 01738 636358

Longcroft Clinic Inglefield St, Dundee DD4 8LT; Tel 01382 503918

12

Tayside University Hospitals NHS Trust

Ninewells Hospital and Medical School, Dundee DD1 9SY;
Tel 01382 660111; Fax 01382 632422
Chair Prof J. McGoldrick
Chief Executive Gerry Marr
Medical Director M.H. Lyall
Director (Nursing and Patient Services) Lesley Summerhill
Director (Human Resource Management) Mrs J. Tolbet
Director (Operations) K. Armstrong
Director (Finance and Information) C. Masson

HOSPITALS

Dundee Dental Hospital and School 2 Park Pl, Dundee
DD1 4HR; Tel 01382 660111; Fax 01382 225163

King's Cross Hospital Clepington Rd, Dundee DD3 8EA;
Tel 01382 660111; Fax 01382 816178

Ninewells Hospital and Medical School Ninewells
Hospital, Dundee DD1 9SY; Tel 01382 660111; Fax 01382
632422

Perth Royal Infirmary Tay Mount Terr, Perth, Perth and
Kinross PH1 1NX; Tel 01738 623311; 01738 623316

Stratcathro Hospital Brechin, Angus DD9 7QA

The Victoria Infirmary NHS Trust

Queens Park Hse, Langside Rd, Glasgow G42 9TT; Tel 0141
201 5809; Fax 0141 201 5825
Chair Rev R.D.N. Campbell
Chief Executive R. Calderwood
Medical Director Dr B.N. Cowan
Director (Human Resources) B. Scully
Director (Finance and Information Systems) F. Seal
Director (Nursing Services) M. Henderson
Annual budget
£63 000 000

West Lothian Healthcare NHS Trust

St. John's Hospital, Howden, Livingston, West Lothian
EH54 6PP; URL www.show.scot.nhs.uk/wlt; Tel 01506
419666; Fax 01506 461280
Chair Stuart Smith
Chief Executive P. Gabbitas
Director (Nursing and Quality) E. Campbell, OBE
Director (Finance and Information) S. Goldsmith
Medical Director Dr B. Montgomery
Director (Operations) J. Jack
Director (Human Resources) L. Khindria

HOSPITALS

Bangour Village Hospital Broxburn, West Lothian
H52 6LW; Tel 01506 419666
Specialism: Psychiatric; elderly care.

St. John's Hospital at Howden Howden West, Livingston,
West Lothian EH54 6PP; Tel 01506 419666
Specialism: General surgery; general medicine;
maternity; geriatric assessment; psychiatry; burns and
plastic surgery; CCU; ITU; orthopaedics; ENT surgery;
paediatrics; oral and maxillo-facial surgery.

St. Michael's Hospital Edinburgh Rd, Linlithgow, West
Lothian EH49 6QS; Tel 01506 842053
Specialism: Geriatric (30)

Tippethill House Armadale Rd, Whitburn, West Lothian
H49 3BQ; Tel 01501 744786
Specialism: Geriatric (60)

Western Infirmary NHS Trust

Dumbarton Rd, Glasgow G11 6NT; Tel 0141 211 2000;
Fax 0141 211 1920

Yorkhill NHS Trust

Yorkhill, Glasgow G3 8SJ;
E-mail linda.mcelroy@scot.nhs.uk; Tel 0141 201 0000;
Fax 0141 201 0836
Chair Sally Kuenssberg
Chief Executive J. Best
Medical Director Morgan Jamieson
Director (Contracts) L. Fleming, AHSM
Director (Finance) Donald Matheson
Director (Nursing and Patient Services) B. Townsend
Director (Human Resources) Mrs H. Ostrycharz

HOSPITALS

The Queen Mother's Hospital Yorkhill, Glasgow G3 8SH;
Tel 0141 201 0550

Royal Hospital for Sick Children Yorkhill, Glasgow G3 8SG;
Tel 0141 201 0000

Health Boards

NHS Argyll and Clyde

Ross Hse, Hawkhead Rd, Paisley, Renfrewshire PA2 7BN;
E-mail public@achb.scot.nhs.uk; Tel 0141 842 7200;
Fax 0141 848 1414
Chair John Mullin
Chief Executive Neil M. Campbell
Director (Medical) Dr L. Jordan
Director (Public Health) Dr Lesley M. Wilkie
Director (Finance) James Hobson
Director (Health Care Planning) Judith A. Illsley
Director (Corporate Communications) Sandy Ferran
Director (Nursing) Mrs C. McGillivray
Annual budget
£450 million

Ayrshire and Arran NHS Board

Boswell Hse, 10 Arthur St, Ayr, South Ayrshire KA7 1QJ;
Tel 01292 611040; Fax 01292 286762
Chair Prof George Irving
Chief Executive W. Hatton, MBA, BA(Hons), DMS, MHSM,
DipHSM, FRSA
Director (Health Improvement) Grace Moore
Director (Finance) D. Lindsay
Director (Public Health) Dr Carol Davidson
Director (Health Policy) Kirsten Major (Acting)

NHS Borders

Newstead, Melrose, TD6 9DB
Chair T. Taylor
Chief Executive J.E. Glennie
Director (Public Health) A. Riley
Director (Finance) R. Kemp

NHS Dumfries and Galloway

Grierson Hse, The Crichton, Bankend Rd, Dumfries,
Dumfries and Galloway DG1 4ZG;
URL www.show.scot.nhs.uk/dghb; Tel 01387 272700;
Fax 01387 252375
Chair J.A. Ross
Chief Executive M.R. Wright
*Chief Administrative Medical Officer and Director (Public
Health)* Dr D. Cox
Director (Finance) Mrs L. Morrison

Fife Health Board

Springfield Hse, Cupar, Fife KY15 5UP; Tel 01334 656200;
Fax 01334 652210
Chair E. Roberton

Chief Executive   G. Brechin
Director (Service Development)   C. Cowan
Director (Public Health)   L. MacDonald
Director (Finance)   R. Pettigrew

CHILD ASSESSMENT UNIT

Gordon Cottage   118 Cocklaw St, Kirkcaldy, Fife KY4 0DJ;
Tel 01383 830441
Consultant Community Paediatrician   Dr T. Scott
Carnegie Clinic, Pilmuir St, Dunfermline, Fife KY12 0QF;
Tel 01383 722911
Consultant Paediatrician   Dr C. Steer
Victoria Hospital, Hayfield Rd, Kirkcaldy, Fife KY2 5AG;
Tel 01592 643355
Community Medicine Specialist   Vacancy
Fife Health Board, Springfield Hse, Cupar, Fife KY15 5UP;
Tel 01334 656200; Fax 01334 652210

HEALTH CENTRES

The Health Centre   Chapel St, High Valleyfield,
Dunfermline, Fife KY12 8SJ; Tel 01383 880511
Leven Health Centre   Victoria Rd, Leven, Fife KY8 4ET;
Tel 01333 425656

HOSPITALS

Adamson Hospital   Bank St, Cupar, Fife KY15 4JN; Tel 01334
652901
Forth Park Hospital   30 Bennochy Rd, Kirkcaldy, Fife
KY2 5RA; Tel 01592 643355
Glenrothes Hospital   1 Lodge Rise, Glenrothes, Fife
KY7 6ER; Tel 01592 743505
Lynebank Hospital   Halbeath Rd, Dunfermline, Fife
KY11 4UW; Tel 01383 623623
Netherlea Hospital   65 West Rd, Newport-on-Tay, Fife;
Tel 01382 543233
Randolph Wemyss Memorial Hospital   Wellesley Rd,
Denbeath, Buckhaven, Fife KY8 1HU; Tel 01592 712427
St. Andrews Memorial Hospital   Abbey Walk, St. Andrews,
Fife; Tel 01334 472327
Stratheden Hospital   Cupar, Fife KY15 5UP; Tel 01334
652611
Townhill Day Hospital   Muir Rd, Townhill, Dunfermline,
Fife; Tel 01383 722966
Weston Day Hospital   West Port, Cupar, Fife; Tel 01334
652163

Forth Valley Health Board

33 Spittal St, Stirling FK8 1DX; Tel 01786 463031; Fax 01786
451474
Chair   Ian Mullen
Chief Executive   F. Mackenzie
Director (Finance Performance Management)   F. Ramsay,
BSc(Hons), CPFA
*Director (Public Health) and Chief Administrative Medical
Officer*   Dr M. McWhirter, MRCP, FFPHM, MBA
Director (Strategic Planning)   B. Baillie

NHS Grampian

Summerfield Hse, 2 Eday Rd, Aberdeen AB15 6RE;
URL www.show.scot.nhs.uk/gdb/index.htm;
E-mail webinfo@ghb.grampian.scot.nhs.uk; Tel 01224
663456; Fax 01224 558609
Chief Executive   Neil M. Campbell
Director (Finance) and Board Secretary   Alex C. Smith
*Chief Administrative Medical Officer and Director (Public
Health)*   Dr E. Baijal
Director (Human Resources) and Chief Adviser (Nursing)
M. Powell

NHS Greater Glasgow

Dalian Hse, PO Box 15329, Glasgow G3 8YZ;
URL www.show.scot.nhs.uk/ggnhsb; Tel 0141 201 4444;
Fax 0141 201 4401
Chair   Prof Sir John P. Arbuthnott, PhD, ScD, FIBiol, FRSE,
FRCPath
Chief Executive   T.A. Divers, OBE
Director (Public Health)   Dr H.G.J. Burns, MBCHB, MPH,
FRCS
Director (Finance)   Wendy Hull, BA (Hons)
Director (Health Promotion)   Evelyn Borland (Acting)
Director (Planning and Community Care))
Miss C.M. Renfrew, MA, MHSM
Director (Communications)   A. McLaws
Assistant Director (Acute Services)   Ms P. Kilpatrick
Assistant Director (Addictions)   Ms D. O'Dwyer
Assistant Director (Community Care)   A. Mackenzie
Assistant Director (Community Care)   D. Walker
Assistant Director (Mental Health)   D. Adams
Assistant Director (Children's Services)   Mrs F. Mercer
Assistant Director (Information)   R. Murdoch
Head (Board Administration)   J.C. Hamilton, MHSM, DIP,
HSM
Manager (Human Resources)   Jill Thompson
Adviser (Pharmaceutical Policy)   S.M. Bryson
Adviser (Nursing)   Sue Plummer, MBA, DMS, RGN, RM,
DN Cert
Consultant in Dental Public Health   D. McCall

Highland Health Board

Beechwood Pk, Inverness, Highland IV2 3HG;
URL www.highlandhealth.org.uk;
E-mail reception@hhb.scot.nhs.uk; Tel 01463 717123;
Fax 01463 235189
Chair   C. Thomson
Director (Public Health and Health Policy)
Dr John G. Wrench
Director (Finance) and Company Secretary   M.S. Iredale, BA,
IPFA
Director (Service Planning and Development)
D.S. Leslie
Director (Health Improvement)   Dr G.V. Stone, MB, ChB,
FFCM, MFCM, DCM
General Manager   Dr R. Gibbins, BA, MBA, PhD

Lanarkshire Health Board

Board Office, 14 Beckford St, Hamilton, South Lanarkshire
ML3 0TA; Tel 01698 281313
Chair   Mr Lex Gold
General Manager   T.A. Divers, MA, BA, MHSM,
DipHSM
*Chief Administrative Medical Officer and Director (Public
Health)*   Dr D. Moir, MD, FFPHM, FRCP, DipMgt,
MBChB
Director (Planning)   B.J. Gill, MA(Hons), IPFA, FCCA,
MHSM, DipHSM
Director (Finance)   C.B. Cowie, LLB, CA
Adviser (Nursing)   T. Lynch, RGM, RMN
Consultant (Public Health Medicine)   Dr C. Clark, BSc,
MBChB, FRCS, MPH, PhD, MFPHM
Consultant (Public Health Medicine)   Dr J. Miller, BSc,
MBChB, DRCOG, MRGGP, MFPHM
Consultant (Public Health Medicine)   Dr J. Wrench, BSc,
MBChB, MSc, DRCOG, MRCGP, MRCP(UK), FFPHM
Consultant (Public Health Medicine)   Dr H.S. Kohli, BSc,
MBChB, DRCOG, MRC, GPMPH, MFPHM
Consultant (Public Health Medicine)   Dr D.T. Cromie,
MBBCh, BAD, DMH, MRCGP, MPH
Consultant (Public Health Medicine)   Dr G.A. Venters,
MBChB, DipAnimal Genetics, PhD, FFPHM
Consultant (Public Health Medicine)   Dr J. Logan, MBChB,
DRCOG, MRCGP, MPA, MFPHM
Specialist (Pharmaceutical Public Health)   E.J.H. Mallinson,
MPharm, FRPharmS, FIMgt, FRSH

12

Consultant (Dental Public Health) M.M. Taylor, MSc, MBA, BDS
Manager (Corporate Affairs) and Board Secretary N.J. Agnew, MHSM, DipHSM

Lothian NHS Board

Deaconess Hse, 148 Pleasance, Edinburgh EH8 9RS;
URL www.nhslothian.scot.nhs.uk; Tel 0131 536 9000;
Fax 0131 536 9009
Chair Brian Cavanagh
Chief Executive Prof James J. Barbour, OBE, BA (Joint Hons), MHSM, FRSA, FFICS
Director (Partnership Development) Margaret Wells
Director (Public Health and Health Policy) Prof Peter Donelly, MC, MPH, MBA, FRCP, FRCPE, FFPHM
Director (Finance and Performance Review) John Matheson, BA, MBA, CPFA

Orkney Health Board

Garden Hse, New Scapa Rd, Orkney, Orkney Islands KW15 1BQ; Tel 01856 885400; Fax 01856 885411
Chair Mrs J. Dewar
Chief Executive Mrs J. Wellden; Tel 01856 885420; Fax 01856 885411
Medical Director Dr George Crooks
Director (Finance and Corporate Services) Roger Dart
Director (Allied Health Professions and Nursing) Miss K. Bree
Chief Administrative Medical Officer and Director (Public Health Medicine) Vacancy

HOSPITAL

Balfour Hospital New Scapa Rd, Kirkwall, Orkney Islands KW15 1BH;
E-mail lorraine.taylor@orkney-ht.scotinhs.uk
Specialism: Medical, surgical, maternity. Number of rooms: Long stay (99)

Shetland NHS Board

Brevik Hse, South Rd, Lerwick, Shetland Isles ZE1 0TG;
URL www.show.scot.nhs.uk/shb; Tel 01595 696767;
Fax 01595 696727
Chair E. Fullerton
Chief Executive S. Laurenson, RGn, DipMgmt (Open)
Director (Public Health) Dr S. Taylor
Director (Patient Services) S. Jack
Director (Finance) D.P.P. Eva, BCom, IPFA

HOSPITALS

Gilbert Bain Hospital Lerwick, Shetland Isles; Tel 01595 743000; Fax 01595 696608

Montfield Hospital Lerwick, Shetland Isles; Tel 01595 743000

NHS Tayside Board

Kings Cross, Clepington Rd, Dundee
URL www.show.scot.nhs.uk/thb/;
E-mail comments@thb.scot.nhs.uk; Tel 01382 424003;
Fax 01382 561818
Chair Peter Bates
Chief Executive Vacancy
Director (Finance) D.J. Clark, CIPFA
Director (Public Health) Dr D. Walker, BSc, MBChB, MSc, MFCM
Director (Planning and Development)/CNA Dr P. Williamson, MA(Hons), PhD, MIM
Head (Personnel) J. Cowie, BA, FIPM, DIPPM

Western Isles Health Board

Health Board Offices, 37 South Beach St, Stornoway, Isle of Lewis HS1 2BB; Tel 01851 702997; Fax 01851 704405
Chair M.A. Matheson, OBE, JP
Chief Executive Murdo Maclennan
Director (Health Gain) Dr M. Watts
Director (Finance) D. Macleod
Director (Health Care) M. George

CHILD DEVELOPMENT CENTRE

Health Centre 20 Springfield Rd, Stornoway, Isle of Lewis PA87 2PS; Tel 01851 702500
Director (Health Care) B. Liddle

DISTRICT HANDICAP TEAM

Western Isles Islands Council Sandwick Rd, Stornoway, Isle of Lewis PA87 2BW; Tel 01851 703773
General Manager (Board) Vacancy

Health Councils and Associations

Scottish Association of Health Councils

8th Fl, Delta Hse, 50 West Nile St, Glasgow, G1 2NP;
URL www.show.scot.nhs.uk/sahc;
E-mail admin1@sahc.sol.co.uk; Tel 0141 225 6880;
Fax 0141 249 9981
Supports local health councils (LHCs), the NHS users' statutory consumer representative. Provides an information and training resource, and promotes the development of public participation in all health-related matters.

Argyll and Clyde Local Health Council

The Gatehouse, Hawkhead Hospital, Hawkhead Rd, Paisley, Renfrewshire PA2 7BL;
E-mail achealth.council@achb.scot.nhs.uk; Tel 0141 840 1336; Fax 0141 848 5007
Chief Officer Rosemary Hill
The Health Council is a statutory NHS organisation established to represent the interests of the public in the NHS in the area.

Ayrshire and Arran Health Council

Ground Fl, Administration Block, Ayrshire Central Hospital, Irvine, North Ayrshire KA12 8SS;
URL www.show.scot.nhs.uk/aahc;
E-mail ayrshire@aahc.demon.co.uk; Tel 01294 323223;
Fax 01294 323222
Chief Officer C. Lambert

Borders Local Health Council

71 High St, Galashiels, Scottish Borders TD1 1RZ;
E-mail moira@blhc.fsnet.co.uk; Tel (24 hours) 01896 661420; Fax 01896 661423
Chief Officer M. Balmer

Dumfries and Galloway Local Health Council

11 Buccleuch St, Dumfries, Dumfries and Galloway DG1 2AT; URL show.nhs.uk/dghc;
E-mail dghealthcouncil@btconnect.com; Tel 01387 261222; Fax 01387 269078
Chief Officer Alan Harvey

Fife Health Council

Hayfield Clinic, Hayfield Rd, Kirkaldy, Fife KYZ 5DG;
E-mail fifenhealthcncl@sol.co.uk; Tel 01592 200555
Chief Officer C. Johnstone

Forth Valley Local Health Council

46 Barnton St, Stirling FK8 1NA;
  URL www.show.scot.nhs.uk/fvlhc;
  E-mail admin@lhc.forth-hb.scot.nhs.uk;
  Tel (24 hour answerphone) 01786 446688; Fax 01786
  471550
Chief Officer   S. McFarlane

Grampian Local Health Council

Westburn Hse, Foresterhill, Westburn Rd, Aberdeen
  AB25 2XG; URL www.show.scot.nhs.uk/glhc;
  E-mail info@glhc.grampian.scot.nhs.uk; Tel 01224
  559444; Fax 01224 552754
Chief Officer   Mrs M. Emslie

Greater Glasgow Health Council

44 Florence St, Gorbals, Glasgow G5 0YZ;
  URL www.glasgowhealthcouncil.org.uk;
  E-mail co@gglhc.demon.co.uk; Fax 0141 429 6367;
  Textphone 0141 429 7698
Chief Officer   D. Crawford

Highland Health Council

The Old Nurses Home, Craig Dunain, Inverness, Highland
  IV3 8PG; Tel 01463 723930; Fax 01463 723939
Chief Officer   Joyce Thompson (Acting)

Lanarkshire Health Council

Airbles Rd, Motherwell, North Lanarkshire ML1 3FE;
  E-mail sheila.mcgoran@lanarkshirehb.scot.nhs.uk;
  Tel (24 hour) 01698 258188; Fax 01698 275706

Lewis and Harris Health Council

20 Kenneth St, Stornoway, Isle of Lewis, HS1 2DR;
  Tel 01851 703292; Fax 01851 702756

Lothian Health Council

21 Torphichen St, Edinburgh EH3 8HX;
  URL www.lhc-online.org;
  E-mail lothian.healthcouncil@lhc.lothian.scot.nhs.uk;
  Tel 0131 229 6605; Fax 0131 229 6220
Chief Officer   Merlyn Branston

Orkney Local Health Council

Custom Hse, 33 Albert St, Kirkwall, Orkney Islands
  KW15 1HL; Tel 01856 879907; Fax 01856 879908
Officer   A. Eltome

Shetland Local Health Council

Gracefield, Sand, Bixter, Shetland Isles ZE2 9NQ;
  E-mail shetlandlhc@ukonline.co.uk; Tel 01595 860257;
  Fax 01595 860257
Chief Officer   Patricia Alderson

Tayside Health Council

Ground Fl, Argyll Hse, Marketgait, Dundee DD1 1QP;
  URL www.show.scot.nhs.uk/thc;
  E-mail taysidehealthcouncil@thb.scot.nhs.uk; Tel (24
  hours) 01382 228212; Fax 01382 202225
Chief Officer   Meg Barclay

Western Isles Health Council

20 Kenneth St, Stornoway, Isle of Lewis HS1 2DR;
  E-mail lhhc@lineone.net; Tel (24 hour) 01851 703292;
  Fax 01851 702756
Chief Officer   D. Ross

Agency

Common Services Agency for the National Health Service in Scotland

Trinity Park Hse, South Trinity Rd, Edinburgh EH5 3SE;
  URL www.show.scot.nhs.uk/csa; Tel 0131 552 6255;
  Fax 0131 552 8651
Chair of Board   Graeme Millar
Chief Executive   Stuart Bain

NORTHERN IRELAND

HSS Trusts

Altnagelvin Hospitals H and SS Trust

Altnagelvin Area Hospital, Glenshane Rd, Londonderry,
  County Londonderry BT47 6SB; Tel 028 7134 5171;
  Fax 028 7161 1222
Chief Executive   S. Burnside, RGN, RMN, RNT, BPhil
Director (Business Services)   R. McCartney, BSc
Director (Pharmaceutical Services and CSSD)   S. O'Kane,
  MPSNI
Director (Nursing)   I. Duddy
Director (Clinical Support Services)   T. Melaugh, MIPM
Director (Finance)   N.J. Smyth, ACIMA
Director (Personnel)   M.J. Doherty, DMS
Director (Estates Management)   A. Moore, BSc, ARICS
Medical Director   Dr G. Nesbitt
Clinical Director (Surgery and Critical Care Directorate)
  P. Bateson
*Clinical Director (General Medicine and Ambulatory Care
  Directorate)*   Dr K. Moles
Clinical Director (Women and Children's Directorate)
  Dr M. Parker
Clinical Director (Pathology)   Dr M. O'Kane
Clinical Director (Imaging Services Directorate)   Dr M. Reilly
Clinical Services Manager (Pathology Services)   Mr K. Garrett
Clinical Services Manager (Imaging Services)   I. Craig
*Clinical Services Manager (Women and Children's Services
  Directorate)*   M. Doherty
*Clinical Services Manager (Medical and Ambulatory Care
  Directorate)*   Miss D. Brennan
*Clinical Services Manager (Surgery and Critical Care
  Directorate)*   Vacancy

HOSPITALS

Altnagelvin Area Hospital (incl Anderson Hse)   Glenshane
Rd, Londonderry, County Londonderry BT47 6SB; Tel 028
7134 5171
  Specialism: Acute (513)

Altnagelvin Day Hospital
  Number of beds: (15)

Spruce House   10 Gransha Hospital, Clooney Rd,
Londonderry, County Londonderry BT47 1TS; Tel 028 7186
0261
  Specialism: Young physically disabled. (17)

Armagh and Dungannon HSS Trust

St. Lukes Hospital, Loughgall Rd, Armagh, County
  Armagh BT61 7NQ; URL www.adhsst.n-i.nhs.uk;
  Tel 028 3752 2381; Fax 028 3752 6302
Chief Executive   Miss P. Stanley
Executive Director (Health Care and Nursing)
  Mrs A. McVeigh

12

Executive Director (Social Services) Mr E. Hamilton
Executive Director (Finance) S. McNally
Medical Executive Director Dr C. Cassidy
Director (Personnel) Mrs H. Ellis
Director (Planning and Performance) Mr P. McCabe
Director (Mental Health and Learning Disability Services)
   Mr K. Toal

HEALTH CENTRES

Armagh Health Centre Dobbin Street La, Armagh, County
Armagh BT61 7QU; Tel 028 3752 3165

Ballygawley Health Centre Old Dungannon Rd,
Ballygawley, County Armagh; Tel 01662 568212

Coalisland Health Centre 10a Lineside, Coalisland,
Dungannon, County Armagh BT71 4LP; Tel 01868 748555

Markethill Health Centre Newry St, Markethill, County
Armagh; Tel 028 3755 1202

Moy Health Centre Charlemont St, Moy, County Armagh;
Tel 01868 784551

Richhill Health Centre Maynooth Rd, Richhill, County
Armagh BT61 9PE; Tel 028 3887 1701

HOSPITALS

Armagh Community Hospital Tower Hill, Armagh, County
Armagh BT61 9DP; Tel 028 3752 2341

Mullinure Hospital Loughgall Rd, Armagh, County
Armagh BT61; Tel 028 3752 2381

South Tyrone Hospital Dungannon, County Tyrone;
Tel 01868 722821
   Specialism: Acute

HOSPITAL FOR PEOPLE WITH LEARNING DISABILITIES

Longstone Hospital for People with Learning Disabilities
Armagh, County Armagh BT61; Tel 028 3752 2381
   Specialism: Mental handicap.

HOSPITAL FOR PEOPLE WITH MENTAL HEALTH NEEDS

St. Luke's Hospital Armagh, County Armagh BT61; Tel 028
3752 2381

Belfast City Hospital HSS Trust

Administration Fl, Belfast City Hospital, Belfast BT9 7AB;
   Tel 028 9032 9241; Fax 028 9032 6614
Chair Joan Ruddock, OBE
Chief Executive J.Q. Coey, FIPM
Medical Director Dr Ken J. Fullerton, MD, FRCP
Director (Nursing) E. Hayes
Director (Finance) Joe Copeland
Director (Personnel) M. Barkley, Grad, IPM

HOSPITAL

Belfast City Hospital Lisburn Rd, Belfast BT9 7AB; Tel 028
9032 9241
   Number of beds: (887)

Causeway HSS Trust

8e Coleraine Rd, Ballymoney, County Antrim BT53 6BP;
   Tel 028 2766 6600; Fax 028 2766 1200
Director (Child and Community Care Services) J.P. Loughrey

HEALTH CENTRES

Ballycastle Health Centre Coleraine Rd, Ballycastle,
County Antrim; Tel 028 2076 2684

Ballymoney Health Centre Newal Rd, Ballymoney, County
Antrim; Tel 028 2766 0300

Coleraine Health Centre Castlerock Rd, Coleraine, County
Londonderry; Tel 028 7034 4831

HOSPITALS

Dalriada Hospital Coleraine Rd, Ballycastle, County
Antrim; Tel 028 7037 6266
   Specialism: General (50)

Robinson Memorial Hospital Newal Rd, Ballymoney,
County Antrim; Tel 028 2766 0322
   Specialism: General (38)

Craigavon and Banbridge Community HSS Trust

Headquarters, Bannvale Hse, Gilford, Craigavon, County
   Down BT63 5JX; Tel 028 3883 1983; Fax 028 3883 1993
Chief Executive W.D. Preston
Chair Graham Martin
Director (Child and Family Care) L.F. Boyle, BSc(Econ/Pol),
   DSS, MSc, CQSW
Director (Elderly and Primary Care) R. Burns, RGN, HV,
   HEdCert
Director (Finance) W. Ronnie Crozier, BSc(Econ), FICAI
Director (Human Resources) K. Donaghy, BA, HND, GIPM,
   MIPM
Director (Planning and Information) Martin Kelly
Director (Mental Health and Disability) Ian Sutherford
Business and Planning Manager (Contracting) S. Hanna
There is a general e-mail format:
<firstinitial>.<surname>@cbct.n-i.nhs.uk

ADMINISTRATION OFFICES

Finance Department 100 Sloan St, Lurgan, Craigavon,
County Armagh BT66 8NT; Tel 028 3832 3262; Fax 028 3832
9483
Director (Finance) W.R. Crozier

Personnel Department Lurgan HSS Centre, 100 Sloan St,
Lurgan, Craigavon, County Armagh BT66 8NT
Manager (Personnel) L. McElrath

CARE OF THE MENTALLY ILL

Psychiatric Unit 68 Lurgan Rd, Portadown, Craigavon,
County Armagh BT63 5QQ; Tel 028 3833 4444; Fax 028 3835
1179
   Specialism: Acute mental health (80); Day care mental
   health (40).

Trasna House Connolly Pl, Trasna Way, Lurgan, Craigavon,
County Armagh BT66 8DN; Tel 02838 347537; Fax 02838
347949

CARE OF OLDER PERSONS

Crozier House Meeting House Rd, Banbridge, County
Down BT32 3ER; Tel 028 4066 2734
Manager Kate McBeth
   Specialism: Residential elderly care (35); respite (4).

Dollingstown Social Centre Alfred Terr, Dollingstown,
Lurgan, Craigavon, County Down BT66 7JX; Tel 028 3832
3680
Contact G. Mcguire; Tel 028 3832 7824
   Specialism: Elderly care (30)

CARE OF PERSONS WITH SPECIAL LEARNING NEEDS

Riverside 10 Moyallan Rd, Gilford, Craigavon, County
Down BT63 5JX; Tel 028 3883 2094
Contact A. Martin
   Specialism: Residential learning disabilities (34).

Windsor Gate Lodge Windsor Ave, Lurgan, Craigavon,
County Armagh BT67 9BN; Tel 028 3832 9652
Contact H. McMullan; Tel 028 3832 4207
   Specialism: Residential learning disabilities (4)

CHILD AND FAMILY CARE

Bocombra Children's Centre 2 Old Lurgan Rd, Portadown, Craigavon, County Armagh BT63 5SG; Tel 028 3833 2479
Contact Paula Hendron
Assessment and residential child care unit. (10)

Child and Family Care Office 2 Old Lurgan Rd, Portadown, Craigavon, County Armagh BT63 5SG; Tel 028 3833 3747; Fax 028 3833 5528
Manager (Child and Family Care) P. Morgan
Manager (Child and Family Care) V. O'Rourke

Child Protection Centre (NSPCC Joint Centre) The Children's Centre, Moyraverty Centre, Craigavon, County Armagh BT65 5HX; Tel 028 3834 3620; Fax 028 3834 3143
Administrative offices for child and family care.

Edenvilla 6 Edenderry Rd, Banbridge, County Down BT32 3AF; Tel 028 4066 2614
Manager M. White
Specialism: Residential child care. (5)

Fostering Resource Centre 2 Old Lurgan Rd, Portadown, Craigavon, County Armagh BT63 5SG; Tel 028 3833 7181
Administrative offices for child and family care.

DAY CARE CENTRES

Banbridge Social Education Centre Meeting Hse Rd, Banbridge, County Armagh BT32 3ER; Tel 028 4062 6773
Manager Louise McCabe
Specialism: Learning disabilities. (30)

Bannvale Social Education Centre 10 Moyallan Rd, Gilford, Craigavon, County Armagh BT63 5JY; Tel 028 3883 1545
Contact L. Knox
Specialism: Learning disabilities (100)

The Beeches Russell Dr, Lurgan, Craigavon, County Armagh BT66 8HD; Tel 028 3834 7537; Fax 028 3834 7949
Specialism: Residential mental illness (9)

Copperfields Meeting Hse Rd, Banbridge, County Down BT32 3ER; Tel 028 4066 2349
Contact Herbie Pearson
Specialism: Physical disability and mental handicap (30)

Eden Social Education Centre 293 Bridge St, Portadown, Craigavon, County Armagh BT63 5BJ; Tel 028 3833 3589
Manager Louise McCabe
Specialism: Learning disabilities (30)

Manor Centre Manor Dr, Lurgan, Craigavon, County Armagh BT66 8QD; Tel 028 3832 6525; 028 3832 8896
Manager Louise McCabe
Specialism: Physical disability; mental health. Number of beds: (80)

The Meadows Day Centre 293 Bridge St, Portadown, Craigavon, County Armagh BT63 5BJ; Tel 028 3833 8145
Contact D. Kelly
Specialism: Elderly; mental health (50)

Psychiatric Day Hospital 68 Lurgan Rd, Portadown, Craigavon, County Armagh BT63 5QQ; Tel 028 3833 4444; Fax 028 3835 1179
Sister-in-Charge Sister Henderson
Specialism: Acute psychiatric day care (40)

Skeagh House 15 Banbridge Rd, Dromore, County Down BT25 1NB; Tel 028 9269 2999
Contact I. Cromie
Specialism: Elderly care (34).

HEALTH CENTRES AND CLINICS AND HEALTH AND SOCIAL SERVICES CENTRES

Banbridge HSS Centre Scarva St, Banbridge, County Down BT32 3AD; Tel 028 4066 2866; Fax 028 4062 6059
Primary health and social care services.

Brownlow HSS Centre 1 Legahory Centre, Legahory, Craigavon, County Armagh BT65 5BE; Tel 028 3834 1431; 028 3834 3011; 028 3834 4973; Fax 028 3834 5983

Contact G. Maguire; Tel 028 3832 7824
Primary health and social care services.

Dromore Clinic 18 Banbridge Rd, Dromore, County Down BT25 1NB; Tel 028 9269 2461
Contact G. Maguire; Tel 028 4066 2866
Primary care services.

Gilford Health Centre Castleview, Gilford, Craigavon, County Down BT63 6JS; Tel 028 3883 1225; 028 3883 1701 028 3883 2091 028 3883 2270; Fax 028 3883 1318
Contact G. Maguire; Tel 028 4066 2866
Primary care services.

Lurgan HSS Centre 100 Sloan St, Lurgan, Craigavon, County Armagh BT66 8NT; Tel 028 3832 7824; Fax 028 3832 9353
Contact G. Macguire
Primary health and social care services.

Portadown HSS Centre Tavanagh Ave, Portadown, Craigavon, County Armagh BT62 3BU; Tel 028 3833 4400; 028 3833 5117; Fax 028 3835 1246
Contact G. Maguire; Tel 028 3839 1212
Primary health and social care services.

RESOURCE CENTRES

Cherrytrees Resource Centre 1a Edenderry Gdns, Portadown, Craigavon, County Armagh BT63 5EA; Tel 028 3839 4088; Fax 028 3839 4095
Specialism: Sensory impairment; physical disability.

Community Mental Handicap Resource Centre Moylinn Hse, Legahory Centre, Craigavon, County Armagh
Specialism: Learning disability team.

Community Mental Health Resource Centre Russell Dr, Lurgan, Craigavon, County Armagh BT66 8HD; Tel 028 3834 7537; Fax 028 3834 7949
Specialism: Mental health service.

SPECIALISED DEPARTMENTS

Occupational Therapy Department 68 Lurgan Rd, Portadown, Craigavon, County Armagh BT63 5QQ; Tel 028 3833 4444; Fax 028 3835 0068
Contact C. Cranston

Speech Therapy Department 68 Lurgan Rd, Portadown, Craigavon, County Armagh BT63 5QQ; Tel 028 3833 4444; Fax 028 3835 0068
Contact R. Nesbitt

Craigavon Area Hospital Group HSS Trust

12

Craigavon Area Hospital, 68 Lurgan Rd, Craigavon, County Armagh BT63 5QQ; Tel 028 3833 4444; Fax 028 3835 0068
Chief Executive John W. Templeton
Director (Nursing and Quality) John Mone

HOSPITALS

Banbridge Polyclinic Linenhall St, Banbridge, County Down; Tel 028 4062 2222

Craigavon Area Hospital 68 Lurgan Rd, Portadown, Craigavon, County Armagh; Tel 028 3833 4444

Lurgan Hospital Sloan St, Lurgan, Craigavon, County Armagh; Tel 028 3832 3262

South Tyrone Hospital Carland Rd, Dungannon, County Tyrone BT71 4AU; Tel 028 8772 2821

Down Lisburn HSS Trust

Lisburn Health Centre, 25 Linenhall St, Lisburn, County Down BT28 1LU; Tel 028 9266 5181; Fax 028 9266 5179
Chief Executive John Compton

HEALTH CENTRES

Community Services Offices 45–47 Main St, Ballynahinch, County Down BT24 8DN; Tel 028 9756 5456; Fax 028 9756 2299

Community Services Offices 20–22 Park Ave, Newcastle, County Down BT33 0DY; Tel 028 4372 2326; Fax 028 4372 6323

Health Centre 12 Pound La, Downpatrick, County Down BT30 6HY; Tel 028 4461 3811; Fax 028 4461 6808

Hillsborough Health Centre 29 Ballynahinch St, Hillsborough, County Down BT26 0AW; Tel 028 9268 3609; Fax 028 9268 9643

Lisburn Health Centre 25 Linenhall St, Lisburn, County Antrim BT28 1LU; Tel 028 9266 5181; Fax 028 9266 5179

Stewartstown Road Health Centre 212 Stewartstown Rd, Dunmurry, Belfast BT17 0FB; Tel 028 9060 2705; Fax 028 9062 9827

HOSPITALS

Downe Hospital Pound La, Downpatrick, County Down BT30 6HY; Tel 028 4461 3311; Fax 028 4461 5699
  Specialism: Mainly acute (92)

Downpatrick Maternity Hospital Struell Wells Rd, Downpatrick, County Down BT30 6RA; Tel 028 4461 3311
  Specialism: Maternity. (20)

Downshire Hospital Ardglass Rd, Downpatrick, County Down BT30 6RA; Tel 028 4461 3311; Fax 028 4461 2444
  Specialism: Psychiatric, psychogeriatric. (240)

Lagan Valley Hospital 39 Hillsborough Rd, Lisburn, County Antrim BT28 1JP; Tel 028 9266 5141; Fax 028 9266 6100
  Specialism: Mainly acute. (315)

Medical Assessment Unit Downe Hospital, Pound La, Downpatrick, County Down BT30 6HY; Tel 028 4461 3311; Fax 028 4461 5699
  Specialism: Elderly. (20)

Thompson House Hospital 19–21 Magheralave Rd, Lisburn, County Antrim BT28 3BP; Tel 028 9266 5646; Fax 028 9267 6026
  Specialism: Physical handicap long stay. (45)

Foyle HSS Trust

Riverview Hse, Abercorn Rd, Londonderry, County Londonderry BT48 6SB; Tel 028 7126 6111; Fax 028 7126 0806
Chief Executive E. Way, BA, AHSM
Director (Health Care) P. Mahon, RGN, SCM, HVcert
Director (Business Services) J. Lusby
Director (Social Care) J. Doherty
Director (Finance) P. McLaughlin, FCCA
Annual budget
£67.3 million

COMMUNITY MENTAL HEALTH TEAMS

Addiction Unit Old Railway Station, Duke St, Londonderry, County Londonderry; Tel 028 7131 1488

Child and Family Community Mental Health Team Old Railway Station, Duke St, Londonderry, County Londonderry; Tel 028 7131 1488

Cityside Community Mental Health Team 22 Crawford Sq, Londonderry, County Londonderry; Tel 028 7137 2230

Community Mental Health Team for the Elderly Slievemore Hse, 2 Village La, Londonderry, County Londonderry; Tel 028 7135 0063

Limavady Community Mental Health Team Arden Centre, Scroggy Rd, Limavady, County Londonderry; Tel 028 7772 2123

Strabane Community Mental Health Team 5 Railway Rd, Strabane, County Tyrone; Tel 028 7138 2963

Waterside Community Mental Health Team Rossdowney Hse, Glendermott Rd, Waterside, County Londonderry; Tel 028 7131 1477

HEALTH CENTRES

Claudy Health Centre 38a Irwin Cres, Claudy, Londonderry, County Londonderry BT47 4AB; Tel 028 7133 8371

Dungiven Health Centre 1 Chapel Rd, Dungiven, Londonderry, County Londonderry; Tel 028 7174 1801

Great James Street Health Centre 51–61 Great James St, Londonderry, County Londonderry BT48 7DF; Tel 028 7136 5177

Limavady Health Centre Scroggy Rd, Limavady, County Londonderry; Tel 028 7176 3131

Shantallow Health Centre Racecourse Rd, Londonderry, County Londonderry BT48 8NF; Tel 028 7135 1350

Strabane Health Centre Upper Main St, Strabane, County Tyrone BT82 8AR; Tel 028 7138 4114

Waterside Health Centre Glendermott Rd, Londonderry, County Londonderry BT47 1BH; Tel 028 7132 0100

HOSPITALS

Gransha Hospital Clooney Rd, Londonderry, County Londonderry BT47 1TF; Tel 028 7186 0261
  Specialism: Mental health (469).

Stradreagh Hospital Gransha Pk, Clooney Rd, Londonderry, County Londonderry; Tel 028 7186 0261
  Specialism: Psychiatric; learning disabilities. Number of beds: (89)

Waterside Hospital Gransha Pk, Clooney Rd, Londonderry, County Londonderry; Tel 028 7186 0007

Green Park Healthcare Trust

Musgrave Park Hospital, Stockman's La, Belfast BT9 7JB; Tel 028 9066 9501; Fax 028 9038 2008
Chief Executive Hilary Boyd
Director (Patient Services) Eleanor Hayes

HOSPITALS

Forster Green Hospital 110 Saintfield Rd, Belfast BT8 4HD; Tel 028 9079 3681
  Specialism: Rehabilitation; respite care; neurology; elderly care; child and family therapy. Number of beds: (120)

Musgrave Park Hospital Stockman's La, Belfast BT9 7JB; Tel 028 9066 9501
  Specialism: Orthopaedics; rheumatology; elderly care; regional spinal cord injuries; rehabilitation; amputee limb fitting. Number of beds: (482)

Homefirst Community HSS Trust

The Cottage, 5 Greenmount Ave, Ballymena, County Antrim BT43 6DA; E-mail chiefexecutive@homefirst.n-nhs.uk; Tel 028 256 33700; Fax 028 256 33733
Chief Executive C. Colhoun
Chair W. Boyd

Mater Hospital HSS Trust

Mater Hospital, Crumlin Rd, Belfast BT14 6AB; URL www.n-i.nhs.uk/mater; Tel 028 9074 1211; Fax 028 9074 1342
Chief Executive E. P. Gordon
Medical Director Dr J. C. McLoughlin, MD, FRCP
Director (Nursing and Quality) Mary Hinds
Director (Finance) Sean Donaghy

Clinical Director Dr Ann Montgomery
Clinical Director B.G. Wilson, MD, FRCS
Clinical Director Dr J. S. McLoughlin, MD, FRCR
Director (Corporate Development) Joan Penden

HOSPITAL

Mater Hospital Crumlin Rd, Belfast BT14 6AB;
URL www.n-i.nhs.uk/mater; Tel 028 9074 1211
    Specialism: General maternity. (229)

Newry and Mourne HSS Trust

Trust Headquarters, 5 Downshire Pl, Newry, County Down
    BT34 1DZ; E-mail trust.headquarters@dhh.n.j.nhs.uk;
    Tel 028 3026 0505
Chair S. Hosan
Chief Executive E. Bowyer
Director (Finance and Planning) M. Dillon
Director (Acute Services) Dr P. Loughran
Director (Nursing and Community Health) Mrs J. O'Hagan
Director (Social Services) J. Flynn
Director (Professions Allied to Medicine) Mrs E. Cavan
Manager (Administrative Services) B. Toal
General Adviser (Medical Services) Dr A. Mulholland
Consultant Community Paediatrician Dr M. Hollinger

HEALTH CENTRES

Bessbrook Clinic Convent Hill, Bessbrook, Newry, County
Down BT35 7AW; Tel 028 3028 30291

Crossmaglen Health Centre Newry Rd, Crossmaglen,
Newry, County Down BT35 9HD; Tel 028 3086 1286

Kilkeel Health Centre Knockchree Ave, Kilkeel, Newry,
County Down BT34 4BP; Tel 028 4176 0960

Newry Health Centre John Mitchel Pl, Newry, County
Down; Tel 028 3083 4200

Newtownhamilton Health Centre 2a Markethill Rd,
Newtownhamilton, Newry, County Down BT35 0BE;
Tel 028 3087 8202

Rathfriland Health Centre John St, Rathfriland, Newry,
County Down BT34 5QH; Tel 028 4063 0666

Warrenpoint Health Centre Summerhill, Warrenpoint,
Newry, County Down BT34 3JD; Tel 028 4177 3388

HOSPITALS

Daisy Hill Hospital 5 Hospital Rd, Newry, County Down
BT35 8DR; Tel 028 3083 5000
    Specialism: Acute (286)

Mourne Hospital Newry St, Kilkeel, Newry, County Down
BT34 4DN; Tel 028 4176 2235

North and West Belfast HSS Trust

Headquarters, Glendinning Hse, 6 Murray St, Belfast
    BT1 6DP; Tel 028 9032 7156; Fax 028 9082 1284
Chair P.A. McCarton
Chief Executive R.G. Black, CSW, MHSM
Director (Finance) P.S. Harvey, BSc(Econ), IPFA, DipMS
Director (Hospital Services) Vacancy
Director (Human Resources and Corporate Affairs) E. Molloy
Director (Operations and Community Care) N. Rooney, BSc,
    MSc, CQSW, CertMS
*Director (Planning, Contracts and Information) and Deputy
    Chief Executive* P.M. Ryan, BA, MSc, DipSS, DipMS
Director (Medical Services – Hospital) Dr C. Marriott
Director (Medical Services – Community) Dr R. McKee
Director (Nursing) B. Connolly

HEALTH CENTRES

Albert Street Health Centre 21 Ross Rd, Belfast BT12 4JR;
Tel 028 9024 2816

Ballyowen Health Centre 179 Andersonstown Rd, Belfast
BT11 9EA; Tel 028 9061 0611; Fax 028 9060 8600

Crumlin Road Health Centre 130–132 Crumlin Rd, Belfast
BT14 6AP; Tel 028 9074 1188; Fax 028 9074 7158

Shankill Health Centre 135 Shankill Pde, Belfast BT13 1DY;
Tel 028 9024 7181; Fax 028 9032 7198

Skegoneill Health Centre 195 Skegoneill Ave, Belfast
BT15 3LL; Tel 028 9077 2471; Fax 028 9077 2449

Whiterock Health Centre 6 Whiterock Gr, Belfast BT12 7RQ;
Tel 028 9032 3153; Fax 028 9043 8112

HOSPITAL

Muckamore Abbey Hospital 1 Abbey Rd, Muckamore,
Belfast BT41 4SH; Tel 028 9446 3333; Fax 028 9446 7730
    Specialism: Learning disabilities (497)

DAY CENTRES

Ballyowen 179 Andersonstown Rd, Belfast BT11 9EA;
Tel 028 9030 1034

Beech Hall 21a Andersonstown Rd, Belfast BT11 9AF;
Tel 028 9062 2939

Carlisle Terrace 2 Carlisle Terr, Belfast BT13 2PR; Tel 028
9023 1135

Glencairn 93 Forthriver Rd, Belfast BT13 3SL; Tel 028 9039
1468

North Belfast 585–589 Crumlin Rd, Belfast BT14 7GB;
Tel 028 9056 6000

Parkmount 704 Shore Rd, Belfast BT15 4HJ; Tel 028 9077
2413

Shankill 135 Shankill Pde, Belfast BT13 1SD; Tel 028 9032
7518

Whiterock 6 Whiterock Gr, Belfast BT12 7RQ; Tel 028 9032
3153

Woodlands 9 Woodland Ave, Belfast BT14 6BY; Tel 028 9075
1215

Northern Ireland Ambulance Service HSS Trust

Ambulance Service Headquarters, 12–22 Linenhall St,
    Belfast BT2 8BS; Tel 01232 246113
Chief Executive P. McCormick, MSL, BA
Chair D. Smyth, OBE

Royal Group of Hospitals and Dental Hospital Health and Social Services

King Edward Bldg, Royal Victoria Hospital, Belfast
    BT12 6BA; URL www.royalhospitals.ac.uk; Tel 028 9024
    0503
Chair Dr P. McWilliams, OBE
Chief Executive W.S. McKee, BSc(Hons), MBA, MHSM
Medical Director Dr Michael McBride
Director (Nursing and Patient Services) D. O'Brien, MBA,
    RGN, SCM, DNCert
Director (Finance) Mrs W. Galbraith
Director (Operations Performance and Planning)
    H. McCaughey, BSc(Hons)
Director (Facilities) C. Burns
Director (Human Resources) M. Mallon
Director (Corporate Services) E. Bates
Head (Corporate Communication) Ms D. Curley

HOSPITALS

Royal Belfast Hospital for Sick Children Falls Rd, Belfast
BT12 6BE; Tel 028 9024 0503
    Specialism: Paediatric. Number of beds: (143 (9 day
    care))

12

Royal Maternity Hospital Grosvenor Rd, Belfast BT12 6BB;
Tel 028 9024 0503
    Specialism: Maternity. Number of beds: (103)
Royal Victoria Hospital Grosvenor Rd, Belfast BT12 6BA;
Tel 028 9024 0503
    Number of beds: (953)

South and East Belfast Health and Social Services Trust

Trust Headquarters, Knockbracken Healthcare Pk, Belfast
    BT8 8BH; URL www.sebt.org;
    E-mail consumer.relations@sebt.n-i.nhs.uk; Tel 028 9056
    5555; Fax 028 9056 5813
Chair B. McLaughlin, CBE
Chief Executive R.S. Ferguson, CQSW
Director (Finance) N.D. Carson, FCCA
Head (Treatment Services) Dr P. Bell
Head (Service Development) Dr G. Rankin
Head (Human Resources) V. Walker
Head (Adult Services) H. Connor, DipSocAdmin, CQSW
Head (Children's Services) E. Nicholl
Head (Operational Support) E. Currie, DipMS, MBIM
Head (Planning) S. O'Brien, BA, DSS, CQSW

HEALTH CENTRES

Cherryvalley Health Centre Kings Sq, Kings Rd, Belfast
BT5 7BP; Tel 028 9079 9321; Fax 028 9040 2069
Dunluce Health Centre Dunluce Ave, Belfast BT9 7AW;
Tel 028 9020 4060; Fax 028 9020 4330
Finaghy Health Centre 13–25 Finaghy Rd South, Belfast
BT10 0BW; Tel 028 9062 8211; Fax 028 9061 2210
Holywood Arches Health Centre Westminster Ave North,
Belfast BT4 1NS; Tel 028 9056 3200; Fax 028 9056 3327
Templemore Avenue Health Centre 98a Templemore Ave,
Belfast BT5 4FW; Tel 028 9045 4321; Fax 028 9045 2640

HEALTH CLINICS

Belvoir Park Clinic 52 Drumart Sq, Belvoir Pk, Belfast
BT8 4DL; Tel 028 9049 1126
Braniel Clinic Glen Rd, Belfast BT5 7DH; Tel 028 9040
1153
Carryduff Clinic Killynure Hse, Church Rd, Belfast
BT8 8DT; Tel 028 9081 4334
Cherryville Clinic 2a Cherryville St, Belfast BT6 8BJ; Tel 028
9045 0887; Fax 028 9045 1161
Cregagh Clinic 331 Cregagh Rd, Belfast BT6 0LG; Tel 028
9079 3918; Fax 028 9070 2874
Dundonald Clinic 16 Church Rd, Dundonald, Belfast
BT16 0LN; Tel 028 9048 2991
Malone Place 31 Malone Pl, Belfast BT12 5FD; Tel 028 9024
2521; Fax 028 9032 9844
Mount Oriel Clinic 53–57 Saintfield Rd, Belfast BT8 4HL;
Tel 028 9070 1845
Templemore Avenue Health Centre 98a Templemore Ave,
Belfast BT5 4FN; Tel 028 9045 4321; Fax 028 9045 2640

HOSPITALS

Albertbridge Road Day Hospital 225 Albertbridge Rd,
Belfast BT5 4PX; Tel 028 9045 6007; Fax 028 9045 2638
    Specialism: Psychiatric.
Knockbracken Mental Health Services Saintfield Rd, Belfast
BT8 8BH; Tel 028 9056 5656; Fax 028 9056 5813
    Specialism: Psychiatric (753)
Shaftesbury Square Hospital 116–120 Great Victoria St,
Belfast BT2 7BG; Tel 028 9032 9808; Fax 028 9031 2208

DENTAL SERVICES

Dental Services Department 31 Malone Pl, Belfast
BT12 5FD; Tel 028 9024 2521

PARA-MEDICAL SERVICES

Occupational Therapy Department Strand Hse, Holywood
Rd, Belfast BT4 1NU; Tel 028 9056 3528; Fax 028 9056 3456
Physiotherapy Department Holywood Arches Health
Centre, Westminster Ave North, Belfast BT4 1NS; Tel 028
9056 3287; Fax 028 9056 3327
Podiatry Department Holywood Arches Health Centre,
Westminster Ave North, Belfast BT4 1NS; Tel 028 9056 3200;
Fax 028 9065 3846
Speech Therapy Department Cherryville Clinic, 2a
Cherryville St, Belfast BT6 8BJ; Tel 028 9045 0887; 028 9045
7025; Fax 028 9045 1161

Sperrin Lakeland HSS Trust

Trust Headquarters, Strathdene Hse, Omagh, County
    Tyrone BT79 0NS; Tel 028 8283 5285; Fax 028 8224 4570
Chief Executive H.S. Mills, BSc, MSc
Director (Human Resources and Operational Services)
    G. McLaughlin, MIPM
Director (Acute Hospital Services) E. Fee, BA, MBA
Tyrone County Hospital, Omagh,
Director (Community Care) D. Bolton, BA, CQSW, DMS
Erne Hospital, Enniskillen,
Medical Director Dr J. Kelly
Director (Finance) Michael MacCrossan
Director (Mental Health and Elderly Services)
    Gabriel Carey
Director (Corporate Affairs) Bridget O'Rawe
Director (Planning, Contracting and Information)
    Vincent Ryan

HEALTH CENTRES AND CLINICS

Carrickmore Health Centre Termon Rd, Carrickmore,
County Tyrone; Tel 028 8076 1242
Including community health and social services.
Castlederg Health Clinic DVHC Grounds, Castlederg,
County Tyrone; Tel 028 8167 1406
Derg Valley Health Centre Castlederg, County Tyrone;
Tel 028 8167 1211
Dromore Health Clinic Dromore, County Tyrone; Tel 028
8289 8137
Enniskillen Health Centre Erne Hospital, Cornagrade Rd,
Enniskillen, County Fermanagh; Tel 028 6632 5638
Including Community Health and Social Services.
Fintona Health Clinic Fintona, County Tyrone; Tel 028 8284
1203
Irvinestown Health Centre Irvinestown, Eniskillen, County
Fermanagh; Tel 028 6862 1212
Including community health and social services.
Lisnaskea Health Centre Drumhaw, Lisnaskea, County
Fermanagh; Tel 028 6772 1566
Omagh Health Centre Mountjoy Rd, Omagh, County
Tyrone; Tel 028 8224 3521
Including health offices and social services office.
Plumbridge Health Clinic Plumbridge; Tel 028 8164 8299
Rathmore Clinic Bellek, Enniskillen, County Fermanagh;
Tel 028 6865 8382

HOSPITALS

Erne Hospital Cornagrade Rd, Enniskillen, County
Fermanagh BT74 6AY; Tel 028 6632 4711
    Specialism: Mainly acute. (283)

Tyrone County Hospital Hospital Rd, Omagh, County Tyrone T79 0AP; Tel 028 8224 5211
Specialism: Acute. (217)

Tyrone and Fermanagh Hospital Omagh, County Tyrone; Tel 028 8224 5211
Specialism: Mental health. (215)

Ulster, Community and Hospitals HSS Trust

Trust Headquarters, Health and Care Centre,
Newtownards, Belfast BT23 4AD; Tel 028 9181 6666;
Fax 028 9151 2131
Chair   S. Grant
Chief Executive   J. McCall
Director (Finance)   P. Cummings
Director (Nursing and Clinical Governance)   S.S. Salmon,
SRN, SCM, HVC, FWTCert, MSc
Director (Medical Services)   Dr R.J. McFarland, BSc, MB,
FRCP, FRCP(Glas)
Director (Business Services0   J.A.N. Semple
Director (Social Work and Quality)   C. Worthington

HOSPITALS

Ards Community Hospital Church St, Newtownards,
County Down BT23 4AS; Tel 028 9181 2661
Number of beds: (301)

Bangor Community Hospital Castle St, Bangor, County
Down BT20 4TA; Tel 028 9145 4184
Number of beds: (88)

Ulster Hospital Dundonald, Belfast BT16 1RH; Tel 028 9048
4511
Number of beds: (687)

HEALTH CENTRES

Health Centre 17 Frederick St, Newtownards, County
Down BT23 4LR; Tel 028 9181 6333; 028 9181 6880 028 9181
7239

Health Centre 1–5 Killaughey Rd, Donaghadee, County
Down BT21 0BL; Tel 028 9188 2176

Health Centre 1 Newtownards Rd, Bangor, County Down
BT20 4BW; Tel 028 9146 9111

Health Centre 5 Newtownards Rd, Comber, Newtownards,
County Down BT23 5AU; Tel 028 9187 2779; 028 9187 8391

ADMINISTRATIVE BUILDING

Newtownards Rd, Bangor, County Down BT23 4LB; Tel 028
9146 8521

SERVICES FOR PEOPLE WITH A SIGHT OR HEARING LOSS

52 Church St, Newtownards, Belfast BT23 4AL; Tel 028 9151
0136; Fax 028 9151 0145; Minicom 028 9151 0137
Programme Manager   Gerry Cunningham

SERVICES FOR PEOPLE WITH A PHYSICAL DISABILITY UNDER 65 YEARS OF AGE

52 Church St, Newtownards, Belfast BT23 4AL; Tel 028 9151
0137; Fax 028 9151 0145; Minicom 028 9151 0137
Programme Manager   Gerry Cunningham

HOSPITAL SOCIAL WORK TEAM

Ulster Hospital, Dundonald, Belfast BT16 1RH
Senior Social Worker   Catherine Reilly; Tel 028 9056 1039

United Hospitals HSS Trust

Trust Headquarters, Bush Hse, Antrim, County Antrim
BT41 2QB; Tel 028 9442 4673; Fax 028 9442 4675
Chief Executive   J. B. Mitchell
Chair   Dr R. H. McGuigan

Health Boards

Eastern Health and Social Services Board

see also chapter 11.
Champion Hse, 12–22 Linenhall St, Belfast BT2 8BS;
URL www.ehssb.n-i.nhs.uk;
E-mail enquiry@ehssb.n-i.nhs.uk; Tel 028 9032 1313;
Fax 028 9055 3681
Chair   David Russell
Chief Executive   Dr P. Kilbane, CBE, MB, FRCP, MSc,
FFPHM
Health Authority.

Northern Health and Social Services Board

see also chapter 11.
County Hall, 182 Galgorm Rd, Ballymena, County Antrim
BT42 1QB; URL www.nhssb.n-i.nhs.uk; Tel 028 2565
3333; (Patient and Client Information Service) 028 2566
2618; (Text Phone) Fax 028 2566 2311
Chair   M. Wood
County Hall, 182 Galgorm Rd, Ballymena, County Antrim
BT42 1QB
Chief Executive   J.S. MacDonnell
Director (Finance)   W. Matthews
Director (Public Health)   Dr J.D. Watson
Director (Nursing and Consumer Services)   E. McNair
Director (Social Services)   M. Wilmont
Director (Pharmaceutical Services)   Dr D.J. Morrison
Director (Dental Services)   A. Millen
Director (Strategic Planning and Commissioning)   E. McClean
Director (Service Performance and Development)   I. Deboys
Director (Primary Care)   D. Boyd

Magherafelt and Cookstown Unit of Management Crown
Bldgs, King St, Magherafelt, County Londonderry; Tel 028
7963 1031
Assistant Director (Social Services)   R.I. McKeown, CSW

HEALTH CENTRES

Bellaghy Health Centre William St, Bellaghy, Magherafelt,
County Londonderry BT45 8HZ; Tel 0164 886215; 0164
886228 0164 886237

Cookstown Health Centre Orritor Rd, Cookstown, County
Tyrone; Tel 0164 87 62995

Maghera Health Centre Church St, Maghera, County
Londonderry; Tel 028 7964 2579

Magherafelt Health Centre Fairhill, Magherafelt, County
Londonderry; Tel 028 7963 2621

Moneymore Health Centre Northland Rd, Moneymore,
Magherafelt, County Londonderry BT45 7Q; Tel 0164 87
48350

HOSPITAL

Mid-Ulster Hospital Hospital Rd, Magherafelt, County
Londonderry; Tel 028 7963 1031
Number of beds: (237)

Southern Health and Social Services Board

see also Chapter 11
Tower Hill, Armagh, County Armagh BT61 9DR; Tel 028
3741 0041; Fax 028 3741 4550
Chair   W.F. Gillespie, OBE, TD, BA, JP, DL

Western Health and Social Services Board

see also Chapter 11
15 Gransha Pk, Clooney Rd, Londonderry, County
Londonderry BT47 6FN; URL www.whssb.org; Tel 028
7186 0086; Fax 028 7186 0311

12

Chair John Bradley
Chief Executive S. Lindsay
Director (Public Health) Dr W.W.M. McConnell, MB, BCh, BAO, MFCM, MRCGP
Director (Finance) P. McLaughlin
Director (Social Care) D. Burke, CQSW, MBA
Clinical Representative (Hospitals) Dr Porteous
Clinical Representative (GPs) Dr E.D.M. Deeney
Chief Nurse M.E.J. Bradley, RMN, RGN, RNT, DipN. BSc(Ea), MSc(ED)
Service Planner T. Haverty, MSc, CSW, DMS, MBASW, MBIM

Health and Social Services Councils

Eastern Board Area

Eastern Health and Social Services Council

1st Fl, McKelvey Hse, 25–27 Wellington Pl, Belfast BT1 6GQ; URL www.ehssc.org; E-mail ecouncil@ehssc.n-i.nhs.uk; Tel 028 9032 1230; (Freephone) 0800 328 5420; Fax 028 9032 1750; Minicom 020 90 321285
Chief Officer J. Graham

Northern Board Area

Northern Health and Social Services Council

8 Broadway Ave, Ballymena, County Antrim BT43 7AA; URL www.nhssc.org; E-mail info@nhssc.n-i.nhs.uk; Tel 028 256 55777; Fax 028 256 55112; Minicom 028 256 55777
Chief Officer N. Graham

Southern Board Area

Southern Health and Social Services Council

Southern HSSC, Quaker Bldgs, High St, Lurgan, County Armagh BT66 8BB; URL www.shsscouncil.net; E-mail reception@shssc.n-i.nhs.uk; Tel 028 3834 9900; Fax 028 3834 9858; Minicom 028 3834 6488
Chief Officer Delia Van Der Lenden

Western Board Area

Western Health and Social Services Council

'Hilltop', Tyrone and Fermanagh Hospital, Omagh, County Tyrone BT79 0NS; E-mail mreilly@hilltop-n-i.nhs.uk; Tel 028 8225 2555; Fax 028 8225 2544
Chief Officer Ms Maggie Reilly; Tel 028 8225 2555; Fax 028 8225 2544; Textphone 028 8224 8389

Agencies

Central Services Agency

25–27 Adelaide St, Belfast BT2 8FH; URL www.csa.n.i.nhs.uk; Tel 028 9032 4431
Chief Executive S.J. Hodkinson, BSc, MSc, FHSM
Director (Finance) P. Gick
Director (FPS) C.M.P. Sheils
Director (Legal Services) A. Maginness
Regional Director (Supplies) T. Molloy
Director (Human Resources) C. MacAllister (Acting)
Director (Nicare) C.M. Sullivan, MSc, PhD, MBCO, MHSM
Ophthalmic Adviser J. Jackson, MBCO, BSc(Hons), PhD
Operational Director (Research and Development) Dr Michael Neely
Head (Counter Fraud Unit) N. Jones

Health Promotion Agency for Northern Ireland

18 Ormeau Ave, Belfast BT2 8HS; URL www.healthpromotionagency.org.uk; Tel 028 9031 1611; Fax 028 9031 1711
Chair Vacancy
Chief Executive Dr B. Gaffney

Nicare (Northern Ireland Centre for Health Care Cooperation and Development)

12–22 Linenhall St, Belfast BT2 8BS; E-mail hqmail@nicare.n-i.nhs.uk; Tel 028 9023 3788; Fax 028 9023 5212
Assistant Director Charlie Carson
Assistant Director Fiona Moore

The Northern Ireland Blood Transfusion Service Agency

Belfast City Hospital Complex, Lisburn Rd, Belfast BT9 7TS; URL www.nibts.org; Tel 028 9032 1414; Fax 028 9043 9017
Chair Mr S. Costello
Chief Executive and Medical Director Dr M. McClelland; E-mail chiefexec@nibts.n-nhs.uk

The Northern Ireland Medical Physics Agency

Musgrave and Clark Hse, Royal Hospital Site, Grosvenor Rd, Belfast BT12 6BA; URL www.ni-nhs.uk/medicalphysics; Tel 028 9063 4430; Fax 028 9031 3040
Chair Prof G. Walmsley
Chief Executive Prof P. Smith; E-mail peter.smith@mpa.n-i.nhs.uk

Part Two

Voluntary, Private and Non-statutory Services

Children, Young People and Families

- **Children's Rights and Adoption Agencies**
  National Organisations
  Children's Rights Organisations
  Approved Adoption Societies
- **Voluntary Organisations, Residential and Day Care Services for Children**
  Residential and Community Projects for Children
- **Other Children's Organisations**
- **Young People**
- **Family Welfare**
- **Organisations for One-Parent Families**
- **Maternity and Motherhood**

Key

(110)	Number of pupils
Mixed	Takes boys and girls
Boys	Takes boys only
Girls	Takes girls only
11–18	Age range of pupils

Abbreviations

ADHD	Attention Deficit Hyperactivity Disorder
ASD	Autism Spectrum Disorder
EBD	Emotional Behavioural Difficulties
LD	Learning Difficulties
LI	Language Impairment
MH	Mentally Handicapped
MLD	Moderate Learning Difficulties
PH	Physically Handicapped
PHAB	Physically Handicapped and Able-Bodied
PMLD	Profound and Multiple Learning Difficulties
PS	Partially Sighted
PtHg	Partially Hearing
SCU	Special Care Unit
SEBD	Severe Emotional Behaviour Difficulties
SEN	Special Educational Needs
SLD	Severe Learning Difficulties
SLDD	Students with Learning Difficulties and Disabilities
SMH	Severely Mentally Handicapped

Children, Young People and Families

CHILDREN'S RIGHTS AND ADOPTION AGENCIES

National Organisations

National Society for the Prevention of Cruelty to Children

Weston Hse, 42 Curtain Rd, London EC2A 3NH;
URL www.nspcc.org.uk; E-mail infounit@nspcc.org.uk;
Tel 020 7825 2500; Fax 020 7825 2525
Director   Mary Marsh
Director (Appeals)   Giles Pegram
Director (Development)   David Prescott
Director (Finance)   John Graham
Director (Personnel)   Liz Booth
Director (Public Policy)   Philip Noyes
Director (Services for Children and Young People)
Jennifer Bernard
Director (Communications)   J. Grounds
The NSPCC is a specialist child protection agency working
in England, Wales and Northern Ireland. Through its
network of over 160 centres, teams and projects and the
National Child Protection Helpline, the NSPCC provides a
wide range of services to children at risk of significant
harm and their families. The pattern of service provided
varies according to local needs. Nationally, the NSPCC acts
as a strong voice for children by seeking to influence law
and social policy. The Society campaigns to change
attitudes towards children and their care.
NSPCC Child Protection Helpline; Tel 0808 800 500,
Textphone 0800 056 0566. Free 24 hour Helpline for advice,
counselling and child protection referrals.

NSPCC PROJECTS

Listed below are contact details for the 180 NSPCC teams
and projects throughout England, Wales and Northern
Ireland.

Divisional Office – North

2nd Fl, Arndale Hse, Crossgates, Leeds, West Yorkshire
LS15 8EU; Tel 0113 229 2200; Fax 0113 229 2240
Divisional Director   Gordon Ratcliffe

Acorn

1 Lostock Gdns, Blackpool FY4 3PP; Tel 01253 345001;
Fax 01253 345025
Manager (Children's Services)   Hein Grosskopf

Almond Tree Project

Bldg 16 AWS Complex, Smuts Rd, Catterick Garrison,
North Yorkshire DL9 3AX; Tel 01748 835704; Fax 01748
836928
Manager (Children's Services)   Janet Thompson

Barnsley Child Protection Team

9 Churchfield Crt, Barnsley, South Yorkshire S70 2JT;
Tel 01226 779494; Fax 01226 771997
Manager (Children's Services)   Margaret Mead
Manager (Children's Services)   Tracey Race

Barnsley Schools Service Team

51 High St, Grimethorpe, Barnsley, South Yorkshire
S72 7BB; Tel 01226 707900; Fax 01226 707919
Manager (Children's Services)   Stephanie Evans

Barrow SAFE Project

The Arch, Walney Rd, Barrow-in-Furness, Cumbria
LA14 5UT; Tel 01229 838746; Fax 01229 814270
Manager (Children's Services)   Wendy Monnelly

Bradford – Hamsaath

117 Little Horton La, Little Hornton, Bradford, West
Yorkshire BD5 0HT; Tel 01274 769800; Fax 01274
769840
Manager (Children's Services)   Sharda Parthasarathi

Calderdale Child Protection Team

St. John's Hse, 2 St. John's La, Halifax, West Yorkshire
HX1 2JD; Tel 01422 339500; Fax 01422 339540
Manager (Children's Services)   Ann Savage
Manager (Children's Services)   Terry Fawthrop

Catalyst Project

7 Chatsworth Sq, Carlisle, Cumbria CA1 1HB; Tel 01228
521829; Fax 01228 574781
Manager (Children's Services)   Liz Benson

Cheshire Child Protection Team

2–8 Henry Street Mews, Henry St, Warrington, Cheshire
WA1 1NU; Tel 01925 418430; Fax 01925 230841
Manager (Children's Services)   Helen Lewandowska
Manager (Children's Services)   Ruth Haig-Ferguson

Cumbria Multi-agency

19–24 Grirgate, Penrith, Cumbria CA11 7NX; Tel 01768
242242
Manager (Children's Services)   Wade Tidbury

Doncaster SSD/NSPCC Post Abuse Therapeutic Team

Rosemead, May Ave, Doncaster, South Yorkshire DN4 9AE;
Tel 01302 856868; Fax 01302 856628
Manager (Children's Services)   Christine E. Furness

Grimsby Project (QPPS)

25 Chantry La, Grimsby, North East Lincolnshire
DN31 2LP; Tel 01472 320450; Fax 01472 320459
Manager (Children's Services)   Susan Proudlove

Hilton House Team

Hilton Hse, 16 Hilton Sq, Pendlebury, Greater Manchester
M27 4DB; Tel 0161 794 4252; Fax 0161 727 0261
Manager (Children's Services)   Thelma Kennedy

Hull Family Centre

Barnstaple Rd, Bransholme, Kingston upon Hull HU7 4HQ;
Tel 01482 837822; Fax 01482 837823
Manager (Children's Services)   Shirley-Anne Rooney

Kaleidoscope

172 Newcastle Rd, Sunderland, Tyne and Wear SR5 1NW;
Tel 0191 516 4600; Fax 0191 516 4640
Manager (Children's Services)   Paula Telford

Lancashire East Child Protection Team

40–42 Wellington St, St. Johns, Blackburn BB1 8AF;
Tel 01254 607070; Fax 01254 605555
Manager (Children's Services)   Tracy Buckley

Leeds Quality Parenting and Family Support

232 Stanningley Rd, Bramley, Leeds, West Yorkshire
LS13 3BA; Tel 0113 217 2200; Fax 0113 217 2240
Manager (Children's Services)   Paul Sharkey

Liverpool SDU

125–127 High St, Wavertree, Liverpool, Merseyside L15 8JS;
Tel 0151 737 1999; Fax 0151 737 2120
Manager (Children's Services)   Pauline Doherty

Manchester City Child Protection Team

5 Wynnstay Gr, Fallowfield, Manchester M14 6XG; Tel 0161
282 3366; Fax 0161 282 0344
Manager (Children's Services)   John Skinner

Meadow House Project

121 Oxford St, Preston, Lancashire PR1 3QY; Tel 01772
200765; Fax 01772 200768
Manager (Children's Services)   Paul Clark

Merseyside Child Protection Team

125–127 High St, Wavertree, Liverpool, Merseyside L15 8JS;
Tel 0151 737 1999; Fax 0151 737 2120
Manager (Children's Services)   Pauline Doherty

Newcastle (Brighton Grove) Therapeutic Team

17 Brighton Gr, Fenham, Newcastle upon Tyne, Tyne
and Wear NE4 5NS; Tel 0191 226 0155; Fax 0191 272
1431
Manager (Children's Services)   Linda Dodds

North West Regional Education Advisor

North West Resource Centre, Horton Hse, SouthLink Bus
Pk, Hamilton St, Oldham, Greater Manchester OL4 1DE;
Tel 0161 628 4444; Fax 0161 628 2560
Manager (Children's Services)   Alison O'Brien

Northumberland Schools Service

c/o Newbiggin Middle School, Cleveland Ave, Newbiggin-
by-the-Sea, Northumberland NE64 6RS; Tel 01670
543651; Fax 01670 543661
Manager (Children's Services)   Patricia Buckley

Northern Regional Education Advisor

Arndale Hse, Station Rd, Leeds, West Yorkshire LS15 8EU;
Tel 0113 229 2200; Fax 0113 229 2240
Manager (Children's Services)   John Stead

Nurturing Project

Havelock Bldgs, Hylton Rd, Sunderland, Tyne and Wear
SR4 8AH; Tel 0191 553 2097; Fax 0191 553 2098
Manager (Children's Services)   Virginia Robinson

Oldham Specialist Assessment Unit

4 Moorhey St, off Lees Rd, Oldham, Greater Manchester
OL4 1JQ; Tel 0161 628 2602; Fax 0161 628 4040
Manager (Children's Services)   Margaret Seed

Partners and Parenting – Newcastle

17 Brighton Gr, Fenham, Newcastle upon Tyne, Tyne and
Wear NE4 5NS; Tel 0191 226 0155; Fax 0191 272 1431
Manager (Children's Services)   Deborah Burgess

Practice Learning Co-ordinator

35 George St, Sheffield, South Yorkshire S1 2PF; Tel 0114
228 9206; Fax 0114 228 9229
Manager (Children's Services)   Mary Sockett

Rainbow House Project

Rainbow Hse, 36–38 Smith Gr, Crewe, Cheshire CW1 3NB;
Tel 01270 588399; Fax 01270 588399
Manager (Children's Services)   Helen Aspden

Redcar and Cleveland Children's Fund

Hinton Hse, 31 Park Road South, Middlesbrough TS5 6LE;
Tel 01642 856400; Fax 01642 856440
Programme Manager   Mark Gray

Regional Employment Advisor

2nd Fl, Arndale Hse, Crossgates, Leeds, West Yorkshire
LS15 8EU; Tel 0113 229 9300; Fax 0113 229 2240
Manager (Children's Services)   Fiona Mulvey

Rotherham Child Protection Team

Thornbank Hse, 38 Moorgate Rd, Rotherham, South
Yorkshire S60 2AG; Tel 01709 789700; Fax 01709 789740
Manager (Children's Services)   Linda Cawley

St. Helens Early Years

St. Helens Parish Church, Church Sq, St. Helens,
Merseyside WA10 1AF; Tel 01744 614682; Fax 01744
697410
Manager (Children's Services)   Carolyn Welsh

Scarborough Family Support Services

Westway Hse, Westway, Eastfield, Scarborough, North
    Yorkshire YO11 3EE; Tel 01723 580700; Fax 01723
    580707
Manager (Children's Services)   Linda Langthorne

Lancashire Schools Team

125 Oxford St, Preston, Lancashire PR1 3QY; Tel 01772
    821635; Fax 01772 825822
Manager (Children's Services)   D. Lang
Manager (Children's Services)   Jill France

Selby Family Support Project

Postengate Surgery, Portholme Rd, Selby, North Yorkshire
    YO8 4QH; Tel 01757 290953; Fax 01757 290953
Manager (Children's Services)   Tim Richardson

Services for Families in Tees Valley

Hinton Hse, 31 Park Road South, Middlesbrough TS5 6LE;
    Tel 01642 856400; Fax 01642 856440
Manager (Children's Services)   Patti Summerfield

Services in South Cumbria

The Arch, Walney Rd, Barrow-in-Furness, Cumbria
    LA14 5UT; Tel 01229 813461; Fax 01229 814329
Manager (Children's Services)   Patricia Palmer

Services in York and North Yorkshire

65 Osbaldwick La, York YO10 3AY; Tel 01904 430455;
    Fax 01904 430818
Manager (Domestic Violence Team)   Cerydwen Evans
Manager (Therapeutic Service)   Debra Radford

Sheffield Support Services for Looked After Children

Centenary Hse, Heritage Pk, 55 Albert Terrace Rd,
    Sheffield, South Yorkshire S6 3BR; Tel 0114 226 1931;
    Fax 0114 226 1936

Sheffield Young People's Centre

35 George St, Sheffield, South Yorkshire S1 2PF; Tel 0114
    228 9200; Fax 0114 228 9229
Manager (Children's Services)   Permala Sehmar

Shield Project

Brian Jackson Hse, 2 North Pde, Huddersfield, West
    Yorkshire HD1 5JP; Tel 01484 411000; Fax 01484 411007
Manager (Children's Services)   Valerie Charles

South Cumbria Child Protection Team

Dallington, Abbey Rd, Barrow-in-Furness, Cumbria
    LA13 9AG; Tel 01229 813461; Fax 01229 813462
Manager (Children's Services)   Patricia Palmer

Stockton DOVES

Corner Hse, 98 Dovecote St, Stockton on Tees, Stockton-
    on-Tees TS18 1HA; Tel 01642 415365; Fax 01642
    415371
Manager (Children's Services)   Marilyn Watson-Dotchin

Support Service for Looked After Children

Centenary Hse, Heritage Pk, 55 Albert Terrace Rd,
    Sheffield, South Yorkshire S6 3BR; Tel 0114 226 1931;
    Fax 0114 226 1936
Manager (Children's Services)   Deb Moore

Sure Start Bramley

30–32 Elder Rd, Bramley, Leeds, West Yorkshire LS13 4DL;
    Tel 0113 255 7755; Fax 0113 257 1850
Manager (Children's Services)   Kathy Shaw

Sure Start Sunderland

Gilpin Hse, Blind La, Houghton le Spring, Tyne and Wear
    DH4 5HX; Tel 0191 553 4010; Fax 0191 553 4013
Manager (Children's Service)   Laura McStea

Sure Start T and D

Loftus Youth and Community Centre, Duncan Pl, Loftus,
    Saltburn-by-Sea, Middlesbrough TS13 4PR; Tel 01287
    644200
Manager (Children's Services)   Julie Conner

Sure Start Whitehaven

NSPCC West Cumbria, Wedgewood Centre, 14 Hollins Cl,
    Whitehaven, Cumbria CA28 8EX; Tel 01946 595300;
    Fax 01946 595316
Manager (Children's Services)   Sue Toomey

Tamarind House

245 Seymour Gr, Old Trafford, Manchester M16 0DS;
    Tel 0161 860 5556; Fax 0161 860 5557
Manager (Children's Services)   John Skinner

There4me

Westminster Hse, 2–8 Henry Street Mews, Henry St,
    Warrington WA1 1NU; Tel 01925 428778
Manager (Children's Services)   John Dunmore

Warrington Young People's Centre

Tim Parry / Johnathan Ball Young People's Centre, Peace Dr,
    Warrington WA5 1HQ; Tel 01925 581200; Fax 01925 581222
Manager (Children's Services)   Helen Lewandowska
Manager (Children's Services)   Ruth Haig-Ferguson

West Cumbria Therapeutic Team

The Wedgewood Centre, 14 Hollins Cl, Whitehaven,
    Cumbria CA28 8EX; Tel 01946 595300; Fax 01946 595316
Care Service Manager   Sue Toomey

Divisional Office – Midlands and West

4th Fl, Alexander Warehouse, The Docks, Gloucester,
    Gloucestershire GL1 2LG; Tel 01452 300616; Fax 01452
    424721
Divisional Manager   Peter Liver

Ashdown Family Centre

Station Rd, Tidworth, Wiltshire SP9 7NR; Tel 01980 846164;
    Fax 01980 847020
Manager (Children's Services)   Gill Cockerton

Bal Raksha Project

65 Melton Rd, Leicester LE4 6PN; Tel 0116 261 0860;
    Fax 0116 268 1773
Manager (Children's Services)   Rama Ramakrishnan

Black Country Inappropriate Sexual Behaviour Project

Fl 3, Riddins Mound Training Centre, Applewood Gr,
    Cradley Heath, West Midlands B64 6EW; Tel 01384
    569232; Fax 01384 566557
Manager (Children's Services)   John Taylor

Bristol and Somerset Schools Team

83–85 North St, Bedminster, Bristol BS3 1ES; Tel 0117 966
4283; Fax 0117 953 5396
Manager (Children's Services)   Anne Coyle

Calne Family Centre

Broken Cross, Calne, Wiltshire SN11 8BN; Tel 01249 813270;
Fax 01249 816361
Manager (Children's Services)   Charlotte Brand

Children's Advice and Representation Service – Shropshire

Suite 2, Cannon Court East, Abbey Lawn, Shrewsbury,
Shropshire SY2 5DE; Tel 01743 281981; Fax 01743 281989
Manager (Children's Services)   Caroline Kibble

Children's Advice and Representation Service – Staffordshire

4 Chapel St, Stafford, Staffordshire ST16 2BX; Tel 01785
228888; Fax 01785 283779
Manager (Children's Services)   Caroline Kibble

Children's Advice and Representation Service – Worcester

3rd Fl, 9 Broad St, Worcester, Worcestershire WR1 3LN;
Tel 01905 617975; Fax 01905 617976
Manager (Children's Services)   C. Kibble

Coventry Surukhia/New Links

Boole Hse, 76 Whitefriars St, Coventry, West Midlands
CV1 2DS; Tel 024 7652 7004; Fax 024 7652 1301
Manager (Children and Families Service)   Surinder Kasli
Care Service Manager (Coventry SHB)   Mark Dalton; Tel 024
7622 2456; Fax 024 7655 1301

Derbyshire Child Protection Team

2–4 Albert Rd, Ripley, Derby DE5 3FZ; Tel 01773 744877;
Fax 01773 570896
Manager (Children's Services)   Jane Williams

Devon and Cornwall Young Witness Support Project

1st Fl, Norwich Union Hse, 12 Bedford St, Exeter, Devon
EX1 1LG; Tel 01392 215345; 01392 410748
Manager (Children's Services)   Sarah Allum

Devon Child Protection Team

First Fl, 52–52a Mutley Plain, Plymouth PL4 6LE; Tel 01752
235120; Fax 01752 235125
Manager (Children's Services)   Gary Gunby

Dove Project

Fl 2, Friary Works, 119 Friar Gate, Derby, Derbyshire
DE1 1EX; Tel 01332 374560; Fax 01322 374566
Manager (Children's Services)   David Matthews

Education Advisor

Wellington Hse, Queen St, Taunton, Somerset TA1 3UF;
Tel 01823 346350; Fax 01823 346366
Education Advisor   Ann Raymond

Education Advisor

1 Crammer St, Nottingham NG3 4GH; Tel 0115 960 5481
Manager (Children's Services)   Claire Trott

East Dorset Child Protection Centre

Spea Hse, Sandford La, Wareham, Dorset BH20 4DY;
Tel 01929 555990; Fax 01929 555999
Manager (Children's Services)   Andrew Conroy

Guernsey Child Protection Centre

16 Fountain St, St. Peter Port, Guernsey GY1 1BX; Tel 01481
723224; Fax 01481 715026
Manager (Children's Services)   Mick Dunbar

Hayle Family Support Unit

58 Queensway, Hayle, Cornwall TR27 4NL; Tel 01736
755828; Fax 01736 752014
Manager (Children's Services)   Peter Barr

Hereford and Worcester Sexually Harmful Behaviour Service

3rd Fl, 9 Broad St, Worcester, Worcestershire WR1 3LN;
Tel 01905 617975; Fax 01905 617976
Manager (Children's Services)   Tony Quinnell

Jersey Pathways Partnership

Le Squez Primary School, School Rd, Le Squez Est, St.
Clement, Jersey; Tel 01534 738143; Fax 01534 738144
Manager (Early Years)   Nola Hopkins

Lincolnshire Children and Families Service

111 Nettleham Rd, off Longdales Rd, Lincoln, Lincolnshire
LN2 1RU; Tel 01522 545225; Fax 01522 540012
Manager (Children's Services)   Vacancy

Midlands Specialist Investigation Service

3rd Fl, Waterlinks Hse, Richard St, Aston, Birmingham,
West Midlands B7 4AA; Tel 0121 333 1000; Fax 0121 333
1001
Manager (Children's Services)   Sarah Fane

North Staffordshire Therapeutic Team

Carole Hse, 17 King St, Newcastle-under-Lyme,
Staffordshire ST5 1JF; Tel 01782 799200; Fax 01782
719666
Manager (Children's Services)   Cathy Small

North Swindon Family Centre

Atworth Cl, Penhill, Swindon SN2 5NP; Tel 01793 705810;
Fax 01793 706589
Manager (Children's Services)   Garry Holmes

Northampton Child and Parent Centre

48 Waterpump Crt, Thorplands, Northampton,
Northamptonshire NN3 8UR; Tel 01604 493336;
Fax 01604 494890
Manager (Children's Services)   El Dora Barnett

Northamptonshire Orchard House Project

Orchard Hse, Gold St, Wellingborough,
Northamptonshire NN8 4EQ; Tel 01933 223920;
Fax 01933 442503
Manager (Children's Services)   Michelle Cannell

Nottinghamshire YPC and Schools Team

1 Cranmer St, Nottingham NG3 4GH; Tel 0115 960 5481;
Fax 0115 969 2998
Manager (Children's Services)   Judy Holloway-Vine

Schools Team – Midlands

Tara House Schools Counselling, 102 Tettenhall Rd, Wolverhampton, West Midlands WV6 0BW; Tel 01902 747722; Fax 01902 747767
Manager (Children's Services) Jim Quinn

Shropshire SHB Service

Suite 2, Cannon Court East, Abbey Lawn, Shrewsbury, Shropshire SY2 5DE; Tel 01743 281980; Fax 01743 281989
Manager (Children's Services) Colin Watt

Somerset Child Protection Centre

Firtzwarren Hse, Queen St, East Reach, Taunton, Somerset TA1 3UG; Tel 01823 346300; Fax 01823 346305
Manager (Children's Services) Chris Curran

South Birmingham Team

446–448 Rednal Rd, West Heath, Birmingham, West Midlands B38 8HX; Tel 0121 477 2299; Fax 0121 477 5717
Manager (Children's Services) Diana Robertson

Staffordshire SHB Service

2nd Fl, The Whitehouse, Chapel St, Uttoxeter, Staffordshire ST16 2BX; Tel 01785 270920; Fax 01785 270929
Manager (Children's Services) F. Richards

Sure Start Beaumont Leys and Stocking Farm

Home Farm Neighbourhood Centre, Home Farm Cl, Beaumont Leys, Leicester LE4 0SU; Tel 0116 235 5213; Fax 0116 236 8411
Manager (Children's Services) Ann Marshall

Sure Start Hayle and St. Ives

42a Penpol Terr, Hayle, Cornwall TR27 4BQ; Tel 01736 756267; Fax 01736 759397
Project Manager Caroline Willis

Sure Start Highfields

28 Saxby St, Leicester LE2 0NE; Tel 0116 254 8270; Fax 0116 254 8292
Project Manager Sumerjit Ram

Swindon Centre

35 Victoria Rd, Swindon SN1 3AS; Tel 01793 431501; Fax 01743 431457
Manager (Children's Services) J. Chipping

Time Out Young People's Centre

38 Walnut Cl, Birmingham, West Midlands B37 7PU; Tel 0121 770 3000; Fax 0121 329 0701
Manager (Children's Services) Rosie Ingham

West Dorset Child Protection Centre

13 Carlton Rd North, Weymouth, Dorset DT4 7PY; Tel 01305 760722; Fax 01305 761720
Manager (Children's Services) Karen Huckle

Divisional Office – South and East

3rd Fl, Arnold Hse, 36–41 Holywell La, London EC2A 3EL; Tel 020 7596 3700; Fax 020 7596 3737
Divisional Manager Safron Rose

After Sexual Abuse Project (ASAP), West Ewell

Swan Hse, 24 Bridge St, Leatherhead, Surrey KT22 8BX; Tel 01372 375372; Fax 01372 387080

Bedfordshire/Luton Children's Services Team

110–112 Leagrave Rd, Luton LU4 8HX; Tel 01582 424888; Fax 01582 439201
Manager (Children's Services) Steve Lock

Bedfordshire/Luton Inter-agency Training Project

110–112 Leagrave Rd, Luton LU4 8HX; Tel 01582 450866

Berkshire Project

320 Stoke Poges La, Slough SL1 3LN; Tel 01753 497800; Fax 01753 497801
Manager (Children's Services) Alison Strugnell

BFree

38 Wager St, London E3 4JE; Tel 020 8983 3555; Fax 020 8983 4505
Manager (Children's Services) Nasima Patel

Buckinghamshire Children's Rights and Advocacy Service

The Coach Hse, 39 Walton Rd, Aylesbury, Buckinghamshire HP21 7SR; Tel 01296 432540; Fax 01296 436147
Project Co-ordinator Charlie Reston

Buckinghamshire Inter-agency Training

66–70 High St, Two Mile Ash, Milton Keynes, Buckinghamshire MK8 8HD; Tel 01908 562244; Fax 01908 568478
Training Officer Geoff Tookey

Child Community Safety (Safe Kids)

76–82 Dock Rd, Tilbury, Essex RM18 7BX; Tel 01375 855210; Fax 01375 855229
Manager (Children's Services) Sarah Wright

Colchester Young Adults Project

66 The High St, Colchester, Essex CO1 1DN; Tel 01206 768333; Fax 01206 561679
Manager (Children's Services) Keith Fellowes

Croydon Therapeutic Service

28 Addiscombe Gr, Croydon, Surrey CR0 5LP; Tel 020 8681 3418; Fax 020 8667 9071
Manager (Children's Services) Jude Toasland
Practice Learning Co-ordinator Judith Niecheial

Education Advisor

5g Mill Crt, Spindle Way, Crawley, West Sussex RH10 1TT; Tel 01293 651842; Fax 01293 651843
Project Leader Julie Mortimer

Essex Young Abusers Project

66 The High St, Colchester, Essex CO1 1DN; Tel 01206 207626; Fax 01733 207645
Manager (Children's Services) Keith Fellowes

Essex Young Witness Project

76–82 Dock Rd, Tilbury, Essex RM18 7BX; Tel 01375 855210; Fax 01375 855229
Manager (Children's Services) Vacancy

Family Alcohol Project

88–91 Troutbeck off Robert St, London NW1 4EJ; Tel 020 7383 3817; Fax 020 7383 4989
Manager (Children's Services) Ann Waller

Grove House Family Centre

Bagleys La, London SW6 2QB; Tel 020 7731 1987; Fax 020 7731 1700
Manager (Children's Services)   Jackie Benjamin

Guardian Ad Litem Project

c/o Croydon CPT, 28 Addiscombe Gr, Croydon, Surrey CR0 5LP
Manager (Children's Services)   Jude Toasland

Guernsey Project

16 Fountain St, St. Peter Port, Guernsey; Tel 01481 723224; Fax 01481 715026
Manager (Children's Services)   Mick Dunbar

Hackney Education Development Team

The Edith Cavell Bldg, Room 42, Enfield Rd, London N1 5BA; Tel 020 8356 7637; Fax 020 8356 7586
Manager (Children's Services)   Brigid Montgomery

Hastings and Rother Schools and Young People's Services

2 Sedlescombe Road South, St. Leonards-on-Sea, East Sussex TN38 0TA; Tel 01424 428833; Fax 01424 718959
Manager (Children's Services)   Ron Fellows

Hear2Help Children and Young People's Services

The Corn Exchange, 22 Church St, Peterborough PE1 1XF; Tel 01733 207620; Fax 01733 207645
Manager (Children's Services)   Lee Mitchell

Hertfordshire Children Services Team

Treetops, 37 Alexandra Rd, Hemel Hempstead, Hertfordshire HP2 5BP; Tel 01442 416500; Fax 01442 234282
Manager (Children's Services)   Paul Ringer

Hertfordshire Project 19

c/o 110–112 Leagreaver Rd, Luton LU4 8HX; Tel 01582 424888; Fax 01582 439201
Manager (Children's Services)   Steve Lock

Home Counties Regional Education Advisor

Broadfield Hse, Brighton Rd, Crawley, West Sussex RH11 9RZ; Tel 01293 449210; Fax 01293 449211
Manager (Children's Services)   J. Mortimer

Home Counties School Counselling Services

Waterside Hse, Woodley Headland, Peartree Bridge, Milton Keynes MK6 3BX; Tel 01908 395793; Fax 01908 395767
Manager (Children's Services)   A. Bartoli

Islington Children's Rights

c/o East London Children, 38 Wager St, London E3 4JE; Tel 020 8983 3555; Fax 020 8983 4505
Manager (Children's Services)   Viv Parker

Ivybridge Family Support Project

Isleworth Centre, 146 Twickenham Rd, Isleworth, Greater London TW7 5DS; Tel 020 8847 0936; Fax 020 8847 0963
Project Manager   Joma Longmore

Jigsaw Project

33 Lampton Rd, Hounslow, Greater London TW3 1JG; Tel 020 8814 1990; Fax 020 8814 0782
Manager (Children's Services)   Doreen Robinson

Maya Angelou Centre

Keston Rd, Tottenham, London N17 6PW; Tel 020 8808 7882; Fax 020 8808 7624
Manager (Children's Services)   Timur Djavit

Norfolk Child Protection Team

246 High St, Gorleston, Great Yarmouth, Norfolk NR31 6RT; Tel 01493 652818; Fax 01493 652427
Manager (Children's Services)   Paul Hitchens

Kent and Medway Family Support and PALS Team

Pear Tree Hse, 68 West St, Gillingham, Kent ME7 1EF; Tel 01634 308200; Fax 01634 300586
Manager (Children's Services)   Stephen Dabrowski

Kent and Medway Treatment Team

Pear Tree Hse, 68 West St, Gillingham, Kent ME7 1EF; Tel 01634 308200; Fax 020 8814 0782
Manager (Children's Services)   Tricia McDade

London Schools Team

c/o Maya Angelou Family Centre, Keston Rd, Tottenham, London N17 6PW; Tel 020 8801 7211; Fax 020 8808 6120
Manager (Children's Services)   Emmanuella Jones

Offender Management Project – London

10 Rathbone Pl, London W1P 1DE; Tel 020 7631 0535
Manager (Children's Services)   Stephen Landy

Milton Keynes Schools Service

Waterside Hse, Peartree Bridge, Woodley Headland, Milton Keynes MK6 3BX; Tel 01908 395793; Fax 01908 395767
Manager (Children's Services)   Bijal Ruparelia

Norfolk – Kids without Fear Project

Arthur Brett Hse, Hellesdon Park Rd, Drayton High Rd, Norwich, Norfolk NR6 5DR; Tel 01603 256090; Fax 01493 652427
Manager (Children's Services)   Vacancy

Oxfordshire Multi-agency Training Project

Yarnton Hse, Rutten La, Yarnton, Oxfordshire OX5 1LP; Tel 01865 841030; Fax 01865 841666

Parkside Assessment and Parental Mental Health Projects

63–65 Lancaster Rd, London W11 1QG; Tel 020 7243 4311; Fax 020 7243 4383
Manager (Children's Services)   Lindsey Calpin

Peterborough Children's and Young People's Service

The Corn Exchange, 22 Church St, Peterborough PE1 1XF; Tel 01733 207620; Fax 01733 207645
Manager (Children's Services)   Sue Minto

Play and Learn Scheme Gillingham

Pear Tree Hse, 68 West St, Gillingham, Kent ME7 1EF;
Tel 01634 300028; Fax 01634 300586
Local Co-ordinator   Elizabeth Jones

Play and Learn Scheme Ramsgate

Ramsgate School, Stirling Way, Ramsgate, Kent CT12 6NB;
Tel 01843 588338; Fax 01843 591303
Local Co-ordinator   Sandra Jones

RESPECT – Croydon Children's Rights Service

Ground Fl, Grosvenor Hse, 160 Gillett Rd, Thornton Heath,
Croydon, Surrey CR7 8SN; Tel 020 8684 6396; Fax 020
8684 2491
Manager (Children's Services)   Viv Parker

South Hampshire Child Protection Centre

The Venture Centre, Venture Tower, Fratton Rd,
Portsmouth PO1 5DL; Tel 023 9286 1675; Fax 023 9281
1239
Manager (Children's Services)   Margaret Ruane

Southampton Child Protection Centre

21 The Avenue, Southampton SO17 1XL; Tel 023 8024 8180;
Fax 023 8024 8188
Manager (Children's Services)   Chris Peel

Southend Safe Communities

Friendship Hse, 484 Southchurch Rd, Southend-on-Sea,
Southend SS1 2QA; Tel 01702 464718; Fax 01702
465744
Manager (Children's Services)   Keith Fellowes

St. Nicholas Centre

66 London Rd, St. Leonards, East Sussex TN37 6AS;
Tel 01424 202796; Fax 01424 202798
Manager (Children's Services)   S. Woudstra

Street Matters: For Young Women

c/o East London Children and Families Centre, 38 Wager
St, Bow, London E3 4JE; Tel 020 8983 3555; Fax 020 8983
4505
Manager (Children's Services)   Nasima Patel

Suffolk Child Protection Team

34 Berners St, Ipswich, Suffolk IP1 3LU; Tel 01473 212576;
Fax 01473 215488
Manager (Children's Services)   Diana Hagger

Sure Start Thorpe Hamlet

221 St. Leonards Rd, Norwich, Norfolk NR1 6JN; Tel 01603
767940; Fax 01603 619973
Programme Manager   Liz Chapman

Surrey Young Witness Project

Swan Hse, 24 Bridge St, Leatherhead, Surrey KT22 8BX;
Tel 01372 375372; Fax 01372 387080
Manager (Children's Services)   Frances Le Roy

Tilbury Children's Project

76–82 Dock Rd, Tilbury, Essex RM18 7BX; Tel 01375 855210;
Fax 01375 855229
Manager (Children's Services)   Sarah Wright

Tower Hamlets Children's Rights

38 Wager St, Bow, London E3 4JE; Tel 020 8983 3555;
Fax 020 8983 4505
Manager (Children's Services)   Viv Parker
Manager (Children's Services – Walksafe)   Purdeep Gill

Wandsworth Schools Pyramid Project

The Edith Cavell Bldg, Room 42, Enfield Rd, Wandsworth,
London N1 5BA; Tel 020 8808 7882; Fax 020 8808 6120
Manager (Children's Services)   Rosie Green

West Sussex SHB and CST – Domestic Violence

Broadfield Hse, Brighton Rd, Crawley, West Sussex
RH11 9RZ; Tel 01293 449200; Fax 01293 449202
Manager (Children's Services)   Anne Thomas

Young Abusers' Service – London

The Peckwater Centre, 6 Peckwater St, Kentish Town,
London NW5 2TX; Tel 020 7530 6422; Fax 020 7530 6423
Manager (Children's Services)   Colin Hawkes

Young People's Advisory Group/Listening London

3rd Fl, Arnold, 36–41 Hollywell La, London EC2A 3EL;
Tel 020 7596 3700; Fax 020 7596 3737

Young People's Centre Tower Hamlets

c/o 38 Wager St, Bow, London E3 4JE; Tel 020 8983 3555;
Fax 020 8983 4505
Manager (Children's Services)   Monawara Bakht

Divisional Office – Wales

Capital Tower, Greyfriars Rd, Cardiff CF10 3AG; Tel 029
2026 7000; Fax 029 2022 3628
Divisional Director   Greta Thomas

Bangor Young People's Centre

Maes Y Ffynnon (Dwr Cymru), Penrhosgarnedd, Bangor,
Gwynedd LL57 2DW; Tel 01248 370775; Fax 01248
354349
Manager (Children's Services)   Chrissie Rolf

Cardiff/Vale Domestic Violence Prevention Project

44 The Parade, Roath, Cardiff CF24 3AB; Tel 029 2044 5201;
Fax 029 2044 5227
Manager (Children's Services)   Shaun Kelly
Manager (Children's Services)   Mark Rivett

Carmarthen Advocacy

The Lodge, 1 Penlan Rd, Carmarthen, Carmarthenshire
SA31 1DN; Tel 01267 220954; Fax 01267 221936

Children's Advocacy and Rights Service, Gwent

2 Bailey St, Newport, Gwent, NP20 4DJ; Tel 01633 252476;
Fax 01633 235960

Children's Advocacy and Rights Service, Swansea

Suite 19, Longford Business Centre, Princess Way, Swansea
SA1 3LW; Tel 01792 482487

Education Advisor – Wales

Unit 1, Cowbridge Crt, Cowbridge Rd East, Cardiff
CF5 5BS; Tel 029 2056 3421; Fax 029 2057 6965
Education Advisor   Jane Harries

Gurnos Family Centre

55–67 Honeysuckle Cl, Gurnos Est, Merthyr Tydfil
CF47 9DD; Tel 01685 373659; Fax 01685 375242
Manager (Children's Services) Diana Griffiths (Acting)

Llwybrau/Pathways Sex Offenders Assessment and Treatment

Gold Tops Hse, 8a Pentonville, Newport NP20 5HB;
Tel 01633 225900; Fax 01633 225907
Manager (Children's Services) Collette Limbrick

Pontypridd Advocacy and Young People's Advocacy Group

Lanelay Terr, Maes-y-Coed, Pontypridd, CF37 1ER;
Tel 01443 400747; Fax 01443 400061

Schools Team – Wales

11 Grosvenor Rd, Wrexham LL11 1BS; Tel 01978 362383;
Fax 01978 352757
Manager (Children's Services) Brenda Bishop

South Wales ASA Project

2 Bailey St, Newport NP20 4DJ; Tel 01633 235962; Fax 01267
235960
Manager (Children's Services) Andrew Burroughs

Swansea Therapeutic and Young Witness Support

143 Middle Rd, Cwmbwria, Swansea SA5 8HE; Tel 01792
579409; Fax 01792 581525
Manager (Children's Services) Victoria Coombes

Young People's Advocacy Group – North Wales

Young People's Centre, Maes Y Ffynnon, Penrhosgarnedd,
Bangor, Gwynedd LL57 2DW; Tel 01248 370775

Divisional Office – Northern Ireland

Jennymount Bus Pk, North Derby St, Belfast BT15 3HN;
Tel 028 9035 1135; Fax 028 9035 1100
Divisional Director Ian Elliott

Ballykeel Sure Start

Unit 1, The Boardroom, 18 Crebilly Rd, Ballymena,
County Antrim BT42 8DN; Tel 028 2564 3555; Fax 028
2563 7525
Project Manager Amanda McCay

Ballymena Family Support

Units 17 and 18 Tower Centre, Lower Mill St, Ballymena,
County Antrim BT43 6AB; Tel 028 2564 7999; Fax 028
2563 0665
Manager (Children's Services) Caroline Holloway

Belfast Family Support – North and West Team

Frank Gillen Centre, Cullingtree Hse, Cullingtree Rd,
Belfast BT12 4JU; Tel 028 9080 3320
Moyard Centre, Moyard Pk, Belfast BT12 7FR; Tel 028 9080
3312
Old Lodge Centre, 134–136 Crumlin Rd, Belfast BT14 6AP;
Tel 028 9080 3318; Fax 028 9074 4235
Manager (Children's Services) Margaret McAlister

Belfast Family Support – South and East/ Down and Lisburn

15a Tates Ave, Belfast BT12 6ND; Tel 028 9080 3315

Belfast Children's Resource Centre

Shankill Centre, 151–157 Shankill Rd, Belfast BT13 1FD;
Tel 028 9031 5005; Fax 028 9023 1058
Manager (Children's Services) Patricia Owens (Acting)

Child Community Safety

Shankill Centre, 151–157 Shankill Rd, Belfast BT13 1FD;
Tel 028 9031 5005; Fax 028 9023 1058
Manager (Children's Services) Martin Crummey
Office Manager Breige Conlon

Craigavon Children and Young People's Centre

The Children and Young People's Centre, Moyraverty
Centre, Craigavon, County Armagh BT65 5HX; Tel 028
3834 1338; Fax 028 3834 s3143
Manager (Children's Services) Sharon Haugh

Education Advisor

Killard Hse, North Rd, Newtownards, County Down
BT23 7AP; Tel 028 9182 6351; Fax 028 9182 6428
Manager (Children's Services) Vacancy

Employment Policies and Business Practices

15 Sedan Ave, Omagh, County Tyrone BT79 7QA; Tel 028
8224 8929; Fax 028 8224 8930
Divisional Development Worker Moninne Dargan

Foyle Children's Resource Team

20 Pump St, Londonderry, County Londonderry BT48 6JG;
Tel 028 7126 6789; Fax 028 7137 1871
Manager (Children's Services) Theresa O'Doherty

Foyle Family Support

42 Dennet Gdns, Waterside, Londonderry, County
Londonderry BT47 2HF; Tel 028 7131 2187; Fax 028 7132
1979
Manager (Children's Services) Deirdre O'Leary

Insight Project

Eme Hse, Tyrone and Fermanagh Hospital, Omagh,
County Tyrone BT79 0NS; Tel 028 8224 5211; Fax 028
3834 3143
Manager (Children's Services) Kevin Lenehan

Independent Visiting Service

15 Sedan Ave, Omagh, County Tyrone BT79 7AQ; Tel 028
8224 8929; Fax 028 8224 8930
Project Worker Una Doherty

Schools Counselling Team – SEELB/BELB

Killard Hse, North Rd, Newtownards, County Down
BT23 7AP; Tel 028 9182 6351; Fax 028 9182 6428
Manager (Children's Services) Cathy Bell

Schools Counselling Team – WELB

15 Sedan Ave, Omagh, County Tyrone BT79 7AQ; Tel 028
8224 8929; Fax 028 8224 8930
Manager (Children's Services) Bronagh Muldoon

Young Witness Service, Antrim

Antrim Courthouse, 30 Castle Way, Antrim, County Antrim
BT41 4AQ; Tel 028 9448 7533; Fax 028 9448 7590
Care Service Manager Avery Bowser

13

Specialist Investigation Services

44 The Parade, Roath, Cardiff CF24 3AB; Tel 029 2083 8080
Head (Specialist Investigation Services) Colin Turner

Specialist Investigation Service – Gloucester

4th Fl, Alexandra Warehouse, The Docks, Gloucester, Gloucestershire GL1 2LG; Tel 01452 300616; Fax 01452 424721
Care Service Manager Stephen Cameron

Specialist Investigation Service – Leeds

Fl 2, Arndale Hse, Station Rd, Crossgates, Leeds, West Yorkshire LS15 8EU; Tel 0113 229 2200; Fax 0113 229 2240
Care Service Manager Joe Cocker

Specialist Investigation Service – London (North)

36 Gloucester Ave, London NW1 7BB; Tel 020 7428 5660; Fax 020 7428 5669
Care Service Manager Beverley Clarke

Specialist Investigation Service – London (South)

44 High St, Penge, London SE20 7HB; Tel 020 8659 7777; Fax 020 8659 9820
Care Service Manager Maureen Carson

Specialist Investigation Service – Mansfield

2 St. Peter's Crt, Station St, Mansfield, Nottinghamshire NG18 1EF; Tel 01623 666770; Fax 01623 666777
Service Manager Sue Bach

Specialist Investigation Service – Midlands

3rd Fl, Waterlinks Hse, Richard St, Aston, Birmingham, West Midlands B7 4AA; Tel 0121 333 1000; Fax 0121 333 1001
Care Service Manager Vacancy

Specialist Investigation Service – North West

100 Lees Rd, Oldham, Greater Manchester OL4 1JN; Tel 0161 484 3300; Fax 0161 484 3310
Care Service Manager Kate Richardson

Specialist Investigation Service – Wales

44 The Parade, Roath, Cardiff CF24 3AB; Tel 029 2044 5200; Fax 029 2044 5220
Care Service Manager Haydn Minton

After Adoption

Head Office, 12–14 Chapel St, Manchester M3 7NH; URL www.afteradoption.org.uk; E-mail (Action Line) information@afteradoption.org.uk; (Talkadoption) helpline@talkadoption.org.uk; Tel 0161 839 4932; (Action Line) 0800 056 8578; (Talkadoption) 0808 808 1234
North East Office, 2nd Fl, Aiden Hse, Tynegate Bus Centre, Sunderland Rd, Gateshead, Tyne and Wear NE8 3HU; E-mail northeast@afteradoption.org.uk; Tel 0191 230 0088; Fax 0191 261 1440
Merseyside Office, 60 Duke St, Liverpool, Merseyside L1 5AA; E-mail merseyside@afteradoption.org.uk; Tel 0151 707 4322; Fax 0151 707 4323
South Wales Office, 2nd Fl, Dominion Hse North, Dominion Arcade, Queen St, Cardiff CF10 2AR; E-mail southwales@afteradoption.org.uk; Tel 029 2066 6597; Fax 029 2066 5289
London Office, 85 Moorgarte, London EC2M 6SA; E-mail london@afteradoption.org.uk; Tel 020 7628 3443; Fax 020 7638 8648

Preston Office, Fishergate Hse, 16 Walton Pde, Preston, PR1 8QT; E-mail preston@afteradoption.org.uk; Tel 01772 258896; Fax 01772 258896
After Adoption provides information, support and counselling through a wide range of services to adopted people, birth parents and relatives, adopted children and young people, adopted families and extended families, and also to professionals working in adoption.
After Adoption operates two helplines: TALKadoption is a unique helpline for young people who want to talk about anything to do with adoption; ACTIONline offers information, counselling and support by telephone.

Children 1st

(Royal Scottish Society for Prevention of Cruelty to Children)
83 Whitehouse Loon, Edinburgh EH9 1AT; E-mail info@children1st.org.uk; Tel 0131 446 2300; Fax 0131 446 2339
Chief Executive Margaret McKay
Director (Finance and Administration) Jacqueline Smith
Director (Children and Family Services) Vacancy
Director (Fundraising) M. Marwick

Children's Rights Organisations

All Party Parliamentary Group for Children

8 Wakley St, London EC1V 7QE; E-mail alinsey@ncb.org.uk; Tel 020 7843 1907; Fax 020 7843 6443
Chair Baroness Massey of Darwen
Chair Hilton Dawson, MP
Clerk to the Group A. Linsey
National Children's Bureau.
To promote interest in issues affecting children and to press for legislative or other action that will benefit children.

British Association for the Study and Prevention of Child Abuse and Neglect (BASPCAN)

10 Priory St, York YO1 6EZ; URL www.baspcan.org.uk; Tel 01904 613605; Fax 01904 642239
National Office Administrator Judy Sanderson
Aims to underline the need for closer co-operation between the medical, legal and social agencies concerned with the problems of child abuse. Membership is drawn from all the professions concerned with this problem, and BASPCAN tries to help by creating local branches, study groups and conferences, by the publication of a journal and by providing information for the media.

Child Poverty Action Group (CPAG)

94 White Lion St, London N1 9PF; URL www.cpag.org.uk; E-mail staff@cpag.org.uk; Tel 020 7837 7979; Fax 020 7837 6414
Director M. Barnes
Provides welfare rights advice and training to advisors. Promotes action to tackle poverty in families with children. Publishes annual guides to social security benefits, the Welfare Benefits Handbook, Child Support Handbook, Fuel Rights Handbook, the Debt Advice Handbook, the Ethnic Minorities' Benefits Handbook, the Council Tax Handbook and a range of social policy publications. Has a range of membership schemes which include the automatic supply of CPAG publications.

Child Poverty Action Group in Scotland

Unit 09 Ladywell, 94 Duke St, Glasgow G4 0UW; Tel (Advice Line (Tues and Weds 1000–1200)) 0141 552 0552; (General enquiries) 0141 552 3303

ChildLine

45 Folgate St, London E1 6GL; URL www.childline.org.uk;
  Tel ('The Line': A special helpline for children living
  away from home (Mon–Fri 0930–2130)) 0800 884444;
  (Administration) 020 7650 3200; (Helpline (24 hours,
  every day) 0800 1111; Fax (Administration) 020 7239
  1001; Minicom (Mon–Fri 1530–2130; Sat and Sun
  1400–20000) 0800 400222
Chief Executive   Carole Easton
ChildLine is the UK's free helpline for children and young
people. It provides a confidential phone counselling service
for any child with any problem, 24 hours a day, every day.
It comforts, advises and protects.
ChildLine also brings to public attention issues affecting
children's welfare and rights.

Children's Legal Centre

University of Essex, Wivenhoe Pk, Colchester, Essex
  CO4 3SQ; URL www.childrenslegalcentre.com;
  E-mail clc@essex.ac.uk; Tel 01206 872466; (Advice Line
  1000–1230 Mon–Fri) 01206 873820; Fax 01206 874026
An independent national charity concerned with law and
policy affecting children and young people. Gives free and
confidential advice and information by letter and telephone
on all aspects of law and policy affecting children and
young people. Runs a free education legal advocacy unit
for parents and children in dispute with schools and LEAs
which operates predominantly in South East England.
Pursues selected cases, initiates research, runs courses and
conferences, operates consultancy service, and monitors
and responds to law, policies and proposals affecting
children and young people. Publishes Childright magazine
(ten per year) and information sheets, briefings and
handbooks on the law affecting children and young
people.

Family Rights Group

The Print Hse, 18 Ashwin St, London E8 3DL;
  URL www.frg.org.uk; E-mail office@frg.org.uk; Tel 020
  7923 2628; Fax 020 7923 2683
Chief Executive   Robert Tapsfield
Gives advice to individuals and agencies; organises
training courses for social workers and others on the law
and good practice relating to children and families
involved in child protection procedures or involved with
the social services department. Publications and
information leaflet available on request; Telephone advice
service available every weekday 1330–1530 on Freephone
0800 731 1696.

Kidscape

2 Grosvenor Gdns, London SW1W 0DH;
  URL www.kidscape.org.uk;
  E-mail contact@kidscape.org.uk; Tel 020 7730 3300;
  Fax 020 7730 7081
A registered charity committed to keeping children safe
from bullying, sexual abuse and harm.
It offers tailor-made on-site training to meet specific
development needs. Courses include child protection,
bullying and aggression, stress management for staff and
counselling skills. Kidscape works closely with parents,
police, social services and teachers.
Offers a telephone helpline for parents of children being
bullied.

The Law Society's Children Panel

The Panel Administrator, Legal Education and Training,
  The Law Society, Ipsley Crt, Redditch, Worcestershire
  B98 0TD; URL www.panels.lawsociety.org.uk;
  E-mail panels@lawsociety.org.uk; Tel 01527 504433
A national panel of solicitors originally known as the Child
Care Panel. It was established in March 1995, following the

publication of the Social Services Committee 1984 report
'Children in Care' to provide details of solicitors available
to conduct child care cases. Following the full
implementation of the Children Act 1989 the Panel was
revised and renamed the Children Panel. Its aim at that
time was to provide representation of children in Public
Law proceedings.
Following a recent review the Panel has been extended to
include representation of all parties in proceedings under
the Children Act 1989 and other family proceedings as
defined in the Children Act 1989.
Details of Panel membership are available on
www.solicitors-online.com or can be obtained from Law
Society Information Services by writing, telephoning or
emailing the above.

Network 81

1–7 Woodfield Terr, Chapel Hill, Stansted, Essex CM24 8AJ;
  URL www.network81.co.uk;
  E-mail network81@tesco.net; Tel 0870 7703262;
  (Helpline) 0870 7703306; Fax 0870 7703263
Administrator   Val Rosier
Manager (National Development)   J. Pashley
Network 81 offers practical help and support to parents
throughout all stages of assessment and statementing as
outlined in the Education Act 1996. The national helpline
offers an individual service linked to a network of local
contacts. They can also offer advice and information on the
organisation and assessment in schools and give guidelines
on how to choose a school. Network 81 produces a range of
literature aimed at familiarising parents with the
assessment and statementing procedures and also
organises several befriender training courses each year.

Northern Ireland Youth and Family Courts Association

84 North Pde, Belfast BT7 2GJ; Tel 028 9064 6217
Hon Secretary   H.R.B. McCandless
Association of lay magistrates appointed by the Lord
Chancellor as being persons having special qualifications
for dealing with juvenile cases. Two such persons, together
with an RM, form a bench in the juvenile court.

South Wales Advocacy Network

12 North Rd, Cardiff CF10 3DY; E-mail
  wales.advocacy.project@the-childrens-society.org.uk;
  Tel 029 2066 8956; (Freephone for children and young
  people) 0800 581862
Network Manager   Gerard Szary
Team Leader (Cardiff)   Sally-Anne Hemingway
Team Leader (Caerphilly and The Vale of Glamorgan)
  Keiron O'Hagan
Team Leader (Bridgend)   Matthew Guy
Team Leader (Swansea, Neath Port Talbot)   Sharon Lovell
Participation Officer   Vacancy
Independent Visitor Co-ordinator   Vacancy
Development Worker   Vacancy
The South Wales Advocacy Network incorporates four
teams, which offer children's rights and advocacy services
in six local authorities. These are Cardiff, Caerphilly, Vale of
Glamorgan, Swansea, Neath Port Talbot and Bridgend. All
of these projects offer services to young people 'looked
after'. The Bridgend project additionally offers advocacy
and mediation to young people at risk of social exclusion.
Within Cardiff, there will also be provision of an
independent visitor service for young people 'looked after'.
The network has a participation worker, whose role is to
promote the inclusion of young people within all the
projects. The network also undertakes development,
consultancy and training in children's rights. A particular
focus has been on young people's rights within the
adolescent mental health system. Research on this issue is
due to be published by The Children's Society.

Voice for the Child in Care (VCC)

Unit 4, Pride Crt, 80-82 White Lion St, London N1 9PF;
URL www.vcc-uk.org.uk; E-mail info@vcc-uk.org;
Tel 020 7833 5792; Fax 020 7713 1950
Hon Chair B. Irvine
Chief Executive John Kemmis
Hon Treasurer G. Gauge
VCC is a national charity committed to empowering
children and young people in public care and campaigning
for change to improve their lives. VCC provides advocacy
services to children and young people in care or in need
and independent services to agencies.

Approved Adoption Societies

The Local authorities in England and Wales act as adoption
agencies under the Children Act 1975 (section 1) and the
Children Act 1989. They state that it is the duty of every
local authority to establish and maintain within their area a
service designed to meet the needs in relation to adoption.
Correspondence and enquiries about adoption should be
addressed to the Director of Social Services for the local
authority concerned.

England

Societies deemed to be approved under the Children Act
1975 by the Secretary of State. The names of the Societies
are listed under the counties in which their
administrative headquarters are registered but their
activities are not necessarily confined to those areas.
Where the information is available the areas covered by
the Societies are listed.

Bedfordshire

St. Francis' Children's Society Collis Hse, 48 Newport Rd,
Woolstone, Milton Keynes MK15 0AA;
URL www.sfcs.org.uk; E-mail enquiries@sfcs.org.uk;
Tel 01908 572700; Fax 01908 572701
Director (Adoption Services) Christine Smith
Director (Business Administration) Richard Gordon
Catchment area: Bedfordshire, Buckinghamshire,
Northamptonshire and Slough.

Berkshire

Parents And Children Together (PACT) 7 Southern Crt,
South St, Reading RG1 4QS; URL www.pactcharity.org;
E-mail info@pactcharity.org; Tel 0118 938 7600; Fax 0118 959
4884
(formerly known as Oxford Diocesan Council for Social
Work Inc)
Chief Executive Y. Gayford
Manager (Adoption) A. Orchard
Manager (Community) Barry Wildsmith
PACT is a registered charity working in the fields of
adoption and community work with vulnerable parents.
Catchment area: Berkshire, Buckinghamshire and
Oxfordshire.

Bristol

Catholic Children's Society (Diocese of Clifton) 58 Alma
Rd, Clifton, Bristol BS8 2DJ; URL www.ccsclifton.org.uk;
E-mail info@ccsclifton.org.uk; Tel 0117 973 4253; Fax 0117
923 8651
Catchment area: Bristol, Bath and North East Somerset,
North Somerset, Somerset, South Gloucestershire,
Gloucestershire, Wiltshire and Swindon.

Cambridgeshire

Adopt Anglia Project, Coram Family 9 Petersfield,
Cambridge, Cambridgeshire CB1 1BB;
URL www.coram.org.uk; Tel 01223 357397; Fax 01223 576602
Project Leader Melanie Atkins
Specialist adoption agency recruiting adoptive families for
children looked after by local authorities. Comprehensive
adoption service offered. Consultation and special
packages can be negotiated.

Cheshire

Adoption Matters 14 Liverpool Rd, Chester, Cheshire
CH2 1AE; URL www.adoptionmatters.org;
E-mail info@adoptionmatters.org; Tel 01244 390938;
Fax 01244 390067
Chief Executive Norman Goodwin
Support Services and Office Manager Valerie Johnson
Comprehensive adoption service to birth parents,
prospective adopters and adopted persons.

Devon

Families for Children Trust Glenn Hse, 96 Old Tiverton Rd,
Exeter, Devon EX4 6LD;
URL www.familiesforchildren.org.uk;
E-mail mail@christiancare.freeserve.co.uk; Tel 01392
278875; Fax 01392 427227
Director (Adoption) C. Davis
Catchment area: Devon, Cornwall, Dorset.

Plymouth Diocesan Catholic Children's Society Ltd Rosary
Hse, 27 Fore St, Heavitree, Exeter, Devon EX1 2QJ;
URL www.plymouth-diocese.org.uk/;
E-mail info@prcdtr.org.uk; Tel 01392 255046
Catchment area: Cornwall, Devon, Old Dorset and the
Scilly Isles.
The charity is not itself a registered adoption agency. It
works in joint venture with its Anglican counterparts to
provide adoption services. Its Anglican Partner is a
registered adoption agency.

Durham

DFW Adoption Agriculture Hse, Stonebridge, Durham,
County Durham DH1 3RY; URL www.dfw-adoption.org;
E-mail dfwadoption@aol.com; Tel 0191 386 3719; Fax 0191
386 4940
Director S. Rayner
Adoption Service.
Catchment area: North East England.

Essex

Barnardo's New Families 54 Head St, Colchester, Essex
CO1 1PB; Tel 01206 562438; Fax 01206 575412
*Manager (Children's Services – London, East Anglia and South
East Region)* Jane Horne

Greater Manchester

Catholic Children's Rescue Society (Diocese of Salford) Inc
390 Parrs Wood Rd, Manchester M20 5NA;
E-mail ccrs1@tiscali.co.uk; Tel 0161 445 7741; Fax 0161 445
7769
Director Rev B. Wilson
Catchment area: South East Lancashire and Greater
Manchester. Mission statement 'Caring for children and
families in the RC Diocese of Salford'.

Manchester Adoption Society 47 Bury New Rd, Sedgley Pk,
Manchester M25 9JY; URL www.manchesteradoption.com;
E-mail info@manchesteradoption.com; Tel 0161 773 0973;
0161 834 9916
Adoption Team and The Goodman Team
Director B. Clatworthy
Catchment area: 25 mile radius of Manchester.

The Goodman Team
Concurrent Planning
Mocha Pde, Lower Broughton, Salford, Greater Manchester
M7 9QE; URL www.manadopt.u-net.com;
E-mail bc@manadopt.u-net.com
Director Brian Clatworthy

Lancashire

Blackburn Diocesan Adoption Agency Ltd St. Mary's Hse,
Cathedral Cl, Blackburn BB1 5AA;
E-mail adoption@bdaa.fsnet.co.uk; Tel 01254 57759;
Fax 01254 670810
Director Brian Williams, CQSW

Catholic Caring Services (Diocese of Lancaster) Ltd 218
Tulketh Rd, Preston, Lancashire PR2 1ES; Tel 01772 732313;
Fax 01772 768726
Director Jim Cullen, BA, MSc, CQSW, DMS
Catchment area: North Lancashire and Cumbria.

Leicestershire

East Midlands Children's Resource Team Lacey Crt,
Charnwood Rd, Shepshed, Leicestershire LE12 9QY;
E-mail east.midlands-crt@childrenssociety.org.uk; Tel 01509
600306; Fax 01509 601191
Project Leader Ursula Towne

London Boroughs

Camden

Coram Family 49 Mecklenburgh Sq, London WC1N 2QA;
Tel 020 7520 0300
Head (Adoption Service) J. Kaniuk
Coram Family is a children's charity that aims to develop
and promote best practice in the care of vulnerable children
and their families. Thomas Coram founded the charity in
1739 when he established the original Foundling Hospital
for abandoned children. Today, established Coram Family
services include: Adoption Service – finding families for
children with complex needs; Fostering New Links –
placements for traumatised 11–18 year olds; Leaving Care
Services – easing the difficult transition to independence;
Child Contact Services – leading agency for supervised
child contact; Parents' Centre – education support and
training for parents.

Croydon

Catholic Children's Society 49 Russell Hill Rd, Purley,
Surrey CR8 2XB; URL www.catholicchildrenssociety.org.uk;
E-mail info@cathchild.org; Tel 020 8668 2181; Fax 020 8763
2274
Director Terence Connor, MA, MSc
Catchment areas: Greater London south of the Thames,
Berkshire, Hampshire, Kent, South Oxfordshire, Surrey,
Sussex, Isle of Wight and the Channel Islands (Roman
Catholic dioceses of Arundel and Brighton, Portsmouth
and Southwark).

Islington

NCH Central Office, 85 Highbury Pk, London N5 1UD;
URL www.nch.org.uk; Tel 020 7704 7000; Fax 020 7226 2537
Community, residential and day care services for children
in need and their families covered nationally through seven
regional offices and over 500 projects in England, Scotland ,
Wales and Northern Ireland.

Kensington and Chelsea

The Catholic Children's Society 73 St. Charles Sq, London
W10 6EJ; URL www.cathchild.org.uk;
E-mail info@cathchild.org.uk; Tel 020 8969 5305; Fax 020
8960 1464

Director Jim Richards
Catchment area: London boroughs north of the Thames,
Staines, Sunbury-on-Thames, Hertfordshire and Essex.
Adoption, fostering, school counselling, family centres,
homelessness work, child psychotherapy and travellers.

Lambeth

Childlink Adoption Society 10 Lion Yard, Tremadoc Rd,
Clapham, London SW4 7NQ;
URL www.adoptchildlink.org.uk;
E-mail enquiries@adoptchildlink.org.uk; Tel 020 7501 1700;
Fax 020 7498 1791
Chief Executive C. Hesslegrave
Catchment Area: Two hours travelling time from central
London.

Redbridge

Barnardo's London, Eastern and South East (LEASE) Scotch
Hse, Tanners La, Barkingside, Ilford, Essex IG6 1QG;
URL www.barnardos.org.uk; Tel 020 8551 0011; Fax 020
8551 8267

Southwark

British Agencies for Adoption and Fostering Skyline Hse,
200 Union St, London SE1 0LX; URL www.baaf.org.uk;
E-mail mail@baaf.org.uk; Tel 020 7593 2000; Fax 020 7593
2001
Catchment area: National.

The Children's Society Head Office, Edward Rudolf Hse,
Margery St, London WC1X 0JL;
URL www.childrenssociety.org.uk;
E-mail info@childsoc.org.uk; Tel 020 7841 4400; Fax 020
7841 4500
Chief Executive Bob Reitemeler
Catchment area: England and Wales.

Independent Adoption Service 121–123 Camberwell Rd,
London SE5 0HB; URL i-a-s.org.uk; E-mail admin@i-a-
s.org.uk; Tel 020 7703 1088; Fax 020 7277 1668

Wandsworth

'SSAFA Forces Help' 19 Queen Elizabeth St, London
SE1 2LP; Tel 020 7403 8783
Director (Social Work) R. Swindley
Enquiries (Staff Officer, Social Work) D. Toni
SSAFA Forces Help employ qualified social work staff to
work with the families of service people based in the UK,
Western Europe, Gibraltar and Cyprus. SSAFA Forces Help
is also a registered adoption agency.

Merseyside

Catholic Children's Society (Shrewsbury Diocese) Inc St.
Paul's Hse, Farmfield Dr, Beechwood, Prenton, Wirral
CH43 7ZT; URL www.cathchildsoc.org.uk;
E-mail info@cathchildsoc.org.uk; Tel 0151 652 1281;
Fax 0151 652 5002
Director Gerard Edwards, MA, PGCE, CQSW, DMS

Nottinghamshire

Catholic Children's Society (RC Diocese of Nottingham) 7
Colwick Rd, West Bridgford, Nottingham NG2 5FR;
URL www.families-are-best.co.uk;
E-mail enquiries@ccsnotts.co.uk; Tel 0115 955 8811; Fax 0115
955 8822
Director Ms M. Dight, MBE
For adopters primarily the East Midlands,
Nottinghamshire, Derbyshire, Leicestershire, Lincolnshire.
Children placed on behalf of all Local Authorities.

Southwell Diocesan Council for Family Care Warren Hse, 2 Pelham Crt, Pelham Rd, Nottingham NG5 1AP; URL www.familycare-nottingham.org.uk; E-mail info@familycare-nottingham.org.uk; Tel 0115 960 3010; Fax 0115 960 8374
Chair of the Council G. Gibson
Director M. Weisz

South Yorkshire

Doncaster Adoption and Family Welfare Society Ltd Jubilee Hse, 1 Jubilee Rd, Wheatley, Doncaster, South Yorkshire DN1 2UE; E-mail info@doncasteradoptionsociety.org.uk; Tel 01302 349909; Fax 01302 340052

West Midlands

Father Hudson's Society Coventry Rd, Coleshill, Birmingham, West Midlands B46 3EB; URL www.fatherhudsons.org.uk; E-mail enquiries@fatherhudsons.org.uk; Tel 01675 434000; Fax 01675 434010
Director K. Caffrey
Manager (Adoption/Fostering) L. Malley
Manager (Residential and Day Services) G. Riley
Manager (Finance and Support Services) T. Bradford
Manager (Community Projects) Vacancy
Registered Charity No. 512992.
Catchment area: Warwickshire, Staffordshire, West Midlands, cities of Birmingham and Coventry, Oxfordshire and Worcestershire.

LDS Family Services 399 Garretts Green La, Garretts Grn, Birmingham, West Midlands B33 0UH; E-mail fam-eng@blschurch.org; Tel 0121 785 4994; Fax 0121 783 1888
Director D. Mark Ricks
Voluntary adoption society for Mormon (LDS) children and families.
Catchment area: England and Wales.

West Yorkshire

Catholic Care (Diocese of Leeds) St. Paul's, 11 North Grange Rd, Headingley, Leeds, West Yorkshire LS6 2BR; URL www.catholic-care.org.uk; E-mail info@catholic-care.org.uk; Tel 0113 388 5400; Fax 0113 388 5401
Director and Company Secretary Martin J. Hirst
Catchment area: West Yorkshire and parts of South Yorkshire and North Yorkshire.

Wales

St. David's Children Society

Formerly Catholic Children and Family Care Society.
Bishop Brown Hse, Durham St, Grangetown, Cardiff CF11 6PB; URL www.adoptionwales.co.uk; E-mail stdavidscs@aol.com; Tel 029 2066 7007; Fax 029 2039 4344
Director Gerry Cooney
Catchment area: Wales and Herefordshire.

Scotland

Barnardo's Family Placement Services 6 Torphichen St, Edinburgh EH3 8JQ; E-mail fps.scotland@barnardos.org.uk; Tel 0131 228 4121; Fax 0131 228 8706
Fostering of children with special needs.

Family Care 21 Castle St, Edinburgh EH2 3DN; Tel 0131 225 6478
Director J. Robinson
Family Care is a charity and voluntary social work agency which operates national and local services for children and families, and people whose lives are affected by adoption. Birthlink Adoption Counselling Centre is a national and international service which operates Scotland's Adoption Contact Register, and a post-adoption service which includes tracing.
Local services are based in Edinburgh and include No. 20 Women and Children's Centre and a children's counselling service.

St. Andrew's Children's Society Ltd (Adoption and Fostering Agency) 7 John's Pl, Leith, Edinburgh EH6 7EL; URL www.standrews-children.org.uk; E-mail info@standrews-children.org.uk; Tel 0131 454 3370; Fax 0131 454 3371
Chair M. McEvoy
Director S.J. Small

St. Margaret's Children and Family Care Society 274 Bath St, Glasgow G2 4JR; E-mail adopt@stmargarets8.fsnet.co.uk; Tel 0141 332 8371; Fax 0141 332 8393

Scottish Adoption Association Ltd 2 Commercial St, Edinburgh EH6 6JA; Tel 0131 553 5060; Fax 0131 553 6422
Director (Adoption Services) Ann Sutton
Catchment area: a 60 mile radius of Edinburgh.
Recruitment and preparation of adoptive families. Placement of young children for adoption. Counselling pregnant women and parents considering adoption for their children. Post-Adoption support and counselling to all affected by adoption.

VOLUNTARY ORGANISATIONS, RESIDENTIAL AND DAY CARE SERVICES FOR CHILDREN

Aberlour Child Care Trust

36 Park Terr, Stirling FK8 2JR; URL www.aberlour.org.uk; E-mail headquarters@aberlour.org.uk; Tel 01786 450335; Fax 01786 473238
Chief Executive Romy Langeland
Director (Operations) Stella Everingham
Director (Finance) Nigel Fairhead
Director (Fundraising) Vacancy
Assistant Director (Young People) Graham McPhie
Assistant Director (Children and Families Affected by Disability) Cameron MacVicar
Assistant Director (Parenting and Young Children's Development) Celia MacIntyre
Assistant Director (Children and Families Affected by Drug and Alcohol Misuse) Valerie Corbett
Assistant Director (North (Children and Families Affected by Disability)) Len Seal
Head (Policy) Keley Bayes

Anderida Adolescent Care Ltd

18a Gildredge Rd, Eastbourne, East Sussex BN21 4RL; Tel 01323 410655; Fax 01323 417546
Director Brian Thompson
Manager (Operations) Allan Hall

Barnardos

Head Office, Tanners La, Barkingside, Ilford, Essex IG6 1QG; Tel 020 8550 8822; Fax 020 8551 6870
Chief Executive R. Singleton, MA, MSc
UK Director (Operations) Dr C. Hanvey

Barnardo's London, East Anglia and South East Region (LEASE)

Scotch Hse, Tanners La, Barkingside, Ilford, Essex IG6 1QG; Tel 020 8551 0011; Fax 020 8551 8267
Director (Children's Services)   D. Pomell

Barnardo's Midlands Region

Brooklands, Great Cornbown, Halesowen, West Midlands B63 3AB; Tel 0121 550 5271; Fax 0121 550 2594
Director (Children's Services)   P. Varcoe

Barnardo's North East Region

Orchard Hse, Fenwick Terr, Jesmond, Newcastle upon Tyne, Tyne and Wear NE2 2JQ; Tel 0191 281 5024; Fax 0191 281 9840
Director (Children's Services)   J. Ewen

Barnardo's North West Region

7 Lineside Cl, Belle Vale, Liverpool, Merseyside L25 2UD; Tel 0151 488 1100; Fax 0151 488 1101
Director (Children's Services)   S. Hayes

Barnardo's Yorkshire Region

Four Gables, Clarence Rd, Leeds, West Yorkshire CS18 4LB; Tel 0113 258 2115; Fax 0113 258 0098
Director (Children's Services)   J. Tebbet

Barnardo's Northern Ireland

542–544 Upper Newtownards Rd, Belfast BT4 3HE; Tel 028 9067 2366; Fax 028 9067 2399
Director (Children's Services)   L. Wilson

Barnardo's Scotland

235 Corstorphine Rd, Edinburgh EH12 7AR; Tel 0131 334 9893; Fax 0131 316 4008
Director (Children's Services)   H. Mackintosh, OBE

Barnardo's Wales and South West

11–15 Columbus Wlk, Brigantine Pl, Atlantic Wharf, Cardiff CF1 5BZ; Tel 029 2049 3387; Fax 029 2048 9802
Director (Children's Services)   J. Stacey

BGWS (Boys and Girls Welfare Society)

BGWS Centre, Schools Hill, Cheadle, Cheshire SK8 1JE; URL www.bgws.org.uk; E-mail enquiries@bgws.org.uk; Tel 0161 283 4848; Fax 0161 283 4747
Chief Executive   Andrew F. Haines, MA, BPhil, CertEd
Objectives
To provide care of and education for children and young people with a diversity of special learning, personal and social needs.

BREAK

Davison Hse, 1 Montague Rd, Sheringham, Norfolk NR26 8WN; URL www.break-charity.org; E-mail office@break-charity.org; Tel 01263 822161; Fax 01263 822181
BREAK provides a range of specialist care services for children, adults and families with special needs. Every year, BREAK provides holidays, short-breaks and respite care for more than 1000 children and adults with learning and physical disabilities at centres in Norfolk.
Other services provided by BREAK: residential family assessments, children's homes, family holidays, day care for adults with learning disabilities. A registered charity, BREAK was founded in 1968.

Castle Homes

The Manor Hse, Squire's Hill, Rothwell, Northamptonshire NN14 6BQ; E-mail castlehomes.co.uk; Tel 01536 711111; Fax 01536 712994
Chief Executive   John Mackenzie
Managing Director (Principal Care)   David Ayers
Private company; KCC, Bromley, Cambridgeshire, Nottinghamshire, Staffordshire, Telford and Wrekin, Essex, South Wales, Shropshire and Cheshire – Reg No. 2178870.

SOUTH EAST REGION

Mainstream Residential

Alexandra House   Deal, Kent; Tel 01536 711111; 0800 917 5671
Arundel House   Dover, Kent; Tel 01536 711111; 0800 917 5671
Victoria House   Dover, Kent; Tel 01536 711111

Intensive Support Programmes

Court Lodge   Maidstone, Kent; Tel 01536 711111
Farm Cottage   Faversham, Kent; Tel 01536 711111
Hobbit House   Meopham, Kent; Tel 01536 711111; 0800 917 5671
Wilford Court   Sittingbourne, Kent; Tel 01536 711111

Emergency Care

Haven House   Sidcup, Kent; Tel 01536 711111; 020 8302 9091 0800 917 5671
A Crisis Care Service which provides a place of safety available throughout the year on a round the clock basis, dealing with breakdowns, remand, respite and where crisis intervention is necessary. This offers a placement for a child or young person, including sibling groups into care for an initial period of 72 hours, but with stays of up to six weeks.

ANGLIAN REGION

Mainstream Residential – Specialist

March House   March, Cambridgeshire; Tel 01536 711111; 0800 917 5671

Intensive Support Programmes

Castle Lodge   Ely, Cambridgeshire; Tel 01536 711111; 0800 917 5671
The Close   Thetford, Norfolk; Tel 01536 711111; 0800 917 5671
Garden Court   Dunmow, Essex; Tel 01536 711111; 0800 917 5671
Strawberry Farm   Cambridge, Cambridgeshire; Tel 01536 711111; 0800 917 5671

MIDLAND REGION

Intensive Support Programme

Newbridge House   Newark, Nottinghamshire; Tel 01536 711111; 0800 917 5671

Mainstream Residential – Specialist

Ashgrove House   Kidsgrove, Stoke-on-Trent; Tel 01536 711111; 0800 917 5671
Wellington House   Wellington, Shropshire; Tel 01536 711111; 0800 917 5671

B G W S

The Boys & Girls Welfare Society is the largest children's charity operating in the north west of England. Working with local authorities, last year BGWS affected the lives of 1800 children with special needs. Our services include:

- More than 20 homes for children and young people with social and emotional difficulties
- 4 homes for children and young people with physical difficulties
- Fostering Service
- Adoption Service
- Bridge College – FE day college for learners with disabilities
- CYCES – The Child and Youth Care Education Service
- Inscape House Special School Cheadle
- Inscape House Special School Salford
- INCA (Inscape Centre for Autism)
- Newbridge Centre (educational, occupational and leisure opportunities for disabled young people up to the age of 30)
- Mediation Service including Legal Aid (Section 29 Franchise for Cheshire)
- Stockport MBC Special Education Needs Parent Partnership
- Outreach/Respite Services – Bespoke packages at commissioners request
- Independent Social Work Services & Consultancy
- Specialised Projects in the Community
- Student Placement Unit
- Training Division
- NVQ Assessment Consortium
- BGWS Training & Conference Centre

Because children and young people matter

t: 0161 283 4848
f: 0161 283 4747

www.bgws.org.uk
Please quote ref: SSYB

CHIEF EXECUTIVE: ANDREW HAINES, M.A., B.Phil, Cert.Ed.
BOYS & GIRLS WELFARE SOCIETY
BGWS Centre, Schools Hill, Cheadle, SK8 1JE
Registered Charity No.209782

Intensive Support Programmes

Hurst Farm Stoke on Tern, Market Drayton, Shropshire TF9 2LD; Tel 01536 711111; 0800 917 5671

Redbrook Grange Redbrook, Whitchurch, Shropshire SY13 3AE; Tel 01536 711111; 0800 917 5671

Whitty Tree House Whitty Tree, Onibury, Craven Arms, Shropshire SY7 9BG; Tel 01536 711111; 0800 917 5671

Emergency Care

Eastgate House 16 Millbank, Wellington, Shropshire TF1 1RZ; Tel 01952 245555; 0800 917 5671
Crisis Child Care Service which provides a place of safety available throughout the year on a round the clock basis, dealing with breakdowns, remand, respite and other crisis. This offers placement for a child or young person, including sibling groups, for an initial period of 72 hours, but with a stay of up to six weeks.

WALES REGION

Mainstream Residential

Cil Ddewi Uchaf (Small Home) Carmarthenshire; Tel 01536 711111; 0800 917 5671

Pentwyn Farm House Monmouthshire; Tel 01536 711111; 0800 917 5671

Catholic Care (Diocese of Leeds)

St. Paul's, 11 North Grange Rd, Headingley, Leeds, West Yorkshire LS6 2BR; URL www.catholic-care.org.uk; E-mail info@catholic-care.org.uk; Tel 0113 388 5400; Fax 0113 388 5401
Director and Company Director Martin J. Hirst

Catholic Children's Society (Arundel and Brighton, Portsmouth and Southwark)

49 Russell Hill Rd, Purley, Surrey CR8 2XB; URL www.cathchild.org; E-mail info@cathchild.org; Tel 020 8668 2181; Fax 020 8763 2274
Director Terence Connor, MA, MSc
Adoption of infants and special needs children including residential preparation, fostering, family community centres, residential homes for children and young people with learning difficulties, 'Home and Away' South London Youth Homelessness project and school counselling.

The Catholic Children's Society (Shrewsbury Diocese) Inc

St. Pauls Hse, Farmfield Dr, Prenton, Wirral CH43 7ZT; E-mail ccs@childsoc.freeserve.co.uk; Tel 0151 652 1281; Fax 0151 652 5002
Director Ged Edwards, MA, PGCE, LQSW, DMS

Catholic Caring Services (Diocese of Lancaster) Ltd

218 Tulketh Rd, Preston, Lancashire PR2 1ES; Tel 01772 732313
Director Jim Cullen
Principal Officer (Children's Services) Vacancy
Principal Officer (Community Services) Mark Wiggin

The Catholic Children's Society (Westminster), The Crusade of Rescue

73 St. Charles' Sq, London W10 6EJ; E-mail cathchild.org.uk; Tel 020 8969 5305; Fax 020 8960 1464
Director Jim Richards
Catchment area: London boroughs north of the Thames, Staines, Sunbury-on-Thames, Hertfordshire and Essex. Adoption, fostering, school counselling, family centres, homelessness work, child psychotherapy and travellers.

The Children's Society

Edward Rudolf Hse, Margery St, London WC1X 0JL; URL www.childrenssociety.org.uk; E-mail info@childrenssociety.org.uk; Tel 020 7841 4400; Fax 020 7841 4500
Chief Executive I. Sparks, MA
Director (Fundraising) Stephen Blunden
Director (Finance and Administration) Charles Nall
Director (Social Work) Penny Dean
Chaplain Missioner Rev D. Rhodes
The Children's Society is a voluntary organisation of the Church of England and the Church in Wales, working with over 40 000 children of all ages through over 100 projects located across England and Wales. Its work includes: street work with young runaways; preventing exclusion from schools; running reviews and bail support programmes for young offenders; advocacy, information and advice for children and young people; involving children in the development of their communities; running family and community centres that work with families on issues and problems affecting them.

East of England Regional Office

20–22 White House Rd, Alpha Bus Pk, Ipswich, Suffolk IP1 5LT; Tel 01473 461911

East Midlands Regional Office

Mayfair Crt, Northgate, Nottingham NG7 7GR; Tel 0115 942 2974

Greater London Regional Office

91–93 Queens Rd, Peckham, London SE15 2EZ; Tel 020 7639 1466

South East Regional Office

The Annexe, Elsfield Hall, 15–17 Elsfield Way, Oxford, Oxfordshire OX2 8FQ; Tel 01865 514161

North East Regional Office

Suite O, Walker Hse, Stockton-on-Tees TS18 1BG; Tel 01642 677302

North West Regional Office

8 Vine St, Kersal, Salford, Greater Manchester M7 3PG; Tel 0161 792 8885

South West Regional Office

Brook Hse, Pennywell Rd, Bristol BS5 0TX; Tel 0117 941 4333

Wales Office

14 Cathedral Rd, Cardiff CF1 9LJ; Tel 029 2039 6974

13

West Midlands Regional Office

Unit 4, Mitre Crt, Sutton Coldfield, West Midlands
    B74 2LZ; Tel 0121 362 8600

Yorkshire and Humberside Regional Office

3rd Fl, Stamford Hse, York YO1 9PW; Tel 01904 627866

Christian Child Care Forum

10 Crescent Rd, South Woodford, London E18 1JB; Tel 020
    8504 2702
UK Co-ordinator   Vacancy
Chair of Trustees   D. Evans
Trustee   D. Pearson
Trustee   G. Kanga
Trustee   K. White
Trustee   S. Rodway
Trustee   J. Marding
Trustee   H. Elliott
Trustee   D. Spicer
The Christian Child Care Forum is a grouping of
organisations and individuals committed to promoting a
vision of contemporary society in which children and
young people have a rightful place, and to responding in
love, from common Christian perspectives, to the needs of
children and families.
By providing a means of sharing experience and insights,
and of increasing understanding and co-operation on
matters of policy and practice, the Forum seeks to sustain
and develop the contribution of Christian resources to the
wellbeing of children and young people.

Christian Family Concern

42 South Park Hill Rd, South Croydon, Surrey CR2 7YB;
    E-mail christfc@surfaid.org.uk; Tel 020 8688 0251;
    Fax 020 8686 7114
Chief Executive   Leslie Hillier
Christian Family Concern provides a range of services to
support families and prevent family breakdown. Birdhurst
Day Nursery provides care and education for 60+ children
aged 0–5 and Birdhurst Kids' Clubs provide after school
care and all day holiday playschemes for 30 children aged
4–11. Vulnerable parents and children benefit from The
Family Drop-In, the Wallis Supported Bedsit Scheme and
the positive parenting programmes. In addition, the
Beracah Bedsit Scheme provides medium term
accommodation for young people aged 18+.

Church of Scotland Board of Social Responsibility

Charis Hse, 47 Milton Rd East, Edinburgh EH15 2SR;
    E-mail info@charis.org.uk; Tel 0131 657 2000; Fax 0131
    657 5000
Convener   Rev Jim Cowie
Director (Social Work)   Ian Manson

Cora Foundation

Cora Hse, Greenock Rd, Bishopton, Renfrewshire
    PA7 5PW; Tel 01505 863697; Fax 01505 863691
Director   Martin McCambridge
Various residential and day education and social care
services.

Coram Family

49 Mecklenburgh Sq, London WC1N 2QA;
    E-mail reception@coram.org.uk; Tel 020 7520 0300
Chief Executive   Dr Gillian Pugh

Coram Family, one of England's oldest children's charities,
has been working continuously with deprived and
disadvantaged children since 1739. They run about 30
projects, working with over 1000 children and young
people in the care system and 600 families and young
children in the local community. Today established Coram
Family services include: Adoption service – finding
families for children with complex needs; Fostering New
Links – placements for traumatised 11–18 year olds;
Leaving Care Services – easing the difficult transition to
independence; Child Contact Services – leading agency for
supervised child contact; Parents' Centre – education
support and training for parents; Family Support
Department – Parenting Service, Family support and early
intervention work.

Daycare Trust

21 St. George's Rd, London SE1 6ES;
    E-mail info@daycaretrust.org.uk; Tel 020 7840 3350;
    Fax 020 7840 3355
Daycare Trust is a national childcare charity. They promote
quality, affordable childcare for children aged 0–14, and
advise parents, providers, practitioners, employers, trade
unions, Government and policy makers on childcare
matters.
Publications, guides, conferences. Also provide and run
campaigns.

Dean and Cauvin Trust

41 Portland St, Edinburgh EH6 4BB; Tel 0131 554 3784
17 Melville St, Edinburgh EH3 7PH
Preparation for independent living.

Fegans Child and Family Care

160 St. James' Rd, Tunbridge Wells, Kent TN1 2HE;
    URL www.fegans.org.uk; E-mail info@fegans.org.uk;
    Tel 01892 538288; Fax 01892 515793
Chief Executive   D.P. Waller

The Fellowship of St. Nicholas

St. Nicholas Centre, 66 London Rd, St. Leonards,
    East Sussex TN37 6AS;
    E-mail fsn@stleonards3.fsnet.co.uk; Tel 01424 423683;
    Fax 01424 460446
Chief Executive   Christine Unsworth
Children's Charity
Providing out of school care; holiday playschemes; art and
photography; double decker fun bus; facilities for room
hire, and a UK on-line IT Centre.

George Muller Foundation

Muller Hse, 7 Cotham Pk, Bristol BS6 6DA;
    URL www.mullers.org; E-mail admin@mullers.org;
    Tel 0117 924 5001
Chief Executive   Julian Marsh
Family centres in Bristol and Weston-super-Mare.

The Integrated Services Programme (ISP)

Church St, Sittingbourne, Kent ME10 3EG;
    URL www.ispchildcare.org.uk;
    E-mail enquiries@ispchildcare.org.uk; Tel 01795 428097;
    (Out of hours) 07693 959070

Managing Director John Whitwell
Specialist childcare services (emergency, assessment, short
and long term) for children and young people aged 0–17
who have suffered the trauma of family breakdown.
ISP provides: foster families, education, social work, speech
and language therapy, educational psychology,
psychotherapy, leaving care and out-reach.

NCH

Central Office, 85 Highbury Pk, London N5 1UD;
    URL www.nch.org.uk; Tel 020 7704 7000; Fax 020 7226
    2537
Chief Executive Deryk Mead
Director (Support Services) Jarvaid Khan
Director (Operations) and Deputy Chief Executive
    Maurice Rumbold, MA
Director (Human Resources) Janice Cook
Pastoral Director Rev Bill Lynn

NCH London Region

Turner Hse, 22 Lucerne Rd, London N5 1TZ; Tel 020 7704
    7070; Fax 020 7704 7080
Director (Children's Services) Barry Barnes

NCH West Midlands Region

Princess Alice Dr, Chester Rd North, Sutton Coldfield, West
    Midlands B73 6RD; URL www.nch.org.uk;
    E-mail hught@nch.org.uk; Tel 0121 355 4615; Fax 0121
    354 4717
Director (Children's Services West Midlands)
    Hugh Thornbery

NCH North East Region

12 Granby Rd, Harrogate, North Yorkshire HG1 4ST;
    E-mail nigelh@nch.org.uk; Tel 01423 524 286; Fax 01423
    501 987
Director (Children's Services) Nigel Harper

NCH North West Region

Aquila Hse, Delta Cres, Westbrook, Warrington WA5 7NR;
    Tel 01925 715380; Fax 01925 715381
Director (Children's Services) Cheryl Eastwood

NCH South East Region

158 Crawley Rd, Roffey, Horsham, West Sussex RH12 4EU;
    E-mail karen.harvey@nch.org.uk; Tel 01403 225900;
    Fax 01403 225911
Director (Children's Services) Karen Harvey (Acting)

NCH South West Region

Horner Crt, 637 Gloucester Rd, Horfield, Bristol BS7 0BJ;
    Tel 0117 935 4440; (Fostering and Adoption) 0117 300
    5360; Fax 0117 300 5365
Director (Children's Services) David Forrest

NCH Scotland

17 Newton Pl, Glasgow G3 7PY;
    URL www.nch.org.uk;
    E-mail christopher.holmes@nch.org.uk; Tel 0141 332
    4041; Fax 0141 332 7002
Director (Children's Services) Christopher Holmes

NCH Cymru

St. David's Crt, 68a Cowbridge Rd East, Cardiff CF11 9DN;
    Tel 029 2022 2127; Fax 029 2022 9952
Director (Children's Services) Graham Illingworth

Norwood

Broadway Hse, 80–82 The Broadway, Stanmore, Greater
    London HA7 4HB; URL www.norwood.org.uk;
    E-mail norwood@norwood.org.uk; Tel 020 8420 6814;
    Fax 020 8420 6800
Chief Executive Norma Brier
Residential, family and community services for socially
disadvantaged Jewish children, and for people of all ages
with learning disabilities.
Registered charity no. 1059050.

Nugent Care Society

99 Edge La, Liverpool, Merseyside L7 2PE;
    URL www.nugentcare.org;
    E-mail info@nugentcare.org; Tel 0151 261 2000; Fax 0151
    261 2001
Director John Kennedy, MA, BA, DMS, MBASW

Peper Harow Foundation

Station Hse, 150 Waterloo Rd, London, SE1 8SB;
    URL www.peperharow.org.uk; Tel 020 7928 7388;
    Fax 020 7261 1307
Chief Executive Mike Willis
Regional Director (North) Alan Worthington
Regional Director (South) Richard Rollinson

Churches' Child Protection Advisory Service

PO Box 133, Swanley, Kent BR8 7UQ;
    E-mail info@ccpas.co.uk; Tel 0845 120 4550; (Helpline)
    0845 120 4551; Fax 0845 120 4552
Director D. Pearson, MBASW, DMS, CSW
CCPAS provides advice, training and support for churches,
organisations, families and individuals on child protection
across the UK. Publishes 'Guidance to Churches', a
comprehensive child protection manual relevant to faith
groups and other organisations in all parts of the UK. Low-
cost telephone helpline (24 hour). Promotes Christian foster
care and adoption. Respite care for children with
disabilities in the West Midlands.

Quarriers

Head Office, Quarriers Village, Bridge of Weir,
    Renfrewshire PA11 3SX; URL www.quarriers.org.uk;
    E-mail enquiries@quarriers.org.uk; Tel 01505 612224;
    01505 616000; Fax 01506 613906
Chief Executive Phil Robinson
Company Secretary Fraser MacDonald

RPS Rainer (The Royal Philanthropic Society, incorporating The Rainer Foundation)

Rectory Lodge, High St, Brasted, Westerham, Kent
    TN16 1JF; URL www.rpsrainer.org.uk;
    E-mail mail@rpsrainer.org.uk; Tel 01959 578200;
    Fax 01959 561891
Chief Executive J. Moseley
RPS Rainer operates over 60 projects nationwide, including
projects for young people leaving care and aftercare; youth
justice including motor projects; bail support and remand
management schemes; Appropriate Adult services; care
and support for young people on release from young

offender institutions; employment, education and training projects for vulnerable and disadvantaged young people; projects working with young women; supported housing including specialist parent and child schemes; mentoring schemes.

St. Christopher's Fellowship

St. Christopher's Hse, 217 Kingston Rd, London
SW19 3NL; E-mail normanashworth@st-chris.co.uk;
Tel 020 8543 3619; Fax 020 8544 1633
Chief Executive   Jonathan Farrow
Assistant Director (Quality Development)
Norman Ashworth
Each year St. Christopher's Fellowship provides care and accommodation to over 600 children and young people in ten London boroughs. Their range of provision includes the London Refuge for runaway children, registered children's homes, supported housing projects, with floating support, and two leaving care projects together with two foyers.

St. Cuthbert's Care

St. Cuthbert's Hse, West Rd, Newcastle upon Tyne,
Tyne and Wear NE15 7PY;
URL www.stcuthbertscare.org.uk;
E-mail enquiries@stcuthbertscare.org.uk; Tel 0191 228
0111; Fax 0191 228 0177
Director   Austin Donohoe
Social Care Agency. Catchment Area: North East (Tyne and Wear, Northumberland, Durham and Teeside).

Salvation Army

101 Newington, Causeway, London SE1 6BN; Tel 020 7367
4879; Fax 020 7367 4712
Director (Family Tracing Service)   Lieutenant Colonel Ron
Smith
Director (Social Work)   Captain Ian Harris
Deputy Director (Social Work)   Major Ray Irving

Anglia Division

2 Barton Way, Norwich, Norfolk NR1 1DR; Tel 01603
724400; Fax 01603 724411

Central North Division

80 Eccles New Rd, Salford, Greater Manchester M5 2RU;
Tel 0161 743 3900; Fax 0161 743 3911

Central South Division

16c Cowley Rd, Uxbridge, Greater London UB8 2LT;
Tel 01895 208800; Fax 01895 208811

East Midlands Division

Paisley Gr, Chilwell, Nottingham NG9 6DJ; Tel 0115 983
5000; Fax 0115 983 5011

East Scotland Division

12a Dryden Rd, Loanhead, EH20 9LZ; Tel 0131 440 9100;
Fax 0131 440 9111

Northern Ireland Division

12 Station Mews, Sydenham, Belfast BT4 1TL; Tel 028 9067
5000; Fax 028 9067 5011

London Central Division

1st Fl, 25–27 Kings Exchange, Tileyard, London N7 9AH;
Tel 020 7619 6100; Fax 020 7619 6111

London North East Division

Maldon Rd, Hatfield Peverel, Essex CM3 3HL; Tel 01245
383000

London South East Division

3 West Crt, Armstrong Rd, Maidstone, Kent ME15 6QR;
Tel 01622 775 5000; Fax 01622 775 5011

North Scotland Division

Deer Rd, Woodside, Aberdeen AB24 2BL; Tel 01224 497000;
Fax 01224 497011

North Western Division

16 Faraday Rd, Wavertree Technology Pk, Liverpool,
Merseyside L13 1EH; Tel 0151 252 6100; Fax 0151 252
6111

Northern Division

Balliol Bus Pk West, Newcastle upon Tyne, Tyne and Wear
NE12 8EW; Tel 0191 238 1800; Fax 0191 238 1811

South and Mid Wales Division

East Moors Rd, Ocean Pk, Cardiff CF1 5SA; Tel 029 2044
0600; Fax 029 2044 0611

South Western Division

Marlborough Crt, Matford Bus Pk, Exeter, Devon EX2 8PF;
Tel 01392 822100; Fax 01392 822111

Southern Division

6/8 Little Park Farm Rd, Segensworth, Fareham,
Hampshire PO15 5TD; Tel 01489 566800; Fax 01489
566811

West Midlands Division

102 Unett St, Hockley, West Midlands B4 6HH; Tel 0121 507
8500; Fax 0121 507 8511

West Scotland Division

4 Buchanan Crt, Cumbernauld Rd, Glasgow G33 6HZ;
Tel 0141 779 5000; Fax 0141 779 5011

Yorkshire Division

1 Cadman Crt, off Hanley Rd, Leeds, West Yorkshire
LS27 0RX; Tel 0113 281 0100; Fax 0113 281 0111
Divisional Commander   Lieutenant Colonel R. Forsyth

The Scottish Institute for Residential Child Care (SIRCC)

5th Fl, Sir Henry Wood Bldg, The University of Strathclyde,
76 Southbrae Dr, Glasgow G13 1PP;
URL www.sircc.strath.ac.uk; Tel 0141 950 3683; Fax 0141
950 3681
Director   Kirstie Maclean
Established on 1st April 2000, The SIRCC aims to ensure that residential child care staff throughout Scotland have access to the skills and knowledge they require to meet the needs of the children and young people in their care.

Spurgeon's Child Care

74 Wellingborough Rd, Rushden, Northamptonshire
NN10 9TY; URL www.spurgeonschildcare.org;
E-mail scc@spurgeons.org; Tel 01933 412412; Fax 01933
412010
Chief Executive   David Culwick
Spurgeon's Child Care is a registered charity which
provides support services for children, young people and
families, working in partnership with Local Authorities,
churches and other groups.
Projects
Over 80 projects across the UK, and 20 overseas, in
Romania, Moldova, Latvia, Uganda, Kenya, Brazil and
Mexico.

REGIONAL OFFICES

Southern Divisional Office

2 Melbourne St, Bedford, Bedfordshire MK42 9AX;
Tel 01234 262959; Fax 01234 261138
Director (Southern Division)   Gary Johnson;
E-mail gjohnson@spurgeonssouth.org.uk
Regional Manager (Bedfordshire)   Sandra Rome;
E-mail srome@spurgeonssouth.org.uk
Regional Manager (East)   Hugh Minty;
E-mail hminty@spurgeonssouth.org.uk
Regional Manager (South West)   Heidi Sydor
The Pound, Ampney Circus, Cirencester, Gloucestershire
GL7 6SA; E-mail spurgeons@swregion.fsnet.co.uk;
Tel 01285 851169

London Regional Office

Bethnel Green Mission, 305 Cambridge Health Rd, London
E2 9LH; E-mail mprince@scclondon.fsnet.co.uk; Tel 020
7613 3223; Fax 020 7613 3223
Regional Manager (London)   Maureen Prince

Northern Divisional Office

8th Fl, St. James's Hse, Pendleton Way, Salford, Greater
Manchester M6 5PW; Tel 0161 736 8991; Fax 0161 736
9662
Director (Northern Division)   Janet Battye;
E-mail janet.battye@spurgeonsnorth.co.uk
Regional Manager (North East)   Ralph Keene;
E-mail sro.spurgeons@btopenworld.co.uk
Regional Manager (North West)   Tudor Humphreys;
E-mail tudor.humphreys@spurgeons.co.uk
Regional Manager (Salford and Greater Manchester)   Glenn
Wood; E-mail glenn.wood@spurgeonsnorth.co.uk
Regional Manager (North)   Vida Slater;
E-mail vida.slater@spurgeonsnorth.co.uk
Regional Manager (Black Country)   Bruce Kirk
51a St. Jude's Road West, Wolverhampton, West Midlands
WV6 0DB; E-mail jmeddings@hotmail.com; Tel 01902
572321; Fax 01902 572520

Overseas Office

58 Heights Ave, Rochdale, Lancashire OL12 6JH;
E-mail jpsmith1000@btopenworld.com; Tel 01706 659320
Overseas Manager   John Smith

Voluntary Service Aberdeen

38 Castle St, Aberdeen AB11 5YU; URL www.vsa.org.uk;
E-mail info@vsa.org.uk; Tel 01224 212021; Fax 01224
580722
Director   W. Howie, MA, BD, STM
One of the largest social care charities in Scotland,
Voluntary Service Aberdeen provides a range of direct
services to help those in need. Expert advice is available
including social work support, also outings and holidays
and help with fuel and transport. Over 1000 volunteers,
supported by VSA also give support to the wider voluntary
sector and administer six other associated but financially
independent local charities.

Residential and Community Projects for Children

Abbreviations: Und – Undenominational;
Inter – Interdenominational; C. of E. – Church of England;
RC – Roman Catholic; Prot – Protestant;
Presb – Presbyterian; Evan – Evangelical

England

Bath and North East Somerset

The Children's Society

Children's Participation Project, Wessex 1st Fl Office, 92b
High St, Midsomer Norton, Bath and North East Somerset
BA3 2DE; Tel 01761 411771; Fax 01761 417553
Project Leader   Jim Davis
The project works with 'new age' traveller families in the
South West and promotes children's rights through
consultation in decision-making and planning. It also
incorporates work that tackles rural poverty as it affects
children and young people.

Bedfordshire

The Children's Society

Regional Monitoring and Evaluation Project 26 Bromham
Rd, Bedford, Bedfordshire MK40 2QD; Tel 01234 344561
Project Leader   Jeff Tye

NCH Action Trust for Children Thames Anglia Region

Mayfield Family Centre 4 Mayfield Rd, Downside,
Dunstable, Bedfordshire LU5 4AP;
E-mail tamfc@mail.nchafc.org.uk; Tel 01582 670695;
Fax 01582 670714
Contact   Julie Clement
Contact   Sue Jones
Contact   Cathy Rogers

Spurgeon's Child Care

Bushmead Avenue Centre 62 Bushmead Ave, Bedford,
Bedfordshire MK40 3QW; Tel 01234 216897; Fax 01234
273537
Manager (Child Care Services)   Lynne Summerfield
Manager (Social Work)   Rosemary Drewett
Manager (Contact)   Sharon Griffiths
Manager (Independent Visitors)   Alison Miller
Contact facilities, social work support to families, group
work, independent visitor's scheme, childminding network
(children with disabilities). Prison playcare.

Bedford Prison
c/o 74 Wellingborough Rd, Rushden, Northamptonshire;
Tel 01933 412412
Prison Play Area Co-ordinator   Val Foster
Prison playcare area (not crèche).
Spurgeon's Child Care.

The Stopsley Project Stopsley Baptist Church, St. Thomas'
Rd, Stopsley, Luton LU2 7XP;
E-mail david.shaw@stopsley.net; Tel 01582 405293;
Fax 01582 418357
Project Manager   D. Shaw
Social work support services, group work.

Berkshire

Barnardos

High Close School Wiltshire Rd, Wokingham RG40 1TT;
Tel 0118 978 5767
Principal A. Paterson

Catholic Children's Society

Familymakers Reading 50 Mount Pleasant, Reading
RG1 2TD; URL www.cathchild.org;
E-mail reading@cathchild.org; Tel 0118 987 5121
Project Manager Catherine Burke
Adoption children 0–10 years and sibling groups.

NCH Action Trust for Children Thames Anglia Region

Greenham House Family Centre Greenham Hse, Greenham
Rd, Newbury, Berkshire RG14 7HS;
E-mail seghfc@mail.nch.org.uk; Tel 01635 45274; Fax 01635
42837
Project Manager R. Lilley

Margaret Wells-Furby Children's Resource Centre Great
Hollands Sq, Bracknell, Bracknell Forest RG12 8UX;
E-mail tamwcrc@mail.nch.org.uk; Tel 01344 456416

Newbury Family Counselling Service c/o Greenham House
Family Centre, Greenham Rd, Newbury, Berkshire
RG14 7HS; Tel 01635 521296
Manager Rosemary Lilley

Birkenhead

Spurgeon's Child Care

Laird Street Family Support Centre Laird Street Baptist
Church, Laird St, Birkenhead, Merseyside CH41 8EN;
E-mail audrey@lairdstreetbirkenhead.org.uk; Tel 0151 653
9400
Centre Manager Audrey Haines
Family support, carers and toddlers.

Birmingham

Barnardos Midland Division

Chess Project Harris Hse, 8 St. Agnes Rd, Birmingham,
West Midlands B13 9PW; Tel 0121 449 8555
Project Leader Lee Richards
Children's health, education and support service.

The Corner Family Project The Corner, 40 Rupert St,
Birmingham, West Midlands B7 4PS;
E-mail corner.family@barnardos.org.uk; Tel 0121 359 2187;
0121 359 5333
Project Leader Teresa Quinn
Project Leader Nicola Myhill

Harris House Project Harris Hse, 8 St. Agnes Rd,
Birmingham, West Midlands B13 9PW; Tel 0121 449
9011
Manager (Children's Services) Shereen Khan

The Children's Society

Wyrley Birch Centre for Parents and Children 36
Parkhouse Dr, Erdington, Birmingham, West Midlands
B23 7UB;
E-mail wyrley-birch-centre@the-childrens-society.org.uk;
Tel 0121 356 7919
Project Leader Ali McCormick

NCH Midlands Region

Birmingham Community Children's Centre 61 Bacchus Rd,
Winson Grn, Birmingham, West Midlands B18 4QY;
Tel 0121 507 9500; Fax 0121 507 9532
Centre Director Caroline Leahy

Birmingham Independent Visitors Project 2–4 Guild Cl,
Ledsam St, Birmingham, West Midlands B16 8EL;
URL www.nch.org.uk; E-mail mdbivs@mail.nch.org.uk;
Tel 0121 455 0120

Birmingham Young Carers (NCH) Carers Centre, Milton
Grange, 16 Handsworth Wood Rd, Handsworth Wood,
Birmingham, West Midlands B20 2DR;
E-mail mdbyc@mail.nch.org.uk; Tel 0121 686 4071
Project Manager Pam Bloor

Bonner House 172 Sellywood Rd, Bournville, Birmingham,
West Midlands B30 1TJ; URL www.nch.org.uk;
E-mail mdbh@mail.nch.org.uk; Tel 0121 472 5839; Fax 0121
471 5114
Project Manager Adrian Over

Kingshurst Family Centre 15 Church Cl, Kingshurst,
Birmingham, West Midlands B37 6HA; Tel 0121 779 6572
Project Manager Sara Roberts

Ladywood Group Projects Ladywood Family Centre, 2–4
Guild Cl, Ladywood, Birmingham, West Midlands
B16 8EL; E-mail ndlfc@nch.org.uk; Tel 0121 456 2728;
Fax 0121 455 9118
Project Manager Maureen McGrath

NCH St. Thomas Centre Bell Barn Rd, Lee Bank,
Birmingham, West Midlands B15 2AF;
E-mail mdstc@mail.nch.org.uk; Tel 0121 464 0016
Deputy Project Manager Jan Pitt

Rutland Children's Rights c/o Adoption NCH (Midlands),
141 Wood End La, Erdington, West Midlands B24 8BD;
URL www.nch.org.uk; E-mail mdap@mail.nch.org.uk;
Tel 0800 085 6634
Children's Rights Officer Anthea Ambrose

Spurgeon's Child Care

Highgate Family Support Centre Highgate Baptist Church,
Conybere St, Birmingham, West Midlands B12 0LY; Tel 0121
440 6788
Project Manager Paul Nuwes
Family support, community-based services, children
and adult counselling, out of school club, holiday
playgroup.

Stepping Stones Family Support Project 16 Jenkins St,
Small Heath, Birmingham, West Midlands B10 0QH;
E-mail sstones@btconnect.com; Tel 0121 772 0613; Fax 0121
772 0613
Project Manager M. Morcom
Home based family support initiatives centre and child
care. Direct work with 5–13 year olds with emotional and
behavioural problems.

Bolton

The Children's Society

The Children's Society in Bolton 49–51 George St,
Farnworth, Lancashire BL4 9RJ;
E-mail bln@childsoc.org.uk; Tel 01204 573155
Project Leader Susan Bramwell

Spurgeon's Child Care

Bolton STAY Project St. Paul's Church, Garside St, Bolton,
Greater Manchester BL1 4AQ;
E-mail dave@urbanoutreachl.freeserve.co.uk; Tel 01204
385848; Fax 01204 399938
Co-ordinator D. Bagley

Bradford

Barnardos Yorkshire Division

Barnardos Allergrange Community Service 91 Saffron Dr, Allerton, Bradford, West Yorkshire BD15 7NQ; E-mail andy.robertson@barnardos.org.uk; Tel 01274 545186; Fax 01274 201677
Project Worker A. Robertson

Barnardos Yorkshire Regional Office
Four Gables, Clarence Rd, Leeds, West Yorkshire LS18 4LB; URL www.barnardos.org.uk

New Families, Yorkshire
43 Briggate, Shipley, Bradford, West Yorkshire BD17 7BP; URL www.barnardos.org.uk/newfamiliesyorkshire; E-mail yorkshire.newfamilies@barnardos.org.uk; Tel 01274 532852
Project Leader D. Jarvis

Catholic Care (Diocese of Leeds)

Bank House 113–117 Barkerend Rd, Bradford, West Yorkshire BD3 9AY; E-mail info@catholic-care.org.uk; Tel 01274 308411; (Head office Catholic Care) 0113 388 5400
A home with 11 places for people aged 18+. Supported living in self-contained flats for people with long term mental health difficulties.

7–9 Crownest Lane 7–9 Crownest La, Bingley, Bradford, West Yorkshire BD16 4HN; Tel 01274 568640
Contact Barbara Dennis
Home for adults with learning difficulties.

Redholt 78 Hollybank Rd, Bradford, West Yorkshire BD7 4QL; E-mail children@ccnedholt.freeserve.co.uk; Tel 01274 573049
Manager E.O. Espinoza
A residential home for six children and young people, offering medium to long-term care. Ages 0–18.

NCH Action for Children North East Region

The Children's Fund Participation Project Information Shop for Young People, 12 Broadway, Bradford, West Yorkshire BD 1JF; Tel 01274 722743
Contact Munaf Patel

Buttershaw Christian Family Centre Buttershaw Baptist Church, The Cres, Bradford, West Yorkshire BD6 3PZ; E-mail mark.phillips@buttershawbaptist.org.uk; Tel 01274 690262
Centre Manager Mark Phillips
Parenting groups, registered playgroup, breakfast cafe, lunch group, after school club, adult literacy, help and support for families. Child Contact Centre.

Bristol

Barnardos Wales and South West Region

Barnardos Shakti Imani Inclusion Project 114 Whitehall Rd, Bristol BS5 9BH; Tel 0117 955 1703
Project Leader Jendayi Serwah
Provides support services for black children aged 5–17 and their families.

Barnardos Lawrence Weston Family Centre Home Farm, Kings Weston La, Lawrence Weston, Bristol BS11 0JE; Tel 0117 982 4578
Project Leader H. Carlton
This project serves the geographical area of North Bristol only.

New Fulford Family Centre 237–239 Gatehouse Ave, Withywood, Bristol BS13 9AQ; Tel 0117 978 2441; Fax 0117 935 8886
11–15 Columbus Walk, Brigantine Pl, Cardiff CF1 5BL
Project Leader Jenny Lewis

NCH Action Trust for Children South West Region

Adoption and Foster Care NCH South West Weir Hse, 93 Whitby Rd, St. Philips, Bristol BS4 4AR; URL www.nch.org.uk; E-mail swaafp@mail.nch.org.uk; Tel 0117 300 5360
Project Manager Jo Jenkin

Bristol Housing Project 78 Belmont Rd, St. Andrews, Bristol BS6 5AT
Project Manager Robin Spencer; Tel 0117 373 5736

Stokescroft Youth Justice Centre Stokes Croft Centre, 59–61 Stokes Croft, Bristol BS1 3QP; Tel 0117 923 2077
Project Manager Steve Waters

Spurgeon's Child Care

Easton Families Project Beaufort St, Easton, Bristol BS5 0PQ; Tel 0117 955 4255; Fax 0117 955 3172
Project Manager Gill Miles

Buckinghamshire

South Bucks Probation Office Easton Crt, 23a Easton St, High Wycombe, Buckinghamshire HP11 1NT; Tel 01494 436421; Fax 01494 450132

The Children's Society

The Family Support Project 135 Jonathans Coffee Hall, Milton Keynes MK6 5DR; Tel 01908 604117
Project Leader Cheryl Arthur (Acting)

NCH Eastern Region

Evelyn Hse B, Lanwades Bus Pk, Kentford, nr Newmarket, Suffolk CB8 7PN; URL www.nch.org.uk

Fullers Slade Family Resource Centre Neighbourhood Hse, 91 Weavers Hill, Fullers Slade, Milton Keynes MK11 2BN; E-mail tafsfrc@mail.nchafc.org.uk; Tel 01908 568813
Project Manager Chris Chapman

Greenleys Family Centre Ardwell La, Greenleys, Milton Keynes MK12 6LU; E-mail tagfc@mail.org.uk; Tel 01908 313622; Fax 01908 312463
Project Manager Linda Farthing

NCH Aylesbury Residential Respite and Day Care Services 201 Buckingham Rd, Aylesbury, Buckinghamshire HP19 9QF; E-mail tarrcds@mail.nch.org.uk; Tel 01296 436249
Project Manager Kim Hinves
Respite and day care services for children with special needs.

Bury

NCH North West Region

Bury Family Centre 72–74 Tenters St, Bury, Greater Manchester BL9 0HX; E-mail nwbufc@mail.nch.org.uk; Tel 0161 764 4811
Project Manager W. Buckland

NCH Family Mediation and Children's Support Services – Greater Manchester 21 Knowsley St, Bury, Greater Manchester BL9 0ST; Tel 0161 797 9910; Fax 0161 763 9311
Project Manager Ben Raites

Calderdale

NCH Calderdale Leaving Care Project 2–3 Savile Row, Savile Park Rd, Halifax, West Yorkshire HX1 2EJ; E-mail neclct@mail.nch.org.uk; Tel 01422 359907; Fax 01422 329393
Project Manager Cathy Appleby

NCH North East Region
12 Granby Rd, Harrogate, West Yorkshire HG1 4ST;
URL www.nchafc.org.uk; Tel 01423 524286

Cambridgeshire

NCH Thames Anglia Region

Evelyn Hse, Lonwades Bus Pk, Kentford, Nr Newmarket,
Suffolk CB8 7PN

Fenland Leaving Care 100 Churchill Rd, Wisbech,
Cambridgeshire PE13 2DN; Tel 01945 466067; Fax 01945
466067
Project Manager Louisa Simpson

Peterborough Family Support Services Peterborough Arts
Centre, Goldhay Way, Peterborough, Cambridgeshire
PE2 5JQ; E-mail enpcp@mail.nch.org.uk; Tel 01733 371173;
Fax 01733 237365
Project Manager Glen Blackburn

The Religious Society of Friends (Quakers)

Friends Therapeutic Community Trust Glebe Hse, Shudy
Camps, Cambridge, Cambridgeshire CB1 6RB;
E-mail info@glebehouse.org.uk; Tel 01799 584359
Deputy Director T. Hornby
Therapeutic community; residential; young men;
(15–19); (17).

Cheshire

Barnardos North West Division

West Cheshire Families Project The Croft, Manning's La
South, Hoole, Chester, Cheshire CH2 3RT; Tel 01244 346482
Project Leader Terry Jones

BGWS Mediation Services Goss Chambers, Goss St,
Chester, Cheshire CH1 2BG; Tel 01244 400658; Fax 01244
343751
Manager (Mediation Services) Ian Chambers

CAFCASS 10 Congleton Rd, Sandbach, Cheshire
CW11 1WJ; E-mail jean.simmons@cafcass.gov.uk; Tel 01270
753502; Fax 01270 759462
Service Manager Jean Simmons
Children and family court advisory support service.

CYCES (Child and Youth Care Education Service) Central
Offices, Schools Hill, Cheadle, Cheshire SK8 1JE;
E-mail cyces@freeserve.co.uk; Tel 0161 283 4832
Principal Sally Wells
Deputy Principal Stuart Bale

Inscape House Salford Walkden Rd, Worsley, Greater
Manchester M28 7FG; E-mail inscape.salford@virgin.net;
Tel 0161 975 2340; Fax 0161 975 2341
Headteacher Mrs F. Brower

Meridian Schools Hill, Cheadle, Cheshire SK8 1JE;
URL www.bgws.org.uk; Tel 0161 283 4775
Service Manager Akilah Akinola
Manager Berat Pottinger

Woodlands Disability Service BGWS Campus, Schools Hill,
Cheadle, Cheshire SK8 1JE; URL www.bgws.org.uk;
E-mail woodlands.bgws@virgin.net; Tel 0161 283 4770
Manager Pat Marsh

The Children's Society

**Children and Young People's Participation Project,
Warrington** 4 Catterall Ave, Orford, Warrington WA2 0JA;
URL www.the-childrens-society.org.uk; Tel 01925 852905
Project Administrator Joyce Davies

62–64 Whitethroat Walk
62–64 Whitethroat Wlk, Oakwood, Birchwood, Warrington
WA3 6PQ; URL www.the-childrens.society.org.uk;
Tel 01925 824340

NCH Action for Children North West Regions

Bolton Parents' Support Network c/o Regional Office, 39–41
Wilson Patten St, Warrington, Warwickshire WA1 1PG

Butterfly Project 33 Wilson Patten St, Warrington
WA1 1PG; E-mail nwbp@mail.nch.org.uk; Tel 01925 655863
Manager Laura Madden

Halton Family Groups (Community Social Work Project)
Suite 1, Unit 1H, Midwood Hse, Midwood St, Widnes,
Cheshire WA8 6BH; E-mail nwhfg@mail.nch.org.uk;
Tel 0151 424 2036; Fax 0151 257 8261
Project Manager Liz Smith

Kings Cross Project

c/o Trinity Church, Peelhouse La, Widnes, Cheshire
WA8 6TJ; E-mail kingscrossproject@dial.pipex.com;
Tel 0151 420 4905
Manager Anne Patchett

Knutsford Family Support Project 12 Northfields,
Knutsford, Cheshire WA16 8JN;
E-mail nwkfsp@mail.nchafc.org.uk; Tel 01565 650647
Project Manager Laura Madden

Lache Family Centre 125 Cliveden Rd, Chester, Cheshire
CH4 8DT; Tel 01244 674494
Project Manager Mark Gaffney

Ventnor Road 1b Ventnor Rd, Heaton Moor, Stockport,
Greater Manchester SK4 4EJ; Tel 0161 442 3779; Fax 0161
442 3779
House Manager Tom McCall

Cornwall

NCH South West Region

Bodmin Family Centre NCH Assessment and Family
Support Service, Priory Rd, Bodmin, Cornwall PL31 2BT;
URL www.nch.org.uk; E-mail swbfc@mail.nchafc.org.uk;
Tel 01208 77662; Fax 01208 76190
Projects Manager John Diaper

Cornwall Leaving Care and After Care Service Enterprise
Hse, St. Austell Bus Pk, Par Moor Rd, St. Austell, Cornwall
PL25 3RF; E-mail swclcacs@mail.nch.org.uk; Tel 01726
815005; Fax 01726 815353
Project Manager Nadia Hewitt

NCH Penzance Family Centre 'Eakring', Alexandra Rd,
Penzance, Cornwall TR18 4LZ; Tel 01736 332020; Fax 01736
331818
Project Manager John Diaper

Polruan Polruan Flats, Polruan Rd, Truro, Cornwall
TR1 1QR; Tel 01872 26526
Contact Roger Blackburn

SPACE The Kernow Bldg, Pound La, Bodmin, Cornwall
PL31 2BT; Tel 01208 77696; Fax 01208 76190
Project Manager Shirley Mills

Coventry

NCH Action for Children Midlands Regions

Coventry Aftercare The Rocklands Centre, 138 Foleshill Rd,
Coventry, West Midlands CV1 4JJ;
E-mail mdca@mail.nch.org.uk; Tel 024 7625 7733; Fax 024
7625 7737
Manager Isobel Pullen

Coventry Cornerstone Family Centre Howard St, Hillfields,
Coventry, West Midlands CV1 4GE; Tel 024 7625 6611;
Fax 024 7623 1346
Project Manager Eileen Woodfield

Coventry and Warwickshire Independent Visitor Project 138
Foleshill Rd, Coventry, West Midlands CV1 4JJ; Tel 024 7625
7733
Contact Nicola Hall

In-Touch Training Project 38 Hill St, Coventry, West Midlands CV1 4AN; E-mail mdittp@mail.nchafc.org.uk; Tel 02476 554443; Fax 02476 552223
Contact Sue Stead

Spurgeon's Child Care

Bedworth Family Support Centre The Old School Hse, 16 Bulkington Rd, Bedworth, West Midlands CV12 9DG; Tel 024 7631 5349; Fax 024 7631 5349
Family support, pre-school and playgroup, crèche, carers and toddlers, nursery equipment library, post-natal support, supervised contact service, parenting skills course, toy library.

Furnace Fields Parents Centre Hazel Gr, Bedworth, West Midlands CV12 9DA; E-mail ann@furnacefields.co.uk; Tel 024 7649 4171
Centre Manager Ann Tabram
Family support service.

Cumbria

Barnardos North West Division

Barrows Green Holiday Activity Centre Barrows Grn, Kendal, Cumbria LA8 0JQ; Tel 01539 560307
Project Leader M. Keighley

CATALYST – NSPCC Cumbria Sex Offender Project 7 Chatsworth Sq, Carlisle, Cumbria CA1 1HB; E-mail northcumbria@nspcc.org.uk; Tel 01228 521829; Fax 01228 514781

NCH North West Region

Banklands Family Centre 25 Banklands, Workington, Cumbria CA14 3EU; Tel 01900 872195
Project Manager Fiona Hogan

Furness Family Centre Dallington, Abbey Rd, Barrow-in-Furness, Cumbria LA13 9AG; Tel 01229 831527
Project Manager Vacancy

NSPCC

The Wedgewood Centre 14 Hollins Cl, Whitehaven, Cumbria CA28 8EX; E-mail wcumbria@nspcc.org.uk; Tel 01946 595300; Fax 01946 595316
Manager (Children's Services) Sue Toomey

Derbyshire

South Derbyshire After Care Project 1st Fl, 11–13 High St, Swadlincote, Derbyshire DE11 8JE; URL www.the-childrens-society.org.uk; E-mail south-derbyshire-after-care@childsoc.org.uk; Tel 01283 819508; Fax 01283 819507
Contact Janice Price

Barnardos Midland Division

The Elms Family Centre 70–72 Elmsleigh Dr, Midway, Swadlincote, Derbyshire DE11 0ER; URL www.barnardos.org.uk; E-mail elms@barnardos.org.uk; Tel 01283 551251
Project Leader N. Martin

Mid Derbyshire Aftercare and Family Link Projects 9 Mundy St, Heanor, Derbyshire DE75 7EB; Tel 01773 717212
Service Manager (After Care) Stuart Robinson
Service Manager (Family Link) T. Easter

NCH Midlands Region

Derbyshire Family Mediation Project 32a Newbold Rd, Chesterfield, Derbyshire S41 7PH; Tel 01246 277422; Fax 01246 277363
Project Manager Liz Ralph

Derbyshire and Derby City Young Carers 3 Leopold St, Derby DE1 2HE; E-mail endeyc@mail.nch.org.uk; Tel 01332 370430; Fax 01332 381616
Project Manager Sally Elliott
Project Manager Sonia Flint
Newbold Road
32a Newbold Rd, Chesterfield, Derbyshire SH1 7PH; E-mail endeyc2@mail.nch.org.uk; Tel 01246 207752
Project Manager Sally Elliott
Project Manager Sonia Flint

North East Derbyshire Aftercare Youthreach, 74 Market St, South Normanton, Derbyshire DE55 2EJ; E-mail mdyrp@mail.nch.org.uk; Tel 01773 583037; Fax 01773 811494
Manager Pam Matthews

Yew Trees, Derbyshire 45 Queen St, Chesterfield, Derbyshire S40 4SF; Tel 01246 277838; Fax 01246 222129
Project Manager Dave Widdowson

Youth Reach 74 Market St, South Normanton, Alfreton, Derbyshire DE55 2EJ; E-mail mdyrp@mail.nch.org.uk; Tel 01773 583037; Fax 01773 811494
Project Manager Pam Matthews

Devon

Chelfham Mill School Chelfham, Barnstaple, Devon EX32 7LA; Tel 01271 850448
Head K. Roberts, BEd, BPhil(EBD)
Boys 7–13 Behavioural difficulties

Dame Hannah Rogers School Woodford Rd, Ivybridge, Devon PL21 9HQ; URL www.damehannah.com; E-mail mail@damehannah.com; Tel 01752 892461; Fax 01752 898101
Principal W.R. Evans
For students with physical difficulties and communication challenges.
Mixed 8–19

West of England School and College for Young People with Little or No Sight Countess Wear, Exeter, Devon; E-mail pholland@westengland.devon.sch.uk; Tel 01392 454200; Fax 01392 428048
Principal P.D. Holland, MEd, BSpEd, DipEd(VI)
(Advisory and Assessment Service for SW region).
Mixed 5–16 (Day nursery 3–5) (Devon/Somerset) FE College 16–21 St. David's Hse MD VI 5–16 (PS and Blind) (Boarding and Day)

The Children's Society

Check Point 7 Victoria Rd, Ellacombe, Torquay, Torbay TQ1 1HV; E-mail cpt@childrenssociety.org.uk; Tel 01803 200100

Children's Rights Torbay 42 Palace Ave, Paignton, Devon TQ3 3HF; E-mail cr@childrensociety.org.uk; Tel 01803 668080; Fax 01803 666796
For young people aged 10 and over.
Project Leader John Noake

Management Committee

British Seamen's Boys' Home Grenville Hse, Berry Head Rd, Brixham, Devon TQ5 9AF; URL www.grenvillehouse.com; E-mail info@grenvillehouse.com; Tel 01803 852797; Fax 01803 852797
Secretary R.M. Williams
Outdoor Education Centre.
Mixed (60) + (12)

NCH South West Region

Beacon Heath Family Centre The Cedars, Beacon La, Exeter, Devon EX4 8LZ; Tel 01392 427063
Project Manager Sally Randell

Chestnut Avenue Family Centre Magnolia Ave, Wonford, Exeter, Devon EX2 6DJ; E-mail swcafe@mail.nch.org.uk; Tel 01392 491802
Project Manager Anne Barnes

Devon Under Eights Customs Hse, The Quay, Exeter, Devon EX2 4AN; Tel 01392 427827
Project Manager Viv Hogan
Administrator Jenny Harris

Elm Park Family Centre 1 Elm Park Villas, Blundells Rd, Tiverton, Devon EX16 4BY; Tel 01884 255783
Project Manager David Jones

Ernesettle Family Centre Ernesettle School, Biggin Hill, Plymouth PL5 2RB; Tel 01752 362657; Fax 01752 369069
Project Manager Heather Reid

Ilfracombe Family Centre Ilfracombe Infants' School, Marlborough Rd, Ilfracombe, Devon EX34 8PN; Tel 01271 863611
Senior Project Worker Karen Lockwood

Leander House Fore St, Devonport, Plymouth PL1 4DW; E-mail swlhd@mail.nch.org.uk; Tel 01752 605174
Project Manager Heather Reid

Nomony Centre St. John's Bridge Rd, Cattedown, Plymouth PL4 0JJ; Tel 01752 667869; Fax 01752 202292
Manager Claire Drummond

Oaklands Park Short Breaks Project Oaklands Park School, John Nash Dr, Dawlish, Devon EX7 9SF; Tel 01626 862884
Project Manager Nigel North

Plymouth Leaving Care Project Bedford Villa, Amity Pl, Plymouth PL4 8EY; E-mail swplca@mail.nch.org.uk
Project Manager Phil Hutty; Tel 01752 213231

Torbay Saturday Club Parkfield Hse, 38 Esplanade Rd, Paignton, Devon TQ3 2NH; Tel 01803 523404; Fax 01803 523404
Co-ordinator Sue Thompson

Torbay Special Needs Playscheme Parkfield Hse, 38 Esplanade Rd, Paignton, Devon TQ3 2NH; Tel 01803 523404; Fax 01803 523414
Co-ordinator Sue Thompson

Valuing Education Beacon Heath Family Centre, The Cedars Beacon La, Exeter, Devon EX4 8LZ; Tel 01392 427063
Contact Sally Randell

Victoria House Family Centre Victoria Hse, Victoria Rd, Barnstaple, Devon EX32 8NP; E-mail swvhfc@mail.nch.org.uk; Tel 01271 321411
Project Manager I. Greaves

NCH – Withy Barn Winsbury Crt, Crownhill, Plymouth PL6 5JU; E-mail swwb@mail.nch.org.uk; Tel 01752 510262; Fax 01752 510263
Project Manager Mark Tucker

Dorset

The Children's Society

The Junction 266 Holdenhurst Rd, Bournemouth BH8 8AY; URL www.childrenssociety.org.uk; E-mail the-junction@childrenssociety.org.uk; Tel 01202 399733; Fax 01202 397656
Project Administrator Debbie Young
Project Leader Paul Weston

NCH South West Region

'Outlooks' NCH Castle Rd, Portland, Dorset DT5 1AU; E-mail swofc@mail.nch.org.uk; Tel 01305 823794
Project Manager I. Veale

Dudley

NCH Midlands Region

Black Country Children's Rights 29 St. James's Rd, Dudley, West Midlands D1Y 3JB; E-mail mddca@mail.nch.org.uk; Tel 01384 212345
Project Manager Ann Cartwright

Stephenson House 292 Stourbridge Rd, Dudley, West Midlands DY1 2EE; Tel 01384 485859; Fax 01384 480047
Contact Irene Hayes

Netherton Park Family Centre Netherton Pk, Netherton, Dudley, West Midlands DY2 9QF; E-mail info@neth-nur.dudley.gov.uk; Tel 01384 818255; Fax 01384 818258
Project Manager Lesley Rowlands-Roberts

Durham

Barnardos North East Division

Barnardos Shared Care North East Suite 4, Durham Business Centre, Langley Moor, Littleburn Ind Est, Durham, County Durham DH7 8HG; Tel 0191 378 4800
Manager (Children's Services) J.A. Latheron

NCH North East Region

NCH Durham and Darlington Family Mediation and Children's Support Services 1st Fl, 72–76 North Rd, Durham, County Durham DH1 4SQ; E-mail nedadfm@mail.nch.org.uk; Tel 0191 386 5418; Fax 0191 386 3057
Project Manager Mary Evans

Seaham Family Centre 56–58 Beech Cres, Parkside, Seaham, County Durham SR7 7QB; Tel 0191 581 9911; Fax 0191 513 1600
Project Manager Josephine Fairless

East Riding of Yorkshire

Beverley Cherry Tree Community Association

Cherry Tree Advice Centre 117 Cherry Tree La, Beverley, East Riding of Yorkshire HU17 0AY; Tel 01482 871993
Advice Service Co-ordinator Simon Pickering

The Children's Society

CAFCASS/Humber Bridge 20 The Weir, Hessle, East Riding of Yorkshire HU13 0RU; E-mail gal@childsoc.org.uk; Tel 01482 640228; Fax 01482 649199
Project Leader Helen Van Gruening
Project Leader Henny Heawood

Essex

Barnardos London, East Anglia and the South East

The Bridge Project Cottage No 9, The Village, Hornes Rd, Barkingside, Ilford, Essex IG6 1BU; E-mail samuel.okwei-nortey@barnardos.org.uk; Tel 020 8551 1107
Project Leader S.N. Okwei-Nortey

Counselling Services Cottage No. 1, Tanners La, Barkingside, Ilford, Essex IG6 1QG; Tel 020 8550 2688
Manager (Children's Services) A.M. Haigh

Day Break 30 Civic Way, Ilford, Essex IG6 1BY; Tel 020 8551 7722
Project Leader V. Bakaria

Hamara Family Project 1b Priory Ave, London E17 7QP; Tel 020 8503 7270
Project Leader A.J. DeBerker

Jigsaw Project (Barnardos) 12 Church Hill, Walthamstow, London E17 3AG; URL www.barnardos.org.uk/jigsaw; E-mail mo.o'reilly@barnardos.org.uk; Tel 020 8521 0033
Manager (Children's Services) Mo. O'Reilly
A fostering and adoption service offering a range of family placement services, a contact facility and direct work room for children.

Sheltered Placement Scheme Scotch Hse, Tanners La, Barkingside, Ilford, Essex IG6 1QG; E-mail sue.burch@barnardos.org.uk
Manager (Human Resources) Sue Burch

Young Women's Project 4a Chillingworth Rd, Holloway, London N7 8QJ; URL www.barnardos.org.uk; E-mail young.women@barnardos.org.uk; Tel 020 7700 2253
Manager (Children's Services) L. Fry

The Children's Society

Mid Essex Drug Awareness Service 114 Springfield Rd, Chelmsford, Essex CM2 6LF; Tel 01245 493311; Fax 01245 491400
Project Leader Tom Aldridge
Opening times: Mon, Wed, Fri 0930–1700, Drop-In 1000–1600, Tues–Thurs, 1000–2030. For preventative, diversionary and support work with under 18's.

NCH Thames Anglia Region

Brentwood Family Centre 24 Norton Rd, Ingatestone, Essex CM4 0AB; Tel 01277 353497; Fax 01277 354691
Project Manager Richard Hill

Essex and Thurrock Independent Visitors Scheme 24 Norton Rd, Ingatestone, Essex CM4 0AB; E-mail taeivs@mail.nchafc.org.uk; Tel 01277 356480; Fax 01277 354691
Manager Mandy Evill

NCH Loughton Family Centre 94 Lawton Rd, Loughton, Essex IG10 2AA; Tel 020 8508 6819
Project Manager Sue Lancaster

RPS Rainer

Carli Project 95 Luncies Rd, Basildon, Essex SS14 1SD; E-mail carli@rpsrainer.fsbusiness.co.uk; Tel 01268 555244; Fax 01268 553941
Project Manager Odette Helman

Catch Project 123–124 The Stow, Harlow, Essex CM20 3AS; URL www.rpsrainer.org.uk; E-mail catch.rpsrainer@ukonline.co.uk; Tel 01279 838003; Fax 01279 306560
Project Manager Vacancy

Essex Motor Project Unit 9, Winstanley Way, Basildon, Essex SS14 3BP; E-mail vic.vant@rpsrainer.org.uk; Tel 01268 273380; Fax 01268 273380

Unit E10
Cowdray Centre, Cowdray Ave, Colchester, Essex CO1 1BP; Tel 01206 768642; Fax 01206 768642
Project Manager Victor Vant

Spurgeon's Child Care

Becontree Baptist Church Becontree Avenue Family Project, Becontree Ave, Dagenham, Essex RN8 3JR; Tel 020 8592 1265
After-school club.

Gloucestershire

NCH South West Region

The Collies Newland St, Whitecliff, Coleford, Gloucestershire GL16 8NB; E-mail swtc@mail.nch.org.uk; Tel 01594 810931
Project Manager Beth Frederick

Residential short break and outreach service for children and young people 5–19, who have a learning and/or physical disability, living in the Forest of Dean social services area.

David Kent House 187 Westward Rd, Stroud, Gloucestershire GL5 4SY; Tel 01453 750976
Project Manager Paul Summersby

The Meadows Meadow La West, Dudbridge, Stroud, Gloucestershire GL5 5JR; Tel 01453 750421; Fax 01453 753479
Linked Projects Manager P. Summersby
Registered Manager Stephen Griffin
Residential short breaks for disabled children.

Spurgeon's Child Care

Matson Churches Youth Community Project Matson Baptist Church, Matson Ave, Gloucester, Gloucestershire GL4 6LA; E-mail robayliffe@mcycp.freeserve.co.uk; Tel 01452 381070
Project Manager (Youth Support) Vacancy
Youth and community work.

St. Aidans Church Coronation Sq, Hesters Way, Cheltenham, Gloucestershire GL51 7SA; URL www.stmarksparish.org; E-mail familyspacehway@tesco.net; Tel 01242 580812
Project Manager P. Blake
Family support work.

Greater Manchester

The Children's Society

The Children's Society Play and Participation Partnership, 103 Union St, Oldham, Greater Manchester OL1 1QH; URL www.childrenssociety.org.uk; E-mail tcs-in-oldham@childrenssociety.org.uk; Tel 0161 785 9909; Fax 0161 785 8956
Project Leader Raja Miah

NCH North West Region

Salford Adolescent and Aftercare 1a Garden St, Eccles, Salford, Greater Manchester M30 0EZ; Tel 0161 707 9495; Fax 0161 707 5661
Contact Mark Connolly

Salford Family Link Mocha Community Centre – Mocha Pde, Lower Broughton Rd, Salford, Greater Manchester M7 1QE; Tel 0161 819 1459; Fax 0161 819 1459
Manager Shelli Nelson

Trafford Young Carers 69 Cross St, Sale, Greater Manchester M33 7HF; E-mail nwtyc@mail.nch.org.uk; Tel 0161 972 0090; Fax 0161 973 4915
Project Manager Rosalind Turnbull

Hampshire

Catholic Children's Society Winchester 7 Bridge St, Winchester, Hampshire SO23 0HN; URL www.cathchild.org; E-mail adoption.winchester@cathchild.org; Tel 01962 842024
Team Manager (Adoption) Di Emery
Project Leader (Foster Care Service) Murray Marks
7a Bridge St, Winchester, Hampshire SO23 0HN; Tel 01962 854652

The Children's Society

Young Carers Initiative Youngs Yard, Finches La, Winchester, Hampshire SO21 1NN; URL www.childrenssociety.org.uk/youngcarers; E-mail young-carers-initiative@childrenssociety.org.uk; Tel 01962 711511
Network Manager Jeremy Coombe

Rights and Participation: Hampshire, Portsmouth and Winchester All Saints Church, Commercial Rd, Portsmouth PO1 4BT; Tel 023 9282 1137
Project Leader Jeremy Coombe

Hampshire Social Services Department

Cambridge Road Centre 4–8 Cambridge Rd, Aldershot, Hampshire GU11 3JZ; Tel 01252 320027
Adolescent and Family Support Team.

Sunbeams Unit Hampshire County Council, Social Services Dept, 4–8 Cambridge Rd, Aldershot, Hampshire GU11 3JZ; Tel 01252 320027; (Direct Line) 01252 322448
Mixed Respite care for children and young people with a learning disability

NCH South East Region

Basingstoke Residential Care 2a Linden Ave, Old Basing, Basingstoke, Hampshire RG24 7HG;
E-mail sela@mail.nch.org.uk; Tel 01256 474598; Fax 01256 843637
Manager John Gardner

Order of Our Lady of Charity

The Mount 358 London Rd, Waterlooville, Portsmouth PO7 7SR; Tel 023 9225 1661
Sister-in-Charge Sr M.R. Hegarty
Mixed 5–18 RC and other religions (8)

RPS Rainer

RPS Rainer City Training Great Western Hse, 34 Isambard Brunel Rd, Portsmouth PO1 2RJ;
E-mail teresa@citytraining.newnet.co.uk; Tel 023 9278 0070; Fax 023 9271 8323
Manager Teresa Sayer-Smith
Work place based vocational training for all young people but with a particular focus on working with those with particular needs, including disadvantaged and disaffected young people.

Catherine Booth House 1 Aylward St, Portsmouth PO1 3PH; Tel 023 9273 7226
Residential Centre
Family centre for 40 men, women and children. Sole referring agency: Portsmouth City Council.
Residential

Cornerstone Community Centre
32 Queen St, Portsmouth; Tel 023 9287 6579
Assistant Manager R. North
Community centre parent/toddler group, counselling – debt and personal, luncheon club for the elderly, meals on wheels, cafeteria open to the public.

Youth and Families Matter Testwood Baptist Church, 283a Salisbury Rd, Totton, Southampton SO40 3LZ;
E-mail yfm-testwoodbaptist@ukgateway.net; Tel 023 8086 0320
Project Manager Roger Frapwell
Family Support Worker Pauline Whitmarsh
Deputy Project Manager Trish Hall
Family support, pre-school, youth and community work, parent support work, parenting courses.

Hereford and Worcester

Barnardos Midland Division

Break Away Trinity Hse, Trinity Rd, Dudley, West Midlands DY1 1JB; Tel 01384 458585
Project Leader J. Tanner

Redditch Family Centre 26 Salop Rd, Redditch, Worcestershire B97 4PS; Tel 01527 550577
Project Leader R. Clift

Warndon Family Centre Shap Dr, Warndon, Worcestershire WR4 9NX; E-mail mdwafc@mail.nchafc.org.uk; Tel 01905 754088; Fax 01905 754088
Contact Sally Jordan

RPS Rainer

Rainbow 1–3 Hylton Rd, 2nd Fl, Worcester, Worcestershire WR2 5JN; Tel 01905 339200; Fax 01905 339201
Manager Steve Massey
Senior Administrator Sandra Bradley
Recruitment, training and support for volunteers to work with offenders. In partnership with Hereford and Worcester Probation Service.

Tutnall Children's Home Trust

Hertfordshire

Stairways 19 Douglas Rd, Harpenden, Hertfordshire; Tel 01582 460055; Fax 01582 462422
Domiciliary Support Service (Children and Adults). Mixed residential care home.
5–19 Short term care Learning disabilities (6) Long-term care adults (21)

NCH Thames Anglia Region

Herts Respite Care 50 Adrian Rd, Abbots Langley, Hertfordshire WD5 0AQ; Tel 01923 267607
Project Manager Glenna Tomlin (Acting)

Phoenix Project 7 Wellfield Rd, Hatfield, Hertfordshire AL10 0BW; E-mail tatpp@mail.nch.org.uk; Tel 01707 260992
Care Leavers Interdependency Project.

Stevenage Family Support Service 3 North Rd, Stevenage, Hertfordshire SG1 4AT; E-mail tasfss@mail.nch.org.uk; Tel 01438 317418; Fax 01438 750525
Project Manager Bridy Speller

Hull

Barnardos Yorkshire Division

Hull 348 Project 348 Holderness Rd, Kingston upon Hull HU9 3DQ; Tel 01482 323671
Project Leader Douglas Green

NCH North East Region

Families First (Hull) 892 Holderness Rd, Kingston upon Hull HU9 4AA; Tel 01482 796123; Fax 01482 782172
Project Manager Jean Sykes

Hull and East Riding Young Carers Project 46 Middle Street North, Driffield, East Riding of Yorkshire YO25 6SS;
E-mail nesdc@mail.nch.org.uk; Tel 01377 272774
Project Manager Sharon Martin

Keys Project 15 x 8th Ave, North Hull Est, Kingston upon Hull HU6 9LB; E-mail nekeys@mail.nchafc.org.uk; Tel 01482 803042
Project Manager Jean Sykes

North Hull Family Centre 86 12th Ave, North Hull Est, Kingston upon Hull HU6 9LE; Tel 01482 803978; Fax 01482 804774
Project Manager Jean Sykes

The Sailors' Families' Society Cottingham Rd, Newland, Kingston upon Hull HU6 7RJ;
E-mail info@sailors-families.org.uk; Tel 01482 342331; Fax 01482 447868
Chief Executive Tim Vernon

South Humber Young Carers The Carers Centre, 11 Redcombe La, Brigg, Lincolnshire DN20 8AU; Tel 01652 652206; Fax 01652 652206
Contact Mavis Crawforth
Contact Bev Davis

Isle of Man

NCH North West Region

Bonwick House Family Resource Centre Bonwick Hse, Lezayre Rd, Ramsey, Isle of Man IM8 2LU; Tel 01624 815918
Project Manager Bernadette Moore

Kent

The Caldecott Community Mersham le Hatch, Ashford, Kent URL www.caldecottfoundation.org; E-mail care@caldecott.org; Tel 01233 503954; Fax 01233 502650
Director D. Marshall
Deputy Director Peter Sandiford
Mixed 6–18 EBD with SEN (76)

Churches Child Protection Advisory Service PO Box 133, Swanley, Kent BR8 7UQ; URL www.ccpas.co.uk; E-mail info@ccpas.co.uk; Tel 0845 1204 550; (Helpline) 0845 1204 551; Fax 0845 1204 552
Director D. Pearson
Provides training and support in child protection/child abuse issues to churches and children's organisations etc across the UK. Advice to social services in dealing with issues of abuse in churches and religious organisations.

Barnardos London, East Anglia and South East Division

Apex Project 128–130 London Rd, Southborough, Tunbridge Wells, Kent TN4 0PL; E-mail apex@barnardos.org.uk; Tel 01892 510650
Project Leader I. Sharpe

Chilston Project The Lodge, Pembury Rd, Tunbridge Wells, Kent TN2 3QJ; Tel 01892 511468; 01892 511469
Project Leader A. Griffin

Meadows School London Rd, Southborough, Tunbridge Wells, Kent TN4 0RJ; Tel 01892 529144
Headteacher Mike Price

Ravensdale Sandhurst Rd, Tunbridge Wells, Kent TN2 3ND; E-mail ravensdale@barnardos.org.uk; Tel 01892 543062
Manager (Children's Services) L. Arney

Castle Homes

Castle Homes – Alexandra House Deal, Kent; Tel 0800 917 5671
Referral Co-ordinator Tel 01536 711111
KCC registered for seven children of either sex aged 11–18 for short-term care and assessment.

Castle Homes – Allenby House 57–59 Victoria Rd, Deal, Kent CT14 7AY; Tel 01304 381324
Officer-in-Charge R. Arthur, DipSW
Placements Officer John Mackenzie; Tel 01304 202010
Placements Officer David Ayers; Tel 01304 202010
KCC registered for nine children of either sex between the ages of 11–18 for long-term care with a therapeutic environment for emotionally disturbed children.
Number of employees
12

Castle Homes – Arundel House 101a Sandwich Rd, Whitfield, Dover, Kent CT16 3JG; Tel 01304 822444
Officer-in-Charge T. Benfield, CSS
Officer-in-Charge I. Benfield, CSS

Placements Officer John Mackenzie; Tel 01304 202010
Placements Officer David Ayers; Tel 01304 202010
KCC registered for five children of either sex aged 0–11. Sibling groups especially cared for in a therapeutic environment for emotionally disturbed children.
Number of employees
7

Castle Homes – Haven House Sidcup, Kent; Tel 020 8302 9091; 0800 917 5671
Referral Co-ordinator Tel 01536 711111
Registered with London Borough of Bexley for five children of both sexes aged 8–18 for emergency placements and crisis intervention, 24-hour intake serviced (collected).

Castle Homes – Victoria House Dover, Kent; Tel 01304 825888
KCC registered for five children of both sexes aged 8—17 for a 12 week assessment to determine possible residential placements.

The Catholic Children's Society

Familymakers Residential and Homefinding Unit 28 Leith Park Rd, Gravesend, Kent DA11 1LW; Tel 01474 352521; 01474 568016; Fax 01474 334967
Project Manager Sybil Roach-Tennant
Two semi-autonomous units with preparation for permanent family placement.
Mixed 5–12

Hubert House Community Centre Mallard Cl, Knights Manor Est, Dartford, Kent DA1 5HU; URL www.cathchild.org; E-mail huberthouse@cathchild.org
Project Leader Caroline Bennett

The Children's Society (London and South East)

The Thanet Community Development Project Unit 9, St. John Business Centre, St. Peter's Rd, Margate, Kent CT9 1TE; E-mail tcd@childsoc.org.uk; Tel 01843 227553; Fax 01843 299566
Project Leader Ivan O'Reilly

NCH South East Region

Harmony Project 85 Dickens Rd, Gravesend, Kent DA12 2JX; URL www.nch.org.uk; E-mail segh@mail.nch.org.uk; Tel 01474 535788

Independent Representation and Complaints Service 39–48 Marsham St, Maidstone, Kent ME14 1HH; E-mail seircs@mail.nch.org.uk; Tel 01622 756678
Project Manager Vacancy

Foster Care NCH Broadstairs 479 Margate Rd, Broadstairs, Kent CT10 2QA; E-mail sefcb@mail.nch.org.uk; Tel 01843 601101; Fax 01843 864636
Project Manager Tracy Livesey

NCH North Downs Project Westchurch Hse, Godfrey Wlk, Ashford, Kent TN23 7XJ; E-mail sendp@mail.nch.org.uk; Tel 01233 612678
Project Manager Jenny Fairweather

NCH South Ashford Playlink Ray Allen Centre, Stanhope Rd, Ashford, Kent TN23 5RN; E-mail sesap@mail.nch.org.uk; Tel 01233 643103; Fax 01233 643103
Manager Stella Sapsford

Tunbridge Wells Harmony ET Centre, Sherwood Park School, Friars Way, Tunbridge Wells, Kent TN2 3UA; Tel 01892 519929

NCH Westwood School 479 Margate Rd, Broadstairs, Kent CT10 2QA; URL www.nch.org.uk; E-mail sews@mail.nch.org.uk; Tel 01843 600820; Fax 01843 600827

Folkestone Early Years Centre Dover Rd, Folkestone, Kent CT20 1QF; URL www.nch.org.uk; E-mail sefey@mail.nch.org.uk; Tel 01303 212720; Fax 01303 212721
Contact Maggie Marshall

PCCA Christian Child Care

Family Advice and Counselling Centre Bethel Centre, Claremont Rd, Hextable, Swanley, Kent BR8 7RF; URL www.pcca.co.uk; E-mail info@pcca.co.uk; Tel 0845 1204 550
Director D. Pearson

RPS Rainer

Kent Triple Key Flat 1, 11 Rendezvous St, Folkestone, Kent CT20 1EY; Tel 01303 226526; Fax 01303 226386
Deputy Project Manager T. Waddell
Leaving care/aftercare project, operating in Ashford, Folkestone and Dover.

Peper Harow Foundation

Please see the Peper Harow main entry, listed elsewhere in this section.
Goldwell with Greenfields Independent Special School Biddenden Rd, Tenterden, Kent TN30 6TD; Tel 01580 292144; Fax 01580 292314
Mixed emotionally disturbed 6–12-year-olds with on-site special school
Greenfields for resident children and day pupils. No area limit.

Lancashire

Action with Young Carers (Bolton) 22 Chorley New Rd, Bolton, Lancashire BL1 4AP; Tel 01204 373989
Blackburn Child Care Society Whalley Rd, Wilpshire, Blackburn BB1 9LL; URL www.bccs-uk.org; E-mail enquiries@bccs-uk.org; Tel 01254 244700; Fax 01254 244701
Director J.A. Tempest
One family group home (schoolchildren).
Interview and examination suite (physical and sexual abuse). (Available for Lancashire Police and Social Services).
Residential remand unit for males aged 11–17.
Bail support service for young people appearing before the youth court (Lancashire and Blackburn and Darwen).
Foster care service for children and young people.
Phone for details.
Children's Rights Service (Rochdale) Dunsterville Hse, Manchester Rd, Rochdale, Greater Manchester OL11 3RB; Tel 01706 869183; (Freephone) 0800 387809
Children's Rights Officer Ann Marie Arnold
Moorland View Children's Home and School Manchester Rd, Clowbridge, Burnley, Lancashire BB11 5PQ; URL www.moorlandview.co.uk; E-mail robin@moorlandview.co.uk; Tel 01282 431144; Fax 01282 455411
Manager Robin Lageard
Meets the needs of children and young people who experience attachment disorders, have experienced sexual, emotional or physical abuse, or have experienced trauma in their lives.
Mixed 11–15
Tameside Children's Rights, Advice and Complaints Service 19–21 Wellington St, Ashton-under-Lyne, Lancashire OL6 6BG; E-mail childrensrights@sova.fsnet.co.uk; Tel 0161 339 7232

Barnardos North West Region

7 Lineside Cl, Belle Vale, Liverpool, Merseyside L25 2UD; Tel 0151 487 5313
Barnardos Chorley Families 2 Harrington Rd, Chorley, Lancashire PR7 1JZ; E-mail chorley.families@barnardos.org.uk; Tel 01257 278994
Manager (Children's Services) Lynda Nolan
South Ribble Families Project Bradbury Hse, 453 Leyland Rd, Lostock Hall, Preston, Lancashire PR5 5SB; Tel 01772 629470
Manager (Children's Services) M. Brennand
Provides a service for disabled children and their families in South Ribble.

Catholic Caring Services (Diocese of Lancaster) Ltd

Catholic Caring Services Residential Children's Centre, 74 Wellington Rd, Preston, Lancashire PR2 1BX; URL www.catholiccaringservices.org.uk; E-mail jimcullen@catholiccaringservices.org.uk; Tel 01772 720654
Residential Team Leader Meryl Allen

The Children's Society

The Children's Society in Rochdale 94 Hill Top Dr, Kirkholt, Rochdale, Lancashire OL11 2RL; Tel 01706 345600; Fax 01706 343490
Project Leader Sue Hyland

NCH North West Region

Bury Family Centre 72–74 Tenters St, Bury, Lancashire BL9 0HX; E-mail nwbufc@mail.nch.org.uk; Tel 0161 764 4811
Contact Barbara Martin
Bypass 106–108 Newport St, Bolton, Lancashire BL3 6AB; E-mail nwb@mail.nch.org.uk; Tel 01204 362002; Fax 01204 388982
Elm Tree Family Support Service 126 Accrington Rd, Burnley, Lancashire BB11 5AE; E-mail nwetfss@mail.nch.org.uk; Tel 01282 452405
Morecambe Young People's Housing Project 40–42 Victoria St, Morecambe, Lancashire LA4 4AL; Tel 01524 831978; Fax 01524 418827
Contact Sarah Elliott
Skelmersdale and Up Holland Family Groups (Community Social Work Project) Office 4, Ecumenical Centre, Northway, Skelmersdale, Lancashire WN8 6PN; Tel 01695 724441
Project Co-ordinator Gail Pulford

NSPCC North West Region

Acorn Centre 1 Lostock Gdns, Blackpool FY4 3PP; Tel 01253 345001
Practice Manager Cindy Hunter

The Nugent Care Society

The Bungalow 346b Newton Rd, Lowton, Warrington, Greater Manchester WA3 1HE; Tel 01942 676555; Fax 01942 674135
Head of Home K. Cooke
Adults with learning disabilities and physical disabilities.
Clarence House School West La, Formby, Merseyside L37 7AZ; Tel 01704 872151; Fax 01704 831001
Deputy Head (Pastoral Care) Donagh McKillop
Residential/day
Mixed 8–17 Special needs

Clumber Lodge Children's Home 88 Victoria Rd, Formby, Merseyside L37 1LP; Tel 01704 872210; Fax 01704 833172
Head of Home Sister B. McKeown
Residential
Three mothers and babies.
   Mixed 0–18 Sexually and physically abused younger children.

Lime House Residential Home Newton Rd, Lowton, Warrington WA3 1HE; Tel 01942 674135; Fax 01942 674135
Head of Home A. Hillidge
   Adults

Nugent House School Carr Mill Rd, Billinge, Wigan, Greater Manchester WN5 5TT; Tel 01744 892551; Fax 01744 895697
Headteacher Mrs J. Bienias
Residential/day
   Boys 7–19 Special needs

Othona Children's Home 427 Liverpool Rd, Birkdale, Southport, Merseyside PR8 3BW; Tel 01704 573888; Fax 01704 570432
Head of Home K. Sutton
   5–18

Spurgeon's Child Care

Bacup Family Centre 2–4 Hawthorne Rd, Bacup, Lancashire OL13 9LQ;
E-mail spurgeons@bacupfamilycentre.fsnet.co.uk; Tel 01706 875720
Centre Manager Leila Allen
Family support, playgroup, crèche, community-based services.

Leyland Project 247 Leyland La, Leyland, Preston, Lancashire PR25 1XL; Tel 01772 436200 (Wade Hall Family Centre)
Project Manager, Youth and Community Worker T. Grose
Community and family support work, Wade Hall project, schools' work, homelessness.

Whitworth Family Centre 33–35 Thorburn Dr, Whitworth, Rochdale, Lancashire OL12 8UJ;
E-mail whitworthcentre@fsmail.net; Tel 01706 356665
Centre Manager L. Moore
Family support, playgroup, crèche, after school clubs, community-based services.

Leeds

The Palace 90–92 Shepherds La, Leeds, West Yorkshire LS7 4DZ
Project Manager Andy Wilson; Tel 0113 262 0093
Youth Clubs
Employment advice and support.
Court support and prison visiting.
Educational visiting.
   Mixed 8–25 Support work with young women.

Barnardos Yorkshire Division

Four Gables, Clarence Rd, Leeds, West Yorkshire CS18 4LB

Churches and Neighbourhood Action 31 Moor Rd, Headingley, Leeds, West Yorkshire LS6 4BG; Tel 0113 274 4940; Fax 0113 274 4942
Manager (Children's Services) Tony Parry

Doncaster Leaving Care Project 63a Warmsworth Rd, Balby, Doncaster, South Yorkshire DN4 0RP;
E-mail dlc@barnardos.org.uk; Tel 01302 858253
Service Manager Tony Parry

Leeds Accommodation Project 2 Rokeby Gdns, Headingley, Leeds, West Yorkshire LS6 3JZ; Tel 0113 275 7314
Project Leader K. Harley
The project recruits volunteers and supported lodgings providers who offer emergency/long term accommodation within their own homes, to care leavers aged 16–21 years.

The project also offers a befriending service to young people preparing for the transition from local authority care into their own tenancies.
The project also provides emergency accommodation for homeless young people aged 16–21 years.

Willow Young Carers Project The Anglers Club, 75a Stoney Rock La, Burmantofts, West Yorkshire LS9 7TB;
E-mail willow@barnardos.org.uk; Tel 0113 240 8368
Project Leader A. Stuart

Catholic Care (Diocese of Leeds)

Adoption and Fostering 11 North Grange Rd, Headingley, Leeds, West Yorkshire LS6 2BR;
URL www.catholic.care.org.uk;
E-mail adoption@catholic-care.org.uk; Tel 0113 388 5400; Fax 0113 388 5401
Team Leader Vera Ogden
Adoption
Counselling service for people wishing to adopt a child. Counselling services for people considering adoption for their baby. Preparation and approval of adoptive parents. Placement of children for adoption. On-going support after adoption for all parties. Counselling around birth records. Covers adoption service for the Leeds and Hallam Dioceses and the southern part of the Middlesbrough Diocese.
Fostering
Pre-adoption fostering service for the above mentioned Dioceses.

Cross Francis Street 3a Cross Francis St, Leeds, West Yorkshire LS7 4BZ; Tel 0113 239 2558
Manager Sheila Jackson
   Home for adults with learning difficulties.

Foundry Mill 4 Foundry Mill Mount, Seacroft, Leeds, West Yorkshire LS14 6TL; Tel 0113 232 6141
   Supported housing for people with mental health problems.

Harrison Crescent 5 Harrison Cres, off York Rd, Leeds, West Yorkshire LS9 6NP; Tel 0113 249 3973
Contact Moira Doyle
Home for children
   0–18

Moor Road 29 Moor Rd, Headingley, Leeds, West Yorkshire LS6 4BG; Tel 0113 278 6562
Home Manager Frances Shaw
Home for children
   0–18

St. Mary's 41 Church St, Boston Spa, Leeds, West Yorkshire LS23 6DG; Tel 01937 842138
Home Manager Owen Corrigan
Home for children
   0–18

School and Community Social Work 11 North Grange Rd, Headingley, Leeds, West Yorkshire LS6 2BR;
URL www.catholic-care.org.uk; Tel 0113 388 5400
Team Leader Ann Guy
Advice and social work support to schools, pupils and their parents and also families and young people in the community. School based service in Bradford, Dewsbury, Featherstone, Halifax, Keighley, Leeds, Menston, Wakefield. Supervised projects in Barnsley and Wath-upon-Dearne.

NCH North East Region

Adoption NCH Yorkshire 11 Queen Sq, Leeds, West Yorkshire LS2 8AJ; URL www.nch.org.uk;
E-mail neap@mail.nch.org.uk; Tel 0113 242 9631; Fax 0113 245 8834
Project Manager Daphne Carrins

Broom Hill Family Centre Nowell Crt, Harehills, Leeds, West Yorkshire LS9 6TW; Tel 0113 235 0877; Fax 0113 235 0455
Project Manager Lynn Coates

Contact Point 272a Dewsbury Rd, Leeds, West Yorkshire LS11 6JT; E-mail necl@mail.nch.org.uk; Tel 0113 277 3997
Project Manager Dan Bordoley

The Children's Society

The LEAP Project 61 Cardigan Rd, Leeds, West Yorkshire LS6 1EB; URL www.childrenssociety.org.uk; E-mail leap-office@childrenssociety.org.uk; Tel 0113 278 0668
Listening, empowering and advocacy project.

The Salvation Army

Mount Cross 139 Broad La, Bramley, Leeds, West Yorkshire LS13 2JP; Tel 0113 257 0810
Residential family centre for 28 family units. Domestic violence and homelessness.

Spurgeon's Child Care

Bramley Family Support Project Hough La, Leeds, West Yorkshire LS13 3RD; Tel 0113 236 0610
Project Manager C. McMullan
Family support community lunch for isolated people, toy library / equipment loan, pre-school preparation, parent and toddler group.

Leicestershire

The Children's Society

The Children and Parents' Centre 28 Saxby St, Highfields, Leicester LE2 0NE; Tel 0116 255 5300
Project Leader Val Fisher

The Glenfield and Melton Project 154 Station Rd, Glenfield, Leicester LE3 8BR; Tel 0116 232 0021
Project Leader Judy Wigfull
Team Manager (Glenfield Bungalow) Caroline Brailsford
Team Manager (Glenfield Bungalow) Gillian Milnes

Melton Bungalow
66 Dalby Rd, Melton Mowbray, Leicestershire LE13 0BH; Tel 01664 411645; Fax 01664 63847
Team Manager (Melton Bungalow) Vanessa Turner

Lincolnshire

Acacia Hall Therapeutic Community Friesthorpe, Lincolnshire; Tel 01673 885816; Fax 01673 885814
Director John Farrow
Governed by Elizabeth Fry Young Offenders' Trust on behalf of The Religious Society of Friends (Quakers). Residential
Boys 10–18

NCH North East Region

NCH Caring Together, Lincolnshire 5 Portland St, Lincoln, Lincolnshire LN5 7JZ; URL www.nch.org.com; E-mail enctl@mail.nch.org.uk; Tel 01522 546516; Fax 01522 575848
Project Manager Beverly McDowell

Families First, Lincolnshire Roseberry Hse, Roseberry Ave, Skegness, Lincolnshire PE25 3HA; E-mail neffl@mail.nch.org.uk

Markham House Family Centre Markham Hse, Swift Gdns, Lincoln, Lincolnshire LN2 4NE; Tel 01522 533313; Fax 01522 533313
Project Manager Sharon Clark

Liverpool

Barnardos North West Region

A Chance To Work Unit B63, Brunswick Small Business Centre, Brunswick Dock, Liverpool, Merseyside L3 4BD; Tel 0151 709 8368
Service Manager Susan G. Branch

Action with Young Carers (Liverpool) Merseyside Hse, 9 South John St, Liverpool, Merseyside L1 8BN
Project Leader S. Bilsborrow

Keeping Children Safe Mornington Terr, 29 Upper Duke St, Liverpool, Merseyside L1 9DY; Tel 0151 709 0540
Project Leader Ann Potter

Liverpool Families 9 Carnatic Rd, Liverpool, Merseyside L18 8BY; E-mail wayne.thomas@barnardos.org.uk; Tel 0151 729 0128; Fax 0151 729 0600

North City Youth Justice 2–4 Lancaster St, Walton, Liverpool, Merseyside L9 1BQ; Tel 0151 530 1051
Manager (Children's Services) R. Harding

North-West Fostering Service 5 Lineside Cl, Liverpool, Merseyside L25 2UD; Tel 0151 488 0822; Fax 0151 488 1101
Manager (Children's Services) John Hardy

South City Youth Persons' Resource Centre 52 Wellington St, Garston, Liverpool, Merseyside L19 2LX; Tel 0151 494 2119; Fax 0151 494 2452
Project Leader P. Wilcox

The Children's Society

Huyton Community Development Project RARC, Woolfall Heath Ave, Huyton, Liverpool, Merseyside L36 3YE; E-mail hcp@childsoc.org.uk; Tel 0151 480 8151; Fax 0151 480 0214
Project Leader Bethan Galliers

Francis Taylor Foundation

St. Gabriel's Assisted Community Home Knolle Pk, Woolton, Liverpool, Merseyside L25 6HT; E-mail beryl@saintgabriels.fsbusiness.co.uk; Tel 0151 428 2119; Fax 0151 421 0531
Care Manager Julia Porter
Semi-independent living for over 16s.
Mixed 3–18

NCH North West Region

Liverpool Leaving Care/Aftercare Service 48–50 Sheil Rd, Liverpool, Merseyside L6 3AE; E-mail nwllc@mail.nch.org.uk; Tel 0151 260 4860
Contact Kevin Stout

Liverpool Supported Accommodation Studio 7, Ward St, Liverpool, Merseyside L3 5XX; Tel 0151 708 5154
Contact Tim Mitchell

Walton Family Centre Cowley Rd, Walton, Liverpool, Merseyside L4 5SY; Tel 0151 525 7456
Project Manager Vacancy

Young Abusers' Consultancy 7 Derwent Sq, Stoneycroft, Liverpool, Merseyside L13 6QT; Tel 0151 228 1118
Contact John Postlethwaite

The Nugent Care Society

Children's Fieldwork Services Team Blackbrook Hse, Blackbrook Rd, St. Helens, Merseyside WA11 9RJ; Tel 01744 605700; Fax 01744 608065
Service Manager C. Shelton
Fostering and adoption and inter county adoption.
Special needs

Holly Road Residential Home 12 Holly Rd, Liverpool, Merseyside L7 0LH; Tel 0151 263 2412
Head of Home B. Forsyth
  Adults Learning disabilities

Individualised Day Support Project Kelton Centre, Woodlands Rd, Liverpool, Merseyside L17 0AN; Tel 0151 729 0717; Fax 0151 729 0124
Individual day support
  Learning disabilities

Nazareth House Children's Home The Villa, Liverpool Rd, Crosby, Liverpool, Merseyside L23 0QT; Tel 0151 928 6418
Head of Home J. Tully
  10–16

Newstead Residential Home 14 Old Mill La, Wavertree, Liverpool, Merseyside L15 8LN; Tel 0151 722 1164
Head of Home P. Hawkins
  Adults with physical disabilities.

Welfare Service 150 Brownlow Hill, Liverpool, Merseyside L3 5RF; Tel 0151 708 0566; Fax 0151 709 0695
Team Leader G. Flynn
Family support
  Material needs, welfare rights. Older people
  (community development).

The Salvation Army

Strawberry Field Community Home Beaconsfield Rd, Woolton, Liverpool, Merseyside L25 6LJ; Tel 0151 428 1647
Contact Kathleen Ranton
Inter
Community home for 20 children
  Mixed 4–14 in full time education

London

Barnardos London, East Anglia and the South East Division

Akwaaba Centre Grinling Pl, Deptford, London SE8 5HG; Tel 020 8691 1062
Project Leader Y. Nariman

Families in Temporary Accommodation 14 Magdalen St, London SE1 2EN
Project Leader J. Reacroft

Families Together 31–33 Spelman St, Spitalfields, London E1 5LQ; Tel 020 7247 7376
Project Leader Jennipher Bagot

Heshima Family Support Centre Coxwell Rd (off Westow St), Upper Norwood, London SE19 3AF; E-mail heshima@barnards/org.uk; Tel 020 8771 0907
Project Leader J. Walker-Reid

Peepul Family Resource Centre 170 Sanderstead Rd, South Croydon, Surrey CR2 0DB; URL www.barnardos.org.uk; E-mail mick.humphries@bardardos.org.uk; Tel 020 8651 6045; Fax 020 8657 5525
Manager (Children's Services) M. Humphries

16+ Project William Morris Hall, 6 Somers Rd, Walthamstow, London E17 6RX; Tel 020 8521 2783
Project Leader R. Truelove

Catholic Children's Society

Bird-in-Bush Commuity Centre 616 Old Kent Rd, London SE15 1JB; E-mail birdinbush@cathchild.org.uk; Tel 020 7639 3030
Project Leader Patricia Hennessey

Catholic Children's Society (Westminster) 73 St. Charles Sq, London W10 6EJ; URL www.cathchild.org.uk; E-mail ccsw@cathchild.org.uk; Tel 020 8969 5305; Fax 020 8960 1464
Director Jim Richards
Catchment area: London boroughs north of the Thames, Staines, Sunbury-on-Thames, Hertfordshire and Essex.

Adoption, fostering, school counselling, family centres, homelessness work, child psychotherapy and travellers.

'Home and Away' Unit 4 and 6, Hermes Hse, 59 Josephine Ave, Brixton, London SW2 2JZ; URL www.cathchild.org; E-mail brixton@cathchild.org; Tel 020 8671 9292; Fax 020 8678 0835
Project Manager Myrtle Bernard
Provision of an integrated package of preventative services aimed at supporting Lambeth young people and their families.

St. Anne's Community Centre 42–46 Harleyford Rd, Vauxhall, London SE11 5AY; E-mail vauxhall@cathchild.org; Tel 020 7735 7049
Project Leader Patrick Doherty

The Children's Society

Barking and Dagenham Under Eights Project 110 North St, Barking, Essex IG11 8LA; Tel 020 8591 9414; Fax 020 8507 1012
Contact Julie McLarnon

Baseline Youth Advice Centre 181 London Rd, Mitcham, Surrey CR4 2JB; E-mail blp@childsoc.org.uk; Tel 020 8646 3033
Line Manager Kate Farley

Battersea Bedsit Project 445–447 Battersea Park Rd, London SW11 4LR; Tel 020 7228 1395
Project Leader Austin Challen

Children and Neighbourhoods in London St. Hilda's East Community Centre, 18 Club Row, London E2 7EY; URL www.cnl.org.uk; E-mail cin@childsoc.org.uk; Tel 020 7613 4107

The East London Network Oxford Hse, Derbyshire St, London E2 6HG; E-mail elp@childsoc.org.uk; Tel 020 7613 2886; Fax 020 7729 8768
Network Manager Jill Healey

Wesley House
Herbert Rd, London E12 6AY; Tel 020 8553 9619

Lambeth Children's Rights Service 95 Westminster Bridge Rd, London SE1 7HR; E-mail lcrs@childsoc.org.uk; Tel 020 7620 2323; Fax 020 7620 1876
Senior Project Worker Yvonne Pearcy
Participation Worker Joycellyn Agyekum-Brenya

Post Adoption and Care Counselling Research Project 91–93 Queen's Rd, Peckham, London SE15 2EZ; E-mail julia.feast@childrenssociety.co.uk; Tel 020 7732 9089; Fax 020 7277 5760
Project Leader Julia Feast

The Rights and Participation Project 24 Deptford Broadway, London SE8 4PA; E-mail rpp@childsoc.org.uk; Tel 020 8691 2520; Fax 020 8691 2518
Participation Worker Tilly Pobee
Project Manager Rajinder Nagra

Shine 48 Union St, London SE1 1TD; E-mail shi@childsoc.org.uk; Tel 020 7403 3854
Project Leader Graham Knight

Young Tenants' Support Project Charan Hse, 18 Union Rd, Clapham, London SW4 6JP; URL www.childrenssociety.org.uk; E-mail young-tenants-support@childrenssociety.org.uk; Tel 020 7498 1616; Fax 020 7498 2211
Project Leader Peter Brown

Christian Child Care Forum

Mill Grove 8–26 Crescent Rd, South Woodford, London E18 1JB; Tel 020 8504 2702; Fax 020 8506 0442
Director K.J. White, MA, MPhil, PhD
A Christian family and residential community offering fostering, residential care and family support. For some children and sibling groups this becomes their family for life.

Christian Family Concern

Christian Family Concern 42 South Park Hill Rd, South Croydon, Surrey; Tel 020 8688 0251
Wallis House bedsit scheme. Hostel for single mothers.

Beracah Bedsit Scheme
For young people 18+.

Beracah
Family support centre (non-residential).

Birdhurst Day Nursery
Under 5s
  Non-residential.

Birdhurst Kids Club
For after school care (non residential) and all day holiday playschemes.
Tel 020 8681 3187

Congregation of Poor Servants of the Mother of God

St. Mary's Home High St, Roehampton, London SW15 4HJ; E-mail ljdowling@aol.com; Tel 020 8788 6186; Fax 020 8788 1054
Service Manager Lisa Dowling
Residential (flats or units of seven), two respite care.
  16+ Learning difficulties

The Depaul Trust

The Lord Clyde Nightshelter 90 Tyers St, Vauxhall, London SE11 5HU; Tel 020 7820 0344; Fax 020 7735 8411
Nightshelter. No newly homeless. Long term homeless with rough sleeping history.
  16–25 year olds.

NCH London Region

Bayswater Families' Centre 14–18 Newton Rd, Bayswater, London W2 5LT; Tel 020 7229 8976; Fax 020 7221 3782
Centre Manager Shelagh Laslett-O'Brien

The Bridge 1st Fl, 34 Upper St, London N1 0PN; E-mail enquiries@thebridgeccds.org.uk; Tel 020 7704 2386; Fax 020 7704 2387
Director Renuka Jeyarajah Dent

CSA National Research Child and Family Department, The Tavistock Centre, London NW3 5BA; Tel 020 7435 7111 ext 2456; Fax 020 7447 3733
Contact Dr Cathy Roberts

The Elwood Family Centre 3 Elwood St, Islington, London N5 1EB; E-mail lnefge@mail.nchafc.org.uk; Tel 020 7704 2754; Fax 020 7359 2685
Contact Deborah Biss

Eye to Eye Mediation 231 Camberwell New Rd, London SE5 0TH; E-mail inetem@mail.nchafc.org.uk; Tel 020 7701 1114; Fax 020 7703 6129
Project Manager Deborah Shead

F.O.C.U.S. 26–28 Northampton Pk, Islington, London N1 2PJ; Tel 020 7226 7072; Fax 020 7704 8942
Contact Cass Williams
Semi independent supported housing after care and mentoring scheme for young people preparing to leave care.

Hackney Young Carers' Project The Print Hse, 18 Ashwin St, London E8 3DL; E-mail inhycp@mail.nch.org.uk; Tel 020 7254 5554; Fax 020 7923 9890
Manager Vera Beining

Haringey Young Carers Red Gables Family Centre, 113 Crouch Hill, Haringey, London N8 9QN; E-mail inhyc@mail.nch.org.uk; Tel 020 8348 4660
Manager Claudia Benjamin

Haven Young Families' Project 1 Ollgar Cl, Shepherds Bush, London W12 0NT; Tel 020 8749 7211; Fax 020 8949 2180
Manager Ange Moore

Imani Family Support Project Battersea Central Mission, PO Box 17, 20-22 York Rd, Battersea, London SW11 3QE; E-mail imani@fish.co.uk; Tel 020 7207 1117
Project Manager Gail Gray

Legard Family Support Unit Legard Hse, Legard Rd, Highbury, London N5 1DE; URL www.nch.org.uk; E-mail inlfsu@mail.nch.org.uk; Tel 020 7354 8415
Project Manager J. Caluori

Phoenix Project 21 Leyton Rd, off Holmes Rd, Wimbledon, London SW19 1LY; E-mail inlrfc@nch.org.uk; Tel 020 8542 3989; Fax 020 8542 1145
Project Manager Ange Moore

London Information Meetings 20 Kendoa Rd, Clapham, London SW4 7NB; Tel 020 7498 0209; Fax 020 7978 2613
Contact Colin Webb

M.A.P. (Mediation for Young People and Families) 20 Marlon Pl, London E8 1LP
Contact Leasa Lambert

Monroe Young Family Centre 33a Daleham Gdns, Camden, London NW3 5BH; Tel 020 7431 5138; Fax 020 7794 0603
Clinical Director Dr Jean Pigott
Intake Manager Patricia Pemberton

Foster Care NCH Options Project 2nd Fl, Unit 4, Stratford Office Village, 4 Romford Rd, Stratford, London E15 4EA; URL www.nch.org.uk; E-mail ino@mail.nch.org.uk; Tel 020 8534 9468; Fax 020 8555 7726
Contact Eddie Royer

Richmond Family Centre 91 Queens Rd, Twickenham, London TW1 4EU; Tel 020 8744 0444; Fax 020 8744 2323
Contact Shirley Stuart

Surviving Together Block D, St Leonard's Hospital, London N1 5LZ; Tel 020 7301 3154; 020 7301 3156; Fax 020 7301 3153
Project Manager Cynthia Kelchure-Cole

Volunteer Initiative Co-ordinator 22 Lucerne Rd, London N5 1TZ; Tel 020 7704 7070; Fax 020 7704 7080

Warren Park Children's Centre Kingston Hill, Kingston, Surrey KT2 7LX; Tel 020 8481 0200; Fax 020 8481 0209
Project Manager Tim Wells

Women's Information and Resource Centre 91 Queens Rd, Twickenham, Greater London TW1 4EU; Tel 020 8744 9888
Contact Kathleen Henderson

Peper Harow Foundation

Please see the Peper Harow main entry, listed elsewhere in this section.

Cumberlow Community 24 Chalfont Rd, South Norwood, London, SE24 4AA; Tel 0208 768 0370
In partnership with Peper Harow and NCH. For mixed emotionally disturbed 15-19 year olds. No area limit.

RPS Rainer

Break Free and Progress Project Palm Tree Crt, Unit 1, 4 Factory La, London N17 9FL; Tel 020 8885 5000; Fax 020 8880 3351
Project Manager Sali Walker

Housing–South London Team Russell Hse, 84–90 Lordship La, East Division, London SE22 8HF; Tel 020 8693 3311; Fax 020 8693 7489
Senior Project Manager Keri Deasy

RPS Rainer Housing–North London Team Emma Hse, 214 High Rd, Tottenham, London N15 4NP; E-mail nlt@rpsrainer.fsnet.co.uk; Tel 020 8808 7698; Fax 020 8808 6705
Senior Project Manager Jacqui Leith
Senior Practitioner Vicky Lofthouse

Wandsworth Independent Living Scheme 203 Lavender Hill, London SW11 5TB; Tel 020 8871 6733; Fax 020 7924 6266
Project Manager M. Harris
Leaving care/aftercare project.

Wandsworth Remand Management Service 177 Blackshaw Rd, London SW17 0DJ; Tel 020 8767 9893; Fax 020 8682 4255
Manager Victoria Staton

The Salvation Army

The Haven Springfield Rd, Sydenham, London SE26 6HG; Tel 020 8659 4033
Centre Manager Captain Mavis Cavell
Community home for 24 children.

Kings Centre Family Project Frampton Park Baptist Church, Frampton Park Rd, Hackney, London E9 7PQ; Tel 020 8985 0877
Project Manager Lorraine Sanie
Family support work.

London Independent Visitors' Scheme 305 Cambridge Heath Rd, Bethnal Green, London E2 9LH; E-mail livs@fsmail.net; Tel 020 7033 0384; Fax 020 7033 0384
Project Manager Maureen Prince

Young Abusers' Project

The Peckwater Resource Centre, 6 Peckwater St, London NW5 2TX; Tel 020 7530 6422; Fax 020 7530 6423
Community based NSPCC project in association with Islington NHS Primary Care Trust.

Manchester

BGWS (Boys' and Girls' Welfare Society)

Crossacres 1 Crossacres Rd, Wythenshawe, Manchester M22 5AD; E-mail crossacres.bgws@virgin.net; Tel 0161 428 5516; Fax 0161 491 3651
Manager Helen Potter

Highlea 51–53 Parsonage Rd, Withington, Manchester M20 4NG; URL bgws.org.uk; E-mail highlea.bgws@virgin.net; Tel 0161 445 4727; Fax 0161 448 1988
Manager Maria McGranaghan

The Bibini Centre

The Bibini Centre for Young People 60a Wood Rd, Whalley Range, Manchester M16 8BC; URL bibini-centreforyoungpeople.com; E-mail information@bibini-centre.fsnet.co.uk; Tel 0161 881 8558; Fax 0161 882 0420
Chief Executive Yoni Ejo
Providing a range of residential and support services to African, Carribean, Asian and Black British children, young people and their families.

Family Support Services St. Wilfred's Enterprise Centre, Off Royce Rd, Manchester M15 5BJ; URL bibini-centreforyoungpeople.com; E-mail valerie@bibini.freeserve.co.uk; Tel 0161 232 7977; Fax 0161 232 7989
Contact Delsierene Waul
Family Support for Black children, young people and their families. Providing disability project worker, Asian project worker, play therapy and asylum seekers and refugee service.

Leaving Care and Home Project 28–30 Peel Gr, Longsight, Manchester M12 4WE; URL bibini-centreforyoungpeople.com; E-mail information@bibinicentre.fsnet.co.uk; Tel 0161 248 8485; Fax 0161 257 0550

Supported flats for Black young people leaving care or in housing need. Provides on-site support, resettlement worker and disability project worker.

Residential Children's Home PO Box 30, Manchester M16 8RR; URL bibini-centreforyoungpeople; E-mail information@bibini-centre.fsnet.co.uk; Tel 0161 881 8558; Fax 0161 882 0420
Residential Manager Maureen Merchant
Children's home for disabled and non-disabled Black children and young people. Provides play therapy, children's rights advocacy and family support/outreach.
10–17

Catholic Children's Rescue Society (Diocese of Salford) Inc

390 Parrs Wood Rd, Didsbury, Manchester M20 5NA; E-mail ccrs@lineone.net; Tel 0161 445 7741
Director/Reverend Secretary Rev B. Wilson
Adoption, fostering, family support services, NAA, social work training.

CCRS – Marietta 25–27 Ruabon Rd, Manchester M20 0LN; Tel 0161 445 7790
Officer-in-Charge Lisa Grundy (Acting)
RC
Children's Home/Family Group Home.
Mixed 0–16

CCRS – Marillac House Laindon Rd, Victoria Pk, Manchester M14 5YJ; Tel 0161 225 1944
Office-in-Charge Sr Susan Whitehead
Supported accommodation for homeless young women, pregnant or with babies.
Female 16–25

CCRS – Marymount 56–68 Parrs Wood Ave, Manchester M20 0NB; Tel 0161 445 4237
Officer-in-Charge Denis Robertson
RC
Family group home/children's home
Mixed 0–16

CCRS – Maryvale 8–10 Rydal Rd, Blackburn BB1 5NR; Tel 01254 681484
Officer-in-Charge Margaret Melia
Supported accommodation for homeless young women, pregnant or with babies.
Female 16–25

CCRS – Mount Carmel 463–465 Parrs Wood Rd, Manchester M20 9NE; Tel 0161 446 2348
Officer-in-Charge Kathryn Delaney
Mixed 0–16 Disabled children/respite care.

CCRS – Radcliffe Road 94 Radcliffe Rd, Bolton, Lancashire BL2 1NY; Tel 01204 385245
Supported accommodation for homeless young women, single, pregnant or with babies.
Female 16–25

CCRS – Wingate 823 Wilmslow Rd, Didsbury, Manchester M20 2SN; Tel 0161 445 9358
Home Manager Nigel Kelleher
RC
Children's home/Family Group home.
Mixed 0–16

Catholic Children's Rescue Society (Diocese of Salford) Inc

390 Parrs Wood Rd, Didsbury, Manchester M20 5NA; E-mail ccrs1@tiscali.co.uk; Tel 0161 445 7741
Director Rev B. Wilson
Telephone applications and enquiries to Duty Officer.

94 Radcliffe Road Bolton, Lancashire BL2 1NY; Tel 01204 385245
Officer-in-Charge Judith Dudgron

The Children's Society Family Centre Oak Rd, Partington, Manchester M31 4LD; URL www.childrenssociety.org.uk; Tel 0161 775 6719; Fax 0161 776 2867
Project Leader Jane Thompson (Acting)

NCH North West Region

NCH Action for Children Irlam Family Centre 18 Fiddlers La, Irlam, Greater Manchester M30 6HN; Tel 0161 775 5340
Project Manager S. Evers

NCH Manchester Family Centre
Referred work only.
77 Alexandra Road South, Whalley Range, Manchester
M16 8GJ; E-mail nwmfc@mail.nch.org.uk; Tel 0161 881
8874; Fax 0161 881 2021
Project Manager C. Baxter
Manchester Family Centre works in partnership with Manchester Social Services Department with families whose young children have been identified as having been abused or at risk of abuse. There are plans to develop additional partnerships in the near future.

Woodhouse Park Family Centre 7 Stoneacre Rd, Woodhouse Pk, Wythenshawe, Manchester M22 1BP; E-mail whp@familycentre.fsnet.co.uk; Tel 0161 498 0292
Manager Martina Street

Safe in the City Victoria Hse, 21 Manor St, Ardwick Grn, Manchester M12 6HE; E-mail scm@childsoc.org.uk
Project Leader Andy McCullough

Social and Therapeutic Services (Stockport) Ltd Orchard Hse, Grenville St, Edgeley, Stockport, Greater Manchester SK3 9ET; Tel 0161 480 8700; Fax 0161 480 7099
Contact Jacqui Ratcliffe
Medium to long term independent children's residential home.

Middlesbrough

Barnardos North East Division

Bridgeway Allendale Rd, Ormesby, Middlesbrough TS7 9LF; Tel 01642 300774
Project Leader C. Moffat

NCH North East Region

Ashington Family Centre Ashington, Northumberland NE63 0SF; Tel 01670 857900; Fax 01670 857901

Hemlington Family Resource Centre 2–6 Dalwood Crt, Hemlington, Middlesbrough TS8 9JG; Tel 01642 598012; Fax 01642 599988
Project Manager Yvonne Cherrington

Monksfield Corbridge Rd, Hexham, Northumberland NE46 1UY; Tel 01434 601594; Fax 01434 601794
Project Manager R. Montague

Norfolk

Kidz Care Project Ltd

The Ferns, Sandy La, West Runton, Cromer, Norfolk
NR27 9LT; URL www.kidzcareproject.co.uk;
E-mail project@kidzcareproject.co.uk; Tel 01263 837895;
Fax 01263 837895
Director Helen James

NCH Thames Anglia Region

Norfolk Independent Visitors 30 St. Faith's La, Norwich, Norfolk NR1 1NN; Tel 01603 764635; Fax 01603 762866
Contact Sarah Beaver

Thetford Family Centre Prospect Hse, 17–19 Raymond St, Thetford, Norfolk IP24 2EA; Tel 01842 753294; Fax 01842 761879
Project Manager Mark Agnew

West Norfolk Shared Housing Scheme King's Lynn, Norfolk PE3Z; Tel 01553 761267; Fax 01553 770236
Contact Peter Baker

West Norfolk Young People's Preparation for Leaving Home Project Old Rectory, 26 Gayton Rd, King's Lynn, Norfolk PE30 4DZ; Tel 01553 761267
Contact Jeanne King

The Willows Marsh La, King's Lynn, Norfolk PE30 3AE; Tel 01553 670990; Fax 01553 670990
Manager Sarah Green-Plumb

E2E The Old Rectory, 26 Gayton Rd, King's Lynn, Norfolk PE30 4DZ; Tel 01553 761267; Fax 01553 770236
Contact Gill Birch
Training in life skills, career planning and NVQ L1 in a selection of training areas.

Peper Harow Foundation

Please see the Peper Harow main entry, listed elsewhere in this section.

Earthsea House Berry's La, Honingham, Norfolk NR9 5AX
Run in partnership with Norfolk County Council for emotionally disturbed Norfolk children aged 5–12 years.

North Lincolnshire

NCH North East Region

Children and Families Project 80 Oswald Rd, Scunthorpe, North Lincolnshire DN15 7PG; Tel 01724 270222; Fax 01724 289956
Project Manager Penny Dodsworth

North Yorkshire

Barnardos Yorkshire Division

Dr B's Restaurant and Coffee Shop 13–15 Knaresborough Rd, Harrogate, North Yorkshire HG2 7SR;
E-mail nadine.good@barnardos.org.uk; Tel 01423 884819
Project Leader N. Good
Trains young people with special learning needs for the catering industry.

Grove Road Project 37a Grove Rd, Harrogate, North Yorkshire HG1 5EW; E-mail grove.road@barnardos.org.uk; Tel 01423 524149; Fax 01423 568016
Project Leader John Townend

Spring Hill School Palace Rd, Ripon, North Yorkshire HG4 3HN; Tel 01765 603320; Fax 01765 607549
Headteacher J. Clarke

NCH North East Region

The Children's Centre Cherry Tree Ave, Scarborough, North Yorkshire YO12 5HL;
E-mail nescrc@mail.nch.org.uk; Tel 01723 341621; Fax 01723 381637
Manager Mavis Crawford
Co-ordinator Judith Kershaw

Independence Scheme 3rd Fl, Europa Hse, 20 The Esplanade, Scarborough, North Yorkshire YO11 2AQ;
E-mail neusbs@mail.nch.org.uk; Tel 01723 364745; Fax 01723 364785
Contact Pat Petterson; Tel 01723 364701
Contact Andrew Arnell

May Lodge Cherry Tree Ave, Scarborough, North Yorkshire YO12 5HL; E-mail neml@mail.nch.org.uk; Tel 01723 364701
Project Manager Mavis Crawforth

Umbrella Short Break Service Europa Hse, 20 The Esplanade, Scarborough, North Yorkshire YO11 2AD; Tel 01723 360389
Project Manager Jillian Young

Northamptonshire

NCH Eastern Region

Daventry and South Northants Family Centre Staverton Rd, Grange Est, Daventry, Northamptonshire NN11 4EY; E-mail endfc@mail.nch.org.uk; Tel 01327 705063; Fax 01327 311683
Project Manager Vacancy

Wellingborough Family Centre 123 Midlands Rd, Wellingborough, Northamptonshire NN8 1LU; E-mail mdwfc@mail.nch.org.uk; Tel 01933 229951; Fax 01933 440721
Project Manager Pauline Jafarian

Peper Harrow Foundation

Please see the Peper Harow main entry, listed elsewhere in this section.

Thornby Hall Thornby, Northamptonshire NN6 8SW; E-mail thornbyhall@thornbyhall.ision.co.uk; Tel 01604 740001; Fax 01604 740353
Director Rene Kennedy, CertEd DipArt Therapy
No area limit.
 Mixed 12–18 Boarding emotionally disturbed.

Midlands Children Support Project 51 Derngate, Northampton, NN1 1UE; Tel 01604 250448
Provides non-residential placement support to children and their carers in Northamptonshire and medium-term residential care at Abington House for mixed emotionally disturbed 9–13-year-olds.

RPS Rainer

Northampton Bail Support Project c/o Northampton Social Services, 53 Billing Rd, Northampton, Northamptonshire NN1 5DB; Tel 01604 602400; Fax 01604 639231
Project Manager John Andrews

Nottinghamshire

Greenfields Childcare and Training Centre 139 Russell Rd, Forest Fields, Nottingham NG7 6GX; Tel 0115 841 8441
Childcare Manager Vacancy

Sherwood Project 2 Clinton Ave, off Hucknall Rd, Nottingham NG5 1AW; Tel 0115 969 1177
Project Leader M. McGrath

The Children's Society

STARS Project Mayfair Crt, North Gate, New Basford, Nottinghamshire NG7 7GR;
E-mail childrens-centre-crabtree@childrenssociety.org.uk; Tel 0115 942 2974
Project Leader Sara Mayer

NCH Eastern Region

Broxtowe Community Support 13–14 Denton Grn, Broxtowe Est, Nottingham NG8 6GD; Tel 0115 976 1240; Fax 0115 979 4200
Contact Jill Green

Broxtowe Family Centre 13–14 Denton Grn, Broxtowe, Nottingham NG8 6GD; Tel 0115 976 1240; Fax 0115 979 4200
Team Manager Jill Green

Number 28 Notts Child and Family Counselling Service 28 Magdala Rd, Nottingham NG3 5DF;
E-mail ennte@mail.nch.org.uk; Tel 0115 985 8308; Fax 0115 985 8805
Project Manager Vacancy

West Notts Independence 101–103 Alfreton Rd, Sutton-in-Ashfield, Nottingham NG17 1FJ;
E-mail enwnip@nch.org.uk
Project Manager Chris Bakewell (Acting)

Spurgeon's Child Care

The Corner Family Centre Mansfield Rd Baptist Church, Corner Sherwood Rise/Gregory Blvd, Nottingham NG6 6JN; E-mail administration@mansfieldroad.fsbusiness.co.uk; Tel 0115 960 4304
Manager Lynette Baxter

Oxfordshire

Fairway Community Development Project Fairway Methodist Church, The Fairway, Banbury, Oxfordshire OX16 0RS; URL www.the-childrens-society.org.uk; E-mail bfc@childsoc.org.uk; Tel 01295 275507; Fax 01295 265073
Regional Manager Lys Buck

Western Corner 118 Burwell Dr, Witney, Oxfordshire OX28 5NA; E-mail wcp@childsoc.org.uk; Tel 01993 772973; Fax 01993 700724
Project Manager Rachael Sherratt

NCH South East Region

Abingdon Family Centre Caldecott School East Site, Caldecott Rd, Abingdon, Oxfordshire OX14 5HB; E-mail seafc@mail.nch.org.uk; Tel 01235 553625
Deputy Manager (Linked Project) Sue Bridgen

The Ark 14 Oxford Rd, Kidlington, Oxfordshire OX5 1AA; Tel 01865 842777
Project Manager A. Marshall
A therapeutic service in Oxfordshire for children and young people and their families who are coping with the consequences of child sexual abuse.

Berinsfield Family Centre Wimblestraw Rd, Berinsfield, Wallingford, Oxfordshire OX10 7LZ;
E-mail sebfc@mail.nch.org.uk; Tel 01865 341310; Fax 01865 341980
Link Project Manager Zuzanna Spackman

Didcot Family Centre 2 Hillary Dr, Didcot, Oxfordshire OX11 8PS; URL www.nch.org.uk;
E-mail sedfc@mail.nch.org.uk; Tel 01235 511444; Fax 01235 511002
Project Manager Sue Spackman (Acting)

Rotherham

Barnardos Yorkshire Division

Redbarn House 36 Station St, Swinton, Mexborough, South Yorkshire S64 8PP; E-mail ann.clegg@barnardos.org.uk; Tel 01709 570344
Headteacher Peter Brandt

The Rowan Education Centre 158 Broom La, Rotherham, South Yorkshire S60 3NW;
E-mail rowan.centre@barnardos.org.uk; Tel 01709 703418
Centre Manager Wendy D. Peake

The Children's Society

South Yorkshire Project Prospect Hse, Muglet La, Rotherham, South Yorkshire S66 7JU;
E-mail south-yorkshire@childrenssociety.org.uk; Tel 01709 812142; Fax 01709 790863
Project Leader Tracey Thompson

Rotherham Bridges Project 14a Nightingale Crt, Nightingale Cl, Rotherham, South Yorkshire;
E-mail nerlc@mail.nch.org.uk; Tel 01709 372985
Project Leader Teresa Roe

NCH North East Region

Rotherham Bridges Project 1 Ash Mount, Doncaster Gate, Rotherham, South Yorkshire S65 1DQ; Tel 01709 828769; Fax 01709 361884
Project Leader Sue May

Rotherham Young Offenders Diversion c/o Regional Office, 12 Granby Rd, Harrogate, North Yorkshire HG1 4ST

Spurgeon's Child Care

Families of Rotherham East Eastwood View Church, Springwell Gdns, Rotherham, South Yorkshire S65 1NH; E-mail fore2@supanet.com; Tel 01709 372075
Project Manager C. Ogle

St. Helens

The Children's Society

The Children's Society in St. Helens Community Work Unit, Ravenhead Foyer, Harris Gdns, Sherdley Rd, St. Helens, Merseyside WA9 5DL; Tel 01744 616614; Fax 01744 616615
Senior Project Leader Cal McKenna

St. Helens Family Centres 4 Whinbury Crt, Clock Face, St. Helens, Merseyside WA9 4GG; Tel 01744 850553; Fax 01744 850544
Project Leader Imogen Parker

Manley Place
1 Manley Pl, Thatto Heath, St. Helens, Merseyside WA9 5DP; Tel 01744 813100; Fax 01744 813100

NCH North West Region

Newton Family Centre 17–19 Victoria Rd, Newton-le-Willows, Merseyside WA12 9RN; E-mail nnnfc@mail.nchafc.org.uk; Tel 01925 227883

St. Helens Family Groups 17–19 Victoria Rd, Earlstown, Newton-le-Willows, Merseyside WA12 9RN; Tel 01925 227883
Contact Ann Simpson

The Nugent Care Society

St. Catherine's Centre Blackbrook Rd, St.Helens, Merseyside WA11 9RJ; E-mail stcatherines@nugentcare.org; Tel 01744 606119; Fax 01744 606201
Principal M. Higgins
Residential
  12–18

Salford

Barnardos North West Division

Salford Families Project 222 Eccles Old Rd, Salford, Greater Manchester M6 8AL; E-mail godfrey.travis@barnardos.org.uk; Tel 0161 707 0222
Project Leader G. Travis
Range of services for Salford families who have a child with a disability.

NCH North West Region

Eccles Family Centre St. Mary's Rd, Eccles, Greater Manchester M30 0AX; E-mail nwefc@mail.nch.org.uk; Tel 0161 789 0566; Fax 0161 789 0566
Project Manager Paul Goodwin

Spurgeon's Child Care

Plum Tree Family Centre 11 Plumtree Crt, Salford, Greater Manchester M6 5BB; Tel 0161 736 1185
Centre Manager J. Cheetham
Centre Manager M. Marley
12 families structured, programmes of work.

Spurgeon's RAPS – Rights and Participation in Salford 73 Sycamore Crt, Paddington Cl, Salford, Greater Manchester M6 5FR; E-mail raps-salford@spurgeons.fsnet.co.uk
Project Manager Melissa Hind
Independent visitors and advocates.

Sefton

The Children's Society

The Children's Society Transition Project 1 Sussex Rd, Southport, Merseyside PR9 0SS; Tel 01704 533833
Project Leader Kevin Thorne

North West Children's Resource Team 24 Lathom Rd, Southport, Merseyside PR9 0JP; Tel 01704 537738
Project Leader Jeff Smith

NCH North West Region

Westdene Children's Residential Unit Park Cres, Southport, Merseyside PR9 9LJ; Tel 01704 531159
Project Manager S. Dale

The Salvation Army

Marshfield 79 Albert Rd, Southport, Merseyside PR9 9LN; Tel 01704 538643
Day nursery for children.
  Mixed 2–5

Sheffield

NCH North East Region

The Bridges 551 Bellhouse Rd, Sheffield, South Yorkshire S5 0ER; Tel 0114 257 7169; Fax 0114 257 1227
Project Manager Paul Grimwood

Sheffield Family Centre 71 Palgrave Rd, Sheffield, South Yorkshire S5 8GS; URL www.nch.org.uk; E-mail nesfc@mail.nch.org.uk; Tel 0114 231 2512; Fax 0114 285 4319
Project Manager Alex Bennett

RPS Rainer

RPS Rainer-South Yorkshire 4th Fl, 40 Castle Sq, Sheffield, South Yorkshire S1 2GF; URL newdirectionsskills4life.org.uk; E-mail elaine@newdirections.f9.co.uk; Tel 0114 275 9291; Fax 0114 275 4649
Service Co-ordinator Elaine Cronin

Shropshire

The Children's Society

Young Carers United 65 Withywood Dr, Malinslee, Telford, Shropshire TF3 2HU; URL www.childrenssociety.org.uk; E-mail ycu@childsoc.org.uk; Tel 01952 502393; Fax 01952 502811

NCH Midlands Region

Shrewsbury Community Support Project Richmond Hse, Rutland, Harlescott Grange, Shrewsbury, Shropshire SY1 3QG; E-mail mdscsp@mail.nch.org.uk; Tel 01743 443497
Project Manager Jacky Yates

Shrewsbury Shared Care (Residential) Placement 49 Reabrook Ave, Belle Vue, Shrewsbury, Shropshire SY3 7PZ; Tel 01743 233101; Fax 01743 233103
Project Manager Allison Ryder

Spurgeon's Child Care

The Kingswell Centre Arthur St, Oswestry, Shropshire SY11 1JN; URL www.kingswell.f9.co.uk; E-mail enquiries@kingswell.f9.co.uk; Tel 01691 655126; Fax 01691 654064
Centre Manager P. Simpson
Youth and community.

Somerset

NCH South West Region

Family Support Services Mendip Wesley Lower School, Christchurch St West, Frome, Somerset BA11 1EA; Tel 01373 451307
Project Manager Elaine Pugsley
NCH Halcon Family Centre 110 Roman Rd, Taunton, Somerset TA1 2BL; E-mail swhfc@mail.nch.org.uk; Tel 01823 256969
Hamp Family Centre Rhode La, Bridgwater, Somerset TA6 6JB; URL www.nch.org.uk; E-mail swhafc@mail.nch.org.uk; Tel 01278 429273
Project Manager Sarah Ives (Acting)
Somerset Inclusion Project Town Hse, 34 Wellington Rd, Taunton, Somerset TA1 5AW; E-mail june.walsham@barnardos.org.uk; Tel 01823 257917
Head of Service June Walsham
Yeovil Family Centre 64 Chelston Ave, Yeovil, Somerset BA21 4PU; Tel 01935 474973
Project Manager Karen Cooper

South Yorkshire

NCH North East Region

Balby Family Resource Centre 1 Sandycroft Cres, Balby, Doncaster, South Yorkshire DN4 0TY; E-mail nebfrc@nch.co.uk; Tel 01302 520270; Fax 01302 570475
Project Manager Denise Lane
Family support, community project for children.
Barnsley Family Link Summerwell, Newsome Ave, Barnsley, South Yorkshire S73 8QS; E-mail nebfl@mail.nchafcorg.uk; Tel 01226 340500; Fax 01226 340780
Project Leader Robert Bowes
Rossington Family Centre NCH Action for Children Grantham St, Rossington, Doncaster, South Yorkshire DN11 0TA; E-mail nerfc@mail.nchafc.org.uk; Tel 01302 863686; Fax 01302 868270
Project Manager John Bailey
St. Edwin's Family Centre 5 Keresforth Cl, Barnsley, South Yorkshire S70 6RS; E-mail nestefc@mail.nch.org.uk; Tel 01226 241171
Project Manager Robert Bowes

Barnardos Yorkshire Region

Priory Family Centre Priory Campus, Pontefract Rd, Barnsley, South Yorkshire S71 5PN; Tel 01226 770619
Project Leader S. Proctor

Stockport

BGWS (Boys and Girls Welfare Society)

Bridge College Curzon Rd, Offerton, Stockport, Greater Manchester SK2 5DG; URL www.bgws.org.uk; E-mail admin@bridgecollege.fsnet.co.uk; Tel 0161 487 4293; Fax 0161 487 4294
Principal Caroline Smale
Vice-Principal Rose Galway (Acting)
Clanhaven 52 Norcross Cl, off Blackstone Rd, Stockport, Greater Manchester SK2 5NH; Tel 0161 483 3869
Manager Sue May
Lerryn 66 Parsonage Rd, Heaton Moor, Stockport, Greater Manchester SK4 4EJ; E-mail lerryn.bgws@virgin.net; Tel 0161 718 3737
Manager Julie Tring
Linden Family Unit 64 Station Rd, Cheadle Hulme, Stockport, Greater Manchester SK8 7BH; E-mail linden.bgws@virgin.net; Tel 0161 485 7235
Unit Manager Christine Clynch
Newbridge Centre Cromer St, off Newbridge La, Stockport, Greater Manchester SK1 2NY; Tel 0161 477 0742; Fax 0161 480 2429
Manager Yvonne Warrington
Deputy C. Bell
Inter
 Mixed 16–30 Needs-based rehabilitation programmes.

Stockton on Tees

The Children's Society

Children's Resource Project North East 40 Mill La, Billingham, Stockton-on-Tees TS23 1HF; E-mail childrens-resource-project-north-east@childrenssociety.org.uk; Tel 01642 559147; Fax 01642 534979
Project Leader Brenda Hall
Youth Justice North East Office B, 27 Yarn Rd, Stockton-on-Tees TS18 3NJ; Tel 01642 657 311; Fax 01642 657 344
Project Leader Keith Munro

NCH North East Region

Stockton Disability Register and Network Hartburn Lodge, Harsley Rd, Hartburn, Stockton-on-Tees TS18 5DL
Contact Lisa Hawkes

Suffolk

The SPACE Project (Suffolk Partnership Achieving Choice and Experience) Warrington Lodge, 3 Warrington Rd, Ipswich, Suffolk IP1 3QU; Tel 01473 215419

NCH Thames Anglia Region

Children in Divorce and Separation Service 3 Dogs Head St, Ipswich, Suffolk IP4 1AE; URL www.itsnotyourfault.org; E-mail tacidas@mail.nch.org.uk; Tel 01473 225845; Fax 01473 225846
Administrative Co-ordinator Anne Poole
Haverhill Family Resource Centre 72 High St, Haverhill, Suffolk CB9 8AP; E-mail tahfrc@mail.nch.org.uk; Tel 01440 714444
Project Manager Russ Edwards
SCSATS 23 Henley Rd, Ipswich, Suffolk IP1 3TF; E-mail enscsats@mail.nch.org.uk; Tel 01473 281239
Project Manager Cheryl Finlayson (Acting)
Suffolk Remand Fostering and Restorative Justice Services 40 Eastgate St, Bury St. Edmunds, Suffolk IP33 1YW; Tel 01284 749062; 01284 749063; Fax 01284 724101
Manager Graham Harrison

Suffolk Leaving Care Service (West) 40 Eastgate St, Bury St. Edmunds, Suffolk IP33 1YW; E-mail enwslc@mail.nch.org.uk; Tel 01284 704019; Fax 01284 724101
Project Manager Bob Walker

Suffolk Leaving Care Service (North) 18–20 Gordon Rd, Lowestoft, Suffolk NR32 1NL; E-mail ennslc@mail.nch.org.uk; Tel 01502 566445; Fax 01502 566447
Project Manager Bob Walker

Suffolk Restorative Justice Service 40 Eastgate St, Bury St. Edmunds, Suffolk IP33 1YW; Tel 01284 749062; 01284 749063; Fax 01284 724101
Contact Graham Harrison

Suffolk Shared Housing Scheme (West) 40 Eastgate St, Bury St. Edmunds, Suffolk IP33 1YW; E-mail enwslc@mail.nch.org.uk; Tel 01284 704019; Fax 01284 724101
Manager Bob Walker

Surrey

Catholic Children's Society 49 Russell Hill Rd, Purley, Surrey CR8 2XB; URL www.catholicchildrenssociety.org.uk; E-mail info@cathchild.org; Tel 020 8668 2181; Fax 020 8763 2274
Adoption Infants/Special Needs.

White Lodge Cottage White Lodge Centre, Holloway Hill, Chertsey, Surrey KT16 0AE; Tel 01932 567131; Fax 01932 570589
Contact C. Davis
Und
Mixed 0–10 Short term care for children with disabilities. (6)

Committee of Management

Cherry Trees School La, East Clandon, Guildford, Surrey GU4 7RS; URL www.cherry-trees.co.uk; Tel 01483 222506
Contact P. Davey
Nine overnight, four day care.
Mixed 0–19 Short term care for children to 19 years with moderate/severe learning disabilities.

NCH London and South East Region

East Surrey Family Link Scheme c/o Pastens, Pastens Rd, Limpsfield, Oxted, Surrey RH8 0RD; Tel 01883 722399; Fax 01883 715283
Project Manager Gillian Smith

Pastens Pastens Rd, Pains Hill, Oxted, Surrey RH8 0RD; E-mail colinm@nch-se.fsnet.co.uk; Tel 01883 723110
Project Manager C. Morley

Surrey Youth Support Service
Incorporating the Leaving Care Team and Community and Placement Support Team.
Churchill Hse, Mayford Grn, Woking, Surrey GU22 0PW; Tel 01483 741900; Fax 01483 721690

RPS Rainer

North Surrey Stepping Out Project 63a High St, Walton-on-Thames, Surrey KT12 1DJ; Tel 01932 225578; Fax 01932 248550
Project Manager T.J. Akerman
Leaving Care/Aftercare Project.

Surrey Remand Management Service Youth Offending Team, Churchill Hse, Mayford Grn, Woking, Surrey GU22 0PW; E-mail adrian.neil@surrey.cc.gov.uk; Tel 01483 723922; Fax 01483 771786
Remand Management A. Neil

RBC Family Foundations

Redhill Baptist Church, Hatchlands Rd, Redhill, Surrey RH1 6AE; Tel 01737 768171; Fax 01737 772351
Family support, community-based services.

Sussex

Anderida Adolescent Care Ltd
Director B. Thompson
Preparing young people in care for independent living.
Private Company No. 2722183; NCSC Registration Office: 18a Gildredge Rd, Eastbourne, East Sussex BN21 4RL; Tel 01323 410655; Fax 01323 417546.
Mixed 15+ Single occupancy for 13+.

CERES 283 Dyke Rd, Hove, East Sussex BN3 6PD; Tel 01273 551023; Fax 01273 508933
Chief Executive L. Lorraine
Residential care home for children with profound physical and learning disabilities and complex health needs.
Family group
10
Children and young adults. Learning difficulties, MH, PH, MLD/SLD, LT

Catholic Children's Society

CERES House 289 Dyke Rd, Hove, East Sussex BN3 6PD; Tel 01273 551023; Fax 01273 508933
Chief Executive L.A. Lorraine
Residential care home for children with profound physical and learning difficulties and complex health needs.
Children and young adults. Severe PH and MH.

Littlehampton Homefinding Unit c/o Flora McDonald School, Whitelea Rd, Littlehampton, West Sussex BN17 7JL; E-mail littlehampton@cathchild.org; Tel 01903 715317; Fax 01903 723642
Project Leader Phillip Mullings
Preparation for family placement.
Mixed 5–12

The Children's Society

Brighton and Hove Portage and Early Support Service 18 Wellington Rd, Brighton, Brighton and Hove BN2 3AA; Tel 01273 682659
Portage Supervisor Jenny Cross

St. Gabriel's Family Centre 18 Wellington Rd, Brighton, Brighton and Hove BN2 3AA; E-mail sgf@childsoc.org.uk; Tel 01273 605040; Fax 01273 608246
Network Manager Vacancy

Fegans Child and Family Care

One Sixty 160 Margate Rd, Ramsgate, Kent CT12 6AA; URL www.fegans.org.uk; Tel 01843 587000
Day Nursery Leader Sue Chevis
Administrator Jay Brown
Daycare facilities for pre-school children.
Contact facilities.

NCH South East Region

Adoption NCH South East 158 Crawley Rd, Roffey, Horsham, West Sussex RH12 4EU; URL www.nch.org.uk; E-mail seap@mail.nch.org.uk; Tel 01403 225916; Fax 01403 225919

Crawley Family Centre 40 Teasel Cl, Broadfield, Crawley, Surrey RH11 9DZ; E-mail secfc@mail.nch.org.uk; Tel 01293 511400
Project Manager Liz Pelham

Eastbourne and Hastings Youth Support Team 5 Brittany Rd, St. Leonards, East Sussex TN38 0RA; URL www.nch.org.uk; E-mail sehryst@mail.nch.org.uk; Tel 01424 446244; Fax 01424 200700

Eastbourne Community Support Services 48 Upperton Gdns, Eastbourne, East Sussex BN21 2AQ; E-mail nchafceastbourne@lineone.net; Tel 01323 723250; Fax 01323 417387
Contact Deborah Hornblow

Elphinstone Family Centre 211 Elphinstone Rd, Hastings, East Sussex TN34 2AX; URL www.nch.org.uk; E-mail seefc@mail.nch.org.uk; Tel 01424 440840; Fax 01424 432541
Practice Manager Phil Riley

Family Link, West Sussex 158 Crawley Rd, Roffey, Horsham, West Sussex RH12 4EU; URL www.nch.org.uk; E-mail sewsfl@nch.org.uk; Tel 01403 225918; Fax 01403 225919
Project Manager Gillian Smith

Palmeira Project 24 Palmeira Ave, Hove, East Sussex BN3 3GB; URL www.nch.org.uk; E-mail sepp@mail.nch.org.uk; Tel 01273 329839; Fax 01273 775497
Project Manager Sarah Leitch
Residential placements for children with severe learning disabilities and challenging behaviour, autism. Five shared care placements. Referrals through Brighton and Hove Social Services.

NCH Tall Trees Family Centre 53 Turkey Rd, Bexhill, East Sussex TN39 5HB; URL www.nch.org.uk; E-mail settfc@mail.nch.org.uk; Tel 01424 730022; Fax 01424 734402
Project Manager T. Hemmings

Spurgeon's Child Care

Littlehampton WIRE Project Wickbourne Chapel, Clun Rd, Littlehampton, West Sussex BN17 7EA; URL www.thewireproject.com; E-mail info@thewireproject.com; Tel 01903 731796
Project Manager Paul Sanderson

Tyne and Wear

Children – North East 89 Denhill Pk, Newcastle upon Tyne, Tyne and Wear NE15 6QE; URL www.children-ne.org; E-mail enquiries@children-ne.org; Tel 0191 256 2444; Fax 0191 256 2446
Director J. Higginson, BA, DASS
Community development for families with young children in rural areas and urban. Eight voluntary home visiting schemes for families with under eights in five local authorities. Development work with young carers and service providers. Development work with fathers. Youth enquiry service. Babysitting initiative. Support for children in school settings.

Barnardos North East Region

The Base 26 Esplanade, Whitley Bay, Tyne and Wear NE26 2AJ; Tel 0191 253 2127; Fax 0191 253 3195
Project Leader Caroline Waitt (Acting)

Family Placement Project (North East) c/o Divisional Office, Orchard Hse, Fenwick, Jesmond, Newcastle upon Tyne, Tyne and Wear NE2 2JQ; Tel 0191 240 4811
Project Leader Vicky Davidson Boyd

Family Resource Centre (Gateshead) 20 Bewick Rd, Gateshead, Tyne and Wear NE8 4DP; URL www.barnardos.org.uk; Tel 0191 478 4667
Project Leader Mary Connor

Killingworth Play Den Citadel East, Killingworth, Tyne and Wear NE12 0UQ; Tel 0191 268 9929
Project Co-ordinator Diane Whorrod

Kirkwood Neighbourhood Centre Kirkwood Dr, North Kenton, Newcastle upon Tyne, Tyne and Wear NE3 3AX; Tel 0191 285 8118
Project Leader Steve Forster
Barnardos. Including North Kenton Advice Centre (Tel 0191 284 2156).

Longbenton Early Years Chesters Ave, Longbenton, Newcastle upon Tyne, Tyne and Wear NE12 8QP; Tel 0191 270 1240; Fax 0191 266 9064
Manager (Children's Services) Alison Winship

New Families (North East) c/o Regional Office, Orchard Hse, Fenwick Terr, Jesmond, Newcastle upon Tyne, Tyne and Wear NE2 2JQ; Tel 0191 240 4814
Manager (Children's Services) Sue Holton

Newcastle Independence Network 4th Fl, Warwick Hse, Grantham Rd, Newcastle upon Tyne, Tyne and Wear NE2 1QX; E-mail sharon.dunbar@barnardos.org.uk; Tel 0191 230 0196
Manager (Children's Services) Sharon Dunbar

Orchard Project Orchard Hse, Fenwick Terr, Jesmond, Newcastle upon Tyne, Tyne and Wear NE2 2JQ; E-mail angela.edwards@barnardos.org.uk; Tel 0191 240 4813; Fax 0191 240 4833
Manager (Children's Services) Angela Edwards
Manager (Children's Services) Penny Leake

Palmersville Training Project Unit 91–92 North Tyne Ind Est, Whitley Rd, Benton, Newcastle upon Tyne, Tyne and Wear NE12 9SZ; Tel 0191 270 1133
Project Leader M. Johnson

South Tyneside Children and Young People's Centre Simonside Lodge, 109 Newcastle Rd, South Shields, Tyne and Wear NE34 9AA; Tel 0191 454 5686
Project Leader C. Watson

Spectrum Barnardo's, Orchard Hse, Fenwick Terr, Newcastle upon Tyne, Tyne and Wear NE2 2JQ; Tel 0191 240 4800
Contact John Smee
Contact Reti Winward

Streetlevel Stanhope Pde, South Shields, Tyne and Wear NE33 4BA; E-mail ros.shrubb@barnardos.org.uk; Tel 0191 455 3027
Project Leader Ros Shrubb

The Children's Society

INLINE Rivendell, 1a Jubilee Rd, Melbourne St, Newcastle upon Tyne, Tyne and Wear NE1 2JJ; E-mail in-line-newcastle@childrenssociety.org.uk; Tel 0191 221 1980; Fax 0191 221 1983
Preparation for independent living, floating support, family mediation, advice and information service. Homeless/potentially homeless young people.

INLINE, Tyneside (Independent Living, North East) 4a Park View, Whitley Bay, Tyne and Wear NE26 2TH; E-mail joerichmond_inline@yahoo.co.uk; Tel 0191 251 4748; Fax 0191 251 9638
Project Manager Joe Richmond
Preparation for independent living, floating support, family mediation, advice and information service. Homeless/potentially homeless young people (16–21 years of age).

Newcastle Diocesan Community Project Denewood, Newcastle upon Tyne, Tyne and Wear NE2 1TL; E-mail newcastle-dcdp@childrenssociety.org.uk; Tel 0191 281 9931; Fax 0191 281 6643
Project Leader Michael Bell

NCH North East Region

Children's Rights Service 3rd Fl, MEA Hse, Ellison Pl, Newcastle upon Tyne, Tyne and Wear NE1 8XS; E-mail necrs@mail.nch.org.uk; Tel 0191 230 3682; Fax 0191 230 5640
Project Manager Vacancy

Cowgate Children's Centre 5–7 Meadowdale Cres, Cowgate, Newcastle upon Tyne, Tyne and Wear NE5 3HL; Tel 0191 286 5507
Project Manager Jane Anderson

Families First Newcastle Wesley Hse, Bond St, Benwell, Newcastle upon Tyne, Tyne and Wear NE4 8BA; Tel 0191 272 4990; Fax 0191 272 5313
Project Manager Sue Ley
Deputy Project Manager Jean Skinner

Independent Persons Scheme 3rd Fl, MEA Hse, Ellison Pl, Newcastle upon Tyne, Tyne and Wear NE1 8XZ; URL www.nch.org.uk; E-mail neips@mail.nch.org.uk; Tel 0191 230 3682; Fax 0191 230 5484
Project Co-ordinator Liz Musto

The Kite 25 Kayll Rd, Sunderland, Tyne and Wear SR4 7TW; E-mail netk@mail.nch.org.uk; Tel 0191 567 4801; Fax 0191 567 1162
Manager Simone Silver Path

NCH Newbiggin Hall Family Project Brian Roycroft Centre, Newbiggin Hall Shopping Centre, Newbiggin Hall Est, Newcastle upon Tyne, Tyne and Wear NE5 4BR; E-mail nenbhfc@mail.nchafc.org.uk; Tel 0191 271 0705
Project Manager Jane Anderson

Northumberland and Tyneside Family Mediation Service MEA Hse, Ellison Pl, Newcastle upon Tyne, Tyne and Wear NE1 8XS; Tel 0191 261 9212
Project Manager Valerie Vaughan
Project Manager Mary Evans

St. Anthony's Children's House 47–49 Caldbeck Ave, Pottery Bank, Walker, Newcastle upon Tyne, Tyne and Wear NE6 3SD; Tel 0191 224 0217
Project Manager Ellen Watts

St. Cuthbert's Care

St. Aidan's Rosehill Rd, Willington Quay, Wallsend, Tyne and Wear NE28 6LQ; Tel 0191 262 3629
Family preparation unit.

Seton St. Vincent's, The Roman Way, West Denton, Newcastle upon Tyne, Tyne and Wear NE15 7LT; Tel 0191 267 4383
Children's unit
7

Thornhill Park 23 Thornhill Pk, Sunderland, Tyne and Wear SR2 7LA; Tel 0191 565 9481
Respite unit for children with learning difficulties.

Wakefield

Barnardos Yorkshire Division

Signpost Constance Green Centre, 24 Cheapside, Wakefield, West Yorkshire WF1 2TF; Tel 01924 304100; Fax 01924 304101
Service Manager L. Richardson

Walsall

Bentley Family Centre Churchill Rd, Bentley, Walsall, West Midlands WS2 0BA; Tel 01922 636767
Project Leader Rev Nigel Carter

NCH Midlands Region

Walsall Resource Centre for Children with Disabilities Pool St, Chuckery, Walsall, West Midlands WS1 2EN; URL www.nch.org.uk/projects/walsallresourcecentre; E-mail mdwrs@mail.nch.org.uk; Tel 01922 636662
Project Manager Sharon Jeffery

Warwickshire

NCH Midlands Region

John Waterhouse Project 87 Rouncil La, Kenilworth, Warwickshire CV8 1FN; E-mail mdjwp@mail.nch.org.uk; Tel 01926 864485
Project Manager Sue Queen

Spurgeon's Child Care

Lillington After School Club 87 Valley Rd, Lillington, Leamington Spa, Warwickshire CV32 7RX; E-mail phil.overton@ntlworld.com; Tel 01926 772937
Project Co-ordinator Phil Overton
After-school club.

West Midlands

Barnardos Midland Division

Dudley Community Routes Blantyre Hse, 4 Barrack La, Halesowen, West Midlands B63 2UX; Tel 01384 411722
Manager (Children's Services) June Hill

Faith in the Black Country Community Project 168 Birmingham Rd, Warley, Oldbury, West Midlands B69 4EH; E-mail faithintheblackcountry.project@barnardos.org.uk; Tel 0121 544 2112
Manager (Children's Services) H. Sherriffe

8 to 18 Family Placement Project Trinity Hse, Trinity Rd, Dudley, West Midlands WV4 5UL; URL www.barnardos.org.uk; E-mail 8to19@barnardos.org.uk; Tel 01384 253652; Fax 01384 257125
Service Manager Bob Woods

Sandcastle Project 7 St. Michael's Crt, Victoria St, West Bromwich, West Midlands B70 8ET; Tel 0121 500 5212
Project Leader K. Footman

St. Christopher's Shared Care 625 Warwick Rd, Solihull, West Midlands B91 1AP; Tel 0121 709 2610; Fax 0121 709 2609
Project Leader Maureen Murray

NCH Midlands Region

NCH Birmingham Independent Visitors Project 2–4 Guild Cl, Ledsam St, Ladywood, Birmingham, West Midlands B16 8EL; E-mail mdivs@mail.nch.org.uk; Tel 0121 455 0120; Fax 0121 455 6362

Adoption NCH 141 Wood End La, Erdington, Birmingham, West Midlands B24 8BD; URL www.nch.org.uk; E-mail mdap@mail.nch.org.uk; Tel 0121 377 7999
Project Manager Sally Heaven-Richards

Sandwell Options

c/o Control Hse, Shaftesbury St, West Bromwich, West Midlands B70 9QD; Tel 0121 569 8403; Fax 0121 525 9282
Project Manager Farzama Mahmood

Smith's Wood Family Centre Wheatfield Cl, Smith's Wood, Solihull, West Midlands B36 0QP
Centre Director Marian Davis

NCH Stourbridge Family Centre School St, Stourbridge, West Midlands DY8 1XE; URL www.nch-stourbridgefc@mail.nch.org.uk; E-mail mdsfc@mail.nch.org.uk; Tel 01384 392665; Fax 01384 444268
Project Manager Sally Wellings

Tudor Close 1 Tudor Cl, Sutton Coldfield, West Midlands B73 6SX; E-mail mdtc@nch.org.uk; Tel 0121 355 5105; 0121 355 5121; Fax 0121 355 5121
Project Manager Chris Telford

PCCA Christian Child Care

Chamberlain House 43 Redruth Rd, Walsall, West Midlands WS5 3EJ; URL www.pcca.co.uk
Enquiries PO Box 133, Swanley, Kent BR8 7UQ; Tel 0845 120 455051
Project Leader P. Humpage
Project Leader A. Humpage
Respite care for children under 13 years with severe disabilities.

West Yorkshire

Catholic Care (Diocese of Leeds)

Craven House 41 Swadford St, Skipton, North Yorkshire
BD23 1QY; Tel 01756 700099
Manager Vee Walker
Home for adults with learning difficulties.

Palace House Road 15 Palace House Rd, Fairfield, Hebden
Bridge, West Yorkshire HX7 6HW; Tel 01422 842238
Contact Louis Zephir
Home for adults with learning difficulties.

West Haven 146 Huddersfield Rd, Dewsbury, West
Yorkshire WF13 2RW; Tel 01924 461720
Manager Peter Simmons
Home for adults with learning difficulties.

The Children's Society

The Children's Society in Keighley 24b Cavendish St,
Keighley, West Yorkshire BD21 3RG; Tel 01535 610227;
Fax 01535 610432
Project Co-ordinator Vacancy

NCH North East Region

Bradford Stepping Stones No 1 Hse, Springfield Complex,
Squire La, Bradford, West Yorkshire BD9 6RA;
E-mail nebiap@mail.nch.org.uk
Community Living Project 'Claremont Lodge', 35
Claremont Dr, Headingley, Leeds, West Yorkshire LS6 4ED;
Tel 0113 274 9531; Fax 0113 274 8876
Project Manager Jeff Moody

Wiltshire

NCH South West Region

Bemerton Heath Family Centre 73a Pinewood Way,
Salisbury, Wiltshire SP2 9HX;
E-mail swbh@mail.nch.org.uk; Tel 01722 411178
Project Manager Vacancy

The Cotswold Community Spine Rd West, Ashton Keynes,
Swindon SN6 6QU; E-mail swcc@mail.nch.org.uk;
Tel 01285 861239

The Friary 73a Pinewood Way, Salisbury, Wiltshire SP1 2SF;
Tel 01722 411178
Project Manager Vacancy

York City

The Children's Society

Children's Resource Project (Yorkshire and The Humber)
George Hse, 18 George St, York YO1 9QB; Tel 01904 634614;
Fax 01904 637007

PACT, Yorkshire George Hse, 18 George St, York YO1 9QB;
E-mail py@childsoc.org.uk; Tel 01904 639056; Fax 01904
672903
Project Leader Lucy Kirkbride

Wales

Blaenau Gwent

NCH Wales

Bettws Family Support c/o Brackla Meadows Family &
Neighbourhood Centre, 3–4 Clos-y-Waun, Bridgend
CF31 2QN; Tel 01656 766067; Fax 01656 766960
Project Manager Megan Nicholas (Acting)

Brackla Meadows Family and Neighbourhood Centre 3–4
Clos-y-Waun, Brackla, Bridgend CF31 2QN; Tel 01656
766067; Fax 01656 766960
Project Manager Megan Nicholas

Cefn Golau Family Centre 105 Attlee Way, CefnGolau,
Tredegar, Blaenau Gwent NP22 3TD
Project Manager Robin Grant

Network Brynmawr 2a Market Sq, Brynmawr, Blaenau
Gwent NP23 4AJ; E-mail wanb@mail.nch.org.uk; Tel 01495
311113
Project Manager Chris Ramus

North Gwent Family Centre Penrhiw Villa, Surgery Rd,
Cwmcelyn, Blaina, Blaenau Gwent NP13 3AY; Tel 01495
290274
Project Manager Vivien Griffiths

TS House 9 Brynteg Rd, Blaina, Blaenau Gwent NP3 3HN;
Tel 01495 292311
Project Manager Chris Ramus

Caerphilly

NCH Wales

Caerphilly Children's Centre Cwrtllanfabon, Energlyn,
Caerphilly CF83 2WP; E-mail waccc@mail.nch.org.uk;
Tel 029 2086 7447
Project Manager D. Paton

Canolfan Teulu Pontottyn Family Centre, Fairview Terr,
Pontlottyn, Caerphilly CF81 9RF;
E-mail wanrvc@mail.nch.org.uk; Tel 01685 843050;
Fax 01685 843650
Project Manager Jenny McMillan

Cardiff

Cardiff Advocacy Team 36 Dogfield St, Cathays, Cardiff
CF24 4QZ; E-mail cat@trosgynnal.org.uk; Tel 029 2066 8956;
(Young peoples' freephone) 0800 581862; Fax 029 2034 4579
Network Manager Gerard Szaby

Welcare Development Llandaff Diocesan Board for Social
Responsibility, 65 Cowbridge Rd West, Ely, Cardiff
CF5 5BQ; Tel 029 2056 5887
Co-ordinator Lynne Park
Mother and baby unit support and assessment as needed;
ante-natal and post-natal care and accommodation;
children and families resource centre, sessional day-care, 18
months–five years. Also nine self-contained flats for single
parent and child. Supported living project.

Barnardos Wales and South West England

Community Links 11–15 Columbus Wlk, Atlantic Wharf,
Cardiff CF10 4BZ; Tel 029 2043 6222; Fax 029 2043 6223
Manager (Children's Services) Sarah Bowen

Barnardo's 8–15s Team 36 Caerau La, Ely, Cardiff
CF5 5HQ; E-mail howard.tomlinson@barnardos.org.uk;
Tel 029 2059 3440
Team Leader Howard Tomlinson

Ely Families Service Ely Family Centre, Grand Ave, Ely,
Cardiff CF5 4LE; E-mail ray.wright@barnardos.org; Tel 029
2057 7074
Manager (Children's Service) R.M. Wright

Family Institute 105 Cathedral Rd, Cardiff CF1 9PH; Tel 029
2022 6532; 029 2022 6533
Project Leader J. Faris

Marlborough Road Partnership 46 Marlborough Rd, Roath,
Cardiff CF23 5BX; E-mail mrp@barnardos.org.uk; Tel 029
2049 7531; Fax 029 2045 3083
Manager (Children's Services) Sally Jenkins

Tros Gynnal Ltd 12 North Rd, Cardiff CF24 4QZ;
E-mail admin@trosgynnal.org.uk; Tel 029 2039 6974
Executive Director Roger Bishop

NCH Wales

Cardiff Options Project 56 Conybeare Rd, Canton, Cardiff CF5 1GD; E-mail waco@mail.nch.org.uk; Tel 029 2066 4359; Fax 029 2021 3023
Project Manager Sian Herrera

Cardiff Respite Care House 92 Rhyd-y-Penau Rd, Cardiff CF23 6PW; E-mail wacrch@mail.nch.org.uk; Tel 029 2075 3513; Fax 029 2075 3820
Manager (Residential Services) Mair Williams

Children and Youth Parenting Team Shaw Cl, Llanrumney, Cardiff CF3 9NX; Tel 029 2036 0556

NCH Pre-School Project c/o Regional Office, St David's Crt, Cardiff CF1 9DN
Contact Melanie Coleman

Carmarthen

Barnardos Wales and South West England

West Wales Project Lyric Bldgs, 7 Queen St, Carmarthen, Carmarthenshire SA31 1JR; Tel 01267 232664; Fax 01267 221805
Project Leader Vacancy

The Children's Society

St. David's Diocesan Team Dark Gate Bldgs, 3 Red St, Carmarthen, Carmarthenshire SA31 1QL; Tel 01267 221551
Project Leader Sue Fletcher

NCH Wales

West Wales Guardian ad Litem Service 33 Quay St, Carmarthen, Carmarthenshire SA31 1PX; Tel 01267 231199
Project Manager Vacancy

Llanelli Community and Family Project 24 Station Rd, Llanelli, Carmarthenshire SA15 1AB; Tel 01554 776323
Project Manager Vacancy

Conwy

NCH Wales

Conwy Children's Rights/Independent Visitor Project Eryl Wen, Eryl Pl, Llandudno, Conwy LL30 2TX; URL www.nch.org.uk; E-mail wacrp@mail.nch.org.uk; Tel 01492 879625; Fax 01492 879625
Contact Glenys Jones

Conwy Family Project Ty Eluned, Towyn Rd, Abergele, Conwy LL22 9AB; E-mail waccafcr@mail.nch.org.uk; Tel 01745 822228; Fax 01745 822687
Project Manager Lesley Gleave

Conwy Snapdragons Network Ty Eluned, Towyn Rd, Abergele, Conwy LL22 9AB; E-mail waccafcr@mail.nch.org.uk; Tel 01745 822228; Fax 01745 822687
Project Co-ordinator Paul Penlington

Conwy Young Carers Ty Eluned, Towyn Rd, Abergele, Conwy LL22 9AB; E-mail waccafcr@mail.nch.org.uk; Tel 01745 822228; Fax 01745 822687
Project Co-ordinator Kath Price

Cyngor Gwynedd

Bryn Melyn Llandderfd Bala, Gwynedd LL23 7RA; URL www.brynmelyngroup.com; E-mail enquiries@brynmelyn.com; Tel 01678 530330; Fax 01678 530460

The Children's Society

Sylfaen 24–26 Seryd Fawr, Caenarfon, Gwynedd LL55 1RL; Tel 01286 677117; Fax 01286 677802
Project Leader Brian Thirsk
Youth homelessness project.

The Presbyterian Church of Wales

Cartref Bontnewydd Bontnewydd, Caernarfon, Gwynedd LL54 7UW; URL www.cartrefbontnewydd.org; E-mail gwybodarth@cartrefbontnewydd.org; Tel 01286 672922; Fax 01286 674114
Trust Director Val Owen
Inter
9
Assessment and training of foster carers, Family Group Conference Project, NVQ Centre. Clywed Project.

Denbighshire

NCH Wales

Denbighshire Capel Seion Capel Seion, Henllan St, Denbigh, Denbighshire LL16 3P; Tel 01745 816350

Denbighshire Children's Residential Service 2 Medea Dr, Rhyl, Denbighshire LL18 3BH; Tel 01745 354483
Contact Sue Henson

Denbighshire Family Support Services Glan-y-Mor, 36 Sandringham Ave, Rhyl, Denbighshire LL18 1NG; Tel 01745 331222; Fax 01745 350200
Project Manager Peter Hibbs
Project Co-ordinator Jane Young

Glan y Mor Family Centre 36 Sandringham Ave, Rhyl, Denbighshire LL18 1NG; Tel 01745 331222; Fax 01745 350200
Project Manager Peter Hibbs

Flintshire

NCH Wales

The Flintshire Family Project Mancot Clinic, Mancot La, Mancot, Flintshire CH5 2AH; E-mail waffs@mail.nch.org.uk; Tel 01244 539537; Fax 01244 539496

Flintshire Children's Residential Service 5 Station Rd, Queensferry, Flintshire CH5 1SU; Tel 01244 810139
Contact Julie Gillbanks

Merthyr Tydfil

The Children's Society

The Children's Society in Merthyr Tydfil 4th Fl, Oldway Hse, Merthyr Tydfil CF47 8UX; Tel 01685 353953
Project Leader Caroline Owen

Monmouthshire

The Children's Society

Valleys Community Development Unit Unit 8 Maritime Offices, Woodland Terr, Maesycoed, Pontypridd, Monmouthshire CF37 1D2; E-mail valleys-community-development-unit@the-childrens-society.org.uk; Tel 01443 485591; Fax 01443 485620
Project Leader Jim Barnaville

Neath Port Talbot

NCH Wales

Neath Port Talbot Family Link Tan y Groes Rd, Port Talbot, Neath Port Talbot; Tel 01639 888678
Contact Jane Kayley

Neath Port Talbot Family Support Project NCH, Severn Cres, Port Talbot, Neath Port Talbot SA12 6TA

Newport

Newport Advocacy Project 26 Charles St, Newport NP9 1JT; Tel 01633 840451
Project Leader Janet Wyllie

Two Way Street Fl 2, 2 Emlyn Wlk, Newport NP9 1EW; E-mail tws@childsoc.org.uk; Tel 01633 243164
Project Leader Mary Flynn

NCH Wales

Family Mediation – NCH Cymru 66 Lower Dock St, Newport NP20 1EF; E-mail wagms@mail.nch.org.uk; Tel 01633 263065
Project Manager Jonathan Price

Newport Community Remand Project 27 Argyle St, Newport NP9 5NE; Tel 01633 857777; Fax 01633 852211
Project Leader Vacancy

Rhondda, Cynon, Taff

Intensive Family Support Service Grange Terr, Llwynypia, Rhondda, Cynon, Taff CF40 2HT; Tel 01443 440846; Fax 01443 430706
Manager (Children's Services) M. Kempenaar

Open Door 21 Morgan St, Pontypridd, Rhondda, Cynon, Taff CF37 2DS; URL www.barnardos.org.uk; Tel 01443 486645
Manager (Children's Services) Ms S. Kemp

NCH Wales

Rhondda Family Support Project, NCH Cymru 293 Brithweunydd Rd, Trealaw, Rhondda, Cynon, Taff CF40 2NZ; URL www.worteyc@mail.nch.org.uk; Tel 01443 433079
Project Manager Nevin Thomas

Ty Cynon Project 52 Pembroke St, Aberdare, Rhondda, Cynon, Taff CF44 7BH; Tel 01685 873708; Fax 01685 871229
Contact Paul Webb

Swansea

The Children's Society, Swansea and Brecon Council of Social Reponsibililty

Good Start for Swansea Children The Family Centre, 45 Broughton Ave, Portmead, Swansea SA5 5JS; Tel 01792 589265
Project Manager Sue Giles

Barnardos Wales and South West England

Barnardos Guardian ad Litem Service in West Glamorgan 76a Walter Rd, Swansea SA1 4QA; Tel 01792 460179; Fax 01792 460193
Panel Manager Felicity Fletcher

Barnardos BAYS Service 32–36 High St, Swansea SA1 1LF; Tel 01792 455105
Manager (Children's Service) Deirdre Conner

NCH Wales

George Thomas House, 361–363 Gower Road, Swansea SA2 7AH; URL www.nchafc.co.uk; Tel 01792 299330
Parents in Partnership George Thomas Hse, 363 Gower Rd, Swansea SA2 7AH; Tel 01222 280773

Vale of Glamorgan

NCH Wales

Headlands School 2 St. Augustine's Rd, Penarth, Vale of Glamorgan CF64 1YY; Tel 029 2070 9771; Fax 029 2070 0515
Headteacher David Haswell

Maes y Coed Children's Centre Gladstone Rd, Barry, Vale of Glamorgan CF63 1NH; E-mail wapfcrp@mail.nch.org.uk; Tel 01446 732755
Project Manager Jane Weeks
Project Worker Vicki Thompson

Penarth Family and Community Resource Centre 14 Albert Cres, Penarth, Vale of Glamorgan CF64 1DA; E-mail wapfcrp@mail.nch.org.uk; Tel 029 2070 4500
Project Manager Jane Weeks

Wrexham

NCH Wales

Longfields 11 Sontley Rd, Wrexham LL13 7EN; E-mail wal@mail.nch.org.uk; Tel 01978 264040; Fax 01978 263600
Manager Maureen Howell

Drws Agored Welshpool Open Door Enterprise Centre, Salop Rd, Welshpool, Powys SY21 7SW; Tel 01938 555009; Fax 01938 555009
Community Development Co-ordinator Liz Davies

NCH Longfields and Wrexham Young Carers Longfields, 11 Sontley Rd, Wrexham LL13 7EN; E-mail wal@mail.nch.org.uk; Tel 01978 264040; Fax 01978 263600
Project Manager (Longfields and Wrexham) Maureen Howell
Project Co-ordinator (Wrexham) Jenny Mackrell

Children's Rights, Tros Gynnal Wrexham Partnership Bldg, First Ave, Gwersyllt, Wrexham LL11 4EH; E-mail wrexham@trosgynnal.org.uk; Tel 01978 757903; Fax 01978 754703

Scotland

Aberdeen City

Partnership Housing Ltd Old Stoneywood Church, Bankhead Rd, Bucksburn, Aberdeen AB21 9QH; URL www.partnershiphousing.org.uk; E-mail contact@partnershiphousing.org.uk; Tel 01224 715544; Fax 01224 715540
Project Manager Matthew Rd
Holiday activity schemes for children in Aberdeen City.

Aberlour Child Care Trust

Children's Services Training and Assessment Centre Room 304, Summerhill Education Centre, Stroneay Dr, Aberdeen AB15 6JA; E-mail cstac@aberlour.org.uk; Tel 01224 346312
Project Manager Fran Littlejohn

Primrosehill Family Centre 8 Sunnybank Rd, Aberdeen AB24 3NG; Tel 01224 483381
Project Manager Jackie Kerr

Barnardos Scotland

Scottish Headquarters, 235 Corstorphine Rd, Edinburgh
EH12 7AR; URL www.barnardos.org.uk; Tel 0131 334
9893; Fax 0131 316 4008

Linksfield 20 Carden Pl, Aberdeen AB10 1UQ; Tel 01224
624090
Manager (Children's Services)   Vacancy

Voluntary Service Aberdeen

Aberdeen Children's Society 38 Castle St, Aberdeen
AB11 5YU; URL www.vsa.org.uk;
E-mail info@vsa.org.uk; Tel 01224 212021; Fax 01224
580722
Director   W. Howie, MA, BD, STM
Aberdeen Children's Society provides a range of
community services to help children in situations of need
including: Social work support; Children and Family
Counsellors; Playgroup, Family Access Centre; Family
support projects; Play equipment library; Christmas toy
scheme; Saturday Fun Club for older children with learning
disabilities.

Linn Moor Residential Special School Peterculter,
Aberdeen AB14 0PJ; URL www.linnmoorschool.co.uk;
E-mail info@linnmoorschool.co.uk; Tel 01224 732246;
Fax 01224 735261
Director   W. Howie, MA, BD, STM
Residential Special School for up to 30 children with
learning disabilities. Individually-designed educational
programmes combined with well planned social activities
and excellent residential care help develop the children's
full potential.

Richmondhill House 18 Richmondhill Pl, Aberdeen
AB15 5EP; URL www.vsa.org.uk; E-mail info@vsa.org.uk;
Tel 01224 212021; Fax 01224 580722
Director   W. Howie, MA, BD, STM
Provides short-term supported accommodation for up to
nine unsupported parents and their children at a time of
crisis. Professional care staff help the parents overcome
difficult emotional problems, develop childcare skills and
build up the confidence and experience necessary to live
independently. Outreach support is also available.

Ayrshire

NCH Scotland

East Ayrshire Family Support Service Lisalanna, Lugar St,
Cumnock, East Ayrshire KA18 1AB; Tel 01290 426880;
Fax 01290 426559
Project Manager   Jo McBain

Borders

Aberlour Child Care Trust

Arberlour Options Lower Langbrae, Main St, St.
Boswells, Scottish Borders;
E-mail borders.options@aberlour.org.uk; Tel 01835 824640;
Fax 01835 824653
Project Leader   Kelvin Beattie
Assistant Director   C. McVicar
36 Park Terr, Stirling FK8 2JR
Offer information, support and practical help to parents
who have a child with additional/special needs.

Borders Respite Care Project 4 St. Cuthbert's Dr, St.
Boswells, Melrose, Scottish Borders TD6 0DF; Tel 01835
823337
Project Leader   K. Beattie
Respite care and holidays for children and young people
with learning disabilities.

Clackmannanshire

NCH Scotland

Broad Horizons Supported Accommodation Project 19
Broad St, Alloa, Clackmannanshire FK10 1AN;
E-mail scbhsap@mail.nchafc.org.uk; Tel 01259 212044;
Fax 01259 210106
Contact   Charlie Gracie

Clackmann Independent Living Project 19 Broad St, Alloa,
Clackmannanshire FK10 1AN;
E-mail scbhsap@mail.nchafc.org.uk; Tel 01259 212044;
Fax 01259 210106
Project Manager   Charlie Gracie

Tullibody Family Project 101a Newmills, Tullibody,
Clackmannanshire FK10 2SE; E-mail sctf@mail.nch.org.uk;
Tel 01259 214695
Project Manager   Eveline Garden

Dumfries and Galloway

Ashbank Trust Ashbank Hse, Troqueer Rd, Dumfries and
Galloway DG2 7SS;
URL www.ashbanktrust.free-online.co.uk;
E-mail chrissie@ashbanktrust.free-online.co.uk; Tel 01387
268270
Manager   C.H. Anderson
Young adults. Learning disability Physical disability (6)

Aberlour Child Care Trust

Aberlour – Crannog Central Carrick Rd, Lochside, Dumfries,
Dumfries and Galloway DG2 9PR; Tel 01387 249033

NCH Scotland

Dumfries and Galloway Family Mediation Service 51
Newall Terr, Dumfries, Dumfries and Galloway DG1 2HH;
E-mail scdagfms@mail.nch.org.uk; Tel 01387 263185
Project Manager   C. Campbell

Upper Nithsdale Family Project Greystone Ave, Kelloholm,
Kirkconnel, Dumfries and Galloway DG4 6RB;
E-mail scunfp@mail.nchafc.org.uk; Tel 01659 66135
Project Manager   M. Halkett

Dundee

Carolina House Trust 23 Roseangle, Dundee DD1 4LS;
E-mail reception@carolina.org.uk; Tel 01382 202029;
Fax 01382 226729
Executive Director   Clive Wood
Residential and Community Projects for young people,
including care rescue service and residential boat project.
ASDAN, AALA and SQA provider of accredited training
for staff, volunteers and young people.

Partners in Advocacy (Dundee Office) Unit 7, Prospect III,
Gemini Cres, Dundee Technology Pk, Dundee DD2 1SW;
URL www.partnersinadvocacy.org.uk;
E-mail dundee@partnersinadvocacy.org.uk; Tel 01382
561113
Advocacy Co-ordinator   Joyce McQuilken

Barnardos Scottish Division

The Bridge Project 1 Dudhope Terr, Dundee DD3 6HG;
Tel 01382 28834
Project Leader   Mandy Sheridan

Dundee Family Support Team 14 Dudhope St, Dundee
DD1 1JS; Tel 01382 224924
Project Leader   D. Anderson

Riverside – Tayside 1 Dudhope Terr, Dundee DD3 6HG;
Tel 01382 221944
Senior Practitioner   Daryl Cuthbert

Children 1st, Royal Scottish Society for the Prevention of Cruelty to Children

Laurelbank Family Centre 2 Dudhope St, Dundee DD1 1JU; Tel 01382 322436; Fax 01382 221465
Project Leader Ian A. Chalmers

NCH Scotland

Dundee Alternatives to Custody Friarfield Hse, Barrack St, Dundee DD1 1PQ; URL www.nch.org.uk; E-mail scdatc@mail.nch.org.uk; Tel 01382 435001; Fax 01382 435073
Project Manager Duncan Mclennan

Dundee Families Project 7 St. Clement Terr, Dundee DD3 9PF; E-mail scdf[@mail.nchafc.org.uk; Tel 01382 828372; Fax 01382 828003
Contact Gill Strachan

Dundee Stopover Project Walker Hse, 9 Wellington St, Dundee DD1 2QA; Tel 01382 227036
Project Manager Muriel Miller

Edinburgh

Dean and Cauvin Trust 41 Portland St, Edinburgh EH6 4BB; Tel 0131 554 3784
Prepartion for independent living.
   Mixed (6)

Partners in Advocacy Unit 6, Abbeymount Techbase, Edinburgh EH7 5AN; URL www.partnersinadvocacy.org.uk; E-mail admin@partnersinadvocacy.org.uk; Tel 0131 478 7723; Fax 0131 478 7729
Director Julienne Dickey
Citizen advocacy and self advocacy for children and adults with learning disabilities.

Barnardos Scottish Division

Blackford Brae Project 91 South Oswald Rd, Edinburgh EH9 2HH; E-mail andrew.saunders@barnardos.org.uk; Tel 0131 662 4997
Principal Andrew Saunders

16 Plus (Edinburgh) 22 Broughton Pl, Edinburgh EH1 3RT; URL www.barnardos.org.uk; E-mail 16plus.edinburgh@barnardos.org.uk; Tel 0131 558 3033
Project Leader Rona Gray

Skylight Project 22 Broughton Pl, Edinburgh EH1 3RT; Tel 0131 557 9944
Project Leader Christine Johnston

NCH Scotland

Court and Hearing Interface Project 17–18 London Rd, Edinburgh EH7 5AT; E-mail sccahip@mail.nch.org.uk; Tel 0131 661 7094
Project Manager J. Docherty

The Edinburgh Intensive Probation Project 17–18 London Rd, Edinburgh EH7 5AT; E-mail scealipp@mail.nch.org.uk; Tel 0131 661 7094
Project Manager J. Docherty

The Gilmerton Road Project 408 Gilmerton Rd, Edinburgh EH17 7JH; Tel 0131 672 1702; Fax 0131 672 1705
Project Manager Barbara Wright

Falkirk

Aberlour Child Care Trust

Langlees Family Centre 26–32 Dunkeld Pl, Langlees, Falkirk FK2 7UD; Tel 01324 638080
Project Manager Liz McMahon
Family centre.

Barnardos Scottish Division

Cluaran Project Watling Lodge, Tamfourhill Rd, Falkirk FK1 4RE; E-mail cluaran.project@barnardos.org.uk; Tel 01324 632903
Project Leader Joanna McCreadie

NCH Scotland

Family Support Service 54 Brown St, Camelon, Falkirk FK1 4QF; E-mail scfssf@mail.nch.org.uk; Tel 01324 633772
Project Manager C. Gent

Fife

Aberlour Child Care Trust

Bellyeoman Road 6 Bellyeoman Road, Dunfermline, Fife KY12 0AD; Tel 01383 724834
Project Manager A. MacArthur
Residential provision for children and young people with profound learning disabilities.

Collydean Project 75 Wilmington Dr, Glenrothes, Fife KY7 6UU; Tel 01592 744195
Project Leader A. McArthur
Respite care for children and young people with learning disabilities and/or physical disability.

Whyteman's Brae 44 Whyteman's Brae, Kirkcaldy, Fife KY1 2LE; E-mail sycamore@aberlour.org.uk; Tel 01592 591500
Service Manager T. Foley
Children and young people exhibiting behavioural disorders.

NCH Scotland

Community Alternative Placement Scheme Pk Hse, 10 Pk Circus Pl, Glasgow G3 6AN; URL www.nch.org.uk; E-mail sccapsmail@nch.org.uk; Tel 0141 331 0584; 0141 331 0585; Fax 0141 333 1097
Practice Team Manager Kay Gibson (Acting)
Alternative to Secure Accomodation for 12–16 yr olds.

Family Mediation Fife 30 North St, Glenrothes, Fife KY7 5NA; E-mail scfmf@mail.nch.org.uk; Tel 01592 751095; Fax 01592 751095
Project Manager Jean Brodie

Glasgow

Aberlour Child Care Trust

Aberlour Outreach Service 201 Drakemire Dr, Glasgow G45 9SS; Tel 0141 634 2434
Depute Project Manager G. McNeill
Mothers with substance dependency and their children; includes day support and outreach.

Glasgow Children's Holiday Scheme 5th Fl, 30 George Sq, Glasgow G2 1EG; E-mail gchs@care4free.net; Tel 0141 248 7255
Co-ordinator Ann Pert
Provides holidays for individual children and families under stress.

No. 1 Project 1 Lancaster Cres, Glasgow G12 0RR; E-mail lancastercres@aberlour.org.uk; Tel 0141 337 6637
Project Manager Sandra Graham (Acting)
Integrated residential rehabilitation project for mothers with substance dependency and their children.

Scarrel Road Castlemilk, Glasgow G45 0DR; Tel 0141 631 1504; Fax 0141 634 7133
Project Manager Rosemary White
Assistant Director Valerie Corbett
Residential rehabilitation unit for mothers with substance dependency and their children.

Archdiocese of Glasgow

Glenlora Cottages 217/227 Glenlora Dr, Glasgow G53 6JS; E-mail glenloracottages@archdioceseofglasgow.freeserve. co.uk; Tel 0141 881 2077
Project Manager Eileen Fraser
Short-term care for persons with learning difficulties.

Barnardos Scottish Division

Faith and Community Project 16 Sandyford Pl, Glasgow G3 7NB; Tel 0141 221 2259; Fax 0141 248 8032
Project Leader L.A. Craise

16 Plus (Glasgow) G14–19 Dundas Business Centre, 38–40 New City Rd, Glasgow G4 9JT; Tel 0141 332 8580
Project Leader Wilma Paterson

Riverside Project (Glasgow) c/o The Brownlee Centre, Gartnaud Hospital, 1053 Great Western Rd, Glasgow G12 0YN; Tel 0141 211 0299

Scottish Adoption Advice Service 16 Sandyford Pl, Glasgow G3 7NB; E-mail saas@barnardos.org.uk; Tel 0141 248 7530
Project Leader R. Mcmillan
Project Leader J. Atherton

NCH Scotland

Preparation for Life Alexandria 28 Bridge St, Alexandria, Glasgow G83 0TA; Tel 01389 757822
Project Manager S. Kielty

Ruchill Child and Family Centre Smeaton St, Ruchill, Glasgow G20 9JS; URL www.nch.org.uk; E-mail scrfp@mail.nch.org.uk; Tel 0141 945 1653; Fax 0141 946 6644
Project Manager Elaine Robertson

NCH San Jai Chinese Project 53 Rose St, Glasgow G3 6SF; E-mail scsjcp@mail.nch.org.uk; Tel 0141 332 3978; Fax 0141 332 2665
Contact Dorothy Neoh

Children 1st, Royal Scottish Society for the Prevention of Cruelty to Children

Children and Families Counselling Project 522 Kilmarnock Rd, Glasgow G43 2BL; E-mail glasgowproject@children1st.org.uk; Tel 0141 637 4144
Project Manager June Welsh

Highlands

NCH Scotland

Highland Intensive Probation 2nd Fl, 46 Church St, Inverness, Highland IV1 1EH; E-mail schip@mail.nchafc.org.uk; Tel 01463 717227; Fax 01463 236335
Project Manager Liz Taylor

Inverness Family Project 186 Smithton Pk, Inverness, Highland IV2 7PF; Tel 01463 794404
Project Manager Liz Taylor

Inverclyde

NCH Scotland

Inverclyde Intensive Probation Unit and Children's Hearing (GAP) Project 9 Terrace Rd, Greenock, Inverclyde PA15 1DJ; URL www.nch.org.uk; E-mail sciipu@mail.nch.org.uk; Tel 01475 727363
Roxburgh Hse, Roxburgh St, 7 Duncan St, Greenock, Inverclyde PA15 4JT; Tel 01475 723044
Practice Team Manager Alan Hind

The Salvation Army

Inverclyde Centre 98 Dalrymple St, Greenock, Inverclyde PA15 1BZ; Tel 01475 783608
23 family units

Moray

Aberlour Child Care

Alba Place 6 Alba Place, Elgin, Moray IV30 4JN; E-mail albaplace@aberlour.org.uk; Tel 01343 542301
Project Leader T. Cripps
Children and young people with learning disabilities.

Moray Youth Action 7 Parade Spur South, Pinefield Ind Est, Elgin, Moray IV30 6AJ; Tel 01343 546214
Service Manager Trisha Hall
Provides LED support to vulnerable young people aged 10–24. Project encompasses community development, support in mainstream education, employment, training, housing, youth crime, group and individual work. Referral via social work.

NCH Scotland

Moray Alternative Placement Scheme (MAPS) Winchester Hse, 1 King St, Elgin, Moray IV30 1EU; Tel 01343 549557; Fax 01343 549558
Practice Manager Jennifer Collins

Moray Family Resource Project Winchester Hse, 1 King St, Elgin, Moray IV30 1EU; Tel 01343 549557; Fax 01343 549558
Contact David Williams
Contact Naomi Graham

Moray Independent Living Project Winchester Hse, Iking St, Elgin, Moray IV30 1EU; Tel 01343 549557; Fax 01343 549558
Manager Glynis Weatherby

Moray Intensive Support Winchester Hse, 1 King St, Elgin, Moray IV30 1EU; Tel 01343 549557; Fax 01343 549558
Manager Jennifer Collins

Moray Project Office Winchester Hse, 1 King St, Lossiemouth, Moray IV31 1EU; Tel 01343 549557; Fax 01343 549558
Contact David Williams

Moray Residential Unit – Buckie 50 Land St, Buckie, Moray AB56 1QS; Tel 01542 839069; Fax 01542 839068
Contact Francis Davidson

Moray Residential Unit – Elgin 6 Rowan Lea, Elgin, Moray IV30 6FP; E-mail scmrue@mail.nchafc.org.uk; Tel 01343 569006
Contact David Williams

North Lanarkshire

Barnardos Scottish Division

CHOSI Motherwell Town Hall, Business Centre, 1–11 High Rd, Motherwell, North Lanarkshire ML1 3HU; E-mail chosi@barnardos.org.uk; Tel 01698 230242
Project Leader D. Noble

NCH Scotland

North Lanarkshire Young Carers Project Town Hall Business Centre, 1–11 High Rd, Motherwell, North Lanarkshire ML1 3HU; Tel 01698 258801
Contact Sean Harkin

Perth and Kinross

NCH Scotland

PACT Project 149–151 Dunkeld Rd, Perth, Perth and Kinross PH1 5AU; E-mail scpact@mail.nchafc.org.uk; Tel 01738 639265; Fax 01738 633203
Alternative to Care
Project Manager Marion Dingwall

Barnardos Scottish Division

Space Project Dryburgh Education Centre, Napier Dr, Dundee DD2 2TF; E-mail qbspac01@barnardos.org.uk; Tel 01382 436621; Fax 01382 436624
Project Leader G. Haddow

Renfrewshire

The Board of Managers Cora Foundation

Good Shepherd Centre Bishopton, Renfrewshire PA7 5PF; Tel 01505 862814; Fax 01505 864167
Principal F. McCann

South Ayrshire

Barnardos Scottish Division

Ayr Homelessness Service 62 Viewfield Rd, Ayr, South Ayrshire KA8 8HH; Tel 01292 610479
Senior Practitioner E. Riach

South Lanarkshire

South Lanarkshire Homelessness Service 40 Bloomgate, Lanark, South Lanarkshire ML11 9ET; Tel 01555 663039
Project Leader A. O'Flynn

NCH Scotland

NCH Clydesdale Youth Project 13 St. Vincent Pl, Lanark, South Lanarkshire ML11 7LA; Tel 01555 665341
Project Manager Vacancy

Shotts Playcare HM Prison, Canthill Rd, Shotts, South Lanarkshire ML7 4LE; Tel 01501 824000
Project Manager Colin Campbell

Stirling

Aberlour Child Care

'Off the Record' Project 27 Murray Pl, Stirling FK8 1DQ; E-mail offtherecord@aberlour.org.uk; Tel 01786 450518; (Freephone) 0800 027 6001
Project Leader A. Robinson
Information, advice and counselling service for young people. Sexual health clinic.

Unit 2 Project 42 Lomond Cres, Cornton, Stirling FK9 5DN; E-mail unit2@aberlour.org.uk; Tel 01786 461334; Fax 01786 451771
Provides individual, groupwork, befriending and family work, as an alternative to residential care for young people in difficulties.

Lecropt School Bridge of Allan, Stirling FK9 4NB; Tel 01786 834498
Principal H. Jones
Teaching, social work and support staff plus child psychotherapist.

NCH Scotland

Hillview Family Project 13 Cultenhove Pl, St. Ninian's, Stirling FK7 9DU; Tel 01786 446283
Project Manager Jean Anderson

West Lothian

Barnardos Scottish Division

Bo'ness Family Centre Duchess Nina Hse, Cadzow Cres, Bo'ness, West Lothian EH51 9AY; Tel 01506 823118
Manager (Children's Services) Angela Curran

Family Placement Services 6 Torphichen St, Edinburgh EH3 8JQ; Fax 0131 228 8706
Project Leader B. Heavey

FASS 8 Hazel Gr, Craigshill, Livingston, West Lothian EH54 5JW; E-mail fass@barnardos.org.uk; Tel 01506 438666
Project Leader Fiona Bennett

West Lothian Family Support Team Melbourne Hse, 94 Mid St, Bathgate, West Lothian EH48 1QF; Tel 01506 656325
Manager (Children's Services) Isobel Denholm

Western Isles

NCH Scotland

Western Isles Independent Living 30 Bayhead, Stornoway, Isle of Lewis; Tel 01851 705080; Fax 01851 706504
Contact Sheila Erskine

Western Isles Children and Families Support Service 30 Bayhead, Stornoway, Isle of Lewis HS1 2DU; Tel 01851 706804; Fax 01851 706804
Manager Sheila Erskine
Manager Valerie Russell

Western Isles Project 30 Bayhead, Stornoway, Isle of Lewis HS1 2DU; Tel 01851 706804
Contact Sheila Erskine

Western Isles Residential Unit Hillcrest, 41 Goathill Rd, Stornoway, Isle of Lewis HSI 2NX; Tel 01851 703963; Fax 01851 706804
Contact Sheila Erskine
Contact Adele Humphreys

Northern Ireland

County Antrim

Barnardos Northern Ireland Division

Sharonmore 208 Ballyduff Rd, Newtownabbey, County Antrim BT36 6UX; Tel 028 9084 3351
Project Leader M. Mckeown

Belfast

Barnardos Northern Ireland Division

Barnardo Professional Foster Care 230 Belmont Rd, Belfast BT4 2AW; E-mail lynda.glass@barnardos.org.uk; Tel 028 9065 2288
Project Leader Lynda Glass

Choices for Children 230 Belmont Rd, Belfast BT4 2AW; E-mail choices.forchildren@barnardos.org.uk; Tel 028 9065 8105
Manager (Children's Services) Kevin McCormick

Dr B's Kitchen 9 Bridge St, Belfast BT1 1LT; Tel 028 9032 1213
Service Manager C. McCaughey

Leaving Care Admin Base, 171 University St, Belfast BT7 1HR; Tel 028 9023 1300
Project Leader Shelagh McCauahan

PACT 25 Windsor Ave, Belfast BT9 6EE; Tel 028 9068 2286
Manager (Children's Services) Benny McDaniel

Willow Grove Project 10 Church St, Banbridge, County Down BT32 4AA; Tel 028 4062 6782
Project Leader A. White

Windsor Avenue FRC 23 Windsor Ave, Lisburn Rd, Belfast BT9 6EE; E-mail windsor.avenue@barnardos.co.uk; Tel 028 9066 7586
Manager (Children's Services) Cathal Mullan

The Salvation Army

Glen Alva Family Centre 19 Cliftonville Rd, Belfast
BT14 6JN; E-mail glenalva@tiscali.co.uk; Tel 028 9035 1185
20 family units.

Thorndale Family Centre Duncairn Ave, off Antrim Rd,
Belfast BT14 6BP; Tel 028 9035 1900; Fax 028 9035 1310
34 family units, four single women units. Playgroup up to
24 children 3-5 years.

County Down

Belfast Central Mission

Advice Centre Grosvenor Hse, 5 Glengall St, Belfast
BT12 5AD; Tel 028 9024 1917; Fax 028 9024 0577
Inner city support centre offering practical help and
comfort to those in need.

Craigmore House 97 Donaghadee Rd, Millisle, County
Down BT22 2BZ; URL www.belfastcentralmission.org;
E-mail craigmore@belfastcentralmission.org; Tel 028 9188
2599; Fax 028 9188 8713
Residential adolescent unit for eight young people aged
between 12 and 18.

Kirk House 110 Kings Rd, Belfast BT5 7BX;
URL www.belfastcentralmission.org; Tel 028 9040 2938;
Fax 028 9040 2939
Residential accommodation for older people based on the
'housing with care' model.

Marmion Adolescent Unit 126 Church Rd, Holywood,
County Down BT18 9BY; Tel 028 9042 2408; Fax 028 9042
5523
Residential adolescent unit for 8–10 young people aged
between 12 and 18.

The Quayside Project 16 South St, Newtownards, County
Down BT23 4JT; Tel 028 9182 7783; Fax 028 9182 7784
Young people leaving care.

Simpson Family Resource Centre 40 Manse Rd, Bangor,
County Down BT20 3DE; Tel 028 9127 1538

Londonderry

Barnardos Northern Ireland Division

Home from Home Project 36a Westland Rd, Magherafelt,
County Londonderry BT45 5AY; Tel 028 7963 1344
Residential Unit, Cherry Lodge, 90–91 Ashdale,
    Randalstown, County Antrim
Manager Mary Tennyson

OTHER CHILDREN'S ORGANISATIONS

Action for Sick Children (National Association for the Welfare of Children in Hospital)

1st Fl, 300 Kingston Rd, London SW20 8LX;
    E-mail enquiries@actionforsickchildren.org.uk; Tel 020
    8542 4848; Fax 020 8542 2424
Joins parents and professionals in promoting high quality
health care for sick children at home and in hospital.
Publications and library/information service for parents
and professionals.

AFASIC

50–52 Great Sutton St, London EC1V 0DJ;
    URL www.afasic.org.uk; E-mail info@afasic.org.uk;
    Tel 020 7490 9410

Runs an information and support service for parents
and professionals and campaigns for better facilities for
speech and language-impaired children and young
people.

Aid for Children with Tracheostomies (ACT)

9 Elmdale Cres, Northfield, Birmingham, West Midlands
    B31 1SL; Tel 0121 411 1348; Fax 0121 411 1348
Secretary J. Earles
Helps parents and families of children who have had a
tracheostomy and the children themselves. Newsletter,
information, equipment available. Fund raising.

The Association for Brain-Damaged Children and Young Adults

Clifton Hse, 3 St. Paul's Rd, Foleshill, Coventry, West
    Midlands CV6 5DE; E-mail abdcya@btclick.com; Tel 024
    7666 5450; Fax 024 7666 5450
Office Manager Mrs E. Markey
For young people with profound learning disabilities. This
service is available in the coventry area only. Provides
short-stay respite-care home, and residential home.

Association for Children with Heart Disorders

89 Buckstone Rd, Edinburgh EH10 6UX;
    URL www.achd.org.uk;
    E-mail jameskelman@btinternet.com; Tel 0131 445
    4868
Chairman Jim Kelman
Six area groups in Scotland provide local contact and
meetings, support for families and fund-raising for
equipment, etc.

Birth Defects Foundation

Hornlock Way, Cannock, Staffordshire WS11 7GF;
    URL www.birthdefects.co.uk;
    E-mail enquiries@bdfnewlife.co.uk; Tel 01543 468888;
    Fax (Family Helpline) 01543 468999

The Bobath Centre

Bradbury Hse, 250 East End Rd, East Finchley, London
    N2 8AU; URL www.bobathlondon.co.uk;
    E-mail info@bobathlondon.co.uk; Tel 020 8444 3355;
    Fax 020 8444 3399
Treatment centre for children with cerebral palsy and
adults with neurological disorder (charity). Postgraduate
training centre for paediatricians, physiotherapists,
occupational and speech and language therapists on the
Bobath approach to the treatment of cerebral palsy.

Cancer and Leukaemia in Childhood (CLIC)

Abbey Wood, Bristol BS34 7JU; URL www.clic.co.uk;
    E-mail clic@clic.co.uk; Tel 0117 311 2600; Fax 0117 311
    2649
Cancer and Leukaemia in Childhood was founded in 1976
to support children suffering from cancer by improving
treatment, promoting research and providing practical
assistance to sick children and their families throughout the
UK.
Examples of CLIC's work include establishing one of the
first Chairs in Paediatric Oncology in the country,
pioneering the opening of 'Home from Home' for the
families of patients, creating a research unit to examine the
molecular genetics of childhood cancer, and establishing a
network of CLIC nurses across the country to provide care
in the child's own home.
CLIC is wholly dependent on voluntary donations and
legacies: we need your support to continue the care for
children with cancer.

The Charterhouse Group of Therapeutic Communities

150 Waterloo Rd, London SE1 8SB;
URL www.charterhousegroup.org.uk;
E-mail chg@btclick.com; Tel 020 7803 0550; Fax 020 7261 1307

An association of member organisations that provide for the care, treatment and education of emotionally deprived and damaged children and young people in residential and day settings, and whose work is based on psychodynamic principles.

The Child Brain Injury Trust

The Radcliffe Infirmary, Woodstock Rd, Oxford,
Oxfordshire OX2 6HE; E-mail info@cbituk.org; Tel 01865 552467; Fax 01865 552574
Chief Executive   Lisa Turan

Child Growth Foundation

2 Mayfield Ave, Chiswick, London W4 1PW;
URL www.heightmatters.org.uk

Runs training courses for staff working with the children in the importance of regular growth screening, in particular linking malnutrition, failure to thrive and obesity – as critical indicators of non-endocrine growth disorders such as child abuse.
Registered Charity Number 274325

Child Watch

Registered Charity No. 518067
19 Spring Bank, Hull, Kingston upon Hull HU3 1AF;
URL childwatch.org.uk; E-mail info@childwatch.org.uk;
Tel 01482 325552; (Helpline) 01482 325 552; Fax 01482 585214

Childwatch provides BAC Standards counselling and group therapy for victims (physical, mental or sexual). Counselling can be provided face to face or by telephone. Referral service. Assisted holidays.
A range of information packs are available: Help and advice by telephone is provided Mon–Fri between 0900–1900. Cost of main information pack £2.50.

Childlink Adoption Society

10 Lion Yard, Tremadoc Rd, London SW4 7NQ;
URL www.adoptchildlink.org.uk;
E-mail enquiries@adoptchildlink.org.uk; Tel 020 7498 1933; Fax 020 7498 1791
Chief Executive   Caroline Hesslegrave

Children in Scotland (SCAFA)

Princes Hse, 5 Shandwick Pl, Edinburgh EH2 4RG;
URL www.childreninscotland.org.uk;
E-mail info@childreninscotland.org.uk; Tel 0131 228 8484; Fax 0131 228 8585
Chief Executive   Dr Bronwen Cohen
Organises conferences, produces regular magazines, provides information, training and research for members, acts as a consultative body on questions relating to children and families and aims to promote a more effective partnership between voluntary and statutory agencies. Information pack available, free on request.

Children's Express (CE)

Exmouth Hse, 3–11 Pine St, London EC1R 0JH;
URL www.childrens-express.org;
E-mail enquiries@childrens-express.org; Tel 020 7833 2577; Fax 020 7278 7722
Director (Development)   Fiona Wyton (Acting)
Children's Express (CE) is an innovative programme of personal development and learning through journalism for young people aged 8-18. The programme targets urban areas of disadvantage and operates in the evening, at weekends and during school holidays. Members take the roles of reporters and editors to research and report on subjects of their choice. They produce stories that are edited, marketed and distributed widely through national, regional and local print and broadcast outlets. The programme provides diversity and range of experience, increases self-esteem and self-confidence, improves literacy and communication and gives children a real sense of purpose and value.
Children's Express has been operating successfully for years in the UK. It has three full-time bureaux, in London, Belfast and Newcastle (in partnership with Save the Children) and a part-time satellite bureau, in Sheffield. Satellite bureaux are run in partnership with local authorities, youth projects and education action zones. Over the next few years they aim to engage more children in the programme by increasing capacity in existing bureaux, creating bureaux in Scotland and Wales, using outreach work to access disadvantaged communities and developing materials on their website (www.childrens-express.org) to support Citizenship in schools and youth groups.

Children's Play Council

8 Wakley St, London EC1V 7QE;
URL www.ncb.org.uk/cpc; E-mail cpc@ncb.org.uk;
Tel 020 7843 6016; Fax 020 7278 9512
Director   Tim Gill

Children's Scrap Project

137 Homerton High St, London E9 6AS; Tel 020 8985 6290
Project Manager   Morris Bennett
Collects, stores and distributes clean, safe, industrial waste for use by children's groups in art, craft and play activities. Provides information on the use of waste materials.

The Children's Trust

Tadworth Crt, Tadworth, Surrey KT20 5RU;
URL www.thechildrenstrust.org.uk; Tel 01737 365000; Fax 01737 365001
Director (Children's Services)   Sally Jenkinson
The Children's Trust exists to offer appropriate care, treatment and education to children with exceptional needs and profound disabilities and to give support to their families. Services offered include: rehabilitation for children with acquired brain injury; short- and medium-term care for children with profound and multiple disabilities; hospice care for children with degenerative conditions; care and therapy programmes for children with exceptional needs (including children who are ventilated); residential education for children and young people aged 5–19 years with profound and multiple learning difficulties.

Cleft Lip and Palate Association (CLAPA)

235–237 Finchley Rd, London NW3 6LS;
URL www.clapa.com; E-mail info@clapa.com; Tel 020 7431 0033; Fax 020 7431 8881
Chair   M. Mars
Chief Executive   Gareth Davies
Supports parents of cleft lip and palate children; publishes and distributes educational materials for parents and workers in the field; raises funds; provision of feeding equipment.

The Compassionate Friends

53 North St, Bristol BS3 1EN; Tel (National Helpline) 0117 953 9639; (Office) 0117 966 5202; Fax (Office) 0117 966 5202
Support and Friendship for Bereaved parents and their families by those similarly bereaved. A self-help group of parents whose son or daughter has died from any age and from any cause. Quarterly newsletters, postal library, range of leaflets. Personal and group support. Befriending, rather than counselling.

13

Contact a Family

209–211 City Rd, London EC1V 1JN;
URL www.cafamily.org.uk;
E-mail info@cafamily.org.uk; Tel 020 7608 8700;
(Freephone helpline for parents Mon–Fri, 1000–1600)
0808 808 3555; Fax 020 7608 8701; Textphone 0808 808
3556
Chief Executive Francine Bates
Support for families who care for disabled children. To
introduce and link families whose children have rare
disorders and offer mutual support and information.
Publication of specialist directory of conditions and rare
disorders and a range of factsheets.

Council for Disabled Children (CDC)

National Children's Bureau, 8 Wakley St, London
EC1V 7QE; URL www.ncb.org.uk;
E-mail mbremmers@ncb.org.uk; Tel 020 7843 1900
Aims to keep under review policy and practice in meeting
the needs of children with disabilities and special needs
and their families. Provides a forum for voluntary and
statutory agencies interested in all aspects of disabled
children; information, consultancy, training and
publications.

Derwen College for the Disabled

Oswestry, Shropshire SY11 3JA; Tel 01691 661234; Fax 01691
670714
Director D.J. Kendall, BEng, FCA, MEd
Further education, social development and vocational
training of young people with learning difficulties and
disabilities. Residential courses (usually three years'
duration).

Enquire

Princes Hse, 5 Shandwick Pl, Edinburgh EH2 4RG;
URL www.childreninscotland.org.uk/enquire;
E-mail enquire.seninfo@childreninscotland.org.uk;
Tel 0845 123 2303; Fax 0131 228 9852
Manager (SEN Information and Advice)
Yvonne Cassidy
Manager (SEN Information and Advice) Dinah Aitken
Enquire is a national helpline for special educational needs
in Scotland funded by the Scottish Executive. Enquire
provides information and advice as well as free
publications to parents, professionals and voluntary
organisations working with and for children and young
people who have special educational needs.

Family Information Group

Resource Centre, Gooshays Dr, Harold Hill, Romford,
Essex RM3 9HJ; Tel 01708 378141; Fax 01708 347913
Centre Manager Sharon Hinds
Provides support and assistance to families who have a
child with a disability or learning difficulties and/or
special needs. Office hours 0930–1500 (Mon–Fri). Also
provides playgroup for children 2.5–5 years.

Find Us Keep Us

Mytton Mill, Montford Bridge, Shrewsbury, Shropshire
SY4 1HA; URL www.saccs.co.uk;
E-mail finduskeepus@saccs.co.uk; Tel 01743 850086;
Fax 01743 850172
Part of the SACCS group, Find US Keep Us is a voluntary
agency providing specialist, long-term foster placements
for traumatised children and young people. They offer a
child centered service, including a programme of
meticulous planning, preparation and support for
children and carers. Their aim is to deliver recovery for
every child through professional family placement
services.

FYD Friends for Young Deaf People

East Crt Mansion, College La, East Grinstead, West Sussex
RH19 3LT; Tel 01342 323444 (Voice); Minicom 01342 312639
President Morag Rosie, MBE
Encourages young deaf people to improve their self
confidence, self esteem and independence through
recreational and educational projects.

Hamilton Lodge School for Deaf Children

Walpole Rd, Brighton, Brighton and Hove BN2 OLS;
URL hamiltonlodgeschool.co.uk;
E-mail hamilton.lodge@ukonline.co.uk; Tel 01273
682362; Fax 01273 695742
Principal Mrs A.K. Duffy, MEd
Non-maintained special school.
Weekly boarding school for profoundly deaf children aged
5–18 years, mixed.

Hyperactive Children's Support Group

71 Whyke La, Chichester, West Sussex PO19 7PD;
URL www.hacsg.org.uk; E-mail web@hacsg.org.uk;
Tel 01243 551313; Fax 01243 552019
Founder/Director Sally Bunday
To help and support hyperactive/ADHD/allergic children
and their parents; to conduct research and promote
investigation into the incidence of hyperactivity in the
UK–its causes and treatments; to disseminate information
concerning this condition; send sae for details.

Joint Educational Trust

King William Hse, 2a Eastcheap, London EC3M 1AA;
URL jetcharity.org; E-mail julie.burns@virgin.net; Tel 020
7283 3445; Fax 020 7283 3446
An educational charity to meet the needs of children at risk
up to the age of 13.

Kidsactive – Play and Opportunity for Disabled Children

Pryor's Bank, Bishops Pk, London SW6 3LA;
E-mail info@kidsactive.org.uk; Tel 020 7736 4443;
Fax 020 7731 4426; Minicom 020 7384 2596
Chief Executive D. Fox
Runs six adventure playgrounds for disabled children and
young people in London and promotes play for disabled
children nationally through training, consultancy and
publications, eg. side by side: guide lines for inclusive play,
and bi-annual newsletter.

Lady Hoare Trust for Physically Disabled Children

1st Fl, 89 Albert Embankment, London SE1 7TP;
URL www.ladyhoaretrust.org.uk;
E-mail info@lhtchildren.org.uk; Tel 020 7820 9989;
Fax 020 7582 8251
Chief Executive Michael Ryan
The Trust gives practical and financial support to children
with juvenile chronic arthritis/limb disabilities through a
nationwide network of qualified social workers. Further
details/local contacts from the above address.

The Lucy Faithfull Foundation

Bordesley Hall, The Holloway, Alvechurch, Birmingham,
West Midlands B48 7QA; URL www.lucyfaithfull.co.uk;
Tel 01527 591922; Fax 01527 591924
The Lucy Faithfull Foundation is a child protection agency
operating across the UK. It provides assessment and
intervention for adult male and female perpetrators of
child sexual abuse and adolescent males and females
engaged in inappropriate sexual behaviours.
The Foundation works with adults where sexual abuse has
been alleged but not proven. They also offer therapy for
child and adult survivors of sexual abuse.

M.F.P.A. Trust Fund for the Training of Handicapped Children in the Arts

Willowpool, Jasons Hill, Orchard Lea, Chesham, Buckinghamshire HP5 3QW
Trustee   Trevor Wells
Trustee   P.E. Driver
Trustee   Florence Burr
Gives financial help to physically and mentally-handicapped children who could benefit from participation in painting, music or drama. Some special schools dealing with these subjects could also qualify for an award.

Madina House Children's Home

146 Gloucester Pl, London NW1 6DT; Tel 020 7262 5314
Madina House provides care and support based on Muslim principles for children including non-Muslims who need short or medium term placements.

National Association for Children of Alcoholics (NACOA)

PO Box 64, Fishponds, Bristol BS16 2UH;
URL www.nacoa.org.uk; E-mail help@nacoa.org.uk;
Tel (Admin) 0117 924 8005; (Helpline) 0800 358 3456
Director   Hilary Henriques
Chair   John Fenston
Administrator   Jenny Parmer
NACOA provides information, advice and support for children of alcoholics and training to professionals.

National Association for Gifted Children

Suite 14, Challenge Hse, Sherwood Dr, Bletchley, Milton Keynes MK3 6DP; URL www.nagcbritain.org.uk;
E-mail amazingchildren@nagcbritain.org.uk; Tel 0845 450 0221; Fax 0870 770 3219
Director   Dr Stephen D. Tommis
Provides activities and support for gifted children and their parents, and professionals associated with their education and health. Counselling available.

National Association for Gifted Children in Scotland

PO Box 2024, Glasgow G32 9YD;
E-mail nagcs.org@talk21.com; Tel 0141 639 4797
Chair   D.M. Henderson
Counsellor   Susan Divecha
Aims to bring together and support parents, teachers and others interested in educational provision, as well as the social and emotional development of children and young people.
A confidential counselling and support service is available to individuals and their families, by telephone or in person. Membership of NAGCS for individuals or organisations is £15 pa.

National Association for Maternal and Child Welfare

1st Fl, 40–42 Osnaburgh St, London NW1 3ND; Tel 020 7383 4117
Chief Executive   Valerie Farebrother

National Association of Child Contact Centres

Minerva Hse, Spaniel Row, Nottingham NG1 6EP;
URL www.naccc.org.uk; E-mail contact@naccc.org.uk;
Tel 0845 4500 280; Fax 0845 4500 420
Child Contact Centres are safe meeting places where the children of a separated family can enjoy contact with the non-resident parent, and sometimes other family members, in a child friendly environment where there is no viable alternative.

National Association of Toy and Leisure Libraries/Play Matters

68 Churchway, London NW1 1LT; URL www.natll.org.uk;
E-mail admin@natll.ukf.net; Tel 020 7387 9592; Fax 020 7383 2714
Director   Glenys Carter
NATLL/Play Matters is the national body for toy and leisure libraries throughout the UK. Toy Libraries lend good quality, carefully chosen toys to all families with young children, including children with special needs. They also offer a befriending, supportive service to parents and carers.
Leisure libraries offer a similar service to adults with special needs and to their carers.
NATLL offers advice, information and support for people setting up and running toy and leisure libraries; sells a range of publications on the topic of toys and play; organises training courses for the voluntary and statutory sectors; produces the annual 'Good Toy Guide'.

National Childminding Association

8 Masons Hill, Bromley, Kent BR2 9EY; Tel 020 8464 6164; Fax 020 8290 6834
Chief Executive   Gill Haynes
A charity providing support and advice to childminders, parents and childminding workers, central and local government and employees. Free information pack available – send sae. The National Childminding Association is working for the well-being of all children through an organisation accessible to all.

National Children's Bureau

8 Wakley St, London EC1V 7QE; URL www.ncb.org.uk;
E-mail membership@ncb.org.uk; Tel 020 7843 6000;
Fax 020 7278 9512
President   Baroness Helena Kennedy, QC
Chair   Anne Sofer
Chief Executive   Paul Ennals
Treasurer   I. Dewar
The National Children's Bureau promotes the interests and well-being of all children and young people across every aspect of their lives. It advocates the participation of children and young people in all matters affecting them. It challenges disadvantage in childhood.
The National Children's Bureau achieves its mission by: ensuring the views of young children and young people are listened to and taken into account at all times; playing an active role in policy development and advocacy; undertaking high quality research and work from an evidence based perspective; promoting multidisciplinary, cross-agency partnerships; identifying, developing and promoting good practice; disseminating information to professionals, policy makers, parents and children and young people. The National Children's Bureau has adopted and works within the UN Convention on the Rights of the Child.
The National Children's Bureau themes for 2000–2005
Promoting participation and young citizenship; communicating positive attitudes and images; ensuring effective care, education and support; enhancing health and well-being; celebrating diversity, valuing difference; developing safe and positive environments.

Children in Wales 25 Windsor Pl, Cardiff CF10 3BZ;
E-mail ciw@globalnet.co.uk; Tel 01222 342434
Contact   Catriona Williams

Children in Scotland Princes Hse, 5 Shandwick Pl, Edinburgh EH2 4RG;
URL www.childreninscotland.org.uk;
E-mail info@childreninscotland.org.uk; Tel 0131 228 8484
Contact   Dr Bronwen Cohen

Council for Disabled Children 8 Wakley St, London EC1V 7QE; Tel 020 7843 6000; Fax 020 7278 9512
Director   P. Russell

National Children's Centre

Brian Jackson Hse, New North Pde, Huddersfield, West Yorkshire HD1 5JP; URL www.nccuk.org.uk; E-mail info@nccuk.org.uk; Tel 01484 519988; Fax 01484 435150
Chief Executive Simon Cale
Action programme for the young, school refusers, families, children with special needs, young offenders, homeless families and unemployed.

National Deaf Children's Sports Association (NDCSA)

Thorn Park School, Thorn La, Bradford, West Yorkshire BD9 6RY; Tel 01274 773770; Fax 01274 770387
Secretary M. Pulford
Aims to organise sporting activities for deaf schoolchildren between schools in Great Britain, including athletics, swimming, netball, football and cross-country. All communications to the Secretary.

The Orange Grove Foster Care Agency

Orange Grove Hse, 203–205 West Malvern Rd, West Malvern, Worcestershire WR14 4BB; URL www.theorangegrove.co.uk; E-mail theorangegrove@compuserve.com
Executive Director Granville Orange
Director (Child Care) Nicci Willock
The Orange Grove is an independent foster care agency. Established in 1996, it provides long and short term placements for children with highly motivated and well supported carers to local authorities throughout the country.

Ormiston Children and Families Trust

333 Felixstowe Rd, Ipswich, Suffolk IP3 9BU; E-mail enquiries@ormiston.org; Tel 01473 724517; Fax 01473 274255
Chief Executive Diana Read
Manager (Communications) Jenny Bibby

The Fostering Network

87 Blackfriars Rd, London SE1 8HA; URL www.fostering.net; E-mail network@fostercare.org.uk; Tel 020 7620 6400; (Helpline (Mon, Tues, Thur, Fri)) 020 7620 2100; Fax 020 7620 6401
Executive Director G. McAndrew
The Fostering Network is committed to raising standards of care for all children and young people who are fostered.
The Fostering Network's services include publications, training, consultancy, advice and mediation projects and a telephone Helpline.
The Fostering Network has over 18 000 members. These include local authorities, voluntary organisations and foster carers. Membership is open to all those concerned with children and young people in care.
The Fostering Network in Scotland Ingram Hse, 2nd Fl, 227 Ingram St, Glasgow G1 1DA; URL www.fostering.net; E-mail network@fostercare-scotland.org.uk; Tel 0141 204 1400; Fax 0141 204 6588
Manager B. Ritchie

Pearson's Holiday Fund

PO Box 3017, South Croydon, Surrey CR2 9PN; Tel 020 8657 3053
General Secretary Bryan K.H. Rogers
The Fund provides financial grants to assist disadvantaged children/young people aged between four and 16 (inclusive), living in the UK, to have holidays, outings, or to take part in group respite activities in the UK that take them away for a little while from their otherwise mundane or restricted environment and which would not be possible without some external financial support.
Applications for grants should be submitted by appropriate third party referring agencies (eg. social workers, health visitors, teachers, doctors, ministers of religion, organisers of holiday activities/projects, etc). The Fund does not respond to direct applications from families.
Guidance notes re applications for Grants may be obtained on application to the General Secretary.

Peper Harow Foundation

Station Hse, 150 Waterloo Rd, London SE1 8SB; Tel 020 7928 7388; Fax 020 7261 1307
Chief Executive Michael Willis
Regional Director (South) Brian Bishop
Regional Director (North) Alan Worthington
Provides specialist residential care, treatment and education services designed to keep seriously disturbed children and adolescents, incorporating support to families; carers and after care, and based on psychodynamic principles.

Perthes Association

PO Box 773, Guildford, Surrey GU1 1XN; URL www.perthes.org.uk; E-mail perthes@cableol.co.uk; E-mail help@perthes.org.uk; Tel (Administration) 01483 534431; (Helpline) 01483 306637
Executive Director Lisa Pritchard
Gives advice on the practical and financial help available, and provides support for parents of children suffering from Perthes disease (a potentially crippling disease of the hip) and other forms of osteochondritis and multiple epiphyseal dysplasia.

Pre-school Learning Alliance

69 Kings Cross Rd, London WC1X 9LL; URL www.pre-school.org.uk; E-mail pla@pre-school.org.uk; Tel 020 7833 0991; Fax 020 7837 4942
Chief Executive M. Lochrie
Provides help and support for pre-schools, field staff and parent and toddler groups through a network of local workers and a small HQ staff.

The Prince's Trust

18 Park Sq East, London NW1 4LH; Tel 0800 842842; Fax 020 7543 1200
Chief Executive Sir Tom Shebbeare
The Prince's Trust offers practical solutions to help young people get their lives working.
Helps people aged between 14 and 30 in all parts of the UK.
The focus is on young people who are struggling at school, have been in care, are unemployed or have been in trouble with the law.
The Prince's Trust has offices all over the country and provides services that best meet local needs, so some programmes are not available in all areas.

REACH (The Association for Children with Hand or Arm Deficiency)

25 High St, Wellingborough, Northamptonshire NN8 4JZ; URL www.reach.org.uk; E-mail reachorg@aol.com; Tel 01933 274126; Fax 01933 274126
National Co-ordinator Sue Stokes
Offers support to parents of children with any hand or arm deficiency.

Retinoblastoma Society

The Royal London Hospital, Whitechapel Rd, London
E1 1BB; URL www.rbsociety.org.uk;
E-mail rbinfo@rbsociety.org.uk; Tel 020 7377 5578;
Fax 020 7377 0740
Provides support and information for families affected by
retinoblastoma. Links families in the same situation. Raises
awareness of the childhood eye cancer with health
professionals and the general public. Funds and promotes
retinoblastoma related research.

reunite – International Child Abduction Centre

PO Box 7124, Leicester LE1 7XX; URL www.reunite.org;
E-mail reunite@dircon.co.uk; Tel (Admin Line) 0116 255
5345; (Advice Line) 0116 255 6234; Fax 020 255 6370
Director   Denise Carter

Royal Gardeners Orphan Fund

14 Scholars Mews, Welwyn Garden City, Hertfordshire
AL8 7JQ; E-mail rgof@btopenworld.com; Tel 01707
333663; Fax 01707 333663
Secretary   Kate Wallis

Royal Pinner School Foundation

110 Old Brompton Rd, South Kensington, London
SW7 3RB; Tel 020 7373 6168
Secretary   David Crawford
Travelling sales representatives' and manufacturers' agents'
children awarded assistance towards educational expenses
including clothing, trips, etc.o where need exists.

Rutherford School

1a Melville Ave, South Croydon, Surrey CR2 7HZ; Tel 020
8688 7560
Chair (Rutherford School)   S. Ellis
Headteacher   Ruth Hills
Provides education, care and therapy for young children
who have profound and multiple learning difficulties,
physical disabilities, and often complex medical needs to
enable each child to reach their maximum potential.
2–12. Day only extended school year.

SACCS Care Ltd

Mytton Mill, Montford Bridge, Shrewsbury, Shropshire SY4
1HA; URL www.saccs.co.uk; E-mail saccs@saccs.co.uk;
Tel 01743 850015; Fax 01743 851060
SACCS Care provides integrated child-centered services for
traumatised children between the ages of 4 and 12 years on
referral.Children are offered residential care, therapeutic
parenting, individual therapy, life story and family
placement services. This provision is supported by an
ongoing programme of professional staff development.
SACCS is an organisation at the forefront of delivering
planned and measurable recovery for the child.

Scottish Society for Autistic Children (SSAC)

Hilton Hse, Alloa Bus Pk, Whins Rd, Alloa,
Clackmannanshire FK10 3SA;
E-mail autism@autism-in-scotland.org.uk; Tel 01259
720044; Fax 01259 720051
Chief Executive   Donald J. Liddell
The Scottish Society for Autism is the leading provider of
services for autism in Scotland. They run a residential
school for children, residential and specialist day services
for adults, the only respite care centre for autism in the UK,
nationwide family support services, training for carers and
professionals, support self-help groups and local societies
and produce information and a members' magazine. They
undertake community care assessments and give guidance
on diagnosis, assessment and care management. Advice on
all aspects of autism is available from professional staff.

SOS – Children's Villages UK

32a Bridge St, Cambridge, Cambridgeshire CB2 1UJ;
URL www.sos-uk.org.uk; E-mail info@sos-uk.org.uk;
Tel 01223 365589; Fax 01223 322613
Chief Executive   Daniel Fox
SOS Children's Villages UK supports the worldwide work
of SOS Children's Villages in caring for orphaned and
abandoned children and young people, until they achieve
independence, regardless of race, creed, gender or politics.

Ulster Society for Promoting the Education of the Deaf and the Blind

85 Jordanstown Rd, Newtownabbey, County Antrim
BT37 0QE; Tel 028 9086 3541; Fax 028 9086 4356
Principal   Stephen L. Clarke, BA, DipEd, CertTOD,
DipSpEd(VI)
Operates Jordanstown School, a boarding and day school
for visually impaired and auditory impaired children.

YOUNG PEOPLE

ABAYOMI and Hammersmith Crisis Centre

182 Hammersmith Rd, London W6 7DJ; Tel 020 8741 3335
Co-ordinator   R. Timmerman
Therapeutic service for Afro-Caribbeans up to the age of 35.

Army Cadet Force Association

E Block, Duke of York's HQ, London SW3 4RR; Tel 020 7730
9733; 020 7730 9734; Fax 020 7730 8264
General Secretary   Brigadier J.E. Neeve
The Army's voluntary youth organisation with a strength
of approx 41 000 boys and girls between the ages of 13 and
18 years.

Boys' Brigade

Felden Lodge, Felden, Hemel Hempstead, Hertfordshire
HP3 0BL; URL www.boys-brigade.org.uk;
E-mail enquiries@boys-brigade.org.uk; Tel 01442 231681;
Fax 01442 235391
Brigade Secretary   Malcolm Hayden

British Youth Council

2 Plough Yard, Shoreditch High St, London EC2A 3LP;
URL www.byc.org.uk; E-mail mail@byc.org.uk; Tel 020
7422 8640; Fax 020 7422 2646
Chief Executive   Bill Freeman
National forum for young people in Britain, with the aim of
advancing their interests and views.

Bryn Melyn Group

PO Box 202, Bala, Gwynedd, LL23 7ZB;
URL www.brynmelyngroup.com;
E-mail enquiries@brynmelyngroup.com; Tel 01678
540598; Fax 01678 540682
Development Executive   Janet Rich

Mentors for Young People 2 High St, Dawley, Telford,
TF4 2ET; URL www.mentorsforyoungpeople.com;
E-mail enquiries@brynmelyngroup.com; Tel 01952 504715;
Fax 01952 504751
Director   Greg Watson

Rubicon for Young People Alkington Rd, Whitchurch,
Shropshire SY13 1SR; URL www.brynmelyngroup.com;
E-mail enquiries@rubiconforyoungpeople.com; Tel 01948
666587; Fax 01948 667246
Director   Steve Gray

Churches' Youth Service Council

143a University St, Belfast BT7 1HP; Tel 028 9032 3217;
   Fax 028 9032 3247
Training and Development Officer   Vacancy
Provides training and support for part-time leaders who
work with young people. Also offers consultancy service
and resources to churches.

Coram Leaving Care Services

Yonge Park 1 Yonge Pk, London N4 3NU;
E-mail brian@clcs35.fsnet.co.uk; Tel 020 7607 4341
Senior Worker   Brian Lewis

Coleridge Road 21 Coleridge Rd, London S4 3NY;
E-mail brian@clcs35.fsnet.co.uk; Tel 020 7607 0365; 020 7700
1920
Senior Worker   Brian Lewis
Aims to prepare young people in care for leaving.
Residential provision for boys and girls aged 16–19.

First Key

Oxford Chambers, Oxford Pl, Leeds, West Yorkshire
LS1 3AX; URL www.first-key.co.uk;
E-mail info@firstkeyleeds.com; Tel 0113 244 3898;
   Fax 0113 243 2541
Director   Peter Hardman
Advisory service working with local authorities and
other agencies in developing appropriate provision, skills
and organisational responses to young people leaving
care.

GFS Platform for Young Women

Townsend Hse, 126 Queen's Gate, South Kensington,
   London SW7 5LQ; URL www.gfsplatform.org.uk;
   E-mail admin@gfsplatform.org.uk; Tel 020 7589 9628;
   020 7589 9629; Fax 020 7225 1458
Chief Executive   Caroline Cayzer
Seeks to enable girls and women to develop their whole
potential, personally, socially and spiritually. Work
includes youth and community work and branch
membership.

Girls' Brigade England and Wales

PO Box 196, 129 Broadway, Didcot, Oxfordshire OX11 8XN;
   URL www.girlsbrigadeew.org.uk;
   E-mail gb@girlsbrigadeew.org.uk; Tel 01235 510425;
   Fax 01235 510429
National Director   Ruth Gilson
Chair   Vivienne Aitchison
Uniformed Christian youth organisation for girls.

Girls Venture Corps Air Cadets

Phoenix Hse, 3 Handley Sq, Finningley Airport, Doncaster,
   South Yorkshire DN9 3GH;
   E-mail gvcachqi@btopenworld.com; Tel 01302 775019;
   Fax 01302 775020
Corps Director   Mrs B. Layne, MBE
Uniformed organisation for girls aged 11–20. Opportunities
for flying, skiing, outdoor pursuits. Aims to develop
members into responsible citizens.

Girlguiding UK

17–19 Buckingham Palace Rd, London SW1W 0PT;
   URL www.girlguiding.org.uk;
   E-mail chq@girlguiding.org.uk; Tel 020 7834 6242;
   Fax 020 7828 8317
Chief Executive   Denise King

Highbury Roundhouses Youth and Community Centre

71 Ronalds Rd, London N5 1XB;
   URL www.highburyroundhouse.org.uk;
   E-mail admin@highburyroundhouse.org.uk; Tel 020
   7359 5916
Locally managed centre providing youth club, pensioners'
lunch club, under fives' activities, adult education classes,
social and recreational activities, play schemes, festivals,
multi-racial events.

National Association of Clubs for Young People

371 Kennington La, London SE11 5QY;
   URL www.nacyp.org.uk; E-mail office@nacyp.org.uk;
   Tel 020 7793 0787
National Director   Colin Groves, FIPD, FIMgt
Over 400 000 young people attend more than 3000 clubs in
45 county and equivalent associations throughout the UK,
providing a unique youth network which reaches many of
the country's most disadvantaged areas. CYP programmes
include sporting, creative, adventurous, training,
conference and international exchange opportunities. The
programmes are sufficiently wide ranging to meet local
and regional needs. Training is offered to club members for
their personal and social development; to senior members
in leadership skills; and to volunteers in practical club
management. CYP runs comprehensive insurance schemes;
provides legal advice; IT support, and offers grant funding
to affiliates.

National Youth Agency

17–23 Albion St, Leicester LE1 6GD; Tel 0116 285 3700;
   Fax 0116 247 3777
Chief Executive   Tom Wylie
Provides information and support for informal and social
education of young people. Funded by local authorities
and central government, it aims to provide a national focus
for the youth service, both statutory and voluntary, and for
all those who work with young people in the community. It
provides curriculum materials, support for policy
development, endorsement and accreditation of training
and a full range of information and publishing services.

New Horizon Youth Centre

68 Chalton St, London NW1 1JR;
   URL www.new-horizon-youth-centre.org;
   E-mail newh97a@aol.com; Tel 020 7388 5570; 020 7388
   5580; Fax 020 7388 5848
Drop-in centre (seven days a week) young people (16–22
years). Offers housing advice, referrals, activities and
facilities.

Ockenden International

Constitution Hill, Woking, Surrey GU22 7UU;
   E-mail oi@ockenden.org.uk; Tel 01483 772012; 01483
   772013; Fax 01483 750774
Provides care and education for disabled refugees;
Community development for refugees overseas.

Coombe Head Bunch La, Haslemere, Surrey GU27 1AJ;
Tel 01428 641861
Accommodation for refugees receiving medical treatment
under the Government's 'Ten or More' scheme.

RPS Rainer

Fresh Start Project 2nd Fl, 6 Liverpool Terr, Worthing, West
Sussex BN11 1TA; URL www.rpsrainer.org.uk;
E-mail jane.chilton@rpsrainer.org.uk; Tel 01903 219600
Project Manager   J. Chilton

The Scout Association

Gilwell Pk, Chingford, London E4 7QW;
URL www.scouts.org.uk; E-mail info.centre@scout.org.uk;
Tel 020 8433 7100; Fax 020 8433 7103
Secretary David J.C. Shelmerdine
Scouting prepares young people for responsible
citizenship. Camp sites and hostel facilities available for
other youth organisations and educational uses.

Sea Cadet Corps

202 Lambeth Rd, London SE1 7JF; Tel 020 7928 8978;
Fax 020 7928 8914
Commodore of the Sea Cadet Corps Commodore R.M.
Parker, RN
National voluntary youth organisation for boys and girls
aged 12–18. Character development based on nautical
activities and traditions.

Shaftesbury Homes and Arethusa

The Chapel, Royal Victoria Patriotic Bldg, Trinity Rd,
London SW18 3SX; E-mail info@shaftesbury.org.uk;
Tel 020 8875 1555; Fax 020 8875 1954
Chief Executive Alison Chesney
Social Work Director Chris Carey
A leading provider of residential child care and leaving
care services in London and the South East currently
operational in Islington, Southwark, Wandsworth, Lambeth
and Suffolk. In addition, the charity operates an Education
Support and Advocacy service, Supported Housing
projects and a Venture centre in Kent.

Student Volunteering UK

Oxford Hse, Derbyshire St, London E2 6HG;
URL www.studentvol.org.uk;
E-mail information@studentvol.org.uk; Tel 020 7739
0918; 020 7739 4565
Chief Executive Kelly A. Drake
Supports, promotes and develops existing student
community action groups and encourages student-based
voluntary community work.

UK Youth

Kirby Hse, 20–24 Kirby St, London EC1N 8TS;
URL www.ukyouth.org; E-mail info@ukyouth.org;
Tel 020 7242 4045; Fax 020 7242 4125
Chief Executive John Bateman
Supports and develops high quality youth work and
informal educational opportunities for all young people,
thereby helping them to achieve their full potential and
develop life skills to help them make a successful transition
to adulthood.

Woodcraft Folk

13 Ritherdon Rd, London SW17 8QE; Tel 020 8672 6031;
Fax 020 8767 2457
National Secretary A. Piercy
A national voluntary children's and youth organisation for
boys and girls from six years of age upwards. Its activities are
based around weekly group meetings and outdoor activities.

YMCA England

(Incorporated)
640 Forest Rd, London E17 3DZ; Tel 020 8520 5599
National Secretary Kevin Williams
Offers accommodation, and training for unemployed,
homeless or disadvantaged young people, outdoor and
environmental education, recreational facilities and many
opportunities for adults to use their time in constructive
and positive ways. Also has its own college for training
youth and community workers both full time and by
distance learning.

YoungMinds

102–108 Clerkenwell Rd, London EC1M 5SA;
URL www.youngminds.org.uk;
E-mail enquiries@youngminds.org.uk; Tel (Admin) 020
7336 8445; (Parents' Information Service – freephone
helpline) 0800 018 2138; Fax 020 7336 8446

Youth Action Northern Ireland (YANI)

(formerly NI Association of Youth Clubs)
Hampton, Glenmachan Pk, Belfast BT4 2PJ;
URL www.youthaction.org;
E-mail info@youthaction.org; Tel 028 9076 0067
YANI is a voluntary youth development agency committed
to the social and economic inclusion of young people in
communities.

Youth Support

PO Box 45408, London SE26 6WG;
URL www.youthsupport.co.uk;
E-mail services@youthsupport.net; Tel 020 8659 9926
Director Dr Diana Birch
Concentrates on day assessments; 'outpatient' assessments;
pre-placement assessments; pre-placement reports;
community and outreach work and assessments or
rehabilitation of families and individuals either in their
own accommodation or in accommodation provided by
local authorities.

FAMILY WELFARE

Adoption UK

Manor Farm, Appletree Rd, Chipping Warden, Banbury,
Oxfordshire OX17 1LH;
E-mail admin@adoptionuk.org.uk; Tel (Administration)
01295 660121; (Membership, Advice and Helpline) 0870
770 0450; Fax 01295 660123
Director Jonathan Pearce
Editor (Adoption Today Magazine) Karam Radwan
Information and support service for prospective and
existing adoptive families. Newsletter features children
needing new families. Membership subscription £26.95 pa,
£250 for adoption agencies. Information pack free. Over 140
local contacts throughout the UK.

Both Parents Forever in Association with M.I.S.T.E.R.X

39 Cloonmore Ave, Orpington, Kent BR6 9LE; Tel 01689
854343
Co-Director John Bell
National self-help group for parents and grandparents
following divorce, separation and care proceedings.
Information pack: Parents' or Grandparents' rights in all
family proceedings; Parental reponsibility; Residence
orders; Contact orders; Education and medical reports;
Social workers; Court welfare officers; Child abduction.
Files on help available overseas on child abduction. In
association with M.I.S.T.E.R.X. domestic violence against
men.

BAAF (British Association for Adoption and Fostering)

Skyline Hse, 200 Union St, London SE1 0LX;
URL www.baaf.org.uk;
www.nationaladoptionweek.org.uk;
E-mail mail@baaf.org.uk; Tel 020 7593 2000; Fax 020 7593
2001
Chief Executive Felicity Collier

13

Director (Policy, Research and Development)
    John Simmonds
Association of member agencies and individuals working to promote good practice in adoption, fostering and social work with children and families. Services include training consultancy, publications, public advice and information. Also operates a family finding service through our magazine Be My Parent.

Chichester Diocesan Association for Family Support Work

New Church Hse, 211 New Church Rd, Hove, Brighton and
    Hove BN3 4ED; Tel 01273 421021; Fax 01273 421041
Team Leader   Mrs Jo Lambert

The Compassionate Friends (Support for Bereaved Parents)

53 North St, Bristol BS3 1EN; URL www.tcf.org.uk;
    E-mail info@tcf.org.uk; Tel (Helpline (7 days 1000–2230))
    0117 953 9639; (Office (5 days 0930–1730)) 0117 966 5202;
    Fax 0117 914 4368
The Compassionate Friends (TCF) is a nationwide organisation of bereaved parents and their families offering understanding, support and encouragement after the death of a child or children. Help is offered to any parent whose son or daughter has died at any age and from any cause, and is extended to siblings and grand-parents. Support is offered through a Helpline, group support meetings, one-to-one visiting, telephone and/or letter contact, a range of publications and leaflets, a quarterly newsletter (also available on cassette), a siblings newsletter, a postal library, retreats and an annual weekend gathering. Befriending support not counselling.

Family Care

21 Castle St, Edinburgh EH2 3DN; Tel 0131 225 6441;
    Fax 0131 225 6478
Director   Julia Robinson
Family Care is a charity and voluntary social work agency with national and local services for children and families, and people whose lives are affected by adoption. Birthlink Adoption Counselling Centre is a national and international service which operates Scotland's Adoption Contact Register, and a post-adoption service which includes tracing. Family Care also provides a free confidential counselling service for children, young people and their families residing in Edinburgh City.

Family Education Trust

The Mezzanine, Elizabeth Hse, 39 York Rd, London
    SE1 7NQ; URL www.famyouth.org.uk;
    E-mail fyc@ukfamily.org.uk; Tel 020 7401 5480; Fax 020
    7401 5471
Director   Robert Whelan
Established to carry out or promote research into the social, medical, economic and psychological consequences of family breakdown and to publish the results of such research; to make information available to those in government, education, medicine and social services who have responsibility for policies affecting the family.

Family Service Units

URL www.fsu.org.uk
Registered charity no. 212114.
Barking and Dagenham Family Service Unit c/o Small World Family Centre, 2 Queens Rd, Barking, Ilford, Essex IG11 8GD; E-mail dianna.calixte@fsu.org.uk; Tel 020 8270 6019; Fax 020 8270 6020
Manager   Dianna Calixte

Birmingham (East) Family Service Unit 723 Coventry Rd, Small Heath, Birmingham, West Midlands B10 0JL; E-mail eb.fsu@virgin.net; Tel 0121 772 4217; Fax 0121 753 2375
Manager   Jennifer Semahimbo

Birmingham (South) Family Service Unit 45 Barretts Rd, Pool Farm, Birmingham, West Midlands B38 9HU; E-mail sbfsu@virgin.net; Tel 0121 459 4232; Fax 0121 458 4323
Manager   Stephanie Ward

Bradford Family Service Unit 207 Cutler Heights La, Bradford, West Yorkshire BD4 9JB; E-mail famsubrad@aol.com; Tel 01274 651652; Fax 01274 782020
Manager   Christine Clavering

Camden Family Service Unit Dowdney Cl, off Bartholomew Rd, Kentish Town, London NW5 2BP; E-mail camdenfsu@talk21.com; Tel 020 7424 1602; Fax 020 7424 1606
Manager   Raj Pandya

Central Office 207 Old Marylebone Rd, London NW1 5QP; URL www.fsu.org.uk; E-mail centraloffice@fsu.org.uk; Tel 020 7402 5175; Fax 020 7724 1829

Edinburgh Family Service Unit 18 West Pilton Pk, Edinburgh EH4 4EJ; Tel 0131 552 0305; Fax 0131 551 3976
Manager   Liz Dahl

Leeds (East) Family Service Unit 15 Lavender Wlk, Leeds, West Yorkshire LS9 8TX; E-mail info@eastleeds.fsu.org.uk; Tel 0113 248 4847; Fax 0113 249 2331
Manager   Mike Wood

Leeds (West) Family Service Unit 3 Chiswick St, Leeds, West Yorkshire LS6 1QE; E-mail wlfsu@aol.com; Tel 0113 275 7600; Fax 0113 278 9990
Manager   Andy Lloyd

Leicester Family Service Unit 26 Severn St, Leicester LE2 0NN; E-mail info@leicester.fsu.org.uk; Tel 0116 254 3352; Fax 0116 275 5216
Manager   Anne Marsden

Liverpool Family Service Unit 13 Croxteth Rd, Liverpool, Merseyside L8 3SE; E-mail liverpoolfsu@fsu.org.uk; Tel 0151 726 0066; Fax 0151 726 0053
Manager   Carey Burton

London (South) Family Service Unit 5 Baldwin Cres, London SE5 9LQ; E-mail southlondonfsu@fsu.org.uk; Tel 020 7733 6291; Fax 020 7924 0975
Manager   Sonia Modeste

London (West) Family Service Unit 289 Westbourne Park Rd, London W11 1EE; E-mail info@westlondonfsu.org.uk; Tel 020 7229 9941; Fax 020 7221 7168
Manager   Saleha Islam

Manchester Family Service Unit Varley St, Miles Platting, Manchester M40 7AH; E-mail mcrsecretary@hotmail.com
Manager   Melanie McGuiness

Rochdale Family Service Unit 37 St. Alban's St, Rochdale, Lancashire OL16 1UT; E-mail leroy.johnson@fsu.org.uk; Tel 01706 648997; Fax 01706 759886
Manager   Leroy Johnson

Sheffield Family Service Unit 88 Upper Hanover St, Sheffield, S3 7BQ; E-mail allumpaulfsu@aol.com; Tel 0114 275 0981; Fax 0114 272 0280
Manager   Paul Allum

Thamesmead Family Service Unit 2 Maran Way, Thamesmead, Erith, Kent DA18 4BP; E-mail tfsu.staffteam@btconnect.com; Tel 020 8310 6570; Fax 020 8312 4277
Manager   Ted Walsh

Waltham Forest Family Service Unit 344 Hoe St, London E17 9PX; E-mail brendah.malahleka@fsu.org.uk; Tel 020 8509 0119; Fax 020 8520 7180
Manager   Brenda Malahleka

Family Welfare Association

501–505 Kingsland Rd, London E8 4AU;
E-mail fwa.headoffice@fwa.org.uk; Tel 020 7254 6251;
Fax 020 7249 5443
Chief Executive Helen Dent
FWA provides social work and social care services to
families and individuals including drop-in centres, family
centres, counselling and befriending services, residential
homes for people returning to the community after periods
of psychiatric care. FWA administers trusts so that
individual grants can be made for a range of basic needs.

HOME-START

2 Salisbury Rd, Leicester LE1 7QR;
E-mail info@home-start.org.uk; Tel 0116 233 9955;
Fax 0116 233 0232
Chief Executive Brian Waller
A central organisation providing training, information and
guidance to individual HOME-START schemes which in turn
offer support, friendship and practical help in the home to
families with under fives experiencing difficulties. Referrals
to Home-Start are usually made by social workers or health
visitors but families are also encouraged to self-refer.

Institute of Family Therapy

24–32 Stephenson Way, London NW1 2HX;
URL www.instituteoffamilytherapy.org.uk;
E-mail ift@psyc.bbk.ac.uk; Tel 020 7391 9150; Fax 020
7391 9169
Counsellor Barry Mason
Counsellor Desa Markovic
Counsellor Linda McCann
The Institute provides a psychotherapy and counselling
service for couples and families experiencing difficulties in
their relationships. Fees are charged on a sliding scale.
Referrals can be self referrals although commissioned work
is undertaken for local authorities and courts. There is also
a Family Mediation Service for couples who are separating
or divorcing.

International Social Service (UK)

Cranmer Hse, 39 Brixton Rd, London SW9 6DD; Tel 020
7735 8941; Fax 020 7582 0696
Contact S. Gilbert
Enquiries overseas for Social Services Departments, UK
welfare agencies and others via professionally qualified
international network; relatives tracing service; information
about intercounty adoption procedures; foreign marriage
advisory service.

LIFE-LINE – Family Help for Violence in the Home

The Old Bakehouse, Main Rd, Ashbourne, Derbyshire
DE6 3ED; Tel 01335 370825
Director S. Dyas
Offers ongoing support and advice to families and children
suffering physical, sexual, mental and/or emotional abuse
and incest, working in every area of Britain. Abused and
abuser.

Middlemore Homes

SS Stevens Ave, Bartley Grn, Birmingham, West Midlands
B32 3SD; Tel 0121 427 2429
General Secretary T. Soden
Social work agency giving day care support to
underprivileged families. Runs Middlemore Family Centre.

National Family Mediation

9 Tavistock Pl, London WC1H 9SN;
URL www.nfm.u-net.com / 10am-2pm;
E-mail general@nfm.org.uk; Tel 020 7383 5993; Fax 020
7383 5994

Chief Executive Matthew Devlin
Manager (Administration and Systems) M. Lee
Association of 65 local family mediation services for
separating or divorcing couples. Family Mediation Services
help couples make joint decisions about a range of issues
(e.g. how to separate, what to say to the children,
distribution of money and property) with a particular focus
on arrangements for their children. National Family
Mediation provides details of local services. It co-operates
with related bodies in the voluntary and statutory sector
and is a founder member of the UK College of Family
Mediators.

National Council for the Divorced and Separated

168 Loxley Rd, Malin Bridge, Sheffield, South Yorkshire
S6 4TE
Chair Harry Taylor
National Secretary Pat Webster
Information support and social clubs. Aims to identify and
promote the interests and welfare of widowed people and
people whose marriages have ended in divorce or
separation.

Parentline Plus

520 Highgate Studios, 53–79 Highgate Rd, London
NW5 1TL; URL www.parentlineplus.org.uk;
E-mail centraloffice@parentlineplus.org.uk; Tel 020 7284
5500; (Helpline) 0808 800 2222; Fax 020 7284 5501;
Textphone 0800 783 6783
Chief Executive Dr Dorit Bravin
Organisation
Parentline Plus is a national charity, focused on families.
Formed following the merger of Parentline the National
Stepfamily Association, and Parent Network.
Aims
Works with adults, children and young people providing
support to families. Works to shape and expand what is
understood by parenting in order to highlight the diverse
nature of modern families and of those who parent.
Works to increase the support available to all those who
parent and contribute to the welfare of children by
increasing people's understanding of the demands of
parenting.
Services
Confidential freephone helpline run by Parentline Plus. It
offers help and support to anyone caring for children.
Helpline 24 hours, seven days a week. Textphone Helpline
for hearing impaired and speech impaired people.
Accredited parenting courses run nationwide.
Development of innovative projects which provide support
to families. Information and publications on a variety of
family issues. In-house training and consultancy for
professionals working with families and advice and
training to companies on developing policies which take
into account family change.

Parents Anonymous London

6–9 Manor Gdns, Islington, London N7 6LA; Tel 020 7263
8918
A telephone helpline, manned by volunteers who work on
a rota, trained to listen to people's distress and to 'stay with
them' on the telephone while they gain comfort, support
and encouragement to enable them to go on. Primarily
concerned with the safety and care of children who might
be under threat or in danger because their carers cannot
cope any more.

REFUGE

2–8 Maltravers St, London WC2R 3EE;
E-mail info@refuge.org.uk; Tel (24 hr National Domestic
Violence Helpline) 0808 808 9999; (Central office) 020
7395 7700; Fax 020 7395 7721
Assistant to Chief Executive Joanne Drinkwater

Provides refuge accommodation for abused women and children. Offers emotional support and practical advice. Provides psychological counselling for women and children. Runs an outreach and resettlement project for children living in refuges. Provides 24-hour domestic violence helpline.

Stillbirth and Neonatal Death Society (SANDS)

28 Portland Pl, London W1N 4DE; URL www.uk-sands.org; E-mail support@uk-sands.org; Tel (Administration) 020 7436 7940; (Helpline (Mon–Fri 0930–1700. All other times, answering machine)) 020 7436 5881; Fax 020 7436 3715
SANDS provides support for bereaved parents and their families when their baby dies at or soon after birth. The key elements of that support are National Telephone Helpline Service; UK-wide network of local self-help groups run by and for bereaved parents; information and publications for bereaved parents and healthcare professionals.

Sussex ADHD Support Group

PO Box 50, East Grinstead, West Sussex RH19 2YE; Tel 01293 428025
Parents support group.

ORGANISATIONS FOR ONE-PARENT FAMILIES

Families Need Fathers

Registered Charity Number 276889.
134 Curtain Rd, London EC2A 3AR; URL www.fnf.org.uk; E-mail fnf@fnf.org.uk; Tel 020 7613 5060; Fax 020 7739 3410
Chair   John Baker
A national self-help society which is primarily concerned with the problems of maintaining a child's relationship with both parents after family breakup. Founded in 1974, FNF is the principal charity providing advice and support on children's issues for separated, divorced and unmarried parents. It has a national network of volunteer telephone contacts and branches which hold regular 'Walk-in, Talk-in' sessions. Holds conferences on, and encourages research into, the problems facing children and parents after family breakup. Seeks to change and improve the present legal processes involved in divorce so as to eliminate unnecessary and protracted legal conflict. Publishes a quarterly journal 'McKenzie' and useful booklets and factpacks.

Gingerbread

7 Sovereign Cl, Sovereign Ct, London E1W 3HW; URL www.gingerbread.org.uk; E-mail office@gingerbread.org.uk; Tel (Advice line) 0800 018 4318; Fax 020 7488 9333
National Chair   Margaret O'Sullivan
Chief Executive   Gwen Vaughan
Gingerbread is the leading association of self-help groups of lone parent families. As a national organisation, Gingerbread aims to promote and support local self-help groups for lone parent families, to represent the needs and views of lone parent families to relevant policy makers and other service providers and to provide an expert information and advice service for individual lone parents. Lone parents and their children as well as other interested individuals and organisations may join their local Gingerbread group (phone the national office for local group details) or may subscribe directly to the national organisation.

The advice line is available weekdays (0900–1700) to give free, confidential advice on matters of concern to lone parents such as divorce and separation, maintenance, access, social security and housing .
Gingerbread produces a range of publications including a quarterly magasine Ginger, Junior Ginger and policy briefing papers and information service for professionals. They also run working and consultancy services on user involvement and lone parent family issues. Write or phone for further information.

One Parent Families

255 Kentish Town Rd, London NW5 2LX; URL www.oneparentfamilies.org.uk; E-mail info@oneparentfamilies.org.uk; Tel 020 7428 5400; Fax 020 7482 4851
President   I. Hay Davison
Chair   Suzanna Taverne
Hon Treasurer   G. Judge
Director   Kate Green
Works to improve the position of Britain's one million one-parent families by offering information to individual lone parents; information and training services to professionals and agencies working with lone parents; providing information to the public so that the needs of one-parent families are more widely recognised and understood; pressing central and local government and other bodies for the policies and services which one-parent families need.
General
The National Council is a government-aided voluntary organisation and a registered charity. Donations are welcome.
Lone Parents' Services
Free information packs and booklets for lone parents on issues such as welfare benefits, housing, divorce, maintenance, legal rights, bereavement.
Return to Work courses for lone parents wishing to re-enter employment, addressing the particular difficulties they face including childcare, finances, confidence building, and employment and training opportunities.
Self help groups can subscribe, at a reduced rate, to an information manual and associated services.
Professionals working with Lone Parents' Services
Information manual on lone parents' rights. Subscribers are mailed updates three times a year and can use a national Enquiry Line staffed by expert advisers who can provide further advice on all issues affecting lone parents.
Training courses regionally based covering all aspects of lone parents' rights.
Publications about lone parenthood can be bought – ask for latest Publications List.
Researchers' and Policy Makers' Services
Briefings and reports are produced regularly, and provide up-to-date information on current policy developments in relation to one-parent families.

One Parent Families Scotland

13 Gayfield Sq, Edinburgh EH1 3NX; URL www.opfs.org.uk; E-mail info@opfs.org.uk; Tel 0131 556 3899; (Helpline) 0800 018 5026; Fax 0131 557 9650
Convenor   Pauline Brogan
Director   S. Robertson, MSocSci
Deputy Director   I. Maxwell
Members are lone parents, and other individuals or organisations working with lone parent families. Publishes information leaflets and briefings and a regular newsletter and campaign on relevant policy issues. Also provides a range of locally based services including adult education groups, support groups for lone fathers and lesbian mothers and childcare and a contact centre.
OPFS has produced a directory of sitter services in Scotland and is developing support for lone parents returning to education, training and employment.

Voluntary Service Aberdeen

(Aberdeen Association of Social Service)
38 Castle St, Aberdeen AB11 5YU; URL www.vsa.org.uk;
     E-mail info@vsa.org.uk; Tel 01224 212021; Fax 01224
     580722
Director   W. Howie, MA, BD, STM
As one of the largest social care charities in Scotland,
Voluntary Service Aberdeen provides a range of direct
services to help those in need. Expert advice is available
including social work support; outings and holidays; help
with fuel and transport; and a Carers Centre. Over 1000
volunteers, supported by VSA help with befriending and
practical tasks, community projects and the five Thrift
Shops throughout the city. VSA also gives support to the
wider voluntary sector and administers six other associated
but financially independent local charities.

Welcare

The Welcare Service for Parents and Children, Trinity Hse,
     4 Chapel Crt, Borough High St, London SE1 1HW;
     E-mail anne-marie.garton@dswark.org.uk; Tel 020 7403
     8686
Director   Anne-Marie Garton
Social work, counselling, advocacy and group work with
parents and children in need. Community projects and
family centres. Work is supported by local authority grants
and church funding. Area covered: Nine South London
Boroughs and parts of East Surrey (Diocese of Southwark).

Welcare – Wales

Diocese of Llandaff Board for Social Responsibility, 65
     Cowbridge Rd West, Cardiff CF5 5BQ; Tel 029 2056 5887
Manager (Welcare Development)   Christine Murrell
Welcare Parenting Support Unit provide ante-natal and
post-natal monitoring and assessment service a high level
of support and accommodation in a residential setting. On
site crèche and Play Development facility.
Welcare Hafan providing self-contained, temporary
accommodation in a semi-supported environment. Low level
of support. On-site crèche and Play Development facility.
Both projects involve Interagency and Primary Health Care
Team support.
Welcare Resource Centre providing community playgroup
and pre-play group service.
All three projects operate on one site at the Welcare
Development.

MATERNITY AND MOTHERHOOD

Association of Breastfeeding Mothers

PO Box 207, Bridgwater, Somerset TA6 7YT;
     URL www.abm.me.uk; E-mail info@abm.me.uk; Tel 020
     7813 1481
Lactation Consultant   Pam Lacey
A voluntary organisation promoting and providing
support for breastfeeding.

Association for Improvements in the Maternity Services (AIMS)

5 Ann's Crt, Grove Rd, Surbiton, Surrey KT6 4BE;
     E-mail chair@aims.org.uk; Tel 0870 765 1433; Fax 0870
     765 1454
Hon Chair   Beverley Lawrence Beech
Offers information, support and advice to parents about all
aspects of maternity care, including parents' rights, the
choices available, technological interventions, natural
childbirth and complaints procedures. Produces a series of
information leaflets and a quarterly journal. SAE please.

Association for Post-Natal Illness

145 Dawes Rd, Fulham, London SW6 7EB;
     URL www.apni.org; E-mail info@apni.org; Tel 020 7386
     0868; Fax 020 7386 8885
Secretary   D. Nehme
Self-help group for women suffering from post-natal
depression. National telephone network provides support
from ex-sufferers. Advice and information available to
sufferers and health professionals.

Baby Milk Action

23 St. Andrews St, Cambridge, Cambridgeshire CB2 3AX;
     URL www.babymilkaction.org;
     E-mail info@babymilkaction.org; Tel 01223 464420;
     Fax 01223 464417
Director (Policy)   P. Rundall
Baby Milk Action aims to save infant lives and to end the
avoidable suffering caused through inappropriate infant
feeding by working within a global network to strengthen
independent, transparent and effective controls on the
marketing of the baby feeding industry worldwide. To
achieve this, Baby Milk Action works to end the
inappropriate marketing policies and practices of the baby
feeding industry, and to ensure that mothers and infants
worldwide are effectively represented wherever decisions
affecting infant feeding are made.

BLISS – The National Charity for The Newborn (Baby Life Support Systems)

Camelford Hse, 87–89 Albert Embankment, London
     SE1 7TP; URL www.bliss.org.uk;
     E-mail information@bliss.org.uk; Tel 020 7820 9471;
     (Helpline) 0500 618140; Fax 020 7820 9567
Head (Information and Parent Support)   Shanit Marshall
National charity for sick newborn and premature babies.
Provides neonatal equipment for hospitals nationwide,
sponsors nurse training, funds research and runs a free
helpline for parents of 'special care babies'.

Cheshire House

22 St. Mary's Rd, Sale, Cheshire M33 6SA;
     URL www.cheshirehouse.net;
     E-mail cheshirehse@aol.com; Tel 0161 905 2711; Fax 0161
     962 4626
Manager (Operationals)   Susan FitzPatrick
24 hour O&A Centre specialising in parenting;
comprehensive risk assessment; life skills; training for
independence in self-contained flats plus 24 hour video
monitoring. Review; case conference; court; weekly reports.
Consultant psychologist available on request. High staff
ratio.

The Cry-sis Helpline

BM Cry-Sis, London WC1N 3XX;
     URL www.cry-sis.org.uk; E-mail info@cry-sis.org.uk;
     Tel 020 7404 5011
Provides telephone helpline to parents with excessively
crying, sleepless and demanding babies. Also available
leaflets on these subjects. Work alongside health vistors and
doctors and take part in important research into these
subjects. SAE please for postal enquiries.

Debendox Action Group

21 Corden Ave, Mickleover, Derby DE3 5AQ; Tel 01332
     517896
Chair   J.B. Hall
Improves market surveillance of drugs, especially those
used during pregnancy and assists members to obtain
compensation from the manufacturer of Debendox.

Foresight, The Association for the Promotion of Pre-conceptual Care

28 The Paddock, Godalming, Surrey GU7 1XD;
URL www.foresight-preconception.org.uk; Tel 01483
427839; Fax 01483 427668
Founder and Director   B. Barnes
Aims to get couples into optimum health before conception
to enhance the chances of delivering a healthy baby.

Ichthus Breaking Free Centre

4 Valkyrie Rd, Westcliff on Sea, Southend SS0 8BU;
E-mail ichthusbreaking@aol.com; Tel 01702 434 460;
Fax 01702 340 855
Director   Ms Bennett-Hernandez
Mother and baby home for 13–19 year olds. Nationwide
service.

LIFE

Life Hse, Newbold Terr, Leamington Spa, Warwickshire
CV32 4EA; URL www.lifeuk.org; E-mail info.lifeuk.org;
Tel 01926 311667; 01926 316737 01926 421587 (National
Hotline) 0800 849 4545
Honary Administrator   N.A. Scarisbrick
Free pregnancy testing and counselling throughout UK.
Accommodation for homeless pregnant women and
unsupported mothers with babies up to 12 months;
counselling after abortion. Infertility relief programme.

Maternity Alliance

Unit 3.3, 2–6 Northburgh St, London EC1V 0AY;
URL www.maternityalliance.org.uk;
E-mail info@maternityalliance.org.uk; Tel (2nd tier
advice) 0845 601 3386; (Advice) 020 7490 7638 (Office)
020 7490 7639; Fax 020 7014 1350
Officer (Information)   Mary Ann Foxwell

Campaigns for and gives information on improvements in
the health care, social and financial support and legal rights
of mothers, fathers and babies.

The Miscarriage Association

c/o Clayton Hospital, Northgate, Wakefield, West
Yorkshire WF1 3JS;
URL www.miscarriageassociation.org.uk;
E-mail info@miscarriageassociation.org.uk; Tel 01924
200799; Fax 01924 298834

National Childbirth Trust

Alexandra Hse, Oldham Terr, Acton, London W3 6NH;
URL www.nctpregnancyandbabycare.com;
E-mail enquiries@national-childbirth-trust.co.uk;
Tel (Mon–Thur 0900–1700, Fri 0900–1600) 0870 444 8707;
(Administration and Office (0900–1700, Fri 0900–1600))
0870 770 3236; (Breastfeeding Line (0800–2200 seven
days a week)) 0870 444 8708
Chair   Dorotka Griffin
Research, information and support in pregnancy, childbirth
and early parenthood; ante-natal classes, breastfeeding
counselling, post-natal support. Ring UK office for nearest
branch.

Twins and Multiple Births Association (TAMBA)

Tamba, 2 The Willows, Gardner Rd, Guildford, Surrey
GU1 4PG; URL www.tamba.org.uk;
E-mail enquiries@tamba.org.uk; Tel 0870 770 3308;
(TAMBA Twinline helpline (1900–2200 weekdays and
1000–2200 weekends)) 0800 138 0509
Tamba aims to provide information and mutual support
networks for families of twins, triplets and more
highlighting their unique needs to all involved in their
care.

Education – Independent Special Schools and Other Educational Organisations

14

- ■ Independent and Non-Maintained Special Schools
- ■ Further Education and Training for Special Needs
- ■ Special Educational Needs
- ■ Other Educational Organisations

Key

(110)	Number of pupils
Mixed	Takes boys and girls
Boys	Takes boys only
Girls	Takes girls only
11–18	Age range of pupils

Abbreviations

ADHD	Attention Deficit Hyperactivity Disorder
ASD	Autism Spectrum Disorder
EBD	Emotional Behavioural Difficulties
LD	Learning Difficulties
LI	Language Impairment
MH	Mentally Handicapped
MLD	Moderate Learning Difficulties
PH	Physically Handicapped
PHAB	Physically Handicapped and Able-Bodied
PMLD	Profound and Multiple Learning Difficulties
PS	Partially Sighted
PtHg	Partially Hearing
SCU	Special Care Unit
SEBD	Severe Emotional Behaviour Difficulties
SEN	Special Educational Needs
SLD	Severe Learning Difficulties
SLDD	Students with Learning Difficulties and Disabilities
SMH	Severely Mentally Handicapped

Education – Independent Special Schools and Other Educational Organisations

INDEPENDENT AND NON-MAINTAINED SPECIAL SCHOOLS

England

Bolton

Birtenshaw Hall School Darwen Rd, Bromley Cross, Bolton, Greater Manchester BL7 9AB; URL www.birtenshawhall.bolton.sch.uk; E-mail enquiries@birtenshawhall.bolton.sch.uk; Tel 01204 304230; Fax 01204 597995
Headteacher C.D. Jamieson, DipSpEd, MEd
  Mixed 3–19 Physical disabilities with associated learning difficulties. Multi-disciplinary staff team (Day, weekly, termly 52-week, Residential) (46)

Bristol

St. Christopher's School Carisbrooke Lodge, Westbury Pk, Bristol BS6 7JE; URL www.st-christophers.bristol.sch.uk; E-mail st-christophers@stchristophers.bristol.sch.uk; Tel 0117 973 3301; 0117 973 6875; Fax 0117 974 3665
  5–19 Severe and complex learning difficulties 40–52 week boarding.

Buckinghamshire

MacIntyre School, Wingrave Leighton Rd, Wingrave, Buckinghamshire HP22 4PD; URL www.macintyre-care.org; E-mail wingrave@macintyre-care.org; Tel 01296 681274; Fax 01296 681091
Headteacher Stephen Smith (Acting)
  Mixed 10–19 Residential school providing a 52-week 24-hours-a-day curriculum for students with severe learning disabilities.

Calderdale

The William Henry Smith School Boothroyd, Brighouse, West Yorkshire HD6 3JW; URL www.whsschool.org.uk; E-mail headteacher@whsschool.org.uk; Tel 01484 710123; Fax 01484 721658
Headteacher B.J. Heneghan
  Boys 8–16 SEBD (Boarders (64), Day (8))

Cheshire

Chaigley School Lymm Rd, Thelwall, Warrington WA4 2TE; URL www.chaig.u-net.com; E-mail admin@chaig.u-net.com; Tel 01925 752357; Fax 01925 757983
Principal Drew Crawshaw
No area limit.
  Boys 8–16 EBD (Day, Boarders)

The David Lewis School, Children's Epilepsy Assessment and Children's Brain Injury Rehabilitation Service Mill La, Warford, Alderley Edge, Cheshire SK9 7UD; URL www.davidlewis.org.uk; E-mail school@davidlewis.org.uk; Tel 01565 640066; Fax 01565 640166
No area limit.
A Children's Brain Injury Rehabilitation service provides an education and rehabilitation service to children with an acquired brain injury; identifying and enabling the new learning required by the child, their family, educators and therapists. Comprehensive, flexible and needs-led services are provided by an experienced inter-disciplinary team.
  Mixed 7–19 Epilepsy and other associated special needs. (Boarders) up to 52 week provision if required. (65)

Delamere Forest School Blakemere La, Norley, Frodsham, Cheshire WA6 6NP; E-mail admin@dfschool.u-net.com; Tel 01928 788263; Fax 01928 788263
Headteacher Harvey Burman
No area limit: day pupils of any denomination.
  Mixed 5–17 EBD, social and educational difficulties, language and speech therapy, physiotherapy. (Day, Weekly Boarders, Full Boarders) (52)

Heaton School St. James' Rd, Heaton Moor, Stockport, Cheshire SK4 4RE; Tel 0161 432 1931; Fax 0161 432 1931
Team Leader (Extended Education) Ann Thornton
All Projects, OCR (Oxford and Cambridge and Royal Society), NSP (National Skills Profile), Basic Food Hygiene Certificate, ASDAN – towards independence.
  SLD/PMLD

Royal School for the Deaf Cheadle Hulme, Cheshire SK8 6RQ; URL www.rsdmanchester.org; E-mail info@rsdmanchester.org; Tel 0161 610 0100; Fax 0161 610 0101
Headteacher Hilary Ward
No area limit.
  Mixed 5–20 Deaf, deaf/blind, deaf/multiple handicapped. (Day, Boarders (52 week accommodation available)) (70)

The Saint John Vianney Lower School Didsbury Rd, Heaton Mersey, Stockport, Greater Manchester SK4 2AA; URL www.stjohnvianney.co.uk; E-mail stjohnvianney.co.uk; Tel 0161 432 0510; Fax 0161 422 2095
Headteacher M.M. O'Donoghue
Areas
Manchester, Trafford, Cheshire, Tameside, Oldham, Salford, Stockport, Bolton, Bury.
Salford Roman Catholic Diocesan Trustees.
  Mixed 4–11 MLD (Day) (80)

The Saint John Vianney Upper School Rye Bank Rd, Firswood, Stretford, Manchester M16 0EX; Tel 0161 881 7843; Fax 0161 881 6948
Headteacher J. Cusick
  11–16 MLD (Day) (96)

Cumbria

Eden Grove School Bolton, Appleby, Cumbria CA16 6AJ; E-mail susanmullen@prioryhealthcare.com; Tel 017683 61346; Fax 017683 61356
Headteacher Ian McCready, MA Ed, BA, ADDipSpEd, CertEd
No area limit.
  Boys 8–19 EBD (50 week and 38 week). MLD, some autistic disorders.

Lowgate House School, Witherslack Group of Schools
Levens, Kendal, Cumbria LA8 8NJ; Tel 015395 60124; Fax 015395 60648
Principal J. Bowers
Headteacher Mrs J. Richardson
  Boys 7–12 EBD (Boarders 13 + 4 Day pupils)

Derbyshire

Alderwasley Hall School Alderwasley, Belper, Derbyshire DE56 2SR; URL www.alderwasley-hall-school.co.uk/; E-mail alderwasleyhallschool@honormead.stinternet.com; Tel 01629 822586
  Mixed 5–19 Speech, language and communication disorders. (Boarders (100)) and (Day (30))

Derby College for Deaf People Ashbourne Rd, Derby DE22 3BH; URL www.dcdp.org; E-mail enquiries@dcdp.org; Tel 01332 297500; Fax 01332 221602

Eastwood Grange School Milken La, Ashover, Chesterfield, Derbyshire S45 0BA; Tel 01246 590255; Fax 01246 590215
  11–16+ Emotional and behavioural difficulties (Boarders)

Royal School for the Deaf, Derby Ashbourne Rd, Derby DE22 3BH; URL www.rsd-derby.org; E-mail admin.rsdd@virgin.net; Fax 01332 299708; Minicom 01332 362512
  Mixed 3–16 Deaf (Day and Weekly Boarders)

Devon

Chelfham Mill Chelfham, Barnstaple, Devon EX32 7LA; URL www.chelfhammillschool.com; E-mail chelfham@aol.com; Tel 01271 850448
Headteacher Katy Roberts, BEd, BPhil
  Boys 7–13 (Day, Boarders) (58)

Dame Hannah Rogers School Woodland Rd, Ivybridge, Devon PL21 9HQ; URL www.damehannah.com; E-mail mail@damehannah.com; Tel 01752 892461; Fax 01752 898101
Principal W. R. Evans
The school meets the needs of students with physical difficulties and associated learning challenges, including communication problems.
  Mixed 8–19 PH, communication problems. (Day/Weekly/Termly) (55)

Grenville College Dyslexia Unit Grenville College, Bideford, Devon EX39 3JR; URL www.grenville.devon.sch.uk; E-mail grenville.devon.sch.uk; Tel 01237 472212; Fax 01237 477020
Headteacher M.C.V. Cane, BSc, PhD
Director (Dyslexia Unit) A. Lane, BEd
The unit is a large department with three full-time teachers in English skills for dyslexics who are fully integrated into the curriculum
  Mixed 2–11 (Juniors) 11–18 (Seniors) (Day, Boarders (from 8)) (350)

Royal West of England Residential School for the Deaf
Exeter, Devon EX2 4NF; Tel 01392 272692; Fax 01392 431146
Headteacher John F. Shaw
  Mixed 3–19 Deaf/partially hearing, deaf/blind (Day, Weekly Boarders) (100)

Trengweath School Hartley Rd, Plymouth PL3 5LW; E-mail glynis.pratchett@scope.org.uk; Tel 01752 771975; 01752 773735; Fax 01752 793388
Headteacher Glynis Pratchett
  Mixed 3–19 PH, CP, PMLD, LD Boarders (18)

Vranch House School Pinhoe Rd, Exeter, Devon EX4 8AD; URL www.vranchhouse.org; E-mail education@vranchhouse.org; Tel 01392 468333; Fax 01392 463818
Headteacher Ms M. Boon, BA, MSc, MPhil
An independent school approved under the 1981 Education Act.
  Mixed 2–12 PH, communication problems (Day) (25)

West of England School and College for Children with Little or No Sight Countess Wear, Exeter, Devon EX2 6HA; E-mail info@westengland.devon.sch.uk; Tel 01392 454200; Fax 01392 428048
Principal Paul Holland, MEd, BSpEd, DipEd(VI)
Further Education College (16–22). Advisory service for South West Region, Regional Assessment Service. Day nursery and pre-school assessment unit.
St. David's House – unit for multi-disabled visually impaired children, 5–16 years.
  Mixed 4–22 Visually impaired. (Day, Boarders)

Whitstone Head School Whitstone, Holsworthy, Devon EX22 6TJ; E-mail sethgent@whitstonehead.sagehost.co.uk; Tel 01288 341251; Fax 01288 341207
Headteacher D. McLean-Thorne
  Mixed 11–16 EBD (32 Boarders, 4 Day)

Doncaster

Fullerton House School Off Tickhill Sq, Denaby, Doncaster, South Yorkshire DN12 4AR; URL www.hesleygroup.co.uk; E-mail doconnor@hesleygroup.co.uk; Tel 01709 861663; Fax 01709 869635
Headteacher David O'Connor, BA, PGCE, AdvDip
  Mixed 8–19 Complex difficulties resulting from autism and/or severe learning difficulties, residential (52 wk) (36)

Wilsic Hall School Wadworth, Doncaster, South Yorkshire DN11 9AG; URL www.hesleygroup.co.uk; E-mail mhenderson@hesleygroup.co.uk; Tel 01302 856382; Fax 01302 853608
Headteacher Martin Henderson, MA, AdvDip (SpEd), CertEd
  Mixed 11–19 Complex difficulties resulting from autism and/or severe learning difficulties (residential) (52 wk) (33)

Yorkshire Residential School for the Deaf Leger Way, Doncaster, South Yorkshire DN2 6AY; Tel 01302 322822; Fax 01302 361808
Director H. Heard, MA, FcollP
  Mixed 2–16+ (Day, Boarders) (100)

Dorset

The Forum School Shillingstone, Blandford Forum, Dorset DT11 0QS; URL www.hesleygroup.co.uk; E-mail gwaters@hesleygroup.co.uk; Tel 01258 860295; Fax 01258 860552
Headteacher Mrs Gay Waters, CertEd, BPhilEd
No area limit
  Mixed 7–14 Autism, Asperger syndrome Residential (termly) (46)

Langside School Langside Ave, Parkstone, Poole BH12 5BN; E-mail john@langside-school.fsnet.co.uk; Tel 01202 518635
Headteacher J. Ashby
Head (Care) P. Parsons
Dorset SCOPE.
  Mixed 2–19 Special needs (Day) (40)

Philip Green Memorial School Boveridge Hse, Cranborne, Wimborne, Dorset BH21 5RU; E-mail pgmschool@hotmail.com; Tel 01725 517218; Fax 01725 517968
Mixed 11–19 MLD/SLD (Boarders) (32)

Portfield School Parley La, Christchurch, Dorset BH23 6BP; URL www.portfield.ik.org; E-mail portfield-school@twas.org.uk; Tel 01202 573808; Fax 01202 580532
Headteacher Andrew Mears, BSc
Mixed 3–18+ Autism and similar (Day, Boarders) (80)

Purbeck View School Northbrook Rd, Swanage, Dorset BH19 1PR; URL www.hesleygroup.co.uk; E-mail sgoulding@hesleygroup.co.uk; Tel 01929 422760; Fax 01929 427627
Headteacher Sue Goulding, BA(Hons), PGCE, AdvDipSEN
No area limit.
Mixed 11–19 Autism, Asperger syndrome (Boarders, termly) (44)

Victoria Education Centre 12 Lindsay Rd, Poole BH13 6AS; Tel 01202 763697
Headteacher Paul A. Warner, BEd, AdvDip
No area limit but generally from Southern Counties.
Mixed 2–19 PD, Medical (Day, Boarders) (113)

East Sussex

Chailey Heritage School North Chailey, Lewes, East Sussex BN8 4EF; Tel 01825 724444; Fax 01825 723773
Headteacher A.C. Bruce
Deputy Headteacher S. Yates
Manager (Finance) M. Cornwell
Mixed 2–19 PH (Day, Boarders) (100)

Hamilton Lodge School Walpole Rd, Brighton, Brighton and Hove BN2 0LS; URL hamiltonlodgeschool.co.uk; E-mail hamilton.lodge@ukonline.co.uk; Tel 01273 682362; Fax 01273 695742
Principal Mrs A.K. Duffy, MEd
National.
Mixed 5–18 Severely/profoundly deaf (Day, Weekly Boarders) (80)

Northease Manor School Lewes, East Sussex BN7 3EY; URL www.northeasemanor.e-sussex.sch.uk; E-mail northease@msn.com; Tel 01273 472915; Fax 01273 472202
Headteacher P. Stanley, BEd, CertEd
Mixed 10–17 Specific learning difficulties (Dyslexia) (Day, Boarders) (90)

St. John's School & College Walpole Road, Brighton, Brighton and Hove BN2 0AF; Tel 01273 244000; Fax 01273 244038

St. Mary's School Wrestwood Rd, Bexhill, East Sussex TN40 2LU; URL www.st-marys.bexhill.sch.uk; E-mail stmarys@wrestwood.freeserve.co.uk; Tel 01424 730740; Fax 01424 733575
Principal and Chief Executive D. Cassar, MA, CCYW, CEd, MIMgt, FRSA
No area limit.
Mixed 7–19 Speech and language, MLD, PH and social communication/medical. (Day (17), Boarders (83), VI Form (44))

Essex

Doucecroft School 163 High St, Kelvedon, Colchester, Essex CO5 9JA; URL www.essexautistic.org.uk; E-mail kc@essexautistic.org.uk; Tel 01376 570060
Further Education Department, 86 High St, Kelvedon, Colchester, Essex CO5 9AA
Headteacher K. Cranmer
Essex Autistic Society.
Mixed 3–16 16–19 Autistic and Asperger's syndrome. 26 plus at school; 12 at Further Education Department.

Jacques Hall Foundation Harwich Rd, Bradfield, Manningtree, Essex CO11 2XW; E-mail jacqueshall@prioryhealthcare.com; Tel 01255 870311; Fax 01255 870377
Admissions and Assessment Office Chris Nicholson
A therapeutic community for disturbed adolescents aged 11–18 on long-term placements with special education provision.
Therapeutic community

MacIntyre Woodacre, 38 D'Arcy Rd, Tiptree, Colchester, Essex CO5 0RR; Tel 01621 819769; Fax 01621 819078
Service Manager S. Raw
Residential and day care for people with learning disabilities
(14)

St. John's RC Special School Turpins La, Woodford Green, Essex IG8 8AX; Tel 020 8504 1818; Fax 020 8559 2409
Headteacher B.C. Sainsbury
Areas
Redbridge, Barking, Newham, Havering, Waltham Forest, Haringey, Barnet, Hackney, Tower Hamlets, Enfield, Islington, Essex, Camden.
Mixed 5–16+ MLD/SLD (100)

Woodcroft School Whitakers Way, Loughton, Essex IG10 1SQ; Tel 020 8508 1369; Fax 020 8502 4855
Headteacher Margaret Newton
Areas
Essex, Hertfordshire, Waltham Forest, Redbridge, Hackney, Tower Hamlets and neighbouring LEAs.
Mixed 2–11+ Severe special needs, disabled, autism, learning, behaviour and relationship difficulties (Day) (24)

Gloucestershire

Cotswold Chine Home School Box, Stroud, Gloucestershire GL6 9AG; E-mail mail@cotswold-chine.org.uk; Tel 01453 837550; Fax 01453 834970
No area limit.
Committee for Steiner Special Education.
Mixed 9–18 (Boarders) (42)

St. Rose's School Stratford Lawn, Stroud, Gloucestershire GL5 4AP; URL www.stroses.gloucs.sch.uk/index.html; Tel 01453 763793; Fax 01453 752617
Headteacher Christopher Hale (Acting)
Mixed 5–18 Nursery (2–5) Extended education unit (16–18) PH, Communication Technology. (Day, Boarders)

Hampshire

Coxlease School Clay Hill, Lyndhurst, Hampshire SO43 7DE; URL www.coxleaseschool.co.uk; E-mail mail@coxleaseschool.co.uk; Tel 02380 283633; Fax 02380 282515
Principal S.F. Cliffen, BEd(Hons)
Boys 9–17 EBD, behavioural and social problems, mild medical conditions, victims and victimisers. (Boarders) (45)

Grateley House School Grateley House School, Grateley, Andover, Hampshire SO42 7RE; URL www.hesleygroup.co.uk; E-mail sking@hesleygroup.co.uk; Tel 01264 889751; Fax 01264 889212
Headteacher Sue King, BA(Hons), DipSpEd, NPQH
No area limit.
Mixed 11–16 Asperger syndrome, ADHD, Tourette's syndrome. (Residential (termly)) (39)

Hill House School Rope Hill, Boldre, Lymington, Hampshire SO41 8NE; URL www.hesleygroup.co.uk; E-mail jwright@hesleygroup.co.uk; Tel 01590 672147; Fax 01590 670535
Headteacher Jenny Wright, BEd, MA(Ed), AdvDipSEN
No area limit.
Mixed 11–19 Autism and associated learning difficulties, residential (52 wk). (22)

Hope Lodge School 22 Midanbury La, Bitterne Pk, Southampton SO18 4HP; E-mail mf@hope-lodge.fsnet.co.uk; Tel 023 8063 4346; Fax 023 8023 1789
Headteacher Allison Hope-West
46 students aged 4–19 and eight residential plus two day students aged 16–19 at Aspil House. Autism and Asperger syndrome (Day, Weekly Boarders) (55)

The Loddon School Wildmoor La, Sherfield on Loddon, Hook, Hampshire RG27 0JD; Tel 01256 882394; Fax 01256 882929
Headteacher Marion Cornick
The Loddon School Company.
Mixed 8–18 SLD, autism, challenging behaviour (Boarders) (27)

Rosewood School Bradbury Centre, 300 Aldermoor Rd, Southampton SO16 5NA; URL roseroad.co.uk; E-mail cathrynspiller@roseroad.co.uk; Tel 023 8079 1234; Fax 023 8051 3473
Headteacher C. Spiller
Rose Road Association.
Mixed 2–19 PMLD (Day) (24)

The Sheiling School Horton Rd, Ashley, Ringwood, Hampshire BH24 2EB; URL www.sheilingschool.co.uk; E-mail enquiries@sheilingschool.co.uk; Tel 01425 477488; Fax 01425 479536
Home life, education and training for children and young adults with special needs. Comprising: The Sheiling School 6–16, mixed, (40); The Senior School (further education and training) 16–19, mixed, (20).
Moderate to severe learning difficulties, emotional and behavioural difficulties, speech impairment, autism, brain damage, epilepsy and Downs Syndrome, Fragile X, Williams Syndrome, MLD and SLD. (Day, Weekly Boarders, 38 week residential) (50)

St. Edward's School Melchet Crt, Sherfield English, Romsey, Hampshire SO51 6ZR; E-mail admin@st-edwards.hants.sch.uk; Tel 01794 884250; 01794 884271; Fax 01794 884904
Headteacher L.P. Bartel, BEd(Hons)
Independent.
Boys 10–16 EBD, SPLD (65)

Southlands School Vicar's Hill, Boldre, Lymington, Hampshire SO41 5QB; URL www.hesleygroup.co.uk; E-mail sgething@hesleygroup.co.uk; Tel 01590 675350; Fax 01590 671891
Headteacher Sue Gething, BEd
No area limit.
Boys 9–16 Southlands caters for boys with Asperger Syndrome.
Southlands offers education and care and places emphasis on life skills and personal and social education in order to enable as independent a transition to adult life as possible. Emphasis is also placed on Information and Communication Technology skills and development (Residential (termly)) (6) (43)

Treloar School Upper Froyle, Alton, Hampshire GU34 4LA; URL www.treloar.org.uk; E-mail admissions@treloar.org.uk; Tel 01420 526400; Fax 01420 526426
Admissions Officer Helen Burton
Treloar School is a leading centre for education, independence training, therapy, opportunities and care for physically disabled young people, some of whom may also have communication or sensory impairments, or learning difficulties. Treloars welcomes young people with a broad range of abilities, from those studying for GCSEs to those working on modified modular curriculum. The School's Key Stage 1 programme is based on the principles of conductive education. The on-site medical centre is staffed 24 hours a day; dedicated therapy teams and rehabilitation engineers work with specialist teaching and care staff to enable each individual to achieve their best.
Mixed 5–16 Wide range of physical disabilities (25 Day, 10 Boarders)

The Wing Centre Vicars Hill, Boldre, Lymington, Hampshire SO41 5QB; URL www.hesleygroup.co.uk; E-mail anightingale@hesleygroup.co.uk; Tel 01590 675350; Fax 01590 671891
Headteacher Angela Nightingale, BEd(Hons)
No area limit.
Male 16–19 Asperger Syndrome. The Wing Centre offers further education and care, emphasising life skills and personal and social education to enable a smooth transition to adult life. Emphasis is also placed on Information and Communication Technology skills and development. Residential, termly. (20)

Herefordshire

Into Independence 112 Ryeland St, Hereford, Herefordshire HR4 0LD; Tel 01432 274632; Fax 01432 274632
Preparation for and support in independent living.
Mixed Socially and emotionally disturbed with range of SEN.

Hertfordshire

Meldreth Manor School Fenny La, Meldreth, Royston, Hertfordshire SG8 6LG; E-mail meldreth.manor@scope.org.uk; Tel 01763 268000; Fax 01763 268099
Headteacher Eric Nash
SCOPE.
Mixed 9–19+ PH, SLD, profound learning difficulties, visual/hearing impairment. (Day, Residential) (64)

Radlett Lodge School (National Autistic Society) Harper La, Radlett, Hertfordshire WD7 9HW; URL www.nas.org.co.uk; E-mail radlett.lodge@nas.org.uk; Tel 01923 854922; Fax 01923 859922
Headteacher L. Tucker
London Boroughs and Home Counties.
National Autistic Society.
Mixed 3–11 (Day, 5-Day Boarders) (49)

Sedgemoor High St, Baldock, Hertfordshire SG7 5NL; URL www.sedgemoor.net; E-mail hwinchester@sedgemoor.net; Tel (Referrals) 01460 258000; Fax 01460 258028
National Director Gary Dawkins
The essence of work at Sedgemoor is a commitment to facilitate real, personal growth and development in the young people for whom they care. They believe that professional practice in Special Education and Residential Care is good enough only if it would be good enough for one's own children. They provide services in Residential Care, Education, Fostering and Emergency Placement, Specialist Care.

St. Elizabeth's RC Special School Much Hadham, Hertfordshire SG10 6EW; E-mail enquiries@stelizabeths.org.uk; Tel 01279 843451; (School Office) 01279 844270
Principal Mrs Clare-Ann Walker
No area limit.
Mixed 5–19 Epilepsy and associated disorders, communication difficulties, autism, SLD and MLD. (Day, (12), Boarders (68))

Isle of Wight

St. Catherine's School Grove Rd, Ventnor, Isle of Wight PO38 1TT; URL www.stcatherines.org.uk; E-mail stcaths@onthepc.co.uk; Tel 01983 852722
Provision made for some children to attend local secondary schools.
No area limit.
Mixed 7–19 Speech and language disorders (Boarders) (70)

14

Kent

Dorton House School Seal, Sevenoaks, Kent TN15 0ED; URL www.rlsb.org.uk; E-mail dortonhouseschool@rlsb.org.uk; Tel 01732 592650; Fax 01732 592670
Royal London Society for the Blind
No area limit.
Mixed 5–16 Visually impaired. (Day, Boarders)

Greenfields School Biddenden Rd, Tenterden, Kent TN30 6TD; Tel 01580 292523
A Peper Harow independent special school for 6–12 year olds, for day pupils as well as children resident at Goldwell, residential centre.

Helen Allison School Longfield Rd, Meopham, Kent DA13 0EW; Tel 01474 814878; Fax 01474 812033
Headteacher Jacqui Ashton Smith
Mixed 5–19 Autism (Day, Weekly Boarders) (70)

Meadows School London Rd, Southborough, Tunbridge Wells, Kent TN4 0RJ; Tel 01892 529144; Fax 01892 527787
Headteacher M. Price
Term-time only. Holiday provision can be arranged by APEX Project in certain circumstances.
Barnardo's London Division
Mixed 11–16 EBD, SEN (Day, Boarders) (56)

Ripplevale School Ripple, Deal, Kent CT14 8JG; E-mail ripplevale.school@hotmail.com; Tel 01304 373866; Fax 01304 381011
Headteacher Don Wilton
London and Southern Counties. Rural location. Small class sizes. Specialist teachers. Classroom support.
Boys 9–16 Emotional/behavioural difficulties. (Day, Boarders)

The Royal School for Deaf Children, Margate and Westgate College for Deaf People Victoria Rd, Margate, Kent CT9 1NB; URL www.royalschoolfordeaf.kent.sch.uk; www.westgate-college.org.uk; E-mail enquiries@royalschoolfordeaf.kent.sch.uk; Tel 01843 227561; Fax 01843 227637
Headteacher C. Owen, BA(Hons), MA(Ed)
England, Wales and the Channel Islands.
Mixed 4–16 school, 16–25 college. Deaf, deaf with additional disabilities, deaf/blind, multisensory impaired. (Day, Boarders) (180)

Lancashire

Beech Tree School Meadow La, Bamber Bridge, Preston, Lancashire PR5 8LN; URL www.scope.org.uk/beechtree; E-mail beechtreeschool@easynet.co.uk; Tel 01772 323131; Fax 01772 322187
Headteacher Lucy Bayliss
SCOPE.
Mixed 7–16 SLD and challenging behaviour. (Boarders, 52 weeks)

Nugent House School Carr Mill Rd, Billinge, Wigan, Greater Manchester WN5 7TT; E-mail janebienas@zen.co.uk; Tel 01744 892551
Headteacher Jane L.G. Bienias, MEd, BEd
Nationwide. Nugent Care Society.
Boys SEN associated with emotional and behavioural disorders (Day, Boarders) (93)

Pontville School and 16+ Transition Unit Black Moss La, Ormskirk, Lancashire L39 4TW; E-mail office@pontville.co.uk; Tel 01695 578734; Fax 01695 579224
A member of the Witherslack Group of Schools Limited.
Headteacher R. Farbon
Attached to the school is a special transition unit for vocational education: 16–19, Mixed, Social and independence skills.
British Isles.
Mixed 11–19 (Day, Boarders) (10)

Rossendale School Moorside Farm, Ramsbottom, Lancashire BL0 0RT; Tel 01706 822779

Headteacher D.G. Duncan
Fully approved by the DfEs under section 347 (1) of the 1996 Education Act. Fully registered with the Social Services Department under the 1989 Children's Act as a school dealing specifically with Statemented pupils displaying emotional difficulties and who may have associated behavioural disorders exacerbated by the following syndromes; Aspergers, ADD, ADHD, Tourettes, Fragile X, Smith McGuiness, Noonan's or any other similarly related disorder.

Royal Cross Primary School Elswick Rd, Ashton-on-Ribble, Preston, Lancashire PR2 1NT; URL www.wemp.freeserve.co.uk/reps; E-mail royalcross@primaryschool.fsnet.co.uk; Tel 01772 729705
Headteacher R. Nottingham
Mixed 4–11 School for deaf children with a unit for hearing children with speech/language disorders. (Day)

Underley Hall School Kirkby Lonsdale, Carnforth, Lancashire LA6 2HE; E-mail underleyes@hotmail.com; Tel 015242 71206; Fax 015242 72581
Headteacher John Parkinson
Boys 9–16+ EBD (52 week Boarding) (70)

Underley Garden School Kirkby Lonsdale, Carnforth, Lancashire LA6 2DZ; E-mail underleyes@hotmail.com; Tel 015242 71569; Fax 015242 72581
Headteacher Colin Tomlinson
Mixed 9–16+ EBD (52 week Boarders) (49)

Witherslack Group of Schools (Cedar House) Kirkby Lonsdale, Carnforth, Lancashire LA6 2HW; Tel 015242 71181
Principal J. Bowers
Headteacher A.W. Cousins
Mixed 9–16 EBD, SpLd, ADHD (Day, Boarders) (70)

Leeds

St. John's Catholic School for the Deaf Church St, Boston Spa, Wetherby, West Yorkshire LS23 6DF; URL www.stjohns.org.uk; E-mail info@stjohns.org.uk; Tel 01937 842144; Fax 01937 541471
Headteacher Thomas Wrynne, BEd, MA, TOD
Mixed 3–19 Deafness

Leicestershire

The Grange Therapeutic School Knossington, Oakham, Leicestershire LE15 8LY; E-mail mjbsmith@btconnect.com; Tel 01664 454264; Fax 01664 454234
Director and Bursar Mrs A. Smith
Boys 8–16 EBD (Boarders) (60)

Liverpool

Royal School for the Blind Church Rd North, Wavertree, Liverpool, Merseyside L15 6TQ; Tel 0151 733 1012
Headteacher J.P. Byrne
No area limit.
Mixed 3–19 Visually impaired with moderate to severe learning difficulties and a range of additional disabilities. (Day, Boarders) Junior and Senior (60–75)

St. Vincent's School for the Blind and Partially Sighted Yew Tree La, West Derby, Liverpool, Merseyside L12 9HN; URL www.stvin.com; E-mail stvincents@compuserve.com; Tel 0151 228 9968; 0151 259 5266; Fax 0151 252 0216
Headteacher Anthony MacQuarrie
Mixed 4–17 visual handicap (Day, Boarders) (79)

London

Outset Ltd Telemax Hse, 15 New Bedford Rd, Luton LU1 1SA; URL www.outset.org.uk; E-mail hq@outset.org.uk; Tel 0870 200 0001; Fax 0870 200 0110

IT Employment Outset develops opportunities for people with disabilities.
All disabilities catered for.
16–63

Pield Heath House RC School Pield Heath Rd, Uxbridge, Greater London UB8 3NW;
E-mail pieldheath@btconnect.com; Tel 01895 233092; 01895 258507; Fax 01895 256497
Headteacher Sr Julie Rose
No area limit.
Mixed 7–19 MLD/SLD, speech and language difficulties. (Day, Boarders)

RNIB Sunshine House School 33 Dene Rd, Northwood, Greater London HA6 2DD; Tel 01923 822538; Fax 01923 826227
No area limit.
RNIB.
Mixed 2–11 Visually impaired (Day, Boarders) (56)

Rutherford School 1a Melville Ave, South Croydon, Surrey CR2 7HZ; URL www.garwoodfoundation.org.uk; Tel 020 8688 7560
Chair J. Norris
Headteacher Ruth Hills
The Garwood Foundation.
Physical, complex medical needs, severe or profound and multiple learning difficulties.

Merseyside

Birkdale School for Hearing-Impaired Children 40 Lancaster Rd, Birkdale, Southport, Merseyside PR8 2JY;
URL www.bshic.co.uk;
E-mail admin@birkdale-school.merseyside.org; Tel 01704 567220; Fax 01704 568342
Headteacher Anne Wood, BEd(Hons)
Mixed 5–19 (Day, Weekly Boarders, Termly Boarders) (35)

Clarence House School West La, Freshfield, Formby, Liverpool, Merseyside L37 7AZ; Tel 01704 872151; Fax 01704 831001

Peterhouse School Preston New Rd, Churchtown, Southport, Merseyside PR9 8PA;
URL www.autisminitiatives.org/peterhouse;
E-mail peterhouse.admin@autisminitiatives.org; Tel 01704 506682; Fax 01704 506683
Head (Education) Graham Birtwell
Autistic Spectrum Disorder

Wargrave House School 449 Wargrave Rd, Newton-le-Willows, Merseyside WA12 8RS; Tel 01925 224899; Fax 01925 291368
Headteacher Pamela Maddock
Mixed 5–19 Autistic spectrum disorders. (Day, Boarders) (68)

West Kirby Residential School Meols Dr, West Kirby, Wirral CH48 5DH; Tel 0151 632 3201
Headteacher G.W. Williams

Newcastle upon Tyne

Northern Counties School Great Northern Rd, Newcastle upon Tyne, Tyne and Wear NE2 3BB;
URL www.northern-counties-school.co.uk;
E-mail info@northerncounties.newcastle.sch.uk; Tel 0191 281 5821; Fax 0191 281 5060
Headteacher Mrs F.M. Taylor
3–19 full/part-time Hearing impairment, sensory impairment, multiple disability. (Day, Boarders) (86)

Norfolk

Sheridan House Special School and Therapeutic Community Southburgh, Thetford, Norfolk IP25 7TJ;
URL www.prioryhealthcare.com;
E-mail sheridanhouse@prioryhealthcare.com; Tel 01953 850494; Fax 01953 851498
Principal Mrs S.J. Sayer
Referrals Ms P. Young
10–16 (12)

North Yorkshire

Breckenbrough School Thirsk, North Yorkshire YO7 4EN;
URL www.breckenbroughschool.org.uk;
E-mail office@breckenbrough.org.uk; Tel 01845 587238
Headteacher T.G. Bennett
Boys 9–17 (Boarders)

Spring Hill School Palace Rd, Ripon, North Yorkshire HG4 3HN; E-mail janet.clarke@barnardos.org.uk; Tel 01765 603320
Headteacher J.E. Clarke, MA
Mixed Learning difficulties, behavioural problems

Northamptonshire

Potterspury Lodge School Towcester, Northamptonshire NN12 7LL; URL www.potterspurylodge.co.uk;
E-mail mail@potterspurylodge.co.uk; Tel 01908 542912; Fax 01908 543399
Principal G. Lietz
Boys 8–16 EBD, Autism, Asperger syndrome. Termly and Weekly Boarders, Day (54)

Thornby Hall Thornby, Northamptonshire NN6 8SW;
E-mail thornbyhall@thornbyhall.ision.co.uk; Tel 01604 740001; 01604 740353; Fax 01604 740311
A Peper Harow school.
Assistant Director (Placements) Warren Sherratt
Mixed 12–18 EBD (Boarders)

Nottingham

I CAN's Dawn House School Helmsley Rd, Rainworth, Mansfield, Nottinghamshire NG21 0DQ;
URL www.ican.org.uk; E-mail dawnhouse@ican.org.uk; Tel 01623 795361; Fax 01623 491173
Mixed 5–16 Speech, language and communication difficulties, small teaching groups. (Day and residential) (81)

Rutland House School 1 Elm Bank, Mapperley Rd, Nottingham NG3 5AJ; E-mail rutland.house@scope.org.uk; Tel 0115 962 1315
Headteacher Carole Oviatt-Ham
Pre-school nursery facilities for children with cerebral palsy; Primary and secondary departments are all on separate sites. Residential pupils at secondary school live in bungalows in the city of Nottingham.
Mixed 2–19 PH, MSI, Complex needs (Day, Boarders) (35)

Sutherland House School Sutherland Rd, Nottingham NG3 7AP; Tel 0115 987 3375
Mixed 3–19 Autistic (Day) (70)

Oxfordshire

Bessels Leigh School Besselsleigh, Abingdon, Oxfordshire OX13 5QB; Tel 01865 390436; Fax 01865 390688
Headteacher J. Boulton, BEd, MEd, DipPsyc(OU)
Boys 10–17 EBD, educational problems (Boarders) (36)

The Mulberry Bush School Standlake, Witney, Oxfordshire OX29 7RW;
E-mail john.diamond@mulberrybush.oxon.sch.uk;
Tel 01865 300202; Fax 01865 300084
Director John Diamond, MA, BA
Registered with the Department for Education and Employment and inspected by National Care Standards Commission.
Mixed 5–12 (entry age up to 9) Severe emotional disturbance, average and above average intelligence (Boarders) (36)

14

Prospects
FOR YOUNG PEOPLE

Provides a range of services and resources for children and young people.

- **Prospects – Bersham –** medium/long term residential care and education.
- **Dewis** and **Tŷ Cornel –** short term residential care, education and assessment.
- **Outreach –** preparation for adulthood within the community.
- **Individual Placements –** Specialist resources for young people whose needs cannot be met in a group setting.
- **Other Services –** Independent visitors, advocacy, comprehensive risk assessment, community based support and individually tailored special projects.
- **Training Consultancy & Publications –** Supporting continuous professional development.

For further information contact:
Vicky Simms (Placement and Referral Manager)
Prospects for Young People, 12 Grosvenor Road, Wrexham LL11 1BU
Telephone 01978 313777 Facsimile 01978 313888

e-mail referrals@prospectsforyp.co.uk
www.prospectsforyp.co.uk

Penhurst School New St, Chipping Norton, Oxfordshire OX7 5LN; Tel 01608 647020; Fax 01608 647029
Headteacher Richard Aird
Mixed 5–19 PH, profound learning difficulties (respite care). (Boarders (Weekly and termly arrangements)). (21)

Swalcliffe Park School Trust Swalcliffe, Banbury, Oxfordshire OX15 5EP; E-mail admin@swalcliffepark.co.uk; Tel 01295 780302; Fax 01295 780006
Headteacher Ray Hooper
Boys 11–16 (some 16+) EBD, Asperger's syndrome, ADHD (Boarders) (57)

Shropshire

Cotsbrook School Higford, Shifnal, Shropshire TF11 9ET; Tel 01952 468502; Fax 01952 468507
Director J.G. Airth, MEd, AdvDipEd
Deputy Director D. Lynn, DipSH
All placement enquiries/referrals to Placements Office, Cotsbrook Community Ltd, P.O.Box 562, Tweedale, Shropshire, TF11 9HG
Mixed 11–16 Severely Emotionally/Socially and Educationally Disturbed (Boarders)

Crisis Care Middle Knuck, Mainstone, Bishop's Castle, Shropshire SY9 5NA; Tel 01588 640584; Fax 01588 640896
Manager Jacqui Stone
Short term, adventure activity based Crisis Placements with Education and Counselling.
Mixed Socially and emotionally disturbed with range of SEN.

Cruckton Hall School Cruckton, Shrewsbury, Shropshire SY5 8PR; URL www.cruckton.demon.co.uk; E-mail pdm@cruckton.com; Tel 01743 860206
Headteacher P.D. Mayhew
Re-recognised under the 1981 Education Act.
Boys 9–18 SEN, Asperger's syndrome Residential (68)

Learning for Life, Hilltop Residential Special School
Hilltop Centre, Fishmore Rd, Ludlow, Shropshire SY8 3DP;
URL www.corvedalecare.co.uk;
E-mail learningforlife@corvedalecare.net; Tel 01584 875231
Headteacher P. Hurd, BA(Hons), PGCE(AdvDipEdMan)
Individual tuition and group tuition of less than four
Mixed 10–16

Overley Hall School Wellington, Telford, Shropshire TF6 5HE; URL www.overleyhall.com;
E-mail info@overleyhall.com; Tel (24 hours) 01952 740231; (from 0700 hrs) 01952 740262
Headteacher W. O'Hagan, BA, PGCE, RNMH
No area limit.
Mixed 9–19+ (Adult facility available) SLD, PMLD Challenging behaviour, autism. Boarders (52 weeks boarding available) (18)

RNIB Condover Hall School Condover, Shrewsbury, Shropshire SY5 7AH; URL www.condoverhallschool.com;
E-mail harry.dicks@rnib.org.uk; Tel 01743 872320; Fax 01743 873310
Principal Harry Dicks
No area limit.
Royal National Institute for the Blind.
Mixed Blind with additional handicaps, deaf/blind (Day, Boarders 38 week and 52 week) (55)

Somerset

The Marchant-Holliday School North Cheriton, Templecombe, Somerset BA8 0AH;
E-mail marholsch.office@talk21.com; Tel 01963 33234; Fax 01963 33432
Headteacher J.M. Robertson, BEd(Hons), DipEd
Area
Southern England.
DES listed.
Boys 7–12 EBD (Boarders, Day) (36)

Sedgemoor Ashwell Pk, Ilminster, Somerset TA19 9DX;
URL www.sedgemoor.net;
E-mail winchester@sedgemoor.net; Tel (Referrals) 01460
258133; Fax 01460 258028
National Director Gary Dawkins, BA(Hons), DQSW,
DMS
The essence of work at Sedgemoor is a commitment to
facilitate real personal growth and development in the
young people for whom they care. They believe that
professional practice in Special Education and Residential
Care is good enough only if it would be good enough for
one's own children. They provide services in Residential
Care, Education, Fostering and Emergency Placement.

South Gloucestershire

Sheiling School, Camphill Community Thornbury
Thornbury Pk, Thornbury, Bristol BS35 1HP;
URL www.sheilingschool.org.uk;
E-mail mail@sheilingschool.org.uk; Tel 01454 412194;
Fax 01454 411860
Residential and day school for special needs 6–19. Rudolph
Steiner Curriculum.
    Mixed 6–19 Multiple handicaps (not severely PH). (Day,
    Boarders) (35)

South Yorkshire

The Robert Ogden School Clayton La, Thurnscoe,
Rotherham, South Yorkshire S63 0BE;
URL www.nas.org.uk; E-mail robert.ogden@nas.org.uk
formerly Storm House School
Headteacher A. Dishman, MA(Psych), BEd
A school of the National Autistic Society
    Mixed 7–19 Autistic (Weekly Boarders termly and 50
    week) (33) (Day) (134)

Staffordshire

Bladon House School Newton Solney, Burton-upon-Trent,
Staffordshire DE15 0TA;
URL www.bladon-house-school.co.uk;
E-mail bladonhouseschool@honormead.btinternet.com;
Tel 01283 563787
    Mixed 5-19 MLD, SLD, speech and language disorders.
Longdon Hall School Longdon Grn, Rugeley, Staffordshire
WS15 4PT; Tel 01543 490634; Fax 01543 492140
    Mixed

Suffolk

The Ryes School Little Henny, Sudbury, Suffolk CO10 7EA;
URL www.theryesschool.org.uk;
E-mail office@ryes-school-demon.co.uk; Tel 01787 374998;
Fax 01787 371995
Headteacher Torsten Friedag
    7–16, 16–24 (Senior)

Surrey

I CAN's Meath School Brox Rd, Ottershaw, Surrey
KT16 0LF; URL www.ican.org.uk;
E-mail meath@ican.org.uk; Tel 01932 872302; Fax 01932
875180
Headteacher
    Mixed 5–12 speech, language and communication
    difficulties, small teaching groups. (Day, Weekly and
    Flexi Boarders and Part Boarding) 10 (extra needs class
    (6))
Link Primary and Secondary School 138 and 82–86
Croydon Rd, Beddington, Surrey CR0 4PG; Tel (Primary)
020 8688 5239; (Secondary) 020 8688 7691
Headteacher G. Stewart
    Mixed 6–16+ Language and communication difficulties.
    (Day) (76)

Moor House School Hurst Green, Oxted, Surrey RH8 9AQ;
URL www.moorhouse.surrey.sch.uk;
E-mail info@moorhouse.surrey.sch.uk; Tel 01883 712271;
Fax 01883 716722
Principal Alan Robertson
A school for pupils with severe specific speech and
language impairments, who are within the range of
intelligence found in a mainstream classroom. Provision
includes small teaching groups and intensive speech and
language therapy. There is additional support from a multi
disciplinary team which includes a nurse and an
occupational therapist.
    Mixed 7–16 severe specific speech and language
    impairment. (Boarders) (80)
St. Dominic's School Hambledon, Godalming, Surrey
GU8 4DX; E-mail office@stdominicsschool.org.uk; Tel 01428
682741; 01428 684693; Fax 01428 685018
Principal Gerry Chapman
    Mixed 9–16 Specific learning difficulties, speech and
    language problems (Day, Weekly Boarders) (100)
St. Joseph's School Cranleigh, Surrey GU6 7DH; Tel 01483
272449; Fax 01483 276003
Headteacher R.R. Dasey
    Mixed 7–14 (14–19). MLD/SLD, associated difficulties,
    speech and language difficulties. (Day, Residential) (75)
The National Centre for Young People with Epilepsy St.
Piers La, Lingfield, Surrey RH7 6PW;
URL www.ncype.org.uk; E-mail mail@ncype.org.uk;
Tel 01342 832243; Fax 01342 834639
Formerly St. Piers School. The National Centre for Young
People with Epilepsy (NCYPE) is the largest provider of
specialised services for young people with epilepsy
offering assessment, treatment, residential care and
education for children and young people from 5–19. St.
Piers School offers a mixture of learning through
individually tailored programmes with access to the
National Curriculum. St. Piers Further Education College
provides state of the art facilities and the curriculum is
developed through two main areas: Life Skills programme
and vocational training programme. In addition to
education, therapy and care on-site, consultant led medical
services are offered in partnership with great Ormond
Street Hospital for Children NHS Trust.
Registered charity no 311877.
    Mixed (200)
St. Margaret's School Tadworth Crt, Tadworth, Surrey
KT20 5RU; E-mail stmargarets@thechildrenstrust.org.uk;
Tel 01737 365810; Fax 01737 365819
Headteacher J.E. Cunningham
    Mixed 5–19 Children with PMLD with complex medical
    needs, degenerative conditions and additional sensory
    impairment. (Day, Boarders (48 week education year) (40)

Tyne and Wear

The Percy Hedley School Station Rd, Forest Hall,
Newcastle upon Tyne, Tyne and Wear NE12 8YY;
URL www.percyhedley.org.uk;
E-mail school@percyhedley.org.uk; Tel 0191 266 5451
Headteacher N.O. Stromsoy, MA, DipSE
Bursar R. Baron
    Mixed 3–18 PH, speech and language disorders. (Day,
    Boarders) (170)
Thornhill Park School 21 Thornhill Pk, Sunderland, Tyne
and Wear SR2 7LA; Tel 0191 514 0659; Fax 0191 510 8242
Headteacher David Walke
    Mixed 2–19 (Day, Boarders) (91)

West Berkshire

The Annie Lawson School Ravenswood Village, Nine Mile
Ride, Crowthorne, West Berkshire RG45 6BQ;
E-mail annie.lawson@norwood.org.uk; Tel 01344 755508;
Fax 01344 762317
Headteacher Mark Hughes, MEd, BEd
    Mixed 11–19 SLD/PMLD, Autism (Residential) (22)

Mary Hare School Arlington Manor, Snelsmore Common, Newbury, West Berkshire RG14 3BQ; URL www.maryhare.org.uk; E-mail office@maryhare.org.uk; Tel 01635 244200
Headteacher Dr Ivan G. Tucker, PhD
Mixed 5–19 Deaf/partially hearing (Day and Boarders) (230)

West Sussex

Farney Close School Bolney Crt, Bolney, Crossways, Haywards Heath, West Sussex RH17 5RD; URL www.farneyclose.co.uk; E-mail head@farneyclose.co.uk; Tel 01444 881811; Fax 01444 881957
Headteacher B. Robinson, MA, BEd(Hons)
Mixed 11–16 EBD (Day, Boarders) (78)

Ingfield Manor School Five Oaks, Billingshurst, West Sussex RH14 9AX; E-mail conductiveeducation@rmplc.co.uk; Tel 01403 782294
Headteacher C. Jay
Advised and supported by Peto Institute, Budapest. A Centre of Excellence for Conductive Education.
3–11 Cerebral palsy (Day, Weekly Boarders) (40)

Philpots Manor School West Hoathly, East Grinstead, West Sussex RH19 4PR; Tel 01342 810268; (Office) 01342 811382; Fax 01342 811363
Training Course (16–18) (16).
Mixed 6–16 A mixed boarding school for children with emotional and behavioural disturbances and learning difficulties. Numbers 54 from 6–16 years, 16 from 16–18 years. EBD, MLD (Boarders) (54)

Wiltshire

Burton Hill School Malmesbury, Wiltshire SN16 0EG; E-mail principal@shaftesbury-bh.prestel.co.uk; Tel 01666 822685; Fax 01666 826022
Headteacher P. Drake
Mixed 8–19 PH with learning difficulties (Day, Boarders) (41)

Wirral

West Kirby Residential School Meols Dr, West Kirby, Wirral CH48 5DH; E-mail wkrshead@aol.com; Tel 0151 632 3201; Fax 0151 632 0621
Head (Care) Yvonne Blackledge
Mixed 5–16+ Emotional and social problems, Asperger's syndrome. (Day, Boarders) (105)

Wokingham

High Close School Wiltshire Rd, Wokingham RG40 1TT; Tel 0118 978 5767
Headteacher A. Paterson
Day unit for 6–11 year olds
Mixed 10–16 Residential, educational, emotional/behavioural difficulties

Wales

Aran Hall School Rhydymain, Dolgellau, Gwynedd LL40 2AR; URL www.aranhall-school.co.uk; E-mail mferguson@aranhall-school.co.uk; Tel 01341 450641; Fax 01341 450637
Headteacher Mark Ferguson
Mixed 11–19 SLD and challenging behaviours (Boarders, 52 Weeks)

Bryn Melyn for Young People Llandderfel, Bala, Gwynedd LL23 7RA; URL www.brynmelyngroup.com; E-mail enquiries@brynmelyn.com; Tel 01678 530330; Fax 01678 530460
Head (Care) L. Walters
Head (Care) S. Goulding
See Chapter 13 for main entry.

Craig-y-Parc School Heol y Parc, Pentyrch, Cardiff CF15 9NB; E-mail ngharvey@aol.com; Tel 029 2089 0361; 029 2089 0397; Fax 029 2089 1404
Headteacher Neil Harvey, CertEd, BEd(Hons), MEd
Mixed 4–19 Cerebral Palsy, commmunication disorders, PMLD. (Day, Weekly Boarders and Full Boarders during term time. Flexible respite.) (55)

Headlands 2 St. Augustine's Rd, Penarth, Vale of Glamorgan CF64 1YY; E-mail wahs@mail.nch.org.uk; Tel 029 2070 9771
Headteacher David Haswell
Mixed EBD/ASD (Day, Boarding)

MacIntyre School, Womaston Walton, Presteigne, Powys LD8 2PT; URL www.macintyre-care.org; E-mail womaston@macintyre-care.org; Tel 01544 230308; Fax 01544 231317
Headteacher M. Bertulis
Mixed 11–19 Residential school providing a 52 week 24-hours-a-day curriculum for students with severe learning disabilities. (16)

Mental Health Care (Furze Mount) Ltd Copthorn Rd, Upper Colwyn Bay, Conwy LL28 5YP; Tel 01492 532678; Fax 01492 531280
All enquiries to Mental Health Care Group
Alexander Hse, Highfield Pk, Llandyrnog, Denbighshire LL16 4LU; Tel 01824 790600; Fax 01824 790341
Home registered for adults primarily with learning disabilities.

Prospects for Young People Bersham Rd, Bersham, Wrexham LL14 4HS; URL www.prospectsforyp.co.uk; E-mail admin@prospectsforyp.co.uk; Tel 01978 313777; Fax 01978 313888
Manager Ian Whelan, DipSW; NEBS Certificate in Management
Co-Director Stephen Elliott, CQSW, MBA
Head (Education) Kathryn Martin, BEd (Hons), Cert Ed, Advdip
Provides nine places for young people aged between 11–16 years on a medium/long-term basis with education available on site, as well as offering access to a developmental outreach service.

Tregynon Hall School Tregynon, Newtown, Powys SY16 3PG; E-mail tregynonhall@btinternet.com; Tel 01686 650330
Director Maureen E. Holmes, BA(Hons), ATC, BSc(Hons)
Director P.G. Holmes, CertEd
Mixed 9–16 (Boarders) (26)

Scotland

Camphill Blair Drummond Blair Drummond Hse, Stirling FK9 4UT; Tel 01786 841573; Fax 01786 841188
Further education and training
Mixed (16+) Learning disabilities (Residential) (40)

Camphill Rudolf Steiner Schools Central Office, Murtle Hse, Bieldside, Aberdeen AB15 9EP; URL www.camphillschools.org.uk; E-mail office@crss.org.uk; Tel 01224 867935; Fax 01224 868420
Mixed 3–19 Complex special needs. (Day, Boarders) (83)

Corseford Residential School Milliken Pk, Howwood Rd, Kilbarchan, Renfrewshire PA10 2NT; Tel 01505 702141; Fax 01505 702445
Headteacher M. Boyle
Mixed 5–18 (early education unit 0–5) Cerebral Palsy (75)

Donaldson's College West Coates, Edinburgh EH12 5JJ; URL www.donaldsons-coll.edin.sch.uk; E-mail admin@donaldsons-coll.edin.sch.uk; Tel 0131 337 9911; Fax 0131 337 1654
Principal Janet Allan
Mixed 3–18 (plus further education/higher education). (Day, Boarders) (75)

14

East Park School 1092 Maryhill Rd, Glasgow G20 9TD;
URL enquiries@eastpark.co.uk;
E-mail eastpark@compusave.com; Tel 0141 946 8315;
Fax 0141 946 2838
Headteacher L. Gray
Mixed 5–19 MH, PH (28)

Harmeny Education Trust Ltd Harmeny School, Mansfield
Rd, Balerno, Midlothian EH14 7JY;
URL www.harmeny.org.uk;
E-mail harmeny@btinternet.com; Tel 0131 449 3938;
Fax 0131 449 7121
Chief Executive P. Webb, BEd, ADipEd(Cantab)
Mixed 6–12 SEBD, ADHD, SpLD (Boarders (30)
Residential, (6) Day)

Hillside School Hillside, Aberdour, Fife KY3 0RH;
Tel 01383 860731; Fax 01383 860929
Headteacher A. Harvey, DCE, BA, DISPE(SEN)
Independent EBD Boys 10–16 (Boarders) (30)

Linn Moor Residential School Peterculter, Aberdeen
AB14 0PJ; URL www.linnmoorschool.co.uk;
E-mail info@linnmoorschool.co.uk; Tel 01224 732246;
Fax 01224 735261
Principal John Davidson
Year-round residential care and specialist education for
children with severe/complex learning disabilities, and
associated social and emotional problems. Autistic children
also feature prominently. Emphasis on individual
development. Residential care provided in small family
groups.
Mixed 5–18 MH (Boarders) (30)
Administrative Centre Voluntary Service Aberdeen, 38
Castle St, Aberdeen AB11 5YU; URL www.vsa.org.uk;
E-mail info@vsa.org.uk; Tel 01224 212021

Ochil Tower (Rudolf Steiner) School Auchterarder, Perth
and Kinross PH3 1AD; URL www.ochiltowerschool.org.uk;
E-mail info@ochiltowerschool.org.uk; Tel 01764 662416;
Fax 01764 662416
Admissions and Reviews Hilary Ruprecht
Mixed 6–18 Special care (Day, Boarders) (34)

Red Brae School 24 Alloway Rd, Maybole, South Ayrshire
KA19 8AA; Tel 01655 883104; 01655 889608
General Manager Leah Galbraith
10–16

The Royal Blind School Craigmillar Pk, Edinburgh
EH16 5NA; URL www.royalblindschool.org.uk;
E-mail office@royalblindschool.org.uk; Tel 0131 667 1100;
Fax 0131 662 9700
Co-ordinator (Social Work) Joyce Alexander
3–19 Visually impaired, V1 and additional handicaps.
(140)

Starley Hall School Aberdour Rd, Burntisland, Fife
KY3 0AG; E-mail info@starleyhallschool.co.uk; Tel 01383
860314; Fax 01383 860956
Director Philip Barton
EBD/AD/HD (Day, Boarders)

Struan House School 27 and 33 Claremont, Alloa,
Clackmannanshire FK10 2DG; Tel 01259 213435; Fax 01259
211851
Headteacher J. Taylor
5–18 Autistic Residential and Day (28)

Westerlea School 11 Ellersly Rd, Edinburgh EH12 6HY;
E-mail westerlea.school@capability-scotland.org.uk;
Tel 0131 337 1236; Fax 0131 346 4412
Headteacher M. Thomson
Mixed 3–16+ years (early education unit 0-36 months)
Pupils with complex needs (physical, communication,
health, intellectual) 6–9

Woodlands School Corsbie Rd, Newton Stewart, Dumfries
and Galloway DG8 6JB; Tel 01671 402480
Residential special school offering individual education,
CATP plans, national certification.
Mixed 8–17 Behavioural problems (Boarders (52 and 38
week)) (24)

Northern Ireland

Jordanstown Schools 85 Jordanstown Rd, Newtownabbey,
County Antrim BT37 0QE; Tel 028 9086 3541; Fax 028 9086
4356
Headteacher Stephen L. Clarke
Mixed 3–19 Auditory, visual (Day, Boarders) (104)

FURTHER EDUCATION AND TRAINING FOR SPECIAL NEEDS

England

Bath

RNID Care Services – South West Region Watery La,
Twerton, Bath, Bath and North East Somerset BA2 1RN;
URL www.mid.org.uk; Tel 01225 332818; Fax 01225 480825
Deputy Director Craig A. Crowley
Deaf and all communication difficulties, learning
disabilities, visual impairment, autism, elderly and
nursing. (Day, Boarders) (60)

Birmingham

Queen Alexandra College Court Oak Rd, Harborne,
Birmingham, West Midlands B17 9TG;
E-mail enquiries@qac.ac.uk; Tel 0121 428 5050; Fax 0121 428
5048
Principal Sue Wright
Queen Alexandra College offers Further Education
vocational guidance and training and assessment.
Mixed 16+ Visual impairment and other disabilities.
(Day, Boarders) (120)

Bristol

Cintre House 54 St. John's Rd, Clifton, Bristol BS8 2HG;
E-mail cintre@freeuk.com; Tel 0117 923 9979; Fax 0117 946
7842
Chief Executive Catherine Twine
Manager Jacqueline Mears
Manager (Administration) Jo Winnard
Courses/Training
Woodwork, Home Economics, Life Skills, Organic
Gardening, Arts and Crafts, Personal Development.
Mixed 16+ (Day, Boarders)

The Hatch Camphill Community St. John's Hse, Kington La,
Thornbury, Bristol BS35 1NA;
E-mail hatchcamphill@cs.com; Tel 01454 413010; Fax 01454
414705
Courses/Training
Weaving, Woodwork, Garden, Farm, Domestic
Learning difficulties. (25)

Cambridgeshire

Papworth Assessment and Development Centre Papworth
Everard, Cambridge, Cambridgeshire CB3 8RG; Tel 01480
357260; Fax 01480 831919
Manager Scott Chapman
Manager (Training) Joanne Abbott
The Papworth Trust provides a vocational assessment
service for school, college leavers and more senior
individuals with disabilities who wish to access the labour
market at supported or open employment levels.
Part time clients three day vocational assessments, career
counselling.
Assessments with an occupational psychologist last for
three days and accommodation can be provided. A full

report of cognitive and physical abilities, occupational interests, personality and work competence can be given to prospective employers.

Career counselling, computability and ergonomic assessment can be included if required.

Physical disabilities, learning difficulties, congenital and acquired disability. All intellectual levels. (Day, Boarders)

Cornwall

Churchtown Outdoor Adventure Centre Lanlivery, Bodmin, Cornwall PL30 5BT; Tel 01208 872148; Fax 01208 873377

Duchy College Stoke Climsland, Callington, Cornwall PL17 8PB; URL www.cornwall.ac.uk/duchy; E-mail admissions@duchy.cornwall.ac.uk; Tel 01579 372222; Fax 01579 372200
Admissions (Stoke Climsland – Residential)
E-mail admissions@duchy.cornwall.ac.uk; Tel 01579 372233; Fax 01579 372200
Admissions (Rosewarne) Amanda Menear (Rosewarne Centre); E-mail enquiries@duchy.cornwall.ac.uk; Tel 01209 722100; Fax 01209 722159
A considerable range of learning difficulties are catered for. (Day, Boarders) (2500)

Peredur Garden and Craft Centre Trebullom, Altarnun, Launceston, Cornwall PL15 7RF; Tel 01566 86075; 01566 86575; Fax 01566 86975
Manager Mr S.W. Rundel
Manager Mrs S.W. Rudel
18 upwards Emotionally disturbed

Cumbria

Lindeth College of Further Education The Oaks, Lindeth, Bowness-on-Windermere, Cumbria LA23 3NH; E-mail nic.lc@btconnect.com; Tel 015394 46265; Fax 015394 88840
Principal Nicola Buckley
An inclusive residential further education course for students with learning difficulties/disabilities. Age range 16–25 years.
(44)

Derby

Green Laund Further Education Centre The Grange, Hospital La, Mickleover, Derby DE3 0DR; URL www.green-laund.co.uk; E-mail green-laund@clara.co.uk; Tel 01332 512855; Fax 01332 512867
Manager Val Parkes; Tel 01332 512855
approved by DSS and Learning and Skills Council
Mixed 19–25+ (Boarders)

Devon

Oakwood Court College 7–9 Oak Park Villas, Dawlish, Devon EX7 0DE; URL www.oakwoodcourtcollege.co.uk; E-mail admin@oakwoodcourtcollege.co.uk; Tel 01626 864066; Fax 01626 866770
Vice-Principal Mrs J. Butler
Mixed 16–25 Behavioural disorders, learning disabled, learning difficulties, vocational and independence training. (Boarders 52 week placement available))

St. Loye's Foundation (Training for Disabled People for Employment) Fairfield Hse, Topsham Rd, Exeter, Devon EX2 6EP; URL www.stloyes.co.uk; E-mail info@stloyes.ac.uk; Tel 01392 255428; Fax 01392 420889
Principal Margaret Peat
St. Loye's College was established in 1937 with the object of providing quality training for people with disabilities and long-term health problems so that they could compete on equal terms with the abled bodied in employment.

Assessment, pre-vocational and vocational training including: Training in Customer Care, Catering, Combined Business Skills, Electronics (including CISCO), Engineering, Horology, Horticulture, Joinery, and Warehousing. Employment rehabilitation and occupational therapy training is also available.
Disabilities catered for
Physical, Learning Difficulties, Behavioural, and Mental Disabilities
18–63 Residential (200)

Hesley Village and College Stripe Rd, Tickhill, Doncaster, South Yorkshire DN11 9HH; URL www.hesleygroup.co.uk; E-mail sekins@hesleygroup.co.uk; Tel 01302 861620; Fax 01302 861621
Headteacher Sue Ekins, MEd, Dip.Sp.Ed
No area limit.
Mixed 16 plus Complex difficulties resulting from autism and/or severe learning difficulties. Residential (52 week). (46)

Dorset

The Fortune Centre of Riding Therapy Avon Tyrrell, Bransgore, Christchurch, Dorset BH23 8EE; URL www.fortunecentre.org; E-mail info@fortunecentre.org; Tel 01425 673297; Fax 01425 674320
Director Jennifer Dixon-Clegg

Ivers College Hains La, Marnhull, Sturminster Newton, Dorset DT10 1JU; URL www.ivers.co.uk; E-mail iver.college@btinternet.com; Tel 01258 820164
Principal L. Matthews
Learning disabilities encompassing additional needs of communication, emotional and behavioural difficulties. (Boarders) Day (46)

Durham

Finchale Training College Durham, County Durham DH1 5RX; URL www.finchale.college.co.uk; E-mail finchale.college@mailbox.as; Tel 0191 386 2634; Fax 0191 386 4962
(200)

East Sussex

The Mount Camphill Community The Mount, Wadhurst, East Sussex TN5 6PT; URL www.camphill.org.uk; E-mail themount@camphill.clara.net; Tel 01892 782025; Fax 01892 782917
(37)

Hampshire

Minstead Training Project Minstead Lodge, Minstead, nr Lyndhurst, Hampshire SO43 7FT; E-mail mtp@milestonenet.co.uk; Tel 023 8081 2254; Fax 023 8081 2297
(50)

Peter Symonds' College Owens Rd, Winchester, Hampshire SO22 6RX; E-mail psc@psc.ac.uk; Tel 01962 852764; Fax 01962 849372
Principal Neil Hopkins
Three boarding houses for up to 100 students.
Dyslexia. (Day) Full and part time students. (2000)

Treloar College Holybourne, Alton, Hampshire GU34 4EN; URL www.treloar.org.uk; E-mail admissions@treloar.org.uk; Tel 01420 547400; Fax 01420 742708
Admissions Officer Helen Burton
Treloar college is a national specialist college of further education, providing education, independence training, therapy, opportunities and care for physically disabled young people, some of whom may also have

14

communication or sensory impairments, or learning difficulties. Treloar welcomes young people with a broad range of abilities, from those studying AS and A2 levels to those working on towards independence programmes. The on-site health centre is staffed 24 hours a day; dedicated therapy teams and rehabilitation engineers work with specialist teaching and care staff to enable each individual to achieve their best.

    Mixed 16+ Wide range of physical disabilities. (Day) (10) (Boarders) (165)

Herefordshire

Royal National College for the Blind College Rd, Hereford, Herefordshire HR1 1EB; URL www.rncb.ac.uk; E-mail info@rncb.ac.uk; Tel 01432 265725; Fax 01432 376628
Principal Roisin Burge
    (Mixed) 16 plus (Residential)

Kent

The Caldecott Community Mersham le Hatch, Ashford, Kent TN25 5NH; E-mail caldecottsch@aol.com; Tel 01233 503954; Fax 01233 502650
Director Derek Marshall
    Mixed (64)

Dorton College of Further Education Seal Dr, Seal, Sevenoaks, Kent TN15 0AH; Tel 01732 592602; Fax 01732 592601
Principal Mike Morris, BSc, BPhil, CQSW, CertEd, DMS
    Mixed 16+ Visually impaired (Day, Boarders)

Nash College of Further Education Coney Hill Education Centre, Croydon Rd, Hayes, Bromley, Kent BR2 7AG; E-mail pa@nashfecollege.org.uk; Tel 020 8462 7419; Fax 020 8462 0347

Headteacher Agnes Flynn, RNLDdip
Shaftesbury Society.
    Mixed 16–25+ PH, speech and language disorders, sensory impairment. (Day, Boarders)

Lancashire

Beaumont College Slyne Rd, Lancaster, Lancashire LA2 6AP; URL www.scope.org.uk; E-mail beaumontcollege@hotmail.com; Tel 01524 541400; Fax 01524 846896
Principal Stephen Briggs
Residential and day courses for students aged 16–25 with learning difficulties and/or disabilities.

Leicester

Broadview Centre Gateway College, Leicester LE2 7BY; URL www.gateway.ac.uk; E-mail cspencer@gateway.ac.uk; Tel 0116 255 3079; Fax 0116 254 9857
    16+ (Day) Physical Disabilities, Learning Disabilities

Leicestershire

RNIB Vocational College Radmoor Rd, Loughborough, Leicestershire LE11 3BS; URL www.rnibvocoll.ac.uk; E-mail enquiries@rnibvocoll.ac.uk; Tel 01509 611077; Fax 01509 232013

Lincolnshire

Broughton House College Brant Broughton, Lincoln, Lincolnshire LN5 0SL; URL www.hesleygroup.co.uk; E-mail bnoble@hesleygroup.co.uk; Tel 01400 272929; Fax 01400 273438

Headteacher Bob Noble, CertEd, DipEd
Mixed 16–25 Complex difficulties resulting from autism and/or severe learning difficulties (Residential, 52 week) (25)

Norfolk

Banham Marshalls College Mill Rd, Banham, Norwich, Norfolk NR16 2HU; URL www.banhammarshalls.com; E-mail info@banhammarshalls.com; E-mail director@banhammarshalls.com; Tel 01953 888656
Director G. Robson
Vice-Principal D. Oakley
Education from primary age up to GCSE and beyond, pre- and vocational courses. Pupils with special needs, including emotional, behavioural, learning and speech and language difficulties.
EBD, SLD Speech and Language

North East Lincolnshire

Linkage College, Weelsby Campus Weelsby Rd, Grimsby, North East Lincolnshire DN32 9RU; Tel 01472 241044; Fax 01472 242375
Chief Executive Dr Bob Price
Admissions Trefor Howard
Moderate learning difficulties, severe learning difficulties, autistic, Asperger's syndrome, epilepsy, hearing impairment, speech and language difficulties, William's Syndrome and other physical disabilities.
Full time pupils (Boarders) (80)

North Yorkshire

Askham Bryan College Pickering Centre, Swainsea La, Pickering, North Yorkshire YO18 8NE; Tel 01751 473431; Fax 01751 473431
Special Needs. Wheelchair Access.
(700)

Henshaws College Bogs La, Harrogate, North Yorkshire HG1 4ED; URL www.hsbp.co.uk; E-mail college@hsbp.co.uk; Tel 01423 886451; Fax 01423 885095
Headteacher Jane Cole
Provide further education and training for students aged 16+ with visual impairment and additional physical or learning difficulties. They aim to make a visible difference to all students by focusing on their abilities. Their student-centred approach means that each student follows an individual programme which combines the skills for independent living with pre-vocational and vocational skills. Each student's programme of study is reviewed on a regular basis. The college believes that combining personal, social and work skills into one comprehensive programme supports students in making the transition into adult life. Courses are accredited through a range of nationally recognised Awarding Bodies. Additional courses are available through supported attendance at local mainstream colleges or training providers. Physiotherapy, Hydrotherapy, Speech and Language Therapy and Occupational Therapy are available on campus, with counselling services arranged where needed.

Northamptonshire

Hinwick Hall College of Further Education (Special Needs) Hinwick, Wellingborough, Northamptonshire NN29 7JD; URL www.hinwick.demon.co.uk; E-mail cromwell@hinwick.demon.co.uk; Tel 01933 312470; Fax 01933 412470
Principal E.E. Sinnott
16–19+ PH, LD, communication disorders. (Day, Boarders) (56)

Nottinghamshire

County Horticulture and Work Training Brook Farm, Linby, Nottinghamshire NG15 8AE; URL www.nottscc.gov.uk/brooke-farm; E-mail kenwyn.smith@nottscc.gov.uk; Tel 0115 632638; Fax 0115 968 0646

Peterborough

Sense East (The Manor House Further Education College) The Manor Hse, 72 Church St, Market Deeping, Peterborough PE6 8AL; E-mail enquiries@senseeast.org.uk; Tel 01778 344921; Fax 01778 380078
Regional Director Ges Roulstone
Aged 17+. (Day, Boarders) Full-time (88)

Shropshire

Derwen College Oswestry, Shropshire SY11 3JA; URL www.kendall@micro-plus-web.net; E-mail david.kendall@micro-plus-web.net; Tel 01691 661234; Fax 01691 670714

Loppington House Further Education Unit and Adult Centre Loppington, Wem, Shropshire SY4 5NF; E-mail office@loppingtonhouse.co.uk; Tel 01939 233926; Fax 01939 235255

Somerset

Farleigh College Newbury, Nr Mells, Frome, Somerset BA11 3RG; E-mail brads@zetnet.co.uk; Tel 01373 814980; Fax 01373 814984
Headteacher S.W. Bradshaw
10–18 SpLD, Asperger's syndrome (50)

Lufton Manor College Lufton, Yeovil, Somerset BA22 8ST; URL lineone.net/lufton.manor; E-mail lufton.manor@lineone.net; Tel 01935 403120; Fax 01935 402126
Principal Rupert Elliott
4–5

Staffordshire

Strathmore House Residential Care Home 27 Queens Park Ave, Dresden, Stoke-on-Trent ST3 4AU; E-mail information@strathassoc.freeserve.co.uk; Tel 01782 596849; Fax 01782 313508

Surrey

The Grange Centre for People with Disabilities Rectory La, Bookham, Leatherhead, Surrey KT23 4DZ; E-mail contact@grange-centre.fsnet.co.uk; Tel 01372 452608; Fax 01372 451959
Director P.H. Wood
Residential care and sheltered housing, therapeutic daycare and vocational training in embroidery, dressmaking, and life skills – computers, literacy, independent living.
18–60 PD, LD (50)

Merrist Wood College Worplesdon, Guildford, Surrey GU3 3PE; URL www.merristwood.ac.uk; E-mail info@merristwood.ac.uk; Tel 01483 884000; Fax 01483 884001
Principal John G. Riddle
A wide range of disabilities catered for.
Part-time (400)
Education and Training for Land-based and related sports, leisure and recreation industries.
16+ Full-time (600)

Queen Elizabeth's Foundation Brain Injury Centre Park Rd, Banstead Pl, Banstead, Surrey SM7 3EE; E-mail bp@bansteadplace.freeserve.co.uk; Tel 01737 356222; Fax 01737 359467

Manager Eileen Jackman
Senior Social Worker Sue Messenger, CQSW
Queen Elizabeth's Foundation Brain Injury Centre is a specialist provision for young adults with acquired brain injuries.
    Mixed 16–35 PH (Boarders, Non residential)

Queen Elizabeth's Foundation Training College Leatherhead Crt, Leatherhead, Surrey KT22 0BN; URL www.qefd.org; Tel 01372 841100; Fax 01372 844156
Marketing Co-ordinator Sandria Lewindon
No area limit.
Queen Elizabeth's Foundation offers 16 Business Studies and Technical courses each leading to nationally recognised qualifications, including NVQs, City & Guilds and RSA examinations.
Support services include Open Learning, Employment Development, Job Club and 24-hour nursing support.
    18+ All disabilities except total blindness or profound deafness. (Residential, Non-residential) (215)

RNIB Redhill College Philanthropic Rd, Redhill, Surrey RH1 4DG; URL www.rnib.org.uk/services/redhill.htm; E-mail ptaylor@rnib-redhill.ac.uk; Tel 01737 768935; Fax 01737 778776
Principal Tracey de Bernhardt-Dunkin
Registered blind or partially sighted students with a wide range of disabilities and learning disabilities.
    Mixed 16+ adult (Day, Boarders) (120)

Tyne and Wear

Thornbeck College 14 Thornhill Pk, Sunderland, Tyne and Wear SR2 7LA; E-mail thornbeckcollege@aol.com
Principal Officer A. Tutty
Deputy Principal C. Dempster
    18+ Residential Provision for life if appropriate.

West Midlands

Hereward College Bramston Cres, Tile Hill La, Coventry, West Midlands CV4 9SW; URL www.hereward.ac.uk; E-mail enquiries@hereward.ac.uk; Tel (Minicom available) 024 76461231; Fax 024 7669 4305
Principal C. Cole
Assistant Principal Keith Robinson
Deputy Principal Janis Firminger, BA, CertEd, MEd, BPhil
Students
Residential 106, Day 440
Residential facilities include study bedrooms in three halls, a bungalow and houses (max capacity 105).
Hereward is a residential College of Further Education for disabled students. Residential students with disabilities from across the UK study alongside their non-disabled peers in a hi-tech and supportive environment in which equality of opportunity is paramount.

Wiltshire

Fairfield Opportunity Farm Dilton Marsh, Westbury, Wiltshire BA13 4DL; Tel 01373 823028; Fax 01373 859032
Learning Disabilities
Teaching ratio of 1:4.
    16+ (Day, Residential)

Worcestershire

RNIB New College Worcester Whittington Rd, Worcester, Worcestershire WR5 2JX;
URL www.rnibnewcollege.worcs.sch.uk;
E-mail hodgetts@rnibncw.demon.co.uk; Tel 01909 763933; Fax 01905 763277
Principal Nick Ratcliffe, MA, JP
No area limit.
Royal National Institute for the Blind.
    Mixed 11–19 Blind and visually impaired (Day, Weekly, Boarders) (100)

Wales

Coleg Elidyr Rhandirmwyn, Llandovery, Carmarthenshire SA20 0NL; E-mail colegrhan@aol.com; Tel 01550 760400; Fax 01550 760331
Secretary (Further Education Group) Jetty Eijgelaar
College of Further Education and Training for Young People with Learning Difficulties and Disabilities, Behavioural and Emotional Difficulties.
Funding: FFEC, FEFCW. LEA. Three sites: Rhandirmyn, Glasallt Fawr, Llangadog and Victoria Hse, Llangadog.
Fully registered with the Local Registration Unit (Carmarthen)
    Residential (24 hour curriculum). Full social and cultural programme of activities and events. (65)

Scotland

Beannachar Banchory-Devenick, Aberdeen AB12 5YL; URL beannachar.co.uk; E-mail beannachar@talk21.com; Tel 01224 869138; Fax 01224 869250
Co-Director E.A. Phethean
Training.
    Mixed 18–28 Mental, emotional, physical handicap (Day, Boarders) (30)

Easter Anguston Residential Farm Training Centre Peterculter, Aberdeen AB14 0PJ; URL www.vsa.org.uk; www.easteranguston.org.uk; E-mail info@easteranguston.org.uk; Tel 01224 733627; Fax 01224 734949
Principal Officer Vacancy
Year-round residential farm training and care for young people with learning disabilities.
    Mixed 16+ (Day, Boarders) (16)
Administrative Centre Voluntary Service Aberdeen, 38 Castle St, Aberdeen AB11 5YU; URL www.vsa.org.uk; E-mail info@vsa.org.uk; Tel 01224 212021

Garvald West Linton Ltd Dolphinton, West Linton, Scottish Borders EH46 7HJ; URL www.garvald-wl.org.uk; E-mail info@garvaldwest.fsnet.co.uk; Tel 01968 682211; Fax 01968 682611
Manager Martin Dawson
    Mixed 16+ Brain damage, Down's syndrome, autism, fragile X syndrome. (Boarders, Day) (32)

Tigh-A'-Chomainn Camphill Ltd 4 Craigton Cres, Peterculter, Aberdeenshire AB14 0SB; E-mail gcalderwoo@aol.com; Tel 01224 732656
Providing a setting (community home) for furthering independence within the open community for adults with special needs.
    Mixed 16–30 (6+)

Northern Ireland

Camphill Community, Glencraig Craigavad, Holywood, County Down BT18 0DB; E-mail office@glencraig.org.uk; Tel 028 9042 3396
All forms of learning disability, residential, includes Camphill Glencraig (Rudolf Steiner) Curative Schools 5–19 mixed and Camphill Glencraig Young Adult Training Scheme (Rudolf Steiner) 18–25, mixed, residential,

St. Gerards Educational Resource Centre Gort Na Mona, Upper Springfield Rd, Belfast BT12 7QP; Tel 028 9024 5593
Contact A.J. McGlone, BA, MEd, DASE, TCert
RC MLD
    Mixed 5–16+ Day (240)

SPECIAL EDUCATIONAL NEEDS

14

AFASIC 50–52 Gt Sutton St, London EC1V 0DJ; URL www.afasic.org.uk; E-mail info@afasic.org.uk; Tel 020 7490 9410; (Helpline (local call rate)) 08453 555577; Fax 020 7251 2834
Chief Executive Linda Cascelles

Allington Manor Psychological Services (SEPS) Allington La, Fair Oak, Eastleigh, Hampshire SO50 7DE; Tel 023 8069 2621
Consultant Psychologist Prof Dr L.F. Lowenstein, MA, DipPsych, PhD, BPs, Chartered Psychologist Assessment-psychodiagnostic for individuals with problems.
Diagnosis and therapy on premises. Also provides vocational assessment.
From average to below average ability and children of superior intelligence with moderate to fairly severe learning and/or behavioural difficulties.
Mixed 10–16+

Association of Blind and Partially-Sighted Teachers and Students BM Box 6727, London WC1N 1XX; E-mail nicola.matthews@btinternet.com
Chair Nicola Matthews

Association for Residential Care Arc Hse, Marsden St, Chesterfield, Derbyshire S40 1JY; URL www.arcuk.org.uk; E-mail contact.us@arcuk.org.uk; Tel 01246 555043; Fax 01246 555045
Chief Executive James Churchill
Consortium of residential care practitioners for people with learning disabilities. Specialises in distance learning courses for staff in home and day centres linked to NVQs. Offers advice and guidance on range of issues relating to residential care e.g. contracts, etc.

Basic Skills Westminster Adult Education Service, Amberley Rd Centre, London W9 2JJ; URL www.waes.ac.uk; E-mail basicskillsadmin@waes.ac.uk; Tel 020 7641 8188
Course Manager (Basic Skills) Lorraine Brook
Course Manager (Basic Skills) Paul Croft; E-mail pcroft@waes.ac.uk; Tel 020 7641 8120

British Association of Teachers of the Deaf 21 The Haystacks, High Wycombe, Buckinghamshire HP13 6PY; E-mail secretary@batod.org.uk; Tel 01494 464190; Fax 01494 464190

British Deaf Association (BDA) 1–3 Worship St, London EC2A 2AB; URL www.bda.org.uk; E-mail helpline@bda.org.uk; Tel 020 7588 3520; (Voice – calls charged at national rate) 0870 770 3300; Fax 020 7588 3527; Textphone 0800 6522 965
Chief Executive Jeff McWhinney
Advances and protects the interests of deaf people.

British Dyslexia Association 98 London Rd, Reading RG1 5AU; URL www.bda-dyslexia.org.uk/; E-mail info@dyslexiahelp-bda.demon.co.uk; Tel (Helpline) 0118 966 8271; Fax 0118 935 1927
Chief Executive Steve Alexander
Advice, helpline, befriending, publications, encourages research, accreditation of specialist dyslexia courses.

British Institute of Learning Disabilities Information and Resource Centre, Wolverhampton Rd, Kidderminster, Worcestershire DY10 3PP; E-mail bild@bild.demon.co.uk; Tel 01562 850251; Fax 01562 851970
Chief Executive Dr J. Harris
Finance and Administration Officer J. Fear
Information Officer Vacancy

Capability Scotland 22 Corstorphine Rd, Edinburgh EH12 6HP; URL www.capability-scotland.org.uk; E-mail capability@capability-scotland.org.uk; Tel 0131 337 9876; Fax 0131 346 7864
Chief Executive A.D.J. Dickson

Director (Quality) Mike Martin
Director (Finance) Richard Hellewell
Director of Services Sandra Kerley
Capability Scotland is the largest disability organisation in Scotland providing a range of facilities for children and adults with physical and/or learning disabilities.
Capability operates three schools. Westerlea is a day school in Edinburgh for children and young people with complex needs. Corseford in Renfrewshire is a residential school for children with physical disabilities which also offers year round residential and respite accomodation. Stanmore House in Lanark offers term time education with 52 week residential and respite accomodation.
Capability Scotland also works in partnership with local authorities to support inclusive education for children with disabilities.

Centre for Accessible Environments (Architectural Advice and Information) Nutmeg Hse, 60 Gainsford St, London SE1 2NY; URL www.cae.org.uk; E-mail info@cae.org.uk; Tel 020 7357 8182
Chief Executive S. Langton-Lockton, BA(Oxon)
Works to improve the design of the built environment to accommodate the needs of all users, including elderly and disabled people. Offers an information service on technical matters, publishes design guidance and a journal, Access by Design; administers a register of architects with experience of designing for disabled people; runs an extensive seminar programme; carries out access audits of buildings.

Citizen Advocacy Information and Training 162 Lee Valley Technopark, Ashley Rd, London N17 9LN; URL www.citizenadvocacy.org.uk; E-mail cait@teleregion.co.uk; Tel 020 8880 4545; Fax 020 8880 4113
Director Sally Carr
Aims to promote the development of citizen advocacy in the London area, and provides information and networking on a national basis.
Registered Charity Number 1035082

Commonwealth Society for the Deaf–Sound Seekers 34 Buckingham Palace Rd, London SW1W 0RE; URL www.sound-seekers.org.uk; E-mail sound.seekers@btinternet.com; Tel 020 7233 5700; Fax 020 7233 5800
Chair Graham Archer, CMG
Encourages the provision of services for deaf people–mainly children in the developing countries of the Commonwealth.

The Council for the Advancement of Communication with Deaf People (CACDP) Durham University Science Pk, Block 4, Stockton Rd, Durham, County Durham DH1 3UZ; URL www.cacdp.org.uk; E-mail durham@cacdp.org.uk; Tel 0191 383 1155; Fax 0191 383 7914; Answerphone 0191 383 7915
Chief Executive Miranda Pickersgill
The Council for the Advancement of Communication with Deaf People (CACDP) aims to improve communication between deaf and hearing people by the development of curricula and examinations in communication skills.
CACDP offers certification in British Sign Language, Lipspeaking, Communicating with Deafblind People and People and Deaf Awareness, and carries out the selection, training, monitoring and registration of examiners.
CACDP maintains a register of qualified and trainee interpreters and publishes annually a national directory of sign language interpreters, lipspeakers, interpreters for deafblind people and speech to text reporters who are not only of a required standard but are also available to undertake interpreting assignments.

Counselling in Education 24 Queens Rd East, Beeston, Nottingham, NG9 2GS; Tel 0115 922 5663
Secretary J. Antcliffe
A division of the British Association of Counselling.

CLA Charitable Trust Caunton Grange, Caunton, Newark, Nottinghamshire NG23 6AB;
URL www.clacharitabletrust.org.uk; Tel 01636 636171;
Fax 01636 636171
Director Peter Geldart
The CLA Charitable Trust helps to provide facilities for the disabled to take part in country sports and recreation and training in agriculture and horticulture. It also promotes education in the countryside for disadvantaged children and young people. It only operates in England and Wales. It does not give grants to support individuals.

Caspari Foundation for Educational Therapy and Therapeutic Teaching (FAETT) 1 Noel Rd, London N1 8HQ;
URL www.caspari.org.uk

DIAL UK–Disablement, Information and Advice Lines St. Catherine's, Tickhill Rd, Doncaster, South Yorkshire DN4 8QN; URL www.dialuk.org.uk;
E-mail enquiries@dialuk.org.uk; Tel 01302 310123;
Fax 01302 310404
Assistant Director (Information) Jo Carr
DIAL UK is the national organisation for the DIAL network of over 140 disability information and advice services. DIAL groups are run by people with direct experience of disability, who give free, independent, impartial advice to disabled people, carers and professionals.
DIAL UK provides a number of services to disability advice centres, including a reference information service, training and management support. Contact DIAL UK for details of local disability advice centres.

Down's Syndrome Scotland 158–160 Balgreen Rd, Edinburgh EH11 3AU; URL www.dsscotland.org.uk;
E-mail info@dsscotland.org.uk; Tel 0131 313 4225; Fax 0131 313 4285
Provides information, practical advice and support to people with Down's syndrome and their families; presses for better services and seeks to increase public awareness of the condition. Local branches offer a wide range of activities throughout Scotland. Publishes a magazine and information series.

Dyslexia Centre The Helen Arkell Dyslexia Centre, Frensham, Farnham, Surrey GU10 3BW;
E-mail general_enquiries@arkellcentre.org.uk; Tel 01252 792400; Fax 01252 795669

Dyslexia in Scotland Stirling Business Centre, Stirling FK8 2DZ; URL www.dyslexia-in-scotland.org;
E-mail info@dyslexia-in-scotland.org; Tel 01786 446650;
Fax 01786 471235
Provides information and practical help for children and adults with dyslexia (specific learning difficulties). Resource centre open Mon–Fri 1000–1600 free to members.

Dyslexia Institute Head Office, 133 Gresham Rd, Staines, Greater London TW18 2AJ; URL www.dyslexia-inst.org.uk;
E-mail info@dyslexia-inst.org.uk; Tel 01784 463851;
Fax 01784 460747
Chief Executive S. Cramer
Advice and counselling; teaching and teacher training services offered by nationwide centres. Further information from Head Office (enclose sae).

Elizabeth FitzRoy Support Caxton Hse, Lower St, Haslemere, Surrey GU27 2PE; URL www.efitzroy.org.uk;
E-mail info@efitzroy.org.uk; Tel 01428 656766; Fax 01428 643262
Chief Executive Steve Jenkin
Residential homes and day services for people with a learning disability.
Registered Charity Number 1011290

ENABLE 6th Fl, 7 Buchanan St, Glasgow G1 3HL;
URL www.enable.org.uk; E-mail enable@enable.org.uk;
Tel 0141 226 4541; Fax 0141 204 4398
Director N. Dunning
Concerned with all aspects of the needs of people with learning disabilities and their families in Scotland.

Grace Eyre Foundation 31 Avondale Rd, Hove, Brighton and Hove BN3 6ER;
URL www.grace-eyre-foundation.co.uk;
E-mail graceeyre@freenet.co.uk; Tel 01273 793887;
Fax 01273 734338
The Grace Eyre Foundation is a Registered Charity (No. 1020192) and a Company Limited by Guarantee (No. 2806429). Its aim is to provide support and practical assistance for people with learning disabilities. Since 1913 the foundation has promoted community placements arranged in a variety of settings. Placements are in small or larger registered care homes, and in independent or semi-independent living schemes. It offers a continuous support, monitoring and supervision service through adult placement services. It also offers respite care and annual review and placement services for individuals who may be resident at a distance from their own local authority. The foundation's day services offer a wide variety of activities and sessions designed to promote each individual's abilities and range of interests.

Helen Arkell Dyslexia Centre
See Dyslexia Centre

The Home Farm Trust (HFT) Merchants Hse, Wapping Rd, Bristol BS1 4RW; Tel 0117 927 3746; Fax 0117 922 5938
Chief Executive Brian Perowne
HFT provides a range of services, residential, day services, supported living, supported employment, advocacy, carers' support and respite for a very wide range of needs – from people with challenging behaviour or profound disabilities through to those living independently.

Hornsby International Dyslexia Centre Wye St, London SW11 2HB; URL www.hornsby.co.uk;
E-mail dyslexia@hornsby.co.uk; Tel 020 7223 1144; Fax 020 7924 1112
Head of Centre Dr Ruth Dawson

'I CAN' 4 Dyer's Bldgs, Holborn, London EC1N 2QP;
URL www.ican.org.uk; E-mail info@ican.org.uk; Tel 0870 010 4066; Fax 0870 010 4067
Information officer Solomon Hughes
I CAN is the national educational charity for children with speech and language difficulties. I CAN's services include an Early Years Programme, Special Schools, a Mainstream Programme, professional development, information and innovative partnership projects.

Kith and Kids c/o the Irish Centre, Pretoria Rd, London N17 8DX; E-mail projects@kithandkids.org.uk; Tel 020 8801 7432; Fax 020 8885 3035
Director Marjolein de Vries
Family Support Co-ordinator Carol Schaffer
Parent self-help group actively working for empowerment and inclusion of the whole family, through a range of project services.

Lead Scotland (Linking Education and Disability) Queen Margaret University College, Clerwood Terr, Edinburgh EH12 8TS; URL lead.org.uk; E-mail enquiries@lead.org.uk; Tel 0131 317 3439; Fax 0131 339 7198
Lead Scotland empowers and enables physically and/or sensory impaired adults in Scotland, to access learning opportunities, providing home-based support.

Leonard Cheshire 30 Millbank, London SW1P 4QD; Tel 020 7802 8200; Fax 020 7802 8250
Director of Services Fiona Street
Regional Director (Scotland) Stephen Neale
Regional Director (South West) Peter Denning
Regional Director (North West) John Winkler
Regional Director (Central) Marion Lambert
Regional Director (North East and Yorkshire) Jonathan Giles
Regional Director (South) David Ford
Regional Director (Eastern) Malcolm Bower-Brown
Regional Director (London and Kent) Rosemarie Mitchell
Regional Director (Wales and West Midlands) Michael O'Leary
Regional Director (Northern Ireland) Roisin Foster
Leonard Cheshire is an international disability care charity, providing wide ranging care and support for more than 10 000 people with physical and learning disabilities. In

NCYPE ⌐·⌐

14

The National Centre
for Young People
with Epilepsy

Epilepsy affects over 75,000 children and young people in the UK. For some 15,000 epilepsy can be a life shattering condition, with profound repercussions on their emotional, social and intellectual development. For these young people specialised care, education, assessment and treatment is crucial.

The National Centre for Young People with Epilepsy (NCYPE), a registered charity, is the major provider of these specialised services to young people throughout the UK. NCYPE provides a day and residential school and further education college, an on-site medical centre, epilepsy assessment and rehabilitation services. NCYPE works in partnership with Great Ormond Street Hospital for Children NHS Trust and the Institute of Child Health.

To find out more please contact The Admissions Co-ordinator at
NCYPE, St Piers Lane, Lingfield, Surrey RH7 6PW
Tel 01342 831243, Fax 01342 834639.
www.nycpe.org.uk.

Registered charity 311877

developing new and existing services, Leonard Cheshire works in partnership with service users as well as health authorities, social service departments and housing associations. Leonard Cheshire is committed to offering disabled people real choices – whether it is by living at home with the assistance of home support services, in independent and supported housing schemes, at community resource centres, or specialist care in residential and nursing services.
Registered Charity Number 218186

Living Options (Creative Young People Together)
Kimbridge Hse, Kimbridge Rd, Bracklesham Bay, Chichester, West Sussex PO20 8PE;
URL www.livingoptions.org.uk;
E-mail livingoptions@hotmail.com; Tel 01243 671865
Chair Val Fethney
Living Options provide opportunities for disabled young people (18+) to live in the community in small group homes and experience independence.

MacIntyre Care 602 South Seventh St, Milton Keynes MK9 2JA; URL www.macintyre-care.org;
E-mail mail@macintyre-care.org.uk; Tel 01908 230100;
Fax 01908 234379
A national charity providing a wide range of flexible services across the UK for over 500 adults and children with learning disabilities. Services include residential accommodation, support living schemes, day services and education and training opportunities, as well as two residential schools.

The Marlowe Child and Family Services PO Box 283, Gloucester, Gloucestershire GL19 4YA;
URL www.themarlowe.f2s.com; E-mail via website;
Tel 01452 700855; Fax 01452 700866
Director (Care) Steve Miller, MA

Provides a range of specialist needs, care and education to children and young people.

MENCAP – Royal Society for Mentally Handicapped Children and Adults Mencap National Centre, 123 Golden La, London EC1Y 0RT; URL www.mencap.org.uk;
E-mail information@mencap.org.uk; Tel 020 7454 0454;
Fax 020 7608 3254
Chair Brian Baldock, CBE
Chief Executive F. Heddell
Mencap is the leading charity working with people with learning disabilities in England, Wales and Northern Ireland. Mencap campaigns to ensure that people with a learning disability have the best possible opportunities to live as full citizens. It aims to influence new legislation and raise the profile of learning disability issues. It undertakes research into issues affecting people with a learning disability. Through its national network of 15 sectors and more than 450 affiliated local societies, Mencap is able to offer local services, support and advice to people with learning disability and their parents/carers.
The services Mencap offers include: support and advice through its Family Adviser Service; housing and residential accommodation; employment via the Pathway Employment Service; leisure via National Federation of Gateway Clubs; holidays advice; education at its own three Further Education colleges; information; unique bookshop.

MIND (The Mental Health Charity) Granta Hse, 15–19 Broadway, London E15 4BQ; URL www.mind.org.uk;
E-mail contact@mind.org.uk; Tel 020 8519 2122; (MIND info line (Open Mon-Fri 0915-1715 for information support)) 0845 766 0163; Fax 020 8522 1725
Chief Executive Richard Brook
MIND (the National Association for Mental Health) is the leading mental health charity in England and Wales. MIND

works for a better life for an estimated one in four people who will experience mental or emotional distress. It does this by:
– Advancing the views, needs and ambitions of people experiencing mental distress.
– Promoting inclusion and challenging discrimination.
– Influencing policy through effective campaigning and education.
– Providing quality services which meet the expressed needs of people experiencing mental distress and which reflect the requirements of a diverse community.
– Achieving equal legal rights and civil rights through campaigning and education.
With over 50 years of experience MIND is a major national network of over 200 local MIND Associations covering most major towns and rural areas in England and Wales. These are separately registered charities operating under the Mind brand. The MIND network is the largest charitable provider of mental health services in the community. The work of the Local Associations is strengthened and supported by staff and activities of National MIND through its offices in London and Wales.

National Association for Special Educational Needs (NASEN) NASEN Hse, 4–5 Amber Business Village, Amber Cl, Amington, Tamworth, Staffordshire B77 4RP; URL www.nasen.org.uk; E-mail welcome@nasen.org.uk; Tel 01827 311500

National Association for Tertiary Education for Deaf People (NATED) c/o SASU, Coventry Technical College, Coventry, West Midlands CV1 3GD
Secretary A.H. Hart
Promotes the exchange of views and experiences of all those concerned in further education and higher education for the hearing impaired.

National Association of Advisory Officers for Special Educational Needs Maryland, Prince's St, Tunbridge Wells, Kent TN2 4SL; E-mail diana.robinson@btclick.com; Tel 01892 534054; Fax 01892 534034
Hon Secretary Diana Roninson

The National Autistic Society 393 City Rd, London EC1V 1NG; Tel 020 7833 2299; Fax 020 7833 9666
Chief Executive Vernon Beauchamp
Pioneers the development of a range of educational and support services; runs schools and adult centres; works in partnership with local authorities; offers families and carers information, advice and support; works to improve awareness of autism; offers a diagnostic and assessment service; provides training and promotes research; produces a wide range of literature.

National Deaf Children's Society 15 Dufferin St, London EC1Y 8UR; URL www.ndcs.org.uk;
E-mail helpline@ndcs.org.uk; Tel (Freephone Helpline (voice and text)) 0808 800 8880; Fax 0207 251 5020
Chief Executive S. Daniels
Advice on welfare, education and equipment for deaf children and their families, and information on all aspects of childhood deafness. Consultancy and advice to SSD's on services to deaf users.
Opening hours: Mon–Fri 1000–1700.

Norwood Broadway Hse, 80–82 The Broadway, Stanmore, Greater London HA7 4HB; URL www.norwood.org.uk; E-mail norwood@norwood.org.uk; Tel 020 8954 4555; Fax 020 8420 6800
Patron Her Majesty The Queen
President Sir Trevor Chinn, CVO
Chair John Libson
Chief Executive Norma Brier
Norwood is one of the UK's leading Children and Family Services Care organisations. Each year, Norwood supports thousands of children, families and people with learning disabilities and social disadvantage. Its range of specialist support services includes Ravenswood Village, Children and Family Centres, Learning Disability Services, Special Education Services and Fostering and Adoption Services.

Norwood's expertise in the field of fostering and adoption was recognised in 2001, when the organisation was appointed to operate the Adoption Register for England and Wales, on behalf of the Government and the National Assembly for Wales. This is a stand-alone project entirely funded by the Government.
Wherever practical they offer services to everyone, irrespective of religion or ethnic background.

Nottinghamshire Deaf Society Institute for the Deaf, 22 Forest Rd West, Nottingham NG7 4EQ;
URL www.nottsdeaf.org; E-mail nds@nottsdeaf.org; Tel 0115 970 0516; Fax 0115 942 3096
Director Tim Hastings
Aims to promote the social welfare, educational and recreational facilities for deaf people in Nottingham and Nottinghamshire.

Outset Ltd Telemax Hse, 15 New Bedford Rd, Luton LU1 1SA; E-mail hq@outset.org.uk; Tel 0870 2000 001; Fax 0870 2000 110
Chief Executive Philip Bartey
Press and PR Officer M. Davies
Operates a network of innovative vocational training and employment projects in London, Luton, the North West, the West Midlands. Projects focus on the training and employment of people with disabilities in the area of information technology and computerised office skills.
Outset's Consultancy division offers organisations and employers a comprehensive range of information, advice, consultancy, research and development services on all aspects of employing and training people with disabilities. Also offers disability awareness training.

Paget Gorman Society (Paget Gorman Signed Speech) 2 Dowlands Bungalows, Dowlands La, Smallfield, Surrey RH6 9SD; URL www.pgss.org;
E-mail prup@compuserve.com; Tel 01342 842308
Chief Examiner Mrs P.R Philips

Phab Summit Hse, Wandle Rd, Croydon, Surrey CR0 1DF; URL www.phabengland.org.uk;
E-mail info@phabengland.org.uk;
Director (Operations) Philip Lockwood

Rathbone 4th Fl, Churchgate Hse, Oxford St, Manchester M1 6EU; E-mail info@rathbone-ci.co.uk; Tel 0161 236 5358; (Special Education Advice Line) 0800 917 6790; Fax 0161 238 6356
Chief Executive Julian Roberts (Acting)

Visual Impairment Centre for Teaching and Research University of Birmingham, School of Education, Edgbaston, Birmingham, West Midlands B15 2TT; URL www.education.bham.ac.uk/research/victar; E-mail victar-enquiries@bham.ac.uk; Tel 0121 414 6733
Secretary Mrs J. Whittaker

Royal College of Psychiatrists 17 Belgrave Sq, London SW1X 8PG; URL www.rcpsych.ac.uk;
E-mail infoservices@rcpsych.ac.uk; Tel 020 7235 2351; Fax 020 7245 1231
Dean Prof C. Katona

The Royal National Institute for Deaf People (RNID) 19–23 Featherstone St, London EC1Y 8SL; URL www.rnid.org.uk; E-mail informationline@rnid.org.uk; Tel 020 7296 8000; (Administration) 020 7296 8001; (Information Line) 0808 808 9000; (Information Line (voice)) 0808 808 0123; Fax 020 7296 8199
Chair David Livermore
The RNID represents the UK's 8.7 million deaf, deafened, hard of hearing and deaf blind people. The RNID's vision is for deaf people to exercise the right to full citizenship and to enjoy equal opportunities.
As a membership charity, it aims to achieve a radically better quality of life for deaf and hard of hearing people. It does this in the following ways: campaigning and lobbying to change laws and government policies; providing information and raising awareness of deafness, hearing loss and tinnitus; training courses and consultancy on deafness and disability; communication services including sign language interpreters; training of interpreters, lipspeakers

and speech-to-text operators; seeking lasting change in education for deaf children and young people; employment programmes to help deaf people into work; Typetalk, the national telephone relay service for deaf and hard of hearing people; residential and community services for deaf people with special needs; equipment and products for deaf and hard of hearing people; social, medical and technical research.

The RNID has offices in Manchester, Birmingham, Bath, Cardiff, London, Belfast and Glasgow. These offices provide information and access to the RNID's services.
RNID Helpline PO Box 16464, London EC1Y 8TT; URL www.rnid.org.uk; E-mail helpline@rnid.org.uk; Tel 0808 808 0123; Textphone 0808 808 9000
RNID Midlands 1st Fl, Monaco Hse, Birmingham, West Midlands B5 7AS; E-mail ruth.beer@rnid.org.uk; Tel 0121 622 2726; Fax 0121 622 5774; Textphone 0121 622 1191
RNID North National Computing Centre, Armstrong Hse, Manchester M1 7ED; E-mail jenny.harkison@rnid.org.uk; Tel 0161 242 2316; Fax 0161 242 2317; Answerphone 0161 242 2272
RNID Northern Ireland Wilton Hse, 5 College Sq North, Belfast BT1 6AR; E-mail nicola.hall@rnid.org.uk; Tel (Voice and text) 028 9032 9738; Fax 028 9031 2032
RNID Scotland 9 Clairmont Gdns, Glasgow G3 7LW; E-mail frances.mcdonnell@rnid.org.uk; Tel (Voice and text) 0141 353 2225; Fax 0141 331 2640
RNID South West 10 Stillhouse La, Bedminster, Bristol, BS3 4EB; E-mail libbie.shepherd@rnid.org.uk; Tel 0117 963 0147; (Voice and text) 0117 963 0146; Fax 0117 963 0142
RNID Wales Fl 3, 33–35 Cathedral Rd, Cardiff CF1 9HB; E-mail david.hart@rnid.org.uk; Tel (Voice) 029 2033 3034; Fax 029 2033 3035; Textphone 029 2033 3036

Royal National Institute of the Blind (RNIB) 105 Judd St, London WC1H 9NE; URL www.rnib.org.uk; E-mail helpline@rnib.org.uk; Tel (RNIB Helpline) 0845 766 9999; Fax 020 7388 2034
Director-General Prof I.W. Bruce, BSocSc, CIMGT
General enquiries; RNIB Resource Centre, London; benefit rights; education; employment and leisure enquiries; services for local societies; health, social and environmental services; reference library; advice on wills and legacies; enquiries on multiple disability; physiotherapy support. Office hours are: Mon–Thu 0900–1715 and Fri 0900–1700. RNIB is the leading charity working with people with sight problems throughout the UK. It has over 60 different services to help people at all stages of their lives. RNIB helps children and young people with sight problems get a good start in life by running a range of support services for them and their families. Its schools and colleges cater for all abilities. For people of working age, RNIB provides training, rehabilitation and help to find and keep jobs. They help older people by advising on social security and other benefits, and devising products to help with daily living. For those who need extra care, they run four residential care homes. For blind and partially-sighted people of all ages it runs the popular Talking Book Service; tape and braille services, holidays and information on everything from hobbies to health.
RNIB Customer Services
For: equipment and games sales and enquiries; transcription and library services; magazines; Braille, Moon, large print and tape; services and advice; Tel 0845 702 3153–for the price of a local call. E-mail cservices@rnib.org.uk.
RNIB Cymru Trident Crt, East Moors Rd, Cardiff CF24 5TD; URL www.rnib.org.uk; Tel 0292 045 0440; Fax 0292 044 9550
RNIB Northern Ireland 40 Linenhall St, Belfast BT2 8BA; URL rnib.org.uk; Tel 028 9032 9373; Fax 028 9043 9118
RNIB Peterborough PO Box 173, Peterborough PE2 6WS; URL www.rnib.org.uk; Tel 01733 370777; Fax 01733 371 555
RNIB Scotland Dunedin Hse, 25 Ravelston Terr, Edinburgh EH4 3TP; URL www.rnib.org.uk; Tel (Edinburgh) 0131 311 8500; (Glasgow) 0141 357 3525; Fax 0131 311 8529
RNIB Talking Book Service Mount Pleasant, Wembley, Greater London HA0 1RR; Tel 020 8903 6666; (Typetalk) 0800 959598; Fax 020 8903 6916

Customer Services Supervisor Ian Leask
Postal Library Service for blind and partially-sighted people, of any age, offering a wide range of professionally recorded books on special easy-to-use playback equipment. The Library is open every weekday from 0800–1700. There is an annual membership subscription (often paid by Local Authority). Information on current subscription rates may be obtained from RNIB Talking Book Service Customer Services Department. The service covers the whole of the British Isles.
RNIB Transcription Centre Northwest 67 High St, Tarporley, Cheshire CW6 0DP; E-mail tarporley@rnib.org.uk; Tel 01829 732115; Fax 01829 732408

SCOPE Cerebral Palsy Helpline, PO Box 833, Milton Keynes MK12 5NY; URL www.scope.org.uk; E-mail cphelpline@scope.org.uk; Tel 0808 800 3333

SENNAC (Special Educational Needs National Advisory Council) Dept. of Education, Liverpool University, Merseyside L69 3BX; Tel 0151 722 3819; Fax 0151 794 2512
Hon Secretary Ian Petrie

Sense, The National Deafblind and Rubella Association
11–13 Clifton Terr, Finsbury Pk, London N4 3SR; URL www.sense.org.uk; E-mail enquiries@sense.org.uk; Tel 020 7272 7774; Fax 020 7272 6012
Chief Executive Dr Tony Best
Campaigns for the needs of deafblind children and adults and other people with sensory impairments. Provides advice, support, information and services for them, their families and professionals in the field. Provides services including educational and advisory services for families with young deafblind children; a network of family self-help groups, long-term residential care in community group homes, holidays and respite care, services and support for people with Usher and older people with acquired deafblindness, communicator guides, and runs courses and conferences.

Skill: National Bureau for Students with Disabilities 4th Fl, Chapter Hse, 18–20 Crucifix La, London SE1 3JW; URL www.skill.org.uk; E-mail info@skill.org.uk; Tel (General (Voice/Minicom)) 020 7450 0620; (Tel Information Service (1330–1630 MonThurs)) 0800 328 5050; Fax 020 7450 0650; Minicom (Information Service) 0800 068 2422
Chief Executive Barbara Waters
Information and advice on post-16 education, training and employment for people with disabilities and learning difficulties. Publications and information booklets available.
Skill in Northern Ireland Unit 2, Jennymount Crt, North Derby St, Belfast BT15 3HN; E-mail admin@skillni.demon.co.uk; Tel (Voice and Minicom) 028 9028 8700; Fax 028 9028 7002
Director Alison Anderson
Director Maria Murray
Skill in Scotland Norton Pk, 57 Albion Rd, Edinburgh EH7 5QY; E-mail admin@skillscotland.org.uk; Tel 0131 475 2348 (and Minicom); Fax 0131 475 2397
Director John Ireson

Speechmark Publishing Ltd Telford Rd, Bicester, Oxfordshire OX26 4LQ; URL www.speechmark.net; E-mail info@speechmark.net; Tel 01869 244644; Fax 01869 320040
Publisher Ian Franklin
Marketing Manager Su Underhill
Sales Manager Sally Dickinson
Publishing for social workers, speech and occupational therapists, special education and elderly care. Wide range of books and resources for use in hospital, day centres and homes. Publishes colourcards and practical materials for social activities and groupwork.

United Kingdom Sports Association for People with Learning Disability (UKSAPLD) Ground Fl, Leroy Hse, 436 Essex Rd, London N1 3QP; E-mail office@uksapld.freeserve.co.uk; Tel 020 7354 1030; Fax 020 7354 2593
Chief Executive Geoff Smedley

Provides increased opportunities for people with learning disability to participate in sport and recreation; co-ordinates the work of member organisations; acts as a national forum; increases awareness of the value of physical activity to professionals involved with people with learning disability.

United Response 113–123 Upper Richmond Rd, Putney, London SW15 2TL; URL www.united-response.co.uk; E-mail info@united-response.co.uk; Tel 020 8246 5200; Fax 020 8780 9538
Chief Executive Su Sayer
National voluntary organisation providing accommodation, employment and support, day services, adult family placement and outreach domiciliary support to people with learning disabilities and mental health problems throughout England. Services in 75 locations. Excellent local management support in 15 area offices, strengthened by support from a central office.

Values into Action Oxford Hse, Derbyshire St, London E2 6HG; Tel 020 7729 5436; Fax 020 7729 7797
Director Jean Collins
Pressure group working for a better quality of life for people with learning difficulties through publications, newsletters, lobbying and research.

Volunteer Reading Help (VRH) Charity Hse, 14–15 Perseverance Works, 38 Kingsland Rd, London E2 8DD; URL www.vrh.org.uk; E-mail enquiry@vrh.clara.net; Tel 0870 7744 300
Chief Executive Heather Brandon
Volunteer Reading Help (VRH) enables children to become confident and literate for life and imparts a love of reading through the sustained support of trained volunteers. The children are chosen by the teachers. There are 43 branches. Charity funded by DfES, LEAs, schools, charitable trusts, companies and individuals.

Walsingham Community Homes Walsingham Hse, 1331–1337 High Rd, Whetstone, London N20 9HR; Tel 020 8343 5600; Fax 020 8446 9156
Chief Executive M. Snell
National Ecumenical charity offering residential care to people with learning disabilities, in small, locally based Christian run homes.

OTHER EDUCATIONAL ORGANISATIONS

Association of Education Committees Charitable Trust (AEC Trust) Midland Personal Financial Services, 70 Pall Mall, London SW1Y 5EY

Community Learning Scotland Rosebery Hse, 9 Haymarket Terr, Edinburgh EH12 5EZ; URL www.communitylearning.org; E-mail info@cls.dircon.co.uk; Tel 0131 313 2488; Fax 0131 313 6800
Chief Executive Charlie McConnell
CLS is the national community learning and development agency, acting as a focus and source of advice of Government on community learning and youth issues.

Educational Guidance Service for Adults 4th Fl, 40 Linenhall St, Belfast BT2 8BA; URL www.egsa.org.uk; E-mail guidance@egsa.dnet.co.uk; info@egsa.dnet.co.uk; Tel 028 9024 4274; Fax 028 9024 0892
Director Eileen Kelly
Provides independent guidance and information for adults interested in returning to or continuing in learning.

Heatherbank Museum of Social Work Trust Glasgow Caledonian University, City Campus, Cowcaddens Rd, Glasgow G4 0BA; URL www.lib.gcal.ac.uk/heatherbank; E-mail a.ramage@gcal.ac.uk; Tel 0141 331 8637; Fax 0141 331 3005

Curator Alastair Ramage
Aims to promote history of social work, social reform and social conditions. Reference library and picture library. Open Monday–Friday 0900–1630. Closed Saturday and Sunday and public holidays. Groups welcome by appointment.

Home Link Community Education Centre 16a Mildenhall Way, Childwall, Liverpool, Merseyside L25 2SR; Tel 0151 498 4881
Communication Education Worker Ruth Kennedy

National Campaign for Nursery Education BCM Box 6216, London WC1N 3XX
Chair Jo White
Works for increased provision of state nursery education by local authorities by public campaigning. Voluntary organisation with national executive (SAE for reply).

The National Society for Epilepsy (NSE) Chesham La, Chalfont St. Peter, Buckinghamshire SL9 0RJ; URL www.epilepsynse.org.uk; www.e-epilepsy.org.uk; Tel 01494 601300; (Helpline) 01494 601400; Fax 01494 871927
The National Society for Epilepsy (NSE) is the largest medical epilepsy charity in the UK, specialising in residential care, rehabilitation and resettlement, assessment and research, in addition to offering a comprehensive range of information and training services.
Residential care for people with complex epilepsy is currently provided in 15 individual care homes on a single site at Chalfont St. Peter, South Buckinghamshire. Increasing emphasis is placed on rehabilitation and resettlement programmes, including supported living and supported housing.
A state-of-the-art epilepsy assessment centre opened in January 2002. In addition to reviews of diagnosis and treatment, the centre provides facilities for assessment of individual's abilities for independent living. A unique feature is the direct link into the NSE's existing MRI unit which opened in 1996.
Training programmes are tailored to suit specific requirements of any audience and can be delivered on and off-site. Information services include a national helpline, an information website at www.epilepsynse.org.uk, a website for professional audiences at www.e-epilepsy.org.uk.and a community-based Epilepsy Information Network.
The NSE works in close collaboration with the National Hospital for Neurology and Neurosurgery and the Institute of Neurology in London.

The New Learning Centre 211 Sumatra Rd, London NW6 1PF; URL www.parenting-skills.co.uk; E-mail tnlc@dial.pipex.com; Tel 020 7794 0321; Fax 020 7431 8600
Skills for Success at School and Harmony in the Home
Director (Learning and Behaviour Specialist) Noel Janis-Norton
The New Learning Centre is a tutorial and guidance service offering: Parenting Skills Classes and workshops on 'Calmer, Easier, Happier Parenting'. Tapes and publications for parents, teachers and professionals who work with families. Classes for children: academic skills, learning strategies, motivating positive attitudes and behaviour.

Society for the Social History of Medicine (SSHM) Dept of History, University of Aberdeen, Meston Wlk, Old Aberdeen, Aberdeen AB24 3FX; URL www.sshm.org; Tel 01224 272456; Fax 01224 272203
Honorary Secretary Dr Lesley Diack
Promotes the study of all aspects of the social history of medicine, having reference to the patients as well as the practitioner and to health as well as disease.

Welsh Joint Education Committee 245 Western Ave, Cardiff CF5 2YX; URL www.wjec.co.uk; E-mail info@wjec.co.uk; Tel 029 2026 5000
Chief Executive Wyn G. Roberts
Association of local authorities in Wales. Examining board for GCSE and GCE A level and vocational examinations. Curriculum development for Welsh language.

Organisations Working with Diversity

15

- ■ **Commission for Equality and Human Rights**
- ■ **Racial Equality**
  Commission for Racial Equality
  Racial Equality Councils
  Other Racial Equality Organisations
- ■ **Sexual and Gender Matters**

Organisations Working with Diversity

Commission for Equality and Human Rights

In November 2003 the new single body replaces the Commission for Racial Equality, the Disability Rights Commission and the Equal Opportunities Commission. It will address discrimination on grounds of religion, sexuality, age, gender, race and disability.

Disability

see Chapter 25

Older Persons' Welfare

see Chapter 18

Racial Equality

Commission for Racial Equality

The Commission was set up under the Race Relations Act 1976 to help enforce the legislation and to promote equality of opportunity and good relations between people of different racial groups. The Commission has the general responsibility of advising the government on the working of the Act and is also a principle source of information and advice for the general public about the Act. The Commission has discretion to assist individuals who consider themselves victims of discrimination. The Race Relations (Amendment) Act 2000, which places a positive duty on public bodies to promote and deliver racial equality in the way they provide their services as employees, has enhanced the CRE's powers of enforcement.

Chair   Trevor Phillips
Chief Executive   Daniel Silverstone
Director (Human Resources and Organisational Development)   Maxine Ayton
Director (Legal Services)   Anthony Robinson
Director (London and South)   Clifford Stewart
Director (North)   Eric Seward
Director (Midlands)   Andrew Housley
Director (Communications and Information)   Vacancy
Director (Finance and Support Services)   Kevin Ross
Director (Strategy and Delivery)   Seamus Taylor
Director (Countries, Regions and Communities)   Dharmendra Kanani
Head (CRE Scotland)   Vacancy
Head (CRE Wales)   Vacancy

OTHER OFFICES

Birmingham
3rd Fl, Lancaster Hse, 67 Newhall St, Birmingham, West Midlands B3 1NA;
URL www.cre.gov.uk/about/offices_midlands.html; Tel 0121 710 3000; Fax 0121 710 3001

Leeds
Yorkshire Bank Chambers, 1st Fl, Infirmary St, Leeds, West Yorkshire LS1 2JP;
URL www.cre.gov.uk/about/offices_north.html; Tel 0113 389 3600; Fax 0113 389 3601

Manchester
Maybrook Hse, 5th Fl, 40 Blackfriars St, Manchester M3 2EG;
URL www.cre.gov.uk/about/offices_north.html; Tel 0161 835 5500; Fax 0161 835 5501

Scotland
The Tun, 12 Jacksons Entry, Edinburgh EH8 8PJ;
URL www.cre.gov.uk/scotland/index.html;
E-mail scotland@cre.gov.uk; Tel 0131 524 2000

Wales
3rd Fl, Capital Tower, Greyfriars Rd, Cardiff CF10 3AG;
URL www.cre.gov.uk/wales/index.html; Tel 029 2072 9200; Fax 029 2072 9220

Racial Equality Councils

Greater London

Barking and Dagenham Council for Racial Equality 18 North St, Barking, Essex IG11 8AW; Tel 020 8594 2773
Chair   Gurjeet K. Smith
Race Equality Officer   Sheila Delaney

Barnet Racial Equality Council 1 Friern Pk, North Finchley, London N12 9DE; E-mail barnet_rec@hotmail.com; Tel 020 8445 6051; Fax 020 8446 0445
Director   E. Magba-Kamara
Chair   Ashitey Ollennu

Bexley Council for Racial Equality Library Bldg, Walnut Tree Rd, Erith, Kent DA8 1RA;
E-mail bexleycre@hotmail.com; Tel 01322 340316; Fax 01322 330728
Director   J. Haider
Chair   K.S. Heer

Bromley Racial Equality Council 196 High St, Penge, London SE20 7QB; E-mail brec@onetel.net.uk; Tel 020 8776 8838

Camden BME Alliance 44 Hampstead Rd, London NW1 2PY; E-mail info@cbmea.org.uk; Tel 020 7388 6030; Fax 020 7388 6040

Racial Equality Partnership Croydon 4th Fl, Oakley Hse, 1a Katharine St, Croydon, Surrey CR0 1NX; Tel 020 8688 8122

Ealing Racial Equality Council 2 The Green, London W5 5DA; Tel 020 8579 3861; Fax 020 8566 5581
Director Godfrey Cremer
Chair Josephine De Souza

Enfield Racial Equality Council Community Hse, 311 Fore St, Edmonton, London N9 0PZ; Tel 020 8373 6271; 020 8373 6272; Fax 020 8373 6281
Director Chandra Bhatia
Chair Mr. C.M Anwar

Greenwich Council for Racial Equality 1st Fl, 1–4 Beresford Sq, Woolwich, London SE18 6BB;
URL www.gcre.supanet.co.uk; E-mail gcre@supanet.com; Tel 020 8855 7191; Fax 020 8317 3707
Director Makhan Singh Bajwa

Hackney Action for Racial Equality 62 Beechwood Rd, London E8 3DY; E-mail jappavoo@hare-62.fsnet.co.uk; Tel 020 7241 2244; Fax 020 7241 2280
Director Joanne Appavoo
Chair Andre Joseph

Haringey Racial Equality Council 14 Turnpike La, London N8 0PT; E-mail haringeyrec@aol.com; Tel 020 8889 6871; Fax 020 8889 6455
Director Derma Ioannou

Harrow Council for Racial Equality 64 Pinner Rd, Harrow, Greater London HA1 4HZ; E-mail hcre@hotmail.com; Tel 020 8427 6504; Fax 020 8863 0005
Director Prem Pawar

Hounslow Racial Equality Council Racial Equality Council, 45 Treaty Centre, Hounslow, Greater London TW3 1ES; E-mail hrec123@hotmail.com; Tel 020 8583 2525
Director Satvinder Buttar
Chair Julius Fletcher

Kingston Racial Equality Council Welcare Hse, 53 Canbury Park Rd, Kingston upon Thames, Surrey KT2 6LQ; Tel 020 8547 2332; Fax 020 8247 9515
Director John Azah

Lewisham Racial Equality Council 48 Lewisham High St, London SE13 5JH; Tel 020 8852 9808; Fax 020 8297 1975
Director Emmanuell Kusemamuriwo

Race Equality in Newham 478 Barking Rd, London E13 8QB; URL www.ncre.co.uk; E-mail valerie.brown@ncre.co.uk; Tel 020 7473 5349
Chair Anna Shillingford

Redbridge Racial Equality Council l, Methodist Church, Ilford, Essex IG1 2JZ; Tel 020 8514 0688
Director Michael Nunoo
Chair Mr G. Ali

Southwark Race and Equalities Council 3rd Fl, 36a Rye La, Peckham, London SE15 5BS; Tel 020 7635 8882; Fax 020 7635 9990
Director Surinder Dhillon
Chair Sonya Murison

Sutton Racial Equality Council 2 Grove Cottage, Grove Pk, High St, Carshalton, Surrey SM5 3BB;
URL www.suttonrec.org.uk;
E-mail admin@suttonrec.org.uk; Tel 020 8770 6199; Fax 020 8770 6198
Director Beau Fadahunsi
Chair Anne Shaw

Tower Hamlets Race Equality Council 2nd Fl, Attlee Hse, Toynbee Hall, 28 Commercial St, London E1 6LS; Tel 020 7377 8077; Fax 020 7377 5299
Director Dr C. Maprayil
Chair Mrs Taifur Rashid

Waltham Forest Race Equality Council 806 High Rd, Leyton, London E10 6AE; Tel 020 8279 2425; Fax 020 8279 2496
Director M.M. Khan
Race Equality Officer (CW) Kulvinder Dhaliwal
Race Equality Officer (G) Chris Arian

Wandsworth Racial Equality Council 107 Trinity Rd, London SW17 7SQ; Tel 020 8682 3201
Director Abdul Chaudhary

South East England

Aylesbury Vale Racial Equality Council Buckinghamshire County Council, Old County Hall, Aylesbury, Buckinghamshire HP20 1UA; E-mail avrec@ukonline.co.uk; Tel 01296 425334; Fax 01296 425334
Director Hari Wadhwa

Bedford Racial Equality Council 36 Mill St, Bedford, Bedfordshire MK40 3HD; URL www.bedfordrec.org; E-mail bedfordrec@aol.com; Tel 01234 340728; 01234 350459; Fax 01234 327487
Chair Kuldip Rupra
Chief Officer Wendy Anderson-Welsh

Essex Racial Equality Council Lower Ground Fl, Civic Centre, Victoria Ave, Southend on Sea, Southend SS2 6EP; E-mail erecsouthend@supanet.com; Tel 01702 333351; Fax 01702 333351
Director Clive Mardner

Essex Racial Equality Council (Basildon Office) Pitsea Area Housing Office, 13 Northlands Pavement, Pitsea, Essex SS13 3DU; Tel 01268 465066; 01268 465068; Fax 01268 465067

Ipswich and Suffolk Council for Racial Equality 46a St. Matthews St, Ipswich, Suffolk IP1 3EP;
URL www.iscre.org.uk; E-mail office@iscre.org.uk; Tel 01473 408111; Fax 01473 400084
Director Sam Budu

Medway Racial Equality Council Municipal Bldgs, Canterbury St, Gillingham, Kent ME7 5LA; E-mail mrec51@hotmail.com; Tel 01634 333880
Director Azhar Mahmood
Director Shila Jassal

Milton Keynes Racial Equality Council Acorn Hse, 377 Midsummer Blvd, Milton Keynes MK9 3HP; Tel 01908 606224; 01908 606828; Fax 01908 606828
Director Navrita Atwal
Providing policy development, community support, assistance to indiviuals and public education in matters of equal opportunities. Access to a high quality, but low cost, translation service is also available to both public and private sectors.

North West Kent Racial Equality Council Enterprise Hse, Dartford, Kent DA1 2AU;
URL www.nwk-rec@freeserve.co.uk;
E-mail dea_nwkrec@hotmail.com; Tel 01322 287251
Director Dev Sharma

Norwich and Norfolk Racial Equality Council Boardman Hse, Redwell St, Norwich, Norfolk NR2 4SL; Tel 01603 442211; Fax 01603 442210
Director Anne Matin
Administration Officer Dorothy Rex

Slough Race Equality Council Coleridge Hse, 5–7 Park St, Slough SL1 1PE;
E-mail sloughraceequalitycouncil.direct@btinternet.com; Tel 01753 691266; Fax 01753 517329
Director Sajidah Chaudhary

Watford Racial Equality Council 149 The Parade, Watford, Hertfordshire WD17 1RH; Tel 01923 237005; Fax 01923 240398
Director Shanaz Mirza

Woking Community Relations Forum The Maybury Centre, Board School Rd, Woking, Surrey GU21 5HD; Tel 01483 721444; 01483 750970; Fax 01483 750548
Manager (Woking Community Relations Forum) Ilham Abou-Rahme
Community English Scheme The Maybury Centre, Board School Rd, Woking, Surrey GU21 5HD; Tel 01483 721444
Co-ordinator Elaine McGinty

Woking Interpreting and Translating Service (WITS) The Maybury Centre, Board School Rd, Woking, Surrey GU21 5HD; Tel 01483 750970
Co-ordinator Nighat Jobeen

Wycombe and District Race Equality Council 272 Desborough Rd, High Wycombe, Buckinghamshire HP11 2QR; E-mail wycombe.rec@virgin.net; Tel 01494 527616; Fax 01494 448764
Director Ranjit Dheer

South West England

Banbury District Racial Equality Council 3 Borough Hse, Marlborough Rd, Banbury, Oxfordshire OX16 5TH; Tel 01295 264518

Bath and North East Somerset Racial Equality Council 5 Pierrepont Pl, Bath, Bath and North East Somerset BA1 1JX; URL www.bathnesrec.freeserve.co.uk; E-mail rec@bathnesrec.freeserve.co.uk; Tel 01225 442352; Fax 01225 329 879
Director R.D. Jones

Bristol Racial Equality Council Colston Hse, Colston St, Bristol BS1 5AQ; E-mail bristolrec@aol.com; Tel 0117 929 7899; Fax 0117 922 7713
Director Peter Courtier

Council for Racial Equality in Cornwall PO Box 89, Truro, Cornwall TR1 1ZD; Tel (Answer phone) 01637 852410
Chair Eileen Bortey

Devon and Exeter Racial Equality Council Wat Tyler Hse, King William St, Exeter, Devon EX4 6PD; E-mail derec@talk21.com; Tel 01392 422566; Fax 01392 422566

Oxfordshire Racial Equality Council The Old Court Hse, Floyds Row, St. Aldates, Oxford, Oxfordshire OX1 1SS; Tel 01865 791891; Fax 01865 726150
Director John Sailsman

Plymouth and District Racial Equality Council Virginia Hse, 40 Looe St, Plymouth PL4 0EB; E-mail plymouthrec@aol.com; Tel 01752 312640; Fax 01752 312643
Director Carola Salvordori
Chair Nigel Barnard (Acting)

Reading Council for Racial Equality 2–4 Silver St, Reading RG1 2ST; E-mail becky@rcre.co.uk; Tel 0118 986 8755; Fax 0118 931 4786
Director R. Sohpal

Swindon Racial Equality Council Faringdon Hse, 1 Faringdon Rd, Swindon SN1 5AR; E-mail swindonrec@srec.fnet.co.uk; Tel 01793 528545; Fax 01793 430524
Director J.S. Bassi
Charity No. 900449

Wiltshire Racial Equality Council Bridge Hse, Stallard St, Trowbridge, Wiltshire BA14 9AE; URL www.wiltsrec.org.uk; E-mail info@wiltsrec.org.uk; Tel 01225 766439; Fax 01225 766988
Director Dr Joe Sang

West Midlands

Coventry Racial Equality Council 3rd Fl, Market Chambers, Shelton Sq, Coventry, West Midlands CV1 1DG; Tel 024 7663 2236; Fax 024 7663 2441
Director P.K. Bedi
Chair Roger Manning

Dudley Racial Equality Council 16a Stone St, Dudley, West Midlands DY1 1NS; URL www.rewm.org/recdud.htm; E-mail dudley@racialequalitycouncil.freeserve.co.uk; Tel 01384 456166; Fax 01384 861010
Director Kenneth Rodney
Chair Martyn J. Copus

East Staffordshire Racial Equality Council Voluntary Services Centre, Union St, Burton-upon-Trent, Staffordshire DE14 1AA; E-mail a.kabal@btclick.com; Tel 01283 510456; Fax 01283 510456
Director A. Kabal

North Staffordshire Racial Equality Council Equality Hse, 75–77 Raymond St, Henley, Stoke-on-Trent ST1 4DP; URL www.nsrec.org.uk; E-mail nsrec@btconnect.com; Tel 01782 407930
SDVS Centre, 131–141 Northwalls, Stafford, Staffordshire ST16 3AD; E-mail diane.nsrec@ntlbusiness.com
Director Mohammed Tufail
Deputy Director Diane Dunley

Redditch Community Relations Council c/o All Womens Hse, Sandycroft, West Ave, Redditch, Worcestershire B98 7DH; Tel 01527 64252
Chair Madge Tillsley, MBE
Secretary Betty Passingham

Rugby Racial Equality Council 5 Pennington St, Rugby, Warwickshire CV21 2AZ; E-mail recrugby@aol.com; Tel 01788 576424
Race Equality Officer J. Hussain

Telford and Shropshire Race Equality Council 26 Church St, Wellington, Shropshire TF1 1DS; Tel 01952 240736
Director Joy Warren

Walsall Strategic Race Equality Partnership The Challenge Bldg, Hatherton Rd, Walsall, West Midlands WS1 1YB; Tel 01922 654705
Chief Officer Stuart Anthony

Warwick District Race Equality Council 10 Hamilton Terr, Leamington Spa, Warwickshire CV32 4LY; E-mail a.kumari@wdrec.co.uk; Tel 01926 457940
Director Anita Kumari

Wolverhampton Racial Equality Council 2 Clarence Rd, off Clarence St, Wolverhampton, West Midlands WV1 4HZ; Tel 01902 572046; Fax 01902 572050
Director Dr E.L. Emanuel
Chair Bhajan Devsi

Worcestershire Racial Equality Council Queen Elizabeth Hse, The Trinity, Worcester, Worcestershire WR1 2PW; URL www.rewm.org; E-mail worcesterrec@aol.com; Tel 01905 29283
Chief Executive Mohammed P. Aslam
Chair Cllr Dan Wickstead

East Midlands

Cambridge Ethnic Community Forum 62–64 Victoria Rd, Cambridge, Cambridgeshire CB4 3DU; URL cecf.co.uk; E-mail info@cecf.co.uk; Tel 01223 315877; Fax 01223 315877
Contact Bryn Hazell

Charnwood Racial Equality Council 66 Nottingham Rd, Loughborough, Leicestershire LE11 1EU; E-mail crec@btconnect.com; Tel 01509 261651; Fax 01509 267826
Executive Director A. Devani

Derby Racial Equality Council 31 Normanton Rd, Derby DE1 2GJ; E-mail derbyrec@btconnect.com; Tel 01332 372428; Fax 01332 206289
Director Tony Walsh

Northampton Racial Equality Council Doddridge Centre, 109 St. James Rd, Northampton, Northamptonshire NN5 5LD; Tel 01604 753837; Fax 01604 753837
Director Vacancy

Nottingham and District Racial Equality Council 67 Lower Parliament St, Nottingham NG1 3BB; Tel 0115 958 6515; Fax 0115 959 0624
Director Milton Crosdale

Peterborough Racial Equality Council 34 Fitzwilliam St, Peterborough PE1 2RX; E-mail prec@lineone.net; Tel 01733 341061; 01733 554630; Fax 01733 312080
Director Harmesh Lakhanpaul

15

Wellingborough and District Racial Equality Council c/o Victoria Centre, Palk Rd, Wellingborough, Northamptonshire NN8 1HT;
URL www.wellingboroughrec.org.uk;
E-mail racialeq@aol.com; Tel 01933 278000; Fax 01933 272409
Director Paul Crofts

Yorkshire and North East England

Darlington and Durham County Racial Equality Council CVS Bldg, Church Row, Darlington DL1 5QD;
URL www.darlingtonrec.org.uk;
E-mail ddcrec@care4free.net; Tel 01325 283900
Director Tony Lindsay (Acting)
Chair Mrs P. Poinen

Doncaster Racial Equality Council 1 Chequer Rd, Doncaster, South Yorkshire DN1 2AA; Tel 01302 730391

Kirklees Racial Equality Council 4th Fl, 10–18 John William St, Huddersfield, West Yorkshire HD1 1BA;
E-mail kirklees.rec@virgin.net; Tel 01484 540225/6;
Fax 01484 429828
Director Jamil Akhtar (Acting)
Chair Mr A.Y. Lunat, OBE

Leeds Racial Equality Council 116–118 Harrogate Rd, Chapel Allerton, Leeds, West Yorkshire LS7 4NY;
E-mail jr.leedsrec@cwcom.net; Tel 0113 268 6900; Fax 0113 268 5492
Director John Roberts
Chair A. Nasias

Rotherham Racial Equality Council Imperial Bldgs, 11–13 Corporation St, Rotherham, South Yorkshire S60 1NP;
Tel 01709 373065; Fax 01709 373065
Director Mohammed Almas Abbasi
Chair T. Johnson

Sheffield Racial Equality Council 3rd Fl, 9–11 Norfolk Row, Sheffield, South Yorkshire S1 2PA;
E-mail sheffieldrec@whsmithnet.co.uk; Tel 0114 203 9325;
Fax 0114 276 7732
Director Valerie Lawrence (Acting)

Tyne and Wear Racial Equality Council 4th Fl, MEA Hse, Ellison Pl, Newcastle Upon Tyne, Tyne and Wear NE1 8XS;
Tel 0191 232 7639; Fax 0191 232 5751
Director Simon Banks

North West England

Blackburn with Darwen Racial Equality Council St. John's Centre, St. John's Pl, Victoria St, Blackburn BB1 6DW;
E-mail chowdry@blackburnrecfsnet.co.uk; Tel 01254 261924; Fax 01254 697722
Director Abdul Hamid Chowdry

Bolton Racial Equality Council Office Unit 4 Bolton Market, Ashburner St, Bolton, Lancashire BL1 1TQ;
E-mail brec.staff@zoom.co.uk; Tel 01204 331002; Fax 01204 331046
Director J. Hall

Bury Racial Equality Council Oddfellows Hse, 94 Manchester Rd, Bury, Greater Manchester BL9 0TH;
Tel 0161 761 4533; Fax 0161 761 4422
Honorary Secretary Samuel Cohen

Cheshire, Halton and Warrington Racial Equality Council 2 Hunters Wlk, Canal St, Chester, Cheshire CH1 4EB;
URL www.chawrec.demon.co.uk;
E-mail office@chawrec.demon.co.uk; Tel 01244 400730;
Fax 01244 400722

Crewe Central Community Group Mill Hse, Brook St, Crewe, Cheshire CW2 7DE; Tel 01270 587429
Community Development Worker Heather Grant

Manchester Council for Community Relations 3rd Fl, Elisabeth Hse, St Peter's Sq, Manchester M2 3DF; Tel 0161 228 0710; Fax 0161 228 0745
Director N. Khan Moghal

Preston and Western Lancashire Racial Equality Council Town Hall Annexe, Birley St, Preston, Lancashire PR1 2RL;
URL www.prestonrec.org.uk;
E-mail admin@prestonrec.org.uk; Tel 01772 906422;
Fax 01772 906685
Chief Executive M.F. Desai

Rochdale Racial Equality Council Deen Hse, Station Rd, Rochdale, Lancashire OL11 1DS;
E-mail equality@rec-rochdale.co.uk; Tel 01706 352374;
Fax 01706 711259
Director Mohammad Naeem

Tameside Racial Equality Council 20 Warrington St, Ashton-under-Lyne, Greater Manchester OL6 6AS;
E-mail trec@btopenworld.com; Tel 0161 343 3399; Fax 0161 343 2424
Director A. Ali

Partnership for Racial Equality c/o Beechcroft, 67 Whetstone La, Wirral, Birkenhead, Merseyside CH41 2SW;
Tel 0151 666 2799; Fax 0151 666 2794
Project Co-ordinator Garrick Prayogg

Wales

Race Equality First, Cardiff The Friary Centre, Cardiff CF10 3FA; E-mail race.equality@enablis.co.uk; Tel 029 2022 4097; Fax 029 2022 9339
Director Jazz Iheanacho

South East Wales Racial Equality Council 124 Commercial St, Newport NP20 1LY; E-mail sewrec@ukonline.co.uk;
Tel 01633 250006; Fax 01633 264075

Swansea Bay Racial Equality Council Third Fl, Grove Hse, Grove Pl, Swansea SA1 5DF; Tel 01792 457035; Fax 01792 459374
Director Mr T. Idris

The Valleys Race Equality Council 33 Gelliwastad Rd, Pontypridd, Rhondda, Cynon, Taff CF37 2BN;
E-mail valrec@valrec.freeserve.co.uk; Tel 01443 401555;
Fax 01443 403111

Scotland

Central Scotland Racial Equality Council Community Education Centre, Annex West, Park St, Falkirk FK1 1RE;
E-mail csrecl@aol.com; Tel 01324 610950; Fax 01324 610955
Chief Executive M. McCrum
Racial Equality Officer Richard Pitts

Edinburgh and Lothians Racial Equality Council (ELREC) 14 Forth St, Edinburgh EH1 3LH;
E-mail elrec@lrec.demon.co.uk; Tel 0131 556 0441; Fax 0131 556 8577
Chief Executive Alastair Christie
Handling cases of racial harassment/discrimination: free advice and support; community development work; youth outreach; promoting equal opportunities and racial equality.

Fife Racial Equality Council 2 Acorn Crt, Glenrothes, Fife KY7 5LZ; E-mail fife.rec@btinternet.com; Tel 01592 610211;
Fax 01592 610591
Director Selma Rahman
Promoting equality of opportunity through casework; community development; policy development; public education.

Grampian Racial Equality Council 9a Little Belmont St, Aberdeen AB10 1JG; URL www.grec.co.uk;
E-mail info@grec.co.uk; Tel 01224 625895
Director Barney Crockett

Tayside Racial Equality Council Arthurstone Library, 5 Arthurstone Terr, Dundee DD4 6RT;
URL www.sol.co.uk./t/erec/; E-mail erec@sol.co.uk;
Tel 01382 454595; Fax 01382 454564
Chief Officer John White

Other Racial Equality Organisations

Amnesty International, United Kingdom 99–119 Rosebery Ave, London EC1R 4RE; URL www.amnesty.org.uk; Tel 020 7814 6200; Fax 020 7833 1510

Catholic Association for Racial Justice (CARJ) 9 Henry Rd, Manor Hse, London N4 2LH; Tel 020 8802 8080; Fax 020 8211 0828
Chair Haynes Baptiste
Director Stephen Corriette
Membership organisation of black and white Catholics working for racial justice in church and society, locally, regionally and nationally; educational, voluntary, charitable. Publications programme; youth initiative; promoting annual Racial Justice Sunday in Catholic community.

CITAS (Community Interpreting Translation and Access Service) Pailingswick Hse, 241 King St, London W6 9LP; E-mail interpreting@citas.org.uk; Tel 020 8748 4187; Fax 020 8741 4127
Co-ordinator Malika Hammidou

Committee for United Kingdom Citizenship PO Box 138, London WC1B 3RW; Tel 020 7580 0897; Fax 020 7436 2418
Secretary Praful Patel

Council of Christians and Jews 5th Fl, Camelford Hse, 87–89 Albert Embankment, London SE1 7TP; URL www.ccj.org.uk; E-mail cjrelations@ccj.org.uk; Tel 020 7820 0090; Fax 020 7820 0504
Director Sr Margaret Shepherd
Education Officer Jane Clements
Education Advisor Rev Jonathan Gorsky
The Council of Christians and Jews brings together the Christian and Jewish communities in this country in a common effort to fight the evils of prejudice, intolerance and discrimination between people of different religions, races and colours, and to work for the betterment of human relations, based on mutual respect, understanding and goodwill.

Ghana Union London 431 Caledonian Rd, London N7 2LT; Tel 020 7700 5634; Fax 020 7700 3225
Chair Ima Plahar

The Gypsy Council for Education, Culture, Welfare and Civil Rights European and UK Central Office, 8 Hall Rd, Aveley, Essex RM15 4HD; URL www.thegypsycouncil.org; E-mail thegypsycouncil@btinternet.com; Tel 01708 868986; Fax 01708 868986
Works for all issues and overseas. Send an sae for information.

The Gypsy Council (Romani Kris) Greenacres Caravan Pk, Hapsford, Frodsham, Cheshire WA6 0JS; Tel 01928 723138; Fax 01928 723138
1996 (all-Gypsy organisation since 1973)
President Hughie Smith
Aims
To obtain adequate accommodation for Gypsies as defined in legislation on good-facility, well-managed permanent residential and transit sites, an integrated State school education for Gypsy children and access to good health care and education for Gypsy families.
Type of work done
Liaison with local authorities on all issues relating to Gypsy site provision and management, obtaining stopping time for Gypsies forced to camp illegally by the national shortfall of official sites; supporting private Gypsy site initiatives; attending conferences as speakers and publishing reports on subjects of relevance to the Gypsy community (price lists available on application).

Hindu Centre 39 Grafton Terr, off Malden Rd, London NW5 4JA; Tel 020 7485 8200

Immigration Advisory Service County Hse, 2nd Fl, 190 Great Dover St, London SE1 4YB; URL www.iasuk.org; E-mail advice@iasuk.org; Tel 020 7357 6917; (24 hour helpline) 020 7378 9191; Fax 020 7378 0665
Chief Executive K. Best

Indian Workers' Association 112a The Green, Southall, Greater London UB2 4BQ; Tel 020 8574 7283; 020 8574 6019; Fax 020 8574 4636
Chair P.S. Khabra, MP
Secretary J.S. Khangura
Research, advocacy, publishing and educational charity whose principal aim is to secure justice for minority (and non-dominant majority) groups suffering discrimination.

Indo-British Cultural Exchange Limited PO Box 138, London WC1B 3RW; URL www.surdhwani.org.uk; Tel 020 7580 0897; Fax 020 7436 2418
Voluntary organisation, activities include arts, theatre, cultural.

Institute of Race Relations 2–6 Leeke St, London WC1X 9HS; URL www.irr.org.uk; Tel 020 7837 0041; Fax 020 7278 0623
Director A. Sivanandan
Secretary J. Bourne

International Voluntary Service Old Hall, East Bergholt, Colchester, Essex CO7 6TQ; E-mail ivsni@gn.apc.org; Tel 01206 298215; Fax 01206 299043
Regional Co-ordinator Steve Davies
Organises voluntary work in Britain and volunteer exchange worldwide.

Regional Offices

Northern Region Office
Castlehill Hse, 21 Otley Rd, Leeds, West Yorkshire LS6 2AA; Tel 0113 230 4600; Fax 0113 230 4610
Regional Co-ordinator Jenni Danson

Southern Region Office
Old Hall, East Bergholt, Colchester, Essex CO7 6TQ
Regional Co-ordinator Steve Davies

Scotland Office
7 Upper Bow, Edinburgh EH1 3JN; Tel 0131 226 6722; Fax 0131 226 6723
Regional Co-ordinator Neil Harrower

International Voluntary Service Northern Ireland 122 Great Victoria St, Belfast BT2 7BG; E-mail placements@ivsni.co.uk; Tel 028 9023 8147; Fax 028 9024 4356
Offers voluntary work opportunities, mostly for two to three weeks at a time, both in Northern Ireland and throughout Europe and North America.

Joint Council for the Welfare of Immigrants 115 Old St, London EC1V 9RT; URL www.jcwi.org.uk; E-mail info@jcwi.org.uk; Tel (Administration) 020 7251 8708; (Advice) 020 7251 8706; Fax 020 7251 8707
Chief Executive Habib Rahman

London Youth Matters (LYM) Pastures Youth Centre, Davies La, London E11 3DR; E-mail londonyouth@compuserve.com; Tel (and minicom) 020 8558 1233; Fax 020 8558 7878
Chair B. Donoghue
Co-ordinator B. Slavin
LYM is the umbrella body for the voluntary sector of the youth service in London. Its aim is to represent, support, maintain and raise the profile of the youth services and young people in London. LYM traces its origins back to 1945 when the London and Middlesex Standing Conference of Youth Organisations was formed under the aegis of the London Council for Social Service (now London Voluntary Service Council). LYM draws its membership from the major voluntary sector youth organisations in London together with local bodies in most of the London boroughs. LYM also has strong links with the local authority youth services.

National Association of Asian Probation Staff (NAAPS) 4th Fl, Glen Hse, 200 Tottenham Court Rd, London W1T 7PL; E-mail shamin.khan@london.probation.gsx.gov.uk; Tel 020 7323 7087; 020 7323 7088; Fax 020 7323 7097
Chair and NAADS National Administrator Shamin Khan; Mobile 07973 047330
Vice-Chair Inderbir Kaur; Tel 021 248 6381
Project Manager Mohd Dhullah; Tel 01332 553572

Co-ordinator (Training) Mansinder Purewal; Tel 0121 248 6230
Co-ordinator (YOT) Mohammed Mustafa; Tel 01733 746540
Co-ordinator (Yorkshire/Humberside) Asra Sharif; Tel 01274 704500
Co-ordinator (North) Mohammed Suleman; Tel 0191 240 7348
Co-ordinator (West Midlands) Narinder Barhra Karmet; Tel 0121 248 6400
Co-ordinator (Midlands) Gurden Singh; Tel 0115 966 9306
Co-ordinator (East of England) Yasser Al-Kilani; Tel 01268 412241
Co-ordinator (South West) Julianna Forrester; Tel 01793 536612
Co-ordinator (London) Ahmed Moulvi; Tel 020 8262 6937
Co-ordinator (London) Amrita Singh; Tel 020 8570 0626
Treasurer Cookie Oliver; Tel 01923 240144
Membership Secretary Asra Sharif; Tel 01274 704500; Mobile 07967 683384
Encourages and maintains a support group of members for promoting Asian perspective on professional issues. Initiates and campaigns for changes within the criminal justice system to adjust the imbalance of disadvantages suffered by all ethnic minority groups.

National Association of Teachers of Travellers (NATT) The Cricket Road Centre, Cricket Rd, Oxford, Oxfordshire OX4 3DW; URL www.natt.org.uk; E-mail traved@a-s-e-t.demon.co.uk; Tel 01865 428089; Fax 01865 428089
President Lucy Beckett
Professional voluntary association organised and run by teachers working with travelling children in support services and mainstream schools.

REU Unit 35, King's Exchange, Tileyard Rd, London N7 9AH; URL www.reu.org.uk; Tel 020 7619 6220; Fax 020 7619 6230
The indpendent national agency providing race equality consultancy, research, development and training in social care.

ROTA (Race on the Agenda) 356 Holloway Rd, London N7 6PA; URL www.rota.org.uk; E-mail rota@rota.org.uk; Tel 020 7700 8135; Fax 020 7700 8192
Director Marina Ahmad
Race on the Agenda (ROTA) is the policy, information and research organisation for the Black voluntary sector in London. ROTA works towards the elimination of racial discrimination and promotes equality of opportunity. We achieve our aims through providing research information to aid the Black and Minority Ethnic voluntary sector to be informed and to maximise the involvement of their respective communities.

Runnymede Trust 133 Aldersgate St, London EC1A 4JA; Tel 020 7600 9666
Chief Executive Sukhvinder Stubbs

Shri Swaminarayan Mandir 105–119 Brentfield Rd, Neasden, London NW10 8LD; URL www.swaminaravan.org; www.mandir.org; E-mail shm@swaminaravan-baps.org.uk; Tel 020 8965 2651; Fax 020 8965 6313

Turkish Cypriot Cultural Association (TCCA) 14a Graham Rd, London E8 1BZ; E-mail turkcultural@btinternet.com; Tel 020 7249 7410; Fax 020 7241 5643
Chair Zeka Alsancak, M.B.E
Co-ordinator Sermet Mustafa
Help to the Turkish community with their educational, social, cultural and mental health problems; care for unmarried mothers, children, youth and elderly; advice, counselling, interpreting; teaching Turkish and English; organising excursions, lectures, and cultural activities.

UN High Commissioner for Refugees 21st Fl, Millbank Tower, 21–24 Millbank, London SW1P 4QP; E-mail gbrlo@unhcr.ch; Tel 020 7828 9191; Fax 020 7630 5349
Representative for the United Kingdom and Ireland A. Dawson-Shepherd
Deputy Representative M. Kingsley-Nyinah

United Nations Association (UNA) 3 Whitehall Crt, London SW1A 2EL; URL www.una-uk.org; E-mail info@una-uk.org; Tel 020 7930 2931; Fax 020 7930 5893
Director M. Harper
The United Nations Association (UNA) exists to make people of all ages in the UK more aware of the work and potential of the United Nations in global affairs. UNA campaigns to seek a fuller commitment by the British government to the principles and machinery of the UN. Its particular interests include the UN and conflict interests; sustainable development and the global environment; human rights and refugee issues. It runs model UN events as a contribution to global citizenship education.

West Midlands Consortium Education Service for Travelling Children The Graiseley Centre, Pool St, Wolverhampton, West Midlands WV2 4NE; E-mail wmcestc@dial.pipex.com; Tel 01902 714646; Fax 01902 714202
Co-ordinator Pat Holmes
Education and field welfare support for Gypsy and traveller children and families.

Sexual and Gender Matters

Beaumont Society 27 Old Gloucester St, London WC1N 3XX; URL www.beaumontsociety.org.uk; Tel (Enquiries) 01582 412220
An organisation run for transvestites, transsexuals and their special needs. All enquiries treated in strictest confidence. Information Line (recorded message) Tel 01582 412220; Wives and Partners Helplines (South) 01223 441246; (Central) 01684 578281; (Scotland) 01389 380389

The Beaumont Trust BM Charity, London WC1N 3XX; Tel 07000 287878
Helps and supports transsexuals and transvestites, their wives, partners, families, friends and professional advisers. Educates the public about their conditions. Registered charity.

The Gender Trust PO Box 3192, Brighton, Brighton and Hove BN1 3WR; URL www.gendertrust.com; E-mail gentrust@mistral.co.uk; Tel (Administration) 01273 234024
Registered charity helping specifically transsexuals and those caring for them with information, counselling, and referral. Membership organisation. Provides a quarterly journal Guide to Transsexualism. Speakers for conferences and conferences organised. Membership organisation including Associates of the Trust. Helpline. Regional and local contacts.

London Lesbian and Gay Switchboard PO Box 7324, London N1 9QS; URL www.llgs.org.uk; www.queeny.org.uk; Tel 020 7837 7324
24 hour telephone information and advice service, legal, safer sex and HIV/Aids referrals for lesbians and gay men.

Lothian Gay and Lesbian Switchboard Ltd PO Box 169, Edinburgh EH3 6S9; E-mail lgls.org; Tel (Administration line) 0131 556 8997; (Helpline (19302200 every evening) 0131 556 4049; (Lothian Lesbian Line (Mon and Thurs evenings 1930–2200) 0131 557 0751
Provides education, information, support and advice for gay men and lesbians on sexuality, relationships, safer sex and sexual health.

Outright Scotland PO Box 23253, Edinburgh EH1 3XD; URL www.outright-scotland.org.uk
Secretary Andrew Wilson
Working for lesbian, gay, bisexual and transgender equality in Scotland.

Women's Organisations

see Chapter 16

Advice and Counselling

16

- Citizens Advice
- Citizens Advice Bureaux
- Consumer Advice Centres
- Independent Advice Centres
- Marriage Guidance
- Genetic Advisory Centres
- Registered Pregnancy Advice Bureaux
- Samaritans
- Bereavement
- Drug and Alcohol Abuse
- Family Planning, Aids and Sexually-transmitted Diseases Counselling
- Psychotherapy
- Women's Organisations
- Youth Counselling Services
- Other Organisations

Advice and Counselling

For further information on the British Association for Counselling see Chapter 25.
This chapter, on advisory and counselling services, has been created in order to bring together details of services that are available to the general public in specific circumstances. Apart from drug and alcohol abuse, women's organisations and youth counselling, the chapter does not cover organisations which set out to assist specific groups, e.g. disabled persons, with the general problems they face. Help for these sorts of need is described elsewhere in the book. Some of the organisations listed here deal mainly with one type of problem – marriage and the family, or consumer protection, for instance. In these cases, advice is available to anyone who needs it. The main generalist organisation is the Citizens' Advice Bureau service. There are bureaux covering all parts of the UK and their advice and practical assistance are free and confidential and cover every conceivable subject. They are therefore a useful resource for anyone with a problem or counselling need for which a specialist organisation does not exist locally. The British Association for Counselling (see Chapter 22), provides support for counsellors and opportunities for their personal growth, education and training. It is also a source of information and advice concerning both counsellors and counselling. Also, at national and international levels it represents counselling.

Citizens Advice

Formerly National Association of Citizens Advice Bureaux.
Myddelton Hse, 115–123 Pentonville Rd, London N1 9LZ; Tel 020 7833 2181; Fax 020 7833 4371
Chief Executive David Harker
The Citizens Advice Bureaux Service (over 1054 CAB outlets in the UK) is valued as a confidential and impartial advisory service offered by a voluntary organisation, which covers the widest possible range of subjects, and is sensitive to emerging social trends and defects in legislation. Citizens Advice employs a central office staff and regional officers to support the Service in the development of new bureaux, training, registration and the maintenance of standards. Central Office also produces the main information system, updated monthly. Additionally, the information staff provide a telephone and postal consultancy service to bureaux. Last year, the bureaux dealt with over six million new enquiries and this cumulative experience is often used by Government and other committees of enquiry. Central office has no facilities for advice-giving to the general public, who should be referred to their local bureau.

Area Offices and Officers – England, Wales and Northern Ireland

East Region

Cambridge Office
8 Wellington Mews, Wellington St, Cambridge, Cambridgeshire CB1 1HW; Tel 01223 356322; Fax 01223 467346

Luton Office
Raglan Hse, 28–34 Alma St, Luton LU1 2PL; Tel 01582 480377; Fax 01582 487550

London Region

London Office
136–144 City Rd, London EC1V 2QN; Tel 020 7549 0800; Fax 020 7253 4341
Regional Director (London Region) Bobbie Pote

Midlands Region

Birmingham Office
5th Fl, Norfolk Hse, Birmingham, West Midlands B5 4LJ; Tel 0121 643 3456; Fax 0121 633 3881

Nottingham Office
1st Fl, Blenheim Crt, Nottingham NG1 3JJ; Tel 0115 941 8315; Fax 0115 950 5862
Regional Director (Midlands) C. Bates

North Region

North East
3rd Fl, Block D, Portland Hse, New Bridge St, Newcastle upon Tyne, Tyne and Wear NE1 8AL; Tel 0191 233 0700; Fax 0191 233 0722
Regional Director (North) D. Shaw

Yorkshire and Humberside
5th Fl, Wade Hse, Leeds, West Yorkshire LS2 8NG; Tel 0113 283 1655; Fax 0113 283 1658

North West Region

Liverpool Office
Suite 193, 1st Fl, Liverpool, Merseyside L2 0XQ; Tel 0151 282 9000; Fax 0151 282 9010

South Region

Chandlers Ford Office
Units 1 and 2, The Anchor Business Centre, Eastleigh,
Hampshire SO53 4UB; Tel 023 8027 3355; Fax 023 8025
5130
Regional Director (South) O. Barnard

Tunbridge Wells Office
80–82 St. John's Rd, Tunbridge Wells, Kent TN4 9PH;
Tel 01892 539275; Fax 01892 512662

West Region

Bristol Office
10th Fl, Tower Hse, Bristol BS1 3BN; Tel 0117 930 0037;
Fax 0117 930 0038
Regional Director (West) P. Woods

Exeter Office
Suite 5, 2nd Fl, Exeter, Devon EX4 3BH; Tel 01392 425517;
Fax 01392 438690

Wales

Aberystwyth Office
Y Felin, Mill St, Aberystwyth, Ceredigion SY23 1JB;
Tel 01970 626105; Fax 01970 625377

Cardiff Office
Ground Fl, Quebec Hse, Cardiff CF1 9AB; Tel 029 2034
0043; Fax 029 2034 1541

St. Asaph/Llanelwy Office
7 St. Asaph Bus Pk, Glascoed Rd, St. Asaph, Denbighshire
LL17 0LJ; Tel 01745 586400; Fax 01745 585554

Citizens Advice Bureaux

England

Bath and North East Somerset

Bath Citizens Advice Bureau 2 Edgar Bldgs, Bath, Bath and
North East Somerset BA1 2EE; Tel 01225 463333; Fax 01225
481667

North East Somerset Citizens Advice Bureau Town Hall,
The Island, Bath, Bath and North East Somerset BA3 2HQ;
Tel 01761 418599; Fax 01761 410853

Bedfordshire

Bedford and District Citizens Advice Bureau 38 Mill St,
Bedford, Bedfordshire MK40 3HD; Tel 01234 354384;
Fax 01234 210065

Dunstable Citizens Advice Bureau Grove Hse, 76 High
Street North, Dunstable, Bedfordshire LU6 1NF; Tel 01582
661384; Fax 01582 665629

Leighton Linslade Citizens Advice Bureau Bossard Hse,
West St, Leighton Buzzard, Bedfordshire LU7 7DA;
Tel 01525 373878; Fax 01525 371161

Luton Citizens Advice Bureau 24–26 King St, Luton,
Bedfordshire LU1 2DP; Tel 01582 731616; Fax 01582 487705

Mid Bedfordshire (Ampthill) Citizens Advice Bureau 10
Bedford St, Ampthill, Bedfordshire MK45 2NB; Tel 01525
404511; Fax 01525 402742

Blackburn

Blackburn with Darwen Citizens Advice Bureau St. John's
Centre, Victoria St, Blackburn BB1 6DW; Tel 01254 671211;
Fax 01254 675934

Blackpool

Blackpool Citizens Advice Bureau 6–10 Whitegate Dr,
Devonshire Sq, Blackpool, Lancashire FY3 9AQ; Tel 01253
308400; Fax 01253 308425

Bracknell Forest

Bracknell Citizens Advice Bureau 42 The Broadway,
Bracknell, Bracknell Forest RG12 1AG; Tel 08450 505161;
Fax 01344 867171

Bristol

Bristol Citizens Advice Bureau 12 Broad St, Bristol BS1 2HL;
Tel 0117 921 1664; Fax 0117 934 9829

Buckinghamshire

Amersham Citizens Advice Bureau 47 Hill Ave, Amersham,
Buckinghamshire HP6 5BX; Tel 01494 433262; Fax 01494
431815

Aylesbury Citizens Advice Bureau 2 Pebble La, Aylesbury,
Buckinghamshire HP20 2JH; Tel 0870 126 4056; Fax 01296
338075

Bletchley Citizens Advice Bureau 3–5 The Concourse,
Brunel Centre, Milton Keynes MK2 2ES; Tel 01908 378569;
Fax 01908 378272

Buckingham, Winslow and District Citizens Advice Bureau
Whealdon Hse, Market Hill, Buckingham,
Buckinghamshire MK18 1JX;
E-mail buckinghamcab@dial.pipex.com; Tel 01280 816707;
Fax 01280 824494

Chesham Citizens Advice Bureau 5 Market Sq, Chesham,
Buckinghamshire HP5 1HG; Tel 01494 784279; 01494
792932; Fax 01494 791391

High Wycombe and District Citizens Advice Bureau 8 Easton
St, High Wycombe, Buckinghamshire HP11 1NP; Tel 08701
264045; Fax 01494 536437

Milton Keynes Central Citizens Advice Bureau Acorn Hse,
361 Midsummer Blvd, Milton Keynes MK9 3HP; Tel 08701
264050; Fax 01908 692686

Cambridgeshire

Cambridge Citizens Advice Bureau 72–74 Newmarket Rd,
Cambridge, Cambridgeshire CB5 8DZ; Tel 01223 361418;
Fax 01223 315137

Ely Citizens Advice Bureau 70 Market St, Ely,
Cambridgeshire CB7 4LS; Tel 0870 7510 933

Fenland Citizens Advice Bureau 12 Church Mews, Wisbech,
Cambridgeshire PE13 1HL; Tel 01945 464367; Fax 01945
475658

Huntingdon Citizens Advice Bureau 6 All Saints Passage,
Huntingdon, Cambridgeshire PE39 3LE; Tel 01480 388900;
Fax 01480 388903

St. Neots Citizens Advice Bureau 28 New St, St. Neots,
Cambridgeshire PE19 1AJ; Tel 01480 388905; Fax 01480
388907

Whitemoor Citizens Advice Bureau Visitors' Centre,
Longhill Rd, March, Cambridgeshire PE15 0PR; Tel 01354
660653; Fax 01354 661909

Channel Islands

Guernsey Citizens Advice Bureau Bridge Ave, The Bridge,
St. Sampsons, Guernsey GY2 4QS; Tel 01481 242266

Jersey Citizens Advice Bureau The Annexe, St. Paul's
Community Centre, St. Helier, Jersey JE2 3WP;
URL www.cab.org.je; E-mail advice@cab.org.je; Tel 01534
724942; Fax 01534 617508

Cheshire

Altrincham Citizens Advice Bureau The Town Hall, Market St, Altrincham, Greater Manchester WA14 1PG; Tel 0870 126 4094; Fax 0161 912 5793

Birchwood Citizens Advice Bureau 46 Benson Rd, Birchwood, Warrington WA3 7PW; Tel 01925 824952; Fax 01925 831861

Cheadle and Gatley Citizens Advice Bureau Cheadle Library, Ashfield Rd, Cheadle, Cheshire SK8 1BB; Tel 0161 428 3153; Fax 0161 428 6691

Chester Citizens Advice Bureau Folliott Hse, Northgate St, Chester, Cheshire CH1 2HQ; Tel 0870 126 4119; Fax 01244 315726

Crewe Citizens Advice Bureau 50 Victoria St, Crewe, Cheshire CW1 2JL; Tel 01270 212401; Fax 01270 251158

Ellesmere Port Citizens Advice Bureau 10 Shrewsbury Rd, Ellesmere Port, Cheshire CH65 8AP; Tel 0151 355 3428; Fax 0151 357 3853

Lymm Citizens Advice Bureau Whitbarrow Rd, Lymm, Cheshire WA13 9AG; Tel 01925 753247; Fax 01925 756896

Macclesfield Citizens Advice Bureau Sunderland Hse, Sunderland St, Macclesfield, Cheshire SK11 6JF; Tel 01625 426303; Fax 01625 503108

Marple Citizens Advice Bureau Council Ofices, Memorial Pk, Marple, Stockport, Cheshire SK6 6BB; Tel 0161 427 6023; Fax 0161 427 1716

Nantwich Citizens Advice Bureau The Gables, Beam St, Nantwich, Cheshire CW5 5NF; Tel 01270 625565; Fax 01270 629079

Northwich Citizens Advice Bureau 48 Chester Way, Northwich, Cheshire CW9 5JA; Tel 01606 42393; Fax 01606 331850

Runcorn Citizens Advice Bureau Ground Fl, Grosvenor Hse, Runcorn, Cheshire WA7 2ER; Tel 01928 710000; Fax 01928 719449

Sale Citizens Advice Bureau 73 Chapel Rd, Sale, Cheshire M33 1EG; Tel 0870 126 4904; Fax 0161 976 3985

Stockport Citizens Advice Bureau 39 Greek St, Stockport, Cheshire SK3 8AX; Tel 08701 2040 40; Fax 0161 480 4447

Widnes Citizens Advice Bureau Unit 6, Victoria Square Shopping Centre, Widnes, Cheshire WA8 6DJ; Tel 0151 495 3207; Fax 0151 420 5802

Winsford Citizens Advice Bureau The Brunner Guildhall, High St, Winsford, Cheshire CW7 2AU; Tel 01606 594497; Fax 01606 555905

Cleveland

Hartlepool Citizens Advice Bureau 87 Park Rd, Hartlepool TS26 9HP; URL www.hartcab.demon.co.uk; E-mail cab@hartcab.demon.co.uk; Tel 01429 273223; Fax 01429 868803

Middlesbrough Citizens Advice Bureau 3 Bolckow St, Middlesbrough TS1 1TH; Tel 01642 864455; Fax 01642 802312

Cornwall

Bodmin Citizens Advice Bureau CAB Offices, Shire Hall, Bodmin, Cornwall PL31 2DQ; Tel 01208 74835

Bude, Holsworthy and District Citizens Advice Bureau Neetside, Bude, Cornwall EX23 8LB; Tel 01288 354531

Camborne (Kerrier) Citizens Advice Bureau The Community Centre, South Terr, Camborne, Cornwall TR14 8SU; Tel 0845 120 3702

Falmouth Citizens Advice Bureau Mulberry Passage, Market Strand, Falmouth, Cornwall TR11 3DB; Tel 01326 313340

Liskeard Citizens Advice Bureau Duchy Hse, 21 Dean St, Liskeard, Cornwall PL14 4AB; Tel 01579 344444; Fax 01579 348338

Newquay Citizens Advice Bureau The Public Library, Marcus Hill, Newquay, Cornwall TR7 1BD; Tel 01637 871645; Fax 01637 851440

Penzance (Penwith) Citizens Advice Bureau The Guildhall, St. John's Rd, Penzance, Cornwall TR18 2QR; Tel 01736 365438

St. Austell Citizens Advice Bureau 28 Market Hill, St. Austell, Cornwall PL25 5QA; Tel 01726 63131; Fax 01726 66181

Saltash Citizens Advice Bureau Ground Fl, 18 Belle Vue Rd, Saltash, Cornwall PL12 6ES; Tel 01752 845515; Fax 01752 849774

Truro Citizens Advice Bureau The Library, Union Pl, Truro, Cornwall TR1 1EP; Tel 01872 278960; Fax 01872 263481

Cumbria

Barrow-in-Furness Citizens Advice Bureau Ramsden Hall, Abbey Rd, Barrow-in-Furness, Cumbria LA14 5QW; Tel 0870 126 4016; Fax 01229 830379

Carlisle Citizens Advice Bureau Carlyle's Crt, Mary's Gate, Carlisle, Cumbria CA3 8RN; E-mail carlisle.cab@gtnet.gov.uk; Tel 01228 633900

Cumbria Rural Citizens Advice Bureau The Library, Ellerthwaite Rd, Windermere, Cumbria LA23 2AJ; Tel 015394 46464; Fax 015394 46505

Eden Citizens Advice Bureau 2 Sandgate, Penrith, Cumbria CA11 7TP; Tel 01768 863564; Fax 01768 899070

Kendal Citizens Advice Bureau Blackhall Rd, Kendal, Cumbria LA9 4BT; Tel 01539 720112; Fax 01539 734294

Millom and District Citizens Advice Bureau Entrance B, Advice Centre, Millom, Cumbria LA18 5BA; Tel 01229 772395

Ulverston and North Lonsdale Citizens Advice Bureau Town Hall Annexe, Theatre St, Ulverston, Cumbria LA12 7AQ; Tel 01229 585585

Whitehaven Citizens Advice Bureau 3 Duke St, Whitehaven, Cumbria CA28 7EW; Tel 01946 693321; Fax 01946 693137

Workington Citizens Advice Bureau Vulcans La, Workington, Cumbria CA14 2BT; Tel 01900 604735; Fax 01900 870482

Derbyshire

Chesterfield Citizens Advice Bureau 6–8 Broad Pavement, Chesterfield, Derbyshire S40 1RP; Tel 01246 209164

High Peak Citizens Advice Bureau Bradbury Community Hse, Market St, Glossop, Derbyshire SK13 8AR; Tel 01457 855869; Fax 01457 855869

Derby Citizens Advice Bureau Progressive Bldgs, Sitwell St, Derby DE1 2JT; Tel 01332 343120; 01332 366548; Fax 01332 291310

Matlock Citizens Advice Bureau 29 Bank Rd, Matlock, Derbyshire DE4 3NF; Tel 01629 582449; 01629 583539; Fax 01629 583539

North East Derbyshire Citizens Advice Bureau 126 High St, Clay Cross, Chesterfield, Derbyshire S45 9EE; Tel 01246 863550

Staveley Citizens Advice Bureau Staveley Hall, Church St, Chesterfield, Derbyshire S43 3TN; Tel 01246 473668

Devon

Barnstaple Citizens Advice Bureau Central Library and Records Office, Tuly St, Barnstaple, Devon EX31 1EJ; Tel 01271 388600

Bideford Citizens Advice Bureau 28a Bridgeland St, Bideford, Devon EX39 2PZ; E-mail cab-bideford@ndirect.co.uk; Tel 01237 473161; Fax 01237 425272

16

Devonport Citizens Advice Bureau Devonport Guildhall, Ker St, Devonport, Devon PL1 4EL; Tel 01752 565522; Fax 01752 607367

Exeter Citizens Advice Bureau Wat Tyler Hse, 3 King William St, Exeter, Devon EX2 4RD; URL www.eclipse.co.uk/exeter.cab; Tel 01392 201210; Fax 01392 201203

Exmouth Citizens Advice Bureau Town Hall, St. Andrew's Rd, Exmouth, Devon EX8 1AW; Tel 01395 264645; Fax 01395 269202

Honiton (East Devon) Citizens Advice Bureau Honiton Library and Information Centre, 48–50 New St, Honiton, Devon EX14 8BS; Tel 01404 44213; Fax 01404 47927

Ilfracombe Citizens Advice Bureau The Candar, Ilfracombe, Devon EX34 9ER; Tel 01271 863549

Newton Abbot Citizens Advice Bureau Bank House Centre, 5b Bank St, Newton Abbot, Devon TQ12 2JL; Tel 01626 203141

Okehampton Citizens Advice Bureau The Ockment Centre, North St, Okehampton, Devon EX20 1AR; Tel 01837 52574; Fax 01837 52105

Paignton Citizens Advice Bureau 29 Palace Ave, Paignton, Devon TQ3 3EQ; Tel 01803 521726; Fax 01803 558262

Plymouth Citizens Advice Bureau Virginia House Settlement, 1st Fl, Plymouth PL4 0EB; Tel 01752 207088; Fax 01752 207087

South Hams Citizens Advice Bureau Mansion Hse, 36 Fore St, Totnes, Devon TQ9 5RP; Tel 01803 862392

Tavistock Citizens Advice Bureau Kingdon Hse, North St, Tavistock, Devon PL19 0AN; Tel 01822 612359; Fax 01822 618990

Teignmouth Citizens Advice Bureau Teignmouth Library, Fore St, Teignmouth, Devon TQ14 8DY; Tel 01626 776770

Tiverton (Mid Devon) Citizens Advice Bureau 28 Gold St, Tiverton, Devon EX16 6PY; Tel 01884 253688

Torquay Citizens Advice Bureau Castleton, 11 Castle Rd, Torquay, Torbay TQ1 3BN; Tel 01803 297799; Fax 01803 296930

Dorset

Bournemouth Citizens Advice Bureau The West Wing, Town Hall, Bournemouth BH2 6DX; Tel 01202 290967; 01202 292561; 01202 558324; Fax 01202 290975

Bridport Citizens Advice Bureau 45 South St, Bridport, Dorset DT6 3NY; Tel 01308 459594; Fax 01308 456769

Christchurch Citizens Advice Bureau 2 Sopers La, Christchurch, Dorset BH23 1JG; Tel 01202 482023; Fax 01202 488441

Dorchester and District Citizens Advice Bureau 1 Acland Rd, Dorchester, Dorset DT1 1JW; Tel 01305 262220; Fax 01305 257126

East Dorset Citizens Advice Bureau The Old Fire Station, Hanham Rd, Wimborne, Dorset BH21 1AS; Tel 01202 884738; Fax 01202 848110

North Dorset Citizens Advice Bureau The Courtyard, Newbury Crt, Gillingham, Dorset SP8 4HZ; Tel 01747 822117; Fax 01747 826300

Poole Citizens Advice Bureau 54 Lagland, Poole BH15 1QG; Tel 01202 678517; Fax 01202 661797

Sherborne Citizens Advice Bureau Manor Hse, Newland, Sherborne, Dorset DT9 3JL; Tel 01935 815305; 01935 815681; Fax 01935 815694

Weymouth and Portland Citizens Advice Bureau 2 Mulberry Terr, Great George St, Weymouth, Dorset DT4 8NQ; Tel 01305 782798; Fax 01305 770325

Durham

Chester-le-Street Citizens Advice Bureau 1 Ashley Terr, Chester-le-Street, County Durham DH3 3EY; Tel 0191 389 3000; Fax 0191 389 1619

Darlington Citizens Advice Bureau Bennet Hse, 14 Horsemarket, Darlington DL1 5PT; Tel 01325 380755; Fax 01325 380824

Derwentside Citizens Advice Bureau 41a Front St, Stanley, County Durham DH9 0ST; Tel 01207 237858; Fax 01207 237272

Durham Citizens Advice Bureau Ruth First Hse, Providence Row, Durham, County Durham DH1 1RP; Tel 0191 384 2638; Fax 0191 384 3886

Easington and District Citizens Advice Bureau Rear of 14 Upper Yoden Way, Town Centre, Peterlee, County Durham SR8 1AX; Tel 0191 586 2639; Fax 0191 587 2695

Sedgefield and District Citizens Advice Bureau Town Hall, High St, Spennymoor, County Durham DL16 6DG; Tel 01388 420146; Fax 01388 420145

Teesdale District Citizens Advice Bureau Woodleigh, Flatts Rd, Barnard Castle, County Durham DL12 8AA; Tel 01833 631486; Fax 01833 631486

Wear Valley Citizens Advice Bureau Lightfoot Inst, Kingsway, Bishop Auckland, County Durham DL14 7JN; Tel 01388 606661; Fax 01388 661629

Essex

Basildon Citizens Advice Bureau The Basildon Centre, St. Martin's Sq, Basildon, Essex SS14 1DL; Tel 01268 522210; Fax 01268 272575

Billericay Citizens Advice Bureau Burghstead Lodge, 143 High St, Billericay, Essex CM12 9AB; Tel 01277 651858; Fax 01277 633830

Braintree Citizens Advice Bureau 2 St. Michael's Rd, Braintree, Essex CM7 7EX; Tel 01376 324129; Fax 01376 331350

Brentwood Citizens Advice Bureau 10 Crown St, Brentwood, Essex CM14 4BA; Tel 01277 222888; Fax 01277 264999

Castle Point Citizens Advice Bureau 168 Long Rd, Canvey Island, Essex SS8 0JP; Tel 01268 511889; Fax 01268 515166

Chelmsford Citizens Advice Bureau 47 Broomfield Rd, Chelmsford, Essex CM1 1SY; Tel 01245 257144; 01245 345720; Fax 01245 281388

Colchester Citizens Advice Bureau Winsleys Hse, High St, Colchester, Essex CO1 1UG; Tel 01206 765331; Fax 01206 563523

Epping Citizens Advice Bureau 50a Hemnall St, Epping, Essex CM16 4LS; Tel 01992 574989

Harlow Citizens Advice Bureau Harlow Advice Centre, Rooms 1 and 2, Harlow, Essex CM20 1ND; Tel 01279 424400; Fax 01279 635443

Harwich Citizens Advice Bureau 24 Kingsway, Dovercourt, Harwich, Essex CO12 3AB; Tel 01255 502462

Loughton Citizens Advice Bureau St. Mary's Parish Centre, High Rd, Loughton, Essex IG10 1BB; Tel 020 8502 0031; Fax 020 8532 0243

Maldon Citizens Advice Bureau St. Cedd's Hse, Princes Rd, Maldon, Essex CM9 7NY; Tel 01621 841195; Fax 01621 841282

Rayleigh Citizens Advice Bureau Civic Suite, Hockley Rd, Rayleigh, Essex SS6 8EB; Tel 01268 770782; Fax 01268 741359

Rochford Citizens Advice Bureau Rochford Day Centre, Back La, Rochford, Essex SS4 1AY; Tel 01702 545552

Thurrock Citizens Advice Bureau 1 New Rd, Grays, Thurrock RM17 6NG; Tel 01375 381023; Fax 01375 375519

Uttlesford Citizens Advice Bureau 18 Church St, Saffron Walden, Essex CB10 1JW; Tel 01799 526582; Fax 01799 513702

Waltham Abbey Citizens Advice Bureau Side Entrance, Town Hall, Waltham Abbey, Essex EN9 1DE; Tel 01992 710353; Fax 01992 710802

Wickford Citizens Advice Bureau Gibraltar Wlk, High St, Wickford, Essex SS12 9AX; Tel 01268 732094; Fax 01268 560868

Witham Citizens Advice Bureau Public Hall, Collingwood Rd, Witham, Essex CM8 2DY; Tel 01376 516222; Fax 01376 502190

Gloucestershire

Cheltenham and District Citizens Advice Bureau 14 Royal Cres, Cheltenham, Gloucestershire GL50 3DA; E-mail cabcheltenham@msn.com; Tel 01242 522491; Fax 01242 228801

Cirencester Citizens Advice Bureau 2–3 The Mews, Cricklade St, Cirencester, Gloucestershire GL7 1HY; Tel 01285 652908

Forest of Dean Citizens Advice Bureau Town Hse, Lords Hill Wlk, Forest of Dean, Coleford, Gloucestershire GL16 8BD; Tel 01594 833717

Gloucester and District Citizens Advice Bureau 75–81 Eastgate, Gloucester, Gloucestershire GL1 1PN; Tel 01452 527202; 01452 528017; 01452 529826; Fax 01452 381507

Stroud and District Citizens Advice Bureau Unit 8, 1st Fl, Stroud, Gloucestershire GL5 2BP; Tel 01453 762084

Greater Manchester

Ashton-in-Makerfield Citizens Advice Bureau The Old Town Hall, Bryn St, Ashton-in-Makerfield, Lancashire WN4 9AY; Tel 01942 725668; Fax 01942 714794

Atherton Citizens Advice Bureau York St, Atherton, Greater Manchester M46 9JD; Tel 01942 873849; Fax 01942 870950

Blackley Citizens Advice Bureau 251 Charlestown Rd, Blackley, Greater Manchester M9 7BD; E-mail cab-blackley@mcrl.poptel.org.uk; Tel 0161 795 3530; Fax 0161 795 3953

Bolton Citizens Advice Bureau 26–28 Mawdsley St, Bolton, Greater Manchester BL1 1LF; E-mail boltoncab@zdnetmail.co.uk; Tel 01204 900200; Fax 01204 900212

Bradford Citizens Advice Bureau 28 Chaddesley, Bradford, Greater Manchester M11 3SW; Tel 0161 223 9328; Fax 0161 220 7274

Bury Citizens Advice Bureau 148 The Rock, Bury, Lancashire BL9 0PP; Tel 0161 761 5355; Fax 0161 763 6653

Eccles Citizens Advice Bureau 40–44 Church St, Eccles, Greater Manchester M30 0DF; Tel 0161 789 1540; Fax 0161 707 6012

Failsworth Citizens Advice Bureau 1 Ashton Rd West, Failsworth, Greater Manchester M35 0EQ; Tel 0161 633 4291; Fax 0161 682 6546

Gorton Citizens Advice Bureau 111 Wellington St, Gorton, Greater Manchester M18 8TX; Tel 0161 231 1607; Fax 0161 231 2093

Harpurhey Citizens Advice Bureau Community Services Centre, Paget St, Manchester M40 7UU; Tel 0161 205 6291; Fax 0161 205 8654

Hazel Grove Citizens Advice Bureau 5 Hatherlow La, Hazel Grove, Stockport, Cheshire SK7 4EP; Tel 0161 456 3335; 0161 456 5404; Fax 0161 483 6821

Heywood Citizens Advice Bureau 46 Market St, Heywood, Rochdale, Greater Manchester OL10 4LY; Tel 01706 624214; Fax 01706 622778

Hindley Citizens Advice Bureau 152 Market St, Hindley, Greater Manchester WN2 3AY; Tel 01942 255069; Fax 01942 256727

Hope Hospital Citizens Advice Bureau Stott La, Salford, Greater Manchester M6 8HD; Tel 0161 787 4713; Fax 0161 787 5621

Hulme Citizens Advice Bureau Claremont Resource Centre, Rolls Cres, Hulme, Greater Manchester M15 5FS; Tel 0161 226 6729; 0161 226 9847; 0161 227 9384; Fax 0161 227 8162

Irlam and Cadishead Citizens Advice Bureau 595 Liverpool Rd, Irlam, Greater Manchester M44 5BE; Tel 0161 775 1849; Fax 0161 777 6626

Leigh Citizens Advice Bureau 6 The Avenue, Leigh, Lancashire WN7 1ES; Tel 01942 708708; Fax 01942 708120

Longsight Citizens Advice Bureau 384 Dickenson Rd, Longsight, Manchester M13 0WQ; Tel 0161 224 4300; Fax 0161 256 0245

Lower Broughton Citizens Advice Bureau Lucy St, off Great Clowes St, Salford, Greater Manchester M7 9ZT; Tel 0161 792 1609; Fax 0161 792 9760

Manchester Central Citizens Advice Bureau Swan Bldgs, 20 Swan St, Manchester M4 5JW; URL www.poptel.org.uk/cab; Tel 0161 834 9844; Fax 0161 834 9163

Middleton Citizens Advice Bureau Milton St, Middleton, Greater Manchester M24 6NT; Tel 0161 284 4666; Fax 0161 284 4560

Oldham Citizens Advice Bureau 24 Clegg St, Oldham, Lancashire OL1 1PL; E-mail oldham.cab@oldhamcab.btinternet.com; Tel 0161 620 3226; 0161 633 4291; Fax 0161 633 3242

Old Trafford Citizens Advice Bureau 139 Stamford St, Old Trafford, Manchester M16 9LT; Tel 0161 232 1816; Fax 0161 232 8463

Ordsall Citizens Advice Bureau 4 Trafford Rd, Salford, Greater Manchester M5 2TD; Tel 0161 848 8865; Fax 0161 877 4944

Partington Citizens Advice Bureau Council Offices, Central Rd, Manchester M31 4FY; Tel 0161 775 4256; Fax 0161 912 5411

Prestwich Citizens Advice Bureau 7 Fairfax Rd, Prestwich, Manchester M25 5AS; Tel 0161 773 7835; Fax 0161 773 0181

Radcliffe Citizens Advice Bureau 1–3 Blackburn St, Radcliffe, Greater Manchester M26 1NN; Tel 0161 723 3767; Fax 0161 724 7274

Rochdale Citizens Advice Bureau 1 Faulkner St, Rochdale, Greater Manchester OL16 1RS; Tel 0161 284 4666; Fax 01706 864778

Royton Citizens Advice Bureau Macauley Hse, 1 Macauley St, Oldham, Lancashire OL2 6PQ; Tel 0161 633 4291; Fax 0161 665 2183

Salford Citizens Advice Bureau Pendleton Hse, Broughton Rd, Salford, Greater Manchester M6 6LS; Tel 0161 736 4983; Fax 0161 737 2630

Stretford Citizens Advice Bureau Stretford Library, Bennett St, Stretford, Greater Manchester M32 8AG; Tel 0161 912 5170; Fax 0161 912 5159

Swinton Citizens Advice Bureau 95 Chorley Rd, Swinton, Greater Manchester M27 4AA; Tel 0161 794 5028; Fax 0161 727 8403

Tameside District Citizens Advice Bureau 9 George St, Ashton-under-Lyne, Tameside OL6 6AQ; Tel 0161 330 2156; Fax 0161 344 2139

Urmston Citizens Advice Bureau 2 Moorfield Wlk, Crofts Bank Rd, Urmston, Greater Manchester M41 0TT; URL www.citizensadvicebureau.freeserve.co.uk; E-mail urmston_cab@hotmail.com; Tel 0161 748 4469; Fax 0161 912 2764

Wigan Citizens Advice Bureau Gerard Winstanley Hse, Crawford St, Wigan, Greater Manchester WN1 1NG; Tel 01942 234292; Fax 01942 829122

16

Withington Citizens Advice Bureau Withington Methodist Church, 439 Wilmslow Rd, Withington, Greater Manchester M20 4AN; Tel 0161 445 7376; Fax 0161 438 0773

Worsley Citizens Advice Bureau 1 Memorial Rd, Worsley, Greater Manchester M28 3AQ; Tel 0161 790 5489; Fax 0161 790 4558

Wythenshawe Citizens Advice Bureau Alpha Hse, Rowlands Way, Wythenshawe, Greater Manchester M22 5RG; Tel 0161 437 6336; Fax 0161 436 6114

Hampshire

Aldershot Citizens Advice Bureau Prince's Gdns, High St, Aldershot, Hampshire GU11 1BJ; Tel 01252 22097

Alton Citizens Advice Bureau 7 Cross and Pillory La, Alton, Hampshire GU34 1HL; Tel 01420 84399; Fax 01420 844645

Andover Citizens Advice Bureau Ground Fl, East Wing, Andover, Hampshire SP10 2BN; Tel 01264 365534; Fax 01264 333853

Basingstoke Citizens Advice Bureau 19–20 Westminster Hse, The Library, Basingstoke, Hampshire RG21 1LS; Tel 01256 322814; Fax 01256 327001

Bishop's Waltham Citizens Advice Bureau The Library, Bank St, Bishop's Waltham, Hampshire SO2 1AN; Tel 01489 896376; Fax 01489 896376

Eastleigh Citizens Advice Bureau 101 Leigh Rd, Eastleigh, Hampshire SO50 9DR; Tel 023 8061 3949; Fax 023 8065 2446

Fareham Citizens Advice Bureau 2nd Fl, County Library Bldg, Fareham, Hampshire PO16 7EN; Tel 01329 233412; Fax 01329 283004

Farnborough Citizens Advice Bureau Elles Hall, Meudon Ave, Farnborough, Hampshire GU14 7LE; Tel 01252 542708; Fax 01252 370921

Fleet and District Citizens Advice Bureau Civic Offices, Harlington Way, Fleet, Hampshire GU13 8AE; Tel 01252 617922; Fax 01252 626905

Gosport Citizens Advice Bureau 2 Thorngate Way, Gosport, Hampshire PO12 1HR; Tel 023 9252 2224; Fax 023 9252 0112

Havant Citizens Advice Bureau 21a East St, Havant, Hampshire PO9 1AA; Tel 023 9271 7700; Fax 023 9249 9154

Leigh Park Citizens Advice Bureau Leigh Park Community Centre, 230 Dunsbury Way, Havant, Hampshire PO9 5BG; Tel 023 9271 7700

Lymington Citizens Advice Bureau 91–92 High St, Lymington, Hampshire SO41 9AP; Tel 01590 672685; Fax 01590 677868

New Milton Citizens Advice Bureau Stannington, 14 Spencer Rd, New Milton, Hampshire BH25 6BZ; Tel 01425 612679; Fax 01425 612679

Petersfield Citizens Advice Bureau The Old Surgery, 18 Heath Rd, Petersfield, Hampshire GU31 4DY; Tel 01730 264887; Fax 01730 233037

Portsmouth Citizens Advice Bureau Drummond Hse, Dugald Drummond St (off Greetham St), Portsmouth PO1 2BB; Tel 023 9282 8621; Fax 023 9286 4536

Ringwood and Fordingbridge Citizens Advice Bureau 5 Fridays Crt, High St, Ringwood, Hampshire BH24 1AB; Tel 01425 473330; Fax 01425 473330

Romsey and District Citizens Advice Bureau 5 Abbey Wlk, Church St, Romsey, Hampshire SO51 8JQ; Tel 01794 516378; Fax 01794 519379

Southampton Citizens Advice Bureau 3 Kings Park Rd, Southampton SO15 2AT; Tel 023 8022 1406; 023 8033 3868; Fax 023 8023 7284

Tadley Citizens Advice Bureau Franklin Ave, Tadley, Hampshire RG26 4ET; Tel 0118 981 7660; Fax 0118 982 0545

Totton and District Citizens Advice Bureau 91 Junction, Totton, Southampton SO40 3BU; Tel 023 8086 3978; Fax 023 9287 2534

Waterlooville Citizens Advice Bureau Swiss Cottage, 9 St. George's Wlk, Waterlooville, Hampshire PO7 7TU; Tel 023 9271 7700; Fax 023 9271 7699

Waterside Citizens Advice Bureau The Grove, 25 St. John's St, Southampton SO45 6BZ; Tel 023 8084 5447

Whitehill and Bordon Citizens Advice Bureau Forest Community Centre, Pinehill Rd, Bordon, Hampshire GU35 0BS; Tel 01420 477747; Fax 01420 488943

Winchester Citizens Advice Bureau The Winchester Centre, 68 St. George's St, Winchester, Hampshire SO23 8AH; Tel 01962 848000; Fax 01962 848005

Yateley and District Citizens Advice Bureau Royal Oak Cl, Yateley, Hampshire GU46 7UD; Tel 01252 878410

Hereford

Hereford and District Citizens Advice Bureau 1a St. Owen St, Hereford, Herefordshire HR1 2JB; Tel 01432 266456

Leominster and District Citizens Advice Bureau 9 Broad St, Leominster, Herefordshire HR6 8HL; Tel 01568 615959; Fax 01568 620106

Ross-on-Wye Citizens Advice Bureau 20 Gloucester Rd, Ross-on-Wye, Herefordshire HR9 5LQ; Tel 01898 566346

Hertfordshire

Abbots Langley Citizens Advice Bureau The Old Stables, St. Lawrence's Verge, Abbots Langley, Hertfordshire WD5 0AS; Tel 01923 267949; Fax 01923 266335

Bishop's Stortford Citizens Advice Bureau 74 South St, Bishop's Stortford, Hertfordshire CM23 3AZ; Tel 01279 655363; Fax 01279 306698

Buntingford Citizens Advice Bureau North Entrance, The Manor Hse, Buntingford, Hertfordshire SG9 9AB; Tel 01763 272024; Fax 01763 271698

Bushey Citizens Advice Bureau 8 Rudolph Rd, Bushey, Hertfordshire WD2 3DU; Tel 020 8950 8726; Fax 020 8950 0175

Cheshunt Citizens Advice Bureau Bishop's College, Old Bldg, Cheshunt, Hertfordshire EN8 9XP; Tel 01992 635858; Fax 01992 629722

Elstree and Borehamwood Citizens Advice Bureau The Community Centre, 2 Allum La, Elstree, Hertfordshire WD6 3PJ; Tel 020 8953 4643; 020 8953 9961; Fax 020 8207 0951

Hatfield Citizens Advice Bureau 1st Fl, Queensway Hse, Hatfield, Hertfordshire AL10 0LW; Tel 01707 262607; Fax 01707 275189

Hemel Hempstead Citizens Advice Bureau 19 Hillfield Rd, Hemel Hempstead, Hertfordshire HP2 4AA; Tel 01442 213368; 01442 263501; Fax 01442 239658

Hertford Citizens Advice Bureau Tooke Hse, 20 Bull Plain, Hertford, Hertfordshire SG14 1DT; Tel 01992 581441; Fax 01992 504374

Hitchin Citizens Advice Bureau Thomas Bellamy Hse, Bedford Rd, Hitchin, Hertfordshire SG5 1HL; Tel 01462 622999; Fax 01462 625550

Hoddesdon Citizens Advice Bureau The Spinning Wheel, 30 High St, Hoddesdon, Hertfordshire EN11 8BP; Tel 01992 460976; Fax 01992 445007

Letchworth Citizens Advice Bureau The Old Grammar School, Broadway, Letchworth, Hertfordshire SG6 2DG; Tel 01462 685393; Fax 01462 685393

Oxhey and District Citizens Advice Bureau 4 Bridlington Rd, South Oxhey, Watford, Hertfordshire WD1 6AF; Tel 020 8421 0911; 020 8428 9591; Fax 020 8421 5266

Potters Bar Citizens Advice Bureau The Wyllyotts Centre, Wyllyotts Pl, Potters Bar, Hertfordshire EN6 2HN; Tel 01707 650348; 01707 659804; Fax 01707 664352

Rickmansworth Citizens Advice Bureau Northway, Rickmansworth, Hertfordshire WD3 1EH; Tel 01923 720424; Fax 01923 711488

Royston Citizens Advice Bureau Town Hall, Royston, Hertfordshire SG8 7DA; Tel 01763 238020; 01763 238027; Fax 01763 238017

St. Albans Citizens Advice Bureau 29 Upper Lattimore Rd, St. Albans, Hertfordshire AL1 3UA; Tel 01727 833855; 01727 855269; Fax 01727 833855

Stevenage Citizens Advice Bureau Swingate Hse, Danestrete, Stevenage, Hertfordshire SG1 1AF; Tel 01438 369491; Fax 01438 722067

Ware and District Citizens Advice Bureau Meade Hse, 85 High St, Ware, Hertfordshire SG12 9AD; Tel 01920 463495; Fax 01920 484908

Watford Citizens Advice Bureau The Advice Centre, St. Mary's Churchyard, Watford, Hertfordshire WD1 2BE; Tel 01923 234949; Fax 01923 231889

Welwyn Garden City Citizens Advice Bureau Campus East, Welwyn Garden City, Hertfordshire AL8 6LY; Fax 01707 393415

Humberside

Boothferry District Citizens Advice Bureau 80 Pasture Rd, Goole, East Riding of Yorkshire DN14 6HE; Tel 01405 762054; Fax 01405 761035

Bransholme Citizens Advice Bureau 18–20 Madron Cl, Barnstaple Rd, Bransholme, Kingston upon Hull HU7 4PR; Tel 01482 838392; Fax 01482 820900

East Yorkshire Citizens Advice Bureau 5a Prospect Arcade, Bridlington, East Riding of Yorkshire YO15 2AL; Tel 01262 605660; Fax 01262 605644

Holderness Citizens Advice Bureau 44 Hull Rd, Withernsea, Kingston upon Hull HU19 2EG; Tel 01964 613745; Fax 01964 615179

Hull Citizens Advice Bureau 2 Charlotte St Mews, Hull, Kingston upon Hull HU1 3BQ; Tel 01482 224608; Fax 01482 211526

Scunthorpe Citizens Advice Burreau 12 Oswald Rd, Scunthorpe, East Riding of Yorkshire DN15 7PT; Tel 01724 863623; Fax 01724 270815

Isle of Wight

Newport Citizens Advice Bureau Exchange Hse, St. Cross St, Newport, Isle of Wight PO30 5BZ; Tel 01983 522611; 01983 826160; Fax 01983 520594

Kent

Ashford Citizens Advice Bureau Seabrooke Hse, 10 Norwood St, Ashford, Kent TN23 1QT; Tel 01233 626185; Fax 01233 610653

Broadstairs Citizens Advice Bureau Pierremont Gdns, Broadstairs, Kent CT10 1JH; Tel 01843 869350

Canterbury Citizens Advice Bureau 3 Westgate Hall Rd, off St. Peter's La, Canterbury, Kent CT1 2BT; Tel 01227 761493; 01227 763348; Fax 01227 787505

Chatham (Medway) Citizens Advice Bureau The Whitehouse, Riverside, Chatham, Medway ME4 4SL; Tel 01634 843723; Fax 01634 842808

Cranbrook and District Citizens Advice Bureau Council Offices, High St, Cranbrook, Kent TN17 3LU; Tel 01580 713561; Fax 01580 714936

Dartford Citizens Advice Bureau Enterprise Hse, 8 Essex Rd, Dartford, Kent DA1 2AU; Tel 01322 224686; Fax 01322 291017

Deal Citizens Advice Bureau 23 Victoria Rd, Deal, Kent CT14 7AS; Tel 01304 374938; Fax 01304 374333

Dover Citizens Advice Bureau Maison Dieu Gdns, Maison Dieu Rd, Dover, Kent CT16 1RW; Tel 01304 202567; Fax 01304 202442

Edenbridge Citizens Advice Bureau 68 High St, Edenbridge, Kent TN8 5AR; Tel 01732 865131; Fax 01732 863220

Faversham Citizens Advice Bureau 43 Stone St, Faversham, Kent ME13 8PH; URL www.members.aol.com/dijphall/favcab; Tel 01795 536996; Fax 01795 537101

Folkestone (Shepway) Citizens Advice Bureau 20 Church St, Folkestone, Kent CT20 1SE; Tel 01303 220709; Fax 01303 249310

Gillingham Citizens Advice Bureau 46 Green St, off High St, Gillingham, Kent ME7 5TJ; Tel 01634 572033; 01634 573444; Fax 01634 280596

Gravesham Citizens Advice Bureau 8 and 9 Parrock St, Gravesend, Kent DA12 1ET; Tel 01474 361239; Fax 01474 362030

Herne Bay Citizens Advice Bureau The South Room, Christ Church, Herne Bay, Kent CT6 5NR; Tel 01227 363312

Maidstone Citizens Advice Bureau 2 Bower Terr, Tonbridge Rd, Maidstone, Kent ME16 8RY; Tel 01622 674032; Fax 01622 751816

Malling Citizens Advice Bureau Clout's Memorial Institute, 9 High St, Maidstone, Kent ME19 6QH; Tel 01732 845501; Fax 01732 842275

Paddock Wood Citizens Advice Bureau The Wesley, Commercial Rd, Tonbridge, Kent TN12 6DS; URL www.pwcab.freeserve.co.uk; E-mail manager@pwcab.freeserve.co.uk; Tel 01892 832977; Fax 01892 834533

Sevenoaks Citizens Advice Bureau Buckhurst La (next to the Library), Sevenoaks, Kent TN13 1HW; URL www.ds.dial.pipex.com/7oakscab; E-mail 7oakscab@dial.pipex.com; Tel 01732 454443; Fax 01732 463164

Sittingbourne Citizens Advice Bureau 17a Station St, Sittingbourne, Kent ME10 3DU; Tel 01795 473652; Fax 01795 431315

Swanley and District Citizens Advice Bureau 16 High St, Swanley, Kent BR8 8BG; Tel 01322 664949; Fax 01322 613136

Tenterden Citizens Advice Bureau Town Hall, High St, Tenterden, Kent TN30 6AN; Tel 01580 762371

Tonbridge Citizens Advice Bureau Castle Lodge, Castle St, Tonbridge, Kent TN9 1BH; Tel 01732 350099; Fax 01732 363335

Tunbridge Wells Citizens Advice Bureau 31 Monson Rd, Tunbridge Wells, Kent TN1 1LS; URL www.twcab.freeserve.co.uk; Tel 01892 538388; Fax 01892 539506

Lancashire

Bacup Citizens Advice Bureau 4 Rochdale Rd, Bacup, Lancashire OL13 9NZ; Tel 01706 873367; Fax 01706 873367

Barnoldswick Citizens Advice Bureau The Old Police Station, Manchester Rd, Barnoldswick, Lancashire BB8 5NZ; Tel 01282 814814; Fax 01282 814815

Burnley Citizens Advice Bureau 47 Parker La, Burnley, Lancashire BB1 2BU; Tel 01282 424655; Fax 01282 414617

Chorley Citizens Advice Bureau 19 St. George's St, Chorley, Lancashire PR7 1AA; Tel 01257 279807; Fax 01257 273085

Colne Citizens Advice Bureau 2 Duke St, Colne, Lancashire BB8 0SU; Tel 01282 867188; Fax 01282 859478

Fleetwood Citizens Advice Bureau 43 Lord St, Fleetwood, Lancashire FY7 6DU; Tel 01253 873091; Fax 01253 772909

Haslingden Citizens Advice Bureau 1–3 Burgess St, Haslingden, Rossendale, Lancashire BB4 5QT; Tel 01706 227515; Fax 01706 830885

16

Hyndburn Citizens Advice Bureau 20–22 Whalley Rd, Accrington, Lancashire BB5 1AA; Tel 01254 232447; Fax 01254 394331

Kirkham and Rural Fylde Citizens Advice Bureau Council Offices, Moor St, Kirkham, Preston, Lancashire PR4 2AU; Tel 01772 682588

Lancaster Citizens Advice Bureau 87 King St, Lancaster, Lancashire LA1 1RH; Tel 01524 384950; Fax 01524 846447

Lytham St. Anne's Citizens Advice Bureau Ashton Gardens Gatehouse, 5 St. George's Rd, Lytham St. Anne's, Lancashire FY8 2AE; Tel 01253 720710; Fax 01253 725907

Morecambe Citizens Advice Bureau Oban Hse, 87–89 Queen St, Morecambe, Lancashire LA4 5EN; Tel 01524 400400; Fax 01524 400401

Nelson Citizens Advice Bureau Broadway, Nelson, Lancashire BB9 9SJ; Tel 01282 616750

Preston Citizens Advice Bureau Town Hall Annexe, Birley St, Preston, Lancashire PR1 2QE; Tel 01772 822416; Fax 01772 25447

Ribble Valley Citizens Advice Bureau 19–21 Wesleyan Row, Parson La, Clitheroe, Lancashire BB7 2JY; Tel 01200 428966; Fax 01200 428966

Skelmersdale Citizens Advice Bureau 110–112 Firbeck, Birchgreen, Skelmersdale, Lancashire WN8 6PW; Tel 01695 723110; Fax 01695 722692

Thornton Cleveleys Citizens Advice Bureau 99 Victoria Road West, Thornton-Cleveleys, Lancashire FY5 3LD; Tel 01253 850658; Fax 01253 867563

Leicestershire

Charnwood Citizens Advice Bureau John Storer Hse, Ward's End, Loughborough, Leicestershire LE11 3HA; Tel 01509 267374

Coalville and District Citizens Advice Bureau The Library, High St, Coalville, Leicestershire LE67 2EA; Tel 01530 835500; Fax 01530 510540

Harborough District Citizens Advice Bureau 11a St. Marys Rd, Market Harborough, Leicestershire LE16 7DS; Tel 01858 466850

Hinckley Citizens Advice Bureau The Chestnuts, 25 Mount Rd, Hinckley, Leicestershire LE10 1AD; Tel 01455 636051

Leicester Citizens Advice Bureau 2a New Wlk, off King St, Leicester LE1 6TF; Tel 0116 255 4212; Fax 0116 255 1041

Lutterworth Citizens Advice Bureau Information Centre, Church Gate, Lutterworth, Leicestershire LE17 4AN; Tel 01455 557375

Melton Citizens Advice Bureau 3a Park Rd, Melton Mowbray, Leicestershire LE13 1TT; Tel 01664 565882; 01664 568812

Oadby and Wigston Citizens Advice Bureau Wigston Library, Bull Head St, Wigston, Leicestershire LE18 1PA; Tel 0116 288 7861; Fax 0116 281 1094

Rutland Citizens Advice Bureau 56 High St, Oakham, Rutland LE15 6AL; Tel 01572 723012; Fax 01572 722568

Lincolnshire

Advicelincs 2nd Fl, Corn Exchange Chambers, Sleaford, Lincolnshire NG34 7SP; Tel (Freephone) 0800 252155

Advicelincs Citizens Advice Bureau 25–26 The Cres, Spalding, Lincolnshire PE11 1AF; URL www.adlincs.dircon.co.uk; Tel 0321 423 8428; Fax 01775 712316

Boston Citizens Advice Bureau 26 South St, Boston, Lincolnshire PE21 6HT; Tel 01205 352666; Fax 01205 354715

East Lindsey Citizens Advice Bureau 33 Drummond Rd, Skegness, Lincolnshire PE25 3EB; Tel 01754 760661; Fax 01754 611956

Grantham and District Citizens Advice Bureau 26–27 St. Catherines Rd, Grantham, Lincolnshire NG31 6TT; Tel 01476 567084; Fax 01476 571237

Lincoln and District Citizens Advice Bureau Beaumont Lodge, Beaumont Fee, Lincoln, Lincolnshire LN1 1UL; Tel 01522 828600; Fax 01522 828601

Sleaford and District Citizens Advice Bureau The Cedar Bldg, Moneys Yard, Sleaford, Lincolnshire NG34 7TW; Tel 01529 307077

South Holland Citizens Advice Bureau 25–26 The Cres, Spalding, Lincolnshire PE11 1AF; Tel 01775 766668; 01775 769693; Fax 01775 712373

Stamford and District Citizens Advice Bureau 39 High St, Stamford, Lincolnshire PE9 2BB; Tel 01780 757621; Fax 01780 480819

London Division

Barking

Barking Citizens Advice Bureau 55 Ripple Rd, Barking, Essex IG11 7NT; Tel 020 8594 6715; Fax 020 8591 0440

Dagenham Citizens Advice Bureau 339 Heathway, Dagenham, Essex RM9 5AF; Tel 020 8592 1084; Fax 020 8593 2511

Rainham Citizens Advice Bureau Family Centre, 21 Broadway, Rainham, Essex RM13 1BR; Tel 01708 720350; Fax 01708 52475

Barnet

Barnet Citizens Advice Bureau CABx Home Visiting Service, 40–42 Church End, Hendon, London NW4 4JT; Tel 020 8203 9778

Finchley Citizens Advice Bureau Hertford Lodge Annexe, East End Rd, Finchley, London N3 3QE; Tel 020 8349 0954; Fax 020 8349 9840

Grahame Park Citizens Advice Bureau The Concourse, Grahame Pk, Hendon, London NW9 5XA; Tel 020 8205 4141; Fax 020 8205 8506

Hendon Citizens Advice Bureau 40–42 Church End, Hendon, London NW4 4JT; Tel 020 8202 5177; 020 8203 5801; Fax 020 8203 3202

New Barnet Citizens Advice Bureau 30 Station Rd, Barnet, London EN5 1PL; Tel 020 8449 0975; Fax 020 8441 2384

Bexley

Bexleyheath Citizens Advice Bureau 8 Brampton Rd, Bexleyheath, Kent DA7 4EY; Tel 020 8303 5100; Fax 020 8303 9524

Brent

Willesden Citizens Advice Bureau 270–272 High Rd, Willesden, London NW10 2EY; Tel 020 8459 2780; Fax 020 8451 3714

Wormwood Scrubs Project 140 Ladbroke Gr, London W10 5ND; Tel 0870 122 2313 ext 560; Fax 020 8968 4281

Bromley

Beckenham and Penge Citizens Advice Bureau 20 Snowdon Cl, Avenue Rd, Penge, London SE20 7RU; Tel 020 8778 0921; Fax 020 8776 6056

Bromley Citizens Advice Bureau The Old Library, 83 Tweedy Rd, Bromley, Kent BR1 1RG; Tel 020 8464 6023; Fax 020 8466 0851

Erith Citizens Advice Bureau 1 Walnut Tree Rd, Erith, Kent DA8 1RA; Tel 01322 340481; Fax 01322 340481

Orpington Citizens Advice Bureau Wallis Hse, 1 Church Hill, Orpington, Kent BR6 0HE; Tel 01689 827732; Fax 01689 823411

Camden

Camden HIV/AIDS Project 94 Avenue Rd, London NW3; Tel 020 7483 4283; Fax 020 7483 1858

Hornsey Citizens Advice Bureau 7 Hatherley Gdns, London N8 9JJ; Tel 020 8862 1400

Kentish Town Citizens Advice Bureau 242 Kentish Town Rd, Kentish Town, London NW5 2AB; Tel 020 7485 7034; Fax 020 7485 5150

Kilburn Citizens Advice Bureau 200 Kilburn High Rd, Kilburn, London NW6 4JD; Tel 020 7372 6888; Fax 020 7328 4744

Turnpike Lane Citizens Advice Bureau 14a Willoughby Rd, London N8 0JJ; Tel 020 8348 2338; Fax 020 8348 9491

City of London

City of London Citizens Advice Bureau 32 Ludgate Hill, London EC4M 7DR; Tel 020 7236 1156; Fax 020 7329 4547

Haringey Refugee Advice Line Tel 0800 413 848

Holborn Citizens Advice Bureau 3rd Fl, Holborn Library, London WC1X 8PA; Tel 020 7404 1497; Fax 020 7404 1507

Croydon

Addington Citizens Advice Bureau 1a Overbury Cres, New Addington, Croydon, Surrey CR0 0LR; Tel 01689 846890; Fax 01689 845105

Croydon Citizens Advice Bureau Money Advice Unit, Strand Hse, Thornton Heath, Surrey CR7 8RG; Tel 020 8665 5911; Fax 020 8689 2377

Thornton Heath Citizens Advice Bureau Strand Hse, Zion Rd, Croydon, Surrey CR7 8RG; Tel 020 8684 2236; Fax 020 8683 4790

Enfield

Edmonton Citizens Advice Bureau Edmonton Methodist Church, Lower Fore St, London N9 0PN; Tel 020 8807 4253; Fax 020 8807 1730

Greenwich

Greenwich Citizens Advice Bureau Money Advice Service, Old Town Hall, London SE18 6PN; Tel 020 8317 3342; 020 8317 8266; Fax 020 8317 0609

Eltham Citizens Advice Bureau Eltham Library, High St, Eltham, London SE9 1TS; Tel 020 8850 6044; Fax 020 8850 7774

Woolwich Citizens Advice Bureau The Old Town Hall, Polytechnic St, Woolwich, London SE18 6PN; Tel 020 8854 9607; Fax 020 8316 7571

Hackney

Dalston Citizens Advice Bureau 491–493 Kingsland Rd, Dalston, London E8 4AU; Tel 020 7249 8616; Fax 020 7249 7699

Hackney Citizens Advice Bureau 236–238 Mare St, Hackney, London E8 1HE; Tel 020 8986 8446; Fax 020 8985 0462

Hammersmith

Fulham Citizens Advice Bureau The Pavilion, 1 Mund St, Fulham, London W14 9LY; Tel 020 7385 1322; Fax 020 7385 6750

Harrow

Harrow Citizens Advice Bureau Civic Centre, Station Rd, Harrow, Greater London HA1 2XH; Tel 020 8427 9443; Fax 020 8863 3267

Havering

Hornchurch Citizens Advice Bureau 59a Billet La, Hornchurch, Essex RM11 1AX; Tel 01708 445983; Fax 01708 443221

Romford Citizens Advice Bureau 7–9 Victoria Rd, Romford, Essex RM1 2DT; Tel 01708 763414; Fax 01708 739319

Hillingdon

Hayes Citizens Advice Bureau Hayes One-Stop, 49–51 Station Rd, Hayes, Greater London UB3 4BE; Tel 01895 277300; Fax 020 8606 2939

Ruislip Citizens Advice Bureau 9 Eastcote Rd, Ruislip, Greater London HA4 8BD; Tel 01895 277300; Fax 01895 622818

Uxbridge One Stop Citizens Advice Bureau Link La, Civic Centre, Uxbridge, Greater London UB8 1UW; Tel 01895 277300; Fax 01895 277306

Yiewsley and West Drayton Citizens Advice Bureau 106 High St, Yiewsley, Greater London UB7 7QJ; Tel 01895 277300; Fax 01895 430421

Hounslow

Brentford and Chiswick Citizens Advice Bureau The Town Hall, Heathfield Terr, London W4 4JN; Tel 020 8994 4846; Fax 020 8995 4674

Feltham Citizens Advice Bureau People's Centre, High St, Feltham, Greater London TW14 4AH; Tel 020 8707 0077; Fax 020 8707 0077

Hounslow Citizens Advice Bureau 45 Treaty Centre, High St, Hounslow, Greater London TW3 1ES; Tel 020 8570 2983; Fax 020 8862 5619

Islington

Holloway Citizens Advice Bureau Caxton Hse, 129 St. John's Way, London N19 3RQ; Tel 020 7272 5577; Fax 020 7272 1383

Islington Citizens Advice Bureau 135 Upper St, Islington, London N1 1QP; Tel 020 7359 0619; Fax 020 7226 1955

Kensington and Chelsea

Chelsea Citizens Advice Bureau Chelsea Old Town Hall, Kings Rd, London SW3 5EE; Tel 020 7351 2114; Fax 020 7351 5240

Kensington Citizens Advice Bureau 1 Thorpe Cl, London W10 5XL; Tel 020 8960 3322; Fax 020 8968 0345

Kingston-upon-Thames

Chessington and Hook Citizens Advice Bureau Library Crt, Elm Rd, Chessington, Surrey KT9 1AS; Tel 020 8255 6060; Fax 020 8255 6093

Kingston and Surbiton Citizens Advice Bureau Neville Hse, 55c Eden St, Kingston upon Thames, Surrey KT1 1BW; Tel 020 8549 0818; Fax 020 8255 6060

Malden and Coombe Citizens Advice Bureau 41 Blagdon Rd, New Malden, Surrey KT3 4AF; Tel 020 8255 6060; Fax 020 8255 6083

Surbiton Citizens Advice Bureau Library Extension, Ewell Rd, Surbiton, Surrey KT6 6AF; Tel 020 8255 6060; Fax 020 8255 6073

Lambeth

Streatham Citizens Advice Bureau Ilex Hse, 1 Barrhill Rd, Streatham, London SW2 4RJ; Tel 020 8674 8993; Fax 020 8678 6593

Lewisham

Catford Citizens Advice Bureau 120 Rushey Grn, Catford, London SE6 4HQ; Tel 020 8690 3190; Fax 020 8690 0067

Lewisham Citizens Advice Bureau Money Advice Service, 80 Downham Way, Bromley, Kent BR1 5NX; Tel 020 8695 5477; Fax 020 8695 9924

Sydenham Citizens Advice Bureau 299 Kirkdale, Sydenham, London SE26 4QD; Tel 020 8690 3190; Fax 020 8776 7499

16

Merton

Merton Citizens Advice Bureau Money Advice Service, 326 London Rd, Mitcham, Surrey CR4 3ND; Tel 020 8640 3194; Fax 020 8685 9483

Mitcham Citizens Advice Bureau 326 London Rd, Mitcham, Surrey CR4 3ND; Tel 020 8288 0450; Fax 020 8685 9483

Morden Citizens Advice Bureau 7 Crown Pde, Morden, Surrey SM4 5DX; Tel 020 8715 0707; Fax 020 8715 0550

Redbridge

Citizens Advice Line for London PO Box 1401, Ilford, Essex IG1 2DP; Tel (Advice Line) 020 8478 51431

Redbridge Citizens Advice Bureau 2nd Fl South, Broadway Chamber, Ilford, Essex IG1 4DU; Tel 020 8514 1314; Fax 020 8514 5700

Richmond

Hampton Citizens Advice Bureau The White Hse Community Centre, 45 The Avenue, Hampton, Surrey TW12 3RN; Tel 020 8941 8330; Fax 020 8941 7443

Richmond Citizens Advice Bureau Linfield Hse, 26 Kew Rd, Richmond, Surrey TW9 2NA; Tel 020 8940 2501; Fax 020 8332 0708

Sheen Citizens Advice Bureau Sheen Lane Centre, Sheen La, London SW14 8LP; Tel 020 8876 1513; Fax 020 8878 5105

Tooting and Balham Citizens Advice Bureau Bedford Hse, 4th Fl, Tooting, London SW17 7BQ; Tel 020 8333 6960; Fax 020 8378 5892

Twickenham Citizens Advice Bureau The Advice Centre, 61 Heath Rd, Twickenham, Greater London TW1 4AW; Tel 020 8892 5917; Fax 020 8744 1167

Southwark

Bermondsey Citizens Advice Bureau 8 Market Pl, Southwark Park Rd, London SE16 3UQ; Tel 020 7231 1118; Fax 020 7231 4410

Peckham Citizens Advice Bureau 97 Peckham High St, London SE15 5RS; Tel 020 7639 4471; Fax 020 7732 2497

Sutton

Beddington and Wallington Citizens Advice Bureau 16 Stanley Park Rd, Wallington, Surrey SM6 0EU; Tel 020 8669 3435; Fax 020 8770 4928

St. Helier Citizens Advice Bureau 5–6 Rose Hill Court Pde, St. Helier Ave, Morden, Surrey SM4 6JS; Tel 020 8640 4170; Fax 020 8648 9128

North Cheam Citizens Advice Bureau 320 Malden Rd, North Cheam, Sutton, Surrey SM3 8EP; Tel 020 8770 4851; Fax 020 8770 4917

Sutton Citizens Advice Bureau Central Library, St. Nicholas Way, Sutton, Surrey SM1 1EA; Tel 020 8643 5291; Fax 020 8770 4929

Tower Hamlets

Tottenham Citizens Advice Bureau Tottenham Town Hall, Town Hall Approach Rd, London N15; Tel 020 8808 6555

Tower Hamlets East Citizens Advice Bureau 86 Bow Rd, London E3 4DL; Tel 020 8980 3728; Fax 020 8981 8761

Whitechapel Citizens Advice Bureau Unit 32, Greatorex St, London E1 5NP; Tel 020 7247 4172; Fax 020 7375 2256

Waltham Forest

Leytonstone Citizens Advice Bureau Greater London Hse, 547–551 High Rd, Leytonstone, London E11 4PB; Tel 020 8556 5693; Fax 020 8558 7911

Walthamstow Citizens Advice Bureau 167 Hoe St, Walthamstow, London E17 3AL; Tel 020 8520 0939; Fax 020 8509 9611

Wandsworth

Battersea Legal Services 14 York Rd, Battersea, London SW11 3QA; Fax (Advice) 020 7978 5348

Putney Citizens Advice Bureau 228 Upper Richmond Rd, Putney, London SW15 6TG; Tel 020 8333 6960; Fax 020 8479 0049

Wandsworth Money Advice Service 215 Balham High Rd, Tooting, London SW17 7BQ; Tel 020 8871 5740

Westminster

Paddington Citizens Advice Bureau 441 Harrow Rd, Paddington, London W10 4RE; Tel 020 8960 2051; Fax 020 8960 4244

Pimlico Citizens Advice Bureau 140 Tachbrook St, London SW1V 2NE; Tel 020 7834 5727; Fax 020 7233 7854

St. Marylebone Citizens Advice Bureau Room 26, Westminster Council Hse, London NW1 5PT; Tel 020 7798 1157; Fax 020 7798 1164

Strand Royal Courts of Justice Royal Courts of Justice, Strand, London WC2A 2LL; Tel 020 7405 2225; Fax 020 7936 7167

Maidenhead and Windsor

Maidenhead Citizens Advice Bureau Redcote Hse, Holmanleaze, Maidenhead, Windsor and Maidenhead SL6 8AW; Tel 01628 621006; Fax 01628 778052

Medway

Rochester Citizens Advice Bureau The Guildhall, 17 High St, Rochester, Kent ME1 1PY; Tel 01634 407549; 01634 843723; Fax 01634 818906

Merseyside

Anfield Citizens Advice Bureau 41 Townsend La, Anfield, Liverpool, Merseyside L6 0BX; Tel 0151 263 4754; Fax 0151 260 8446

Bebington Citizens Advice Bureau 57 New Chester Rd, New Ferry, Bebington, Wirral CH62 1AB; Tel 0151 645 8793; Fax 0151 644 9478

Birkenhead (Charity) Ltd Citizens Advice Bureau 50 Argyle St, Birkenhead, Merseyside CH41 6AF; Tel 0151 647 6517; (Appointments only) 0151 674 3826; Fax 0151 647 3026

Bootle Citizens Advice Bureau 297 Knowsley Rd, Bootle, Merseyside L20 5DF; Tel 0151 922 1114; Fax 0151 933 0734

Crosby Citizens Advice Bureau Prince St, Waterloo, Liverpool, Merseyside L22 5PB; Tel 0151 928 9702; Fax 0151 920 1243

Formby Citizens Advice Bureau 11 Duke St, Formby, Liverpool, Merseyside L37 4AN; Tel 01704 875078; Fax 01704 833015

Garston Citizens Advice Bureau 17 James St, Garston, Liverpool, Merseyside L19 2NJ; Tel 0151 427 7419; Fax 0151 494 1683

Kensington (Merseyside) Citizens Advice Bureau Rathbone Community, Industrial Bldg, Liverpool, Merseyside L7 5ND; Tel 0151 260 6393; Fax 0151 261 1010

Knowsley Central (Huyton) Citizens Advice Bureau Community Services Centre, Lathom Rd, Liverpool, Merseyside L36 9XZ; Tel 0151 489 5098; Fax 0151 489 0113

Knowsley North (Kirkby) Citizens Advice Bureau 2 Newton Gdns, Kirkby, Merseyside L32 8RR; Tel 0151 546 2284

Knowsley South (Halewood) Citizens Advice Bureau 5–21 Raven Court Shopping Centre, Leathers La, Liverpool, Merseyside L26 0UP; Tel 0151 486 3593; Fax 0151 443 2061

Liverpool City Citizens Advice Bureau 3rd Fl, Hepworth Chambers, Liverpool, Merseyside L1 3AA; Tel 0151 709 8989; Fax 0151 709 5959

Liverpool County Court Service 4th Fl, Queen Elizabeth II Law Courts, Liverpool, Merseyside L2 1XA; Tel 0151 473 7373 ext 4156

Netherley Citizens Advice Bureau Unit G, Belle Vale Shopping Centre, Netherley, Merseyside L25 2RF; Tel 0151 487 0027; Fax 0151 487 8342

Old Swan Citizens Advice Bureau 536 Prescot Rd, Old Swan, Liverpool, Merseyside L13 3DB; Tel 0151 220 0125; Fax 0151 254 1958

Southport Citizens Advice Bureau 24 Wright St, Southport, Merseyside PR9 0TL; Tel 01704 531456; Fax 01704 564821

Speke Citizens Advice Bureau Damwood Hall, North Pde, Liverpool, Merseyside L24 2SB; Tel 0151 486 4737; Fax 0151 486 4737

St. Helen's Citizens Advice Bureau Waterloo St, St. Helen's, Merseyside WA10 1PU; Tel 01744 22935; Fax 01744 758720

Toxteth Citizens Advice Bureau 254 Park Rd, Toxteth, Liverpool, Merseyside L8 8DX; Tel 0151 280 8484; Fax 0151 280 5781

Wallasey Citizens Advice Bureau 237–243 Liscard Rd, Wallasey, Merseyside CH44 5TH; Tel 0151 639 7858; 0151 639 7859; Fax 0151 630 5118

Walton (Merseyside) Citizens Advice Bureau 131 County Rd, Walton, Liverpool, Merseyside L4 3QF; Tel 0151 525 1639; Fax 0151 521 5880

West Kirby Citizens Advice Bureau 1 Acacia Gr, West Kirby, Wirral CH48 4DD; Tel 0151 625 9802; Fax 0151 625 0625

Norfolk

Dereham Citizens Advice Bureau Assembly Rooms, Ruthem Pl, East Dereham, Norfolk NR19 2TX; Tel 01362 697776; Fax 01362 692546

Diss, Eye and Harleston Citizens Advice Bureau Shelfhanger Rd, Diss, Norfolk IP22 3EH; Tel 01379 651333; Fax 01379 640530

Fakenham and District Citizens Advice Bureau The Community Centre, Oak St, Fakenham, Norfolk NR21 9DY; Tel 01328 856040; Fax 01328 856024

Great Yarmouth Citizens Advice Bureau 2 Stonecutters Way, Great Yarmouth, Norfolk NR30 1HF; E-mail advice@gtyarmouthcab.freeserve.co.uk; Tel 01493 856665; Fax 01493 331950

Holt Citizens Advice Bureau Kerridge Way, Holt, Norfolk NR25 6DN; Tel 01263 713849; Fax 01263 713753

King's Lynn Citizens Advice Bureau Thoresby College, Queen St, King's Lynn, Norfolk PE30 1HX; Tel 01553 774719; Fax 01553 660900

Marham Citizens Advice Bureau 28 Grange Cres, Upper Marham, Norfolk PE33 9LA; Tel 01760 338347

Norfolk Citizens Advice Bureau Money Advice, Units 12, Norwich, Norfolk NR2 4TE; Tel 01603 763961; Fax 01603 763961

North Walsham and District Citizens Advice Bureau New Rd, North Walsham, Norfolk NR28 9DE; Tel 01692 402570; Fax 01692 405847

Norwich Citizens Advice Bureau The Advice Arcade, 4 Guildhall Hill, Norwich, Norfolk NR2 1JH; URL www.gurney.co.uk / cab; Tel 01603 262478; 01603 626145; Fax 01603 765007; 01603 878828

Thetford Citizens Advice Bureau 15 Earls St, Thetford, Norfolk IP24 2AB; Tel 01842 752777; 01842 753382; Fax 01842 750986

Watton Citizens Advice Bureau The Cabin, Harvey St, Watton, Norfolk IP25 6EB; Tel 01953 882746

Wymondham Citizens Advice Bureau 14 The Bridewell, Norwich Rd, Wymondham, Norfolk NR18 0NS; Tel 01953 603977; Fax 01953 600217

North East Lincolnshire

Grimsby Citizens Advice Bureau 6 Town Hall St, Grimsby, North East Lincolnshire DN31 1HN; Tel 01472 359005; Fax 01472 269838

North West Somerset

Weston-super-Mare (Woodspring) Citizens Advice Bureau Roselawn, 7 Walliscote Grove Rd, Weston-super-Mare, North Somerset BS23 1UT; Tel 01934 621908; Fax 01934 412558

North Yorkshire

Hambleton Citizens Advice Bureau 9 South Pde, Northallerton, North Yorkshire DL7 8SE; Tel 01609 770309; Fax 01609 773365

Harrogate Citizens Advice Bureau Victoria Park Hse, 18 Victoria Ave, Harrogate, North Yorkshire HG1 5QY; URL www.harrogate.cab.demon.co.uk; Tel 01423 503756; 01423 567150; Fax 01423 565192

Richmondshire Citizens Advice Bureau The Old School, Dundas St, Richmond, North Yorkshire DL10 7AB; Tel 01748 823978; Fax 01748 823965

Ripon Citizens Advice Bureau 5 Duck Hill, Ripon, North Yorkshire HG4 1BL; Tel 01765 603297; Fax 01765 690306

Ryedale Citizens Advice Bureau Ryedale Community Hse, Wentworth St, Malton, North Yorkshire YO17 0BN; Tel 01653 692740; Fax 01653 692809

Scarborough and District Citizens Advice Bureau 62 Roscoe St, Scarborough, North Yorkshire YO12 7BY; Tel 01723 368710; Fax 01723 354795

Selby Citizens Advice Bureau 16 Park St, Selby, North Yorkshire YO8 4PW; Tel 01757 702031; Fax 01757 213325

Skipton Citizens Advice Bureau St. Andrew's Church Hall, Newmarket St, Skipton, North Yorkshire BD23 2JE; Tel 01756 700210; 01756 792821; Fax 01756 796631

Northamptonshire

Corby Citizens Advice Bureau No. 1 Corby Advice Centre, George St, Corby, Northamptonshire NN17 1QG; Tel 01536 203552; Fax 01536 407599

Daventry and District Citizens Advice Bureau The Abbey, Market Sq, Daventry, Northamptonshire NN11 4BH; Tel 01327 706464; Fax 01327 701644

Kettering Citizens Advice Bureau The Oasis Centre, 10 Market St, Kettering, Northamptonshire NN16 0AH; Tel 01536 482321; Fax 01536 312313

Northampton Citizens Advice Bureau 72a St. Giles St, Northampton, Northamptonshire NN1 1JW; Tel 01604 636000; Fax 01604 231224

Rushden Citizens Advice Bureau Bakehouse Office, 46 Duck St, Rushden, Northamptonshire NN10 9SD; Tel 01933 317311; Fax 01933 411537

Wellingborough Citizens Advice Bureau 2b High St, Wellingborough, Northamptonshire NN8 4HR; Tel 01933 274343; Fax 01933 229781

Northumberland

Alnwick and District Citizens Advice Bureau The Bondgate Centre, 22 Bondgate Without, Alnwick, Northumberland NE66 1PN; Tel 01665 604135; Fax 01665 605849

Blyth Valley Citizens Advice Bureau Eric Tolhurst Centre, 3–13 Quay St, Blyth, Northumberland NE24 2AS; Tel 01670 367779; Fax 01670 545942

Castle Morpeth Citizens Advice Bureau Tower Bldgs, 9 Oldgate, Morpeth, Northumberland NE61 1PY; Tel 01670 518814; Fax 01670 511085

16

Eastern Borders Citizens Advice Bureau 5 Tweed St, Berwick-upon-Tweed, Northumberland TD15 1NG; Tel 01289 330222; Fax 01289 305025

Tynedale Citizens Advice Bureau The Community Centre, Gilesgate, Hexham, Northumberland NE46 3NP; Tel 01434 605254; Fax 01434 607611

Wansbeck Citizens Advice Bureau Station Villa, Kenilworth Rd, Ashington, Northumberland NE63 8AA; Tel 01670 818360; Fax 01670 812573

Nottinghamshire

Ashfield Citizens Advice Bureau 22 Market St, Sutton-in-Ashfield, Nottinghamshire NG17 1AG; Tel 01623 557686; Fax 01623 555345

Bassetlaw Citizens Advice Bureau Central Ave, Worksop, Nottinghamshire S80 1EJ; Tel 01909 476049; Fax 01909 530566

Beeston Citizens Advice Bureau Albion St, Beeston, Nottingham, Nottinghamshire NG9 2PA; Tel 0115 922 1074; Fax 0115 943 6362

Eastwood Citizens Advice Bureau Library and Information Centre, Nottingham Rd, Eastwood, Nottinghamshire NG16 3GB; Tel 01773 718065; 01773 760641; Fax 01773 533687; 01773 768363

Mansfield Citizens Advice Bureau Queens Wlk, Mansfield, Nottinghamshire NG18 1JX; Tel 01623 627163; Fax 01623 427472

Newark and District Citizens Advice Bureau 2 Castlegate, Newark, Nottinghamshire NG24 1AX; Tel 01636 704391; Fax 01636 640819

Nottingham and District Citizens Advice Bureau 24–30 Castle Gate, Nottingham NG1 7AT; Tel 0115 958 5280; Fax 0115 958 5628

Ollerton and District Citizens Advice Bureau 5 Forest Crt, Forest Rd, Newark, Nottinghamshire NG22 9PL; Tel 01623 861808; Fax 01623 836156

Oxfordshire

Abingdon Citizens Advice Bureau The Charter, Abingdon, Oxfordshire OX14 3LX; Tel 01235 521894; Fax 01235 537050

Banbury and District Citizens Advice Bureau Cornhill Hse, 26 Cornhill, Banbury, Oxfordshire OX16 8NG; Tel 01295 264637; Fax 01295 269960

Bicester Citizens Advice Bureau The Garth, Launton Rd, Bicester, Oxfordshire OX6 0JB; Tel 01869 321076; Fax 01869 248606

Didcot and District Citizens Advice Bureau Civic Hall, Britwell Rd, Didcot, Oxfordshire OX11 7JN; Tel 01235 813632

Henley and District Citizens Advice Bureau Market Pl, Henley on Thames, Oxfordshire RG9 2AQ; Tel 01491 572129

Oxford Citizens Advice Bureau 95 St. Aldates, Oxford, Oxfordshire OX1 1DA; Tel 01865 247578; Fax 01865 202715

Thame Citizens Advice Bureau Market Hse, North St, Thame, Oxfordshire OX9 3HH; Tel 01844 214827; Fax 01844 214827

Witney Citizens Advice Bureau 33a High St, Witney, Oxfordshire OX8 6LP; Tel 01993 705691; Fax 01993 771245

Peterborough

Peterborough Citizens Advice Bureau Alma Hse, 41a Park Rd, Peterborough PE1 2TH; Tel 01733 346516; Fax 01733 340028

Reading

Reading Citizens Advice Bureau 21 Chatham St, Reading RG1 7JF; Tel 0118 950 2829; 0118 958 3513; 0118 959 8059; Fax 01734 394442

Reading Community Welfare Rights Unit 17 Chatham St, Reading RG1 7JF; Tel 01734 505292; 01734 505296; Fax 01734 571673

Shropshire

Bridgnorth and District Citizens Advice Bureau Whitburn St, Bridgnorth, Shropshire WV16 4QT; Tel 01746 763838; Fax 01746 763766

Madeley Citizens Advice Bureau The People's Centre, High St, Telford, Shropshire TF7 5AU; URL www.madeley-high-street.freeserve.co.uk; E-mail cab@madeley.org.uk; Tel 01952 585824; Fax 01952 684830

North Shropshire Citizens Advice Bureau Lord Clive Chambers, St. Mary's St, Market Drayton, Shropshire TF9 1AA; Tel 01630 657137; Fax 01630 658126

Oswestry and Border Citizens Advice Bureau 16 Lower Brook St, Oswestry, Shropshire SY11 2HJ; Tel 01691 654425; Fax 01691 657564

Shrewsbury Citizens Advice Bureau The Roy Fletcher Centre, 12–17 Cross Hill, Shrewsbury, Shropshire SY1 1JE; Tel 01743 357855

South Shropshire Citizens Advice Bureau 2 College St, Ludlow, Shropshire SY8 1AN; Tel 01584 876454; 01584 876933; Fax 01584 876454

Telford Citizens Advice Bureau Meeting Point Hse, Southwater Sq, Telford, Wrekin TF3 4HS; Tel 01952 291101; Fax 01952 200322

Wellington Citizens Advice Bureau 35 Church St, Wellington, Wrekin TF1 1DG; Tel 01952 223232

Slough

Slough Citizens Advice Bureau 27 Church St, Slough SL1 1PL; Tel 01753 522004; 01753 522189; Fax 01753 693830

Somerset

Bridgwater (Sedgemoor) Citizens Advice Bureau 1 Castle St, Bridgwater, Somerset TA6 3DD; Tel 01278 455236

Frome Citizens Advice Bureau St. John's Cottage, Church Steps, Frome, Somerset BA11 1PL; Tel 01373 465496; Fax 01373 452289

Shepton Mallet Citizens Advice Bureau The Amulet, 7 Market Pl, Shepton Mallet, Somerset BA4 5AG; Tel 01749 343010

Taunton Citizens Advice Bureau Sussex Lodge, 44 Station Rd, Taunton, Somerset TA1 1NS; Tel 01823 282235

Yeovil (South Somerset) Citizens Advice Bureau Petter's Hse, Petter's Way, Yeovil, Somerset BA20 1SH; Tel 01935 421167; Fax 01935 410561

Southend

Southend-on-Sea Citizens Advice Bureau 1 Church Rd, Southend-on-Sea, Southend SS1 2AL; Tel 01702 610610; Fax 01702 469999

South Gloucestershire

Kingswood and District Citizens Advice Bureau 117 High St, Staple Hill, Bristol BS16 5HF; Tel 0117 956 9174; Fax 0117 957 4212

South Yorkshire

Askern and District Citizens Advice Bureau 59 Manor Rd, Askern, Doncaster, South Yorkshire DN6 0BE; Tel 01302 701339; Fax 01302 709137

Barnsley Citizens Advice Bureau 10 Regent St South, Barnsley, South Yorkshire S70 2HT; Tel 01226 206492; Fax 01226 298840

Doncaster Citizens Advice Bureau The Guildhall Advice Centre, Old Guildhall Yard, Doncaster, South Yorkshire DN1 1QW; Tel 01302 735225; 01302 735232; Fax 01302 735230

Mexborough and District Citizens Advice Bureau The Lindsay Centre, Hallgate, Mexborough, South Yorkshire S64 0JT; Tel 01709 585827; Fax 01709 578476

Pitsmoor Citizens Advice Bureau 28–30 Spital Hill, Sheffield, South Yorkshire S4 7LG; Tel 0114 275 5376; Fax 0114 276 9454

Rotherham Citizens Advice Bureau Centenary Market Bldgs, Eastwood La, Rotherham, South Yorkshire S65 1EQ; Tel 01709 513523; Fax 01709 513815

Sharrow Citizens Advice Bureau 416–418 London Rd, Sheffield, South Yorkshire S2 4ND; Tel 0114 258 3322; Fax 0114 258 3363

Stainforth Citizens Advice Bureau 14 Church Rd, Stainforth, South Yorkshire DN7 5AA; Tel 01302 842845; Fax 01302 845187

Staffordshire

Biddulph Citizens Advice Bureau 10 Tunstall Rd, Biddulph, Stoke-on-Trent ST8 6HH; Tel 01782 519332; Fax 01782 519341

Burntwood and District Citizens Advice Bureau 7 Cannock Rd, Chase Terr, Burntwood, Staffordshire WS7 8JS; Tel 01543 682936

Burton-upon-Trent Citizens Advice Bureau Voluntary Services Centre, Union Street Car Pk, Burton-upon-Trent, Staffordshire DE14 1AA; Tel 01283 510993; Fax 01283 566493

Cannock Citizens Advice Bureau 48 Allport Rd, Cannock, Staffordshire WS11 1DZ; Tel 01543 502236

Cheadle Citizens Advice Bureau Council Office Car Park, Harborne Rd, Cheadle, Staffordshire ST10 1JY

Kidsgrove Citizens Advice Bureau Claire Hse, Liverpool Rd, Stoke-on-Trent ST7 4EH; Tel 01782 786529; Fax 01782 777587

Leek Citizens Advice Bureau 20 St. Edwards St, Leek, Staffordshire ST13 5DS; Tel 01538 373243

Lichfield Citizens Advice Bureau 29 Levetts Fields, Lichfield, Staffordshire WS13 6HY; Tel 01543 252730; Fax 01543 414255

Newcastle-under-Lyme Citizens Advice Bureau 25–27 Well St, Newcastle-under-Lyme, Staffordshire ST5 1BP; Tel 01782 617381; Fax 01782 713202

Rugeley Citizens Advice Bureau 7 Brook Sq, Rugeley, Staffordshire WS15 2DU; Tel 01889 577042; Fax 01889 586126

Stafford Citizens Advice Bureau Stafford District, Voluntary Services Centre, Stafford, Staffordshire ST16 3AD; Tel 01785 258673

Stoke-on-Trent District Citizens Advice Bureau Advice Hse, Cheapside, Stoke-on-Trent ST1 1HL; URL www.stoke.cab.org.uk; Tel 01782 219427; Fax 01782 269632

Stone Citizens Advice Bureau St. Mary's Chambers, 19 Station Rd, Stone, Staffordshire ST15 8JT; Tel 01785 814806

Tamworth Citizens Advice Bureau 1st Fl, The Philip Dix Centre, Tamworth, Staffordshire B79 7DN; Tel 01827 709645; Fax 01827 709644

Uttoxeter Citizens Advice Bureau Rear Annexe, Town Hall, Uttoxeter, Staffordshire ST14 7HN; Tel 01889 568500; Fax 01889 567058

Stockton-on-Tees

Stockton and District Citizens Advice Bureau Bath La, Stockton-on-Tees TS18 2EQ; Tel 01642 607445; Fax 01642 612666

Suffolk

Beccles Citizens Advice Bureau 1 Ballygate, Beccles, Suffolk NR34 9NA; Tel 01502 717715; Fax 01502 716212

Brandon Citizens Advice Bureau Old School Hse, Market Hill, Brandon, Suffolk IP27 0AA; Tel 01842 811511; Fax 01842 813116

Bungay Citizens Advice Bureau 8 Chaucer St, Bungay, Suffolk NR35 1DT; Tel 01986 895827; Fax 01502 892144

Bury St. Edmunds Citizens Advice Bureau Risbygate Centre, 90 Risbygate, Bury St. Edmunds, Suffolk IP33 1SQ; Tel 01284 753675; 01284 755039; Fax 01284 763056

Felixstowe Citizens Advice Bureau 2–6 Orwell Rd, Felixstowe, Suffolk IP11 7HD; Tel 01394 275958; Fax 01394 275325

Halesworth Citizens Advice Bureau 25 Market Pl, Halesworth, Suffolk IP19 8AY; Tel 01986 874541; Fax 01502 874522

Haverhill Citizens Advice Bureau 4 Swan La, Haverhill, Suffolk CB9 8AH; Tel 01440 704012; Fax 01440 713212

Ipswich and District Citizens Advice Bureau 19 Tower St, Ipswich, Suffolk IP1 3BE; Tel 01473 219777; Fax 01473 286548

Leiston Citizens Advice Bureau Council Offices, Main St, Leiston, Suffolk IP16 4ER; Tel 01728 832193; Fax 01728 832544

Lowestoft Citizens Advice Bureau The Advice Centre, 36 Gordon Rd, Lowestoft, Suffolk NR32 1NL; Tel 01502 518510; 01502 565875; Fax 01502 515825

Mildenhall Citizens Advice Bureau Willow Hse, 40 St. Andrew's St, Mildenhall, Suffolk IP28 7HB; Tel 01638 712094; Fax 01638 715567

Newmarket Citizens Advice Bureau Foley Gate, Wellington St, Newmarket, Suffolk CB8 0HY; Tel 01638 661694; 01638 665999; Fax 01638 668111

Saxmundham Citizens Advice Bureau 26b High St, Saxmundham, Suffolk IP17 1AB; Tel 01728 603057; Fax 01728 602102

Sudbury Citizens Advice Bureau Belle Vue, Newton Rd, Sudbury, Suffolk CO10 6RG; Tel 01787 374671; Fax 01787 881564

Surrey

Ash Citizens Advice Bureau Ash Hill Rd, Ash, Aldershot, Hampshire GU12 5DP; Tel 01252 315569; Fax 01252 316612

Camberley Citizens Advice Bureau Surrey Heath Hse, Knoll Rd, Camberley, Surrey GU15 3HD; Tel 01276 707500; Fax 01276 707508

Caterham and Warlingham Citizens Advice Bureau Soper Hall, Harestone Valley Rd, Caterham, Surrey CR3 6YN; Tel 01883 344777; Fax 01883 341745

Cranleigh Citizens Advice Bureau Village Way, Cranleigh, Surrey GU6 8AF; Tel 01483 273378; Fax 01483 271054

Dorking Citizens Advice Bureau 231 High St, Dorking, Surrey RH4 1RT; Tel 01306 876805; Fax 01306 741416

Epsom and Ewell Citizens Advice Bureau 7 The Pde, E psom, Surrey KT18 5DU; Tel 01372 720205; Fax 01372 732587

16

Esher and District Citizens Advice Bureau Harry Fletcher Hse, High St, Esher, Surrey KT10 9RN; Tel 01372 464770; Fax 01372 470488

Farnham Citizens Advice Bureau Bright Hse, off East St, Farnham, Surrey GU9 7SB; Tel 01252 716319; Fax 01252 726218

Godalming and District Citizens Advice Bureau 10 Queen St, Godalming, Surrey GU7 1BD; Tel 01483 428212; Fax 01483 421779

Guildford Citizens Advice Bureau 15 Haydon Pl, Guildford, Surrey GU1 4LL; Tel 01483 576657; 01483 576699; Fax 01483 450185

Haslemere Citizens Advice Bureau Well Lane Hse, High St, Haslemere, Surrey GU27 2LB; Tel 01428 643413; Fax 01428 656130

Heathlands Citizens Advice Bureau Beech Hse, Church Rd, Camberley, Surrey GU16 5AD

Horley Citizens Advice Bureau Albert Rooms, 92 Albert Rd, Horley, Surrey RH6 7HZ; Tel 01293 786346; Fax 01293 785521

Leatherhead Citizens Advice Bureau Wesley Hse, Bull Hill, Leatherhead, Surrey KT22 7AH; Tel 01372 375522; Fax 01372 379166

Oxted Citizens Advice Bureau The Portacabin, The Ellice Road Car Park, Oxted, Surrey RH8 0PY; Tel 01883 715525; Fax 01883 730259

Runnymede Citizens Advice Bureau Civic Offices, Station Rd, Addlestone, Surrey KT15 2AH; Tel 01932 477080; 01932 842266; Fax 01932 827187

Staines Citizens Advice Bureau Community Link, Knowle Grn, Staines, Greater London TW18 1XB; Tel 01784 444220; Fax 01784 446394

Sunbury and Shepperton Citizens Advice Bureau 1b Staines Road West, Sunbury-on-Thames, Greater London TW16 7AB; Tel 01932 765041

Walton, Weybridge and Hersham Citizens Advice Bureau Elm Gr, Hersham Rd, Walton-on-Thames, Surrey KT12 1LH; Tel 01932 248660; Fax 01932 221680

Woking Citizens Advice Bureau Provencial Hse, 26 Commercial Way, Woking, Surrey GU21 1EN; Tel 01483 763840; Fax 01483 776350

Sussex

Bexhill and Rother Citizens Advice Bureau Voluntary Services Centre, 38 Sackville Rd, Bexhill, East Sussex TN39 3JE; Tel 01424 215055; 01424 734549; Fax 01424 734513

Bognor Regis Citizens Advice Bureau Town Hall, Clarence Rd, Bognor Regis, West Sussex PO21 1LD; Tel 01243 820644; Fax 01243 842981

Brighton Citizens Advice Bureau 39–41 Surrey St, (opposite Brighton Station), Brighton, Brighton and Hove BN1 3PB; Tel 01273 207551; Fax 01273 776376

Burgess Hill Citizens Advice Bureau Delmon Hse, 38 Church Rd, Burgess Hill, West Sussex RH15 9AE; Tel 01444 241252; Fax 01444 871309

Chichester and District Citizens Advice Bureau Bell Hse, 6 Theatre La, Chichester, West Sussex PO19 1SR; Tel 01243 784231; Fax 01243 538914

Crawley Citizens Advice Bureau The Tree, 103 High St, Crawley, West Sussex RH10 1DD; Tel 01293 529717; Fax 01293 551443

Crowborough Citizens Advice Bureau Thorpe Hse, Croft Rd, Crowborough, East Sussex TN6 1DL; Tel 01892 655303; Fax 01892 653841

Eastbourne Citizens Advice Bureau 66 Grove Rd, Eastbourne, East Sussex BN21 4UH; Tel 01323 410110; 01323 417177; Fax 01323 412072

East Grinstead Citizens Advice Bureau Cantalupe Hse, Cantalupe Rd, East Grinstead, West Sussex RH19 3BZ; Tel 01342 321638; Fax 01342 410240

Hailsham Citizens Advice Bureau Southview, Western Rd, Hailsham, East Sussex BN27 3DN; Tel 01323 842336; Fax 01323 849762

Hastings Citizens Advice Bureau 24 Cornwallis Terr, Hastings, East Sussex TN34 1EB; Tel 01424 430400; 01424 721386; Fax 01424 442253

Haywards Heath Citizens Advice Bureau Oaklands, Paddock Hall, Haywards Heath, West Sussex RH16 1HG; Tel 01444 454575; 01444 459866; Fax 01444 414799

Horsham Citizens Advice Bureau East Wing, Public Library, Horsham, West Sussex RH12 1PJ; Tel 01403 217257; Fax 01403 218548

Hove and Portslade Citizens Advice Bureau 1 Tisbury Rd, Hove, Brighton and Hove BN3 3BQ; Tel 01273 734811; Fax 01273 202631

Lancing and Sompting Citizens Advice Bureau Parish Hall, South St, Lancing, West Sussex BN15 8AJ; Tel 01903 755585; Fax 01903 754194

Lewes Citizens Advice Bureau 3 North St, Lewes, East Sussex BN7 2PA; Tel 01273 473082

Littlehampton Citizens Advice Bureau 14–16 Anchor Springs, Littlehampton, West Sussex BN17 6BP; Tel 01903 724010; Fax 01903 733237

Seaford Citizens Advice Bureau 23 Church St, Seaford, East Sussex BN25 1HD; Tel 01323 890875; 01323 896209

Shoreham and Southwick Citizens Advice Bureau Volunteer Centre, Pond Rd, Shoreham by Sea, West Sussex BN43 5WU; Tel 01273 453756; Fax 01273 462754

Uckfield Citizens Advice Bureau Civic Centre, Bell Farm La, Uckfield, East Sussex TN22 1AE; E-mail citizens@dial.pipex.com; Tel 01825 764940; Fax 01825 767181

Worthing and District Citizens Advice Bureau 11 North St, Worthing, West Sussex BN11 1DU; Tel 01903 231972; 01903 232116

Tyne and Wear

Gateshead Citizens Advice Bureau 5 Regent Terr, Gateshead, Tyne and Wear NE8 1LU; Tel 0191 477 1392; Fax 0191 477 4922

Newcastle (City) Citizens Advice Bureau Westgate Hse, 46 Westgate Rd, Newcastle upon Tyne, Tyne and Wear NE1 1SH; Tel 0191 232 0832; Fax 0191 232 0461

South Tyneside Citizens Advice Bureau Edinburgh Bldgs, 2 Station Approach, South Shields, Tyne and Wear NE33 1HR; Tel 0191 456 0157; Fax 0191 454 7090

Washington Citizens Advice Bureau The Elms, 19 Front St, Washington, Tyne and Wear NE37 2BA; Tel 0191 416 6848; Fax 0191 415 3494

Whitley Bay Citizens Advice Bureau 109 Park View, Whitley Bay, Tyne and Wear NE26 3RH; Tel 0191 252 6841

Warrington

Warrington Citizens Advice Bureau 21 Reylands St, Warrington WA1 1EJ; Tel 01925 574547; Fax 01925 652547

Warwickshire

Bedworth Citizens Advice Bureau Old Market Tavern, 25 Congreve Wlk, Bedworth, Warwickshire CV12 8LX; Tel 024 7631 1119; Fax 024 7664 0710

North Warwickshire Citizens Advice Bureau Coleshill Hse, Coleshill Rd, Atherstone, Warwickshire CV9 1BW; Tel 01827 716988; Fax 01827 712852

Nuneaton Citizens Advice Bureau Barlow Hse, Back St, Nuneaton, Warwickshire CV11 4HG; Tel 024 7634 4708; 024 7638 3954; Fax 024 7664 1719

Rugby Citizens Advice Bureau 1st Fl, Chestnut Hse, Rugby, Warwickshire CV21 2AQ; Tel 01788 541000; Fax 01788 544903

Stratford-upon-Avon Citizens Advice Bureau 7a Rother St, Stratford-upon-Avon, Warwickshire CV37 6LU; Tel 01789 293299

Warwick and District Citizens Advice Bureau 28 Hamilton Terr, Leamington Spa, Warwickshire CV32 4LY; Tel 01926 421515; Fax 01926 885983

West Berkshire

Newbury Citizens Advice Bureau 16 Bartholomew St, Newbury, West Berkshire RG14 5LL; Tel 01635 40205; Fax 01635 524011

West Midlands

Acocks Green Citizens Advice Bureau York Hse, 2b Station Rd, Birmingham, West Midlands B27 6DN; Tel 0121 708 1871; Fax 0121 706 8276

Bilston Citizens Advice Bureau William Leigh Hse, 15 Walsall St, Wolverhampton, West Midlands WV14 0AT; Tel 01902 572000; Fax 01902 572008

Birmingham Citizens Advice Bureau Colmore Circus Subway, Bull St, Birmingham, West Midlands B4 6AJ; Tel 0121 236 0864

Birmingham Consumer Advice Centre 155–157 Corporation St, Birmingham, West Midlands B4 6PH; Tel 0121 236 3271; Fax 0121 233 2368

Brierley Hill Citizens Advice Bureau Cottage St, Brierley Hill, West Midlands DY5 1RE; Tel 01384 263430; 01384 482301; Fax 01384 482301

Chelmsley Wood Citizens Advice Bureau Stephenson Dr, Chelmsley Wood, Birmingham, West Midlands B37 5TA; Tel 0121 770 5915; 0121 770 9985; Fax 0121 779 6707

Coventry Citizens Advice Bureau Fleet Hse, Corporation St, Coventry, West Midlands CV1 1EG; Tel 024 7622 7474; Fax 024 7652 5315

Cradley Heath Citizens Advice Bureau Community Centre, Reddal Hill Rd, Warley, Oldbury, West Midlands B64 4JG; Tel 01384 636988; Fax 01384 410760

Dudley Citizens Advice Bureau Marlborough Hse, 11 St. James' Rd, Dudley, West Midlands DY1 1JG; Tel 01384 816066; Fax 01384 816069

Halesowen Citizens Advice Bureau 49 Summer Hill, Halesowen, West Midlands B63 3BU; Tel 01384 816181; Fax 01384 816191

Handsworth Citizens Advice Bureau 197 Churchill Pde, Birchfield Rd, Handsworth, West Midlands B19 1LL; Tel 0121 523 3226; Fax 0212 523 3227

Kings Heath Citizens Advice Bureau 1 Station Rd, Kings Heath, Birmingham, West Midlands B14 7SS; Tel 0121 444 0706; Fax 0121 444 8159

Kingstanding Citizens Advice Bureau 404 Kinstanding Rd, Kingstanding, Birmingham, West Midlands B44 8LD; Tel 0121 683 6883; Fax 0121 683 6884

Low Hill Citizens Advice Bureau The Bungalow, rear of Dale Hse, Wolverhampton, West Midlands WV10 9BG; Tel 01902 305446; Fax 01902 305455

Northfield Citizens Advice Bureau 734–740 Bristol Road South, Northfield, Birmingham, West Midlands B31 2NN; Tel 0121 476 6856

Oldbury Citizens Advice Bureau Municipal Bldgs, Halesowen St, Warley, Oldbury, West Midlands B69 3DB; Tel 0121 552 2022; Fax 0121 552 2442

Shirley Citizens Advice Bureau Shirley Centre, 274 Stratford Rd, Solihull, West Midlands B90 3AD; Tel 0121 745 3148; Fax 0121 745 6863

Smethwick Citizens Advice Bureau 370–372 High St, Smethwick, Warley, Oldbury, West Midlands B66 3PJ; Tel 0121 558 8500; Fax 0121 555 6291

Solihull Citizens Advice Bureau Alice Hse, 10 Homer Rd, Solihull, West Midlands B91 3QQ; Tel 0121 705 2211; Fax 0121 705 5192

Stourbridge Citizens Advice Bureau 69 Market St, Stourbridge, West Midlands DY8 1AQ; Tel 01384 816222; Fax 01384 816220

Sutton Coldfield Citizens Advice Bureau 2 South Cottage, Farthing La, Sutton Coldfield, West Midlands B72 1RN; Tel 0121 354 8344; 0121 355 0319; Fax 0121 354 9727

Tipton Citizens Advice Bureau Tipton Alliance, Neptune Health Pk, Tipton, West Midlands; Tel 0121 607 6411; Fax 0121 607 6413

Walsall Citizens Advice Bureau 139–144 Lichfield St, (opposite the Town Hall), Walsall, West Midlands WS1 1SE; Tel 01922 612111; 01922 612333; Fax 01922 648018

West Bromwich Citizens Advice Bureau 22 Lombard St, West Bromwich, West Midlands B70 8RT; Tel 0121 553 4423; Fax 0121 525 8019

Wolverhampton Citizens Advice Bureau 26 Snow Hill, Wolverhampton, West Midlands WV2 4AD; Tel 01902 773626; Fax 01902 421791

Yardley Citizens Advice Bureau 202–204 Church Rd, Yardley, West Midlands B25 8TU; Tel 0121 784 6455; Fax 0121 624 6111

West Yorkshire

Batley Citizens Advice Bureau Town Hall Annexe, Brunswick St, Batley, West Yorkshire WF17 5DT; Tel 01924 326066; Fax 01924 326062

Bradford Citizens Advice Bureau 17 Canal Rd, Bradford, West Yorkshire BD1 4AT; E-mail cab-bradford@merl.poptel.org.uk; Tel 01274 390170; 01274 725325; Fax 01274 370177

Brighouse Citizens Advice Bureau 1 Hall St, Brighouse, West Yorkshire HD6 1JY; Tel 01484 714066

Chapeltown Citizens Advice Bureau Willow Hse, New Roscoe Bldgs, Leeds, West Yorkshire LS7 4BZ; Tel 0113 262 9479; Fax 0113 237 4894

Dewsbury Citizens Advice Bureau The Town Hall, Dewsbury, West Yorkshire WF12 8DG; Tel 01924 461491; Fax 01924 462257

Elland Citizens Advice Bureau Providence United Reformed Church, Huddersfield Rd, Elland, West Yorkshire HX5 9AH; Tel 01422 376080; Fax 01422 377738

Halifax Citizens Advice Bureau 37 Harrison Rd, Halifax, West Yorkshire HX1 2AF; Tel 01422 342917; Fax 01422 348036

Keighley Citizens Advice Bureau The Library Annexe, Spencer St, Keighley, West Yorkshire BD21 3BN; Tel 01535 605454; Fax 01535 601326

Leeds Citizens Advice Bureau 31 New York St, Leeds, West Yorkshire LS2 7DT; Tel 0113 245 7679; Fax 0113 246 1160

Otley Citizens Advice Bureau Courthouse St, Otley, West Yorkshire LS21 1BG; Tel 01943 466976; Fax 01943 464395

Pontefract Citizens Advice Bureau 1b Charter Hse, Jackson's Crt, Pontefract, West Yorkshire WF8 1DE; Tel 01977 793768; Fax 01977 795098

South Elmsall Citizens Advice Bureau Westfield Resource and Enterprise Centre, Westfield La, Pontefract, West Yorkshire WF9 2PU; Tel 01977 642179; Fax 01977 640537

Spen Valley Citizens Advice Bureau The Town Hall, Church St, Cleckheaton, West Yorkshire BD19 3RH; Tel 01274 877607; Fax 01274 862491

16

Wakefield Citizens Advice Bureau 27 King St, Wakefield, West Yorkshire WF1 2SR; Tel 01924 372563; Fax 01924 200837

Wiltshire

Kennet Citizens Advice Bureau Commercial Rd, Devizes, Wiltshire SN10 1EH; Tel 01380 722242; 01380 728771; Fax 01380 728848

North Wiltshire Citizens Advice Bureau 3 Avon Reach, Monkton Hill, Chippenham, Wiltshire SN15 1EE; Tel 01249 443046; Fax 01249 445812

Salisbury and District Citizens Advice Bureau 18 College St, Salisbury, Wiltshire SP1 3AL; E-mail advice@cabsalisbury.force9.co.uk; Tel 01722 327222; Fax 01722 410262

Swindon Citizens Advice Bureau 1 Faringdon Rd, Swindon SN1 5AR; Tel 01793 528303; Fax 01793 613270

West Wiltshire Citizens Advice Bureau Mill Hse, 58 Stallard St, Trowbridge, Wiltshire BA14 9AE; Tel 01225 763865; Fax 01225 774069

Wokingham

Wokingham Citizens Advice Bureau Wellington Hse, Wellington Rd, Wokingham RG40 2AB; URL www.wokingham-cab.org.uk; E-mail user@whamcab.doctornet.co.uk; Tel 01734 775604; 01734 890389; Fax 01734 782277

Worcestershire

Bromsgrove and District Citizens Advice Bureau 47 Worcester Rd, Bromsgrove, Worcestershire BG1 7DN; Tel 01527 831480; Fax 01527 574536

Malvern Hills Citizens Advice Bureau The Grange, Grange Rd, Malvern, Worcestershire WR14 3HA; Tel 01684 563611

Redditch Citizens Advice Bureau Central Chambers, 20 Unicorn Hill, Redditch, Worcestershire B97 4QU; Tel 01527 66664; Fax 01527 596588

Worcester Citizens Advice Bureau 2a St. Nicholas St, Worcester, Worcestershire WR1 1UW; Tel 01905 611371; Fax 01905 20478

Wychavon (Evesham) Citizens Advice Bureau 110 High St, Evesham, Worcestershire WR11 4EJ; Tel 01386 443737

Wyre Forest Citizens Advice Bureau 21–22 New Rd, Kidderminster, Worcestershire DY10 1AF; Tel 01562 823953; Fax 01562 864774

York City

York Citizens Advice Bureau 3 Blossom St, York YO2 1AU; Tel 01904 636066; Fax 01904 620571

Wales

Blaenau Gwent

Abertillery Citizens Advice Bureau The Council Offices, Mitre St, Abertillery, Blaenau Gwent NP3 1BX; Tel 01495 212424

Bridgend

Bridgend Citizens Advice Bureau 1b Merthyr Mawr Rd, Bridgend CF31 3NH; Tel 01656 654951; Fax 07070 659726

Maesteg Citizens Advice Bureau Council Offices, Talbot St, Maesteg, Blaenau Gwent CF34 9DA; Tel 01656 734662; Fax 01656 735948

Caerphilly

Bargoed and District Citizens Advice Bureau 41b Hanbury Sq, Bargoed, Caerphilly CF81 8QU; Tel 01443 831112; Fax 01443 839872

Blackwood Citizens Advice Bureau 2 Hall St, Blackwood, Caerphilly NP2 0NR; Tel 01495 224456

Caerphilly Citizens Advice Bureau Park La, Caerphilly CF8 1AA; Tel 029 2088 2105; Fax 029 2088 8440

Risca Citizens Advice Bureau Park Rd, Risca, Caerphilly NP1 6BJ; Tel 01633 614731; Fax 01633 614731

Cardiff

Butetown Citizens Advice Bureau Community Centre, Loudon Sq, Cardiff CF1 5JF; Tel 029 2048 1638; Fax 029 2045 2798

Central Cardiff Citizens Advice Bureau 71 Bridge St, Cardiff CF1 2EE; Tel 029 2039 8676; Fax 029 2034 5951

Cowbridge Citizens Advice Bureau Rear of 79 Eastgate, Cowbridge, Cardiff CF7 7AA; Tel 01446 775411; Fax 01446 775311

Ely (North) Citizens Advice Bureau 91 Grand Ave, Ely, Cardiff CF5 4LF; Tel 029 2056 5469

Ely (South) Citizens Advice Bureau 36 Caerau La, Ely, Cardiff CF5 5HQ; Tel 029 2059 3175; Fax 029 2059 2529

Grangetown Citizens Advice Bureau Grangetown Library, Redlaver St, Cardiff CF1 7HJ; Tel 029 2039 6629

Llanedeyrn Citizens Advice Bureau Community Education Centre, Power Hse, Cardiff CF3 7PN; Tel 029 2054 0202; Fax 029 2054 1664

Llanrumney Citizens Advice Bureau c/o Day Centre, Minehead Rd, Cardiff CF3 9TH; Tel 029 2077 7466; Fax 029 2079 0425

Llantwit Major Citizens Advice Bureau The Old School, Wine St, Llantwit Major, Cardiff CF61 1RZ; Tel 01446 796594; Fax 01446 795200

Trowbridge Citizens Advice Bureau 113 Caernarvon Way, Trowbridge, Cardiff CF3 8RX; Tel 029 2079 9585; Fax 029 2036 0504

Carmarthen

Ammanford Citizens Advice Bureau 14 Iscennen Rd, Ammanford, Carmarthenshire SA18 3BG; Tel 01269 591091

Carmarthen Citizens Advice Bureau 113 Lammas St, Carmarthen, Carmarthenshire SA31 3AP; Tel 01267 234488; Fax 01267 223748

Haverfordwest Citizens Advice Bureau 19 Cartlett, Haverfordwest, Carmarthenshire SA61 2LH; Tel 01437 765216; Fax 01437 765245

Llanelli Citizens Advice Bureau 4a Cowell St, Llanelli, Carmarthenshire SA15 1UU; Tel 01554 759626; Fax 01554 759091

Ceredigion

Aberystwyth Citizens Advice Bureau 12 Cambrian Pl, Aberystwyth, Ceredigion SY23 1NT; Tel 01970 612817; Fax 01970 612442

Cardigan and District Citizens Advice Bureau Napier St, Cardigan, Ceredigion SA43 1ED; Tel 01239 613707; Fax 01239 612988

Conwy

Llangollen Citizens Advice Bureau 9 Oak St, llangollen, Clwyd, Conwy LL20 8NR; Tel 01978 860983; Fax 01978 860983

Cyngor Gwynedd

Bangor Citizens Advice Bureau 60 Deiniol Rd, Bangor, Gwynedd LL57 2RF; Tel 01248 352598; Fax 01248 370482

Meiriennydd Citizens Advice Bureau Mill St, Dolgellau, Gwynedd LL40 1PY; Tel 01341 423070; Fax 01341 423600

Porthmadog Citizens Advice Bureau St. David's Bldg, Lombard St, Porthmadog, Gwynedd LL49 9AB; Tel 01766 513304; Fax 01766 514080

Pwllheli Citizens Advice Bureau 9 Church Pl, Pwllheli, Gwynedd LL53 5DT; Tel 01758 614798; Fax 01758 701682

Denbighshire

Denbigh Citizens Advice Bureau The Church Institute, Lenten Pool, Denbigh, Denbighshire LL16 3LG; Tel 01745 814336; Fax 01735 814336

Prestatyn Citizens Advice Bureau 1 Nant Hall Rd, Prestatyn, Denbighshire LL19 9LR; Tel 01745 855400; Fax 01745 886949

Rhyl Citizens Advice Bureau 11 Water St, Rhyl, Denbighshire LL18 1SP; Tel 01745 334568; Fax 01745 343036

Ruthin Citizens Advice Bureau Town Hall, Wynnstay Rd, Ruthin, Denbighshire LL15 1YN; Tel 01824 703483; Fax 01824 703483

Flintshire

Flint Citizens Advice Bureau 65 Church St, Flint, Flintshire CH6 5AF; Tel 01352 733187; Fax 01352 730674

Holywell Citizens Advice Bureau Old Library, Post Office La, Holywell, Flintshire CH8 7LH; Tel 01352 711262; Fax 01352 714134

Mold Citizens Advice Bureau The Annexe, Terrig Hse, Mold, Flintshire CH7 1EG; Tel 01352 753520; Fax 01352 757159

Shotton Citizens Advice Bureau 34a Chester Road West, Shotton, Deeside, Flintshire CH5 1BY; Tel 01244 819553; Fax 01244 822382

Monmouthshire

Abergavenny Citizens Advice Bureau 2 Lower Monk St, Abergavenny, Monmouthshire NP7 5NA; Tel 01873 854761

Caldicot Citizens Advice Bureau The Cross, Caldicot, Newport NP6 4HY; Tel 01291 423840

Chepstow Citizens Advice Bureau The Gate Hse, High St, Chepstow, Monmouthshire NP6 5LH; Tel 01291 623437; Fax 01291 622660

Monmouth Citizens Advice Bureau 23a Whitecross St, Monmouth, Monmouthshire NP5 3BY; Tel 01600 712590; Fax 01600 772449

Neath Port Talbot

Neath Citizens Advice Bureau 17 Gnoll Park Rd, Neath, Neath Port Talbot SA11 3BT; Tel 01639 635545; Fax 01639 639754

Port Talbot Citizens Advice Bureau 36 Forge Rd, Port Talbot, Neath Port Talbot SA13 1NU; Tel 01639 895057; Fax 01639 892992

Newport

Newport Citizens Advice Bureau 8 Corn St, Newport NP9 1DJ; Tel 01633 265688; Fax 01633 213792

Pembrokeshire

Pembroke and District Citizens Advice Bureau 10 Meyrick St, Pembroke Dock, Pembrokeshire SA72 6UT; Tel 01646 683805; Fax 10646 686552

Powys

Brecon and District Citizens Advice Bureau 12 Castle St, Brecon, Powys LD3 9BU; Tel 01874 624595; Fax 01874 611144

Machynlleth and District Citizens Advice Bureau The Care Centre, Forge Rd, Machynlleth, Powys SY20 8EQ; Tel 01686 703131; Fax 01686 703134

Montgomeryshire District Citizens Advice Bureau Ladywell Hse, Frolic Street Entrance, Newtown, Powys SY16 1JB; URL www.montcab.powys.org.uk; E-mail montycab@powys.org.uk; Tel 01686 626557; Fax 01686 624873

Radnor Citizens Advice Bureau Old Town Hall, Temple St, Llandrindod Wells, Powys LD1 5DL; Tel 01597 823508; Fax 01597 833000

Ystradgynlais Citizens Advice Bureau 47 Commercial St, Ystradgynlais, Swansea SA9 1JH; Tel 01639 849427; Fax 01639 849260

Rhondda, Cynon, Taff

Cynon Valley Citizens Advice Bureau Old Library, Daffryn Rd, Mountain Ash, Rhondda, Cynon, Taff CF45 4DA; Tel 01443 475633

Merthyr Tydfil Citizens Advice Bureau Tramroadside North, Merthyr Tydfil CF47 0AP; Tel 01685 379997

Pontypridd Citizens Advice Bureau 5 Gelliwastad Rd, Pontypridd, Rhondda, Cynon, Taff CF37 2BP; Tel 01443 409963; Fax 01443 402621

Swansea

Swansea Citizens Advice Bureau 208 High St, Swansea SA1 1PE; Tel 01792 652902; Fax 01792 480849

Torfaen

Torfaen Citizens Advice Bureau 21 Caradoc Rd, Cwmbran, Torfaen NP44 1PP; Tel 01633 482464; Fax 01633 876121

Vale of Glamorgan

Barry Citizens Advice Bureau 119 Broad St, Barry, Vale of Glamorgan CF62 7TZ; Tel 01446 733894; Fax 01446 739558

Penarth Citizens Advice Bureau West House Cottage, Stanwell Rd, Penarth, Vale of Glamorgan CF64 2YG; Tel 029 2070 5555; Fax 029 2070 4566

Wrexham

Wrexham Citizens Advice Bureau 2 North Arcade, Chester St, Wrexham LL13 8BA; Tel 01978 364639; Fax 01978 363332

Citizens Advice Scotland

Edinburgh Citizens Advice Bureau
26 George Sq, Edinburgh EH8 9LD; E-mail info@cas.org.uk; Tel 0131 667 0156; Fax 0131 668 4359
Chief Executive Officer Kaliani Lyle
Head (Policy/Public Affairs) S. McPhee
Manager (Finance) Seonid Fowler
Press Officer Ian Brown
Advisory Officer (Lothian) Fiona Dow
Fundraiser Anita Milne

Glasgow Citizens Advice Bureau
4 Park Gdns, Glasgow G3 7YE; Tel 0141 332 8341
Advisory Officer Stuart Divers

Inverness Citizens Advice Bureau
1st Fl, David Whyte Hse, 57 Church St, Inverness, Highland IV1 1DR; Tel 01463 237696
Advisory Officer C. Greer (Grampian, Highland, Orkney, Shetland)

Aberdeen City

Aberdeen Citizens Advice Bureau 47 Market St, Aberdeen AB11 5PZ; Tel 01224 586255

Aberdeenshire

Banff and Buchan Citizens Advice Bureau Marischal Chambers, Drummers Corner, Peterhead, Aberdeenshire AB42 6ZP; Tel 01779 471515

Angus

Angus (Arbroath) Citizens Advice Bureau 11 Millgate, Arbroath, Angus DD11 1NN; Tel 01241 870661

Angus (Forfar) Citizens Advice Bureau 175 East High St, Forfar, Angus DD8 2HH; Tel 01307 467096/7

Angus (Montrose) Citizens Advice Bureau 38 Murray St, Montrose, Angus DD10 8LB; Tel 01674 673263

Clackmannanshire

Clackmannanshire Citizens Advice Bureau 47 Drysdale St, Alloa, Clackmannanshire FK10 1JA; Tel 01259 723880

Dundee

Dundee Citizens Advice Bureau 97 Seagate, Dundee DD1 2ER; Tel 01382 227171; 01382 227172

East Ayrshire

East Ayrshire Citizens Advice Bureau 3 John Dickie St, Kilmarnock, East Ayrshire KA1 1HW; Tel 01563 544744

East Lothian

Haddington Citizens Advice Bureau 38 Market St, Haddington, East Lothian EH41 3JE; Tel 01620 824471

East Renfrewshire

Barrhead Citizens Advice Bureau 216 Main St, Barrhead, Glasgow G78 1SN; Tel 0141 881 2032

Edinburgh

Edinburgh (Central) Citizens Advice Bureau 58 Dundas St, Edinburgh EH3 6QZ; Tel 0131 557 1500

Edinburgh (Gorgie/Dalry) Citizens Advice Bureau Fountainbridge Library, 137 Dundee St, Edinburgh EH11 1BG; Tel 0131 474 8080

Edinburgh (Leith) Citizens Advice Bureau 166 Great Junction St, Edinburgh EH6 5LJ; Tel 0131 554 8144

Edinburgh (Pilton) Citizens Advice Bureau 661 Ferry Rd, Edinburgh EH4 2TX; Tel 0131 332 9434

Edinburgh (Portobello) Citizens Advice Bureau 191 Portobello High St, Edinburgh EH15 1EU; Tel 0131 669 7138; 0131 669 9503

Falkirk

Grangemouth and Bo'ness Citizens Advice Bureau 1 Kerse Rd, Grangemouth, Falkirk FK3 8HW; Tel 01324 483467

Glasgow

Dumbarton Citizens Advice Bureau 6–14 Bridge St, Dumbarton, East Dunbartonshire G82 1NT; Tel 01389 765345

Glasgow (Albion Street) Citizens Advice Bureau 48 Albion St, Glasgow G1 1LH; Tel 0141 552 5556

Glasgow (Bridgeton) Citizens Advice Bureau 35 Main St, Glasgow G40 1QB; Tel 0141 554 0336

Glasgow (Drumchapel) Citizens Advice Bureau 49 Dunkenny Sq, Drumchapel, Glasgow G15 8NE; Tel 0141 944 0205; 0141 944 2612

Glasgow (Easterhouse) Citizens Advice Bureau 46 Shandwick Sq, Glasgow G34 9DS; Tel 0141 771 2328

Glasgow (Maryhill) Citizens Advice Bureau 1145 Maryhill Rd, Glasgow G20 9AZ; Tel 0141 946 6373

Glasgow (Parkhead) Citizens Advice Bureau 1361–1363 Gallowgate, Glasgow G31 4DN; Tel 0141 554 0004

Rutherglen and Cambuslang Citizens Advice Bureau School Hse, 2 MacCallum Ave, Rutherglen, Glasgow G73 3AL; Tel 0141 647 5100

Highland

Caithness Citizens Advice Bureau 7a Brabster St, Thurso, Caithness, Highland KW14 7AP; Tel 01847 894243; 01847 896796

Inverness Citizens Advice Bureau 103 Academy St, Inverness, Highland IV1 1LX; Tel 01463 235345

Lochaber Citizens Advice Bureau Dudley Rd, Fort William, Highland PH33 6JB; Tel 01397 705311

Nairn Citizens Advice Bureau 6 High St, Nairn, Highland IV12 4BJ; Tel 01667 456677

Ross and Cromarty Citizens Advice Bureau Balallan, 4 Novar Rd, Alness, Highland IV17 0QG; Tel (extensions at Dingwall and Tain) 01349 883333

Midlothian

Dalkeith Citizens Advice Bureau 8 Buccleuch St, Dalkeith, Midlothian EH22 1HA; Tel 0131 660 1636; 0131 663 3688

Musselburgh Citizens Advice Bureau 141 High St, Musselburgh, Midlothian EH21 7DD; Tel 0131 653 2544; 0131 653 2748

Penicuik Citizens Advice Bureau 14a John St, Penicuik, Midlothian EH26 8AB; Tel 01968 675259

Moray

Moray Citizens Advice Bureau 30–32 Batchan St, Elgin, Moray IV30 1BH; Tel 01343 550088

North Lanarkshire

Airdrie Citizens Advice Bureau Resource Centre, 14 Anderson St, Airdrie, North Lanarkshire ML6 0AA; Tel 01236 754109; 01236 754376

Bellshill Citizens Advice Bureau 6 Hamilton Rd, Bellshill, North Lanarkshire ML4 1AQ; Tel 01698 748615

Coatbridge Citizens Advice Bureau Unit 10, Fountain Business Centre, Ellis St, Coatbridge, North Lanarkshire ML5 3AA; Tel 01236 421447; 01236 421448

Cumbernauld Citizens Advice Bureau 3rd Fl, 2 Annan Hse, Town Centre, Cumbernauld, North Lanarkshire G67 1DP; Tel 01236 723201

Motherwell and Wishaw Citizens Advice Bureau 32 Civic Sq, Motherwell, North Lanarkshire ML1 1TP; Tel 01698 251981; 01698 259389

Perth and Kinross

Perth Citizens Advice Bureau 4–12 New Row, Perth, Perth and Kinross PH1 5QB; Tel 01738 624301; 01738 624302

Renfrewshire

Paisley Citizens Advice Bureau 45 George St, Paisley, Renfrewshire PA1 2JY; Tel 0141 889 2121

Scottish Borders

Central Borders Citizens Advice Bureau 25 Albert Pl, Galasheils, Scottish Borders TD1 3DL; Tel 01896 753889

Peebles Citizens Advice Bureau 42 Old Town, Peebles, Scottish Borders EH45 8JF; Tel 01721 721722

Roxburgh Citizens Advice Bureau 15a High St, Hawick, Scottish Borders TD9 9BZ; Tel 01450 374266

South Lanarkshire

East Kilbride Citizens Advice Bureau 24 Cornwall Way, East Kilbride, South Lanarkshire G74 1JR; Tel 01355 263698

Hamilton Citizens Advice Bureau Almada Tower, 67 Almada St, Hamilton, South Lanarkshire ML3 0HQ; Tel 01698 283477

Stirling

Denny and Dunipace Citizens Advice Bureau 24 Duke St, Denny, Stirling FK6 6DD; Tel 01324 823118; 01324 825333

West Dunbartonshire

Clydebank Citizens Advice Bureau 34 Alexander St, Clydebank, West Dunbartonshire G81 1RZ; Tel 0141 952 7921

Stirling Citizens Advice Bureau The Norman MacEwan Centre, Cameronian St, Stirling FK8 2DX; Tel 01786 470239; 01786 470257

West Lothian

Livingston Citizens Advice Bureau Suite Seven, Shiel Hse, Shiel Wlk, Livingston, West Lothian EH54 5EH; Tel 01506 432977

Citizens Advice Northern Ireland

County Antrim

Antrim Citizens Advice Bureau 10d High St, Antrim, County Antrim BT41 4AN; Tel 028 9442 8176; Fax 028 9446 9243

Ballymena Citizens Advice Bureau 28 Mount St, Ballymena, County Antrim BT43 6BW; Tel 028 2564 4398; Fax 028 2563 1686

Belfast (Antrim Road) Citizens Advice Bureau 211 Antrim Rd, Belfast BT15 2GW; Tel 028 9050 3000; Fax 028 9074 7230

Belfast (Central) Citizens Advice Bureau 6 Callender St, Belfast BT1 5BN; Tel 028 9050 3000; Fax 028 9031 2336

Belfast (East Belfast) Citizens Advice Bureau 342 Newtownards Rd, Belfast BT4 1HE; Tel 028 9050 3000; Fax 028 9045 2735

Belfast (Falls) Citizens Advice Bureau 8 Springfield Rd, Belfast BT12 7AG; Tel 028 9050 3000; Fax 028 9043 8741

Belfast (Shankill) Citizens Advice Bureau 179 Shankill Rd, Belfast BT13 1FP; Tel 028 9050 3000; Fax 028 9022 2040

Belfast (Suffolk and Andersonstown) Citizens Advice Bureau 208 Andersonstown Rd, Belfast BT11 9EB; Tel 028 9030 1916; Fax 028 9062 3594; Minicom 028 9062 3594

Carrickfergus Citizens Advice Bureau 65 North St, Carrickfergus, County Antrim BT38 7AE; Tel 028 9335 1808; Fax 028 9335 5850

Glengormley Citizens Advice Bureau 3b Ballyclare Rd, Glengormley, Newtownabbey, County Antrim BT36 5EU; Tel 028 9084 4592; Fax 028 9083 8528

Larne Citizens Advice Bureau Park Lodge, 49 Victoria Rd, Larne, County Antrim BT40 1RT; Tel 028 2826 0379

Lisburn Citizens Advice Bureau The Bridge Community Centre, 50 Railway St, Lisburn, County Antrim BT28 1XG; Tel 028 9266 2251; Fax 028 9260 2933

Rathcoole Citizens Advice Bureau Dunnaney Centre, Rathmullan Dr, Rathcoole, Newtownabbey, County Antrim BT37 9DQ; Tel 028 9085 2271; Fax 028 9036 5770

County Armagh

Armagh Citizens Advice Bureau 9 McCrums Crt, Armagh, County Armagh BT61 7RS; Tel 028 3752 4041; Fax 028 3752 7029

Lurgan Citizens Advice Bureau Town Hall, 6 Union St, Lurgan, Craigavon, County Armagh BT66 6AS; Tel 028 3832 3571; Fax 028 3834 7219

Portadown Citizens Advice Bureau Town Hall, 7 Edward St Portadown, Craigavon, County Armagh BT62 3LX; Tel 028 3835 3260; Fax 028 3836 1181

County Down

Ards Citizens Advice Bureau North Down and Ards Community Health and Care Unit, 39 Regent St, Newtownards, County Down BT23 4AD; Tel 028 9181 9257; Fax 028 9181 0134

Banbridge and District Citizens Advice Bureau Old Town Hall School, Scarva St, Banbridge, County Down BT32 3DA; Tel 028 4062 2201; Fax 028 4062 2249

Bangor and District Citizens Advice Bureau 1a Springfield Ave, Bangor, County Down BT20 5BY; Tel 028 9127 0009; Fax 028 9127 0574

Downpatrick Citizens Advice Bureau Maghinis Hse, 8–10 Irish St, Downpatrick, County Down BT30 6BP; Tel 028 4461 4110; Fax 028 4461 6432

Holywood Citizens Advice Bureau Queens Hall, Sullivan Pl, Holywood, County Down BT18 9JF; Tel 028 9042 8288; Fax 028 9042 6758

Newry Citizens Advice Bureau River Hse, 41c The Mall, Newry, County Down BT34 1AN; Tel 028 3026 2934; Fax 028 3026 9224

County Fermanagh

Fermanagh Citizens Advice Bureau Belmore Mews, 2 New St, Enniskillen, County Fermanagh BT74 6AH; Tel 028 6632 4334; Fax 028 6632 9633

County Londonderry

Coleraine Citizens Advice Bureau 24 Lodge Rd, Coleraine, County Londonderry BT52 1NB; Tel 028 7034 4817; Fax 028 7034 2501

Londonderry Citizens Advice Bureau 1–3 Guildhall St, Derry, Londonderry, County Londonderry BT48 6BJ; Tel 028 7136 2444; Fax 028 7126 1030

County Tyrone

Cookstown Citizens Advice Bureau 15a Molesworth St, Cookstown, County Tyrone BT80 8NX; Tel 028 8676 6126; Fax 028 8676 9396

Dungannon Citizens Advice Bureau 5–6 Feeney's La, Dungannon, County Tyrone BT70 1TX; Tel 028 8772 5299; Fax 028 8772 5872

Strabane Citizens Advice Bureau 17 Dock St, Strabane, County Tyrone BT82 8EE; Tel 028 7138 2665; Fax 028 7138 3818

16

Consumer Advice Centres

The following list of centres offering advice on consumer problems has been supplied by the Consumers' Association. Their status varies, some being run by local authorities and some by the Citizens Advice Bureau service. In all cases, however, they are prepared to offer help both to consumers and to suppliers of consumer goods and services. In the case of the local authority departments, they are concerned with inspection and the enforcement of consumer legislation. Where no centre is named in the list for a particular locality, the nearest Citizens Advice Bureau will advise in the first instance.

Consumers' Association Ltd

2 Marylebone Rd, London NW1 4DF; URL www.which.net; E-mail editor@which.net; Tel 020 7770 7000

England

Bristol

Bristol Consumer Advice Centre Trading Standards Dept, Rackhay, Bristol BS1 4HY; Tel 0117 925 097

Buckinghamshire

Aylesbury Consumer Advice Centre Trading Standards Dept, County Hall, Aylesbury, Buckinghamshire; Tel 01296 5000 ext 593
Mon–Thurs 0900–1730; Fri 0900–1700.

Aylesbury Consumer Advice Centre 23a Walton St, Aylesbury, Buckinghamshire; Tel 01296 5000 ext 593
Mon–Fri 1000–1500.

High Wycombe Consumer Advice Centre Little Market Hse, High Wycombe, Buckinghamshire; Tel 01494 28531
Mon–Fri 1000–1600 (Wed closed).

Cambridgeshire

Cambridge Consumer Advice Centre Trading Standards Complaints Division, Lion Yard, Cambridge, Cambridgeshire; Tel 01223 311318

Cheshire

Chester Consumer Advice Centre Trading Standards Dept, Backford Hall, Chester, Cheshire CH1 6EA; Tel 01244 59123

Crewe Consumer Advice Centre Trading Standards Dept, Delamere Hse, Crewe, Cheshire CW1 2JZ; Tel 01270 583177

Macclesfield Consumer Advice Centre Trading Standards Dept, Park La, Macclesfield, Cheshire SK11 8LG; Tel 01625 26391

Northwich Consumer Advice Centre Trading Standards Dept, Watling St, Northwich, Cheshire CW9 5ET; Tel 01606 3961

Stockport Consumer Information and Advice Centre 9 Princes St, Stockport, Cheshire SK1 1SL; Tel 0161 480 0315
Mon–Sat 0845–1700; Thurs 0845–1300.

Croydon

Croydon Consumer Advice Centre Central Library, 9 Katherine St, Croydon, Surrey; Tel 020 8680 4299

Derbyshire

Chesterfield Consumer Advice Centre Trading Standards Dept, New Beetwell St, Chesterfield, Derbyshire; Tel 01246 32563
Mon–Thurs 0900–1700; Fri 0900–1630.

Derby Consumer Advice Centre Trading Standards Department, 23 St. Mary's Gate, Derby; Tel 01332 49817; 01332 49818
Mon–Fri 0900–1600.

Devon

Barnstaple Consumer Advice Centre Trading Standards Dept, Civic Centre, Barnstaple, Devon EX31 1ED; Tel 01271 72511 ext 7004

Exeter Consumer Advice Centre Trading Standards Dept, 28 Barnfield Rd, Exeter, Devon EX1; Tel 01392 77977 ext 3475

Plymouth Consumer Advice Centre Trading Standards Dept, 415 Crownhill Rd, Plymouth PL5 2LJ; Tel 01752 363121

Torquay Consumer Advice Centre Trading Standards Dept, Town Hall, Torquay, Torbay TQ1 3SA; Tel 01803 38204

Durham

Darlington Consumer Advice Office Town Hall, Darlington; Tel 01325 60651

Durham City Consumer Advice Office 80a Claypath, Durham, County Durham; Tel 0191 43520

East Riding of Yorkshire

Bridlington Fair Trading Advice Centre 4 St. John's Ave, Bridlington, East Riding of Yorkshire; Tel 01262 679832
Mon–Fri 1030–1300, 1400–1600.

Goole Fair Trading Advice Centre Goole Library, Goole, East Riding of Yorkshire; Tel 01405 21867
Wed, Fri 1230–1630.

East Sussex

Hastings Consumer Advice Centre Trading Standards Dept, Bohemia Rd, Hastings, East Sussex TN34 1EX; Tel 01424 434424
Mon–Thurs 0830–1700; Fri 0830–1600.

Essex

Braintree Consumer Advice Centre Trading Standards Dept, 19 Bocking End, Braintree, Essex; Tel 01376 222729
Mon–Thurs 0900–1730; Fri 0900–1630.

Chelmsford Consumer Advice Centre Trading Standards Dept, Beehive La, Chelmsford, Essex; Tel 01245 355381
Mon–Thurs 0900–1730; Fri 0900–1630.

Colchester Consumer Advice Centre Trading Standards Dept, Stanwell Hse, Colchester, Essex; Tel 01206 571448
Mon–Thurs 0900–1730; Fri 0900–1630.

Grays Consumer Advice Centre Director of Housing and Community Services, 68 High St, Grays, Thurrock; Tel 01375 384184

Harlow Consumer Advisory Service Advice Centre, Harlow, Essex CM20 1HD; Tel 01279 446622

Gloucestershire

Gloucester Consumer Advice Centre Trading Standards Dept, Hillfield Hse, Gloucester, Gloucestershire GL1 3LD; Tel 01452 426200

Hartlepool

Hartlepool Consumer Advice and Information Centre 1–3 Victoria Rd, Hartlepool; Tel 01429 245750
Mon–Thurs 0900–1630; Fri 0930–1600.

Hertfordshire

Hemel Hempstead Consumer Advice Centre 15 Hillfield Rd, Hemel Hempstead, Hertfordshire; Tel 01442 63501 Mon–Fri 1000–1600; Sat 1000–1200.

Watford Consumer Advice Centre 149 The Pde, Watford, Hertfordshire; Tel 01923 31889 Mon–Fri 1000–1630.

Kent

Maidstone Consumer Advice Centre Trading Standards Dept, Springfield, Maidstone, Kent ME14 2LS; Tel 01622 671411 Mon–Fri 0830–1700.

Leicestershire

Leicester Consumer Advice Centre 90 Granby St, Leicester LE1 1DJ; Tel 0116 255 5848 Tues–Fri 1000–1700; Sat 1000–1300.

London Boroughs

Camden

Camden Consumer Aid Centre 242 Kentish Town Rd, London NW5; Tel 020 7485 7034 Mon–Wed 1000–1500; Fri 1000–1300; Thurs 1000–1300.

Greenwich

Greenwich Information and Consumer Advice Centre 43 Wellington St, Woolwich, London SE18; Tel 020 8854 8888 ext 2274/5 Mon–Fri 0930–1700.

Hackney

Hackney Consumer Advice Centre 236 Mare St, London E8; Tel 020 8986 8446 Mon, Wed, Thurs 1000–1400; Tues 1700–1900.

Hammersmith and Fulham

Shepherd's Bush Advice Centre 338 Uxbridge Rd, London W12 7LL; Tel 020 8743 6953 Mon, Thurs, Fri 0930–1200; Tues 1400–1600; Mon, Wed 1800–2000.

Haringey

Haringey Consumer Advice Centre 136 High Rd, Wood Green, London N22; Tel 020 8888 8442 Tues–Sat 0930–1630; Thurs 0930–1300.

Lambeth

Brixton Consumer Advice Centre 13 Electric Ave, London SW2; Tel 020 7737 3311 Tues–Sat 0930–1600; Wed 0930–1300.

Lambeth Walk Consumer Advice Centre Lambeth Wlk Shopping Precinct, Lambeth Wlk, London SE1; Tel 020 7737 3311 Tues–Sat 0930–1600; Wed 0930–1300.

Streatham Consumer Advice Centre 85–87 Streatham High Rd, London SW16; Tel 020 7737 3311 Tues–Sat 0930–1600; Wed 0930–1300.

Lewisham

Lewisham Counsumer Services Department 185 Lewisham High St, London SE13 6AA; Tel 020 8852 9121

Newham

Newham Advice Centre 5 Beckton Rd, Canning Town, London E16; Tel 020 8534 4545 ext 5925/5929 Mon–Fri 1000–1200.

Newham Advice Centre Town Hall, Barking Rd, London E6 2RP; Tel 020 8472 1430 ext 3055/3056 Mon–Fri 0900–1700.

Newham Advice Centre 99 The Gr, Stratford, London E15; Tel 020 8534 4545 ext 5480 Mon–Fri 0900–1700.

Southwark

Southwark Consumer Advice Centre 376 Walworth Rd, London SE17 2NG; Tel 020 7703 5049

Tower Hamlets

Tower Hamlets Consumer Advice Centre Cheviot Hse, 227–233 Commercial Rd, London E1 2BN; Tel 020 7790 1818 ext 219 Mon, Tues, Fri 1000–1400; Wed, Thurs 1330–1600.

Waltham Forest

Waltham Forest Aid Centre 807 High Rd, Leyton, London E10; Tel 020 8558 0033 Mon–Fri 1000–1715; Sat 0900–1300.

Westminster

Westminster Consumer Advice Centre Westminster Council Hse, Marylebone Rd, London NW1 5PT; Tel 020 7828 8070 Mon–Fri 0900–1630.

Merseyside

Birkenhead Consumer Advice Centre 7 Borough Pavement, Birkenhead, Merseyside L41 2XX; Tel 0151 647 5404 Mon–Fri 0845–1700.

Bootle Consumer Advice Centre 88 The Hexagon, Bootle, Merseyside; Tel 0151 933 0088 Mon–Fri 0845–1700.

Kirkby Consumer Advice Centre Council of Social Service Bldg, Kirkby, Merseyside L32 8SE; Tel 0151 546 8636 Mon–Fri 0845–1700.

Liverpool Consumer Advice Centre Trading Standards Dept, 62 Great Crosshall St, Liverpool, Merseyside L3 2AT; Tel 0151 227 5234 ext 2112/3 Mon–Fri 0845–1700.

St. Helens Consumer Advice Centre Trading Standards Dept, Chalon Way, St. Helens, Merseyside WA10 1AS; Tel 01744 55351 Mon–Fri 0845–1700.

Middlesbrough

Middlesbrough Consumer Advice and Information Centre 125 Albert Rd, Middlesbrough; Tel 01642 245750 Mon–Thurs 0900–1630; Fri 0930–1600.

Norfolk

Norwich Consumer Advice Centre Advice Services, 24 Exchange St, Norwich, Norfolk NR2 1AX; Tel 01603 613864

Northumberland

Alnwick Consumer Advice Centre Trading Standards Dept, Fenkle St, Alnwick, Northumberland; Tel 01665 602412 Mon–Thurs 0830–1700; Fri 0830–1630.

Hexham Consumer Advice Centre Trading Standards Dept, Loosing Hill, Hexham, Northumberland Mon–Thurs 0830–1700; Fri 0830–1630.

Morpeth Consumer Advice Centre Trading Standards Dept, Southgate Hse, Morpeth, Northumberland NE61 2DP; Tel 01670 56112 Mon–Thurs 0830–1700; Fri 0830–1630.

16

Oxfordshire

Oxford Consumer Advice Centre Trading Standards Dept, Rewley Rd, Oxford, Oxfordshire; Tel 01865 815605
Mon–Thurs 0830–1700; Fri 0830–1600.

Peterborough

Peterborough Consumer Advice Centre Trading Standards Complaints Division, St. Peter's Rd, Peterborough;
Tel 01733 64278
Mon–Fri 0900–1700.

Reading

Reading Consumer Advice Centre PO Box 17, Reading; Tel 01734 55911 ext 2294/2243
Mon–Fri 0900–1600.

Redcar and Cleveland

Redcar Consumer Advice and Information Centre County Library, Redcar, Redcar and Cleveland; Tel 01642 475526
Mon–Thurs 1000–1630; Fri 0930–1600.

South Yorkshire

Barnsley Consumer Advice Centre 19–21 Upper Charter Arcade, Barnsley, South Yorkshire S70 1RF; Tel 01226 83139
Doncaster Consumer Advice Centre Arndale Centre, Doncaster, South Yorkshire DN1 1PZ; Tel 01302 62680
Rotherham Consumer Advice Centre Bridge St, Rotherham, South Yorkshire S60 1QZ; Tel 01709 382972
Sheffield Consumer Advice Centre 17–19 Matilda St, Sheffield, South Yorkshire S1 3LB; Tel 0114 273 8044

Stockton-on-Tees

Stockton-on-Tees Consumer Advice and Information Centre County Library, Stockton-on-Tees; Tel 01642 615355
Mon–Thurs 0900–1630; Fri 0930–1600.

Surrey

Dorking Consumer Advice Centre Trading Standards Dept, PO Box 99, Dorking, Surrey; Tel (24 hour answerphone) 01306 86286
Mon–Fri 0915–1645.

Tyne and Wear

Gateshead Consumer Advice Centre 24–26 Trinity Sq, Gateshead, Tyne and Wear NE8 1DX; Tel 0191 477 1002
Mon–Thurs 0830–1630; Fri 0830–1600.
Jarrow Consumer Advice Centre 23 Grange Rd, Jarrow, Tyne and Wear NE32 3JY; Tel 0191 489 3414
Mon–Thurs 0830–1630; Fri 0830–1600.
Newcastle Consumer Advice Centre 9–11 Princess Sq, Newcastle upon Tyne, Tyne and Wear NE1 8EN; Tel 0191 610 937
Mon–Thurs 0830–1630; Fri 0830–1600.
Sunderland Consumer Advice Centre 62 High St West, Sunderland, Tyne and Wear SR1 3DP; Tel 0191 40631
Mon–Thurs 0830–1630; Fri 0830–1600.
Wallsend Consumer Advice Centre 81–83 High Street West, Wallsend, Tyne and Wear NE28 8JD; Tel 0191 262 0903
Mon–Thurs 0830–1630; Fri 0830–1615.

Warrington

Warrington Consumer Advice Centre Trading Standards Dept, Bank St, Warrington WA1 2AW; Tel 01925 36006

West Midlands

Birmingham Consumer Advice Centre Ringway Hse, Birmingham, West Midlands 6AF; Tel 0121 236 3271
Mon 0930–1200; Tues, Thurs, Fri 0930–1600; Wed 0930–1500.
Birmingham Consumer Advice Centre Trading Standards Dept, County Hall, Birmingham, West Midlands; Tel 0121 300 6236
Mon–Fri 0900–1300, 1400–1715.
Coventry Consumer Advice Centre 2nd Fl, Coventry, West Midlands CV1 EG; Tel 024 7627 474; 024 7627 475; 024 7627 476
Mon–Fri 0900–1245, 1300–1700.
Coventry Consumer Advice Centre Trading Standards Dept, Blackburn Hse, Coventry, West Midlands CV3 4AN; Tel 024 7650 4317; 024 7650 4387
Mon–Fri 0900–1300, 1400–1715.
Walsall Consumer Advice Centre 5 Lower Hall La, Walsall, West Midlands; Tel 01922 611331
Mon–Fri 0915–1700; Sat 0930–1200.
Wolverhampton Consumer Advice Centre Civic Centre, Wolverhampton, West Midlands; Tel 01902 27811
Mon–Fri 0900–1700; Sat 1000–1230.
Wolverhampton Consumer Advice Centre 184 Stafford St, Wolverhampton, West Midlands WV1 1NA; Tel 01902 773626
Mon–Fri 1000–1700; Sat 1000–1230.
Wolverhampton Consumer Advice Centre Trading Standards Dept, Salop St, Wolverhampton, West Midlands; Tel 01902 55433

West Sussex

Chichester Consumer Advice Centre Trading Standards Dept, The Tannery, Chichester, West Sussex PO19 3HN; Tel 01243 777336
Mon–Fri 0900–1700.
Crawley Consumer Advice Centre Trading Standards Dept, 28 Springfield Rd, Crawley, West Sussex; Tel 01293 51900
Mon–Fri 0900–1700.
Worthing Consumer Advice Centre Trading Standards Dept, Portland Bldgs, Worthing, West Sussex; Tel 01903 37492
Mon–Fri 0900–1700.

Wiltshire

Swindon Consumer Advice Centre 24 Milton Rd, Swindon SN1 5JE; Tel 01793 22909; 01793 23920
Mon–Fri 0930–1230, 1400–1600.

Wales

Neath Port Talbot

Neath Consumer Advice Centre Consumer Protection Dept, Neath Area Office, Neath, Neath Port Talbot; Tel 01639 9850584
Mon–Thurs 0830–1700; Fri 0830–1630.
Pontardawe Consumer Advice Centre Consumer Protection Dept, Lliw Valley Area Office, Swansea; Tel 01792 864816
Mon–Thurs 0830–1700; Fri 0830–1630.
Port Talbot Consumer Advice Centre Consumer Protection Dept, Port Talbot Area Office, Port Talbot, Neath Port Talbot; Tel 01639 883273
Mon–Thurs 0830–1700; Fri 0830–1630.

Rhondda, Cynon, Taff

Aberdare Consumer Advice Centre 45 Dean St, Aberdare, Rhondda, Cynon, Taff CF44 7BN; Tel 01685 871097
Mon–Thurs 0830–1700; Fri 0830–1630.

Pontypridd Consumer Advice Centre Consumer Protection Dept, Forest Gr, Pontypridd, Rhondda, Cynon, Taff; Tel 01443 405340
Mon–Thurs 0830–1700; Fri 0830–1630.

Swansea

Swansea Consumer Advice Centre Consumer Protection Dept, County Hall, Swansea; Tel 01792 471567
Mon–Thurs 0830–1700; Fri 0830–1630.

Scotland

Scottish Consumer Council

Royal Exchange Hse, 100 Queen St, Glasgow G1 3DN;
URL www.scotconsumer.org.uk;
E-mail scc@scotconsumer.org.uk; Tel 0141 226 5261;
Fax 0141 221 0731
Chair Graeme Millar
SCC promotes and represents the interests of Scottish consumers especially the disadvantaged. Researches areas of consumer concern and resulting published reports are used to influence and persuade relevant bodies, such as central and local government, nationalised and independent industries and public, professional and private sector services to act in consumers' interests.

Argyll and Bute

Dunoon Consumer Protection Dept, Argyll Sub Region, Dunoon, Argyll and Bute PA23 7AP; Tel 01369 4374 ext 5
Mon–Thurs 0845–1645; Fri 0845–1555.

East Ayrshire

Kilmarnock Consumer Protection Dept, Western Rd, Kilmarnock, East Ayrshire KA3 1LL; Tel 01563 21502
Mon–Fri 0845–1645.

Edinburgh

Edinburgh Consumer Advice Centre, Shrubhill, Edinburgh; Tel 0131 553 5456
Mon–Thurs 0830–1630; Fri 0830–1550.

Falkirk

Falkirk Consumer Advice Centre, Trading Standards Dept, Falkirk; Tel 01324 20021 ext 245
Mon–Fri 0900–1700.

Fife

Glenrothes Trading Standards Dept, Fife Hse, Glenrothes, Fife KY7 5LT; Tel 01592 754411
Mon–Fri 0900–1230, 1330–1700.

Glasgow

Glasgow Consumer Advice Centre, St. Enoch Hse, Glasgow G1 4BH; Tel 0141 226 3511
Mon–Sat 0845–1645.

Glasgow Consumer Protection Dept, Glasgow Sub Region, Glasgow G1 5RQ; Tel 0141 552 0596
Mon–Thurs 0845–1645; Fri 0845–1555.

Highland

Inverness Consumer Protection Dept, Regional Bldgs, Inverness, Highland; Tel 01463 234121
Mon–Tues 0900–1730; Wed–Fri 0900–1700.

Inverclyde

Greenock Consumer Protection Dept, 3 Wallace Pl, Greenock, Inverclyde PA15 1JB; Tel 01475 24400
Mon–Fri 0845–1645.

Greenock Information and Advice Centre, 23 Clyde Sq, Greenock, Inverclyde PA15 1NB; Tel 01475 86850
Mon–Fri 0845–1645; Sat 0845–1230.

North Ayrshire

Irvine Consumer Advice Centre, 3 Fullarton Sq, Irvine, North Ayrshire KA12 8EJ; Tel 01294 72135
Mon–Sat 0900–1700.

North Lanarkshire

Coatbridge Consumer Protection Dept, 175 Bank St, Coatbridge, North Lanarkshire ML5 1HA; Tel 01236 23666
Mon–Thurs 0845–1645; Fri 0845–1555.

Motherwell Consumer Advice Centre, 81 Merry St, Motherwell, North Lanarkshire ML1 1JJ; Tel 01698 66513
Mon–Thurs 0845–1645; Fri 0845–1555.

Renfrewshire

Paisley Consumer Advice Centre, The Piazza, Paisley, Renfrewshire PA1 1EN; Tel 0141 887 7632
Mon–Thurs 0845–1645; Fri 0845–1555.

Paisley Consumer Protection Dept, Renfrew Sub Region, Paisley, Renfrewshire PA1 1LG; Tel 0141 889 5454
Mon–Thurs 0845–1645; Fri 0845–1555.

Shetland Islands

Lerwick Consumer Advice Office, 3 Commercial Rd, Lerwick, Shetland Isles; Tel 01595 3864
Mon–Thurs 0900–1700; Fri 0900–1600.

South Ayrshire

Ayr Consumer Protection Dept, Ayr Sub Region, Ayr, South Ayrshire KA7 1EN; Tel 01292 267093
Mon–Thurs 0845–1645.

South Lanarkshire

East Kilbride Consumer Advice Centre, Cornwall Way, East Kilbride, South Lanarkshire G74 1JR; Tel 0135 52 25343
Mon–Thurs 0845–1645; Fri 0845–1555.

Hamilton Consumer Advice Centre, 54–56 Quarry Sq, Hamilton, South Lanarkshire ML3 7AU; Tel 01698 282561; 01698 283761
Mon–Sat 0845–1655.

Hamilton Consumer Protection Dept, Lanark Sub Region, Hamilton, South Lanarkshire ML3 0AL; Tel 01698 282828
Mon–Thurs 0845–1645; Fri 0845–1555.

Stirling

Stirling Stirling Trading Standards Dept, Forrest Rd, Stirling FK8 14H; Tel 01786 73932
Mon–Fri 0900–1700.

West Dunbartonshire

Clydebank Consumer Protection Dept, 627 Dumbarton Rd, Clydebank, West Dunbartonshire G81 4GT; Tel 0141 952 2204
Mon–Thurs 0845–1645; Fri 0845–1555.

Dumbarton Consumer Protection Dept, Dumbarton Sub Region, Dumbarton, West Dunbartonshire G82 3PU; Tel 01389 65151
Mon–Thurs 0845–1645; Fri 0845–1555.

16

Western Isles

Stornoway Consumer Protection Dept, Sandwick Rd, Stornoway, Isle of Lewis; Tel 01851 3773 Mon–Thurs 0900–1730; Fri 0900–1700.

Northern Ireland

Belfast

Belfast City Council Consumer Advice Centre 6 Callender St, Belfast BT1 5BN; E-mail consumeradvice@belfastcity.gov.uk; Tel 0289 032 8260; Fax 0289 023 7675 Mon, Tue, Thur 0930–1630; Wed 0930–1400, Fri 0930–1615.

Independent Advice Centres

adviceUK

12th Fl, New London Bridge Hse, 25 London Bridge St, London SE1 9ST; URL www.adviceuk.org.uk; E-mail admin@adviceuk.org.uk; E-mail <firstname>.<lastname>@adviceuk.org.uk; Tel 020 7407 4070; Fax 020 7407 4071
Chair Keith Bennett
Chief Executive Steve Johnson
Co-ordinates and supports a wide range of independent advice centres. Formerly the Federation of Independent Advice Centres (FIAC).

170 Community Project 170 New Cross Rd, New Cross, London SE14 5AA

Account 3, Women's Consultancy Services 1–9 Birkbeck St, London, E2 6JZ

Action for Sick Children 300 Kingston Rd, London SW20 8LX

ADFAM National Waterbridge Hse, 32–36 Loman St, London SE1 0EE

Advice and Community Resource Centre 59 Withington Rd, Whalley Range, Manchester M16 7EX

Advice and Representation Centre University of Wales Institute Cardiff Student Union, Llandaff Campus, Cardiff CF5 2YB

Advice and Representation Centre (ARC) Buckinghamshire Chilterns University Student Union, Queen Alexander Rd, High Wycombe, Buckinghamshire HP11 2JZ

Advice and Resource Centre–GAMH Shaftesbury Hse, 3rd Fl, Glasgow G2 6AY

Advice Centre Hull University Union, Cottingham Rd, Hull, Kingston upon Hull HU6 7RX

Advice Centre, Students' Union Sheffield Hallam University, Nelson Mandela Bldg, Pond St, Sheffield, South Yorkshire S1 2BW

Advice Centre, Union of Students at UCE University of Central England, Franchise St, Birmingham, West Midlands B42 2SU

Advice Information and Counselling in Huntingdon Appin Hse, Ferrars Rd, Huntingdon, Cambridgeshire PE29 3DR

Advice Lincs 4–6 Bear La, Spalding, Lincolnshire PE11 3XA

Advice on Individual Rights in Europe 74–76 Eurolink Business Park Centre, 49 Effra Rd, London, SW2 1BZ

Advice Rights Bus Station, Harefield Rd, Nuneaton, Warwickshire CV11 4HR

Advisory Centre for Education (ACE) 1c Aberdeen Studios, 22 Highbury Gr, London N5 2DQ

Advocacy Project (Scotland) Ltd 72 London Rd, Glasgow G1 5NP

Advocacy Service–Perth and Kinross The Gateway, North Methven St, Perth, Perth and Kinross PH1 5PP

AEKTA Project 16 Holyhead Rd, Birmingham, West Midlands B21 0LT

Afghan Association of London (Harrow) Suite 1, 84–88 Pinner Rd, Harrow, London HA1 4HZ

African Legal Advisory Service Trocoll Hse, Suite 306, Wakering Rd, Barking, London IG11 8PD

Afro-Asian Advisory Service 53 Addington Sq, London SE5 7LB

Afro-Caribbean Care Group for the Elderly Claremont Resource Centre, Rolls Cr, Hulme, Manchester M15 5FS; E-mail accg@fsnet.co.uk

Afro-Caribbean Resource Centre 339 Dudley Rd, Winson Grn, Birmingham, West Midlands B18 4HB; E-mail acre@lineone.net

Age Concern (Castlederg) 33a Main St, Castlederg, County Tyrone BT81 7AS

Age Concern Barking and Dagenham The White House, 884 Green La, Dagenham, London RM8 1BY

Age Concern Brent 120 Craven Park Rd, Harlesden, London NW10 8QD

Age Concern Bristol Canningford Hse, 38 Victoria St, Bristol, BS1 6BY

Age Concern Coleraine 1 Waterside, Coleraine, County Antrim BT51 3DP

Age Concern England (Information) Correspondence only. Astral Hse, 1268 London Rd, Norbury, London SW16 4ER

Age Concern Northern Ireland 3 Lower Cres, Belfast BT7 1NR

Age Concern Southampton 1 Sacon Gate, Southampton SO14 3HA

Albanian Youth Action Unit E209, 2nd Fl, East Bldg, Westminster Business Sq, Durham St, London SE11 5JH

Alcohol Counselling and Prevention Service 34 Electric La, Brixton, London SW9 8JT

All Saints Haque Centre 25–27 Vicarage Rd, All Saints, Wolverhampton, West Midlands WV2 1BZ

Alone in London Advice and Advisory Services 188 King's Cross Rd, London, WC1X 9DE

Andover Crisis and Support Centre 15–17 New St, Andover, Hampshire SP10 1EL

Anglia Student Union Advice Service (ASUAS) Anglia Students Union, Anglia Polytechnic University, Chelmsford, Essex CM1 1LL

Angolan Advice and Information Centre Imperial Hse, 54 Willoughby La, London N17 0SP

APASENTH The Brady Arts Centre, 192–195 Hanbury St, London, E15 1HJ

Arch (North Staffs) Ltd 110 Lichfield St, Hanley, Stoke-on-Trent ST1 3DS

Ardler Information Point c/o Ardler Neighbourhood Centre, Turnberry Ave, Dundee DD2 3TP

Ardoyne Association 11 Etna Dr, Belfast BT14 7NN

Asian Resource Centre 101Hamstead Rd, Handsworth, Birmingham, West Midlands B20 2QS

Asian Women's Adhikar Association Waterloo Terr, 222 Newhampton Road East, Wolverhampton, West Midlands WV1 4BA

Asian Women's Advisory Service 161 Mare St, London E8 3RH

Asian Women's Resource Centre 108 Craven Pk, Harlesden, London NW10 8QE

Aston Legal Centre United Evangelical Project (UEP), 29 Trinity Rd, Birmingham, West Midlands B6 6AJ

Aston University Students Guild Advice Centre The Triangle, Birmingham, West Midlands B4 7ES

Aston-Mansfield 'The Junction', 318 Barking Rd, Plaistow, London E13 8HL

Asylum Aid 28 Commercial St, London E1 6LS

Avon (Univ Settlement) Community Association 115 High St, Shirehampton, Bristol BS11 0DE

Axis 12 St. Georges Sq, Huddersfield, West Yorkshire HD1 1JF

Ballynafeigh Advice Centre 283 Ormeau Rd, Belfast BT7 3GG

Ballysally Community Association 101 Daneshill Rd, Coleraine, County Derry BT52 2QJ

Ballysillan Advice Service 921–933 Crumlin St, Belfast BT14 8FG

Banbury Young Homelessness Project The Bridge, 49 Castle St, Banbury, Oxfordshire OX16 8NU

Banchory Advice Centre West Church Hall, Mount St, Banchory, Aberdeen AB31

Bangladesh Welfare Association (UK) Ltd 39 Fournier St, London E16 0E

Bangladesh Youth Movement (BYM) 21–23 Henriques St, London, E1 1NB

Bangladeshi Ekota Project c/o CREC, 66 Nottingham Rd, Loughborough, Leicestershire LE11 1EU

Barking and Dagenham CVS Faircross Community Complex, Hulse Ave, Barking, Essex IG11 9UP

Barnet Housing Aid Centre 36b Woodhouse Rd, North Finchley, London N12 0RG

Barnet Law Service 9 Bell La, London, NW4 2BP

Barnstaple Youth Enquiry Service 25 Castle St, Barnstaple, Devon EX31 1DR

Barton Hill Advice Service Unit 32 Easton Bus Pk, Felix Rd, Easton, Bristol BS5 0PT

Basement Project 4 Hogarth Rd, Earls Court, London SW5 0PT; E-mail thebasementproject@yahoo.co.uk

Bassetlaw Housing Advice Centre (BHAC) 13 Queen St, Worksop, Nottinghamshire S80 2AN

Battle Against Tranquillisers PO Box 658, Bristol BS99 1XP

BCAT-The Black Sexual Health Organisation Unit 8, Chapeltown Enterprise Centre, 231–235 Chapeltown Rd, Leeds, West Yorkshire LS7 3DX

Beaconsfield Advisory Centre 18 Aylesbury End, Old Town, Beaconsfield, Buckinghamshire HP9 1LW

Bebington TUC Unemployed Centre 101 New Chester Rd, New Ferry, Merseyside L62 4RA

Bed and Breakfast Project HOCT The Crypt, Holy Cross Church, Cromer St, London, WC1N 8JU

Bedford Community Rights Centre 27b Tavistock St, Bedford, Bedfordshire MK40 2RB

Belfast Unemployed Resource Centre 45–49 Donegall St, Belfast BT1 2FG

Bell Farm Church South Rd, West Drayton, London UB7 9LW

Bellenden Neighbourhood Advice Centre Copleston Centre, Copleston Rd, Peckham, London SE15 4AN

Bellinge Community House 15 Hamerhill Crt, Northampton, Northamptonshire NN3 9BU

Benefit Advice Shop 19 Bedford St, Rhyl, Clwyd, LL!8 1SY

Bestwood Advice Centre 21 Gainsford Cres, Bestwood Est, Nottingham NG5 5FH

Better Life for Women and Families Unit 18, Enterprise Centre, 1a Willan Rd, Broadwater Farm, Tottenham, London N17 6NG

Bhagini Centre Ltd 177–179 Narborough Rd, Leicester LE3 0PE

BHAM Racial Attacks Monitoring Unit PO Box 9289, Birmingham, West Midlands B15 2EA

BHT Housing Aid and Legal Centre 113–117 Queens Rd, Brighton, Brighton and Hove BN1 3XG

Birkbeck College London Student Union Advice Centre Birkbeck College London, Malet St, London WC1E 7HX

Birmingham Business Debtline Birmingham Settlement, 318 Summer La, Birmingham, West Midlands B19 3RL

Birmingham Money Advice and Grants 138 Digbeth, Birmingham, West Midlands B5 6DR

Birmingham Tribunal Unit 5th Fl, Ruskin Chambers, 179–203 Corporation St, Birmingham, West Midlands B4 6RP

Birmingham TUC Centre for the Unemployed 448 Stratford Rd, Sparkhill, Birmingham, West Midlands B11 4AE

BISU–Welfare Advice Centre Bolton Institute Students Union, Deane Campus, Bolton, Lancashire BL3 5AB

Blackbird Leys Neighbourhood Support Centre 96 Blackbird Leys Rd, Blackbird Leys, Oxford, Oxfordshire OX4 5HS

Blackfriars Advice Centre
Correspondence address only.
c/o 199 Walworth Rd, London SE17 1RL

Blackliners Units 46–47, Eurolink Business Centre, 49 Effra Rd, London SW2 1BZ

Blackpool Centre for the Unemployed 29 Queen St, Blackpool FY1 1NL

Blackpool Refuge Resource Centre 98a Park Rd, Blackpool, FY1 4ES

Blakenhall Community Advice Centre 164 Dudley Rd, Wolverhampton, West Midlands WV2 3DN

Blind Centre for Northern Ireland 70 North Rd, Belfast, BT5 5NJ

Boldon Lane Neighbourhood Advice Centre 89–91 Boldon La, South Shields, Tyne and Wear NE34 0AS

Borderline 48 Grosvenor Gdns, London SW1W 0EB

Bradford Campus Student Union Welfare Service The Sound Gallery, Great Horton Rd, Bradford, West Yorkshire BD7 1AY

Bradford City Centre Project Limited YMCA Bldg, Trinity Rd, Bradford, West Yorkshire BD5 0JG

Breakthrough Advice and Advisory Centre Plaistow Christian Church, 663 Barking Rd, Plaistow, London, E13 9EX

Brent Association of Disabled People 154 Harlesden Rd, Willesden, London NW10 3RX

Brent Bereavement Services Willesden Community Hospital, Harlesden Rd, London NW10 3RY

Brent Carers Centre Wembley Centre for Health and Care, 116 Chaplin Rd, Wembley, Greater London HA0 4UZ

Brent Irish Advisory Service (BIAS) The Old Library Bldg, Willesden Green Library Centre, Willesden, London NW10 2ST

Bridge Housing Advice Centre The Annexe, Southfield Rd, Loughborough, Leicestershire LE11 2TS

Bridge That Gap The Bridge, 31–33 Bridge St, Andover, Hampshire SP10 1BE

Brighton Unemployed Centre Families Project Prior Hse, 6 Tilbury Pl, Brighton, Brighton and Hove BN2 2GY

Brighton University Student Union Welfare Unit Cockcroft Bldg, Lewes Rd, Brighton, Brighton and Hove BN2 4GJ

Brigstowe Project 96–98 Stapleton Rd, Bristol BS5 0PR

Bristol Debt Advice Centre 2nd Fl, 48–54 West St, St. Philips, Bristol BS2 0BL

16

Bristol Drugs Project 11 Brunswick Sq, Bristol BS2 8PE

Brixton Advice Centre 167 Railton Rd, Herne Hill, London SE24 0LU

Burnley Community Advice Centre 144 St. James St, Burnley, Lancashire BB11 1NR

Byker Advice and Information Project 21 Raby Cross, Byker, Newcastle upon Tyne, Tyne and Wear NE6 2FF

Cambridge Independent Advice Centre 41 Mill Rd, Cambridge, Cambridgeshire CB1 2AW

Camden Chinese Community Centre 173 Arlington Rd, London NW1 7EY

Camden Federation of Private Tenants 11–17 The Marr, Curnock Est, London NW1 0HE

Camden Tribunal and Rights Units 2 Grafton Yard, London NW5 2ND

Cancer Resource Store 64 Mount Pleasant, Liverpool, Merseyside L3 5SD; URL www.cancerstoreuk.com

Canning Town Advice Centre 11 Hermit Rd, Canning Town, London E16 4HP

Cannock Chase Advice Centre 23 Park Rd, Cannock, Staffordshire WS11 1JN

Canterbury Housing Advice Centre 2nd Fl, 24 Burgate, Canterbury, Kent CT1 2HA

Cape Hill and Windmill Development Trust 1st Fl, Hamilton Hse, Grove La, Smethwick, West Midlands B66 2SG; E-mail thetrust@capehill.windmill.fsnet.co.uk

Caradon Housing Youth Project The Basement, Parade Hse, Liskeard, Cornwall PL14 6AA

Cardiff Energy Advice Centre Terminus Bldg, Wood St, Cardiff CF1 1EQ

Cardiff Move-on 195 Newport Rd, Cardiff CF24 1AJ

Cardiff University Union Student Advice Centre Park Pl, Cardiff CF1 3QN

Cardiff Womens Aid 20 Moira Terr, Adamsdown, Cardiff CF2 1ES

Care and Repair (Cheltenham) Ltd The Resource Centre, 340 High St, Cheltenham, Gloucestershire GL50 3JF

Care and Repair Carmarthenshire 21–23 High St, Ammanford, Dyfed, Carmarthenshire SA18 2NA

Care and Repair Cymru Norbury Hse, Norbury Rd, Fairwater, Cardiff CF5 3AS

Carers Centre (North and West Oxfordshire) 27 Horse Fair, Banbury, Oxfordshire OX16 0AE

Carers Centre for Brighton and Hove Ltd 113–117 Queens Rd, Brighton, Brighton and Hove BN1 3XG

Carers' Council Allies in Adult Mental Health Nottingham Voluntary Action Centre, 7 Mansfield Rd, Nottingham, NG1 3FB

Carers Information and Support Service 28 Chislehurst Rd, Orpington, Kent BR6 0DG

Carers of Barking and Dagenham 15 Althorne Way, Dagenham, Essex RM10 7AV

Carila–Latin American Welfare Group Manor Gardens Centre, 6–9 Manor Gdns, London N7 6LA

CARIS Haringey 107 Hampden Rd, Hornsey, London N8 0HU

Carterton Advice and Neighbourhood Centre Methodist Church Bldgs, Burford Rd, Carterton, Oxfordshire OX18 3AG

CASA Alcohol Services 75 Fortess Rd, Camden, London NW5 1AG

Cast Advice Crisis Pregnancy and Parenting Centre HCF Romford Centre, 2 Craigdale Rd, Hornchurch, Essex RM11 1AX

Castle Advice Service Duke St Neighbourhood Centre, 207 Duke St, Sheffield, South Yorkshire S2 5QP

Catholic Housing Aid Society (CHAS) 209 Old Marylebone Rd, London NW1 5QT

Central London Advice Service Derry Hse, Penfold St, London NW8 8HJ

Centre 33 33 Clarendon St, Cambridge, Cambridgeshire CB1 1JX

Centre 70 Community Association Ltd 46 Knights Hill, West Norwood, London SE27 0JD

Centre for Armenian Information and Advice Hayashen, 105a Mill Hill, Acton, London W3 8JF

Centre for Corporate Accountability 4th Fl, 197-199 City Rd, London EC1V 1JN; URL www.corporateaccountability.org; E-mail info@corporateaccountability.org

Centre for Full Employment 73 West St, Sheffield, South Yorkshire S1 4EQ

Centre of Filipinos St. Francis Community Centre, 13 Hippodrome Rd, Notting Hill, London, W11 4SF; E-mail cf@clara.net

Ceredigion Access 6 Water St, Aberaeron, Ceredigion SA46 0DG

Changing Faces 1–2 Junction Mews, London W2 1PN

Chapelgreen Advice Centre 35 Station Rd, Chapeltown, Sheffield, South Yorkshire S35 2XE

Charnwood Racial Equality Council 66 Nottingham Rd, Loughborough, Leicestershire LE11 1EU

CHAS (Bristol) Housing Advice Centre 86–88 Stokes Croft, Bristol BS1 3RJ

CHAS Housing Aid Sedgefield Terr, Bradford, West Yorkshire BD1 2RU

CHAS Housing Aid (Kirklees) Unit 8, Empire Hse, Dewsbury, West Yorkshire WF12 8DJ

CHAS Housing Aid–Kirklees 1st Fl, Standard Hse, Huddersfield, West Yorkshire HD1 2JF

CHAS Palace PO Box 524, Croydon, Surrey CR9 2QR

Cheetham Hill Advice Centre 1 Morrowfield Ave, Cheetham Hill, Manchester M8 9AR

Chelmsley Advice and Resource Agency Keeper's Lodge, Chelmsley Rd, Birmingham, West Midlands B37 7RS

Cheltenham and Gloucester College of Higher Student Union Welfare Advice Centre Students Union Central Complex, PO Box 220, Cheltenham, Gloucestershire GL50 2QF

Cheltenham Housing Aid Centre Ltd 31 Prestbury Rd, Cheltenham, Gloucestershire GL52 2PP

Cheshire Asbestos Victims Support Group 3 Fryer St, Runcorn, Cheshire WA7 1ND; URL www.cavsg.org.uk; E-mail information@cavsg.org.uk

Children's Information Service 11 Leopold St, Sheffield, South Yorkshire S1 2GY

Children's Legal Centre University of Essex, Whivenhoe Pk, Chelmsford, Essex CO4 3SQ

Children's Rights Service West London YMCA, The Drop-in Centre, 82 Matlock La, Ealing, London W5 5BJ; E-mail admin@londonymca.org

Chinese Association of Tower Hamlets 680 Commercial Rd, London, E14 7HA; E-mail londonchinese@hotmail.com

Chinese Community Centre 2nd Fl, 28–29 Gerrard St, London W1V 7LP

Chinese Information and Advice Centre 1st Fl, 53 New Oxford St, London WC1A 1BL

Chinese Welfare Association 133–135 University St, Belfast BT7 1HQ

Choice in Hackney 2nd Fl, D Block, St. Leonard's Primary Care Centre, Nuttal St, London N1 5LZ

Chub Bilsthorpe Resource Centre The Village Hall, Cross St, Newark, Nottinghamshire NG22 8QY

Churchdown Project Advice Service, 35 Coriander Dr, Churchdown, Gloucestershire GL3 1LD

Churches Advice Centre 91 Spencer Rd, Waterside, County Londonderry BT47 6AE

Citizen Advice and Rights, Cowdenbeath 322 High St, Cowdenbeath, Fife KY4 9NT

Citizen Advice and Rights, Dunfermline 4 Abbey Park Pl, Dunfermline, Fife KY12 7PD

Citizen Advice and Rights, Glenrothes 119 Canmore Rd, Glenrothes, Fife KY7 4BJ

Citizen Advice and Rights, Kirkcaldy 15 Wemyssfield, Kirkcaldy, Fife KY1 1XN

Citizens Advice and Rights, Cupar 11 St. Catherine's St, Cupar, Fife KY15 4LS

Citizen's Advice and Rights, Fife Room 114, Unicorn Hse, Glenrothes, Fife KY7 5NS

Citizens Advice and Rights, Levenmouth Wellesley Rd, Methil, Fife KY8 3QR

City Centre Project Ltd 52 Oldham St, Manchester M4 1LE

Clapham Community Project St. Anne's Hall, Venn St, Clapham, London SW4 0AX

Claudy Rural Development Association 35 Irwin Cres, Claudy, Londonderry, County Londonderry BT47 4AB

Cleveland Housing Advice Centre 16 Borough Rd, Middlesbrough TS1 5DW

Clifton Welfare Rights Advice Centre c/o Green Lane Youth and Community Centre, Green La, Nottingham NG11 9AY

Clydebank Unemployed Community Resource Centre 1 Stanford St, Whitecrook, Clydebank, West Dunbartonshire G81 1RW

Coastal Homeless Action Group (CHAG) 43 The High St, Saxmundham, Suffolk IP17 1AJ

Coleraine Women's Aid (Women's Centre) 23 Abbey St, Coleraine, County Londonderry BT52 1DU

Colin Community Groups Association 220 Springfield Rd, Belfast BT12 7DR

College of Health St. Margaret's Hse, 21 Old Ford Rd, London E2 9PL

Collingham Rural Advice and Resource Centre Memorial Hall, 67 High St, Collingham, Near Newark, Nottinghamshire NG23 7LB

Colon Cancer Concern 9 Rickell St, London, SW6 1RU; URL www.coloncancer.org.uk; E-mail admin@coloncancer.org.uk

Columbian Refugee Association 161 Lambeth Wlk, London SE11 6EE

Communicare 233 Kings Rd, Reading, Berkshire RG1 4LS

Community Advice and Information Service 85 Crampian Rd, Aviemore, Highland PH22 1RH

Community Advice Programme 2 The Green, Ealing, London W5 5DA

Community Car Share Network The Studio, 32 The Colts, Leeds, West Yorkshire LS2 7EW; URL www.carshareclubs.org.uk; E-mail office@carshareclubs.org.uk

Community Debt Advice Centre 12 Mill Rd, Burgess Hill, West Sussex RH15 8DR

Community Development and Legal Project Cedar Lodge, 37 Charlton Church La, London, SE7 7AG

Community Development Centre North Belfast 22 Cliftonville Rd, Belfast BT14 6JX

Community House 27–29 Birk Ave, Kendray, Barnsley, South Yorkshire S70 3AG; E-mail lawrence@communityhouse42.fsnet.co.uk

Community Information Centre 16 Market Pl, Wantage, Oxfordshire OX12 8AE

Community Links Canning Town Public Hall, 105 Barking Rd, Canning Town, London E16 4HQ

Community of Congolese Students in UK Room C, Lyndhurst Hall, Warden Rd, London, NW5 4RE

Community Self Build Agency Unit 26, Finsbury Business Centre, London EC1R 0NE

Community Space Centre St. John-at-Hackney Church, Lower Clapton Rd, London E5 0PD

Coney Hill Neighbourhood Project 1a Stanway Rd, Coney Hill, Gloucester, Gloucestershire GL4 4RE

Connect 141–121 Bridgend YMCA, Angel St, Bridgend CF31 4AD

Corby and District Welfare Rights Advice Service 2 Corby Advice Centre, George St, Corby, Northamptonshire NN17 1QG

Corpus Christi Services Springhill Dr, Belfast BT12 7QD

County Trust (CASH) 3 Gregories Crt, Gregories Rd, Beaconsfield, Buckinghamshire HP9 1HQ

Coventry University Student Union Advice Centre Students' Union, Coventry University, Priory St, Coventry, West Midlands CV1 5FJ

Craigavon Independent Advice Centre Moylinn Hse, 21 Legahory Centre, Craigavon, County Armagh BT65 5BE

Credit Action Trust 6 Regent Terr, Cambridge, Cambridgeshire CB2 1AA

Creggan Community Care The Old Clinic, Fanad Dr, Derry, County Derry BT48 9OE

Cricklewood Homeless Concern (CHC) 60 Ashford Rd, London, NW2 5TU

Crookes Rights and Advice Centre Crookes Endowed Centre, Crookes, Sheffield, South Yorkshire S10 1UB

Crossover 619 Bordesley Grn, Birmingham, West Midlands B9 5XZ

Croxteth Advice Centre 35 Moss Way, Croxteth, Liverpool, Merseyside L11 0BL

Croydon Housing Aid Society Ground Fl, The Old Hse, Croydon, Surrey CR9 0UN

Croydon Youth Information and Counselling Service Drop In, 132 Church St, Croydon, Surrey CR0 1RF

Cystic Fibrosis Trust 11 London Rd, Bromley, Kent BR1 1BY

Daneshouse Road Advice Centre (BACSC Ltd) 53 Daneshouse Rd, Burnley, Lancashire BB10 1AF

Darnall and District Advice Service 626 Staniforth Rd, Darnall, Sheffield, South Yorkshire S9 4LN

Daventry Welfare Rights Advice Group The Abbey, Market Sq, Daventry, Northamptonshire NN11 4BH

Day–Mer Turkish and Kurdish Community Centre Former Library, Howard Rd, Hackney, London N16 8PR

Deaf Advice Service Sheffield 173 Arundel Gate, Sheffield, South Yorkshire S1 2LQ

Deptford and New Cross Credit Union Ltd Pepys Resource Centre, Old Library, Deptford Strand, London SE8 3AQ

Derbyshire Housing Aid Ltd 46 Curzon St, Derby DE1 1LL

Derbyshire Unemployed Workers Centre 54 Saltergate, Chesterfield, Derbyshire S40 1JR

Derry Community Social Services Centre 1a High St, Londonderry, County Fermanagh BT48 6LT

Derwentside Women's Aid PO Box 13, Consett, County Durham DH8 8RL

DIAL Llantrisant and District c/o Mrs D Rees (Chair), 53 Lanely Rd, Talbot Green, Rhondda, Cynon, Taff CF1 8HY

DIAL Tameside The Festival Hall, Peel St, Denton, M34 3JX

DIAL Waltham Forest 1a Warner Rd, Walthamstow, London E17 7DY

16

Diaspora (Sudanese Community Group) Unit C2, 3 Bradbury St, London, N16 6JN; URL www.diaspora.org.uk; E-mail diaspora@compuserve.com

Dilligence Advice and Information Service PO Box 22627, London, N4 2ZG; E-mail dais@excite.co.uk

Disability Action Portside Bus Pk, 189 Airport Road West, Belfast BT3 9ED

Disability Action (Derry) 58 Strand Rd, Derry, County Derry BT48 7AG

Disability Action in Barnet 954 Barnet Rd, North Finchley, London N12 9RX; URL www.dabb.org.uk; E-mail disability@dabb.org.uk

Disability Action in Islington 90–92 Upper St, Islington, London N1 0NP

Disability Advice and Information Network Sembal Hse, Handel Terr, Southampton SO15 2FH

Disability Advice and Welfare Network 64 Bickerstaffe St, St. Helens, Merseyside WA10 1DH

Disability Advice Service Lambeth 336 Brixton Rd, London, SW9 7AA

Disability Alliance ERA Universal Hse, 88–94 Wentworth St, London E1 7SA

Disability Association Barking and Dagenham Welfare Rights Welfare Benefits Department, 51 Ripple Rd, Barking, Essex IG11 7NT

Disability Discrimination Act RAP 6 New Court Rd, Springfield, Chelmsford, Essex CM2 6BZ

Disability in Camden
Correspondence only.
Peckwater Centre, Peckwater St, London, NW5 2TX

Disability Law Service 38–45 Cavell St, London, E1 2BP; E-mail advice@dls.org.uk

Disability North The Dene Centre, Castle Farm Rd, Newcastle upon Tyne, Tyne and Wear NE3 1PH

Disability Solutions The Dudson Centre, Hope St, Stoke-on-Trent ST1 5DD

Disability West Midlands Prospect Hall, College Wlk, Selly Oak, West Midlands B29 6LE

Disabled People's Alliance Northants YMCA Bldg, 4–5 Cheyne Wk, Northampton, Northamptonshire NN1 5PT

Disablement Resource Unit MCVS, Mount Vernon Grn, Liverpool, Merseyside L7 8TF

Disablement Welfare Rights Advice Service Canolfan Lafan, 2 Glanrafon, Bangor, Gwynedd LL57 1LH

DISC Cobblers Hall, Burn La, Newton Aycliffe, County Durham DL5 4SE

Doncaster Partnership for Carers Ltd Lansdowne Centre, Lansdowne Rd, Doncaster, South Yorkshire DN2 6QN

Dorest Lesbian and Gay Helpline PO Box 316, Bournemouth BH1 4HL

Dostiyo, Asian Women and Girls Organisation 62–66 Dunster St, Northampton, Northamptonshire NN1 3JY

Dove House Integrated Advice Centre 32 Meenan Sq, Bogside, Derry, County Derry BT48 9EX

Downs Syndrome Association 155 Mitcham Rd, Tooting, London SW17 9PG

DRIVE 42 Garway, Woolton, Liverpool, Merseyside L25 5LR

Druglink 47 Victoria Rd, Swindon SN1 3AY

Dudley Advice Centre 104 Dixons Green Rd, Dudley, West Midlands DY2 7DJ; E-mail dudleyadvicecentre@yahoo.co.uk

Dundee Drugs and AIDS Project 76 Bell St, Dundee DD1 1HF

Dunfermline Advocacy Initiative 2 Halbeath Rd, Dunfermline, Fife KY12 7QX

Dungiven Community Resource Centre 114 Main St, Dungiven, Londonderry, County Derry BT47 4LG

Accommodation Office, Durham Student Union Dunelm Hse, New Elvet, Durham, County Durham DH1 3AN

Durham Students' Union Welfare Service Dunelm Hse, New Elvet, Durham, County Durham DH1 3AN

Earls Court Homeless Families Project 17 Bramham Gdns, London SW5 0JJ

Early Years Project Alessi Centre, Belfast BT13 2BZ

East Belfast Independent Advice Centre 85 Castlereagh St, Belfast BT5 4NF

East Bristol Advice and Information Centres Unit 51, Easton Business Centre, Felix Rd, Easton, Bristol, BS5 0HE; E-mail ebaic@lineone.net

East End Advice Centre 5 Whitevale St, Glasgow G31 1QW

East European Advice Centre 370–377 Uxbridge Rd, London W12 7LL

East Finchley Advice Service 42 Church La, East Finchley, London N2 8DT

East London Out Project 56–60 Grove Rd, Walthamstow, London E17 9BN

East London Somali Association 728 Romford Rd, Manor Park, London, E12 6BT

East Sussex Disability Association 1 Faraday Cl, Hampden Pk, Eastbourne, East Sussex BN22 9BH; E-mail info@esda.org.uk

East Sutherland Village Advisory Service Alba, Main St, Golspie, Sutherland, Highland KW10 6TG

Ebor Gardens Advice Centre PO Box YR6, Leeds, West Yorkshire LS9 7UT
Correspondence address.

EEAC Bonnington Mill, 72 Newhaven Rd, Edinburgh EH6 5QG

Elders' Voice Carlton Centre, Granville Rd, London, NW6 2BX; E-mail elders.voice@lineone.net

Ellesmere Port Trade Union Resource Centre King St, Ellesmere Port, Cheshire L65 4AZ

Endeavour Repaircare 8 Sydenham Rd, Hartlepool TS25 1QB

Energy Conservation and Solar Centre Unit 327, 30 Gt Guildford St, London SE1 0HS

Energy Projects Plus Manor Trust Bldg, 79 Gorsey La, Wallasey, Merseyside CH44 4HF; E-mail advice@epplus.org.uk

Energy Projects Plus-Cheshire Rooms 2–4, Brunmer Guildhall, High St, Winsford, Cheshire CW7 2AU

Enniskillen Welfare Rights Advice Centre 3–7 Queen St, Enniskillen, County Fermanagh BT74 7ES

Equity Trust Fund 222 Africa Hse, 64 Kingsway, London WC2B 6BD

Essex University Student Union Advice Centre Wivenhoe Pk, Colchester, Essex CO4 3SQ

Ethiopian Advice and Support Centre Palingswick Hse, 241 King St, London W6 9LP

Ethiopian Community in Britain 2a Lithos Rd, London, NW3 6EF

Ethiopian Refugee Community in Lambeth 1 Stockwell Grn, London SW9 9HP

Evelyn Oldfield Unit LVS Resource Centre, 356 Holloway Rd, London, N7 6PA; E-mail evelynoldfieldunit@compuserve.com

Evelyn One–Nine–O Centre 190 Evelyn St, Deptford, London SE8 5DB

Exeter Drugs Project Dean Clarke Hse, Southernbay East, Exeter, Devon EX1 1PQ

Exeter Homeless Action Group 16 Bartholomew St East, Exeter, Devon EX4 3BG

Eye to Eye Youth Counselling Service Beddau CEC, Bruncelynog School, Beddau, Rhondda, Cynon, Taff CF38 2AE

Eyres Monsell Tenants Association 20 The Exchange, Eyres, Leicester, Leicestershire LE2 9BA

Face Advice Centre 118 Ferham Rd, Rotherham, South Yorkshire S61 1DY

Faces in Focus 102 Harper Rd, London SE1 6AQ

Falls Community Council 275–277 Falls Rd, Belfast BT12 6FD

Falls Women's Centre 173 Mulholland Terr, Falls Rd, Belfast BT12 6AF

Family Support Project Stockport C P Society, Granville Hse, Stockport, Greater Manchester SK4 4JZ

Fazakerley Advice Information and Resources Ltd The Community Centre, Formosa Dr, Liverpool, Merseyside L10 7LQ

Federation of Voluntary Sector Care Providers 2nd Fl, 32–36 Rye La, Peckham, London SE15 5BS; URL www.the.fed@virginnet.co.uk

Fife Advocacy Project Office 3, Fraser Bldgs, Kirkcaldy, Fife KY1 2NL

Fife Community Mediation 24 Hill St, Kirkcaldy, Fife KY1 1HX

Filwood Hope 11–13 Filwood Broadway, Knowle West, Bristol BS4 1JL

Financial Fitness Resource Team 19 Boyle St, Greenock, Strathclyde, PA15 1ER

Finsbury Park Action Group Alexandra National Hse, 330 Seven Sisters Rd, London N4 2PJ

Finsbury Park Homeless Families Project c/o Alexandra National Hse, 330 Seven Sisters Rd, London N4 2PJ

Firth Park Advice Centre 9 Stubbin La, Firth Pk, Sheffield, South Yorkshire S5 6QG

Fitzrovia Neighbourhood Association Fitzrovia Neighbourhood Centre, 39 Tottenham St, London W1P 9PE

Fitzwilliam Road Education and Welfare Rights Centre 112 Fitzwilliam Rd, Rotherham, South Yorkshire S65 1PX

Fold Housing Trust 3 Redburn Sq, Hollywood, County Down BT18 9HZ

Foleshill Information and Advice Centre 449 Foleshill Rd, Foleshill, Coventry, West Midlands CV6 5AQ

Forest Fields Advice Centre 69 Wiverton Rd, Forest Fields, Nottingham NG7 6NU

Forest Road Unemployed Community Residential Centre Forest Rd, Cinderford, Gloucestershire GL14 2NT

Foxhill and Parson Cross Advice Service 31 Wolfe Rd, Foxhill, Sheffield, South Yorkshire S6 1BT

Foyle Downs Syndrome Trust Spencer Hse, Spencer Rd, Waterside, County Londonderry BT47 1AA

Foyle Homeless Action and Advice Service 8 London St, Derry, County Londonderry BT48 6RQ

Friend Community Mental Health Residential Centre 39a–b Oxford St, Weston-super-Mare, North Somerset BS23 1TN

Frontline Housing Advice Ltd Hudson Hse, 1 Stockwell Grn, London SW9 9HP

Fulham Legal Advice Centre 679a Fulham Rd, London SW6 5PZ

Furness Drug and Alcohol Concern 52 Paradise St, Barrow-in-Furness, Cumbria LA14 1JG

Galliagh Community Development Group 82a Brookdale Pk, Galliagh, Londonderry, BT48 6HQ

Galliagh People's Support Group 27 Galliagh Pk, Galliagh, Londonderry, BT48 8DD

GALOP Unit 2g, Leroy Hse, London N1 3QP

GAVO Newport Resource Centre 35 Commercial Rd, Newport NP20 2PB

GDVSAP 75–81 Eastgate St, Gloucester, Gloucestershire GL1 1PN

Genesis Money Advice Project Mission Hall, Mission Sq, Brentford, Greater London TW8 0SD

Gingerbread Advice Line 7 Sovereign Cl, Sovereign Ct, London E1W 3HW

Gingerbread Northern Ireland 169 University St, Belfast BT7 1HR

Girlington Advice Centre Girlington Rd, Bradford, West Yorkshire BD8 9NN

Glenluce Quality Caring Centre 62 Knocknagoney Ave, Belfast, BT4 2PZ

Gloucester Forum for Young Single Homelessness 4 Wellington St, Gloucester, Gloucestershire GL1 1RA

Gloucester Tenants Federation 1st Fl, 75–81 Eastgate St, Gloucester, Gloucestershire GL1 1PN

Gordon Rural Action 55 Gordon St, Huntly, Aberdeenshire AB54 8EQ

Granton Information Centre 134 West Granton Rd, Edinburgh EH5 1PE

Greater Manchester Hazards Centre Ltd 23 New Mount St, Manchester M4 4DE

Greater Manchester Immigration Aid Unit 400 Cheetham Hill Rd, Manchester M8 9LE

Greater Manchester Low Pay Unit 23 New Mount St, Manchester M4 4DE

Greater Turf Lodge Residents Association 36a Norglen Dr, Belfast, BT11 8DH

Greenwich Carers Centre 170–172 Powis St, Woolwich, London SE18 6NL

Greenwich Energy Efficiency Advice Centre 1st Fl, The Old Town Hall, Woolwich, London SE18 6PN

Greenwich Housing Rights 25 Hare St, Woolwich, London SE18 6NE

Greenwich University Student Union Advice Service Bathway, Woolwich, London SE18 6QX

Greenwich Women's Centre 45 Hare St, Woolwich, London SE18 6NE

Hackney Carers Centre Unit 17, 11–20 Tudor Gr, London E9 7QL

Hackney Cypriot Association 5 Balls Pond Rd, London, N1 4AX

Hackney Women's Aid PO Box 8586, London, E8 3AZ

Halton Trade Union Unemployed Community Residential Centre Old Police St, Mersey Rd, Runcorn, Cheshire WA7 1DF

Hammersmith and Fulham Private Tenants' Rights Project 142–144 King St, London W6 0QU

Hammersmith Women's Aid PO Box 2018, Shepherd's Bush, London, W12 8NP

Harbour Centre (Plymouth) Ltd 9–10 Ermington Terr, Mutley, Plymouth PL4 6QG

Haringey Cons. of Disabled People and Carers 551b High Rd, Tottenham, London N17 6SB

Haringey Women's Forum 2 Factory La, Tottenham, London, N17 9FL

Harlow Welfare Rights and Advice Service Harlow Advice Centre, 2 Eastgate, Harlow, Essex CM20 1ND

Hastings Advice and Representation Centre 8 Cambridge Rd, Hastings, East Sussex TN34 1DJ

16

Haywards Heath Debt Advice Centre Elizabeth Hse, 13 Heath Rd, Hayward Heath, West Sussex RH16 3AY; URL www.debt-advice.org.uk; E-mail enquiries@debt-advice.org.uk

Healthy Gay Living Centre 40 Borough High St, London SE1 1XS

Heath Town Support and Information Centre 236 Chervil Rise, Heath Town, Wolverhampton, West Midlands WV10 0HR

Hebburn Neighbourhood Advice Centre 10 Victoria Road West, Hebburn, Tyne and Wear NE31 1LD

Heeley Advice Centre Heeley Grn Centre, 344 Gleadless Rd, Sheffield, South Yorkshire S2 3AH

Help Project St. Helens Community Advice Centre, Christian Life Centre, St. Helens, Merseyside WA10 2DT

Help the Aged 1st Fl, Ascot Hse, 24–31 Shaftesbury Ave, Belfast BT2 7DB

Heslers Way Neighbourhood Project 34 Edinburgh Pl, Cheltenham, Gloucestershire GL51 7SA

Highfield and St. Matthews Community Employment Project 6 Seymour St, Highfields, Leicester, LE2 0LB

Highland Advice and Information Network 57 Church St, Inverness, Highland IV1 1DR

Hillcrest House 14–17 Jasmine Ct, Gobnascale, County Londonderry BT47 2DZ

Hinckley YMCA Young People's Information Centre 7 Lancaster Rd, Hinckley, Leicestershire LE10 0AW

Hispanic Welfare Association Head Office, 11 Sackville Rd, Southend-on-Sea, SS2 4JQ

Hitslink Advice Agency 39 Abingdon Rd, Leicester LE2 1HA

Holbrooks Community Care Association Holbrooks Information Centre – The Park, Holbrook La, Holbrooks, Coventry, Warwickshire CV5 4LD; URL www.holbrooks.clara.net; E-mail hcca@holbrooks.clara.net

Holmewood Outreach Advice Centre Madison Ave, Holme Wood, Bradford, West Yorkshire BD4 0JE

Homes for Homeless People Cyranian Hse, 9–11 Union St, Luton LU1 3AN

Hope Debt Advice Centre 118 Brickhill Dr, Bedford, Bedfordshire MK41 9QZ

Hope House Advice Service Hope Hse, 117 Jumpers Rd, Christchurch, Dorset BH23 2JS

Hornsey YMCA Care and Repair Hornsey YMCA, 184 Tottenham La, Hornsey, London N8 8SG

Housing Advice Centre 2–14 Telford Rd, London W10 5SH

Housing Advice Centre Anchor Hse, 116 Kingston Cres, Portsmouth PO2 8AL

Housing Advice Resource Project (HARP) 227 High St, Northallerton, North Yorkshire DL7 8DW

Housing Aid and Advice Centre for Swale Central Hse, Central Ave, Sittingbourne, Kent ME10 4NU

Housing Interaction Trust Drill Hall Cottage, Bellingdon Rd, Chesham, Buckinghamshire HP5 2HA

Housing Rights Service 72 North St, Belfast BT1 1LD

Housing Young People in Shrewsbury Roy Fletcher Centre, Suite H, Shrewsbury, Shropshire SY1 1JE

Hoxton Trust Legal Advice Service 156 Hoxton St, Hackney, London N1 6SH

HSOCA Salby Centre, 190 Great Dower St, Tottenham, London N17 8JL; E-mail hsoca@hotmail.com

Hucknall and District Voluntary Advice Centre Council Offices, Watnall Rd, Nottingham NG15 7LA

Hull Independent Housing Aid Centre 60 Beverley Rd, Hull, Kingston upon Hull HU3 1YE

Huyton Unemployed Centre CVS Bldg, Lathom Rd, Liverpool, Merseyside L36 9XZ

ICIS 35 Worthing Rd, East Preston, Littlehampton, West Sussex BN16 1BQ

Imece, Turkish Speaking Women's Group 2 Newington Green Rd, London, N1 4RX

Immigration Advisory Service County Hse, 190 Great Dover St, London SE1 4YB

Impact (DAS) Limited 4 Dudley St, Grimsby, Lincolnshire DN31 2AB

Imperial College Union Advice Service Beit Quad, Prince Consort Rd, London SW7 2BB

Independent Advice Unit Keele University Students' Union, Keele, Staffordshire ST5 5BJ

Independent Theatre Council 12 The Leather Market, Weston St, London SE1 3ER

Indo-American Refugee and Migrant Association 1st Fl, Universal Hse, 88–94 Wentworth St, London E1 7SA

Information Service Ground Fl, Royal Bldgs, Main St, Tobermory, Isle of Mull, Strathclyde, PA75 6NU; URL www.info.mull.com

Integrated Asian Advice Service 24 Green End, Woolwich, London SE16 6JY

Interchange Legal Advisory Service Interchange Studios, Dalby St, Camden, London NW5 3NQ

Inverclyde Advice and Employment Rights 16 Nicholson St, Greenock, Strathclyde, PA25 1JX

IPSEA 4 Ancient House Mews, Woodbridge, Suffolk IP12 1DH

Ipswich Disabled Advice Bureau Room 11, 19 Tower St, Ipswich, Suffolk IP1 3BG

Ipswich Housing Action Group PO Box 122, Ipswich, Suffolk IP1 3RU

Iranian Association Palingswick Hse, 241 King St, London, W6 9DT

Iranian Community Centre 266–268 Holloway Rd, London N7 6NE

Irish Community Care Merseyside 60 Duke St, Liverpool, Merseyside L1 5AA

Irish Support and Advice Centre The Irish Centre, Blacks Rd, Hammersmith, London W6 9DT

Island Advice Centre Island Hse, 4 Roserton St, London E14 9PG

Island Women's Refuge PO Box 5, Sandown, Isle of Wight PO37 6HG

Isle of Wight Independent Housing Advice Exchange Hse, St. Cross La, Newport, Isle of Wight PO30 5BZ

Islington Age Concern 6–9 Manor Gdns, Islington, London N7 6LA

Islington Carers Forum Unit 1, 53 Hargrave Rd, London N19 5SH

Islington People's Rights 2 St. Paul's Rd, Islington, London N1 2QN

Islington Women's Advice Group (WAG) c/o North Islington Law Centre, 161 Hornsey Rd, London N7 6DU

Jewish Association for the Mentally Ill 16a North End Rd, Golders Green, London NW11 7PH

Just Ask Advisory and Counselling Service Dellow Centre, 82 Wentworth St, London E1 7SA

Justice 59 Carter La, London EC4V 5AQ

Kalayaan! St. Francis Centre, Pottery La, London W11 4NQ

Kensington and Chelsea Staying Put Offices 6 and 7, Canalside Hse, London W10 5AA

Kent Information Federation Ground Fl, Cygnet Hse, Gravesend, Kent DA12 1BQ

Kent Law Clinic Eliot College, University of Kent, Canterbury, Kent CT2 7NS

Kent University Union Advice and Information Services Mandela Bldg, The University, Canterbury, Kent CT2 7NW

Key House Project 20 Low St, Keighley, West Yorkshire BD21 3PN

Keyworth Advice Centre Correspondence address only. 22 Commercial Rd, Keyworth, Nottingham NG12 5JS

Kilburn Youth Resource Centre 107 Kingsgate Rd, London, NW6 2JH

Kings College London Student Union Advice Centre 1st Fl, Macadam Bldg, London WC2R 2NS

Kings Cross Homelessness Project 48 Mecklenburg Sq, London WC1N 2NU

Kingsmead Advice Service 8–9 Kingsmead Way, Kingsmead Est, Hackney, London E9 5QG

Kingston Churches Action on Homelessness 36a Fife Rd, Kingston upon Thames, Surrey KT1 1SU

Kiran Asian Women's Aid PO Box 899, Leytonstone, London E11 1AA

Kirkby Unemployed Centre Westhead Ave, Northwood, Kirkby, Merseyside L33 0XN

Kiveton Park Independent Advice Centre Kiveton Park Library, Wales Rd, Sheffield, South Yorkshire S26 6RB

Knoll Advice Centre St. Richard's Church and Community Centre, Egmont Rd, Hove, Brighton and Hove BN3 7FP

Knowsley Pensioners Advocacy and Information Service CVS Bldg, Cherryfield Dr, Kirby, Merseyside L32 8SE

Kugos Advice Centre Kingston University Students' Union, Penrhyn Rd, Kingston upon Thames, Surrey KT1 2EE

Kurdish Community Centre Fairfax Hall, 11 Portland Gdns, London N4 1HU

Kurdish Information and Advocacy Centre Caxton Hse, 129 St. John's Way, London, N19 3RQ

Lambeth Chinese Community Association 69 Stockwell Rd, London SW9 9PY

LAMP 67 Regent Rd, Leicester LE1 6YF

Lancaster University Student Union Advice Centre Slaidburn Hse, Bailrigg, Lancaster, Lancashire LA1 4YA

Langsett Advice and Area Resource Centre Creswick St, Sheffield, South Yorkshire S6 2TN

Latin American Association Legal and Social Advice Priory Hse, Kingsgate Pl, London NW6 4TA

Latin American Disabled People's Project Unit 7, 42 Braganza St, London SE17 3RJ

Latin American Elderly Project Ringcross Community Centre, Lough Rd, London N7 8RH

Latin American Women's Aid The Print Hse, 16 Ashwin Rd, London, E8 3DL

Latin American Women's Rights Service Tindlemanor, 52–54 Featherstone St, London EC1Y 8RT

Lay Advocacy Limited Ground Fl, 18 Cradock St, Swansea SA6 8AA; E-mail layadvocacy@wales.btinternet.com

Leeds DDA Service Shire View, 72 Headingly La, Leeds, West Yorkshire LS6 2DJ

Leeds Metropolitan Student Union Advice Service LMUSU–Student Advice, B Bldg, Leeds, West Yorkshire LS1 3HE

Leeds Occupational Benefits Advice Centre 88 North St, Leeds, West Yorkshire LS2 7PN

Leeds Occupational Health Project 88 North St, Leeds, West Yorkshire LS2 7PN

Legal Advice Centre (University House) 104 Roman Rd, Bethnal Green, London E2 0RN

Leicester Charity Organisations Society 20a Millstone La, Leicester, LE1 5JN

Leicester Money Advice Ltd 20 Millstone La, Leicester LE1 5RA

Leicester Racial Equality Council Epic Hse, 3rd Fl, Leicester LE1 3SH

Leicester YMCA 7 East St, Leicester LE1 6EY

Lesbian and Gay Employment Rights Unit 1g, Leroy Hse, London N1 3QP

Lewisham Refugee Network Parker Hse, 144 Evelyn St, Deptford, London SE8 5DD

LIAISE Mount Zion Hse, Edward St, Lurgan, Craigavon, County Armagh BT66 6DB

Ligoniel Improvement Association Wolfhill Centre, 148 Ligoniel Rd, Belfast BT14 8DT

Limavady Community Development Initiative Roe Valley Hospital, 24d Benevenagh Dr, Limavady, County Londonderry BT49 0AQ

Lincoln Women's Aid PO Box 125, Lincoln, Lincolnshire LN1 1HA

Lisburn Welfare Rights Group 171 Avemore Rd, Lisburn, County Antrim BT28 1NE

Liverpool Association of Disabled People Lime Court Centre, Upper Baker St, Liverpool, Merseyside L6 1NB

Liverpool One Parent Families Trust 24 Hardman St, Liverpool, Merseyside L1 9AX

Liverpool University Guild Advice Centre Liverpool University Students' Union, PO Box 187, Liverpool, Merseyside L69 7BR

LLAWRACC The Old Police Station, 80 Lark La, Liverpool, Merseyside L17 8UU

London Advice Services Alliance 2nd Fl, Universal Hse, London E1 7SA

London Congo-Brazzar Association Unit B2, 3 Bradbury St, Dalston, London N16 83N

London Connection 12 Adelaide St, London WC2N 4HW

London East Aid Network (LEAN) 35 Romford Rd, Stratford, London E15 4LY

London Hazards Centre Hampstead Town Hall Centre, 213 Haverstock Hill, London NW3 4QP

London Irish Women's Centre 59 Stoke Newington Church St, Stoke Newington, London N16 0AR

London Legal Advice Centre 62 Battersea Park Rd, London SW11 4JP

London School of Economics Students' Union Advice Centre E297, East Bldg, London WC2A 2AE

Lonsdale District Carers The Carers Centre, 4–6 Regents Rd, Morecambe, Lancashire LA3 1OG; E-mail lonsdale@carers.freeserve.co.uk

Loughborough Student's Union and Advice Centre Union Bldg, Ashby Rd, Loughborough, Leicestershire LE11 3TT; E-mail advice@lborosu.org.uk

Low Pay Unit 23–25 Shipquay St, Derry, County Derry BT48 6DL

Low Pay Unit Belfast 45–49 Donegall St, Belfast, BT1 2FG

Lower North Belfast Community Council 21 York Rd, Belfast BT15 3GU

Luton Law Centre 28 Clarendon Rd, Luton LU2 7PQ

Manchester Carers Centre Beswick Hse, Beswick Row, Manchester M4 4PR

Manchester Metropolitan Students' Union Advice Centre 99 Oxford Rd, Manchester M1 7EL

Manningham Project 203 Lumb La, Bradford, West Yorkshire BD8 7SG

16

Manor Rights and Advice Service 300 Prince of Wales Rd, Manor, Sheffield, South Yorkshire S2 1FF

Mansfield Unemployed Workers Centre Beech Hse, 2 Beech Ave, Mansfield, Nottinghamshire NG18 1EY

Mansfield Welfare Rights Initiative The Community Project, 141 Newgate La, Mansfield, Nottinghamshire NG18 2QD

Mary Ward Legal Centre 26–27 Boswell St, London WC1N 3JZ

Maryhill Representaiton Unit The Quadrangle, 59 Ruchill St, Glasgow G20 9PY

Marylebone Bangladesh Society 2 Boscobel St, London NW8 8PS

Maternity Alliance 45 Beech St, London EC2P 2LX

Matson Neighbourhood Project Matson La, Matson, Gloucester, Gloucestershire GL4 6DX

Meadows Advice Group Queens Walk Community Centre, Queens Wlk, Nottingham NG2 2DF

Meniere's Society 98 Maybury Rd, Woking, Surrey GU21 5HX

Meridian Money Advice Keeper's Cottage, St. Alfege's Church Hall, Greenwich, London SE10 8AW

Merthyr Care and Repair Office 105 and 206, Ground Fl, Ty Kair Hardire, Riverside Crt, Avenue de Clichy, Merthyr Tydfil CF47 8XF

Merton Unemployed Workers Centre 88 High St, Colliers Wood, London SW19 2BT

Metro Centre Unit 401, 49 Greenwich High Rd, London SE10 8JL

Micro–Assistance in Continuing Education Cenmac, Charlton Park School, Charlton Park Rd, London SE7 6JB

Middlesex University Students Union Rights and Advice Centre Trent Pk, Bramley Rd, London N14 4YZ

Migrant Advisory and Advocacy Service Town Hall, High St, Southall, Greater London UB1 3HA

Migrant and Refugees Community Forum 2 Thorpe Cl, Ladbroke Gr, London, W10 5XL

Migrants Resource Centre 24 Churton St, London SW1V 2LP

Miles Platting Advice Centre 3 Queensbury Pde, Miles Platting, Manchester M40 7DW

Millen Advice Point 56 Manchester Rd, Swindon SN1 2AQ

Milton Keynes Welfare Rights Group Ltd Acorn Hse, 373 Midsummer Blvd, Milton Keynes MK9 3HP

Mind in Manchester 23 New Mount St, Manchester M4 4DE

Mind Yourself 15 Magazine St, Derry, County Londonderry BT48 5HH

Mixenden Parents Resource Centre 30–34 Stanningley Rd, Mixenden, Halifax, West Yorkshire HX2 8RJ

Money Advice and Community Support Service Community Base, 113–117 Queens Rd, Brighton, Brighton and Hove BN1 3XG

Money Advice Centre and National Debtline Birmingham Settlement, 318 Summer La, Birmingham, West Midlands B19 3RL

Money Advice Project Newlands Centre, 871 Springfield Rd, Glasgow, G31 4HZ

Money Advice Support Team (MAST) Happyhillock Neighbourhood Base, 65 Happyhillock Rd, Dundee DD4 8LR

Montgomeryshire Citizen Advocacy Ltd Dolerw, Milford Rd, Newtown, Powys SY16 2EQ

Montserrat Community Support Trust Unit C4, 3 Bradbury St, London, N16 8JN

MOSAIC: Shaping Disability Services The Guild Hall, Cotton St, Leicester, LE1 1QB

MTUCURC Advice Unit 4 Hardman St, Liverpool, Merseyside L1 9AX

MU Money Advice Service 18 College Grn, Gloucester, Gloucestershire GL1 2LR

Multi-agency Supported Tenancies Scheme 4 Bell Dean Rd, Allerton, Bradford, West Yorkshire BD8 0EQ

Multi-Lingual Community Rights Shop 213 Camberwell Rd, Camberwell, London SE5 0HG

Murray Hall Community Trust Neptune Health Pk, Sedgley Road West, Tipton, West Midlands DY4 8LU

NABS 32 Wigmore St, London W1H 9DF

Napier Students' Association Welfare Advice Service 12 Merchiston Pl, Edinburgh EH10 4NR

National Council for One Parent Families 255 Kentish Town Rd, London NW5 2LX

National Group on Homeworking Office 26, 30–38 Dock St, Leeds, West Yorkshire LS10 1JF

National Schizophrenia Fellowship Wyndhurst, Knockbracken, Belfast BT8 8BH

National Youth Advocacy Service 1 Downham Road South, Heswall, Wirral L60 5RG

Neighbourhood Development Association 69 Falls Rd, Belfast BT12 4PD

New Horizon Youth Centre 68 Challon St, London, NW1 1JR

Newcastle University Student Advice Centre Kings Wlk, Newcastle upon Tyne, Tyne and Wear NE1 8QB

Newcastle VIP Benefits Project Lynnwood Business Development Centre, Lynnwood Terr, Newcastle upon Tyne, Tyne and Wear NE4 6UL

Newham Action Against Domestic Violence St. Mark's Centre, Tollgate Rd, London E6 4YA

Newham Asian Women's Project 661 Barking Rd, Plaistow, London E13 9EX

Newham Chinese Association 505 Barking Rd, Plaistow, London E13 8PS

Newham United Tamil Association 728 Romford Rd, Manor Pk, London, E12 6BT

Newry Welfare Rights Centre Ballybot Hse, 28 Cornmarket, Newry, County Down BT34 8BG

No Limits 278 Shirley Rd, Southampton SO15 3HL
Wheatsheaf Hse, 24a Bernard St, Southampton, Hampshire SO14 3AY
406–408 Portsmouth Rd, Sholing, Southampton SO19 9AT

Nomad Homeless Advice and Support Unit 30 Rockingham La, Sheffield, South Yorkshire S1 4FW

North Bristol Advice Centre 2 Gainsborough Sq, Lockleaze, Bristol BS7 9XA

North East Windhill Community Association Church St, Windhill, Shipley, West Yorkshire BD18 2NR

North Edinburgh Drug Advice Centre 10 Pennywell Crt, Edinburgh EH4 4TZ

North London Action for the Homeless Our Lady of Good Council, Bouverie Rd, London N16 0AJ

North of England Refugee Service 2 Jesmont Rd West, Newcastle upon Tyne, Tyne and Wear NE2 4PQ

Northampton Care and Repair 7–15 St. John's Terr, Northampton, Northamptonshire NN1 1HA

Northampton Women's Aid PO Box 315, Northampton, Northamptonshire NN1 1LS

Northamptonshire Rape/Incest Crisis Centre 2nd Fl, 3–7 Hazelwood Rd, Northampton, Northamptonshire NN1 1LG

Northern Complainant Aid Fund Checkpoint, 45 Westgate, Bradford, West Yorkshire BD1 2TH

Northern Ireland Council for Ethnic Minorities 3rd Fl, Ascot Hse, 24–31 Shaftesbury Sq, Belfast BT2 8DB

Northern Refugee Centre Alpha Hse, 10 Canver St, Sheffield, South Yorkshire S1 2BE

Northlands 13 Pump St, Derry, County Londonderry BT48 6JG

Northwest Surrey Association of Disabled People Provincial Hse, 26 Commercial Way, Woking, Surrey GU21 1GN

Norwich and District Legal Services Committee Advice Arcade, 4 Guildhall Hill, Norwich, Norfolk NR2 1JP

Notre Dame Refugee Centre Notre Dame de France, 5 Leicester Pl, London WC2H 9BP

Nott Trent University Union of Students Advice Centre Byron Hse, Shakespeare St, Nottingham NG1 4GH

Nottinghamshire Outworkers Support Group c/o Nottingham Racial Equality Council, 67 Lower Parliament St, Nottingham NG1 3BB

Nucleus Legal Advice Centre 298 Old Brompton Rd, London SW5 9JF

NUS-USI 29 Bedford St, Belfast BT2 7EJ

Oasis Town Centre Project 143c Lower High St, Merthyr Tydil, CF47 8EB

Off the Record–Bath and North East Somerset Open House Centre, Manvers St, Bath, Bath and North East Somerset BA1 1JW

Off the Record–Bristol 2 Horfield Rd, St. Michaels Hill, Bristol BS2 8EA

Off the Record–Richmond 2 Church St, Twickenham, Greater London TW1 3NJ

OGWR Dash 74 Nolton St, Bridgend CF31 3BP

Oldham Independent Housing Aid Centre 5 Ascroft Crt, Peter St, Oldham, Greater Manchester OL1 1HP

Omagh Independent Advice Services 15 High St, Omagh, County Tyrone BT78 1BA

One Parent Families 21 Priory St, York YO1 1ET

Open Door (Fife) James St, Dunfermline, Fife KY12 7QE

Open Door Eastbourne 67 Susans Rd, Eastbourne, East Sussex BN21 3TG

Organisation of Blind African Caribbeans 1st Fl, Gloucester Hse, London SE5 0RZ

Orrell Park Advice Centre 6 Moss La, Liverpool, Merseyside L9 8AJ

OUR Community Association 112–114 Frank Webb Ave, Crewe, Cheshire CW1 3NE

Ownership Options in Scotland Ltd Unit 2, the John Cotton Centre, 10 Sunnyside, Edinburgh EH7 5RA

Oxford Brookes Student Union Advice Centre Helena Kennedy Student Centre, Headington Hill Campus, Oxford, Oxfordshire OX3 0BP

Oxford Community Care Advice and Action Group Rivermead Centre, Abingdon, Oxfordshire OX1 4XD

Oxford Community Work Agency Ltd Barton Neighbourhood Centre, Underhill Circus, Oxford, Oxfordshire OX3 9LS

Oxford House Immigration Project Derbyshire St, Bethnal Green, London E2 6HG

Oxford Housing Rights Centre 11 New Rd, Oxford, Oxfordshire OX1 1LT

Oxford Unemployed Workers and Claimants Union East Oxford Community Centre, Princes St, Oxford, Oxfordshire OX4 1HU

Oxfordshire Chinese Community and Advice Centre 44b Princes St, Oxford, Oxfordshire OX4 1DD

PACE 34 Harthern Rd, London, N7 9JL

Padstones Reedham Hse, 2 Britwell Rd, Burnham, Buckinghamshire SL1 8AG

Pakistan Women's Welfare Association 225 Seven Sisters Rd, London N4 2DA

Parentline East Midlands Market Office, Sheep Market, Stamford, Lincolnshire PE9 2SL

Parents Consortium Information Service Allsworth Crt, 40 St. David's Rd, Hextable, Kent BR8 7RJ

Parents of Autistic Children Together c/o Eileen Fairbrass Centre, Pembroke Gdns, Dagenham, Essex RM10 7YP

Parks Advice Point 70 Cavendish Sq, Pk South, Swindon SN3 2LR

People of Herts Want Equal Rights Chells Enterprise Village, Chells Way, Stevenage, Hertfordshire SG2 0LZ

People's Voices 1 King George V Rd, Amersham, Buckinghamshire HP5 6BE

People's Voices East Anglia Unit 18, COLBEA, 154 Magdalen St, Colchester, Essex CO1 2JX

PEX – Action on Pesticide Exposure Eurolink Centre, 49 Effra Rd, London SW2 1BE

Planning Aid for Scotland Bonnington Mill, 72 Newhaven Rd, Edinburgh EH6 5QG

Playcare Merton 16 Buckfast Rd, Mordon, London SM4 5LY

Plymouth Communities Against Poverty 16 Miers Cl, Barne Barton, Plymouth, PL5 1DJ

Plymouth Community Partnership Ltd The Old Treasury Bldg, Catherine St, Plymouth PL1 2AD

Plymouth Eddystone Group 36 Looe St, The Barbican, Plymouth PL4 0EB

Plymouth Energy Advice Centre 142 Union St, Plymouth PL1 3HL

Plymouth TUC Unemployed Workers' Centre 40 Tavistock Pl, Drake Circus, Plymouth PL4 8AX

Plymouth University Student Union Exmouth Douglas Ave, Exmouth, Devon EX8 2AT

Podsmead Neighbourhood Project 15a Scott Ave, Podsmead, Gloucester, Gloucestershire GL2 5BD

Portsmouth Community Advice Centre The Paulsgrove Community Centre, Marsden Rd, Portsmouth PO6 4JD

Portsmouth Community Advice Centres Buckland Community Centre, Malins Rd, Portsmouth PO2 1BL

Portsmouth Minorities Support Group Albemarle Hse, Osbourne Rd, Southsea, Hampshire PO5 3BL

Powys Benefit Take-up Campaign c/o Radnor Care and Repair, Arvon Hse, Temple St, Llandindad Wells, Powys LD1 5DP

PRAXIS Pott St, London E2 0EF

Prescot and Whiston Trade Union Unemployed Centre Prescot One Stop Shop, Prescot Shopping Centre, Knowsley, Merseyside L34 5GA

Preston and Western Lancashire R E C PO Box 10, Town Hall Annexe, Preston, Lancashire PR1 2RL

Princess Royal Trust Vale Royal Carers Centre Unit 8, Lower Ground Fl, Northwich, Cheshire CW9 5LG

Prisoners Advice Service Unit 305, Hatton Sq, London EC1N 7RJ

Prisonlink (NACRO) 169 Onmeau Rd, Belfast, BT7 1SQ

Public Concern at Work Suite 306, 16 Baldwins Gdns, London EC1N 7RJ

Race Equality Council for Gloucestershire 15 Brunswick Rd, Gloucester, Gloucestershire GL1 1HG

RAISE 211 Walton Rd, Liverpool, Merseyside L4 4AJ

16

Reading University Student Union Student Advice Centre White Knights, PO Box 230, Reading RG6 6AZ

Redbridge Disability Association (REDA) 98–100 Ilford La, Ilford, Essex IG1 2LD

Redbridge Refugee Forum Broadway Chambers, 1 Cranbrook Rd, Ilford, Essex IG1 4DU

Redress Trust Ltd 6 Queen Sq, London WC1N 3AR

Refugee Advice Centre 702 High Rd, Leyton, London E10 6JP

Refugee Education and Training Advisory Service World University Service (UK), 14 Dufferin St, London EC1X 8PD

Refugee Legal Centre Sussex Hse, 39–45 Bermondsey St, London SE1 3XF

Release 3rd Fl, 388 Old St, London EC1V 9LT

Renewal Programme (Turnaround) 170 Harold Rd, London E13 0SE

Resource Centre Derry Ltd Carnhill Est, Shantallow, Derry, County Londonderry BT48 8DA

Reunite PO Box 24875, London E1 6FR

Rights of Women 52–54 Featherstone St, London EC1Y 8RT

Rights Office PO Box 12775, Edinburgh EH8 9YG

Rights Project 290–292 Wingrove Ave, Newcastle upon Tyne, Tyne and Wear NE4 9AA

Rights Shop (Bethnal Green) 296 Bethnal Green Rd, London E2 0AG

Rights–Luton TUC Centre for the Unemployed Enterprise Hse, 7 Gordon St, Luton LU1 2QP

Ringwood Debt Advice Centre c/o Stonechat Cl, Ferndown, Dorset BH22 9CH

Roehampton Institute London Students' Union Hirst Union Bldg, Digby Stuart College, London SW15 5PH

Romford Independent Legal Advice Centre c/o Romford County Court, 2a Oaklands Ave, Romford, Essex RM1 4DP

Rose Hill and Donnington Advice Centre The Cabin, The Oval, Oxford, Oxfordshire OX4 4SF

Rosemount Resource Centre Westway, Rosemount, Derry, County Londonderry BT48 9NT

Rotherham Occupational Health Project Room 9, Imperial Bldgs, Rotherham, South Yorkshire S60 1PA

Roundabout Centre 1 Stanley Rd, Bidston, Birkenhead, Merseyside L41 7BG

Royal Association for Deaf People St. Bede's Centre for Deaf, 412 Clapham Rd, London SW9 9DA

Royal Holloway College Student Union Welfare Office Royal Holloway College, Egham Hill, Egham, Surrey TW20 0EX

Royds Community Association Sunnybank Hse, 506 Huddersfield Rd, Bradford, West Yorkshire BD12 6AD; URL www.royds.org.uk; E-mail jayne@royds.org.uk

Saffron Resource Centre 432 Saffron La, Leicester LE2 6SB

SAHIR House 80 Rodney St, Liverpool, Merseyside L1 9AR

SAIVE The Dudson Centre, Hope St, Stoke-on-Trent ST1 5DD

Salford TUC Unemployment and Community Residential Centre 84–86 Liverpool Rd, Eccles, Salford, Greater Manchester M30 0WZ

Saltlley and Nechelle Law Centre 2 Alun Rock Rd, Saltley, Birmingham, West Midlands B8 1JB

Sane–Saneline London 1st Fl, City Side, London E1 1EE

Sane–Saneline Macclesfield 1 Queen Victoria St, Macclesfield, Cheshire SK11 6LP

Sane–Saneline South West Units 1 and 2, The Greenway Centre, Bristol BS10 5PY

Sangham Advice Centre 210 Burnt Oak Broadway, Burnt Oak, Greater London HA8 6AP

Scarf 1 Cotton St, Aberdeen AB11 5EE

Scargill Walk Centre 32 Scargill Wlk, Eastwood, Nottingham NG16 3AY

Scobmo 8–10 Carters Grn, West Bromwich, West Midlands B70 9LW

Scoop Aid 277 Rutland Rd, Pitsmoor, Sheffield, South Yorkshire S3 9PZ

Scottish Low Pay Unit 24 Sandyford Pl, Glasgow G3 7NG

Search Project 74 Adelaide Terr, Benwell, Newcastle upon Tyne, Tyne and Wear NE4 9JN

Sefton Pensioners Advocacy Centre 7 Yellow Hse La, Southport, Merseyside PR8 1ER

Sefton Unemployment and Community Appeals Centre St. Thomas' Church, Seaforth Rd, Seaforth, Merseyside L21 4PX

Seniorline Help the Aged, Pentonville Rd, London N1 9UZ

Serene incorporating The Crysis Helpline BM Cry-sis, London WC1N 3XX

Shaftesbury Centre Milfoil Dr, Langney, Eastbourne, East Sussex BN23 8BR

Shankill Women's Centre c/o Shankhill Centre, 151–157 Shankill Rd, Belfast BT13 1FD

Sheffield Advice Centres Group Highfield Hse, 20 St. Barnabas Rd, Sheffield, South Yorkshire S2 4TF

Sheffield Alcohol Advisory Service 646 Abbeydale Rd, Sheffield, South Yorkshire S7 2BB

Sheffield and Rotherham Asbestos Group Unit 311, Aizlewood's Mill, Nursery St, Sheffield, South Yorkshire S3 8GG

Sheffield Carers Centre 33–35 Charles St, Sheffield, South Yorkshire S1 2HU

Sheffield Occupational Health Advisory Service 3rd Fl, Queen's Bdgs, Sheffield, South Yorkshire S1 2DX

Sheffield University Student Union Student Advice Centre Students' Union, Western Bank, Sheffield, South Yorkshire S10 2TG

Sheila Kay Fund 2nd Fl, 60 Duke St, Liverpool, Merseyside L1 5AA

Shelter Housing Action for Hastings 48 Cambridge Gdns, Hastings, East Sussex TN34 1EN

Shelter Housing Aid and Research Project 13 Welford Rd, Leicester, LE2 7AD

Shelter London and South Kingsbourne Hse, 229–231 High Holborn, London WC1V 7DA

Shelter Notts Housing Advice Service 15 Broad St, Nottingham NG1 3AJ

Sheringham Advice Centre 6 De Morley Garth, Sheringham, Norfolk NR26 8JG

Sherwood Advice Centre Sherwood Methodist Church, Devon Dr, Nottingham NG5 2EN

Shiney Advice and Resource Project (SHARP) 14 Beatrice Terr, Shiney Row, Houghton-le-Spring, Tyne and Wear DH4 4QW

Shrewsbury Homes for All The Roy Fletcher Centre, 12–17 Cross Hill, Shrewsbury, Shropshire SY1 1JE

Signpost Stockport for Carers Torkington Centre, Torkington Rd, Hazel Gr, Stockport, Greater Manchester SK7 4PY

Signposts 58 Regent Rd, Morecambe, Lancashire LA3 1TE

SITRA Bramah Hse, 65–71 Bermondsey St, London SE1 3XF

Skill 4th Fl, Chapter Hse, London SE1 3JW

Smart Criminal Justice Services 4a East Ave, Oxford, Oxfordshire OX4 1XW

Smethwick Energy Action Ltd 96 Cape Hill, Smethwick, Warley, West Midlands B66 4PH

Society for the Blind 2 Queen's Cres, St. George's Cross, Glasgow G4 9BW

Somali Bravanese Welfare Association in Barnet Bravanese Centre, 116 Coppalla Rd, Muswell Hill, London N10 1JS

South Birmingham Young Homeless Project The Depot, Belton Gr, Longbridge, Birmingham, West Midlands B45 9PE

South Bradford Community Network Odsal Community Centre, Crawford Ave, Odsal, Bradford, West Yorkshire BD6 1HX

South Bristol Advice Services Leinster Hse, Leinster Ave, Knowle, Bristol, West Yorkshire BS4 1NL

South Bromley Youth Forum (SBYF) 27 Aberfeldy St, Poplar, London E14 0NU

South London Tamil Welfare Group (SLTWG) 36 High St, Colliers Wood, London SW19 2AB

South Riverside Community Development Centre Brunel St, Riverside, Cardiff CF1 8ES

South Sefton TUCU and CRC St. Thomas' Church Hall, Seaforth Rd, Liverpool, Merseyside L21 4PJ

South West Belfast Advice Partnership 3 Carnamore Pk, Belfast BT11 9TP

Southall Black Sisters 52 Norwood Rd, Southall, London UB2 4DW

Southall Rights 54 High St, Southall, London UB1 3DB

Southampton and District Unemployed Centre 11 Porchester Rd, Woolston, Southampton SO19 2JB

Southwark Disablement Association 2 Bradenham Cl, Albany Rd, London SE17 2QB

Southwark Homeless Information Project 612 Old Kent Rd, London SE15 1JB

Southwark Irish Pensioners Project 19 Spa Rd, Bermondsey, London, SE16 3CN

Southwark Pensioners Centre 305–307 Camberwell Rd, London SE5 0HQ

Southwark Refugee Project 161 Summer Rd, Peckham, London SE15 6JL

Southwark Vietnamese-Chinese Community Thomas Calton Education Centre, Alpha St, Peckham, London SE15 4NX

Speakeasy Advice Centre 4 Arabella St, Roath, Cardiff CF2 4TA

Springfield Charitable Association Advice Centre Montague Centre, Broadway, Belfast BT12 6BZ

St. Ann's Welfare Rights Advice Group The Neighbourhood Centre, Robin Hood Chase, Nottingham NG3 4EZ

St. Botolph's Project 2 White Church La, London E1 7QR

St. Giles Trust 64–68 Camberwell Church St, Camberwell, London SE5 8JB

St. James Community Support and Advice Centre 223a Frederick Rd, Aston, Birmingham, West Midlands B6 6BP

St. John's Community Centre 64 Albert Rd, North Woolwich, London E15 2JB

St. Luke's Advisory Service 64 Old Shoreham Rd, Brighton, Brighton and Hove BN1 5DD

St. Oswalds Community Advice Centre 228 Jardine Cres, Tile Hill, Coventry, West Midlands CV4 9PL

St. Paul's Advice Centre Association 146 Grosvenor Rd, St. Paul's, Bristol BS2 8YA

St. Philip's Money Advice Centre St. Philip's Church Centre, 41 Moore Ave, Bournemouth BH11 8AT

Staffordshire Alcohol Advisory Service 29 Eastgate St, Stafford, Staffordshire ST16 2LZ

Stapleford Advice Bureau c/o County Library, Church St, Stapleford, Nottingham NG9 8GA

Step Forward 234 Bethnal Green Rd, London E2 9AA; E-mail sforward@hostels.org.uk

Step One Unemployment Centre Glyn Hse, 70 Broadway, Peterborough PG1 2SU

Stepping Stones Debt Counselling Service St. Paul's Church, Oak Rd, Bursledon, Southampton, SO31 8DT

Stocksbridge Advice Centre The Library, Manchester Rd, Sheffield, South Yorkshire S36 1DH

Stoke-on-Trent and Staffordshire Deaf Society Ellis Memorial Centre, Wellesley St, Shelton, Stoke-on-Trent ST1 4NF

Stonehouse Neighbourhood Project 10 High St, Stonehouse, Gloucestershire GL10 2NG

Stonwall Housing 2a Leroy Business Centre, 436 Essex Rd, London N1 3DP; E-mail stonewall@hostels.org.uk

Stratton Advice Point Upper Stratton Library, Beechcroft Rd, Swindon SN2

Student Advice and Information Centre Southampton University Students' Union, Highfield, Southampton SO17 1BJ

Student Advice Bureau South Bank University Student Union, Keywork St, London SE1 6NG

Student Advice Bureau University College Worcester, Henwick Gr, Worcester, Worcestershire WR2 6AJ

Student Advice Centre Bournemouth University Students' Union, Talbot Campus, Poole BH12 5BB

Student Advice Centre Southampton Institute Students' Union, East Park Terr, Southampton SO14 0YN

Student Advice Centre (Stafford and Stoke) Staffordshire University Union of Students, Beaconside, Stafford, Staffordshire ST18 0AD

Student Information and Advice Centre Liverpool Students' Union, Haigh Bldg, Liverpool, Merseyside L1 9DE

Student Information and Advice Centre Newman College Health Centre, Genners La, Birmingham, West Midlands B32 3NT

Students' Union Advice Centre University of Sussex Students' Union, 1st Fl, Brighton, Brighton and Hove BN1 9QF

Students' Union Advice Centre University of the West of England, Frenchay Campus, Bristol BS16 1QY

Students' Union Support and Advice Centre University of Plymouth, Drake Circus, Plymouth PL1 4AA

Sunderland University Student Union Advice Centre 1st Fl, Wearmouth Hall, Sunderland, Tyne and Wear SR1 3SD

Support Limited Sinfin Community Enterprise Centre, Sheridan St, Derby, Derbyshire DE24 9HG

Supportive Parents for Special Children 3rd Fl, Royal Oak Hse, Royal Oak Ave, Bristol BS1 4GB

Survivors of Child Abuse Oakes Hse, 53 London Rd, Gloucester, Gloucestershire GL1 3HF

Swan Advice Network Leigh Hse, 1 Wells Hill, Bath, Bath and North East Somerset BA3 3RN

Swansea Care and Repair 35 Mansel St, Swansea, SA1 5SN

Swaythling Information Centre The Bunker, 284 Burgess Rd, Southampton SO16 3BE

Tameside Welfare Rights Unit 200 Market St, Hyde, Cheshire SK14 1HB

Tamil Refugee Action Group 2nd Fl, 449–451 High Rd, Willesden, London NW10 2JJ

Tamil Relief Centre Community Hse, 311 Fore St, Edmonton, London N9 0PZ

Tannochside Information and Advice Centre 14 Thorniewood Rd, Tannochside, Uddingston, North Lanarkshire G71 5QQ

Tar Anall 539 Falls Rd, Belfast BT11 9AB

Tar Isleach 133 Hillman St, Belfast BT15 2FX

Target 3 52 Deptford Broadway, Deptford, London SE8 4PH

Taxaid Linburn Hse, 342 Kilburn High Rd, London NW6 2QJ

TBF: the teacher support network Hamilton Hse, Mabledon Pl, London WC1H 9BE

TEDS Cottage 7, Garth Olwg, Pontypridd, Rhondda, Cynon, Taff CF38 1BT

Terrence Higgins Trust Advice Centre 52–54 Grays Inn Rd, London WC1X 8JU

Terrence Higgins Trust West Queen Anne Hse, 8–10 West St, Old Market, Bristol BS2 0BH

Thameside Community Support, Advice Centre Bastable Ave, Thames View Est, Barking, Essex IG11 0NG

Thorneby Information and Advice Centre 27 and 31 Loftus Rd, Thorneby, Stockton-on-Tees, TS17 6EG

Thorpe Edge Advice Service 14 York Hse, Idlethorpe Way, Bradford, West Yorkshire BD10 9ES

Threshold Housing Advice 126 Uxbridge Rd, Shepherds Bush, London W12 8AA

Time to Talk The Abbey, Market Sq, Daventry, Northamptonshire NN11 4BH

Torfaen People's Centre Trosnant Hse, Trosnant St, Pontypool, Torfaen NP4 8AT

Torry Resources Advice Group 26 Menzies Rd, Aberdeen AB11 9BA

Tottenham Legal Advice Centre 754–758 High Rd, Tottenham, London N17 0AL

TPAS (Scotland) 74–78 Saltmarket, Glasgow, G1 5LD

Trade Union Safety Team 70 Sallengate, Chesterfield, Derbyshire S40 1JR

Trinity Centre St. Paul's Hill, Winchester, Hampshire SO22 5AE

Turkish Cypriot Community Association 117 Green Lanes, London, N16 9DA

Turkish Cypriot Women's Project 140a Falkland Rd, Hornsey, London N8 0NP

Turlin Moor Money Advice Project St. Gabriel's Church, Keysworth Rd, Poole BH16 5BH

Turriff Advice Centre Masonic Bldg, Gladstone Terr, Turriff, Aberdeenshire AB53 4AT

UCLU Rights and Advice Centre University College London Union, 25 Gordon St, London WC1H 0AH

UELSU Advice and Information Service Union Bldg, Longbridge Rd, Dagenham, Essex RM8 2AS

UKCOSA 9–17 St. Alban's Pl, Islington, London N1 0NX

UMIST Student Association Advice Centre Sackville St, PO Box 88, Manchester M60 1QD

Union of UEA Students Advice Unit Union Hse, University of East Anglia, Norwich, Norfolk NR4 7TJ

University of Brunel Students Information and Advice Service Brunel University, Cleveland Rd, Uxbridge, Greater London UB8 3PH

University of Central Lancashire Student Union Advice Centre Fylde Rd, Preston, Lancashire PR1 2TQ

University of Huddersfield Students Union Advice Centre UHSU, Milton Hall, Queensgate, Huddersfield, West Yorkshire HD1 3DH

University of Luton Students Union Advice Centre Europa Hse, Vicarage St, Luton, LU1 3HZ

University of Teesside Union Advice Centre Borough Rd, Middlesbrough TS1 3BA

University of Wales Swansea Student Union Advice Centre 3rd Fl, Union Hse, Swansea SA2 8PP

University of Wales, Bangor Student Union Deiniol Rd, Bangor, Gwynedd LL57 2TH

University of Exeter Guild of Students Advice Centre 1st Fl, Devonshire Hse, Exeter, Devon EX4 4PZ

UNU Student Advice Centre Portland Bldg, University Pk, Nottingham NG7 2RD

Upper Anderstown Welfare and Advice Group Tullymore Community Centre, 37a Tullymore Gdns, Belfast BT11 6NE

USDU Student Advice Centre University of Derby Students' Union, Kedleston Rd, Derby DE22 1GB

Victoria Road Advice Centre c/o 126 Obelisk Rd, Woolston, Southampton SO19 9DP Correspondence address only.

Vine Advice Centre 227 Crumlin Rd, Belfast BT14 7DY

Voluntary Action North East Lincolnshire 14 Town Hall St, Grimsby, Humberside, DN31 1HN

Wallasey Welfare Advice Centre Natwest Bldgs, 89 Brighton St, Wallasey, Merseyside L44 6QJ

Wallsend People's Centre 10 Frank St, Wallsend, Tyne and Wear NE28 6RN

Walsall Deaf People's Centre 59a Lichfield St, Walsall, West Midlands WS4 2BX

Waltham Forest Association of Disabled People Unit 13–14, Alpha Business Centre, South Grove, London E17 7NX

Waltham Forest MENCAP The Mencap Centre, 1a Mallock Rd, Leyton, London E10 6BN

Wandsworth Carers Centre 181 Wandsworth High St, London SW18 4JE

Wapping Bangladesh Association Wapping Youth Club, Tench St, London E1W 2QD; E-mail wapping.bangladesh@virgin.net

Warwick Student Union Advice and Welfare Services University of Warwick, Coventry, West Midlands CV4 7AL

Warwickshire Welfare Rights Advice Service 1 Stratford St, Nuneaton, Warwickshire CV11 5BS

Waterloo Action Centre 14 Baylis Rd, London SE1 7AA

WAVE Trauma Centre 5 Chichester Park South, Belfast BT15 5DW

WAVE Trauma Centre, Armagh 9 Dobbin St, Armagh, County Armagh BT61 7QQ

Wear Body Positive 32 West Sunnyside, City Centre, Sunderland, Tyne and Wear SR1 1BU

Wearside Disablement Centre Trust 5 Mary St, Sunderland, Tyne and Wear SR1 3NH

WECIL Ltd Courtlands, Leinster Ave, Knowle, Bristol BS4 1AR

Welfare and Education Centre De Montfort Student Union, 4 Newarke Cl, Leicester LE2 7BJ

Welfare Benefits Unit 17 Priory St, York YO1 6ET

Welfare Rights Advice Service Junction 7, 3–7 Hazelwood Rd, Northampton, Northamptonshire NN1 1LG

Well Woman Centre–Swindon Health Hydro, Milton Rd, Swindon SN1 5JA

Wellingborough District Resource Education Centre c/o Victoria Centre, Park Rd, Wellingborough, Northamptonshire NN8 1HT

Wellingborough Welfare Rights Advice Group c/o NCH Family Centre, 123 Midland Rd, Wellingborough, Northamptonshire NN8 1LU

Wesley Housing Project PO Box 257, Keighley, West Yorkshire BD21 5BB; E-mail info@wesleyhousing.fsnet.co.uk

West Bridgeford Advice Centre 16 The Leys, Normonton-on-the Wolds, Nottinghamshire NG12 5NU

West Everton Community Council 33 Everton Brow, Everton, Liverpool, Merseyside L3 8SU

West Fife Community Drugs Project 93 Pittencrieff St, Dunfermline, Fife KY12 8AN

West Hampstead Community Association 60–62 Mill La, London NW6 1NJ

West Midlands Low Pay Unit 3rd Fl, Wolverley Hse, Birmingham, West Midlands B5 6BJ

West Somerset Advice Bureau The Lane Centre, Market House La, Minehead, Somerset TA24 5NW

West Swindon Family and Community Project 15 Gainsborough Way, Freshbrook, Swindon SN5 8PD

West View Advice and Resource Centre 30 Miers Ave, West View, Hartlepool TS24 9HH

Westminster Advocacy Service for Senior Residents 56 Dean St, London W1V 5HJ

Westwood Advice and Information Centre 45 Featherstall Road North, Oldham, Greater Manchester OL9 6QA

Whitby Resource Centre (T/A Network) The Colosseum, Victoria Pl, Whitby, North Yorkshire YO21 1EZ

White City Community Project 110–112 Finlay Rd, Gloucester, Gloucestershire GL4 6TF

Wigan Independent Advice Centre Suite 25, Rodney Hse, Wigan, Greater Manchester WN1 1BT

Willenhall Community Money Advice Centre 104 Remembrance Rd, Willenhall, Coventry, West Midlands CV3 3DP

Willowbrook Centre 48 Willowbrook Rd, Peckham, London SE15 6BW

Windsor Advisory Centre William St, Windsor, Windsor and Maidenhead SL4 4BA

Windsor Women's Centre 34 Ebor St, Belfast BT12 6HY

Wirral SEN Parent Partnership Charing Cross Methodist Neighbourhood Centre, Claughton Rd, Binderhead, Wirral, CM41 4DX

Woking Information for Disability Enquiries Provincial Hse, 26 Commercial Way, Woking, Surrey GU21 1EN; E-mail info@askwide.org.uk

Women's Aid Federation England PO Box 391, Bristol BS99 7WS

Women's Community Action Group c/o St. Mark's Church Hall, Brookhey Dr, Kirby, Merseyside L33 9TE

Women's Health 52–54 Featherstone St, London EC1Y 8RT

Women's Health Information and Support Service Jordan Hse, 7 St. Benedict St, Norwich, Norfolk NR2 4PE

Women's Link; Women's Housing Advice in London Rooms 417–419, London Fruit and Wool Exchange, Brushfield St, London E1 6EL

Women's Support Network 30 Donegal St, Belfast BT1 2GQ

Womenspace Room 51, Estate Bldgs, Huddersfield, West Yorkshire HD1 1JW

Wood End Advice and Information Centre 146 Hillmorton Rd, Wood End, Coventry, West Midlands CV2 1FX

Woodcroft Advice Centre Livingstone Hse, 102 Watling Ave, Edgware, Greater London HA8 0LN

Woodseats Advice Centre 927 Chesterfield Rd, Woodseats, Sheffield, South Yorkshire S8 0SS

Worcester Welfare Rights Centre The Angel Centre, 1 Angel Pl, Worcester, Worcestershire WR1 3QN

Worlds End Neighbourhood Advice Centre 2 Worlds End Pl, Chelsea, London SW10 0HE

WPARH Whiteheads Bldg, 26a Snowhill, Wolverhampton, West Midlands WV2 4AF

Wycombe Women's Aid Ltd c/o The Priory Centre, 11 Priory Rd, High Wycombe, Buckinghamshire HP13 6SL

Yemeni Community Association Veto, Vestry Hall, 43 Athercliffe Common, Sheffield, South Yorkshire S9 2AE

Yemeni Refugee Association 9 Gower St, Sheffield, West Yorkshire S4 7HA

Yorkshire and Humberside Low Pay Unit 102 Commercial St, Batley, West Yorkshire WF17 5DP

Young Homeless Project 38 High St, Leamington Spa, Warwickshire CV31 1LW

Young Minds Trust 2nd Fl, 102–108 Clerkenwell Rd, London EC1M 5SA

Young People's Centre 69 Ship St, Brighton, Brighton and Hove BN1 1AE

Young Person's Advisory Service 36 Bolton St, Liverpool, Merseyside L3 5LX

Youth Action 2000 Streetwise, Phoenix Youth Centre, Hawes La, High Wycombe, Kent BR4 9AE

Youth Action Wiltshire – The Advice Centre Bridge Centre, Bath Rd, Chippenham, Wiltshire SN15 2AA (Correspondence address).

Youth Advice Centre Hove YMCA, 65 Blatchington Rd, Hove, Brighton and Hove BN3 8PP

Youth Enquiry Service Plymouth 14–16 Union St, Plymouth PL1 2FR

Zacca-Lisanga Selby Centre, Selby Rd, London N17 8JN; E-mail zacca-lisanga@ukonline.co.uk

Breich Valley Information Service (BVIS)
10 Main St, Fauldhouse, West Lothian EH47 9HX; E-mail amorrison.bvis@virgin.net; Tel 01501 770276
Manager Anne Morrison
Collection, collation and dissemination of information for the benefit of all sections of the community.

Citizen Advocacy Information and Training (CAIT)
Unit 162, Lee Valley Technopark, Ashley Rd, Tottenham Hale, London N17 9LN;
URL www.citizenadvocacy.org.uk;
E-mail cait@teleregion.co.uk; Tel 020 8880 4545; Fax 020 8880 4546
Director Sally Carr
CAIT aims to promote and support citizen advocacy by offering training and information (including a quarterly newsletter) to citizen advocacy schemes. The objective of citizen advocacy is to encourage all of us to become more involved in the welfare of vulnerable people in our communities, to speak on the behalf of another person and to protect their interests.

Disability Advice Service (East Suffolk)
Cedar Hse, Pytches Rd, Woodbridge, Suffolk IP12 1EP; Tel 01394 387070; Fax 01394 387070
Manager Margaret Shaw
Advice for people with disabilities, their carers and professionals; welfare benefits advice; holidays, equipment, education, employment, local facilities, sport, leisure, travel and transport.

Gordon Rural Action (GRAIN)
55 Gordon St, Huntly, Aberdeenshire AB54 8EQ; Tel 01466 793676; Fax 01466 794209
Development Officer Margaret Lobley
Senior Advice Worker K. Brown
A Council of Voluntary Service which helps support and set up community groups, Carers Support Service which helps support carers of all ages, Volunteer Centre helps find volunteering opportunities for the public and Advice Centres which give advice on benefits, employment issues and money/debt advice.

16

Stonehaven Advice, Information and Resources (STAIR)
2a Market La, Stonehaven, Aberdeenshire; Tel 01569 766578
Chair L. Laing
Vice-Chair M. Tennent
Secretary E.D. Byars
Treasurer E. Whitelaw
Free confidential, impartial, independent advice, help and information.

Marriage Guidance

Relate Central Office

Herbert Gray College, Little Church St, Rugby,
Warwickshire CV21 3AP; URL www.relate.org.uk;
E-mail enquiries@relate.org.uk; Tel 01788 573241;
Fax 01788 535007
Chief Executive Angela Sibson
Director (Field Services and Training) S. Bagnall
Head (Finance) Andrew Turnbull
Centres throughout England, Wales and Northern Ireland
enable Relate to offer counselling, psychosexual therapy
and educational services to those wanting help with adult
couple relationships, whether they are married or not.
These services are provided by trained counsellors who
benefit from continuing supervision. The services are
usually made available by appointment and are planned to
match clients' specific needs. They are based on Relate's
policy for offering clients confidentiality.

England

Aldershot, Farnborough and Fleet Relate 12 Arthur St,
Aldershot, Hampshire GU11 1HL; Tel 01252 324679
Contact Claire Howe

Basingstoke and District Relate The Orchard, White Hart
La, Basingstoke, Hampshire RG21 4AF; Tel 01256 324364
Contact Evelyn Askew

Berkshire Relate (HQ) 281 Basingstoke Rd, Reading
RG2 0JA; Tel 0118 987 6161
Chief Executive Karen Ross

Bolton and Wigan Relate Brunswick Hse, 32 Bradford St,
Bolton, Lancashire BL2 1JJ; Tel 01204 528302
Contact Christine Whittle

Bournemouth, Poole and Christchurch Relate 1 Stratfield
Saye, 20–22 Wellington Rd, Bournemouth BH8 8JN;
Tel 01202 311231
Contact Roni Jones

Brighton, Hove, Worthing and District Relate 58 Preston Rd,
Brighton, Brighton and Hove BN1 4QF; Tel 01273 697997
Contact Trish Owen

Bury Oldham and Rochdale Relate 9 Parkhills Rd, Bury,
Lancashire BL9 9AU; Tel 0161 764 4113
Contact Joyce Siddall

Central Middlesex Relate Civic Centre Complex, Station
Rd, Harrow, Greater London HA1 2XH; Tel 020 8427 8694;
Fax 020 8861 8471
Director Hazel Hewett

Chesterfield and North Derbyshire Relate Othen Hse, 7
Sheffield Rd, Chesterfield, Derbyshire S41 7LL; Tel 01246
231010
Contact Lynn Tory

Coventry and District Relate New Hse, Hertford Pl,
Coventry, West Midlands CV1 3JZ; Tel 024 7622 5863
Contact Suzanne Gibbon

Dacorum Relate The Gables, 3 St. Mary's Rd, Hemel
Hempstead, Hertfordshire HP2 5HL; Tel 01442 262618
Contact Mike Hockings

Dorset Relate 2 Poundbury Business Centre, Poundbury,
Dorchester, Dorset DT1 3WA; Tel 01305 262285
Contact Anne O'Neill

East Staffordshire Relate
Voluntary Services Centre, Union St, Burton-upon-Trent,
Staffordshire DE14 1AA; Tel 01283 561697
Manager David Dodgson

Gloucestershire Relate 27 Park Rd, Gloucester,
Gloucestershire GL1 1LH; Tel 01452 522071
Contact Kenneth Hitchings

Guernsey Relate 5 Smith St, St. Peter Port, Guernsey GY1
2JN; URL www.guernseycharities.org.gg; Tel 01481 730303
Manager Claire Wherry

Jersey Relate 2 Charles Hse, Charles St, St. Helier, Jersey
JE2 4SF; Tel 01534 734980
Office Manager Pauline Michel

Kingston upon Hull and East Riding of Yorkshire Relate 1
Charlotte St Mews, Worship St, Hull, Kingston upon Hull
HU1 3BP; Tel 01482 329621
Contact Deborah Andrew
Contact Judy Brattan

Leeds Relate The Gallery, Oxford Chambers, Oxford Pl,
Leeds, West Yorkshire LS1 3AX; Tel 0113 245 2595
Contact Judith Whitehead

Lincoln, Grantham and District Relate 16 St. Martin's La,
Lincoln, Lincolnshire LN1 1HY; Tel 01522 524922
Contact Chris Guiton

Mid and West Wales Relate Ty Merthyr, Little Water St,
Carmarthen, Carmarthenshire SA31 1ER; Tel 01267 236737
Contact Helen Thomas

Milton Keynes Relate 47 Aylesbury St, Wolverton,
Buckinghamshire MK12 5HX; Tel 01908 310010
Contact Jane Street

North and South West Sussex Relate 3 Station Rd, Crawley,
Sussex RH10 1HY; Tel 01293 517925
Contact Sue Quinn

North East London Relate Langtons, Billet La, Hornchurch,
Essex RM11 1XL; Tel 01708 441722
Director Lily Williams

North Hertfordshire and Stevenage Relate The Old
Grammar School, Broadway, Letchworth, Hertfordshire
SG6 3PS; Tel 01462 679139
Contact Sheelagh Taylor

North London Relate 31 Genotlin Rd, Enfield, Greater
London EN1 2AG; Tel 020 8367 7712
Director Jane Collins

North Wales Relate (HQ) 8 Riviere's Ave, Colwyn Bay,
Conwy LL29 7DP; Tel 01492 5339 20
Contact Alex Jaundrill

Northern Ireland Relate 76 Dublin Rd, Belfast BT2 7HP;
Tel 028 9032 3454
Chief Executive Gerald Clerk

Nottinghamshire Relate 96 Mansfield Rd, Nottingham
NG1 3HD; Tel 0115 950 7836
Contact Bridget Gilliatt

Pennine Relate 38 Clare Rd, Halifax, West Yorkshire
HX1 2HX; Tel 01422 363845
Contact Sue Fisher
Contact Judith Rowley

Plymouth and District Relate 3 Blenheim Rd, Plymouth
PL7 8LJ; Tel 01752 213131
Contact Sue Hirons

Reigate, Epsom and Districts Relate 44c Church St,
Reigate, Surrey RH2 0AJ; Tel 01737 245212
Contact Mike Bland

Rugby and North East Warwickshire Relate 11 Little Church
St, Rugby, Warwickshire CV21 3AW; Tel 01788 565675
Contact Sarah Curtis

Shropshire and Herefordshire Relate The Roy Fletcher
Centre, 12–17 Cross Hill, Shrewsbury, Shropshire SY1 1JE;
Tel 01743 344010
Contact Lyn Foley

Somerset Relate The Mrytle Tree, 34 Bridge St, Taunton, Somerset TA1 1UD; Tel 01823 275983
Contact Mary Adamson

South East Sussex Relate 22 Church St, Old Town, Eastbourne, East Sussex BN21 1HS; Tel 01323 410001
Contact Maureen Anstey

South Staffordshire Relate Mansell Hse, 22 Bore St, Lichfield, Staffordshire WS13 6LL; Tel 01543 304858
Contact Kathleen Rotton

South Warwickshire Relate Pageant Hse, 2 Jury St, Warwick, Warwickshire CV34 4EW; Tel 01926 403340
Manager Mary Upton

Walsall Relate 15 Lower Hall La, Walsall, West Midlands WS1 1RL; Tel 01922 626004
Manager Stuart Mountford

West Kent Relate Kelly Hse, Warwick Rd, Tunbridge Wells, Kent TN1 1YL; Tel 01892 529927; Fax 01892 515518
Contact Brenda Henson

Wiltshire Relate (HQ) 24a Church St, Trowbridge, Wiltshire BA14 8DY; Tel 01225 765310
Contact Amanda Foyster

Wolverhampton Relate 346 Newhampton Rd Est, Wolverhampton, West Midlands WV1 4AD; Tel 01902 428447
Contact Kate Farnell

York and Harrogate Relate 13 Dragon Pde, Harrogate, North Yorkshire HG1 5BZ; Tel 01423 502173
Contact Joseph McGuiness

Couple Counselling Scotland

18 York Pl, Edinburgh EH1 3EP;
URL www.couplecounselling.org;
E-mail enquiries@couplecounselling.org; Tel 0131 558 9669
Chief Executive Hilary Campbell
Business Services Maureen Blakely
Principal (Sexual and Relationship Therapy) Sue Maxwell

Argyll and District Couple Counselling
For all appointments Tel 01631 563297.

Ayrshire Couple Counselling
Tel (Appointments) 01292 265270

Border Region Couple Counselling
42 High St, Galashiels, Scottish Borders TD1 1SE
For appointments Tel 01896 754440.

Central Region Couple Counselling
Housing and Social Services Dept, Drummond Hse, Stirling FK8 2EG; Tel 01786 471177

Dumfries and Galloway Couple Counselling
Mount St. Michael, Craigs Rd, Dumfries, Dumfries and Galloway DG1 4UT; E-mail info@ccdg.co.uk; Tel 01387 251245; Fax 01387 248113

Fife Region Couple Counselling
St. Bryce Kirk Church Centre, St. Bycedale Ave, Kirkcaldy, Fife KY1 1ET; E-mail admin@ccfife.fsnet.co.uk; Tel 01592 597444

Glasgow Marriage Counselling Service
27 Sandyford Pl, Glasgow G3 7NB; Tel 0141 248 5249; Fax 0141 226 4122

Grampian Region Couple Counselling
14 Rose St, Aberdeen AB10 1UA;
E-mail p.okroj@btinternet.com; Tel 01224 648412; Fax 01224 658275

Highland Region Marriage Counselling
6 View Pl, Inverness, Highland IV2 4SA; Tel 01463 712888; Fax 01463 712210

Inverclyde and District Couple Counselling
Dept of Social Work, Dalrymple Hse, Greenock, Renfrewshire PA15 1UN; Tel 01475 714100; Fax 01475 730699

Lanarkshire Couple Counselling
The Cottage, 14 Airbles Rd, Motherwell, North Lanarkshire ML1 2PN; Tel 01698 254709

Lothian Couple Counselling
9a Dundas St, Edinburgh EH3 6QG;
URL www.cclothian.btinternet.co.uk;
E-mail cclothian.btinternet.co.uk; Tel 0131 556 1527; Fax 0131 558 9526

Orkney Couple Counselling
43 Junction Rd, Kirkwall, Orkney Islands KW15 1AR; Tel 01856 872797

Shetland Couple Counselling
4 Pirate La, Lerwick, Shetland Isles ZE1 0DY; Tel 01595 692719

Tayside Couple Counselling
201 Blackness Rd, Dundee DD1 5PN;
E-mail couplecounselling@taysidedd1.fsnet.co.uk; Tel 01382 640123

Marriage Care

Clitherow Hse, 1 Blythe Mews, London W14 0NW;
URL www.marriagecare.org.uk;
E-mail angela@marriagecare.org.uk; Tel 020 7371 1341; (National Helpline (Mon–Fri 1000–1600)) 0845 660 6000; Fax 020 7371 4921
Chief Executive Terry Prendergast
Director (Training) Joe Mannion
Functions
An organisation drawn mainly from the Catholic community offering relationship counselling, to those who are married, gay, lesbian or single, where there are family or personal relationship problems. Marriage Care also provides Relationship Education, Marriage Preparation and Enrichment and a Telephone Helpline for those in crises. All those who provide services are volunteers and trained to professional standards, with the counselling training externally validated. Complete confidentiality applies to all services offered by Marriage Care.

England

Barnet and Enfield Marriage Care
30 Station Rd, New Barnet, Hertfordshire; Tel 020 7243 1898

Birmingham Marriage Care
37 Victoria Rd, Acock's Grn, Birmingham, West Midlands B27 7XZ; Tel 0121 708 1900

Blackheath Marriage Care
5 Creswell Pk, Blackheath, London SE3 9RD; Tel 020 8297 0883

Blackpool and Fylde Marriage Care
25a Clifton St, Blackpool FY1 1JD; Tel 01253 751867

Bolton Marriage Care
7 Marefair, Horwich, Bolton, Lancashire BL6 6DH; Tel 0845 603 9216; 01204 699843

Bournemouth and Poole Marriage Care
121a Old Christchurch Rd, Bournemouth; Tel 01202 425566

Brighton Marriage Care
5 Surrenden Rd, Preston Pk, Hove, Brighton and Hove
BN1 6PA; Tel 01273 220111

Bristol Marriage Care
58 Alma Rd, Clifton, Bristol BS8 2DQ; Tel 0117 973 3777

Carlisle Marriage Care
c/o The Rectory, Warwick Sq, Carlisle, Cumbria CA1 1LB;
Tel 01228 818596

Chelmsford and Colchester Marriage Care
c/o 128 New London Rd, Chelmsford, Essex CM2 0AE;
Tel 01245 490169

Chester and Ellesmere Port Marriage Care
16 St. Peter's Way, Mickle Trafford, Chester, Cheshire
CH2 4EJ; Tel 01244 676799

Cleveland Marriage Care
John Paul II Centre, 55 Grange Rd, Middlesbrough
TS1 5AU; Tel 01642 248118

Coventry Marriage Care
13 Stoney Rd, Coventry, West Midlands CV1 2NP; Tel 024
7622 0065

Crawley Marriage Care
c/o Christian Education Centre, 4 Southgate Dr, Crawley,
West Sussex; Tel 01293 550567

Croydon Marriage Care
c/o Catholic Children's Society, 49 Russell Hill Rd, Purley,
Surrey CR8 2XB; Tel 01737 644321

Eastbourne Marriage Care
c/o 3 Princes Rd, Langney, Eastbourne, East Sussex
BN23 6HS; Tel 01323 417460

Gibraltar Marriage Care
215 Main St, Gibraltar; Tel 00350 71717

Gloucestershire Marriage Care
39 Rodney Rd, Cheltenham, Gloucestershire GL50 1HX;
Tel 01242 234882

Hallam Marriage Care
524 Queens Rd, Sheffield, South Yorkshire S2 4DT; Tel 0114
258 0000

Havering and Brentwood Marriage Care
c/o Clitherow Hse, 1 Blythe Mews, Blythe Rd, London
W14 0NW; Tel 0845 660 6000

Hereford and Worcester Marriage Care
St. Francis Xavier Hse, 19 Broad St, Hereford,
Herefordshire; Tel 01432 360459

Ilford Marriage Care
Kenwood Gardens Health Centre, Cranbrook, Ilford, Essex
IG1; Tel 020 8554 8070

Ipswich Marriage Care
PO Box 249, Capel, St Mary, Ipswich, Suffolk IP4 2DY;
Tel 01473 311976

Leeds Marriage Care
Hinsley Hall, 62 Headingly La, Leeds, West Yorkshire
LS6 2BX; Tel 0113 261 8045; 0113 270 3940

Leicester and Rutland Marriage Care
c/o Friends Meeting Hse, Queens Rd, Leicester; Tel 0800
389 3801

Lincolnshire North Marriage Care
Our Lady of Lincoln Presbytery, Laughton Way, Ermine
Est, Lincoln, Lincolnshire LN2 2HE; Tel 0800 389 3801

Liverpool and Wirral Marriage Care
c/o Nugent Care Society, 99 Edge La, Liverpool,
Merseyside L7 2PE; Tel 0151 261 2003

London Marriage Care
46 Notting Hill Gate, London W11 3HZ; Tel 020 7243 1898

Manchester and Salford Marriage Care
Clitherow Hse, Lower Chatham St, Manchester M15 6BY;
Tel 0161 236 5426; 0845 603 9216

Marriage Care South West
4 Colne La, Ivybridge, Devon PL21 0PN; Tel 01392 426494

Medway Towns Marriage Care
The White Hse, Riverside, Chatham, Kent ME4 4SL;
Tel 01634 828839

Milton Keynes Marriage Care
City Counselling Centre, 320 Saxon Gate West, Milton
Keynes MK9 2ES; Tel 01908 696606

Newmarket and Cambridge Marriage Care
14 Exeter Rd, Newmarket, Suffolk CB8 8LT; Tel 01638
560580

North East Hampshire and West Surrey Marriage Care
St. Joseph's Parish Centre, Queen's Rd, Aldershot,
Hampshire; Tel 01483 756555

North Staffordshire Marriage Care
44 Jasper St, Hanley, Stoke-on-Trent ST1 3DA; Tel 01782
213018

Northampton Marriage Care
20a Park Ave North, Northampton, Northamptonshire
NN3 2HS; Tel 0800 389 3801

Norfolk Marriage Care
Cathedral Hse, Unthank Rd, Norwich, Norfolk NR2 2PA;
Tel 01692 598885

Nottingham and Derby Marriage Care
4 Oxford St, Nottingham NG1 5BH; Tel (Derby) 01332
294940; (Nottingham) 0800 389 3801

Oldham Marriage Care
14 Waterloo St, Oldham, Greater Manchester; Tel 0845 603
9216

Oxford Marriage Care
The Healthy Living Centre, Oxford Rd, Temple Cowley,
Oxfordshire OX4 2ES; Tel 01865 749806

Peterborough Marriage Care
17 Manor Hse St, Peterborough PE1 2TL; Tel 01733
346456

Portsmouth Marriage Care
c/o 32 Mill Rd, Denmead, Waterlooville, Portsmouth
PO7 6PA; Tel 0239 226 4880

Preston Marriage Care
218a Tulketh Rd, Preston, Lancashire PR2 1ES; Tel 01772
731956

Reading Marriage Care
56 Western Ave, Woodley, Reading RG5 3BH; Tel 0118 977
0971

Rochdale Marriage Care
c/o 11 Rudgwick Dr, Brandlesholme, Bury, Lancashire
BL8 1YA; Tel 0845 603 9216

South and Mid Cheshire Catholic Marriage Care
Eaton Hse, Eaton St, Crewe, Cheshire CW2 7EG; Tel 01270
879911

South Buckinghamshire Marriage Care
15 Rectory Ave, High Wycombe, Buckinghamshire
HP13 6HN; Tel 01494 525875

Southampton Marriage Care
4 Maytree Cl, Badger Farm, Winchester, Hampshire
SO22 4JE; Tel (Southampton) 023 8051 2607;
Fax (Winchester) 01962 861806

Southend Marriage Care
c/o 64 Keswick Ave, Hullbridge, Essex SS5 6JW; Tel 01702
233344

Southport Marriage Care
188 Lord St, Southport, Merseyside PR9 0QL; Tel 01704
567666

Stockport Marriage Care
Outpatients Dept, St. Thomas's Hospital, Stockport,
Greater Manchester SK3 8HB; Tel 0845 603 9216; (day
time only) 0161 419 4355

Trafford Marriage Care
Greystones, 305 Manchester Rd, Altrincham, Greater
Manchester WA14 5PH; Tel 0161 969 3331

Tyneside Marriage Care
3rd Fl, Mea Hse, Ellison Pl, Newcastle upon Tyne, Tyne and
Wear NE1 8XS; Tel 0191 232 0342

Warrington Marriage Care
c/o 9 Museum St, Warrington WA1 1JA; Tel 01925 635448

Wigan Marriage Care
1 Parsons Wlk, Wigan, Greater Manchester WN1 1RU;
Tel 0845 603 9216

Wiltshire Marriage Care
19 Wyndale Cl, Stratton St. Margaret, Swindon SN3 4UZ;
Tel 01793 821818

Wimbledon Marriage Care
Guild Hse, 30 Worple Rd, London SW19 4EF; Tel 020 8947
8285

Wolverhampton, Walsall and Dudley Marriage Care
23 Glebe St, Walsall, West Midlands WS1 3NX; Tel 01902
847701

Wales

Cardiff Marriage Care
Bishop Brown Hse, Durham St, Grange Town, Cardiff
CF1 7PB; Tel 023 9252 2482

Newport Marriage Care
8 Corn St, Newport NP9 1DJ; Tel 01633 252868

Swansea Marriage Care
115 Walter Rd, Swansea SA1 5RE; Tel 01639 896699

Wrexham Marriage Care
Peace and Justice Centre, Kingsmills Rd, Wrexham
LL13 8HN; Tel 01978 351795

Scottish Marriage Care

1st Fl Suite, 72 Waterloo St, Glasgow G2 7DA;
URL www.scottishmarriagecare.org;
E-mail info@scottishmarriagecare.org; Tel 0141 222
2166

Aberdeen
Margaret Hse, 132 Huntly St, Aberdeen AB1 1SU; Tel 01224
643174

Ayrshire
9 Atholl Gdns, Kilwinning, South Ayrshire KA13 7DQ;
Tel (Appointments) 01294 551210

Dundee
24–28 Lawside Rd, Dundee DD3 6XY; Tel 01382 227551

Edinburgh
113 Whitehouse Loan, Edinburgh EH10 1BB; Tel 0131 623
8919; (Appointments) 0131 669 5144

Falkirk
Hope St, Falkirk FK1 5AT; Tel (Appointments) 01324
665700; (Centre) 01324 638426

Glasgow
196 Clyde St, Glasgow G1 4JY; Tel (Appointments) 0141 204
1239; Fax 0141 221 1962

Inverness
42 Kenneth St, Inverness, Highland IV3 5DH; Tel 01463
230690

Motherwell
Coursington Rd, Motherwell, North Lanarkshire ML1 1PP;
Tel (Appointments) 01355 235595

Paisley
50 Greenock Rd, Paisley, Renfrewshire PA3 2LE;
Tel (Appointments) 0141 889 6972

Stirling
Drummond Hse, Wellpark, Stirling; Tel 01324 665700

Jewish Marriage Council

23 Ravenshurst Ave, London NW4 4EE;
URL www.jmc.uk.org; E-mail info@jmc-uk.org; Tel 020
8203 6311; (Crisis Line (Miyad)) 0800 652 9249
Administrator   Sue Cash
Provides confidential counselling services for single,
married and divorced people; discussion groups for
youths, engaged couples and and young married couples
and support groups for divorced and separated people, as
well as a Marriage Bureau (Connect) and mediation
service.

Family Mediation Scotland (FMS)

127 Rose St, South La, Edinburgh EH2 4BB;
URL www.familymediationscotland.org.uk;
E-mail info@familymediationscotland.org.uk; Tel 0131
220 1610; Fax 0131 220 6895
The objective of FMS is to ensure that family mediation
services provide a professional standard of service and are
available to couples in dispute over the care of their
children, throughout the community in every part of
Scotland.

Affiliated Services

Family Mediation Ayrshire
63 Titchfield St, Kilmarnock, South Ayrshire KA1 1QS;
Tel 01563 572429

Family Mediation Borders
PO Box 13753, Scottish Borders;
E-mail isobel@fmborders.freeserve.co.uk; Tel 01721
724170

Family Mediation Central Scotland
16 Melville Terr, Stirling FK8 2NE;
E-mail familymediationcentre@scotlandf.freeserve.co.uk;
Tel 01786 472984

Family Mediation Glasgow
1 Melrose St, (off Queen's Cres), Glasgow G4 9BJ;
E-mail familymediation@westofscotland.freeserve.co.uk;
Tel 0141 332 2731

Family Mediation Grampian
27 Huntly St, Aberdeen AB10 1TJ;
E-mail familymediation@grampian2.freeserve.co.uk;
Tel 01224 630050

Family Mediation Highland
62 Academy St, Inverness, Highland IV1 1LP;
E-mail familymediation@highland2.freeserve.co.uk;
Tel 01463 712100

Family Mediation Lothian
37 George St, Edinburgh EH2 2HN;
E-mail lothian@familymediation.freeserve.co.uk;
Tel 0131 226 4507

Family Mediation Moray
17 Institution Rd, Elgin, Moray IV30 1QT;
E-mail familymediation@moray1.fsnetico.uk; Tel 01343
540801

Family Mediation North Aberdeenshire
8 Love La, Peterhead, Aberdeenshire; Tel 01779 490790

Family Mediation Orkney
43 Junction Rd, Kirkwall, Orkney Islands KW15 1AR;
E-mail funorkney@netscapeonline.co.uk; Tel 01856
870571

Family Mediation Tayside
132a Nethergate, Dundee DD1 4ED;
E-mail fm.tayside@virgin.net; Tel 01382 201343

Family Mediation Western Isles
The Bridge Community Centre, Bayhead, Stornoway, Isle of
Lewis HS1 2DU; Tel 01851 706868

NCH Action for Children Dumfries and Galloway Family Mediation Service
1 Newall Terr, Dumfries, Dumfries and Galloway
DG1 1LN; Tel 01387 263185

NCH Action for Children Family Mediation Fife
30 North St, Glenrothes, Fife KY7 5NA;
E-mail scdayfuns@mail.nchafc.org.uk; Tel 01592 751095

Genetic Advisory Centres

England

London

North East Thames

Genetic Clinic
Moorfields Eye Hospital, City Rd, London EC1V 2PD;
Tel 020 7253 3411 ext 2346
Consultant Surgeon A.T. Moore, FRCS, FCOphth

Institute of Child Health
30 Guilford St, London WC1N 1EH; URL www.ich.ac.uk;
Tel 020 7242 9789; Fax 020 7831 0488

Paediatric Department
Colchester General Hospital, Turner Rd, Colchester, Essex
CO4 5JL
Consultant Dr B. Sihra
Consultant Dr J. Symons, FRCP, DCH
Consultant Dr S. Mukerji, FRCP, DCH
Consultant Dr S. Battacharyya, MRCP
Consultant Dr A. Robinson

North West Thames

Galton Laboratory
Department of Biology, University College London,
London NW1 2HE; URL www.ucl.ac.uk; Tel 020 7679
7411; Fax 020 7383 2048

North West London Regional Genetics Service
Kennedy-Galton Centre, North West London Hospitals
NHS Trust, Watford Rd, Harrow, Greater London
HA1 3UJ; Tel 020 8869 2795; Fax 020 8869 3106
Head of Department Prof A. Kessling
Chief Cytogeneticist Mrs K. Waters
Chief Molecular Geneticist Mr S. Payne

South East Thames

Psychiatric Genetic Clinic
The Maudsley Hospital, Denmark Hill, London SE5 8AZ;
Tel 020 7703 6091
Referrals Dr P.C. Sham, MRCPsych

Clinical Genetics
7th Fl, New Guy's Hse, Guy's Hospital, St. Thomas St,
London SE1 9RT; Tel 020 7955 4648; Fax 020 7955
2550
Chair (Division of Medical and Molecular Genetics UMDS)
Prof E. Solomon, PhD
Consultant (Clinical Geneticist) and Head of Service
Dr S. Mohammed, MD, MRCP

Merseyside

Chester Genetic Counselling Clinic
Countess of Chester Hospital NHS Trust, Chester, Cheshire;
Tel 01244 364754
Consultant Paediatrician and Regional Genetic Counsellor
Dr D.W. Fielding

Liverpool

Merseyside and Cheshire Clinical Genetics Service
Alder Hey Children's Hospital, Eaton Rd, Liverpool,
Merseyside L12 2AP; Tel 0151 252 5238; Fax 0151 252
5951
Consultant Clinical Geneticist Dr A. Fryer
Senior Lecturer (Clinical Genetics) Dr I. Ellis

The Endocrine Clinic
Royal Liverpool Hospital, Prescot St, Liverpool, Merseyside
L7 8XP; Tel 0151 706 2000

North Western

Manchester

Willink Biochemical Genetics Unit
Royal Manchester Children's Hospital, Pendlebury,
Manchester M27 4HA; E-mail ed.wraith@cmmc.nhs.uk;
Tel 0161 727 2137/8; Fax 0161 727 2137

Northern

Newcastle upon Tyne
Institute of Human Genetics, International Centre for Life,
Central Parkway, Newcastle upon Tyne, Tyne and Wear
NE1 3BZ; Tel 0191 241 8600; Fax 0191 241 8799
Head of Department Prof J. Burn

Clinics

Regional Genetics Service Institute of Human Genetics,
International Centre for Life, Central Parkway, Newcastle
upon Tyne, Tyne and Wear NE1 3BZ; Tel 0191 241 8600
Central Clinics
Royal Victoria Infirmary Freeman Hospital, Newcastle
upon Tyne, Tyne and Wear

Peripheral Clinics

Genetics Clinic, Ashington
Ward 10, Ashington Hospital, Ashington, Northumberland

Genetics Clinic, Bishop Auckland
Bishop Auckland General Hospital, Cockton Hill Rd, County Durham DL14 6AD

Genetics Clinic, Carlisle
Central Clinic, Victoria Pl, Carlisle, Cumbria

Genetics Clinic, Darlington
Antenatal Clinic, Darling Memorial Hospital, Darlington

Genetics Clinic, North Tees
Outpatient Department and Children's Outpatients Department, North Tees General Hospital, Hardwick Rd, Stockton, Tyne and Wear TS19 8PE

Genetics Clinic, Middlesbrough
Antenatal Clinic and Children's Outpatient Department, South Cleveland General Hospital, Middlesbrough

Genetics Clinic, Whitehaven
West Cumberland Hospital, Hensingham, Whitehaven, Cumbria

Genetics Clinic, Sunderland
Children's Outpatient Department, Sunderland District General Hospital, Kayll Rd, Sunderland, Tyne and Wear SR4 7TP

Genetics Clinic, Kendal
Outpatient Department, Westmorland General Hospital, Kendal, Cumbria

Genetics Clinic, Hartlepool
Outpatient Dept and Childrens Outpatient Dept, Hartlepool General Hospital, Holdforth Rd, Hartlepool, TS24 9AH

Genetic Clinic
James Cook University Hospital, Marton Rd, Middlesbrough, TS4 3BW

Oxford Regional Genetics Service

Department of Clinical Genetics, Oxford Radcliffe Hospital, Headington, Oxfordshire OX3 7LJ; Tel 01865 226066; Fax 01865 226011
Lead Clinician   Dr H. Stewart

South Western

Peninsula Clinical Genetics Service
Royal Devon and Exeter Hospital, Barrack Rd, Exeter, Devon EX2 5DW; E-mail debbie.bristow@rdehc-tr.swest.nhs.uk; Tel 01392 403151
Consultant Clinical Geneticist   Dr P. Turnpenny
Consultant Clinical Geneticist   Dr C. Brewer
Consultant Clinical Geneticist   Dr J. Rankin

Trent

Sheffield Centre for Human Genetics
Sheffield Children's Hospital, Sheffield, South Yorkshire S10 2TH; E-mail o.quarrell@sheffield.ac.uk; Tel 0114 271 7025; Fax 0114 273 7467

Wessex

Southampton
Wessex Clinical Genetics Service, Princess Anne Hospital, Southampton SO16 5YA; URL www.suht.nhs.uk/wcgs/; E-mail genetics@suht.swest.nhs.uk; Tel 023 8079 6162; Fax 023 8079 4346
Clinical Geneticist   Dr I.K. Temple

Clinical Geneticist   Dr D. Eccles
Clinical Geneticist   Dr A.L. Collins
Clinical Geneticist   Dr A. M. Lucassen
Clinics also held at: North Hants Hospital; West Dorset Hospital, Dorchester; Poole General Hospital; St. Mary's Hospital, Portsmouth; Odstock Hospital, Salisbury; Royal Hants County Hospital, Winchester; St. Mary's Hospital, Isle of Wight. All enquiries to Southampton.

West Midlands

Birmingham
Regional Clinical Genetics Service, Birmingham Women's Hospital, Birmingham, West Midlands B15 2TG; Tel 0121 627 2630; Fax 0121 627 2618
Professor of Medical Genetics and Honorary Consultant in Clinical Genetics   Prof E. Maher
Genetic Clinics held in Birmingham and in the following Health Districts: Burton-upon-Trent; Coventry; Hereford; Nuneaton; Rugby; Sandwell; Shrewsbury; Stafford; Stoke-on-Trent; Walsall; Warwick; Wolverhampton; Worcester. Please telephone for further details.

Yorkshire

Yorkshire Regional Genetics Service, Ashley Wing, Leeds, West Yorkshire LS9 7TF; Tel 0113 206 5145; Fax 0113 246 7090
Consultant Clinical Geneticist (Lead Clinician)   Dr C. Chu
Consultant   Dr E. Sheridan
Specialist Registrar   Dr A. Jackson
Register Counsellor   A. Wilcocks
Manager and Genetic Counsellor   F. Robson
Family Support Worker (Neurofibromatosis)   Diane Friend

Wales

Institute of Medical Genetics, University of Wales College of Medicine, Heath Pk, Cardiff CF14 4XN; URL www.uwcm.ac.uk/study/medicine/medical-genetics; Tel 029 2074 4028
The Insitute contains the Regional Medical Genetics Service for Wales and co-ordinates genetic counselling clinics throughout Wales

Scotland

North Eastern

Medical Genetics, Polwarth Bldgs, Medical School, Fosterhill, Aberdeen AB9 2ZD; E-mail n.haites@abdn.ac.uk; Tel 01224 681818 ext 53003
Head (Molecular Genetics and Cytogenetics)   Prof N. Haites

Northern

Paediatric Unit, Raigmore Hospital, Inverness, Highland; Tel 01463 704000; Fax 01463 711322
Consultant Paediatrician   Dr G. Farmer
Consultant Paediatrician   Dr J. McDonald
Consultant Paediatrician   Dr I. MacDonald
Consultant Paediatrician   Dr T. Reddy

South East of Scotland

Clinical Genetic Service, Western General Hospital, Crewe Rd, Edinburgh EH4 2XU; Tel 0131 651 1012; Fax 0131 651 1013

Tayside

Genetic Counselling Clinic
Ninewells Hospital and Medical School, Dundee DD1 9SY; Tel 01382 632035; Fax 01382 496382
Consultant Clinical Geneticist   Dr David R. Goudie; E-mail david.r.goudie@tnht.scot.nhs.uk

16

Human Genetic Laboratories
Ninewells Hospital and Medical School, Dundee DD1 9SY;
Tel 01382 632035; Fax 01382 496362
Consultant Clinical Geneticist Dr D. Goudie

Western

West of Scotland Regional Genetics Service, Institute of
Medical Genetics, Yorkhill, Glasgow G3 8SJ;
URL www.gla.ac.uk/medicalgenetics;
E-mail j.m.connor@clinmed.gla.ac.uk; Tel 0141 201 0365;
Fax 0141 357 4277
Head (Centre) Prof J.M. Connor

Northern Ireland

Regional Genetics Centre, Fl A, Tower Block, Belfast City
Hospital, Belfast BT9 7AB; Tel 028 9032 9241
ext 2851/2873; Fax 028 9023 6911

Registered Pregnancy Advice Bureaux

Facilities for provision of legal abortion operations in
Britain can be divided into two main categories: those on
NHS premises and those elsewhere. The Abortion Act
1967 lays down that, outside of the NHS, premises on
which pregnancies can be terminated must be specially
'approved' for that purpose. 'Approved' premises can
themselves be divided into nursing homes and clinics run
for commercial purposes and those which are part of
non-profit-making charities. In addition, during the past
15 years, there has grown up a network of pregnancy
advisory bureaux: some deal only with patients seeking
abortion, some deal with all aspects of fertility and
infertility, and others have broadened their role and now
deal with a wide variety of needs in addition to problems
connected with pregnancy. These bureaux also can be
divided into charitable and commercial categories.
Advisory services are not themselves controlled by
statute but voluntarily agree to be inspected and
'registered' by the Department of Health, because the
Department of Health requires the proprietors of all
places who seek 'approval' to perform abortion
operations to give certain undertakings. Amongst these
undertakings are a number regarding the 'Register of
Pregnancy Advice Bureaux and they include that 'the
Nursing Home must not admit for treatment any
abortion patient referred by a pregancy advice bureau or
referral agency of any kind which is not on the list of
those registered by the Secretary of State as notified to
approved nursing homes from time to time' and 'Advice
bureaux which do not charge a fee for their services are
not registered, but approved nursing homes must not
accept patients direct from such sources. Non fee-
charging agencies should be asked to refer patients either
to a doctor or to a registered bureau'. As well as being
categorised on the basis of whether they are charities,
whether they charge their clients and what sort of
services they provide, these bureaux can be divided into:
(1) Those that are charities and refer patients only to
clinics which are also charities; (2) Those that are charities
but refer some or all of their patients to commercial
clinics; (3) Those that are commercial and refer their
patients to commercial clinics. The following list shows
all the currently Department of Health registered
pregnancy advice bureaux, indicating those which are
run by registered charities and those which make
referrals to commercial clinics.
Officer (Public Relations) Diane Munday

British Pregnancy Advisory Service (BPAS)

Austy Manor, Wootton Wawen, Solihull, West Midlands
B95 6BX; URL www.bpas.org; E-mail info@bpas.org;
Tel 01564 793225
Chief Executive Ian H. Jones
The British Pregnancy Advisory Service, established in
1967, is a registered non-profit making charitable
organisation, with 33 Consultation Centres and eight
Clinics, and three day care centres located nationwide.
Although counselling, advising and performing
termination of pregnancy is the primary element of BPAS
operations, the organisation also undertakes further
services relating to fertility control, including: emergency
contraception, sterilisation, vasectomy and vasectomy
reversal.

Amersham Consultation Centre
Outpatients Department, Amersham Hospital, Whielden
St, Amersham, Buckinghamshire HP7 9JD;
URL www.bpas.org; E-mail info@bpas.org; Tel 08457
304030

Bath Consultation Centre
Sawclose Clinic, Bridewell La, Bath, Bath and North East
Somerset BA1 1EX; URL www.bpas.org;
E-mail info@bpas.org; Tel 08457 304030

Birmingham Consultation Centre
1st Fl, Guildhall Bldgs, Birmingham, West Midlands
B2 4BT; URL www.bpas.org; E-mail info@bpas.org;
Tel 08457 304030
Provides post-coital contraception.

Pregnancy Advisory Service (Blackpool)
93 Abingdon St, Blackpool FY1 1PP;
E-mail pas.blackpool@mailsaq.net; Tel 01253 293096;
(Evenings and weekends) 01253 353154
Manager Brenda Featherstone
Open Mon–Fri 0900–1700.

Bournemouth Consultation Centre
23 Ophir Rd, Bournemouth BH8 8LS; URL www.bpas.org;
E-mail info@bpas.org; Tel 08457 304030
Provide post-coital contraception.

Brighton Consultation Centre
Wistons Site, Chatsworth Rd, Brighton, Brighton and Hove
BN1 5DW; URL www.bpas.org; E-mail info@bpas.org;
Tel 08457 304030
Provides post-coital contraception.

Bristol Consultation Centre
Frenchay Hospital, Frenchay Park Rd, Bristol BS16 1LE;
URL www.bpas.org; E-mail info@bpas.org; Tel 08457
304030

Cannock Consultation Centre
Cannock Chase Hospital, Brunswick Rd, Cannock,
Staffordshire WS11 2XY; URL www.bpas.org;
E-mail info@bpas.org; Tel 08457 304030

Cardiff Consultation Centre
3rd Fl, Westminster Hse, Cardiff CF1 1DX;
URL www.bpas.org; E-mail info@bpas.org; Tel 08457
304030
Provides post-coital contraception.

Chester Consultation Centre
98a Foregate St, Chester, Cheshire CH1 1HB;
URL www.bpas.org; E-mail info@bpas.org; Tel 08457
304030
Provides post-coital contraception.

Coventry Consultation Centre
Ground Fl, Unit 4, Coventry, West Midlands CV1 3RA;
URL www.bpas.org; E-mail info@bpas.org; Tel 08457
304030
Provides post-coital contraception.

Doncaster Consultation Centre
The Bungalow, 1a Avenue Rd, Doncaster, South Yorkshire
DN2 4AH; URL www.bpas.org; E-mail info@bpas.org;
Tel 08457 304030
Provides post-coital contraception.

Glasgow Consultation Centre
1st Fl, 245 North St, Glasgow G3 7DL; URL www.bpas.org;
E-mail info@bpas.org; Tel 08457 304030

Leeds Consultation Centre
3rd Fl, 7 Eastgate, Leeds, West Yorkshire LS2 7LY;
URL www.bpas.org; E-mail info@bpas.org; Tel 08457
304030
Provides post-coital contraception.

Leigham Lodge Consultation Centre
76 Leigham Court Rd, Streatham, London SW16 2QA;
URL www.bpas.org; E-mail info@bpas.org; Tel 08457
304030

Liverpool Consultation Centre
20 Rodney St, Liverpool, Merseyside L1 2TQ;
URL www.bpas.org; E-mail info@bpas.org; Tel 08457
304030
Provides post-coital contraception.

London Central Consultation Centre
26–27 Bedford Sq, London WC1B 3HH;
URL www.bpas.org; E-mail info@bpas.org; Tel 08457
304030

Luton Consultation Centre
1st Fl, 2 Gordon St, Luton LU1 2QP; URL www.bpas.org;
E-mail info@bpas.org; Tel 08457 304030
Provides post-coital contraception.

Manchester Consultation Centre
75 Lever St, Manchester M1 1FL; URL www.bpas.org;
E-mail info@bpas.org; Tel (24 hours) 0161 228 1887
Manager   Avril Dunn
Pregnancy testing services with immediate results. Advice
available on contraception, emergency contraception and
sterilisations. Referral for abortion after consultation and
medical assessment. Reversal of both sterilisation and
vasectomy available.

Milton Keynes Consultation Centre
Luing Cowley Centre, Milton Keynes Hospital, Milton
Keynes MK6 5LD; Tel 08457 304030
Provides post-coital contraception.

Peterborough Consultation Centre
URL www.bpas.org; E-mail info@bpas.org; Tel 08457
304030

Preston Consultation Centre
2nd Fl, Shereton Hse, Preston, Lancashire PR1 2QP;
URL www.bpas.org; E-mail info@bpas.org; Tel 08457
304030

Richmond Consultation Centre
15 Rosslyn Rd, Twickenham, Greater London TW1 2AR;
URL www.bpas.org; E-mail info@bpas.org; Tel 08457
304030

Sheffield Consultation Centre
Park Health Centre, 190 Duke St, Sheffield, South Yorkshire
S2 5QQ; URL www.bpas.org; E-mail info@bpas.org;
Tel 08457 304030
Provides post-coital contraception.

Stoke Pregnancy Advisory Service
1a George St, Newcastle-under-Lyme, Staffordshire
ST5 1JX; Tel 01782 632784
Manager   Ms C. Hopewell
Referrals to clinics in Manchester or Birmingham. Service
includes sterilisation, post coital pill, smear test and very
early pregnancy tests.

Swindon Consultation Centre
Swindon Health Centre, Carfax St, Swindon SN1 1ED;
URL www.bpas.org; E-mail info@bpas.org; Tel 08457
304030

Telford Consultation Centre
Apley Clinic, Princess Hospital, Apley Castle, Telford,
TF6 6TF; URL www.bpas.org; E-mail info@bpas.org;
Tel 08457 304030

Torquay Consultation Centre
BPAS Gynae Clinic, Torbay Hospital, Lawes Bridge,
Torquay, Devon TQ2 7AA; URL www.bpas.org;
E-mail info@bpas.org

East Midlands Pregnancy Advisory Service (EMPAS)

493 Mansfield Rd, Nottingham NG5 2JJ; Tel 0115 962 1450
Director   E. Sensecall
Director   T.J. Sensecall
Makes referrals to commercial clinics.

Lifeline Pregnancy Counselling and Care

7a Albany St, Edinburgh EH1 3PY; Tel 0131 557 2060
Senior Counsellor   Sarah Home
Provides free professional counselling and help to women
suffering physically or psychologically in consequence of
unintended pregnancy, childbirth, abortion, miscarriage,
post-natal depression etc. Free pregnancy tests and material
aid. Charity no SCO 26943.

Marie Stopes International

Head Office, 153–157 Cleveland St, London W1T 6QW;
URL www.mariestopes.org.uk; Tel 020 7574 7400;
(Health screening and family planning) 0845 300 0460;
(Male and female sterilisation) 0845 300 0212;
(Termination of pregnancy) 0845 300 8090; Fax 0117 900
5501
Director (Clinic Services)   Liz Davies
A registered charity with a network of nearly 40 centres
across the UK providing male and female sterilisation,
termination of pregnancy, health screening, family
planning and emergency after-sex contraception. Main
centres in London, Leeds, Manchester, Bristol, Maidstone
and Reading.

Marie Stopes Centre (Bristol)
3 Great George St, Bristol, BS1 5RR; Tel 0845 300 8090

Marie Stopes Centre (Leeds)
10 Queen Sq, Leeds, West Yorkshire LS2 8AJ; Tel 0845 300
8909

Marie Stopes Centre (Maidstone)
10 Brewer St, Maidstone, Kent, ME14 1RU; Tel 0845 300
8090

Marie Stopes Centre (Manchester)
2 St. John St, St. John St Chambers, Manchester M3 4DB;
Tel 0845 300 8090

16

Marie Stopes House
108 Whitfield St, London W1P 6BE; Tel 0845 300 8090

Marie Stopes Centre (Reading)
121 London St, Reading RG1 4QA; Tel 0845 300 8090

Pregnancy and Counselling Service (Stoke)

1a George St, Newcastle-under-Lyme, Staffordshire
ST5 1JX; Tel 01782 632784
Manager Ms C. Hopewell
Referrals to clinics in Manchester or Birmingham. Service
includes sterilisation, post coital pill, smear test and very
early pregnancy tests.

Samaritans

The Upper Mill, Kingston Rd, Ewell, Surrey KT17 2AF;
URL www.samaritans.org.uk;
E-mail admin@samaritans.org.uk; Tel 020 8394 8300;
Fax 020 8394 8301
Patron HRH The Prince of Wales
Chair Bernard Finnemore
Hon Consultant Dr Sally Pidd
Hon Treasurer Tony Lee
Chief Executive Simon Armson
Director (Training) J. Guenault
Director (Finance and Administration) Sue Scregg
Director (Marketing) David Richards
Director (Caller Services) Jackie Wilkinson
Functions
The Samaritans is a registered charity which provides
confidential and emotional support to people in crisis. The
Samaritans is available 24 hours a day for everyone passing
through crisis and at risk of suicide. The following is a list
of branches arranged alphabetically or call 08457 909090 or
e-mail jo@samaritans.org.

England and Wales

East Midlands

Banbury
The Samaritans, 33 Albert St, Banbury, Oxfordshire
OX16 8DG; Tel 01295 270000

Boston
The Samaritans, 52 Wormgate, Boston, Lincolnshire
PE21 6NS; Tel 01205 311311

Chesterfield
The Samaritans, 2 Rose Hill, Chesterfield, Derbyshire
S40 1LW; Tel 01246 270000

Derby
The Samaritans, 110 Burton Rd, Derby DE1 1TG; Tel 01332
364444

Grantham
The Samaritans, 27 St. Catherine's Rd, Grantham,
Lincolnshire NG31 6TT; Tel 01476 591551

Kettering
The Samaritans, 111 Montagu St, Kettering,
Northamptonshire NN16 8XL; Tel 01536 416999

Leicester
The Samaritans, 1a Elmfield Ave, Leicester LE2 1RB;
Tel 0116 270 0007

Lincoln
The Samaritans, 17 Hungate, Lincoln, Lincolnshire
LN1 1ES; Tel 01522 528282
Groups at Retford, Boston and Grantham.

Mansfield and District
The Samaritans, 1a Grove St, Mansfield, Nottinghamshire
NG18 1EL; Tel 01623 422224

Milton Keynes
The Samaritans, 161 Fishermead Blvd, Milton Keynes
MK6 2AB; Tel 01908 667777

Northampton
The Samaritans, 2 St. Michael's Ave, Northampton,
Northamptonshire NN1 4JQ; Tel 01604 637637

Nottingham
The Samaritans, 18 Clarendon St, Nottingham NG1 5HQ;
Tel 0115 941 1111

Peterborough
The Samaritans, 32–34 St. John's St, Peterborough PE1 5DD;
Tel 01733 312727

Eastern England

Basildon and Thurrock
The Samaritans, 16 Little Lullaway, Basildon, Essex
SS15 5JJ; Tel 01268 412000

Bedford
The Samaritans, 23 Foster Hill Rd, Bedford, Bedfordshire
MK40 2ES; Tel 01234 211211

Bury St. Edmunds and West Suffolk
The Samaritans, 46 Well St, Bury St. Edmunds, Suffolk
IP33 1EQ; Tel 01284 750000

Cambridge
The Samaritans, 4 Emmanuel Rd, Cambridge,
Cambridgeshire CB1 1JW; Tel 01223 364455

Chelmsford and Mid-Essex
The Samaritans, 12 Critchett Terr, Chelmsford, Essex
CM1 2QN; Tel 01245 357357

Colchester, Tendring and Suffolk
The Samaritans, 12 Vineyard St, Colchester, Essex
CO2 7DG; Tel 01206 561234

Great Yarmouth
The Samaritans, 62 North Quay, Great Yarmouth, Norfolk
NR30 1JB; Tel 01493 842800

Hertfordshire/Essex
The Samaritans, 14 Cross St, Ware, Hertfordshire
SG12 7AH; Tel 01279 421110; 01920 464099

Ipswich and East Suffolk
The Samaritans, 140 St. Helen's St, Ipswich, Suffolk
IP4 2LE; Tel 01473 211133

King's Lynn
The Samaritans, 26 Queen St, King's Lynn, Norfolk
PE30 1HT; Tel 01553 761616

Lowestoft and Waveney
The Samaritans of Lowestoft and Waveney, 14 Beach Rd,
Lowestoft, Suffolk NR32 1EA; Tel 01502 500800

Luton
The Samaritans, 33 Cardiff Rd, Luton LU1 1PP; Tel 01582
720666

North Hertfordshire and Stevenage
The Samaritans, 5 Nuns Cl, Hitchin, Hertfordshire
SG5 1EP; Tel 01438 316161; 01462 455333

Norwich
The Samaritans, 19 St. Stephen's Sq, Norwich, Norfolk
NR1 3SS; Tel 01603 611311

Southend-on-Sea
The Samaritans, 154 York Rd, Southend-on-Sea, Southend SS1 2DZ; Tel 01702 611911

London

Bexley and Dartford
The Samaritans, 35 Glynde Rd, Bexleyheath, Kent DA7 4HB; Tel 020 8301 1010

Brent
The Samaritans, 7 Meyrick Rd, London NW10 2EL; Tel 020 8459 8585

Bromley and Orpington
The Samaritans, 9b Station Rd, Orpington, Kent BR6 0RZ; Tel 01689 833000

Croydon
The Samaritans of Croydon and Sutton, 2b Kidderminster Rd, Croydon, Surrey CR9 2BQ; Tel 020 8681 6666

Ealing
The Samaritans, 26 Junction Rd, Ealing, London W5 4XL; Tel 020 8560 2345

Enfield-Haringey-Barnet
The Samaritans, 40 Queens Rd, Bounds Green, London N11 2QU; Tel 020 8889 6888

Festival Branch
The Samaritans, 8 Latimer Rd, London SW19 1EP; Tel 020 8544 1695

Harrow
The Samaritans, 44 Station Rd, Harrow, Greater London HA1 2SQ; Tel 020 8427 7777

Havering
The Samaritans, 107 North St, Romford, Essex RM1 1ER; Tel 01708 740000

Hillingdon
The Samaritans, 2 Press Rd, Uxbridge, Greater London UB8 1AT; Tel 01895 253355

Kingston upon Thames
The Samaritans, 12 St. Andrew's Rd, Surbiton, Surrey KT6 4DT; Tel 020 8399 6676

Lewisham
The Samaritans, 362 New Cross Rd, London SE14 6AG; Tel 020 8692 5228

London (Central)
The Samaritans, 46 Marshall St, London W1V 1LR; Tel 020 7734 2800

Putney
The Samaritans, 106 Felsham Rd, Putney, London SW15 1DQ; Tel 020 8789 9121; 020 8789 9122

Redbridge
The Samaritans, 8 Mildmay Rd, Ilford, Essex IG1 1DT; Tel 020 8553 9900

South West Hertfordshire
The Samaritans, 45 St. John's Rd, Watford, Hertfordshire WD1 1QB; Tel 01923 233333

Waltham Forest
The Samaritans, 663 Lea Bridge Rd, Leyton, London E10 6AL; Tel 020 8520 9191

North

Carlisle
The Samaritans, 12 Corporation Rd, Carlisle, Cumbria CA3 8XB; Tel 01228 544444

Darlington
The Samaritans, 13 Woodland Rd, Darlington DL3 7BJ; Tel 01325 465465

Durham
The Samaritans of Central Durham, 26 Sutton St, Durham, County Durham DH1 4BW; Tel 0191 384 2727

Hartlepool
The Samaritans, 58 Avenue Rd, Hartlepool TS24 8AT; Tel 01429 276767

Newcastle
The Samaritans of Tyneside, 15 Portland Terr, Newcastle upon Tyne, Tyne and Wear NE2 1QS; Tel 0191 232 7272

Northumbria
The Samaritans, 25 North Seaton Rd, Ashington, Northumberland NE63 0AG; Tel 01670 814222

Sunderland
The Samaritans, 13 Grange Cres, Stockton Rd, Sunderland, Tyne and Wear SR2 7BN; Tel 0191 567 7177

Teeside
The Samaritans, 147 Borough Rd, Middlesbrough TS1 3AT; Tel 01642 217777

Whitehaven
The Samaritans of West Cumbria, 71 George St, Whitehaven, Cumbria CA27 7PU; Tel 01946 694266

North East Region

Barnsley
The Samaritans, 77 Pitt St West, Barnsley, South Yorkshire S70 1BN; Tel 01226 202222

Bradford
The Samaritans, 6 Mornington Villas, Manningham, Bradford, West Yorkshire BD8 7HB; Tel 01274 547547

Bridlington
The Samaritans, 60 North St, Bridlington, East Riding of Yorkshire YO15 2DY; Tel 01262 400400

Doncaster
The Samaritans, 36 Thorne Rd, Doncaster, South Yorkshire DN1 2JA; Tel 01302 327474

Grimsby
55 Alexandra Rd, Grimsby, North East Lincolnshire DN31 1RD; Tel 01472 353111; 01472 353112

Halifax and Calderdale
The Samaritans, 8 Hopwood La, Halifax, West Yorkshire HX1 5HW; Tel 01422 349349

Harrogate
The Samaritans, 5 Mount Pde, Harrogate, North Yorkshire HG1 1BX; Tel 01423 525352

Huddersfield
The Samaritans, 47 Trinity St, Huddersfield, West Yorkshire HD1 4DN; Tel 01484 533388

Hull
The Samaritans, 75 Spring Bank, Kingston upon Hull HU3 1AG; Tel 01482 323456

Leeds
The Samaritans of Leeds, 93 Clarendon Rd, Leeds, West Yorkshire LS2 9LY; Tel 0113 245 6789

Northallerton and The Dales
The Samaritans of Northallerton and The Dales, 7 Crosby Rd, Northallerton, North Yorkshire DL6 1AA; Tel 01609 776161

16

Rotherham
The Samaritans, 22 Percy St, Rotherham, South Yorkshire S65 1ED; Tel 01709 361717

Scarborough
The Samaritans, 79 Dean Rd, Scarborough, North Yorkshire YO12 7QS; Tel 01723 368888

Scunthorpe
The Samaritans, Lyndum Hse, 2 Lyndum St, Scunthorpe, North Lincolnshire DN15 6QU; Tel 01724 860000

Sheffield
The Samaritans, 26 Rockingham La, Sheffield, South Yorkshire S1 4FW; Tel 0114 276 7277

Wakefield
The Samaritans, Charlotte St, Wakefield, West Yorkshire WF1 1UL; Tel 01924 377011

Worksop
The Samaritans, Samaritan Hse, 71 Eastgate, Worksop, Nottinghamshire S80 1RE; Tel 01909 531153

York
The Samaritans, 89 Nunnery La, York YO23 1AH; Tel 01904 655888

North West

Barrow, Furness and South Lakes
The Samaritans of Barrow, Furness and South Lakes, 16 Hartington St, Barrow-in-Furness, Cumbria LA14 5SL; Tel 01229 825656

Blackburn
The Samaritans of Blackburn, Hyndburn and Ribble Valley, 105 New Park St, Blackburn BB2 1DF; Tel 01254 662424

Blackpool
The Samaritans, 16 Edward St, Blackpool FY1 1BA; Tel 01253 622218

Bolton
The Samaritans, 16 Bark Street East, Bolton, Lancashire BL1 2BQ; Tel 01204 521200

Bury
The Samaritans, 13 Knowsley St, Bury, Lancashire BL9 0ST; Tel 0161 764 0055

Buxton and High Peak
The Samaritans of Buxton and High Peak, 19 High St, Buxton, Derbyshire SK17 6ET; Tel 01298 260000

Isle of Man
The Samaritans, 5 Victoria Pl, Douglas, Isle of Man; Tel 01624 663399

Lancaster and District
The Samaritans, 21 Sun St, Lancaster, Lancashire LA1 1EW; Tel 01524 61666

Liverpool and Merseyside
The Samaritans of Liverpool and Merseyside, 25 Clarence St, Liverpool, Merseyside L3 5TN; Tel 0151 708 8888

Macclesfield
The Samaritans of Macclesfield and District, Read Hse, 2 Boden St, Macclesfield, Cheshire SK10 6LL; Tel 01625 426000

Manchester and Salford
The Samaritans of Manchester and Salford, 72–74 Oxford St, Manchester M1 5NH; Tel 0161 236 8000

Northwich
The Samaritans of Mid-Cheshire, 1 St. Paul's Pl, Witton St, Northwich, Cheshire CW9 5DZ; Tel 01606 43211; 01606 43212

Pendle, Burnley and Rossendale
The Samaritans of Pendle, Burnley and Rossendale, 15 Market Sq, Nelson, Lancashire BB9 7LP; Tel 01282 694929

Preston
The Samaritans, 11 St Wilfred St, Preston, Lancashire PR1 2US; Tel 01772 822022

Rochdale, Oldham and District
The Samaritans, Rochdale, Lancashire OL11 1BU; Tel 01706 868686

Southport
The Samaritans of Southport and District, 32 Union St, Southport, Greater Manchester PR9 0QE; Tel 01704 538038

Stockport
The Samaritans, Churchgate Hse, 96 Churchgate, Stockport, Cheshire SK1 1YJ; Tel 0161 480 2222

Warrington, Halton and St. Helens
The Samaritans, 46 Arpley St, Warrington WA1 1LX; Tel 01925 235000; 01925 235001

Wigan
The Samaritans, 73 Dicconson St, Wigan, Greater Manchester WN1 2AT; Tel 01942 492222

South East

Ashford
The Samaritans, 22 Queen St, Ashford, Kent TN23 1RG; Tel 01233 610000

Brighton, Hove and District
The Samaritans, 102 Clarendon Rd, Hove, Brighton and Hove BN3 3WQ; Tel 01273 772277

Canterbury
The Samaritans, 32 Northgate, Canterbury, Kent CT1 1BL; Tel 01227 457777

Eastbourne and District
The Samaritans, The Haven, 13 Bolton Rd, Eastbourne, East Sussex BN21 3JT; Tel 01323 735555

Folkestone and Hythe
The Samaritans, 9 Cambridge Gdns, Folkestone, Kent CT20 1DB; Tel 01303 255000

Guildford
The Samaritans, 69 Woodbridge Rd, Guildford, Surrey GU1 4RD; Tel 01483 505555

Hastings and Rother
The Samaritans, 26 St. Andrew's Sq, Hastings, East Sussex TN34 1SR; Tel 01424 436666

Horsham and Crawley
The Samaritans, 21 Denne Rd, Horsham, Sussex RH12 1JE; Tel 01403 276276; 01293 515151

Leatherhead
The Samaritans, 7 Church Rd, Leatherhead, Surrey KT22 8AT; Tel 01372 375555

Maidstone
The Samaritans, 48 Grecian St, Maidstone, Kent ME14 2TS; Tel 01622 674444; 01622 674445

Medway, Gravesham and Swale West
The Samaritans, Priory Rd, Strood, Rochester, Kent
ME2 2EG; Tel 01634 730981

Reigate
The Samaritans of East Surrey, 4b High St, Reigate, Surrey
RH2 9AY; Tel 01737 248444

Tunbridge Wells
The Samaritans, 7 Lime Hill Rd, Tunbridge Wells, Kent
TN1 1LJ; Tel 01892 532323

Weybridge
The Samaritans of North West Surrey, Ledger Dr,
Addlestone, Surrey KT15 1AT; Tel 01932 844444

Worthing
The Samaritans, 2 Lennox Rd, Worthing, West Sussex
BN11 1DA; Tel 01903 205555

South West

Bath
The Samaritans, 10 Newbridge Hill, Bath, Bath and North
East Somerset BA1 3PU; Tel 01225 429222

Bristol
The Samaritans, 37 St. Nicholas St, Bristol BS1 1TP; Tel 0117
983 1000

Cornwall and Truro
The Samaritans, 19 Treyew Rd, Truro, Cornwall TR1 2BY;
Tel 01872 277277

Exeter, Mid and East Devon
The Samaritans, 10 Richmond Rd, Exeter, Devon EX4 4JA;
Tel 01392 411711

North Devon
The Samaritans of North Devon and North Cornwall at
Barnstaple and Bude, 2 Summerland St, Barnstaple,
Devon EX32 8JJ; Tel 01271 374343

Plymouth
The Samaritans, 20 Oxford Pl, Plymouth PL1 5AJ; Tel 01752
221666

South Devon
The Samaritans, 21 Warren Rd, Torquay, Torbay TQ2 5TQ;
Tel 01803 299999

Taunton and Somerset
The Samaritans, 16 Wood St, Taunton, Somerset TA1 1UN;
Tel 01823 288998

Weston-super-Mare
137a High St, Weston-super-Mare, North Somerset
BS23 1HN; Tel 01934 632555

Weymouth
The Samaritans of Dorset, 13 King St, Weymouth, Dorset
DT4 7BJ; Tel 01305 771777; 01305 771778

Yeovil
The Samaritans, 10 Everton Rd, Yeovil, Somerset
BA20 1UF; Tel 01935 476455

Southern England

Basingstoke
The Samaritans, 5 Essex Rd, Basingstoke, Hampshire
RG21 1TA; Tel 01256 462333

Bognor Regis
The Samaritans, 13 Argyle Rd, Bognor Regis, Sussex
PO21 1DY; Tel 01243 826333

Bournemouth
The Samaritans of Bournemouth and District, 1 Durrant
Rd, Bournemouth BH2 6LE; Tel 01202 551999

Bracknell
The Samaritans, Hope Cottage, 2 Mount Pleasant,
Bracknell, Bracknell Forest RG12 9AD; Tel 01344
455556

Chilterns
The Samaritans, 149 Station Rd, Amersham,
Buckinghamshire HP6 5DJ; Tel 01494 432000

Farnborough and District
The Samaritans, 182a Farnborough Rd, Farnborough,
Hampshire GU14 7JW; Tel 01252 513222

Guernsey
The Samaritans, 2 Forest La, St. Peter Port, Guernsey
GY1 1WJ; Tel 01481 715515

Isle of Wight
The Samaritans, 14 East St, Newport, Isle of Wight
PO30 1JL; Tel 01983 521234

Jersey
The Samaritans, 30 Hue St, St. Helier, Jersey JE2 3RE;
Tel 01534 725555

Newbury
The Samaritans, 58 West St, Newbury, West Berkshire
RG13 1BD; Tel 01635 42452

Oxford
The Samaritans, 123 Iffley Rd, Oxford, Oxfordshire
OX4 1EJ; Tel 01865 722122

Portsmouth
The Samaritans, 296 London Rd, North End, Portsmouth
PO2 9JN; Tel 023 9269 1313; 023 9269 1314; 023 9269
1515

Reading
The Samaritans, 59a Chomley Rd, Reading, Berkshire
RG1 3NB; Tel 0118 926 6333

Salisbury and District
The Samaritans, 42 Milford St, Salisbury, Wiltshire SP1 2BP;
Tel 01722 323355

Slough, Windsor and Maidenhead
The Samaritans of Slough, Windsor and Maidenhead, 17
Uxbridge Rd, Slough SL1 1SN; Tel 01753 531011; 01753
531012

Southampton
The Samaritans, 64 St. Andrew's Rd, Southampton
SO14 0BA; Tel 023 8063 2888

Swindon
The Samaritans, 6 Curtis St, Swindon SN1 5JU; Tel 01793
537373

Winchester
The Samaritans, 13 Upper High St, Winchester, Hampshire
SO23 8UT; Tel 01962 860633

West Midlands and North Wales

Bangor (North Wales)
The Samaritans, 5 Abbey Rd, Bangor, Gwynedd LL57 2EA;
Tel 01248 354646

Birmingham
The Samaritans, 13 Bow St, Birmingham, West Midlands
B1 1DW; Tel 0121 666 6644
Associate Group at Tamworth.

16

Brecon and Radnor
The Samaritans, Flat 2, Sandringham, Temple St, Llandrindod Wells, Powys LD1 5DP; Tel 01597 823000

Brierley Hill
The Samaritans, 'Beryl Hse', 8 Albion St, Brierley Hill, West Midlands DY5 3EE; Tel 01384 78111

Chester and District
The Samaritans, 36 Upper Northgate St, Chester, Cheshire CH1 4EF; Tel 01244 377999

Coventry and District
The Samaritans, 57 Moor St, Earlsdon, Coventry, West Midlands CV5 6ER; Tel 024 7667 8678

Crewe
The Samaritans of South Cheshire, 2 Hall O'Shaw St, Crewe, Cheshire CW1 4AE; Tel 01270 216666

Leek and Staffordshire Moorlands
The Samaritans, 27 Fountain St, Leek, Staffordshire ST13 6JS; Tel 01538 384100

Rhyl
The Samaritans, 23 Bedford St, Rhyl, Denbighshire LL18 1SY; Tel 01745 354545

Shrewsbury
The Samaritans, Swan Hse, Coleham Head, Shrewsbury, Shropshire SY3 7BJ; Tel 01743 369696

Solihull
The Samaritans, Station Approach, Solihull, West Midlands B91 1LE; Tel 0121 704 2255

Stafford
Stafford Samaritans, Garden St, Stafford, Staffordshire ST17 4DD; Tel 01785 243333

Stoke-on-Trent and Newcastle
The Samaritans of Stoke-on-Trent and Newcastle District, 3 Shelton New Rd, Stoke-on-Trent ST1 4PH; Tel 01782 213555

Stratford
The Samaritans, 1 Shakespeare St, Stratford-upon-Avon, Warwickshire CV37 6RN; Tel 01789 298866

Tamworth
The Samaritans, The Philip Dix Centre, Corporation St, Tamworth, Staffordshire B79 7DN; Tel 01827 709637; 01827 709638

Telford
The Samaritans, 115 King St, Telford, TF1 1NU; Tel 01952 256161

Walsall
The Samaritans, Bott La, Walsall, West Midlands WS1 2JQ; Tel 01922 624000

Wolverhampton
The Samaritans, 54 Newhampton Road West, Wolverhampton, West Midlands WV6 0RU; Tel 01902 426422; 01902 426423

South Wales and the Marches

Aberystwyth
The Samaritans of Aberystwyth, Maengwyn, 5 Trinity Rd, Aberystwyth, Ceredigion SY23 1LU; Tel 01970 624535

Bangor and North Down
The Samaritans, 92 Dufferin Ave, Bangor, Gwynedd BT20 3AD; Tel 028 9146 4646

Bridgend
The Samaritans, 2 Green St, Bridgend CF31 1HF; Tel 01656 662333

Cardiff and District
The Samaritans, 75 Cowbridge Road East, Canton, Cardiff CF1 9AF; Tel 029 2034 4022

Cheltenham and District
The Samaritans, Victoria Hse, Back Albert Pl, Pittville, Cheltenham, Gloucestershire GL52 2HN; Tel 01242 515777

Gloucester
The Samaritans, 9 Park End Rd, Gloucester, Gloucestershire GL1 5AT; Tel 01452 306333

Haverfordwest
The Samaritans, 1 Albert St, Haverfordwest, Pembrokeshire SA61 1TA; Tel 01437 766699

Herefordshire
The Samaritans, 44a Berrington St, Hereford, Herefordshire HR4 0BJ; Tel 01432 269000

Newport and Gwent
Newport and Gwent Samaritans, 43 Stow Hill, Newport NP9 1JH; Tel 01633 259000

Swansea
The Samaritans, 17 St. John's Rd, Manselton, Swansea SA5 8PR; Tel 01792 655999

Worcester
The Samaritans, 9 Sansome Pl, Worcester, Worcestershire WR1 1UA; Tel 01905 21121

Scotland

Aberdeen and District
The Samaritans, 60 Dee St, Aberdeen AB11 6DS; Tel 01224 574488

Borders
The Samaritans, 4 Kirk Wynd, Selkirk, Scottish Borders TD7 4AW; Tel 01750 20000

Caithness
The Samaritans, 7 Riverside Pl, Caithness, Highland KW14 8BZ; Tel 01847 895656

Correspondence
Taigh Foise, 2 Drummond Pk, Crook of Devon, Kinross, Perth and Kinross KY13 0UX

Dumfries and Galloway
The Samaritans, 104 Loreburn St, Dumfries, Dumfries and Galloway DG1 1HW; Tel 01387 253555

Dundee
The Samaritans, 10 Victoria Chambers, Dundee DD1 1JN; Tel 01382 226666

Dunfermline
The Samaritans, 22 Townhill Rd, Dunfermline, Fife KY12 0QX; Tel 01383 722222

Edinburgh and The Lothians
The Samaritans, 25 Torpichen St, Edinburgh EH3 8HX; Tel 0131 221 9999

Elgin
The Samaritans, 21 Greyfriars St, Elgin, Moray IV30 1LF; Tel 01343 543000

Falkirk
The Samaritans, 19 Orchard St, Falkirk FK1 1RF; Tel 01324 622066

Glasgow
The Samaritans, 210 West George St, Glasgow G2 2DQ;
Tel 0141 248 4488

Hamilton
The Samaritans, 4 Selkirk Pl, Hamilton, South Lanarkshire
ML3 6RQ; Tel 01698 429411

Inverclyde
The Samaritans, 65 Cathcart St, Greenock, Renfrewshire
PA15 1DE; Tel 01475 721212

Inverness
The Samaritans, 65 Cathcart St, Inverness, Highland
IV3 5DT; Tel 01463 713456

Kilmarnock
The Samaritans of Ayrshire, 43 Titchfield St, Kilmarnock,
East Ayrshire KA1 1QS; Tel 01563 531313

Kirkcaldy
246 St. Clair St, Kirkcaldy, Fife KY1 2BD; Tel 01592 654242

Orkney
The Samaritans, 43 Junction Rd, Kirkwall, Orkney,
KW15 1AR; Tel 01856 875875

Perth
The Samaritans, 59 King St, Perth, Perth and Kinross
PH2 8JB; Tel 01738 626666

Shetland
Linda Rose Hse, Charlotte St, Lerwick, Shetland Isles ZE1;
Tel 01595 694449

Stornaway
The Samaritans, 13 Macleod Rd, Stornoway, Isle of Lewis
HS1 2HI; Tel 01851 703777

Ireland

Athlone
The Samaritans, 3 Court Devenish, Athlone, County
Westmeath, Republic of Ireland; Tel 353 902 73133

Ballymena
The Samaritans, 45 Mount St, Ballymena, County Antrim
BT43 6BP; Tel 028 256 50000

Belfast
The Samaritans, 5 Wellesley Ave, Belfast BT9 6DG; Tel 028
9066 4422

Coleraine
The Samaritans, 20 Lodge Rd, Coleraine, County
Londonderry BT52 1NB; Tel 028 703 20000

Cork
The Samaritans, Coach St, Cork, Republic of Ireland;
Tel 353 21 271323

Craigavon
The Samaritans, 162 Thomas St Portadown, Craigavon,
County Armagh BT62 3BD; Tel 028 3833 3555

Derry
The Samaritans, 16 Clarendon St, Derry, County Derry
BT48 7ET; Tel 028 7126 5511

Drogheda
The Samaritans, 3 Leyland Pl, Stockwell St, Drogheda,
Republic of Ireland; Tel 00 35341 984 3888; 00 35341 984
3889

Dublin
The Samaritans, 112 Marlborough St, Dublin, 1, Republic of
Ireland; Tel 3531 8727700

Ennis and Clare
Sunville, Kilrush Rd, Ennis, County Clare; Tel 353 68
29777

Galway
The Samaritans, 14 Nun's Island, Galway, Republic of
Ireland; Tel 353 91 561222

Kilkenny and Carlow
The Samaritans, Barrack St, Kilkenny, Republic of Ireland;
Tel 00 35356 65554; 00 35356 65750

Limerick and Tipperary
The Samaritans, 20 Barrington St, Limerick, Republic of
Ireland; Tel 353 61 412111

Newbridge
The Samaritans, 3 McIlwaine Terr, County Kildare,
Republic of Ireland; Tel 353 45 435299

Newry
The Samaritans, 19 St. Colman's Pk, Newry, County Down
BT34 2BX; Tel 028 3026 6366

Omagh
The Samaritans, 20 Campsie Rd, Omagh, County Tyrone
BT79 0AG; Tel 028 8224 4944

Sligo
12 Chapple St, Sligo, Republic of Ireland; Tel 353 71 42011

Tralee
44 Moyderwell, Tralee, County Kerry, Republic of Ireland;
Tel 353 66 71 22566

Waterford
The Samaritans, 16 Beau St, Waterford, Republic of Ireland;
Tel 353 51 872114

Bereavement

Cruse, Bereavement Care
126 Sheen Rd, Richmond, Surrey TW9 1UR;
E-mail info@cruse.bereavementcare.org.uk; Tel 0870 167
1677; Fax 020 8940 7638
Patron HM The Queen
President Dr C. Murray Parkes, OBE
Chair M. Pearson
Chief Executive Anne Viney
Regional Officer (Central) S. Godfrey
Suffolk Hse, 123 High St, Cottenham, Cambridgeshire
CB4 4SD; Tel 01954 250509
Regional Manager (North West) Catherine Rose
1st Fl, 21 Palace St, Bolton, Lancashire BL1 2DR
Regional Manager (London and South Eastern)
S. Edgeworth
79 Stanmore Hill, Stanmore, Greater London HA7 3DZ;
Tel 020 8954 7399; Fax 020 8954 7399
National Manager (Wales) Richard Patterson
Ty Energlyn, Heol-Las, Caerphilly, CF83 2WP; Tel 029 2088
6913
National Manager (Scotland) Stewart Wilson
Cruse Scottish Headquarters, 33–35 Boswall Parkway,
Edinburgh EH5 2BR; Tel 0131 551 1511; Fax 0131 551
5234
National Manager (Northern Ireland) Anne Townsend
Cruse, Piney Ridge, Belfast BT8 8BH; Tel 028 9079 2419;
Fax 028 9079 2474
Cruse Bereavement Care is the UK's largest and only
national organisation that helps and supports anyone who
has been bereaved by death. Since 1959 Cruse has been
providing advice, counselling and information on practical
matters for bereaved people entirely free of charge. Cruse
has learnt that it is time and talking that help soothe the
immediate pain and sorrow. Time and talking are

fundamental to all the services we offer to anyone bereaved. Cruse's bereavement support is delivered through a network of over 5500 highly committed volunteers working in the community, in 150 branches across the UK. Last year 55 000 sought our help and advice. Cruse also offers training, support, information and publications to those working to care for bereaved people through education and information services. As a national charity Cruse depends upon the generosity of individuals to continue our work helping bereaved people.

Referrals

Self referral is the usual way most people contact Cruse, however, where the bereaved person has given their consent, we may accept referrals from the family, or the various caring professions.

London Bereavement Relief Society
Nasmith Hse, 175 Tower Bridge Rd, London SE1 2AH; Tel 020 7407 7585; Fax 020 7403 6711
Secretary W.N. Barr, CA
Provides one-off cash grants within the first four months of bereavement to widows and widowers in need who live in London postal districts.

National Association for Widows
3rd Fl, National Office, 48 Queen's Rd, Coventry, West Midlands CV1 3EH; URL www.widows.uk.net; Tel 024 7663 4848
President Vacancy
Founder J. Hemer
Offers information, advice and support to all widows and to all those concerned to help widows with the problems they face in society today. Head Office provides a free and confidential advice and information service, while branches throughout the country provide the basis of a supportive social life for many widows. Younger widows contact list now also available. Readings list available from Head Office.

National Federation of Solo Clubs
Rooms 7–8, Ruskin Chambers, Birmingham, West Midlands B4 6RY; Tel 0121 236 2879
For widowed, divorced and separated people and single people between 21–70 years of age. Please send sae for lists of clubs and information.

War Widows' Association of Great Britain
President The Baroness Strange
Chair Kath Evans
41 Glamis Crt, Vicarage La, Fareham, Hampshire PO14 2LB
Honorary Secretary Mrs. R. A. Campbell
7 Pentreath Avenue, Guildford, Surrey GU2 5TA; Tel 01483 852 056
Public Relations Officer Deborah Bowles
11 Chichester Cl, Bury St. Edmunds, Suffolk IP33 2LZ
The officially recognised organisation representing all war widows of Great Britain, working for their financial benefit and welfare.

Drug and Alcohol Abuse

Regional Offices

Accept Services (Alcohol Community Centre for Education, Prevention, Treatment and Research)
724 Fulham Rd, London SW6 5SE; Tel 020 7371 1777
An independent charity which offers a range of services to problem drinkers, their families and friends. Services include assessment, one to one counselling, group work, day and evening programme, drop-in sessions and information workshops for doctors, social workers, nursing and welfare officers and others from the helping professions. A telephone counselling and advice service operates during office hours. Self-referrals accepted.

Action on Smoking and Health (ASH)
102 Clifton St, London EC2A 4HN; URL www.ash.org.uk; E-mail action.smoking.health@dial.pipex.com; Tel 020 7739 5902; Fax 020 7613 0531
Manager (Research) Amanda Sandford

Addaction
67–69 Cowcross St, London EC1M 6PU; Tel 020 7251 5860; Fax 020 7251 5890
Chief Executive Peter Martin
Provides community-based services to reduce the harm caused by drug and alcohol abuse, including needle exchanges and HIV testing; education programmes and projects; consultancy and training; works in partnership with communities, statutory authorities and voluntary organisations.

Addaction Brighton and Hove 12 St. George's Pl, Brighton, Brighton and Hove, BN1 4GB; Tel 01273 690575; Fax 01273 607576

Addaction Crawley Drugs Advice Centre The Annex, 103 High St, Crawley, Sussex RH10 1DD; Tel 01293 548350; Fax 01293 652856

Addaction Devon Probation Office 49 Polsloe Rd, Exeter, Devon EX1 2DT; Tel 01392 254317; Fax 01392 431832

Addaction Hastings 6 Trinity St, Hastings, East Sussex TN34 1HG; Tel 01424 441548; Fax 01424 722207

Addaction Leicester Criminal Justice Project 25a New Wlk, Leicester, Leicestershire LE1 6TE; Tel 01162 550121
Project Manager Natalie Smith
Specifically targeting drug using individuals who are involved in acquisitive crime or drug related crime.

Addaction Lincoln Elm Hse, 9–13 Monks Rd, Lincoln, Lincolnshire LN2 5HL; Tel 01522 511993
Director (Services) Michael Storer
Community based tier two, low threshold service providing referral, assessment, support services, advice and information. The project also manages the local arrest referral scheme and in partnership with the Probation Service manages the assessment and delivery of Drug Testing and Treatment Orders.

Addaction Southern Derbyshire Beckett St, Derby, Derbyshire DE1 1HT; Tel 01332 374 400; 01332 374 700; Fax 01332 374 701
An intregrated community based service comprising the following elements: street agency, GP shared care scheme, day programme and the criminal justice project. Addaction Southern Derbyshire will provide a wide range of services to drug and alcohol users across Southern Derbyshire.

Addaction Walsall 231 Stafford St, Walsall, West Midlands WS2 8PJ; Tel 01922 646262
Project Manager Hugh Jobber
Community based tier one/two, low threshold service providing referral, assessment, support services, advice, information and needle exchange. The project also manages the local arrest referral scheme.

Addaction Woking Probation Centre White Rose Centre, Oriental Rd, Woking, GU22 7PJ; Tel 01483 718460; Fax 01483 718459

ADFAM
Waterbridge Hse, 32–36 Loman St, London SE1 0EE; E-mail admin@adfam.org.uk; Tel (Office) 020 7928 8898; Fax 020 7928 8923
Chief Executive Vivienne Evans
ADFAM is the UK charity for the families and friends of drug users, providing separate publications for partners, parents and children of drug users, publication for the families of drug using prisoners, and a Family Support Group Pack for those wanting to set up a support service or group in their community. Our community development project provides training and ongoing support and advice for professionals and parents wanting to set up support

services or groups in their area. Our Prison Project provides support to the Families of Drug Using Prisoners at Prison Visitors Centres London-wide and to professionals England-wide.

Advice and Counselling on Alcohol and Drugs (ACAD)
Chief Executive Graham Fanti
Registered charity covering Bristol, South Gloucestershire, Bath and North East Somerset and North Somerset. Aims to reduce alcohol and other drug related harm via information, advice and counselling to alcohol or drug misusers and affected others. Minimum support house available.

Al-Anon Family Groups UK and Eire
61 Great Dover St, London SE1 4YF;
URL www.al-anonuk.org.uk; E-mail alanonuk@aol.com;
Tel (Confidential helpline service (1000–2200)) 020 7403 0888; Fax 020 7378 9910
Al-Anon is worldwide and offers understanding and support for families and friends of problem drinkers, whether the alcoholic is still drinking or not. Alateen, a part of Al-Anon, is for young people aged 12–20 who have been affected by someone else's drinking, usually that of a parent. For details of meetings throughout the UK and Eire please contact the above.

Alcohol Advice Centre (Shetland)
44 Commercial St, Lerwick, Shetland Isles ZE1 0AB;
E-mail aac@core4free.net; Tel 01595 695363; Fax 01595 692801

Alcohol Advisory and Counselling Service
Director Fiona Angus
Offers confidential counselling service to drinkers and their relatives; coercive referrals from industry and courts; prison work; alcohol policies for industry; training, education, prevention.

Alcohol Concern
Waterbridge Hse, 32–36 Loman St, London SE1 0EE;
URL www.alcoholconcern.org.uk;
E-mail contact@alcoholconcern.org.uk; Tel 020 7928 7377; Fax 020 7928 4644
Chief Executive Eric Appleby
Alcohol Concern is the national agency on alcohol misuse. It works both to reduce the costs of alcohol misuse and to develop the range and quality of helping services available to problem drinkers and their families. Since it began work in 1984, Alcohol Concern has built up expertise on a wide range of alcohol-related issues. It uses this to influence and support health and social policies both nationally and locally.

Alcohol Counselling and Prevention Services (ACAPS)
34 Electric La, Brixton, London SW9 8JT;
URL www.acaps.co.uk; E-mail info@acaps.co.uk; Tel 020 7737 3579; Fax 020 7737 2719
Director Peter Bennett
Providing individual counselling for problem drinkers, their friends and relatives; providing education, training and consultancy service for professionals who encounter problem drinkers among their clients; providing information and advice in connection with alcohol. Special services include: lesbian, gay, bisexual project, NEXT STEPS work preparation project, homeless training project, young people's project, complementary therapy, drugs and alcohol outreach.

Alcohol Focus Scotland
2nd Fl, 166 Buchanan St, Glasgow G1 2LW;
E-mail jacklaw@alcohol-focus-scotland.org.uk; Tel 0141 572 6700; Fax 0141 333 1606
Chief Executive Jack Law
National co-ordinating body for local councils on alcohol in Scotland, responsible for training and standards of service delivery and for promoting education about healthy, sensible drinking styles.

Alcohol Recovery Project
68 Newington Causeway, London SE1 6DF;
URL www.arp-uk.org; E-mail jbentley@arp_uk.org;
Tel 020 7403 3369; Fax 020 7357 6712
Director (Corporate Development) Julie Bentley
Provides counselling and intervention work for people alcohol problems in informal 'drop-in' centres, residential houses and through support in peoples homes.

Alcohol Services (CIC) – Liverpool
Merseyside Hse, 9 South John St, Liverpool, Merseyside
URL www.mcas.org.uk; E-mail liverpoolas@c-i-c.co.uk;
Tel 0151 707 1221; Fax 0151 709 1576
Operational Manager S.A. Ashton
Service Manager (Liverpool) Roger Newton
Provides a community-based counselling, referral and after care service to those with an alcohol problem and a service to relatives, hospitals, other statutory workers and employers. Service free and totally confidential. Also at out-post centres around the Merseyside and Cheshire region.

Knowsley, St. Helens, Warrington and Halton Alcohol Services (CIC)
County Hse, St. Helens, Huyton, Merseyside L36 9UL; E-mail huytonas@c-i-c.co.uk; Tel 0151 481 0776
Service Manager Cathy Morris

Sefton Alcohol Service (CIC)
22 Union St, Southport, Merseyside PR9 0QE; E-mail seftonas@c-i-c.co.uk; Tel 01704 542332
Service Manager Neil Watson

Alcoholics Anonymous
PO Box 1, Stonebow Hse, Stonebow, York YO1 7NJ;
URL www.alcoholics-anonymous.org.uk; Tel 01904 644026; (National Helpline) 0845 769 7555
Fellowship of people who share their experience, strength and hope with each other and help others recover from alcoholism.

Alcoholics Anonymous (Scotland)
Northern Service Office (Scotland), 50 Wellington St, Glasgow G2 6HJ; Tel 0141 226 2214; Fax 0141 221 9450

Alcoholics Anonymous (Northern Ireland)
7 Donegal St Pl, Belfast BT1 2FN; Tel 028 9043 4848

Aquarius (Birmingham)
Head Office: 6th Fl, The White Hse, 111 New St, Birmingham, West Midlands B2 4EU;
URL www.aquarius.org.uk;
E-mail whitehouse@aquarius.org.uk; Tel 0121 632 4727
Director R.M. Purser
Assistant Director A. Fleming
Offers free alcohol counselling services and staff training in Birmingham, Dudley, Sandwell, Solihull and Wolverhampton. Registered charity.

Aquarius (Northampton)
4 St. Georges St, Northampton, Northamptonshire NN1 2TR; URL www.aquarius.org.uk;
E-mail aquarius.9@zoom.co.uk; Tel 01604 632421; Fax 01604 636495
Unit Administrator Mary Dyer-Atkins
Comprehensive day service and six month residential project for people affected by alcohol, drug or tranx problems. Individual counselling and groups including a women's support group and men's group. Aftercare support including second stage houses and programmes.

ASH Scotland
8 Frederick St, Edinburgh EH2 2HB;
URL www.ashscotland.org.uk;
E-mail ashscotland@ashscotland.org.uk; Tel 0131 225 4725; Fax 0131 220 6604
Chief Executive M. Moore
Our main activities centre on a public information service, campaigning and action-based projects. Campaigning to reduce the numbers of young people smoking and for effective support services for smokers.

16

Ayrshire Council on Alcohol
2 Bridge La, Kilmarnock, East Ayrshire KA1 1QH; Tel 01563
541155; Fax 01563 573232
65 Fort St, Kilmarnock, East Ayrshire KA7 1E
Aims to provide a counselling service to those whose lives
are affected by the misuse of alcohol.

Bethany Lodge
Hebron Trust, 12 Stanley Ave, Norwich, Norfolk NR7 0BE;
URL www.hebrontrust.org.uk;
E-mail philippa@hebrontrust.org.uk; Tel 01603 439905;
Fax 01603 700799
Administrator P. Morris
Project Leader A. Gathercole
Bethany Lodge accommodates up to four women (18–45
yrs) with severe drug and alcohol problems who have
responsibility for one or more children (0–12 yrs).
Treatment and rehabilitation is provided in a safe and
secure family environment with individual attention for
each person. Children attend school and the ethos of a
family home rather than an institution. The team of
professional staff includes family support workers.

Bexhill Project
Phoenix Hse, Colwall Crt, 1 Pages Ave, Bexhill-on-Sea, East
Sussex TN39 3AP; URL www.phoenixhouse.org.uk;
E-mail bexhill@phoenixhouse.org.uk; Tel 01424 732171;
Fax 01424 733480

The Blenheim Project
321 Portobello Rd, London W10 5SY;
URL www.theblenheimproject.org;
E-mail info@theblenheimproject.org; Tel (10001700
Helpline) 020 8960 5599
The Blenheim Project is a drugs agency which works with
drug users, their friends and families. Needle exchange and
alternative therapies available. Drop In 1300–1600 Mon,
Wed–Fri. Counselling service. Crack day programme.

Brighton Family Service
160 Dyke Rd, Brighton, Brighton and Hove BN1 5PA;
E-mail brighton@phoenixhouse.org.uk; Tel 01273
558645; Fax 01273 566919
Service Manager Mercia Powis

British Temperance Society
Stanborough Pk, Watford, Hertfordshire WD25 9JZ;
Tel 01923 672251; Fax 01923 893212
Director R.J.B. Willis
Offers an educational service to provide information on the
effects of alcohol and drug abuse on the human body. 'Stop
Smoking' courses, films for hire, leaflets on smoking,
alcohol and drugs; health lecturers available for schools
etc.

CAN
81 St. Giles St, Northampton, Northamptonshire NN1 1JF;
URL www.can.org.uk;
E-mail administration@can.org.uk; Tel 01604 627027;
Fax 01604 629557
Chief Executive James Spence
CAN is the comprehensive independent agency for alcohol,
drug and homelessness problems for the whole of
Northamptonshire. We have 30 years' experience in
providing counselling, advice and information on
substance misuse. The following services are offered to
individuals, couples, friends and family groups; individual
counselling, advice and information, needle exchange
drop-in, telephone helpline, written material, self-help
material, information packs for students, talks to groups/
organisations, training. We have workers who specialise in
helping people from ethnic minorities. In addition to our
main and part-time centres we operate anywhere else in the
county by special arrangement. We provide a day centre
and outreach to homeless drinkers and drugtakers, plus
extensive education and prevention work, and work with
offenders in prison and the community.

Brackley Tel 01604 622121
(Appointments arranged in Brackley).

CAN Community Drug Programme (Luton and Bedford)
Guild Hse, 28 Guildford St, Luton LU1 2NR;
E-mail cancdp@aol.com; Tel 01582 400237
(Referral only for structured group work day care
programmes).

Corby 43 High St, Corby, Northamptonshire NN17 1UU;
E-mail cancdp@aol.com; Tel 01536 201973
Drop-in centre 0930–1630 Mon–Fri.

Daventry Tel 01604 622121
(Centre open by appointment only).

Kettering Tel 01536 201973
(Centre open by appointment only).

Towcester Tel 01604 622121
(Appointments arranged in Towcester).

Wellingborough 41 Oxford St, Wellingborough,
Northamptonshire NN8 4JG; Tel 01933 223796

City Road (Crisis Intervention)
352–358, London EC1V 2PY; URL www.cityroads.co.uk;
E-mail mail@odysseytrust.org; Tel (24 hour advice and
information) 020 7278 8671
Residential care home for drug users in crisis living in
London. Staffed by a multi-disciplinary team, including
nurses, providing a 24hr response and care.

Clouds Alcohol and Drug Dependency Treatment Centre
Clouds Hse, East Knoyle, Salisbury, Wiltshire SP3 6BE;
URL www.clouds.org.uk;
E-mail admin@clouds.org.uk; Tel 01747 830733;
Fax 01747 830783
Chief Executive N. Barton
Registered Charity Number 296637.

Coke Hole Bridge
(part of Yeldall Bridges)
20a Town Mills Hse, Bridge St, Andover, Hampshire
SP10 1BL; Tel 01264 361745; Fax 01264 335105
Coke Hole Bridge runs Ashley Copse: a residential care
home for recovering drug and alcohol dependents: There
are places available for up to 16 women (aged 18–50) and
children (aged 1–11).

Community Drug Project (CDP)
146 Camberwell Rd, London SE5 0EE;
URL www.communitydrugproject.org;
E-mail cdpokr@compuserve.com; Tel 020 7277 4580;
Fax 020 7277 4590
Director S. Wickenden
Advice and support for people with drug problems; help in
reducing drug-related harm; referrals to detoxification and
rehabilitation programmes; needle exchange; Primary
Health Care Clinic and Acupuncture Sessions. Structured
day programme; Criminal Justice Liaison Service; Specialist
outreach service for crack-cocaine users.

Cornwall Alcohol and Drugs Agency Limited
CADA Hse, Infirmary Hill, Truro, Cornwall TR1 2HY;
E-mail info@cadasw.co.uk; Tel 01872 263001; Fax 01872
263002
Client Services Director Karon Clark
Concerned with practical measures to prevent and alleviate
the distressing consequences to health, family and
community life induced by alcohol, drug and substance
misuse.

Cowal Council on Alcohol and Drugs
Ballochyle Hse, Kirk St, Dunoon, Argyll, Argyll and Bute
PA23 7DP; URL www.ballochylehouse.btinternet.com;
E-mail ccad@btinternet.com; Tel 01369 704406
Co-ordinator Gary Morgan
Provides counselling and support to those suffering
because of addictive problems. Also available for advice,
information and consultancy on alcohol and drug issues.

Cranstoun Drug Services
4th Fl, Broadway Hse, 112–134 The Broadway, Wimbledon, London SW19 1RL; URL www.cranstoun.org; E-mail info@cranstoun.org.uk; Tel 020 8543 8333; Fax 020 8543 4348

Drug Treatment Centre and Opiate Injectables Clinic
Opiate Injectables Clinic, Chelsea and Westminster Hospital, 369 Fulham Rd, London SW10 9NH; Tel 020 8846 6111; Fax 020 8846 6112
Open Mon and Fri 0900–1230, Tue 0900–1230, 1400–1830; Wed and Thu 0900–1230, 1400–1630.
Central and North West London Trust Substance Misuse Service.
Nurse-led team includes keyworker system of nurses, consultant psychiatrist/lead clinician, social workers and medical staff, psychology, OT and family therapy. Provides outpatient assessment and treatment, individual and group work, advisory and referral through the Central Assessment and Primary Care Service (CAPS). Unit at 69 Warwick Rd. (Drop-in service also available at 69 Warwick Rd.)

Drugaid
16 Clive St, Caerphilly CF83 1GE; E-mail drugaid@talk21.com
Director Stephanie Hoffman
Service Manager Gail Castle
Service Manager Caroline Evans
Training Co-ordinator Beth Archard
Counselling, support and information aimed at drug, alcohol and solvent users, their families, local communities, services, groups and professionals, covering Caerphilly, Merthyr Tydfil, Rhondda, Cynon, Taff, Blaenau Gwent. Open access services for self and third party referrals. Targetted services for young people and offenders. Needle exchange also available.

DrugScope
32–36 Loman St, London SE1 0EE; URL www.drugscope.org.uk; E-mail services@drugscope.org.uk; Tel 020 7928 1211; Fax 020 7928 1771
Director (Information and Customer Services) J. Field
DrugScope is today one of the UK's leading centres of expertise on drugs. Our aim is to inform policy development and reduce drug-related risk. We provide quality drug information, promote effective responses to drug taking, undertake research at local, national and international levels, advice on policy-making, encourage informed debate and speak for our member bodies working on the ground.

Dumbarton Area Council on Alcohol
West Bridgend Lodge, Dumbarton, West Dunbartonshire G82 4AD; E-mail email@daca0.fsnet.co.uk; Tel 01389 731456; Fax 01389 734690
Manager C. Dennett
Operates a counselling service in Dumbarton, Clydebank and Helensburgh with related day and evening social and recreational facilities. Social Skills groups, self-help and family counselling.

Edinburgh and Lothian Council on Alcohol
6 Clifton Terr, Edinburgh EH12 5DR; Tel 0131 337 8188; Fax 0131 337 9825
Free confidential advice, counselling and information for anyone worrying about their own or someone else's drinking. Supported accommodation in West Lothian.

Elizabeth House Association
94 Redcliffe Gdns, London SW10 9HH; Tel 020 7370 1279

The Emmanuel Community
4 Withington Rd, Manchester M16 8AA; Tel 0161 232 0904
Registered Treatment facility for alcoholics and children 0-5 years (includes registered baby unit). Treats mothers with their children and women on their own. Primarily addiction to alcohol and other problems.

Damascus Road Association Withington Rd, Manchester M16 8AA

Families Anonymous (FA)
The Doddington and Rolo Community Association, Charlotte Despard Ave, Battersea, London SW11 5HD; URL www.famanon.org.uk; E-mail office@famanon.org.uk; Tel 0845 120 0660; 020 7498 4680
FA self-help groups meet regularly and are open to anyone concerned about drug abuse or related behavioural problems of a relative or friend.
Office hours Mon–Fri 1300–1600. Out of hours contact telephone numbers on 24 hour answerphone.

Gamblers Anonymous and Gam-Anon
PO Box 88, London SW10 0EU; URL www.gamblersanonymous.org.uk; E-mail private@gamblersanonymous.org.uk; Tel (London) 08700 508 880; (Midlands) 0121 233 1335; (North East) 0114 262 0026; (North West) 0161 976 5000; (Northern Ireland) 01504 351329; (Scotland) 0141 630 1033
To help individuals and their families to cope with problems created by compulsive gambling.

Gloucestershire Drug and Alcohol Service (GDAS)
Hepworth Hse, 115 Southgate St, Gloucester, Gloucestershire GL1 1UT; Tel 01452 552801; Fax 01452 551139
Chief Executive Peter Steel
Administrator Louise Owen
23 King Street Stroud, Gloucestershire GL5 3BX; Tel 01453 755711; Fax 01453 755632
Team Leader Dave Bean
Administrator Catherine Simmons
Montrose House Wellington St, Cheltenham, Gloucestershire GL50 1XY; Tel 01242 584881; Fax 01242 584882
Team Leader Bev Polson
Administrator Lyn Holder
1 Spa Road Gloucester, Gloucestershire GL1 1UY; Tel 01452 381166; Fax 01452 550581
Team Leader Pam Zygo
Administrator Pauline Vidal
4 Whitfield Street Gloucester, Gloucestershire GL1 1NA; Tel 01452 385757; Fax 01452 521144
Team Leader Pam Zygo
Administrator Dave Parton

Gloucestershire Drug Project
24 Cambray Pl, Cheltenham, Gloucestershire GL50 1JN; Tel 01242 570003; Fax 01242 263561
4 Commercial Road
Project Director T. Shea
Agents for Community Care Assessments.

Greenhill Barton Christian Centres Ltd
Christian Addiction Release Centre, Greenhill Barton, Pitney Hill, Langport, Somerset TA10 9AB; E-mail greenhillbarton.freeserve.co.uk; Tel 01458 259100; Fax 01458 259100
Centre Director Peter Rodenhurst
Centre Director Mary Rodenhurst
Christian family centred community for those seeking release from addiction.

Gwent Drugs Service
139 Lower Dock St, Newport NP9 1EE; Tel 01633 216777
Manager (Drugs Service) Rose France
Project Open Mon–Fri 0900–1700.
Advice and information, prescribing clinic, counselling, drop-in, needle and pharmacy exchange services. For drug users, and families/friends of drug users.

16

Hebron House
12 Stanley Ave, Thorpe Hamlet, Norwich, Norfolk
NR7 0BE; URL www.hebrontrust.org.uk;
E-mail philippa@hebrontrust.org.uk; Tel 01603 439905;
Fax 01603 700799
Administrator P. Morris
Project Leader C. Chalk
Offers residential rehabilitation for women aged 18–45 who
are chemically dependent (alcohol or drugs). Abstinence
regime developed from Christian philosophy. Client-
focused approach based on the importance of relationships,
including the 12 steps in small, supportive community.
Residents are not pressurised to adopt Christian beliefs.

HOPE UK
25(F) Copperfield St, London SE1 0EN;
URL www.hopeuk.org; E-mail enq@hopeuk.org; Tel 020
7928 0848; Fax 020 7401 3477
Executive Director George Ruston, MSc
Alcohol and drug education for children and young people
through literature, talks and DRUGNET alcohol and other
drug education programme for the voluntary youth sector.

Hungerford Drug Project – Turning Point
32a Wardour St, Soho, London W1D 6QR;
E-mail hungerford@turning-point.co.uk; Tel 020 7437
3523; Fax 020 7287 1274
Project Manager Andy Symons
Project Manager Andrew Woolridge
Team Leader (LGBT Service – Antidote) Monty Moncrieff
Team Leader Paddy Screech
Advice, information, referral and counselling agency for
people with drug related problems, their families and
friends. Offers professional advice and training to generic
workers. Telephone Helpline: Mon–Fri 1400–1730, Mon–Fri
1000–1300, Wed 1800–2100; Drop-in: Mon–Fri 1400–1700;
Shatsu: Mon, Thur 1000–1700; Counselling: by
appointment.

ICS (Inverclyde Counselling Service)
2a Newton St, Greenock, Renfrewshire PA16 8UJ; Tel 01475
785695
Manager John Oliver
Private and confidential one to one counselling for people
with an alcohol problem or those who are affected by
another's.

Addaction
59 Magdalen St, Exeter, Devon EX2 4HY;
URL www.addaction.org.uk;
E-mail m.greener@addaction.org.uk; Tel 01392 255151;
Fax 01392 498977
Area Manager Mary Greener
Provides advice, information, education and counselling.
Residential therapy at two houses, prisons, police and the
probation services.

Inward House Projects
Highfield View, Quernmore Rd, Lancaster, Lancashire
LA1 3JT; URL www.inwardhouse.co.uk;
E-mail inward@btinternet.com; Tel 01524 37519
Chief Executive Jerry Sutton
Residential rehabilitation, community based aftercare,
supported housing, prison drug rehabilitation, probation
support services for people recovering from substance
misuse, training and education.

Jersey Council on Alcoholism
28 West Park Ave, St. Helier, Jersey JE2 3PJ;
URL www.geocities.com/jcoa_ci;
E-mail jcoa@localdial.com; Tel 01534 726672
Counsellor Barry Jordan, TCert, BPhil, MA(SW),
CQSW
Administrator Mark Thompson
Residential dry house for those who have had a drink
problem but have made a commitment to live without
alcohol; one to one counselling.

Ley Community Drug Services
Sandy Croft, Sandy La, Yarnton, Oxford, Oxfordshire
OX5 1PB; URL www.ley.co.uk; E-mail enq@ley.co.uk;
Tel 01865 378600; Fax 01865 842238
Residential therapeutic community for drug and alcohol
abusers both sexes.

Life for the World Trust
Wakefield Bldg, Gomm Rd, High Wycombe,
Buckinghamshire HP13 7DJ; URL www.lftw.org;
E-mail lfw@cwcom.net; Tel 01494 462008; Fax 01494
446268
Christian charity providing rehabilitation for drug or
alcohol misusers, plus training education, advice and
consultancy for service providers.

London Drug Policy Forum
Town Clerk's Office, PO Box 270, London EC2P 2EJ;
E-mail david.mackintosh@corporation.gov.uk; Tel 020
7332 3084; Fax 020 7332 1168
Policy Adviser David Mackintosh
The London Drug Policy Forum is funded by the
Corporation of London to assist, support and advise policy
makers on drug issues affecting the capital. The Forum
works with the London Boroughs, Drug Action Teams,
Health Authorities, drug agencies and Government
Departments to promote good practice on education and
prevention, community safety and improving services for
drug users.

The Medical Council on Alcoholism
3 St. Andrew's Pl, London NW1 4LB;
E-mail mca@medicouncilalcol.demon.co.uk; Tel 0207 487
4445; Fax 0207 935 4479
Executive Director Dr Peter Abraham, FRCPsych
Founded by medical practitioners in 1967 with a view to
co-ordination of effort and the better understanding of
alcoholism and its prevention, and the treatment and
after-care of alcoholics. Currently devoted mainly to
education and supplying information to health
professionals by means of the Journal, Newsletter,
regional advisers, seminars, symposia, handbooks and
direct communications from the office of the Medical
Council on Alcoholism. Also assists doctors in need of
help in relation to alcohol.

Mid Argyll Council on Alcohol
45 Chalmers St, Ardishaig, Argyll, Argyll and Bute
PA30 8EY; E-mail midargyllcad@btopenworld.com;
Tel 01546 602 880
Provides an advice, counselling and information service
dealing with alcohol and drug related problems and other
addictions. 24 hour ansamachine. Court and industrial
referrals

Moray Council on Addiction
252 High St, Elgin, Moray IV30 1NS;
URL www.mysite.freeserve.com/mca;
E-mail mca@moray.gov.uk; Tel 01343 552211; Fax 01343
547000
Director Lynn Geddes
Free confidential counselling and advisory service to those
with problems resulting from their own or someone else's
alcohol or drug use. Education, information and literature
available.

Mount Carmel
12 Aldrington Rd, Streatham, London SW16 1TH;
URL www.mountcarmel.org.uk;
E-mail mountcarmeluk@yahoo.co.uk; Tel 020 8769 7674;
Fax 020 8696 0412
The purpose of Mount Carmel is to support individual men
and women in their recovery from alcoholism and help
them to achieve a fulfilled and sober life.
Residential, day programme and move-on house.

National Council on Gambling (NCG)
Grovelands, Priory Hospital, London N14 6RA; Tel 020
8364 1376
Chair   Dr E. Moran
Hon Secretary   Vacancy
Aims to educate the public about gambling, to further
research and to help those whose lives have been impaired
by gambling.

North Edinburgh Drug Advice Centre
Muirhouse Shopping Centre, 10 Pennywell Crt, Edinburgh
EH4 4TZ; E-mail drugs@nedac.freeserve.co.uk; Tel 0131
332 2314
Project Manager   D. Campbell
Appointments for anyone with a drug-related problem,
and for their relatives.

**Options (New Forest) Alcohol and Drug Counselling and
Information Service**
21 New St, Lymington, Hampshire SO41 9BH;
E-mail lymington@optionscounselling.co.uk; Tel 01590
677300; Fax 01590 676748
Director (Operations)   Nikki Keeley
Counselling and information for people with alcohol
and/or drug-related problems and their families.
Counsellor training programme. Education and training for
Social Services and Probation and other statutory and
voluntary bodies. Library and reference facilities.
Counselling and Information Centres at Hythe, Lymington,
Ringwood and Totton.

**Options Alcohol and Drug Counselling and Information
Service**
147 Shirley Rd, Southampton SO15 3FH;
E-mail southampton@optionscounselling.co.uk; Tel 023
8063 0219; Fax 023 8039 0800
21 New St, Lymington, Hampshire SO41 9BH;
E-mail lymington@optionscounselling.co.uk
105 Leigh Rd, Eastleigh, Hampshire S050 9DR;
E-mail eastleigh@optionscounselling.co.uk; Tel 023 8062
0260; Fax 023 8062 9949
Chief Executive   Peter Keeley
Counselling and information for people with substance
misuse problems and their families. Counsellor training
programme. Education and training for Social Services and
Probation and other statutory and voluntary bodies.
Library and reference facilities.

**Orkney Alcohol Counselling and Advisory Service
(OACAS)**
43 Junction Rd, Kirkwall, Orkney Islands KW15 1AR;
URL www.oacas.org.uk; E-mail enquiries@oacas.org.uk;
Tel 01856 874738
Practice Supervisor and Co-ordinator   Simon Gordon
Free counselling and support services: advice,
information, education for those affected by alcohol
problems – own drinking, relatives, others. Service strictly
confidential and tailored to meet individual needs of
clients. Referrals through self, GP, social work, employers
or courts. Also general and drugs counselling. Open
1000–1700 Mon to Fri and by appointment evenings and
weekends.

Phoenix House (Central Office)
3rd Fl, Asra Hse, 1 Long La, London SE1 4PG;
URL www.phoenixhouse.org.uk;
E-mail info@phoenixhouse.org.uk; Tel 020 7234 9756;
Fax 020 7234 9770
Chief Executive   Bill Puddicombe
National charity and social landlord that provides
residential and non-residential care for people with a drug
or alcohol problem and their families. Care provision
includes single adult and family residential rehabilitation
and community support, prison and ex-offender liaison
services, street level outreach work, advocacy and tenancy
support.

Phoenix House (Alpha Service)
Wickham Rd, Southampton SO32 3PD;
URL www.phoenixhouse.org.uk; Tel 01489 878527;
Fax 01489 877555
Senior Practitioner   Ann Mills
Service Manager   Roy Phillips
Alpha Service is a mixed community of residents living and
working together in a large Victorian house set in seven
acres of grounds in the heart of the Hampshire countryside.
Our main aim is to support people who are dependent on
drugs, alcohol or solvents to lead a better life style and
return them to society with a higher self esteem and con-
fidence, without dependence on drugs, alcohol or solvents.

Phoenix House Adult Residential Service (London)
1 Eliot Bank, London SE23 3XE;
URL www.phoenixhouse.org.uk;
E-mail london@phoenixhouse.org.uk; Tel 020 8699 7152;
Fax 020 8291 9442
Service Manager   Florence Olupitan
Manager (Community Service)   Paul Ferry
Adult residential, community and street level outreach
services.

Phoenix House in Scotland
586 Keppochhill Rd, Glasgow G22 5HS; Tel 0141 332 0121
Manager (Care Practice)   Marion Quinn
Adult residential service for males and females aged 18+.
Detoxification service also provided.

Phoenix House, Aberdeen Community Service   17
Palmerston Rd, 1st Fl Left, Aberdeen AB11 5PQ; Tel 01224
589130; Fax 01224 589129
Service Manager   Debbie Kelbie (Acting)

Phoenix House, Glasgow Community Service   Unit 481,
Templeton Business Centre, Templeton St, Glasgow, G40
1DA; E-mail glasgowcomservedtto@phoenixhouse.org.uk;
Tel 0141 551 0703; Fax 0141 556 1374

Phoenix House, North

Phoenix House Adult Residential Service (Sheffield)   Storth
Oaks, 229 Graham Rd, Ranmoor, South Yorkshire S10 3GS;
URL www.phoenixhouse.org.uk;
E-mail sheffieldbusinessman@phoenixhouse.org.uk;
Tel 0114 230 8230; Fax 0114 230 2361
Service Manager   Jeremy Booker

Phoenix House Adult Residential Service (South Shields)
Westoe Dr, South Shields, Tyne and Wear NE33 3EW;
URL www.phoenixhouse.org.uk;
E-mail tyneside@phoenixhouse.org.uk; Tel 0191 454 5544;
Fax 0191 427 7787
Service Manager   Phamie Muir (Acting)

Phoenix House Adult Residential Service (Wirral)   Upton
Rd, Bidston, Wirral CH43 7QF;
URL www.phoenixhouse.org.uk;
E-mail wirral@phoenixhouse.org.uk; Tel 0151 652 2667;
Fax 0151 653 6118
Service Manager   Joey Neill

Phoenix House Family Service (Sheffield)   29–31 Collegiate
Cres, Broomhall, Sheffield, South Yorkshire S10 2BJ;
E-mail sheffieldfamily@phoenixhouse.org.uk; Tel 0114 268
5131; Fax 0114 268 5741
Service Manager   Monica Hargreaves
Community Service Manager

Phoenix House, Tyneside Community Service   Scotswood
Community Project, 221 Woodstock Rd, Scotswood,
Newcastle upon Tyne, NE15 6HE;
URL www.phoenixhouse.org.uk; Tel 0191 274 8720

Phoenix House, Alpha Service   Phoenix House, Alpha
Service, Wickham Rd, Droxford, Hampshire SO32 3AD;
URL www.phoenixhouse.org.uk;
E-mail alpha@phoenixhouse.org.uk; Tel 01489 877478;
01489 877555
Service Manager   Roy Phillips
Business Manager   Mark Styles

Phoenix House Adult Residential Service (Bexhill) Colwall Crt, 1 Pages Ave, Bexhill, East Sussex TN39 3AP; URL www.phoenixhouse.org.uk; E-mail bexhill@phoenixhouse.org.uk; Tel 01424 732171; Fax 01424 733480
Service Manager Chris Reddington

Phoenix House Family Service (Brighton) 160 Dyke Rd, Brighton, Brighton and Hove BN1 5PA; E-mail brighton@phoenixhouse.org.uk; Tel 01273 558 645; Fax 01273 566 919
Service Manager Mercia Powis

Release
National Drugs and Legal Services, 388 Old St, London EC1V 9LT; URL www.release.org.uk; E-mail info@release.org.uk; Tel (Daytime Helpline 1000–1800) 020 7729 9904; (Office) 020 7729 5255; Fax 020 7729 2599
Free and confidential advice and counselling on drugs, drug related legal problems, and criminal legal emergencies. Information and training for professionals working with drug users. Publications on drugs.

Re-Solv
30a High St, Stone, Staffordshire URL www.re-solv.org; E-mail information@re-solv.org; E-mail helpline@re-solv.org; Tel 0808 800 2345; 01785 817885; Fax 01785 813205
Manager Jon McVey

Sheffield Alcohol Advisory Service
646 Abbeydale Rd, Sheffield, South Yorkshire S7 2BB; URL www.sheffieldaas.org.uk; E-mail saasmail.freeserve.co.uk; Tel 0114 258 7553; Fax 0114 258 8466
Information, advice and counselling service for those affected by alcohol; 6 bedded dry house (a registered project so residents may retain their own accommodation); training courses on drugs, alcohol and relevant skills for volunteers and those working in the field.

Society for the Study of Addiction
National Addiction Centre, 4 Windsor Wlk, London SE5 8AF; URL www.addiction.ssa.org; E-mail membership@addiction-ssa.org; Tel 020 7848 0841; Fax 020 7703 5787
Open to members of the medical and allied profession to encourage the scientific study of addiction.

Surrey Alcohol and Drug Advisory Service
Head Office, 14 Jenner Rd, Guildford, Surrey GU1 3PL; URL www.sadas.org.uk; E-mail info@sadas.org.uk; Tel (Central Appointments Bureau) 01483 590150; Fax 01483 590160
Confidential advice information and counselling for alcohol and drug-related problems. Outreach, criminal justice and young people's services. Additional counselling venues countrywide.

Head Office and Surrey-wide Appointments 14 Jenner Rd, Guildford, Surrey GU1 3PL; URL www.sadas.org.uk; Tel 01483 590150

TCA Alcohol Advice and Information Centre
13 King St, Dundee DD1 2JD; URL www.alcoholtayside.com; E-mail enquiries@tca.sol.co.uk; Tel 01382 223965; Fax 01382 227142
TCA's over-riding purpose is to provide an efficient and effective service to adults and young people whose lives are adversely affected by alcohol and drug misuse. It offers one-to-one counselling, advice, information, group work programmes, mentoring and diversionary work, and supports and initiates preventative work through schools awareness sessions, community projects and multi-agency initiatives.

Turning Point
New Loom Hse, 101 Back Church La, London E1 1LU; E-mail info@turning-point.co.uk; Tel 020 7702 2300; Fax 020 7702 1456
Chief Executive Victor Adebowale
National charity helping people with drink, drug and mental health problems and learning disabilities. Operates over 100 projects around the county providing rehabilitation, day care and street level advice and counselling service for people seeking help.

Wirral Project
Upton Rd, Bidston, Wirral L43 7QF; Tel 0151 652 3289
Care Practice Manager J. Logan
Provides residential rehabilitation including detoxification for people who have had drug problems, helps the more acute cases of dependency and advises workers in the field.

Women's Alcohol Centre (Part of the Alcohol Recovery Project)
66a Drayton Pk, London N5 1ND; URL www.arp-uk.org; Tel 020 7226 4581
Alcohol Services Worker Elaine Werkun
Alcohol Services Worker Patricia Burgess
Alcohol Services Worker Vacancy
Team Leader Vacancy
House Worker Stella Odunewu
Offers individual alcohol-focussed sessions, groups, support, advice and a residential service to women who are worried about their drinking. Crèche facility on request.

Yeldall Christian Centres
Yeldall Manor, Blakes La, Hare Hatch, Reading, Berkshire RG10 9XR; URL www.yeldall.org.uk; E-mail yeldall@aol.com; Tel 0118 940 4411
Provides long-term rehabilitation programme for drug and alcohol dependants; single homeless project and training.

Family Planning, AIDS and Sexually Transmitted Diseases Counselling

Brook Young People's Information Service
Brook Central, 421 Highgate Studios, 53–79 Highgate Rd, London NW5 1TL; URL www.brook.org.uk; Tel 020 7323 1522; Fax 020 7580 6740
Chair Nigel Webb
Chief Executive Jan Barlow
Helpline Manager Shanta Everington
Doctors, nurses and counsellors provide free advice on, and supplies for, contraception, pregnancy testing, infection, and sexual and emotional problems for young people under 25. 44 centres in Bristol, Burnley, Birmingham, Edinburgh, Liverpool, London, Milton Keynes, Belfast, Birkenhead, Cornwall, Jersey, Manchester, Oldham, Wigan, Sandwell and Dudley, Inverness, Blackburn and Eccles.

Brook Publications
PO Box 883, Oxford, OX4 5NT; URL www.brook.org.uk; E-mail publications@brookcentres.org.uk; Tel 01865 719 410; Fax 01865 748 746

CABI Publishing
A division of CAB International.Wallingford, Oxfordshire OX10 8DE; URL www.cabi-publishing.org; E-mail publishing@cabi.org; Tel 01491 832111; Fax 01491 829198
Product Manager Richard Sullivan
Content Director (Division of Human, Animal and Social Sciences) E. Dodsworth
Editor (Tropical Diseases Bulletin) James Brooks
Co-Editor (Abstracts on Hygiene and Communicable Diseases) Louise Acres
Co-Editor (Abstracts on Hygiene and Communicable Diseases) Valerie Pritchard

CABI Publishing produces many publications and electronic services in the human health and disease area, including books, journal, CD-ROMs and electronic databases. Publications and services include: CAB HEALTH, a human health and disease database containing over 600 000 records from 1973 to present. CAB HEALTH is available online, on CD-ROM, and on the Internet. Abstracts on Hygiene and Communicable Diseases and Tropical Diseases Bulletin, both monthly abstract journals. British Journal of Nutrition, Nutrition Research Reviews, Proceedings of the Nutrition Society and Public Health Nutrition, all published on behalf of the Nutrition Society. For full information about any of our publications and services please contact Richard Sullivan, Product Manager, Marketing Department, at the address above.

Crusaid
1–5 Curtain Rd, London EC2A 3JX;
URL www.crusaid.org.uk
National charity; since 1986 has raised over £21m for the care and support of people with HIV/AIDS; provides capital grants for projects and for direct relief of individual hardship in the UK; Office in Scotland.

The Ella Gordon Unit
St. Mary's Hospital, Milton Rd, Portsmouth PO3 6AD;
Tel 023 9286 6301; Fax 023 9286 6311
Consultant (Contraception and Sexual Health)
Dr Sarah Randall
Contraception and Sexual Health Services: Clinic/Cervical Cancer Screening; Sterilisation Counselling; Psychosexual Counselling; Menopause and Premenstrual Syndrome Clinics, Unplanned Pregnancy Assessment Clinic; Pre/post abortion counselling; Sexsense Clinics for young people.

fpa
2–12 Pentonville Rd, London N1 9FP;
URL www.fpa.org.uk; Tel (General) 020 7837 5432; (Helpline) 0845 310 1334
Chief Executive A. Weyman
Provides a nationwide helpline and information service and education and training providing courses in personal relationships and sexuality for relevant professions. Offices provide service throughout the UK. Mail order book service from fpa Direct (01865 719 418 www.fpsales.co.uk).

Herpes Viruses Association
41 North Rd, London N7 9DP; URL www.herpes.org.uk;
Tel (Helpline) 020 7609 9061; (Office) 020 7607 9661
Director M.J. Nicholson
Provides information and advice to people with herpes simplex and to general public and health professionals. Counselling available if required. Reacts to misrepresentation of the virus in the media; promotes a more accurate public awareness of herpes simplex. Publishes leaflets, a booklet and a quarterly journal for members. (Affiliate membership for professional bodies available). Please send sae for further details.

Lighthouse West London
111–117 Lancaster Rd, London W11 1QT;
URL www.tht.org.uk; E-mail info@tht.org.uk; Tel 020 7792 1200; Fax 020 7229 1258
Care and support centre for people affected by HIV and AIDS. Services include an informal drop-in area, a café, support groups and counselling, education and training programmes, home support, complementary and creative therapies, children centre.

Macfarlane Trust
Alliance Hse, 12 Caxton St, London SW1H 0QS; Tel 020 7233 0342; Fax 020 7233 0839
Established by the Government in 1987 to assist: a) people with haemophilia who are HIV positive and their dependants; b) parents caring for people with haemophilia who are HIV positive and are living with them.

Applications either by patient, family, doctor or social worker to above. Assistance includes advice and information as well as financial help.

MAINLINERS
38–40 Kennington Park Rd, London SE11 4RS;
E-mail linersmain@aol.com; Tel (Administration) 020 7582 5434; (Advice) 020 7582 5226; (General) 020 7582 3338; Fax 020 7582 6999
HIV prevention agency working with current and ex drug users and sex workers. Bi-monthly newsletter free to drug users and HIV+ people. Hepatitis C support group, National Hepatitis C Resource Centre, Working Women's Service, Mobile Outreach Needle Exchange, SMART (street drop-in drugs agency), Mainliners Youth Service, On-Line Advice Service, Training and Conference programme, Information dissemination.

National AIDS Trust
New City Cloisters, 196 Old St, London EC1V 9FR;
URL www.nat.org.uk; E-mail info@nat.org.uk; Tel 020 7814 6767; Fax 020 7216 0111
NAT is the UK's leading HIV and AIDS policy and advocacy organisation working to ensure that people in power take action on HIV both within the UK and internationally. NAT also runs a number of campaigns on key issues and organises the Diana, Princess of Wales Lecture on AIDS.

Positively Women
347–349 City Rd, London EC1V 1LR;
URL www.positivelywomen.org.uk;
E-mail info@positivelywomen.org.uk;
Tel (Administration) 020 7713 0444; (Client Services) 020 7713 0222; Fax 020 7713 1020
National charity offering support for women living with HIV by women living with HIV. Support and advocacy; crèche facilities and therapeutic services for children affected by HIV; information and advice; training and volunteering opportunities. It also works towards empowering women living with HIV to make informed choices; ensuring that the voice of HIV positive women is heard.

The Terrence Higgins Trust
52–54 Gray's Inn Rd, London WC1X 8JU;
URL www.tht.org.uk; E-mail info@tht.org.uk; Tel 020 7405 2381; 020 7831 0330 (Helpline (1200–2200 daily)) 020 7242 1010
Chief Executive Nick Partridge
Provides counselling, social and legal support for people affected by HIV and AIDS.

Psychotherapy

Albany Trust Counselling
c/o The Art of Health and Yoga, 280 Balham High Rd, London SW17 7AL; Tel 020 8767 1827
Administrator S. Stephen
Professionally qualified psychotherapists and counsellors offer long and short-term therapy for people with relationship and psychosexual problems.

Arbours Association
6 Church La, London N8 7BU;
E-mail info@arboursassociation.org; Tel 020 8340 7646
Director J. Berke, MD
Director Thomas Ryan
Charity providing intensive, personal and psychotherapeutic support for individuals, couples or families in emotional distress. Facilities include the Crisis Centre, three therapeutic communities, a psychotherapy service and a four-year training programme in analytical psychotherapy.

16

Association of Therapeutic Communities
Pine Street Day Centre, 13–15 Pine St, London EC1R 0JH;
   URL www.therapeuticcommunities.org; Tel 020 8950
   9557; Fax 020 8950 9557
Training, conferences, bulletins and international journal
for workers in residential/day care communities in the
field of mental health.

**The Institute of Psychosynthesis and London
Psychosynthesis Clinic**
65a Watford Way, Hendon, London NW4 3AQ; Tel 020 8202
   4525; Fax 020 8202 6166
Training in psychosynthesis and psychotherapy and
clinic.

London Centre for Psychotherapy
32 Leighton Rd, London NW5 2QE;
   URL www.lcp-psychotherapy.org.uk; Tel 020 7482 2002;
   Fax 020 7482 4222
A registered charity providing individual or group
psychotherapy and counselling at moderate fees. Self-
referrals or referrals made by doctors, social agencies and
other contacts are all taken.

The Severnside Institute for Psychotherapy
11 Orchard St, Bristol BS1 5EH;
   URL www.sipsychotherapy.org.uk;
   E-mail fionamcginn.sip@virgin.net; Tel 0117 923 2354;
   Fax 0117 923 2354

UK College for Complementary Healthcare Studies
St Charles Hospital, Exmoor St, London W10 6DZ; Tel 020
   8964 1206
Principal   M. Langford
Provides a wide range of courses in counselling,
hypnotherapy, reflexology and therapeutic massage.

Women's Organisations

Asian Women's Association
40 Argyle Rd, Ilford, Essex IG1 3SN;
   E-mail harvinder@asianwomenassociation.fsnet.co.uk;
   Tel 020 8518 0725
Co-ordinator (Community Development)   Harvinder Sarohi-
   Parhar
Deals with the problems of Asian women in the Redbridge
Area. Specialises in domestic violence issues.

Bristol Women's Aid
248 Stapleton Rd, Easton, Bristol BS5 0NT;
   URL www.priorityyouth.demon.co.uk; Tel (Helpline)
   0117 977 1888
Bristol Women's Aid offers information and support to
women and children fleeing domestic violence (physical,
sexual and mental abuse) and rererral to safe, supportive,
temporary accommodation. Helpline open Mon–Fri
1000–1500 (24 hour answerphone).

Co-operative Women's Guild
446 Hertford Rd, Enfield, Greater London EN3 5QH;
   Tel 020 8804 5905
Democratic women's organisation aiming to educate
women, campaign for women's issues and strive for
peace.

Corona Worldwide (Women's Corona Society)
South Bank Hse, Black Prince Rd, London SE1 7SJ;
   URL www.coronaworldwide.org;
   E-mail coronahq@hotmail.com; Tel 020 7793 4020
President   Elizabeth Hunter
Chair   Maureen Withey
Honorary Treasurer   Jennifer Atkinson
Aims to provide information and advice for men and
women going to live and/or work overseas. Voluntary and
non-political. Network in UK and overseas.

Edinburgh Women's Rape and Sexual Abuse Centre
PO Box 120, Brunswick Rd, Edinburgh EH7 5WX;
   E-mail ewrasac@aol.com; Tel (Helpline) 0131 556 9437;
   Fax 0131 558 1612
Provides support and information to women and girls who
have been raped and sexually assaulted at any time in their
lives. Campaigns to raise awareness and change the views
in society about rape and child sexual abuse. Training and
consultancy is offered.

Free Church Women's Forum
27 Tavistock Sq, London WC1H 9HH;
   E-mail pauline@cte.org.uk; Tel 020 7529 8132; Fax 020
   7529 8134
President   C. Clucas
Secretary   P. Main, BSc
Promotes voluntary work on behalf of people in need and
supports the ministry of women.

Glos Domestic Violence Support and Advocacy Project
75–81 Eastgate St, Gloucester, Gloucestershire GL1 1PN;
   URL www.domesticviolencesupport.org.uk;
   E-mail jill@glosdvsupp.freeserve.co.uk; Tel (Advice
   Service) 01452 500115
Advice, support and advocacy for women and men
experiencing and having experienced domestic violence.
24 hour, 7 day helpline.

The Labour Party
16 Old Queen St, London SW1H 9HP;
   URL www.labour.org.uk; E-mail join@labour.org.uk;
   Tel 08705 900 200
National Women's Officer   Rachel McLean

Lambeth Women's Workshop Ltd
Unit C22, Pk Hall Trading Est, Martell Rd, West Norwood,
   London SE21 8EA;
   URL www.lambethwomensworkshop.co.uk;
   E-mail workshop.lww@virgin.net; Tel 020 8670 0339
Voluntary organisation with 20 years experience.
NVQ Wood Occupations NVQ Level 1, ICA
Lambeth Women's Workshop runs a roll-on roll-off course
for three days a week, approximately 24 weeks in length.
Whilst on the course, trainees have the opportunity to learn
how to: hang doors, fit locks, make a window, learn how to
make basic joints, use power tools safely, attach skirting
and architrave. Trainees study core units such as: health
and safety at work, communications, work relations,
efficiency, selection and use of equipment, loading and
unloading and finishing products. Trainees also participate
in the following: One day First Aid course (certificated); Job
Seeking Skills course; Three weeks' work experience with
local employers. Trainees are provided with: monthly travel
pass; childcare allowance for under fives; safety boots.

Lloyd Thomas Charity for Women and Girls
The Trustees, 16 Mortimer St, London W1T 3JL;
   E-mail info@fhaonline.org.uk; Tel 020 7436 3304; Fax 020
   7436 3302
Application through social worker or similar welfare agent.
The charity makes grants to poor women and girls in
desperate need of a holiday break. Limited funds.

London Friend
86 Caledonian Rd, London N1 9DN;
   URL www.londonfriend.org.uk;
   E-mail office@londonfriend.org.uk; Tel (Helpline) 020
   7837 3337; (Office) 020 7833 1674; Fax 020 7278 3119
Offers counselling, helplines social and support groups to
all lesbians and gay men and those unsure of their
sexuality. Counselling is available for individuals and
couples and is free. Counsellors are lesbians and gay men
who work to the BAC code of ethics.

London Rape Crisis Centre
PO Box 69, London WC1X 9NJ; Tel (Mon–Fri 1000–1800;
   1800–2200 answerphone, Sat and Sun 1000–2200) 020
   7837 1600; (Office) 020 7916 5466

Manager (Training Development) Kris Black
A telephone and face to face counselling service run by women for women and girls who have been raped or sexually assaulted at any time in their lives.

Southwark Muslim Women's Association
Bellenden Old School, Bellenden Rd, London SE15 4DG;
URL www.smwa.org.uk; E-mail smwasmwa@aol.com;
Tel 020 7732 8053; Fax 020 7732 3310
Director Zafar Iqbal
The Southwark Muslim Women's Association (SMWA) aims to counter disadvantages and discrimination faced by Muslim communities in Southwark, with a special emphasis on meeting the needs of women, children and elders.

National Association of Ladies' Circles of Great Britain and Ireland (NALC)
NALC Headquarters Office, Provincial Hse, Cooke St, Keighley, West Yorkshire BD21 3NN;
URL www.ladies-circle.org.uk;
E-mail hq@ladies-circle.org.uk; Tel 01535 607617
Association Secretary Mary Hebden
Fellowship and fund-raising with community service involvement.

National Association of Women's Clubs
5 Vernon Rise, King's Cross Rd, London WC1X 9EP; Tel 020 7837 1434
Admin Officer Pauline Chittick
Co-ordinates non-political, non-sectarian affiliated women's clubs in UK, providing information services, weekend schools and an Annual Conference.

National Council of Women of Great Britain
36 Danbury St, London N1 8JU; URL www.ncwgb.org;
E-mail ncwgb@danburystreet.freeserve.co.uk; Tel 020 7354 2395; Fax 020 7354 9214
President Hilary Sillars
Works at local and national level to affect change and improvement in quality of life for all.

National Federation of Women's Institutes
104 New Kings Rd, London SW6 4LY;
URL www.womens-intitute.co.uk;
E-mail cspa@nfwi.org.uk; Tel 020 7371 9300; Fax 020 7736 3652
General Secretary Jana Osborne

National Housewives Association (NHA)
Secretary Mary Shelley
12 Chestnut Dr, Pinner, Greater London HA5 1LY
Aims to put forward housewives' views, constructive comments, ideas to producers, manufacturers, MPs, Euro MPs etc; provide information and advice to housewives on various topics as the need arises and to campaign on their behalf.

NWR (National Women's Register)
3a Vulcan Hse, Vulcan Road North, Norwich, Norfolk NR6 6AQ; URL www.nwr.org; E-mail office@nwr.org; Tel 01603 406767; Fax 01603 407003
Office Administrator Angela Norman
Enables women to meet informally in each other's homes to hold discussions on topics unconnected with their everyday surroundings. Promotes friendship, communication skills, builds confidence and understanding of others' points of view. Also runs educational workshops and day conferences affiliated to the above activities. Newsletter; national correspondence magazine; research bank for members; postal book groups and houseswap facilities at a national level with many other local offshoots.

Rights of Women
52–54 Featherstone St, London EC1Y 8RT;
E-mail info@row.org.uk; Tel (Advice line) 020 7251 6577 (open at specific times only); (Office) 020 7251 6575; (Office) 020 7251 6576; Fax 020 7490 5377

Free confidential telephone legal advice for women on a range of issues including family law, relationship breakdown, children, domestic violence, immigration, employment and housing. Also undertake research and policy work to promote women's interests in relation to the law.

Scottish Women's Aid
Norton Pk, 57 Albion St, Edinburgh EH7 5QY;
URL www.scottishwomensaid.co.uk;
E-mail info@scottishwomensaid.org.uk; Tel 0131 475 2372; Fax 0131 475 2384
National Worker (Network and Administration) Dorothy Fall
National Worker (Legal Issues) Louise Johnson
National Worker (Children's Rights and Support) Claire Houghton
National Worker (Children's Rights and Outreach) Heather Coady
National Worker (External Training) Nel Whiting
National Worker (Refuge Development) Kate Arnot
National Worker (Internal Training) Indigo V
National Worker (Finance) Diane Wilson
National Worker (Permanent Housing) Lydia Okroj
Registered charity giving information, support and refuge to women, children and young people who have experienced domestic abuse.

Society for Promoting the Training of Women (Women's Loan Training Fund)
Deep Carrs Farm Cottage, Golf Course Dr, Lindrick Common, Worksop, Nottinghamshire S81 8BQ;
Tel 01909 475891
Secretary Mrs Morgan Thompson, BA
Grants interest-free loans for tuition fees and maintenance to women undertaking recognised training. Repayments as percentage of salary when trainee begins to earn. SAE for reply.

Welsh Women's Aid/Cymorth i Fenywod yng Nghymru
Aberystwyth Office: 4 Pound Pl, Aberystwyth, Ceredigion SY23 1LX; Tel 01970 612748; Fax 01970 627892
38–48 Crwys Rd, Cardiff CF2 4NN
Co-ordinator (National Children's Research and Campaign) Sian Howys
National Co-ordinator (Management and Annual Conference) C. Brown
National Co-ordinator (Mid Wales Regional Work) Sasha Williams
National Co-ordinator (Information) Gwenda Williams
The co-ordinating body for 34 Women's Aid groups throughout Wales. These groups aim to provide support, information and temporary crisis accommodation for women and children experiencing domestic violence. The national organisation provides support, information and training for these groups and campaigns on their behalf on issues affecting women experiencing physical, mental and sexual abuse.

Cardiff Office 38–48 Crwys Rd, Cardiff CF2 4NN; Tel 029 2039 0874; Fax 029 2039 0878
National Co-ordinator (Social Security) Sue Bowyer
National Co-ordinator (Housing) Vacancy
National Co-ordinator (Press and Publicity) Lata Griffith Unny
National Co-ordinator (South East Wales Regional Work) G. Allen
National Co-ordinator (Finance) Sally Jones
National Co-ordinator (South West Wales Regional Work) Collette Morgan
National Co-ordinator (Police and Legal) Deana Millward

Rhyl Office 26 Wellington Rd, Rhyl, Denbighshire LL18 1BN; Tel 01745 334767; Fax 01745 331502
National Co-ordinator (Childwork) Helen Shedker
National Co-ordinator (North Wales Regional Work) Mel Evans
National Co-ordinator (Employment) Wendy Roberts
National Co-ordinator (Statistics and Research) Pam Davies

16

WNCCC – Cancer Aware
1st Fl, Charity Hse, 14–15 Perseverance Works, London
E2 8DD; URL www.wnccc.org.uk;
E-mail admin@wnccc.org.uk; Tel 020 7729 4688; Fax 020
7613 0771
WNCCC – Cancer Aware aims to encourage and support
the prevention and early detection of cancer in women.
This will be achieved by the provision of information and
support materials, training and guidance, to government,
health professionals and the general public.

Women Prisoners Resource Centre
Office 4, Canalside Hse, London W10 5AA; Tel 020 8968
3121
Information and advice to women returning to London, or
who have recently left prison. Include work with both
statutory and voluntary agencies looking at services they
provide for women offenders.

Women's Aid Federation of England
PO Box 391, Bristol BS99 7WS;
URL www.womensaid.org.uk;
E-mail info@womensaid.org.uk; Tel (24 hr National
Domestic Violence Helpline) 08457 023 468;
(Administration) 0117 944 4411; Fax 0117 924 1703
National Helpline for Women who need information,
advice and refuge from domestic violence 08457 023 468.
Finds temporary refuge for women and their children, who
have suffered physical, mental and sexual abuse. Also
offers support and advice for women not in a refuge. For
general information and leaflets telephone the Admin tel
no. Donations and Covenants welcome. National
co-ordinating office for refuges throughout the country.
Provides information, publications, training and
consultancy on domestic violence. Resources and
co-ordinates the work of women's refuges. Promotes good
practice in service provision. Lobbies on behalf of women's
refuges and women and children.

Women's Health
52 Featherstone St, London EC1Y 8RT;
URL www.womenshealthlondon.org.uk;
E-mail health@womenshealthlondon.org.uk;
Tel (Helpline (0930–1330 daily)) 0845 125 5254; Fax 020
7250 4152; Minicom 020 7490 5489

Women's International League for Peace and Freedom
37 Hollingworth Rd, Petts Wood, Orpington, Kent
BR5 1AQ; URL www.gnape-org/ukwilpf;
E-mail rosalie.huzzard@btinternet.com; Tel 020 8467
5307
Works for international peace with justice for all and
welcomes women of every age, race, faith and political
opinion.

Women's Link: Women's Housing Advice in London
Room 417, London Fruit and Wool Exchange, Brushfield St,
London E1 6EL; URL www.womenslink.org.uk;
E-mail advice@womenslink.org.uk; Tel 020 7248 1200
Accommodation advisory service for low income and
homeless women in London; postal and telephone
enquiries, and appointments advice service four days a
week. Ex-offenders outreach and casework. Publishes
Hostels in London directory yearly as well as other
activities. Website.

Women's Refuge Salisbury
Beckingsale Hse, 121 Rampart Rd, Salisbury, Wiltshire
SP1 1JA; Tel 01722 324348
Manager
Short-term residential home for physically / mentally
abused women (and their children).

The Women's Therapy Centre
10 Manor Gdns, London N7 6JS;
URL www.womenstherapycentre.co.uk;
E-mail enquiries@womenstherapycentre.co.uk; Tel 020
7263 6200

Offers group and individual psychotherapy to women
from a feminist perspective. Special interest in women's
eating problems and in working with Black and Ethnic
women and lesbians. One year course and study days for
women working with women. Advice and information
about therapy services nationwide.

YWCA of England and Wales
Clarendon Hse, 52 Cornmarket St, Oxford, Oxfordshire
OX1 3EJ; URL www.ywca-gb.org.uk;
E-mail info@ywca-gb.org.uk; Tel 01865 304200;
Fax 01865 204805
The YWCA in England and Wales works with young
women aged 11–30 from any racial ethnic or religious
background. Its network of 18 projects are based in or reach
out to deprived communities and support young women
experiencing poverty, unemployment, violence and abuse
and campaign to overcome the barriers to their full
participation in society.

Youth Counselling Services

The following list of counselling, advisory or information
services for young people has been supplied by the
National Association of Young People's Counselling and
Advisory Services. This list does not imply anything about
quality of service. The particular nature of the service
varies, but in general they are at least somewhere any
young person can contact for information and support.

Youth Access

1–2 Taylors Yard, 67 Alderbrook Rd, London SW12 8AD;
E-mail admin@youthaccess.org.uk; Tel 020 8772 9900;
Fax 020 8772 9746
Director   B. Rayment
Membership association for services which provide
information, advice and counselling to young people.

Brook Advisory Centres

153a East St, London SE17 2SD; URL www.brook.org.uk;
E-mail information@brookcentres.co.uk; Tel 020 7708
1234
National charity objects of which are the prevention and
mitigation of the suffering caused by unwanted pregnancy
by educating young persons in matters of sex and
contraception and developing among them a sense of
responsibility in regard to sexual behaviour.

Bristol Brook Young People's Clinic
Manager (Centre)   Anna Hutley
Clinical Manager   Dr Tracey Masters

Brook in Birmingham
59–65 John Bright St, Birmingham, West Midlands B1 1BL;
URL www.brook.org.uk;
E-mail info@brookinbirmingham.org.uk; Tel 0121 643
5341
Chair (Executive Committee)   Jagdip Ral
Chief Executive   Penny Barber

City Centre   59–65 John Bright St, Birmingham, West
Midlands B1 1BL; URL www.brook.org.uk;
E-mail birmingham@brooksexadvice.com

Brook in Burnley
64 Bank Pde, Burnley, Lancashire BB11 1TS; Tel 01282
416596
Centre Manager   A.H. Rolfe

London
Chair of Trustees   Angela Dawe
Chief Executive   Lyne Hurley
Sexual health service for young people.
Open Mon–Sat.

Brixton Brook Advisory Centre 53 Acre La, London SW2 5TN; Tel 020 7274 4995

Brook in Barking Central Clinic, Vicarage Dr, Barking, Essex IG11 7NF; Tel 020 8276 7021
Walk-in service, no appointment necessary.

Deptford Brook Advisory Centre Waldron Health Centre, Stanley St, Deptford, London SE8 4BG; Tel 020 8691 0417; (Information) 020 7703 9660

East Street Brook Advisory Centre 153a East St, London SE17 2SD; Tel 020 7703 9660; Fax 020 7277 2103

Hayes Brook Advisory Centre Minet Clinic, Avondale Dr, Hayes, Greater London UB3 3PF; URL www.brook.org.uk; Tel 020 8813 7050; (Appointments) 020 7387 8700

Ilford Brook Advisory Centre John Telford Clinic, Cleveland Rd, Ilford, Essex IG1 1EE; Tel 020 7580 2991; (Drop-in service) 020 8478 6982

Lewisham Brook Advisory Centre Central Lewisham Clinic, 410 Lewisham High St, London SE13 6LL; Tel 020 8690 3922; (Appointments) 020 7703 9660

Lower Clapton Brook Advisory Centre Lower Clapton Health Centre, 36 Lower Clapton Rd, London E5 0PD; Tel 020 8986 7111; (Appointments) 020 7580 2991

Manor Gardens Brook Advisory Centre 6 Manor Gdns, off Holloway Rd, London N7 6LA; Tel 020 7272 4231

Redbridge Brook Advisory Centre John Telford Clinic, Ilford, Essex IG1 1EE; Tel 020 8478 6982
Under 25s only.

Rotherhithe Brook Advisory Centre
Manager (Centre) Ms Wordsworth

SHINE
Young People's Sexual Health.
SHINE clinics:
Tuesdays 1630–1830 West Beckton Health Centre.
Wednesdays 1630–1830 West Ham Lane Health Centre.
Saturdays 0930–1130 West Ham Lane Health Centre.
Thursday 1700–18.30 Shrewsbury Road Health Centre.

Uxbridge Brook Advisory Centre First Fl, Fountains Mill, Uxbridge, Greater London UB8 1JR; Tel 01895 813595; (Appointments) 020 7580 2991

Merseyside Brook Advisory Centre
81 London Rd, Liverpool, Merseyside L3 8JA; Tel 0151 207 4000; Fax 0151 207 4144
Manager Sue Ryrie
Charity providing contraceptive and sexual health service for young people (under 25).

Milton Keynes Brook Advisory Centre
Acorn Hse, 355 Midsummer Blvd, Milton Keynes MK9 3HP; Tel 01908 669215; Fax 01908 607262

Caledonia Youth

5 Castle Terr, Edinburgh EH1 2DP; URL www.caledoniayouth.org; E-mail information@caledoniayouth.org; Tel 0131 229 3596; Fax 0131 221 1486

Caledonia Youth – Glasgow
Atlantic Chambers, 45 Hope St, Glasgow G2 6AE; E-mail information@caledoniayouth.org; Tel 0141 222 2302

Regional Organisations

England

Bristol

The Clocktower Association (Community Project)
Tower Rd North, Warmley, Bristol BS30 8XU; E-mail clocktower@ukgo.com; Tel 0117 967 1655

Chair Mr M. Packer
Administration Assistant Rebecca Grigg
We offer a venue for courses and training, meetings and community arts.

Off the Record–Bristol
2 Horfield Rd, St Michael's Hill, Bristol, Gloucestershire BS2 8EA; Tel (Helpline:) 0808 808 9120; Fax (Office) 0117 922 6747
Free, confidential advice, information and counselling services via a drop-in service and telephone helpline, open Mon 0930–1800, Tue, Wed 1130–2000 counselling appointment system (counselling only available for people up to 25 years old).

Buckinghamshire

Way In
Townsend Hse, Townsend Rd, Chesham, Buckinghamshire HP5 2AW; E-mail wayinchesham@hotmail.com; Tel (Administration) 01494 793304; (Helpline) 01494 791177; Fax 01494 792202
Chair (Management Committee) Trevor Glover-Wright
Co-ordinator Gill Dickinson
Free and confidential support for young people aged 11–25.

Youth Concern (Aylesbury)
The Uptown Coffee Bar, The Arches, Market Sq, Aylesbury, Buckinghamshire HP20 1TW; Tel 01296 431183; Fax 01296 483567
Contact Roger Priest
Contact Suzanne Cheshire

Youth Enquiry Service
52 Frogmoor, High Wycombe, Buckinghamshire HP13 5DG; URL www.yeswycombe.org.uk; E-mail wycyes@waitrose.com; Tel 01494 437373; Fax 01494 452853
Co-ordinator and Youth and Community Worker Martin Skinner

Youth Information Service
Saxon Crt, Avebury Blvd, Milton Keynes MK9 3HS; Tel 01908 604700; Fax 01908 253671
Chair Executive Committee Esme Hopson
Manager Yvonne McLaughlin

Cambridgeshire

Centre Thirty Three
33 Clarendon St, Cambridge, Cambridgeshire CB1 1JX; URL www.centre33.org.uk; E-mail help@centre33.org.uk; Tel (Counselling and information service for young people (25 and under)) 01223 314763; (Helpline) 01223 316488; Fax 01223 566633
Chair Management Committee Paul Morrish
Centre Manager Alan Humphreys

Cumbria

Castlerigg Manor Catholic Residential Youth and Conference Centre
Castlerigg Manor, Manor Brow, Keswick, Cumbria CA12 4AR; URL www.castleriggmanor.com; E-mail castleriggmanor@hotmail.com; Tel 017687 72711; Fax 017687 75302

Essex

Colchester Youth Enquiry Service Ltd (YES)
45–46 East Stockwell St, Colchester, Essex CO1 1SR; URL www.colchesteryes.org.uk; E-mail info@colchesteryyes.org.uk; Tel 01206 710771
Manager Louise Fairey
Administrator and Receptionist Carol Chapman
Housing Advocate Sarah Aldous

16

Romford Counselling Service
Romford YMCA, Rush Green Rd, Romford, Essex
    RM7 0PH; URL www.romfordymca.org;
    E-mail counselling@romford.ymca.org; Tel 01708 766211;
    Fax 01708 754211
Manager (Couselling Service)   Margaret White
General Secretary   Pip Wilson

Gloucestershire

Share Young People's Counselling Service
80 Eastgates, Gloucester, Gloucestershire GL1 1QN;
    Tel 01452 524019 (counselling)
Manager   Alan Bain, MBE

Greater Manchester

42nd Street
2nd Fl, Swan Bldgs, 20 Swan St, Manchester M4 5JW;
    E-mail theteam@fortysecondstreet.org.uk; Tel 0161 832
    0170
Chair (Management Committee)   J. Batsleer
Mental health organisation for young people aged 14–25;
accepts referrals from various sources (including self-
referral); offers individual counselling and a large number
of groups, including a drop-in.

Signpost
Young People's Advice and Information Centre, St.
    Andrew's Hall, Brownley Rd, Wythenshawe,
    Manchester M22 ODW;
    URL www.signpostadvice.org.uk;
    E-mail signpost@signpostadvice.org.uk; Tel 0161 436
    5432; 0161 436 5433; Fax 0161 437 1055

Hampshire

Off the Record (Havant)
Threeways, 138 Purbrook Way, Leight Pk, Havant,
    Hampshire PO9 3SU; Tel (Clientline) 023 9243 3999
A confidential and free counselling and information service
for young people aged 11–25.

Off the Record (Portsmouth)
250 Fratton Rd, Portsmouth PO1 5HH; Tel (Clientline) 023
    9281 5322; (Office only) 01705 785111
A confidential and free counselling and information service
for young people aged 11–25.

Herefordshire

CLD Youth Counselling Trust
Hereford Hse, 3 Offa St, Hereford, Herefordshire HR1 2LL;
    Tel 01432 359132; Fax 01432 359132
Manager   Mrs C. Lewis-Davies
We offer a free specialist and easily accessible youth
counselling service in Herefordshire for young people aged
13–25 years who are disadvantaged because of emotional,
psychological or behavioural difficulties.

Way 2 Go Information and Support Service
Manager   Di Gosling
We offer free information, support, advocacy and practical
help for young people aged 11–25 years.

Hertfordshire

Signpost
Young People's Counselling and Information Service,
    206–210 Lower High St, Watford, Hertfordshire
    WD17 2EL; Tel 01923 239495
Project Manager   Samantha Sharpe
Outreach Worker   Vacancy

Isle of Wight

Isle of Wight Youth Trust
1 St. John's Pl, Newport, Isle of Wight PO30 1LH; Tel 01983
    529569; Fax 01983 537175
Director   Eileen Monks

Kent

Bromley Y
17 Ethelbert Rd, Bromley, Kent BR1 1JA
Chair   Dr Christine Stone
Director   Pietro Battista

Youth Action 2000
The Phoenix Youth Centre, Hawes La, West Wickham,
    Kent; Tel 020 8777 7938
Contact   Iain Khan Gilchrist

The Crib   Fenge Centre for Community Education, 101a
Parish La, Penge, London SE20; Tel 020 8778 3566
Project Leader   Sheena Horner
Mobile travel drop-in centre (converted single-decker bus)
which visits Crystal Palace, Penge and Anerley providing
an informal educational programme for young people who
choose not to use existing services.

London

Alone in London Service
188 Kings Cross Rd, London WC1X 9DE; Tel 020 7278 4224;
    Fax 020 7837 7943
President   Dame Margaret Booth, DBE
Patron   Emma Thompson
Director   Gaynor Quilter
Key Objectives
To help resolve any immediate housing crisis; to help
define any problems underlying the housing crisis; to help
obtain statutory services to which there is a right; to help,
where appropriate, re-establish positive family links and
provide resettlement to 'city of origin' with support; to
support the acquisition of living skills; to support the
transition to full independence.
Advice; concentrates on solving the most immediate
problems for young homeless people such as finding a
place to sleep at night and then to recommend the most
appropriate services to define and address the underlying
causes of the young person's homelessness.
Advocacy; including benefit entitlement, accessing services
under the 1989 Children's Act, Representation for refugees
and for young people in court. Supported housing; structured to encourage young people to gain the skills necessary to
live independently. Resettlement; ensuring that the transition from supported to independent living is successful.
Family mediating; enabling young people to forge positive
contact with their families while they are at home or in re-
establish contact when they have left home.
Satellite services for Advocacy and Advice are also offered
at our Lewisham Site.
We have provided 2136 young people with direct support
and counselling; advice on a range of housing options, 317
with advocacy, while 291 have been seen by our family
mediating service. We have worked with 1012 new young
people.

The Brandon Centre
Counselling and Psychotherapy for young people.
26 Prince of Wales Rd, London NW5 3LG;
    URL www.brandon-centre.org.uk;
    E-mail reception@brandon-centre.org.uk; Tel 020 7267
    4792
Director   Geoffrey Baruch, PhD
Administrator   Sarah Charlton

Brent Adolescent Centre
51 Winchester Ave, London NW6 7TT; Tel 020 7328 0918;
    Fax 020 7328 0918

Preventive mental health service for young people aged 14–21 years old. Provides assessment and treatment to young people and psychological support to parents.

Connection at St. Martin's
12 Adelaide St, London WC2N 4HW;
E-mail info@cstn.org.uk; Tel 020 7766 5544; Fax 020 7930 9194
Chair (Management Committee) Ian Hobbs
Chief Executive Colin Glover

Coram Leaving Care Services
Semi-independence houses.
6–8 York Mews, London NW5 2UJ; Tel 020 7284 9895; Fax 020 7482 7394

Boys2Men Groupwork Project Tel 020 7373 8256

Coram Aftercare Services 70 Kingsgate Rd, London NW6 4TE; Tel 020 7372 8256

Coram Education Support Service Silverdale Project, Old Tenant Hall, Harrington St, London NW1; Tel 020 7388 4109; Fax 020 7383 4986

Coram Leaving Care Service 1 Yonge Pk, London N4 3NU; Tel 020 7607 4341; Fax 020 7700 8497
Semi-independence House.

High Support House 13 Campbell Rd, Bow, London E3 4DS; Tel 020 8981 4883; Fax 020 8981 4871

Coram Mentoring Service Tel 020 7372 7882

Semi-independence House 21 Coleridge Rd, London, N4 2NY; Tel 020 7607 0365; 020 7700 1920; Fax 020 7609 5503
Contact this house for referrals to all semi-independent houses.

Ealing Youth Counselling and Information Service
55 High St, Acton, London W3 6NE; Tel 020 8992 8182; Fax 020 8992 8182

Faces in Focus
102 Harper Rd, London SE1 6AQ;
URL www.facesinfocus.org.uk;
E-mail general@facesinfocus.org.uk; Tel 020 7403 2444; Fax 020 7207 2982
Project Director G.J. Tomkins

Face 2 Face
Chestnuts Hse, 398 Hoe St, Walthamstow, London E17 9BR;
URL face2face-wf.org.uk;
E-mail face2face@edu.lbwf.gov.uk; Tel 020 8509 1210; Fax 020 8509 3030
Contact Jo Seward
Contact Janet Blair

New Horizon Youth Centre
68 Chalton St, London NW1 1JR; E-mail newh97a@aol.com; Tel 020 7388 5570; 020 7388 5580; Fax 020 7388 5548

Off Centre
Hackney Young People's Counselling Service
25–27 Hackney Gr, London E8 3NR;
URL www.offcentre.org.uk; E-mail info@offcentre.org.uk; Tel 020 8985 8566; 020 8986 4016; Fax 020 8985 0044
Director Michelle Rogers
Manager (Counselling Services) Michelle Springer-Benjamin

One Step Project
Campden Institute, 95 Lancaster Rd, London W11 1QQ;
E-mail info@one-stepdemon.co.uk; Tel 020 7598 4924
Project Leader Sonia McCollin

Open Door
Open Door, Young People's Consultation Service, 12 Middle La, Crouch End, London, N8 8PL;
URL www.opendooronline.org;
E-mail enquiries@opendooronline.org; Tel 020 8348 5947; Fax 020 8341 1684
Director Charlotte Jarvis

Young People's Counselling Service
Tavistock Centre, 120 Belsize La, London NW3; Tel 020 7435 7111 ext 2337; (Direct line) 020 7447 3787
Contact Sandra Masterson
The Young People's Counselling Service, part of the Tavistock Clinic, is a part of National Health Service Trust.

Youth AID (Lewisham) – Advice, Information, Development
17 Brownhill Rd, London SE6 2HG;
E-mail youthaid@aol.com; Tel 020 8697 2152/7435

Youthreach (Greenwich)
c/o Greenwich YMCA, Woolwich Dockyard, London SE18 5PQ; Tel 020 8854 7744
Co-ordinator Marion Maynard

Merseyside

Young Persons' Advisory Service
36 Bolton St, Liverpool, Merseyside L3 5LX;
URL www.ypas.org.uk; E-mail support@ypas.co.uk; Tel 0151 707 1025; Fax 0151 707 1252
An independent agency offering free, confidential counselling,advice,information and support to young people aged 16–25 years from Merseyside.
Mon 1000–2000; Tue and Thur 1000–1600; Wed 1000–2000; Fri 1000–1530; Drop-in open Mon–Thur 1200–1630; Fri 1200–1530; office hours 0930–1700.

Middlesex

Hounslow Youth Counselling Service
78 St. John's Rd, Isleworth, Greater London TW7 6RU;
E-mail hycs@lineone.net; Tel 020 8568 1818
Chair (Management Committee) A. Kelly
Co-ordinator P. David

Link Youth Counselling and Information Service
Fountains Mill, 81 High St, Uxbridge, Greater London UB8 1JR; Tel 01895 238884; Fax 01895 238556
Confidential service for people aged 14–25 years in Hillingdon. Please phone or call for an apppointment. Self referral.

Norfolk

Matthew Project–Drug Aid
24 Pottergate, Norwich, Norfolk NR2 1DX;
URL www.matthewproject.org;
E-mail thematthewproject@btinternet.com; Tel 01603 626123; (Helpline) 01603 764754; Fax 01603 630411
Chair P. Hoey
Director J. Bryant

Northamptonshire

Green Door Counselling and Information Service
The Connaughty Centre, Cottingham Rd, Corby, Northamptonshire NN17 1SY; Tel 01536 200520
Chair Cllr Alexis Hill
Co-ordinator Gill Neary
Mon, Tue, Wed 15.30–1800; Thu 1000–1300; 1530–1800; Fri 1530–1800.

Kettering Youth Information
William Knibb Centre, Montagu St, Kettering, Northamptonshire NN16 8AE;
E-mail info@ketteringyouthinformation.co.uk; Tel 01536 412537; (Helpline) 01536 510089
Information, advice, counselling, pregnancy tests, condoms available. Free and confidential service.
Information, advice, counselling on drugs, alcohol, solvents, gambling.

16

Service Six
Rock St, Wellingborough, Northamptonshire NN8 4LW;
E-mail info@service6.freeserve.co.uk; Tel 01933 226615;
Fax 01933 226602

Nottinghamshire

Ollerton and District Citizen's Advice Bureau
5 Forest Crt, New Ollerton, Newark, Nottinghamshire
NG22 9PL; Tel 01623 861808; Fax 01623 836156

Youth Enquiry Service (YES)
Sutton Youth and Community Centre, High Pavement,
Sutton-in-Ashfield, Nottinghamshire NG17 1EE;
Tel 01623 550706
Co-ordinator Lyndsey Radford
Team Leader Mandy Revel
Area Youth Officer Bill Blackamore
Service offers free, confidential counselling and
information for young people and their parents/carers.

Reading

No 5 Young People's Counselling and Information Centre
2–4 Sackville St, Reading RG1 1NT;
E-mail ask@no5info.freeserve.co.uk; Tel 0118 901 5668

Slough

SPACE
81–83 Windsor Rd, Slough SL1 2JL;
URL myweb.tiscali.co.uk/space.counselling;
E-mail space.counselling@tiscali.co.uk
Co-ordinator Toni Brown
Support Co-ordinator Hazel Dier

Suffolk

I.S. (Information and Support Services)
Community Education Centre, Camps Rd, Haverhill,
Suffolk CB9 8HB

IS: Information and Support for Young People
20–21 Commercial Rd, Lowestoft, Suffolk NR32 2TD;
Tel 01502 513547; Fax 01502 572879
Young person's information and counselling centre. Open
Tuesdays and Thursdays 1530–1730. Appointments may be
available at other times.

YAC – Information and Support Services to Young People
13 Curriers La, Ipswich, Suffolk IP1 2AQ; Tel 01473 212165;
Fax 01473 255677

Surrey

Croydon Drop-In for Young People
Director Kim Bennett
Development Worker (Outreach) Derek Taylor
Administration Penny Sene
Counselling Co-ordinator Rhona Kenny
Drop In provides a free and confidential information,
advice, advocacy and counselling service to young people
in Croydon aged 11–25..

Open House
Guildford Youth Counselling Service, Bridge St, Guildford,
Surrey GU1 4SB; Tel 07932 047778
Counselling Co-ordinator Dr Richard Cole
Director and Chief Executive (YMCA) Pete Brayne

Open Door Youth Counselling Service
1 Grove Cottage, Grove Pk, High St, Carshalton, Surrey
SM5 3BB; URL www.opendooryouthcounselling.com;
E-mail angela.opendoor@ukgateway.net; Tel 020 8770
4388
Manager and Development Co-ordinator Angela E.H. Watson

Sussex

Open Door Eastbourne
67 Susans Rd, Eastbourne, East Sussex BN21 3TG;
E-mail opendooreastbourne@pact.org.uk; Tel 01323
725155/738853; Fax 01323 734601
Project Manager F. Johnson
Project Co-ordinator Tim Bower
Information, support and counselling for young people
aged 13–25.

Windsor and Maidenhead

Windsor and Maidenhead Youth and Counselling Service
22 Cookham Rd, Maidenhead, Windsor and Maidenhead
SL6 8AJ; URL www.no22.co.uk; Tel 01628 636661
Chair of the Executive R. Berry
Co-ordinator Mary Luxon

West Midlands

Open Door Youth Counselling
480a Bristol Rd (entrance in Alton Rd), Selly Oak,
Birmingham, West Midlands B29 6BD;
E-mail opendoor@opendooryouthcounselling.co.uk;
Tel (Client) 0121 472 2071; (Office) 0121 472 8676
Chair (Executive Committee) Mark Prever
Director (Services) Carmel Mullan-Hartley
Counselling Co-ordinator Helen Shilvock

The What Centre
Advice, Information and Counselling Centre, Young
People
23 Coventry St, Stourbridge, West Midlands DY8 1EP;
URL www.thewhatcentre.co.uk;
E-mail thewhatcentre@aol.com; Tel 01384 379992
Centre Manager Julie Duffy

Wiltshire

Connections Youth Counselling Service
178 Victoria Rd, Swindon SN1 3DF;
E-mail connections@connectionsycs.fsbusiness.co.uk;
Tel (Administration) 01793 612969; (Helpline) 01793
695255; Fax 01793 525099
Administrator Gillian Stephens

Worcestershire

Youthcomm
Youthcomm, c/o City Youth Centre Spring Gdns,
Worcester, Worcestershire WR1 2AE;
URL www.youthcomm.org.uk;
E-mail get@youthcomm.org.uk; Tel 01905 726663;
(Freephone) 0800 096 1425
Co-ordinator (Youthcomm) Adrian Newman

Young Enquiry/Youthcomm
Young Enquiry Service, c/o City Youth Centre, Spring
Gdns, Worcester, Worcestershire WR1 2AE
Contact Richard Wood
Youth Adviser Sandra Sterckx

Yorkshire

Scarborough Youth Enquiry Service (YES)
4 Elders St, Scarborough, North Yorkshire YO11 1DZ;
Tel 01723 375563
Senior Worker Sylvia Settle

Selby Youth Enquiry Service
Youth Hse, New La, Selby, North Yorkshire YO8 0FW;
Tel 01757 709249

Whitby Youth Enquiry Service (YES)
Rafters, New Quay Rd, Whitby, North Yorkshire
    YO21 1DH; E-mail yes@whitbycomed.com; Tel 01947
    601477
Senior Youth Worker   Sandra Evans

York Youth Enquiry Service (YES)
1 Bootham, York YO30 7BN; URL www.yorkyes.co.uk;
    E-mail mail@yorkyes.co.uk; Tel 01904 623850; Fax 01904
    643184
Project Co-ordinator   Dawn Moores

Youth and Community Service
Skipton Youth and Community Centre, Otley St, Skipton,
    North Yorkshire BD23 1ET; Tel 01756 798015
District Worker   Shaun Wiseman

Youth Enquiry Service
Bedale High School, Fitzalan Rd, Bedale, North Yorkshire
    DL8 ZEQ; Tel 01677 422043

Youth Enquiry Service
14 Bower Rd, Harrogate, North Yorkshire HG1 1BA;
    E-mail info@harrogateyes.org; Tel 01423 524174
Senior Worker   Morag F. Linfoot
Office is open Mon–Fri 1030–1300, other times by
arrangement.

Wales

City Centre Youth Project/GrassRoots
58 Charles St, Cardiff CF10 2GG; Tel 029 2023 1700
Advice, information and support service for under 25s.
Workshop facilities including video production, publishing
and computers, photography and art, music and sound
studio and drama.

Scotland

Family Planning and Reproductive Health Care
2–6 Sandyford Pl, Glasgow G3 7NB; Tel 0141 211 8130;
    Fax 0141 211 8139
Director   Dr A. Bigrigg
Manager (Support Services)   Jennifer Schofield

Off The Record
27 Murray Pl, Stirling FK8 1DQ;
    E-mail offtherecord@aberlour.org.uk; Tel 01786
    450518

Speakeasy
44 Adelaide St, Craigshill, Livingston, West Lothian
    EH54 5HQ; Tel 01506 430718; (Freefone) 0800
    220424

Northern Ireland

Contact Youth Counselling Services
The Bridge, 135–139 Ravenhill Rd, Belfast BT6 8DR;
    E-mail info@contactyouth.org; Tel (Contact Youth) 028
    9054 7848; (Youthline) 0808 808 8000
Chair   Dee Kelly
Director   N. Patterson

'Just Ask' Adolescent Service
Newry and Mourne Health and Social Services Trust, John
    Mitchel Pl, Newry, County Down BT34 2BU;
    E-mail majellacasey@dhh.n-i.nhs.uk; Tel 028 3083 4250;
    Fax 028 3026 5830

Other Organisations

ABAYOMI Counselling and Resource Centre
182 Hammersmith Rd, London W6 7DJ; Tel 020 8741 3335;
    Fax 020 8741 4473
Manager   Robert Timmerman
The project provides a culturally and racially appropriate
psychotherapy and counselling and support service to
African Caribbean's aged between 16 and 65 years.

Adoption UK
Manor Farm, Appletree Rd, Chipping Warden, Banbury,
    Oxfordshire OX17 1LH;
    E-mail admin@adoptionuk.org.uk; Tel 01295 660121;
    (Membership, Advice and Helpline) 0870 7700 450;
    Fax 01295 660123
Director   Jonathan Pearce
Editor (Adoption Today Magazine)   Karam Radwan
Information and support service for prospective and
existing adoptive families. Bi-monthly Journal features
children needing new families. Membership subscription
£26.95 p/a, £250.00 for adoption agencies. Information
pack free. Over 140 local contacts throughout the UK.

Alzheimer Scotland
22 Drumsheugh Gdns, Edinburgh EH3 7RN;
    URL www.alzscot.org; E-mail alzheimer@alzscot.org;
    Tel 0131 243 1453; (24 hour Dementia Helpline) 0808 808
    3000; Fax 0131 243 1450
Chief Executive   Jim Jackson
Convener   Alan Jacques
Training Officer   Jennifer Marlborough
Information Manager   Kate Fearnley
Provides information and services for people with
dementia and the people who care for them and works to
improve public policies for them.

At Ease
Free advisory service for people in the forces and their
families.
28 Commercial St (nr Aldgate East station), London E1 6LS;
    Tel (Sundays 1700–1900) 020 7247 5164

BAAF Adoption and Fostering
Skyline Hse, 200 Union St, London SE1 0LX;
    URL www.baaf.org.uk; E-mail mail@baaf.org.uk; Tel 020
    7593 2000; Fax 020 7593 2001
Chief Executive   Felicity Collier
A voluntary organisation that works in the best interest of
children separated from their birth parents and exists to
promote good practice in adoption and fostering. An
umbrella organisation for statutory and voluntary adoption
and fostering agencies. BAAF provides training,
information and consultancy, a wide range of publications
including a quarterly professional journal 'Adoption and
Fostering'. Also operates a family finding service. Be My
Parent is published bi-monthly and includes profiles of
children awaiting adoption. Focus on Fives is a fortnightly
newsletter for approved families which features children
under five. BAAF Link is a computer database which links
approved familes and children all around the UK. There
are six BAAF regional and national centres in England,
Scotland and Wales.

Birmingham Settlement
318 Summer La, Newtown, Birmingham, West Midlands
    B19 3RL; URL www.birminghamsettlement.org.uk;
    Tel 0121 248 3000; Fax 0121 248 3070
Chair   Hilary Shayler
Chief Executive   Susan Spencer
Director (Finance)   Carol Pearce
Multi purpose voluntary agency providing advice and
regeneration services: community care and development
including day centres, home-based community care work,
advice and advocacy and group support; debt and money

advice includes National Debtline, Business Debtline, local money advice centre and national money advice training unit. Also training, volunteering and employment support projects for local residents, specifically targeting women.

The Bisbey Partnership: Psychology and Counselling Services

Gainsborough Hse, 9 Portland Rd, East Grinstead, West Sussex RH19 4EB; E-mail loribeth@khys.demon.co.uk; E-mail steve.bisbey@talk21.com; Tel 01342 323107; Fax 01342 324316

Certified Trauma Specialist S. Bisbey, BSc(Psych), CTS
Psychologist F. Hewstone, BSc(Psych)

Specialises in treatment of post-traumatic stress disorder, relationship difficulties and abortion issues.

Both Parents Forever

39 Cloonmore Ave, Orpington, Kent BR6 9LE; Tel 01689 854343

Co-Director John Bell

National self-help group for parents and grandparents following divorce, separation and care proceedings. Information pack: parents'/grandparents' rights in all family proceedings: parental responsibility; residence orders; contact orders; education/medical reports; social workers; court welfare officers; child abduction. Files on help available overseas on child abduction. In association with MISTERX help to men who are victims of domestic violence.

Breakspear Hospital

Hertfordshire Hse, Wood La, Hemel Hempstead, Hertfordshire HP2 4FD;
E-mail info@breakspearmedical.com; Tel 01442 261333; Fax 01442 266388

Medical Director Dr J.A. Monro

Private Sector Medical Services for the treatment of allergy and environmental illness.

Careline

Cardinal Heenan Centre, 326 High Rd, Ilford, Essex IG1 1QP; URL www.carelineuk.org; Tel (Administration) 020 8514 5444; (Counselling) 020 8514 1177

Administrator Angela Sharp

Charity providing confidential crisis telephone counselling to children, young people and adults on any issue including relationship problems, child abuse, HIV/AIDS, depression, anxieties and phobias. Face-to-face counselling service for adults in local area only.

Catholic Children's Society (Shrewsbury Diocese Inc)

St Paul's Hse, Farm Field Dr, Birkenhead, Merseyside L43 7ZT; E-mail childsoc@diocshr.dircon.co.uk; Tel 0151 652 1281; Fax 0151 652 5002

Director Ged Edwards

Child Poverty Action Group (CPAG)

94 White Lion St, London N1 9PF; URL www.cpag.org.uk; Tel 020 7837 7979; Fax 020 7837 6414

Director Martin Barnes
Training Administrator Judy Allen

Provides welfare rights, advice and training to advisors (not direct to clients). Publishes guides to social security benefits. Promotes action to tackle poverty in families with children.

Child Poverty Action Group in Scotland Unit 09 Ladywell,

94 Duke St, Glasgow G4 0UW; URL www.cpag.org.uk; Tel (Advice Line (Tues–Weds 1000–1200) 0141 552 0552; (General Enquiries) 0141 552 3303

Continence Foundation

307 Hatton Sq, 16 Baldwins Gdns, London EC1N 7RJ;
E-mail continence-help@dial.pipex.com; Tel 020 7404 6875; (Helpline (Mon–Fri 0930–1630) 0845 345 0165; Fax 020 7404 6876

Director Dr Judith Wardle

Charity offering advice, education and information on urinary and faecal incontinence. Helpline for the public.

Crisis Point

7 Rochdale Rd, Collyhurst, Manchester M4 4HS; Tel 0808 808 2007; Textphone 0808 808 2117

Opening Times Tue–Sun 2000–0000. We operate call-back when Crisisline is closed where people are invited to leave non-urgent messages for response, usually within 24 hours.

Crisisline

A free and confidential helpline specifically for the people of Manchester which provides listening, support, advice and information for anyone in personal crisis, suffering stress, anxiety, depression, generally worried about their mental health or in need of support with long term mental health problems.

Crisisline opened in October 1999. A Turning Point project Funded by National Charities Lottery Board. See entry for Turning Point, this chapter. The helpline is run by a team of specially trained and experienced volunteers.

DIAL UK

St Catherine's, Tickhill Rd, Doncaster, South Yorkshire DN4 8QN; URL www.dialuk.org.uk; Tel 01302 310 123; Fax 01302 310 404

Chief Executive Dorothy McGahan

National organisation co-ordinating DIAL disability advice centres. Network of over 100 local information and advice services for disabled people, carers and professional service providers covering all aspects of disability. DIAL advice services are run by people with direct experience of disability.

Divorce Mediation and Counselling Service

38 Ebury St, London SW1W 0LU; Tel (Mon–Fri 1000–1630) 020 7730 2422

A charity offering mediation to separating or divorcing couples. The service works particularly with children's issues and also offers counselling.

Heathrow Travel-Care

Room 1308, Queens Bldg, Heathrow Airport, Hounslow, Greater London TW6 1BZ;
E-mail heathrow-travel_care@baa.co.uk; Tel 020 8745 7495; Fax 020 8745 4161; Minicom 020 8745 7564

Team Leader Sandie Cox

Independent social work service for passengers and employees at Heathrow Airport. Qualified staff offer information and advice.

The KCC Foundation

Counselling, consultancy and training

2 Wyvil Crt, Trenchold St, London SW8 2TG;
URL www.kcc-international.com;
E-mail kensington_consultation_centre@compuserve.com;
Tel (For home counties) 01438 311974; (London – Head Office) 020 7720 7301

Listening Post

Brunswick Methodist Church, Brunswick Pl, Newcastle upon Tyne, Tyne and Wear NE1 7BJ; Tel 0191 232 1692

Director and Training Team Leader John A. Morris

Free, confidential listening service for anyone who needs it. Just walk in–no appointment needed. Mon–Sat 1200–1500 and stress counselling by appointment Mon 1300–1700, Wed 1400–1700.

Mediation UK

Alexander Hse, Telephone Ave, Bristol BS1 4BS;
URL www.mediationuk.org.uk;
E-mail enquiries@mediationuk.org.uk; Tel 0117 904 6661; Fax 0117 904 3331

Director Tony Billinghurst

Charitable organisation representing mediation services throughout the UK and promoting mediation as a way of resolving disputes.

Meeting Point Trust Ltd

Meeting Point Hse, Southwater Sq, Telford, TF3 4HS;
URL www.meetingpointhouse.co.uk;
E-mail reception@meetingpointhouse.co.uk; Tel 01952 292888; Fax 01952 291168

Message Home Helpline
Roebuck Hse, 284 Upper Richmond Road West, London
SW14 7JE; URL www.missingpersons.org;
E-mail m.home@missingpersons.org; Tel (Freephone)
0800 700 740; (Office) 020 8392 4550; Fax 020 8487 8297
Manager Joanne Cannon

OPAS (The Pensions Advisory Service)
11 Belgrave Rd, London SW1V 1RB;
URL www.opas.org.uk; Tel 0845 601 2923; Fax 020 7233
8016
Director (Administration) B. Wilkins
Independent and voluntary organisation established for the
purpose of giving free help and advice to members of the
public on all matters concerning pension schemes
including personal pensions and state schemes; Available
to all those who think they have pension rights including
scheme members, pensioners, those with deferred pensions
and dependants.

Shingles Support Society
41 North Rd, London N7 9DP;
URL www.herpes.org.uk/shingles; Tel (Helpline) 020
7609 9061; (Office) 020 7607 9661; Fax available on
request
Director M. Nicholson
For people with shingles or PHN (post-herpetic neuralgia
following shingles) the SSS provides information and
advice on self-help therapies and fully referenced drug
treatment sheets for their GPs. Send SAE (with small
donation) to receive 19 pages.

Speakability
1 Royal St, London SE1 7LL;
URL www.speakability.org.uk;
E-mail speakability@speakability.org.uk; Tel 020 7261
9572; (Helpline) 080 8808 9572; Fax 020 7928 9542
Chief Executive Anne Keatley-Clarke
Speakability works with people with aphasia to overcome
the barriers they face by: supporting people living with
aphasia through its information service, national network
of groups and training courses and workshops; influencing
individuals and organisations in order to improve services
for people with aphasia and raising funds to support these
aims.

Sussex Family Mediation Service
Garton Hse, 22 Stanford Ave, Brighton, Brighton and Hove
BN1 6AA; E-mail sxfms@supanet.com; Tel 01273 550563;
Fax 01273 555412
Service Manager Leo Jago

Westminster Pastoral Foundation
23 Kensington Sq, London W8 5HN;
URL www.wpf.org.uk;
E-mail appeals@wpf.org.uk; Tel 020 7361 4800; Fax 020
7361 4808
Westminster Pastoral Foundation provides high quality
counselling and psychotherapy to those with mental and
emotional problems, high quality professional training in
counselling psychotherapy and conducts research into
methods of treatment.

16

Voluntary Service and Voluntary Health and Welfare Organisations

17

- ■ **Voluntary Services**
  England
  Wales
  Scotland
  Northern Ireland
- ■ **Community Service Volunteers**
- ■ **Women's Royal Voluntary Service**
- ■ **British Red Cross Society**
- ■ **St. John Ambulance**
- ■ **St. Andrew's Ambulance Association**
- ■ **National Association of Hospital and Community Friends**
- ■ **Other Voluntary Organisations**

Voluntary Service and Voluntary Health and Welfare Organisations

Voluntary Service England

Action with Communities in Rural England (Acre)

Somerford Crt, Somerford Rd, Cirencester, Gloucestershire
GL7 1TW; URL www.acre.org.uk;
E-mail acre@acre.org.uk; Tel 01285 653477; Fax 01285
654537
Co-ordinator (Policy and Information) Catherine Best
ACRE is the national association of rural community
councils, whose shared purpose is to improve the quality
of life of local communities and particularly of
disadvantaged people, in rural England. Its aim is to
facilitate the development of thriving, diverse and
sustainable communities throughout rural England.

Bedfordshire Rural Communities Charity

The Old School, Cardington, Bedford, Bedfordshire
MK44 3SX; E-mail brcc@bedsrcc.org.uk; Tel 01234
838771; Fax 01234 838149
Executive Director J. Ridge

Community Council for Berkshire

Epping Hse, 55 Russell St, Reading RG1 7XG;
E-mail ccberks@aol.com; Tel 0118 961 2000; Fax 0118 961
2600
Director Elaine Cooke

Buckinghamshire Community Action

Unit B The Firs, Aylesbury Rd, Bierton, Aylesbury,
Buckinghamshire HP22 5DX;
URL www.bucks-comm-action.org.uk;
E-mail bca@bucks-comm-action.org.uk; Tel 01296
421036; Fax 01296 330721
Chief Executive Catherine Johnstone

Cambridgeshire ACRE

32 Main St, Littleport, Ely, Cambridgeshire CB6 1PJ;
E-mail enquiries@cambsacre.org.uk; Tel 01353 860850;
Fax 01353 862040
Chief Executive Kirsten Bennett

Cheshire Community Council

96 Lower Bridge St, Chester, Cheshire CH1 1RU;
E-mail cheshire@comcouncil.freeserve.co.uk; Tel 01244
323602; Fax 01244 315389
Principal Officer Vivien Ellis

Cornwall Rural Community Council

9a River St, Truro, Cornwall TR1 2SQ;
E-mail info@cornwallrcc.co.uk; Tel 01872 273952;
Fax 01872 241511
Chief Executive O. Baines

Voluntary Action Cumbria

The Old Stables, Redhills, Penrith, Cumbria CA11 0DT;
E-mail sheilathompson@ruralcumbria.org.uk; Tel 01768
242130; Fax 01768 242134
Director K. Braithwaite

Derbyshire Rural Community Council

Church St, Wirksworth, Derbyshire DE4 4EY;
E-mail drcc@derbysrcc.org.uk; Tel 01629 824797;
Fax 01629 826053
Chief Officer M. Harris

Community Council of Devon

County Hall, Topsham Rd, Exeter, Devon EX2 4QB;
E-mail info@devonrcc.org.uk; Tel 01392 382533;
Fax 01392 382062
Chief Executive J. Talbot

Dorset Community Action

Community Hse, The Barracks, Bridport Rd, Dorchester,
Dorset DT1 1YG;
E-mail denise.paice@dorsetcommunityaction.org.uk;
Tel 01305 250921; Fax 01305 216420
Director J. Raimes

Durham Rural Community Council

Park Hse, Station Rd, Lanchester, Durham, County
Durham DH7 0EX; E-mail info@durhamrcc.org.uk;
Tel 01207 529621; Fax 01207 529619
Director L. Vallance

Rural Community Council of Essex

Mackmurdo Hse, 79 Springfield Rd, Chelmsford, Essex
CM2 6JG; E-mail celia.love@essexrcc.org.uk; Tel 01245
352046; Fax 01245 495427
Director N. Shuttleworth

Gloucestershire Rural Community Council

Community Hse, 15 College Grn, Gloucester,
Gloucestershire GL1 2LZ; E-mail gbsrcc@grcc.org.uk;
Tel 01452 528491; Fax 01452 528493
Director S. Wright

Community Action Hampshire

Beaconsfield Hse, Andover Rd, Winchester, Hampshire SO22 6AT; E-mail info@action.hants.org.uk; Tel 01962 854971; Fax 01962 841160
Chief Executive   R. Tulloch

Community First Herefordshire and Worcestershire

141 Church St, Malvern, Worcestershire WR14 2AN; E-mail info@communityhw.org.uk; Tel 01684 573334; Fax 01684 573367
Chief Executive   Richard Quallington

Community Development Agency for Hertfordshire

Birchwood Ave, Hatfield, Hertfordshire AL10 0PS; E-mail cdaforherts@boltblue.com; Tel 01707 695500; Fax 01707 695529
Director   J. Beswarick

Humber and Wolds Rural Community Council

14 Market Pl, Howden, Goole, East Riding of Yorkshire DN14 7BJ; E-mail brencocliff@hwrc.fsbusiness.co.uk; Tel 01430 430904; Fax 01430 432037
Director   Mary Cornwall

Isle of Wight Rural Community Council

3 Langley Crt, Pyle St, Newport, Isle of Wight PO30 1LA; E-mail mail@iwrcc.org.uk; Tel 01983 524058; Fax 01983 526905
Chief Executive   Sue Dovey

Kent Rural Community Council

15 Manor Rd, Folkestone, Kent CT20 2AH; E-mail info@kentrcc.org.uk; Tel 01303 850816; Fax 01303 850244
Director   C. Davies

Community Futures Lancashire

15 Victoria Rd, Fulwood, Preston, Lancashire PR2 4PS; E-mail ccl@communityfutures.org.uk; Tel 01772 717461; Fax 01772 900250
Chief Officer   D. Partington

Leicestershire and Rutland Rural Community Council

Community Hse, 133 Loughborough Rd, Leicester LE4 5LQ; E-mail sturner@ruralcc.org.uk; Tel 0116 266 2905; Fax 0116 266 0153
Director   Jeremy Prescott

Community Council of Lincolnshire

Church La, Sleaford, Lincolnshire NG34 7DF; E-mail office@cclincs.com; Tel 01529 302466; Fax 01529 414267
Chief Executive   S. Bland

Norfolk Rural Community Council

20 Market Pl, Hingham, Norfolk NR9 4AF; E-mail nrcc@norfolkrcc.demon.co.uk; Tel 01953 851408; Fax 01953 850695
Chief Executive Officer   J. Dixon

Northamptonshire ACRE

Hunsbury Hill Centre, Northampton, Northamptonshire NN4 9QX; E-mail acre@nacre.powernet.co.uk; Tel 01604 765888; Fax 01604 708571
Director   David Quayle

North Somerset Community Action

Church Hse, 74 Long Ashton Rd, Bristol BS41 9LE; E-mail mail@community-action.org.uk; Tel 01275 393837; Fax 01275 394563
Chief Executive   Vanessa Collier

Community Council of Northumberland

Tower Bldgs, 9 Oldgate, Morpeth, Northumberland NE61 1PY; E-mail info@ccn.org.uk; Tel 01670 517178; Fax 01670 511400
Director   D. Francis

Nottinghamshire Rural Community Council

Newstead Miners Welfare Community Centre, Tilford Rd, Newstead Village, Nottingham, Nottinghamshire NG15 0BS; E-mail enquiries@nottsrcc.org.uk; Tel 01623 727600; Fax 01623 720148
Chief Executive   B. Middleton

Oxfordshire Rural Community Council

Jericho Farm, Worton, Witney, Oxfordshire OX29 4SZ; E-mail orcc@oxonrcc.org.uk; Tel 01865 883488; Fax 01865 883191
Chief Executive   J. Hardwicke

Community Council for Somerset

Victoria Hse, Taunton, Somerset TA1 3JZ; E-mail pat@somersetrcc.org.uk; Tel 01823 331222; Fax 01823 323652
Chief Executive   David Smith

Community Council of Staffordshire

Friars Mill, Friars Terr, Stafford, Staffordshire ST17 4DX; E-mail communitycouncil@staffs.org.uk; Tel 01785 242525; Fax 01785 242176
Chief Executive   Andrew Halden

Suffolk ACRE

Suffolk Hse, 2 Wharfedale Rd, Ipswich, Suffolk IP1 4JP; E-mail info@suffolk.org.uk; Tel 01473 242500; Fax 01473 242530
Chief Executive   W. Gibson

Surrey Community Action

Astolat, New Inn La, Burpham, Guildford, Surrey GU4 7HL; E-mail info@surreyca.org.uk; Tel 01483 566072; Fax 01483 440508
Head (Communities Unit)   Abby Thomas

Action in Rural Sussex

Sussex Hse, 212 High St, Lewes, East Sussex BN7 2NH; E-mail info@ruralsussex.org.uk; Tel 01273 473422; Fax 01273 483109
Chief Executive   J. Leggett

Tees Valley Rural Community Council

New Exchange Bldgs, Queens Sq, Middlesbrough TS2 1AA; E-mail tvrcc@onyxnet.co.uk; Tel 01642 213852; Fax 01642 253289
Senior Rural Officer   Diane Harbron

Warwickshire Rural Community Council

Unit 25, Stoneleigh Deer Pk, Stareton, Kenilworth, Warwickshire CV8 2LY; E-mail enquiries@wrccrural.org.uk; Tel 024 7653 1280; Fax 024 7653 1296
Chief Officer   A. Chappell

Community First, Wiltshire

Wyndhams, St. Joseph's Pl, Devizes, Wiltshire SN10 1DD;
E-mail reception@communityfirst.org.uk; Tel 01380
722475; Fax 01380 728476
Director Ken Grimes

Yorkshire Rural Community Council

William Hse, Shipton Rd, Skelton, York YO30 1SF;
E-mail yrcc@williamhouse.co.uk; Tel 01904 645271;
Fax 01904 610985
Director Ian Strong

National Council for Voluntary Organisations (NCVO)

(Formerly National Council of Social Service)
Regent's Wharf, 8 All Saints St, London N1 9RL;
URL ncvo-vol.org.uk; E-mail ncvo@ncvo-vol.org.uk;
Tel 020 7713 6161; (Helpline) 0800 2798 798; Fax 020 7713
6300
Chief Executive S. Etherington
Director (Public Policy) Cambell Robb
Director (Planning and Support Services)
Catherine Wood
Director (Membership Services) Ben Kernighan
Head (Marketing) Diane Lightfoot
Head (Services Team) Jane Hatfield
The aims of NCVO are to provide a range of resources that
will increase the effectiveness of voluntary organisations; to
protect the interests and independence of voluntary
organisations; to promote the common interests of
voluntary organisations, particularly among policy makers
at government level. With its membership of national
voluntary agencies, its European and international
connections and its close affiliation with Rural Community
Council, Councils for Voluntary Service and Community
Associations, NCVO is in a position to encourage and
extend the participation of voluntary organisations in
responding to social issues. NCVO offers a range of
services to its members and other voluntary organisations,
including information, financial and legal advice. Its
publishing imprint is NCVO Publications which publishes
books on issues generic to the voluntary sector. Extensive
publications list available and magazine, NCVO News,
published ten times a year.

National Association of Councils for Voluntary Service (NACVS)

177 Arundel St, Sheffield, South Yorkshire S1 2NU;
URL www.nacvs.org.uk; E-mail nacvs@nacvs.org.uk;
Tel 0114 278 6636; Fax 0114 278 7004; Textphone 0114 278
7025
Chief Executive Kevin Curley
The National Association of Councils for Voluntary Service
(NACVS) is the growing network of over 300 Councils for
Voluntary Service (CVS) throughout England. The
Association helps to promote voluntary and community
action by supporting member CVS and by acting as a
national voice for the local voluntary and community
sector.

East of England

Basildon, Billericay and Wickford Council for Voluntary Service
CVS Office, Basildon Centre, St. Martin's Sq, Basildon,
Essex SS14 1DL; URL www.bbwcvs.org.uk;
E-mail enquiries@bbwcvs.org.uk; Tel 01268 288870
Chief Officer Lorna Wallace

Braintree District Voluntary Support Agency
Room 5, Colne Hse, 96 Mount Chambers, Braintree, Essex
CM7 9BY; URL www.bdvsa.org.uk;
E-mail bdvsa@bdvsa.org; Tel 01376 550507; Fax 01376
550092
Chief Officer Judy Cuddeford

Brentwood Council for Voluntary Service
c/o Brentwood Borough Council, Council Offices, Ingrave
Rd, Brentwood, Essex CM15 8AY;
E-mail enquiries@brentwoodcvs.org.uk; Tel 01277
222299; Fax 01277 260836
Chief Officer John Glanville

Broxbourne Voluntary Sector Development Agency
1–3 Albury Grove Rd, Cheshunt, Hertfordshire EN8 8NS;
URL www.bvsda.co.uk; E-mail bvsda@aol.com;
Tel 01992 638633; Fax 01992 638644
Chief Officer Ian Richardson

Cambridge Council for Voluntary Service
Llandaff Chambers, 2 Regent St, Cambridge,
Cambridgeshire CB2 1AX;
URL www.cambridge.cvs.org.uk;
E-mail enquiries@cambridge.cvs.org.uk; Tel 01223
464696; Fax 01223 500486
Chief Officer Lorna Davies

Cambridgeshire ACRE
32 Main St, Littleport, Ely, Cambridgeshire CB6 1PJ;
URL www.cambsacre.org.uk; Tel 01353 860850;
Fax 01353 862040
Chief Officer Kirsten Bennett;
E-mail kirsten.bennett@cambsacre.org.uk

Castle Point Association of Voluntary Services
The Tyrells Centre, 39 Seamore Ave, Benfleet, Essex
SS7 4EX; E-mail cavs.vb@virgin.net; Tel 01268 638416
Chief Officer Chris Moran

Chelmsford Council for Voluntary Service
1st Fl, 47 Broomfield Rd, Chelmsford, Essex CM1 1SY;
URL www.essexcc.gov.uk/community/chelmsfordcvs;
E-mail chelmsfordcvs@ukcharity.com; Tel 01245 351888;
Fax 01245 280731
Chief Officer Joan Hutchison

Colchester Community Voluntary Services
Winsley's Hse, High St, Colchester, Essex CO1 1UG;
URL www.ccvs.org; E-mail information@ccvs.org;
Tel 01206 505250; Fax 01206 500367
Chief Officer Samantha Drummond

Dacorum Council for Voluntary Service
48 High St, Hemel Hempstead, Hertfordshire HP1 3AF;
E-mail reception.dcvs@dial.pipex.com; Tel 01442 253935;
Fax 01442 239775
Chief Officer Julia Mayo

Epping Forest Council for Voluntary Service
Homefield Hse, Civic Offices, High St, Epping, Essex
CM16 4BZ; URL www.eppingforest.cvs.org.uk;
E-mail epping.cvs@virgin.net; Tel 01992 564178
Chief Officer Sally Hassan

Fenland and District Council for Voluntary Service
37–39 High St, March, Cambridgeshire PE15 9JJ;
URL www.fenland.cvs.org.uk;
E-mail fenlandcvs@hotmail.com; Tel 01354 659772;
Fax 01354 659772

Harlow Council for Voluntary Service
3 Wych Elm, Hamstel Rd, Harlow, Essex CM20 1QP;
URL www.harlocvs.demon.co.uk;
E-mail della.nash@harlocvs.demon.co.uk; Tel 01279
308308; Fax 01279 308313
Chief Officer Val Jepps

17

Community Development Agency for Hertfordshire
Birchwood Ave, Hatfield, Hertfordshire AL10 0PS;
URL www.cdaforherts.org.uk;
E-mail jeanbeswarick@cdaforherts.freeserve.co.uk;
Tel 01707 695500; Fax 01727 867491
Chief Officer Jean Beswarick

Hertsmere Community Voluntary Support
Allum Lane Community Centre, Allum La, Elstree,
Hertfordshire WD6 3PJ;
URL www.hertsmere.cvs.org.uk;
E-mail cvs@hertsmerecvs.fsnet.co.uk; Tel 020 8207 4504;
Fax 020 8207 1467
Chief Officer Robin Charnley

Hunts Forum of Voluntary Organisations
The Primrose Centre, Primrose La, Huntingdon,
Cambridgeshire PE29 1WG;
E-mail huntsfor@dialstart.net; Tel 01480 415178;
Fax 01480 415222
Chief Officer Sally Tubberdy

Ipswich and District Council for Voluntary Service
1 Cornhill, Ipswich, Suffolk IP1 1AQ;
E-mail enquiries@ipswich-cvs.org.uk; Tel 01473 251834;
Fax 01473 251848
Chief Officerr Richard Middleton

Voluntary Action Luton
15 New Bedford Rd, Luton LU1 1SA;
E-mail info@valuton.org.uk; Tel 01582 733418; Fax 01582
733013
Chief Officer Anne Laing

Maldon and District Council for Voluntary Service
The Square, Holloway Rd, Maldon, Essex CM9 4ER;
E-mail cvs.maldon@tiscali.co.uk; Tel 01621 851891;
Fax 01621 851896
Chief Officer Kevin Wearing

Mid Bedfordshire Council for Voluntary Service
10 Bedford St, Ampthill, Bedford, Bedfordshire MK45 2NB;
URL www.midbedscvs.org.uk;
E-mail midbedcvs@care4free.net; Tel 01525 841160
Chief Officer Mark Smith

North Bedfordshire Council for Voluntary Service
The Bedford Centre for Voluntary Services, 43 Bromham
Rd, Bedford, Bedfordshire MK40 2AA;
E-mail cvs@northbedscvs.org.uk; Tel 01234 354366;
Fax 01234 347503
Chief Officer Diane Wynne-Powell

North Hertfordshire Council for Voluntary Service
4 Grove Rd, Hitchin, Hertfordshire SG5 1SE;
E-mail nhcvs@care4free.net; Tel 01462 450022; Fax 01462
432999
Chief Officer Mervyn Terrett

Norwich and Norfolk Voluntary Services
Charing Cross Centre, St. John Maddermarket, Norwich,
Norfolk NR2 1DN; URL www.nvs.org.uk;
E-mail admin@nvs.org.uk; Tel 01603 614474; Fax 01603
764109
Chief Officer Ann Polley

Peterborough Council for Voluntary Service
3 Lincoln Crt, Lincoln Rd, Peterborough, Cambridgeshire
PE1 2RP; URL www.pcvs.care4free.net;
E-mail pcvs@care4free.net; Tel 01733 342683; Fax 01733
559057
Chief Officer John Cunningham

Rayleigh Association of Voluntary Services
The Foyer, 134 High St, Rayleigh, Essex SS6 7BX;
URL www.rravs.org.uk; E-mail rravs@rravs.org.uk;
Tel 01268 775255; Fax 01268 775255
Chief Officer Derek Helsen

Southend Association of Voluntary Services
SAVS Centre, 29–31 Alexandra St, Southend on Sea,
Southend SS1 1BW; URL www.savs-southend.co.uk;
E-mail info@savs-southend.co.uk; Tel 01702 356000;
Fax 01702 356011
Chief Officer Maureen Frewin

Voluntary and Community Action South Bedfordshire
Bossard Hse, West St, Leighton Buzzard, Bedfordshire
LU7 1DA; E-mail vols@sbcvo.freeserve.co.uk; Tel 01525
850559; Fax 01525 850559
Chief Officer John Gelder

St. Albans District Council for Voluntary Service
31 Catherine St, St.Albans, Hertfordshire AL3 5BJ;
URL www.stalbans.gov.uk/cvs;
E-mail peggy@cvsstalbans.freeserve.co.uk; Tel 01727
852657; Fax 01727 852656

Stevenage Council for Voluntary Service
Stevenage Voluntary Centre, Swingate, Stevenage, Hertford-
shire SG1 1RU; E-mail admin@stevenagecvs.solis.co.uk;
Tel 01438 353951; Fax 01438 722238
Chief Officer Ann Jansz

Suffolk ACRE Ltd
Suffolk Hse, 2 Wharfedale Rd, Ipswich, Suffolk IP4 4JP;
URL www.suffolkacre.org.uk;
E-mail info@suffolkacre.org.uk; Tel 01473 242500;
Fax 01473 242530
Chief Officer Wil Gibson

Suffolk Association of Voluntary Organisations (SAVO)
Dickson Hse, 43a Woodbridge Rd East, Ipswich, Suffolk
IP4 5QN; URL www.savo-online.com;
E-mail enquiries@savo.co.uk; Tel 01473 273273;
Fax 01473 725040

Tendring Community Voluntary Service
Imperial Hse, Rosemary Rd, Clacton-on-Sea, Essex
CO15 1NZ; URL www.tendring.cvs.org.uk;
E-mail tendringcvs@charity2000.fsnet.co.uk; Tel 01255
425692; Fax 01255 425126
Chief Officer Sharon Alexander

Three Rivers Council for Voluntary Service
24 Ebury Rd, Rickmansworth, Hertfordshire WD3 1BN;
URL www.threerivers-cvs.org.uk;
E-mail threerivers.cvs@virgin.net; Tel 01923 711174;
Fax 01923 711174
Chief Officer Mary Green

Thurrock Council for Voluntary Service
1st Fl, Thameside Complex, Cromwell Rd, Richmond Rd,
Grays, Essex RM17 5PD;
URL www.thurrock-community.org.uk;
E-mail tcvs1@unitynet.co.uk; Tel 01375 374093;
Fax 01375 374093
Chief Officer Natalie Warren

Council for Voluntary Service Uttlesford
12b Stortford Rd, Great Dunmow, Essex CM6 1DA;
E-mail cvs@uttlesford8.fsbusiness.co.uk; Tel 01371
878400; Fax 01371 878400
Chief Officer Sue Sumner

The Voluntary Network
1 Kingston Villa, Newmarket, Suffolk CB8 8EW;
URL www.newmarket-suffolk.com/forum;
E-mail voluntary-network@ntlworld.com; Tel 01638
608047; Fax 01638 600178
Chief Officer David Pitt

Watford Council for Voluntary Service
149 The Parade, Watford, Hertfordshire WD17 1RH;
URL www.watford.cvs.org.uk; Tel 01923 254400;
Fax 01923 213377
Chief Officer Avani Modasia

Waveney Community Forum Council for Voluntary Service
12 Grove Rd, Lowestoft, NR32 1EB;
E-mail info@wavenycf.org.uk; Tel 01502 582201
Chief Officer Sandra Jarvis

Welwyn and Hatfield Council for Voluntary Service
The Bill Salmon Centre, 88 Town Centre, Hatfield,
Hertfordshire AL10 0JW; URL www.whcvs.org.uk;
E-mail info@whcvs.org.uk; Tel 01707 274861; Fax 01707
258845
Chief Officer Carmen Dillion

West Norfolk Council for Voluntary Service
16 Tuesday Market Pl, King's Lynn, Norfolk PE30 1JN;
E-mail info@westnorfolk.cvs.org.uk; Tel 01553 760568;
Fax 01553 774399
Chief Officer Heather Farley,

East Midlands

Amber Valley Council for Voluntary Service
33 Market Pl, Ripley, Derbyshire DE5 3HA;
URL www.ambervalleycvs.org.uk;
E-mail admin@avcvs.org; Tel 01773 512076
Chief Officer Sue Naish

Ashfield Links Forum
The Council Offices, Fox St, Nottingham, Nottinghamshire
NG17 1BD; E-mail links@ashfieldlinks.org.uk; Tel 01623
555551; Fax 01623 555513
Chief Officer David Gilding

Bassetlaw Community and Voluntary Service
The Dukeries Centre, Park St, Worksop, Nottinghamshire
S80 1HH; URL www.bcvs.org.uk;
E-mail hello@bcvs.org.uk; Tel 01909 476118; Fax 01909
480501
Chief Officer Michael Newstead

Council for Voluntary Service Blaby District
The Parish Rooms, The Old School, Blaby Rd, Enderby,
Leicestershire LE19 4AP;
E-mail bcvs@cvsb.freeserve.co.uk; Tel 0116 275 1918;
Fax 0116 275 1942
Chief Officer Malcolm Flaherty

Voluntary Action Bolsover
Kitchencroft, Oxcroft La, Bolsover, Derbyshire S44 6NF;
URL www.bolsover.cvs.org.uk;
E-mail vabolsover@kitchencroft.fsnet.co.uk; Tel 01246
241730; Fax 01246 828660
Chief Officer Tom Winsborough

Boston District Council for Voluntary Service
The Len Medlock Voluntary Centre, St. George's Road,
Boston, PE21 8YB; URL www.bostoncvs.org.uk;
E-mail enquiry@bostoncvs.org.uk; Tel 01205 365580
Chief Officer Sarah Tanner

Charnwood Community Council
John Storer Hse, Wards End, Loughborough, Leicestershire
LE11 3HA; URL www.charnwoodcvs.org.uk;
E-mail enquiries@charnwoodcvs.org.uk; Tel 01509
631750; Fax 01509 230132
Chief Officer Neil Lambert

**Chesterfield and North East Derbyshire Council for
Voluntary Service and Action**
Ground Fl, Blenheim Crt, 17 Newbold Rd, Chesterfield,
Derbyshire S41 7PG; E-mail linkscvs@btconnect.com;
Tel 01246 274844; Fax 01246 274844
Chief Officer Carol Lawton

Derby Council for Voluntary Service
4 Charnwood St, Derby DE1 2GT; URL www.cvsderby.co.uk;
E-mail cvs@cvsderby.co.uk; Tel 01332 346266; Fax 01332
205069; Minicom 01332 341576
Chief Officer Mark Scothern

Derbyshire Dales Council for Voluntary Service
Council Offices, 3 Bath St, Bakewell, Derbyshire DE45 1BY;
E-mail enquiries@derbyshiredales.cvs.org.uk; Tel 01629
812154; Fax 01629 812491
Chief Officer Peter Fenton

Erewash Council for Voluntary Service
Parkland Connexion, Leopold St, Long Eaton,
Nottinghamshire NG10 4QE;
URL www.erewashcvs.org.uk;
E-mail enquiries@erewashcvs.org.uk; Tel 0115 849 0400;
Fax 0115 849 0370
Chief Officer Peter Edwards

Gedling Council for Voluntary Service
Park View Offices, Arnot Hill Pk, Nottingham Rd,
Nottingham NG5 6LU;
E-mail admin@gedlingcvs.org.uk; Tel 0115 926 6750;
Fax 0115 967 4545
Chief Officer Pam Wisher

Grantham and District Volunteer Bureau
26–27 St. Catherine's Rd, Grantham, NG31 6TT;
E-mail granthamvb@care4free.net; Tel 01476 570085;
Fax 01476 574367
Chief Officer Susan Swinburn

Voluntary Action Hinckley and Bosworth
12 Waterloo Rd, Hinckley, Leicestershire LE10 0QD;
URL www.hinckleycvs.org.uk;
E-mail hinckcvs@aol.com; Tel 01455 633002; Fax 01455
633002
Chief Officer Judy Handford

High Peak Council for Voluntary Service Planning
1a Bingswood Ind Est, Bingswood Ave, Whaley Bridge,
High Peak, Derbyshire SK23 7LY;
URL www.highpeakcvs.org.uk;
E-mail hello@highpeakcvs.org.uk; Tel 01663 735350
Chief Officer Kevin Skingsley

Voluntary Action Leicester
9 Newark St, Leicester LE1 5SN;
URL www.voluntaryactionleicester.org.uk;
E-mail info@voluntaryactionleicester.org.uk; Tel 0116
258 0666; Fax 0116 257 5059
Chief Officer Kevan Liles

Leicestershire and Rutland Council for Voluntary Service
Beaumont Enterprise Centre, Boston Rd, Leicester,
Leicestershire LE4 1HB; URL www.c-cp.org.uk;
E-mail gill@c-cp.org.uk; Tel 0116 234 1577
Chief Officer Gill Wolerton

Community Council of Lincolnshire
The Old Mart, Church La, Sleaford, NG34 7DF;
URL www.cclincs.com;
E-mail karen.watts@cclincs.com
Chief Officer Simon Bland

Mansfield Community and Voluntary Service
Community Hse, 36 Wood St, Mansfield, Nottinghamshire
NG18 1QA; URL www.mcvs.dial.pipex.com;
E-mail info@mansfieldcvs.org; Tel 01623 651177;
Fax 01623 635258
Chief Officer Sharon Clancy

Melton Borough Council for Voluntary Service
Windsor Hse, Windsor St, Melton Mowbray,
Leicestershire LE13 1BU;
E-mail cvsmelton@melton.solis.co.uk; Tel 01664
410007; Fax 01664 482902
Chief Officer Kathleen McKinley

NAVO
20 St. John St, Mansfield, Nottinghamshire NG18 1QJ;
E-mail navol@aol.com; Tel 01623 651170
Chief Officer Jon North

17

Newark and Sherwood Council for Voluntary Service
85 Millgate, Newark, Nottinghamshire NG24 4UA;
    URL www.newarkandsherwoodcvs.fsnet.co.uk;
    E-mail mschofield@nandscvs.org; Tel 01636 679539;
    Fax 01636 612296
Chief Officer   Julia Hughes

North West Leicestershire Council for Voluntary Service
Marlene Reid Centre, 85 Belvoir Rd, Coalville,
    Leicestershire LE67 3PH;
    E-mail mail@nwlcvs.demon.co.uk; Tel 01530 510515;
    Fax 01530 814632
Chief Officer   Martin Gage

Council for Voluntary Service Northampton and County
13 Hazelwood Rd, Northampton, Northamptonshire
    NN1 1LG; URL www.cvsnorthamptonshire.org.uk;
    E-mail cvs@cvsnorthamptonshire.org.uk; Tel 01604
    624121
Chief Officer   Mary Hopkins

Nottingham Council for Voluntary Service
7 Mansfield Rd, Nottingham NG1 3FB;
    URL www.nottinghamcvs.co.uk;
    E-mail ncvs@nottinghamcvs.co.uk; Tel 0115 934 8400;
    Fax 0115 934 8440
Chief Officer   Jane Sterck

Self Help Nottingham
Ormiston Hse, 32–36 Pelham St, Nottingham, NG1 2EG;
    URL www.selfhelp.org.uk;
    E-mail barbara-anne@selfhelp.org.uk; Tel 0115 911 1662;
    Fax 0115 911 1660
Chief Officer   Barbara-Anne Walker

Voluntary Action for Oadby and Wigston
Centre for Development and Volunteering, 132a Station Rd,
    Wigston, Leicestershire LE18 2DL;
    E-mail jpb@vaow.solis.co.uk; Tel 0116 281 0026; Fax 0116
    288 6423
Chief Officer   Wendy Aubrey
Chief Officer   Maureen Fisher

Rushcliffe Council for Voluntary Service
Park Lodge, Bridgford Rd, West Bridgford,
    Nottinghamshire NG2 6AT;
    URL www.rushcliffecvs.org.uk;
    E-mail paula@rushcliffecvs.org.uk; Tel 0115 981 6988;
    Fax 0115 974 8097
Chief Officer   Ian Bradford

Voluntary Action Rutland
Rutland Volunteer Centre, Barleythorpe Rd, Oakham,
    Rutland, Leicestershire LE15 6QH;
    E-mail v.a.r@rutnet.co.uk; Tel 01572 722622; Fax 01572
    722622
Chief Officer   Kathy Braddock
Chief Officer   Liz Tagg

South Derbyshire Council for Voluntary Service
48 Grove St, Swadlincote, Derbyshire DE11 9DD;
    URL beehive.thisisderbyshire.co.uk/sdcvs;
    E-mail office@southderbyscvs.org.uk; Tel 01283 550163;
    Fax 01283 550168
Chief Officer   Jo Smith

South Holland Voluntary Rural Council
2 Victoria St, Spalding, PE11 1EA;
    E-mail resources@vicstreet.fsbusiness.co.uk; Tel 01775
    766226; Fax 01775 766226
Chief Officer   Liz Peto

South Leicestershire Council for Voluntary Service
The Settling Rooms, St. Mary's Pl, Springfield St, Market
    Harborough, Leicestershire LE16 7DR;
    E-mail sleicscvs@aol.com; Tel 01858 433232; Fax 01858
    461617
Chief Officer   Stephen Banbury

London

Barking and Dagenham Council for Voluntary Service
Faircross Community Complex, Hulse Ave, Barking, Essex
    IG11 9UP; E-mail enquiriescvsbd@aol.com; Tel 020 8591
    5275; Fax 020 8591 0363
Chief Officer   Mark Thackham

Barnet Voluntary Service Council
1st Fl, Britannia Hse, 960 High Rd, London N12 9RY;
    URL www.barnetvsc.org.uk;
    E-mail admin@barnetvsc.org.uk; Tel 020 8446 6624;
    Fax 020 8446 6628
Chief Officer   Julie Hawkins

Bexley Voluntary Service Council
8 Brampton Rd, Bexleyheath, Kent DA7 4EY;
    E-mail information@bvsc.co.uk; Tel 020 8304 0911;
    Fax 020 8298 9583
Chief Officer   Janet Smith

Brent Association for Voluntary Action ((BRAVA))
25 High St, London NW10 4NE; URL www.brava.org.uk;
    E-mail info@brava.org.uk; Tel 020 8838 1350; Fax 020
    8838 1361
Chief Officer   Anju Bhatt

Community Links Bromley
Community Hse, South St, Bromley, Kent BR1 1RH;
    URL www.communitylinksbromley.org.uk;
    E-mail admin@communitylinksbromley.org.uk; Tel 020
    8315 1900; Fax 020 8315 1924
Chief Officer   Barbara Cracknell

Voluntary Action Camden
293–299 Kentish Town Rd, London NW5 2TJ;
    URL www.vac.org.uk; E-mail vac@vac.org.uk; Tel 020
    7284 6550; Fax 020 7284 6551
Chief Officer   Simone Hensby

Croydon Voluntary Action
97 High St, Thornton Heath, Surrey CR7 8RY;
    E-mail cva@cvalive.org.uk; Tel 020 8684 3862; Fax 020
    8665 1334
Chief Officer   Steve Phaure

Ealing Community and Voluntary Service
24 Uxbridge Rd, London W5 2BP;
    E-mail evsc@evsc.demon.co.uk; Tel 020 8579 6273;
    Fax 020 8567 4683
Chief Officer   Andy Roper

Enfield Voluntary Action
Community Hse, 311 Fore St, London N9 0PZ;
    E-mail evaction@tiscali.co.uk; Tel 020 8373 6268; Fax 020
    8373 6267
Chief Officer   Paula Jeffery

Greenwich Voluntary Action Council
The Old Town Hall, Polytechnic St, London SE18 6PN;
    E-mail gvac@ndirect.co.uk; Tel 020 8316 4774; Fax 020
    8316 4755
Chief Officer   Sharon Walker

Hackney Agency for Volunteering (HAVE)
92 Dalston La, Dalston, London E8 1NG;
    URL www.hackneyvoluntaryaction.org.uk;
    E-mail info@hackneyvoluntaryaction.org.uk; Tel 020
    7241 4443; Fax 020 7241 0043
Chief Officer   Janice Rafael

Voluntary Sector Resource Agency Hammersmith and Fulham
Aspen Hse, 1 Gayford Rd, London W12 9BY;
    E-mail info@vsra.org.uk; Tel 020 8762 0862; Fax 020 8749
    3874
Chief Officer   Penelope Harrison,

Haringey AVCO
Room 334, Lee Valley Technopark, Ashley Rd, London
N17 9LN; E-mail info@havcoharengey.org.uk; Tel 020
8800 4087
Chief Officer Roger Jones

Harrow Assocation of Voluntary Service
The Lodge, 64 Pinner Rd, Harrow, Greater London
HA1 4HZ; E-mail havs1@aol.com; Tel 020 8863 6707;
Fax 020 8863 8401
Chief Officer Margaret Nunn

**Havering Association of Voluntary and Community
Organisations (HAVCO)**
Community Hse, 19–21 Eastern Rd, Romford, Essex
RM1 3NT; URL www.havco.org.uk;
E-mail directorhavco@aol.com; Tel 01708 742881;
Fax 01708 744373
Chief Officer Kim Guest

Hillingdon Association of Voluntary Services
Key Hse, 106 High St, Yiewsley, West Drayton, Greater
London UB7 7BQ; URL www.havs.org.uk;
E-mail enquiries@havs.org.uk; Tel 01895 442722;
Fax 01895 442754
Chief Officer Carol Coventry

Hounslow Voluntary Sector Forum
Unit 9, Hounslow Business Pk, Alice Way, Hanworth Rd,
Hounslow, Greater London TW3 3UD;
E-mail hvsf@yahoo.co.uk; Tel 020 8572 5929; Fax 020
8572 9027
Chief Officer Rory Gillert

Islington Voluntary Action Council
322 Upper St, London N1 2XQ; URL www.ivac.org.uk;
E-mail information@ivac.org.uk; Tel 020 7226 4862;
Fax 020 7359 7442
Chief Officer David Abse

Kensington and Chelsea Social Council
Unit 1, Cloisters, 5 Kensington Church St, London W8 4LD;
URL www.kcsc.org.uk; E-mail info@kcsc.demon.co.uk;
Tel 020 7937 9512; Fax 020 7937 9526
Chief Officer Augustine Omara

Kingston Voluntary Action
Siddeley Hse, 50 Canbury Park Rd, Kingston-upon-
Thames, Surrey KT2 6LX; URL www.kva.org.uk;
E-mail info@kva.org.uk; Tel 020 8255 3335; Fax 020 8255
8804
Chief Officer Hilary Garner

Lambeth Voluntary Action Council
95 Acre La, London SW2 5TU; URL www.lambethvac.org.uk;
E-mail lvac@lambethvac.org.uk; Tel 020 7737 1419;
Fax 020 7737 4328
Chief Officer Conrad Hollingsworth

Voluntary Action Lewisham
120 Rushey Grn, Catford, London SE6 4HQ;
URL www.lewcvs.dircon.co.uk;
E-mail louise@lewcvs.dircon.co.uk; Tel 020 8314 9411;
Fax 020 8314 1315
Chief Officer Martin Howie

London Voluntary Service Council
London Voluntary Sector Resource Centre, 356 Holloway
Rd, London N7 6PA; URL www.lvsc.org.uk;
E-mail lvsc@lvsc.org.uk; Tel 020 7700 8107; Fax 020 7700
8108
Chief Officer Christina Schwabenland

Merton Voluntary Service Council
The Vestry Hall, London Rd, Mitcham, Surrey CR4 3UD;
E-mail info@mvsc.co.uk; Tel 020 8685 1771; Fax 020 8685
0249
Chief Officer Christine Frost

Newham Voluntary Service Council
Ithaca Hse, 27 Romford Rd, Stratford, London, E15 4LJ;
URL www.nvsc.org.uk; E-mail admin@nvsc.org.uk;
Tel 020 8519 9500; Fax 020 8519 9500
Chief Officer Sarah Ruiz

Redbridge Council for Voluntary Service
1st Fl, North Broadway Chambers, 1 Cranbrook Rd, Ilford,
Essex IG1 4DU; E-mail simon@redbridgecvs.net; Tel 020
8554 5049; Fax 020 8478 9640
Chief Officer Marcia Samuels

Richmond-upon-Thames Council for Voluntary Services
The Centre for Voluntary Services, 1 Princes St, Richmond-
upon-Thames, Surrey TW9 1ED;
URL www.richmondcvs.org.uk;
E-mail action@richmondcvs.org.uk; Tel 020 8255 8500;
Fax 020 8401 1967
Chief Officer Chris Whelan

Southwark Action for Voluntary Organisations
64 Camberwell Rd, London SE5 0EN;
URL www.savo.org.uk;
E-mail admin@savo.org.uk; Tel 020 7703 8733;
Fax 020 7703 9393
Chief Officer Jonathan Moore

Sutton Centre for Voluntary Service
Unilink Hse, 21 Lewis Rd, Sutton, Surrey SM1 4BR;
URL www.suttonvcs.org.uk;
E-mail info@suttoncvs.org.uk; Tel 020 8643 3277; Fax 020
8643 4178
Chief Officer Sue Robson

Tower Hamlets Community Organisations Forum
1st Fl, Norvin Hse, 45–55 Commercial St, London E1 6BD;
URL www.towerhamlets.org.uk;
E-mail admin@towerhamlets.cvs.org.uk; Tel 020 7426
9970
Chief Officer Jez Reeve,

Voluntary Action Waltham Forest
Unit 37, Alpha Business Centre, South Grove Rd,
Walthamstow, London E17 7NX;
E-mail vawf@dial.pipex.com; Tel 020 8521 0377; Fax 020
8521 1672
Chief Officer Ajamu Mutumwa

Wandsworth Volunteer Bureau
170 Garratt La, London, SW18 4DA; URL www.wvb.co.uk;
E-mail wvb@zoo.co.uk; Tel 020 8870 4319; Fax 020 8871
3502
Chief Officer Stefan Kuchar

Voluntary Action Westminster
37 Chapel St, London NW1 5DP; URL www.vawcvs.org;
E-mail general@vawcvs.org; Tel 020 7723 1216; Fax 020
7723 8929
Chief Officer Bernard Collier

North East

**2D (Teesdale and Wear Valley Council for Voluntary
Service)**
Unit 4, Crook Business Centre, New Rd, Crook, North
Yorkshire DL15 8QE; URL www.2d.org.uk;
E-mail m.armstrong@2d.org.uk; Tel 01388 762220;
Fax 01388 762225
Chief Officer Michele Armstrong

Blyth Valley Council for Voluntary Service
22 Beaconsfield St, Blyth, Northumberland NE24 2DP;
E-mail enquiries@blythvalley.cvs.org.uk; Tel 01670
353623; Fax 01670 359976
Chief Officer Thom Bradley

17

CAVOS (Community and Voluntary Organisations Sedgefield)
Block 2, 1st Fl, St. Cuthbert's Hse, Durham Way North, Aycliffe Ind Pk, County Durham, North Yorkshire DL5 6HW; URL www.cavos.org.uk; E-mail sbvb@freenet.co.uk; Tel 01325 313930
Chief Officer Robyn Holms

Chester-le-Street and District Council for Voluntary Service and Volunteer Bureau
Volunteer Centre, Clarence Terr, Chester-le-Street, County Durham DH3 3DQ; URL www.chesterlestreetcvsvb.org.uk; E-mail clscvs@cvsvb.fsnet.co.uk; Tel 0191 389 1960; Fax 0191 389 1960
Chief Officer Belinda Lowis

Darlington Council for Voluntary Service and Volunteer Bureau
Church Row, Darlington DL1 5QD; E-mail darlingtoncvs@onyxnet.co.uk; Tel 01325 266888; Fax 01325 266899
Chief Officer Kevin Richards

Derwentside Council for Voluntary Service
The Louisa Centre, Front St, Stanley, County Durham DH9 0TE; E-mail dcvs@derwentside.org.uk; Tel 01207 218855; Fax 01207 218849
Chief Officer Janice Docherty

Durham City District Council for Voluntary Service
7 Milliennium Pl, Durham, County Durham DH1 1WA; E-mail cvs@supanet.com; Tel 0191 384 4801; Fax 0191 384 4801
Chief Officer Julie Taylor

Durham Rural Community Council
Park Hse, Station Rd, Lanchester, County Durham DH7 0EX; E-mail drcc@onyxnet.co.uk; Tel 01207 529621; Fax 01207 529619
Chief Officer Leigh Vallance

Easington District Council of Voluntary Service
13 Upper Yoden Way, Peterlee, County Durham SR8 1AL; E-mail cvs_easington_district@care4free.net; Tel 0191 586 5427; Fax 0191 518 0889
Chief Officer Vacancy

Gateshead Voluntary Organisations Council
John Haswell Hse, 8–9 Gladstone Terr, Gateshead, Tyne and Wear NE8 4DY; URL www.gvoc.org.uk; E-mail gvoc@dial.pipex.com; Tel 0191 478 4103; Fax 0191 477 1260; Minicom 0191 478 4103
Chief Officer Pauline Nelson

Hartlepool Voluntary Development Agency
Rockhaven, 36 Victoria Rd, Hartlepool TS26 8DD; URL www.hvda.co.uk; E-mail info@hvda.co.uk; Tel 01429 262641; Fax 01429 265056
Chief Officer Keith Bayley

Newcastle upon Tyne Council for Voluntary Service
MEA Hse, Ellison Pl, Newcastle upon Tyne, Tyne and Wear NE1 8XS; URL www.cvsnewcastle.org.uk; E-mail ncvs@cvsnewcastle.org.uk; Tel 0191 232 7445; Fax 0191 230 5640; Minicom 0191 232 7445
Chief Officer Carole Howells

North Tyneside Voluntary Organisations Development Agency
Linskill Centre, Linskill Terr, North Shields, Tyne and Wear NE30 2AY; URL www.voda.org.uk; E-mail voda@voda-nt.demon.co.uk; Tel 0191 200 5790; Fax 0191 200 5791; Textphone 0191 200 6428
Chief Officer Jan Worters

Community Council of Northumberland
Tower Bldgs, 9 Oldgate, Morpeth, Northumberland NE61 1PY; E-mail info@ccn.org.uk; Tel 01670 517178; Fax 01670 511400
Chief Officer David Francis

Redcar and Cleveland Voluntary Development Agency
2nd Fl, Craighton Hse, West Terr, Redcar, North Yorkshire TS10 3BU; URL www.rcvda.org.uk; E-mail enquiries@rcdva.org.uk; Tel 01642 440571; Fax 01642 289177
Chief Officer Martin Harvey

South Tyneside Council for Voluntary Service
John Hunt Hse, 27 Beach Rd, South Shields, Tyne and Wear NE33 2QA; E-mail southtynesidecvs@btconnect.com; Tel 0191 456 9551; Fax 0191 456 0603
Chief Officer Allyson Stewart

Stockton Borough Voluntary Development Agency
27 Yarm Rd, Stockton-on-Tees TS18 3NJ; URL www.sbvda.net; E-mail office@stocktonvda.org; Tel 01642 355292; Fax 01642 355294
Chief Officer David Dorman-Smith

Sunderland Council for Voluntary Service
Riverview Hse, West Wear St, Sunderland, Tyne and Wear SR1 1ND; URL www.sunderland.com/voluntary; E-mail voluntary@sunderland.com; Tel 0191 565 1566; Fax 0191 568 0740
Chief Officer Gillian McDonough

Tees Valley Rural Community Council
2nd Fl, New Exchange Bldgs, Queen's Sq, Middlesbrough TS2 1AA; URL www.ovtv.org.uk; E-mail tvrcc@onyxnet.co.uk; Tel 01642 213852
Chief Officer Diane Harbron

Tynedale Voluntary Action
Hexham Community Centre, Gilesgate, Hexham, Northumberland NE46 3NP; URL www.tva.org.uk; E-mail tva@tva.org.uk; Tel 01434 601201; Fax 01434 606201
Chief Officer Mike Coleman

Wansbeck Council for Voluntary Service
107–109 Station Rd, Ashington, Northumberland NE63 8RS; URL www.wansbeckcvs.org.uk; E-mail enquire@wansbeck.cvs.org.uk; Tel 01670 858688; Fax 01670 813179
Chief Officer Sheila McGuckin,

North West

Barrow and District Council for Voluntary Service
Burlington Hse, Michaelson Rd, Barrow-in-Furness, Cumbria LA14 2RJ; URL www.barrowcvs.org.uk; E-mail network@bcvs.demon.co.uk; Tel 01229 823144; Fax 01229 823155
Chief Officer Janet Short

Bebington Centre for Voluntary Service
Voluntary Service Centre, 65 The Village, Bebington, Wirral CH63 7PL; URL www.merseyworld.com/bebington; E-mail info@bebingtoncvs.solis.co.uk; Tel 0151 643 7275; Fax 0151 643 7271
Chief Officer Annette Roberts

Blackburn with Darwen Council for Voluntary Service
St. John's Centre, Victoria St, Blackburn BB1 6DW; URL www.bwdcvs.org; E-mail mail@bwdcvs.org; Tel 01254 583957; Fax 01254 693932
Chief Officer Dorothy Whitaker

Blackpool, Wyre and Fylde Council for Voluntary Service
95 Abingdon St, Blackpool FY1 1PP;
E-mail admin@cvsblackpool.fsbusiness.co.uk; Tel 01253
624505; Fax 01253 295800
Chief Officer Carol Neale

Bolton District Council for Voluntary Service
Bridge Hse, Pool St South, Bolton, Lancashire BL1 2BA;
URL www.zen.co.uk/home/page/bcvs;
E-mail mail@boltoncvs.org.uk; Tel 01204 396011;
Fax 01204 373694; Minicom 01204 396011
Chief Officer Alison Hill

**Burnley, Pendle and Rossendale Council for Voluntary
Service**
ELVSRC, Rachel Kay-Shuttleworth Bldg, 62–64 Yorkshire
St, Burnley, Lancashire BB11 3BT;
URL www.bprcvs.co.uk; E-mail bprcvs@care4free.net;
Tel 01282 433740; Fax 01282 416146
Chief Officer Terry Hephrun

Bury CVS
6 Tenderten St, Bury, BL9 0EG; E-mail info@burycvs.org.uk;
Tel 0161 447 8450
Chief Officer Mike France

Carlisle Council for Voluntary Service
27 Spencer St, Carlisle, Cumbria CA1 1BE;
E-mail enquiries@carlisle.cvs.org.uk; Tel 01228 512513;
Fax 01228 512513
Chief Officer Lynne Sneap

Chester Council for Voluntary Service
Folliott Hse, 53 Northgate St, Chester, Cheshire CH1 2HQ;
E-mail enquiries@chestercvs.co.uk; Tel 01244 323527;
Fax 01244 315487
Chief Officer Alan Chapman

Chorley and South Ribble Council for Voluntary Service
Astley Hall Farmhouse, Hallgate, Astley Village, Chorley,
Lancashire PR7 1XA; E-mail c-sr.cvs@blueyonder.co.uk;
Tel 01257 263254; Fax 01257 234358
Chief Officer Cindy Bolton

Congleton District Council for Voluntary Service
11 Hope St, Sandbach, Cheshire CW11 1BA;
URL www.cdcvs.comcarenet.net;
E-mail cdcvs@comcarenet.net; Tel 01270 763100;
Fax 01270 763160
Chief Officer Jan Charles

**Crewe and Nantwich Council for Voluntary Service and
Volunteer Bureau**
Ashton Hse, 1a Gatefield St, Crewe, Cheshire CW1 2JP;
URL www.crewecvs.freeserve.co.uk;
E-mail wendy@crewecvs.freeserve.co.uk; Tel 01270
211545; Fax 01270 211545
Chief Officer Wendy Gjerstad

Voluntary Action Cumbria
The Old Stables, Redhills, Penrith, Cumbria CA11 0DT;
URL www.ruralcumbria.org.uk;
E-mail katebraithwaite@ruralcumbria.org.uk; Tel 01768
242130; Fax 01768 242134
Chief Officer Kathryn Braithwaite,

Eden Council for Voluntary Service
4b Redhills Bus Pk, Penrith, Cumbria CA11 0DT;
E-mail mailroom@edencvs.co.uk; Tel 01768 242138;
Fax 01768 210295
Chief Officer Karen Bowen

**Ellesmere Port and Neston Council for Voluntary Service
and Volunteer Bureau**
4 Shrewsbury Rd, South Wirral, Cheshire CH65 8AP;
E-mail janet@epncvs.net; Tel 0151 357 2931; Fax 0151 356
7491
Chief Officer Gareth Williams

Greater Manchester Centre for Voluntary Organisations
The St. Thomas Centre, Ardwick Green North, Manchester
M12 6FZ; URL www.gmcvo.org.uk;
E-mail gmcvo@gmcvo.org.uk; Tel 0161 277 1000;
Fax 0161 273 8296
Chief Officer Alex Whinnom

Halton Voluntary Action
Sefton Hse, Public Hall St, Runcorn, Cheshire WA7 1NG;
URL www.haltonva.org.uk;
E-mail haltonva@haltonva.org.uk; Tel 01928 592405;
Fax 01928 568713
Chief Officer Deborah Dalby

Heswall and District Council for Voluntary Service
Hillcroft, Rocky La, Heswall, Wirral CH60 0BY;
URL www.hdcvs.freeserve.co.uk;
E-mail enquiries@heswall.cvs.org.uk; Tel 0151 342 6115;
Fax 0151 342 6115
Chief Officer Joyce Spaven

**Hyndburn and Ribble Valley Council for Voluntary
Service**
Hyndburn Office, 21 Cannon St, Accrington, Lancashire
BB5 1NJ; E-mail hyndburncvs@btconnect.com; Tel 01254
879966; Fax 01254 879944
Chief Officer Christine Fish

Knowsley Council for Voluntary Service
Community Services Centre, Lathom Rd, Huyton,
Knowsley, Merseyside L36 9XZ;
URL www.knowsleycvs.org.uk;
E-mail kcvs@cybase.co.uk; Tel 0151 489 1222; Fax 0151
443 0251
Chief Officer Linda Walker

Lancaster District Council for Voluntary Service
Trinity Community Centre, Middle St, Lancaster,
Lancashire LA1 1JZ;
URL www.lancaster.cvs.org.uk;
E-mail email@lancaster.cvs.org.uk; Tel 01524 63760;
Fax 01524 68988
Chief Officer Fiona Gordon

Liverpool Council for Voluntary Service
14 Castle St, Liverpool, Merseyside L2 0NJ;
URL www.lcvs.org.uk;
E-mail info@liverpoolcss.org; Tel 0151 236 7728;
Fax 0151 258 1153
Chief Officer Alan Lewis

Local Solutions (formerly Merseyside CVS)
Mount Vernon Grn, Hall La, Liverpool, Merseyside L7 8TF;
URL www.localsolutions.org.uk;
E-mail info@localsolutions.org.uk; Tel 0151 709 0990;
Fax 0151 709 9326
Chief Officer Malcolm Pearson

Macclesfield District Council for Voluntary Service
81 Park La, Macclesfield, Cheshire SK11 6TX;
URL www.maccvol.btinternet.co.uk;
E-mail mdcvs@btclick.com; Tel 01625 428301; Fax 01625
619101
Chief Officer Keith Atherton

Voluntary Action Manchester
North Sq, 11–13 Spear St, Manchester M1 1JU;
URL www.vamanchester.org.uk;
E-mail vam@vamanchester.org.uk; Tel 0161 236 3206;
Fax 0161 228 0464
Chief Officer Robert Arnold

Oldham Development Agency for Community Action
Unit 12, Manchester Chambers, Oldham, Lancashire
OL1 1LF; URL www.odaca.net;
E-mail admin@odaca.net; Tel 0161 633 6222; Fax 0161
624 7451
Chief Officer Paula Boshell

17

Preston Council for Voluntary Service
Princes Bldg, 50–52 Lancaster Rd, Preston, Lancashire
PR1 1DD; URL www.preston.cvs.org.uk;
E-mail pcvs@voluntarysectorpreston.freeserve.co.uk;
Tel 01772 251108; Fax 01772 561264
Chief Officer Joan Burrows

Council for Voluntary Service Rochdale and Volunteer Development Agency
156–158 Drake St, Rochdale, Lancashire OL16 1PX;
E-mail cvsrochdale@care4free.net; Tel 01706 631291;
Fax 01706 710769
Chief Officer Julia Hayne

Salford Council for Voluntary Service
Old Town Hall , off Irwell Pl, Eccles, Salford, Greater
Manchester M30 0EJ; E-mail office@salfordcvs.co.uk;
Tel 0161 787 7795; Fax 0161 789 0818
Chief Officer David Mottram

Sefton Council for Voluntary Service
The Old Museum, Church Rd, Waterloo, Merseyside
L22 5NB; URL www.sefton.cvs.org.uk;
E-mail mail@seftoncvs.org.uk; Tel 0151 920 0726;
Fax 0151 920 1036
Chief Officer Angela White

Council for Voluntary Action South Lakeland
Stricklandgate Hse, 92 Stricklandgate, Kendal, Cumbria
LA9 4PU; E-mail info@cvasl.org.uk; Tel 01539 729168;
Fax 01539 725561
Chief Officer David Jones

St. Helens District Council for Voluntary Service
100 Corporation St, St. Helens, Merseyside WA10 1TB;
URL www.sthelenscvs.org.uk;
E-mail enquiries@sthelenscvs.org.uk; Tel 01744 21755;
Fax 01744 603544
Chief Officer Kate Williams

Stockport Council for Voluntary Service
Russell Morley Hse, 8–16 Lower Hillgate, Stockport,
Cheshire SK1 1JE; URL www.stockportcvs.co.uk;
E-mail info@stockportcvs.co.uk; Tel 0161 477 0246;
Fax 0161 477 8585
Chief Officer Lin Thomas

Tameside Third Sector Coalition
Suite 3, St Michael's Crt, St Michael's Sq, Ashton-under-
Lyme, Tameside OL6 6XN; URL www.t3sc.org.uk;
E-mail info@t3sc.org.uk; Tel 0161 339 4985; Fax 0161 339
9070
Chief Officer Moira Cunningham

Trafford Council for Voluntary Service
106a Harley Rd, Sale, Cheshire M33 7FP;
E-mail traffordcvs@lc24.net; Tel 0161 976 2448; Fax 0161
976 2433
Chief Officer Barbara Bleeker

Vale Royal Council for Voluntary Service
Waterside Hse, Navigation Rd, Northwich, Cheshire
CW8 1BE; E-mail info@valeroyalcvs.org.uk; Tel 01606
723180; Fax 01606 723181
Chief Officer Arthur Neil

Warrington Council for Voluntary Service
5 Hanover St, Warrington WA1 1LZ;
E-mail info@warrington.cvs.org.uk;
E-mail enquiries@warrington.cvs.org.uk; Tel 01925
630239; Fax 01925 630519
Chief Officer Mary Barbour

West Cumbria Council for Voluntary Service
1st Fl, Lowther Bldgs, 21b Lowther St, Whitehaven, Cumbria
CA28 7DG; E-mail chris@westcumbriacvs.solis.co.uk;
Tel 01946 852955; Fax 01946 852958
Chief Officer Christine Coombes

West Lancashire Council for Voluntary Service
Sandy Lane Centre, 49 Westgate, Skelmersdale, Lancashire
WN8 8LP; URL www.wlcvs.org;
E-mail enquiries@wlcvs.org; Tel 01695 733737; Fax 01695
558073
Chief Officer Barrie Moreton

Wigan and Leigh Council for Voluntary Service
93 Church St, Leigh, Greater Manchester WN7 1AZ;
URL www.wigan-vb-cvs.co.uk;
E-mail info@wigancvs.co.uk; Tel 01942 514234;
Fax 01942 514352
Chief Officer Sarah Mumby

Wirral Council for Voluntary Service
46 Hamilton Sq, Birkenhead, Wirral CH41 5AR;
URL www.wirralcvs.org.uk;
E-mail melanie@jonescvs.fsnet.co.uk; Tel 0151 647 5432;
Fax 0151 650 1402
Chief Officer Jean Benfield

South East

Action in Rural Sussex
Sussex Hse, 212 High St, Lewes, Sussex BN7 2NH;
URL www.srcc.org.uk; E-mail info@srcc.org.uk;
Tel 01273 473422
Chief Officer Pat Buesnel

Adur Council for Voluntary Service
6 Tarmount La, Shoreham by Sea, West Sussex BN43 6DA;
E-mail choff@adurcvs.solis.co.uk; Tel 01273 441662;
Fax 01273 441662
Chief Officer Pauline Price

Arunwide Council for Voluntary Service
Dove Lodge, 49 Beach Rd, Littlehampton, West Sussex
BN17 5JG; URL www.arun-cvs.fsnet.co.uk;
E-mail manager@arun-cvs.org.uk; Tel 01903 726228;
Fax 01903 726229
Chief Officer Hilary Spencer

Banbury and District Council for Voluntary Service
27 Horsefair, Banbury, Oxfordshire OX16 0AE; Tel 01295
279515; Fax 01295 279515
Chief Officer Jim Flux

Basingstoke Voluntary Services
The Orchard, White Hart La, Basingstoke, Hampshire
RG21 4AF; URL www.voluntaryservices.com;
E-mail bvs@voluntaryservices.com; Tel 01256 423800;
Fax 01256 423825
Chief Officer Christine Steer

Community Council for Berkshire
Epping Hse, 55 Russell St, Reading, Berkshire RG1 7XG;
E-mail ccberks@aol.com; Tel 0118 961 2000; Fax 0118 961
2600
Chief Officer Edward Crask

Bexhill Community Partnership
c/o Sidley Community Association, 121 Ninfield Rd,
Bexhill on Sea, East Sussex TN39 5BD;
E-mail mfisher@bexhillcp.fsnet.co.uk; Tel 01424 217259;
Fax 01424 217259
Chief Officer Martin Fisher

Bracknell Forest Voluntary Action
Coopers Hill Centre, Bagshot Rds, Bracknell, Bracknell
Forest RG12 7QS; E-mail info@bfva.org; Tel 01344
304404; Fax 01344 411878
Chief Officer Sue Telfer

Brighton and Hove Community and Voluntary Sector Forum
Community Base, 113 Queens Rd, Brighton, East Sussex
BN1 3XG; E-mail anna@cvsectorforum.org.uk; Tel 01273
234044; Fax 01273 234733
Chief Officer Anna King

Buckinghamshire Community Action
Unit B, The Firs, Aylesbury, Buckinghamshire HP22 5DX;
URL www.bucks-comm-action.org.uk;
E-mail bca@bucks-comm-action.org.uk; Tel 01296
421036; Fax 01296 331464
Chief Officer   Catherine Johnstone

Central Surrey Council for Voluntary Service
The Cedars, 14 Church St, Epsom, Surrey KT17 4QB;
E-mail centralsurreycvs@btconnect.com; Tel 01372
722911; Fax 01372 722911
Chief Officer   Bob Frisby

Chichester and District Council for Voluntary Service
60a North St, Chichester, West Sussex PO19 1NB;
E-mail katemoore@chichestercvs.fsnet.co.uk; Tel 01243
528615; Fax 01243 528615
Chief Officer   Kate Moore

Voluntary Action (Chiltern and South Bucks)
150 High St, Chesham, Buckinghamshire HP5 1EF;
E-mail office@vacsb.org.uk; Tel 01494 793470; Fax 01494
778987
Chief Officer   Diane Rutter

Crawley Council for Voluntary Service
The Tree, 103 High St, Crawley, West Sussex RH10 1DD;
E-mail info@crawleycvs.org; Tel 01293 526248; Fax 01293
529069
Chief Officer   Susan Knight

East Grinstead Council for Voluntary Service
Old Court Hse, College La, East Grinstead, West Sussex
RH19 3LS; E-mail mail@egcvs.fsnet.co.uk; Tel 01342
238080; Fax 01342 324664
Chief Officer   Felicity Cudworth

Voluntary Action for East Hampshire
48 Station Rd, Liss, Hampshire GU33 7AA;
URL www.action.hants.org.uk;
E-mail info@vaeh.org.uk; Tel 01730 301334; Fax 01730
301019
Chief Officer   Audrey Hollingbery

East Kent Council for Voluntary Service
Beach Hse, Beach St, Herne Bay, Kent CT6 5PT;
URL www.cvs-east-kent.org.uk;
E-mail enquiries@cvs-east-kent.org.uk; Tel 01227 373293;
Fax 01227 742575
Chief Officer   Ian McKewan

Eastbourne Association of Voluntary Service
8 Saffrons Rd, Eastbourne, East Sussex BN21 1DG;
URL www.eavs.org; E-mail info@eavs.org.uk; Tel 01323
639373; Fax 01323 410977
Chief Officer   Lesley Goble

Eastleigh Community Services
ECS Hse, 16 Romsey Rd, Eastleigh, Hampshire
SO50 9AL; URL www.ecs-vol.org;
E-mail reception@ecs-vol.org; Tel 023 8090 2400;
Fax 023 8090 2413
Chief Officer   Ken Dufton

**Elmbridge Council for Voluntary Service Steering
Committee**
Tudor Glade, c/o 12 Ashley Rise, Walton-on-Thames,
Surrey KT12 1ND; E-mail emerson@globalnet.co.uk;
Tel 01932 222759
Chief Officer   Kate Emerson

Fareham Community Action
5 Osborn Rd South, Fareham, Hampshire PO16 7DF;
URL www.farehamaction.org.uk;
E-mail admin@farehamaction.org.uk; Tel 01329 231899;
Fax 01329 311001
Chief Officer   Paul O'Beirne

Farnham Voluntary Service Council
Vernon Hse, West St, Farnham, Surrey GU9 7DR;
E-mail cvs@fvscfarnham.freeserve.co.uk; Tel 01252
725961; Fax 01252 737424
Chief Officer   Tony Shepherd

Gosport Voluntary Action
Bury Hse, Bury Rd, Gosport, PO12 3PX;
E-mail mail@gva.org.uk; Tel 023 9258 3836; Fax 023 9252
6323
Chief Officer   David Miles

Guildford Association of Voluntary Service
39 Castle St, Guildford, Surrey GU1 3UQ;
E-mail k.peters@gavs.org.uk; Tel 01483 504626;
Fax 01483 304229
Chief Officer   Vacancy

Community Action Hampshire
Beaconsfield Hse, Andover Rd, Winchester, Hampshire
SO22 6AT; URL www.action.hants.org.uk;
E-mail info@action.hants.org.uk; Tel 01962 854971;
Fax 01962 841160
Chief Officer   Richard Tulloch

Hart Voluntary Action
Harlington Way, Fleet, Hampshire GU51 4AE;
URL www.hartvolaction.org.uk;
E-mail info@hartvolaction.org.uk; Tel 01252 815652;
Fax 01252 811841
Chief Officer   Pam Worsfold

Hastings Voluntary Action
31a Priory St, Hastings, East Sussex TN34 1EA;
URL www.hastingsvoluntaryaction.org;
E-mail infoworker@hastingsvoluntaryaction.org;
Tel 01424 444010; Fax 01424 432877
Chief Officer   Steve Manwaring

Havant Council of Community Service
21 East St, Havant, Hampshire PO9 1AA;
E-mail havantccs@tiscali.co.uk; Tel 023 9264 5777;
Fax 023 9278 2300
Chief Officer   Sue Spencer

Horsham Area Council for Voluntary Service
Harvest Hse, 53–55 North St, Horsham, West Sussex
RH12 1RN; URL www.horsham.co.uk/hacvs;
E-mail john.moss@btclick.com; Tel 01403 255277;
Fax 01403 248700
Chief Officer   John Moss

ICIS
35 Worthing Rd, East Preston, Littlehampton, Sussex
BN16 1BQ; URL www.icis-westsussex.org.uk;
E-mail helpline@icis-westsussex.org.uk; Tel 0800 859929
Chief Officer   Anne Netley

Isle of Wight Rural Community Council
3 Langley Crt, Pyle St, Newport, Isle of Wight PO3 1LA;
URL www.iwrcc.org.uk; E-mail mail@iwrcc.org.uk;
Tel 01983 524058; Fax 01983 526905
Chief Officer   Sue Dovey

Kent Rural Community Council
15 Manor Rd, Folkestone, Kent CT20 2AH;
URL www.kentrcc.org.uk;
E-mail crispin.davies@kentrcc.org.uk; Tel 01303 850816;
Fax 01303 850244
Chief Officer   Crispin Davies

Council for Voluntary Service Medway
52 New Road Ave, Chatham, Kent ME4 6BG;
URL www.cvsmedway.cvs.org.uk;
E-mail postmaster@cvs-medway.demon.co.uk; Tel 01634
812850; Fax 01634 840611
Chief Officer   Gillian Wells

17

Mid and South East Kent Council for Voluntary Service
Berwick Hse, 8 Elwick Rd, Ashford, Kent TN23 1PF;
E-mail ashford@msekentcvs.fsnet.co.uk; Tel 01233
610171; Fax 01233 647021
Chief Officer Ann Roots

Mid Sussex (South) Council for Voluntary Service
38 Church Rd, Burgess Hill, West Sussex RH15 9AE;
E-mail midsussexsouth@cvsms.solis.co.uk; Tel 01444
258102; Fax 01444 258102
Chief Officer Janice Spence

Milton Keynes Council of Voluntary Organisations
Acorn Hse, 351 Midsummer Blvd, Milton Keynes
MK9 3HP; URL www.mkcvo.cvs.org.uk;
E-mail general@mkcvo.co.uk; Tel 01908 661623;
Fax 01908 200979
Chief Officer Ruth Stone

Community First New Forest
Public Offices, 65 Christchurch Rd, Ringwood, Hampshire
BH24 1DH; URL www.hants.gov.uk/nfvsc;
E-mail sonia@nfvsc.org; Tel 01245 482773; Fax 01425
482666
Chief Officer Andrew Strong

North West Kent Council for Voluntary Service
Enterprise Hse, 8 Essex Rd, Dartford, Kent DA1 2AU;
E-mail jim.nwkcvs@btinternet.com; Tel 01322 291060;
Fax 01322 291102
Chief Officer Jim Baker

Oxfordshire Council for Voluntary Action
The Old Court Hse, Floyds Row, Oxford, Oxfordshire OX1
1SS; URL www.ocva.org.uk; E-mail admin@ocva.org.uk;
Tel 01865 251946; Fax 01865 204138
Chief Officer Gwyn Huish

Portsmouth Council of Community Service
338 Commercial Rd, Portsmouth PO1 4BT;
E-mail enquiries@portsmouthccs.org.uk; Tel 023 9282
7110; Fax 023 9287 3785
Chief Officer Susan Newcombe

The Priory Centre (High Wycombe Council for Voluntary Service)
11 Priory Rd, High Wycombe, Buckinghamshire HP13 6SL;
URL www.priorycentre.org.uk;
E-mail wyccvs@nascr.net; Tel 01494 523440; Fax 01494
523247
Chief Officer Bill Reid

Reading Voluntary Action
8 Cross St, Reading, Berkshire RG1 4DJ;
E-mail rva@volaction.demon.co.uk; Tel 0118 957 4123;
Fax 0118 958 6131
Chief Officer Mike Martin

Reigate and Banstead Council for Voluntary Service
76 Station Rd, Redhill, Surrey RH1 1PL;
URL www.reigatebanstead.cvs.org.uk;
E-mail reigate.cvs@virgin.net; Tel 01737 763156;
Fax 01737 772098
Chief Officer Lynne Loving

Runneymede Association of Voluntary Services
12–13 The Sainsbury Centre, Chertsey, Surrey KT16 9AG;
URL www.ravs.dial.pipex.com;
E-mail ravs@dial.pipex.com; Tel 01932 571122; Fax 01932
566077
Chief Officer Heather Cook

Rushmoor Voluntary Services
Community Centre, Meudon Ave, Farnborough, Hampshire
GU14 7LE; URL www.users.dircon.co.uk/ rvs;
E-mail rvs@dircon.co.uk; Tel 01252 540162; Fax 01252
370500
Chief Officer Sally Saunderson

Rye and District Council for Voluntary Service
25 Cinque Ports St, Rye, East Sussex TN31 7AD;
E-mail mail@rdcvs.fsnet.co.uk; Tel 01797 225466;
Fax 01797 229448
Chief Officer Gina Sanderson

Slough Council for Voluntary Service
27 Church St, Slough, Berkshire SL1 1PL;
E-mail enquiries@slough.cvs.org.uk; Tel 01753 524176;
Fax 01753 535869
Chief Officer Adrian Hailer

South Downs Council for Voluntary Service
66 High St, Lewes, East Sussex BN7 1XG;
URL www.southdowns.cvs.org.uk;
E-mail enquiries@southdowns.cvs.org.uk; Tel 01273
483832; Fax 01273 483834
Chief Officer Colin Brown

Southampton Voluntary Services
18 Oxford St, Southampton SO14 3DJ;
URL www.southamptonvs.org.uk;
E-mail information@southamptonvs.org.uk; Tel 023 8022
8291; Fax 023 8022 2929; Minicom 023 8022 8291
Chief Officer Jo Ash

Voluntary Action in Spelthorne
Community Link, Knowle Grn, Staines, Greater London
TW18 1XB; E-mail sarahclarke-vais@lineone.net;
Tel 01784 446358; Fax 01784 446358
Chief Officer Sarah Clarke

Surrey Voluntary Service Council
'Astolat', Coniers Way, New Inn La, Guildford, Surrey
GU4 7HL; URL www.surreygateway.net;
E-mail info@surreyca.org.uk; Tel 01483 566072;
Fax 01483 440508
Chief Officer Julia Grant

Voluntary Service – Surrey Heath
Community Link, Surrey Heath Hse, Knoll Rd, Camberley,
Surrey GU15 3HH; URL www.vssh.org.uk;
E-mail chris@vssh.org.uk; Tel 01276 707565; Fax 01276
707567
Chief Officer Christine Furneaux

Swale Volunteering and Community Development Centre
Central Hse, Central Ave, Sittingbourne, Kent ME10 4NU;
URL www.swalevb.care4free.net;
E-mail swalevb@care4free.net; Tel 01795 473828;
Fax 01795 420336
Chief Officer Sandra Thorne

Tandridge Council for Voluntary Service
The Star Centre, The Library, Gresham Rd, Oxted, Surrey
RH8 0BQ; Tel 01883 722593; Fax 01883 715785
Chief Officer Andy Parr

Test Valley Community Services
Romsey Town Hall, Bell St, Romsey, Hampshire SO51 8GY;
URL www.tcvs.org.uk; E-mail romsey@tvcs.org.uk;
Tel 01794 519998; Fax 01794 517122
Chief Officer Janet Blann

Vale Volunteers
Hoseworth Hse, Oxford Rd, Aylesbury, HP19 3EQ;
URL www.valevolunteers.org.uk;
E-mail valevols@bucksnet.co.uk; Tel 01296 337456;
Fax 01296 718871
Chief Officer Karen Boddy

Wealden Federation of Voluntary Organisations
The Quickbourne Suite, Uckfield Civic Centre, Belfarm La,
Uckfield, East Sussex TN22 1AE;
URL www.wfvo.org.uk; E-mail info@wfvo.org.uk;
Tel 01825 767801; Fax 01825 767801
Chief Officer John Kelly

West Berkshire Council for Voluntary Service
Wichcombe Hse, 123–126 Bartholemew St, Newbury, West
Berkshire RG14 5BN;
URL www.westberkshire.cvs.org.uk;
E-mail westberkscvs2@hotmail.com; Tel 01635 523861;
Fax 01635 529722
Chief Officer   Karen Morton

West Kent Council for Voluntary Service
19 Monson Rd, Tunbridge Wells, Kent TN1 1LS;
URL www.westkentcvs.org.uk;
E-mail info@westkentcvs.org.uk; Tel 01892 530330;
Fax 01892 532539
Chief Officer   Caroline Shaw

Winchester Area Community Action
The Winchester Centre, 68 St. George's St, Winchester,
Hampshire SO23 8AH; URL www.waca.org.uk;
E-mail waca@waca.org.uk; Tel 01962 842293; Fax 01962
848029
Chief Officer   Diana Wooldridge

Windsor and Maidenhead Voluntary Action
67 St. Leonard's Rd, Windsor, Berkshire SL4 3BX;
URL www.wmvolaction.org.uk;
E-mail wmvolaction@aol.com; Tel 01753 622433;
Fax 01753 622433
Chief Officer   Fiona Winrow

Woking Association of Voluntary Service
Provincial Hse, 26 Commercial Way, Woking, Surrey
GU21 1EN; URL www.wavs.demon.co.uk;
E-mail info@wavs.org.uk; Tel 01483 751456; Fax 01483
740929
Chief Officer   Lesley Kitchen

Wokingham District Council for Voluntary Service
St. Nicolas Church Hall, Sutcliffe Ave, Reading, Berkshire
RG6 7JN; E-mail info@wdcvs.org; Tel 0118 926 5775;
Fax 0118 926 4551
Chief Officer   Martin Gilman

Worthing Council for Voluntary Service
3rd Fl, Colonnade Hse, Warwick St, Worthing, West Sussex
BN11 1DH; E-mail worthingcvs@btopenworld.com;
Tel 01903 528620; Fax 01903 528611
Chief Officer   Julia Carrette

South West

Bournemouth Council for Voluntary Service
Boscombe Link, 3–5 Palmerston Rd, Bournemouth
BH1 4HN; E-mail contactus@bournemouthcvs.co.uk;
Tel 01202 466130; Fax 01202 466130
Chief Officer   Jonathan Burke

Cheltenham Council for Voluntary Service
c/o Cheltenham CAB , 14 Royal Cres, Cheltenham,
Gloucestershire GL50 3DA;
URL www.cheltenham.cvs.org.uk;
E-mail ccvs@cheltenhamcvs.solis.co.uk; Tel 01242
227737; Fax 01242 704432
Chief Officer   Frances Robertson

Community First
Wyndhams, St. Joseph's Place, Devizes, SN10 1DD;
URL www.communityfirst.org;
E-mail kgrimes@communityfirst.org.uk; Tel 01380
722475
Chief Officer   Kenneth Grimes

Community Projects Trust
2a Fore St, Mount Folly, Bodmin, Cornwall PL31 2HQ;
URL www.community-projects-trust.org.uk;
E-mail comprojtru@aol.com; Tel 01208 75799
Chief Officer   Trevor Murden

Cornwall Voluntary Sector Forum
Cornwall Social Economy Unit, 14 Chapel St, Cornwall
TR14 8ED; URL www.cornwallrcc.co.uk/asps/
extra9.asp; E-mail kathryn@cornwallrcc.co.uk; Tel 01209
614952; Fax 01209 614951
Chief Officer   Rob Pickering

Cotswold Council for Voluntary Service
Cirencester Centre, 23 Sheep St, Cirencester, Gloucestershire
GL7 1QW; URL www.sc-vs.com; E-mail jane@sc-vs.com;
Tel 01285 658802; Fax 01285 659337
Chief Officer   Jane Winstanley

Dorset Community Action
Community Hse, The Barracks, Bridport Rd, Dorchester
DT1 1YG; URL www.dorsetcommunityaction.org.uk;
E-mail admin@dorsetcommunityaction.org.uk; Tel 01305
250921
Chief Officer   Jane Raimes

East Devon Council for Voluntary Service
Newholme Volunteer Centre, Northcote La, Honiton,
Devon EX14 1HS; URL www.edvsa.org.uk;
E-mail edvsa@eurobell.co.uk; Tel 01404 549045;
Fax 01404 549048
Chief Officer   Sue Tucker

Exeter Council for Voluntary Service
Wat Tyler Hse, King William St, Exeter, Devon EX4 6PD;
URL www.exetercvs.org.uk;
E-mail cvs@exetercvs.org.uk; Tel 01392 202055;
Fax 01392 202054
Chief Officer   John Bunting

Forest Voluntary Action Forum
The Belle Vue Centre, Cinderford, Gloucestershire
GL14 2AB; E-mail fvaf@ukonline.co.uk; Tel 01594
822073; Fax 01594 822073
Chief Officer   Tim Fretter

Gloucester Centre for Voluntary Services
75–81 Eastgate St, Gloucester, Gloucestershire GL1 1PN;
URL www.gloucestercvs.org.uk;
E-mail info@gloucestercvs.org.uk; Tel 01452 332424;
Fax 01452 332131
Chief Officer   Helen Hughes

Involve – Voluntary Action in mid-Devon
28 Gold St, Tiverton, Devon EX16 6PY;
URL www.involve-middevon.org.uk;
E-mail alison.goff@involve-middevon.org.uk; Tel 01884
255734
Chief Officer   Janine Lawley

Voluntary Action Kennet
Office D, 12 River St, Pewsey, Wiltshire SN9 5DH;
URL www.vak.org.uk; E-mail staff@vak.org.uk;
Tel 01672 564140; Fax 01672 564114
Chief Officer   Margaret West

The Learning Curve
St. George, 3-4 New Road, Chippenham, SN15 1EJ;
URL www.learningcurve.org.uk;
E-mail enquiries@learningcurve.org.uk; Tel 01249 464686
Chief Officer   Tim Ward

North Devon Voluntary Action Forum
c/o CAB , Belle Meadow Crt, Albert La, Barnstaple, Devon
EX32 8RJ; E-mail ndvaf@eurobell.co.uk; Tel 01271
377964; Fax 01271 377961
Chief Officer   Penny Jackson

North Dorset Volunteer Action
7 East St, Blandford Forum, Dorset DT11 7DU;
URL members.tripod.com/ndvolunteer;
E-mail office@ndcva.plus.com; Tel 01258 454678;
Fax 01258 454678
Chief Officer   Mike Oram

17

North Somerset LDWG
c/o Youth Community Service, Woodhurst Rd, Weston-super-Mare, BS23 3JR;
E-mail youth.community@n-somerset.gov.uk; Tel 01934 644075; Fax 01934 644168
Chief Officer   Philip Humphries

North Wiltshire Council for Voluntary Service
3–4 New Rd, Chippenham, Wiltshire SN15 1EJ;
URL www.cvsnw.org.uk; E-mail jj@cvsnw.org.uk;
Tel 01249 654089; Fax 01249 642561
Chief Officer   Janice Fortune

Okehampton and District Council for Voluntary Service and Volunteer Bureau
The Ockment Centre, North St, Okehampton, EX20 1AR;
E-mail oke-vb@eurobell.co.uk; Tel 01837 55047;
Fax 01837 55047
Chief Officer   Karen Nolan

Penwith Community Development Trust
Parade St, Penzance, Cornwall TR18 4BU;
E-mail pcdt@supanet.com; Tel 01736 330045; Fax 01736 331088
Chief Officer   Sue Guard

Plymouth Guild of Voluntary Service
Ernest English Hse, Plymouth PL1 2DA;
URL www.plymguild.demon.co.uk;
E-mail guild@plymguild.demon; Tel 01752 201766;
Fax 01752 201214
Chief Officer   George Plenderleith

Poole Council for Voluntary Service
Poole Advice Centre, 54 Lagland St, Poole BH15 1QG;
E-mail poolecvs@poolecvs.fsnet.co.uk; Tel 01202 682046;
Fax 01202 667187
Chief Officer   Christopher Beale

Salisbury and District Council for Voluntary Service
Greencroft Hse, 42–46 Salt La, Salisbury, Wiltshire SP1 1EG;
URL www.salisbury.cvs.org;
E-mail salisbury.cvs@ruralnet.org.uk; Tel 01722 421747;
Fax 01722 415544; Minicom 01722 421747
Chief Officer   Trevor Hazelgrove

South Gloucestershire Council for Voluntary Service
Elton Room, The Chantry, 52 Castle St, Thornbury,
BS35 1HB; URL www.southgloucestershire.cvs.org.uk;
E-mail development@southgloucestershire.cvs.org.uk;
Tel 01454 865205
Chief Officer   Rebecca Quick

South Hams Council for Voluntary Service
13 Leechwell St, Totnes, Devon TQ9 5SX;
URL www.southhamscvs.org.uk;
E-mail cvs@southhamscvs.org.uk; Tel 01803 862266;
Fax 01803 862230
Chief Officer   Ian Campbell

Stroud and District Council for Voluntary Service
10 The High St, Stonehouse, Gloucestershire GL10 2NA;
E-mail sdcvs@yahoo.co.uk; Tel 01453 828082; Fax 01453 828082
Chief Officer   Merci Rebati

Voluntary Action Swindon
1 John St, Swindon, Wiltshire SN1 1RT;
E-mail info@vas-swindon.org; Tel 01793 538398;
Fax 01793 538900
Chief Officer   Philip Baker

Taunton Deane Council for Voluntary Service
Old Municipal Bldgs, Corporation St, Taunton, Somerset
TA1 4AQ; URL www.taunton.cvs.org.uk;
E-mail enquiries@taunton.cvs.org.uk; Tel 01823 284470;
Fax 01823 333892
Chief Officer   Jenny Sparks

Tavistock and District Council for Voluntary Service
7 King St, Tavistock, PL19 0DS;
URL www.tavistock.cvs.org.uk;
E-mail tav-vb@eurobell.co.uk; Tel 01822 618224;
Fax 01822 618230
Chief Officer   Jan Simpson

Teignbridge Council for Voluntary Service
Maltings Resource Centre, Teign Rd, Newton Abbot, Devon
TQ12 4AA; URL www.teigncvs.org.uk;
E-mail mail@teigncvs.org.uk; Tel 01626 203050;
Fax 01626 203053
Chief Officer   Sandra Perry

Torbay Voluntary Service
11 Castle Rd, Torquay, Torbay TQ1 3BB;
URL www.torbayvs.co.uk; E-mail info@torbayvs.co.uk;
Tel 01803 212638; Fax 01803 213263
Chief Officer   Carole Schneider

Torridge Voluntary Services
14–14a Bridgeland St, Bideford, Devon EX39 2QE;
URL www.caringabouttorridge.org.uk;
E-mail pauline.tvs.bideford@lineone.net; Tel 01237 425554; Fax 01237 425554
Chief Officer   Pauline Smith

West Somerset Council for Voluntary Service
7 Quirke St, Minehead, Somerset TA24 5TZ;
E-mail wscvs@aol.com; Tel 01643 707484; Fax 01643 708824
Chief Officer   Graham Sutton

Voluntary Action West Wiltshire
Bridge Hse, Stallard St, Trowbridge, Wiltshire BA14 9AE;
E-mail vaww@globalnet.co.uk; Tel 01225 767993;
Fax 01225 776313
Chief Officer   Veronica McAndry

VOSCUR
The Create Centre, Smeaton Rd, Bristol, BS1 6XN;
URL www.voscur.org; E-mail info@voscur.org; Tel 0117 909 9949; Fax 0117 909 3346
Chief Officer   Jean Erskine

Yeovil and District Council for Voluntary Service
Petters Hse, Petters Way, Yeovil, Somerset BA20 1SH;
E-mail yeo.cvs@btconnect.com; Tel 01935 475914;
Fax 01935 411852
Chief Officer   Jean Newman

West Midlands

Birmingham Voluntary Service Council
138 Digbeth, Birmingham, West Midlands B5 6DR;
URL www.bvsc.org; E-mail admin@bvsc.org; Tel 0121 643 4343; Fax 0121 643 4541
Chief Officer   Jane Slowey

Bridgnorth Voluntary Action
Bridgnorth College, Stourbridge Rd, Bridgnorth,
Shropshire WV15 6AL; URL www.bridgnorth-va.net;
E-mail cvs@bridgnorth-va.net; Tel 01746 766477;
Fax 01746 766806
Chief Officer   Robert Money

Chase Council for Voluntary Service
CVS Bldgs, Arthur St, Cannock, Staffordshire WS11 2HD;
URL www.chase.cvs.org.uk;
E-mail cvs@chase.solis.co.uk; Tel 01543 500404;
Fax 01543 500406
Chief Officer   Kent Parson

Coventry Voluntary Service Council
6th Fl, Coventry Point, Market Way, Coventry, West
Midlands CV1 1EA; URL www.coventry-vsc.org.uk;
E-mail info@coventry-vsc.org.uk; Tel 024 7622 0381;
Fax 024 7625 7720
Chief Officer   Janice Nichols

Droitwich Spa and Rural Council for Voluntary Service
The Old Library Centre, 65 Omberley St East, Droitwich
Spa, Worcestershire WR9 8QS;
E-mail droitwichrescen@btclick.com; Tel 01905 779115;
Fax 01905 772010
Chief Officer Sue Poyer

Dudley Council for Voluntary Service
7 Albion St, Brierley Hill, West Midlands DY5 3EE;
URL www.dudleycvs.org.uk;
E-mail info@dudleycvs.org.uk; Tel 01384 78166;
Fax 01384 484587
Chief Officer Gillian Cooper

Community Action and Support – East Staffordshire
Voluntary Services Centre, Union St, Burton upon Trent,
Staffordshire DE14 1AA;
E-mail stellah@cases-vol.org.uk; Tel 01283 543414;
Fax 01283 512365
Chief Officer Stella Hudson

Hereford Voluntary Action
3 St. Peter's Cl, Hereford, HR1 2DL;
URL www.herefordshireva.org; E-mail hvc@wyenet.co.uk;
Tel 01432 343932; Fax 01432 352901
Chief Officer Philippa Money

Herefordshire and Worcestershire Community First
141 Church St, Malvern, WR14 2AN;
URL www.communityhw.org.uk;
E-mail info@communityhw.org.uk; Tel 01684 573334;
Fax 01989 567526
Chief Officer Richard Quallington

Council for Voluntary Service Ledbury and District
CVSLD Office, Salters Yard, Bye St, Ledbury, Herefordshire
HR8 2AA; E-mail admin@voluntaryactionledbury.org.uk;
Tel 01531 636006; Fax 01531 636333
Chief Officer Geoff Knock

Lichfield and District Council for Voluntary Services
Mansell Hse, 22 Bore St, Lichfield, Staffordshire WS13 6LL;
E-mail rosevakis@ldcvs.org.uk; Tel 01543 303030;
Fax 01543 303034
Chief Officer Rose Vakis

Community Action Malvern and District
3rd Fl, 28–30 Belle Vue Terr, Great Malvern, Worcestershire
WR14 4PZ; E-mail comact@malvernca.solis.co.uk;
Tel 01684 580638; Fax 01684 575155
Chief Officer Mike McKnight

Newcastle-under-Lyme Council for Voluntary Service
12 Andrew Pl, Newcastle-under-Lyme, Staffordshire
ST5 1DL; URL www.ncvsinstaffs.org;
E-mail general@nulcvs.co.uk; Tel 01782 629269;
Fax 01782 740186
Chief Officer Karen Phillips

North Shropshire VB
c/o SBC, The Manse, Doddington, Whitchurch, Shropshire
SY13 1DZ; E-mail nsvb@genie.co.uk; Tel 01948 667650;
Fax 01948 667651
Chief Officer Louise Stokes

North Warwickshire Council for Voluntary Service
Community Hse, Coleshill Rd, Atherstone, Warwickshire
CV9 1BN; URL www.nwcvs.org;
E-mail info@nwcvs.org.uk; Tel 01827 718080; Fax 01827
720416
Chief Officer Jacquie Aucott

Nuneaton and Bedworth Council for Voluntary Service
72 High St, Nuneaton, Warwickshire CV11 5DA;
URL www.cvsnunbed.co.uk;
E-mail lizs@cvsnunbed.co.uk; Tel 024 7638 5765; Fax 024
7637 4871
Chief Officer Liz Stuart

Oswestry Community Action
Cube, Oswald Rd, Oswestry, SY11 1RB;
URL www.qube-oca.ac.uk; E-mail qube@wnsc.ac.uk;
Tel 01691 656882; Fax 01691 680862
Chief Officer Trudi Graham

RAWM
2nd Fl, Waterlinks Hse, Richard St, Birmingham, B7 4AA;
URL www.rawm.org.uk; E-mail rawm@rawm.co.uk;
Tel 0121 359 9100
Chief Officer Chris Bonnard

Rugby Council for Voluntary Service
Council for Voluntary Services Hse, 19–20 North St, Rugby,
Warwickshire CV21 2AG;
E-mail rugbycvs@rugbycvs.org.uk; Tel 01788 574258;
Fax 01788 550786
Chief Officer Nicholas Wharton

Sandwell Council of Voluntary Organisations
128b Oldbury Rd, Smethwick, West Midlands B66 1JE;
E-mail leoner@scvo-sandwell.org.uk; Tel 0121 558 7434;
Fax 0121 558 9336
Chief Officer Leoner Garner

Voluntary Action Shrewsbury
Roy Fletcher Centre, 12–17 Crosshills, Shrewsbury,
Shropshire SY1 1JE;
URL www.shrewsburyvolunteers.cvs.org.uk;
E-mail info@shrewsburyvolunteers.cvs.org.uk; Tel 01743
341700; Fax 01743 244594
Chief Officer Peter Dunhill

Community Council Shropshire
1 College Hill, Shrewsbury, Shropshire SY1 1LT;
URL www.collegehill.org.uk;
E-mail enquiries@shropshire-rcc.org.uk; Tel 01743
360641; Fax 01743 233335
Chief Officer Julia Baron

Solihull Council for Voluntary Service
The Priory, Church Hill Rd, Solihull, West Midlands
B91 3LF; E-mail enquiries@solihull.cvs.org.uk; Tel 0121
704 1619; Fax 0121 711 4066
Chief Officer Andrew Moore

South Shropshire Voluntary Action
2a Palmers Hse, 7 Corve St, Ludlow, Shropshire
SY8 1DB; URL www.ssva.org.uk;
E-mail info@ssva.org.uk; Tel 01584 877756; Fax 01584
876177
Chief Officer Tina Healy

South Staffordshire Council for Voluntary Services
1 Stafford St, Brewood, Stafford, Staffordshire ST19 9DX;
E-mail volsec@sscvs.solis.co.uk; Tel 01902 851675;
Fax 01902 851685
Chief Officer Marian Thomas

Stafford District Voluntary Services
131–141 North Walls, Stafford, Staffordshire ST16 3AD;
URL www.sdvs.org.uk; E-mail admin@sdvs.org.uk;
Tel 01785 606670; Fax 01785 606669
Chief Officer Helen R. Dart

Staffordshire Moorlands Council for Voluntary Service
Bank Hse, 20 St. Edward St, Leek, Staffordshire ST13 5DS;
E-mail leek@smcvs.co.uk; Tel 01538 381356; Fax 01538
381356
Chief Officer David Titterton

Voluntary Action Stoke-on-Trent
The Dudson Centre, Hope St, Hanley, Stoke-on-Trent
ST1 5DD; E-mail info@vast.org.uk; Tel 01782 683030;
Fax 01782 683199
Chief Officer Mark Forrester

17

Stratford upon Avon District Council for Voluntary Service
The Hospital, Arden St, Stratford-upon-Avon, Warwickshire CV37 6NX; URL www.stratfordcvs.org.uk; E-mail alanb@care4free.net; Tel 01789 298115; Fax 01789 262886
Chief Officer   Alan Bartlett

Tamworth Council for Voluntary Service
The Carnegie Centre, Corporation St, Tamworth, Staffordshire B79 7DN; E-mail enquiries@tamworth-cvs.org.uk; Tel 01827 709657; Fax 01827 709660
Chief Officer   Simon Johnson

Telford and Wrekin Council for Voluntary Service
Meeting Point Hse, Southwater Sq, Telford, Wrekin TF3 4HS; E-mail telfordandwrekincvs@btinternet.com; Tel 01952 291350; Fax 01952 290384
Chief Officer   Michael Lloyd

Walsall Council for Voluntary Service
Jerome Chambers, 16a Bridge St, Walsall, West Midlands WS1 1HP; E-mail services@walsall-cvs.org.uk; Tel 01922 619840; Fax 01922 619848
Chief Officer   Angie Bradley-Davies

Council for Voluntary Service – Warwick District
109 Warwick St, Leamington Spa, Warwickshire CV32 4QZ; URL www.cvswd.spacomputers.com; E-mail information@cvswd.org.uk; Tel 01926 881151; Fax 01926 315112
Chief Officer   Stephen Nightingale

Wolverhampton Voluntary Sector Council
2–3 Bell St, Wolverhampton, West Midlands WV1 3TR; URL www.wolvesvsc.demon.co.uk; E-mail wvsc@wolverhampton.cvs.org.uk; Tel 01902 773761; Fax 01902 310270
Chief Officer   Ian Ellis

Worcester City Volunteer Bureau
33 Tything, Worcester, Worcestershire WR1 1JL; E-mail wcvb@btconnect.com; Tel 01905 24741; Fax 01905 723688
Chief Officer   Sally Ellison

Community Action Wyre Forest
Burgage Lodge, Franche Rd, Kidderminster, Worcestershire DY11 5AD; E-mail cawf@onetel.net.uk; Tel 01562 67008; Fax 01562 67008
Chief Officer   Sascha McDonald

Yorkshire and Humber

Voluntary Action Barnsley
35 Queens Rd, Barnsley, South Yorkshire S71 1AN; URL www.vabarnsley.org.uk; E-mail info@vabarnsley.org.uk; Tel 01226 242726; Fax 01226 206580
Chief Officer   Penny Stanley

Bingley Voluntary Action
Cardigan Hse, Ferncliffe Rd, Bingley, West Yorkshire BD16 2TA; E-mail bingley_voluntary_action@yahoo.co.uk; Tel 01274 781222; Fax 01274 400050
Chief Officer   Margaret Jackman

Boothferry Council for Voluntary Service
The Courtyard, Boothferry Rd, Goole, East Riding of Yorkshire DN14 6AE; URL www.boothferrycvs.org.uk; E-mail cvs@boothferrycvs.demon.co.uk; Tel 01405 837123; Fax 01405 837124
Chief Officer   Mike Moore

Bradford Community and Voluntary Service
19–25 Sunbridge Rd, Bradford, West Yorkshire BD1 2AY; URL www.bradfordcvs.org.uk; E-mail admin@computingbradford.org.uk; Tel 01274 722772; Fax 01274 393938
Chief Officer   Anthony Clipsom

Calderdale Council for Voluntary Service
1st Fl, Venture Hse, 1–9 Silver St, Calderdale, West Yorkshire HX1 1HS; URL www.cvac.org.uk; E-mail info@cvac.org.uk; E-mail enquiries@calderdale.cvs.org.uk; Tel 01422 348777; Fax 01422 348779
Chief Officer   Sajid Hashmi

Craven Voluntary Action
33 Coach St, Skipton, North Yorkshire BD23 1LQ; E-mail cravenva@totalise.co.uk; E-mail enquiries@craven.cvs.org.uk; Tel 01765 701056; Fax 01765 701611
Chief Officer   Caroline Long

Doncaster Council for Voluntary Service
Community Hse, 7 Netherhall Rd, Doncaster, South Yorkshire DN1 2PH; URL www.doncastercvs.org.uk; E-mail enquiries@doncastercvs.org.uk; Tel 01302 813333; Fax 01302 813335
Chief Officer   Norma Wardman

East Yorkshire Council for Voluntary Service
Bridlington Community Resource Centre, 4–6 Victoria Rd, Bridlington, East Riding of Yorkshire YO15 2BW; URL www.eycvs.org.uk; E-mail eycvs.bridlington@care4free.net; Tel 01262 677555; Fax 01262 401747
Chief Officer   Vacancy

Harrogate and Area Council for Voluntary Service
Community Hse, 46–50 East Pde, Harrogate, North Yorkshire HG1 5RR; URL www.harrogate.org; E-mail cvs@harrogate.org; Tel 01423 504074; Fax 01423 502126
Chief Officer   Hazel McGrath

Hull Council for Voluntary Service
Voluntary Organisations Centre, 29 Anlaby Rd, Hull, Kingston upon Hull HU1 2PG; URL www.hull.cvs.org.uk; E-mail hullcvs@hcvs.karoo.co.uk; Tel 01482 324474; Fax 01482 580565
Chief Officer   Dave Rogers

Humber and Wolds Rural Community Council
14 Market Pl, Howden, Goole, DN14 7BJ; E-mail h&wrcc@ruralnet.org.uk; Tel 01430 430904; Fax 01430 432037
Chief Officer   Mary Cornwell

Ilkley and District Council for Voluntary Service
Riddings Hall, Riddings Rd, Ilkley, West Yorkshire LS29 9LU; URL www.ilkley.org/cvs; E-mail ilkleycvs@icvs.fsnet.co.uk; Tel 01943 603348; Fax 01943 609906
Chief Officer   Gill Bowskill

Keighley Voluntary Services
Voluntary Services Centre, 135 Skipton Rd, Keighley, West Yorkshire BD21 3AU; E-mail info@keighleyvs.org; E-mail enquiries@keighley.cvs.org.uk; Tel 01535 665258; Fax 01535 691436
Chief Officer   Caroline Schwaller

Voluntary Action Kirklees
15 Lord St, Huddersfield, West Yorkshire HD1 1QB; E-mail vak@voluntaryactionkirklees.co.uk; E-mail enquiries@kirklees.cvs.org.uk; Tel 01484 518457; Fax 01484 518457
Chief Officer   Neil Bennett

Voluntary Action – Leeds
Stringer Hse, 34 Lupton St, Leeds, West Yorkshire
    LS10 2QW; URL www.val.org.uk;
    enquiries@leeds.cvs.org.uk; E-mail info@val.org.uk;
    Tel 0113 297 7920; Fax 0113 297 7921
Chief Officer   Rhona Davidson

North Bank Forum
Titus Salt Hse, Newland, Cottingham Rd, Kingston upon
    Hull, HU6 7RJ; URL www.northbankforum.org.uk;
    E-mail volorgs@nbforum.demon.co.uk; Tel 01482
    472458
Chief Officer   Rachel-Anne Heywood

Voluntary Action North East Lincolnshire
14 Town Hall St, Grimsby, DN31 1HN;
    E-mail vanel@care4free.net; Tel 01472 231123
Chief Officer   Helen Hardy
Chief Officer   Sally Nunn

Voluntary Action North Lincolnshire
41 Frances St, Scunthorpe, DN15 6NS;
    URL beehive.thisisscunthorpe.co.uk;
    E-mail fact@vanl.org; Tel 01724 845155; Fax 01724
    281599
Chief Officer   Carole Phillips

North Yorkshire Forum for Voluntary Organisations
Unit S, Alanbrooke Industrial Pk, Station Rd, Thirsk, North
    Yorkshire YO7 3SE; URL www.nyfvo.org.uk;
    E-mail nyfvo@nyfvo.org.uk; Tel 01845 578228; Fax 01845
    578249
Chief Officer   Neil Irving

Northallerton and District Voluntary Service Association
Community Hse, 10 South Pde, Northallerton, North
    Yorkshire DL7 8SE; E-mail post@ndvsa.co.uk; Tel 01609
    780458; Fax 01609 770570
Chief Officer   Hazel Kirby

Richmondshire Volunteer Centre
6 Flints Terr, Richmond, North Yorkshire DL10 7AH;
    URL www.communigate.co.uk/ne/richmondshirecvs;
    E-mail rcvs@pgen.net; Tel 01748 822537; Fax 01748
    822537
Chief Officer   Kay Lerigo

Ripon Council for Voluntary Service
Sharow View, Allhallowgate, Ripon, North Yorkshire
    HG4 1LF; E-mail riponcvs@riponcvs.demon.co.uk;
    Tel 01765 603631; Fax 01765 603329
Chief Officer   Lynette Barnes

Voluntary Action Rotherham
Durlston Hse, 5 Moorgate Rd, Rotherham, South Yorkshire
    S60 2EN; E-mail varotherham@tinyonline.co.uk;
    Tel 01709 829821; Fax 01709 829822
Chief Officer   Janet Wheatley

Ryedale Voluntary Action
Ryedale Community Hse, Wentworth St, Malton, North
    Yorkshire YO17 0BN; E-mail post@rva-cvs.org.uk;
    Tel 01653 600120; Fax 01653 695377
Chief Officer   Paul Hayward

Scarborough District Council for Voluntary Service
Allatt Hse, 5–6 West Parade Rd, Scarborough,
    North Yorkshire YO12 5ED;
    E-mail post@sdcvs.demon.co.uk; Tel 01723 362205;
    Fax 01723 507570
Chief Officer   Colin Barnes

Selby District Association of Voluntary Service
Abbey Yard Centre, Abbey Yard, Selby, North Yorkshire
    YO8 4PN; E-mail selbyavs@hotmail.com; Tel 01757
    291111; Fax 01757 290311
Chief Officer   Gill Cashmore

Voluntary Action Sheffield
69 Division St, Sheffield, South Yorkshire S1 4GE;
    URL www.vas.org.uk; E-mail admin@vas.org.uk;
    Tel 0114 249 3360; Fax 0114 249 3361; Minicom 0114 249
    3360
Chief Officer   Nick Warren

Shipley Council for Voluntary Service
Kirkgate Community Centre, Kirkgate, Shipley, West
    Yorkshire BD18 3EH;
    E-mail daverogers@scvs.go-legend.net; Tel 01274 591777;
    Fax 01274 530790
Chief Officer   Dave Rogers

Thirsk, Sowerby and District Community Care Association
14a Market Pl, Thirsk, North Yorkshire YO7 1LD;
    E-mail gill.middleton@tscca.co.uk; Tel 01845 523115;
    Fax 01845 525605
Chief Officer   Gill Middleton

Voluntary Action Wakefield District
13 Upper York St, Wakefield, West Yorkshire WF1 3LQ;
    URL www.wakefield.cvs.org.uk;
    E-mail enquiries@vawd.org.uk; Tel 01924 367418;
    Fax 01924 787370
Chief Officer   Peg Alexander

Whitby and District Volunteer Centre
Church Hse Centre, Flowergate, Whitby, North Yorkshire
    YO21 3BA; E-mail whitbydva@tiscali.co.uk; Tel 01947
    605256; Fax 01947 821819
Chief Officer   Rosanne Wyatt Bull

York Council for Voluntary Service
Priory Street Centre, 15 Priory St, York YO1 6ET;
    URL www.yorkcvs.org.uk/;
    E-mail yorkcvs@yorkcvs.org.uk; Tel 01904 621133;
    Fax 01904 630361
Chief Officer   Colin Stroud

Yorkshire Rural Community Council
William Hse, Shipton Rd, Skelton, York, YO30 1XF;
    E-mail yrcc@williamhouse.co.uk; Tel 01904 645271;
    Fax 01904 610985
Chief Officer   Ian Strong

National Council for Voluntary Youth Services (NCVYS)

2 Plough Yard, Shoreditch High Street, London EC2A 3LP;
    URL www.ncvys.org.uk; E-mail mail@ncvys.org.uk;
    Tel 020 7422 8630; Fax 020 7422 8631
Chief Executive   S. Rauprich
The National Council for Voluntary Youth Services
(NCVYS) is the independent voice of the voluntary sector
in England. A diverse network of over 160 national
voluntary and community youth organisations and
regional and local youth networks. NCVYS has been
working since 1936 to raise the profile of youth work, share
good practice and influence policy that has an impact on
young people and the organisations that support them.

Community Matters (National Federation of Community Organisations)

12–20 Baron St, London N1 9LL;
    URL www.communitymatters.org.uk;
    E-mail communitymatters@communitymatters.org.uk;
    Tel 020 7837 7887
Chair   Jackie Graham
Director   David Tyler
Hon Treasurer   Des Davis
Community Matters helps and speaks for community
organisations, with over 1000 members from England,

17

Wales and Scotland. It gives a national voice, assists the work and development of community organisations, promotes neighbourhood concerns, and gives support and advice services. The Community organisations it services are neighbourhood groups bringing together and developing the community through education, recreation, leisure/social welfare. Operating democratically they give a voice to the neighbourhood and run collective facilities.

Regional Office
6–8 York Pl, Leeds, West Yorkshire LS1 2DS; Tel 0113 244 3844
Deputy Director (Policy) Keith Kemp

LOCAL FEDERAL ORGANISATIONS OF THE NATIONAL FEDERATION OF COMMUNITY ORGANISATIONS

Barnsley Federation of Community Organisations Steering Group
101 New Lodge Cres, New Lodge, Barnsley, South Yorkshire S71 1SO; Tel 01226 289484
Secretary Terry Baggett

Carlisle and District Federation of Community Organisations
'Whinlatter', Heads Nook, Brampton, Carlisle, Cumbria CA8 9AJ; E-mail malcolmjackson2@compuserve.com; Tel 01228 791876
Press Officer Malcolm Jackson

Community Matters Buckinghamshire
Holman St, Aylesbury, Buckinghamshire HP19 3LJ; E-mail communitymattersbucks@tesco.net; Tel 01296 392498
Community Development Worker Claire Pollak

Community Matters Hertfordshire
(Hertfordshire except Dacorum)
99 Downlands, Chells Manor, Stevenage, Hertfordshire SG2 7BJ
Secretary Vacancy

Community Matters Portsmouth
157 Elm Gr, Southsea, Portsmouth PO5 1LJ; Tel 03292 827798
Treasurer Jill Wilson

Greater Manchester Federation of Community Organisations
(Metropolitan Boroughs of Bolton, Bury, Manchester, Oldham, Rochdale, Salford, Stockport, Trafford and Wigan)
Park View Centre, Hardman St, Chestergate, Stockport, Greater Manchester SK3 0DH; Tel (Day) 0161 476 2819; (Evenings) 0161 282 5329
Secretary Rose Walker

Havering Federation of Community Organisations
13 Norwood Ave, Romford, Essex RM7 0QD; Tel 01708 765306
Secretary Nigel Meyer

Oxford Federation of Community Organisations
Rose Hill Community Centre, The Oval, Rose Hill, Oxford, Oxfordshire OX4 4UY; Tel 01865 792168
Secretary Jim Barlow

South West Federation of Community Organisations
(Cornwall, Devon, Plymouth, Dorset and Somerset)
5 Turbill Gdns, Chaddlewood, Plymouth PL7 2XF; E-mail communitymatters@davidevery.clara.net; Tel 01752 330176
Secretary David Every

Swindon Federation of Community Organisations
Freshbrook Community Centre, Worsley Rd, Freshbrook, Swindon SN5 8LY; Tel 01793 871017
Chair Terry Iles

Tameside Association of Community Organisation
(Tameside, in Greater Manchester)
23 Ashbrook Ave, Denton, Manchester M34 2QJ; E-mail blowndes@mcri.poptel.org.uk; Tel 0161 273 6048 (Work); Fax 0161 336 5506
Secretary/Treasurer Barbara Lowndes

Walsall and District Federation of Community Organisations
Riley Hse, 25 Anchor Rd, Aldridge, West Midlands WS9 8PT; Tel 01922 720866
Chair and Acting Secretary Les Leak

West Sussex Federation of Community Organisations
34 Stanley Rd, Worthing, West Sussex BN11 1DT; E-mail ew.centre@talk21.com; Tel 01903 204805
Secretary Diane Bewley

Wolverhampton Federation of Community Organisations
(Wolverhampton, in the West Midlands)
51 Redhurst Dr, Ford Hse, Wolverhampton, West Midlands WV10 6QN; Tel 01902 781670
Secretary Lilian Bowkley

INDEPENDENT FEDERATIONS

Blyth Valley Federation of Community Organisations
Eric Tolhurst Centre, 3–13 Quay Rd, Blythe, Northumberland NE24 2AS; Tel 01670 540969
Secretary Vacancy

Community Associations of Peterborough
6 Egar Way, Bretton, Peterborough PE3 9AE; Tel 01733 267478
Vice-Chair Marion Hammett

Durham Association of Youth and Community Organisations
The Old School Hse, Front St, Framwellgate Moor, Durham, County Durham DH1 5BL; Tel 0191 384 9266
Chair Mary Tribe

Hull Federation of Community Organisations
c/o Lonsdale Community Centre, 8 Lonsdale St, Hull, Kingston upon Hull HU3 6PA; E-mail hullfed@infco.karoo.co.uk; Tel 01482 564691
Contact Sue Mellor

North East Council for Community Organisations
c/o Jarrow Community Association, Cambrian St, Jarrow, Tyne and Wear NE32 3QN; Tel 0191 483 2784
Secretary Malcolm Hardy

Sunderland Federation of Community Associations
6 Maples Ave, Silkworth, Sunderland, Tyne and Wear SR3 1DW
Secretary Sadie Thurlbeck

Voluntary Service Wales

Wales Council for Voluntary Action/ Cyngor Gweithredu Gwirfoddor Cymru (WCVA)

Baltic Hse, Mount Stuart Sq, Cardiff CF10 5FH; URL www.wcva.org.uk; E-mail enquiries@wcva.org.uk; Tel 02920 431700; Fax 02920 431701
North Wales Office, 13 Wynnstay Rd, Colwyn Bay, Conwy LL29 8NB; Tel 01492 539800
Head Office, Baltic Hse, Mount Stuart Sq, Cardiff, CF10 5FH; Tel 02920 431 777
Chief Executive Graham Benfield
Deputy Chief Executive Phil Jarrold

Director (Research) Lynda Garfield
Director (Communications) Lindsey Williams
Director (Grants) Geraint Humphreys
North Wales Office, 13 Wynnstay Rd, Colwyn Bay, Conwy
   LL29 8NB; Tel 01492 539800
Director (Volunteering) Sue Pickavance
Director (Finance) John Hewitt
Director (Training) Eileen Murphy
Head (Contracts) Roy Haley
North Wales Office, 13 Wynnstay Rd, Colwyn Bay, Conwy
   LL29 8NB
Head (Europe) Phil Fiander
Head (Grants) Sue Spurrier
Community Initiatives Policy Officer Alice Greenlees
Grants Assessor Andrew Owen
Help Officer Sioned Hughes
Policy Officer Gwenan Davies
Mid Wales Office, Park La Hse, 7 High St, Welshpool,
   Powys SY21 7JP; Tel 01938 552379
European Funding Adviser Ingela Mann
Mid Wales Office, Park La Hse, 7 High St, Welshpool,
   Powys SY21 7JP
European Projects Advisor Kevin Peacock

Mid Wales Office
Park Lane Hse, 7 High St, Welshpool, Powys SY21 7JP;
   Tel 01938 552379; Fax 01938 552092

North Wales Office
13 Wynnstay Rd, Colwyn Bay, Conwy LL29 8NB; Tel 01492
   539800; Fax 01492 539801

Welsh Association of County Voluntary Organisations

COUNCILS FOR VOLUNTARY SERVICE

Voluntary Action Cardiff
3rd Fl, Shand Hse, Fitzalan Pl, Cardiff CF24 0BE; Tel 029
   2048 5722; Fax 029 2046 4196
Director Paul Warren

Carmarthenshire Association of Voluntary Services
Ty Carwyn, 3 St. Peter's St, Carmarthen, Carmarthenshire
   SA31 1LN; E-mail director@cavs.org.uk; Tel 01267
   236367; Fax 01267 239933
Director Ieuan Williams

Denbighshire Voluntary Services Council
Naylor Leyland Centre, Well St, Ruthin, Denbighshire
   LL15 1AF; Tel 01824 702441; Fax 01824 705412
Chief Officer E. Godden

Gwent Association of Voluntary Organisations
8 Pentonville, Newport NP20 5XH;
   E-mail info@gavowales.org.uk; Tel 01633 213229;
   Fax 01633 221812
Director Mrs J.M. Render

Neath Port Talbot Council for Voluntary Service
Ty Margaret Thorne, 17–19 Alfred St, Neath, Neath Port
   Talbot SA11 1EF; E-mail nptcvs@ukonline.co.uk;
   Tel 01639 631246; 01639 642302; Fax 01639 646947
Neath Port Talbot Council for Voluntary Service exists to
support, promote and develop the participation of
community groups, voluntary organisations and
individuals in the voluntary sector throughout the Neath
Port Talbot area.
Opening times: Mon, Tue, Thur and Fri 0930–1230 and
1330–1630; Wed 1030–1230 and 1330–1630. Sat, Sun closed.

Powys Association of Voluntary Organisations
Davies Memorial Gallery, Newtown, Powys SY16 2NZ;
   Tel 01686 626220; Fax 01686 621537
Community Development Worker John Harrington
Community Development Worker Michele Muireagena

Sub-Offices
Brecknock
Brecon, Powys LD3 7AW; Tel 01874 622631; Fax 01874
   611952
Community Development Worker Tony Bell
Community Development Worker Hayley Price

Radnorshire
Middleton St, Llandrindod Wells, Powys; Tel 01597 822191;
   Fax 01597 824856
Director Linda Pepper

Swansea Council for Voluntary Service
7 Walter Rd, Swansea SA1 5NF; URL www.scvs.org;
   E-mail scvs@scvs.org.uk; Tel 01792 544000; Fax 01792
   544037
Director C. Green

Yyns Môn Voluntary Services
Room 20, Môn Training, Pengrorsedd Ind Est, Llangetui,
   Ynys Môn, Isle of Anglesey LL77 7JA;
   URL www.menternet.org.uk/ymvs/index.htm;
   E-mail wfxvs@anglesey.gov.uk; Tel 01248 752550;
   Fax 01248 752551

17

Voluntary Service Scotland

Scottish Voluntary Organisations

Voluntary Service Aberdeen
38 Castle St, Aberdeen AB11 5YU; URL www.vsa.org.uk;
   E-mail info@vsa.org.uk; Tel 01224 212021; Fax 01224
   580722

Arran Council for Voluntary Service
Park Terr, Lamlash, Isle of Arran KA27 8NB;
   E-mail arrancvs@scvo.org.uk; Tel 01770 600611;
   Fax 01770 600611
Manager Jan Schofield

Arran Citizens Advice Bureau
North Ayrshire Citizens Advice Service, Park Terr,
   Lamlash, Isle of Arran; Tel 01770 600210

Association of Local Voluntary Organisations
2 Hope St, Lanark, South Lanarkshire ML11 7LZ;
   URL www.alvo.org.uk; E-mail alvo@scvo.org.uk;
   Tel 01555 661233; Fax 01555 662633
Information, support, training and resources to Clydesdale
voluntary sector.

Ayrshire Federation of Community Associations
Community Education Service, 43 Birkshill, North Irvine,
Contact R.H. Giles

Voluntary Action in Badenoch and Strathspey
2 Inverewe Grampian Rd Shopping Centre, Aviemore,
   Highland PH22 1RH ; E-mail vabs@scvo.org.uk;
   Tel 01479 810004; Fax 01479 811058

BRIDGE Council for Voluntary Service
Voluntary Resource Centre, 17 South St, Mintlaw,
   Aberdeenshire AB42 5EL;
   E-mail bridgecvs@care4free.net; Tel 01771 624787;
   Fax 01771 624791
BRIDGE – a council for voluntary services in North
Aberdeenshire.

Berwickshire Association for Voluntary Service
9 Currie St, Duns, Scottish Borders TD11 3DL;
E-mail bavs@scvo.org; Tel 01361 883137; Fax 01361
883137
Contact A.J. Fowler

Blantyre Volunteer Group
75 Calder St, Blantyre, Glasgow G72 0AU; Tel 01698 821656;
Fax 01698 712284

Borders
Borders Forum of Councils of Voluntary Service
Contact John Wilson

Caithness Voluntary Group
Steven and Son, Harbour Quay, Wick, Caithness, Highland
KW1 5ER; E-mail cvg.net@virgin.net; Tel 01955 603453;
Fax 01955 603661

Central Borders Association of Voluntary Service
6a Roxburgh St, Galashiels, Scottish Borders TD1 1PF;
E-mail cbavs@scvo.org.uk; Tel 01896 752787; 01896
755370; Fax 01896 759661
Contact Janine Gordon

City of Glasgow Society of Social Service
30 George Sq, Glasgow G2 1EG; Tel 0141 248 3535
Contact Joyce Stevenson

**Community and Voluntary Organisations Council
(CAVOC)**
112 Windmillhill St, Motherwell, North Lanarkshire
ML1 1TA; URL www.cavoc.org.uk;
E-mail cavoc@btclick.com; Tel 01698 275469

Council for Voluntary Organisations in Kyle and Carrick
52 Main St, Ayr, South Ayrshire KA8 8EF; Tel 01292
282897

Dundee Voluntary Action
Number Ten, 10 Constitution Rd, Dundee DD1 1LL;
URL dra@number10.org; E-mail dva@number10.org;
Tel 01382 305732; Fax 01382 305729

East Kilbride Voluntary Organisations Council
14 Pankhurst Pl, Village, East Kilbride, South Lanarkshire
G74 4BH; URL www.ekvoc.org.uk;
E-mail ekvoc@scvo.org.uk; Tel 01355 237302

East Lothian Voluntary Organisations Network
82 High St, Tranent, East Lothian EH33 1HH; Tel 01875
615423
A council of voluntary service for East Lothian.

East Sutherland Council of Social Service
Pulrossie Farm, Dornoch, Highland IV25 3RL; Tel 0186 288
206
Contact Alison Burnett

Voluntary Action Resource Centre (Falkirk and District) Ltd
Falkirk Voluntary Centre, Old Sheriff Crt, Hope St, Falkirk
FK1 5AT; E-mail info@varc.org.uk; Tel 01324 636571;
Fax 01324 624269

Fife Day Care Services
70 Main St, Lochgelly, Fife KY5 9AA; Tel 01592 782889;
Fax 01592 784859

Council for Voluntary Service Fife
23–27 Randolph St, Buckhaven, Fife KY8 1AT;
URL cvsfife.org.uk; E-mail cvsfife@quista.net; Tel 01592
414588; Fax 01592 414591
Contact C. Patrick

Voluntary Organisations North East Fife
Volunteer Hse, 69–73 Crossgate, Cupar, Fife KY15 5AS;
URL www.vonef.org.uk; E-mail vonef@aol.com; Tel 0134
654080

Glasgow Community Councils Resource Centre
8 John St, Glasgow G1 1HP; Tel 0141 227 4723
Contact P. Lausen

Glasgow Council for the Voluntary Sector
11 Queen's Cres, Glasgow G4 9AS; URL www.gcvs.org.uk;
E-mail information@gcvs.org.uk; Tel 0141 332 2444;
Fax 0141 332 0175

Gordon Federation of Community Halls and Associations
c/o Ron Lyall, The Crags, Skene, Aberdeenshire AB32 7EQ;
Tel 0133 016 669

Hamilton Volunteer Group
57 Argyle Drive, Burnbank, Hamilton, South Lanarkshire
ML3 9EG; Tel 01698 891755; Fax 01698 420798

Harris Voluntary Service
Old Hostel, Tarbert, Harris, Isle of Harris, HS3 3BG;
E-mail hcvs@scvo.org.uk; Tel 01859 502171; Fax 01859
502303

Inverclyde Voluntary Council of Social Service
Unit 6, Drumfrochar Ind Est, Greenock, Inverclyde
PA15 4JY; Tel 01475 791938; 01475 791939
Hon President J. Barlas, MBE

Islay and Jura Council of Voluntary Service
Highfield, High St, Bowmore, Isle of Islay, Argyll and Bute
PA43 7JE; E-mail anne.clark2@virgin.net; Tel 01496 810743

Kilmarnock Volunteer Services
6 Grange St, Kilmarnock, East Ayrshire KA1 2AR; Tel 01563
541142

**Kincardine – Deeside Federation of Village Halls and
Associations**
Mar Lodge, Braemar, Aberdeenshire; Tel 01339 741427
Contact Sandra Dempster

Voluntary Action Lewis
30 Francis St, Stornoway, Isle of Lewis HS1 2ND;
E-mail valewis@cali.co.uk; Tel 01851 702632; Fax 01851
703035
Contact A. Nicholson

Lothian
Caring in Craigmillar, Ground Fl, 63 Niddrie Mains Terr,
Edinburgh EH16 4NX; Tel 0131 661 5852

Voluntary Action West Lothian
19 Jarvey St, Bathgate, West Lothian EH48 4EZ; Tel 01506
634115

Midlothian Voluntary Action
4–6 White Hart St, Dalkeith, Midlothian EH22 1AE;
E-mail mva@btinternet.com; Tel 0131 663 9471

Moray Voluntary Service Organisation
30–32 High St, Elgin, Moray IV30 1BU;
E-mail mvso@moray.gov.uk; Tel 01343 541 713;
Fax 01343 550554

**New Choices Volunteer Centre/Clackmannanshire
Community Transport Scheme**
14–16 Bank St, Alloa, Clackmannanshire FK10 1HP;
Tel 01259 215237; Fax 01259 215237

Nithsdale Council of Voluntary Service
Holywood Bldg, Old Assembly Cl, Irish St, Dumfries, Dum-
fries and Galloway DG1 2PH; E-mail info@ncvs.org.uk;
Tel 01387 269161; Fax 01387 269026

North West Sutherland Council for Community Action
The Schoolhouse, Strathnaver, Kinbrace, Highland
KW11 6UA; URL www.bratach.co.uk;
E-mail secretary.nws@btopenworld.com; Tel 01641
561214; Fax 01641 561211

North and West Sutherland Council of Social Service
Cruamar, Lochiver, Lairg, Highland IV27 4LD; Tel 0157 14
291
Contact N.A. MacAskill

Voluntary Action Inverness
1 Connel Crt, Ardconnel St, Inverness, Highland IV2 3EY;
E-mail vai@scvo.org.uk; Tel 01463 220922; Fax 01463
713691

Voluntary Action Orkney
Anchor Bldg, 6 Bridge St, Kirkwall, Orkney Islands
KW15 1HR; E-mail enquiries@vaorkney.org.uk;
Tel 01856 872897; Fax 01856 873167
Executive Director Norma Campbell, MBE

**Peebleshire Federation of Village Halls and Tweeddale
Association of Voluntary Organisations**
The Volunteer Resource Centre, Newby Crt, School Brae,
High St, Peebles, Scottish Borders EH45 8AL;
E-mail marlene.borthwick@tavo.org.uk; Tel 01721
723123
Manager Marlene Borthwick

Perth and Kinross Association of Voluntary Service Ltd
The Gateway, North Methven St, Perth, Perth and Kinross
PH1 5PP; E-mail pkavs@scvo.org.uk; Tel 01738 567076;
Fax 01738 440717

Ross-shire Voluntary Action
Thorfin Hse, Bridgend Bus Pk, Dingwall, Highland
IV15 9SL; URL www.rossvolact.org.uk;
E-mail alan@rossvolact.org.uk; Tel 01349 862431;
Fax 01349 861818

**Roxburgh Association of Voluntary Service and Roxburgh
Volunteer Centre**
1 Veitchs Cl, Jedburgh, Scottish Borders TD8 6AY;
E-mail ravs@scvo.org.uk; Tel 01835 863554; 01835 864728
Manager Heather Batsch
Manager Sue Bennett

Shetland
Shetland Council of Social Service, 11 Mounthooly St,
Lerwick, Shetland Isles ZE1 0BJ;
E-mail shetlandcss@zetnet.co.uk; Tel 01595 693816;
Fax 01595 696787
Executive Officer J.C. Irvine

Skye and Lochalsh Council for Voluntary Organisations
Tigh Lisiqarry, Bridge Rd, Portree, Isle of Skye IV51 9ER;
URL www.slcvo.co.uk; E-mail slcvo@scvo.org.uk;
Tel 01478 612921
Manager Chrisanne MacDonald

Stewartry Council of Voluntary Service
17 Castle St, Kirkcudbright, Dumfries and Galloway DG6
4JA; E-mail info@stewartrycvs.org.uk; Tel 01557 331346

Uist Council of Voluntary Organisations
Bldg 41, Airport Rd, Balivanich, Benbecula, Western Isles
HS7 5LA; E-mail ucvo@cali.co.uk; Tel 01870 602117
Manager Mr C. Atkin

Voluntary Groups – East Sutherland
ALBA, Main St, Golspie, Sutherland, Highland KW10 6TG;
E-mail ann@vges.org.uk; Tel 01408 633001; Fax 01408
634347

Western Isles
Voluntary Action Barra and Vatersay, Castlebay, Isle of
Barra HS9 5XD; Tel 01871 810401; Fax 01871 810638
Contact Jessie MacNeil

Voluntary Organisations Information Centre
98 High Blantyre Rd, Burnbank, Hamilton, South
Lanarkshire ML3 9HW; Tel 01698 821538
Contact W. Hamilton

Voluntary Service Northern Ireland

Bryson House

28 Bedford St, Belfast BT2 7FE;
URL www.brysonhouse.co.uk;
E-mail charity@brysonhouse.com; Tel 028 9032 5835;
Fax 028 9043 9156
Chair John Steele
Hon Treasurer W.F. Caldwell
Hon Secretary S. Bryson
Executive Director Jo Marley
Executive Director John McMullan
Agency for voluntary social action, responding to the needs
of the community in a practical way. Provides voluntary
services where there is an established need which is not
covered by statutory provision; pioneers innovative
projects to deal with problems such as community care,
unemployment, urban decay and marital stress; offers
nursery and other accommodation in Bryson House to
voluntary organisations; offers a range of consultancy,
advice and support services to Northern Ireland's
voluntary and community groups: substantial training
schemes for unemployed young people.

Bedtime Service
Bryson Hse, 28 Bedford St, Belfast BT2 7FE; Tel 028 9032
5835
Contact Eleanor McCrory
Volunteers helping elderly at bedtime.

Belfast Hills Unit
Knockbracken Healthcare Pk, Saintfield Rd, Belfast
BT8 8BH; E-mail bryson.house@lineone.net; Tel 028 9040
1684
Researching the problems of urban decay, and working at
improving the conditions and attitudes which contribute to
it. Practical support is provided for communities wishing
to improve their environment.

Community Development Programme
Bryson Hse, 28 Bedford St, Belfast BT2 7FE; Tel 028 9032
5835
Contact John McMullan
Works with local communities to improve their areas by
creating partnerships between statutory authorities and
local communities.

Computer Training Programme
Contact Monica Gallagher
Offers a wide range of classes from basic computer skills to
specialised training for specific software packages.

Energy First
1–11 May St, Belfast, BT1 4NA;
URL www.belfast-energy.demon.co.uk;
E-mail all@belfleac.demon.co.uk; Tel 02890 240664
Contact Orla Ward
Energy First is the umbrella organisation for the Bryson
House energy efficiency projects which include the Belfast
Energy Efficiency Advice Centre, Heatsmart, and the
Belfast Energy Agency. They provide free impartial energy
efficiency advice and give talks and presentations. The
Agency also has responsibility for the promotion of grants
and cashbacks and provides a free Home Energy Survey.
You can contact any of the projects.

Environmental Education Programme
Bryson Hse, 28 Bedford St, Belfast BT2 7FE;
E-mail james.thompson@nireland.com; Tel 028 9032
5835
Contact J. Thompson
Delivers environmental education courses to primary
schools throughout the province.

17

Family Support (Dunmurry/Lisburn)
Colin Family Centre, Pembrook Loop Rd, Dunmurry,
   Belfast BT17 0PH; Tel 028 9061 4433
Contact   Dawn Thompson

Family Support (North and West)
67 Woodvale Rd, Belfast BT13 6BW; Tel 028 9074 0926
Contact   Dawn Thompson

Family Support (North Down and Ards)
438 Frances St, Newtownards, County Down BT23 3DX;
   Tel 028 9182 3688
Contact   Dawn Thompson

Family Support (South and East)
28 Bedford St, Belfast BT2 7FE; Tel 028 9047 40926
Contact   Dawn Thompson
Offering practical help and emotional support to families
who are under stress, or where there is a risk that children
may be admitted to care.

Home from Hospital (South and East)
Bryson Hse, 28 Bedford St, Belfast BT2 7FE; Tel 028 9032
   5835
Contact   Elizabeth Lightbody

Laundry Service
Bryson Hse, 28 Bedford St, Belfast BT2 7FE
Contact   Eleanor McCrory
Bringing relief to households where one or more members
are suffering from incontinence.

Neighbourly Care (North Down and Ards)
Ards Development Bureau, 43–45 Francis St,
   Newtownards, County Down BT23 7DX;
   E-mail volunteerunitards@utvinternet.com; Tel 028 9182
   2556
Seeks to provide local flexible help to dependent
individuals and to identify, motivate and support
community members willing to share responsibility for
caring.

New Deal Training Programme
Contact   Trevor Wright;
   E-mail trevor.wright@brysonhouse.com
Provides a 46-place work experience training programme
for people who have been long-term unemployed.

No Age to Golden Age
An energy efficiency and home safety project targeted at
vulnerable individuals and families suffering from fuel
poverty. The programme, working within six Council areas
around the province, offers free advice to the householder
backed by the installation of energy saving, home safety
and water conserving measures.

Recycling Centre
Unit 3, 16 Prince Regent Rd, Belfast BT5 6QR;
   URL www.rubbish2resource.com;
   E-mail cashforcans@freeuk.com; Tel 02890 401 070;
   Fax 02890 401 050
Contact   Eric Randall
Kerbside recycling service offered in the greater Belfast area
and mobile collection of aluminium cans.

Student Unit
Contact   Pat McCarthy
Providing community social work placements in the
voluntary sector for social work students.

Home from Hospital North and West
67 Woodvale Rd, Belfast BT13 6BN; Tel 028 9075 4576
Contact   Marie Ruddock

Home from Hospital North Down and Ards
43–45 Francis St, Newtownards, County Down BT23 7DX

Volunteer Unit North Down and Ards
43–45 Francis St, Newtownards, County Down BT23 7DX;
   Tel 028 9182 2556
Providing volunteer opportunities throughout North
Down and Ards.

Northern Ireland Council for Voluntary Action (NICVA)

61 Duncairn Gdns, Belfast BT15 2GB; URL www.nicva.org;
   E-mail nicva@nicva.org; Tel 02890 877777; Fax 02890
   877799
Director   Seamus McAleavey
Information Officer   Elaine Campbell
NICVA is the umbrella body for voluntary, community and
charitable groups in Northern Ireland, providing its 550
affiliated members with information, advice and training
on a wide range of issues from management consultancy
and finance through to policy development and lobbying.
NICVA adopts a community development approach,
attempting to empower local communities to pursue their
own needs and agendas. Enquiries to the Information Officer.

Community Service Volunteers (CSV)

Headquarters, 237 Pentonville Rd, London N1 9NJ;
   URL www.csv.org.uk;
   E-mail 100631.1720@compuserve.com; Tel 020 7278 6601;
   Fax 020 7837 9621
Executive Director   Elisabeth Hoodless, CBE, JP
CSV creates opportunities for people to play an active part
in the life of their community through volunteering,
education, training and the media. Full-time volunteers
work mostly away from home with people who need their
help; CSV trains unemployed people for careers including
community care, horticulture, building, tourism and
enterprise; CSV Education encourages service learning
through publications, demonstration projects and a
nationwide student tutoring network; RSVP (Retired and
Senior Volunteer Programme) matches older people to
need through nationwide local groups of volunteers; CSV
Media works in partnership with radio and television to
provide media training and support services and produce
social action broadcasting.

Wales
4th Fl, Arlbee Hse, Greyfriars Rd, Cardiff CF10 3AE;
   E-mail csvcymrv@dial.pipex.com; Tel 029 2066 6737;
   Fax 029 2066 6738

Scotland
Wellgate Hse, 200 Cowgate, Edinburgh EH1 1NQ; Tel 0131
   622 7755

LOCAL OFFICES

Birmingham
St. Peter's Urban, Village Trust, Birmingham, West
   Midlands B8 3TE; URL www.csv.org.uk;
   E-mail mike@csvenvironment.org.uk; Tel 0121 327 1351;
   Fax 0121 328 7135

Bristol
17 Midland Rd, St. Phillips, Bristol BS2 0JT;
   URL www.csv.org.uk; Tel 0117 941 1114; Fax 0117 941
   2990

Cardiff
4th Fl, Arlbee Hse, Greyfriars Rd, Cardiff CF10 3AE;
   URL www.csv.org.uk; E-mail csvcymru@dial.pipex.com;
   Tel 029 2066 6737; Fax 029 2066 6738

Glasgow

236 Clyde St, Glasgow G1 4JH; URL www.csv.org.uk;
 E-mail csvvpglasgow@compuserve.com; Tel 0141 204
 1681; Fax 0141 204 1681

Tyneside

4th Fl Mea Hse, Ellison Pl, Newcastle upon Tyne, Tyne and
 Wear NE1 8XS; URL www.csv.org.uk; Tel 0191 232 6616;
 (NWNI) 0191 284 8371; (Training) 0191 213 5050

CSV Education

CSV, 237 Pentonville Rd, London N1 9NJ;
 URL www.csv.org.uk; E-mail dgar@csv.org.uk; Tel 020
 7278 6601; Fax 020 7278 1020
Director   Peter Hayes

CSV Media

See chapter 27
Director   Sue Farrington; Tel 020 7278 6601; Fax 020 7278
 7912

RSVP

CSV, 237 Pentonville Rd, London N1 9NJ;
 URL www.csv.org.uk;
 E-mail executiveofficer@rsvphq.fsnet.co.uk; Tel 020 7278
 6601; Fax 020 7833 8434
Director   Denise Murphy

Anglia

Tel 01733 394780

Isle of Wight

Tel 01983 864258
Contact   P. Wright

Kent/East Sussex

Tel 01227 459980
Contact   Muriel Jennings

London South

Tel 020 8300 5982
Contact   W. Barker

Glasgow

Tel 0141 882 7097
Contact   Ken Nicholson
Contact   Joan Fair
Contact   David Brookes

Midlands

Tel 0115 925 7353
Contact   Clive Donald

North West

Contact   Alan Brown

Outer London North

Tel 020 8440 2455
Contact   Bill Ibbotson

Outer London South

Tel 020 8777 5781
Contact   Louise Martin

Wales

Contact   Barne Cooper

South Wales

Tel 029 2062 7077
Contact   Vacancy

South West

Tel 01643 851484
Contact   A. Sherrett

Thames Valley

Tel 01625 39468
Contact   R. Robinson

Wessex

Tel 01202 673936
Contact   E. Paing

West

Tel 0117 962 8649
Contact   Bob Maggs

Yorkshire

Tel 01904 610198
Contact   J. Swain

CSV Environment

CSV Environment Manager   Mike Williams; Tel 0121 322
 2008; Fax 0121 322 2008

Bristol

Tel 0117 946 5216

Hereford

Tel 01432 356687

London

Tel 020 7278 6601

Midlands

Tel 0121 322 2008

Scotland

Tel 0141 248 6864

Wales

Tel 029 2066 6737

CSV Training and Enterprise

Manager   Bill Garland; Tel 020 7278 6601; Fax 020 7278
 2474

Avon Training

7–10 Lawford St, Bristol BS2 0DH;
 E-mail csvavontng@compuserve.com; Tel 0117 908 2266;
 Fax 0117 908 2277
Manager   Nicky Weekes

Avon Enterprise

Tel 0117 922 5585

17

Hereford Training

44 Berrington St, Hereford, Herefordshire HR4 0BJ;
E-mail tricia.csv.hfdtraining.demon.co.uk; Tel 0143 235
6687; Fax 0143 234 2707
Manager Tricia Hales

CVS Newcastle

3rd Fl, Stanesgate Hse, 2 Groat Market, Newcastle Upon
Tyne, Tyne and Wear NE1 1UQ;
E-mail margaret.csvnewc@dial.pipex.com; Tel 0191 232
6616; Fax 0191 230 0180
Manager Margaret Gibb

Northern Ireland

Young Help Trust, 23–31 Waring St, Belfast BT1 2DX;
E-mail younghelp@dnet.co.uk; Tel 028 9056 0120;
Fax 028 9056 0121
Manager Jeanette Murray

Scotland

Springboard Lanark Trust, 12–14 Draffen St, Motherwell,
Lanarkshire, ML1 1NL;
E-mail springboardlanark@dial.pipex.com; Tel 01698
258157; Fax 01698 276635
Manager Patricia Tinney

Springboard Bromley Trust

Bromley College, Rookery La, Bromley, Kent BR2 8HE;
E-mail administration@sbbro.demon.co.uk; Tel 020 8462
1222; Fax 020 8462 0094
Manager John Pink

Springboard Hackney Trust

1–9 Downham Rd, London N1 5AA;
E-mail vida.bond@springboardht.org.uk; Tel 020 7684
2345; Fax 020 7684 2346
Manager Vida Bond

Springboard Islington Trust

91–93 Parkhurst Rd, London N7 0LP;
E-mail springbd@dircon.co.uk; Tel 020 7700 0336;
Fax 020 7607 9770
Manager Gloria Appiah

Springboard Southwark Trust

821 Old Kent Rd, London SE15 1NY;
E-mail trocque@aol.com; Tel 020 7639 1007; Fax 020 7639
1767
Manager Terry Rocque

Springboard Sunderland Trust

184 Roker Ave, Sunderland, Tyne and Wear SR6 0BS;
E-mail spring.sun@dial.pipex.com; Tel 0191 564 0291;
Fax 0191 514 2429
Manager Colin Wilson

Training Options

236 Clyde St, Glasgow G1 4JH;
E-mail cvstrops@compuserve.com; Tel 0141 204 1681;
Fax 0141 221 9636
Manager Margaret Fox

CVS Training Wales

CVS Hse, Williams Way off Penrath Rd, Cardiff CF10 5DY;
E-mail allan@csvtw.freeserve.co.uk; Tel 029 2041 5700;
Fax 029 2041 5756
Manager Allan Hopkins

Volunteer Programme

Director Rebecca Rendle; Tel 020 7278 6601; Fax 020 7837
9318

Midlands Region

9th Fl, Elizabeth Hse, 22 Suffolk St, Queensway,
Birmingham, West Midlands B1 1LS;
E-mail bham@cvsmidlands.demon.co.uk; Tel 0121 643
8080; Fax 0121 643 6434
Region Director John Anderson

East Region

2nd Fl, 52 Burleigh St, Cambridge, Cambridgeshire
CB1 1DJ; E-mail csv@cambridgecsv.freeserve.co.uk;
Tel 01223 728460; Fax 01223 470122
Region Director Sue Gwaspari

London Region

237 Pentonville Rd, London N1 9NJ;
E-mail csvlondonvp@compuserve.com; Tel 020 7643
1408; Fax 020 7278 2864
Region Director Helen Drake

North Region

3rd Fl, Auburn Hse, Upper Piccadilly, Bradford, West
Yorkshire BD1 3NU;
E-mail csvnorthregion@bradford27.fsbusiness.co.uk;
Tel 01274 737266; Fax 01274 772190
Region Director Renee Gorman

East Scotland

Wellgate Hse, 200 Cowgate, Edinburgh EH1 1NQ;
E-mail is@connectfree.co.uk; Tel 0131 622 7766; Fax 0131
622 7355
Region Director Is Szoneberg

South East Region

Wenlock Hse, 41-43 North St, Brighton, Brighton and Hove
BN1 1RH; E-mail csv.brighton@ukonline.co.uk;
Tel 01273 748811; Fax 01273 748855
Region Director Billy Dann

South West Region

17 Midland Rd, St. Philips, Bristol BS2 0JT;
E-mail vpgloucester@csv.org.uk; Tel 0117 908 0070;
Fax 0117 908 1103
Region Director Paula Cannings

Wales

4th Fl, Arlbee Hse, Greyfriars Rd, Cardiff CF10 3AE;
E-mail csvcymru@dial.pipex.com; Tel 02920 666737;
Fax 02920 666738
Region Director Deryl Dix

West Scotland

236 Clyde St, Glasgow G1 4JH;
E-mail csvvpglasgow@compuserve.com; Tel 0141 204
1681; Fax 0141 204 0668
Region Director Kay Boyd

Women's Royal Voluntary Service

Milton Hill Hse, Milton Hill, Steventon, Abingdon,
Oxfordshire OX13 6AD; URL www.wrvs.org.uk;
E-mail volunteer@wrvs.org.uk; Tel 01235 442917;
Fax 01235 861166
Chair Tina Tietjen
Chief Executive G. Burton

WRVS is a registered charity and the largest practical voluntary organisation in Britain. The service has approximately 113 000 members. A growing 15 per cent of the members are men.

WRVS provides care and assistance in every major county town and city. Members are involved in a comprehensive range of projects and activities in response to local needs. Activities are split into four main areas – community services, food services, hospital services and emergency services.

Care in the Community and Food Services

Working closely with local authorities, activities include delivery of Meals on Wheels, Books on Wheels and providing other home support services, running contact centres for children of separated parents, running crèches, lunch clubs and tea bars in magistrates' courts and prisons.

Care in Hospitals

Activities include providing essential comfort and support to patients, staffing information desks for hospital visitors, assisting in blood donor centres, trolley shops for patients and running tea bars and shops for patients, staff and visitors.

Care in Emergencies

WRVS volunteers are available 24 hours a day to assist in any emergency/disaster. The volunteers provide assistance and refreshments to the rescue teams–ambulance, fire brigade, police etc. They set up rest centres for victims, provide them with emergency clothing and feeding and staff information points. Assistance is also given during community events with the provision of refreshments, crèches, information points etc.

Channel Islands

c/o WRVS Head Office, Milton Hill Hse, Abingdon, Oxfordshire OX13 6AF; Tel 01235 442903; Fax 01235 861166
Chair Tina Tietjen

Guernsey

Jubilee Day Centre, Grandes Maisons Rd, St. Sampson, Guernsey GY2 4JH; Tel 01481 47518; Fax 01481 47347

Jersey

25 Providence St, St. Helier, Jersey JE2 4SQ; Tel 01534 874838

Scotland

Edinburgh

44 Albany St, Edinburgh EH1 3QR; Tel 0131 556 4284; Fax 0131 557 5431

Wales

WRVS Wales

6 Cleeve Hse, Cardiff CF4 5GJ; Tel 029 2074 7717; Fax 029 2074 7796

British Red Cross Society

9 Grosvenor Cres, London SW1X 7EJ; Tel 020 7235 5454; Fax 020 7245 6315
Patron HM The Queen
Chair John McClure
Chief Executive Sir Nicholas Young
The British Red Cross is recognised in the Geneva Conventions as a Voluntary Aid Society – a role which requires the Society to work alongside the medical services in preparing for and responding to those crises resulting from war or aggression. That role is just as relevant during peacetime. Whatever the crisis, large or small, the British Red Cross provides services to help. From responding to emergencies such as Dunblane, providing first aid cover and training or helping people come through their own personal crises via services such as Transport and Escort and International Tracing, the British Red Cross is prepared to meet the needs of vulnerable people.

Founded in 1870, the British Red Cross has 30 000 volunteers offering services to their local community. These services are: Medical Loan, Transport and Escort, Health and Social Care, First Aid duties, Message and Tracing. For further details, please contact your local British Red Cross Branch.

The Society contributes to international relief by raising funds and providing relief and personnel through the International Committee of the Red Cross or the Federation of Red Cross Societies in Geneva and thence through the Red Cross Society of the country concerned.

17

England

Avon
Red Cross Hse, Alma Rd Ave, Bristol BS8 2DX; Tel 0117 973 8242

Bedfordshire
Red Cross County Office, 99 Ashburnham Rd, Bedford, Bedfordshire MK40 1EA; Tel 01234 349166

Berkshire
90 Eastern Ave, Reading RG1 5SF; Tel 0118 966 6645

Buckinghamshire
123 London Rd, High Wycombe, Buckinghamshire HP11 1BY; Tel 01494 525361

Cambridgeshire
2 Shaftesbury Rd, Cambridge, Cambridgeshire CB2 2BW; Tel 01223 354434

Cheshire
Memorial Hse, Northwich Rd, Knutsford, Cheshire WA16 0AW; Tel 01565 650201

Cornwall
Red Cross Hse, Lighterage Hill, Truro, Cornwall TR1 2XR; Tel 01872 272471

County Durham and Teeside
Flass Hse, Waddington St, Durham, County Durham DH1 4BG; Tel 0191 386 4367

Cumbria
Woolpack Yard, Kendal, Cumbria LA9 4NG; Tel 01539 721504

Derbyshire
Red Cross Hse, Matlock Grn, Matlock, Derby DE4 3EG; Tel 01629 582171

Devon
Ermen Hse, Butts Rd, Exeter, Devon EX2 5BD; Tel 01392 273932

Dorset
Red Cross County Office, Westminster Rd, Wareham, Dorset BH20 4SW; Tel 01929 551555

Essex
Red Cross Hse, 200 New London Rd, Chelmsford, Essex CM2 9AD; Tel 01245 490090; (Training Department) 01245 350433

Gloucestershire
Red Cross Hse, Cainscross, Stroud, Gloucestershire
GL5 4JQ; Tel 01453 762288

Greater Manchester
Bladbury Hse, Unit 4, Ohio Ave, Central Pk, Salford,
Greater Manchester M5 2GT; Tel 0161 888 8900

Hampshire
Red Cross Hse, Weeke, Winchester, Hampshire SO22 5JD;
Tel 01962 865174

Herefordshire and Worcestershire
Red Cross Hse, Green Hill, Worcester, Worcestershire
WR5 2AE; Tel 01905 351212

Hertfordshire
Baker St, Hertford, Hertfordshire SG13 7HT; Tel 01992
586609

Hull and East Riding
182 Chanterlands Ave, Hull, East Riding of Yorkshire
HU5 4DJ; Tel 01482 499830

Isle of Wight
Red Cross Hse, 1 Hunnycross Way, Newport, Isle of Wight
PO30 52D; Tel 01983 522718

Kent
Red Cross Hse, 25 College Rd, Maidstone, Kent ME15 6SX;
Tel 01622 690011

Lancashire
Pittman Crt, Pittman Way, Preston, Lancashire PR2 9ZG;
Tel 01772 709555

Leicestershire and Rutland
Red Cross Hse, 244 London Rd, Leicester LE2 1RN; Tel 0116
270 5087

Lincolnshire
22 London Rd, Grantham, Lincolnshire NG31 6EJ; Tel 01476
563378

London
3rd Fl, Tuition Hse, London SW19 4DT; Tel 020 8944 8909

Merseyside
Bradbury Hse, Tower St, Liverpool, Merseyside L3 4BJ;
Tel 0151 709 7799

Norfolk
Coronation Rd, Norwich, Norfolk NR6 5HD; Tel 01603
426361; 01603 426362

North Yorkshire
Red Cross Hse, Zetland St, Northallerton, North Yorkshire
DL6 1NB; Tel 01609 772186; (Training Department) 01609
775941

Northamptonshire
Red Cross Hse, Hatton Cl, Northampton,
Northamptonshire NN3 6SU; Tel 01604 495010

Northumbria
Croft Hse, Western Ave, Newcastle upon Tyne, Tyne and
Wear NE4 8SR; Tel 0191 273 7961; (Training Department)
0191 273 1673

Nottinghamshire
Great Freeman St, Nottingham NG3 1FR; Tel 0115 988
1710

Oxfordshire
Red Cross Hse, Colwell Dr, Abingdon, Oxfordshire
OX14 1AU; Tel 01235 555811

Shropshire
Sutton Lodge, Betton St, Shrewsbury, Shropshire SY3 7NY;
Tel 01743 351348

Somerset
Red Cross Hse, Livingstone Way, Taunton, Somerset
TA2 6BD; Tel 01823 273700

South Yorkshire
53 Clarkegrove Rd, Sheffield, South Yorkshire S10 2NH;
Tel 0114 266 0656; (Industrial Training) 0114 268 2722

Staffordshire
24 St. Leonard's Ave, Stafford, Staffordshire ST17 4LU;
Tel 01785 258155

Suffolk
Red Cross Hse, Lamdin Rd, Bury St. Edmunds, Suffolk
IP32 6NU; Tel 01284 767215

Surrey
Red Cross Headquarters, Woodlands Rd, Guildford, Surrey
GU1 1RL; Tel 01483 572396

Sussex
3 Howard Terr, Brighton, Brighton and Hove BN1 3TR;
Tel 01273 737514

Warwickshire
19 Coventry Rd, Cubbington, Leamington Spa,
Warwickshire CV32 7JN; Tel 01926 832446

West Midlands
Bradbury Hse, 7 Lowe St, Birmingham, West Midlands
B12 0ER; Tel 0121 766 5444

West Yorkshire
Beech Hse, 333 Leeds Rd, Bradford, West Yorkshire
BD10 9AB; Tel 01274 620999

Wiltshire
Red Cross Hse, Gains La, Devizes, Wiltshire SN10 1QU;
Tel 01380 730131

Isle of Man

Red Cross Hse, Derby Rd, Douglas, Isle of Man IM2 3EN;
Tel 01624 621857

Channel Islands

Jersey Committee
Serendine, La Petite Sente, St. Helier, Jersey JE2 6SN;
Tel 01534 852638

Bailiwick of Guernsey
Red Cross Hse, Rohais, St. Peter Port, Guernsey; Tel 01481
723088

Wales

Calon Cymru
31 Park St, Newtown, Powys SY16 1EF; Tel 01686 626663

Glamorgan/Morgannwg
Ground Fl, Riva Hse, Ynys Bridge Crt, Gwaelod-y-Garth,
Cardiff CF4 8YY; Tel 029 2081 0021

Gwent
35 Stow Park Circle, Newport NP9 4HF; Tel 01633 267131;
01633 267132

North Wales/Gogledd Cymru
Oxford Rd, Llandudno, Gwynedd LL30 1DH; Tel 01492
877886

South West Wales
16 Spilman St, Carmarthen, Carmarthenshire SA31 1JY;
Tel 01267 237874

Scotland

Head Office, Alexandra Hse, Glasgow G2 4HL; Tel 0141 332
9591

Argyll, Bute and Dumbartonshire
116 East Princes St, Helensburgh, Argyll and Bute
G84 7DQ; Tel 01436 672507

Ayrshire and Arran
18 Wellington Sq, Ayr, South Ayrshire KA7 1HA; Tel 01292
263946

Borders
1 Wheatlands Mill, Wheatlands Rd, Galasheils, Scottish
Borders TD1 2HQ; Tel 01896 751888

Dumfries and Galloway
Nith Ave, Dumfries, Dumfries and Galloway DG1 1EF;
Tel 01387 252858

Fife
Frankfield Hse, 22 Carlyle Rd, Kirkcaldy, Fife KY1 1DB;
Tel 01592 260252

Forth Valley
Red Cross Hse, 1 Glebe Ave, Stirling FK8 2HZ; Tel 01786
474620

Glasgow and Renfrewshire
2 Swan St, Glasgow G4 0AX; Tel 0141 332 1607

Highland and Western Isles
Forbes Hse, 36 Huntly St, Inverness, Highland IV3 5PR;
Tel 01463 231620

Lanarkshire
6 Auchingramont Rd, Hamilton, South Lanarkshire
ML3 6JT; Tel 01698 286354

Lothian
Beaverhall Hse, 27 Beaverhall Rd, Edinburgh EH7 4JE;
Tel 0131 557 9898

North East Scotland and Northern Isles
Red Cross House, 22 Queens Rd, Aberdeen AB1 4RT;
Tel 01224 647741

Tayside
51 Cowgate, Dundee DD1 2JF; Tel 01382 200084

Northern Ireland

(Regional Office)
87 University St, Belfast BT7 1HP; Tel 028 9024 6400

Belfast
125 University St, Belfast BT7 1HP; Tel 028 9032 2325

Down
The Lady Mairi Bury Hse, 20 Hamilton Rd, Bangor, County
Down BT20 4LE; Tel 028 9147 3343

Northern
Unit 5, The Courtyard, Ballymena, County Antrim
BT42 1HL; Tel 028 9065 8303

Western
54 High St, Omagh, County Tyrone BT78 1BP; Tel 028 8225
1116

The Order of St. John Ambulance

Priory of England and the Islands, 27 St. John's La, London
EC1M 4BU; Tel 020 7324 4000; Fax 020 7324 4001
Functions
St. John Ambulance exists to provide First Aid and medical
support services, caring services in support of community
needs and education, training and personal development to
young people. In pursuit of these aims, St. John
Ambulance: is the UK's leading First Aid training
organisation; trains nearly half a million people in First Aid
every year; has over 46 000 volunteers, well over half of
whom are under the age of 18; has two youth groups,
Badgers for 6–10 year olds and Cadets for 10–18 year olds;
provides Care in the Community services including a
library service and care for the elderly and homeless
people.
Local Authorities or anyone else wishing to consult or
enlist the aid of St. John Ambulance should refer to their
County Headquarters (see below) or to London
Headquarters (see above), addressing all enquiries to the
Chief Executive Officer.

Headquarters
Chief Commander   Peter Brown, EQ, BEM
Chief Executive   R. Holmes, CB

England

Avon St. John Ambulance
The Harry Crook Centre, Raleigh Rd, Bedminster, Bristol
BS3 1AP; E-mail sja@stjohnavon.demon.co.uk; Tel 0117
953 3880; Fax 0117 953 3890

Bedfordshire St. John Ambulance
St. John Hse, 34 St. John's St, Bedford, Bedfordshire
MK42 0DH; E-mail bedfordshire@st-john.co.uk;
Tel 01234 216200; Fax 01234 353163

Berkshire St. John Ambulance
County HQ, Church Rd, Woodley, Reading RG5 4QN;
E-mail sjaberks@sjaberks.demon.co.uk; Tel 0118 933
5500; Fax 0118 933 5555

Buckinghamshire St. John Ambulance
Robert Payne Training Centre, Tindal Rd, Aylesbury,
Buckinghamshire HP20 1HR;
E-mail countyhq@bucks.sja.org.uk; Tel 01296 393857;
01296 423886

Cambridgeshire St. John Ambulance
3 Barton Rd, Cambridge, Cambridgeshire CB3 9JZ;
Tel 01223 355334; Fax 01223 350630

Cheshire St. John Ambulance
PO Box 683, Valley Dr, Liverpool Rd, Chester, Cheshire
CH1 1FA; E-mail countyhq@cheshire.sja.org.uk;
Tel (24 hour Answer Service) 01244 383407; Fax 01244
383406

Cornwall St. John Ambulance
Par Moor Rd, Par, Cornwall PL24 2SQ;
E-mail countyhq@cornwall.sja.org.uk; Tel 01726 815967;
Fax 01726 817777

Cumbria St. John Ambulance
Scalegate Rd, Upperby, Carlisle, Cumbria CA2 4PQ;
E-mail carlisle@sja.u-k.org; Tel 01228 528684; Fax 01228
590134

Derbyshire St. John Ambulance
County HQ and Training Centre, Derby Rd, Chesterfield, Derby S40 2ED;
E-mail countyhq@derbyshire.sja.org.uk; Tel 01246 200272; 01246 200273; Fax 01246 558306
Commander   Ken Cook
County Director   R.K. Pedley, FICA
Commissioner   Gp Capt R. Bates, AFC, RAF(Retd.)

Devon St. John Ambulance
County HQ, 7–9 Marlborough Crt, Manaton Cl, Matford Business Pk, Exeter, Devon EX2 8PF;
E-mail countyhq@devon.sja.org.uk; Tel 01392 824445; Fax 01392 824446

Dorset St. John Ambulance
County HQ, St. John Hse, Bridport Rd, Poundbury, Dorchester, Dorset DT1 2NH;
E-mail countyhq@dorset.sja.org.uk; Tel 01305 751169; Fax 01305 751150

Durham St. John Ambulance
St. John's Rd, Meadowfield, Durham, County Durham DH7 8TZ; E-mail countyhq@durham.sja.org.uk; Tel 0191 378 1111; Fax 0191 378 3892

Essex St. John Ambulance
County HQ and Training Division, One Fox Cres, Chelmsford, Essex CM1 2BN;
E-mail countyhq@essex.sja.org.uk; Tel 01245 265678; Fax 01245 496240

Gloucestershire St. John Ambulance
St. John Hse, 67 London Rd, Gloucester, Gloucestershire GL1 3HF;
E-mail countyhq@gloucestershire.sja.org.uk; Tel 01452 527227; Fax 01452 505755

Greater Manchester St. John Ambulance
St. John Hse, Egerton Rd, Fallowfield, Manchester M14 6XX; E-mail countyhq@gman.sja.org.uk; Tel 0161 225 2764; Fax 0161 257 3082

Guernsey St. John Ambulance
Headquarters, Rohais, St. Peter Port, Guernsey GY1 1YN;
E-mail bailwick@sja.org.uk; Tel 01481 727129; Fax 01481 728881

Hampshire St. John Ambulance
St. John Hse, Worthy La, Winchester, Hampshire SO23 7AB;
E-mail countyhq@hampshire.sja.org.uk; Tel 01962 863366; Fax 01962 864942

Hereford St. John Ambulance
Widemarsh St, Hereford, Herefordshire HR4 9HN;
E-mail countyhq@herefordshire.sja.org.uk; Tel 01432 272837; Fax 01432 263563

Hertfordshire St. John Ambulance
HQ, The White Hse, Argyle Way, Stevenage, Hertfordshire SG1 2AD; E-mail countyhq@herts.sja.org.uk; Tel 01438 740044; Fax 01438 740403

Hull St. John Ambulance
Priory Hse, Popple St, Hull, Kingston upon Hull HU9 1LP;
E-mail countyhq@hside.sja.org.uk; Tel 01482 588564; Fax 01482 588590

Isle of Man St. John Ambulance
Glenrutchery Rd, Douglas, Isle of Man IM2 6BG;
E-mail countyhq@sja.org.uk; Tel 01624 674387; Fax 01624 626270

Isle of Wight St. John Ambulance
12 Manners View, Dodner Pk, Newport, Isle of Wight PO30 5FA; E-mail info@isleofwight.sja.org.uk; Tel 01983 822794; Fax 01983 525564

Jersey St. John Ambulance
14–16 Midvale Rd, St. Helier, Jersey JE2 3YR;
E-mail stjohn.ambulance@jerseymail.co.uk; Tel 01534 35611; Fax 01534 617520

Kent St. John Ambulance
31 Town Hill, West Malling, Maidstone, Kent ME19 6QL;
E-mail countyhq@kent.sja.org.uk; Tel 01732 874446; Fax 01732 846894

Lancashire St. John Ambulance
79 Garstang Rd, Fulwood, Preston, Lancashire PR1 1LD;
E-mail countyhq@lancashire.sja.org.uk; Tel 01772 252239; Fax 01772 883941

Leicestershire St. John Ambulance
112 Regent Rd, Leicester LE1 7LT;
E-mail countyhq@leics.sja.org.uk; Tel 0116 255 3954; Fax 0116 247 1455

Lincolnshire St. John Ambulance
The Cardinal's Hat, 268 High St, Lincoln, Lincolnshire LN2 1JG; E-mail countyhq@lincolnshire.sja.org.uk; Tel 01522 523701; Fax 01522 567617

London (Prince of Wales's) District St. John Ambulance
Edwina Mountbatten Hse, 63 York St, Marylebone, London W1H 1PS;
E-mail districthq@st-john-ambulance.org.uk; Tel 020 7258 3456; Fax 020 7724 0968

Merseyside St. John Ambulance
PO Box 90, 2 Edgar St, Liverpool, Merseyside L69 3RB;
E-mail countyhq@merseyside.sja.org.uk; Tel 0151 298 2838; Fax 0151 298 2899

Norfolk St. John Ambulance
7–13 Rose La, Norwich, Norfolk NR1 1PL;
E-mail stjohn@norfolk@btinternet.com; Tel 01603 621649; Fax 01603 766195

North Yorkshire and Teesside St. John Ambulance
Lumley Cl, Thirsk Ind Pk, Thirsk, North Yorkshire YO7 3TD; E-mail countyhq@hyt.sja.org.uk; Tel 01845 521910; Fax 01845 526363

Northamptonshire St. John Ambulance
The Mill, Millbrook Cl, St. James' Mill Rd, Northampton, Northamptonshire NN5 5JF;
E-mail countyhq@northants.sja.org.uk; Tel 01604 597800; Fax 01604 758866

Northumbria St. John Ambulance
St. John Hse, Westgate Rd, Newcastle upon Tyne, Tyne and Wear NE4 9PQ;
E-mail countyhq@northumbria.sja.org.uk; Tel 0191 273 7938; Fax 0191 226 1330

Nottinghamshire St. John Ambulance
County HQ, 561 Valley Rd, Basford, Nottingham NG5 1JG;
E-mail countyhq@notts.sja.org.uk; Tel 0115 978 4625; Fax 0115 979 0183

Oxfordshire St. John Ambulance
St. John Hse, 2–4 High St, Kidlington, Oxfordshire OX5 2DN; E-mail countyhq@oxfordshire.sja.org.uk; Tel 01865 378228; Fax 01865 841792

Shropshire St. John Ambulance
St. John Hse, Priory Rd, Shrewsbury, Shropshire SY1 1RU;
E-mail countyhq@shropshire.sja.org.uk; Tel 01743 231280; Fax 01743 243465

Somerset St. John Ambulance
St. John Hse, 60 Staplegrove Rd, Taunton, Somerset TA1 1DH; E-mail countyhq@somerset.sja.org.uk; Tel 01823 345920; Fax 01823 345927

South and West Yorkshire St. John Ambulance
Healey Rd, Ossett, Wakefield, West Yorkshire WF5 8LN;
E-mail countyhq@swy.sja.org.uk; Tel 01924 262726;
Fax 01924 270714

Staffordshire St. John Ambulance
County HQ, 18 Lichfield Rd, Stafford, Staffordshire
ST17 4LJ; E-mail countyhq@staffordshire.sja.org.uk;
Tel 01785 257124; Fax 01785 224451

Suffolk St. John Ambulance
Priory Hse, Duckemere, Bramford, Ipswich, Suffolk
IP8 4AJ; E-mail countyhq@suffolk.sja.org.uk; Tel 01473
241500; Fax 01473 241480

Surrey St. John Ambulance
St. John Hse, Stocton Cl, Guildford, Surrey GU1 1HA;
E-mail countyhq@surrey.sja.org.uk; Tel 01483 567163;
Fax 01483 888111

Sussex St. John Ambulance
23 Farncombe Rd, Worthing, West Sussex BN11 2AY;
E-mail enquiries@sussex.sja.org.uk; Tel 01903 235599;
Fax 01903 207119

Warwickshire St. John Ambulance
HQ, National Agricultural Centre, Stoneleigh Pk,
Kenilworth, Warwickshire CV8 2TA;
E-mail countyhq@warwickshire.sja.org.uk; Tel 024 7669
6521; Fax 024 7669 0121

West Midlands St. John Ambulance
Nelson Memorial Hall, 100 Lionel St, Birmingham, West
Midlands B3 1DG; E-mail countyhq@wmids.sja.org.uk;
Tel 0121 236 6660; Fax 0121 212 2003

Wiltshire St. John Ambulance
15 High St, Devizes, Wiltshire SN10 1AT;
E-mail countyhq@wiltshire.sja.org.uk; Tel 01380 728362;
Fax 01380 720557

Worcestershire St. John Ambulance
148 Wylds La, Worcester, Worcestershire WR5 1DN;
E-mail info@worcs.sja.org.uk; Tel 01905 359512;
Fax 01905 764639

Wales

Priory for Wales

Priory Hse, Meridian Crt, North Rd, Cardiff CF4 3BL;
E-mail training@stjohnwales.co.uk; Tel 029 2062 7627;
Fax 029 2062 7687
Priory Chief Executive

Northern Ireland

Northern Ireland (Commandery of Arts)

Erne Knockbracken Healthcare Pk, Saintfield Rd, Belfast
BT8 8RA; E-mail districthq@ni.sja.org.uk; Tel 028 9079
9393; Fax 028 9079 3303

St. Andrew's Ambulance Association

St. Andrew's Hse, 48 Milton St, Glasgow G4 0HR; Tel 0141
332 4031; Fax 0141 332 6582
Chief Executive   Brendan J.P. Healy
Manager (Training)   Jim Dorman
Manager (Finance)   Alan McQueen
Manager (Corps Support)   Gordon Connell
St. Andrew's Ambulance Association is a long established

charity and is Scotland's premier provider of First Aid
Training and Services. Through their volunteers they
provide First Aid at thousands of public events throughout
the country each year.

National Association of Hospital and Community Friends

11–13 Cavendish Sq, London W1G 0AN;
URL www.hc-friends.org.uk;
E-mail info@hc-friends.org.uk; Tel 0845 450 0285
Chair   The Baroness Emerton
Chief Executive   David Wood
The National Association of Hospital and Community
Friends is the representative body for over 800 Leagues of
Friends who work within hospitals and the communities
throughout the UK. Each League is an autonomous charity.
Activities undertaken by Friends are diverse including:
fundraising; visiting services; libraries; hospital radio;
shops/trolleys and teabars; befriending and carer support
schemes; lunch clubs; day centres; transportation; guiding
services and much more. The National Association
supports this work by providing representation, specialist
advice and information, insurance and group deposit
schemes, training, publications, grants, conferences and
local support networks. Membership is open to charitable
voluntary organisations whose work is dedicated to
helping those disadvantaged by ill-health or disability.

Other Voluntary Organisations

Centre for Civil Society

Formerly the Centre for Voluntary Organisation.
London School of Economics, Houghton St, London
WC2A 2AE; URL www.lse.ac.uk/depts/ccs;
E-mail ccs@lse.ac.uk; Tel 020 7955 7205; 020 7955 7375;
Fax 020 7955 6039
Prof   Jude Howell
A university-based programme working collaboratively
with voluntary agencies, broadly in the field of
organisation and management. The centre has an
integrated programme and the main activities are courses,
training, consultancy, research, publications and MSc
(postgraduate) courses for those working in and with the
British voluntary sector and in non-governmental
organisations in Europe and the Third World.

International Voluntary Service

(Registered Office) Old Hall, East Bergholt, Colchester,
Essex CO7 6TQ; URL www.ivsgbn.demon.co.uk;
E-mail ivs@ivsgbsouth.demon.co.uk; Tel 01206 298215;
Fax 01206 299043
Field Worker   Steve Davies
Organises voluntary work worldwide and regular local
voluntary work groups.

North

Castlehill House, 21 Otley Rd, Leeds, West Yorkshire
LS6 2AA; URL www.ivsgbn.demon.co.uk;
E-mail ivs@ivsggn.demon.co.uk; Tel 0113 230 4600;
Fax 0113 230 4610
Field Worker   Col Collier

Scotland

7 Upper Bow, Edinburgh EH1 3JN;
URL www.ivsgbn.demon.co.uk;
E-mail ivs@ivsgbscot.demon.co.uk; Tel 0131 226 6722;
Fax 0131 226 6723

17

Northern Ireland

International Voluntary Service Northern Ireland, 122 Great Victoria St, Belfast BT2 7BG; URL www.ivsni.dnet.co.uk; Tel 028 9023 8147; Fax 028 9024 4356

National Centre for Volunteering

Regent's Wharf, 8 All Saints St, London N1 9RL; Tel 020 7520 8900; Fax 020 7520 8910
Chief Executive Christopher Spence, MBE
The National Centre for Volunteering is an independent organisation which promotes excellence in volunteering in England in the public, private and voluntary sectors. The Centre provides support, advice, research, publications and information relating to volunteering. The Centre's development work includes promoting and supporting volunteering in Health and Social Care.

National Early Years Network

Formerly VOLCUF
77 Holloway Rd, London N7 8JZ; E-mail info@neyn.org.uk; Tel 020 7607 9573; Fax 020 7700 1105
Chief Executive Eva Lloyd
The National Early Years Network is a national umbrella organisation for all those running or managing services for children under eight. It promotes the development of quality services for children through publications, training and its journal, Coordinate.

REACH

89 Albert Embankment, London SE1 7TP;
URL www.reach-online.org.uk;
E-mail mail@reach-online.org.uk; Tel 020 7582 6543;
Fax 020 7582 2423
Director Sue Evans
Finds part-time, expenses-only opportunities for experienced managers and professional people of all ages and backgrounds who want to use their skills working as part-time volunteers to help voluntary organisations with charitable aims. Free placement service available throughout the UK.

Scottish Council for Voluntary Organisations

Mansfield Traquair Centre, 15 Mansfield Pl, Edinburgh EH3 6BB; URL www.scvo.org.uk;
E-mail enquiries@scvo.org.uk; Tel 0131 556 3882;
Fax 0131 556 0279
Director (Development and Programmes) John Ferguson
Promotes and supports voluntary action in Scotland and provides services to the voluntary sector.

SCOVO (Standing Conference Of Voluntary Organisations for People with a Learning Disability in Wales)

5 Dock Chambers, Bute St, Cardiff CF10 5AG;
URL www.scovo.org.uk; E-mail enquiries@scovo.org.uk;
Tel 029 2049 2443; Fax 029 2048 1043
Chair Mark Sadler
Director J.G. Crowe
SCOVO, as the collective voice of the voluntary sector, seeks to promote the rights of people with a learning disability to have valued lives, by working in partnerhip with other organisations, service users and their parents/carers, campaigning, supporting the voluntary sector and its interests, providing and promoting good practice.

Voluntary Service Aberdeen

38 Castle St, Aberdeen AB11 5YU; URL www.vsa.org.uk; E-mail info@vsa.org.uk; Tel 01224 212021
Director William Howie, MA, BD, STM
Aberdeen's major charity, Voluntary Service Aberdeen, is an independent agency working with the city's elderly, children in special need, one-parent families, those with learning disabilities or mental health problems, and people facing financial hardship. The agency provides direct residential care services, community services, financial assistance and helps promote the voluntary sector. Responsible for six independent charities: Agecare Aberdeen, Linn Moor Residential School, Easter Anguston Farm Training Centre, Aberdeen Children's Society, Richmondhill House, St. Aubin's Project.

St Aubin's Project

Northfield Lodge, Provost Fraser Dr, Aberdeen AB16 7JY;
URL www.vsa.org.uk; E-mail info@staubins.org.uk;
Tel 01224 680684; Fax 01224 680684
Helping individuals with a long history of mental health problems and years of institutionalised living behind them return to the community. Care ranges from short-term stay rehabilitation to long-term supported residential accommodation.

Volunteer Development Scotland (VDS)

Stirling Enterprise Pk, Stirling FK7 7RP;
URL www.vds.org.uk; E-mail vds@vds.org.uk; Tel 01786 479593
Chief Executive George Thomson
VDS is the National Centre for Volunteering and Community involvement.

Focus
The Basement, 309 Gray's Inn Rd, London WC1X 8QF
Contact Maria Walsh O'Reilly

Older Persons' Welfare Organisations

- **Age Concern**
  - England
  - Wales
  - Scotland
  - Northern Ireland
- **Other Organisations**

Older Persons' Welfare Organisations

Age Concern

Age Concern England

Founded 1940.
Astral Hse, 1268 London Rd, London SW16 4ER;
  URL www.ageconcern.org.uk;
  E-mail ace@ace.org.uk; Tel 020 8765 7200; (Helpline
  (open 0700–1900 seven days a week) 0800 009966;
  Fax 020 8765 7211
Royal Patron   HRH The Prince of Wales, KG, KTGCB
Director General   Gordon Lishman, OBE
Aims
Age Concern England, a registered charity, in its role as a
National Council on Ageing, brings together Age Concern
organisations from across the UK and over 100 national
organisations, including the main professional bodies and
directly representational organisations of older people. It
works closely with Age Concerns Scotland, Cymru and
Northern Ireland. Nationally, Age Concern England is
involved in campaigning, parliamentary work, policy
analysis, research, specialist information and advice
provision, publishing and the training of professionals
and volunteers working with older people throughout the
country. A member of the federation of over 400 Age
Concern organisations operating in England, Age Concern
England provides both financial and development
support to assist the other members in their provision of
vital local services. Supported by the work of many
thousands of volunteers, these services often include
daycare, home visiting, lunch clubs, repair and gardening
services.

Local Committees

Bath

Age Concern Bath and North East Somerset
18 Kingsmead Sq, Bath, Bath and North East Somerset
  BA1 2AE; URL www.acban.freeserve.co.uk;
  E-mail staff@acban.freeserve.co.uk; Tel 01225 466135;
  Fax 01225 464321
Chief Officer   Joan Travis

Bedfordshire

Age Concern Bedfordshire
80–82 Bromham Rd, Bedford, Bedfordshire MK40 2QH;
  E-mail d.verney-acb@talk21.com; Tel 01234 360510;
  Fax 01234 360562
Chief Officer   Karen Birkin

Age Concern Luton
17a Manchester St, Luton LU1 2QB; Tel 01582 456812
Chief Officer   Collette McKeaveney

Berkshire

Age Concern Berkshire
St. Andrew's Hse, Wilton Rd, Reading RG30 2SS;
  E-mail acb@acberk.org; Tel 0118 959 4242; Fax 0118 956
  9403
Director   Geoff Chivers

Blackburn

Age Concern Blackburn with Darwen
4 King St, Blackburn BB2 2DH;
  URL www.ageconcernblackburn.co.uk;
  E-mail admin@ageconcernblackburn.co.uk; Tel 01254
  266620; Fax 01254 266621
Chief Officer   Pauline Walsh

Blackpool

Age Concern Blackpool
3 Cookson St, Blackpool FY1 3EF;
  URL www.ageconcern-blackpool.org.uk;
  E-mail ac-blackpool@breathemail.net; Tel 01253 622812;
  Fax 01253 751252
Chief Executive   Ruth Lambert

Bristol

Age Concern Bristol
Canningford Hse, 38 Victoria St, Bristol BS1 6BY;
  E-mail ageconcern@acbristol.freeserve.co.uk;
  Tel (Administration) 0117 929 7537; (Advice and
  Information) 0117 922 5353; (Insurance) 0117 922 1933;
  Fax 0117 922 1911
Director   Maya Bimson

Buckinghamshire

Age Concern Buckinghamshire
145 Meadowcroft, Aylesbury, Buckinghamshire HP19 3HH;
  E-mail ageconcern@ageconcernbucks.org.uk; Tel 01296
  431127; (Information and Advice) 01296 431911;
  Fax 01296 330783
Director   Josephine Brader

Age Concern Milton Keynes
6 Burners La, Kiln Farm, Milton Keynes MK11 3HB;
  E-mail milton_keynes@ageconcern.org.uk; Tel 01908
  305900; Fax 01908 305901
Chief Executive   Ellen Clark

Age Concern Slough
The Old Library, William St, Slough SL1 1XX;
  E-mail chris@acslough.org.uk; Tel 01753 822890;
  Fax 01753 571054
Chief Officer   Tracey Morgan

Cambridgeshire

Age Concern Cambridgeshire
2 Victoria St, Chatteris, Cambridgeshire PE16 6AP;
E-mail accambs@aol.com; Tel (Administration) 01354
696650; (Information) 01354 696677; Fax 01354 696119
Director Gloria Culyer

Age Concern Peterborough
The Lindens, 86 Lincoln Rd, Peterborough PE1 2SN;
E-mail office@agecp.fsnet.co.uk; Tel 01733 564185;
Fax 01773 311137
Chief Officer Pat Strachan

Cheshire

Age Concern Cheshire
314 Chester Rd, Hartford, Northwich, Cheshire CW8 2AB;
URL www.ageconcerncheshire.com;
E-mail mail@accheshire.u-net.com; Tel (General
Enquiries) 01606 881660; (General Enquiries) 01606
881662; (General Enquiries) 01606 881663; (Insurance)
01606 881661; Fax 01606 881667
Chief Executive Jill Walter

Age Concern East Cheshire
Chester Hse, 122 Chestergate, Macclesfield, Cheshire
SK11 6DU; E-mail east.cheshire@ageconcern.org.uk;
Tel 01625 612958; Fax 01625 511582
Chief Executive Madelyn Bridge

Age Concern Halton
44 Church St, Runcorn, Cheshire WA7 1LR;
E-mail enquiries_runcorn@ac-halton.org.uk; Tel 01928
590926; Fax 01928 591455
Director Melissa Critchley

Cornwall and the Isles of Scilly

Age Concern Cornwall and the Isles of Scilly
5a Little Castle St, Truro, Cornwall TR1 3DL;
URL www.ageconcerncornwall.org.uk;
E-mail acc@ageconcerncornwall.org.uk; Tel 01872
279693; (Information and Advice) 01872 264370;
Fax 01872 276479
Chief Executive Paul Brinsley

Cumbria

Age Concern Barrow and District
Lakeland Pennine Bldg, Abbey Rd, Barrow-in-Furness,
Cumbria LA14 1XL;
E-mail info@ageconcernbarrow.co.uk; Tel 01229 831425;
Fax 01229 822425
Chief Officer Adrienne Poole

Age Concern Carlisle and District
20 Spencer St, Carlisle, Cumbria CA1 1BG;
E-mail age@ageconcarl.enterprise-plc.com; Tel 01228
536673; Fax 01228 597039
Director Jessica Riddle

Age Concern Eden
Resource Centre, Sandgate, Penrith, Cumbria CA11 7TP;
E-mail edenage@talk21.com; Tel 01768 863618; Fax 01768
863792
Chief Officer Valerie Brook

Age Concern North West Cumbria
Old Customs Hse, West Strand, Whitehaven, Cumbria
CA28 7LR; URL www.ageconcern-nwc.org.uk;
E-mail pubaffairs@ageconcern-nwc.org.uk; Tel 01946
66669; Fax 01946 591182
Director Mary Bradley

Age Concern South Lakeland
Stricklandgate Hse, Stricklandgate, Kendal, Cumbria
LA9 4PU; E-mail acsl@stricklandgate-house.org.uk;
Tel 01539 728118; Fax 01539 732473
Director Mary Christian

Derbyshire

Age Concern Derbyshire
29a Market Pl, Heanor, Derbyshire DE75 7EG;
E-mail derbyshire@ageconcern.org.uk; Tel 01773 768240;
Fax 01773 533277
Director Keith Briars

Devon

Age Concern Devon
6–7 Southernhay West, Exeter, Devon EX1 1JG;
E-mail a.c.palmer@talk21.com; Tel 01392 250085;
Fax 01392 435421
Chief Officer Ann Palmer

Age Concern Exeter
138 Cowick St, Exeter, Devon EX4 1HS;
E-mail mail@exeter-age-concern.freeserve.co.uk;
Tel 01392 202092; Fax 01392 204113
Director Martyn Rogers

Age Concern Plymouth
Plymouth Age Concern Centre, Elspeth Sitters Hse,
Hoegate St, Plymouth PL1 2JB; Tel 01752 665424;
Fax 01752 251618
Managing Director Cyndi Hall

Age Concern Torbay
Sandwell Hse, 4 Dendy Rd, Paignton, Devon TQ4 5DB;
URL www.ageconcerntorbay.org.uk;
E-mail ageconcerntorbay@ageconcerntorbay.org.uk;
Tel 01803 555181; Fax 01803 555182
Director Robin Causley

Dorset

Age Concern Bournemouth
700 Wimborne Rd, Winton, Bournemouth BH9 2EG;
E-mail bournemouth@ageconcern.org.uk; Tel 01202
530530; Fax 01202 530598
Chief Officer Hazel Walker

Durham

Age Concern Darlington and District
Bradbury Hse, Beaumont St West, Darlington DL1 5SX;
E-mail darlington@ageconcern.org.uk; Tel 01325 362832;
Fax 01325 383543
Chief Officer Peter Walshaw

Age Concern Durham County
7 Atherton St, Durham, County Durham DH1 4DJ;
E-mail info@ageconcern-durham.org.uk; Tel 0191 386
3856; Fax 0191 383 1528
Chief Officer Harriet Gibbon

East Sussex

Age Concern Brighton, Hove and Portslade
57 Ditchling Rd, Brighton, Brighton and Hove BN1 4SD;
E-mail acbrighton@cwcom.net;
E-mail ageconcernbhp@netscapeonline.co.uk; Tel 01273
570732; Fax 01273 624196
Director Dorothy Engmann

Age Concern East Sussex
54 Cliffe High St, Lewes, East Sussex BN7 2AN;
E-mail acesussex@talk21.com; Tel 01273 476704;
Fax 01273 486833
Director Diane Parr

Essex

Age Concern Colchester
Stockwell Hse, 43 East Stockwell St, Colchester, Essex
CO1 1SS; E-mail age@accolchstr.freeserve.co.uk;
Tel 01206 500967; Fax 01206 500984
Chief Officer   Rachel Fahie

Age Concern Essex
112 Springfield Rd, Chelmsford, Essex CM2 6LF;
URL www.ageconcernessex.co.uk;
E-mail user@acsx.demon.co.uk; Tel 01245 264499;
Fax 01245 346107
Chief Officer   Mrs Terry Cassels

Age Concern Havering
HOPWA Hse, Inskip Dr, Hornchurch, Essex RM11 3UR;
E-mail havering@ageconcern.org.uk; Tel 01708 796600;
Fax 01708 796606
Chief Officer   Graham Rooks

Age Concern Redbridge
3rd Fl, 17 Station Rd, Ilford, Essex IG1 4DW;
E-mail andy.petty@acredbridge.co.uk; Tel 020 8220 6000;
Fax 020 8478 4767
Director   Andrew Petty

Gloucestershire

Age Concern Gloucestershire
Bleak Hse, 26 Station Rd, Gloucester, Gloucestershire
GL1 1EW; URL www.ageconcernglos.org.uk;
E-mail acglos-admin@dial.pipex.com; Tel 01452 422660;
Fax 01452 384028
Director   Sue Grove

Age Concern South Gloucestershire
34 St. Mary St, Thornbury, Bristol BS35 2AT;
E-mail ageconcern.southglos@thornet.co.uk; Tel 01454
858754; (Information and Advice) 01454 858750;
Fax 01454 858751
Chief Officer   David Harwood

Greater London

Age Concern London
54 Knatchbull Rd, London SE5 9QY;
URL www.aclondon.org.uk;
E-mail pjones@aclondon.org.uk; Tel 020 7346 5970;
Fax 020 7274 6014
Director   Paula Jones

Age Concern Barking and Dagenham
White Hse, 884 Green La, Dagenham, Essex RM8 1BX;
E-mail barking_and_dagenham@ageconcern.org.uk;
Tel (Administration and Insurance) 020 8270 4948;
(Administration and Insurance) 020 8720 4947; (General
Enquiries) 020 8270 4946; (General Enquiries) 020 8270
4947; (General Enquiries) 020 8270 4949
Chief Officer   Samantha Mauger

Age Concern Barnet
Meritage Ctr, Church End, Hendon, London NW4 4JT;
E-mail barnet_hendon@ageconcern.org.uk; Tel 020 8203
5040; Fax 020 8203 6099
Chief Officer   Mark Robinson

Age Concern Bexley
Manor Hse, Grassington Rd, Sidcup, Kent DA14 6BY;
E-mail phillip.watson@ageconcern.org.uk; Tel 020 8300
0883; Fax 020 8300 2495
Chief Officer   Phillip Watson

Age Concern Brent
120 Craven Park Rd, London NW10 8QD;
E-mail brent@ageconcern; Tel 020 8965 7711; Fax 020
8961 8976
Chief Officer   Sue Newman

Age Concern Bromley
Community Hse, South St, Bromley, Kent BR1 1RH;
E-mail info@acbromley.org.uk; Tel 020 8315 1850;
Fax 020 8315 1851
Chief Executive   Maureen Falloon

Age Concern Camden
The Margaret Hepburn Centre, 11 St. Chad's St, London
WC1H 8BG; E-mail accam@dial.pipex.com; Tel 020 7837
3777; Fax 020 7278 1904
Chief Officer   Pauline Cheeseman

Age Concern Ealing Borough
135 Uxbridge Rd, West Ealing, London W13 9AU;
E-mail ageconcernealing-btardesk@btinternet.com;
Tel 020 8567 8017; Fax 020 8566 5696
Executive Director   Sylvia Scheherer

Age Concern Enfield
Community Hse, 311 Fore St, Edmonton, London N9 0PZ;
E-mail age.concern.enfield@teleregion.co.uk;
Tel (Advice) 020 8345 5577; (Office) 020 8373 6314;
Fax 020 8373 6314; 020 8373 6317
Chief Officer   Tony Seagroatt

Age Concern Greenwich
14 Plumstead Rd, Woolwich, London SE18 7BZ;
E-mail greenwich@ageconcern.org.uk; Tel 020 8854 6079;
Fax 020 8316 1123
Director   Jacky Grant

Age Concern Hackney
22 Dalston La, Hackney, London E8 3AZ;
E-mail achackney@achackney.fsnet.co.uk; Tel 020 7254
0715; Fax 020 7249 0339
Manager   Liz Groves

Age Concern Hammersmith and Fulham
105 Greyhound La, London W6 8NJ;
URL www.achf.org.uk; E-mail info@achf.org.uk; Tel 020
7386 9085; Fax 020 7386 5740
Chief Executive   Vacancy

Age Concern Haringey
Tottenham Town Hall, Approach Rd, Tottenham, London
N15 4RY; E-mail haringey@ageconcern.org.uk; Tel 020
8801 2444; Fax 020 8365 1732
Director   Robert Edmonds

Age Concern Harrow
Exchequer Bldg, Civic Centre, Station Rd, Harrow, Greater
London HA1 2UJ; E-mail arrol.betty@ageconcern.org.uk;
Tel 020 8424 9344; Fax 020 8424 8544
Director   Betty Arrol

Age Concern Hillingdon
Globe Hse, Bentinck Rd, West Drayton, Greater London
UB7 7RQ;
E-mail enquiries@ageconcernhillingdon.org.uk;
Tel 01895 431331; Fax 01895 430045
Chief Officer   Christine Commerford

Age Concern Hounslow
Alexandra Hse, Albany Rd, Brentford, Greater London
TW8 0NE; E-mail hounslow@ageconcern.org.uk; Tel 020
8560 6969; Fax 020 8560 9119
Chief Officer   Jenny Siddons

Islington Age Concern
6–9 Manor Gdns, Islington, London EC1V 4NJ; Tel 020 7281
6018; Fax 020 7561 9917
Director   Joanne Luff

Age Concern Kensington and Chelsea
27 Adam and Eve Mews, London W8 6SH;
E-mail silversurfers@ackc.fsnet.co.uk; Tel 020 7938 3944;
Fax 020 7376 2591
Chief Officer   Helen Fraquet

18

Age Concern Kingston upon Thames
Raleigh Hse, 14 Nelson Rd, New Malden, Surrey KT3 5EA;
E-mail info@ageconcernkingston.org; Tel 020 8942 8256;
Fax 020 8336 0322
Chief Officer Liz Aitchison

Age Concern Lambeth
6 Electric Ave, Brixton, London SW9 8JX; Tel 020 7733 0528;
Fax 020 7346 6814
Director Vacancy

Age Concern Lewisham
20 Brownhill Rd, Catford, London SE6 2EN;
E-mail ageconcernlewisham@hotmail.com; Tel 020 8695
0895; Fax 020 8695 0895
Chief Officer Jacqui Ives

Age Concern Newham
228a Romford Rd, Forest Gate, London E7 9HZ;
E-mail acnewham@btconnect.com; Tel 020 8503 1511;
Fax 020 8503 1771
Chief Officer Sue McCarthy

Age Concern Tower Hamlets (ACTH)
82 Russia La, London E2 9LU; URL www.acth.org.uk;
E-mail main@acth.org.uk; Tel 020 8981 7124; Fax 020
8980 1546
Director Gary Jones

Age Concern Waltham Forest
Ground Fl, Zenith Hse, 210 Church Rd, Leyton, London
E10 7JQ; URL www.ageconcernwf.org.uk;
E-mail age.concern.waltham.forest1@virgin.net; Tel 020
8558 5512; Fax 020 8558 0383
Director Scott Dunbar

Age Concern Wandsworth
4 Arndale Wlk, Wandsworth Shopping Centre, Wandsworth,
London SW18 4BX; E-mail david@ac-wandsworth.org.uk;
Tel 020 8870 2020; Fax 020 8870 2123
Director David Sidonio

Age Concern Westminster
268–272 Edgware Rd, London W2 1DS; Tel 020 7724 6930;
Fax 020 7724 7045
Director Vicky Jensen

Greater Manchester

Age Concern Bolton
72–74 Ashburner St, Bolton, Lancashire BL1 1TN;
E-mail postmaster@ageconcernbolton.org.uk; Tel 01204
382411; Fax 01204 365541
Chief Officer Gareth Evans

Age Concern Manchester
77 Lever St, Manchester M1 1FL;
E-mail ageconcernmanchester@supanet.com; Tel 0161
236 3339; Fax 0161 236 2968
Chief Officer Ray Gridley

Age Concern Metro Bury
Jubilee Centre, Clarence Pk, Moseley Ave, Bury, Lancashire
BL9 6NG; E-mail acmetrobury@lineone.net; Tel 0161 763
9030; Fax 0161 763 3314
Chief Officer Beryl Pilkington

Age Concern Metro Oldham
10 Church La, Oldham, Greater Manchester OL1 3AN;
E-mail oldham.ageconcern@btclick.com; Tel 0161 633
0213; Fax 0161 620 6197
Chief Executive Yvonne Lee

Age Concern Metro Rochdale
12 South Pde, Rochdale, Lancashire OL16 1LR;
E-mail acmr.rochdale@cwcom.net; Tel 01706 712515;
Fax 01706 712616
Chief Officer Alan Haughton

Age Concern Salford
51 Regent St, Eccles, Manchester M30 0BP;
E-mail metropolitan_salford@ageconcern.org.uk;
Tel 0161 788 7300; Fax 0161 707 9533
Director Sharon Brearley

Age Concern Stockport
Churchgate Hse, 96 Churchgate, Stockport, Cheshire
SK1 1YJ; URL www.ageconcernstockport.org;
E-mail stockport@ageconcern.org.uk; Tel 0161 477 1213;
Fax 0161 429 8386
Director Margaret Brade

Age Concern Tameside
131 Katherine St, Ashton-under-Lyne, Lancashire
OL6 7AW; E-mail rachel@actameside.freeserve.co.uk;
Tel 0161 308 5000; Fax 0161 308 5001
Director Joyce Howarth
Director Jean Hurlston

Age Concern Trafford
20a Station Rd, Urmston, Manchester M41 9JN;
E-mail admin@ageconcerntrafford.org.uk; Tel 0161 747
9901; Fax 0161 746 8200
Director Anne-Marie Jones

Age Concern Wigan Borough
68 Market St, Wigan, Greater Manchester WN1 1HX;
Tel 01942 241972; 01942 241973; Fax 01942 241980
Chief Officer Stuart Murray

Hampshire

Age Concern Hampshire
1 St. Cross Rd, Winchester, Hampshire SO23 9JA; Tel 01962
868545; (Information and Advice Freephone) 0800 328
7154; Fax 01962 842358
Director Chris Perry

Age Concern Portsmouth
The Old George Centre, 16 Kingston Rd, Portsmouth
PO1 5RZ; E-mail user@concernportsmouth.fsnet.co.uk;
Tel 023 9286 2121; Fax 023 9273 1020
Chief Officer Tom Shepherd

Age Concern Southampton
Unit 1, Grd Fl, Saxon Gate, Back of the Walls, Southampton
SO14 3HA; E-mail ageconcern.southampton@virgin.net;
Tel (Advice and Information) 023 8036 8636; (Office) 023
8036 8618; Fax 023 8036 8615
Chief Officer Sandra Smith

Hereford and Worcester

Age Concern Hereford and Worcester
6 Sansome St, Worcester, Worcestershire WR1 1UH;
E-mail ageconcern@achw.org.uk; Tel 01905 726652;
Fax 01905 610620
Chief Executive Magda Praill

Hertfordshire

Age Concern Dacorum
Hemel Hempstead Day Centre, Half Moon Yard, Hemel
Hempstead, Hertfordshire HP1 3AE;
E-mail dacorum@ageconcern.org.uk; Tel 01442 259049;
Fax 01442 218383
Chief Officer Caroline Player

Age Concern Hertfordshire
4 Silver Crt, Watchmead, Welwyn Garden City,
Hertfordshire AL7 1TS; E-mail hq@acherts.org.uk;
Tel 01707 323272; (Information Line) 0845 6013446;
Fax 01707 332464
Chief Executive Officer Marion Birch

Humberside

Age Concern East Riding of Yorkshire
Morley's Cottage, Morley's Yard, Walkergate, Beverley,
East Riding of Yorkshire HU17 9BY;
E-mail sylviascott@ageconcern.org.uk; Tel 01482 869181;
Fax 01482 861065
Chief Officer Sylvia Scott

Age Concern Hull
The Healthy Living Centre, Bradbury Hse, Porter St, Hull,
Kingston upon Hull HU1 2RH;
E-mail info@ageconcernhull.org; Tel 01482 242644;
Fax 01482 226176
General Manager Dorrie Grassby

Isle of Man

Age Concern Isle of Man
19 Drinkwater St, Douglas, Isle of Man IM1 1AT;
E-mail aciomhq@advsys.co.uk; Tel 01624 613044;
Fax 01624 672951
Chief Officer Robert Clucas

Isle of Wight

Age Concern Isle of Wight
14 Pyle St, Newport, Isle of Wight PO30 1JW;
E-mail felicite.brooker@ageconcern.org.uk; Tel 01983
525282; Fax 01983 837547
Director Felicite Booker

Lancashire

Age Concern Hyndburn
24–26 Whalley Rd, Accrington, Lancashire BB5 1AA;
E-mail ac.hyndburn@btinternet.com; Tel 01254 871010;
Fax 01254 396624
Chief Executive Patrick Collister

Age Concern Lancashire
57 St.Thomas's Rd, Chorley, Lancashire PR7 1JE;
E-mail lancashire@ageconcern.org.uk; Tel 01257 233200;
Fax 01257 479012
Chief Officer Geraldine Moore

Age Concern Preston and South Ribble
Arkwright Hse, Stoneygate, Preston, Lancashire PR1 3XT;
E-mail acpsr511598@aol.com; Tel 01772 552850;
Fax 01772 552866
Chief Executive Linda Chivers

Leicestershire and Rutland

Age Concern Leicestershire and Rutland
Lansdowne Hse, 113 Princess Rd East, Leicester LE1 7LA;
E-mail enquiries@ageconcernleics.com; Tel 0116 299
2233; Fax 0116 299 2244
Executive Director Anthony Donovan

Age Concern Leicester
Clarence Hse, 46 Humberstone Gate, Leicester LE1 3PJ;
E-mail rodney.freer@ageconcern.org.uk; Tel 0116 222
0555; Fax 0116 251 4601
Executive Director John Scruton

Lincolnshire

Age Concern Kesteven
Council Offices, Eastgate, Sleaford, Lincolnshire NG34 7EB;
E-mail kesteven@ageconcern.org.uk; Tel 01529 302843;
Fax 01529 303399
Chief Officer Valerie Vowles

Age Concern Boston and South Holland
County Hall, Boston, Lincolnshire PE21 6DY; Tel 01205
310010 ext 4995; Fax 01522 552277
Chief Officer Barbara M. Blatherwick

Age Concern Lincoln
The Day Centre, Park St, Lincoln, Lincolnshire LN1 1UQ;
Tel 01522 527694; Fax 01522 567212
Chief Officer Diane Garner

Age Concern Lindsey
The Old School Hse, Manor Hse St, Horncastle, Lincoln,
Lincolnshire LN9 5HF;
E-mail info@ageconlin.freeserve.co.uk; Tel 01507 524242;
Fax 01507 525242
Chief Officer Malcolm Baxter

Merseyside

Age Concern Knowsley
Community Services Centre, Lathom Rd, Huyton,
Knowsley, Merseyside L36 9XZ;
URL www.acknowsley.fsnet.co.uk;
E-mail contact@acknowsley.fsnet.co.uk; Tel 0151 480
4632; Fax 0151 449 3106
Chief Executive David P. Rimmer

Age Concern Liverpool
Sir Thomas Hse, 5 Sir Thomas St, Liverpool, Merseyside
L1 6BW; E-mail liverpool@ageconcern.org.uk;
Tel (General) 0151 330 5678; (Information and Advice)
0151 236 4440; Fax 0151 330 5679
Chief Executive Dil Daly

Age Concern St. Helens
24–28 Claughton St, St. Helens, Merseyside WA10 1RZ;
E-mail philipacsthelens@hotmail.com; Tel 01744 454530;
Fax 01744 422656
Director Philip Longworth

Age Concern Wirral
42–44 Market St, Birkenhead, Merseyside CH41 5BT;
Tel 0151 666 2220; Fax 0151 650 0212
Chief Officer Myrtle Lacey

Middlesbrough

Age Concern Teesside
190 Borough Rd, Middlesbrough TS1 2EH;
E-mail teesside@ageconcern.org.uk; Tel 01642 805500;
Fax 01642 240904
Chief Officer Dave Punshon

Norfolk

Age Concern Norfolk
300 St. Faith's Rd, Old Catton, Norwich, Norfolk NR6 7BJ;
E-mail acn@acnorfolk.org.uk; Tel 01603 787111;
Fax 01603 301371
Director Rex Humphrey

Age Concern Norwich
Advice Arcade, 4 Guildhall Hill, Norwich, Norfolk
NR2 1JH; E-mail acnorwich@acnorwich.demon.co.uk;
Tel 01603 496333; Fax 01603 496320
Chief Officer Brenda Arthur

North Yorkshire

Age Concern North Yorkshire
49 East Pde, Harrogate, North Yorkshire HG1 5LQ;
E-mail murieljacny@aol.com; Tel 01423 502253;
Fax 01423 507903
Chief Executive Alexandra Bird

Age Concern Scarborough and District
39 Aberdeen Wlk, Scarborough, North Yorkshire
YO11 1BD; Tel 01723 379058; (Administration) 01723
366502; Fax 01723 341711
Chief Officer Brenda Stephenson

18

Age Concern York
Norman Collinson Hse, 70 Walmgate, York YO1 9TL;
E-mail sally@ageconcernyork.org.uk; Tel 01904 627995;
Fax 01904 658463
Chief Officer Sally Hutchinson

Northamptonshire

Age Concern Northampton and County
Cliftonville Day Centre, Cliftonville Rd, Northampton,
Northamptonshire NN1 5BU;
E-mail liam.condron@ageconcern.org.uk; Tel 01604
611200; Fax 01604 611201
Chief Officer Liam Condron

Northumberland

Age Concern Northumberland
Wansbeck Business Centre, Rotary Parkway, Ashington,
Northumberland NE63 8QZ; E-mail acnhq@tiscali.co.uk;
Tel 01670 528220; Fax 01670 528219
Chief Officer Gary Brown

Nottinghamshire

Age Concern Nottingham and Nottinghamshire
Bradbury Hse, 12 Shakespeare St, Nottingham NG1 4FQ;
URL www.ageconcernnotts.org.uk;
E-mail info@ageconcernnotts.org.uk; Tel 0115 844 0011;
Fax 0115 841 4460
Chief Executive Michael Tinkler

Oxfordshire

Age Concern Oxfordshire, City and County
St. Edmunds Hse, 39 West St. Helens St, Abingdon,
Oxfordshire OX14 5BW;
E-mail marydaniel@ageconcernoxon.com; Tel 01235
849400; Fax 01235 849449
Chief Officer Mary Daniel

Shropshire, Telford and Wrekin

Age Concern Shropshire, Telford and the Wrekin
3 Mardol Gdns, Shrewsbury, Shropshire SY1 1PR; E-mail
shorpshiretelfordandthewrekin@ageconcern.org.uk;
Tel 01743 233123; 01743 233666; Fax 01743 248848
Chief Officer Tricia Maddox

Somerset

Age Concern Somerset
County Headquarters, The Market Hse, Fore St, Taunton,
Somerset TA1 1JD; E-mail somerset@ageconcern.org.uk;
Tel 01823 322113; Fax 01823 324128
Chief Executive Libby Lisgo

South Yorkshire

Age Concern Barnsley
12–18 Eldon St, Barnsley, South Yorkshire S70 2JB;
E-mail barnsley@ageconcern.org.uk; Tel 01226 211161;
Fax 01226 211162
Director Philip Wormald

Age Concern Metropolitan Doncaster
109 Thorne Rd, Doncaster, South Yorkshire DN2 5BE;
E-mail vickieferres@care4free.net; Tel 01302 812345;
Fax 01302 812813
Director Vickie Ferres

Age Concern Rotherham
49–53 St. Ann's Rd, Rotherham, South Yorkshire S65 1PF;
E-mail co@acr.yorks.freeserve.co.uk; Tel 01709 829621;
Fax 01709 821327
Chief Executive Kate Adams

Age Concern Sheffield
10 Carver St, Sheffield, South Yorkshire S1 4FS;
E-mail ageconcernsheffield@ic24.net; Tel 0114 275 7964;
Fax 0114 275 1832
Director Pam Perriam

Staffordshire

Age Concern North Staffordshire
6–8 Albion St, Hanley, Stoke-on-Trent ST1 1QH; Tel 01782
286209; Fax 01782 209099
Chief Officer Jane Emms

Age Concern South Staffordshire
28 Salter St, Stafford, Staffordshire ST16 2JU; Tel (Advice)
01785 600610; (Office) 01785 600603; (Office) 01785
600605; Fax 01785 228211
Chief Executive Nick Maslen

Suffolk

Suffolk Age Concern
County Office, 8 Northgate St, Ipswich, Suffolk IP1 3BZ;
URL www.ageconcernsuffolk.org.uk;
E-mail office@ageconcernsuffolk.org.uk; Tel 01473
257039; Fax 01473 287955
Chief Officer Daphne Savage

Surrey

Age Concern Croydon
158–162 London Rd, Croydon, Surrey CR0 2TD;
URL www.croydon.gov.uk/healthinfo/agecroydon;
E-mail croydon@ageconcern.org.uk; Tel 020 8680 5450;
Fax 020 8288 9229
Director Stuart Routledge

Age Concern Richmond upon Thames
The ARC at Meadows Hall, Church Rd, Richmond, Surrey
TW10 6LN; E-mail ageconcernrut@hotmail.com; Tel 020
8940 8066; Fax 020 8940 5744
Chief Officer Ryan Sampson

Age Concern Surrey
Rex Hse, William Rd, Guildford, Surrey GU1 4QZ;
E-mail admin@acsurrey.org.uk; Tel 01483 503414;
Fax 01483 454614
Director Tony Lee

Age Concern Sutton Borough
2 Lower Sq, Civic Centre, St. Nicholas Way, Sutton, Surrey
SM1 1EA; E-mail mharper@acsutton.freeserve.co.uk;
Tel (Administration) 020 8770 4092; Fax 020 8770 4093
Chief Officer Marion Harper

Tyne and Wear

Age Concern Gateshead
341–343 High St, Gateshead, Tyne and Wear NE8 1EQ;
E-mail ageconcern.gateshead@lineone.net; Tel 0191 477
3559; Fax 0191 478 5307
Chief Officer Ann Marshall

Age Concern Newcastle
MEA Hse, Ellison Pl, Newcastle upon Tyne, Tyne and Wear
NE1 8XS;
URL web.onyxnet.co.uk/support-acnewcastle.co.uk;
E-mail mariann.douglas@ageconcern.org.uk; Tel 0191
232 6488; Fax 0191 235 9925
Chief Executive Sue Pearson

Age Concern North Tyneside
13 Saville St West, North Shields, Tyne and Wear
NE29 6QP; URL www.ageconcernnorthtyne.org;
E-mail alma.caldwell@age-nt.demon.co.uk; Tel 0191 280
8484; Fax 0191 280 8485; Minicom 0191 280 8486
Chief Executive Officer Alma Caldwell

Age Concern South Tyneside
19 Beach Rd, South Shields, Tyne and Wear NE33 2QA;
E-mail agecon2000@yahoo.co.uk; Tel 0191 456 6903;
Fax 0191 455 7431
Chief Officer   John Briers

Age Concern Sunderland
Bradbury Ctr, Stockton Rd, Sunderland, Tyne and Wear
SR2 7AQ; E-mail graeme@ac-sunderland.org.uk;
Tel 0191 514 1131; Fax 0191 567 0378
Director   Graeme Lyall

Warwickshire

Age Concern Warwickshire
10 Clemens St, Leamington Spa, Warwickshire CV31 2DL;
E-mail ho@ageconcernwarks.co.uk; Tel 01926 883118;
Fax 01926 452857
Director   Elizabeth Phillips

West Midlands

Age Concern Birmingham
5th Fl, Centro Hse, 16 Summer La, Birmingham, West
Midlands B19 3SD;
E-mail mail@ageconcernbirmingham.co.uk; Tel 0121
2131130; Fax 0121 6838840
Chief Executive   Shirley Goode

Age Concern Coventry
Alvyn Smith Hse, 7 Warwick Row, Coventry, West
Midlands CV1 1EX; E-mail sueburgin@hotmail.com;
Tel 024 7623 1999; Fax 024 7663 4210
Chief Officer   Sue Burgin

Age Concern Dudley
The Junction, 1 Cradley Rd, Netherton, Dudley, West
Midlands DY2 9RA; E-mail dudley@ageconcern.org.uk;
Tel 01384 354508; Fax 01384 354511
Chief Officer   Sally Huband

Age Concern Sandwell
15–17 Bull St, West Bromwich, West Midlands B70 6EU;
E-mail info@ageconcernsandwell.org.uk; Tel 0121 500
1860; Fax 0121 500 1861
Chief Executive Officer   Mike Allen

Age Concern Solihull
The Priory, Churchill Rd, Solihull, West Midlands B91 3LF;
E-mail info@acsolihull.fsnet.co.uk; Tel 0121 705 9128;
Fax 0121 704 0139
Chief Executive Officer   Anne Hastings

Age Concern Walsall
50 Lower Hall La, Walsall, West Midlands WS1 1RJ;
E-mail enquiry@ageconcernwalsall.fsnet.co.uk; Tel 01922
638825; Fax 01922 615713
Chief Officer   Debbie Niemann

Age Concern Wolverhampton
Hupton Hse, 93–94 Darlington St, Wolverhampton, West
Midlands WV1 4EX;
E-mail mail@acwolverhampton.demon.co.uk; Tel 01902
572060; Fax 01902 572080
Chief Executive   Gerard Walsh

West Sussex

Age Concern West Sussex
County Office, 2 Chapel St, Chichester, West Sussex
PO19 1BU; E-mail post@acwestsussex.org; Tel 01243
775588; (Insurance) 01903 232324; Fax 01243 527553;
(Insurance) 01903 233245
Director   Robyn Clayton

West Yorkshire

Bradford and District
19 Sunbridge Rd, Bradford, West Yorkshire BD1 2AY;
E-mail bradford@ageconcern.org.uk; Tel 01274 395144;
Fax 01274 723744
Chief Officer   Carol Wooller

Age Concern Calderdale
5–6 Park Rd, off Hopwood La, Halifax, West Yorkshire
HX1 2TS; E-mail info@ageconcerncalderdale.org.uk;
Tel 01422 252040; Fax 01422 262000
Chief Executive   Tim Swift

Age Concern Kirklees
3rd Fl, Empire Hse, Wakefield Old Rd, Dewsbury, West
Yorkshire WF12 8DH; E-mail agekirk@btinternet.com;
Tel 01924 459938; Fax 01924 450269
Chief Executive   Helen Atanacio

Age Concern Leeds
188a Woodhouse La, Leeds, West Yorkshire LS2 9DX;
E-mail ageconcern.leeds@dial.pipex.com; Tel 0113 245
8579; Fax 0113 244 4640
Chief Executive   Rev Carol Wardman

Age Concern Wakefield
7 Bank St, Castleford, West Yorkshire WF10 1JD;
E-mail ageconcernwakdis@netscapeonline.co.uk;
Tel 01977 552114; (Information) 01977 552476;
(Insurance) 01977 552475; Fax 01977 518549
Chief Officer   Barbara McCulloch

Wiltshire

Age Concern Salisbury and District
21 Brown St, Salisbury, Wiltshire SP1 2AS; Tel 01722 335425;
Fax 01722 325362
Chief Officer   Phyllis Dayes

Age Concern Swindon
14 Milton Rd, Swindon SN1 5JE;
E-mail swindon@ageconcern.org.uk; Tel 01793 692166;
Fax 01793 485011
Director   Jo Osorio

Age Concern Wiltshire
Founded 1952.
13 Market Pl, Devizes, Wiltshire SN10 1HT; Tel 01380
727767; Fax 01380 728797
Director   Liddy Davidson

Age Concern Wales

1 Cathedral Rd, Cardiff CF11 9SD;
URL www.accymru.org.uk;
E-mail enquiries@accymru.org.uk; Tel 0292 037 1566;
Fax 0292 039 9562
Director   R. Taylor

Local Organisations

Cardiff

Age Concern Cardiff and the Vale
91–93 Caerphilly Rd, Birchgrove, Cardiff CF14 4AE;
E-mail information@age.concern-cardiff.org.uk; Tel 0292
052 1052; Fax 0292 052 0357
Director   J. Hawkins

Denbighshire

Age Concern North Wales Central
12–14 Hall Sq, Denbigh, Denbighshire LL16 3NU;
URL www.ageconcern-nw-central.co.uk;
E-mail agecon.n.w.cent@btconnect.com; Tel 01745
816947; Fax 01745 815912
Chief Officer   B. Williams

18

Gwynedd

Age Concern Gwynedd a Mon
Fordd Santes Helen, Caernarfon, Gwynedd LL55 2YD;
 URL www.age-concern-gwnedd-a-mon.sagenet.co.uk;
 E-mail john@ageconcerngwynedd.co.uk; Tel 01286
 677711; Fax 01286 674389
Chief Officer J.C. Jones

Mid Glamorgan

Age Concern Morgannwg
7 Gelliwasted Rd, Pontypridd, Rhondda, Cynon, Taff
 CF37 2BP; URL www.ageconcernmorgannwg.org.uk;
 E-mail chief.officer@ageconcernmorgannwg.org.uk;
 Tel 01443 485505; Fax 01443 401000
Chief Officer A. Higgins

Newport

Age Concern Gwent
12 Baneswell Rd, Newport NP9 4BP;
 E-mail ageconcern.gwent@business.ntl.com; Tel 01633
 763330; Fax 01633 259246
Chief Officer David Murray

Pembrokeshire

Age Concern Pembrokeshire
2a Holloway, Haverfordwest, Pembrokeshire SA61 2JL;
 URL www.age-concern-pembrokeshire.co.uk;
 E-mail info@age-concern-pembrokeshire.org.uk;
 Tel 01437 769972; Fax 01437 763620
Chief Officer Jane Slade

Swansea

Age Concern Sir Gâr
Temporary Offices, Ardmean Hse, 27–28 Blue St,
 Carmarthen, Carmarthenshire SA31 3LE; Tel 01267
 233721; Fax 01267 233783
Chief Officer Glan Morris

Age Concern West Glamorgan
138 Walter Rd, Swansea SA1 5RQ;
 URL www.ageconcernswansea.org.uk;
 E-mail director@ageconcernswansea.org.uk; Tel 01792
 641164; Fax 01792 301355
Director Sue Richards

Age Concern Scotland

Founded 1943.
Leonard Small Hse, 113 Rose St, Edinburgh EH2 3DT;
 URL www.ageconcernscotland.org.uk;
 E-mail enquiries@ascot.org.uk; Tel 0131 220 3345;
 Fax 0131 220 2279
Chair Betty Bridgeford
Director Maureen O'Neill
Contact Information Manager David Brownlee
Membership
600
Funded by
Donations; Grants from Scottish Executive; Regional
Councils; Health Boards.
Aims
To improve services for older people and campaign on their
behalf.
Undertakes
Pressure/lobbying; library and information service;
fundraising; funding body.
Subject areas
Disability; housing; income maintenance; pre-retirement;
post-retirement; education etc.

Age Concern Northern Ireland

Founded 1977.
3 Lower Cres, Belfast BT7 1NR;
 URL www.ageconcernni.org; Tel 0289 024 5729; Fax 0289
 023 5497
Director C. Common
Funded by
DHSS, Health and Social Security, NLCB, charitable trusts,
fundraising.
Staff
135 paid full-time; Voluntary 1000+.
Aims
Acts as social advocate, provides direct services,
information and publications for older people.
Undertakes
Advice/information; health promotion; community
development; advocacy; research; education for older
people; pressure/lobbying; seminars/conferences; library
and information service; fundraising; care services.
Subject areas
Disability; housing; income maintenance; domiciliary care;
residential care; pre-retirement; health; post-retirement;
reminiscence; death and bereavement; education; carers'
support; transport; research/information service; care or
housing, community development.

Other Organisations

The Abbeyfield Society

53 Victoria St, St. Albans, Hertfordshire AL1 3UW;
 URL www.abbeyfield.com; E-mail post@abbeyfield.com;
 Tel 01727 857536; Fax 01727 846168
Chief Executive Brian House
Abbeyfield provides accommodation with care for older
people in sheltered housing. Residents have their own self-
furnished rooms, usually with en suite facilities; a
housekeeper ensures that two meals a day are provided. In
addition to approximately 800 sheltered houses, Abbeyfield
has around 70 care houses.

AgeCare Aberdeen

38 Castle St, Aberdeen AB11 5YU; URL www.vsa.org.uk;
 E-mail info@vsa.org.uk; Tel 01224 212021
Director W. Howie, MA, BD, STM
Aims
To improve the lives of people over retirement age in
Aberdeen. Provides care homes and sheltered housing plus
three activity centres for active retired people. Social work
team offers material aid and grants are available for
community groups. Weekend day care, home support
service for older people with dementia, social transport
schemes and volunteer befriending groups work with the
housebound. Promotes the development of new services
for older people.

Age Concern Institute of Gerontology

Kings College London, Franklin Wilkins Bldg, Waterloo Rd,
 London SE1 9NN
Director Janet Askham

Almshouse Association

Billingbear Lodge, Carters Hill, Wokingham RG40 5RU;
 URL www.almshouses.org; E-mail naa@almshouses.org;
 Tel 01344 452922; Fax 01344 862062
Director Anthony Leask
Advises members on any matters concerning almshouses
and welfare of the elderly. Promotes improvements and
provision of almshouses. Reviews and takes action on
legislation.

Anchor Trust

1st Fl, 408 Strand, London WC2R 0NE;
URL www.anchor.org.uk;
E-mail enquiries@anchor.org.uk; Tel 020 759 9100;
Fax 020 759 9101
Chief Executive John Belcher
Chair David Peryer
Anchor Trust is England's largest not-for-profit provider of housing, care and support to older people. Services include retirement housing, integrated housing with care, leasehold housing, a national community alarm service, home care, home improvement and adaptations, residential and nursing care. Anchor works with older people to increase their independence and quality of life and to broaden the range of their choices in where and how they live.

British Association for Service to the Elderly (BASE)

Founded 1968. Formerly known as the Geriatric Care Association.
The Guildford Institute of the University of Surrey, Ward St, Guildford, Surrey GU1 4LH; E-mail base@intonet.co.uk; Tel 01483 451036; Fax 01483 451034
Aims
To improve standards of care of elderly people through a national programme and others.

Care Concern

20 Pentonville Rd, London N1 9XB; Tel 020 7837 7345;
Fax 020 7833 8272
Care Concern is an independent day care provider for elders with high dependency needs and specialising in ethnic minorities.

British Geriatrics Society (BGS)

31 St. John's Sq, London EC1M 4DN;
URL www.bgs.org.uk; E-mail info@bgs.org.uk; Tel 020 7608 1369; Fax 020 7608 1041
Administrative Director A. Mair
Hon Secretary Dr K. Kelleher
The principal activities of the Society are in promoting scientific development of geriatric medicine and in influencing the providers of medical and social services for elderly people to improve the quality and provision of such services. The Society also administers funds to permit and reward research and promotes measures which will improve health throughout adult life to ensure better fitness on achieving old age.

British Pensioners and Trade Unions Action Association

76 Hinckley Rd, Coventry, West Midlands CV2 2EU;
E-mail jacksprung@maeunlimited.net; Tel 024 7661 4125
General Secretary Jack Sprung
Represents senior citizens on various committees and campaigns on their behalf for pensions, NHS and community care, energy and transport.

Carers UK

Ruth Pitter Hse, 20–25 Glasshouse Yard, London EC1A 4JT;
URL www.carersonline.org.uk;
E-mail info@ukcarers.org; Tel 020 7490 8818; (Freephone CarersLine (1000–1200 and 1400–1600 Mon–Fri) 0808 808 7777
Chief Executive Diana Whitworth
Carers UK is a campaigning organisation. They provide information and advice on all aspects of caring to both carers and professionals. The CarersLine is a free advice line for carers staffed by welfare rights, community care and benefits advisers, and answers over 22,000 carers' enquiries each year.

Carers UK have a UK-wide network of offices, branches and individuals offering support to carers and providing vital feedback on local practices and policies towards carers.

Carers Wales

River Hse, Yns Bridge Crt, Gwaelod y Garth, Cardiff CF15 9SS; Tel 029 2081 1370

Carers Scotland

91 Mitchell St, Glasgow G1 3LN; Tel 0141 221 9141

Carers Northern Ireland

58 Howard St, Belfast BT1 6PJ; URL www.carersni.org; Tel 028 9043 9843

Carers UK North of England

23 Mount St, Manchester M4 4DE; Tel 0161 953 4233

Centre for Policy on Ageing (CPA)

Founded 1947.
19–23 Ironmonger Row, London EC1V 3QP;
URL www.cpa.org.uk
Director and Information Enquiries G. Crosby
Aims
CPA is an independent information and policy unit aiming to promote better services and informed debate by formulating and developing policies and good practice. There is a varied publications list and comprehensive information service including Age Info CD-ROM and Age Information on the Web.
Undertakes
Research, education for elderly people; pressure / lobbying; seminars / conferences; library and information service; consultancy.
Staff
7
Subject areas
Housing; income maintenance; community care; residential and nursing home care; health; social care; employment; education; ethnic minorities; transport; leisure; religion and spirituality; information needs.

CSV (Community Service Volunteers)

237 Pentonville Rd, London N1 9NJ; URL www.csv.org.uk;
E-mail information@csv.org.uk; Tel 020 7278 6601
UK-wide charity and volunteer agency. For Retired and Senior Volunteer Programme see RSVP.

Contact The Elderly

15 Henrietta St, London WC2E 8QG; URL www.contact-the-elderly.org; E-mail info@contact-the-elderly.org; Tel 0800 716543; Fax 020 7379 5781
Director M. Hartwell
A voluntary service providing companionship and outings for elderly isolated people who live alone without family close by.

Counsel and Care (CCE)

Founded 1954.
Twyman Hse, 16 Bonny St, London NW1 9PG;
URL www.counselandcare.org.uk;
E-mail advice@counselandcare.org.uk;
Tel (Administration) 020 7241 8555; (Advice Line (local rate 1000–1300)) 0845 300 7585; Fax 020 7267 6877
Chief Executive Martin Green
Aims
Counsel and Care provides a free advisory service for older people and carers. Grants can be made for single needs.

18

Undertakes

Advice; pressure/lobbying; information service. Provides advice and information to persons over 60, their carers, friends and relatives on a range of issues, including community care, hospital discharge, continuing NHS care and finding suitable accommodation.

Elderly Accommodation Counsel (EAC)

Founded 1985.
3rd Fl, 89 Albert Embankment, London SE1 7TP;
    URL www.housingcare.org.uk;
    E-mail enquiries@e-a-c.demon.co.uk; Tel 020 7820 1343;
    Fax 020 7820 3970
Director J. Galvin
Manager (Operations) Lyn Middleton
Aims
The only national specialist Advice Line providing advice/information on Housing and Care choices for older people. EAC maintains a nationwide database of all forms of accommodation-sheltered housing for sale and rent, almshouses, care homes providing personal care, care homes providing nursing care, close care and extra care schemes. Advisors also give detailed advice and guidance to help enquirers choose and fund the accommodation most suited to their needs.

EXTEND (Movement to Music for the Over 60s and Less Able People of Any Ages)

EXTEND Exercise Training Ltd, 2 Place Farm,
    Wheathampstead, Hertfordshire AL4 8SB;
    E-mail admin@extend.org.uk; Tel 01582 832760;
    Fax 01582 832760
Secretary Ernie Scott

Forces Pensions Society

68 South Lambeth Rd, London SW8 1RL;
    URL www.forpen.co.uk; E-mail helen@forpen.co.uk;
    Tel 020 7582 0469; Fax 020 7820 7583
General Secretary Major General J.C.M. Gordon, CBE
To procure, where equitable, improvement in the Armed Forces Pension Scheme for members of the armed forces and their dependants. Assists members on service pension problems.

Friends of the Elderly

40–42 Ebury St, London SW1W 0LZ; URL www.fote.org.uk;
    E-mail enquiries@fote.org.uk; Tel 020 7730 8263; Fax 020
    7259 0154
Chief Executive Geoffrey Dennis
Friends of the Elderly promotes independence for older people in their own homes through community-based care services, with grants to those on low incomes to help cope with problems ranging from long-term mobility and home repairs to immediate, basic daily needs. The Friends provide residential homes based on Christian values with nursing care on site and is in process of upgrading all homes to meet the needs of the increasingly frail, together with the provision of safe and homely dementia care.

Grace and Compassion Benedictines

St. Benedict's, 1 Manor Rd, Kemp Town, Brighton, Sussex
    BN2 5EA; URL www.dabnet.org/gcb.htm;
    E-mail generalate@graceand compassion.co.uk;
    Tel 01273 680720; Fax 01273 680527
Prioress General Mother Mary Garson, MA, OSB, ABPsS,
    FRSA
Aims to give a home and love to elderly persons in need; interdenominational; men and women equally welcome.

Help the Aged

Founded 1961
207–221 Pentonville Rd, London N1 9UZ
Director General M. Lake, CBE
Information Manager Nicky Lappin
Aims
Help the Aged's purpose is to secure and uphold the rights of older people everywhere. Working with them, they identify the needs and champion the issues that help better their lives. Through research, campaigning and fundraising, they develop solutions, drive activities and inspire others to do the same.
Undertakes
Help the Aged provides information and advice to older people via SeniorLine, a free telephone advice service. Call 0808 800 6565 (0808 808 7575 from Northern Ireland); lines are open on weekdays from 0900 to 1600. Help the Aged also provides a wide range of free advice leaflets. Other activities include campaigning and lobbying; grantmaking; fundraising and fundraising advice.

Merton and Morden Guild of Social Service

Looe Hse, 34a Aberconway Rd, Morden, Surrey SM4 5LF;
    E-mail mmguild@hotmail.com; Tel 020 8640 1640
General Secretary J. Duncan
Voluntary organisation primarily for the welfare of elderly people. Registered Charity No 206143.

MHA Care Group

Epworth Hse, Stuart St, Derby DE1 2EQ;
    URL www.mha.org.uk; Tel 01332 296200; Fax 01332
    296925
Chief Executive Roger Davies
Provides a range of accommodation and care services based on Christian principles which are open to all older people in need whatever their beliefs. Methodist Homes cares for over 2000 older people in 49 residential homes and 31 sheltered housing schemes. There are also three specialist homes for those with dementia and a dual registered home. The befriending arm, Live at Home, now works in 41 local communities.

Nursing Home Fees Agency (NHFA)

St. Leonard's Hse, Mill St, Eynsham, Oxford, Oxfordshire
    OX29 4JX; URL www.nhfa.co.uk;
    E-mail enquiries@nhfa.co.uk; Tel 01865 733000;
    Fax 01865 733001
Chief Executive P. Spiers
The NHFA provides a free specialist advisory service to older people or their relatives on financial and legal problems arising when entering nursing or residential care, including advice on how best to meet the cost of care from resources available, with an aim to protect and preserve capital whilst also paying increasing fees. Advice and guidance on DWP benefits, local authority assessments, health authority responsibilities, important legal matters and tax problems, comprehensive fact sheets and information available on request. NHFA care advice line freephone 0800 998833.

OPAS (The Pensions Advisory Service)

11 Belgrave Rd, London SW1V 1RB;
    URL www.opas.org.uk; E-mail enquiries@opas.org.uk;
    Tel 020 7233 8080; Fax 020 7233 8016
Director (Administration) B. Wilkins
Independent and voluntary organisation established for the purpose of giving free help and advice to members of the public on all matters concerning pension schemes including personal pensions; available to all those who think they have pension rights including scheme members, pensioners, those with deferred pensions and dependants.

Otto Schiff Housing Association

Central Office, The Bishops Ave, London N2 0BG; Tel 020 8209 0022; Fax 020 8201 8089

Overseas Service Pensioners' Association

138 High St, Tonbridge, Kent TN9 1AX;
URL www.ospa.org.uk; Tel 01732 363836
Secretary   D.F.B. Le Breton
Represents, safeguards and promotes the interests of colonial and overseas civil service pensioners and their widows and dependants in all matters relating to their pensions.

The Pensions Trust for Charities and Voluntary Organisations

Verity Hse, 6 Canal Wharf, Leeds, West Yorkshire LS11 5BQ; Tel 0113 234 5500; Fax 0113 234 5599
Chief Executive   Richard K. Stroud, BA, FPMI
The Pensions Trust is a non-profit-making organisation and the leading specialist provider of occupational pension schemes to employers and employees within the voluntary sector. With net assets of over £2.0 billion the trust numbers 2500 organisations including more than 83 000 individual members participating in its pension schemes.

Pilgrim Homes

Registered Charity Number 242266; Registered Social Landlord 170822
Nasmith Hse, 175 Tower Bridge Rd, London SE1 2AL;
URL www.pilgrimhomes.org.uk;
E-mail info@pilgrimhomes.org.uk; Tel 020 7407 5466;
Fax 020 7403 4533
Pilgrim Homes is a national charity founded in 1807 to care for needy, elderly Christians. Today the society has nine care schemes throughout the country offering a range of care in a dedicated Christian setting to elderly Christians who subscribe to the society's basic Protestant beliefs.

Pre-Retirement Association (PRA)

9 Chesham Rd, Guildford, Surrey GU1 3LS;
URL www.pra.uk.com; E-mail info@pra.uk.com;
Tel 01483 301170; Fax 01483 300981

Director   Dr M.A. Davies
The PRA aims to provide educational programmes for those facing the change to a lifestyle outside full-time paid employment by encouraging mid-life planning and planning for retirement or redundancy. The PRA acts as a national focus for the development of this work with links to European, North American and Commonwealth countries. It has a resource centre and provides a wide range of courses for those retiring or redundant, for company personnel staff, or for those wishing to develop as pre-retirement tutors. Registered charity 801246.

RSVP (Retired and Senior Volunteer Programme)

Director   Denise Murphy; Tel 020 7643 1385
Manager (National Development)   John McCarthy; Tel 020 7643 1386
CSV's Retired and Senior Volunteer Programme harnesses the skills and experience of older people to enrich schools, hospitals and community projects and to protect our environment. All serve through local groups organised by volunteer organisers supported by volunteer regional co-ordinators.

St. Vincent de Paul Society (England and Wales)

14 Blandford St, London W1H 4DP; URL www.svp.org.uk;
E-mail svpuk@btconnect.com; Tel 020 7935 9126; Fax 020 7935 9136
President   J. O'Connor
Registered charity. Enquirers from London region should contact London Regional Office, 24 George St, London W1H 5RB; Tel 020 7935 7625; Fax 020 7935 6561.
Registered Charity Number 1053992

Wireless for the Bedridden Society

159a High St, Hornchurch, Essex RM11 3YB; Tel 01708 621101; (Freephone) 0800 0182137; Fax 01708 620816
Chief Executive   Barry A. Hobbs
Provides free radio and television sets for the housebound, disabled and elderly who cannot afford sets for themselves. Covers all parts of the UK.

18

Travel, Mobility and Holidays

19

- Organisations which provide assistance with travel arrangements for people with a variety of disabilities or special needs

Travel, Mobility and Holidays

This chapter does not claim to be a complete list of firms and organisations which can offer assistance with travel arrangements. Inclusion of an editorial entry does not imply approval; equally exclusion does not imply disapproval. Entries are listed in alphabetical order. For a list of older persons' welfare organisations, see Chapter 18; for a general list of disability and communication and visual impairment organisations, see Chapter 25

Action for Blind People (formerly London Association for the Blind)

14–16 Verney Rd, London SE16 3DZ; URL www.afbp.org; E-mail info@afbp.org; Tel 0800 915 4666; Fax 020 7635 4829
Chief Executive   Stephen Remington
A national charity working with blind and partially-sighted people, their families and carers. Provides employment support, accommodation, grants and welfare benefits advice, as well as information and advice on many other aspects of visual impairment. Mobile information and advice service travels throughout the country.

Alexander Forbes Mobility Services

2nd Fl, The Heights, 59–65 Lowlands Rd, Harrow, Greater London HA1 3AE; E-mail bruntonp@forbes.co.uk; Tel 020 8869 5500; Fax 020 8869 5506
Insurance schemes for electric and manual wheelchairs and mobility scooters against accidental damage, fire, theft, third party liability and breakdown.

Alfred Bekker

Kellythorpe, Driffield, East Riding of Yorkshire YO25 9DJ; Tel 01377 241700; Fax 01377 241767
Chief Officer   Karen Bekker
Manufacturers of hand controlling equipment, steering aids etc. Full or part conversions to cars, vans, trucks and lorries. Mobile fitters throughout the country. Employs 27 disabled fitters. Also offers accommodation adapted for wheelchair users. Rooms with colour TV, tea/coffee making equipment and specially designed en suite bathrooms.

Anglia Railways Train Services Limited

St. Clare Hse, Princes St, Ipswich, Suffolk IP1 1LY; URL www.angliarailways.co.uk; E-mail info@angliarailways.co.uk; Tel 08700 402020; Fax 01473 693915

Arriva Trains Merseyside Ltd

Rail Hse, Lord Nelson St, Liverpool, Merseyside L1 1JF; Tel 0151 702 2071

Arriva Trains Northern Ltd

Main Headquarters, Station Rise, York YO1 1HT; Tel 01904 522808; Fax 01904 524889

Arthritis Care

18 Stephenson Way, London NW1 2HD; URL www.arthritiscare.org.uk; Tel 020 7380 6500; Fax 020 7380 6505
Arthritis Care is the only national charity working proactively with and for people with arthritis, providing development courses, self-help groups in self-management. In addition they work through 650 local branches and groups with more than 7000 volunteers providing information, publications and hotels.

Atlas Conversions

75 Alverstone Rd, Portsmouth PO4 8RP; URL www.atlasconversions.co.uk; E-mail sales@atlasconversions.co.uk; Tel 023 9275 6265
General Manager   Joe Cordina
Producers of mini buses, wheelchair-accessible and easy access vehicles.

Automobile Association Ltd (the 'AA')

Norfolk Hse, Priestley Rd, Basingstoke, Hampshire RG24 9NY; URL www.theaa.com; E-mail customer.services@theaa.com; Tel (General Information) 0870 6000371; (Helpline for disabled members and non-members) 0800 262050; Fax 0990 143484
The Manager (Disability Helpline)
Founded in 1905, the AA is Britain's biggest motoring organisation, with 9.4m members. A free Disability Helpline and a biennial 'Disabled Travellers' Guide' (free to AA members), are made available, and there are preferential membership rates for Orange Badge holders. The disability helpline provides information on all aspects of mobility for disabled motorists and information for people with disabilities who wish to take out or renew AA membership.

Avon Tyrrell Activity and Residential Centre

Bransgore, Hampshire BH23 8EE; URL www.avontyrrell.org.uk; E-mail info@avontyrrell.org.uk; Tel 01425 672347; Fax 01425 673883
Estate Manager   R. Bonney
The National Training and Residential Centre of the charity 'UK Youth', located in the New Forest. Avon Tyrrell provides accommodation, activities and environmental education for organised groups of children and young people, in full board or self catering accommodation.

BAA plc

130 Wilton Rd, London SW1V 1LQ; URL www.baa.com;
  Tel 020 7834 9449; Fax 020 7932 6699

BAA plc owns and operates seven major UK airports: Heathrow, Gatwick, Stansted and Southampton in the South East; and Glasgow, Edinburgh and Aberdeen in Scotland. Responsibility for the easy transit of disabled travellers through these airports is shared with airlines and handling agents. Such passengers should inform their airline in advance of their movements so that suitable arrangements can be made and assistance given. Help Points are installed in baggage reclaim halls, on forecourts and close to disabled spaces in short-term car parks at Heathrow. All terminal buildings are fitted with lifts, ramps and escalators to ensure easy access for everyone. Information for passengers with special needs can be found on the BAA website. Care in the Air, giving general advice to disabled passengers, is available from The Secretary, Air Transport Users Council, 5th Fl, Kingsway Hse, 103 Kingsway, London WC2B 6QX.

Batricar Independent Mobility

43 Avishayes Rd, Chard, Somerset TA20 1NZ;
  E-mail batricarindmob@aol.com; Tel 01460 67220;
  Fax 01460 67220; Stroud Office, Philip Cl; Tel 01453
  826981; Fax 01453 826981

Suppliers of new and reconditioned battery-powered three and four wheeled mobility vehicles, wheelchairs, manual and power, walking aids, wheelchair power packs and care aids. All products suitable for the elderly and disabled between the ages of 10 and 110.

Bendrigg Trust

Bendrigg Lodge, Old Hutton, Kendal, Cumbria LA8 0NR;
  URL www.bendrigg.org.uk;
  E-mail office@bendrigg.org.uk; Tel 01539 723766;
  Fax 01539 722446

Principal   T. Clarke

An independent, non-profit-making venture, The Bendrigg Trust is a registered charity specialising in courses for people with a physical disability, people with learning disabilities, disadvantaged, unemployed and other youth groups, working with up to 40 people for two to seven days. Bendrigg Lodge is fully accessible for wheelchair users. A wide range of both indoor and outdoor activities with specialist instruction is available. Also a self-contained, fully fitted annexe 'Oakwood', ideal for smaller groups up to 20.

BJK Insurance Brokers Ltd

1 Riverside Crt, Castle St, Barnstaple, Devon EX31 1EY;
  E-mail info@bjknibbs.co.uk; Tel 01271 345005

Special scheme for insurance of multi-seat vehicles used by youth, disabled and community organisations. Property, personal accident and liability insurance specialists for these organisations. Registered insurance brokers. Schemes for professional indemnity insurance for community transport groups, Shopmobility projects and bonus and excess protection insurance for volunteers. Travel cover for community and charitable organisations including those with pre-existing medical conditions.

Birmingham PHAB Camps

2 Lenchs Grn, Edgbaston, Birmingham, West Midlands
  B5 7PX; Tel 0121 440 5727

Provides holidays for groups consisting of equal numbers of physically disabled and able-bodied children/young people in July and August each year. One camp takes 25 children aged 8–10 years; one is for 25 children aged 11–13 years; one is for 25 children aged 14–16 years; and one is for 30 young adults aged 16–20 years. Also runs a holiday for 20 children aged 8–18 years with multiple disabilities and profound learning difficulties. Referrals are mainly by schools around Birmingham and occasionally from social workers. The camps are held at various residential centres in the British Isles and are staffed by unpaid volunteers, normally aged 17–30 years, including a qualified nurse on each.They are not suitable children with autistic or behavioural problems. All children must live in the Birmingham area.

BREAK

Davison Hse, 1 Montague Rd, Sheringham, Norfolk
  NR26 8WN; URL www.break-charity.org;
  E-mail office@break-charity.org; Tel 01263 822161;
  Fax 01263 822181

BREAK provides a range of specialist care services including holidays, short-breaks and respite care for children and adults with learning and physical disabilities at two centres in Norfolk. Guests come from all over the country and the holiday programme combines full 24-hour care with outings, entertainment and activities.
The fully accessible centres are open all year round and can each accommodate up to 10 guests per week. Facilities at both centres include: accessible transport, indoor heated swimming pool, sensory room, specialised toys/games and a wide range of adaptations for the safety and comfort of guests. Groups, with or without accompanying carers, are welcome. Family holidays are available at certain times of the year.
BREAK also provides afffordable self-catering holidays for families with special needs at a wheelchair-friendly chalet at Westward Ho! in Devon.

British Limbless Ex-Service Men's Association (BLESMA)

Frankland Moore Hse, 185–187 High Rd, Chadwell Heath,
  Romford, Essex RM6 6NA; URL www.blesma.org;
  E-mail blesma@btconnect.com; Tel 020 8590 1124;
  Fax 020 8599 2932

General Secretary   J.W. Church, MBE

BLESMA Homes at Blackpool and Crieff, Perthshire, provide residential, convalescent and holiday accommodation for limbless ex-service men and their widows. Limited accommodation is available for other war pensioners. Open all the year. Forms of application available from BLESMA Headquarters or local branches.

British Polio Fellowship

(Registered: The Infantile Paralysis Fellowship)
The Runway, Eagle Office Centre, South Ruislip, Greater
  London HA4 6SA; URL www.britishpolio.org;
  E-mail info@britishpolio.org

National Welfare Officer   Dorothy Nattrass

The British Polio Fellowship exists to support people who have had polio and their carers in a variety of ways. Information available on the late effects of polio/post-polio syndrome.

British Red Cross Society

9 Grosvenor Cres, London SW1X 7EJ; Tel 0207 235 5454;
  Fax 0207 245 6315

The British Red Cross provides a number of services for vulnerable people in their local communities. These include the short term loan of medical equipment; the transporting of those unable to make essential journeys unaided; and care for those recently discharged from hospital. All of these services are delivered by trained and skilled volunteers. For more information, please contact your local British Red Cross branch.

British Rheumatism and Arthritis Association

see Arthritis Care

British Ski Club for the Disabled

Randlehayes Farm, Aylesbeare, Exeter, Devon EX5 2JN;
URL www.bscd.org.uk; E-mail rcann@bscd.org.uk;
Tel 01395 232915; Fax 01395 232330
Vice-Chair and Membership Secretary Rosemary Cann
Provides facilities for disabled people to partake in
recreational skiing on artificial slopes and snow holidays.
Training is available to become a guide.

Bromakin Ltd

12 Prince William Rd, Belton Pk, Loughborough,
Leicestershire LE11 0GU; URL www.bromakin.co.uk;
E-mail sales@bromakin.co.uk; Tel 01509 217569
Managing Director Peter Carruthers
Company Secretary Sheila Carruthers
Manufacturers and distributors of high-performance
wheelchairs and sports equipment.

Calvert Trust Keswick

Little Crosthwaite, Keswick, Cumbria CA12 4QD;
URL calvert-trust.org.uk;
E-mail enquiries.calvert.keswick@dial.pipex.com;
Tel 017687 72254; Fax 017687 71920
Centre Director J. Crosbie
Outdoor activity centre for people with disabilities.
Multi-activity courses guided by experienced instructors.
Activities include sailing, canoeing, pony riding and trap
driving, problem solving, riding, swimming, orienteering,
rock-climbing and abseiling, nature trails etc. Fully
accessible accomodation with en-suite facilities.
(Accommodation also available for self-catering groups
who wish to run their own activities outside the centre.)

Camping for the Disabled

Unit B1 Greenwood Crt, Cartmel Dr, Shrewsbury,
Shropshire SY1 3TB
Contact Jean Griffiths
Offers advice to disabled and their families on camping
and caravanning. Encourages experienced disabled
campers to pool information and experiences to help
others. Organises group camps at adapted sites. Organises
group booking to cut costs. Compiles lists of accessible sites
in Britain and Europe. Membership £2.50 a year for up to
five members of a family. Requests for site information
should be accompanied by a SAE and the enquirer should
state the particular region of a country he/she is interested
in.

Cardiff Railway Company Limited

10th Fl, Brunel Hse, Cardiff CF2 1SA; Tel 029 2043 0000

Cefndy Enterprises

Cefndy Rd, Rhyl, Denbighshire LL18 2HG; Tel 01745
343877; Fax 01745 355806
Marketing Assistant D. Holmes-Langstone
Healthcare manufacturer/supplier: commodes, overbed
tables, trolleys, bath aids, shower aids, grab rails and
toileting aids.

Central Trains Limited

PO Box 4323, Birmingham, West Midlands B2 4JB; Tel 0121
645 1140

Cheam Invicta Club

Bungalow Secretary P. Webbe
43 Wrayfield Rd, Cheam, Surrey SM3 9TJ; Tel 020 8644 9537
Bungalow at Elmer Sands, Middleton-on-Sea, open all the
year round: self-catering with four double bedrooms, one
with a hoist, sofa bed in lounge, accommodating 10 people.

Up to five wheelchairs. Large lounge, dining room, kitchen,
bathroom with hoist, shower room, two toilets. Fully
adapted for wheelchairs. About five minutes from the
beach on a private estate, and five miles from Bognor.
Bookings are taken from 31 October for the following year.
SAE to be sent with all enquiries please.

Children's Country Holidays Fund

1st Fl, 42–43 Lower Marsh, London SE1 7RG;
URL www.childrensholidays-ccnt.org; Tel 020 7928 6522;
Fax 020 7401 3961
Chief Executive M. Bishop
Offers summer holidays to London children in need aged
between 5–12, and to London families. Parents are required
to make a small contribution towards the cost of the
holidays, according to their means. Applications should be
made by social workers, teachers, health visitors, etc. to the
Chief Executive or appropriate London Organiser.

The Children's Trust

See Chapter 13
Tadworth Crt, Tadworth, Surrey KT20 5RU; Tel 01737
365000; Fax 01737 365001
Offers short-term residential care for children with
profound and multiple disabilities, available 365 days of
the year on a flexible basis. Also, hospice care for children
with terminal conditions. A rehabilitation service for
children with acquired brain injury is also available. The
Children's Trust operates St. Margaret's School at Tadworth
Court which is an independent residential school for
children with profound and multiple learning difficulties.
The School is open 49 weeks of the year.

The Chiltern Railway Company Limited

Western Hse, 14 Rickfords Hill, Aylesbury,
Buckinghamshire HP20 2RX; Tel 01296 332100

Churchtown

Lanlivery, Bodmin, Cornwall PL30 5BT;
E-mail churchtown@saqnet.co.uk; Tel 01208 872148;
Fax 01208 873377
Director D. Owens, MPhil, MIBiol
Courses in rural studies, field studies, outdoor pursuits,
leisure activities, photography, painting, pottery etc. Full
care facilities for people with physical and/or intellectual
special needs. Holidays and respite care throughout the
year. Registered residential home. Self catering, accessible
family lodges.

The Cirdan Sailing Trust

3 Chandlers Quay, Maldon, Essex CM9 4LF;
URL www.cirdan-faramir.co.uk;
E-mail info@cirdan-faramir.co.uk; Tel 01621 851433;
Fax 01621 840045
Head (Marketing and Fundraising) Leonie Turner
Exists to provide sailing adventure for groups of young
people (accompanied by their leaders) from youth
organisations across the spectrum. The Trust runs large
sailing vessels staffed by qualified officers. Prices can be
subsidised so needy groups can utilise facilities. Details
available on request.

Communities Scotland

27–29 Palmerston Pl, Edinburgh EH12 5AP;
URL www.communitiesscotland.gov.uk;
E-mail rossc@communitiesscotland.gov.uk; Tel 0131 313
0044; Fax 0131 479 5498
Manager Colin Ross
Communities Scotland: Community Learning and
Development Team provides a national focal point for
these areas of work.

19

Community Transport

Head Office, PO Box 66, Manchester M19 2XT; Tel 0161 477 2962
Chief Executive Murray Seccombe
Company Secretary Peter Cooper
Minibus loan to non-profit organisations–many minibuses have tail lifts. Drivers available. Also collects unwanted furniture to recycle it for reuse by low-income individuals and families. Projects in Coventry, Birmingham, Sandwell, Wolverhampton, Salford, Newcastle upon Tyne.

Connect Youth (CNY)

British Council, 10 Spring Gdns, London SW1A 2BN;
URL www.connectyouthinternational.com;
E-mail connectyouth.enquiries@britishcouncil.org;
Tel 020 7389 4030; Fax 020 7389 4033
Contact Information Unit, Connect Youth
Connect Youth (CNY), a department of the British Council, promotes international exchanges for British young people with youth groups from other countries. Connect Youth is also the UK National Agency for the European Commission's YOUTH Programme. This programme offers various actions ranging from group exchanges to voluntary service and is run across 30 countries in Europe. Priority is given to young people who would not normally have the opportunity for an international experience. In addition to this programme, they also provide UK government funds for bilateral exchanges with USA, Israel, Japan, China and a host of other countries. They also run the Causeway British-Irish programme to promote exchanges between young people in Britain and Ireland.

Connex South Eastern Limited

Friars Bridge Crt, 41–45 Blackfriars Rd, London SE1 8PG;
Tel 020 7620 5000

Cowal (Mobility) Aids Ltd

Cowal Crt, Heath End Rd, High Wycombe,
Buckinghamshire HP15 6HL;
URL www.cowalmobility.co.uk;
E-mail sales@cowalmobility.co.uk; Tel 01494 714400;
Fax 01494 714818
Managing Director Roy K. Walters
Manufacture and fit all types of controls and seating for disabled drivers and passengers, which can also be supplied ready assembled. Sole UK distributors of Cowal GZ 91 (and 'Wymo') wheelchair lifts to car roof top devices. Electronic accelerator and person hoist also manufactured and fitted. Motability accredited.

CSV (Community Service Volunteers)

237 Pentonville Rd, London N1 9NJ; URL www.csv.org.uk;
E-mail information@csv.org.uk; Tel 020 7278 6601
Head (Press) Jonathan Tuchner
CSV offers young people between the ages of 16–35 the opportunity to volunteer full–time, away from home, for between four months and one year. In return volunteers receive board, lodging, fares and pocket money. Projects nationwide range from mentoring young offenders to supporting people with disabilities so that they might live independently. Older volunteers meet needs in their own communities through RSVP, CSV's Retired and Senior Volunteer Programme.

Cystic Fibrosis Trust

11 London Rd, Bromley, Kent BR1 1BY;
URL www.cftrust.org.uk;
E-mail enquiries@cftrust.org.uk; Tel 020 8464 7211;
(Benefits Advice) 0845 859 1010; (General Helpline) 0845 859 1000; (Welfare Grants) 0845 859 1020; Fax 020 8313 0472

Chief Executive Rosie Barnes
The Cystic Fibrosis Trust raises money to fund vital hospital and university research into improved treatments and the search for a cure for CF. It also provides support, information and advice for people with CF, their families and friends.

CZC Rail Ltd

Customer Services, Station Rd, Cambridge,
Cambridgeshire CB1 2JW; Tel 0845 601 4873; Fax 01223 453606

Diabetes UK

10 Parkway, London NW1 7AA;
URL www.diabetes.org.uk; E-mail info@diabetes.org.uk;
Tel 020 7424 1000; (Diabetes UK Careline) 020 7424 1030;
Fax 020 7424 1001
Chief Executive Paul Streets
A charity which exists to help people with diabetes and their carers and which supports diabetes research. It organises family weekends and holidays for children with diabetes and their parents and also campaigns on behalf of people with diabetes. For information and advice on all aspects of diabetes call the Diabetes UK Careline.

Disabled Drivers' Association (DDA)

National Headquarters, Ashwellthorpe, Norwich, Norfolk NR16 1EX; URL www.dda.org.uk;
E-mail ddahq@aol.com; Tel (0900–1700) 0870 770 3333
Charity run by and for disabled persons to promote independence through mobility and inform and advise on mobility related problems; c. 24 000 members in UK, and 35 local DDA Groups. Substantial discounts available to disabled members on continental and island car ferries. The DDA produces a quarterly magazine Magic Carpet, free to members and full of advice and information on relevant topics.

Disabled Motorists' Federation (DMF)

c/o Chester-le-Street and District CVS Volunteer Centre,
Clarence Terr, Chester-le-Street, County Durham
DH3 3DQ; E-mail jkillick2214@compuserve.com;
Tel 0191 416 3172; Fax 0191 416 3172
Chair Joyce Williams
President Vacancy
Honorary Secretary Mr J.E. Killick
145 Knoulberry Rd, Blackfell, Washington, Tyne and Wear NE37 1JN
Umbrella organisation for disabled motorists' clubs. DMF provides national representation, support, free quarterly magazine for members and helps establish new clubs where no provision exists. RAMP provides route plans and maps incorporating roadside accessible facilities (hotels, restaurants, attended service stations, toilets etc.) free to members. The service is available to non–members for £5.00 per route. DMF is now developing a similar service for continental travel called EURAMP. RAMP/EURAMP request line is 01743 761181.

Durham County Association for the Disabled

Ground Fl Rear, Town Hall, Spennymoor, County Durham
DL16 6JD; E-mail dcad@alphaphe.com; Tel 01388 812288
Chair H. Hesler
Organising Secretary Marie Ward
Offers a general advice service on all subjects. Produces newsletters. Organises holidays. Close liaison with statutory and voluntary disabled organisations. Affiliated to RADAR (Royal Association for Disability and Rehabilitation). Social events. DIAL information service.

Elap Engineering Ltd

Fort St, Accrington, Lancashire BB5 1QG;
URL www.elap.co.uk; E-mail mail@elap.co.uk; Tel 01254
871599; Fax 01254 389992
Contact   C. Garrett
Supply a range of conversion kits, to convert the existing
front passenger or driver's seat to rotate out through the
doorway of car. Where a kit is not possible, can supply a
complete replacement rotating/sliding seat in both two and
four door vehicles, enabling easy, dignified access.

English Tourism Council

Thames Tower, Black's Rd, Hammersmith, London
W6 9EL; E-mail cveitch@englishtourism.org.uk; Tel 020
8563 3383; Fax 020 8563 3113
The English Tourism Council seeks to encourage the
tourism industry to cater for all people regardless of age or
disability and create a genuinely welcoming and accessible
environment. A new National Accessible Scheme has been
introduced which seeks to identify and acknowledge those
places to stay that meet the needs of wheelchair users and
others with mobility problems as well as people with
sensory (hearing/visual) impairment. The scheme is
supported by Government, as well as a wide range of
expert organisations in the disability field such as Tourism
For All Consortium and Holiday Care.

Eurostar (UK) Ltd

Eurostar Hse, London SE1 8SE; Tel 020 7922 6180

Fairthorne Manor

South East Hampshire YMCA, Fairthorne Manor, Curdridge,
Southampton SO30 2GH; URL www.fairthorne.co.uk;
E-mail info@fairthorne.co.uk; Tel 01489 785228;
Fax 01489 798936
Centre operates all year for day groups and residentially.
Accommodation in residential blocks (160) and summer
tented accommodation for 180. Activities includes sailing,
canoeing, archery, orienteering, climbing, environmental
activities, crafts and a variety of field and wide games. Staff
include qualified instructors and a live-in Warden and
Houseparent. Ramps for wheelchairs in most areas of the
Centre including ground floor bedrooms with wide doors;
special toilet and shower facilities adjacent. The staff have
experience in dealing with a wide range of special needs
but children should be accompanied by their own staff. The
Manor also operates a fully inclusive playscheme for up to
500 children per day. Enquiries for tailored residential
courses or adventure holidays welcomed.

Family Fund

PO Box 50, York YO1 9ZX; URL www.familyfund.org.uk;
E-mail info@familyfund.org.uk; Tel 0845 130 45412;
Fax 01904 652625
Chief Executive   Marion Lowe
Family Fund is an independent organisation whose purpose
is to ease the stress on families who care for severely disabled
and seriously ill children under 16, by providing grants and
information related to the care of the child. The Fund is
funded by the national governments of England, Northern
Ireland, Scotland and Wales. Grants given include washing
machines, holidays, leisure activities, driving lessons,
bedding and clothing. Further details of the disability and
financial guidelines of the Fund are available from the
Information Officer. Applications should be made in writing
giving the child's full name and date of birth, address, brief
details of his/her disability and the kind of help required.

Ford Motor Company Ltd

Eagle Way, Brentwood, Essex CM13 3BW; Tel 01277 253000;
Fax 01277 253067
Participates in the Motability contract hire scheme and
offers substantial discounts to disabled people. Those
without mobility allowances, but who are registered
disabled, may still qualify for Ford's own outright purchase
scheme and special discounts. For a free information pack
ring free of charge on 0800 111222.

Gatwick Express Limited

52 Grosvenor Gdns, London SW1W 0AU; Tel 020 7973 5000

Gerald Simonds Healthcare Ltd

9 March Pl, Gatehouse Way, Aylesbury, Buckinghamshire
HP19 8UA; URL www.gerald-simonds.co.uk;
E-mail info@gerald-simonds.co.uk; Tel 01296 380200;
Fax 01296 380279
Managing Director   H.G. Simonds
Gerald Simonds Healthcare Ltd is a specialist supplier of
mobility and seating equipment, whose objective is to offer
disabled people of all ages the highest possible degree of
mobility, comfort and self-respect. It achieves this by
providing carefully selected products, backed up by
outstanding service both before and after purchase. The
product range includes lightweight manual wheelchairs by
Etac, Quickie and Kuschall, custom built to suit the user's
individual needs and abilities; stand-up wheelchairs by
Levo of Switzerland; add-on power-drives for manual
wheelchairs; powered wheelchairs and scooters; Jay
Medical wheelchair seating products for pressure relief and
postural control and stability; and the Vicair range of
pressure relieving mattresses and wheelchair cushions.

Gowrings Mobility Limited

Bone La, Newbury, Berkshire RG14 5UE;
URL www.gowringsmobility.co.uk;
E-mail sales@gowringsmobility.co.uk; Tel 0845 608 8040;
Fax 01635 529400
Manufacturer and supplier of wheelchair passenger vehicles.

Great North Eastern Railway Limited

Main Headquarters, Station Rise, York YO1 1HT; Tel 01904
653022

Great Western Trains Company Limited

Milford Hse, 1 Milford St, Swindon, SN1 1HL;
URL www.firstgreatwestern.co.uk; Tel 08457 000125

HF Holidays Ltd

Imperial Hse, Edgware Rd, London NW9 5AL;
URL www.hfholidays.co.uk;
E-mail info@hfholidays.co.uk; Tel 020 8905 9388; Fax 020
8205 0506
Chief Executive   Peter Chapman
Non-profit-seeking organisation with country houses
throughout UK. Open all year. Group bookings and
conferences welcome. Specialists in walking and special
interest holidays. No extra charge for single rooms.
Telephone for a brochure.

Highball Scheme (Birmingham)

9 While Rd, Sutton Coldfield, West Midlands B72 1ND;
Tel 0121 354 2799
Bookings Officer   Dave Benton
Operates Children's Holiday Centre at Hanley Swan,
Worcester, near the Malvern Hills. Adventure weekend
holidays throughout the year for deprived children aged
5–14 years, living in or near Birmingham. Can be hired by
children's organisations and schools. Contains fully
equipped kitchen, dining facilities, playroom, eight
bedrooms of different sizes with double and single bunk
beds. Will accommodate 40 children and 15 staff. No resident
staff; groups hiring the centre must provide their own food.
Available throughout the year subject to prior bookings.

19

Holiday Care

7th Fl, Sunley Hse, 4 Bedford Pk, Croydon, Surrey
CR0 2AP; URL www.holidaycare.org.uk;
E-mail info@holidaycare.org; Tel (Administration) 0845
124 9974; (Info) 0845 124 9971; (Reservations) 0845 124
9973; Fax 0845 124 9972
Manager Derek Moore
Holiday Care is the central resource on holiday information
for disabled tourists, older persons and carers in the UK
and overseas: Nearly 100 leaflets and information sheets on
holiday opportunities in the UK and overseas are
produced. These include accessible hotels, farmhouses,
guest houses and self-catering; activity holidays; holidays
organised for disabled people or where care is available;
and transport advice. Anyone wishing to become a 'Friend
of Holiday Care' is able to book inspected UK hotel or self-
catering accommodation featured in their guides.This
accommodation has been inspected for accessibility and
Friends of Holiday Care receive discounted rates when
booking at Hilton, Copthorne and Novotel Hotels using the
Holiday Care Reservations service.

Holidays for Disabled People

PO Box 164, Totton, Southampton SO40 9WZ;
URL members.aol.com/h4dp1/; E-mail h4dp1@aol.com;
Tel 01252 332452
Holidays for Disabled people organises one week holiday
each year at a leading holiday centre in the UK, catering for
groups and individuals who have a physical disability.
Helpers are provided at no extra charge. Unless otherwise
stated, a doctor will be present. Optional daily excursions
are arranged, using specially adapted vehicles, and evening
entertainment provided. In addition, holiday organisers
arrange several smaller breaks, usually abroad.

International Voluntary Service (IVS)

IVS South, Old Hall, Colchester, Essex CO7 6TQ;
URL ivs-gb.org.uk; E-mail ivs@ivsgbsouth.demon.co.uk;
Tel 01206 298215
International workcamps from end of June to September
(also some in winter and spring), usually lasting between 2-
4 weeks. Teams of 6–20 volunteers from all over the world,
minimum age 18, help community-based groups and
organisations with playschemes, environmental and
conservation work, holiday activities with/for disabled
people, women's projects, Third World solidarity, etc. Some
projects involve a study element, often on international or
Third World themes. Volunteers with disabilities can be
accepted on some of these projects on an individual basis,
as part of the team. Volunteers are also sent to workcamps
outside the UK. Free board and lodging. Travel expenses
cannot be paid.

IVS North

Castlehill Hse, 21 Otley Rd, Leeds, West Yorkshire
LS6 3AA; E-mail ivsgbn@ivsgbn.demon.co.uk; Tel 0113
230 4600; Fax 0113 230 4610

IVS Scotland

7 Upper Bow, Edinburgh EH1 2JN;
E-mail ivs@ivsgbscot.demon.co.uk; Tel 0131 226 6722;
Fax 0131 226 6723

IVS Northern Ireland

30 Shaftesbury Sq, Belfast BT2 7DB; E-mail colin@ivsni.co.uk;
Tel 028 9023 8147; Fax 028 9024 4356

Invacare Ltd

South Rd, Bridgend Ind Est, Bridgend, Mid Glamorgan,
CF31 3PY; Tel 01656 664321; Fax 01656 667532
Managing Director Roy Hawkes
Invacre Ltd is the UK division of one of Europe's largest
manufacturers of mobility aids and rehabilitation
equipment. Manufacturers of an extensive range of

Powerchairs in the UK, their range encompasses lightweight and specialist manual wheelchairs, Profiling Beds
and products to enhance positioning, posture and provide
pressure relief.

Island Line Limited

Ryde St. Johns Rd Station, St. Johns Rd, Ryde, Isle of Wight
PO33 2BA; URL www.island-line.co.uk;
E-mail comments@island-line.co.uk; Tel 01983 812591

Iona Community

Iona Abbey, Isle of Iona, Argyll and Bute PA76 6SN;
E-mail ionacomm@iona.org.uk; Tel 01681 700404;
Fax 01681 700460
Ecumenical Christian community with three centres, in
beautiful Hebridean island settings. All welcome, including
socially, educationally, environmentally disadvantaged and
physically and mentally challenged people. The Abbey (45
beds) is open Mar–Oct, as is the Macleod Centre, which
sleeps 48 and has disabled access and facilities for young
people: The Camas Centre, Bunessan, Isle of Mull, offers
challenge in an outdoor setting for small groups, 15–20
people. Brochure from the above address. Financial
assistance available in certain circumstances.

John Grooms (Grooms Holidays)

50 Scrutton St, London EC2A 4XQ;
URL www.johngrooms.org.uk;
E-mail charity@johngrooms.org.uk; Tel 08456 584478;
Fax 01446 775060
John Grooms is a national charity which together with its
sister organisation, John Grooms Housing Association, works
with disabled people, enabling them to have greater
independence, choice and freedom. Grooms Holidays, run by
John Grooms, has award-winning hotels and 16 self-catering
apartments around the UK, all of which are accessible to
people with disabilities, including wheelchair users.
Accommodation varies from a chalet in the Lake District to
an apartment on the south coast. Grooms Holidays aims to
provide breaks that are affordable, memorable and accessible.
Other services provided by John Grooms are: nine residential
and nursing homes, a brain injury rehabilitation centre for
Suffolk residents, employment training for people with
disabilities at horticultural nursery. John Grooms Housing
Association is the largest specialist builder of wheelchair
accessible housing in the UK.
Publications
Free, colour holiday brochure with pictures, prices and
local attractions; Residential care brochure – describing all
John Grooms care services; Grooms News – free magazine
three times a year; Information pack – general leaflets
describing John Grooms work; Annual reports and
accounts. All publications free for reasonable quantities.

Keep Able Ltd

Sterling Pk, Pedmore Rd, Brierley Hill, West Midlands
DY5 1TB; URL www.keepable.co.uk;
E-mail sales@keepable.co.uk; Tel 01384 473704
Keep Able, the specialist equipment retailer, has nine stores
across the UK. Their comprehensive product range
includes mobility, seating, beds, stairlifts, bathing and aids
for daily living. Professional advice is available in all stores
and home visits can be arranged. A free mail order
catalogue is available.
Specialist facilities
A growing area of business involves the provision of
specialist support and seeing systems for wheelchair
application. Working with clients and health-care
professionals their staff can help find appropriate seating
and mobility solutions. An important feature of Keep
Able's service allows the provision of hoisting and
equipment training for health-care practitioners. They have
particular expertise in this field.

Keep Able Ltd Birmingham

182–186 Robin Hood La, Hall Grn, Birmingham, West
Midlands B28 0LG; Tel 0121 777 8383; Fax 0121 778 2579

Keep Able Ltd Bournemouth

779–781 Wimborne Rd, Moordown, Bournemouth
BH9 2BD; Tel 01202 549121; Fax 01202 549141

Keep Able Ltd Bristol

278–280 Gloucester Rd, Horfield, Bristol BS7 8PD; Tel 0117
924 6620; Fax 0117 924 0125

Keep Able Ltd Kettering

Unit 38c, Telford Way, Kettering, Northamptonshire
NN16 8UN; Tel 01536 525153; Fax 01536 515077

Keep Able Ltd London

615–619 Watford Way, Apex Corner, Mill Hill, London
NW7 3JN; Tel 020 8201 0810; Fax 020 8201 0840

Keep Able Ltd Staines

11–17 Kingston Rd, Staines, Greater London TW18 4QX;
Tel 01784 440044; Fax 01784 449900

Keep Able Ltd Wolverhampton

9b Cleveland St, Wolverhampton, West Midlands
WV1 3HH; Tel 01902 711881; Fax 01902 714513

Keep Able Ltd Worcester

Unit 5, Lowesmoor Wharf, Worcester, Worcestershire
WR1 2RS; Tel 01905 28575; Fax 01905 724936

Kent Association for Disabled People

The Chequers Centre, Pads Hill, Romney Pl, Maidstone,
Kent ME15 6AT; Tel 01622 756444
County Administrator   Susan Russell
Aims to promote the welfare and interests of disabled
people throughout the county of Kent. Provides holidays
with care. There are seven autonomous local branches,
providing social activities and self-help groups for
members. Advice and information service on all aspects of
disability.

Kessingland Beach Holiday Village

Kessingland Beach, Beach Rd, Lowestoft, Suffolk
NR33 7RW; Tel 01502 740636; Fax 01502 740907
Contact   Tracey Lawrence
Can accommodate groups of people with special needs
(parties of up to 20) of all ages, accompanied by helpers
and supervising staff. Chalet accommodation completely
modified, modernised and furnished for two, four or five
people. Lounge area, fitted kitchen, fully carpeted,
background heating, bathroom suites and colour television.
All accommodation including recreational and dining
facilities is on ground floor level with entry ramps
provided where necessary. Full range of daytime sports
and entertainment available plus nightly cabarets and live
bands. Free indoor and outdoor heated pools. Holiday
Village is alongside the sea in country area, five miles from
Lowestoft. Open April to October. Self-catering, half-board
holidays.

League of Welldoers

119–133 Limekiln La, Liverpool, Merseyside L5 8SN;
E-mail info@theleague.liv.org.uk; Tel 0151 207 1984
Chief Executive   Philip Rooney

Leonard Cheshire

see Chapter 14
30 Millbank, London SW1P 4QD;
URL www.leonard-cheshire.org.uk;
E-mail info@london.leonard-cheshire.org.uk; Tel 020
7802 8200; Fax 020 7802 8250

Park House Hotel

Sandringham, King's Lynn, Norfolk PE35 6EH; Tel 01485
543000
Manager   Jonathon Walpole
Park House is a unique holiday and short stay respite care
facility for people with physical disabilities and their
carers. Dual registered for the provision of both nursing
and residential care, Park House provides holiday and
respite care accomodation to the highest possible standard
all year round.

Liverpool Association of Disabled People (LAD)

Lime Court Centre, Upper Baker St, Liverpool, Merseyside
L6 1NB; URL www.ladp.org.uk;
E-mail ladisabled@freenetname.co.uk; Tel 0151 263 8366;
Fax 0151 263 1855; Minicom 0151 260 3187
LAD is a campaigning organisation controlled by disabled
people. Has a welfare rights project and offers a wide range
of information advice. Including access audits.

Lloyd Thomas Charity for Women and Girls

c/o FHA, 16 Mortimer St, London W1N 7RD; Tel 020 7436
3304
Administrator   S. Jewell
Application through social worker or similar welfare agent.
Makes grants to poor women and girls in desperate need of
a holiday break.

London Transport

1b Broadway, London SW1H 0BD; Tel 020 7222 5600;
(Travel information) 020 7222 1234
Elderly and disabled residents of Greater London travel
free on London Transport buses and underground trains
from 0900 until 0300 Mondays and Fridays, but on
Saturdays, Sundays and Public holidays are valid
at any time. They also travel free on British Rail trains in
the London area from 0930 Mondays–Fridays and any time
Saturdays, Sundays and Public holidays. The non-elderly
blind travel free on buses and the underground at all times.
These concessions to elderly and disabled London
residents are financed by the London Borough Councils.
Child fares on London buses and the underground are
available to children in the 5-13 age group; children under
five travel free. Young persons aged 14 and 15 will be
charged adult fares unless they can produce a Child Rate
Photocard. Photocards can be obtained (free of charge) by
personal application at underground stations or Pass
Agents on production of a passport size photograph and
evidence of age (Birth Certificate, NHS Medical Card or
Passport). Child fares are not available on the buses after
2200. This restriction does not apply to Child Travelcards
and Bus Passes. From January 4, 1998 all 16–17 year olds
were eligible to apply for a 16–17 photocard. This enables
the holder to purchase the equivalent of a monthly Adult
LT Card or Bus Pass at a discounted rate. Photocards can be
obtained (free of charge) by personal application at Pass
Agents and underground stations on production of a
passport size photograph and evidence of age, i.e passport,
birth certificate or medical card. On trains and buses with a
large standing space near the entry doors there are notices
by certain seats suggesting that able-bodied passengers
make them available, if required, for elderly and
handicapped people.

Maison des Landes Hotel

St. Ouens, Jersey JE3 2AA; Tel 01534 481683; Fax 01534
485327
Purpose-built hotel for disabled guests and their families,
and fully accessible for wheelchair-users. The hotel offers
accommodation for up to 40 people in single, twin and
family rooms, all ensuite and each with tea and coffee
making facilities. The hotel welcomes individuals, families,
school parties and groups of all ages. Guests must be

19

capable of tending to their personal needs or bring a carer. Special diets are catered for, with prior notice. Available for guests' use are: electric ceiling and mobile hoists, electric wheelchairs (£5 daily hire charge), manual wheelchairs and various other specialised equipment. The hotel's facilities include: indoor heated swimming pool, satellite TV lounge, pool table and darts, patio areas for BBQs (weather permitting). Emergency pager in each room. District Nurse on call by arrangement. Rates: £39–£52 per person per night full board, to include transfer to and from airport and ferry terminals, and daily outings in specially adapted minibuses. Open mid March to end October. Early booking is advised.

MENCAP

MENCAP National Centre, 123 Golden La, London EC1Y 0RT; URL www.mencap.org.uk; E-mail info@mencap.org.uk; Tel 020 7454 0454; Fax 020 7608 3254
President   Lord Rix, CBE, DL
Chief Executive   Jo Williams
Chair   Brian Baldock, CBE
Aims
Mencap is the leading charity working with children and adults with learning disabilities in England, Wales and Northern Ireland. Mencap campaigns to ensure that people with a learning disability have the best possible opportunities to live as full citizens. It aims to influence new legislation and raise the profile of learning disability issues. It undertakes research into issues affecting people with a learning disability.
Activities
Through its national network of 15 sectors and more than 450 affiliated local societies Mencap is able to offer local services, support and advice to people with learning disability and their parents/carers.
Membership
Individuals can become members for £12, or if they join through their local Mencap/Gateway group for £1
Services
Support and advice through its Family Adviser Service; housing and residential accommodation; employment via the Pathway Employment Service; leisure via National Federation of Gateway Clubs; holidays; advice; education at its own three FE colleges; information; unique bookshop.
Publications
Range of information leaflets. Viewpoint: The Newspaper of Mencap and Gateway.

Midland Main Line Limited

Midland Hse, Nelson St, Derby DE1 2SA; Tel 01345 221125

Millfield Enterprises Courses

Millfield School, Street, Somerset BA16 0YD
Headmaster   P.M. Johnson
Commercial Manager   D.R.H. Humphrey, FIMgt, MInstAM; Tel 01458 444320; Fax 01458 840584

Mind, The Mental Health Charity

Granta Hse, London E15 4BQ; URL www.mind.org.uk; E-mail contact@mind.org.uk; Tel 020 8519 2122; (Mind Information Line (Inner London)) 020 8522 1728; (Mind Information Line (Outer London)) 0845 766 0163; Fax 020 8522 1725
Chief Executive   J. Clements
Mind works for a better life for the estimated one in four people who will experience mental or emotional stress at some time in their lives. It does this by advancing the views, needs and ambitions of people experiencing mental distress; promoting inclusion and challenging discrimination; influencing policy through effective campaigning and education; providing quality services

which meet the expressed needs of people experiencing mental distress and which reflect the requirements of a diverse community; achieving equal legal and civil rights through campaigning and education.

Mobility Centre Queen Elizabeth's Foundation

Damson Way, Fountain Dr, Carshalton, Surrey SM5 4NR; E-mail info@mobility.qe-org; Tel 020 8770 1151; Fax 020 8770 1211
Director   Sascha von Lieven-Knapp
This purpose-built centre provides a wide-reaching mobility service for physically disabled and elderly people. Information is available on any outdoor mobility problem, driving ability, car adaptation and passengers' transfer assessments are given, driving tuition and wheelchair assessments. The Centre has residential accommodation, a tarmac road system with a selection of adapted cars and outdoor vehicles together with a large covered area for the testing of powered and manual wheelchairs. Training courses for therapists and driving instructors are also provided.
Overnight accessible accommodation is available.

Mobility Information Service

National Mobility Centre, Unit B1, Greenwood Crt, Cartmel Dr, Shrewsbury, Shropshire SY1 3TB; URL www.mis.org.uk; E-mail mis@nmcuk.freeserve.co.uk; Tel 01743 463072; Fax 01743 463065
Chief Officer   Jean Griffiths
Provider of information on purchase of vehicles, adaptations to vehicles, wheelchairs and other mobility equipment. Driving tuition by an ADI in specially adapted vehicles. Advice given on DLA and a wide ranging information service provided on mobility concerns. Information packs, leaflets and stickers available for disabled drivers and or passengers. Mirrors, steering knobs, gear shift lock release and easy off parking brake release aids sold by mail order, prices on application.

Motability

Goodman Hse, Station Approach, Harlow, Essex CM20 2ET; Tel 01279 635666
A national charity which helps disabled people to become mobile by making a wide range of cars, scooters and powered wheelchairs available through contract-hire and hire-purchase schemes.

Mothers' Union

The Mary Sumner Hse, 24 Tufton St, London SW1P 3RB; E-mail mu@themothersunion.org.uk; Tel 020 7222 5533; Fax 020 7222 1591
Provides range of family support projects, including holidays for disadvantaged families, prison visiting childcare, parenting courses etc. Information from local co-ordinators or Action and Outreach Unit at above address.

Multiple Sclerosis Society of Great Britain and Northern Ireland

MS National Centre, 372 Edgware Rd, London NW2 6ND; URL www.mssociety.org.uk; E-mail info@mssociety.org.uk; Tel 020 8438 0700; Fax 020 8438 0701
Chief Executive   P. Cardy
Has eight holiday and short-stay homes open all year round for people with multiple sclerosis. Short-stay homes offer a high degree of care for more severely disabled guests. All homes have trained care and nursing staff to support and assist guests as required. Each home has been adapted for disabled guests and has a lift, hoists and other equipment as necessary.

Short-stay homes

Brambles Respite Care Centre
Suffolk Cl, Massetts Rd, Horley, Surrey; Tel 01293 771644
28 guests. Hydrotherapy, physiotherapy, range of occupational therapy activities. Bookings to The Administrator.

Helen Ley House
Bericote Rd, Blackdown, Leamington Spa, Warwickshire;
    Tel 01926 313550
23 guests. Bookings to the Administrator. Range of
therapies and activities available.

Danygraig Respite Care Centre
Newton, Porthcawl, Brigend, Bridgend CF35 5SR; Tel 01656
    782643
Eight guests. Bookings to the Manager.

Holiday homes

The Richard Cave Home (Leuchie House), North Berwick
Leuchie Hse, North Berwick, East Lothian; Tel 01620 892864
22 guests. Bookings to The Manager. Range of activities
available.

Holmhill Grantown on Spey
Holmhill, Woodside Ave, Grantown-on-Spey, Moray
    PH26 3JR; Tel 01479 873085
12 guests. Bookings to The Manager. Range of activities
available.

Kenninghall
Kenninghall Multiple Sclerosis Centre, 13 Shakespeare Rd,
    Worthing, West Sussex BN11 4AR; Tel 01903 238945
14 guests. Bookings to The Manager. Range of activities
available.

Orcombeleigh
22 Douglas Ave, Exmouth, Devon; Tel 01395 272644
20 guests. Booking to the Manager. Range of therapies and
activities available.

Woodlands Respite Care Centre
120 Thief La, Hull Rd, York YO1 3HU; Tel 01904 430600
20 beds, en suite facilities hydrotherapy physiotherapy.
Booking to the Administrator.

Muscular Dystrophy Campaign

7–11 Prescott Pl, London SW4 6BS;
    URL www.muscular-dystrophy.org;
    E-mail info@muscular-dystrophy.org; Tel 020 7720 8055;
    Fax 020 7498 0670
The Muscular Dystrophy Campaign is the national charity
which invests in research to find treatments and cures for
people who are affected by any of the conditions known as
muscular dystrophy or by a related neuromuscular disorder.
These conditions are largely characterised by wasting and
weakening of muscle tissue. They affect both adults and
children and lead to varying degrees of disability. The
Campaign provides support in the form of expert medical
care at Muscle Centres; information; advice; a team of
Family Care Officers; and financial assistance with essential
equipment. The charity relies on voluntary donations to
fund its work.

National Federation of GATEWAY Clubs

MENCAP National Centre, 123 Golden La, London
    EC1Y 0RT; Tel 020 7454 0454
Chairman   Roger Galletley
National Officer   P. Mendonca
Advances the personal development of people with
learning disabilities through greater leisure opportunities
by promoting personal choice and independence and
encouraging full participation, integration and involvement
in club and community. There are 730 clubs throughout
England, Wales and Northern Ireland and over 5000
participants in the Gateway Award Scheme.

National Society for the Prevention of Cruelty to Children (NSPCC)

42 Curtain Rd, London EC2A 3NH;
    URL www.nspcc.org.uk;
    E-mail skerly@nspcc.org.uk; Tel 020 7825 2752; Fax 020
    7825 2965
Family Resources Officer   Sylvia Kerly
Organises holidays for children and families. The scheme
only applies to children and families receiving services
from the NSPCC, and holiday arrangements cannot be
made for others. Resources of other organisations and
holiday centres are used by the NSPCC, which does not
own residential establishments.

National Trust

The Stackpole Centre, Home Farm, Pembroke,
    Pembrokeshire SA71 5DQ; Tel 01646 661425;
    (Bookings) 01646 661618; Fax 01646 661425
Centre Co-ordinator   Julie Freeman
Self catering holiday centre for people with or without
disabilities, equipped with a 150-seat theatre and
hydrotherapy pool with leisure suite.

National Trust for Places of Historic Interest or Natural Beauty

Rowan, Kembrey Pk, Swindon SN2 8YL;
    URL www.nationaltrust.org.uk;
    E-mail accessforall@nationaltrust.org.uk; Tel 0870 458
    4000
Publishes annually Information for Visitors with
Disabilities booklet, describing access at properties of
interest to visitors with disabilities, single copies free from
National Trust, Membership Department, PO Box 39,
Bromley, Kent BR1 3XL). Also produced in large print and
on tape. The Trust's Members' Magazine is provided on
tape as a free service for members with visual disabilities.
An annually updated 'touch' list is available, giving details
of items that can be enjoyed by touch in historic buildings
in the care of the Trust. Produced also in large print and in
Braille. Enquiries, but not requests for literature 020 7447
6742; Fax 01793 462944.

National Tyres and Autocare

Regent Hse, Heaton La, Stockport, Greater Manchester
    SK4 1BS; Tel 0161 480 7461 ext 209; (Freephone) 0800
    626666
Chief Executive   Hans Brandt
With over 400 branches throughout the country, National
Tyres and Autocare is one of the UK's leading fast fit and
fleet care specialists. National offers a comprehensive
service, including exhaust systems, AA Approved brake
centres, MOTs, shock absorbers and tyres at the most
competitive prices available.

North London Railways Limited

Melton Hse, 65–75 Clarendon Rd, Watford, Hertfordshire
    WD1 1DP; Tel 01923 207413

One Parent Family Holidays

Kildonan Courtyard, Barrhill, Girvan, South Ayrshire
    KA26 0PS; URL www.opfh.org.uk;
    E-mail opfholiday@aol.com; Tel 01465 821288
Chief Officer   Mr C. Chatfield
Arrange one parent family holidays with particular
emphasis on Continental holidays at low cost in tents,
apartments and pensions in France, USA and elsewhere in
the company of other lone families. Also organises holidays
on behalf of groups of lone parents, widows and
organisations. Sae for information.

19

Park Place Residential Home for the Elderly

1 Manchester Rd, Buxton, Derbyshire SK17 6SE; Tel 01298 25648

Peter Le Marchant Trust

Canalside Moorings, Beeches Rd, Loughborough, Leicestershire LE11 2NS; Tel 01509 265590
Trust Administrator L. Smith
Provides holidays and day trips for disabled people in specially-built boats which include hydraulic lifts, telephones, resuscitation equipment, showers etc. Trips operate from the Trust's moorings at Loughborough. The Trust also runs a six-berth cruiser for families with a disabled member on the Norfolk Broads. A 65' narrow boat, operating from Loughborough, sleeping eight, gives holidays to families or groups of friends with a seriously ill or disabled person. Please contact the Administrator for details of hire charges.

Proudline Associates

16 Ely Gdns, Tonbridge, Kent TN10 4NZ; Tel 01732 367827
Partner B.J.A. Hicks, BScEng, MICE
Contact Mrs Hicks
To give independence to the disabled with the No-Morflat puncture-proof inner tube to allow trouble-free travel and a holiday with no problems.

Psoriasis Association

7 Milton St, Northampton, Northamptonshire NN2 7JG; Tel 01604 711129; Fax 01604 792894
Chief Executive Gladys Edwards
Advises psoriatics and their families on useful precautions while on holiday, particularly when abroad, and on the various overseas resorts which cater for sufferers from this condition.

Queen Elizabeth's Foundation

The Development Centre, Dorincourt, Oaklawn Rd, Leatherhead, Surrey KT22 0BT; URL www.qefd.org; E-mail dominic.lodge@developmentcentre.org; Tel 01372 841301
Principal Dominic Lodge
A residential centre for young adults with physical disabilities. The centre exists to assist people with disabilities to have autonomous, less dependent, progressive and ambitious futures through its learning programme.

Queen Elizabeth's Foundation Brain Injury Centre

Banstead Pl, Park Rd, Banstead, Surrey SM7 3EE; URL www.qefd.org/braininjury; E-mail rehab@braininjurycentre.org.uk; Tel 01737 356222; Fax 01737 359467
Senior Social Worker Sue Messenger
Head (Education) Barbara Weston
Head (Therapy) Daphne Skingle
Head (Administration) Sue McGlade
Psychologist Lynne Hensor
One of the most progressive units in the country for the rehabilitation of young adults who have acquired disabilities as a result of brain injury caused by accident, illness or a neurological disorder. A team of therapists and teachers with social work and clinical psychological input develop an individual programme for each client. New services include a transitional programme and vocational rehabilitation.

Queen Elizabeth's Foundation Training College

Woodlands Rd, Leatherhead, Surrey KT22 0BN; URL www.qefd.org; Tel 01372 841100
Marketing Co-ordinator Melanie Edgson
Queen Elizabeth's Foundation Training College provides residential training for disabled adults. It accepts trainees from 18 years plus and offers 16 Business Studies and Technical courses, each leading to nationally recognised qualifications, inluding NVQs, City and Guilds and RSA examinations. Support services include Open Learning Department Employment Development Team with Job Club and 24-hour nursing support.

Ratcliff Tail Lifts Ltd

Bessemer Rd, Welwyn Garden City, Hertfordshire AL7 1ET; URL www.ratcliff.co.uk; E-mail info@ratcliff.co.uk; Tel 01707 325571; Fax 01707 327752
Sales Director V. Martin
Manufacturers of passenger lifts for fitting into the side/rear of ambulances, minibuses, larger buses, coaches and mobile libraries, thus enabling disabled people to be safely and easily raised from ground level into the vehicle.

Raymar Healthcare Ltd

Unit 10, Fairview Est, Newtown Rd, Henley on Thames, Oxfordshire RG9 1HG; E-mail info@raymarhealthcare.com; Tel 01491 578401; Fax 01491 412041
Managing Director M. Corby
Suppliers and repairers of cushions and mattresses for the prevention and treatment of pressure sores. Also provides wheelchair ramps.

Renault UK Ltd

The Rivers Office Pk, Denham Way, Maples Cross, Rickmansworth, Hertfordshire WD3 9YS; E-mail motability@renault.co.uk; Tel 01582 679104; Fax 01582 679105
Manager (Operations) Caroline Chapman
The Renault Motability Programme is fully supported by the Renault Dealer Network and together with their Special Sales Department will be able to answer all your questions and discuss your individual requirements. Please call 0800 387626 for further information.

Reselco Limited

Unit 2, Inwood Bus Pk, Whitton Rd, Hounslow, Greater London TW3 2EB; URL www.reselco.com; E-mail sales-info@reselco.com; Tel 020 8569 6363; Fax 020 8569 6660
Managing Director A.C. Tidmarsh
Vehicle supply, finance, insurance, advice on vehicle suitability. All types of controls, clutch, brake and steering adaptations; seat modifications, repositioning and electric movement. Replacement and new seats for all vehicles. Control repositioning, electric parking brakes. Wheelchair securing systems. Whole vehicle conversions. Hoists, ramps and hydraulic platforms for all types of vehicle. Remote operation and switching of ancilliary functions including our Infra Red Hand Grip system. Security systems, electric windows, cruise controls, reversing aids, fire extinguisher systems. Collection and delivery of your vehicle. Tailor made mobility solutions.

Riding for the Disabled Association (incorporating Carriage Driving)

Lavinia Norfolk Hse, Avenue 'R', Stoneleigh Deer Park Business Village, Stareton, Kenilworth, Warwickshire CV8 2LY; Tel 024 7669 6510; Fax 024 7669 6532
Provides riding and driving for disabled people and produces a list of riding holidays in February/March each year. Only available to those who ride/drive with an RDA Member Group. Details about the Association's riding holidays and also its Member Groups, of which there are over 640 throughout the UK, are available from the above address/telephone no.
Registered charity no. 244108.

Rifton Equipment

Darvell, Robertsbridge, East Sussex TN32 5DR;
URL www.rifton.com;
E-mail sales@communityproducts.com; Tel 01580
883301; Fax 01580 883331
Regional Manager M. Huleatt
Leading supplier of furniture and supportive/mobility
equipment for children with special needs. Products
include gait trainers, toileting and bathing aids and
tricycles. All Rifton items are designed in close co-
operation with therapists. Supplied only from the above
address.

Roma Medical Aids Ltd

Unit 23, Vale Bus Pk, Cowbridge, Vale of Glamorgan
CF71 7PF; URL www.romamedical.co.uk;
E-mail sales@romamedical.co.uk; Tel 01446 774519;
Fax 01446 774077
Director Simon Dalton
Director John Pitt
Director Harmar Roberts

MG Rover Motability

PO Box 368, Dunstable, Bedfordshire LU5 5YR; Tel 0845 704
5310
Mobility allowance recipients are eligible for mobility HP
or contract hire.

Royal Armoured Corps War Memorial Benevolent Fund

RHQ RTR, Bovington, Wareham, Dorset BH20 6JA;
Tel 01929 403331
Secretary Major A. Henzie (Retd)
The primary aim of the Fund is to provide speedy and
temporary relief in cases of poverty and distress for former
members of the Royal Armoured Corps and their
dependants. Priority is given to those who served in
wartime regiments of the RAC, now disbanded, with no
regimental funds of their own. Limited assistance is offered
to former, post-war members of the RAC as each existing
regiment has benevolent funds of its own.

Royal Association for Disability and Rehabilitation (RADAR)

12 City Forum, 250 City Rd, London EC1V 8AF;
URL www.radar.org.uk; E-mail radar@radar.org.uk;
Tel 020 7250 3222; Fax 020 7250 0212; Minicom 020 7250
4119
RADAR is a national organisation working with and for
physically-disabled people. The Association's policy is to
remove architectural, economic and attitudinal barriers
which impose restrictions on disabled people, and to
ensure that disabled people are able to play their full role in
the community. RADAR is particularly involved in the
areas of civil rights, employment, mobility, social services,
housing, and social security. The Association produces a
number of publications, and operates in conjunction with
an affiliated network of around 500 local and national
organisations.

Royal Hospital for Neuro-disability – Research and Development

West Hill, Putney, London SW15 3SW; Tel 020 8780 4500;
Fax 020 8680 4501
Chief Executive Peter Franklyn
Director (Medical and Research Services) Dr Keith Andrews
Director (Research) Prof Maria Stokes
Research at the Royal Hospital for Neuro-disability applies
basic and applied research methods to improve the
understanding and treatment of complex disabilities
resulting from damage to the nervous system. The research

aims to evaluate current clinical practices and develop new
treatments to further improve the treatment and care of
patients.
Research proposals are approved by the Hospital's Medical
and Research Advisory Committee as well as an external
ethics committee. Many projects are conducted in
collaboration with high calibre academic institutions, with
an emphasis on appropriate multidisciplinary mix.
External funding is required for each project and the
research programme is underpinned by support funding
from the NHS R and D Executive.

Other Voluntary Services

Royal Hospital for Neuro-disability, West Hill, Putney,
London SW15 3SW; E-mail info@neuro-disability.org.uk;
Tel 020 8780 4500; Fax 020 8780 4501
Admissions Manager Carol Groves
The Royal Hospital for Neuro-Disability in Putney, London
is a hospital and home offering short and long term
specialist services providing assessment, rehabilitation,
disability management, physical and cognitive management, nursing and respite care for adults aged 18 upwards
who have high dependancy needs as a result of acquired
brain injury or progressive neurological disabilities.
The brain injury service provides a continuum of care for
people ranging from those in persistant vegetative state to
those requiring skills to allow re-integration into the
community. Long term care is available in a number of
specialist units including one for young people with
disability and another for those suffering from
Huntington's disease. All areas are supported by a broad
range of clinical and non-clinical services.
Direct external referrals are also encouraged from outside
the Hospital to the Dental Surgery, Technology Clinic and
Special Seating Service.

Travel, Mobility and Holidays

Royal Hospital for Neuro-disability, West Hill, Putney,
London SW15 3SW; E-mail info@neuro-disability.org.uk;
Tel 020 8780 4500; Fax 020 8780 4501
The Royal Hospital for Neuro-disability specialises in the
treatment and care of people with profound or complex
disabilities, resulting from disease or damage to the brain
or nervous system. The Hospital cares for approximately
275 residents and during the past year 991 patients' trips
have been organised. These include visits to the theatre,
sporting events, shopping, rock and pop music concerts,
museums and galleries, films, excursions, dance and
classical music trips. A monthly outings list enables
patients, relatives and volunteers to access community
events together. The Patient Activities Office at the Hospital
also assists with organising holidays.

Royal National Institute of the Blind

105 Judd St, London WC1H 9NE; URL www.rnib.org.uk;
E-mail helpline@rnib.org.uk; Tel 020 7388 1266; (RNIB
Helpline) 0845 766 9999; Fax 020 7388 2034
There are two million people in the UK with sight
problems. RNIB's pioneering work helps anyone with a
sight problem – not just with braille, Talking Books and
computer training, but with imaginative and practical
solutions to everyday challenges. They fight for equal
rights for people with sight problems and fund pioneering
research into preventing and treating eye disease. As a
charity they rely on generosity. If you or someone you
know has a sight problem, RNIB can help.

St. John's Ambulance, Social Care Department

St. John's Ambulance NHQ, 27 St. John's La, Clerkenwell,
London EC1M 4BU; URL www.sja.org.uk; Tel 020 7324
4000; Fax 020 7324 4001
A section of a National Voluntary organisation providing
community care services and community development
work with adults and young people. This includes training

19

packages and publications for carers, primary health care for homeless people, work with young carers, health promotion activities for youth and hospital library services. Work is carried out in partnership with other organisations and statutory service providers. Most services are provided on a voluntary basis by trained members of St. John Ambulance and supported by paid staff.

Salvador Caetano Coachbuilders Ltd

Hambledon Rd, Waterlooville, Hampshire PO7 7UA;
   URL www.caetano.co.uk; E-mail src@caetano.co.uk;
   Tel 02392 258211; Fax 02392 255611
Director and General Manager   Ian Tubbs
Sales Administrator   Maria Kay
Manufacturers of community buses and coaches.

Scottish Youth Hostels Association (SYHA)

7 Glebe Cres, Stirling FK8 2JA; Tel 01786 891400; Fax 01786 891333
Chief Executive   L. MacDonald
There are around 60 youth hostels in Scotland enabling schools and groups to enjoy natural, cultural, educational and recreational opportunities to the full. Their youth hostels offer good, comfortable accommodation and a friendly, relaxed, international atmosphere. There are TV rooms, good self-catering facilities and many hostels offer excellent value catering options. SYHA are a non-profit making organisation. For groups they offer a central booking service and a wide range of tours can be arranged to suit individual requirements.

The Scout Association

Gilwell Pk, Bury Rd, Chingford, London E4 7QW;
   URL www.scoutbase.org.uk;
   E-mail info.centre@scout.org.uk; Tel 020 8498 5400;
   Fax 020 8498 5407
Information on projects with volunteer leaders who work with young people in activities to encourage self-reliance. Provides inexpensive indoor and outdoor accommodation, conference facilities etc. at hostels, camp sites and activity centres throughout the UK, many with facilities for the disabled.

Scout Holiday Homes Trust

Gilwell Pk, Chingford, London E4 7QW;
   URL www.scoutbase.org.uk/hq-info/holhomes;
   E-mail scout.holiday.homes@scout.org.uk; Tel 020 8433 7290; Fax 020 8433 7184
Booking Secretary   L. Peters
Caravans and chalets (for up to six people) around the country, with ramps for wheelchairs, self-catering.. Not recommended for totally dependent wheelchair users. No scouting connection necessary. For persons with special needs and their families and all families or groups whose quality of life is diminished by disability, infirmity or misfortune.

ScotRail Railways Limited

Caledonian Chambers, 87 Union St, Glasgow G1 3TA;
   URL www.scotrail.co.uk;
   E-mail enquiries@scotrail.co.uk; Tel 08700 005151

Scripture Union Holidays

207–209 Queensway, Bletchley, Milton Keynes MK2 2EB;
   URL www.scriptureunion.org.uk;
   E-mail holidays@scriptureunion.org.uk; Tel 01908 856177; Fax 01908 856012
One mixed summer holiday for able-bodied and physically-handicapped young people aged 16–19 including a variety of indoor and outdoor activities and excursions.

Shaftesbury Society

16 Kingston Rd, South Wimbledon, London SW19 1JZ;
   Tel 020 8239 5555; Fax 020 8239 5580
Special schools, further education for younger people; shared housing and residential care for adults with physical or learning disabilities; hostels for young homeless people; urban community projects, supported living services.

Skegness Sands

(formerly Derbyshire Miners' Holiday Centre)
Winthorpe Ave, Skegness, Lincolnshire PE25 1QZ;
   Tel 01754 762231
Manager (Sales)   Sarah Cater

South West Trains Limited

Friars Bridge Crt, 41–45 Blackfriars Rd, London SE1 8NZ;
   Tel 020 7928 5151

SPARKS

Heron Hse, Dean Farrar St, London SW1H 0DX;
   URL www.sparks.org.uk; E-mail info@sparks.org.uk;
   Tel 020 7799 2111; Fax 020 7222 2701
SPort Aiding medical Research for KidS. Raises money for vital research so that children are born healthy. Its aim is to bring research to clinical application. Money is raised through fun sporting and social events.

Special Families Home Swap Register

Erme Hse, Station Rd, Plympton, Plymouth, PL7 2AU;
   E-mail specialfamiliestrust@care4free.net; Tel 01752 347577
Service for physically disabled people whereby members can swap their specially adapted homes with each other for breaks and holidays worldwide, confident that their needs will be met as in their own home. There is no charge to be listed and all members receive a free copy. If they feel the service to be of value, they are asked to make a donation towards the scheme's administration costs. The Special Families Home Swap Register is a non-profit making organisation, any surplus arising goes to the Special Families Trust, a charity for disabled children and their families in Devon and Cornwall (registered charity number 1001147).

Stirling University

Stirling FK9 4LA; URL www.stir.ac.uk/theuni/conference;
   E-mail conferences@stir.ac.uk; Tel 01786 467140; 01786 467141; Fax 01786 467143
Commercial Manager   E. O'Hare
Accessible campus (good motorway, road and rail links with the rest of Britain) can be used by small groups with helpers for vacations from early June to early September and January to early February. Single bedroom accommodation in Halls (no lifts), but paraplegic facilities at circulation level. Catering offered in separate areas of the campus; self-catering facilities can be offered to organisers by special arrangement. Also one-storey chalets and six-person self-catering flats in blocks; no lifts, but some flats at ground floor level. Shops, theatre, bars, sports facilities, etc. on campus.

Sunrise Medical Limited

High St, Wollaston, West Midlands DY8 4PS;
   URL www.sunrisemedical.co.uk;
   E-mail sunmail@sunmed.co.uk; Tel 01384 446688;
   Fax 01384 446699
Vice-President (Sales, UK Operational)   Chris Fullerton
Manager (Marketing, UK Operational)   Tony Mercer
Sunrise Medical Limited is part of a worldwide market leader in the manufacture and distribution of products for

the disabled and elderly in the areas of rehabilitation, recovery and respiratory. Brands include: Sterling, Minivator, Quickie, Coopers, Oxford DeVilbiss, DynaNox and Parker Bath.

Tall Ships Youth Trust (incorporating the Sail Training Association)

2a The Hard, Portsmouth PO1 3PT;
  E-mail info@tallships.org; Tel 023 9283 2055; Fax 023 9281 5769
Chief Executive   Christine Law
The Tall Ships Prince William and Stavros S Niarchos take young people aged between 16 and 25 on challenging adventure voyages offering teambuilding and personal development. Voyages last from ten to 14 nights covering up to 1000 miles. Sailing areas include Northern Europe, Canary Islands, the Azores and the Caribbean. No sailing experience or special equipment required. The young people from all walks of life are the working crew of the ships. Advice on seeking sponsorship is offered. Cash grants may be available.

Thames Trains Limited

Venture Hse, 37–43 Blagrave St, Reading RG1 1PZ; Tel 0118 908 3623

Thameslink Rail Limited

Friars Bridge Crt, 41–45 Blackfriars Rd, London SE1 8NZ;
  URL www.thameslink.co.uk; Tel 0845 330 6333

Training Enterprise and Education Directorate

For addresses see Chapter 3.
Operates a scheme providing assistance with fares to work for certain severely disabled people. Applications should be made in the first instance to local jobcentres.

Trefoil House

Gogarbank, Edinburgh EH12 9DA;
  URL www.trefoil.org.uk; E-mail info@trefoil.org.uk;
  Tel 0131 339 3148; Fax 0131 317 7271
Holiday Centre for people with disabilities catering for individuals, families and groups. Closed for holidays until March 2006.

Vic Hughes Coaches

61 Fern Gr, Feltham, Greater London TW14 9AY; Tel 020 8831 0770; 020 8831 9393; Fax 020 8831 0660
Transportation for the handicapped, disabled or elderly. Specialised vehicles with tail lifts.

Virgin Trains Limited

Meridian, 85 Smallbrook Queensway, Birmingham, West Midlands B5 4HA; Tel 0121 654 7400

Visit Scotland

PO Box 121, Livingston, West Lothian EH54 8AF;
  URL www.visitscotland.com; Tel 0845 225 5121
Visit Scotland produces an accommodation guide series, Where to Stay. All titles feature accommodation holding a disabled award made following inspection against recognised criteria. There are 140 Tourist Information Centres located throughout Scotland whose staff are able to deal with on-the-spot enquiries.

Voluntary Association for Surrey Disabled

10 Havenbury Est, Station Rd, Dorking, Surrey RH4 1ES;
  Tel 01306 741 500; 01306 741 600; Fax 01306 741 600
Senior Charity Administrator   Mrs S. Lavington

Group holidays arranged for adults with a physical disability. Parties accompanied by volunteer helpers. Escorted or unescorted guests welcome. Holiday parties are at various venues in this country and occasionally abroad. Guests unable to meet the full cost may be considered for financial assistance. The Association also owns an adapted bungalow in Elmer Sands, near Bognor Regis that is available for individual holidays. This bungalow sleeps up to 10 people. For the group holidays, applications restricted to residents in the administrative county of Surrey. Other services include information on all aspects of disability, the sale and loan of disability equipment, two adapted mini buses available for hire to groups and individuals.

Wales Tourist Board

Production Services Dept, Brunel Hse, Cardiff CF24 0UY;
  Tel 029 2047 5214; Fax 029 2048 2436
Publishes accommodation guides/maps. A View of Wales Magazine (free). Wales – Where to Stay Guide (£4.95). Wales Tourist Map (£2.50); available at Tourist Information Centres, newsagents and bookshops or by post from the above address. Price is inclusive of postage.

Wessex Medical Equipment Company Limited

Budds Lane Ind Est, Romsey, Hampshire SO51 0HA;
  Tel 01794 830303; Fax 01794 512621
Managing Director   J. Lane
National Sales Manager   N. Durham
Manufacturers of aids for people with disabilities, which include a range of electrically-operated hoists, compact wheelchair vertical lifts. For public accessibility a range of short rise platform lifts up to five metres. Also platform stairlifts.

West Anglia Great Northern Railway Limited

Hertford Hse, 1 Cranwood St, London EC1V 9QS

Winged Fellowship Trust

Angel Hse, 20–32 Pentonville Rd, London N1 9XD;
  URL www.wft.org.uk; E-mail admin@wft.org.uk; Tel 020 7833 2594 ext 2594
Chief Executive   Pat Wallace
Head (Contracts)   Graham Smithers
Provider of holidays for disabled people. The trust has five accessible centres in Cornwall, Southampton, Essex, Nottinghamshire and Merseyside where trained staff and volunteers can provide 24-hour personal support and care on-call. All centres cater for adults with physical disabilities and the centre in Cornwall provides additional holidays for children and adults with learning disabilites. They welcome block bookings from local authorities.

Women's Royal Voluntary Service (WRVS)

Milton Hill Hse, Milton Hill, Abingdon, Oxfordshire OX13 6AF; Tel 01235 442954; Fax 01235 861166
Chair   Tina Tietjen
WRVS provides social transport, library services, Good Neighbours schemes, Meals on Wheels, Meals With Care, luncheon and social clubs for the older/housebound person. Contact centres are also provided for estranged parents/grandparents to meet with their children/grandchildren in neutral surroundings. Toy libraries are also a developing service within WRVS. Some Prison visitor centres are managed by WRVS on behalf of the Prison Service providing a neutral venue outside the prison for relatives/friends visiting convicted and remand prisoners. WRVS emergency services also provide a support role to the statutory emergency services in the event of an emergency via feeding, rest centres and reception facilities. WRVS also provides tea bars, shops and trolleys, a mobile retail service, for patients and visitors in hospitals. Patron: Her Majesty the Queen.

19

York University Student Community Action Children's Holidays (YSCA)

The Student Centre, University of York, Heslington, York
YO1 5DD; URL www.ysca.org.uk;
E-mail su-ysca@york.ac.uk; Tel 01904 433133; Fax 01904
433664

YSCA runs holidays for disadvantaged children, aged 6–16.
The holidays are free but volunteers pay for their own
travel expenses. The camps are run for five weeks during
the Summer holidays and two weeks during the Easter
holidays.

Youth Hostels Association (England and Wales) Ltd (YHA)

Trevelyan Hse, Dimple Rd, Matlock, Derbyshire DE4 3XB;
URL www.yha.org.uk;
E-mail customerservices@yha.org.uk; Tel 01629 592600;
Fax 01629 592702

The Youth Hostel Association is the biggest budget
accomodation provider in England and Wales. It operates
230 Youth Hostels with locations ideal for study or
recreation.

Advice is available for educational liaison and to help
organise group visits. Additional facilities are provided
such as leader rooms, group leader packs, classrooms,
National Curriculum Linked Packages and GNVQ Tutor
Information Pack.

106 Youth Hostels are perfect for families, 80 are suitable
for children under three. The family packages are
designed to be flexible, with designated family rooms
and special children's menus. For weekend breaks in the
country, bucket and spade trips to the beach or
sightseeing holidays the YHA has great places at
affordable prices.

Please contact the Customer Services Department for
advice on Youth Hostels suitable for people with
disabilities.

Denominational Social Services Organisations

20

- Baptist Union of Great Britain
- Church of England
- Church of Scotland
- Church in Wales
- Ecumenical and Inter-Denominational Organisations
- Judaism
- Methodist Church
- Presbyterian Church
- Quakers (Religious Society of Friends)
- Roman Catholic Church
- The Salvation Army
- United Reformed Church, Church and Society

Denominational Social Services Organisations

Baptist Union of Great Britain

PO Box 44, Baptist Hse, Didcot, Oxfordshire OX11 8RT;
E-mail baptistuniongb@baptist.org.uk; Tel 01235 517700;
Fax 01235 517715
General Secretary   Rev D.R. Coffey, BA

Department for Research and Training in Mission
Team Administrator   Fiona Pollock

Church of England

Canterbury Diocesan Association for the Deaf
Diocesan Hse, Lady Wootton's Grn, Canterbury, Kent
CT1 1NQ
Chaplain and Honorary Secretary   Vacancy
Secretary and Reader   J. Seatherton; Tel 01227 454477
Aims
To meet the spiritual, pastoral and social needs of deaf
people.

Church Lads' and Church Girls' Brigade
2 Barnsley Rd, Wath-upon-Dearne, Rotherham, South
Yorkshire S63 6PY; URL www.clcgb.org.uk;
E-mail generalsecretary@clcgb.org.uk; Tel 01709 876535;
Fax 01709 878089
General Secretary   Col (Retd) A.J. Reed Screen
A uniformed organisation within the Church of England
which offers adventure, challenge and responsibility for
children and young people through fun, faith and
fellowship.

Church of England Board for Social Responsibility
Secretary   D.P. Skidmore
Church Hse, Great Smith St, Westminster, London
SW1P 3NZ; Tel 020 7898 1521; Fax 020 7898 1536

DIOCESAN SOCIAL RESPONSIBILITY ADVISERS

England

Bath and Wells
Contact   Helen Stanton
The Old Deanery, Wells, Somerset BA5 2UG
Area covered
Avon and Somerset

Birmingham
Officer (Social Responsibility)   Diocesan Council for Social
Responsibility, 175 Harborne Park Rd, Birmingham,
West Midlands B17 0BH

Area covered
West Midlands

Blackburn
Contact   Rev Canon Chris Rich
Blackburn Diocesan Offices, Cathedral Cl, Blackburn
BB1 5AA
Area covered
Lancashire

Bristol
Contact   Rev Harold Clarke
St. Nicholas Hse, Lawford St, Bristol BS5 0RE
Area covered
Avon and North Wiltshire

Canterbury and Rochester
Contact   Rev D. Grimwood
Diocesan Council for Social Responsibility, 60 Marsham St,
Maidstone, Kent ME4 1EW
Area covered
Greater London and Kent

Carlisle
Contact   Rev Colin Saxon
Church Hse, West Walls, Carlisle, Cumbria CA3 8UE
Area covered
Cumbria

Chelmsford
Contact   Rev Canon Roger Matthews
The Chelmsford Council for Social Responsibility, 53 New
St, Chelmsford, Essex CM1 1NG
Area covered
Essex and Greater London

Chester
Contact   Rev Canon Bob Powley
Chester Diocesan Board for Social Responsibility, Diocesan
Hse, Chester, Cheshire CH1 4PN
Area covered
Cheshire and Merseyside

Chichester
Contact   Rev Barry Smith
Chichester Board for Social Responsibility, Diocesan
Church Hse, Hove, Brighton and Hove BN3 4ED
Area covered
East and West Sussex

Coventry
Contact   Rev Elizabeth M. Cowley
Board for Social Responsibility, Coventry Cathedral,
Coventry, West Midlands CV1 5ES
Area covered
Warwickshire and West Midlands

Derby
Contact   Joy Bates
Derby Diocesan Council for Social Responsibility, Derby
Church Hse, Derby DE1 3DR
Area covered
Derbyshire

Durham
Contact Rev Caroline Dick
The Vicarage, 26 Upsall Dr, Darlington DL3 8RB
Area covered
Cleveland, Durham and Tyne and Wear

Ely
Contact Dr Hilary Lavis
Ely BSR, Bishop Woodford Hse, Ely, Cambridgeshire
   CB7 4DX
Area covered
Cambridgeshire and Norfolk (parts of)

Exeter
Contact Martyn Goss
Diocesan Board for Christian Care, 96 Old Tiverton Rd,
   Exeter, Devon EX4 6LD
Area covered
Devonshire

Gloucester
Contact Rev Canon Adrian Slade
38 Sydenham Villas Rd, Cheltenham, Gloucestershire
   GL52 6DZ
Area covered
Gloucestershire

Guildford
Contact Bassi Mirzania
Diocesan Hse, Quarry St, Guildford, Surrey GU1 3XG
Area covered
Hampshire and Surrey

Hereford
Contact Jackie Boys
1 Carter Gr, Hereford, Herefordshire HR1 1NT
Area covered
Herefordshire, Worcestershire and Shropshire

Leicester
Contact Rev Martin Wilson
Leicester Diocesan Board for Social Work, 278 East Pk Rd,
   Leicester LE5 5AY
Area covered
Leicestershire

Lichfield
Contact Vanessa Geffen
Diocesan Board for Social Responsibility, The Church at
   Rowley St, Stafford, Staffordshire ST16 2RH
Area covered
North Shropshire and Staffordshire

Lincoln
Church in Society Office, Church Hse, Lincoln, Lincolnshire
   LN2 1PU
Area covered
Humberside and Lincolnshire

Liverpool
Contact Ultan Russell
Board for Social Responsibility, Church Hse, Liverpool,
   Merseyside L1 3DW
Area covered
Cheshire, Greater Manchester, Lancashire and
Merseyside

London
Contact Rev Chris Brice
Christian Action and Responsibility, London Diocesan Hse,
   London SW1P 4AU
Area covered
Most of Greater London, north of the Thames

Manchester
Social Responsibility Officer Alison Peacock
Board for Social Responsibility, 2869 Church Hse,
   Manchester M3 2GJ
Area covered
Greater Manchester

Newcastle
Contact Barry Stewart
Church Hse, Grainger Pk Rd, Newcastle upon Tyne, Tyne
   and Wear NE4 8SX

Area covered
Tyne Wear and Northumberland

Norwich
Contact Alison Howard
Diocesan Board for Social Responsibility, Derham Rd,
   Norwich, Norfolk NR9 5ES
Area covered
Norfolk and Suffolk

Oxford
Contact Jo Saunders
Diocesan Board for Social Responsibility, Diocesan Church
   Hse, Oxford, Oxfordshire OX2 0NB
Area covered
Berkshire, Buckinghamshire and Oxfordshire

Peterborough
Contact Rev Neil Purvey-Tyrer
Diocesan Family and Social Welfare Council, 222
   Dogsthorpe Rd, Peterborough PE1 3PB
Area covered
Cambridgeshire, Leicestershire and Northamptonshire

Portsmouth
Contact Rev Canon David Tonkinson
Diocesan Council for Social Responsibility, All Saints
   Church, Portsmouth PO1 4BT
Area covered
Hampshire and Isle of Wight

Ripon
Contact Maureen Browell
Diocesan Council for Social Responsibility, Leeds Church
   Inst, Leeds, West Yorkshire LS2 7JF
Area covered
North and West Yorkshire

St. Albans
Contact Canon Richard Wheeler
Diocesan Board for Social Responsibility, 41 Holywell Hill,
   St. Albans, Hertfordshire AL1 1HE
Area covered
Bedfordshire, Greater London and Hertfordshire

St. Edmundsbury and Ipswich
Social Responsibility Officer
Diocesan Board for Social Work, Diocesan Hse, Ipswich,
   Suffolk IP1 13BG
Area covered
Suffolk

Salisbury
Contact Rev Tim Woods
Diocesan Council for Social Responsibility, Church Hse,
   Salisbury, Wiltshire SP1 2QB
Area covered
Dorset and Wiltshire

Sheffield
Contact Rev Michael Wagstaff
Diocesan Church Hse, 95–99 Effingham St, Rotherham,
   South Yorkshire S65 1BL
Area covered
South Yorkshire

Sodor and Man
Contact Mrs Wendy Fitch
Diocesan Committee for Social Responsibility, 1 Kelly Cl,
   Ramsey, Isle of Man
Area covered
Isle of Man

Southwark
Contact Rev Canon Bruce Saunders
Social Responsibility Dept, Trinity Hse, London S
   E1 1HW
Area covered
Most of Greater London, south of the Thames and part of
Surrey

Southwell
Contact Patricia Stoat
Diocesan Board for Social Responsibility, Warren Hse,
   Nottingham NG3 1HL

Area covered
Nottinghamshire

Truro
Contact Alan Chesney
Devoran Vicarage, Truro, Cornwall TR3 6PA
Area covered
Cornwall

Wakefield
Contact Canon Ian Gaskell
Advisory Council for Social Responsibility, Church Hse,
 Wakefield, South Yorkshire WF1 1LP
Area covered
South and West Yorkshire

Winchester
Contact Jane Fisher
Diocesan Council for Social Responsibility, 9 The Cl,
 Winchester, Hampshire SO23 9LS
Area covered
Dorset, Hampshire and Channel Islands

Worcester
Contact Alison Webster
Diocesan Board for Social Responsibility, The Old Palace,
 Worcester, Worcestershire WR1 2JE
Area covered
Herefordshire and Worcestershire

York
Contact Andrew Dorton
Stillington Vicarage, York YO6 1LA
Area covered
Cleveland, Humberside and North Yorkshire

Scotland

Social Responsibility Committee of the Mission Board,
 General Synod of the Scottish Episcopal Church, 21
 Grosvenor Cres, Edinburgh EH12 5EE; Tel 0131 225
 6357

Ireland

Northern Dioceses
Church of Ireland Board of Social Responsibility, Church of
 Ireland Hse, Belfast BT1 2QH; Tel 028 9023 3885

Church of England Pensions Board

29 Gt Smith St, Westminster, London SW1P 3PS; Tel 020
 7898 1800; Fax 020 7898 1801
Secretary R.G. Radford, AIA
Provides pensions and retirement accommodation for the
clergy and their spouses, clergy widow(er)s, deaconesses or
licensed church workers and their widow(er)s.

LDS Family Services

LDS Family Services, 1st Fl, 399 Garretts Grn La, Garretts
 Grn, Birmingham, West Midlands B33 0UH;
 E-mail eng-lds-@ldschurch.org; Tel 0121 785 4994;
 Fax 0121 783 1888
Agency Director Mark Ricks
Voluntary Adoption Society for The Church of Jesus Christ
of Latter Day Saints (Mormons).

Church of Scotland

Church of Scotland Board of Social Responsibility

Charis Hse, 47 Milton Road East, Edinburgh EH15 2SR;
 URL cofscotland.org.uk/boards/socialresp;
 E-mail info@charis.org.uk; Tel 0131 657 2000; Fax 0131
 657 5000
Director (Social Work) I.D. Baillie

The social work of the Church of Scotland is administered
by the Board of Social Responsibility which provides a
service of residential and day care as well as engaging in
the study of social and ethical issues facing society today.
The Board operates Homes for older people throughout
Scotland and a range of projects, and other supportive
Centres for people of all ages who through pressure of
circumstances or inherent weakness need assistance and
support. It responds to problems such as alcohol and drug
dependency, and to develop informed opinion and an
effective Christian response to issues of alcohol and drugs,
health and healing, child abuse, family matters, euthanasia,
human sexuality and abortion.

Church of Scotland Guild

121 George St, Edinburgh EH2 4YN;
 URL www.cos-guild.org.uk;
 E-mail guild@cofscotland.org.uk; Tel 0131 225 5722;
 Fax 0131 220 3113
General Secretary Alison Twaddle
The Church of Scotland Guild is a movement within the
Church of Scotland which invites and encourages both
women and men to commit their lives to Jesus Christ and
enables them to express their faith in worship, prayer and
action. This is expressed in a variety of caring projects. The
Church's social services are provided by its Board of Social
Responsibility, to which the Guild is linked.

Church in Wales

20

The Council for Mission and Ministry, 3a Cathedral Rd,
 Cardiff, CF11 9XF; Tel 0292 070 5278; Fax 0292 071 2413
Officer (Church and Society) Rev Robin Morrison

Bangor

Diocesan Division for Social Responsibility, Canolfan yr
 Esgobaeth, Clos y Gadeirlan, Bangor, Gwynedd
 LL57 1RL;
 E-mail madelaine.dbf.bangor@churchinwales.org.uk;
 Tel 01248 353360; Fax 01248 362191
Officer (Social Responsibility) Rev Madelaine Brody
Through its offshoot charitable company 'Cywaith Joseff
(Joseph's Co-operative)' the diocese has active involvement
in a range of housing and homelessness projects. It has a
commitment to credit unions and the encouragement of
parenthood skills among young people in schools.

Llandaff

Diocese of Llandaff, Board for Social Responsibility, Cardiff
 CF5 2EE; Tel 029 2057 8899; Fax 029 2057 6198
Executive Officer Rev G. Foster
Diocese of Llandaff Board for Social Responsiblity:
incorporating The Welcare Development, Cardiff and the
St. Illtud's Day Care Centre, Llantwit Major.

St. Asaph

Diocesan Council for Social Responsibility, The Vicarage,
 Denbigh, Denbighshire LL16 4NN; Tel 01745 890250
Officer (Social Responsibility) Rev M. Williams

St. Davids

Diocesan Council for Social Responsibility, Dark Gate
 Bldgs, 3 Red St, Carmarthen, Carmarthenshire
 SA31 1QL; Tel 01267 221551

Swansea and Brecon

Diocesan Social Responsibility, Eastmore Centre, St.
 Barnabus Church, Hawthorne Ave, Uplands, Swansea
 SA2 0LP; Tel 01792 402616
Contact Rev P. Williams

Ecumenical and Inter-Denominational Organisations

Churches Together in Britain and Ireland

Bastile Crt, 2 Paris Gdn, London SE1;
URL www.ctbi.org.uk; E-mail info@ctbi.org.uk; Tel 020 7523 2121
General Secretary Dr David Goodbourn
Co-ordinating Secretary (Church and Society)
Rev John Kennedy
Commission Secretary (Racial Justice) Rev Arlington Trotman (Churches Commission for Racial Justice)

Judaism

Association of Jewish Ex-Servicemen and Women

Registered Charity Number 1082148.
Ajex Hse, 5a East Bank, London N16 5RT;
URL www.ajex.org.uk; E-mail ajexuk@talk21.com;
Tel 020 8800 2844; Fax 020 8880 1117
General Secretary J. Weisser
Assists Jewish ex-servicemen and women and dependants in need. To promote social service schemes for the benefit of sick, disabled and deprived including ex-service people. Ajex Charitable Foundation. Donations and bequests welcomed.

Association of Jewish Refugees in Great Britain (AJR)

Jubilee Hse, Merion Ave, Stanmore, Greater London HA7 4RL; URL www.ajr.org.uk;
E-mail enquiries@aja.org.uk; Tel 020 8385 3070; Fax 020 8385 3080
Assists former refugees (from Nazi oppression) and their families, primarily from Central Europe, by providing a wide range of services. These include regular financial support for the needy, weekly advice sessions on benefit and pension problems, the operation of a popular Day Centre, sheltered accommodation, financial aid for a number of residential homes for the aged, a meals-on-wheels service, a team of full-time social workers and volunteers, and a widely-read journal.

Jewish Aged Needy Pension Society

34 Dalkeith Gr, Stanmore, Greater London HA7 4SG;
Tel 020 8958 5390
Administrator Sheila A. Taylor
Provides pensions and other assistance to those elderly in the Jewish community who find themselves in reduced circumstances.

Jewish Association for the Physically Handicapped

7–10 Chandos St, London W1G 9DQ; Tel 020 7447 9000
Treasurer Paul Warren, FCA
Provides grants to physically handicapped for provision of aids and facilities.

Jewish Blind and Disabled (JBD)

The working name of the Jewish Blind and Physically Handicapped Society
164 East End Rd, London N2 0RR; E-mail info@jbd.org;
Tel 020 8883 1000; Fax 020 8444 6729
Director (Social Work) Natalie Black
Founded in 1969, JBD is an independent charity not affiliated to any other organisation. JBD provides caring

sheltered housing to improve the quality of life, maximise freedom of choice, respect dignity at all times and help achieve independent living for visually and physically disabled people.

Jewish Care

Stuart Young Hse, 221 Golders Green Rd, London NW11 9DQ; URL www.jewishcare.org;
E-mail info@jcare.org; Tel 020 8922 2000; (Jewish Care Direct) 020 8922 2222; Fax 020 8922 1998
Chief Executive Simon Morris (acting)
Services include care for older people, people with mental health problems, physical disabilities or visual impairments, as well as people suffering from strokes, Parkinson's disease, Alzheimer's disease and other forms of dimentia. Services are also available for unemployed people, Holocaust survivors and refugees, as well as people who have been bereaved, recently separated or divorces. Programmes are also offered in community centres for children and younger people.

Area Offices

Jewish Care North East London Office
Jewish Family Centre, 85 Lordship Rd, London N16 0QY;
Tel 020 8880 2244

Jewish Care North West London Office
Stuart Young Hse, 221 Golders Green Rd, London NW11 9DQ; Tel 020 8922 2222

Jewish Care Redbridge Office
Dennis Centre, 84 Beehive La, Ilford, Essex IG1 3RS; Tel 020 8922 2222

Jewish Child's Day

707 High Rd, North Finchley, London N12 0BT;
URL www.jewishchildsday.co.uk;
E-mail info@jewishchildsday.co.uk; Tel 020 8446 8804;
Fax 020 8446 7370
Life President J. Jacobs
Chair J. Moss
Vice-Chair A. Ingram
Vice-Chair V. Campus
Hon Secretary S. Dorfman
Executive Director P. Shaw
Aims
To help organisations working for Jewish children in need.

Jewish Deaf Association

Julias Newman Hse, Woodside Park Rd, London N12 8RP;
URL www.jda.org.uk;
E-mail mail@jda.dircon.co.uk; Tel 020 8446 0502; Fax 020 8445 7451; Answerphone (Advisory Centre) 020 8446 0214; Minicom 020 8446 4057
Chair Evelyn Gee
Executive Director Susan Cipin
Caters for social, cultural, educational and welfare needs of Jewish deaf and hard of hearing people. Day centre for elderly, profoundly deaf members on Wednesday, offering Kosher three-course lunch, and social activities in afternoon. Resource centre for deaf and hard of hearing people of all faiths, able to demonstrate a wide range of technological aids to improve the quality of lives of deaf and hard of hearing people.

JLGB (Jewish Lads' and Girls' Brigade)

Camperdown, 3 Beechcroft Rd, South Woodford, London E18 1LA; URL www.jlgb.org;
E-mail office@jlgb.org; Tel 020 8989 5743; 020 8989 8990;
Fax 020 8518 8832
Commandant Jill Attfield
Chair Charles Kay, MBE
Secretary (Brigade Staff) R.S. Weber
The JLGB is a national voluntary youth organisation

committed to enriching the lives of Jewish young people (8–11 years and 11–17 years) through a diverse range of experiences and activities, in a friendly, safe and structured environment, encouraging development within the Jewish and wider community.
The 'Uniformed Division' operates through uniformed groups around the UK; the 'Outreach Kiruv Project' offers similar activities to young people not wishing to join the uniformed groups and operates in schools, youth clubs and other youth groups. The 'Hand-in-Hand Project' offers opportunities for voluntary service through a network of local groups either within an existing club/school/centre or by establishing a separate independent group.
The JLGB is a registered charity.

League of Jewish Women

6 Bloomsbury Sq, London WC1A 2LP;
URL www.leagueofjewishwomen.org.uk;
E-mail office@leagueofjewishwomen.org.uk; Tel 020 7242 8300; Fax 020 7242 8313
Hon Secretary Jean Karsberg
Voluntary welfare service organisation whose 5000 members serve the general community in all spheres of need. Concerned with current social issues.

Norwood

Broadway Hse, 80–82 The Broadway, Stanmore, Greater London HA7 4HB; URL www.norwood.org.uk; Tel 020 8954 4555; Fax 020 8420 6800
Patron HM The Queen
President Sir T. Chinn
Chair J. Libson
Chief Executive N. Brier
Director (Service Development) Ruth Fasht
Norwood is a Jewish child and family services charity which offers services to children, young people, adults, people with learning disabilities and their families, irrespective of religion or ethnic background where practical. Provision includes a range of counselling and support services to children and their families dealing with problems of child abuse, financial hardship and family breakdown; extensive community services are also provided to people with learning disabilities and their families including Unity, a recreational scheme and the deli, a vocational training project. Residential services include an adolescent unit, semi-independent bedsits, a respite care house, a network of community homes and Ravenswood Village; day services include the Kennedy Leigh Centre and family centres in Hendon, Hackney and Redbridge.

World Jewish Relief (formerly Central British Fund)

(Formerly Central British Fund), The Forum, 74–80 Camden St, London NW1 0EG; Tel 020 7691 1771
Executive Director Vivienne Lewis

Methodist Church

Independent Methodist Churches

Registered Office and Resource Centre, Fleet St, Pemberton, Wigan, Greater Manchester WN5 0DS;
URL www.imcgb.org.uk;
E-mail resourcecentre@imcgb.org.uk; Tel 01942 223526; Fax 01942 227768
Manager A.M. Rigby

The Methodist Church

Methodist Church Hse, 25 Marylebone Rd, London NW1 5JR; URL www.methodist.org.uk;
E-mail co-ordsec@methodistchurch.org.uk; Tel 020 7486 5502; Fax 020 7467 5228

Quaker Peace and Social Witness

Friends Hse, Euston Rd, London NW1 2BJ;
URL www.quaker.org.uk; E-mail qpsw@quaker.org.uk; Tel 020 7663 1000; Fax 020 7663 1001
General Secretary Linda Fielding
The department of the Religious Society of Friends in Britain which is concerned especially with international understanding, peace and economic and social justice.

Quakers (Religious Society of Friends)

Quaker Voluntary Action

Friends Meeting Hse, 6 Mount St, Manchester M2 5NS;
E-mail mail@qva.org.uk; Tel 0161 819 1634
Executive Secretary Sue Dixon
Quaker Voluntary Action (QVA) brings together people from different countries and backgrounds to live and work together on short and medium-term community needs projects throughout Britain. QVA volunteers help to run playschemes, organise community art festivals, work in youth centres, work with disabled children etc. QVA welcomes volunteers with disabilities on projects with suitable facilities. The needs of physically-disabled volunteers are taken into consideration when projects are planned, but it is a good idea to contact the office to discuss any special needs. QVA also sends volunteers on projects abroad (Europe, USA, Japan, Africa). Projects run in summer and last 2–3 weeks plus, minimum age is 18 and with no upper age limit. Food and accommodation are free. QVA charges a registration fee and volunteers pay own travel and insurance. For an info pack send a large stamped s.a.e. to the address above.

20

Presbyterian Church

Presbyterian Church of Wales

53 Richmond Rd, Cardiff CF24 3WJ;
URL www.ebcpcw.org.uk; E-mail ebcpcw@aol.com;
Tel 029 2049 4913; Fax 029 2046 4293
General Secretary Rev W.G. Edwards, BA, BD

Church and Society Board

32 Garth Dr, Liverpool, Merseyside L18 6HW;
E-mail dbenrees@freeuk.com; Tel 0151 724 1989;
Fax 0151 724 5691
Secretary Rev Prof D.B. Rees, BA, BD, MA, MSc (Econ), ThD, PhD, FRSA
Presbyterian Church of Wales.
The Church maintains one children's home at Bontnewydd, nr Caernarfon; community workers at Community House Church, Eton Rd, Newport, Gwent, Rhyl Christian Family Centre, Waren Rd, Rhyl, and Noddfa Caernarfon; one youth training centre; The College, Bala, Gwynedd (Rev W. Bryn Williams); The Lay Training Centre, Trefeca, Talgarth, Powys (Rev Gethin Rhys); and Youth Holiday Centre, Tresaith, Dyfed.

Presbyterian Orphan and Children's Society

Church Hse, Belfast BT1 6DW;
E-mail orph-child@presbyterianireland.org; Tel 028 9032 3737
Secretary and Treasurer W.P. Gray, MSSc, PhD, MinstLM
The Society is a Christian organisation. Its aim is to help families and young people of the Presbyterian Church in Ireland in whatever way it can. In 2002 the Society allocated grants in the region of £375 000 to children and

young people. The Society is currently involved in various initiatives, including the funding of a family worker, Contact Centre and the funding of Mother and Toddler Groups, Crèches, etc, belonging to and administered by the Presbyterian Church.

Roman Catholic Church

Catholic Housing Aid Society (CHAS)

209 Old Marylebone Rd, London NW1 5QT;
  URL www.chasnational.org.uk;
  E-mail info@chasnational.org.uk; Tel 020 7723 7273;
  (Housing Advice Line) 020 7723 5928; Fax 020 7723 5943
Director R. Rafferty
Main areas of work are housing advice, research and education. Nine local housing advice groups.

Catholic Men's Society of Great Britain

Metropolitan Cathedral Bldgs, 152 Brownlow Hill, Liverpool, Merseyside L3 5RQ; Tel 0151 709 5078
Secretary Chris Bolger
Aims
To help men to become responsible Christians through personal, spiritual and social formation.

Catholic Youth Services

39 Eccleston Sq, London SW1V 1BX;
  URL www.catholicyouthservices.org;
  E-mail cys@cbccw.org.uk; Tel 020 7901 4870; Fax 020 7901 4873
Director Helen Bardy
Assistant Director J. Lloyd
Head (Office and Communication) Z. Tolman
Youth Service agency of the Catholic Bishops' Conference of England and Wales.

National Commission for Social Care

19a Park Circus, Glasgow G3 6BE;
  E-mail nacosoca@business.ntl.com; Tel (Child Protection Information Line) 0141 572 0253; (General Enquiries) 0141 331 0083; Fax 0141 332 2190
National Co-ordinator David McCann
To co-ordinate and advise all organisations linked to the Catholic Church in Scotland on matters relating to social care. To advise Bishops' Conference on social care matters.

Prison, Advice and Care Trust (PACT)

Lincoln Hse, 1–3 Brixton Rd, London SW9 6DE;
  URL www.imprisonment.org.uk;
  E-mail info@pact.uk.net; Tel 020 7582 1313; (Family Support Services) 020 7278 3981; Fax 020 7735 6077
Director Myra Fulford
In London, professional counsellors offer a service to prisoners on remand. Welfare staff offer advice, support and information to families of prisoners. The Trust is actively involved in the management of crèche facilities and The Visitors' Centres at Wormwood Scrubs, Belmarsh, Pentonville and Holloway. We work in close collaboration with statutory and voluntary agencies.

St. Joseph's Society for the Relief of the Aged Poor

St. Joseph's Almshouse, 42 Brook Grn, London W6 7BW;
  Tel 020 7603 9817; Fax 020 7602 1005
Secretary S.D. Dolan
Provides funding for diocesan-based projects dealing with the aged. Also provides subsidised accommodation in Brook Green.

Caritas – Social Action

39 Eccleston Sq, London SW1V 1BX;
  URL www.caritas-socialaction.org.uk;
  E-mail caritas@cbcew.org.uk; Tel 020 7901 4875; Fax 020 7901 4874
Director Sarah Lindsell
Promotes Catholic social action in England and Wales. An umbrella body for Catholic charities.

The Salvation Army

101 Newington Causeway, London SE1 6BN; Tel 020 7367 4500
Commander (UK Territorial) Commissioner Alex Hughes
Chief Secretary Lt Col V. Poke
Secretary (Programme) Col K. Burridge
Director (Social Services) Cap Ian Harris
Director (Family Training Service) Lt Col Ron Smith

Counselling Services (for emotional, social, sexual, marital, or spiritual problems)
1 Water La, Stratford, London E15 4LU; Tel 020 8356 5480; Fax 020 8536 5489

Divisional Headquarters

Salvation Army Anglia Division
2 Barton Way, Norwich, Norfolk NR1 1DL; Tel 01603 724400; Fax 01603 724411

Salvation Army Central Northern Division
80 Eccles New Rd, Salford, Greater Manchester M5 4DU; Tel 0161 743 3900; Fax 0161 743 3911

Salvation Army Central South Division
16c Cowley Rd, Uxbridge, Greater London UB8 2LT; Tel 01895 208800; Fax 01895 208811

Salvation Army East Midlands Division
Paisley Gr, Chilwell, Nottingham NG9 6DJ; Tel 0115 983 5000; Fax 0115 983 5011

Salvation Army East Scotland Division
5 East Adam St, Edinburgh EH8 9TF; Tel 0131 662 3300; Fax 0131 662 3311

Salvation Army Ireland Division
Station Mews, Sydenham, Belfast BT4 1TL; Tel 028 9067 5000; Fax 028 9067 5011

Salvation Army London Central Division
1st Fl, 25–27 Kings Exchange, Tileyard Rd, London N7 9AH; Tel 020 7619 6100; Fax 020 7619 6111

Salvation Army London North East Division
Maldon Rd, Hatfield Peverel, Essex CM3 2HL; Tel 01245 383000; Fax 01245 353011

Salvation Army London South East Division
East Crt, Enterprise Rd, Maidstone, Kent ME15 6JF; Tel 01622 775000; Fax 01622 775011

Salvation Army Northern Division
Balliol Bus Pk, Newcastle upon Tyne, Tyne and Wear NE12 8EW; Tel 0191 238 1800; Fax 0191 238 1811

Salvation Army North Scotland Division
Deer Rd, Woodside, Aberdeen AB24 2BL; Tel 01224 496000; Fax 01224 497011

Salvation Army North Western Division
16 Faraday Rd, Wavertree Technology Pk, Liverpool, Merseyside L13 1EH; Tel 0151 252 6100; Fax 0151 252 6111

Salvation Army South and Mid Wales Division
East Moors Rd, Ocean Pk, Cardiff CF24 5SA; Tel 029 2044 0600; Fax 029 2044 0611

Salvation Army Southern Division
6–8 Little Park Farm Rd, Segensworth, Fareham,
Hampshire PO15 5TD; Tel 01489 566800; Fax 01489
566811

Salvation Army South Western Division
Marlborough Crt, Matford Bus Pk, Exeter, Devon EX2 8PF;
Tel 01392 822100; Fax 01392 822111

Salvation Army West Midlands Division
102 Unett St, Birmingham, West Midlands B19 3BZ;
Tel 0121 507 8500; Fax 0121 507 8511

Salvation Army West Scotland Division
4 Buchanan Crt, Cumbernauld Rd, Glasgow G33 6HZ;
Tel 0141 779 5000; Fax 0141 779 5011

Salvation Army Yorkshire Division
1 Cadman Crt, off Hanley Rd, Leeds, West Yorkshire
LS27 0RX; Tel 0113 281 0100; Fax 0113 281 0111

Salvation Army Prison Welfare and After-Care
101 Newington Causeway, London SE1 6BN; Tel 020 7367
4849; Fax 020 7367 4712
Liaison Officer   Major Marion Henderson

United Reformed Church, Church and Society

86 Tavistock Pl, London WC1H 9RT; URL www.urc.org.uk;
E-mail church.society@urc.org.uk; Tel 020 7916 2020;
Fax 020 7916 2021
General Secretary   Rev Dr David Cornick
Secretary (Church and Society)   Dr Andrew Bradstock
Church and Society maintains contact with churches
throughout the country and acts as a centre of information
and communications over the range of social responsibility
agenda.

20

Professional Bodies and Trade Associations

21

- ■ **Professional Bodies**
- ■ **Joint Negotiating Councils and Committees**
- ■ **Trades Unions**
- ■ **Other Professional Organisations**

Professional Bodies and Trade Associations

Professional Bodies

Alliance of Deaf Service Users and Providers

Chair   Karen Hope
Services to Deaf People, Hollybush Hse, Nuneaton, Warwickshire CV11 4AR; Tel 024 7634 406; 024 7635 1166
Secretary   Gail Norton
Centre for the Deaf, Centenary Hse, Leeds, West Yorkshire LS2 8AY
Aims to advance, promote and maintain appropriate personal social services to deaf people and their families through a partnership of people involved with or interested in services to deaf people. Reflects the changing nature of social services, the growing emphasis through changes in legislation and practice on partnerships with people who may use services, to develop those services to best meet their identified needs. Full ADSUP membership (£10) is open to people who use, deliver, plan or are interested in the quality of personal social services to deaf people. Membership entitles one to a reduced subscription rate for Deafness £5 pa.

Association of British Dispensing Opticians

199 Gloucester Terr, London W2 6LD;
   URL www.abdo.org.uk; E-mail general@abdo.org.uk; Tel 020 7298 5100; Fax 020 7298 5111
General Secretary   Sir Anthony Garrett, CBE
The ABDO is a membership and representative body for dispensing opticians and also an examining body. The qualification FBDO is recognised by the General Optical Council.

Association of Charity Officers

Beechwood Hse, Wyllyotts Cl, Potters Bar, Hertfordshire EN6 2HN; E-mail info@aco.uk.net; Tel 01707 651777; Fax 01707 660477
Director   Valerie J. Barrow
Aims to encourage efficiency and co-operation between member charities and considers the effect of legislation on charities and beneficiaries. There are more than 200 member charities offering help to all sections of the community. Particular expertise in benevolence and can offer advice and training to professionals assisting their clients. ACO itself has no funds for grant aid but members offer direct help to individuals and a range of specialised services, many of which are widely used by the statutory authorities. Newsletter. Report (8) on the impact of fees top-up in homes for elderly beneficiaries on charities commissioned by the Association of Charity Officers and undertaken by the Age Concern Institute of Gerontology obtainable from: The Age Concern Institution of Gerontology, Cornwall Hse Annexe, King's College

London, Waterloo Rd, London SE1 8TX. Booklet Individuals in Need: Guidelines for Grantmakers – ISBN 0 9528724 0 4, published by ACO, available from ACO (£5.00). Report of 1996: Preserved Rights to Income Support for Residents in long-term care (with Age Concern England), available from Age Concern, 1268 London Rd, London, SW16 4ER. Benchwork Study 1997/2001/2002. Report: Fees paid to GPs for services provided to Residents of Care Accommodation for Older People, 2000/2001 (Feb 2001 ISBN 0452 8724). Charities Helping People in Need 1997 available from ACO, please send A4 sae. Internal directory. Mainly self-funding, some project grant aid from Home Office.

Association of Child Psychotherapists

120 West Heath Rd, London NW8 7TU;
   URL www.acp.uk.net; E-mail acp@dial.pipex.com; Tel 020 8458 1609
Secretary   A. Lee-Lazone; Tel 020 8458 1609; Fax 020 8458 1482
Concerned with training, registration, professional standards, careers structure in the NHS, salaries, and giving information to the public. Therapists work in the NHS and in private practice with children, young people and parents.

Association of Community Workers

Stephenson Bldg, Elswick Rd, Newcastle upon Tyne, Tyne and Wear NE4 6SQ;
   E-mail lesleyleach@acwl.fsbusiness.co.uk; Tel 0191 272 4341
Administrative Officer   Lesley Leach
Provides a forum for critical discussion of community work issues. Supports members, represents, campaigns and publishes relevant material. Membership open.

Association for Continence Advice (ACA)

102a Astra Hse, Arklow Rd, New Cross, London SE14 6EB;
   E-mail info@aca.uk.com; Tel 020 8692 4680; Fax 020 8692 6217
Company Secretary   Barbara Angell
Multidisciplinary membership association of professionals with special interest in health and social care of people with bladder and bowel problems in the promotion of continence and the better management of incontinence.

Association for Education Welfare Management

National Secretary   Jennifer A. Price
The Whiskers, 1 The Boundary, Bradford, West Yorkshire BD8 0BQ; Tel 01274 542295
Promotes good practice and support for managers of education social work and education welfare service within the local education authority structure.

21

Association of Educational Psychologists

26 The Avenue, Durham, County Durham DH1 4ED;
   Tel 0191 384 9512; Fax 0191 386 5287
Association Secretary Mary Jenkin
Professional association for educational psychologists and
a registered trade union for educational psychologists in
England, Wales and Northern Ireland.

Association for Family Therapy

12a Executive Suite, St. James Crt, Wilderspool Causeway,
   Warrington WA4 6PL; URL www.aft.org.uk;
   E-mail s.kennedy@aft.org.uk; Tel 01925 444 414
Chair Judith Lask
Executive Officer Sue Kennedy
Aims to promote practice, teaching and research into
family therapy. Membership is open to all those engaged in
work with families. Publishes a quarterly Journal of Family
Therapy and a bi-monthly magazine: Context.

Association of Social Care Communicators

Royal Borough of Kensington and Chelsea, Town Hall,
   Hornton St, London W8 7NX; Tel 020 7361 3661; Fax 020
   7361 3764
Chair Tim Ellis
Vice-Chair Michelle Bill
Vice-Chair David Coope
National organisation linking and supporting information
workers in social services, social work departments, health
and voluntary sectors.
Aims to raise the profile of public information as a service
in its own right; improve the quality and range of
information available to service users and staff; encourage
the exchange of ideas between information workers
throughout the country; act as a support group offering a
chance to discuss the particular problems of providing
quality public information.

British Acupuncture Council

63 Jeddo Rd, London W12 9HQ;
   E-mail info@acupuncture.org.uk; Tel 020 8735 0400;
   Fax 020 8735 0404
Chair Jasmine Uddin, MBAcC
The British Acupuncture Council works to maintain
common standards of education, ethics, discipline and
codes of practice to ensure the health and safety of the
public at all times. It is committed to promoting research
and enhancing the role that traditional accupuncture can
play in the health and well-being of the nation.

British Association of Art Therapists

Mary Ward Hse, 5 Tavistock Pl, London WC1H 9SN;
   URL www.baat.org; E-mail baat@ukgateway.net; Tel 020
   7383 3774; Fax 020 7387 5513
Enquiries c/o The Secretary of the Association.
The British Association of Art Therapists, which was
founded in 1964, is the professional body representing art
therapists in Great Britain.

British Association for Counselling and Psychotherapy

1 Regent Pl, Rugby, Warwickshire CV21 2PJ;
   URL www.bacp.co.uk; E-mail bacp@bacp.co.uk;
   Tel (Office) 0870 443 5252; Fax 0870 443 5161
Chief Executive (Acting) Alan Jamieson
Divisions
Association for Pastoral and Spiritual Care and Counselling
(ASPCC); Association for University and College
Counselling (AUCC); Association for Counselling at Work
(ACW); Counselling in Education (CIE); Faculty of
Healthcare Counsellors and Psychotherapists Ltd (FHCP);
Personal Relationship Groupwork (PRG); Race and
Cultural Education in Counselling (RACE).
Exists to represent counselling at a national and
international level; to promote understanding and
awareness of counselling; to maintain and raise standards
of counsellor training and practice, and to increase the
availability of trained and supervised counsellors.
Produces directories annually on counselling and
psychotherapy resources and training. BAC has codes of
ethics and practice for counsellors, counselling skills,
trainers in counselling and the supervision of counsellors.
Information telephone line or letter (A5 sae please) to
members of the public who want names of counsellors.

British Association of Domiciliary Care

Director Maggie Uttley, MBE
2 Hornbeams, The Street, Reading RG7 1QY; Tel 0118 988
   2954; Fax 0118 988 2954
A professional association representing and supporting
Domiciliary Care Managers from all sectors. Publishing
Good Practice Guidelines; organising seminars and
workshops; advising and consulting with members;
Lobbying Government and other bodies.

British Association and College of Occupational Therapists

106–114 Borough High St, London SE1 1LB;
   URL www.cot.org.uk; E-mail cot@cot.co.uk; Tel 020 7357
   6480; Fax 020 7450 2299
Professional association for occupational therapy staff and
students with members in the NHS, local authorities and in
private practice.

British Association for Paediatric Nephrology (BAPN)

Renal Office, Gt Ormond St Hospital for Children NHS
   Trust, London WC1N 3JH; Tel 020 7893 8346; Fax 020
   7829 8841
President Dr. M. Savage
Treasurer Dr Rodney Gilbert
Secretary (Research) Dr Nick Webb
Secretary Dr Lesley Rees
To promote high standards of care for children with renal
disease and to foster research in this area.

British Association of Psychotherapists

37 Mapesbury Rd, London NW2 4HJ;
   URL www.bap-psychotherapy.org; Tel 020 8452 9823;
   Fax 020 8452 5182
Chief Executive B. Elise Ormerod
Promotes the knowledge and skills of psychotherapy, and
the education, training and competence of adult and child
psychotherapists. Offers a prompt assessment and referral
system for children, adolescents and adults requiring
psychotherapy. Offers in addition some short courses for
related professions.

British Association for Sexual and Relationship Therapy

PO Box 13686, London SW20 9ZH; URL www.basrt.org.uk;
   E-mail info@basrt.org.uk
Provides two conferences a year on psychosexual topics
open to professional non-members. Publishes an
international journal. Please send sae for details of local sex
therapists.

British Association of Social Workers

16 Kent St, Birmingham, West Midlands B5 6RD;
   URL www.basw.co.uk; E-mail i.johnston@basw.co.uk;
   Tel 0121 622 3911; Fax 0121 622 4860
Director I. Johnston

England Office
E-mail n.mapstone@basw.co.uk

Northern Ireland Office
216 Belmont Rd, Belfast BT4 2AT;
E-mail e.ashenhurst@basw.co.uk; Tel 028 9067 2247

Scottish Office
17 Waterloo Pl, Edinburgh EH1 3BG;
E-mail r.stark@basw.co.uk; Tel 0131 556 9525

Wales Office
33 Plas St. Pol de Leon, Penarth Marina, Penarth, Vale of
Glamorgan CF64 1TR; E-mail p.lloyd@basw.co.uk;
Tel 029 2071 0784

British Association of Teachers of the Deaf

175 Dashwood Ave, High Wycombe, Buckinghamshire
HP12 3DB; URL www.batod.org.uk;
E-mail secretary@batod.org.uk; Tel 01494 464190;
Fax 01494 464190
Secretary Paul Simpson
Aims to promote the education of all hearing-impaired
children, young persons and adults. Promotes the interests
and status of all teachers of the hearing impaired,
producing a refereed journal with learned papers and also
an association magazine with articles of topical interest,
five times per year.

British Hypnotherapy Association

67 Upper Berkeley St, London W1H 7QX;
URL www.hypnotherapy-association.org; Tel 020 7723
4443
Chair R.K. Brian
Hon Secretary Alison Wookey
Refers enquirers about hypnotherapy for emotional
problems, relationship difficulties, psychosexual
problems, phobias, neurotic behaviour patterns etc to the
nearest therapist on register. Maintains a register of
competent psychotherapists who, when appropriate, can
utilise hypnosis to aid recall. The register is confined to
therapists with at least four years' relevant training and
who comply with high standards of competence and
ethics in their work. Also issues publications, arranges
talks and articles, and recommends appropriate training
courses.
Aims
To raise standards of treatment of nervous problems; to
care for the interests of patients and members; to collate
and disseminate information on hypnotherapy.

British Institute of Learning Disabilities (BILD)

Campion Hse, Green St, Kidderminster, Worcestershire
DY10 1JL; URL www.bild.org.uk;
E-mail enquiries@bild.org.uk; Tel 01562 723010;
Fax 01562 723029
Officer (Information) Norman Mills
Aims
To contribute to and improving quality of life for people
with learning disabilities through training, education,
dissemination of information and publishing books and
journals.

British Medical Association

BMA Hse, Tavistock Sq, London WC1H 9JP;
URL www.bma.org.uk; E-mail info.web@bma.org.uk;
Tel 020 7387 4499; Fax 020 7383 6400
Secretary Jeremy Strachan
A voluntary, professional association of doctors, an
independent trade union, a scientific and educational body
and a publishing house.

The British Psychological Society

St. Andrew's Hse, 48 Princess Rd East, Leicester,
Leicestershire LE1 7DR; E-mail mail@bps.org.uk;
Tel 0116 254 9568; Fax 0116 247 0787
Hon General Secretary Prof A. Colley
Chief Executive Barry Brooking
The only learned society and professional body
incorporated by Royal Charter to promote psychology
within the UK.

Children and Family Court Advisory and Support Services (CAFCASS)

Cafcass Headquarters, 13th–14th Fls, Archway Tower, 2
Junction Rd, London N19 5HQ;
URL www.cafcass.gov.uk;
E-mail cafcass@cafcass.gov.uk; Tel 020 7210 4400;
Fax 020 7210 4422

Carers UK

Ruth Pitter Hse, 20–25 Glasshouse Yard, London EC1A 4JT;
URL www.carersonline.org.uk;
E-mail info@ukcarers.org; Tel 020 7490 8818;
(CarersLine) 0808 808 7777; Fax 020 7490 8824
Chief Executive D. Whitworth
A charity and UK wide organisation of carers. Provides
information, advice and support to carers through 'Caring'
Magazine, CarersLine and leaflets. Carries out research and
lobbies to improve recognition of and services for carers.
Offers training and information to social care and health
professionals.

Chartered Institute of Environmental Health (CIEH)

Chadwick Crt, 15 Hatfields, London SE1 8DJ;
URL www.cieh.org; E-mail media@cieh.org; Tel 020 7928
6006; Fax 020 7827 5865
The CIEH website contains useful information on food
safety policy and all press releases.

Chartered Institute of Housing (CIH)

Octavia Hse, Westwood Way, Coventry, West Midlands
CV4 8JP; URL www.cih.org;
E-mail customer.services@cih.org; Tel 024 7685 1700;
Fax 024 7669 5110

Chartered Society of Physiotherapy

14 Bedford Row, London WC1R 4ED;
URL www.csp.org.uk; E-mail pr@csphysio.org.uk;
Tel 020 7306 6666; Fax 020 7306 6611
Chief Executive Phil Gray
Director (Communications) Neil Tester
The CSP is the professional association and educational
body and trade union for the UK's 38 000 chartered
physiotherapists, physiotherapy students and assistants
CSP members work primarily in the NHS, but also in the
independent sector, education, research, occupational
health and voluntary sector.

Coal Industry Social Welfare Organisation

CISWO, The Old Rectory, Rectory Dr, Whiston, Rotherham,
South Yorkshire S60 4JG; Tel 01709 728115; Fax 01709
839164
Director (Social Work) Geraldine Pearce
CISWO aims to enhance the quality of life for individuals
and communities in coalfield and former coalfield areas.
The organisation provides social care community
development services, and has links with individuals,
miners' welfare schemes, partnership agencies and
charitable trusts.

21

Consumers' Association

2 Marylebone Rd, London NW1 4DF; Tel 020 7770 7000;
    Fax 020 7770 7600
Chief Executive   S. Mckechnie
Undertakes research and comparative testing of goods
and services. Represents the consumer interest and
campaigns for improvements in both the public and
private sector.

The Ergonomics Society

Devonshire Hse, Devonshire Sq, Loughborough,
    Leicestershire LE11 3DW; URL www.ergonomics.org.uk;
    E-mail ergsoc@ergonomics.org.uk; Tel 01509 234904;
    Fax 01509 235666
President   Magdalen Galley
Chair   Roger Haslam
Business Manager   John Cotton
Promotes education and awareness of ergonomics and
maintains professional standards.

General Medical Council

178 Great Portland St, London W1W 5JE;
    URL www.gmc-uk.org; Tel 020 7580 7642; Fax 020 7915
    3641
Chief Executive and Registrar   Finlay Scott

Independent Healthcare Association (IHA)

Westminster Tower, 3 Albert Embankment, London
    SE1 7SP; URL www.lha.org.uk; Tel 020 7793 4620;
    Fax 020 7820 3738
Chair   Clare Hollingsworth
Chief Executive   Barry Hassell
Executive Director (Community Care)   Ann Mackay
IHA promotes good standards of health and social care in
the independent sector. Members of include providers of
acute mental health and community care. IHA's
Community Care Group consists of nursing homes,
residential homes and home care providers. IHA represents
the interests of its members to government and other
groups involved in health and social care.

Institute of Career Guidance

27a Lower High St, Stourbridge, West Midlands DY8 1TA;
    URL www.icg-uk.org; E-mail hq@icg-uk.org; Tel 01384
    376464; Fax 01384 440830
Chief Executive   Bryony Pawinska
The Institute in consultation with its members and
associates defines and promotes the ethics, principles and
practice of high quality careers guidance for all.

Institute of Chartered Secretaries and Administrators

16 Park Cres, London W1B 1AH; URL www.icsa.org.uk;
    E-mail info@icsa.co.uk; Tel 020 7580 4741; Fax 020 7323
    1132
The professional examining body for Chartered Secretaries
with a membership that encompasses individuals in
organisations across the corporate, public and not-for-profit
sectors.

Institute of Health Promotion and Education

Department of Oral Health and Development, University
    Dental Hospital, Manchester M15 6FH;
    URL www.ihpe.org.uk;
    E-mail anthony.blinkhorn@man.ac.uk; Tel 0161 275 6610;
    Fax 0161 275 6299
Secretary   Prof Anthony Blinkhorn
A recognised professional association offering full or
associate membership to those engaged in the practice of
health promotion and education.

Institute of Healthcare Management

PO Box 33239, London SW1W 0WN;
    URL www.ihm.org.uk; E-mail enquiries@ihm.org.uk;
    Tel 020 7881 9235; Fax 020 7881 9236
Chief Executive   Maurice Cheng
The IHM is the professional institute for all concerned with
the management of healthcare services, providing
management education and development, publications,
conferences and regional activities, and contributing to
national policy.

The Institute of Welfare

Institute of Registered Welfare Officers.
Newland Hse, 137–139 Hagley Rd, Edgbaston,
    Birmingham, West Midlands B16 8UA;
    URL www.instituteofwelfare.co.uk;
    E-mail info@instituteofwelfare.co.uk; Tel 0121 454 8883;
    Fax 0121 454 7873
Administrator   L. Johnson

Justices' Clerks' Society (JCS)

2nd Fl, Port of Liverpool Bldg, Pier Head, Liverpool,
    Merseyside L3 1BY; URL www.jc.society.co.uk;
    E-mail secretariat@jc-society.co.uk; Tel 0151 225 0790;
    Fax 0151 236 4458
Chief Executive   Sid Brighton
Promotes the science of law and observes the operation of
the law especially that administered by justices of the peace
in the UK. Watches proposals for legislation in matters
affecting the jurisdiction and administration of justice by
justices of the peace in England and Wales and takes such
steps in regard to the support of, or opposition to, such
proposals as may seem expedient.

Magistrates' Association

28 Fitzroy Sq, London W1T 6DD;
    E-mail magistrates-association.org.uk; Tel 020 7387 2353;
    Fax 020 7383 4020
Chief Executive   Sally Dickinson
The Association organises meetings, conferences,
discussions and publications (including a monthly journal).
It is a consultative body and represents the interests of
magistrates.

Medical Women's Federation

Tavistock House North, Tavistock Sq, London WC1H 9HX;
    URL www.medicalwomensfederation.co.uk;
    E-mail mwf@btconnect.com; Tel 020 7387 7765; Fax 020
    7388 9216
Aims
For equal opportunities for women doctors and patients.

National Association of Advisory Officers for Special Educational Needs

Hon Secretary   D. Robinson
Maryland, Princes St, Tunbridge Wells, Kent TN2 4SL;
    E-mail diana.robinson@btclick.com
Information and debating facility for members on
subscription.

National Association of Councillors

Civic Centre, Gateshead, Tyne and Wear NE8 1HH;
    E-mail cllr.pmole@gateshead.gov.uk; Tel 0191 433 3000;
    Fax 0191 477 9253
Chair   Cllr S. Campbell
General Secretary (Contact)   Cllr P.J. Mole
Director (Finance)   Cllr J. Kelly
Paliamentary Officer   G. Morris
National Women's Officer   Cllr R. Simpson

Regional branches
Northern, Welsh, Scottish, Northern Ireland, Midland, Southern.
Membership
8000.
Functions
To represent and further the interests of elected members. To initiate consideration of matters of interest and to provide a forum for councillors to discuss common issues and exchange ideas. To provide for the education and training of councillors. To negotiate with central government or other bodies to improve the status of councillors.

National Association of Prison Visitors

32 Newnham Ave, Bedford, Bedfordshire MK41 9PT;
    E-mail info@napu.org.uk; Tel 01234 359763; Fax 01234 359763
Secretary   A.G. McKenna
Prison visitors establish a genuine relationship with the people they visit built on trust.

Napo

4 Chivalry Rd, Battersea, London SW11 1HT;
    URL napo.org.uk; E-mail info@napo.org.uk; Tel 020 7223 4887; Fax 020 7223 3503
General Secretary   Judy McKnight
Assistant General Secretary   Harry Fletcher
Assistant General Secretary   Jonathan Ledger
Assistant General Secretary   Cordell Pillay
Professional association and trade union active in social, penal and employment policy. TUC affiliated.

National Association of Professionals Concerned with Language Impaired Children (NAPLIC)

c/o Speech and Language Therapy, Parsons Green Centre, 5–7 Parsons Grn, London SW6 4UL; Tel 020 8846 7987
President   Ann Locke
Chair   Claire Withey
Secretary (Membership)   Deirdre Goodger
Treasurer   Deidre Goodger
Promotes professional awareness of the needs of the language impaired child and encourage teaching skills.

NHS Education for Scotland

22 Queen St, Edinburgh EH2 1NT; Tel 0131 226 7371;
    Fax 0131 225 9970
Manager (Corporate Services)   David Ferguson (Acting)

National Consumer Council

20 Grosvenor Gdns, London SW1W 0DH;
    URL www.ncc.org.uk; E-mail info@ncc.org.uk; Tel 020 7730 3469
The purpose of the National Consumer Council is to make all consumers matter. The Council puts forward the consumer interest, particularly that of disadvantaged groups in society, by researching, campaigning and working with those who can make a difference to achieve beneficial change. A non-profit company limited by guarantee and funded partly by the Department of Trade and Industry.

Welsh Consumer Council

5th Fl, Longoross Crt, 47 Newport Rd, Cardiff CF24 0WL;
    URL www.wales-consumer.org.uk;
    E-mail info@wales-consumer.org.uk; Tel 02920 255454;
    Fax 02920 255464

Scottish Consumer Council

Royal Exchange Hse, 100 Queen St, Glasgow G1 3DN;
    URL www.scotsconsumer.org.uk;
    E-mail scc@scotconsumer.org.uk; Tel 0141 226 5261;
    Fax 0141 221 0731

General Consumer Council for Northern Ireland
Elizabeth Hse, 116 Holywood Rd, Belfast BT4 1NY;
    URL www.gccni.org.uk; E-mail info@gccni.org.uk;
    Tel 028 9067 2488; Fax 028 9065 7701

The NHS Confederation

1 Warwick Row, London SW1E 5ER;
    URL www.nhsconfed.net; Tel 020 7959 7272; Fax 020 7959 7273
Chief Executive   Dr Gill Morgan
Represents the organisations that make up the NHS. Around 95% of organisations across the UK are members.
Mission
Dedicated to improving health policy and practice by linking members in the development of policy and ideas; creating a range of opportunities for members' views to be heard; encourage agenda-setting debate; campaigning for change; working in partnership with other organisations; building awareness and understanding of issues; providing a single reference point for expert comment; supporting NHS leadership and management.

Police Federation of England and Wales

15–17 Langley Rd, Surbiton, Surrey KT6 6LP; Tel 020 8399 2224; 020 8399 2228
General Secretary   C. Elliott
Established by Act of Parliament, representing members of Police Forces below the rank of Superintendent in all matters affecting their welfare and efficiency.

Police Superintendents' Association of England and Wales

National Headquarters, 67a Reading Rd, Pangbourne, Berkshire RG8 7JD; URL www.policesupers.com; E-mail enquiries@policesupers.com; Tel 0118 984 4005; Fax 0118 984 5642
National Secretary   Chief Superintendent D. Palmer
National Deputy Secretary   Chief Superintendent P. Aspey
Represents the interests of all superintending ranks on matters relating to pay, pensions and conditions of service.

Prison Officers' Association

Cronin Hse, 245 Church St, London N9 9HW; Tel 020 8803 0255; Fax 020 8803 1761

The Queen's Nursing Institute

3 Albemarle Way, London EC1V 4RQ;
    URL www.qni.org.uk; E-mail info@qni.org.uk
Director   Mrs J. Hesketh
A charitable organisation concerned with innovation in primary healthcare nursing and the welfare of community nurses.

Royal College of Midwives

15 Mansfield St, London W1G 9NH; URL www.rcm.org.uk; E-mail info@rcm.org.uk; Tel 020 7312 3535; Fax 020 7312 3536
General Secretary   Dame Karlene Davis, DBE, DSc (Hon) MA, BEd (Hons) MTD, RM, RN
Educational and professional organisation to promote the art and science of midwifery and maintain professional standards. An independent trade union with approx. 35 000 members.

Royal College of Nursing of the UK (RCN)

20 Cavendish Sq, London W1M 0AB; URL rcn.org.uk; Tel 020 7409 3333; Fax 020 7355 1379
General Secretary   Dr Beverly Malone, PhD
Adviser (Mental Health)   Cris Allan
The RCN is the world's largest professional union of nurses, an independent trade union and an establishment of higher education.

21

Royal College of Physicians of London

11 St. Andrew's Pl, London NW1 4LE; Tel 020 7935 1174; Fax 020 7487 5218
Chief Executive Philip Masterton-Smith
The College was founded in 1518. Its present objectives are the preservation of standards of medicine, the continuing education of physicians and research.

Royal College of Psychiatrists

17 Belgrave Sq, London SW1X 8PG;
E-mail infoservices@rcpsych.ac.uk; Tel 020 7235 2351; Fax 020 7245 1231
Secretary V. Cameron
The College aims to advance the science and practice of psychiatry and to promote study and research work in all disciplines connected with understanding and treatment of mental disorder.

Royal College of Speech and Language Therapists

2 White Hart Yard, London SE1 1NX; URL www.rcslt.org; E-mail postmaster@rcslt.org; Tel 020 7378 1200; Fax 020 7403 7254
Professional Director Kamini Gadhok
As a professional body, the RCSLT is responsible for appropriate standards of clinical practice, ethical conduct and promotion of academic knowledge. There is an information service which operates in office hours.

Royal Institute of Public Health

28 Portland Pl, London W1B 1DE; URL www.riph.org.uk; E-mail info@riphh.org.uk; Tel 020 7580 2731
Chief Executive Nichola Wilkins, BA(Hons), MMedSci
An independent, not for profit, membership organisation dedicated to promoting public health and hygiene, through information, education and training, quality testing and policy development.
Worldwide membership of public health professionals.

Royal Society of Medicine

1 Wimpole St, London W1G 0AE; URL www.rsm.ac.uk; E-mail membership@rsm.ac.uk; Tel 020 7290 2900; Fax 020 7290 2992
Executive Director Dr Anne Grocock
A learned society providing academic and club services through its library, publications, meetings, conferences, restaurant, hotel, buttery and bar. The Society also serves as a venue for private meetings and conferences.

The Royal Society for the Promotion of Health

Founded 1876
38a St. George's Dr, London SW1V 4BH;
URL www.rsph.org; E-mail rshealth@rshealth.org.uk; Tel 020 7630 0121; Fax 020 7976 6847
Patron HM The Queen
Promotion of health through conferences, lectures, the conduct of various examinations and the production of a journal; making representations to government and public bodies.

Scottish Police Federation

5 Woodside Pl, Glasgow G3 7QF; URL www.spf.org.uk; E-mail spf@scottishpolicefederation.org.uk; Tel 0141 332 5234
General Secretary D.J. Keil
A staff association which looks after the conditions of service and the welfare of the members of the police service in Scotland from the rank of chief inspector to that of cadet.

Social Care Association

Thornton Hse, Hook Rd, Surbiton, Surrey KT6 5AN; URL www.socialcareassoc.com; E-mail sca@scaed.demon.co.uk; Tel 020 8397 1411; Fax 020 8397 1436
Chief Executive Richard Clough, OBE
Deputy Chief Executive Nick Johnson
SCA is the professional association and leading voice for all involved in social care. It provides associate, corporate and individual membership and has an advice and legal help-line service as well as offering consultancy, care practice audits, arbitration, best value review and training services.

Socialist Health Association (SHA)

(Formerly the Socialist Medical Association)
Toynbee Hall, 28 Commercial St, London E1 6LS;
URL www.sochealth.fsnet.co.uk;
E-mail sha@sochealth.fsnet.co.uk; Tel 020 7377 0403; Fax 020 7377 0403
Director John Briggs
Defence, extension and improvement of the NHS. Prevention of ill-health and positive encouragement of good health. Affiliated to the Labour Party. Publishes journal, reports, briefings. It is a membership organisation which acts as a think tank and pressure group on health and health-related issues.

Society of Chiropodists and Podiatrists

1 Fellmongers Path, Tower Bridge Rd, London SE1 3LY; URL www.feetforlife.org; E-mail enq@scpod.org; Tel 0845 450 3720; Fax 0845 450 3721
Chief Executive Joanna Brown (Acting)
The professional body for chiropodists and podiatrists in the UK, registered with the Health Professions Council, and an independent listed trade union. Validates and provides advanced courses. Publishes monthly journal Podiatry Now and quarterly academic journal British Journal of Podiatry, and a range of foot health literature. Member of the International Federation of Podology (FIP).

Topss England

Albion Crt, 5 Albion Pl, Leeds, West Yorkshire LS1 6JL; URL www.topss.org.uk; Tel 0113 245 1716; Fax 0113 243 6417
Chair Arthur Keefe
Chief Executive Andrea Rowe
Topss England is the employment-led strategic body for education, training and workforce development in social care, including social work. It works closely with the Department of Health and regulatory bodies in social care. In Northern Ireland, Scotland and Wales the Topss functions are undertaken by their respective social care councils, with whom Topss England works in partnership.

Joint Negotiating Councils and Committees

England and Wales

Employers' Organisation for Local Government

Layden Hse, 76–86 Turnmill St, London EC1M 5QU; URL www.lg-employers.gov.uk; Tel 020 7296 6600; Fax 020 7296 6666
Executive Director Charles Nolda
EO negotiates salary structures, and terms and conditions of employment on behalf of local government employers for over three million staff; provides human resources information and advice, maps trends in working patterns through surveys and research.

Joint Negotiating Committee for Chief Officers of Local Authorities

EO, Layden Hse, London EC1M 5QU;
URL www.lg-employers.gov.uk;
E-mail individual.name@lg-employers.gov.uk; Tel 020 7296 6600
Secretary (Employers')   Charles Nolda

Joint Negotiating Committee for Justices' Clerks

Secretary (Employers')   Charles Nolda
Layden Hse, 76–86 Turnmill St, London EC1M 5LG; Tel 020 7296 6600
Secretary (Officers' Side)   Alan Leighton
c/o 1PMS, 75-79 York Rd, London, SE1 7AQ; Tel 020 7902 6000

Joint Negotiating Committee for Magistrates' Courts Staff

Secretary (Employers' Side)   Charles Nolda
Layden Hse, 76–86 Turnmill St, London EC1M 5LG; Tel 020 7296 6600
Secretary (Trade Union Side)   Rosie Eagleson
Association of Magistrial Officers, 1 Fellmongers' Path, 176 Tower Bridge Rd, London SE1 3LY; Tel 020 7403 2244

Joint Negotiating Committee for Teachers in Residential Establishments

Secretary (Employers' Side)   Charles Nolda
Employers Organisation, Layden Hse, 76–86 Turnmill St, London EC1M 5LG; Tel 020 7296 6600; Fax 020 7296 6666
Secretary (Staff Side)   Barry Fawcett
Hamilton Hse, Mabledon Pl, London WC1H 9BD; Tel 020 7388 6191

Joint Negotiating Committee for Youth and Community Workers

Secretary (Employers' Side)   Charles Nolda
Employers' Organisation, Layden Hse, 76–86 Turnmill St, London EC1M 5LG; Tel 020 7296 6600; Fax 020 7296 6666
Secretary (Staff Side)   Barry Fawcett
Hamilton Hse, Mabledon Pl, London WC1H 9BD; Tel 020 7388 6191

National Joint Council for Local Government Services

Incorporating the National Joint Council for Local Authorities' Administrative, Professional, Technical and Clerical Services, the National Joint Council for Local Authorities' Services (Manual Workers) (England and Wales), and the Residential and Allied Staffs Committee.
Secretary (Employers' Side)   Charles Nolda
Layden Hse, 76–86 Turnmill St, London EC1M 5LG; Tel 020 7296 6600
Secretary (Trade Union Side – TGWU)   Jack Dromey
Secretary (Trade Union Side – GMB)   Mick Graham
Secretary (Trade Union Side – UNISON)   Heather Wakefield

National Joint Council for Workshops for the Blind

Secretary (Employers' Side)   Charles Nolda
Layden Hse, 76–86 Turnmill St, London EC1M 5LG; Tel 020 7296 6600
Secretary (Trade Union Side)   Joe Mann
National League of the Blind and Disabled, Central Office, Swinton Hse, 324 Gray's Inn Rd, London WC1X 8DD; Tel 020 7837 6103

Scotland

Joint Negotiating Committee for Chief Officials of Local Authorities (Scotland)

Secretary (Employers' Side)   Vacancy
Rosebery Hse, 9 Haymarket Terr, Edinburgh EH12 5XZ; Tel 0131 474 9200
Secretary (Officials' Side)   J. Di Paola
Unison, Douglas Hse, Edinburgh EH4 3UR; Tel 0131 226 2662

Scottish Joint Council for Local Goverment Employees

Secretary (Employers' Side)   O. Aitken
Rosebery Hse, 9 Haymarket Terr, Edinburgh EH12 5XZ; Tel 0131 474 9200
Secretary (Staff Side)   J. Di Paola
Douglas Hse, 60 Belford Rd, Edinburgh EH4 3UQ; Tel 0131 226 2662

Scottish Joint Negotiating Committee for Local Government employees

Secretary (Employers' Side)   O. Aitken
Rosebery Hse, 9 Haymarket Terr, Edinburgh EH12 5XZ; Tel 0131 474 9200
Secretary (Trade Unions')   Robert Parker
Fountain Hse, 1/3 Woodside Cres, Glasgow G3 7UJ; Tel 0141 332 8641

Scottish Joint Negotiating Committee for Teaching Staff in School Education (SJNC/SE)

Secretary (Management Side)   D. Brown
Rosebery Hse, 9 Haymarket Terr, Edinburgh EH12 5XZ; Tel 0131 474 9200
Secretary (Teachers' Side)   K. Wimbor
46 Moray Pl, Edinburgh EH3 6BH; Tel 0131 225 6244

21

Trades Unions

Association of Teachers and Lecturers (ATL)

7 Northumberland St, London WC2N 5RD;
URL www.askatl.org.uk; E-mail info@atl.org.uk; Tel 020 7930 6441; Fax 020 7930 1359
General Secretary   Mary Bousted, BA(Hons), MA, PhD
Teachers' and Lecturers' trade union and professional association with membership throughout England, Wales and Northern Ireland.

Association of University Teachers

Egmont Hse, 25–31 Tavistock Pl, London WC1H 9UT;
E-mail hg@aut.org.uk; Tel 020 7670 9700
General Secretary

British Union of Social Work Employees (BUSWE)

BUSWE Hse, 208 Middleton Rd, Crumpsall, Manchester M8 4NA; E-mail buswe@buswe.fsnet.co.uk; Tel 0161 720 7727; Fax 0161 795 4524
Founded in 1971 BUSWE is a fully certified independent trade union. It is the only specialist trade union encompassing all aspects and branches of the social work profession. Concerned with achieving fair and equitable pay and conditions of service for all social work employees and with the professional development of all aspects of social work. BUSWE has recognition arrangements with NSPCC and throughout the voluntary sector and with some local authorities.

Community and Youth Workers Union (CYWU)

302 The Argent Centre, 60 Frederick St, Birmingham, West
   Midlands B1 3HS; URL www.cywu.org.uk;
   E-mail kerry@cywu.org.uk; Tel 0121 233 3344; Fax 0121
   233 3345
President   Bob Allen
General Secretary   Doug Nicholls
Specialist trade union for mentors, personal advisers youth,
community, and play workers, representing the majority of
full and part-time staff in national and local negotiations.

GMB Trades Union

22–24 Worple Rd, Wimbledon, London SW19 4DD;
   E-mail gmb.research@geo2.poptel.org.uk; Tel 020 8947
   3131; Fax 020 8944 6552
The Union has a membership of over 700 000 and is the
fourth largest in the UK. Approximately one third of the
Union's membership is employed in the public services.
The union is represented on the following Negotiating
Councils in Local Government: National Joint Council for
Local Government Services; Joint Negotiating Committee
for Local Authority Craft and Associated Employees. The
Union is represented on the following Negotiating
Councils in the Health Services: General Whitley Council;
Administrative and Clerical Staffs Council; Ancillary Staffs
Council; Nurses and Midwives Council; Ambulance
Council; Maintenance Staff Council.

NATFHE – The University and College Lecturers' Union

27 Britannia St, London WC1X 9JP;
   URL www.natfhe.org.uk; E-mail hq@natfhe.org.uk;
   Tel 020 7837 3636; Fax 020 7278 9383
NATFHE represents lecturers in post-school further, higher
and adult education. Approximately 85% of all full-time
lecturers in the services belong to the Association which is
affiliated to the Trades Union Congress. The pay and
conditions of service of further education lecturers are
determined by the Association of Colleges and of higher
education lecturers by the Universities and Colleges
Employers' Association. NATFHE is the major organisation
on the teachers' side in negotiations with these bodies and
is also the major FE association on the Teachers'
Superannuation Working Party which negotiates teachers'
pensions. NATFHE represents the views of FHE lecturers
on many national and local educational bodies and has a
large number of specialist subject sections to which
lecturers in particular disciplines can belong.

National Association of Schoolmasters/Union of Women Teachers (NASUWT)

Registered Offices and Administrative Headquarters;
   Hillscourt Education Centre, Rose Hill, Rednal,
   Birmingham, West Midlands B45 8RS;
   URL www.teachersunion.org.uk;
   E-mail nasuwt@mail.nasuwt.org.uk; Tel 0121 453 6150;
   Fax 0121 457 6208
President   Terry Bladen
Hon Treasurer   Sue Rogers
General Secretary   Eamon O'Kane, MA, DipEd
Deputy General Secretary   Chris Keates
Assistant General Secretary   Jerry Bartlett
Assistant Secretary (Salaries and Pensions)   Brian Clegg, BSc
Assistant Secretary (Education)   Olwyn Elizabeth Gunn,
   DipEd(Adv)
Assistant Secretary (Membership Services)   Paul MacLachlan,
   BSc
Assistant Secretary (Industrial Relations)   Joe Boone
Assistant Secretary (Legal)   Mary Howard, BA
Assistant Secretary (Finance)   Jane O'Callaghan
Assistant Secretary (Personnel and Development)
   Nick Parker
Assistant Secretary (Policy and Equality)   Patrick Roach

National Society for Education in Art and Design (NSEAD)

The Gatehouse, Corsham Crt, Corsham, Wiltshire
   SN13 0BZ; URL www.nsead.org.uk;
   E-mail johnsteers@nsead.org; Tel 01249 714825;
   Fax 01249 716138
General Secretary   J. Steers, NDD, ATC, DAE, PhD
Aims to have a significant influence in all areas of art and
design education; to have representation on important
national and regional bodies; to continually define and
reassess policies in all areas of art, craft, and design
education; to maintain contacts with other societies and
groups which have an interest in these topics; to safeguard
the interests and protect the employment of members by
providing legal advice and assistance in professional
matters whenever possible or desirable.
Publications
Journal of Art and Design Education (Blackwells)
published three times per annum.

National Union of Teachers (NUT)

Hamilton Hse, Mabledon Pl, London WC1H 9BD; Tel 020
   7388 6191; Fax 020 7387 8458
The largest teachers' organisation in England and Wales. As
well as representing teachers in mainstream education, it
represents teachers in community and youth work, special
schools, intermediate treatment and CHES observation and
assessment centres.

Professional Association of Nursery Nurses (PANN)

2 St. James' Crt, Friar Gate, Derby DE1 1BT;
   URL www.pat.org.uk; E-mail pann@pat.org.uk;
   Tel 01332 372 337; Fax 01332 290310
General Secretary   Jean Gemmell
Professional Officer (PANN Section)   T. Pritchard
Chair (PANN Section)   D. Lawson
Vice-Chair (PANN Section)   L. Porter
PANN is a separate section within the Professional
Association of Teachers (PAT). As a section it is run by
nursery nurses for nursery nurses and promotes
professionalism within nursery nursing. Working within
the larger PAT it is a trade union able to offer protection
and support to members.

Professional Association of Teachers (PAT)

(Incorporating the Professional Association of Nursery
Nurses – PANN)
2 St. James' Crt, Friar Gate, Derby DE1 1BT;
   URL www.pat.org.uk; E-mail hq@pat.org.uk; Tel 01332
   372337; Fax 01332 290310
General Secretary   Jean Gemmell, BSc, BEd
Senior Professional Officer (Education)   Alison Johnston,
   BEd
Professional Officer (PANN)   Tricia Pritchard
A trade union with around 35 000 members including
school teachers, further and higher education lecturers,
education support staff, nursery nurses and nannies
throughout the UK. The Association promotes
professionalism and has a rule that prohibits members
from taking strike action. PAT also has an office in
Edinburgh.

Secondary Heads Association (SHA)

(Formed from the amalgamation of the Association of
Headmistresses and the Head Masters' Association)
130 Regent Rd, Leicester LE1 7PG; E-mail info@sha.org.uk;
   Tel 0116 299 1122; Fax 0116 299 1123
President   Anne Welsh
George Stephenson High School, Southgate, Killingworth,
   Newcastle upon Tyne, Tyne and Wear NE12 0SA;
   Tel 0191 200 8347; Fax 0191 200 8349

Vice-President Tim Andrew

Chesham High School, White Hill, Chesham, Buckinghamshire HP5 1BA; Tel 01494 782854; Fax 01673 775414

SHA is the professional association exclusively for leaders of secondary schools and colleges.

Transport and General Workers Union (TGWU)

128 Theobald's Rd, Holburn, London WC1X 8TN; Tel 020 7611 2500; Fax 020 7611 2555

General Secretary Bill Morris

Deputy General Secretary Margaret Prosser

Britain's biggest general union with 900 000 members in workplaces across the UK. In 1999, five Sectors were established to represent today's workplace and workers: food and agriculture, manufacturing, services, transport, and women, race and equalities. There are also eight Transport and General Regions across the British Isles, each with its own committee, ensuring a strong regional input. Sectors and Regions come together at the General Executive Council.

UNISON

1 Mabledon Pl, London WC1H 9AJ;
URL www.unison.org.uk;
E-mail localgovt@unison.co.uk; Tel 020 7551 1121;
Fax 020 7551 1195

General Secretary Dave Prentis

National Officer (Social Services) Owen Davies

UNISON is the UK's largest union with 1.4 million members including 350 000 in social work and social care.

National Association of Teachers of Travellers (NATT)

Avon ConsortiumTraveller Education Service,
Charborough Rd, Filton, Bristol BS34 7RA;
URL www.natt.org; Tel 0117 969 0534; Fax 0117 969 0535

President Marion R. Rowlands (Avon TES)

Professional Association organised and run by teachers working with Travelling Children in Support Services and mainstream schools.

Dyslexia in Scotland

Dyslexia in Scotland, Stirling Business Centre, Stirling FK8 2DZ; URL www.dyslexia-in-scotland.org;
E-mail info@dyslexia-in-scotland.org; Tel 01786 446650;
Fax 01786 471235

Other Professional Organisations

Elizabeth Finn Trust

1 Derry St, London W8 5HY;
URL www.elizabethfinntrust.org.uk;
E-mail jonathan.welfare@elizabethfinn.org.uk; Tel 020 7396 6700; Fax 020 7396 6739

Chief Executive Jonathan Welfare

Runs care homes and offers financial assistance to those in need.

Printers' Charitable Corporation

7 Cantelupe Mews, Cantelupe Rd, East Grinstead, West Sussex RH19 3BG;
URL printerscharitablecorporation.co.uk;
E-mail sandra@pccorp.fsnet.co.uk; Tel 01342 318882;
Fax 01342 318887

Sheltered housing in Basildon and Bletchley and a nursing home in Bletchley. Financial assistance for eligible people from the printing industry. Applications to the Director and Secretary.

The Royal Scottish Agricultural Benevolent Institution

Ingliston, Edinburgh EH28 8NB; URL www.rsabi.org.uk;
E-mail rsabi@rsabi.org.uk; Tel 0131 333 1023; Fax 0131 333 1027

Provides financial in kind help, welfare advice, friendship and support to any person in difficulty who is or has been in agriculture, fish farming, rural estate work, horticulture and forestry in Scotland and their dependants.

Schoolmistresses and Governesses Benevolent Institution

SGBI Office, Queen Mary Hse, Pk Rd, Chislehurst, Kent BR7 5PY

Director and Secretary

Helps ladies who have been employed, or self-employed, for the major part of their working lives in all facets of education.

Social Workers' Educational Trust (British Association of Social Workers)

16 Kent St, Birmingham, West Midlands B5 6RD; Tel 0121 622 3911

Honorary Secretary Gill Aslett

Assists qualified social workers with two years experience, who are undertaking further studies and research.

The Theatrical Guild

Charity Number: 206669

PO Box 22712, London N22 5WQ;
URL www.the-theatrical-guild.org.uk;
E-mail admin@the-theatrical-guild.org.uk; Tel 020 8889 7570

Chief Administrator K. Nichols

Helps everyone who has worked in the professional theatre, especially backstage and front of house staff and, in conjunction with other theatrical charities, actors and actresses. Students need not apply.

21

Education and Training in Health, Welfare and Social Work

22

- National Bodies
- Other Training Institutions
- Universities and University Colleges
- Colleges and Institutes of Higher Education
- Colleges of Further Education
- Adult Colleges

Education and Training in Health, Welfare and Social Work

National Bodies

Health Professions Council (HPC)

Park Hse, 184 Kennington Park Rd, London SE11 4BU;
URL www.hpc-uk.org; E-mail info@hpc-uk.org; Tel 020
7582 0866; Fax 020 7820 9684
The HPC is a council set up to safeguard the health and
well-being of patients using the services of the health
professions it regulates and to ensure that the public has
access to and is treated by health professionals who are
qualified and competent.

IHCD Health and Care Limited

IHCD, St. Bartholomew's Crt, Bristol BS1 5BT; Tel 0117 929
1029
IHCD Health and Care Limited is an autonomous business
unit within Edexcel Foundation. IHCD Health and Care
Limited maintains its own identity and offers health and
care qualifications for employers.

Nursing and Midwifery Council (NMC)

23 Portland Pl, London W1B 1PZ; URL www.nmc-uk.org

Social Care Institute for Excellence (SCIE)

1st Fl, Goldings Hse, 2 Hay's La, London SE1 2HB;
URL www.scie.org.uk; Tel 020 7089 6840; Fax 020 7089
6841
Chair   Dr Jane Campbell
Chief Executive   Bill Killgallon
Head (Corporate Services)   Victoria McNeill
The Social Care Institute for Excellence (SCIE) is an
independent body established in October 2001 to raise
standards of practice and improve outcomes for service
users across the social care sector.
Its role, in partnership with users and other stakeholders, is
to review the knowledge available from academic research,
user and carer expertise and current good practice, and
make it available electronically and in other media; develop
guidelines and tools to improve practice and service
provision; and to promote the use of knowledge to support
change in social care organisations.

Other Training Institutions

Adlerian Society (of the United Kingdom) and the Institute for Individual Psychology

73 South Ealing Rd, London W5 4QR;
URL www.adleriansociety.co.uk; Tel 020 8567 8360;
Fax 020 8567 8360
Hon Treasurer   Ann Hariades

Contact (Buckinghamshire)   Lilian Beattie; Tel 01296 622153
Contact (Cambridge)   Anthea Millar; Tel 01223 314827
Contact (Cumbria)   Ken Tyllsen; Tel 01539 620952
Contact (London)   Ann Hariades; Tel 020 8997 4163
Contact (Oxford)   Grendon Haines; Tel 01865 727760
To advance public education in the work of Alfred Adler
via lectures, workshops, training courses for counsellors,
ongoing therapeutic groups, a residential weekend and
parent support groups, teacher support groups, part-time
training to run parent and teacher support groups, family
counselling, individual counselling.
Training courses, lectures, workshops and referrals are
available for various areas.

AFTA Thought Training Consultants Limited

Unit C8–10 Brunswick Business Centre, Brunswick Dock,
Liverpool, Merseyside L3 4BD;
URL www.aftathought.co.uk;
E-mail info@aftathought.co.uk; Tel 0151 708 7774;
Fax 0151 709 3416
Director   Mary Austin
Director   Dawn Taylor
Formed in 1989, AFTA Thought Training Consultants
design and deliver training and related services to the
public sector. Specialises in the following areas of training
provision: Managing Violence or Aggression within the
Workplace; Managing Challenging Behaviour (for
residential workers and foster carers); Child Protection,
Promoting and Ensuring Safe Working Practice within a
Care Context; Domestic Violence Awareness; Bullying and
Harassment; Child Protection Working Together, NVQ
related training, Protection of Vulnerable Adults; Managing
Diversity.
AFTA Thought also provides a recruitment and selection
service specifically aimed at agencies wishing to assess and
recruit staff who will be working alongside children and
vulnerable adults.

British Association for Counselling and Psychotherapy (BACP)

BACP Hse, 35–37 Albert St, Rugby, Warwickshire
CV21 2SG; URL www.bacp.co.uk;
E-mail bacp@bacp.co.uk; Tel 0870 443 5252; Fax 0870 443
5160
Chair   Ms V. Potter
Deputy Chair   Ms N. Barden
President   Dame Fiona Caldicott
Divisions   Mrs G. Green
Association for Pastoral and Spiritual Care and Counselling
Tony Bryer
Association for University and College Counselling
John Cowley
Association for Counselling at Work   Barry McInnes
Counselling in Education   Mark Prever
Faculty of Healthcare Counsellors and Psychotherapists
Shane Buckeridge

22

Personal Relationship Groupwork   Justine Oldfield-Rowell Represents counselling and psychotherapy at national and international level, aiming to promote counselling and psychotherapy throughout society and to raise standards of training and practice. Provides support for counsellors, psychotherapists and those using counselling skills working in areas such as education, medical settings and the workplace. BACP produces directories on counselling and training resources and provides information on these and other subjects. Publications include the journals Counselling and Psychotherapy Journal (CPJ), Counselling and Psychotherapy Research (CPR) and Healthcare Counselling and Psychotherapy Journal (HCPJ). Also available are information sheets and booklets on specific counselling and psychotherapy topics.
BACP Information Office can give information or letter (please send A5 sae) to members of the public who want to be put in touch with counsellors, psychotherapists or counselling agencies on a national basis.

British Association of Psychotherapists

37 Mapesbury Rd, London NW2 4HJ;
    URL www.bap-psychotherapy.org;
    E-mail mail@bap-psychotherapy.org; Tel 020 8452 9823;
    Fax 020 8452 0310
Chief Executive   B.E. Ormerod

For Dementia Training

6 Camden High St, London NW1 0JH;
    URL www.fordementia.org.uk;
    E-mail training@fordementia.org.uk; Tel 020 7874 7222;
    Fax 020 7874 7219
Director   M. Minoletti
Provides training courses for anyone looking after older people, at home, in hospital or in residential homes. The aim is to improve the quality of care by increasing the knowledge and skills of carers. In house and open courses are available.

CHT (Community Housing and Therapy)

see Chapter 25, Mental Health

Conference Centre@NCH

Princess Alice Dr, Chester Rd North, Sutton Coldfield, West
    Midlands B73 6RD; Tel 0121 355 4615; Fax 0121 354 4717
Manager (Conference Centre)   Jackie Casewell
The centre provides five meeting rooms for conferences and training courses, and can offer a tailor-made package to suit customers' individual requirements.

Co-operative College

Stanford Hall, Loughborough, Leicestershire LE12 5QR;
    E-mail alan.wilkins@co-opcollege.zee.web.co.uk;
    Tel 01509 857204
Head (Learning)   Alan Wilkins
Offers six month residential Accelerated Access Programme for mature voluntary/community activists. No formal academic qualifications required. Scholarships available. Also an extensive NVQ programme that may be suitable for voluntary and community organisations.

Dramatherapy Programmes, University of Surrey Roehampton

The University of Surrey, Roehampton, Southlands College,
    London SW15 5SL; URL www.roehampton.ac.uk;
    E-mail enquiries@roehampton.ac.uk; Tel 020 8392 3232
Programme Convener   Ditty Dokter
Provides individual and group dramatherapy which is applied in treatment and rehabilitation for people with mental health problems; provides training for professionals and resources for institutions.

Family Institute, Cardiff

School of Care Sciences, Glyn Tol Campus, University of
    Glamorgan, Pontypridd, CF37 1DL; Tel 01443 483820
Senior Lecturer in Psychotherapy   Brenda Cox
Senior Lecturer in Psychotherapy   Billy Hardy
Senior Lecturer in Psychotherapy   Jeff Faris
Provides training in family therapy from introductory to advanced levels and in advanced counselling and supervision; publishes and engages in research. Independent psychotherapy and consultation service to the public.

Foxes Academy

The Esplanade, Minehead, Somerset TA24 5QP; Tel 01643
    704450; Fax 01643 708249
Contact   S. Jenkins
Contact   Maureen Tyler-Moore
Residential training hotel for people with learning disabilities. Accredited three year course.

Framework

20 Shawclough Dr, Rochdale, Lancashire OL12 7HG;
    URL www.framework.org.uk;
    E-mail penny@framework.org.uk; Tel 01706 648067;
    Fax 01706 648067
Framework is a small group of independent consultants working in the not-for-profit sector. It is interested in improving effectiveness in organisations – including action to change management practice, to handle conflicts, to surface and deal with difficult emotions, plan better strategies and develop quality and equality. It operates locally, regionally, nationally and internationally.

Gerda Boyesen Centre for Biodynamic Psychology

15 The Ridgeway, Acton, London W3 8LW; Tel 020 8993
    5777
Chair   Gerda Boyesen
Training Director   Ziggi Bach
Secretary   Lisa Dodson
Dedicated to the teaching of the methods of Gerda Boyesen, founder of Biodynamic Psychology.

The Gestalt Centre

62 Paul St, London EC2A 4NA;
    URL www.gestaltcentre.co.uk;
    E-mail mail@gestaltcentre.co.uk; Tel 020 7613 4480;
    Fax 020 7613 4737
Centre Co-ordinator   Jacqueline Wearn
Provides training in counselling and psychotherapy, from foundation courses to postgraduate level. Member of UK Council for Psychotherapy and British Association for Counselling and Psychotherapy.

Gestalt South London

28 Wandle Rd, London SW17 7DW; Answerphone 020 8767
    9857
Psychotherapist   Anna Farrow
Psychotherapist   Barbara Stones
Psychotherapist   Sonia Malikban
Psychotherapist   Jutta Ten Merkel
Psychotherapist   Sally McLaughlin
Psychotherapist   Carol Siederer
Offers psychotherapy/counselling for individuals and couples. It also provides clinical supervision for experienced and trainee psychotherapists.

Groupwork Consultation and Training Ltd (GCT)

PO Box 363, Southsea, Hampshire PO4 0YP;
    URL www.groupct.demon.co.uk;
    E-mail dave@groupct.demon.co.uk; Tel 023 9275 0030
Director   David Warren-Holland

Courses are held at various venues in London and are also available on an in-service basis. Courses include a three-day introduction to basic groupwork skills; intensive four-day intermediate level course; and a year-long accredited advanced groupwork certificate of training awarded by Greenwich College, recognised as efficient by the British Accreditation Council. Short courses include offending behaviour, drug and alcohol problems, young people leaving care, supervision, working with resistant clients, co-working and leadership, anger management, cognitive behavioural groupwork, groupwork with perpetrators of domestic violence.

Guild of Psychotherapists

47 Nelson Sq, London SE1 0QA;
E-mail adminguild@btopenworld.com; Tel 020 7401 3260; Fax 020 7401 3472
Chair   J. Fisher
Administrative Secretary   G. Graham
Administrative Secretary   C. Butler
Promotes the relief of psychological illness or disorder by providing psychotherapy for the public benefit. Also education and training in analytical psychotherapy. Psychoanalytic psychotherapy training (minimum of four years training) leads to membership of the Guild and UKCP registration.

Institute for Psychotherapy and Social Studies

West Hill Hse, 6 Swains La, London N6 6QU;
Answerphone 0171 284 4762
Chair (Training)   Veronica Norburn
Vice-Chair   Sue Sntel
Concerned with the training of psychoanalytic psychotherapists; offers psychotherapy to individuals and couples through network of qualified members and trainees. (Fees are on a sliding scale and some low-cost therapy is available.)

Institute of Family Therapy

24–32 Stephenson Way, London NW1 2HX;
URL www.instituteoffamilytherapy.org.uk;
E-mail ift@psyc.bbk.ac.uk; Tel 020 7391 9150; Fax 020 7391 9169
Provides postgraduate training in family and couple therapy as well as a clinical service to families and couples facing a range of relationship and personal problems.

Institute of Group Analysis

1 Daleham Gdns, London NW3 5BY;
URL www.groupanalysis.org;
E-mail iga@igalondon.org.uk; Tel 020 7431 2693; Fax 020 7431 7246
Chair of Council   D. Vincent

Institute of Psychiatry

De Crespigny Pk, Denmark Hill, London SE5 8AF;
URL www.iop.kcl.ac.uk/iop/home.shtml; Tel 020 7848 0335; Fax 020 7848 0620
Dean   Dr G. Szmukler
Secretary   Laurence Benson
The Institute of Psychiatry is a school of King's College London, University of London and works jointly with the South London and Maudsley NHS Trust to provide research and postgraduate teaching in psychiatry, psychology and allied disciplines, including basic and clinical neurosciences. The Institute is recognised by the World Health Organization as a collaborating centre for research and training in mental health.
Its mission is to promote excellence in the research, development and teaching of psychiatry and its allied subjects and to apply and disseminate this knowledge with the aim of preventing mental disorder and the development of treatment for the relief of suffering.

Institute of Psychoanalysis

Byron Hse, 112a Shirland Rd, London W9 2EQ;
URL www.psychoanalysis.org.uk; Tel 020 7563 5000
Charitable institute providing building and staff to run the British Psycho-Analytical Society and to provide treatment; provides training to become a qualified psychoanalyst and conducts research.

Institute of Transactional Analysis

PO Box 1101, Wigton CA7 9YH; URL www.ita.org.uk;
E-mail admin@ita.org.uk; Tel 0845 009 9101
Administrator   Charlie King
Council Secretary   Mark Widdowson
Advances the education of the public with regard to the study, theory and practice of transactional analysis and its application in accordance with the recognised standards of professional competence in the practice of transactional analysis in the United Kingdom of Great Britain and Northern Ireland.
List of trainers and regional practitioners available from the Institute; trainers provide own training programmes which may lead to certified Transactional Analyst in clinical, educational, organisational and counselling specialisations (3–5 years part-time).

Laban Centre London

Laurie Gr, New Cross, London SE14 6NH;
URL www.laban.co.uk; E-mail info@laban.co.uk; Tel 020 8692 4070; Fax 020 8694 8749
Course Leader   V. Jobbins

Lincoln Clinic and Centre for Psychotherapy

19 Abbeville Mews, 88 Clapham Park Rd, London SW4 7BX; URL www.lincoln-psychotherapy.org.uk;
E-mail training@lincoln-psychotherapy.org.uk; Tel 020 7978 1110; Fax 020 7720 4721
Referrals Psychotherapist (Reduced Fee Scheme)   N. Griffiths
Referrals Psychotherapist (Full Fee)   S. Cowley
Administrator   A. Amoah
Administrator (Training)   B. Scally; Tel 020 7978 1110
Training in psychoanalytic psychotherapy; consultation and assessment for patients with emotional difficulties who feel that psychotherapy would be helpful; psychoanalytical psychotherapy for patients for whom this is appropriate.

London Association of Primal Psychotherapists

West Hill Hse, 6 Swains La, London N6 6QU; Tel 020 7267 9616; Fax 020 7267 9616
Psychotherapist   Susan Cowan-Jenssen
Psychotherapist-Training Co-ordinator   Marsha Nodelman
Provides psychotherapy in a safe and contained environment where feelings can be experienced and integrated. The Association believes that it is the unexpressed feelings of earlier traumas and traumatic relationships that causes suffering.

London Clinic of Psychoanalysis

112a Shirland Rd, London W9 2EQ;
URL www.psychoanalysisclinic.org.uk; Tel 020 7563 5002
Clinic Director   P. Crockatt
Provides a clinical psychoanalytic service with contributions according to patient's financial situation. The staff are senior therapists completing a psychoanalytic training.

Maca (Mental After Care Association)

1st Fl, Lincoln Hse, 296–302 High Holborn, London WC1V 7JH; URL www.maca.org.uk;
E-mail maca@maca.org.uk; Tel 020 7061 3400; Fax 020 7061 3401
Training available to outside agencies.

22

Metanoia Institute

Registered Charity No. 1050175
13 North Common Rd, London W5 2QB;
   URL www.metanoia.ac.uk; E-mail info@metanoia.ac.uk;
   Tel 020 8579 2505; Fax 020 8566 4349
Counselling and psychotherapy training institute.
Metanoia offers nationally and internationally accredited
diploma, MSc, Doctorate and other postgraduate courses in
a number of counselling and psychotherapy approaches:
person-centred, transactional analysis, Gestalt, integrative,
and counselling psychology. Graduation from the
psychotherapy courses leads to UKCP registration. The BA,
MSc and Doctorate are offered in collaboration with
Middlesex University.
All courses are modular and can be studied part-time to fit
with other life commitments. Attendance at an
introductory workshop is a prerequisite of most courses.
Metanoia operates an Accreditation of Prior Learning
scheme by means of which students may apply to join the
BA/Diploma or MSc courses part way through a training
programme.
Also available is the Metanoia Counselling and
Psychotherapy Service offering a confidential and
professional service for the local community which
provides a quality assessment and support at lower cost,
and the Metanoia Referral Directory which is intended to
assist people who are seeking counselling or
psychotherapy.

The Minster Centre

Registered Charity No. 104205217 Mapesbury Rd, London
NW2 4HU; URL www.minstercentre.org.uk;
E-mail info@minstercentre.org.uk; Tel 020 8450 3311;
Fax 020 8450 1177
Director   Helen Davis
Administrator   Tina Hunt
Co-ordinator   Marion Fitzpatrick
A training and accrediting member of the Humanistic and
Integrative Psychotherapy Section of the United Kingdom
Council for Psychotherapy (UKCP).
A member of the British Association of Counselling and
Psychotherapy (BACP). The training has been accepted by
the BAC Course Recognition Scheme.
Offers psychotherapy and counselling for individuals and
groups. Specialised counselling projects for refugees and
for male perpetrators of domestic violence and their ex
partners. Full and low-cost psychotherapy/counselling.

National Society for Epilepsy (NSE)

see Chapter 23

National Society for the Prevention of Cruelty to Children

42 Curtain Rd, London EC2A 3NH; Tel 020 7825 2500

National Child Protection Training Group
see NSPCC main entry in Chapter 13
3 Gilmour Cl, Beaumont Leys, Leicester LE4 1EZ; Tel 0116
234 7200
Head of Child Protection Training   E. Hendry
A range of child protection training and development
services for individuals and agencies who work with
children. These include an annual programme of
conferences and short courses, an accredited post-
qualifying course, Training for Trainers, specially designed
training delivered on-site, training packs and videos. A
Training Resource Unit is provided for reference purposes,
free of charge. The Training Group is a Registered Provider
under the CCETSW Scheme.

NSPCC National Training Centre
3 Gilmour Cl, Beaumont Leys, Leicester LE4 1EZ; Tel 0116
234 7200; Fax 0116 234 0464

Centre Manager   F. Payne
The centre provides facilities for courses, conferences,
meetings and exhibitions including residential provision.

Nordoff-Robbins Music Therapy Centre

2 Lissenden Gdns, London NW5 1PP;
   URL www.nordoff-robbins.org.uk;
   E-mail admin@nordoff-robbins.org.uk; Tel 020 7267
   4496; Fax 020 7267 4369
Head (Training)   Dr Julie Sutton
The centre is a registered charity providing weekly music
therapy sessions for over 300 children, adolescents and
adults with a wide range of special needs, including
learning disability, emotional and behavioural difficulties
and mental health problems. The centre also offers a two
year professional training leading to a Master of Music
Therapy degree, and short introductory courses and
conferences.

Pellin Institute

15 Killyon Rd, London SW8 2XS; URL www.pellin.org;
   E-mail people@pellin.org; Tel 020 7720 4499
Director/Member (UK Council on Psychotherapy)
   Peter Fleming
Training in the techniques and methods of Contribution
Training Psychotherapy and Counselling and Gestalt
Therapy. Graduates are able to apply these practical skills
to all professions involved with social, emotional and
mental health.

Philadelphia Association

4 Marty's Yard, 17 Hampstead High St, London NW3 1QW;
   URL philadelphia-association.co.uk;
   E-mail paoffice@globalnet.co.uk; Tel 020 7794 2652;
   Fax 020 7794 2652
Hon Secretary   P. Gordon
Hon Treasurer   R. Mayo
Administrator   Lavinia Hunter
Aims to relieve mental distress through low-cost
residential community households and private
psychotherapy service. Provides educational forum,
publications and training in psychotherapy and
phenomenology, accredited by UKCP.

Prospect Training and Consultancy

3 Outram Rd, Felpham, West Sussex PO22 7AL; Tel 01243
   841211; Fax 01243 841211
Principal Partner and Course Director   C. Hardy, MA,
   BScSoc(Hons), CQSW, DipSocPol and SocAdmin, Ce
Principal Partner and Course Director   W. Stafford, MA,
   BASoc(Hons), CQSW, DipinAppSocStudies
Prospect exists with the aim of providing specialist training
and consultancy support for professional and managerial
staff in all the welfare services, and their agencies, along
with an independent social work service to clients. Prospect
continues to build on 11 years of experience to offer
provisions, some of which, such as providing a full
offenders work training, make it unique. Aims are achieved
through the following activities: a professional updating
and specialist education, through courses in the fields of
child protection, work with offenders, and residential and
daycare with children and young people; making this
training accessible nationwide by using open learning,
work-based programmes in full or short course formats;
courses that span from post-qualifying to NVQ (including
for managers) in order to give a comprehensive provision;
specialist child protection, inspections and related work
with schools. This and the NVQ work is conducted jointly
with the Professional Development Matters (PDM)
partnership. Independent social work, as well as Guardian
ad Litem work. Consultancy for managers and/or staff
ranging from policy and practice to management buy-outs.
Publications – articles for journals, books, journal and book

editing – and sessions at conferences, including the total organisation if required. Drawing on a wide network of specialists for the most relevant inputs to those using these services.

Quantum Care Ltd

4 Silver Crt, Watchmead, Hertfordshire AL7 1TS;
 URL www.quantumcare.co.uk;
 E-mail info@quantumcare.co.uk; Tel 01707 393293;
 Fax 01707 368250
Chief Executive   Maria Ball
Director (Finance and Business)   Nick Lee
Manager (Training)   Sue Harrison
Provider of residential and other care services for older people and a not-for-profit company. Training for front-line care staff in local authorities or voluntary organisations to ensure effective delivery of care services to a wide range of client services. Training provided by established care provider in modern training suite. Tailor-made courses can be provided to individual organisations.

Reconstruct Ltd

26 Sarum Complex, Salisbury Rd, Uxbridge, Greater London UB8 2RZ; URL www.reconstuct.co.uk;
 E-mail office@reconstruct.co.uk; Tel 01895 251352;
 Fax 01895 251852
Reconstruct offers a range of services to social services departments including training, consultancy, project management and the organisation of independent visiting, assessments and chairing.

Redwood Women's Training Association

20 North St, Middleton, Manchester M24 6BD; Tel 0161 643 1986
UK Administrator   Julie Phillips

Regent's College

School of Psychotherapy and Counselling, Inner Circle, Regent's Pk, London NW1 4NS; URL www.spc.ac.uk;
 E-mail spc@regents.ac.uk; Tel 020 7487 7406; Fax 020 7487 7446
Academic Dean   Prof Ernesto Spinelli

Richmond Fellowship Training and Consultancy Services

80 Holloway Rd, London N7 8JG;
 URL www.richmondfellowship.org.uk;
 E-mail peter.allen@richmondfellowship.org.uk; Tel 020 7697 3300; Fax 020 7697 3301
Head (Training and Consultancy Services)   Peter Allen
Tailored training and consultation in different mental health issues, team building, groupwork and supervision. Also offers the two year Richmond Fellowship Diploma in Community Mental Health accredited by Middlesex University.

RNIB Scotland, Edinburgh and the Lothians

12 Hillside Cres, Edinburgh EH7 5DZ;
 E-mail rniblothian@rnib.org.uk; Tel 0131 557 1004;
 Fax 0131 557 4001
Assistant Director (Community Services)   B.E. Merchant

The Sainsbury Centre for Mental Health

134–138 Borough High St, London SE1 1LB;
 URL www.scmh.org.uk; E-mail contact@scmh.org.uk;
 Tel 020 7403 8300; Fax 020 7403 9482
Conference and publications details on request. Registered Charity No. 1091156.

School of Social Work and RNIB Rehabilitation Studies

Faculty of Health and Community Care, University of Central England, Birmingham, West Midlands B42 2SU; Tel 0121 331 6405; Fax 0121 331 6592
Head   Prof Mark Doel
The School offers standard and flexible courses for specialist workers involved in rehabilitation work with blind and partially sighted people of all ages. Courses lead to a Diploma in Higher Education plus Diplomas in Rehabilitation Studies.
All courses lead to the award of a Diploma of Higher Education.

SESAME Institute

Christchurch, 27 Blackfriars Rd, London SE1 8NY;
 URL www.btinternet.com/ sesameuk;
 E-mail sesameinstituteuk@btinternet.com; Tel 020 7633 9690
Co-Director   Mary Smail
Co Director   Diana Cooper
Aims to research and promote the use of drama and movement in therapy and train practitioners in the Sesame Method.

Southwark Social Services Department/ South London and Maudsley NHS Trust/ Institute of Psychiatry, King's College London

Social Work and Social Care Section, Health Services Research Department, De Crespigny Pk, Denmark Hill, London SE5 8AF; Tel 020 7848 0150; Fax 020 7848 0530
Course Director   Dr Alan Rushton

Tacade

1 Hulme Pl, The Crescent, Salford, Greater Manchester M5 4QA; URL www.tacade.com;
 E-mail tacade@dial.pipex.com; Tel 0161 745 8925;
 Fax 0161 745 8923
Contact   L. Marland
Training, resources, information, consultancy and project management on preventive education and life skills.

Tavistock and Portman NHS Trust

120 Belsize La, London NW3 5BA; URL www.tavi-port.org;
 E-mail academic@tavi-port.org; Tel 020 7435 7111
Director (Academic Services)   Mary Joyce

The UK College for Complementary Health Care Studies

Wembley Centre for Health and Care, Barham Hse, 116 Chaplin Rd, Wembley, Greater London HA0 4UZ;
 E-mail info@ukcollege.com; Tel 020 8795 6178; Fax 020 8795 6179
Principal   M. Langford, SRN, RCNT, DipMed/Psych(Lond), DHP, MAPT(UK)
The college offers a range of part-time modular training programmes, offered only or to professional practitioner level, including counselling, hypnotherapy, reflexology, massage, aromatherapy etc. Qualifications include the BTEC Professional Development Certificate in Complementary Health Care, the Vocational Award International and Diploma in Reflexology and the City and Guilds and UK College Joint Skills Testing Certificate in Counselling and Hypnotherapy.

YMCA George Williams College

199 Freemasons Rd, Canning Town, London E16 3PY;
 URL www.ymca.ac.uk; E-mail m.crosby@ymca.ac.uk;
 Tel 020 7540 4900; Fax 020 7511 4900
Principal   Mary Crosby

22

Universities and University Colleges

England

University of Bath

Claverton Down, Bath, Bath and North East Somerset BA2 7AY; URL www.bath.ac.uk; Tel 01225 386212; Fax 01225 386872
Registrar   Jonathan Bursey, MSc

Centre for the Analysis of Social Policy
Professor (Social Policy)   Jane Millar

Research in Progress
Director   Prof J. Millar (family policy, tax credits)

Department of Social and Policy Sciences
Tel 01225 388388

The University of Birmingham

Edgbaston, Birmingham, West Midlands B15 2TT; Tel 0121 414 3344; (Estate Management Office) 0121 414 5950

Institute of Applied Social Studies
Head of Department   D. Stephenson
Director (Social Research)   Prof Marrian Barnes
The department conducts research within a broad range of topics in the areas of social policy and professional practice. Staff in the department have particular interests in service user perspectives and have developed collaborative research links with user and community groups as well as services delivery agencies.

Community, Play and Youth Studies Department
Head of Department/Manager (Programmes)   Amanda Grant
No. of students
260 (CPYW Department)

Marie Burnie House
Weoley Park Rd, Birmingham, West Midlands B29 6LL; Tel 0121 472 7245
Head of School   Prof Hywel Thomas
PA   Caroline Baxter
Registrar   C. Evans

University of Bradford

Richmond Rd, Bradford, West Yorkshire BD7 1DP; URL www.bradford.ac.uk; E-mail course-enquiries@bradford.ac.uk; Tel 01274 233081; Fax 01274 236260
Registrar and Secretary   N.J. Andrew, BA

Bradford Centre for International Development
Head of Department   Patrick Ryan, BSc MA

Department of Social Sciences and Humanities
Head of Department   Dr Barbara Fawcett, BA, MSc, CQSW, PhD

Department of Peace Studies
Head of Department   Shaun Gregory, BSc, PhD

School of Health Studies
Head of Department   Gwendolen Bradshaw (Acting), RN, RM, ADM, PGCEA, MA

University of Brighton

Mithras Hse, Lewes Rd, Brighton, Brighton and Hove BN2 4AT; URL www.brighton.ac.uk; E-mail business.services@brighton.ac.uk; Tel 01273 643222

School of Applied Social Sciences/School of Health Professions/Institute of Nursing and Midwifery
Falmer, Brighton, Brighton and Hove BN1 9PH; URL www.brighton.ac.uk/health/

University of Bristol

Senate Hse, Tyndall Ave, Bristol BS8 1TH; URL www.bristol.ac.uk; Tel 0117 928 9000

The Socio-Legal Centre for Family Studies
3 Priory Rd, Bristol BS8 1TX; Tel 0117 928 8136
The Socio-Legal Centre for Family Studies was established in 1985 as a joint venture between the University of Bristol's Law Faculty and the School of Applied Social Studies, to reflect the cross-disciplinary nature of family justice as an area of academic study and an objective of professional practice. It aims to provide both empirical information and theoretical ideas which will foster the development of a modern and coherent family justice system, responsive to the needs of families and their children

The Norah Fry Research Centre
3 Priory Rd, Bristol BS8 1TX; Tel 0117 923 8137; Fax 0117 946 6553
The Norah Fry Research Centre was established in 1988 as part of the University of Bristol's Department of Mental Health. The centre's principal interests are the evaluation and development of services for people with learning difficulties. Research projects have examined services provided both statutory and non-statutory agencies. Staff members also contribute to undergraduate and postgraduate courses in the university; supervise postgraduate students and organise and contribute to workshops, conferences and seminars. Members of the centre are drawn from a range of academic disciplines and professional backgrounds.

School for Policy Studies
8 Priory Rd, Bristol BS8 1TZ; URL www.bris.ac.uk/depts/sps; E-mail sps-enquiries@bristol.ac.uk; Tel 0117 954 6755; Fax 0117 954 6756
Contact (Early Childhood Studies)   C. Keen; E-mail carol.keen@bristol.ac.uk; Tel 0117 954 6743
Contact (Social Policy)   H. Bush; E-mail h.e.bush@bristol.ac.uk; Tel 0117 954 6745
Contact (Social Work)   H. Purdie; E-mail h.purdie@bris.ac.uk; Tel (Graduate Enquiries) 0117 954 5571
Contact (Family Therapy)   A. Osborn; E-mail a.l.osborne@bristol.ac.uk; Tel 0117 954 6758
The School for Policy Studies informs and examines national and international policy debate by building on its activites which include undergraduate, postgraduate and professional teaching programmes as well as research and consultancy. The school has four core research centres: Family Policy and Child Welfare; Health and Social Care; Urban Studies; Social Exclusion and Social Justice. These centres work collaboratively and accommodate around 55 academic staff from a wide range of disciplines and 70 postgraduate students from both home and overseas. Research is funded by a variety of bodies. The school has a community focus to policy work by helping service providers and users to develop and put into practice initiatives that can improve their locality and day-to-day living. Areas of particular interest at the school and within its centres include the effects of the NHS and community care reforms, child welfare, domestic violence, neighbourhood change and urban regeneration and professional education in universities.

Brunel University

Uxbridge, Greater London UB8 3PH; URL www.brunel.ac.uk; E-mail admissions@brunel.ac.uk; Tel 01895 274000; Fax 01895 232806

University of Buckingham

Hunter St, Buckingham, Buckinghamshire MK18 1EG;
URL www.buckingham.ac.uk;
E-mail admissions@buckingham.ac.uk; Tel 01280 814080;
Fax 01280 822245
Chancellor Sir Martin Jacomb

University of Cambridge

Press Office, The Old Schools, Trinity La, Cambridge,
Cambridgeshire CB2 1TN; Tel 01223 332300; Fax 01223
330262
Chancellor HRH The Prince Philip, Duke of Edinburgh,
HonLLD
Vice-Chancellor Prof Alan Richard

University of Central England in Birmingham

Perry Barr, Birmingham, West Midlands B42 2SU;
URL www.uce.ac.uk; E-mail info@ucechoices.com;
Tel 0121 331 5595
Secretary and Registrar M. Penlington, BA

School of Social Work and RNIB Rehabilitation Studies
Perry Barr, Birmingham, West Midlands B42 2SU;
URL www.hcc.uce.ac.uk; Tel 0121 331 5482; Fax 0121 331
6592
Head of School Prof Mark Doel
Course Director (Social Work Year 1) Jerry Tew
Course Director (Social Work Year 2) Val Sylvester
Course Director (Social Work BSc) Chandi Patel
Course Director (Rehabilitation Studies) Richard Cox

University of Central Lancashire

Vice-Chancellor Malcolm McVicar, BA, MA, PhD

Department of Social Work
University of Central Lancashire, Preston, Lancashire
PR1 2HE; URL www.uclan.ac.uk;
E-mail cservices@uclan.ac.uk

City University

Northampton Sq, London EC1V 0HB;
URL www.city.ac.uk; E-mail registry@city.ac.uk; Tel 020
7040 5060
Academic Registrar A.H. Seville, MA, PhD

Department of Optometry and Visual Science
Head of Department D.F. Edgar, BSc, FCOptom

School of Social and Human Sciences
Dean of School Prof H. Tumber, MA, PhD

Coventry University

Priory St, Coventry, West Midlands CV1 5FB;
URL www.coventry.ac.uk;
E-mail info.reg@coventry.ac.uk; Tel 024 7688 7688;
Fax 024 7688 8638
Vice-Chancellor Michael Goldstein, CBE, BSc, PhD, DSc,
CChem, FRSC
Pro Vice-Chancellor Prof David Gillingham, BSc, DMS,
PhD, FCIM
Pro Vice-Chancellor Prof Donald Pennington, BA, PhD,
CPsy, AFBPS
Dean (School of Health and Social Sciences) Linda Merriman,
MPhil, PhD, DpodM, CertEd

De Montfort University

The Gateway, Leicester LE1 9BH; URL www.dmu.ac.uk;
E-mail enquiry@dmu.ac.uk; Tel 0116 2551 551; Fax 0116
255 0307
Chief Executive and Vice-Chancellor Prof Philip Tasker

School of Health and Community Studies
The Gateway, Leicester LE1 9BH; Tel 0116 255 1551;
Fax 0116 257 7866
Head Prof M.P. Saks, BA, MA, PhD
BA Course Leader (Health Studies) K. Moore
BA Modular Course Leader (Health Studies) Dr A. Watterson
BA Course Leader (Nursing) I. Rudd
BSc Course Leader (Midwifery) J. West
Course Leader (Applied Social and Community Studies)
G. Taylor
Course Leader (Applied Health Studies) S. Dyson
Course Leader (Community Education) K. Chouham
Course Leader (Community Health Nursing) J. Leatham,
MA, RGN, SCM, HVCert, PGCEA
Course Leader (Health Care Practice) S. Ham-Ying
Course Leader (Human Communication) K. Grundy
Course Leader (Human Psychology) D. Rowley
Course Leader (Social Work – Leicester) M. Stewart
Course Leader (Social Work – Milton Keynes)
L. McIntosh-Stewart
Course Leader (Youth and Community Development)
C. Howson
Dip HE Course Leader (Midwifery) M. McLean
Dip HE Course Leader (Nursing) P. Pleasance
MA Course Leader (Midwifery) M. Hamilton
MA Course Leader (Nursing) J. Reece

University of Derby

Kedleston Rd, Derby DE22 1GB; URL www.derby.ac.uk;
E-mail admissions@derby.ac.uk;
E-mail <initial>.<surname>@derby.ac.uk; Tel 01332
590500; Fax 01332 294861
Chancellor Sir C.E. Ball, MA, DUniv, HonDLitt, HonDEd,
FRSA
Vice-Chancellor Prof R.W. Waterhouse, MA, Hon DUniv
Deputy Vice-Chancellor M.R. Hall, FCA, FCMA, FCT
Pro Vice-Chancellor and Registrar J.M. Fry, BSc
Pro Vice-Chancellor R.M. Faithorn, BA, MPhil, PGCE
Pro-Vice-Chancellor Prof Freda Tallantyre, BA, MLitt,
PGCE
Clerk to the Council and Company Secretary R. Gillis, FRSA
Solicitor
Librarian G. Brewer, BA, MA, ACA
Students: 23 641 (16 305 HE students; 7336 FE students).

22

High Peak Campus
Harpur Hill, Buxton, Derby DK17 9JZ;
URL www.highpeak.ac.uk;
E-mail admissions@derby.ac.uk; Tel 01298 71100
Marketing Manager Beverley Cooke
Dean of School (Education, Human Sciences and Law)
Prof David Davies
Dean of School (Health and Community Studies)
Dawn Forman
Head (Early Years, Special Care and Teacher Training) Pat Joyce

University of Durham

University Office, Durham, County Durham DH1 3HP;
URL www.dur.ac.uk; E-mail registrar@durham.ac.uk;
Tel 0191 334 2000; Fax 0191 334 6250
Registrar and Secretary L. Sanders, BA

Department of Sociology and Social Policy
32 Old Elvet, Durham, County Durham DH1 3HN;
URL www.dur.ac.uk; E-mail dave.byrne@durham.ac.uk;
Tel 0191 334 6826
Head of Department Prof David Byrne
No. of students
357

University of East Anglia

University Plain, Norwich, Norfolk NR4 7TJ;
URL www.uea.ac.uk; Tel 01603 456161; Fax 01603 458553
Registrar and Secretary B.J. Summers, BSc

School of Social Work and Psychosocial Studies

Elizabeth Fry Bldg, University of East Anglia, Norwich, Norfolk NR4 7TJ; URL www.uea.ac.uk/swk; E-mail norma.blake@uea.ac.uk; Tel 01603 592068; Fax 01603 593552

Dean Prof David Howe, MA, PhD

The school offers a wide range of courses for qualified social workers and other social care and child welfare professionals. Research activity is concentrated on the relationship between theory and social work and social care practice; child care practice, policy and planning; attachment theory; family violence and conflict resolution; the interaction of law and social work.

The school publishes its own monograph series, which currently lists more than 100 titles.

Centre for Research on the Child and Family

School of Social Work and Psychosocial Studies, Elizabeth Fry Bldg, Norwich, Norfolk NR4 7TJ; URL www.uea.ac.uk/swk/research; E-mail j.warner@uea.ac.uk; Tel 01603 592068; Fax 01603 593552

Co-Director Dr Margaret O'Brien
Co-Director Dr Gillian Schofield

The Centre for Research on the Child and Family undertakes research on aspects of children's lives and the changing nature of the family.

Making Research Count

School of Social Work and Psychosocial Studies, University of East Anglia, Norwich, NR4 7TJ; URL www.making-research-count.org.uk; E-mail s.e. bailey@uea.ac.uk; Tel 01603 592068; Fax 01603 593552

Co-ordinator Sue Bailey

The Making Research Count initiative provides training on 'research literacy' and the principals of evidence based practice.

Current and recently completed research projects and evaluations are in the areas of: Children in Urban Environments; Family Placement; Family Support and Child Protection; International Child Welfare; Families Across the Life-Cycle; Marital and Family Breakdown; Breakfast Clubs.

University of East London

Longbridge Rd, Dagenham, Essex RM8 2AS; URL www.uel.ac.uk; E-mail publicity@uel.ac.uk; Tel 020 8223 3000; Fax 020 8590 7799

School of Education and Community Studies
Head of School Ann Slater

School of Health and Biosciences
Head David Humber

School of Psychology
Head David Rose

School of Social Sciences
Head Barbara Harrison

University of Essex

Wivenhoe Pk, Colchester, Essex CO4 3SQ; URL www.essex.ac.uk/; Tel 01206 873333; Fax 01206 873598

Department of Sociology
Head of Department Prof Lydia Morris
Contact (Environmental Issues and Sociological Theory) Prof E. Benton
Contact (Citizenship, Nation and Rights) Prof Robin Blackburn
Contact (Gender and Mental Health, Social Aspects of Senile) Prof J. Busfield

Contact (Social Anthropology of Latin America, Ethnicity and National Identity, Religion) Dr A.L.E. Canessa Social anthropology of Latin America; Ethnicity and national identity; Religion.
Contact (Crime and Control) Dr Eamonn Carrabine
Contact (Welfare, Children) Dr Pam Cox
Contact (Sexuality and Sexual Behaviour and AIDS) Prof A.P.M. Coxon
Contact (Aspects of 19th Century Gender and Families, Men and Women's Roles) Prof L. Davidoff
Contact (Social Divisions and Household Dynamics) Prof Diane Elson
Contact (Gender, Work, Employment and Migration) Prof M. Glucksmann
Contact (Gender and Ethnicity Issues, Welfare Policies) Dr Jane Hindley
Contact (Health and Criminology) Dr Paul Iganski
Contact (Gender Relations and Gender Divisions, Unemployment and the Labour Market, Social Policy) Prof L. Morris
Contact (Class and Stratification, Gender Family and Household, Stress, Identity and Anxiety in the Western World) Prof R. Pahl
Contact (Poverty) Dr Lucinda Platt
Contact (Problems of Sexual Diversity, Symbolic Interactionism) Prof K. Plummer
Contact (Life History, Gender and Organisations) Dr M. Roper
Contact (Health and Illness, Cultural Studies) Dr C. Samson
Contact (Social Stratification, Theoretical Sociology, Business Ownership and Control) Prof J. Scott
Contact (Environment, Crime and Health, Policing, Joint Health and Social Sciences Initiatives, Development in Policing) Prof N. South
Contact (Human Rights) Dr Yasemin Soysal
Contact (Step Families, Families and Social Mobility) Prof P. Thompson
No. of students
239

University of Exeter

Northcote Hse, The Queen's Dr, Exeter, Devon EX4 4QJ; URL www.exeter.ac.uk; E-mail s.d.franklin@exeter.ac.uk; Tel 01392 661000; Fax 01392 263108

Registrar and Secretary I.H.C. Powell, MA

Centre for Evidence-Based Social Services

Richard's Bldg, St. Luke's Campus, Heavitree Rd, Exeter, Devon EX1 2LU; URL www.ex.ac.uk/cebss; E-mail s.e.bosley@exeter.ac.uk; Tel 01392 262865; Fax 01392 262858

Director of Centre Prof Brian Sheldon, MPhil, PhD, DipSocStud, DipSW, RMN

This research and dissemination centre, attached to the Department of Social Work and Probation Studies, began operation in May 1997. It is funded jointly by the Department of Health and Social Services Departments in the South and South-West of England (£4m over three years in the first instance). Its functions are: to review existing research on the effectiveness of social services and to bring out the implications for management, organisation and practice; to review empirical studies on the nature of social and personal problems (e.g. in childcare, child protection, mental ill health, disability, old age); to undertake or commission evaluative research where gaps exist in the available literature; to work in collaboration with local research and training departments; to contribute to the service-review processes within departments; to liaise with the providers of professional training courses at universities in the region regarding the use of empirical evidence in the curriculum. These developments parallel initiatives in the field of evidence-based medicine and the project as a whole emphasises multidisciplinary co-operation.

Department of Social Work and Probation Studies

Richards Bldg, St. Luke's Campus, Heavitree Rd, Exeter, Devon EX1 2LU; URL www.exeter.ac.uk/swps; E-mail g.m.watson@exeter.ac.uk; E-mail d.k.cooper@exeter.ac.uk; Tel 01392 262873; Fax 01392 262875
Head of Department   Gordon Jack, BSc, MSc, CQSW

University of Hertfordshire

College La, Hatfield, Hertfordshire AL10 9AB; URL www.herts.ac.uk; E-mail main.reception@herts.ac.uk; Tel 01707 284000; Fax 01707 286386
Vice-Chancellor and Chief Executive   Prof R.J.T. Wilson

Faculty of Health and Human Sciences

Department of Social Community and Health Studies, College La, Hatfield, Hertfordshire AL10 9AB; Tel 01707 284401; Fax 01707 284415
Dean of Faculty   Dr Michael Buckenham
Associate Head of Department (Social, Community and Health Studies)   Brian Littlechild, CQSW, BA, MA; E-mail b.littlechild@herts.ac.uk
Head of Research (Department of Social, Community and Health Studies)   Dr Roger Green; E-mail r.d.green@herts.ac.uk
Chair (Research and Consultancy Committee)   Dr Diana Konbrott
Staff Specialist Fields for Supervision of Research
Social security. Health policy. Social work. Social administration. Deviancy. Social policy.
Staff Research Activities and Interests
Police and social services. Social policy. Refugees. Social theory. Care leavers. Working with fathers in child protection work. Young offenders. Adoption. Child protection, criminal careers and criminal sentencing. Health, Social Services and Community Care. The Family and Family Policy. Learning Disabilities. The Welfare State in Britain and Europe. Poverty. Mental Health. Community research. User involvement in practice and policy development. Chronic Illness and Disability.

University of Huddersfield

Queensgate, Huddersfield, West Yorkshire HD1 3DH; URL www.hud.ac.uk; Tel 01484 422288; Fax 01484 516151
Vice-Chancellor   Prof J.R. Tarrant, BSc, PhD
Academic Registrar   Dr V.P. Jeffs, BSc(Hons), MSc, PhD

School of Human and Health Sciences, Social Work Section
Course Leader   Mr G. Rice
A range of of placement opportunities offered in statutory, voluntary and private social work agencies.
No. of students
40 per annum

University of Hull

Cottingham Rd, Hull, Kingston upon Hull HU6 7RX; URL www.hull.ac.uk; Tel 01482 346311

The School of Nursing, Social Work and Applied Health Studies

Cottingham Rd Campus, Cottingham Rd, Hull, HU6 7RX; Tel (Social Work) 01482 466163
Head of School   Richard Hogston
Head and Senior Lecturer (Social Work)   Jonathan Parker, BA(Hons), MSc, MPhil, DipHSW, CQSW

Keele University

Keele, Staffordshire ST5 5BG; URL www.keele.ac.uk
Secretary and Registrar   S.J. Morris, BA

School of Social Relations
Head of School   Prof G. Allan
Director (MA/Diploma in Social Work)   R. Pugh

University of Kent

Canterbury, Kent CT2 7NZ; URL www.kent.ac.uk; Tel 01227 764000
Secretary and Registrar   Nick McHard, BSc, MA(CNAA)

Faculty of Social Science
Dean   Prof John Baldock, BA, MA
Director and Senior Lecturer (Learning Disability)   Peter McGill, BSc, MPhil, AFBPsS, C.Psychol
Director (Personal Social Services Research Unit)   Dr Ann Netten, BA, PhD
Professor (Health Service Studies) and Director (Centre for Health Service Studies)   Andy Alaszewski, BA, MA, PhD(Cantab)
Professor (Social Psychology) and Director (Centre for the Study of Group Processes)   Dominic Abrams, BA, MSc, PhD
Professor (Applied Psychology of Learning Disabilities – Tizard Centre)   Jim Mansell, BSc, MScEcon, FBPsS, CPsychol
Professor (Social Psychology)   Rupert Brown, BSc, PhD
Professor (Social Policy)   Peter Taylor-Gooby, BA, MPhil, Social Admin, PhD
Professor (Health Psychology) and Director (Centre for Research in Health Behaviour)   Derek Rutter, BA, PhD
Professor (Urban Studies) and Head (School of Social Policy, Sociology and Social Research)   Chris Pickvance, BA(Econ), MA(Econ)
Professor (Women's Studies)   Mary Evans, MSc(Econ), DPhil
Professor (Sociology)   Larry Ray, BA, MA DPhil
Professor (Psychoanalytic Psychology)   Janet Sayers, MA(Cantab), PhD, DipClinPsych
Professor (Clinical Psychology of Learning Disability) and Head (Tizard Centre)   Prof Glynis Murphy, BA(Oxon), MA, PhD
Professor (Public Policy and Management)   William Jenkins, BSc, PhD
Reader (Health Care of Older People – Centre for Health Service Studies)   Dr Iain Carpenter, MD, FRCP
Professor (Sociology)   Prof Frank Furedi
Professor (Social Policy and Sociology)   Prof Julia Twigg
Director (European Institute of Social Services)   Andrew Swithinbank

Tizard Centre
University of Kent, Canterbury, Kent CT2 7LZ; URL www.kent.ac.uk/tizard; E-mail tizardgen@kent.ac.uk; Tel 01227 827373; Fax 01227 763674
Director   Prof Glynis Murphy
The Tizard Centre is one of the leading academic groups working in learning disability and mental health services in the UK. From 1996 the centre worked in services for older people. Members of the centre are selected both for their academic record and for their practical experience in services. The centre has excellent links with social services departments, health authorities and other relevant organisations. The primary aims of the centre are: (i) to advance knowledge about the relationship between the organisation of priority care services and their outcomes, and (ii) to help service agencies (both purchasers and providers) develop their own competence to provide and sustain high-quality, comprehensive services for people with learning disabilities or mental health problems. The centre is committed to teaching, research and consultancy that acknowledge diversity and address issues arising from social inequality. The centre has an extensive programme of consultancy and research both nationally and internationally, and also provides short courses and degree and diploma programmes at the University of Kent and elsewhere.

School of Social Policy, Sociology and Social Research
Cornwallis Bldg, University of Kent, Canterbury, Kent CT2 7NF; URL www.kent.ac.uk/sspssr/; E-mail socio-office@kent.ac.uk; Tel 01227 823684; 01227 827816; Fax 01227 824014; 01227 827005
Head   Prof Chris Pickvance
The School of Social Policy, Sociology and Social Research is one of the largest departments of its type in the UK.

22

Centre for Health Services Studies (CHSS)
George Allen Wing, Cornwallis Bldg, University of Kent,
Canterbury, Kent CT2 7NF;
URL www.kent.ac.uk/chss/; Tel 01227 823940;
Fax 01227 827868
Director Prof Andy Alaszewski
CHSS is an interdisciplinary research centre which
supports research in the NHS in Kent and Surrey and has a
programme of national and international health services.
The centre draws together a wide range of research and
disciplinary expertise, including health and social policy,
medical sociology, public health and epidemiology,
geriatric medicine, primary care, physiotherapy, statistical
and information analysis.

Personal Social Services Research Unit (PSSRU)
George Allen Wing, Cornwallis Bldg, University of Kent,
Canterbury, Kent CT2 7NF;
URL www.kent.ac.uk/pssru/; Tel 01227 764000;
Fax 01227 827038
Director Dr Ann Netten
The Personal Social Services Research Unit conducts
research and policy analysis aimed at the improvement of
equity and efficiency of community-based health and social
care services.
The aim of the PSSRU is to continue to undertake high
quality social science research which influences evidence-
based policy-making and practice development. Its
researchers come from a wide range of disciplines and
backgrounds, including the caring professions. The
distinctive unit style of analysis draws on a wide variety of
research approaches, which have been collated and
developed systematically, and are called the 'Production of
Welfare' approach.

European Institute of Social Services (EISS)
Keynes College, University of Kent, Canterbury, Kent
CT2 7NP; URL www.kent.ac.uk/eiss/;
E-mail eiss-group@kent.ac.uk; Tel 01227 823038;
Fax 01227 827246
Director Andrew Swithinbank
The European Institute of Social Services (EISS) is one of
the leaders in the conception, delivery and evaluation of
international social care and health projects, which develop
both social assistance services and combat the social
exclusion of vulnerable groups.
The institute combines academic expertise with UK social
care practice experience and consultancy skills. EISS has a
strong and developing track record of social policy and
practice development both in the EU and in the Accession
countries of Central and Eastern Europe. Its main aim is to
enable social care organisations and the people they serve
to gain maximum benefit from European funding.
EISS runs programmes of research, publications,
conferences and training and provides a membership and
information service, briefing a large community of UK
public and voluntary organisations on EU and wider social
policy developments.

Kingston University

Student Information and Advice Centre, Cooper Hse,
Kingston upon Thames, Surrey KT1 2HX; Tel 020 8547
2000; Fax 020 8547 7080
Vice-Chancellor Peter Scott, HonDLitt, HonLLD

School of Social Work
Combe Martin, Kingston Hill, Kingston upon Thames,
Surrey KT2 7LB
Head of School H. Thompsett, BA, MA, BPhil, CQSW
Programme Director (Undergraduate) David Hodgson, MA,
LLM, CQSW
Programme Director (Postgraduate) Jane Lindsay, MA, MSc,
CQSW
No. of undergraduate students
200
No. of postgraduate students
90

School of Social Science
Head of School Prof J.W. Bailey, BA(Soc), MSc(Econ)
Course Tutor M.A Roberts, BA(Pol), MA(Pol)

Lancaster University

Lancaster, Lancashire LA1 4YW; URL www.lancs.ac.uk;
Tel 01524 65201

Department of Applied Social Science
Lancaster University Cartmel College, Lancaster,
Lancashire LA1 4YL; URL www.lancs.ac.uk; Tel 01524
594095; 01524 594098; 01524 594099; Fax 01524 592475
Head of Department Dr Sue Wise

University of Leeds

Leeds, West Yorkshire LS2 9JT; URL www.leeds.ac.uk;
Tel 0113 243 1751; Fax 0113 244 3923
Secretary J.R. Gair, MA

School of Continuing Education
Chair of the School Malcolm S. Chase, BA, MA, DPhil

Nuffield Institute for Health
Director Prof G. Wistow, BA, MSocSci

School of Psychology
Head of Department Prof John E. Blundell, BSc, PhD

Department of Sociology and Social Policy
Head of Department Paul Baggaley, BA, MA, DPhil

Leeds Metropolitan University

City Campus, Leeds, West Yorkshire LS1 3HE;
URL www.lmu.ac.uk;
E-mail course-enquiries@lmu.ac.uk; Tel 0113 283 3113;
Fax 0113 283 3114
Vice-Chancellor Prof L. Wagner, MA
Admissions Officer Deborah Senior
Faculties/schools/departments
There are four faculties: Leeds Business School; Faculty of
Cultural and Education Studies; Faculty of Health and
Environment; and Faculty of Information and Engineering
Systems. There is also a Centre for Language Study,
Learning and Information Services, Student Support
Services and other central services. There are
approximately 37 000 students and 3000 staff.

Faculty of Health and Environment
Dean Michael Holmes
Deputy Dean Brian Whittington
Head (School of Health and Human Sciences) Diana Daltry
Head (School of Applied Social Sciences) Terry Moran
Head (School of Health and Community Care) Pete Nutman
Head (School of Art, Architecture and Design) Chris Royffe
Head (School of the Built Environment) Robert Hargreaves
No. of students
7600

The University of Leicester

Registrar and Secretary K.J. Julian, MA

School of Social Work
107 Princess Rd East, Leicester LE1 7LA;
E-mail social.work@le.ac.uk; Tel 0116 252 3766; Fax 0116
252 3748
Head of Department Prof Stewart Petersen
No. of students
150

University of Liverpool

Senate Hse, Abercromby Sq, Liverpool, Merseyside
L69 3BX; Tel 0151 794 2000; Fax 0151 708 6502
Registrar M.D. Carr, MA

Department of Sociology, Social Policy and Social Work Studies
Eleanor Rathbone Bldg, Bedford St South, Liverpool,
Merseyside L69 7ZA; E-mail s.braye@liv.ac.uk; Tel 0151
794 3023
Director (Social Work Studies) Suzy Braye
No. of students
100

School of Combined Honours: Faculty of Social and Environmental Studies
Sir Alastair Pilkington Bldg, Liverpool, Merseyside
L69 7SH; Tel 0151 794 1433
Director Andre Brown

University of London

Senate Hse, Malet St, London WC1E 7HU;
URL www.lon.ac.uk; E-mail enquiries@eisa.lon.ac.uk;
Tel 020 7862 8360; Fax 020 7862 8358
Administrative Officer Cynthia Barlow

Birkbeck University of London
Malet St, London WC1E 7HX; URL www.bbk.ac.uk;
E-mail admissions@bbk.ac.uk; Tel 0845 601 0174

Goldsmiths College, University of London
New Cross, London SE14 6NW;
URL www.goldsmiths.ac.uk;
E-mail admissions@gold.ac.uk; Tel (College) 020 7919
7171; (Registry Admissions Office (postgraduate)) 020
7919 7060; (Registry Admissions Office (undergraduate))
020 7919 7766; Fax (College) 020 7717 2240
Warden Prof Ben Pimlott, BA, BPhil, PhD, FRHistS, FRSA,
FBA
Head (Anthropology Department) Prof Nicholas Thomas,
BA, PhD
Head (Educational Studies Department) Prof Eve Gregory,
BA, PGCE, PhD, DipEd
Head (Psychology Department) Dr Jane Powell, BA, MPhil,
PhD, CClinPsychol
Head (Sociology Department) Dr Mike Michael, BA, PhD
Goldsmiths offers a wide range of courses from access and
foundation to certificates, undergraduate and
postgraduate. Call for details.

Imperial College London, Faculty of Medicine and Graduate School of Life Sciences and Medicine
South Kensington Campus, London SW7 2AZ;
URL www.imperial.ac.uk

Institute of Education
20 Bedford Way, London WC1H 0AL; URL www.ioe.ac.uk;
E-mail info@ioe.ac.uk; Tel 020 7612 6000; Fax 020 7612
6097
Director Prof G.J. Whitty
Secretary D.J. Warren, BSc
No. of students
1612 full-time, 2864 part-time.

King's College London
URL www.kcl.ac.uk
Full range of subjects available including Biochemistry,
Dentistry, Nursing and Pharmacology. See website for details.

London School of Economics and Political Science
Houghton St, London WC2A 2AE; URL www.lse.ac.uk;
E-mail stu.rec@lse.ac.uk; Tel 020 7955 7345; Fax 020 7955
7415

Department of Social Policy
Convenor of Department Prof Julian LeGrand
Departmental Manager John Wilkes
The interests of the Department of Social Policy at the LSE
embrace virtually all major issues which confront
individual countries and the world today. How best to
provide health and education; the planning of towns and
the provision of reasonable housing and social services; the
problems posed by ageing populations, poverty and social

exclusion; the role of national and local government and
non-governmental organisations in instigating policy
reform and change.
Today these and many other issues have to be considered
in an increasingly international and dynamic context – one
in which national, European and global matters frequently
interact and merge.
Staff reflect a host of different backgrounds – and they are
continually involved in policy debate and in advising local,
national and international organisations.
Former students fill senior policy-related and academic
positions in countries, literally all around the world.
No. of students in training
100 (undergraduate); 400 (postgraduate and research)

London School of Hygiene and Tropical Medicine
50 Bedford Sq, London WC1B 3DP;
URL www.lshtm.ac.uk/courses;
E-mail registry@lshtm.ac.uk

Royal Free and University College Medical School of University College London
From 1st August 1998 the new medical school entitled the
Royal Free and University College Medical School of
University College London came into existence and
superseded the previous two separate schools of the Royal
Free and UCL. A new medical curriculum was introduced
from September 2000.
University College London, Gower St, London WC1E 6BT;
URL www.ucl.ac.uk; Tel 020 7679 3000; Fax 020 7679
3001
Medicine MB BS.

Royal Holloway, University of London
Department of Health and Social Care, Egham, Surrey
TW20 0EX; URL www.rhul.ac.uk;
E-mail s.m.sweet@rhul.ac.uk; Tel 01784 41434

St. Bartholomew's and the Royal London School of Medicine and Dentistry
Turner St, London E1 2AD; Tel 020 7377 7000

St. George's Hospital Medical School
Cranmer Terr, London SW17 0RE; URL www.sghms.ac.uk;
Tel 020 8725 5466

London Metropolitan University

166–220 Holloway Rd, London N7 8DB;
URL www.londonmet.ac.uk;
E-mail admissions@londonmet.ac.uk; Tel 020 7753 7045;
(Course Enquiries Office) 020 7133 4200
Vice Chancellor Prof Roderick Floud, MA, DPhil, FRHistS

Faculty of Environment and Social Studies
Ladbroke Hse, 62–66 Highbury Gr, London N5 2AD;
URL www.unl.ac.uk/ess/faculty.shtml; Tel 020 7753 5087
Dean of Faculty Dr J. Somerville

Loughborough University

Loughborough, Leicestershire LE11 3TU;
URL www.lboro.ac.uk; Tel 01509 263171
Vice-Chancellor Prof D.J. Wallace, CBE, BSc, PhD, FRS,
FRSE, FInstP, FRSA, MBCS, CEng
Registrar J. Town, BA
Bursar H.M. Pearson, BA(Econ), LLB, ACIS

Department of Social Sciences
Epinal Way, Loughbourough, Leicestershire LE11 3TU;
URL www.lboro.ac.uk/departments/ss;
Tel (Communication and Media studies, Sociology)
01509 223368; (Social Policy, Criminology and Social
Policy) 01509 223383; (Social Psychology) 01509 223365;
Fax 01509 223944
Head of Department Prof Peter Golding
Departmental Administration Lynn Dutton
Clerical Officer (Postgraduate and Research) Deidre Lombard

22

The University of Manchester

3rd Fl, Beyer Bldg, Manchester M13 9PL; Tel 0161 275 2000
Registrar and Secretary E. Newcomb, BA, DipEd, FRSA

ARC Epidemiology Research Unit

Stopford Bldg (University of Manchester), Oxford Rd,
Manchester M13 9PT; Tel 0161 275 5037; Fax 0161 275
5043
Director Prof Alan Silman, MSc, MD, FRCP, FFPHM
The Arthritis and Rheumatism Council maintains an
Epidemiology Research Unit which is a department within
the School of Epidemiology and Health Sciences. The work
of the unit includes the monitoring of all routine morbidity
and mortality statistics on the rheumatic diseases. The unit
undertakes studies on the occurrence of rheumatic diseases
in the community, risk factors for their development, and
predictors of prognosis. In addition it studies the genetic
epidemiology of these conditions. Work is also being done
on the classification and coding of musculoskeletal diseases
for national and international bodies.

Centre for the Development of Continuing Education

Director J.M. Hostler, MA, MEd, PhD
A large programme of part-time short courses designed for
adult students whether their interest is purely personal or
job-related. Courses are available during the daytime, in
the evenings and at weekends. The format ranges from a
series of meetings over one or two terms to single study-
days. Some courses carry the option of university credit
and study over an extended period. There is also a
programme which prepares applicants for designated postgraduate courses at the university. The subject range covers
the arts, social sciences, personal development and
management studies, science and computing.

Centre for Youth Studies

Director Dr Chris Murray, BA, MPhil, PhD European
research, the young confronted with employment; Social
condition of youth in the UK; Life styles, occupation and
source of revenue of young unemployed people.
Contact M. Maquire European research, the young
confronted with employment.
Contact D. Ashton European research, the young
confronted with employment.
Contact Paul Cook Liberation and industrial development
with reference to Kenya, Pakistan and Sri Lanka.
Contact John Craig Security and development in a small
state; The case of Malta; Ethnicity and development in
Malaysia
Contact David Hulme Popular participation in rural
development projects
Contact M.L. Jones Managerial thinking and behaviour;
an African perspective.
Contact P. Mann Development of interdisciplinary team
management in the NHS
Contact J. Mullen Social planning for basic human needs,
with particular reference to Tanzania, Tunisia and Papua
New Guinea.

Faculty of Medicine, Dentistry and Nursing

Centre for Audiology, Education of the Deaf and Speech
Pathology, School of Education, University of
Manchester, Oxford Rd, Manchester M13 9PL
School of Epidemiology and Health Sciences, Stopford
Bldg, University of Manchester, Oxford Rd, Manchester
M13 9PL
Contact (Psychiatric Social Work) Prof Michael Kerfott
Department of Psychiatry, Mathematics Bldg, Manchester
University, Manchester M13 9PL
Contact (MSc Psychiatry) Dr Angela Wieck
Department of Psychiatry, Withington Hospital,
Manchester M20 8LR
Contact (Clinical Psychology) Dr Rachel Calam
Clinical Psychology, Withington Hospital (UMSM),
Manchester M20 8LR
Contact (Child Care and Child Mental Health)
Sheila Thomson

Department of Psychiatry, Mathematics Bldg, The
University of Manchester, Oxford Rd, Manchester
M13 9TL
Contact (Family and Individual Cognitive Behaviour)
John McGovern
School of Nursing, Coupland III Bldg, University of
Manchester, Oxford Rd, Manchester M13 9TL
Contact (Health Care Ethics) Gareth Evans
Faculty of Education, University of Manchester, Oxford Rd,
Manchester M13 9TL
Contact (Mental Health and Social Work) Barbara Hatfield
Department of Psychiatry, Mathematics Bldg, The
University of Manchester, Oxford Rd, Manchester
M13 9PL
Contact (MSc Psychiatry for Developing Countries)
Dr R Gater
Department of Psychiatry, Manchester Royal Infirmary,
Manchester M13 8AL
Contact (Diploma/MSc Systemic Family Therapy) E.J Webster
Department of Psychiatry, Mathematics Bldg, The
University of Manchester, Oxford Rd, Manchester
M13 9TL

Hester Adrian Research Centre

For the study of learning processes in the mentally
handicapped.
Director Prof C.C. Kiernan, BA, PhD
*Project Director (Behaviour Problems of Mentally Handicapped
People)* C. Kiernan
*Project Director (Behaviour Problems of Mentally Handicapped
People)* H. Qureshi
Project Director (Ageing and Mental Handicap) J. Hogg
Project Director (Ageing and Mental Handicap) S. Moss
Project Director (Down's Syndrome) C. Cunningham
Research Fellow (Down's Syndrome) T. Sloper
Research (Down's Syndrome) C. Knussen
Research (Down's Syndrome) A. Rangecroft
Project Co-director (Special Education) C. Robson
Project Co-director (Special Education) J. Sebba
HARC Statistician D. Reeve
Research Projects
Behaviour problems of mentally handicapped people:
epidemiology and service provision; Department of Health
and Social Security 1985.
Ageing and mental handicap: a study of the needs,
epidemiology and service provision for older clients;
Department of Health and Social Security 1985.
Longitudinal study of the process and adaption in a cohort
of children with Down's syndrome and their families;
Department of Health and Social Security 1985–1989.
The impact of in-service courses in special education;
Department of Health and Social Security 1983–1986.

School of Nursing, Midwifery and Health Visiting

Tel (Postgraduate) 0161 275 7561; (Undergraduate) 0161 273
2087; (Undergraduate and Postgraduate) 0161 275 5333

Student Health Service

Senior Medical Officer Dr C.E. Peacock, BSc, MB, ChB,
MFCH

The Manchester Metropolitan University

Department of Applied Community Studies

Manchester Metropolitan University, 799 Wilmslow Rd,
Manchester M20 2RR; URL www.mmu.ac.uk/acs;
E-mail acs.cse@mmu.ac.uk; Tel 0161 247 2098; Fax 0161
247 6844
Head of Department Dr Bill Campbell

Department of Biological Sciences

Manchester Metropolitan University, John Dalton Bldg,
Manchester M1 5GD;
URL www.sci-eng.mmu.ac.uk/biology;
E-mail bio@mmu.ac.uk; Tel 0161 247 1234; Fax 0161 247
6325
Head of Department Prof T. Looker

Department of Health Care Studies

Elizabeth Gaskell, Hathersage Rd, Manchester M13 0JA;
URL www.mmu.ac.uk/hcs;
E-mail health.cse@mmu.ac.uk; Tel 0161 247 2518;
Fax 0161 247 6328
Head of Department   Dr D. Skidmore

Department of Humanities Applied Social Studies

Manchester Metropolitan University, Alsager Faculty,
Stoke-on-Trent ST7 2HL; Tel 0161 247 5373
Head of Department   Prof G. Heathcote

Department of Politics and Philosophy

Manchester Metropolitan University, Geoffrey Manton
Bldg, Manchester M15 6LL;
URL www.mmu.ac.uk/politics;
E-mail polphil-hums@mmu.ac.uk; Tel 0161 247 3436;
Fax 0161 247 6312
Head of Department   Prof M. Bell

Department of Psychology and Speech Pathology

Manchester Metropolitan University, Elizabeth Gaskell,
Manchester M13 0JA;
URL www.psychology.mmu.ac.uk;
E-mail psychology.cse@mmu.ac.uk; Tel 0161 247 2553;
Fax 0161 247 6364
Head of Department   Dr P. Banister

Department of Sociology

Manchester Metropolitan University, Geoffrey Manton
Bldg, Manchester M15 6LL;
URL www.mmu.ac.uk/sociology;
E-mail sociology-hums@mmu.ac.uk; Tel 0161 247 3027;
Fax 0161 247 6321
Head of Department   B. Leach

Middlesex University (MU)

North London Bus Pk, Oakleigh Rd South, London
N11 1QS; URL mdx.ac.uk;
E-mail admissions@mdx.ac.uk; Tel 020 8411 5000;
Fax 020 8411 5649

Health and Social Sciences Department

Dean (Health and Social Sciences)   Prof Margaret House
Curriculum Leader for Nursing   Charmagne Barnes
Head (Social Work)   Helen Cosis-Brown

University of Newcastle upon Tyne

Newcastle upon Tyne, Tyne and Wear NE1 7RU;
URL www.ncl.ac.uk;
E-mail admissions-enquiries@ncl.ac.uk; Tel 0191 222
5594
Students
12 066 undergraduate students, 4273 postgraduate
students.

University of Northumbria

21–22 Ellison Pl, Newcastle upon Tyne, Tyne and Wear
NE1 8ST; URL www.northumbria.ac.uk; Tel 0191 232
6002; Fax 0191 227 4017
University Registrar   C.A. Penna, BA(Hons), ACIS

School of Health, Community and Education Studies

Dean   Prof R. Stephens, BA, MA, CPhil, PhD
Faculty Registrar   J. Braithwaite

University of Nottingham

University Pk, Nottingham NG7 2RD;
URL www.nottingham.ac.uk; Tel 0115 951 5151
Registrar   K.H. Jones, BA, MA

School of Sociology and Social Policy

Head of School   Prof J. Evetts

The Nottingham Trent University

Burton St, Nottingham NG1 4BU; URL www.ntu.ac.uk;
E-mail cor.web@ntu.ac.uk; Tel 0115 941 8418
Vice-Chancellor   Prof Neil Gorman

Department of Health and Human Services

Head of Department   Prof Patricia Higham, BA, LRCC,
PgDip, CertEd, PhD

Department of Social Sciences

Head of Department   Prof David Webb, BA, MA, PhD

The Open University

Initial enquiries
Walton Hall, Milton Keynes MK7 6AA;
URL www.open.ac.uk; Tel 01908 274066
Secretary   A.F. Woodburn, BSc, DPA
Address and telephone numbers for all initial enquiries
about courses and study packs listed above, and for course
brochures: The Course and Information Centre, The Open
University, PO Box 724, Milton Keynes, MK7 6ZS; Tel 01908
653231 (answering services out of office hours). The
University offers a number of awards, including a BA and a
BSc degree, a Diploma in Health and Social Welfare, a
Professional Certificate and Diploma in Management and
an MBA (which includes a Managing Public Services
option). Further details on these awards and the courses
can be obtained from the Call Centre at the address above.

Oxford Brookes University

Gipsy La, Headington, Oxford, Oxfordshire OX3 0BP;
URL www.brookes.ac.uk; E-mail query@brookes.ac.uk;
Tel 01865 484848; Fax 01865 483616
Chancellor   Jon Snow
Vice-Chancellor   Prof Graham Upton, MEd, PhD, CPsychol,
FBPsS
*Deputy Vice-Chancellor (Academic Affairs)/Deputy Chief
Executive*   Prof Linda Challis, BA(Oxon), MSc
Deputy Vice-Chancellor (Business and Resources) and Registrar
Rex Knight
Pro Vice-Chancellor (Research and Consultancy)
Prof Susan McRae
Director (Academic and Student Affairs)   E.N. Winders, BA

School of Social Sciences and Law

Dean   Prof Derek Elsom

School of Health and Social Care

Contact   June Girvin

University of Plymouth

Drake Circus, Plymouth PL4 8AA;
URL www.plymouth.ac.uk;
E-mail prospectus@plymouth.ac.uk; Tel 01752 232232

Faculty of Human Sciences

Drake Circus, Plymouth PL4 8AA;
URL www.hs.plymouth.ac.uk;
E-mail humansciences@plymouth.ac.uk; Tel 01752
233191
Head of Faculty (Administration)   Suzanne Tolan
The Community Justice Research Centre aims to foster
collaboration between practitioners, policy-makers and
academics in the development of efficient and effective
community and social services, underpinned by research. It
provides a focal point for practice-oriented community,
health and social care research in the far South West and
high-quality social research of benefit to the local
community. Recent studies include a profile of poverty and
disadvantage in the South West regions; home care
services; carers' support needs; employment needs of
people with disabilities in Devon; healthcare needs of
families.

22

University of Portsmouth

University Hse, Winston Churchill Ave, Portsmouth
PO1 2UP; URL www.port.ac.uk;
E-mail info.centre@port.ac.uk; Tel 023 9284 8484; Fax 023
9284 2733

School of Social and Historical Studies
Milldam, Burnaby Rd, Portsmouth PO1 3AS; Tel 02392
876543
Head of School   F. Carr, BA, MSc
Research Co-ordinator   G. Moon, BA, PhD
Staff specialist fields for supervision of research include
centre–local relations in local government;
police–community relations; comparative analysis of
pressure groups; comparative health policy; medical
negligence; welfare policy; consumerism in health and
social care; community care; user involvement in service
provision; race/anti-racism in the social care environment.
No. of students
150

Social Services Research and Information Unit (SSRIU)
Under the joint auspices of the University of Portsmouth
and the Portsmouth City Council Department of Social
Services and Hampshire County Council Department of
Social Services.
University of Portsmouth, St. George's Bldg, 141 High St,
Portsmouth PO1 2HY; E-mail ssriu.port.ac.uk; Tel 023
9284 5550; Fax 023 9284 5555
Unit Director   C. Hayden, BSc, PhD
The SSRIU provides research and consultancy services in
the health and social care field. Its core work is for
Hampshire Social Services Department, and Portsmouth
City Council, but contract research is also undertaken for a
wide variety of statutory and non-statutory agencies at a
local, regional and national level. The unit runs a full-time
community care studentship and offers time-limited
research placements for social work practitioners.
Postgraduate supervision is also provided for projects
related to the work of the unit. SSRIU research is organised
into three central themes: the care and control of children;
the interface between health and social care and social
exclusion. Current projects include: the role of health
professionals in the child protection process, the use of
restraint in children's homes, school exclusions in the
primary sector and an evaluation of family group
conferences.

The University of Reading

Whiteknights, PO Box 217, Reading RG6 6AH;
URL www.reading.ac.uk;
E-mail schools.liaison@reading.ac.uk; Tel 0118 378 5123;
Fax 0118 378 4404

School of Health and Social Care
The University of Reading, Woodlands Ave, Reading
RG6 1HY; Tel 0118 378 8851
Head of School   Doug Badger, MSW, BA, CQSW
Course Leader (MA in Therapeutic Child Care)
Dr Linnet McMahon, BA, MSW, PhD, CQSW
Course Leader (MA in Advanced Social Work Studies)
Ann Quinn, BA DipSS
Course Leader (Practice Teaching Programme)   Linda Ward,
BA, MA
Visiting Research Fellow   Phillip Vaughan, MSc, CQSW,
DMS
Social Work Secretary   Lucia Gwinnell
Research interests and projects:
Mentally disordered offenders: Prison mental health, drugs
and alcohol.
Children and young people: School exclusion; play therapy
and social work; infant and child observation; therapeutic
communities for children and young people – processes
and outcomes.
Older people: Involvement of older people in planning
services; social work and palliative care.

Social work education: the processes of learning in social
work education; the processes of teaching in social work
education.
People with disabilities: Social role valorisation; self-
advocacy; parents' views of a special unit for pre-school
children with physical and learning disability.

University of Sheffield

Firth Crt, Western Bank, Sheffield, South Yorkshire
S10 2TN; URL www.sheffield.ac.uk;
E-mail j.a.smith1@sheffield.ac.uk; Tel 0114 222 5300;
Fax 0114 273 8496
Registrar and Secretary   D.E. Fletcher, BA, PhD

Department of Sociological Studies
No. of postgraduate taught students
71 full-time

Sheffield Hallam University

City Campus, Howard St, Sheffield, South Yorkshire
S1 1WB; URL www.shu.ac.uk; E-mail colei@shu.ac.uk;
Tel 0114 225 5555; Fax 0114 225 2430
A range of courses is offered at the School of Health and
Social Care and the school of Social Science and Law.

South Bank University

103 Borough Rd, London SE1 0AA; URL www.sbu.ac.uk;
Tel 020 7815 7815
Deputy Vice-Chancellor and Registrar   R. Phillips

Faculty of Health
Dean   Prof D.T. Sines

Faculty of Humanities and Social Science
Dean   Prof Jeffrey Weeks
These courses offer a firm grounding in social research, and
academic content with is at the cutting edge of highly
topical subjects, taught by leading experts in the field.

University of Southampton

The University, Highfield, Southampton SO17 1BJ;
URL www.soton.ac.uk; E-mail prospenq@soton.ac.uk;
Tel 023 8059 4741; Fax 023 8059 3482
Secretary and Registrar   J.F.D. Lauwerys, BEd, MA
Academic Registrar   Vacancy

Department of Social Work Studies
Head of Department   F. Sheldon
No. of students
80 MSc/DipScs; 80 for BSc/DipSw.

University of Sunderland

Langham Tower, Ryhope Rd, Sunderland, Tyne and Wear
SR2 7EE; E-mail student-helpline@sunderland.ac.uk;
Tel 0191 515 2000
Vice-Chancellor and Chief Executive   Prof Peter Fidler, MBE,
MSc, DipTP, DipSoc, MRTPI
University Secretary   J.D. Pacey, LLB
Academic Registrar   S. Porteous, MA, DPP

School of Health, Natural and Social Sciences
Priestman Bldg, Sunderland, Tyne and Wear SR1 3PZ

University of Surrey

Guildford, Surrey GU2 7XH; URL www.surrey.ac.uk
Academic Registrar   P.W. Beardsley, BA

European Institute of Health and Medical Sciences
Head of Institute   Prof R. Pope
Head (Postgraduate Taught Programmes)   Dr M. C. Murphy,
BSc, PhD

School of Human Sciences: Economics
Head of School   Prof S. Arber
Head of Department   Prof L. Hunt

School of Human Sciences: Psychology
Head of School   Prof S. Arber
Head of Department   C.R. Fife-Schaw

School of Human Sciences: Sociology
Head of Department   G. Cooper
Head of School   Prof S. Arber

University of Sussex

Sussex Hse, Falmer, Brighton, Brighton and Hove
    BN1 9RH; URL www.sussex.ac.uk;
    E-mail information@sussex.ac.uk; Tel 01273 606755
Registrar and Secretary   Neil Gershon, BA

University of Sussex Institute of Education
Education Development Bldg, University of Sussex,
    Brighton, Brighton and Hove BN1 9RG;
    E-mail usie.gso@sussex.ac.uk; Tel 01273 678260; 01273
    678347
Course Convenor   Prof Michael Eraut, BA, PhD
No. of students
16

Social Work and Social Care Group
School of Cultural and Community Studies, Essex Hse,
    University of Sussex, Brighton, Brighton and Hove
    BN1 9RQ; E-mail t.j.golds@sussex.ac.uk; Tel 01273
    606755
Chair (School of Social Work and Social Care)   Imogen Taylor,
    PhD
No. of students
40

Social Policy and Social Work Group
Chair (School of Social Work and Social Care)   Imogen Taylor,
    PhD
Education for the professions; Reflective learning and
practice: Interprofessional work; Teamwork; The Learning
Organisation; Gender issues in practice; Non-traditional
learners; User participation; Carers.

University of Teesside

Middlesbrough TS1 3BA; Tel 01642 342306; Fax 01642
    342399
Director (Social Sciences and Law)   Prof T. Blackman, BA,
    PhD
The School's wide range of courses includes youth studies,
youth work and community development, law and sport
and exercise.

University of Warwick

Coventry, West Midlands CV4 7AL;
    URL www.warwick.ac.uk
Registrar   J.W. Nicholls, BA, PhD(Camb)

Department of Psychology
Chair of Department   Prof K. Lamberts, BA, BSc, MSc,
    PhD

School of Health and Social Sciences
Chair of School   Prof A. Mullender, BA(Sheff), MA(Nott),
    CQSW, AcSS

Department of Sociology
Chair of Department   Prof R.D. Fine, BA(Oxf), PhD

Centre for Primary Health Care Studies
Chair   Prof Jeremy Dale, MA(Camb), PhD, MBBS, FRCGP,
    DRCOG, DipChild

University of the West of England

Frenchay Campus, Coldharbour La, Bristol BS16 1QY;
    URL www.uwe.ac.uk; E-mail admissions@uwe.ac.uk;
    Tel 0117 328 3333; Fax 0117 328 2810

Faculty of Health and Social Care
Glenside Campus, Blackberry Hill, Bristol BS16 1DD;
    URL www.uwe.ac.uk/hsc/;
    E-mail hsc.admissions@uwe.ac.uk; Tel 0117 328 8536;
    Fax 0117 328 8499
Dean of Faculty   Prof Steven West
Programme Leader (BSc(Hons)/Social Work)   Judith Thomas
Programme Leader (BA(Hons) Social Work Studies)
    Liz Frost
No. of students
Full-time (2587), part-time (1279)

University of Westminster

School of Integrated Health
115 New Cavendish St, London W1W 6UW;
    URL www.wmin.ac.uk;
    E-mail cav-admissions@wmin.ac.uk; Tel 020 7911 5883;
    Fax 020 7911 5079
Head of School   Dr Peter Davies, BA(Hons) MA, PhD

University of Wolverhampton

City Campus, Wulfruna St, Wolverhampton, West
    Midlands WV1 1SB; URL www.wlv.ac.uk;
    E-mail enquiries@wlv.ac.uk; Tel 01902 321000; Fax 01902
    322680
Vice-Chancellor   Prof J.S. Brooks, BSc, PhD, DSc, CEng,
    CPhys, FInstP

School of Education
Walsall Campus, Gorway Rd, Walsall, West Midlands
    WS1 3BD; URL www.wlv.ac.uk/sed/;
    E-mail sed-enquiries@wlv.ac.uk; Tel 01902 321050;
    Fax 01902 323177
Dean   Sir Geoff Hampton, KBE, CertEd, BEd, MEd;
    Tel 01902 323179; Fax 01902 323180

School of Health
City Campus, 62–68 Lichfield St, Wolverhampton, West
    Midlands WV1 1DJ; URL www.wlv.ac.uk/soh/;
    Tel 01902 321054
Dean   Prof Mel Sherannes

School of Humanities Languages and Social Sciences
City Campus, Wulfruna St, Wolverhampton, West
    Midlands WV1 1SB; URL www.wlv.ac.uk/shass/;
    E-mail kelly.j.guest@wlv.ac.uk; Tel 01902 321056
Dean   Prof G. Hurd

University of York

Heslington, York, YO10 5DD; URL www.york.ac.uk;
    Tel 01904 430000; Fax 01904 433433

Department of Social Policy and Social Work
Goodricke College, University of York, York
    URL www.york.ac.uk/depts/spsw;
    E-mail ahl4@york.ac.uk; Tel 01904 433483; 01904 433484;
    Fax 01904 433475
Head of Department (Social Policy)   Prof M. Maynard
Head of Department (Social Work)   Prof M. Stein
Director (Social Policy Research Unit)   Prof S.M. Baldwin
Director (Centre for Housing Policy)   Prof J. Ford
Director (Social Work Projects)   Prof I. Sinclair
Research degrees usually include some preliminary course
work in research methods. Subjects may be in the areas of
social policy or social work.
No. of students
270 approx.

22

Wales

Cardiff University

PO Box 921, Cardiff University, Cardiff CF10 3XQ;
URL www.cardiff.ac.uk;
E-mail prospectus@cardiff.ac.uk; Tel 029 2087 4899
Vice-Chancellor   Dr David Grant, CBE, PhD, FREng, FIEE

Cardiff Business School
Director   Prof R. Mansfield
Deputy Director (Research)   Prof M. Reed

Cardiff School of Social Sciences
Glamorgan Bldg, King Edward VII Ave, Cardiff CF10 3WT;
URL www.cardiff.ac.uk/socsi/;
E-mail hayessm@cf.ac.uk; Tel 029 2087 5179; Fax 029 2087 4175
Director   Prof Huw Beynon
Course Director (Centre for Social Work Studies)
Dr A.J. Pithouse
Director (Graduate Studies)   Prof G. Rees

School of Psychology
Cardiff University, PO Box 901, Cardiff CF10 3YG;
URL www.cardiff.ac.uk/psych/; Tel 029 2087 6707
Head of School   Prof D.M. Jones

Employment and the Welsh Economy
Contact   A. Roberts
Contact   M. Munday
A range of projects is being carried out within Cardiff Business School relating to the nature of economics and industrial change in Wales and the implications of these on employment. Some projects focus on the implications of inward investment and others on industrial restructuring.

Training
Contact   R. McNabb
Contact   K. Whitfield
Contact   J. Makepeace
A variety of research is underway in the Business School looking at the economics of training and implications of recent changes in the structure of training provision and the creation of training and enterprise councils.

Public Sector
Contact   G. Boyne
Contact   I. Kirkpatrick
Contact   M. Kitchener
Contact   N. Lane
Contact   P. Morgan
Contact   R. Whipp
Research on a number of aspects of the public sector, including its political restructuring, the introduction of the quasi-market in healthcare and the new managerial approaches found in local authorities.

University of Glamorgan

Vice-Chancellor   Prof Sir Adrian Webb, BSocSci, MSc(Econ)

School of Care Sciences
Glyn Taff, University of Glamorgan, Pontypridd, Rhondda, Cynon, Taff CF37 1DL; Tel 01443 483101; 01443 483102; Fax 01443 483118
Principal/Head of Department   Prof D. Mead, RGN, RCNT, RNT, DipNursing, DipAdvanced Nursing Ph

University of Wales

University Registry, Cathays Pk, Cardiff CF10 3NS;
URL www.wales.ac.uk; E-mail uniwales@wales.ac.uk;
Tel 029 2038 2656; Fax 029 2078 6212
Senior Vice-Chancellor   D. Llwyd Morgan, BA, DPhil, DLitt

University of Wales, Bangor

College Rd, Bangor, Gwynedd LL57 2DG;
URL www.bangor.ac.uk; Tel 01248 351151; Fax 01248 370451

School of Social Sciences
Head of School   Graham Day
Research Projects
Public Appointments: Motivations and Prompts; Local Distinctiveness Initiative; Employment Tribunals – a comparative study; Skills and the labour market; Community and heritage; Management of menstrual problems of women prisoners; Regulating Rural Space; Crime and Disorder in village India; Maximum security prisons; Constructing racial identities in Victorian England and colonial India; the relationship between social scientific research and public policy; National identity in the former USSR; Minority language planning issues.

University of Wales Institute, Cardiff (UWIC)

PO Box 377, Llandaff Campus, Western Ave, Cardiff CF5 2SG; URL www.uwic.ac.uk;
E-mail uwicinfo@uwic.ac.uk; Tel 029 2041 6070; Fax 029 2041 6286
Vice-Chancellor and Principal   Prof A.J. Chapman, BSc, PhD, FBPsS, CPsychol, FRSA
Head (School of Health and Social Sciences)   Dr Pam Harris

University of Wales, Lampeter

Lampeter, Ceredigion SA48 7ED

Department of Voluntary Sector Studies
Lampeter, Ceredigion SA48 7ED; URL www.lamp.ac.uk;
E-mail enquiries@volstudy.ac.uk; Tel 01570 424785; Fax 01570 423600
Course Director   C. Fisher

Scotland

University of Dundee

Nethergate, Dundee DD1 4HN; URL www.dundee.ac.uk;
E-mail secretary@dundee.ac.uk; Tel 01382 344000; Fax 01382 201604
Secretary   Dr D. J. Duncan

Department of Social Work
Faculty of Education and Social Work, Gardyne Rd, West Ferry, Dundee DD5 1NY;
URL www.dundee.ac.uk/socialwork;
E-mail info@socialwork.dundee.ac.uk; Tel 01382 464000
Head of Department   Dr B. Gillies
No. of students
350

The University of Edinburgh

Old College, South Bridge, Edinburgh EH8 9YL;
URL www.ed.ac.uk;
E-mail communications.office@ed.ac.uk; Tel 0131 650 1000
Head of College and Vice-Principal   Prof V. Bruce

Social Policy
Adam Ferguson Bldg, George Sq, Edinburgh EH8 9LL;
Tel 0131 650 3926; Fax 0131 650 3919
Head of Department   Dr M. Adler
Research projects and studies
Evaluation of services for pre-senile dementia sufferers; Legal aid in Scotland; Devolved management of schools; Personal injury actions under small claims procedures; Minutes of agreement in divorce; The Treasury and social policy; European social policy; Gender and transitions in

the local state; Use of computers in analysing qualitative data; Social policy in the Third World; Nurse morale and the quality of psychogeriatric care; International friends and developments in public policy.

Social Work
31 Buccleuch Pl, Edinburgh EH8 9JT;
URL www.socialwork.ed.ac.uk;
E-mail n.bryce@ed.ac.uk; Tel 0131 650 3912; Fax 0131 650 3911
Head (Social Work) Richard W. Perry
No. of students
60 (annual entry).

University of Glasgow
Glasgow G12 8QQ; URL www.gla.ac.uk; Tel 0141 330 2000
Academic Secretary Jan Hulme, MA

Department of Social Work
Lilybank Hse, Bute Gdns, Glasgow G12 8RT;
E-mail esslh@udcf.gla.ac.uk; Tel 0141 330 5029; Fax 0141 330 3543
Head of Department Joan Orme

Glasgow Caledonian University
City Campus, Cowcaddens Rd, Glasgow G4 0BA;
URL www.caledonian.ac.uk;
E-mail helpline@gcal.ac.uk; Tel 0800 027 9171; Fax 0141 331 3005
Principal and Vice-Chancellor Dr I. Johnston, CB, BSc, PhD, CIMgt, FIPD, FRSA
Dean (School of Health and Social Care) Dr Brian Durward

The Robert Gordon University
Schoolhill, Aberdeen AB10 1FR; URL www.rgu.ac.uk;
E-mail i.centre@rgu.ac.uk; Tel 01224 262000
Principal Prof William Stevely, BA, MA, PhDCChem, FRSC, MIBid

School of Applied Social Studies
Garthlee Rd, Aberdeen AB10 7QG;
E-mail assjl@ss1.rgu.ac.uk; Tel 01224 263201; Fax 01224 263222
Head Prof J. Lishman
Registrar Hilary Douglas
General Editor: Research Highlights J. Lishman
Disseminating research to practitioners and policy makers.
J. Love
No. of students
400

University of Stirling
University Secretary Kevin J. Clarke, BA
Research Projects and Officers:
Head (Research in Applied Social Science) Prof A. Bowes
Social Work Research Centre Prof G. McIvor
Centre for Comparative Research in Social Welfare
Prof J. Clasen
Dementia Services Development and Research
Prof M. Marshall

Department of Applied Social Science
Head of Department Prof A.M. Bowes
Director (Social Work Education) Prof C. Rowlings
Director (Housing Education) Dr D. Robertson
Dean of Faculty of Human Sciences Prof D.W.G. Timms
Research Officer Prof A. Bowes Minority ethnic social care, housing and health
Research Officer Prof A. Prout Projects on children and youth.
Research Officer Prof C. Hallett Projects on children and youth; Children's Pathways to Welfare.

Research Officer Dr K. Stalker Community care services in Scotland.
Research Officer Prof G. McIvor Social work and criminal justice.
Research Officer S. Tester Community care in Britain and Europe.
Research Officer Prof M. Marshall Dementia.
Research Officer Cathy Murray Children's Pathways to Welfare.
Research Officer Samantha Punch Children's Pathways to Welfare.
Research Officer I. Anderson Homelessness

University of Strathclyde
Faculty of Education, Jordanhill Campus, 76 Southbrae Dr, Glasgow G13 1PP; URL www.strath.ac.uk; Tel 0141 950 3000
Dean I.R.M. Smith
Official Correspondent (Faculty Officer) Lorna Dougall
Head (Social Work Department) Neil Ballantyne, BSc, DipSW, CQSW
Head of Department (Community Education) C. Rowlands, BA, DYS, MEd
No. of students
150 undergraduates, 100 postgraduates.

Northern Ireland

The Queen's University of Belfast
University Rd, Belfast BT7 1NN; URL web.qub.ac.uk;
E-mail g.kelly@qub.ac.uk; Tel 028 9033 5426; Fax 028 9066 5465

School of Social Work
Director of School John Pinkerton, BSc, MSc, PhD
No. of students in training
56

University of Ulster
Coleraine Campus, Cromore Rd, Coleraine, Co. Londonderry, BT52 1SA
Provost (Coleraine campus) Prof P. Roebuck, CBE, BA, PhD, FRHistS

Faculty of Life and Health Sciences
Dean Prof Bernadette Hannigan, BA(Mod), PhD, FIMBS

Faculty of Social Sciences
Dean Prof Anne Moran, MSc, DPhil pgCUT

Colleges and Institutes of Higher Education

England

Anglia Polytechnic University
Bishop Hall La, Chelmsford, Essex CM1 1SQ;
URL www.apu.ac.uk; Tel 01245 493131

Blackburn College
Feilden St, Blackburn BB2 1LH; Tel 01254 55144
Principal S. Ewing

Care, Health and Childhood Studies Centre
Contact Tricia Fanning, BA(Hons), PGCE, QSW

22

Bradford College

Great Horton Rd, Bradford, West Yorkshire BD7 1AY;
URL www.bradfordcollege.ac.uk;
E-mail schoolsliaison@bilk.ac.uk;
E-mail admissions@bilk.ac.uk; Tel (Admissions Office,
for course enquiries and applications) 01274 433333;
(Schools Liaison Office for general enquiries – voice and
minicom) 01274 433189; Fax (Admissions Office) 01274
431060; (Schools Liaison Office) 01274 433173
Principal Alan Hodgson, MA Cantab
Director (Academic Planning) Dr Gordon Lakin

Buckinghamshire Chilterns University College

Queen Alexandra Rd, High Wycombe, Buckinghamshire
HP11 2JZ; URL www.bcuc.ac.uk;
E-mail pnoden@bcuc.ac.uk; Tel 01494 522141; Fax 01494
461704
Director/Chief Executive Prof P.B. Mogford, MA(Cantab),
PhD
Dean of Faculty Dr Rod Marshall
Main qualifications offered
Buckinghamshire Chilterns University College is a
university college offering its own degrees in the higher
education sector.

Darlington College of Technology

Cleveland Ave, Darlington DL3 7BB;
URL www.darlington.ac.uk;
E-mail enquire@darlington.ac.uk; Tel 01325 503050;
Fax 01325 503000
Principal S.E. Farley

School of Health and Community Studies
Head of School M. French

Edge Hill

St. Helens Rd, Ormskirk, Lancashire L39 4QP;
URL www.edgehill.ac.uk;
E-mail enquiries@edgehill.ac.uk; Tel 01695 575171;
Fax 01695 579997
Chief Executive Dr J. Cater

Newcastle College

see Colleges of Further Education

University College Northampton

Park Campus, Boughton Green Rd, Northampton,
Northamptonshire NN2 7AL;
URL www.northampton.ac.uk;
E-mail marketing@northampton.ac.uk; Tel 01604 735500;
Fax 01604 722083

Faculty of Arts and Social Sciences
Faculty Registry, Park Campus, Boughton Green Rd,
Northampton, Northamptonshire NN2 7AL;
URL www.northampton.ac.uk;
E-mail marketing@northampton.ac.uk; Tel 0800 358
2232; 01604 735500; Fax 01604 722083

Southampton Institute

East Park Terr, Southampton SO14 0YN;
URL www.solent.ac.uk; E-mail enquiries@solent.ac.uk;
Tel 023 8031 9000; Fax 023 8022 2259
Principal Dr Roger Brown, MA(Cantab), PhD
Head of School (Human Sciences and Communication)
Prof James Connelly, BScSocSci, PhD

Warwickshire College, Leamington Spa, Rugby, Moreton Morrel

see Colleges of Further Education

Wales

Coleg Menai

Bangor, Gwynedd LL57 2TP; URL www.menai.ac.uk;
E-mail student.services@menai.ac.uk; Tel 01248 370125;
01248 383333

North East Wales Institute of Higher Education

Plas Coch, Wrexham LL11 2AW; URL www.newi.ac.uk;
E-mail enquiries@newi.ac.uk; Tel 01978 290666;
Fax 01978 290008
Principal Lecturer John Bates
Admissions Officer Keith Mitchell

University of Wales College, Newport

Caerleon Campus, PO Box 179, Newport NP18 3YG;
URL www.newport.ac.uk; E-mail uic@newport.ac.uk;
Tel 01633 430088; 01633 432432
Vice Chancellor and Principal Prof James R. Lusty
Academic Registrar P. Folan
Head of School M. A. Lyons
No. of students
200 full-time; 202 part-time.

Colleges of Further Education

England

Amersham and Wycombe College

Chesham Campus, Lycrome Rd, Chesham,
Buckinghamshire HP5 3LA;
URL www.amersham.ac.uk;
E-mail info@amersham.ac.uk; Tel 01494 735555;
Fax 01494 735588
High Wycombe Campus, Spring La, Flackwell Heath,
Buckinghamshire HP10 9HE; Tel 01494 735555;
Fax 01494 735577
Amersham Campus, Stanley Hill, Amersham,
Buckinghamshire HP7 9HN; Tel 01494 735555; Fax 01494
735566
Principal John Eaton

Barnsley College

PO Box 266, Church St, Barnsley, South Yorkshire S70 2YW;
URL www.barnsley.ac.uk;
E-mail programmeenquiries@barnsley.ac.uk; Tel 01226
730191; Fax 01226 298514
Principal Mr J. West

Health and Social Care
Faculty Director (Health, Care and Services) Chris Hanson

Bexley College

Tower Rd, Belvedere, Kent DA17 6JA;
URL www.bexley.ac.uk; Tel 01322 404000
Principal Bridget Boreham, BA (CertEd), MBA(Ed),
FIMgt
A range of courses is offered in the Services to People
department.

Birmingham College of Food, Tourism and Creative Studies

Summer Row, Birmingham, West Midlands B3 1JB;
URL www.bcftcs.ac.uk; E-mail sfellows@bcftcs.ac.uk;
Tel 0121 693 2281; Fax 0121 608 7100
Principal E.F. McIntyre, BA(Hons), MHCIMA, CBE

Bolton Community College

Horwich Campus, Victoria Rd, Bolton, Lancashire
BL6 6ED; Tel 01204 453629
Programme Manager Don Astley

The Bournemouth and Poole College

North Rd, Parkstone, Poole BH14 0LS;
URL www.thecollege.co.uk; Tel 01202 747600
Principal R. Dimbleby, MA, FRSA

Centre for Health and Social Care
Head of Centre Rob Hardy, MA, CQSW, PhD

Bromley College of Further and Higher Education

The Old Town Hall Site, Tweedy Rd, Bromley, Kent
BR1 3PP; Tel 020 8295 7060; Fax 020 8295 7099
Principal Peter Jones

Social Work Curriculum Team
Curriculum Team Leader Bob Cecil, BA, MA, PGCE

Calderdale College

Francis St, Halifax, West Yorkshire HX1 3UZ; Tel 01422
357357
Principal Monica Box
A range of courses is offered in the Health, Care and
Education Department.

Carlisle College

Victoria Pl, Carlisle, Cumbria CA1 1HS; Tel 01228 819000;
Fax 01228 514677
Principal M. Tattersall

Community Studies Department
Head of Department Helen Gudgeon

City of Bristol College

Ashley Down, Bristol BS7 9BU; Tel 0117 904 5168; Fax 0117
924 9134
Principal B.D. Styles, BA, MSc

The Bristol Centre for Care Studies
Head of Faculty Graham Theedom
Also available are tailor-made training courses for health
and care organisations.

NVQ Flexible/Open Learning Centre
City of Bristol College, The Hartcliffe Centre, Bristol
BS13 0RJ; Tel 0117 904 5626

City College Manchester

City Campus, Whitworth St, Manchester M1 3HB;
URL www.ccm.ac.uk; Tel 0161 279 7252; Fax 0161 236
5576
Principal Willie Mills

Colchester Institute

Sheepen Rd, Colchester, Essex CO3 3LL;
URL www.colch-inst.ac.uk; E-mail info@colch-inst.ac.uk;
Tel 01206 518000; Fax 01206 763041
Principal Danny Clough

Faculty of Music, Arts and Health
Head of Faculty T.V. Smyth, MA, BA, RGN, RMN,
DipNursing, RNT

Cornwall College

No course enquiries

Head Office, Lombard Hse, 8 Palace Rd, St. Austell,
Cornwall PL25 4BU; URL www.cornwall.ac.uk;
Tel 01726 222 718; Fax 01726 65926
Principal Dr A. Stanhope

Cornwall Business School
Head of School Dr C. Cohen

Doncaster College

Waterdale, Doncaster, South Yorkshire DN1 3EX;
URL www.don.ac.uk; E-mail infocentre@don.ac.uk;
Tel 01302 553553; Fax 01302 553559
Principal Dr G.E. Holmes

East Berkshire College

Station Rd, Langley, Slough SL3 8BY; Tel 01753 793000;
Fax 01753 793316
Principal Jean Robertson

School of Health, Caring, Leisure, Beauty and Hairdressing
Head of School Sarah Knowles

East Devon College

Bolham Rd, Tiverton, Devon EX16 6SH; Tel 01884 235200;
Fax 01884 235262
Principal J. Brooks
Curriculum Centre Manager Mike Ashley

Fareham College

Bishopsfield Rd, Fareham, Hampshire PO14 1NH;
Tel 01329 815200
Principal Mr Groves, BSc, MA(Ed), MBA, PGCE

Farnborough College of Technology

Boundary Rd, Farnborough, Hampshire GU14 6SB;
URL www.farn-ct.ac.uk; E-mail info@farn-ct.ac.uk;
Tel 01252 405555; Fax 01252 407041

School of Applied and Health Sciences
Head of School Dr E. Wolfenden

Grantham College

Stonebridge Rd, Grantham, Lincolnshire NG31 9AP;
URL www.grantham.ac.uk;
E-mail enquiry@grantham.ac.uk; Tel 01476 400200;
Fax 01476 400291
Principal Malcolm Saville, BSc(Soc), MA(Ed), PGCE

Grimsby College

Nuns Corner, Grimsby, Lincolnshire DN34 5BQ;
URL www.grimsby.ac.uk; E-mail infocent@grimsby.ac.uk;
Tel 01472 311222; Fax 01472 879924
Principal D. Khan, MA, DipTH, FAIA, FCCA

Care
Manager (Curriculum) B. Hodge

Guildford College of Further and Higher Education

Stoke Pk, Guildford, Surrey GU1 1EZ; Tel 01483 448660
Principal Lynne Sedgmore

Division of Health, Beauty and Community Studies
Head of Division Stephanie Davies

Harrogate College

Hornbeam Pk, Hookstone Rd, Harrogate, North Yorkshire
HG2 8QT; Tel 01423 879466; Fax 01423 879829
Principal/Dean (Further Education) D. Thornton
Deputy Principal J. Dishman

22

Havering College of Further and Higher Education

Quarles Campus, Tring Gdns, Romford, Essex RM3 9ES;
Tel 01708 462869
Principal N. Otley

Department of Social Services, Health and Education
Head of Department M.J. Clark

Hertford Regional College

Ware Centre, Scotts Rd, Ware, Hertfordshire SG12 9JF;
Tel 01920 465441
Principal Paul R. Harvey

Highbury College, Portsmouth

Dovercourt Rd, Cosham, Portsmouth PO6 2SA; Tel 023
9238 3131
Principal Stella Mbubaegbu

School of Health, Science and Care
Head of School Jackie Page

Huddersfield Technical College

New North Rd, Huddersfield, West Yorkshire HD1 5NN;
Tel 01484 536521
Principal and Chief Executive J.E. Coburn

School of Caring
Social Care Section, New North Rd, Huddersfield, West
Yorkshire HD1 5NN; Tel 01484 536521
Head of School J. Watson
Tutor (Social Work) D. Porritt

Isle College, Wisbech

Ramnoth Rd, Wisbech, Cambridgeshire PE13 2JE;
URL www.isle.ac.uk; E-mail courses@isle.ac.uk;
Tel 01945 582561 Ext 351
Principal M. Taylor
Co-ordinator (Tots to Teens) Deborah Hall
Kids' club (after-school care), pre-school, parent and
toddler, holiday club.

Lambeth College

Clapham Centre, 45 Clapham Common Southside, London
SW4 9BL; URL www.lambethcollege.ac.uk;
E-mail courses@lambethcollege.ac.uk; Tel (Course
enquiries) 020 501 5000; (General) 020 7501 5010; Fax 020
501 5041
Principal Ian Ashman

Leicester College

Freemen's Park Campus, Aylestone Rd, Leicester LE2 7LW;
URL www.leicestercollege.ac.uk;
E-mail info@leicestercollege.ac.uk; Tel 0116 224 2000;
Fax 0116 224 2194
Curriculum Area Manager Wendy Brickett

Caring Professions
Curriculum Area Manager Wendy Brickett

Liverpool Community College

Old Swan Centre, Broadgreen Rd, Liverpool, Merseyside
L13 5SQ; Tel 0151 252 1515; Fax 0151 228 9873
Head of Faculty David Green

Programme Area: Health
Head of Faculty D. Green, MSc, MA, CertEd

Lowestoft College

St. Peter's St, Lowestoft, Suffolk NR32 2NB; Tel 01502
583521
Principal G. Parsons

School of Community Studies
Centre Manager J. Sutton

Macclesfield College

Park La, Macclesfield, Cheshire SK11 8LF;
E-mail info@macclesfield.ac.uk; Tel 01625 410000;
Fax 01625 410001
Principal Wendy Wright

Management and Professional Studies
Sector Manager Elizabeth Gorb

Mid-Kent College of Higher and Further Education

Horsted Centre, Maidstone Rd, Chatham, Kent ME5 9UQ;
URL www.midkent.ac.uk; Tel 01634 830633; Fax 01634
830224
Principal and Chief Executive John Levett

Middlesbrough College

Marton Rd, Middlesbrough TS4 3RZ; Tel 01642 333333;
Fax 01642 333310
Principal John Hogg, LLB(Hons) Cert Ed

Faculty of Health, Care and Basic Education
Head of Faculty P. Smith, MSc, BA, DipTEFL

New College, Durham

Framwellgate Moor, Durham, County Durham DH1 5ES;
Tel 0191 375 4000; Fax 0191 375 4216
Principal John Widdowson

New College Nottingham

Basford Hall, Stockhill La, Nottingham NG6 0NB;
URL www.ncn.ac.uk; E-mail enquiries@ncn.ac.uk;
Tel 0115 916 2001
Faculty Head Val Wood

Newark and Sherwood College

Friary Rd, Newark, Nottinghamshire NG24 1PB; Tel 01636
680680
Principal J. Gray

Community Services and Personal Care
Manager P. Towner

Newcastle College

Rye Hill Campus, Scotswood Rd, Newcastle upon Tyne,
Tyne and Wear NE4 7SA; URL www.ncl-coll.ac.uk;
E-mail enquiries@ncl-coll.ac.uk; Tel 0191 200 4000;
Fax 0191 200 4517
Principal and Chief Executive Jackie Fisher

North East Surrey College of Technology

Reigate Rd, Ewell, Surrey KT17 3DS;
URL www.nescot.ac.uk; E-mail hccs@nescot.ac.uk;
Tel (Course enquiries) 020 8394 3038
Chief Executive R. J. Pritchard, MSc, PGCE, DipAES, CBiol,
FRSA

Department of Health, Community and Care Studies
Head of Department S. Dickinson, BSocSc(Hons), PGCE,
MSc

North Hertfordshire College

Monkswood Way, Stevenage, Hertfordshire SG1 1LA;
URL www.nhc.ac.uk; Tel 01462 424242; Fax 01462 443054
Principal   R. Gochin
Curriculum Area Manager   Lesley Davies
Director (Resources and IS)   Simon Botterill

North Lincolnshire College

Monks Rd Campus, Monks Rd, Lincoln, Lincolnshire
LN2 5HQ; Tel 01522 876000; Fax 01522 876200
Principal   John Allen

Division of Community Studies
Head of Division   Patrick O'Keefe

North Lindsey College

Kingsway, Scunthorpe, North Lincolnshire DN17 1AJ;
URL www.northlindsey.ac.uk; Tel 01724 281111;
Fax 01724 294020
Principal   Roger Bennett
Director (Learner Support Services)   Kit Sargent

North Oxfordshire College and School of Art

Broughton Rd, Banbury, Oxfordshire OX16 9QA; Tel 01295
252221; Fax 01295 250381
Principal   G. Wharton

Division of Business and Community Services
Course Leader (Care)   N. Taker
Course Leader (Child Care and Education)   M. French

North Tyneside College of Further Education

Embleton Ave, Wallsend, Tyne and Wear NE28 9NL;
Tel 0191 229 5000; Fax 0191 229 5301
Principal   Les Walton, OBE, BA(Hons), MEd, FRSA

Faculty of Care and General Education
Head of Faculty   Helen Wright

College of North West London

Dudden Hill La, London NW10 2XD;
E-mail course.enquiries@cnwl.ac.uk; Tel (Course
enquiries) 020 8208 8050; Fax 020 8208 5151
Principal   Anthony Holyhead

Faculty of Arts, Community and Leisure Studies
Head of Faculty   Pat Brennan-Barrett

Northampton College

Booth La, Northampton, Northamptonshire NN3 3RF;
Tel 01604 734567; Fax 01604 734394
Principal   Len Closs

Health, Care and Love in Childcare
Head of Faculty   Sue Baker

Oxford College of Further Education

Oxpens Rd, Oxford, Oxfordshire OX1 1SA; Tel 01865
245871
Principal   C.R. Wickens, MSc, CChem, MRSC

Faculty of Arts
Curriculum Manager   Pam Coull

Plymouth College of Further Education

Goschen Centre, Saltash Rd, Plymouth PL2 2BD
Head (Caring Services)   R. Haws

Department of Science and Health
Head of Department   Dr Andy Thompson

Preston College

St. Vincent's Rd, Fulwood, Preston, Lancashire PR2 4UR;
Tel 01772 772200 ext 2229
Principal   S. Ingleson

Academy of Health, Social Care and Early Years
Dean   Judith Broome

St. Helens College

Brook St, St. Helens, Merseyside WA10 1PZ;
URL www.sthelens.ac.uk;
E-mail enquire@sthelens.ac.uk; Tel 01744 733 766

College of Health and Care
Town Centre Campus, Brook St, St. Helens, Merseyside
WA10 1PZ; URL www.sthelens.ac.uk;
E-mail enquire@sthelens.ac.uk; Tel 01744 733766
Head of College   D. Wheatley

The Sheffield College

PO Box 345, Sheffield, South Yorkshire S60 2YY; Tel 0114
260 3603

Health, Community and Social Care
Faculty Director   Vaun Cutts

Somerset College of Arts and Technology

Wellington Rd, Taunton, Somerset TA1 5AX;
E-mail somerset@somerset.ac.uk; Tel 01823 366366;
Fax 01823 366353
Principal   Alison Scott

School of Health and Social Care Studies
Head of School   Nick Davey

Stafford College

Earl St, Stafford, Staffordshire ST16 2QR;
E-mail enquiries@staffordcoll.ac.uk; Tel 01785 223800;
Fax 01785 259953
Principal   Stephen Willis, BSc, MEd

Caring Courses
Head of School   C. Challinor

Stockport College of Further and Higher Education

Wellington Rd South, Stockport, Greater Manchester
SK1 3UQ; URL www.stockport.ac.uk;
E-mail enquiries@stockport.ac.uk; Tel 0845 230 3102
Principal   Peter Roberts, BA(Hons), MA, MEd

Stoke-on-Trent College

Stoke Rd, Shelton, Stoke-on-Trent ST4 2DG;
URL www.stokecoll.ac.uk; E-mail info@stokecoll.ac.uk;
Tel 01782 208208; Fax 01782 603504
Burslem Campus, Moorland Rd, Burslem, Staffordshire
ST6 1JJ; URL www.stokecoll.ac.uk;
E-mail info@stokecoll.ac.uk; Tel 01782 208208; Fax 01782
603504
Principal   G. Moore

Tameside College

Beaufort Rd, Ashton-under-Lyne, Greater Manchester
OL6 6NX; Tel 0161 908 6600
Chief Executive   J. Carrik

22

School of Care, Counselling and Community Work
Head of School Ann Walsh

Telford College of Arts and Technology

Haybridge Rd, Wellington, Shropshire TF1 2NP; Tel 01952 642200; Fax 01952 243657
Principal D.F. Boynton, BSc, MSc, CEng, FRSA

Department of Caring, Health and Art
Head of Department Jane Reeves, BSc(Hons), RGN, CertEd, DipHE

Thanet College

Ramsgate Rd, Broadstairs, Kent CT10 1PN; Tel 01843 605040
Principal G.F. Burney, BSc, MPhil, CEng, MIMechE, CertEd

Early Years and Care Studies
Head of Section R. Evans, BSc(Hons), MA, RGN, RM, CertEd

Tile Hill College of Further Education

Tile Hill La, Coventry, West Midlands CV4 9SU;
URL www.tilehill.ac.uk; E-mail info@tilehill.ac.uk;
Tel 024 7669 4200
Principal P. Taylor, BSc(Hons), ACA

School of Health, Education and Social Work
Head of School Gill Manthorpe, MA(Ed)

Wakefield College

Margaret St, Wakefield, West Yorkshire WF1 2DH;
URL www.wakcoll.ac.uk; Tel 01924 789356; Fax 01924 789340
Principal Heather MacDonald

Faculty of Caring Services
Faculty Manager Liz McFarlane

Warwickshire College, Royal Leamington Spa, Rugby, Moreton Morrell

Warwick New Rd, Leamington Spa, Warwickshire CV32 5JE; URL www.warkscol.ac.uk;
E-mail enquiries@warkscol.ac.uk; Tel 01926 318000
Principal I. Morgan

Caring Courses
Contact Janet Bogyor

West Herts College, Dacorum Campus

Marlowes, Hemel Hempstead, Hertfordshire HP1 1HD;
Tel 01442 221613
Head (Care Studies) Helen Mays, MSc, DMS, RGN

School of Care Studies
Senior School Administrator Josephine Hopkins

West Kent College of Further Education

Brook St, Tonbridge, Kent TN9 2PW; Tel 01732 358101;
Fax 01732 771415
Chief Executive Bill Fearon

Business and Community Studies
Head of Faculty Mandy Hobart

Wiltshire College

Registered with CCETSW as an approved Vocational Education and Training Provider.

Cocklebury Rd, Chippenham, Wiltshire SN15 3QO;
URL www.wiltscoll.ac.uk; E-mail info@wiltscoll.ac.uk;
Tel 01249 464644
Principal G. Bright

Wirral Metropolitan College

Borough Rd, Birkenhead, Wirral CH42 9QD;
URL www.wmc.ac.uk; Tel 0151 551 7894; Fax 0151 551 7401
Principal Ray Dowd

Humanities, Care and Education
Head of Programmes A. Dunn
Programme Team Leader C. Court

Wolverhampton College

Westfield Rd, Bilston, Wolverhampton, West Midlands WV14 6ER; E-mail p.lidster@bilston.ac.uk; Tel 01902 821000; Fax 01902 821101
Head of Department R. Ashwell

Wales

Coleg Gwent

Newport (NASH) Campus, Nash Rd, Newport NP19 4TS;
E-mail pegingtonjc@coleggwent.ac.uk; Tel 01633 466178;
Fax 01633 466090
General Manager David Rees

Care Studies Centre
Manager Brenda Roberts

Coleg Menai

Principal Haydn E. Edwards, BSc, MBA, PhD, FRSC, FIMgt

Health and Social Care Unit
Unit Manager Elaine Pumfrey

Scotland

Aberdeen College

The Gallowgate, Aberdeen AB25 1BN;
URL www.abcol.ac.uk; E-mail enquiry@abcol.ac.uk;
Tel 01224 612000; Fax 01224 612001
Sector Manager Frank Hughes; Tel 01224 612188

Clydebank College

Kilbowie Rd, Clydebank, West Dunbartonshire G81 2AA;
Tel 0141 952 7771
Principal Matt Mochar

Social Care Section
Curriculum Leader Kate Jamie

Dumfries and Galloway College

Heathall, Dumfries, Dumfries and Galloway DG1 3QZ;
URL www.dumgal.ac.uk; E-mail info@dumgal.ac.uk;
Tel 01387 261261; 01387 261265
Principal Tony Jakimciw

Health and Social Studies
Tel 01387 243881
Head of Department Sue Clarke;
E-mail clarkes@dumgal.ac.uk
Programme Manager June Holland;
E-mail hollandj@dumgal.ac.uk

Dundee College

Melrose Campus, Melrose Terr, Dundee DD3 7QX;
URL www.dundeecoll.ac.uk;
E-mail g.grandison@dundee.coll.ac.uk; Tel 01382
834834
Curriculum Manager   Gwen Grandison

Social and Health Studies
Team Leader (Health Care)   Marie McArthur
Team Leader (Child Care)   Brenda Dunn
Team Leader (Social Care)   Helen Duncan
Team Leader (Horticulture)   Gordon Croll
Team Leader (Care)   Anne Hamilton

Inverness College

3 Longman Rd, Longman South, Inverness, Highland
IV1 1SA; Tel 01463 236681; Fax 01463 711977
Principal   P. Hafren (Acting)

Jewel and Esk Valley The Edinburgh and Lothians College

Eskbank Campus, Newbattle Rd, Dalkeith, Midlothian
EH22 3AE; E-mail eforrest@jevc.ac.uk; Tel 0131 660 1010;
Fax 0131 663 3710
Principal   J. Lisgo

Langside College Glasgow

50 Prospecthill Rd, Glasgow G42 9LB;
URL www.langside.ac.uk;
E-mail enquireuk@perseus.langside.ac.uk (UK
Enquiries); enquire int@perseus.langside.ac.uk
(International Enquiries); Tel 0141 649 4991; Fax 0141 632
5252
Principal   A. Graeme Hyslop
Head of Faculty   Jan Watson
Senior Lecturer (Social Care Courses)   David Macallan

Motherwell College

Dalzell Dr, Motherwell, North Lanarkshire ML1 2DD;
URL www.motherwell.ac.uk;
E-mail mcol@motherwell.co.uk; Tel 01698 232323;
Fax 01698 232 527
Principal and Chief Executive   Richard Millham
A range of courses is offered in the caring, social sciences,
languages and communication, and support for learning
and personal and social development departments.

North Glasgow College

110 Flemington St, Glasgow G21 4BX;
URL www.north-gla.ac.uk;
E-mail c.mckay@north-gla.ac.uk; Tel 0141 558 9001
Principal   R. Knox, MA, DipM, MCIM, FRSA, FCMI,
MInstLM

Community Services
Head of Department   C. McKay, BA, MEd

Stevenson College

Bankhead Ave, Sighthill, Edinburgh EH11 4DE; Tel 0131
535 4600; Fax 0131 535 4666
Principal   Dr R. Harris, BA, MEd

Department of Applied Social Studies
Head of Department   N.J. Reynolds

Northern Ireland

Belfast Institute of Further and Higher Education

Millfield Bldg, Belfast BT1 1HS;
URL www.belfastinstitute.ac.uk;
E-mail vboyd@belfastinstitute.ac.uk; Tel 028 9026 5000;
Fax 028 9026 5451
Director   B. Turtle
Deputy Director   T. Neilands
Head (Department of Continuing Education)   P. Scott
Head (Centre for Social Work/Social Care)   V. Boyd
No. of students
3700 (full-time); 35 000 (part-time)

North West Institute of Further and Higher Education

Strand Rd, Londonderry, County Londonderry BT48 7BY;
URL www.nwifhe.ac.uk; Tel 028 7127 6000; Fax 028 7126
0520
Director   P.P. Gallagher, BA(Hons), CCCE, MA(Ed), FRSA

Department of Caring Services
Head of Department   G.R. Cowan, MA, BA(Hons), RMN,
DipMang(Open)

Adult Colleges

22

Ruskin College

Walton St, Oxford, Oxfordshire OX1 2HE;
URL www.ruskin.ac.uk; E-mail enquiries@ruskin.ac.uk;
Tel 01865 554331; Fax 01865 554372
Principal   Lorna Duffin (Acting)
Course Leader   Richard Bryant

The University of Birmingham, Selly Oak Campus

Elmfield Hse, Birmingham, West Midlands B29 6LQ;
Tel 0121 415 2286; Fax 0121 415 2296
Course Director   Ralph Thomas, BA(Hons), MA,
DipAppSocSt
Diploma in Social Work, for both non-graduates and
graduates (2 years), 3rd year leading to BA Hons Applied
Social Sciences. Development Studies, training courses for
experienced field workers and headquarters' staff of
voluntary aid agencies and church development
organisations from different countries. NVQ 4 in Care for
workers in Social Work/Social Care.

Research and Development

- **National Organisations**
- **Specialist Research**

Research and Development

National Organisations

Economic and Social Research Council (ESRC)

Polaris Hse, North Star Ave, Swindon SN2 1UJ;
URL www.esrc.ac.uk; Tel 01793 413000; Fax 01793
413001
Chair Frances Cairncross
Chief Executive Prof Ian Diamond, AcSS
Director (Communications and Information)
Astrid Wissenberg
Director (Policy and Resources) Glyn Davies
Director (Research, Training and Development)
Adrian Alsop
The ESRC is the UK's largest funding agency for research
and postgraduate training relating to social and economic
issues. It provides independent, high-quality, relevant
research to business, the public sector and Government.
The ESRC invests more than £76 million every year in
social science and at any time is supporting some 2000
researchers in academic institutions and research policy
institutes. It also funds postgraduate training within the
social sciences to nurture the researchers of tomorrow.

Institute of Community Studies

18 Victoria Park Sq, Bethnal Green, London E2 9PF;
URL www.community-studies.ac.uk; Tel 020 8980 6263
Director Peter Hall
Administrator John Stevens

Medical Research Council

20 Park Cres, London W1B 1AL; URL www.mrc.ac.uk;
E-mail firstname.surname@headoffice.mrc.ac.uk; Tel 020
7636 5422; Fax 020 7436 6179
Chair Sir Anthony Cleaver, MA, FBCS
Chief Executive Prof Sir George Radda, CBE, FRS
Executive Director N. Winterton, MA
Director (Research Management) D. Dunstan, PhD

National Development Team for People with Learning Disabilities

Europa Hse, Barcroft St, Bury, Greater Manchester BL9 5BT;
URL www.ndt.org.uk; E-mail office@ndt.org.uk;
Tel 0161 447 8807; Fax 0161 447 8877
Chief Executive Joan Maughan

National Society for the Prevention of Cruelty to Children

42 Curtain Rd, London EC2A 3NH;
URL www.nspcc.org.uk; Tel 020 7825 2500
Head (Child Protection Research) Dr P. Cawson

Undertakes and promotes research into child protection
and related issues.
Specialist library on child protection – study facilities by
appointment. See also library website: www.nspcc.org.uk/
inform, aimed at practitioners and researchers.

Policy Studies Institute (PSI)

100 Park Village East, London NW1 3SR;
URL www.psi.org.uk; E-mail postmaster@psi.org.uk;
Tel 020 7468 0468; Fax 020 7388 0914
Director Prof Jim Skea
The Policy Studies Institute (PSI) is one of the leading
independent social and economic research centres in the
UK, contributing benchmark studies to the policy process
since 1932.
PSI is a registered charity, run on a non-profit basis, and is
not associated with any pressure group or commercial
interest. In January 1998 it became a wholly owned
subsidiary of the University of Westminster. PSI's mission
is to inform policy by establishing the facts.

Social Research Association

PO Box 33660, London N16 6WE; URL www.the-sra.org.uk;
E-mail admin@the-sra.org.uk
Chair Ceridwen Roberts

Specialist Research

23

Action Medical Research

Vincent Hse, Horsham, West Sussex RH12 2DP;
URL www.action.org.uk; E-mail info@action.org.uk;
Tel 01403 210406
President General The Lord Guthrie
Chair Stephen May, MA
Chief Executive Simon Moore, CB
Dedicated to preventing and treating disease and disability
by funding vital medical research.

Addiction Research Unit

(Institute of Psychiatry) National Addiction Centre,
Addiction Sciences Bldg, London SE5 8AF; Tel 0171 703
5411
Honorary Director Prof Griffith Edwards

Arthritis Research Campaign

Copeman Hse, St. Mary's Crt, St. Mary's Gate, Chesterfield,
Derbyshire S41 7TD; E-mail info@arc.org.uk; Tel 01246
558033; Fax 01246 558007
Chief Executive Fergus Logan
Medical research charity funding research into the causes
and means of treatment of the rheumatic diseases.

Association for Child Psychology and Psychiatry

St. Saviour's Hse, 39–41 Union St, London SE1 1SD;
    URL www.acpp.org.uk; E-mail acpp@acpp.org.uk;
    Tel 020 7403 7458; Fax 0207 7403 7081
Senior Administrator   Ms I. King

Association for Children with Heart Disorders

26 Elizabeth Dr, Helmshore, Rossendale, Lancashire
    BB4 4JB; URL www.tachd.org.co.uk;
    E-mail gillhitchen@btinternet.com; Tel 01706 213632;
    Fax 01706 213632
Chair   Janet Rathburn
Treasurer   A. McGahon
National Secretary   Gill Hitchen
Scottish Branch   Jim Kelman
To give support and understanding in everyday care and
welfare to parents and families of children with heart
disorders; to improve facilities for children at heart units in
hospitals throughout Great Britain; to maintain standards
of improvement as new techniques develop; to raise funds
to help purchase essential specialised equipment which is
not always forthcoming through normal NHS channels.

Association for Research in the Voluntary and Community Sector (ARVAC)

2d Aberdeen Studios, 22-24 Highbury Gr, London N5 2EA;
    E-mail arvac@arvac.org.uk; Tel 020 7704 2315; Fax 020
    7704 9995
Director   L. Symes
ARVAC was formally established in 1978.
Aims
To promote effective community action through research;
to act as a resource to people interested in research in or on
community organisations; to encourage and facilitate networking and collaboration between people working in this
field; to ensure findings or research on community organisations are made available to policy makers; to play a role in
identifying gaps in our knowledge of the community sector.
Activities
ARVAC organises seminars, conferences and regional
research training workshops. Publishes occasional papers,
pamphlets and a quarterly bulletin. Manages the ARVAC
database.

Association for the Study of Obesity (ASO)

URL www.aso.org.uk
Chair   Dr S. Jebb
Treasurer   N. Norgan
Administrative Officer   C. Hawkins
To promote medical research into the causes, prevention
and treatment of obesity. To facilitate contact between
individuals and organisations interested in any aspect of
the problem of obesity and body weight regulations.

Birth Control Trust

16 Mortimer St, London W1N 7RD;
    URL www.easynet.co.uk/bct/;
    E-mail bct@birthcontroltrust.org.uk; Tel 0171 580 9360;
    Fax 0171 637 1378
Aims to advance medical and sociological research in
contraception, sterilisation and legal abortion and to
publish the results of such research.

Board of Deputies of British Jews

Commonwealth Hse, 1–19 New Oxford St, London WC1A
    1NU; URL www.bod.org.uk; E-mail info@bod.org.uk;
    Tel 020 7543 5400; Fax 020 7543 0010
Director (Community Issues)   M. Schmool, BSocSci
Compiles data on various aspects of the British Jewish
community, and prepares interpretive studies of social and
demographic trends.

British Heart Foundation (BHF)

14 Fitzhardinge St, London W1H 6DH;
    URL www.bhf.org.uk; Tel 020 7935 0185; Fax 020 7486
    5820
Director-General   Major General L.F.H. Busk
Secretary and Director (Finance)   J. Edwards
Director (Fundraising)   A. Morciras
Director (Communications)   B. McBride
Chief Executive (Shops)   K. Blair
Research into causes, diagnosis, treatment and ultimate
prevention of all diseases of the heart and circulation.
Education and information for the general public and the
medical professions. Provision of cardiac care equipment,
nursing care and other patient support services and
coordination of life saving training skills. There are nine
regional offices.

British Society of Audiology (BSA)

80 Brighton Rd, Reading RG6 1PS;
    URL www.b-s-a.demon.co.uk;
    E-mail bsa@b-s-a.demon.co.uk; Tel 0118 966 0622;
    Fax 0118 935 1915
Chair   Prof Linda Luxon
Hon Secretary   A. Reid
Hon Treasurer   G.P. Frost
Aims to further the science of and research in audiology,
and to advance education in audiology.

British Society for Developmental Disabilities (BSDD)

5 Handsworth Dr, Great Barr, Birmingham, West Midlands
    B43 6ED; URL www.bjdd.org; Tel 0121 360 2027
Hon Administrator   J.G. Csucsmi
Aims to mobilise, foster and encourage interest in any of
the problems and aspects of developmental disabilities
by meetings, publications, conferences and any other
means.

British Thoracic Society

17 Doughty St, London WC1N 2PL;
    URL www.brit-thoracic.org.uk;
    E-mail bts@brit-thoracic.org.uk; Tel 020 7831 8778;
    Fax 020 7831 8766
Honorary Secretary   Dr J. T. Macfarlane
Professional medical society. Publishes treatment
guidelines and promotes education and research into such
lung diseases as asthma, bronchitis, emphysema,
pneumonia, tuberculosis, cancer and others.

Cancer Research UK

PO Box 123, Lincoln's Inn Fields, London WC2A 3PX;
    URL www.cancerresearch.uk.org;
    E-mail alex.markham@cancer.org.uk; Tel 020 7242 0200;
    Fax 020 7269 3610
Chief Executive   Prof Alex Markham
Investigation into the causes, prevention, treatment and
cure of cancer through intensive research in the
organisation's own laboratories and hospital units.

Child Accident Prevention Trust (CAPT)

18–20 Farringdon La, London EC1R 3HA;
    URL www.capt.org.uk; E-mail safe@capt.org.uk; Tel 020
    7608 3828; Fax 020 7608 3674
Chair   Robin Hope
Director   K. Phillips
National charity dedicated to reducing the number of
children and young people killed, disabled and seriously
injured as a result of accidents. CAPT is responsible for the
annual Child Safety Week. Provides information to parents,
carers and students. Training and advocacy over child
accident prevention.

Children's Liver Disease Foundation

36 Great Charles St, Birmingham, West Midlands B3 3JY;
    URL www.childliverdisease.org;
    E-mail info@childliverdisease.org; Tel 0121 212 3839;
    Fax 0121 212 4300
Chief Executive   C. Arkley
To create a greater public awareness of the problem of liver
disease in children. Funds research into the causes,
treatment and cures for childhood liver disease. Provides
emotional support, literature and education.

Civil Liberties Trust

21 Tabard St, London SE1 4LA;
    URL www.liberty-human-rights.org.uk;
    E-mail info@liberty-human-rights.org.uk; Tel 020 7403
    3888; Fax 020 7407 5354
Director   Shami Chakrabarti
Registered charity and sister organisation of Liberty, which
carries out research and education and provides legal
assistance on civil liberties issues.

Cystic Fibrosis Trust

11 London Rd, Bromley, Kent BR1 1BY;
    URL www.cftrust.org.uk; Tel 020 8464 7211; Fax 020 8313
    0472
Finances research into cystic fibrosis and helps and advises
parents of affected children and adults.

DrugScope

DrugScope is an independent centre of expertise on drugs,
with an aim to inform policy development and reduce
drug-related risk. It provides quality drug information,
promotes effective responses to drug taking, undertakes
research at local, national and international levels, advises
on policy-making, encourages informed debate and speaks
for its member organisations working on the ground.
The DrugScope website gives access to a wide range of
information including a drugs encyclopaedia and a good
practice and research section with many online
publications. It also enables searching of the library,
treatment service and training databases.
32–36 Loman St, London SE1 0EE;
    URL www.drugscope.org.uk;
    E-mail info@drugscope.org.uk; Tel 020 7928 1211;
    Fax 020 7928 1771
Chair   Sylvie Pearson
Chief Executive   Frank Warburton (Acting)
Manager (Communications)   Rachel Lohan

Information and Library Service

E-mail info@drugscope.org.uk; Tel (Public enquiry line)
    0870 774 3682
The Information and Library Service, staffed by qualified
professionals, answers thousands of enquiries every year
from a wide range of people on drug misuse issues. This
includes drug workers, students and those involved in
education, housing, criminal justice and healthcare
services, as well as the general public and drug users.

Press Office

E-mail press@drugscope.org.uk; Tel (Enquiries) 020 7922
    8607

Eating Disorder Association (EDA)

1st Fl, Wensum Hse, 103 Prince of Wales Rd, Norwich,
    Norfolk NR1 1DW; URL www.edauk.com;
    E-mail info@edauk.com; Tel (Admin) 0870 770 3256;
    (Adult Helpline (Mon–Fri 08302030)) 0845 634 1414;
    (Recorded information service) 0906 302 0012; (Youth
    Helpline (Under 18's: Mon–Fri 16001830)) 0845 634
    7650

EDA offers a range of services, which include national
telephone helplines; a UK-wide network of local self-help
and support groups, postal and telephone contacts; a
comprehensive range of information including leaflets for
young people; membership which includes a quarterly
magazine; lists of treatment available in your area; a
helpline and support service for young people; an annual
conference for members to learn about the latest
developments; a telephone counselling programme for
people with bulimia; training for professionals in health,
education and social care; a professional journal, European
Eating Disorders Review, which provides information and
practical help for professionals in all disciplines; service
specifications guidelines for the treatment of anorexia and
bulimia nervosa; an extensive and informative website.

Foundation for the Study of Infant Deaths (FSID)

Artillery Hse, 11–19 Artillery Row, London SW1P 1RT;
    URL www.sids.org.uk/fsid/; E-mail fsid@sids.org.uk;
    Tel (General enquiries) 0870 757 0885; (Helpline) 0870
    787 0554; Fax 0870 787 0725
Director   Joyce Epstein
Chair   C. Baker
Chair (Scientific Committee)   Prof A. Cox
Chair (Information and Support Committee)
    Rev R. Robinson
FSID is the UK's leading cot death charity aiming to
prevent sudden infant death and promote baby health.
FSID raises funds for research (over £8 million) into the
causes and prevention of cot death, supports bereaved
families and offers information and advice on how to
reduce the risk of cot death to parents, carers and health
professionals.

The Grubb Institute of Behavioural Studies

Cloudesley St, London N1 0HU; URL www.grubb.org.uk;
    E-mail info@grubb.org.uk; Tel 020 7278 8061; Fax 020
    7278 0728
Managing Consultant   Jean Hutton
The Grubb Institute of Behavioural Studies energises
people to transform their behaviour individually and
corporately as they gain insight into their experience of
human systems, institutions and personal relations seen in
the context of psychodynamic and systemic thinking and
the Christian faith. Founded in 1969, it is an applied social
research institute working at critical organisational,
professional, social and spiritual issues which undermine
the effective work of client institutions. In working with
both conscious and unconscious processes, staff draw on
theological concepts and values to provide frameworks of
meaning and purpose. The Institute is an independent non-
profit-making body with full-time staff and a voluntary
Christian Council.

Home and Leisure Accident Surveillance Systems

Bay 435, 1 Victoria St, London SW1H 0ET; Tel 020 7215
    2114
Aims to improve consumer safety. Reports and computer
printout available.

Institute of Cancer Research

123 Old Brompton Rd, London SW7 3RP;
    URL www.icr.ac.uk; Tel 020 7153 5380; Fax 020 7153 5572
Chief Executive   P.W.J. Rigby, PhD
Secretary   J.M. Kipling, FCA
Through association with the Royal Marsden NHS Trust
the institute presents a multi-disciplinary approach to basic
and applied cancer research and training.

ISDD (Institute for the Study of Drug Dependence)

see DrugScope

23

The Centre for Crime and Justice Studies

8th Fl, 75–79 York Rd, London SE1 7AW;
URL www.kcl.ac.uk/ccjs; E-mail ccjs.enq@kcl.ac.uk;
Tel 020 7401 2425; Fax 020 7401 2436
Director Una Padel

Joseph Rowntree Foundation

The Homestead, 40 Water End, York YO30 6WP;
URL www.jrf.org.uk; Tel 01904 629241; Fax 01904 620072
Director Lord Best, OBE
Head (Publishing) Julia Lewis
Research and development in fields of housing; area
regeneration; children, young people and families; work,
income and social policy; social care and disability. As Joseph
Rowntree Housing Trust (housing association) manages over
2000 properties including residential care and nursing homes,
and continuing care retirement community.

LEPRA (British Leprosy Relief Association)

Fairfax Hse, Causton Rd, Colchester, Essex CO1 1PU;
URL www.lepra.org.uk; E-mail lepra@lepra.org.uk;
Tel 01206 562286
Director T. Vasey
Head (Press and Publicity) J. Frame
President Sir C. Bonington, CBE
A medical charity with the object of eradicating leprosy.

Leukaemia Research Fund

Registered Charity Number 216032
43 Great Ormond St, London WC1N 3JJ;
URL www.lrf.org.uk; E-mail info@lrf.org.uk; Tel 020
7405 0101; Fax 020 7242 1488
Chief Executive D.L. Osborne
The only national research charity devoting all its resources
to defeating leukaemia, Hodgkin's lymphoma and other
lymphomas, myeloma and related blood diseases in
children and adults.
It supports an extensive research programme, trains the
leukaemia experts of tomorrow and can provide patient
information and free patient information leaflets.

The Medical Council on Alcohol

3 St. Andrew's Pl, London NW1 4LB;
E-mail mca@medicouncilalcol.demon.co.uk; Tel 020 7487
4445; Fax 020 7935 4479
Executive Director Dr G. Ratcliffe, FRCP
Founded by medical practitioners in 1967 with a view to
co-ordination of effort and the better understanding of
alcoholism and its prevention and the treatment and aftercare of alcoholics. Currently devoted mainly to education
and supplying information to health professionals by
means of the journal, newsletter, regional advisers,
seminars, symposia, handbooks and direct communication
from the office of the Medical Council on Alcohol. Also
assists doctors in need of help with alcohol dependency.

Mental Health Foundation

7th Fl, 83 Victoria St, London SW1H 0HW;
URL www.mentalhealth.org.uk; E-mail mhf@mhf.org.uk;
Tel 020 7802 0300; Fax 020 7802 0301
Chief Executive Dr Andrew McCulloch
The Mental Health Foundation is a national charity
working to improve services for both people with mental
health problems and people with learning disabilities. It is
the only charity to fund and work with both service users
and providers and plays an important role in funding
research and new approaches to prevention, treatment and
care. The Foundation's work includes: allocating grants for
research and community projects; contributing to the
public debate; educating policy makers and healthcare
professionals and striving to reduce the stigma attached to
mental illness and learning disabilities.

Migraine Trust

45 Great Ormond St, London WC1N 3HZ;
URL www.migrainetrust.org;
E-mail info@migrainetrust.org; Tel 020 7831 4818;
Fax 020 7831 5174
Director Ann Rush

Minority Rights Group International

379 Brixton Rd, London SW9 7DE;
E-mail minority.rights@mrgmail.org; Tel 020 7978 9498;
Fax 020 7738 6265
Director Vacancy
Marketing and Publicity Officer Graham Fox
Minority Rights Group International (MRG) is a non-
governmental organisation working to secure the rights of
ethnic, religious and linguistic minorities and indigenous
peoples worldwide, and to promote cooperation and
understanding between communities.
MRG's activities are focused on international advocacy,
training, publishing and outreach and are guided by the
needs expressed by their partner organisations.

Multiple Sclerosis Society of Great Britain and Northern Ireland

MS Society in Great Britain

MS National Centre, 372 Edgware Rd, London NW2 6ND;
URL www.mssociety.org.uk;
E-mail info@mssociety.org.uk; Tel 020 8438 0700;
(Helpline) 0808 800 8000; Fax 020 8438 0701

MS Society in Northern Ireland

34 Annadale Ave, Belfast BT7 3JJ
Chief Executive P. Cardy
Funds research to find a cause and cure of MS and provides
a welfare service for people with multiple sclerosis,
including a telephone counselling service.

Multiple Sclerosis Society Scotland

Registered Charity Number SCO 16433.
Ratho Pk, 88 Glasgow Rd, Ratho Station, Newbridge,
Edinburgh EH28 8PP;
URL www.mssocietyscotland.org.uk;
E-mail enquiries@mssocietyscotland.org.uk; Tel 0131 335
4050
Provides support and advice to its members through
branches all over Scotland. Funds medical research into
MS, offers telephone counselling service, provides
information grants to individuals, offers respite holiday
care.

Muscular Dystrophy Campaign

7–11 Prescott Pl, London SW4 6BS;
URL www.muscular-dystrophy.org;
E-mail info@muscular-dystrophy.org; Tel 020 7720 8055;
Fax 020 7498 0670
Executive Director Christine Cryne
Funds medical research into muscular dystrophy and
allied neuromuscular diseases. Offers help and advice to
those with neuromuscular disorders and their families.
There are family care officers based in hospitals across the
country.

National Asthma Campaign

Providence Hse, Providence Pl, London N1 0NT;
URL www.asthma.org.uk; Tel 020 7226 2260; (Asthma
Helpline Mon–Fri 0900–1700) 0845 701 0203; Fax 020
7704 0740
Chief Executive Donna Covey

The National Centre for Volunteering

Formerly the Volunteer Centre UK
Regent's Wharf, 8 All Saints St, London N1 9RL;
    URL www.volunteering.org.uk;
    E-mail information@thecentre.org.uk; Tel 020 7520 8900;
    (Information service freephone (1030–1230, 14–1600))
    0800 028 3304; Fax 020 7520 8910
Chief Executive   Christopher Spence
Promotes excellence in volunteering, offering a range of
services designed to support volunteer involving
organisations in England. Produces a monthly magazine
'Volunteering' and a range of good practice and research
publications.

National Children's Centre

Brian Jackson Hse, New North Pde, Huddersfield, West
    Yorkshire HD1 5JP; URL www.nccuk.org.uk;
    E-mail info@nccuk.org.uk; Tel 01484 519988; Fax 01484
    435150
Chief Executive   S. Cale
Research and action programmes for children, adolescents
and families.

National Institute of Economic and Social Research

2 Dean Trench St, Smith Sq, London SW1P 3HE;
    URL www.niesc.ac.uk; E-mail library@niesr.ac.uk;
    E-mail enquiries@niesr.ac.uk; Tel (Library) 020 7654
    1907; (Switchboard) 020 7222 7665; Fax 020 7654 1900
Secretary   G. Clisham
Librarian   P. Oliver
An independent charity that aims to increase knowledge of
the social and economic conditions of contemporary
society.

National Meningitis Trust

Fern Hse, Bath Rd, Stroud, Gloucestershire GL5 3TJ;
    URL www.meningitis-trust.org.uk;
    E-mail support@meningitis-trust.org.uk; Tel 01453
    768000
Funds medical research into all aspects of meningitis,
supports meningitis patients and provides information to
raise awareness about the disease.

National Society for Epilepsy (NSE)

Chesham La, Chalfont St. Peter, Buckinghamshire SL9 0RJ;
    URL www.epilepsynse.org.uk; Tel 01494 601300;
    (Helpline (1000–1600 Mon–Fri)) 01494 601400; Fax 01494
    871927
The National Society for Epilepsy is a charity whose
objective is to advance research, treatment, care,
understanding and support for people with epilepsy
nationwide. It provides medical clinics and an asssessment
centre for adults: in conjunction with the National Hospital
for Neurology and Neurosurgery, London. Research
includes causes, effects and treatment of epilepsy.
Residential and respite care for adults with epilepsy and
other disabilities; rehabilitation and supported housing;
information and education: comprehensive leaflets, videos
and epilepsy updates; accredited specialised and general
training; trained volunteers provide information and
support to individuals and families in their own locality;
associate membership: members receive regular
information on treatment, research and topics of interest.

National Society for Research into Allergy (NSRA)

PO Box 45, Hinckley, Leicestershire LE10 1JY;
    E-mail nsra.allergy@virgin.net; Tel 01455 250715;
    Fax 01455 250715
Hon General Secretary   Eunice L. Rose

Charity offering to members allergy elimination diets for
any or multiple food allergy diagnoses. Reaction Magazine
prints relevant and up-to-date information. Membership
£15 annually. Helpline numbers available.

One Plus One, Marriage and Partnership Research

The Wells, 7–15 Roseberry Ave, London EC1R 4SP;
    URL www.oneplusone.org.uk;
    E-mail info@oneplusone.org.uk; Tel 020 7841 3660;
    Fax 020 7841 3670
Director   P. Mansfield
Research/Information Officer   Fiona Hovsepian
Exists to build, through research, a framework for
understanding contemporary marriage and partnership.
One Plus One puts this research into practice through
projects in information, education and training.

Paget Gorman Society (Paget Gorman Signed Speech) (PGSS)

2 Dowlands Bungalows, Dowlands La, Smallfield, Surrey
    RH6 9SD; URL www.pgss.org;
    E-mail prup@compuserve.com; Tel 01342 842308
Chief Executive   Pauline Phillips
Helps children with speech and language handicaps to
communicate with the use of PGSS.

Plunkett Foundation

23 Hanborough Bus Pk, Long Hanborough, Oxfordshire
    OX29 8SG; URL www.plunkett.co.uk;
    E-mail info@plunkett.co.uk; Tel 01993 883636; Fax 01993
    883576
Chief Executive   Richard Moreton
Develops and promotes agricultural and other rural co-
operatives and self-help groups worldwide. Runs training
courses and conferences for co-operative personnel and
social enterprise development in UK and developing
countries. Undertakes rural group consultancy and
research for national and international organisations.
Organises study tours in UK for overseas visitors. Library
information and advisory service available.

Population Investigation Committee

Room PS201, London School of Economics, London
    WC2A 2AE; URL www.lse.ac.uk/depts/pic/;
    E-mail pic@lse.ac.uk; Tel 020 7955 7666; Fax 020 7955
    6831
General Secretary   A. Shepherd
Promotes education and research in the field of population.
Produces a journal carrying articles of international
interest, and also occasional supplements and books.

Research into Ageing

PO Box 32833, London N1 9ZQ; URL www.ageing.org;
    E-mail ria@ageing.co.uk; Tel 020 7843 1550; Fax 020 7843
    1559
Director (Fundraising and Communication)   R. Music
Research into Ageing's purpose is to understand and
challenge the diseases and disabilities which become more
common in later life. It does this by: funding and
promoting leading edge research; encouraging promising
young scientists to investigate healthy ageing; changing
attitudes to old age. Healthy ageing leaflets and other
publications available.

Resource Information Service

The Basement, 38 Great Pulteney St, London W1F 9NU;
    E-mail ris@ris.org.uk; Tel 020 7494 2408; Fax 020 7287
    8928
Publishes directories, CD-ROMs and online information

23

921

systems for organisations providing frontline services to people in need. Publications include the London Hostels Directory, UK Advice Finder. Runs Hostels Online – a website of hostel information and vacancies, and Homeless Pages – a website of homelessness resources.

Restricted Growth Association

PO Box 4744, Dorchester, Dorset DT2 9FA;
    URL www.rgaonline.org.uk; E-mail rgai@talk.com;
    Tel 01308 898445
Chair   A. Tate
Treasurer   John Langridge
President   Dr Charles L. Pocock
Promotes the interests of children and adults of unusually short stature. Gives advice on medical matters and home aids. Organises social activities. Publications: quarterly newspaper and bi-annual information magazine and advisory booklets. Contacts for adoption and fostering of babies of restricted growth.

Royal College of Paediatrics and Child Health

50 Hallam St, London W1W 6DE;
    E-mail enquiries@rcpch.ac.uk; Tel 020 7307 5600; Fax 020 7307 5601
Secretary   Len Tyler
Aims to further the study of child health and to promote excellence in paediatric practice.

Royal Society for the Prevention of Accidents (ROSPA)

Edgbaston Pk, 353 Bristol Rd, Birmingham, West Midlands B5 7ST; URL www.rospa.co.uk;
    E-mail help@rospa.co.uk; Tel 0121 248 2000; Fax 0121 248 2001
Chief Executive   Dr John Hooper
Director (Safety Policy)   John Howard
Deals with safety at work, on the road, in the home and at leisure. Runs training courses and campaigns and promotes safety education.

The Royal Society for the Promotion of Health

38a St. Georges Dr, London SW1V 4BH;
    URL www.rsph.org; E-mail rshealth@rshealth.org.uk;
    Tel 020 7630 0121; Fax 020 7976 6847
Chief Executive   Stuart Royston
The Royal Society for the Promotion of Health exists to promote the continuous improvement in human health worldwide through education, communication, and the encouragement of scientific research. The society was founded in 1876 to promote the health of the people. The scope of the society covers accredited educational systems in public health and food hygiene, food and nutrition, health and safety, preventable medicine, the environment and engineering. Grades of membership are Fellow, Member, Associate Member, and election to a particular grade being dependent upon qualifications held. Activities include publication of a journal, hosting conferences and members' meetings, the delivery of examinations, the accreditation of food packaging for companies who have shown diligence.

The Sainsbury Centre for Mental Health

134–138 Borough High St, London SE1 1LB;
    URL www.scmh.org.uk; Tel 020 7403 8300; Fax 020 7403 9482
The Sainsbury Centre for Mental Health is a registered charity, working to improve the quality of life for people with severe mental health problems. It aims to influence national policy and encourage good practice in mental health services, through a coordinated programme of research, training and development. Conference and publication details on request.

Scottish Association for the Study of Delinquency (SASD)

Flat 0/2, 8 Downhill St, Glasgow G11 5QS; Tel 0141 581 6158
Hon President/Sheriff Principal   C.G.B. Nicholson, QC
Chair   Nial Campbell
Vice-Chair   D. Gunn
Hon Secretary   Elizabeth Kyle
Hon Treasurer   Alisdar McVitie
To create a common meeting ground for the many professional groups and individuals interested in the field of social pathology. Initiates, encourages and promotes research into the causes, prevention and treatment of delinquency and crime.

Sight Savers International (Royal Commonwealth Society for the Blind)

Grosvenor Hall, Bolnore Rd, Haywards Heath, West Sussex RH16 4BX;
    E-mail generalinformation@sightsavers.org; Tel 01444 446600; Fax 01444 446688
Executive Director   R. Porter
Contact   Sue Castle
Programmes for the prevention and cure of blindness and for the education, employment and welfare of visually impaired people in developing countries.

Society for the Study of Fertility

82a High St, Sawston, Cambridge, Cambridgeshire CB2 4HJ; E-mail office@ssf.org.uk; Tel 01223 830665
Chair   Prof Alan McNeilly
Business Secretary   Dr Kate Hardy
Study of biology of reproduction and fertility in both animals and humans. Scientific conferences held regularly for interchange of ideas and information.

The Tavistock Institute

30 Tabernacle St, London EC2A 4UE;
    URL www.tavinstitute.org;
    E-mail central.admin@tavinstitute.org; Tel 020 7417 0407; Fax 020 7417 0566
Secretary   Debbie Sorkin, FCA
Finance Officer   Hitesh Shah
Contact for Mental Health   Fiddy Abraham
Social science research and consultancy organisation having contacts with government and public bodies in many countries.

Tavistock Institute of Medical Psychology

Tavistock Centre, 120 Belsize La, London NW3 5BA;
    URL www.tmsi.org.uk; www.tcec.co.uk;
    E-mail timp@tmsi.org; Tel 020 7435 7111; Fax 020 7435 1080
Director (Tavistock Marital Studies Institute)   C.F. Clulow, PhD
Chair (Tavistock Career and Educational Consultation)   S. Weintrobe, BSc (Hons), NSc ClinPsychol
Company Secretary   Mr D. Obadina, BA(Hons) BS, Grad IPD
Promotes the study and practice of psychotherapy, and through the Tavistock Marital Studies Institute (TMSI) provides a professional service to those experiencing difficulty in their marriage; develops appropriate skills for practitioners in the helping services through training programmes and consultation; undertakes action research relevant to the practice of marital work in various settings.Through the Tavistock Career and Educational Consultation (TCEC), it provides a psychoanalytically oriented vocational and educational guidance service, and provides training and supervision for new consultants in this area.

Visual Impairment Centre for Teaching and Research (VICTAR)

University of Birmingham, School of Education, Edgbaston, Birmingham, West Midlands B15 2TT; URL www.educationbham.ac.uk/research/victar; E-mail victar-enquiries@bham.ac.uk; Tel 0121 414 6733; Fax 0121 414 4865

VICTAR is a research centre that undertakes research on the educational, psychological and general rehabilitative needs of visually impaired people. Disseminates information about research. Carries out teaching and training in the area of visual impairment, and provides advice and resources.

The Williams Syndrome Foundation

161 High St, Tonbridge, Kent TN9 1BX; URL www.williams-syndrome.org.uk; E-mail john.nelson@wsfoundation.btinternet.com; Tel 01732 365152; Fax 01732 360178

Chief Executive John Nelson

The foundation is a registered charity researching the disease. It provides information about the condition, puts parents of affected children in touch with each other, enables children to meet, acquires information for research, works to interest the medical profession in the disease and maintains a record of affected children.

Youthaid

PO Box 30069, 89 Albert Embankment, London SE1 7WR; URL www.vvy.org.uk; E-mail mailbox@vvy.org.uk; Tel 020 7582 7221; Fax 020 7582 7721

Director B. Chatrik

Provides information about the rights and opportunities of young people in training, education, employment and unemployment; conducts research into the position of young people in the labour market.

23

Social Services Media

24

- **Journals**
- **National Daily and Sunday Newspapers**
- **Broadcasting Services to the Community**
  British Broadcasting Corporation
  Independent Television Companies
  Independent Local Radio
- **Other Media Organisations and Services**

Social Services Media

Ageing and the Elderly

Ageing and Society
Cambridge University Press, The Edinburgh Bldg,
Cambridge, Cambridgeshire CB2 2RU;
URL www.cambridge.org; Tel 01223 312393
Editor T. Warnes
Volume 24 in 2004: 6 issues. Institutions print and
electronic: £161, Individuals print plus electronic: £55.
Ageing and Society is an interdisciplinary and international
journal devoted to publishing papers that further the
understanding of human ageing in the wider social and
cultural context. It draws contributions and readers from a
broad spectrum of academic disciplines. In addition to
original articles, Ageing and Society features an extensive
book review section and a regular updating on specified
research areas.

Almshouses Gazette
The Almshouses Association, Billingbear Lodge, Carters
Hill, Wokingham, Berkshire RG40 5RU;
URL www.almshouses.org; E-mail naa@almshouses.org;
Tel 01344 452922; Fax 01344 862062
Director Anthony Leask
Quarterly £0.75 including postage.

Care Assistants Handbooks
Hawker Publications, Culvert Hse, Culver Rd, London
SW11 5DH; E-mail books@hawkerpubs.demon.co.uk;
Tel 020 7720 2108 ext 206; Fax 020 7498 3023
Editor Sue Benson
Price each between £9.95–£14.95 plus £0.95 postage.
A series of five books: for Care Assistants Working with
Elderly People; Community Care Assistants; Working with
People with Dementia; Working with People with Learning
Disabilities; Hospital Care Assistants.

Caring Times
Hawker Publications, Culvert Hse, Culver Rd, London
SW11 5DH;
E-mail caringtimes@hawkerpubs.demon.co.uk; Tel 020
7720 2108; Fax 020 7498 3023
Editor Geoff Hodgson
Monthly subscription £50.00; circulation 18 000.
Aims
The Management magazine for the residential and nursing
home sector. Covers the news, background and business
information for directors, owners and managers of
organisations which own or operate homes in the local
authority, not-for-profit and private sectors.

Caring Today
Vivas Publications Ltd, Martin Mill, Walker La, Hebden
Bridge, West Yorkshire HX7 8SJ;
E-mail vivshep@aol.com; Tel 01422 847078; Fax 01422
847017
Director Vivien Shepherd
Director Alan Shepherd
Six issues per year; £15.00 pa.

Geriatric Medicine
(Part of Inside Communications)
Isis Bldg, Thames Quay, 193 Marsh Wall, London E14 9SG;
URL www.gerimed.co.uk; Tel 020 7772 8466; Fax 020
7772 8597
Managing Editor Alison Boyle
Publisher Peter Sayer; E-mail peter_sayer@mrn.co.uk

Information Bulletin
Age Concern England, Astral Hse, 1268 London Rd,
London SW16 4ER; URL www.ageconcern.org.uk;
Tel 020 8765 7200; Fax 020 8765 7211
Editor Jeremy Fennell (Acting)
Monthly publication. Annual subscription £26.00.
Digest of information on developments which may affect
older people, new legislation, journal articles and
publications.

The Journal of Dementia Care
Hawker Publications Ltd, Culvert Hse, Culvert Rd, London
SW11 5DH;
E-mail dementiacare@hawkerpubs.demon.co.uk; Tel 020
7720 2108; Fax 020 7498 3023
Editor Sue Benson
Bi-monthly publication with circulation of 5000.
Subscription £65.00 pa.
Five conferences annually in the UK and Ireland.
Aims
Multi-disciplinary journal committed to improving the
quality of care offered to people with dementia. Aimed at
all professionals working for people with dementia.

New Literature on Old Age
A guide to new publications, courses and conferences on
ageing.
Centre for Policy on Ageing, 19–23 Ironmonger Row,
London EC1V 3QP; E-mail gcrosby@cpa.org.uk; Tel 020
7553 6500; Fax 020 7553 6501
Director Gillian Crosby
Bi-monthly publication; specimen issues free. Annual
subscription £30.00.
A 'Current awareness' service which provides a
comprehensive guide to new publications, courses,
conferences and meetings on ageing.
Also available on Age Info CD-ROM (published by Centre
for Policy on Ageing). Annual subscription (four issues)
£600 plus VAT. Each issue completely replaces the previous
one.

24

Nursing Older People
17 Peterborough Rd, Harrow, Greater London HA1 2AX;
Tel 020 8423 1066; Fax 020 8423 3867

Old Age
A register of social research.
Centre for Policy on Ageing, 19–23 Ironmonger Row,
London EC1V 3QP; E-mail gcrosby@cpa.org.uk; Tel 020
7553 6500; Fax 020 7553 6501
Director   Gillian Crosby
Provides full details of current and recently completed
research projects in the field of ageing – within the UK –
ranging from anthropology to geography to social
administration.

Pensioners' Voice
National Federation of Retirement Pensions Associations,
Thwaites Hse, Railway Rd, Blackburn, Lancashire
BB1 5AX; Tel 01254 52606; Fax 01254 52606
Editor   R. Stansfield
Six issues per year.
Information, advice and general reading for pensioners.

Quality in Ageing
Pavilion Publishing, The Ironworks, Cheapside, Brighton,
East Sussex BN1 4GD; URL www.pavpub.com;
E-mail info@pavpub.com; Tel 01273 623222; Fax 01273
625526
Marketing Executive   Vicki Smith
Policy, practice and research
This quarterly journal focuses on real issues that concern
older people and those who work with them. Promoting
the best possible of life for older people and the best
possible care and support services for everyone who needs
them. The journal is published in association with BASE
(The British Association for Service to the Elderly).

Selected Bibliographies on Ageing
Title to vary with every issue.
Centre for Policy on Ageing, 25–31 Ironmonger Row,
London EC1V 3QP; Tel 020 7253 1787; Fax 020 7490 4206
Deputy Director   Gillian Crosby;
E-mail gcrosby@cpa.org.uk
Frequency variable; price variable.
An occasional series bringing together annotated references
on a variety of topics within the broad field of ageing.
Also available on Age Info CD-ROM (published by Centre
for Policy on Ageing).

This Caring Business
Martin Mill Cottage, Walker La, Hebden Bridge, HX7 8XJ;
E-mail vivshep@aol.com; Tel 01422 847078; Fax 01422
847017
Editor   Vivien Shepherd
Monthly publication (combined Dec/Jan and July/Aug);
subscription £56.00 cash or credit card pa or £46.00 direct
debit.
Caters for long-term care (commercial editorial) with
different features each month.

Working with Older People
Pavilion Publishing, The Ironworks, Cheapside, Brighton,
East Sussex BN1 4GD; URL www.pavpub.com;
E-mail info@pavpub.com; Tel 01273 623222; Fax 01273
625526
Marketing Executive   Vicki Smith
Working with Older People supports all staff in social
services, health, housing, voluntary or the private sector to
meet the demands of caring the increasing population of
older people in our society. All features are easily accessible
with photographs and diagrams to illustrate key points and
are geared towards informing and supporting practice.

Yours (For the Young at Heart)
EMAP Esprit Ltd, Bushfield Hse, Orton Centre,
Peterborough PE2 5UW; Tel 01733 237111; Fax 01733
288129
Editor-in-chief   Neil Patrick

Monthly publication; £1.10 per issue; subscription £15.15
pa. Circulation of 335 000.
A general magazine for the over 60s providing entertaining
and informative articles plus advice about money, health,
law and personal problems. Campaigns to improve the
lives of elderly people.

Alcohol and Drug Abuse

Alcohol and Alcoholism
International Journal of the Medical Council on
Alcoholism.
Oxford University Press, Great Clarendon St, Oxford,
Oxfordshire OX2 6DP;
URL www.alcalc.oupjournals.org;
E-mail jnls.cust.serv@oup.co.uk
Editor   Mandy Hill

The Drug and Alcohol Professional
Pavilion Publishing, The Ironworks, Cheapside, Brighton,
East Sussex BN1 4GD; URL www.pavpub.com;
E-mail info@pavpub.com; Tel 01273 623222; Fax 01273
625526
Marketing Executive   Vicki Smith
The Drug and Alcohol Professional is a quarterly journal
that has a unique approach to the problems that alcohol
and drug use can cause individuals, and to the types of
intervention, developments, current research, trends and
discussion in the field.

Share
Share Editors, Stonebow Hse, PO Box 1, Stonebow, York
YO1 7NJ
Monthly price of £1; annual subscription £12 inclusive of
postage.
Share is the monthly journal of Alcoholics Anonymous in
England and Wales.

Straight Talk
Waterbridge Hse, 32–36 Loman St, London SE1 0EE;
URL www.alcoholconcern.org.uk; Tel 020 7928 7377
Quarterly publication; £15 subscription per annum.
Aimed at all those who have an interest in tackling alcohol-
related problems.

UK Alcohol Alert
Alliance House Foundation.
Editorial Office, Elmgren Hse, 1 The Quay, St. Ives,
Cambridgeshire PE27 5AR; URL www.ias.org.uk;
E-mail info@ias.org.uk; Tel 01480 466766
Quarterly publication; annual subscription £10.00.
News concerning alcohol and drugs.

Blind and Visually Impaired

The Advocate
National League of the Blind and Disabled, Central Office,
Swinton Hse, 324 Grays Inn Rd, London WC1X 8DD;
Tel 020 7837 6103; Fax 020 7278 0436; Minicom 020 7837
6103
General Secretary   Joe Mann
Registered trade union.
Quarterly publication; subscription price of £1.64.
On-going account of activities in branches.

The British Journal of Visual Impairment
View Publication Trust, York Annexe, Coventry, West
Midlands CV7 9HP
Editor   Kevin Carey
108 High St, Hurstpierpoint, West Sussex BN6 9PX
Aimed at all those professionally concerned with children
and adults who have a visual impairment. Articles cover

aspects of health, welfare, education and employment. Published March, July, November. Index annually. Annual subscription £25.00, three years £70.00 (ISSN 0264 6196). Available in inkprint, braille, tape and disk.

Dbl Review
see Children and Young People

Guiding Star
(A Musical Tape for the Blind)
Music for the Blind, 2 High Park Rd, Southport, Merseyside PR9 7QL; Tel 01704 228010
Editor (News) C. Mills
Presenter D. Mills
Britain's first National Talking Newspaper.
Every 14 days to the blind or partially sighted. Cost according to entry age.
News features, including news not heard on radio or TV; listeners requests; competitions; library stocks over 5 000 000 tune titles. Run by a fully registered charity, The Music for the Blind.

Merry-Go-Round
(A Musical Tape for the Blind)
Music for the Blind, 2 High Park Rd, Southport, Merseyside PR9 7QL; Tel 01704 228010
Presenter D. Mills
Popular middle-of-the-road music for disabled, partially sighted and blind people.
Monthly.

New Beacon
Royal National Institute for the Blind, 224 Great Portland St, London W1N 6AA; Tel 020 7388 1266; Fax 020 7388 0945
Subscriptions, RNIB (Customer Services), PO Box 173, Peterborough, Cambridgeshire PE2 6WS
Editor Ann Lee
Monthly publication at £1.60 (braille or print).
Covers all visual impairment issues, features, news, letters, comment.

Open Hand
Deafblind UK, National Centre for Deafblindness, John and Lucille van Geest Pl, Cygnet Rd, Hampton, Peterborough PE7 8FD; URL www.deafblind.org.uk
Editor Rosemary Sandford
Quarterly publication; annual subscripion £10.00.
A magazine for deafblind people published in Braille, Moon, large print, on tape and disk.

Talking Sense
see Deaf/Hard of Hearing/Speech Impaired

Touch of the Classics
(A Musical Tape for the Blind)
Music for the Blind, 2 High Park Rd, Southport, Merseyside PR9 7QL; Tel 01704 228010
Presenter D. Mills
Classical and light music for disabled, partially sighted and blind people.
Monthly.

Children and Young People

see also Chapter 13

Adoption and Fostering (formerly Child Adoption)
British Agencies for Adoption and Fostering, 200 Union St, London SE1 0LX; URL www.baaf.org.uk; Tel 020 7593 2040; Fax 020 7593 2001
Production Editor Miranda Davies;
E-mail miranda.davies@baaf.org.uk
Quarterly publication priced at £12.00; annual subscription: £49.00 (individuals), £68.00 (institutions) UK.
Articles, news and reviews of social work practice, legal and medical issues concerning children.

Barnardo's Child Care Publications
Barnardo's, Tanners La, Barkingside, Ilford, Essex IG6 1QG; URL www.barnados.org.uk; Tel 020 8550 8822
Information Officer Dorothy Howes
Publishes approx. 10 titles a year.
Covers all aspects of child care services provided by the Barnardo's organisation.

British Association for Early Childhood Education
(Working title: 'Early Education')
Early Education, 136 Cavell St, London E1 2JA; URL www.early-education.org.uk;
E-mail office@early-education.org.uk; Tel 020 7539 5400; Fax 020 7539 5409
Project Manager Jenny Rabin
Journal and newsletter thrice yearly, free to members (annual subscription for membership £25.00).
Early Education promotes the right of all children to education of the highest quality. It provides a multidisciplinary network of support and advice for everyone concerned with the education and care of young children from birth to eight years.

CCHF Newsletter and Leaflet
Children's Country Holidays Fund, 1st Fl, 42–43 Lower Marsh, London SE1 7RG;
URL www.childrensholidays-cchf.org; Tel 020 7928 6522
Free annual publication.

Child: Care, Health and Development
Blackwell Publishing Ltd, 9600 Garsington Rd, Oxford, OX4 2DQ; URL www.blackwellpublishing.com; Tel 01865 776868; Fax 01865 714591
Editor Dr Stuart Logan
Bi-monthly publication; annual subscription for institutions is £235.00 (Europe), £258.00 (overseas), \$410.00 (US and Canada).
Development of all children, particularly those disabled by physical, intellectual, emotional and social problems, and the assessment of new methods to help overcome these problems.

Child and Adolescent Mental Health (formerly Child Psychology and Psychiatry Review)
Association for Child Psychology and Psychiatry, St. Saviour's Hse, 39–41 Union St, London SE1 1SD; Tel 020 7403 7458; Fax 020 7403 7081
Joint Editor Dr Orlee Udwin
Joint Editor Prof Panos Vostanis
Four issues.
Publishers:Blackwell Publishers.
Subscription: Libraries and institutions £70.00, individuals £28.00 (joint subscription with Journal of Child Psychology and Psychiatry savings of 10% available).
Forum for exchange of clinical experience, ideas and research related to clinicians and practitioners.

The Children's Society: Publications
The Children's Society, Edward Rudolf Hse, Margery St, London WC1X 0JL;
E-mail publishing@the-childrens-society.org.uk; Tel 020 7841 4400; Fax 020 7841 4500
Publishes reports and books on practice as well as resources for children, young people and schools in a range of areas of childcare.

Children Now
National Children's Bureau, 8 Wakley St, London EC1V 7QE; E-mail emoore@ncb.org.uk; Tel 020 7843 6048; Fax 020 7278 9512
Editor Emma Moore
Assistant Editor Sarah Vaughan
Quarterly publication free to members. For membership details telephone 020 7843 6047.

24

Childright
Children's Legal Centre, University of Essex, Wivenhoe Pk, Colchester, Essex CO4 3SQ;
 URL www.childrenslegalcentre.com;
 Tel (Administration) 01206 872466; (Advice Line Mon–Fri 10–1230 and 1400–1630) 01206 873820;
 Fax 01206 874026
Ten issues pa. Subscription £45.00 (organisations), £32.00 (individuals), £21.00 (concessionary i.e. students, young people and articled clerks). For International EU Organisations add £5, World Organisations add £15, Individuals add £10.
Explains proposed and implemented legislation affecting children and young people; policy developments, articles and information sheets; publications review.
Also available is an education advocacy unit which specialises in educational disputes – contact through the advice line.

Club Connection
National Association of Clubs for Young People, 371 Kennington La, London SE11 5QY;
 URL www.nacyp.org.uk;
 E-mail office@nacyp.org.uk; Tel 020 7793 0787; Fax 020 7820 9815
Information Officer   Andrew Mabey
Director (Fundraising, Marketing and Communications)   Malcolm M. Tyndall
Quarterly publication.
Club Connection is a free NACYP Publication that allows 3000 affiliated clubs in the UK to network with each other. The magazine has a circulation of 10 000 and a readership of 450 000 people including club leaders and youth workers. The publication contains: National, Regional and Club news, Exciting youth initiatives in the UK, fundraising tips, news, competitions and promotional offers.

Dbl Review
Deafblind International, c/o SENSE, 1113 Clifton Terr, Finsbury Pk, London N4 3SR; Tel 020 7272 7774; Fax 020 7272 6012
Editor   Eileen Boothroyd
Bi-annual publication, free to members of the DbI.
Membership £10.00 per year via SENSE.
International news, information and professional articles on the education of deafblind children and young adults.

Emotional and Behavioural Difficulties
(Journal of the Association of Workers for Children with Emotional Behavioural Difficulties)
Editor   Prof Paul Cooper
University of Leicester, School of Education, 21 University Rd, Leicester, Leicestershire LE1 7RF; Tel 0116 252 3688; Fax 0116 252 3653
Manager (Circulation)   Allan Rimmer
Charlton Crt, East Sutton, Maidstone, Kent ME17 3DQ; Tel 01622 843104; Fax 01622 844220
Professional association for workers in education, social work and health professions dealing with children with emotional and behavioural difficulties.
Four issues per year. Subscription: £132 (libraries), £40 (individuals), £66 (schools), which includes access to the electronic content of the journal at no extra charge. Student discounts, single issue rates and advertising rates are available from Sage publications Tel 020 7374 0645. Further details: www.sagepub.co.uk.

Foster Care Magazine
Fostering Network, 87 Blackfriars Rd, London SE1 8HA;
 URL www.fostering.net;
 E-mail julie.pybus@fostering.net; Tel 020 7620 6443;
 Fax 020 7620 6401
Editor   Julie Pybus
Quarterly publication with annual subscription of £9.00.
News, features and comment on topical fostering issues.

Gingerbread
7 Sovereign Cl, Sovereign Crt, London E1W 3HW;
 URL www.gingerbread.org.uk;
 E-mail office@gingerbread.org.uk; Tel 020 7488 9300;
 (Free Helpline) 0800 0184318; Fax 020 7488 9333
Provides support, advice and information for lone parents and their children.
Network of self help groups. News and information about one parent families and Gingerbread.

Good Toy Guide
National Association of Toy and Leisure Libraries, 68 Churchway, London NW1 1LT; Tel 020 7387 9592;
 Fax 020 7383 2714
One issue per year. Consumer guide to toys tested nationwide in Toy Libraries; includes toys for children with special needs. Various other publications on play – send s.a.e. for list.

Journal of Adolescence
The Journal of the Association for Professionals in Services for Adolescents, Academic Press Ltd, 24–28 Oval Rd, London NW1 7DX; E-mail louise.chantler@hbuk.co.uk
Bi-monthly publication; annual worldwide subscription £198.00.

Journal of Child Psychology and Psychiatry and Allied Disciplines
Association for Child Psychology and Psychiatry, St. Saviour's Hse, 39–41 Union St, London SE1 1SD;
 E-mail jcpp@acpp.co.uk; Tel 020 7403 7458; Fax 020 7403 7081
Joint Editor   Prof J. Stevenson
Joint Editor   Prof Frank C. Verhulst
Joint Editor   Dr. Francesca Happé
Eight issues including Annual Research Review.
Publishers: Blackwells Publishers.
Subscriptions: £232.00 (libraries and institutions).
Theory, research and clinical practice in child and adolescent psychology, and psychiatry and allied disciplines with special reference to developmental psychopathology and disorders.

Maternity Action
Maternity Alliance, Unit 3.3, 2–6 Northburgh St, London EC1V 0AY; URL www.maternityalliance.org.uk;
 E-mail info@maternityalliance.org.uk; Tel (Advice except Fri) 020 7490 7638; (Office) 020 7490 7639;
 Fax 020 7588 8584
Editor   Liz Kendall
Four issues a year at £4.00; annual subscription £16.00.
Features news, reviews and comment on controversial issues and initiatives in maternity rights and services.

National Playbus Association
National Playbus Association, 93 Whitby Rd, Bristol BS4 4AR; URL www.playbus.org.uk;
 E-mail playbus@playbus.org.uk; Tel 0117 977 5375;
 Fax 0117 972 1838
Membership organisation for community mobile projects.
Covers work of all mobile projects and details policy issues, safety, funding and mobile work.

New Generation
(The magazine of the National Childbirth Trust)
National Childbirth Trust, Alexandra Hse, Oldham Terr, London W3 6NH; Tel (Adults) 0870 770 3236;
 (Breastfeeding line) 0870 444 8708; (Enquiry line) 0870 444 8707
Editor   Sonia Leach
Quarterly publication; free to NCT members (membership to NCT is £36.00 for the first year and £26.00 thereafter).
Covers all aspects of education for parenthood. Strong emphasis on research, antenatal preparation, breast-feeding counselling, practical postnatal support and education.
Voluntary and private; advice and counselling; voluntary service; education and training in health and welfare.

Nursery World

Admiral Hse, 66–68 East Smithfield, London E1W 1BX;
URL www.nursery-world.com; Tel 020 7782 3120;
Fax 020 7782 3131
Editor   Liz Roberts
50 issues at £59 pa.
Professional magazine for those involved in the care and education of children in their early years.

Poverty

Child Poverty Action Group, 94 White Lion St, London
N1 9PF; Tel 020 7837 7979; Fax 020 7837 6414
Thrre issues annually at £3.95; annual subscription £21.00
(incl CPAG supporting membership).
In-depth feature articles on aspects of poverty in UK, plus news, facts and figures, research notes etc.

Support for Learning

A Journal of The National Association for Special
Educational Needs (NASEN)
Editor   Caroline Roaf
4–5 Amber Business Village, Amber Cl, Tamworth,
Staffordshire B77 4RP; E-mail welcome@nasen.org.uk;
Tel 01827 311500; Fax 01827 313005
Quarterly publication; subscription details from NASEN Hse.
Covers special education needs of children of all ages and all aspects of provision; keeps readers abreast of current legislation and developments; research reports, good practice in UK and abroad.

Talk

National Deaf Children's Society, 15 Dufferin Sts, London
EC1Y 8UR; URL www.ndcs.org.uk;
E-mail ndcs@ndcs.org.uk; Tel (voice and text) 020 7490
8656; Fax 020 7251 5020
News, views and features on all issues relating to childhood deafness.
Six issues per year; annual subscription £10.00 (UK), £20.00 (overseas). Free to parents and carers of deaf children in UK.

Under Five

Pre-School Learning Alliance, 69 Kings Cross Rd, London
WC1X 9LL; URL www.pre-school.org.uk;
E-mail editor.u5c@pre-school.org.uk; Tel 020 7833 0991;
Fax 020 7837 4942
Contact   Mandy Frielinghams
Monthly excluding Aug and Dec. Annual subscription (non-members) £30.00.
Issues regarding children under five and those who care for them: family concerns, play and development, running pre-schools.

Values Education

Moral Education Centre, St. Martin's College, Bowerham
Rd, Lancaster, Lancashire LA1 3JD
Thrice yearly; £6.00.
Aimed at all concerned with the moral and social well-being of children.

Welfare Rights Bulletin

Child Poverty Action Group, 94 White Lion St, London
N1 9PF; Tel 020 7837 7979
Editor   S. Osborne
Bi-monthly, £4.50. Annual subscription £25.00.
Updates the Welfare Benefits Handbook, useful tactics for dealing with common problem areas and reports on social security case law.

The Who Cares? Trust

Kemp Hse, 152–160 City Rd, London EC1V 2NP;
URL www.thewhocarestrust.org.uk;
E-mail mailbox@thewhocarestrust.org.uk; Tel 020 7251
3117; (FreeCall) 0500 564570; Fax 020 7251 3123
Chief Executive   Susanna Cheal, MBE
The Who Cares? Trust works to improve public care for children and young people living in residential accommodation and foster care through publications such as the national quarterly Who Cares? magazine.
Development programmes include Health, Education, Lifeskills and Preparation for Employment. Additionally the Who Cares? Linkline offers confidential support and information for young people who are or have been in care on the FreeCall number above .

Who Minds?

Magazine of the National Childminding Association
8 Masons Hill, Bromley, Kent BR2 9EY;
URL www.ncma.org.uk;
E-mail elyssa.barr@ncma.org.uk; Tel 020 8464 6164
Editor   Elyssa Campbell-Barr
National charity and membership organisation for childminders and those interested in quality childcare.
Quarterly 40 page publication in full colour, free to members.
Issues concerning childminding and child care in general.
Members' information.

World's Children

Save the Children, 17 Grove La, London SE5 8RD;
URL www.savethechildren.org.uk; Tel 020 7730 5400;
Fax 020 7708 2508
Non-governmental organisation concerned with children's rights and needs.
Quarterly publication sent to donors of over £10.00 a year.
Features on child rights and welfare and Save the Children's work around the world, including the UK. No unsolicited copy.

Young People Now

Haymarket Professional Publications Ltd, 174
Hammersmith Rd, London W6 7JP;
URL www.nya.org.uk;
E-mail ypn.editorial@haynet.com; Tel 020 8606 7500;
(Subscriptions) 020 8267 4319
Editor   Stovin Hayter
Weekly publication.

UK Youth

The magazine of youth groups.
UK Youth, 20–24 Kirby St, London EC1N 8TS;
URL www.ukyouth.org;
E-mail publications@ukyouth.org; Tel 020 7242 4045
Quarterly publication. Annual subscription: £15.00
(individuals), £20.00 (organisations).

Clubs

24

New Vincentian

14 Blandford St, London W1U 4DR; Tel 020 7935 9126;
Fax 020 7935 9136
Contact   Elizabeth Palmer
Free every three months.

Rotary International

Rotary International in Great Britian and Ireland,
Kinwarton Rd, Alcester, Warwickshire B49 6BP;
URL www.rotary-ribi.org; E-mail secretary@ribi.org;
Tel 01789 765411; Fax 01789 765570
Bi-monthly publication. Individual copies £2.00; annual subscription £6.00.

The Soroptimist

The Warehouse, Fleeman Gr, West Bridgford, Nottingham,
Nottinghamshire NG2 5BH; Tel 0115 982 5273; Fax 0115
982 5276
Editor   J.V. Foster
Quarterly publication free to members; annual subscription for non–members: £7.50 (postage free).
News of activities of members of Soroptimist Clubs in 25 countries including service given and international involvement. Also articles of wider general interest.

Tabler
Association of Young Men's Clubs.
Marchesi Hse, 4 Embassy Dr, Edgbaston, Birmingham,
    West Midlands B15 1TP;
    URL www.roundtable.org.uk;
    E-mail hq@roundtable.org.uk; Tel 0121 456 4402;
    Fax 0121 456 4185
Quarterly publication.

Community

ARVAC Bulletin
ARVC, Unit 2d, Aberdeen Studios, 22–24 Highbury Gr,
    London N5 2EA; URL www.arvac.org;
    E-mail arvac@arvac.org.uk; Tel 020 7704 2315; Fax 020
    7704 9995
Information Officer   Aubrey Wade
Quarterly publication. Members pay subscriptions (see
flyers for rates); research news and reports, conferences,
new books and bibliography.

Comm
Published in English and French.
European Regional Clearing Hse for Community Work,
    c/o IEIAS, 179 rue du Debarcadere, B-6001 Marcinelle,
    Belgium
Three issues yearly. Annual subscription BF1450 postage
included.
Forum of exchange to all those engaged in community
work.

Community
The Community Matters magazine.
Community Matters, 8–9 Upper St, London N1 0PQ;
    URL www.communitymatters.org.uk;
    E-mail communitymatters@communitymatters.org.uk;
    Tel 020 7226 0189; Fax 020 7354 9570
Editor   D. Tyler
Quarterly; annual subscription £10.00.
News from community organisations around the country
and on national matters of relevance to community groups
such as legislation, campaigns, funding.

Community Development Journal
FMAS, Southampton Institute, East Park Terr,
    Southampton, Hampshire SO14 0YN;
    E-mail keith.popple@solent.ac.uk; Tel 023 8031 9104;
    Fax 023 8031 9114
Quarterly; annual subscription £82.00 (UK and Europe);
US$145 elsewhere.

Community Safety Journal
Pavilion Publishing, The Ironworks, Cheapside, Brighton,
    East Sussex BN1 4GD; URL www.pavpub.com;
    E-mail info@pavpub.com; Tel 01273 623222; Fax 01273
    625526
Marketing Executive   Vicki Smith
The journal for all professionals working in the field of
community safety.

The Journal of Integrated Care
Pavilion Publishing, The Ironworks, Cheapside, Brighton,
    East Sussex BN1 4GD; URL www.pavpub.com;
    E-mail info@pavpub.com; Tel 01273 623222; Fax 01273
    625526
Marketing Executive   Vicki Smith
The journal provides practical relevance to the needs of
people working in service planning and delivery, whilst
promoting the positive engagement of service users and
carers. There is a focus on partnership working.

SCAN News
Community Learning Scotland, The National Community
Education Agency.

Community Learning Scotland, Rosebery Hse,
    9 Haymarket Terr, Edinburgh EH12 5EZ;
    URL www.communitylearning.org;
    E-mail info@cls.dircon.co.uk; Tel 0131 313 2488; Fax 0131
    313 6800
Editor   Ian Bone
Six issues a year (bi–monthly); annual subscription
£15.00.

Therapeutic Communities
The International Journal for Therapeutic and Supportive
Organisations
School of Social Work and Psychological Studies,
    University of East Anglia, Norwich, Norfolk NR4 7TJ;
    E-mail c.thoday@vea.ac.uk; Tel 01603 592068; Fax 01603
    593552
Editor   A. Ward
Quarterly; annual subscription £35.00 (free to members of
the Association of Therapeutic Communities), £78.00
(institutions).
A multidisciplinary journal for all mental health
professions, their trainers and managers, who want to
share a psychodynamic understanding of what happens in
groups, teams and organisations. The Journal aims to
disseminate knowledge and experience to readers who are
involved in the delivery, development, or design of care
systems.

Counselling

British Journal of Guidance and Counselling
Taylor and Francis Ltd, PO Box 25, Abingdon,
    Oxfordshire OX14 3UE; Tel 01235 401000; Fax 01235
    401550
Editor   A.G. Watts
Four times yearly; annual subscription £188.00
(institutions); £78.00 (individuals).
Includes symposia, research and theoretical papers,
fieldwork articles, book reviews, abstracts.

Counselling and Psychotherapy Journal
British Association for Counselling and Psychotherapy,
    1 Regent Pl, Rugby, Warwickshire CV21 2PJ;
    URL www.bacp.co.uk; E-mail bacp@bacp.co.uk; Tel 0870
    443 5252; Fax 0870 443 5160
Publishing   Niki Cox
10 publications per year. Subscription free to BACP
members; non-members £69.00 (UK), £82 (overseas).
The monthly professional journal for counsellors and
psychotherapists.

Human Systems
The Journal of Systemic Consultation and Management
published by Leeds Family Therapy and Research Centre
and Kensington Consultation Centre.
Kensington Consultation Centre, 2 Wyvil Crt, Trenchold St,
    London SW8 2TG; URL www.kcc-international.com;
    E-mail kensington_consultation_centre@compuserve.com;
    Tel 020 7720 7301
Editor   Dr Peter Stratton
Editor   Philippa Seligman

Journal of Family Therapy
Official journal of the Association for Family Therapy
P073 – Psychotherapy Section, Institute of Family Therapy,
    De Crespigny Pk, London SE5 8AF;
    E-mail jft@iop.kcl.ac.uk; Tel 020 7848 0683; Fax 020 7848
    0205
Editor   Dr. Ivan Eisler
Quarterly; annual subscription £40 (individuals), £140.00
(institutions).
Promotes all aspects of family therapy and systemic
practice.

RELATE News
Herbert Gray College, Little Church St, Rugby,
Warwickshire CV21 3AP;
E-mail enquiries@relate.org.uk; Tel 01788 573241;
Fax 01788 535007
Four issues pa.
Published by RELATE, the couple-counselling charity. This
newsletter is circulated to more than 5000 counsellors, sex
therapists, practice supervisors and centre managers in
England, Wales and Northern Ireland.

Deaf/Hard of Hearing/ Speech Impaired

British Deaf News
7 Empire Crt, Albert St, Redditch, Worcestershire B97 4DA;
URL www.britishdeafnews.com;
E-mail editorial@britishdeafnews.com; Tel 01527 592034;
Fax 01527 592083; Textphone 01527 592044
Editor Catya Neilson
Manager (Advertising) Catherine Sayers
Monthly, £1.95; annual subscription £20 (£15 for BDA
members).
Articles of interest to deaf people and professional workers;
news from the deaf community around the country.

British Journal of Audiology
Academic Press Ltd, 24–28 Oval Rd, London NW1 7DX;
Tel 020 7267 4466
Editor S.D.G. Stephens
Quarterly; annual subscription £43.00 (UK), £56.00 (overseas).
Articles of interest for the specialist and technician in
audiology.

Deafness and Education International
Hearing Concern, 7–11 Armstong Rd, London W3 7JL;
URL www.hearingconcern.com;
E-mail hearingconcern@hearingconcern.com; Tel 020
8743 1110
Editor Dr Clare Gallaway
Three issues pa; annual UK subscription £60.00
(individual), £80.00 (institution) plus postage.

Hearing Concern
Hearing Concern, 7–11 Armstrong Rd, London W3 7JL;
URL www.hearingconcern.org.uk; Tel (Admin) 020 8743
1110
Editor Philip Barron, FIPR
Quarterly on application.

One in Seven
Published by the Royal National Institute for Deaf People.
RNID, 19–23 Featherstone St, London EC1Y 8SL;
URL www.rnid.org.uk;
E-mail membership@rnid.org.uk; Tel 020 7296 8000;
Fax 020 7296 8199; Textphone 020 7296 8001
Managing Editor and Publisher Stephen Iliffe
Editor Dawn Egan
Editor (News) Tim Russell
Six issues pa; annual subscription includes membership to
RNID: £16.50 (individual), £15.00 (standing order), £40.00
(organisations).

Rainbow, Deafblind UK
The association of deafblind and dual sensory impaired
people.
100 Bridge St, Peterborough PE1 1DY;
URL www.deafblinduk.org.uk
Editor Michael Gerwat
Quarterly; annual subscription £20.00 (free to Deafblind
UK members).
The magazine for deafblind and dual sensory impaired
people. Available in Braille, Moon, large print, on tape or
on disk.

Sound Sense
The journal of Tinnitus Association
Tinnitus Action, PO Box 14904, London SE18 3ZX;
E-mail tinnitus@tinnitus.co.uk; Tel 020 8317 8934;
Fax 020 8317 8934
Editor Michael O'Toole
Free circulation.
Articles on research and other matters of interest to those
who have and treat tinnitus.

Talking Sense
c/o Sense, National Deafblind and Rubella Association,
11–13 Clifton Terr, London N4 3SR; Tel 020 7272 7774;
Fax 020 7272 6012
Editor Colin Anderson
Quarterly; annual subscription £10.00.
News and information for anyone concerned with
deafblind and multiply disabled children and adults.

Disability

Access by Design
Centre for Accessible Environments, Nutmeg Hse,
Gainsford St, London SE1 2NY; URL www.cae.org.uk;
E-mail info@cae.org.uk; Tel 020 7357 8182; Fax 020 7357
8183
Address correspondence to the Information Officer
Four publications pa; annual subscription £20.00 (UK),
£24.00 (overseas).
Promotes good practice in design of buildings regarding
access for people with disabilities.

The Advocate
National League of the Blind and Disabled, 2 Tenterden Rd,
London N17 8BE; Tel 020 8808 6030
Annual subscription £4.00.
Propaganda and information for members and interested
bodies.

Bulletin
The Royal Association for Disability and Rehabilitation
(RADAR), 12 City Forum, 250 City Rd, London
EC1V 8AF; E-mail radar@radar.org.uk; Tel 020 7250
3222; Fax 020 7250 0212; Minicom 020 7250 4119
Monthly; annual subscription £15.00.

Compass
see Leonard Cheshire, Chapter 13
International Quarterly Magazine of Leonard Cheshire.
Leonard Cheshire, 30 Millbank, London SW1P 4QD; Tel 020
7802 8200; Fax 020 7802 8250
Editor Alison Couch
Contains news and features on Leonard Cheshire services
all over the world, plus articles on disability issues and
current trends.

Contact
Liverpool Association of Disabled People, Lime Court
Centre, Upper Baker St, Liverpool, Merseyside L6 1NB;
URL www.ladp.org.uk; E-mail ladisabled@aol.com;
Tel 0151 263 8366
Quarterly; annual subscription £2.00.
Information on all aspects of disability for disabled people.

Disability Now
Newspaper for people with all types of disabilities, parents,
carers and professionals, published by Scope.
6 Market Rd, London N7 7PW; Tel 020 7619 7323; Fax 020
7619 7331
Editor Mary Wilkinson
Manager (Marketing and Circulation) Juliana Uduezue
Manager (Advertisement) Richard Gresham
Monthly; annual subscription: £18.00 (individuals), £28.00
(organisations). Also can be ordered from local newsagent.
News, views and features on anything of interest to people
with disabilities including campaigns, discrimination and
employment.

24

Magic Carpet
The Disabled Drivers' Association, Ashwellthorpe,
    Norwich, Norfolk NR16 1EX; E-mail ddahq@aol.com;
    Tel 0870 770 3333
Editor   Clive Frusher
Quarterly publication free to members (membership
currently 22 000); non–members' annual subscription
£10.00 (single), £14.00 (joint).
Covers mobility for the disabled motorist and passenger
and associated subjects.

News of Across
The in-house journal of the Across Trust.
The Across Trust, Bridge Hse, 70–72 Bridge Rd, East
    Molesey, Surrey KT8 9HF; Tel 020 8783 1355
Editor   R.V. Glithero
Three publications pa; free to members; circulation 26 000.
Provides news and information to supporters.

Forces

Blesmag
British Limbless Ex–Service Men's Association, Frankland
    Moore Hse, 185–187 High Rd, Romford, Essex
    RM6 6NA; URL www.blesma.org;
    E-mail blesma@btconnect.com; Tel 020 8590 1124;
    Fax 020 8599 2932
General Secretary   J.W. Church, MBE
Three publications pa.
Covers pensions, entitlements, allowances, casework,
artificial limbs and appliances, branch contributions and
social activities.

Flying Angel News
The Mission to Seafarers, St. Michael Paternoster Royal,
    College Hill, London EC4R 2LR;
    URL www.missiontoseafarers.org;
    E-mail general@missiontoseafarers.org; Tel 020 7248
    5202; Fax 020 7248 4761
Editor   Gillian Ennis
Quarterly newspaper; annual subscription £2.00.
News and features on the shipping industry as it affects
seafarers' lives, and activities of The Mission to Seafarers
and other organisations concerned with the well-being of
seafarers.

Legion Magazine
Centurion Publishing Ltd, 1 Benjamin St, London
    EC1M 5EA; URL www.britishlegion.org.uk; Tel 020 7880
    6200; Fax 020 7296 4214
Editor (Managing)   Claire Townley-Jones
Annual subscription £3.00. News and views of interest to
the 500 000 plus members of the Royal British Legion
nationally, including youth groups.

The Scottish Legion News
For Legion members and the service community.
The Royal British Legion Scotland, New Haig Hse, Logie
    Green Rd, Edinburgh EH7 4HR;
    E-mail ehfs.pub@btconnect.com; Tel 0131 557 2782;
    Fax 0131 557 5819
Editor   N.J. Griffiths
Annual subscription £5.00 (postage free); free on a quota
basis to branches.

Hospitals, Nursing and the Health Service

**Association for Improvements in the Maternity Services
Quarterly Journal**
40 Kingswood Ave, London NW6 6LS;
    URL www.aims.org.uk; E-mail aimsuk@ic24.net

Hon Chair   Beverley Beech
Pressure group for maternity care.
Quarterly; annual subscription £20.00.
Offers information, support and advice to parents about all
aspects of maternity care, including parents' rights, the
choices available, technological interventions, natural
childbirth and complaints procedures. Produces a series of
information leaflets and a quarterly journal.

The British Journal of Forensic Practice
Pavilion Publishing, The Ironworks, Cheapside, Brighton,
    East Sussex BN1 4GD; URL www.pavpub.com;
    E-mail info@pavpub.com; Tel 01273 623222; Fax 01273
    625526
Marketing Executive   Vicki Smith
A quarterly journal aimed at all publications and managers
responsible for delivering, commissioning, planning and
running services for people in forensic services.

British Medical Journal
British Medical Association, BMA Hse, Tavistock Sq,
    London WC1H 9JR; URL www.bmj.com;
    E-mail editor@bmj.com; Tel 020 7387 4499; Fax 020 7383
    6418
Editor   Prof Richard Smith
Annual subscription: £355.00 (companies), £263.00
(libraries), £299.00 (qualified doctors), £263.00
(individuals).
Independent professional journal for doctors and other
health professionals in general practice, hospital, academic,
industrial or welfare positions.

Community Practitioner
40 Bermondsey St, London SE1 3UD; Tel 020 7939 7058
Editor   Melanie Danforth
Monthly; annual subscription £82.00 (UK).
Covers preventive and community health.

Health Service Journal
EMAP PSM, Greater London Hse, Hampstead Rd, London
    NW1 7EJ; URL www.hsj.co.uk; Tel 020 7874 0200;
    Fax 020 7874 0201
For subscriptions
HSJ Subs Dept, TPS, Tower Hse, Sovereign Pk, Lathkill St,
    Market Harborough, Leicestershire LE16 9EF
Editor   P. Davies
Subscriptions: £2.25 (weekly); £95.00 (institutions); £65.95
(individual).

The Health Summary (THS)
32 King Henry's Rd, London NW3 3RP; Tel 020 7722
    5596
Editor   Jill Turner
Monthly; annual subscription £125.00.
Briefing paper on health policy.

Friends Connect
National Association of Hospital and Community Friends,
    2nd Fl, Fairfax Hse, Causton Rd, Colchester, Essex
    CO1 1RJ; Tel 01206 761227; Fax 01206 560244
Editor   Ladan Nourbakhsh
News and features on the work of our 36 000 healthcare
volunteers in the UK.

International Journal of Health Promotion and Education
c/o Centre for Stress Management, 156 Westcombe Hill,
    Blackheath, London SE3 7DH; URL www.ihpe.org.uk;
    E-mail ijhpe@managingstress.com; Tel 020 8318 4448;
    Fax 020 8318 4448
Editor   Prof S. Palmer
Quarterly; annual subscription (non–members) £36.00 per
complete volume (Jan–Dec).
Academic papers on behavioural aspects of health and
illness, health education methodology reports and book
reviews for medical, educational, nutritional and health
science readership.

Journal of Advanced Nursing
Blackwell Science Ltd, Osney Mead, Oxford, Oxfordshire OX2 0EL; E-mail sarah.jewell@blacksci.co.uk; Tel 01865 206206; Fax 01865 721205
Editor-in-Chief Prof James P. Smith, OBE, FRCN
Monthly; annual subscription for individuals: £95.00 (Europe), £104.50 (overseas), $165.00 (US). For institutions: £525.00 (Europe), £577.50 (overseas), $918.00 (US).

Journal of Community Nursing
PTM Publishers Ltd, 282 High St, Sutton, Surrey SM1 1PQ; URL www.jcn.co.uk; E-mail mail@jcn.co.uk; Tel 020 8642 0162; Fax 020 8643 2275
Publisher Stephen H.P. Mell
Editor Fiona Meehan, RGN, RSCN
Annual subscription £52.00.
Contributes towards the maintenance and improvements of standards of community nursing through informed articles on all aspects of the subject.

Journal of the Royal Society for the Promotion of Health
Royal Society for the Promotion of Health, 38a St. George's Dr, London SW1V 4BH; E-mail rshealth@rshealth.org.uk; Tel 020 7630 0121
Hon Editor Prof G.J. Davies, BEd, MSc, PhD, FRSH
Four issues pa. Apply for subscription rates.
Features original research, reviews and articles both from UK and overseas covering the promotion of public health including primary care, nutrition, food safety and hygiene, nutrition, environment and planning.

Nursing Times
Emap Healthcare Ltd, Greater London Hse, Hampstead Rd, London NW1 7EJ; Tel 020 7874 0500; Fax 020 7874 0505
Editor Tricia Reid
Annual subscription: £77.00 (organisations); £48.50–£53 (individuals); £42.50 (students); $287 (USA and Canada), £218.50 (rest of world).
Covers clinical, management, education and research topics in nursing, midwifery and health visiting as well as detailed coverage of developments in health and relevant social services.

Patient Voice
The Patients Association, PO Box 935, Harrow, Greater London HA1 3YJ; Tel 020 8423 9111; (Helpline) 0845 608 4455; Fax 020 8423 9119
Quarterly; annual subscription £20.00.
All aspects of patient care and health care delivery including readers' letters, book reviews, special articles.

The Practitioner
Miller Freeman Professional Ltd, 30 Calderwood St, London SE18 6QH; Tel 020 8316 3036; Fax 020 8316 3078
Editor Gavin Atkin
12 issues pa free to NHS GPs and vocational trainees; single copies £11.50 (UK), $18.00 (overseas); annual subscription £74.50 (UK), $98.00 (overseas).
Directed at general practitioners; to provide review articles and doctors' own projects.

UNISON Focus
1 Mabledon Pl, London WC1H 9AJ ; URL www.unison.org.uk; E-mail unison-focus@unison.org.uk; Tel 0845 355 0845; Fax 020 7387 6692
Editor Helen Barron
Fortnightly publication.
As the largest union in Local Government and the Health Service, UNISON represents the vast majority of Social Service staff. Its two publications, UNISON Focus and U Magazine, report news, features and policies affecting all its members, and UNISON's news and views on major policy, professional, fiscal and industrial relations issues.

Housing and Homelessness

Axis
Garden Hse, Old Potbridge Rd, Winchfield, Hook, Hampshire RG27 8BT; Tel 01252 843407; Fax 01252 843407
Editor Chris Griffin
Alternate months; annual subscription: £42.50 (libraries).
Covers provision, financing and management of rented public housing and low–cost housing for sale; homelessness; housing policy; housing improvement including estate renewal; planning; regeneration.

Housing, Care and Support
Pavilion Publishing, The Ironworks, Cheapside, Brighton, Brighton and Hove BN1 4GD; URL www.pavpub.com; E-mail info@pavpub.com; Tel 01273 623222; Fax 01273 625526
Marketing Executive Jenny Smith
Housing, Care and Support is a journal providing a whole range of information, perspectives, experiences, policy updates and developments in this area. Subjects include the new policies and thinking on daily practice with articles on managers' and practitioners' experiences of getting to grips with new initiatives.

Housing Today
7th Fl, Anchorage Hse, 2 Clove Cres, London E14 2BE; Tel 020 7560 4149
Editor Denise Chevin; E-mail denise_chevil@buildergroup.co.uk
Subscription-based weekly publication.

Housing Studies
For Subcriptions:
Taylor and Francis Publishing Company, PO Box 25, Abingdon, Oxfordshire OX14 3UE
Editor Moira Munro
School of Planning and Housing, ECA/Heriot Watt University, 79 Grassmarket, Edinburgh EH1 2HJ; Tel 0131 221 6164
Six issues pa.
A journal providing a forum for debate on housing in developed economies and the associated political, social and economic concerns. Contributions range from social anthropology to architecture, economics, sociology, social policy and political science.

ROOF
Shelter, 88 Old St, London EC1V 9HU; URL www.roofmag.org.uk; E-mail roof@shelter.org.uk; Tel 020 7505 2161; Fax 020 7505 2167
Editor Emma Hawkey
Bi–monthly £6.00 (back issues); annual subscription £69.00 (institutions), £40.00 (individuals).

24

Law

Civil Liberty Agenda
National Council for Civil Liberties, 21 Tabard St, London SE1; Tel 020 7403 3888
Editor Kate Wilkinson
Quarterly; free to members or annual subscription £6.00 (UK), £8.00 (overseas).
Covers civil liberty issues.

Community Care Law Reports
242 Pentonville Rd, London N1 9UN; Tel 020 7833 2931; Fax 020 7837 6094
Quarterly reports providing authorative and comprehensive coverage of cases relating to all aspects of community care law.

Family Court Reports
Butterworths Tolley, Halsbury Hse, 35 Chancery La,
    London WC2A 1EL; Tel 020 7520 5327; Fax 020 7520 5362
Editor   Anne-Marie Forker, LLB
24 publications pa; annual subscription £160.00 plus postage.
Covers all aspects of family law jurisdiction in terms of law
reports and comment.

Family Law
Jordan Publishing Ltd, 21 St. Thomas St, Bristol BS1 6JS;
    URL www.familylaw.co.uk;
    E-mail editor@familylaw.co.uk; Tel 0117 918 1445;
    Fax 0117 925 0486
Editor   M. McColl
Editor   E.A. Walsh, LLB Solicitor
Monthly; annual subscription: £135.00.

Journal of Social Welfare and Family Law
Routledge Ltd, 11 New Fetter La, London EC4P 4EE;
    Tel 020 7842 2139; Fax 020 7842 2302
Editor   Christina Lyon
Editor   Adrian James
Quarterly; annual subscription £46.00 (individuals), £180.00
(institutions).
Provides coverage of current issues and debates in welfare
and family and social policy in the UK.

Legal Action
Legal Action Group, 242 Pentonville Rd, London N1 9UN;
    URL www.lag.org.uk; E-mail lag@lag.org.uk; Tel 020
    7833 2931; Fax 020 7837 6094
Monthly; annual subscription £81.00.
Magazine for those involved with welfare law and advice
centres.

The Magistrate
Magistrates' Association, 28 Fitzroy Sq, London W1T 6DD;
    URL www.magistrates-association.org.uk
10 issues pa. Cost of magazine included in annual
membership subscription: £26.00 or £29.00 (other
subscribers).
Aims by coverage of relevant issues to help magistrates
and others who work in the criminal justice system to a
heightened awareness of the legal and social context of
their decision-making.

NASPO News
National Association of Senior Probation Officers, 37 Bower
    Mount Rd, Maidstone, Kent ME16 8AX
Editor   John Tracey
152 Mill La, Gresby, Upton, Wirral L49 3NT; Tel 0151 678
    8196
Quarterly, free to members; annual subscription £8.00.
Covers management of resources and team leadership in
the probation service; treatment of offenders, and manage-
ment and practice issues in the criminal justice system.

Probation Journal
Published by the National Association of Probation
    Officers, 3–4 Chivalry Rd, Battersea, London SW11 1HT;
    Tel 020 7223 4887
Hon Editor   Hindpal Singh Bhui
217a Balham High Rd, London SW17 7BP; Tel 020 8671
    0640; Fax 020 8671 0640
Quarterly; individual copies at £5.00; annual subscription
£20.00.
Covers work with offenders, supervision in the community,
social policy issues concerning defendants, prisoners and
ex–offenders, the criminal justice system and penal reform,
and family court welfare work.

Learning Difficulties

British Journal of Developmental Disabilities
Registered Charity Number 265299.

Editorial Office, 'The Globe', 4 Great William St, Stratford-
    upon-Avon, Warwickshire CV37 6RY;
    URL www.bjdd.org; E-mail editor@bjdd.org
Co-ordinating Editor   A.L. Gunzburg
Published in January and July at £18.00 (Europe); £22.00
(overseas).
Provides an international forum for a multi-disciplinary
approach to the problems posed by mental handicap and
learning disabilities in all counties.

British Journal of Learning Disabilities
Blackwell Science Ltd, Osney Mead, Oxford, Oxfordshire
    OX2 0EL; URL www.blackwell-science.com/bld;
    E-mail bld@blacksci.co.uk; Tel 01865 206206
Editor   Dr Dorothy Atkinson
Editor   Dr Jon Walmsley
Quarterly (March, June, Sept, Dec); annual subscription,
£37.00 (individual); £66.00 (organisations).
Contains original articles on all current policies and practices
in relation to the prevention of learning disabilities,
alleviation of its effects and provision of services.

Camphill Pages
Association of Camphill Communities, Gawain Hse, 56
    Welham Rd, Norton, Malton, North Yorkshire
    YO17 9DP; URL www.camphill.org.uk; Tel 01653
    694197; (Local rate) 08454 582178; Fax 01653 600001
Editor   Andy Paton
Published spring, autumn and winter. Published by the
Publications Group of the Association of Camphill
Communities. News, comment, debate and articles on
Camphill Communities and the National Association of
Parents Relatives and Friends.

Camphill Village Trust Annual Review
The Camphill Village Trust, 19 South Rd, Stourbridge, West
    Midlands DY8 3YA; Tel 01384 372122
Company Secretary   Eva Heathcock
Published annually in November. Free on request.
Covers the work of the 11 communities of the Trust with
articles on developments, the cultural, social and working
life of the Trust and its supporters and members. Leading
article touches on philosophy of Camphill Communities.

CARElink
The Care Fund, Phillippines Cl, off Hever Rd, Edenbridge,
    Kent TN5 8BT; URL www.carefund.org.uk;
    E-mail carefund@freeuk.com; Tel 01732 782711;
    Fax 01732 782712
News of fundraising in CARE Communities and Appeal
Groups.

Current Awareness Service (CAS)
British Institute of Learning Disabilities bibliography of
new books, articles, educational events and audio visual
aids.
BILD, Wolverhampton Rd, Kidderminster, Worcestershire
    DY10 3PP; URL www.bild.org.uk; Tel 01562 850251;
    Fax 01562 851970
Monthly; annual subscription on request.

Journal of Applied Research in Intellectual Disabilities
Blackwell Science Ltd, Osney Mead, Oxford, Oxfordshire
    OX2 0EL; Tel 01865 206161; Fax 01865 271205
Editor   Prof David Felce
Editor   Prof Glynis Murphy
Quarterly (March, June, Sept, Dec); annual subscription
£36.00 (individuals); £89.00 (organisations).
Designed to draw together findings of applied research in
learning disabilities undertaken in the UK and overseas by
authors of all professions.

Letters of L'Arche
Quarterly journal of the Federation
c/o L'Arche, 10 Briggate, Silsden, West Yorkshire BD20 9JT;
    URL www.larche.org.uk; E-mail info@larche.org.uk;
    Tel 01535 656186; Fax 01535 656426

International communities created with people with learning disabilities.
Annual subscription £10.00 (UK), £10.50 (EC); individual copies £2.50.
Reports and articles from over 100 worldwide communities: news, philosophy and reflection, personal and professional experience of community with people with learning difficulties.

Living WELL
Pavilion Publishing, The Ironworks, Cheapside, Brighton, East Sussex BN1 4GD; URL www.pavpub.com; E-mail info@pavpub.com; Tel 01273 623222; Fax 01273 625526
Marketing Executive   Vicki Smith
Aims to promote better quality lifestyles for people with learning disabilities. Taking a unique focus on good practice in work, education, leisure and lifestyle the journal helps subscribers to work towards inclusive relationships in the community.

The Tizard Learning Disability Review
Pavilion Publishing, The Ironworks, Cheapside, Brighton, East Sussex BN1 4GD; URL www.pavpub.com; E-mail info@pavpub.com; Tel 01273 623222; Fax 01273 625526
Marketing Executive   Vicki Smith
The key journal for managers, practitioners and researchers who work in their field of learning disability. Published in association with the Tizard Centre at the University of Kent, it bridges the gap between research and development, and everyday practice. With peer-reviewed contributions it provides a representation of interests and balance of perspectives on current issues and developments.

Values into Action
Oxford Hse, Derbyshire St, London E2 6HG; URL www.viauk.org; E-mail general@viauk.org; Tel 020 7729 5436; Fax 020 7729 7797
Director   Dr Jean Collins
Quarterly, free to members of VIA.
Articles on policy issues, news and book reviews for wide readership including people with learning disabilities.

Viewpoint
MENCAP, 123 Golden La, London EC1Y 0RT; URL www.mencap.org.uk/viewpoint; E-mail viewpoint@mencap.org.uk; Tel 020 7696 5599; Fax 020 7454 9193
Editor   Faiza Fareed
Marketing and Advertising   Estelle Bloom; Tel 020 7696 5560
Annual subscription £15.00.
Campaigning newspaper for people with a learning disability, families and professionals. News, features, reviews, diary.

Local Government

Local-Government Association
Local Government Association, Smith Sq, London SW1P 3HZ; URL www.lga.gov.uk; E-mail info@lga.gov.uk; Tel 020 7664 3131
Head (Publishing)   Rosa Van der Meersch

Local Government Chronicle
Greater London Hse, Hampstead Rd, London NW1 7EJ; URL www.lgcnet.com; E-mail (press releases) lgc.newsgroup@emap.com; (editorial) E-mail lgc@lgc.emap.com; Tel 020 7347 1837; Fax 020 7347 1831
Editor   Richard Vize
Weekly £3.25 (by post £4.26); annual subscription £110.00.
The weekly news magazine for senior local government officers.

Local Governance
(Published by INLOGOV)
Institute of Local Government Studies, J. G. Smith Bldg, University of Birmingham, Birmingham, West Midlands B15 2TT
Editor   Peter Watt
Aims to contribute to both theory and practice of local government policy making and strategic management. It creates a basis for a lively and critical exchange of ideas and experience about policy making in the public sector. The editors welcome contributions to the debate from local politicians, corporate and departmental managers and academics.

The MJ
32 Vauxhall Bridge Rd, London SW1V 2SS; Tel 020 7973 6668; Fax 020 7233 5051
Editor   Michael Burton
Weekly; individual copies £2:75; annual subscription £135.00.
Covers the whole local government field and aimed at senior management and elected members.

Mental Health

A Life in the Day
Pavilion Publishing, The Ironworks, Cheapside, Brighton, East Sussex BN1 4GD; URL www.pavpub.com; E-mail info@pavpub.com; Tel 01273 623222; Fax 01273 625526
Marketing Executive   Vicki Smith
A journal for people with an interest in developing 'real life' daytime activities for people who use mental health services including employment, education and the arts. Subscribers are able to share examples of good practice innovation from a wide range of mental health projects around Europe and beyond.

British Journal of Educational Psychology
British Psychological Society, St. Andrew's Hse, 48 Princess Road East, Leicester LE1 7DR
Editor   Prof Julie Dockrell
Press Editor   Julie Neason
£104.00 per volume of four parts (Mar/Jun/Sept/Dec).

The Journal of Mental Health Promotion
Pavilion Publishing, The Ironworks, Cheapside, Brighton, East Sussex BN1 4GD; URL www.pavpub.com; E-mail info@pavpub.com; Tel 01273 623222; Fax 01273 625526
Marketing Executive   Vicki Smith
Coordinates the dissemination of new research outcomes to programme developers and to all those who are involved in policy-making and the implementation of mental health promotion and mental health disorder prevention policies in local or national communities. Peer-reviewed by an expert editorial board. Provides subscribers with a forum for debate on mental health promotion.

International Journal of Social Psychiatry
Avenue Publishing Company, 41 Georges Wood Rd, Brookmans Pk, Hertfordshire AL9 7BX; URL www.ijsp.co.uk; Tel 01707 655015; Fax 01707 655015
Publisher   Shahin Bierer
Editor   Dr Dinesh Bhugra
For social workers, doctors and teachers in hospitals and universities, it presents articles on changing attitudes towards social psychiatry, stressing partnership between the various disciplines.

The Mental Health Review
Pavilion Publications, The Ironworks, Cheapside, Brighton, East Sussex BN1 4GD; URL www.pavpub.com; E-mail info@pavpub.com; Tel 01273 623222; Fax 01273 625526

24

Marketing Executive Vicki Smith
Widely-read and well-respected journal amongst mental health professionals. Articles from leading figures in the field offer readers a medium between policy issues and innovative practices.

Openmind

The Mental Health Magazine.
Openmind, 15–19 Broadway, London E15 4BQ;
URL www.openmindmagazine.org.uk;
E-mail openmind@mind.org.uk; Tel 020 8221 9661;
Fax 020 8221 9681
Editor Sara Dunn
Bi–monthly; individual copies £3.50; annual subscription (2000) £22.00 (individuals), £36.00 (organisations).
Offers an overview of news, issues, research and developments in the field of mental health; encourages debate; provides helpful information.

Occupational Medicine

British Journal of Occupational Therapy
(Official Journal of the College of Occupational Therapists)
106–114 Borough High St, London SE1 1LB; Tel 020 7450 2340; Fax 020 7450 2350
Editor Upma Barnett
Manager (Advertisement) Paula Willock
Monthly.
Publishes articles on health care, practice, education, management and research in occupational therapy.

Ombudsman

Annual Review/Ombudsman News (of the Financial Ombudsman Service)
South Quay Plaza, 183 Marsh Wall, London E14 9SR;
URL www.financial-ombudsman.org.uk;
E-mail enquiries@financial-ombudsman.org.uk; Tel 0845 080 1800; (Switchboard) 020 7964 1000; Fax 020 7965 1001
An independent service for consumers with unresolved complaints about financial firms.
Annual Review is available from June every year. It reports on the work of the Financial Ombudsman Service for the past year.
Ombudsman News is produced monthly and contains commentary and case studies.
Both are available free from the website or upon request.

Physiotherapy

Braille Journal of Physiotherapy
Royal National Institute of the Blind, PO Box 173, Peterborough, Cambridgeshire PE2 6WS;
URL www.rnib.org.uk; E-mail cservices@rnib.org.uk;
Tel 01733 375000
Monthly; annual subscription on request.
Articles from Physiotherapy, Journal of the Chartered Society of Physiotherapy reproduced in braille. The Journal of the Chartered Society of Physiotherapy is also available on tape and computer disk in ASCII and WP formats from RNIB.

Physiotherapy
Chartered Society of Physiotherapy, 14 Bedford Row, London WC1R 4ED; Tel 020 7306 6660; Fax 020 7306 6667
Managing Editor Gillian Adams
Monthly; individual copies £14.00; annual subscription £129.00 (UK), £188.00 (overseas).
Professional articles on physiotherapy plus book reviews, abstracts, correspondence and official reports.

Therapy Weekly
Emap Healthcare, Greater London Hse, Hampstead Rd, London NW1 7EJ;
E-mail melissao@healthcare.emap.co.uk; Tel 020 7874 0360; Fax 020 7874 0368
Editor Melissa Oliveck
Advertising Manager Heather Day
Weekly; annual subscription personal: £35.00; institutional £49.00; student £20.00. Applications from charterd physio, occupational and speech and language therapists will be considered for inclusion on the free circulation list.

Prisons and Offenders

The British Journal of Criminology
Published on behalf of the Centre for Crime and Justice Studies by Oxford University Press.
Great Clarendon St, Oxford, Oxfordshire OX2 6DP;
URL www.bjc.oupjournals.org
Editor Geoffrey Pearson
Advertising Sales Agent Helen Pearson
Quarterly publication.
Annual subscription: Institutions – £155.00 (UK/Europe), US$250.00 (elsewhere); Personal subscribers – £47.00 (UK/Europe), US$79.00 (elsewhere); ESC/ASC/Law and Society Assoc. members – £37.00 (UK/Europe), US$60.00 (elsewhere); Full BSC members – free with membership; CCJS members £20 (UK/Europe), US$30 (elsewhere).

Fresh Start
The Bourne Trust Newsletter, Lincoln Hse, 1–3 Brixton Rd, London SW9 6DE; Tel 020 7582 1313; Fax 020 7735 6077
Editor Donald Kelly
Three publications pa; free on request.
Counselling and social service for prisoners and their families.

Howard Journal of Criminal Justice
The Howard League for Penal Reform, 1 Ardleigh Rd, London N1 4HS; URL www.howardleague.org; Tel 020 7249 7373
Editor Prof David Wilson
Editor Tony Fowles
Editor Frances Crook
Four publications pa; £45.00 (free to Howard League members).
Concerned with all major aspects of the criminal process, penal policy and crime prevention; asserts the importance of an integrated approach.

The NAPV Newsletter
Fleur Field, Kingsdale Rd, Berkhamsted, Hertfordshire; Tel 01442 877974
Editor C. Green
Two publications pa; free (members), £1.50 (non-members).
News of activities of prison visitors and other related interests.

NASPO News
National Association of Senior Probation Officers, 37 Bower Mount Rd, Maidstone, Kent ME16 8AX
Editor John Tracey
152 Mill La, Greasby, Upton, Wirral L49 3NT; Tel 0151 678 8196
Quarterly; free to members; annual subscription £8.00.
Covers management of resources and team leadership in the probation service; treatment of offenders, and management and practice issues in the criminal justice system.

Probation Journal
Published by the National Association of Probation Officers, 3–4 Chivalry Rd, Battersea, London SW11 1HT; Tel 020 7223 4887

Hon Editor   Hindpal Singh Bhui
217a Balham High Rd, London SW17 7BP; Tel 020 8671
    0640; Fax 020 8671 0640
Quarterly; free to members and associates; individual
copies: £6.00 (individuals), £12.00 (organisations);
annual subscription: £24.00 (individuals), £48.00
(organisations).
Covers social work with offenders, supervision in the
community, social policy issues concerning defendants,
prisoners and ex-offenders, the criminal justice system and
penal reform, and family court welfare work.

Public Health and Health Education

Health Education Journal
University Dental Hospital of Manchester, Higher
    Cambridge St, Manchester, Greater Manchester
    M15 6FH; URL www.hej.org.uk; Tel 0161 275 6610
Contact   Prof Anthony Blinkholm
Quarterly (from Jan); annual subscriptions £37.00
(individuals), £65.00 (institutions).
Research, feature articles and research reviews for those
working in the fields of health education and promotion.

Health Promotion International
Journals Subscriptions Department, Oxford University
    Press, Great Clarendon St, Oxford, Oxfordshire 6DP
Editor in Chief   J. Catford
Quarterly publication. Annual subscription: institutions –
£127.00 (UK/Europe), US$225.00 (elsewhere); personal:
£62.00 (UK/Europe), US$110.00 (elsewhere).
Describes international progress in the developing field of
health promotion.

Journal of Public Health Medicine
Official journal of the Faculty of Public Health Medicine
of the Royal College of Physicians in the United
Kingdom.
West Surrey Health Authority, The Ridgewood Centre, Old
    Bisley Rd, Camberley, Surrey GU16 5QE;
    URL www.pubmed.oupjournals.org
Editor   Dr E.G. Jessop
Editor   Dr N. Vetter
Assistant Editor   Karen Hayday
Quarterly; annual subscription: £155.00 (UK/Europe)
US$280.00 (elsewhere); individual copies: £45.00
(UK/Europe); US$88.00 (elsewhere).

Proceedings of the Nutrition Society
10 Cambridge Crt, 210 Shepherds Bush Rd, London
    W6 7NJ; URL www.nutsoc.org.uk;
    E-mail edoffice@nutsoc.org.uk
Editor   Dr G. R. Goldberg
Six issues pa.

**Public Health (A Journal of the Royal Institute of Public
Health)**
The Royal Institute of Public Health, 28 Portland Pl,
    London W1B 1DE; E-mail public.health@riph.org.uk;
    Tel 020 7291 8359; Fax 020 7291 8383
Six issues pa; annual subscription £198.00 (EU), £198.00
(elsewhere).
Devoted to preventive medicine and public health.

Public Health Engineer
The official journal of the Institution of Public Health
    Engineers, Sterling Publications Ltd, 86–88 Edgware Rd,
    London W2 2YW; Tel 020 7258 0066
Editor   F.E. Bruce
Quarterly; individual copies £5.00; annual subscription
£20.00.
Papers presented to the Institution on water supply,
sewerage, wastewater disposal, solid wastes,
environmental pollution, etc.; Institution affairs.

Sociology of Health and Illness
School of Sociology and Social Policy, Nottingham
    University, Nottingham, Nottinghamshire NG7 2RD;
    URL www.blackwellpublishers.co.uk/journals/shil;
    E-mail shi@nottingham.ac.uk; Tel 0115 846 6560;
    Fax 0115 8466349
Editor   R. Dingwall
Editor   V. James
Editor   E. Murphy
Editor   A. Pilnick
Five issues pa and a monograph; £45.00/US$55.00
(individuals); £247.00 /US$477.60 (institutions).
Contains articles and book reviews on health and social
welfare from sociology and related disciplines.

Race Relations and Ethnic Diversity

Journal of Ethnic and Migration Studies
Carfax Publishing Taylor and Francis Ltd, Customer
    Services Dept, Rankine Rd, Basingstoke, Hampshire
    RG24 8PR; URL www.tandf.co.uk/journals;
    E-mail journals.order@tandf.co.uk; Tel 01256 813002;
    Fax 01256 330245
Editor   Russell King
Editorial Manager   Jenny Money
Carfax Publishing Taylor and Francis Ltd, Customer
    Services Dept, 325 Chestnut St, 8th Fl, Philadelphia,
    PA 19106, USA; Tel 1 215 625 8900; Fax 1 215 625 8914
Carfax Publishing Taylor and Francis Ltd, PO Box 352,
    Cammeray, NSW 2062, Australia; Tel 61 2 9958 5329;
    Fax 61 2 9958 2376
Bi-monthly annual subscriptions £400.00/US$651
(institutions); £78.00/US$129 (individuals).
Publishes the results of research on migration, ethnic
conflict, nationalism, discrimination, racism and policies of
integration and citizenship.

Runnymede Bulletin
Runnymede Trust, Suite 106 The London Fruit and Wool
    Exchange, Brushfield St, London E1 6EP;
    URL www.runnymedetrust.org;
    E-mail info@runnymedetrust.org; Tel 020 7377 9222;
    Fax 020 7377 6622
Editor (Publications)   Ros Spry
Quarterly; annual subscription £25.00 (2003).
Covers developments in the field of race relations, ethnicity
and cultural diversity. Promotes diversity via radical
thinking to ensure that the contribution that ethnic
minorities make to society is fully valued and realised.
Research strategy and publications output reflect and
promote the mainstreaming of race issues to influence policy-
making within governmental and institutional bodies.

24

Religion and Morals

All the World
The Salvation Army, International Headquarters, 101
    Queen Victoria St, London EC4P 4EP;
    URL www.salvationarmy.org/alltheworld.nsf; Tel 020
    7332 0101
Editor   Kevin Sims
Quarterly; individual copies £0.40; annual subscription
£3.00 (UK), £3.50 (surface); £4.50 (overseas).

In Touch
The Grail, 125 Waxwell La, Pinner, Greater London
    HA5 3ER; URL www.geocities.com/grailcentre;
    E-mail waxwell@compuserve.com; Tel 020 8866 2195;
    Fax 020 8866 1408
Editor   Mary Grasar
Quarterly; annual subscription £8.00.
Articles on prayer, scripture, book reviews and topical
issues.

Point 3
(The Toc H Magazine)
Toc H, 1 Forest Cl, Wendover, Aylesbury, Buckinghamshire
    HP22 6BT; E-mail info@toch.org.uk; Tel 01296 623911;
    Fax 01296 696137
Bi-monthly; individual copies £0.80; annual subscription
£5.00.
In-house journal which acts as vehicle for communication
between staff and members; informs readers on topical and
relevant issues.

Share It
The Church Army, Independents Rd, London SE3 9LG;
    URL www.churcharmy.org.uk; Tel 020 8318 1226
Three publications pa (including annual report).
News of activities.

Social Work and Social Policy

British Journal of Social Work
School of Social Sciences, Cardiff University, 50 Park Pl,
    Cardiff CF10 3AT; URL www3.oup.co.uk/social
Oxford University Press, Great Clarendon St, Oxford,
    Oxfordshire OX2 6DP; Tel 01865 556767; Fax 01865
    556646
Editor   I. Butler
Editor   M. Drakeford
Six issues pa; annual subscription £225 (Europe), US$370.00
(elsewhere).
Bi-monthly academic journal publishing articles and listing
and reviewing books on social work, social care, social
policy, criminology etc.

Care and Health Magazine
21–27 Seagrave Rd, London SW6 1RP; Tel 0870 901 7773
Publisher   John Buttle
Fortnightly magazine

Community Care
Quadrant Hse, The Quadrant, Sutton, Surrey SM2 5AS;
    URL www.communitycare.co.uk;
    E-mail comcare.news@rbi.co.uk; Tel 020 8652 4861
Editor   Polly Neate
Weekly; individual copies £1.85; annual subscription £78.00
(UK), £125.00 (overseas), £39.00 (student rate).

Critical Social Policy
Published by SAGE Publications in association with
Critical Social Policy Ltd
6 Bonhill St, London EC2A 4PU; URL www.sagepub.co.uk;
    E-mail info@sagepub.co.uk; Tel 020 7374 0645; Fax 020
    7374 8741
Contact   Norman Ginsburg
School of Social Sciences, University of North London,
    62–66 Highbury Gr, London N5 2AD; Tel 020 7753 3283
Quarterly; subscription details from SAGE Publications.
Analysis of social policy and welfare issues from critical
viewpoint.

Crucible
Board for Social Responsibility, Church Hse, Great Smith
    St, London SW1P 3NZ;
    E-mail crucible@bsr.c-of-e.org.uk; Tel 020 7898 1537
Editor   Peter Sedgwick
Editor (Book Reviews)   Andrew Davey
Administrator   Anna Barandella
Quarterly; indiviual copies £3.00; annual subscription
£12.00 postage free.
Christian comment on contemporary social, economic and
political issues.

Groupwork
Whiting and Birch Ltd, 90 Dartmouth Rd, Forest Hill,
    London SE23 3HZ; Tel 020 8244 2421; Fax 020 8244 2448
Editor   Oded Manor

Deputy Editor   Alison Skinner
Three issues pa; annual subscription: £47.50 (institutions),
£27.50 (individuals).
Social work with groups.

Human Relations
The Tavistock Institute, 30 Tabernacle St, London
    EC2A 4UE; E-mail t.jeffers@tavinstitute.org; Tel 020 7417
    0407
Sage Publications, 6–8 Bonhill St, London EC2A 4PU
Editor   Prof Paul Willman
Twelve issues pa; annual subscription: US$677.00 (outside
North America US$474.00), US$104.00 (individuals).

The Journal of Adult Protection
Pavilion Publishing, The Ironworks, Cheapside, Brighton,
    East Sussex BN1 4GD; URL www.pavpub.com;
    E-mail info@pavpub.com; Tel 01273 623222; Fax 01273
    625526
Marketing Executive   Vicki Smith
Gives adult protection professionals access to the high
quality research and innovative service development
needed to develop policy and practice decisions in an
emerging field.

Journal of Practice Teaching in Social Work
Whiting and Birch Ltd, 90 Dartmouth Rd, London
    SE23 3HZ; Tel 020 8244 2421; Fax 020 8244 2448
Editor   Graham Ixer
Annual subscription: £50.00 (libraries), £30.00 (others).

Journal of Social Policy
Cambridge University Press, The Edinburgh Bldg,
    Shaftesbury Rd, Cambridge, Cambridgeshire CB2 2RU;
    Tel 01223 326070; Fax 01233 315052
Editor   Michael Hill
Editor   Helen Jones
Volume 1 in 2004: Two journals in 2004: eight issues.
Institutions print and electronic: £204. Individuals print
plus electronic: £65.
Journal of Social Policy and Social Policy and Society is
now available as one comple bundle. Journal of Social
Policy carries articles on all aspects of social policy in an
international context.
Social Policy and Society brings discussion of
contemporary social policy issues to a wider audience and
provides a valuable teaching and research resource to the
worldwide social and public policy community.
2004 sees subscribers benefiting from a new online
resource, the Social Policy Digest. An invaluable, fully
searchable and regularly updated source of information
about current events across the whole social policy
field.

Practice
School of Nursing, Social Work and Applied Health,
    University of Hull, Cottingham Rd, Kingston-upon-
    Hull, East Riding of Yorkshire HU6 7RX; Tel 01482
    466243; Fax 01482 466306
Editor   Greta Bradley
Editor   Jill Manthorpe
Annual subscription £37.00 (individuals), £57.00
(institutions), £26.00 (BASW members).
Journal for social workers, trainers, researchers, academics
and managers.

Scope
Review of Social Policy and Voluntary Action in N. Ireland
Northern Ireland Council for Voluntary Action, 61 Dunairn
    Gdns, Belfast BT15 2GB; Tel 028 9087 7777; Fax 028 9087
    7799
Managing Editor   Frances McCandless
Monthly (10 times a year), £1.50 (sterling).

Social Caring
21–27 Seagrove Rd, London SW6 1RP; Tel 0870 901 7773
Quarterly magazine of the Social Care Association.

Social Policy and Administration
School of Social Policy, University of Kent, Canterbury, Kent CT2 7RF
Editor John Baldock
Editor (Review) Dr David Dehney
Quarterly; annual subscription £44.00 (individuals) £410.00 (institutions).
Articles by practitioners and academics on issues of social policy and provision, predominantly about Britain, but with well-documented comparative studies of other countries in health, social work, social security, housing and employment. Long review articles of current publications in each issue.

Social Sciences: News from the ESRC
Economic and Social Research Council, Polaris Hse, North Star Ave, Swindon SN2 1UJ; URL www.esrc.ac.uk; E-mail exrel@esrc.ac.uk; Tel 01793 413000
Editor Lesley Lilley
Three free publications pa.
Provides news of developments at ESRC and features results of ESRC-sponsored research.

Social Services Abstracts Bulletin
Democratic Services, Strategic Support Directorate, Newcastle City Council Civic Centre, Newcastle upon Tyne, Tyne and Wear NE99 2BN; URL www.newcastle.gov.uk; E-mail lesley.phillips@newcastle.gov.uk; Tel 0191 211 5041; Fax 0191 211 4959
Editor Lesley Phillips
Monthly.
Abstracts of social services journal articles.

Social Work and Social Sciences Review
Whiting and Birch Ltd, 90 Dartmouth Rd, Forest Hill, London SE23 3HZ; Tel 020 8244 2421; Fax 020 8244 2448
Co-Editor Prof David Thorpe
Co-Editor Bob Sapey
Annual subscription £60.00 (corporate), £35.00 (individual).
Social work, applied research and links to social services.

Social Work Education
Taylor and Francis Ltd, PO Box 25, Abingdon, Oxfordshire OX14 3UE; Tel 01235 401000; Fax 01235 401550
Editor A.G. Watts
Quarterly; annual subscription: £146.00 (institutions), £40.00 (individuals).

Social Work Monographs
University of East Anglia, Norwich, Norfolk NR4 7TJ; E-mail j.hancock@uea.ac.uk; Tel 01603 592087; Fax 01603 593552
Editor Ann McDonald
Ten issues pa; individual copies £7.50 (including postage); available by standing order £6.00 each.
Social Work Monographs publishes the student dissertations from a wide range of universities. We also publish Law Files written by university staff on Child Care, Mental Health and Community Care Law.

Social Work Practice
Taylor and Francis Ltd, PO Box 25, Abingdon, Oxfordshire OX14 3UE; Tel 01235 401000; Fax 01235 401550
Editor A.G. Watts
Quarterly; annual subscription: £144.00 (institutions), £54.00 (individuals).

Specific Health Problems

Abstracts on Hygiene and Communicable Diseases
CABI Publishing, CAB INTERNATIONAL, Wallingford, Oxfordshire OX10 8DE; URL www.cabi-publishing.org; E-mail publishing@cabi.org; Tel 01491 832111; Fax 01491 833508

Director (Health, Animal and Social Science) Elizabeth Dodsworth
Product Manager Richard Sullivan
All aspects of health and disease, including environmental health, community health, diseases and their control and communicable diseases.

Arthritis News
Arthritis Care, 18 Stephenson Way, London NW1 2HD; URL www.arthritiscare.org.uk; E-mail editor@arthritiscare.org.uk; Tel 020 7380 6500; Fax 020 7380 6505
Editor Kate Llewelyn
Bi-monthly, individual copies £2 (free to members); annual subscription £12.00.
A lifestyle magazine for people with arthritis containing practical information interviews, news, competitions and reviews.

Arthritis Today
Magazine for subscribers to the Arthritis Research Campaign.
St. Mary's Gate, Chesterfield, Derbyshire S41 7TD; URL www.arc.org.uk
Editor Jane Tadman
Quarterly; to subscribers to Arc who donate £15.00 pa.

Balance
Diabetes UK, 10 Parkway, London NW1 7AA; URL www.diabetes.org.uk; E-mail balance@diabetes.org.uk; Tel 020 7424 1000
Editor Martin Cullen
Bi-monthly, individual copies £2.00 (free to members).
Current information including products and research, diet advice and recipes, events.

British Journal of Cancer
BJC Main Editorial Office, UCL Department of Oncology, Rm 317 Bland Sutton Bldg, Middlesex Hospital, Mortimer St, London W1N 8AA; URL www.bjcancer.com; E-mail bjc@ucl.ac.uk; Tel 020 7679 9600; Fax 020 7916 8548
Editor-in-Chief Robin Weiss
Editorial Office Andrew Welsh
Publisher Nature Publishing Group

Brittle Bone Society
Charity Shop, 112 City Rd, Dundee DD2 2PW; E-mail bbs@brittlebone.org; Tel 01382 667603
Administrator Raymond Lawrie
Quarterly; annual membership £10.00.

CF Today
Cystic Fibrosis Trust, 11 London Rd, Bromley, Kent BR1 1BY; URL www.cftrust.org.uk; Tel 020 8464 7211; Fax 020 8313 0472
Free quarterly.
Medical and scientific articles, letters and information.

Epilepsy Today
Epilepsy Action, New Anstey Hse, Gate Way Dr, Yeadon, Leeds, West Yorkshire LS19 7XY; URL www.epilepsy.org.uk; E-mail epilepsy@epilepsy.org.uk; Tel 0113 210 8800; Fax 0113 391 0300
Quarterly; subscription £12.00 pa.
Wide-ranging articles about epilepsy and related issues; of interest to all profession working with epilepsy, as well as members of the charity

Exchange
National Eczema Society, Hill House, Highgate Hill, London N19 5NA; Tel 020 7281 3553
Editor Freda Houlton
Quarterly; individual copies £2.00 (free to members).
Society membership £12.00 (UK), £16.00 (overseas).
All aspects of the management of eczema; information on new developments and useful products.

24

HDA Newsletter
Huntington's Disease Association, 108 Battersea High St, London SW11 3HP; Tel 020 7223 7000
Team Leader Cath Stanley
Free twice pa.
All aspects of the medical condition of Huntington's Disease plus news of the Association.

ia Journal
(Journal of ia – The Ileostomy and Internal Pouch Support Group)
PO Box 22, Great Yarmouth, Norfolk NR31 6WA; E-mail editor@iajournal.co.uk; Tel 01493 300999
Editor John Smail, ACIB
Quarterly (Mar/Jun/Sep/Dec); supplied free to members of member organisations.
Anything to do with helping people who have had surgery involving removal of the colon to return to full and active lives.

International Journal of Health Promotion and Education
c/o University Dental Hospital, Higher Cambridge St, Manchester, Greater Manchester M15 6FH; URL www.ihpe.org.uk; Tel 0161 275 6610; Fax 0161 275 6299
Editor Prof S. Palmer
Quarterly; annual subscription (non–members £36.00 per complete volume (Jan–Dec).
Academic papers on behavioural aspects of health and illness, health education methodology reports, and book reviews for medical, educational, nutritional and health science readership.

Journal of Intellectual Disability Research
(Published by Blackwell Publishing Ltd on behalf MENCAP in association with IASSID.
Blackwell Publishing Ltd, 101 George St, Edinburgh EH2 3ES
Editor W.I. Fraser
Eight issues per year; annual subscription: Individuals – £89.00), US$149.00 (USA/Canada); Institutions – £369.00 (Europe), £406.00 (elsewhere), $617.00 (USA/Canada).

Kidney Life
National Kidney Federation, 6 Stanley St, Worksop, Nottinghamshire S81 7HX; URL www.kidney.org.uk; E-mail nkf@kidney.org.uk; Tel 01909 487795; (Helpline) 0845 601 0209; Fax 01909 481723
Editor K. Wright
Quarterly; annual subscription £12.00 (minimum); leaflets free to KPA members.
Covers medical and social items relating to kidney patients together with information on activities of the federation and its 65 member associations.

Migraine News
(Quarterly newsletter.)
The Migraine Trust, 45 Great Ormond St, London WC1N 3HZ; URL www.migrainetrust.org; Tel 020 7831 4818; Fax 020 7831 4818
Managing Editor Danielle Swain
The Migraine Trust funds and promotes research, improves the diagnosis and treatment of migraine and provides support and information for sufferers.
Contains medical articles, literature information and advice available to sufferers; fund-raising activities of self-help groups.

MS Matters
Multiple Sclerosis Society, MS National Centre, 372 Edgware Rd, London NW2 6NDs; URL www.mssociety.org.uk; E-mail membership@mssociety.org.uk; Tel 020 8438 0700; (Helpline Freephone) 0808 800 8000; Fax 020 8438 0701
Bi-monthly; annual subscription £5.00.
A lifestyle magazine for people living with multiple sclerosis.

National Ankylosing Spondylitis Society Newsletter
NASS, PO Box 179, Mayfield, East Sussex TN20 6ZL; URL www.nass.co.uk; E-mail nass@nass.co.uk; Tel 01435 873527; Fax 01435 873027
Twice pa; annual subscription £15.00.
Articles on all aspects of the disease; branch news; correspondence. Other publications as well as physiotherapy cassette and video tape.

NewsBeat
British Heart Foundation, 14 Fitzhardinge St, London W1H 6DH; URL www.bhf.org.uk; Tel 020 7935 0185; Fax 020 7486 5820
Editor Liz Missen
Twice pa, free but donation appreciated to cover costs; sent to all supporters.
Covers the fund-raising work of the heart research charity, including reports on research projects, medical news; regional events.

The Parkinson
Parkinson's Disease Society, 215 Vauxhall Bridge, London SW1V 1EJ; URL www.parkinsons.org.uk; E-mail bcormie@parkinsons.org.uk; Tel 020 7932 1359; Fax 020 7233 9908
Editor Barbara Cormie
Quarterly; free to members of the Parkinson's Disease Society.
Advice and information on living with Parkinson's Disease.

Quarterly Journal of Medicine
Experimental Medicine Unit, University of Wales, Singleton Pk, Swansea SA2 8PP; E-mail qjm@btinternet.com; Tel 01865 248539; Fax 01865 248540
Editor J.M. Hopkin
Monthly; individual copies £18.00 (UK); annual subscription: Institutions – £165.00 (UK), US$285.00 (USA), £165.00 (elsewhere); Individuals – £82.00 (UK), £165 (elsewhere).
Original and review articles on medical science and practice.

Target Md
Official magazine of the Muscular Dystrophy Campaign.
7–11 Prescott Pl, London SW4 6BS; URL www.muscular-dystrophy.org; E-mail info@muscular-dystrophy.org; Tel 020 7720 8055
Editor Leigh Chambers
Quarterly; annual subscription £12.00 (free to members).
Scientific research and management of neuromuscular disorders, personal profiles, fund-raising. Mailed to people with neuromuscular conditions, medical and care professionals.

Talkback
BackCare, 16 Elmtree Rd, Teddington, London TW11 8ST; URL www.backcare.org.uk; E-mail talkback@backcare.org.uk; Tel 020 8977 5474; Fax 020 8943 5318
Quarterly with membership (subscription £20.50).
Up-to-date information on reducing the impact of back pain.

Your Voice
RETHINK, 28 Castle St, Kingston upon Thames, Surrey KT1 1SS; URL www.rethink.org; www.rethink.org/at-ease; E-mail info@rethink.org; Tel 020 8547 3937; Fax 020 8547 3862; (Advice service (1000–1500 Mon–Fri)) 020 8974 6814
Publications Julian Lloyd
Quarterly; annual subscription £15.00 (UK), £22.00 (overseas).
Fellowship affairs and other relevant matters in the wider field of mental health.

Voluntary Service

Carer
Carers National Association, Ruth Pitter Hse, 20–25 Glasshouse Yard, London EC1A 4JS;
URL www.carersuk.demon.co.uk; Tel 020 7490 8818; Fax 020 7490 8824
Bi-monthly; free to subscribers and association members.

Voluntary Sector
Published by the National Council for Voluntary Organisations
Editor Amanda Moss
Regent's Wharf, 8 All Saints St, London N1 9RL; Tel 020 7713 6161; Fax 020 7713 6300
News, features and analysis on issues affecting the voluntary sector
Published ten times pa. Annual subscription £30.00 (voluntary organisations and individuals), £55.00 (statutory organisations and companies). Specimen copy on request. Bulk rates on request.

Third Force News
Scottish Council for Voluntary Organisations, Mansfield Traquair Centre, 15 Mansfield Pl, Edinburgh EH3 6BB;
URL www.scvo.org.uk; Tel 0131 556 3882
Editor Gordon Brown
Annual subscription £110.00.
A newsletter for and about the voluntary sector in Scotland containing features, news, views, information and advice.

VAM News
Voluntary Action Manchester, North Sq, 11–13 Spear St, Manchester, Greater Manchester M1 1JU;
URL www.vamanchester.org.uk;
E-mail vam@vamanchester.org.uk; Tel 0161 236 3206; Fax 0161 228 0464
Bi-monthly, free to voluntary or community groups based in Manchester.
Aimed at voluntary organisations in Manchester.

NATIONAL DAILY AND SUNDAY NEWSPAPERS

Social Services Correspondents

Daily Express
245 Blackfriars Rd, London SE1 9UX; Tel 020 7928 8000
Editor (Home Affairs) Robin Ackroyd

Daily Mail
Northcliffe Hse, 2 Derry St, London W8 5TT; Tel 020 7938 6000; Fax 020 7937 5287
Reporter (Home Affairs) James Clark

Financial Times (UK) Ltd
Number One, Southwark Bridge, London SE1 9HL;
URL www.ft.com; E-mail news.desk@ft.com; Tel 020 7873 3000
Editor (Public Affairs) Nick Timmins

The Guardian
119 Farringdon Rd, London EC1R 3ER;
URL www.guardianunlimited.co.uk/society; Tel 020 7278 2332; Fax 020 7713 4154
Society Editor Patrick Butler
The Guardian's Society section every Wednesday reports and comments on the latest developments within public services.

The Independent and Independent on Sunday
1 Canada Sq, Canary Wharf, London E14 5DL; Tel 020 7293 2000
Correspondent (Social Services) Jack O'Sullivan
Correspondent (Social Services) Judy Judd
Correspondent (Social Services) Ian McKinnon

Sunday Times
1 Pennington St, London E1 9XW; Tel 020 7782 5000

The Times
1 Pennington St, London E1 9XN; Tel 020 7782 5000
Contact Jill Sherman
Broadcasting, Audio-visual Education, Computers in Education

BROADCASTING SERVICES TO THE COMMUNITY

This list of broadcasting companies and organisations also includes, where available, details of the type of social concern programmes and aids which they produce.

British Broadcasting Corporation

BBC White City, 201 Wood La, London W12 7TS;
URL www.bbc.co.uk/learning; Tel 020 8752 5252
Director (Factual and Learning) John Willis
Controller (Learning and Interactive) Liz Cleaver
Head (Public Affairs, BBC Learning) Wendy Jones
Senior Education Officer (BBC Scotland) John Russel
Head (Education and Learning, BBC Wales) Eleri Wyn Lewis
BBC Education Consultant (BBC Northern Ireland) Eric Twaddell
The BBC provides educational output, both formal and informal, for transmission on its public service television and radio services in the UK. In addition, it offers extensive educational content for both children and adults online at www.bbc.co.uk. Formal educational output supports a range of lifeskills and vocational training for adults and various elements of the school curriculum for children. Informal, broadly educative programming is broadcast across the BBC schedule and covers many subject areas. The BBC uses digital technology to build on the strengths and popularity of factual TV and radio programmes and make them the starting point for online learning through which people are encouraged to foster general interests in, for example, science or history or to develop specific skills for work, life and leisure. The BBC works with a range of educational partners, including government departments and agencies, training organisations, museums and universities, colleges and schools. It has a longstanding relationship with the Open University, based on a mutual commitment to lifelong learning.

BBC Television
Television Centre, 80 Wood La, London W12 7RJ;
URL www.bbc.co.uk; Tel 020 8743 8000

BBC Radio
Broadcasting Hse, Portland Pl, London W1A 1AA; Tel 020 8743 8000

BBC Learning Support
BBC White City, 201 Wood La, London W12 7TS; Tel 020 8752 5252
Head (Learning Support) Steve Pollock
Manager (Learning Support) Sheila Browne
Learning Support department producing radio and television programmes on a wide range of subjects. The main areas of output are relationships, information technology, business and management, citizenship, health and technology and promoting the understanding of the

24

world and other cultures. A number of books and videos are published to accompany the programmes. Programmes are transmitted on both BBC1 and BBC2, and across all the radio networks.

BBC Education Publishing Division

BBC White City, 201 Wood La, London W12 7TS; Tel 020 8752 5252
Head (Educational Publishing)   Juliet Waugh
Head (Product Development)   Catherine Boulton
Head (Production)   Susan Ross
The Department produces a wide range of materials to support educational broadcasts, including books and materials for language learning for teachers and students and non-profit making publications.

BBC Production

Perry Bldg, Walton Hall, Milton Keynes MK7 6BH; Tel 01908 655 221
Head (Production)   Chris Palmer
Head (Business and Finance)   Steve Horner
Manager (Operations)   Richard Armiger
Executive Producer   Andrew Law
Executive Producer   Andy Metcalf
Executive Producer   Stephen Haggard
BBC Production at Milton Keynes is the principal supplier of radio, television audio and video cassettes, and interactive multimedia as integral components of Open University courses. It also produces for a range of other clients. The post-production facilities are self-contained at Milton Keynes. Programmes are transmitted on BBC2 weekdays at night and on weekends in the morning.

BBC Worldwide Ltd

BBC Woodlands, 50 Wood La, London W12 0TT; Tel 020 8433 1673
BBC Worldwide Ltd is the commercial consumer arm and a wholly-owned subsidiary of the BBC. BBC Worldwide Children's Learning produces a wide range of learning resources for home and school, including books, DVDs, videos, audio cassettes and online materials.

Regional Offices

BBC Birmingham

BBC Broadcasting Centre, Pebble Mill Rd, Birmingham, West Midlands B5 7QQ; URL www.bbc.co.uk; Tel 0121 432 8888; Fax 0121 432 9949

BBC North

New Broadcasting Hse, PO Box 27, Manchester, Greater Manchester M60 1SJ; Tel 0161 200 2020

BBC Scotland

Broadcasting Hse, Queen Margaret Dr, Glasgow G12 8DG; Tel 0141 339 8844

BBC Wales

Broadcasting Hse, Llantrisant Rd, Llandaff, Cardiff CF5 2YQ; URL www.bbc.co.uk/wales/education; Tel 029 2032 2834
Head (Education and Learning)   Dr Eleri Wyn Lewis; E-mail eleriwyn.lewis@bbc.co.uk

BBC Northern Ireland

BBC Northern Ireland, Broadcasting Hse, Ormeau Ave, Belfast BT2 8HQ; URL www.bbc.co.uk/learning; E-mail education.ni@bbc.co.uk; Tel 028 9033 8000
Education Consultant   Eric Twaddell

Broadcasting Support Services

Director   Keith Smith
This service is independent of the BBC and offers support for a wide range of broadcasts in the areas of social concern and education.

Independent Television Companies

Anglia Television Ltd

Anglia Hse, Norwich, Norfolk NR1 3JG; URL www.angliatv.com; Tel 01603 615151
Managing Director   Graham Creelman
Executive (Broadcast and Regional Affairs)   Jim Woodrow

Carlton Broadcasting

Gas St, Birmingham, West Midlands B1 2JT; URL www.itv.com/carltoncentral; E-mail campaign@carltontv.co.uk; Tel 0121 643 9898
Programmes Include
Annual Social Action Campaign; regional daytime Social Action programmes broadcast four times weekly.

Channel Four Television Corporation

124 Horseferry Rd, London SW1P 2TX; URL www.channel4.com; Tel 01926 436444; Fax 01926 436446
Managing Director   D. Lloyd
Commissioning Editor (Education Programmes)   Mark Galloway
Commissioning Editor (Multicultural Progammes)   Farrukh Dhondy
Commissioning Editor (Independent Film and Video)   Robin Gutch
Programmes include
Cutting Edge, Dispatches, Critical Eye, The Eleventh Hour.

Channel Television

Television Centre, St. Helier, Jersey JE1 3ZD; URL www.channeltv.co.uk; E-mail broadcast@channeltv.co.uk; Tel 01534 816816; Fax 01534 816817
Chief Executive   Huw Davies
Managing Director   Michael Lucas

HTV Group

Managing Director   J. Payne

HTV Wales

Television Centre, Culverhouse Cross, Cardiff CF5 6XJ; URL www.itv.com/htvwales; E-mail public.relations@htv-wales.co.uk; Tel 029 2059 0590; Fax 029 2059 7183
Controller and Director (Programmes)   Elis Owen
Programmes Include
English language programmes on HTV in Wales and Welsh language programmes for transmission on the Fourth Channel in Wales, including parent education and adult education programmes of general interest and community involvement programmes, including volunteer recruitment items, details of self-help schemes and information for those in need.

Independent Television News (ITN) Ltd

200 Gray's Inn Rd, London WC1X 8XZ; URL www.itn.co.uk; Tel 020 7833 3000; Fax 020 7430 4868
Chair   Mark Wood
Chief Executive   S. Purvis

Yorkshire Television Ltd

The Television Centre, Kirkstall Rd, Leeds, West Yorkshire LS3 1JS; Tel 0113 243 8283; Fax 0113 244 5107
Managing Director   Richard Gregory
Director (Programmes)   John Whiston
Manager (Viewer Services)   Barbara Siedlecki
Controller (Factual Programmes)   Chris Bryer
Programmes
Calendar daily news magazine. Editor, Clare Morrow.

Independent Local Radio

All stations broadcast a wide range of social concern items throughout their programmes. Where available brief details of relevant features have been given under individual entries.

Beacon Shropshire
28 Castle St, Shrewsbury, Shropshire SY1 2BQ; Tel 01743 232271; Fax 01743 231944
Programme Controller Steve Martin

BRMB Radio Group
Nine Brindley Pl, 4 Oozells Sq, Birmingham, West Midlands B1 2DJ; URL www.brmb.co.uk; Tel 0121 250 0964

Capital Radio (95.8FM, 1548AM)
30 Leicester Sq, London WC2H 7LE; Tel 020 7766 6000; Fax 020 7766 6195

Classic Gold 1260 (1260 MHz)
PO Box 2020, Bristol BS99 7SN;
E-mail reception@classicgold.musicradio.com; Tel 0117 984 3200; Fax 0117 984 3202

Clyde 1 (102.5FM)
PO Box 1025, Clydebank, Glasgow G81 2HQ;
URL clyde1.com; E-mail clyde1@srh.co.uk; Tel 0141 565 2200; Fax 0141 565 2301

Clyde 2 (1152KHz)
Po Box 1025, Clydebank, Glasgow G81 2HQ;
URL clyde2.com; E-mail clyde2@srh.co.uk; Tel 0141 565 2200; Fax 0141 565 2301
Managing Director and Director (Programmes)
Alex Dickson, OBE

2 CR-FM (102.3FM) Classic Gold 828 (828AM)
5–7 Southcote Rd, Bournemouth BH1 3LR;
URL www.musicradio.com;
E-mail newsbournemouth@creation.com; Tel 01202 259259; Fax 01202 255244

Downtown Radio (96.4, 96.6, 97.1 102.3 102.4, 103.1, 103.4FM; 1026AM)
Newtownards, County Down BT23 4ES;
URL www.downtown.co.uk;
E-mail programmes@downtown.co.uk; Tel 028 9181 5555; Fax 028 9181 5252

Essex FM
Essex Radio plc, Radio Hse, 19–20 Clifftown Rd, , Southend on Sea, Southend SS1 1SX; URL www.koko.com; Tel 01702 333711; Fax 01702 345224
Managing Director (Essex FM/Breeze) Mark Lee
Managing Director (Mercury FM) Sue Clarke
1 East St, Tonbridge, Kent TN9 1AR
Managing Director (Vibe FM) Nigel Taylor
Reflection Hse, Olding Rd, Bury St. Edmunds, Suffolk IP33 3TA
Managing Director (Ten 17) Denise Mickle
Latton Bush Business Centre, Southern Way, Harlow, Essex CM18 7BU
Managing Director (Mercury FM) Denise Mickle
9 Christopher Place Shopping Centre, St. Albans, Hertfordshire AL3 5DQ
Managing Director (Mercury FM) John Kershaw
The Stanley Centre, Kelvin Way, Crawley, West Sussex RH10 2SE
Managing Director (Medway FM) John Hirst
Berkeley Hse, 186 High St, Rochester, Kent ME1 1EY

GEM–AM (999 kHZ AM, Nottingham, 945 kHz AM, Derby)
Radio Trent Ltd, 29–31 Castle Gate, Nottingham NG1 7AP;
E-mail admin@gemam.musicradio.com; Tel 0115 952 7000; Fax 0115 912 9333
Programme Manager Geoff Hemming

GWR FM–Bristol and Bath (96.3 and 103.0FM)
Contact address PO Box 2000, Bristol BS99 7SN;
URL www.gwrfm.co.uk;
E-mail reception@musicradio.com; Tel 0117 984 3200; Fax 0117 984 3202

GWR FM–Wiltshire (97.2 and 102.2FM)
PO Box 2000, Swindon SN4 7EX; Tel 01793 842600; Fax 01793 842602
Managing Director Neil Cooper
Programme Controller Steve Fountain
Commercial radio station, part of the GWR Group.

102.7 Hereward FM/Classic Gold (1332 AM)
Queensgate Centre, PO Box 225, Peterborough PE1 1XJ;
URL www.koko.com; Tel 01733 460460; Fax 01733 281446
Programme Controller Paul Green

Leicester Sound (103.2FM)
Granville Hse, Granville Rd, Leicester, Leicestershire LE1 7RW; Tel 0116 256 1300; Fax 0116 256 1305
Managing Director Phil Dixon;
E-mail phildixon@musicradio.com

London News Radio: LBC (1152AM) and News Direct (97.3FM)
200 Gray's Inn Rd, London WC1X 8XZ; Tel 020 7973 1152; Fax 020 7312 8565

Magic (1152)
Swalwell, Newcastle upon Tyne, Tyne and Wear NE99 1BB; Tel 0191 420 3040; Fax 0191 496 0174
Programme Director Tony McKenzie

Magic AM; South Yorkshire (1548, 1305, 990 MW)
Radio Hse, 900 Herries Rd, Sheffield, South Yorkshire S6 1RH; URL www.magicam.co.uk; Tel 0114 209 1000; Fax 0114 285 3159
Programme Director Anthony Gay
Deputy Programme Director Darrell Woodman

Manx Radio (1368kHz AM, 89 and 97.2 to 103.7MHz stereo FM)
Broadcasting Hse, Douglas Head, Douglas, Isle of Man IM1 5BW; URL www.manxradio.com;
E-mail postbox@manxradio.com; Tel 01624 682600; Fax 01624 682604

Mercia–FM (97.0 and 102.9MHz FM stereo)
Hertford Pl, Coventry, West Midlands CV1 3TT; Tel 020 7686 8200; Fax 020 7686 8209
Managing Director Carlton Dale
Programme Controller Dave Myatt

Mercury FM (102.7 and 97.5FM)
The Stanley Centre, Kelvin Way, Crawley, West Sussex RH10 9SE; URL www.koko.com; Tel 01293 519161; Fax 01293 560927
Programme Controller Simon Osborne
Team Leader (Sales) Amanda Masters
There is a general email address:
<firstname>.<surname>@musicradio.com

Metro FM (97.1FM)
Radio House, Newcastle upon Tyne, Tyne and Wear NE99 1BB; URL www.metroradio.co.uk; Tel 0191 420 0971; Fax 0191 496 0174

Northants 96
19–21 St. Edmunds Rd, Northampton, Northamptonshire NN1 5DY;
E-mail reception@northants96.musicradio.com; Tel 01604 795600; Fax 01604 795601
Office Manager Heidi Llewellyn
Manager (Sales) Caroline Keeley

24

945

Northsound Radio (1035AM and 96.9FM)
45 Kings Gate, Aberdeen AB15 4EL;
URL www.northsound.co.uk; Tel 01224 337000;
Fax 01224 400003
Programme Director   Gerry Burke

Piccadilly Radio Ltd (Piccadilly Key 103 FM and Magic 1152 AM)
Magic 1152, Castle Quay, PO Box 1152, Manchester, Greater
Manchester M15 4NJ; Tel 0161 228 5000; Fax 0161 288 5001
Programme Director   John Dash
Managing Director   Dave Lincoln

Plymouth Sound Limited (261m, 1152kHz, 97.0FM)
Earl's Acre, Plymouth, Devon PL3 4HX; Tel 01752 227272;
Fax 01752 255962

Q103fm
PO Box 103, Vision Pk, Cambridge, Cambridgeshire
CB4 4WW; Tel 01223 235255; Fax 01223 235161
Managing Director   Alistair Wayne

Radio Aire 96.3 FM/Magic 828
51 Burley Rd, Leeds, West Yorkshire LS3 1LR;
URL www.radioaire.co.uk; Tel 0113 283 5500
Director (Programmes)   John O'Hara

Radio City 96.7 and Magic 1548
St. John's Beacon, 1 Houghton St, Liverpool, Merseyside
L1 1RL; URL www.radiocity967.com; Tel 0151 472 6800;
Fax 0151 472 6821

Radio Forth Ltd
Forth One 97.3 MHz, 97.6 MHz and 102.2 MHz; Forth 2
1548 KHz.
Forth Hse, Forth St, Edinburgh EH1 3LF;
URL www.forthone.com; www.forth2.com; Tel 0131 556
9255; Fax 0131 558 3277

Radio Tay Ltd
Tay FM (102.8 MHz and 96.4 MHz); Radio Tay AM (1161
KHz and 1584 KHz)
PO Box 123, Dundee DD1 9UF; URL www.radiotay.co.uk;
E-mail allyb@radiotay.co.uk; Tel 01382 200800; Fax 01382
423252
Managing Director   Ally Ballingall

RAM FM (102.8MHz FM stereo)
The Market Pl, Derby DE1 3AA; Tel 01332 292945;
Fax 01332 292229
Manager (Station)   Phil Dixon

Red Dragon FM
Atlantic Wharf, Cardiff CF10 4DJ;
URL www.reddragonfm.co.uk;
E-mail info@reddragonfm.co.uk; Tel 029 2066 2066
Programme Director   Andy Johnson

Severn Sound 102.4MHz and Classic Gold 774kHz (774kHz, 102.4MHz)
Bridge Studios, Eastgate Centre, Gloucester,
Gloucestershire GL1 1SS; Tel 01452 313200; Fax 01452
313213

SGRfm–Ipswich (97.1FM) and Bury St. Edmunds (96.4FM)
Alpha Bus Pk, 6–12 Whitehouse Rd, Ipswich, Suffolk
IP1 5LT; URL www.koko.com; Tel 01473 461000;
Fax 01473 741200

Signal Radio (102.6 and 96.9fm)/BIG (1170am)
Stoke Rd, Stoke-on-Trent ST4 2SR; URL www.signal1.co.uk;
www.big1170.co.uk; E-mail info@signalradio.com;
Tel 01782 441300; Fax 01782 441341
Director (Station)   Chris Hurst
Programme Manager (Signal 1)   Mark Franklin
Programme Manager (BIG am)   Mark Chivers
General email format
<initial>.<surname>@signalradio.com

Southern FM (102.4FM, 103.5FM)
PO Box 2000, Brighton, Brighton and Hove BN41 2SS;
URL www.southernfm.com;
E-mail info@southernradio.co.uk; Tel 01273 430111;
Fax 01273 430098
Director (Sales)   Deirdre Lythe
Managing Director   R. Hoad

2-TEN FM Today's Better Music Mix (102.9, 97, 103.4FM); Classic Gold (1431 and 1485AM)
PO Box 2020, Reading RG31 7FG;
E-mail 2-tenfm@musicradio.com; Tel 0118 945 4400;
Fax 0118 928 8456

TFM Radio (96.6FM) and Magic 1170 (1170MW)
Yale Cres, Teesdale, Thornaby, Stockton-on-Tees TS17 6AA;
Tel 01642 888222; Fax 01642 868288

TRENT FM (Nottingham and Mansfield) (96.2 and 96.5MHz FM)
29–31 Castle Gate, Nottingham NG1 7AP;
E-mail reception@trentfm.musicradio.com; Tel 0115 952
7000; Fax 0115 912 9333
Programme Controller   D. Stone

96.4FM The Wave/Swansea Sound (1170MW)
Victoria Rd, Gowerton, Swansea SA4 3AB; Tel 01792 511170
(Swansea Sound); 01792 511964 (The Wave); Fax 01792
511171 (Swansea Sound); 01792 511965 (The Wave)
Director (Station)   Andy Griffiths
Head (News)   Emma Thomas

West Sound (1035AM, 96.7, 97.5 103, 97, 96.5FM Stereo)
Radio Hse, 54a Holmston Rd, Ayr, South Ayrshire
KA7 3BE; URL www.westsound.co.uk; E-mail west-
sound@srh.co.uk; Tel 01292 283662; Fax 01292 262607
Managing Director   Sheena Borthwick

Community Radio

Millennium FM (106.8FM)
Harrow Manor Way, Thamemead South, London SE2 9XH;
Tel 020 8311 3112; Fax 020 8312 1930
Managing Director   Rooney Collins

OTHER MEDIA ORGANISATIONS AND SERVICES

BBC

Ceefax
Room 7540, BBC Television Centre, Wood La, London
W12 7RJ
Read Hear pages for the deaf, BBC2, pages 640–649
inclusive.
Volunteer news about voluntary projects on BBC page 649.
Community pages, BBC2, 650–659 inclusive.

Birmingham Tapes for the Handicapped Association
20 Middleton Hall Rd, Kings Norton, Birmingham, West
Midlands B30 1BY; E-mail btha@gofornet.co.uk; Tel 0121
628 3656; Fax 0121 628 3656
Founder and President   Richard J. Harmer
Monthly tape magazine and a tape library service. Tapes
are sent nationwide.

Blind Centre for Northern Ireland
70 North Rd, Belfast BT5 5NJ; URL www.bcni.co.uk;
E-mail info@bcni.co.uk; Tel 028 9050 0999; Fax 028 9065
0001
Chief Executive   Deane Houston

Diabetes UK
10 Parkway, London NW1 7AA;
URL www.diabetes.org.uk;
E-mail info@diabetes.org.uk; Tel 020 7424 1000; Fax 020 7424 1001
Balance available on cassette free for visually impaired members. Information available on loan from RNIB library in Braille or cassette.

Broadcasting Support Services
Registered Charity Number 282264.
Union Hse, 65–69 Shepherds Bush Grn, London W12 8UA;
URL www.bss.org; E-mail marketing@bss.org; Tel 020 8735 5000; Fax 020 8735 5099
Chief Executive Christine Kent
Provides follow-up services, such as helplines, booklets and web sites, for viewers and listeners and runs long-term helplines.

Chatterbox Recording Club
Welland, Stafford St, St. Georges, Telford, Shropshire TF2 9DT; Tel 01952 616410
Secretary R. Armstrong
Established 1965 for tape, letter, email and mini-disk communication anywhere, for the mutual exchange of chat, music and forming of friendships and better understanding between peoples of all nations.

Clearvision Project
Linden Lodge School, 61 Princes Way, London SW19 6JB; URL www.clearvisionproject.org; Tel 020 8789 9575
Director Marion Ripley
Honorary Secretary Kathleen Gaster
Honorary Treasurer Geraldine Gwilliam
A nationwide postal lending library of children's books with Braille text interleaved on clear plastic so that pictures and print are not obscured. The books are ideal for braille-reading children to share with sighted parents, friends and classmates, and for blind parents to read to sighted children; 200+ institutional borrowers; 300+ individual borrowers; registered charity.

CSV Media
237 Pentonville Rd, London N1 9NJ;
E-mail media@csv.org.uk; Tel 020 7278 6601; Fax 020 7278 7912
Director Sue Farrington
CSV Media works in partnership with over 60 local BBC radio stations and Independent local radio and television stations throughout the UK. All of our broadcasts aim to stimulate listeners and viewers to take action – to improve the quality of others' lives and/or their own lives. We produce radio, video, print, web sites, conferences and provide media training for not-for-profit organisations, plus we provide training in media, ICT and work base skills for unemployed people.
CSV Media is the social action broadcasting arm of the national charity CSV (Community Service Volunteers).

East Region
Tel 01473 217363

London and South East Region
Tel 020 7278 6601

Midlands Region
Tel 0121 683 1800

North West Region
Tel 0161 279 4455

South West Region
Tel 01209 219851

Northern Ireland
Tel 028 9023 2621

Scotland
Tel 0141 204 1681

Teletext
Ceefax Community Magazine, CSV Media, 237 Pentonville Rd, London N1 9NJ; Tel 020 7278 6601; Fax 020 7278 7912
Weekly UK platform for news and debate on community issues on BBC 2 Ceefax, pages 650–659.

Concord Video and Film Council (incorporating Graves Medical Audiovisual Library)
22 Hines Rd, Ipswich, Suffolk IP3 9BG;
URL www.concordvideo.co.uk;
E-mail concordvideo@btinternet.com; Tel 01473 726012; Fax 01473 274531
Council Member Lydia Vulliamy
Educational 16mm film and video library. Programmes available for hire or purchase on disability, the elderly, unemployed, ethnic minorities, and many other contemporary issues. Full video catalogue plus updates: £3.00 including updates. Free brochures describing programmes on disabled people, health education, learning difficulties, medical subjects, race relations, psychology and counselling.

Deaf Broadcasting Council
Registered Charity Number 298758
70 Blacketts Wood Dr, Chorleywood, Rickmansworth, Hertfordshire WD3 5QQ;
URL www.deafbroadcastingcouncil.org.uk; Fax 01923 283127
Policy and Liaison Officer Ruth Myers;
E-mail rmyers@waitrose.com
The DBC ensures that deaf people have high quality access to television, video and audio visual communications.

Listening Books
12 Lant St, London SE1 1QH;
URL www.listening-books.org.uk;
E-mail membership@listening-books.org.uk; Tel 020 7407 9417; Fax 020 7403 1377
Listening Books provides a postal audio book library service to anyone with an illness or disability that makes it impossible or difficult to hold a book, turn pages, or read in the usual way. Audio books are provided for both pleasure and learning. Individual Membership costs £50 per year; Organisational Membership starts at £100.

National Music for the Blind
Radio Churchtown Studios, 2 High Park Rd, Southport, Merseyside PR9 7QL; Answerphone (24 hour service) 01704 228010
Founder Director Derek Mills
The only charity authorised by the Post Office to send complete programmes of music via the Free Post system for the blind.
Service comprises five cassettes monthly (Newspaper – Nostalgia in Music – Classics – and a Talking Book; also requests for certain tunes on one programme). Also a talking newspaper Guiding Star and magazines Sound Trax Merry-go-round and Classical.
Recipients: anyone requiring large print books to the totally blind and only one charge on entry – according to age. Telephone for details (no annual charge).
Availability–all recorded items sent via free mail in returnable wallets containing ordinary cassettes only. Hospitals, Nursing Homes and individual blind supplied. A fully Registered Charity No 503665.
Cost: service of five tapes per month for life for a single initial payment which varies with age of joining. Join by telephoning 0900 hrs to 1700 hrs every day of the week.
NB The Guiding Star newspaper is Britain's first national audio newspaper in stereo. Run entirely by a staff of volunteer unpaid workers throughout the UK. This is a library of tapes on loan. All are at least of 90 minutes duration. The Soundtrax magazine is 100 minutes long.

24

947

Talking Newspaper Association of the United Kingdom
Registered Charity Number 293656.
National Recording Centre, Heathfield, East Sussex
   TN21 8DB; URL www.tnauk.org.uk;
   E-mail info@tnauk.org.uk; Tel 01435 866102; Fax 01435
   865422
Chief Executive   T. McDonald
Formed in 1974, initially giving advice and help on starting
up Talking Newspapers in other parts of the UK. In 1984

TNAUK began recording national publications on tape.
Provides a choice of over 185 national newspapers and
magazines for visually-impaired and disabled people,
including details of national and regional radio and
television programmes on audio cassette, computer disk,
E-mail and CD-ROM.
Has a small permanent staff, aided by over 200 volunteer
readers and production helpers.
Annual subscription.

Other Voluntary Organisations

25

- **Armed Forces and Seafarers**
- **Charity Support, Funding and Regulation**
- **Communication and Visual Impairment**
- **Community Work and Development**
- **Disability**
- **Environment**
- **Health Organisations**
- **Housing and Homelessness**
- **Human Rights and Civil Liberties**
- **International and Overseas**
- **Mental Health**
- **Prisons, Offenders and Victims**
- **Training**
- **Unemployment**

Other Voluntary Organisations

Armed Forces and Seafarers

Army Benevolent Fund

41 Queen's Gate, South Kensington, London SW7 5HR;
URL www.armybenfund.org;
E-mail enquiries@armybenevolentfund.com; Tel 020
7591 2000; Fax 020 7584 0889
The fund helps soldiers, ex-soldiers and their families in
real need, financially and practically, and supports national
and service charities which also care for them.

At Ease

28 Commercial St (nr Aldgate East station), London E1 6LS;
E-mail atease@advisory.freeserve.co.uk; Tel (Sundays
1700–1900) 020 7247 5164
Free advisory service for people in the forces and their
families.

ATS and WRAC Association Benevolent Fund

AGC Centre, Worthy Down, Winchester, Hampshire
SO21 2RG; Tel 01962 887478; 01962 887612; Fax 01962
887478
Secretary   Maj J.A Freebairn
Assists women who have served in QMAAC, ATS and
WRAC.

British and International Sailors' Society

Orchard Pl, Southampton SO14 3AT;
URL www.biss.org.uk; E-mail admin@biss.org.uk;
Tel 023 8033 7333; Fax 023 8033 8333
General Secretary   Alan B. Smith
Chair   Capt Andrew Tyrrell
The British and International Sailors' Society is an
international Christian charity, established in 1818,
providing vital welfare and care to seafarers and their
families. The work is administered worldwide through a
network of centres, chaplains and society personnel. The
society operates across 19 countries in over 60 ports –
caring for and providing facilities to the worlds 1.5m
seafarers.

British Limbless Ex-Service Men's Association (BLESMA)

185–187 High Rd, Chadwell Heath, Romford, Essex
RM6 6NA; URL www.blesma.org;
E-mail blesma@btconnect.com; Tel 020 8590 1124;
Fax 020 8599 2932
General Secretary   Mr J.W. Church, MBE
Provision of residential and holiday home accommodation.
All welfare aspects relative to limbless ex-servicemen and
their dependants. Financial assistance available.

Council of Voluntary Welfare Work

Holderness Hse, 51–61 Clitton St, London EC2A 4EY;
Tel 020 7375 3782; Fax 020 7375 3782
General Secretary   Brig W.I.C. Dobbie
Co-ordinates the activities of religious and philanthropic
organisations in the provision of clubs and bookshops for
HM Forces.

Earl Haig Fund Scotland

New Haig Hse, Logie Green Rd, Edinburgh EH7 4HR;
E-mail ceo@ehfs.org.uk; Tel 0131 557 2782; Fax 0131 557
5819
Chief Executive   Commander A.C. Herdman
Relief of distress among ex-service people and dependants
in Scotland.

Ex-Services Mental Welfare Society

Head Office, Tywhitt Hse, Oaklawn Rd,, Leatherhead,
Surrey KT22 0BX; URL combatstress.org.uk;
E-mail contactus@combatstress.org.uk; Tel 01372 841600;
Fax 01372 841601
Chief Executive   Commodore T.D. Elliott, RN
Founded in 1919 in the immediate aftermath of the First
World War. For over 80 years it has been the only
organisation specialising in the care of men and women
of all ranks discharged from the armed services and
Merchant Navy who suffer from injury to the mind. The
Society has a regional network of welfare officers
throughout the UK who visit patients at home or in
hospital, and who assist with the presentation of claims
and appeals for War Disablement Pension. The society
also has the facility of three short-stay treatment
centres.

King George's Fund for Sailors

8 Hatherley St, London SW1P 2YY; URL www.kgfs.org.uk;
E-mail seafarers@kgfs.org.uk; Tel 020 7932 0000; Fax 020
7932 0095
Director General   Commodore B.W. Bryant, RN
Fund-raising for all seafaring charities and giving grants
according to established need.

League of Remembrance

55 Great Ormond St, London WC1N 3HZ; Tel 020 7242
5660; Fax 020 7242 5660
Secretary   B.M. Barchard, OBE, RGN, RSCN
Widows and dependants of members of the armed forces
and retired nurses who need financial assistance and
companionship, work in London hospitals making
dressings and other ward requirements. Relies entirely on
voluntary donations.

The Mersey Mission to Seafarers

Colonsay Hse, 20 Crosby Rd South, Liverpool, Merseyside L22 1RQ; URL www.merseymissiontoseafarers.org; E-mail liverangel@aol.com; Tel 0151 920 3253; Fax 0151 928 0244
Chaplain Roy Paul
Cares for seafarers of all nationalities, of any race, colour or creed, ashore or afloat, serving or retired. Offers a ministry on ship, in hospital, in prison and at home.

The Mission to Seafarers

St. Michael Paternoster Royal, College Hill, London EC4R 2RL; URL www.missiontoseafarers.org; E-mail general@missiontoseafarers.org; Tel 020 7248 5202; Fax 020 7248 4761
Secretary General Rev Canon Bill Christianson
Justice and Welfare Secretary Rev Canon Ken Peters
A voluntary society of the Anglican Church caring for the practical and spiritual welfare of seafarers of all nationalities and creed. This ministry is offered through a network of chaplains and seafarers' centres in over 300 ports worldwide.

'Not Forgotten' Association

2 Grosvenor Gdns, London SW1W 0DH; URL www.nfassociation.freeserve.co.uk; E-mail director@nfassociation.freeserve.co.uk; Tel 020 7730 2400; Fax 020 7730 0020
Director Lieutenant Colonel T.J. Tedder
Provides recreation for disabled ex-service men and women by supplying television sets and licences, financing holidays and arranging day outings. Also in-house entertainment for those confined to hospitals and homes.

The Officers' Association

48 Pall Mall, London SW1 5JY; E-mail ags@oaed.org.uk; Tel 020 7389 5203; Fax 020 7930 9053
General Secretary Maj Gen J.C.B. Sutherell, CB, CBE
Providing advice and assistance to ex-officers in gaining employment. Relief of distress for ex-officers and their dependants. Homes for the elderly and disabled ex-officers.

Regular Forces Employment Association Limited

49 Pall Mall, London SW1Y 5JG; URL www.rfea.org.uk; E-mail ghall@ctp.org.uk; Tel 020 7321 2011; Fax 08700 940795
Chief Executive Peter Johnson, OBE
Finding both employment and staff. Assists those leaving the armed forces to re-establish themselves in civilian life, principally through helping them to find employment. For branches nationwide, see website.

Royal Air Force Benevolent Fund

67 Portland Pl, London W1B 1AR; URL www.raf-benfund.org.uk; E-mail mail@rafbf.org.uk; Tel 020 7580 8343; Fax 020 7636 7005
Controller Air Chief Marshal Sir David Cousins, KCB, AFC, BA
Aims to relieve distress amongst past and present members of all ranks of the RAF, WRAF and their dependants.

Royal Air Forces Association

117½ Loughborough Rd, Leicester LE4 5ND; URL www.rafa.org.uk; Tel 0116 266 5224; Fax 0116 266 5012
Secretary General Edward Jarron

Royal Alfred Seafarers' Society

SBC Hse, Restmor Way, Wallington, Surrey SM6 7AH; E-mail royalalfred@btopenworld.com; Tel 020 8401 2889; Fax 020 8401 2592
General Secretary A.R. Quinton, FCA
A registered charity maintaining care home and sheltered housing facilities at Banstead in Surrey; also a care home at Eastbourne. These establishments are open to all former seafarers and their widows, and non-seafarers may be admitted at the management's discretion.

Royal Armoured Corps War Memorial Benevolent Fund

RHQ RTR, Bovington, Wareham, Dorset BH20 6JA; Tel 01929 403331; Fax 01929 403488
Secretary Major A. Henzie, MBE (Rtd)
Assists members of disbanded wartime units of the RAC and it's Recce Corps or their dependants in cases of poverty or distress.

Royal British Legion

48 Pall Mall, London SW1Y 5JY; URL www.britishlegion.org.uk; E-mail info@britishlegion.org.uk; Tel 0845 772 5725; Fax 020 7973 7399
Secretary General I.G. Townsend
Aims to provide the ex-service community with aid for the needy, pensions advice, convalescent and residential care, disabled employment, small business advice and loan service, job training.

The Royal British Legion Women's Section

48 Pall Mall, London SW1Y 5JY; URL www.britishlegion.org.uk; E-mail women@britishlegion.org.uk; Tel 020 7973 7225
Welfare Adviser C. George
Offers periods of rest and convalescence and provides financial help and educational needs for ex-service women and wives/widows of ex-servicemen.

Royal Cambridge Home for Soldiers' Widows

82–84 Hurst Rd, East Molesey, Surrey KT8 9AH; Tel 020 8979 3788
Superintendent Mrs I.O. Yarnell
Registered charity no. 225674. Surrey Registered Residential Care Home est.1851 by Royal Charter. Residential home, providing single bed-sitter accommodation for widows of soldiers who have served in the ranks of the British Army worldwide, as well as women either single or widowed who have served in the army themselves or in the Nursing Yeomanry and wives of In-pensioners of the Royal Hospital, Chelsea, who are also in need of residential care.

Royal Commonwealth Ex-Services League

48 Pall Mall, London SW1Y 5JG; Tel 020 7973 7263; Fax 020 7973 7308
Secretary-General Colonel B.C.G Nicholson, OBE
Gives assistance to ex-servicemen, their widows and dependants living overseas and whose service was in the armed forces of the crown.

Royal National Mission to Deep Sea Fishermen

43 Nottingham Pl, London W1U 5BX; URL rnmdsf.moonfruit.com; E-mail enquiries@rnmdsf.org.uk; Tel 020 7487 5101; Fax 020 7224 5240
Chief Executive Dan Conley
Concern, comfort and care for shipwrecked, sick, distressed, disabled, retired and seagoing fishermen and their dependants.

The Royal Naval Benevolent Society for Officers

1 Fleet St, London EC4Y 8RN; E-mail rnbt@rnbt.org.uk; Tel 020 7427 7471
Secretary   Commander W.K. Ridley, RN
Financial assistance to RN, RM, RNR, RNVR, RMR, RMFVR and QARNNS officers, both active service and retired, and their dependants.

Royal Naval Benevolent Trust

311 Twyford Ave, Portsmouth PO2 8PE;
  E-mail rnbt@rnbt.org.uk; Tel (Administration) 023 9269 0112; (Grants) 023 9266 0296; Fax 023 9266 0852
Chief Executive   Commander J. Owens, RN
To give help, in cases of need, to serving and ex-serving ratings of the Royal Navy and other ranks of the Royal Marines, and their dependants.

Royal Patriotic Fund Corporation

40 Queen Anne's Gate, London SW1H 9AP;
  E-mail rpat@fish.co.uk
Secretary   Colonel R.J. Sandy
Provides financial help for needy widows, orphans and dependants of members of HM forces by allowances and grants. Help towards education and provides television sets for eligable widows of service-men.

Royal Sailors' Rests (RSR)

Head Office, 311 Twyford Ave, Portsmouth, Hampshire PO2 8PE; URL www.rsr.org.uk; E-mail info@rsr.org.uk; Tel 023 9265 0505; Fax 023 9265 2929
Executive Director   Brian Deverson
Cares for the moral, social and spiritual welfare of Royal Naval personnel and their families.
Registered Charity Number 238748

Royal Seamen's Pension Fund

c/o Shipwrecked Fishermen and Mariners' Royal Benevolent Society, 1 North Pallant, Chichester, West Sussex PO19 1TL;
  E-mail rspf@shipwreckedmariners.org.uk; Tel 01243 787761; Fax 01243 530853
Secretary   Capt. J.E. Dykes
Discretionary grants for merchant navy members who have retired after long and continuous service.
Registered Charity Number 223323

Sailors' Families' Society

Cottingham Rd, Newland, Hull, Kingston upon Hull HU6 7RJ; URL www.sailors-families.org.uk; E-mail info@sailors-families.org,uk; Tel 01482 342331; Fax 01482 447868
Chief Executive   Tim Vernon
Care and upbringing of children, including those with a seafaring background; residential, non-residential and aftercare.

St. Dunstan's Caring for Blind Ex-service Men and Women

12–14 Harcourt St, London W1H 4HD;
  URL www.st-dunstans.org.uk;
  E-mail enquiries@st-dunstans.org.uk; Tel 020 7723 5021; Fax 020 7262 6199
Chief Executive   Robert Leader
St. Dunstan's is a registered charity founded in 1915. Its purpose is to provide rehabilitation, training and lifelong care to blind ex-service men and women, whatever the cause of their blindness.

Scottish Veterans' Garden City Association (Inc)

New Haig Hse, Logie Green Rd, Edinburgh EH7 4HQ;
  E-mail scottish.veterans@charity.vfree.com; Tel 0131 557 1188
General Secretary   Flight Lieutenant A.F. Nelson (RAF, retd)
The association maintains cottages throughout Scotland for the benefit of disabled ex-servicemen and merchant seamen. Disabled ex-members of the police and fire services also qualify.

Scottish Women's Land Army Welfare and Benevolent Fund

Ingliston, Edinburgh EH28 8NB; URL www.rsabi.org.uk;
  E-mail rsabi@rsabi.org.uk; Tel 0131 333 1023; Fax 0131 333 1027
Awards grants to former members of the service in Scotland who may be in need.
Administered by Royal Scottish Agricultural Benevolent Institution.

Seamen's Christian Friend Society

48 South St, Alderley Edge, Cheshire SK9 7ES;
  E-mail headquarters@scfs.org; Tel 01625 590010; Fax 01625 585442
Director   Michael J. Wilson
Aims to minister to seamen of all nationalities, their families and dependants and to provide spiritual, moral and material help if appropriate.

Shipwrecked Fishermen and Mariners' Royal Benevolent Society

1 North Pallant, Chichester, West Sussex PO19 1TL;
  URL www.shipwreckedmariners.org.uk;
  E-mail grants@shipwreckedmariners.org.uk; Tel 01243 787761; Fax 01243 530853
General Secretary   Captain J.E. Dykes, OBE, RN
Regular and occasional financial aid to needy fishermen, mariners or their dependants; also to professional fishermen shipwrecked on the coasts of the British Isles.

SSAFA Forces Help (Soldiers', Sailors', Airmen and Families' Association)

Central Office, 19 Queen Elizabeth St, London SE1 2LP;
  URL www.ssafa.org.uk;
  E-mail info@ssafa.org.uk; Tel 020 7403 8783; Fax 020 7403 8815
Director (Welfare and Housing)   Michael Goldschmidt
Director (Social Work)   Kate Burgess
SSAFA Forces Help is the national caseworking charity helping serving and ex-service men, women and their families in need. Through a national network of 7000 trained volunteers, help and advice are available for people with social, financial, housing, health and employment difficulties. Qualified social workers are in post to support serving personnel and their families in the UK and overseas.
Registered Charity Number 210760

Women's Royal Naval Service Benevolent Trust

311 Twyford Ave, Portsmouth PO2 8RN;
  E-mail wrnsbt@care4free.net; Tel 023 9265 5301
General Secretary   S. Tarabella
Financial assistance in cases of necessity or distress for ex-members of the WRNS who served between September 1939 and November 1993 and their dependants.

Charity Support, Funding and Regulation

BC.UK

c/o ACE Centre, 92 Windmill Rd, Headington, Oxford, Oxfordshire OX7 3LX
Contact
Disseminates information through workshops, lectures, newsletters and publications and provides training for instructors.

Charities Aid Foundation (CAF)

Kings Hill, West Malling, Kent ME19 4TA;
    URL www.cafonline.org;
    E-mail enquiries@cafonline.org; Tel 01732 520000;
    Fax 01732 520001
Chief Executive Stephen Ainger
CAF is a registered charity working to help donors make the most of their giving and charities to make the most of their resources, in the UK and overseas. It operates a charity account for tax-effective giving, has established banking, investment and administrative services to charities and distributes grants enabling registered charities to operate more effectively. CAF publishes a variety of research reports on the voluntary sector including the highly acclaimed charity trends.

Charity Commission

Harmsworth Hse, 13–15 Bouverie St, London EC4Y 8DP;
    URL www.charitycommission.gov.uk
Manager (Public Relations)
The Commission is a government department which regulates charities. It maintains a register of charities, provides legal services and support for charities and investigates and remedies abuse.

The Dialogue Company

68 Green La, Edgware, Greater London HA8 7QA;
    URL www.thedialoguecompany.co.uk;
    E-mail info@thedialoguecompany.co.uk; Tel 020 8958 2020; Fax 020 8958 8008
Managing Partner Stephen Chelms, MA
Unique program of managing creative dialogue with multiple applications; teaching the skills; creating a culture of communication; enabling change; ensuring a structure for teamwork; developing the skills for leadership and supporting leaders; releasing the power of communication for resolving problems and disputes.

LMSC: The Legislation Monitoring Service for Charities, Voluntary Organisations and their Advisers

1 Millbank, London SW1P 3JZ;
    E-mail info@lmsconline.org; Tel 020 7222 1265;
    Fax 020 7222 1250
Director H. Donoghue
Watches for government and EC legislation and policy decisions affecting charities.

Royal Humane Society

Brettenham Hse, Lancaster Pl, London WC2E 7EP;
    URL www.royalhumane.org; E-mail rhs@supanet.com;
    Tel 020 7836 8155
Secretary Major General C. Tyler CB
Gives awards, including medals, for saving or attempts to save human life.

United Trusts

PO Box 14, 8 Nelson Rd, Edge Hill, Liverpool, Merseyside L69 7AA; URL www.unitedtrusts.org.uk;
    E-mail information@unitedtrusts.org.uk; Tel 0151 709 8252; Fax 0151 708 5621
Chair and Honorary Director Fred C. Freeman
Administrator J.H. Pritchard
Registered Charity
Promotes tax-free payroll and other giving through workplace charity funds (termed 'workplace trusts') and local citizen controlled funds (termed 'local trusts'). Gifts can be distributed by donors for any charitable purposes.
Serves in association with United Way (a connected charity) and Charities Aid Foundation.

United Way

PO Box 14, 8 Nelson Rd, Edge Hill, Liverpool, Merseyside L69 7AA; URL www.unitedtrusts.org.uk;
    E-mail information@unitedtrusts.org.uk; Tel 0151 709 8252; Fax 0151 708 5621
Chair and Honorary Director Fred C. Freeman
Administrator J.H. Pritchard
An independent payroll giving agency charity in association with United Trusts (a connected charity) and Charities Aid Foundation mainly in North West England. Service known as Give as You Earn (United Way).

Westminster Amalgamated Charity

(Assistance confined to City of Westminster).
School Hse, Drury La, London WC2B 5SU; Tel 020 7395 9460; Fax 020 7395 9479

Communication and Visual Impairment

Blind and Visually Impaired

Action for Blind People

14–16 Verney Rd, London SE16 3DZ; URL www.afbp.org;
    E-mail info@afbp.org; Tel 020 7635 4800; (Helpline) 0800 915 4666; Fax 020 7635 4900
Chief Executive S. Remington
National charity providing employment support, accommodation, hotels, and leisure services grants. Information and advice, including welfare rights and mobile service. Leaflets in large print, Braille and on tape.
Registered Charity Number 205913

Association of Blind and Partially Sighted Teachers and Students (ABAPSTAS)

BM Box 6727, London WC1N 3XX;
    URL www.abapstas.freeservers.com;
    E-mail nick@npcl.demon.co.uk

Braille Transcription Service

8 Segbourne Rd, Rubery, Birmingham, West Midlands B45 9SX; Tel 0121 453 4268
Administrator Wynne Batchelor
A group of voluntary braillists who work closely with RNIB. Anything required by a blind person will be transcribed if technically possible. Binding can be arranged if required. No charge.

British Retinitis Pigmentosa Society (BRPS)

Registered Charity Number 271729.
PO Box 350, Buckingham, Buckinghamshire MK18 1GZ;
URL www.brps.org.uk; E-mail info@brps.org.uk;
Tel 01280 821334; (Helpline) 01280 860363; Fax 01280
815900
Trustee and Hon Secretary   Lynda Cantor, MBE
The society is a membership organisation run by
volunteers with over 35 branches throughout the UK. The
BRPS aims to raise funds for scientific research to provide
treatments leading to a cure for RP. The BRPS provides a
welfare support and guidance service to its members and
their families.

British Wireless for the Blind Fund

Gabriel Hse, 34 New Rd, Chatham, Kent ME4 4QR;
URL www.blind.org.uk; E-mail info@blind.org.uk;
Tel 01634 832501; Fax 01634 817485
Chief Executive   Mrs M.R. Grainger
Provides radio/CD/radio cassettes on free permanent loan
to registered blind and registered partially sighted people,
over the age of eight, who are resident in the UK and in need.

CALIBRE Cassette Library

Registered Charity Number 286614.
Aylesbury, Buckinghamshire HP22 5XQ;
URL www.calibre.org.uk;
E-mail enquiries@calibre.org.uk; Tel 01296 432339;
Fax 01296 392599
Director   J.R. Palmer
Provides a free lending library of books recorded on ordinary,
standard cassettes, for anyone who cannot read printed
books, whether through blindness or other disablement.

Centre for Sensory Impaired People

17 Gullane St, Partick, Glasgow G11 6AH; Tel 0141 334
5530; Fax 0141 334 5530
Manager   J. Agnew
Services offered to visually impaired people and their
carers include showroom, radio department, large print
and embossed type library, playback tape service, student
recording service, low vision aid unit/registration.

The English National Association of Visually Handicapped Bowlers

18 Hervey St, Lowestoft, Suffolk NR32 2JG;
URL www.lawnbowls.comvis.impaired/england;
E-mail gailh@fish.co.uk
Honorary Secretary   Gail Hepworth
Charity for blind bowlers in England with 60 affiliated
clubs with over 600 members. Has national and
international tournaments (at least nine).

Fife Society for the Blind

Fife Sensory Impairment Centre, Wilson Ave, Kirkcaldy,
Fife KY2 5EF; URL www.f-s-b.org.uk;
E-mail enquiries@f-s-b.org.uk; Tel 01592 412666;
Fax 01592 412888
Chief Executive   Alan J. Suttie
Responsible on an agency basis for all services to visually
impaired persons in Fife region.

Forfarshire Society for the Blind

76 High St, Arbroath, Angus DD11 1AW; Tel 01241 871215;
Fax 01241 871215
Manager   Margaret Tennant
Carries out all statutory duties related to the blind and
partially sighted on behalf of the local authority. A regular
visiting service and provision of aids, financial help with
holidays.

Gardner's Trust for the Blind

Boundary Hse, 91–93 Charterhouse St, London EC1M 6PN;
Tel 020 7253 3757; Fax 020 7253 3761
Secretary   Angela Stewart
Awards grants for music, educational or social welfare
purposes to registered blind or partially sighted persons
living in England and Wales in need; also small pensions.
Applications should be made in writing.
Registered Charity Number 207233

General Welfare of the Blind

37–55 Ashburton Gr, London N7 7DW;
E-mail gwb@btconnect.com; Tel 020 7609 0206; Fax 020
7607 4425
Chair   D.F. Calow
Secretary   Joel Kay, Esq
Chief Executive   Graham Robinson
Employment of blind persons. Factories in London and
Luton. Hostel and houses for personnel. Welfare payments
made to retired and working persons.
Registered Charity Number 210794

Gift of Thomas Pocklington

(Private charity for the blind)
5 Castle Row, Chiswick, London W4 4JQ; Tel 020 8995 0880;
Fax 020 8987 9965
Chief Executive   Ron Bramley, FCIH
Provides residential care homes, sheltered flats and
supported housing for people with sight loss in London,
Birmingham and Devon. Independent housing in other
parts of the country. Finances research into blindness.

Grampian Society for the Blind

Iain Fraser Resource Centre, 21 John St, Aberdeen
AB25 1BT; URL www.grampianblind.org;
E-mail info@grampianblind.org; Tel 01224 625622;
Fax 01224 620122
Provides general and statutory welfare services for the
visually impaired on an agency basis for the social work
departments of Aberdeen, Aberdeenshire and Moray
councils.

Greater London Fund for the Blind

12 Whitehorse Mews, 37 Westminster Bridge Rd, London
SE1 7QD; E-mail info@glfb.org.uk; Tel 020 7620 2066;
Fax 020 7620 2016
Chief Executive   R.E. Edwards
Combined appeal on behalf of 14 organisations which
provide services and support for visually impaired people.

The Guide Dogs for the Blind Association (GDBA)

Hillfields, Burghfield Common, Reading RG7 3YG;
URL www.guidedogs.org.uk;
E-mail guidedogs@gdba.org.uk; Tel 0118 983 5555;
Fax 0118 983 5433
Chief Executive   Geraldine Peacock
GDBA is a registerd charity that depends entirely on public
support to provide guide dogs, mobility and other
rehabilitation services that meet the needs of blind and
partially sighted people.

Henshaws Society for Blind People

John Derby Hse, 88–92 Talbot Rd, Old Trafford, Greater
Manchester M16 0GS; URL www.hsbp.co.uk;
E-mail info@hsbp.co.uk; Tel 0161 872 1234; Fax 0161 848
9889
Chief Executive   Dianne Asher
Henshaws Society for Blind People, a registered charity,
provides services for visually impaired people of all ages,
their carers and professionals, including a College of Futher

Education (Harrogate); Arts and Craft Centre in Knaresborough; Training and Professional Development Centre (Harrogate); and two resource centres (Manchester and Liverpool). Community outreach services include a Patient Support Service at Manchester Royal Eye Hospital, a Family Support Officer and rehabilitation service by contract. As a registered housing association, Henshaws also owns and manages a wide range of residential and community housing across northern England.

Highland Society for the Blind

38–39 Ardconnel St, Inverness, Highland IV2 3EX;
E-mail highlandvisions@hotmail.com; Tel 01463 233663
Manager (Rehabilitation Services)   M.R. Hynd
Rehabilitation services to visually impaired people and sheltered workshop employing blind and severely disabled people. Providing rehabilitation and information services to visually impaired people in the Highland region.

International Glaucoma Association (IGA)

Registered Charity Number 274681
108c Warner Rd, London SE5 9HQ; URL www.iga.org.uk;
E-mail info@iga.org.uk; Tel 020 7737 3265; Fax 020 7346 5929
Patient Support Supervisor   Valerie Greatorex
IGA aims to prevent loss of sight from glaucoma throughout the world. Supplies free information on request. Membership over 14 000. Meetings and newsletters to members. Supports research into glaucoma. Campaigns for improved glaucoma services, and greater public awareness.

ISIS Audio Books

7 Centremead, Osney Mead, Oxford, Oxfordshire OX2 0ES;
URL www.isispublishing.co.uk;
E-mail sales@isis-publishing.co.uk; Tel 01865 250333;
Fax 01865 790358
General Manager   Pauline Horne
Manager (Sales and Marketing)   Mark Merrill
Publishes complete and unabridged books on tape, available for rental or purchase. Also publishers of large print books.

ISIS Large Print Books

7 Centremead, Osney Mead, Oxford, Oxfordshire OX2 0ES;
E-mail audiobooks@isis-publishing.co.uk; Tel 01865 250333; Fax 01865 790358
Managing Director   John Durrant
Publishes large print books for elderly and partially sighted adults. List covers fiction/non-fiction and reference works.

Metropolitan Society for the Blind

Lantern Hse, 102 Bermondsey St, London SE1 3UB;
E-mail enquiries@msb.gb.com; Tel 020 7403 6184; 020 7403 6571; Fax 020 7234 0708
Secretary   A.F. Luck
Visiting, grants, aids, radios, holidays and escort services for blind and partially sighted in 12 inner London boroughs and City of London.

National Federation of the Blind of the United Kingdom

Registered Charity Number 236629
Sir John Wilson Hse, 215 Kirkgate, Wakefield, West Yorkshire WF1 1JG; URL www.nfbuk.org;
E-mail nfbuk@nfbuk.org; Tel 01924 291313; Fax 01924 200244
President   Bill Poole
Pressure group campaigning for an overall improvement in the standard of life for all blind and partially sighted people.

National Library for the Blind

Far Cromwell Rd, Bredbury, Stockport, Greater Manchester SK6 2SG; URL www.nlb-online.org;
E-mail enquiries@nlbuk.org; Tel 0161 355 2000; Fax 0161 355 2098
Chief Executive   Helen Brazier
The National Library for the Blind (NLB) is a gateway to free comprehensive library services for all those who cannot read print and their intermediaries. Its aim is to enable all visually impaired people to have the same access to library services as sighted people. As well as lending a wide range of reading material for all ages from its extensive collection of hard copy Braille and Moon books and Braille music, NLB also provides access to electronic books and reference material via its award-winning website. Membership is free and international and joining is easy. For an information pack please telephone.

National Music for the Blind

2 High Park Rd, Southport, Merseyside PR9 7QL;
URL derek.wsmcafe.com; Tel 01704 228010
Director   Derek Mills
Provides for the blind or partially sighted a simulated radio station on tape and a request for tunes programme. Service of over five million items of music and sounds. Gives grants for repairs to radios and cassettes for blind members. Tape loan service.
Registered Charity Number 503665

Nottinghamshire Royal Society for the Blind

Ortzen St, off Peveril St, Radford, Nottingham NG7 4BN;
URL www.nrsb.org.uk; E-mail info@nrsb.org.uk;
Tel 0115 970 6806; Fax 0115 970 6807
Chief Executive   John Mills
The Nottinghamshire Royal Society for the Blind, founded in 1843, is a long established, respected charity. The society aims to encourage the hopes and aspirations of people with impaired vision. The emphasis is on developing living skills, providing training, information and supportive services throughout Nottinghamshire. Their services range from an integrated early start nursery, adult services and outreach schemes, as well as information recourses at local Hospitals. A keynote is to support those recently diagnosed as being vision impaired by the provision of rehabilitation support and on-going training.
Registered Charity Number 511288

Partially Sighted Society

PO Box 322, Doncaster, South Yorkshire DN1 2XA;
E-mail info@partsight.org.uk; Tel 01302 323132;
Fax 01302 368998
Printing and enlargement service; daily living aids to vision; publication; local contact and support; free catalogue, information and advice.

Royal National Institute of the Blind (RNIB)

see Chapter 14

RNIB Skills Development Centre for Visually Impaired People

RNIB Manor House
Middle Lincombe Rd, Torquay, Devon TQ1 2NG;
URL www.rnib/services/manorpro.htm;
E-mail manorhouse@rnib.org.uk; Tel 01803 214523;
Fax 01803 214143

RNIB Residential Training Centres

RNIB Kathleen Chambers House
97 Berrow Rd, Burnham on Sea, Somerset TA8 2PG;
Tel 01278 782142

RNIB Tate House

28 Wetherby Rd, Harrogate, North Yorkshire HG2 7SA;
Tel 01423 886927

RNIB Wavertree House

Somerhill Rd, Hove, Brighton and Hove BN3 1RN;
URL www.rnib.org.uk

The Royal London Society for the Blind

Dorton Hse, Seal, Sevenoaks, Kent TN15 0EB; Tel 01732
592500; Fax 01732 592506
Chief Executive Brian Cooney
Provides education, training and employment for blind
and partially sighted people.

Scottish National Federation for the Welfare of the Blind

5 Balmashanner Rise, Forfar, Angus DD8 1PD; Tel 01307
460359
Secretary John Duncan
Promotes the wellbeing and protects the interest of the
blind in Scotland.

Scottish National Institution for the War Blinded

PO Box 500, Gillespie Cres, Edinburgh EH10 4HZ;
URL www.rbas.org.uk; E-mail enquiries@rbas.org.uk;
Tel 0131 229 1456; Fax 0131 229 4060
Secretary/Treasurer J.B.M. Munro AIB(Scot)

Sports Club for the Blind (London)

64 Antrim Mansions, Antrim Rd, London NW3 4XL
Chairman Keith De Jersey
38 Sedcote Rd, Enfield, Greater London EN3 4RG
Secretary Ian Hamlyn
64 Antrim Mansions, Antrim Rd, London NW3 4XL;
Tel (Home) 020 7586 4548
For a very small membership fee, many sports and
activities are made available.

Talking Newspaper Association of the UK (TNAUK)

National Recording Centre, Heathfield, East Sussex
TN21 8DB; E-mail info@tnauk.org.uk; Tel 01435 866102;
Fax 01435 865422
National charity providing over 200 national newspapers
and magazines on tape, computer disk, e-mail and CD-
ROM for visually impaired and disabled people. The
service is available for an annual subscription. TNAUK
co-ordinates the efforts of more than 500 local talking
newspaper groups which provide regular taped versions of
local newspapers to the community.
For further information please contact Brenda Hatcher at
TNAUK.

Ulverscroft Large Print Books Ltd

The Green, Bradgate Rd, Leicester LE7 7FU;
URL www.ulverscroft.co.uk;
E-mail sales@ulverscroft.co.uk; Tel 0116 236 4325;
Fax 0116 234 0205
Customer Care Officer Gail Whalley
Publishers of high quality large print books, fiction and
non-fiction including bestselling authors. Abridged and
unabridged audio books also available.

Deaf/Hard of Hearing/Speech Difficulties

Aberdeen and North East Deaf Society

Centre for the Deaf, No 13 Smithfield Rd, Aberdeen
AB24 4NR; URL aberdeennedeaf.com;
E-mail info@aneds.org.uk; Tel 01224 494566; Fax 01224
483894; Minicom 01224 495675

Principal Officer Rosemary Burt, BA(Hons), CQSW, CFPS,
CACDP(Stage 3)
Provides a social work service to all hearing-impaired
people throughout Aberdeen City, Aberdeenshire and
Moray districts. Promotes social, spiritual and recreational
welfare of deaf people. Also provides professional
interpreting service.

ELGIN SUB-OFFICE

28 Institution Road
Clerk Diane Lunan; Tel 01343 556580; Fax 01343 547651

AFASIC

see Chapter 14

BID Services with Deaf People

Centre for Deaf People, Ladywood Rd, Birmingham, West
Midlands B16 8SZ; URL www.bid.org.uk;
E-mail enquiry@bid.org.uk; Tel 0121 246 6100; Fax 0121
246 6125; Minicom 0121 246 6101
Chief Executive Bryan Sheppard
BID Services with Deaf people has an SLA with
Birmingham and Solihull Councils to carry out assessment
and care management and environmental equipment
provision for Deaf people. It also has a well established
tenancy support service (Supporting People) and provide a
Deaf care service for Sandwell and interpreting unit,
employment resource centre and workshops, two
residential homes, youth service, supported living
projects, prison project, communication classes and other
groups.
Information service, two residential homes, prison project,
lip-reading and other groups.
Charity no. 1053184. Company limited by guarantee no.
3124204.

Bradford and District Association for Deaf People

25 Hallfield Rd, Bradford, West Yorkshire BD1 3RP;
E-mail deafbrad@aol.com; Tel 01274 729280; Fax 01274
370482; Textphone 01274 722752
Secretary A. Haythornthwaite
Supports the provision of welfare services and provides
suitable premises for the social, recreational and
educational needs of the deaf. Provides a chapel with
specially conducted and interpreted services.

British Deaf Association

see Chapter 14

British Deaf Sports Council

7 Bridge St, Otley, West Yorkshire LS21 1BQ;
E-mail britdeafsport@btconnect.com.uk; Tel 01943
850214; Fax 01943 850828; Textphone 01943 850081
Promotes and controls amateur sports and games for the
deaf of Great Britain on a national and international
plane.

British Stammering Association

15 Old Ford Rd, Bethnal Green, London E2 9PJ;
URL www.stammering.org;
E-mail mail@stammering.org; Tel 020 8983 1003;
(Helpline (Mon–Fri 1000–1600)) 0845 603 2001; Fax 020
8983 3591
Director Norbert Lieckfeldt
Information and advice on stammering therapy and self-
help activities. Additional benefits for members include
quarterly magazine, library, open days, telephone
networks. Stammering pupils project. Research
information. Parents' Helpline. Telephone helpline.

The British Tinnitus Association

Unit 5, Ground Fl, Acorn Bus Pk, Woodseats Cl, Sheffield,
South Yorkshire S8 0TB; URL www.tinnitus.org.uk;
E-mail info@tinnitus.org.uk; Tel (Freephone enquiry
line) 0800 018 0527; Fax 0114 258 7059
Operations Manager   Val Rose
Offers information about tinnitus and helps to found and
implement self-help groups to provide mutual support and
varying degrees of counselling. Publishes quarterly journal
Quiet £10.00.

Burnley and District Society for the Deaf

The Haven, 26 Reedley Rd, Burnley, Lancashire BB10 2LU;
Tel 01282 612301
Chairman   Kevin Jordan
All enquiries and grant applications to the Chairman. Trust
body for the making of grants to assist the deaf and their
dependants. General advice given, but not a counselling
service.

Cambridge Campaign for Tackling Acquired Deafness (CAMTAD)

8a Romsey Terr, Cambridge, Cambridgeshire CB1 3NH;
Tel 01223 416141; Fax 01223 416141
Chairman   Dr S. Webster
Aims to create awareness of the nature, extent and
problems of acquired deafness and to inform those
affected of the available help. Provides training for
voluntary helpers. Home visits and 17 other drop-in
hearing help sessions, around Cambridge and
surrounding areas.

Centre for the Deaf Bristol

16–18 King Sq, Bristol BS2 8JL; Tel (Voice) 0117 924 9868;
Fax 0117 924 4884; Minicom 0117 944 1344
Provides recreation and leisure activities, social work
support, community support, environmental aids and
equipment, welfare and pastoral service, youth work, sign
languages and lip reading classes, support for deaf and
hard of hearing community groups, information and
advice facilities, advocacy, deaf people with special
learning needs.

Cheshire Deaf Society

Operating as Deafness Support Network
144 London Rd, Northwich, Cheshire CW9 5HH;
E-mail dsn@deafnesssupportnetwork.co.uk; Tel 01606
47831; Fax 01606 49456
Provision of an integrated statutory and voluntary
comprehensive service for all people who are deaf and
hard of hearing of all ages throughout Cheshire, Halton
and Warrington. A professional team of qualified specialist
social work staff provides fieldwork services. An
interpreting service is available for people who use British
Sign Language. Social centres and clubs are provided at
Chester, Northwich, Warrington, Crewe, Congleton and
Macclesfield. Specialist residential care services are also
provided.

Church of the Holy Name Mission to the Deaf

St James' Gdns, Uplands, Swansea SA1 6DY; Tel 01792
470477
Chaplain and Principal Officer   Rev H.V. Parsell
Provides a religious, welfare and social centre for deaf
people.

Commonwealth Society for the Deaf – Sound Seekers

see Chapter 14

Cornwall Association for Deaf and Hard of Hearing People

3–4 Quay Mews, Quay St, Truro, Cornwall TR1 2UL;
E-mail cornwall@deaf.freeserve.co.uk; Tel 01872 225868;
Fax 01872 225868; Minicom 01872 263664
Co-ordinator/Secretary   Angela Williams
Grant aid, information and communication support – sign
language interpreters, lip-speakers, speech to text operators
and loop installation hire.

Cued Speech Association UK

9 Duke St, Dartmouth, Devon TQ6 9PY;
URL www.cuedspeech.co.uk;
E-mail info@cuedspeech.co.uk; Tel 01803 832784;
Fax 01803 835311
Cued Speech is a sound-based system which uses eight
hand-shapes in four positions near the mouth to
supplement the normal lip patterns of speech. It therefore
gives an exact visual representation of spoken language
at the same time as normal speech. Deaf people can then
'see' spoken language in exactly the same way as hearing
people hear it. This allows deaf children to develop their
inner language, and improve literacy, lipreading and
speech. It can also help deafened people communicate in
English and deaf people who want to improve their
English. In addition it can be effective in helping hearing
people with speech and language difficulties. It can be
used with an aural approach or in addition to sign
language.
The Cued Speech Association UK promotes the use of
Cued Speech; provides information about Cued Speech
and its use; runs awareness days and training courses in
Cued Speech and conducts examinations leading to the
Certificate of Proficiency in Cued Speech and
Cuereading.

Cumbria Deaf Association

3 Compton St, Carlise, Cumbria CA1 1HT;
E-mail cumbria.deaf@virgin.net; Tel 01228 606434;
Fax 01228 606433; Minicom 01228 606432
Chief Executive   John M. Brown
Offers a comprehensive service for deaf and hearing
impaired people and acts as agents for the social services
departments. Offers a communication support unit for
Cumbria, youth services, sign language classes, deaf
awareness bureau, learning and skills service, technical
equipment service and care packages.

deafconnect

Centre for Deaf People, Green St, Northampton,
Northamptonshire NN1 1SY;
URL www.deafconnect.org.uk;
E-mail info@deafconnect.org.uk; Tel 01604 250303;
Fax 01604 239041; Minicom 01604 636828
Administrator   Gillian Hill
Information Officer   Jemma Collins;
E-mail jemdconn@aol.com; Tel (voice/minicom) 01604
233440
Family and Children's Worker   Mary McInnes; Tel 01604
628268
Manager (Services)   Lesley Knight
The enabling and empowering of deaf people that they
may live full and independent lives.
Deaf/blind group every 2nd Tuesday each month at 1400.
Def2 group (youth club) meet at 1930 every Monday.
Thursday Club (Retired people) 2nd and 4th Thursday
each month at 1030-1430. Listeners (Hard of Hearing
Group) 2nd Thursday of month at 1000. Deaf social club
Saturdays at 1800 fortnightly. St. Mark's Church at 1000.
National Deaf Children's Society (Northampton region)
monthly. Sunshine Club – summer playscheme and half
term activities for deaf children.

deafPLUS

Prospect Hall, 12 College Wlk, Bristol Rd, Birmingham,
West Midlands B29 6LE; URL www.deafplus.org;
E-mail info@deafplus.org; Tel 0121 415 2080; (Video) 0121
415 2082; Fax 0121 415 2081; Textphone 0121 415 2083
Director   Terry Thompson
deafPLUS is the working name of Breakthrough Deaf-
Hearing Integration – a company limited by Guarantee
(3680467) Registered Charity (1073468).
A voluntary organisation, based in London, Midlands,
South and North whose aim is to develop innovative work
with deaf and hearing people which enables them to
improve their quality of life through contact, information
and training.

Dewsbury, Batley and Spenborough Centre for the Deaf

10 Oxford Rd, Dewsbury, West Yorkshire WF13 4JT;
Tel 01924 461940
Provides social, recreational and spiritual services for the
deaf in North Kirklees.

Diocesan Association for Deaf and Hard of Hearing People in Dorset, Wiltshire and Swindon

c/o Church Hse, Crane St, Salisbury, Wiltshire SP1 2QB;
E-mail deaf.assoc@salisbury.anglican.org; Tel 01722
411977 205; Fax 01722 331159
Chaplain (Wiltshire)   Rev Helen Begley
Chaplain (Dorset)   Rev Peter Aves
Pastoral and practical care of people who are deaf and hard
of hearing.

Edinburgh and East of Scotland Deaf Society

49 Albany St, Edinburgh EH1 3QY;
URL www.deafsociety.org;
E-mail admin@deafsociety.org; Tel 0131 556 3128;
Fax 0131 557 8283; Textphone 0131 557 0419
Charity working with deaf and hard of hearing people and
their families, providing a social work service, technical
advice, communication support, training and community
development sports and leisure activities, youth services
and supported care housing.

Glasgow Society for the Education of Deaf and Dumb

c/o Alexander Sloan, 144 West George St, Glasgow
G2 2HG; E-mail iatm@alexandersloan.co.uk; Tel 0141
354 0354; Fax 0141 354 0355
Secretary and Treasurer   Sandy Mowat
Gives grants individually and through schools and associ-
ations to help young deaf people in many different ways.

Greater Manchester Deaf Blind Club

30 Tolland La, Hale, Cheshire WA15 0LD
Chair   Dr D.H. Thorpe
Aims to promote social meetings and visits monthly, to
organise annual holidays for members, and to oversee
welfare of members daily.

Hampshire Deaf Association

1 and 2 Carlton Commerce Centre, Dukes Rd,
Southampton SO14 0SQ; URL www.deafhampshire.org;
E-mail enquiries@deafhampshire.org; Tel 023 80516516;
Fax 023 8051 6517; Minicom 023 8051 6518
Chief Executive   Graham Whitehead
Provides a range of services for deaf, deafened and hard of
hearing people. Services include; interpreting service, infor-
mation centre, deaf awareness training and consultancy.
East Hill Residential home (Isle of Wight) youth programme,
community support programme and chaplaincy.

Harrow Deaf Children's Society

142 Sharps La, Ruislip, Greater London HA4 7JB;
E-mail clyalfrob@hotmail.com; Tel 01895 621250;
Fax 01895 621250
Chair   Clyde Robinson
Offers support to parents of deaf children.

Harrow Parents Association for Hearing Impaired Children

8 Waxwell Cl, Pinner, Greater London HA5 3ET; Tel 020
8866 8646; Fax 020 8866 8646
Secretary   Gillian Jones
Offers support to parents of deaf children.

Hearing Concern (British Association of the Hard of Hearing)

7–11 Armstrong Rd, London W3 7JL;
URL www.hearingconcern.org.uk;
E-mail info@hearingconcern.org.uk; Tel 020 8743 1110;
(Helpdesk 'Lo call') 0845 0744600 (voice and text);
Fax 020 8742 9043; Textphone 020 8742 9151
Chief Executive   Fiona Robertson
A national membership charity dedicated to hard of
hearing adults in the UK. Offers advice, support and
information through it's national HelpDesk. Publishes
quarterly magazines and various advice leaflets and fact-
sheets on hearing loss.

Leicester and County Mission for the Deaf

Centre for Deaf People, 135 Welford Rd, Leicester LE2 6BE;
URL cfdpleicester.org.uk;
E-mail info@cfdpleicester.org.uk; Tel 0116 257 4800;
Fax 0116 257 4856
Director   P.T. Kilgour, BSC, CPM
Provides personal social work service, community centre,
communication and information services, environmental
aids, pastoral care for deaf and hard of hearing people in
Leicestershire and Leicester.

Link Centre for Deafened People

19 Hartfield Rd, Eastbourne, East Sussex BN21 2AR;
E-mail linkcntr@dircon.co.uk; Tel 01323 638230;
Fax 01323 642968; Textphone 01323 739998
Chief Executive   Dr. L. Gailey
Specialised residential courses for adults with acquired
profound or total hearing loss and their partner/family;
holistic approach.

Mansfield Society for Deaf People

Centre for the Deaf and Hard of Hearing, 1 Wood St,
Mansfield, Nottinghamshire NG18 1QB; Tel 01623
652029; Fax 01623 652029
Centre Organiser   Mrs K. Payne
Provides educational, social and religious facilities for the
deaf and hard of hearing including tinnitus and Menieres
groups, including luncheon clubs, social clubs.

Merseyside Society for Deaf People

Queen's Dr, West Derby, Liverpool, Merseyside L13 0DJ; Tel
(Voice and Minicom) 0151 228 0888; Fax 0151 228 4872
Chief Executive   John Brennan
Acts as agent for the local authority in providing social
work and community work services for deaf people in the
Liverpool, Wirral and Sefton areas of Merseyside. Has a
team of specialist social workers who have fluent
communication in British sign language.

National Deaf Children's Society

see Chapter 14

Newcastle Deaf Centre

2 Summer Hill Gr, Summerhill Sq, Newcastle upon Tyne, Tyne and Wear NE4 6EE; E-mail iris@ncdeafcentre.freeserve.co.uk; Tel 0191 232 4104; Fax 0191 233 2122; Minicom 0191 261 8885

North Regional Deaf Association and North Regional Assocation for the Blind

144 London Rd, Northwich, Cheshire CW9 5HH; E-mail northregions@cwcom.net; Tel (Voice and Minicom) 01606 330362; Fax 01606 49456
Organiser John. F. Banham
To promote better services for the deaf, deafblind, and those with a significant sensory loss. Provides a regular forum to consider issues, new legislation and technical developments. Operates a free personal crisis and short-term advocacy service across the whole of the north of England. Membership open to health/local authorities and to voluntary organisations providing services.

Northern Counties School

Great North Rd, Newcastle upon Tyne, Tyne and Wear NE2 3BB; URL www.northern-counties-school.co.uk; E-mail cris.lewis@northerncounties.newcastle.sch.uk; Tel 0191 281 5821; Fax 0191 281 5060
Headteacher K.J.C. Lewis MA, MSc, DipEd, DipEdDPH
Day and residential education for deaf, deafblind, and multi-disabled children aged 4–19 years. Outreach support and assessment service. Communication classes for parents and public. Total Communication used throughout.

Oxford Diocesan Council for the Deaf (ODCD)

Denchworth Hse, Denchworth, Wantage, Oxfordshire OX12 0DX; Tel 01235 868442
Chaplain Rev R. Williams

Oxford and District Club for the Hard of Hearing

Deaf and Hard of Hearing Centre, St. Ebbe's, Oxford, Oxfordshire OX1 1RL; Tel (Wed 1500–2200) 01865 243447; Fax 01865 249823
Chair Mrs Q. Hamilton
Social, cultural and welfare needs of those handicapped by impaired hearing.

Plymouth Deaf Association

Blake Lodge, Seymour Rd, Mannamead, Plymouth PL3 5AS; Tel 01752 660769; Fax 01752 266286; Minicom 01752 603685
Contact Paul Northam
Provides social activities for the profoundly deaf and hard of hearing. Evening activities are organised including indoor games, bingo.

The Royal Association for Deaf People (RAD)

Walsingham Rd, Colchester, Essex CO2 7BP; URL www.royaldeaf.org.uk; E-mail info@royaldeaf.org.uk; Tel 01206 509509; Fax 01206 769755; Minicom 01206 577090
Chief Executive Tom Fenton
Administrator Vicki Wheeler
Finance Officer Lesley Frearson
Operates in London, Kent, Surrey, Essex

RAD Centre for Deaf People

St. Mark's Centre for Deaf People, Cottage Pl, Chelmsford, Essex CM1 1NL; URL www.royaldeaf.org.uk; E-mail rad.chelmsford@royaldeaf.org.uk; Tel 01245 283777; Fax 01245 346609; Textphone 01245 257704

Contact Regional Manager
Provides a range of services to support deaf and deafblind adults, including sign language interpretation, support groups such as learning disabled, family groups, lunch clubs, training etc.

The Royal National Institute for Deaf People (RNID)

see Chapter 14

RNID Tinnitus Helpline

19–23 Featherstone St, London EC1Y 8SL; URL www.rnid.org.uk; E-mail tinnitushelpline@rnid.org.uk; Tel (Voice (helpline)) 0808 808 6666; Fax 020 7296 8099; Textphone 0808 808 0007
Head (Information and Casework Service) Karen Bradshaw
National telephone service offering information and advice on all aspects of tinnitus and its management. Open Mon–Fri 1000–1500, answerphone at other times. Freephone.

Royal Schools for the Deaf Manchester

Stanley Rd, Cheadle Hume, Cheadle, Cheshire SK8 6RQ; URL www.rsdmanchester.org; E-mail info@rsdmanchester.org; Tel (and Minicom) 0161 610 0100; Fax 0161 610 0101
Head (Post-16) Dr Bernie White
Comprehensive educational provision for hearing-impaired children with additional or complex needs including the deaf/blind, children in autistic spectrum and those with challenging behaviour. Educational provison for children with communication difficulties. Facilites for further and continuing education. (5–19 years). Day or residential provision. Residential provision for 52 weeks.

St. Vincent's Centre for Deaf People

51 Tobago St, Glasgow G40 2RH; Tel 0141 554 8897; 0141 554 8898; Fax 0141 551 8904; Textphone 0141 550 1616
Project Manager Elizabeth Lafferty

The Scottish Council on Deafness

Suite 62, 1st Fl, 93 Hope St, Glasgow G2 6LD; URL www.scod.org.uk; E-mail admin@scod.org.uk; Tel 0141 248 2474; Fax 0141 248 2479
Co-ordinates the work of all organisations working with and for deaf people in Scotland to improve the human and civil rights of deaf people living in Scotland.

Scottish Workshop with the Deaf

Donaldson's College, West Coates, Edinburgh EH12 5JJ; Tel 0131 337 9911; Fax 0131 337 1654
Hon Chair Irene Fortune
Multi-disciplinary organisation consisting of workers concerned with deafness and deaf people themselves. One of the main aims is to encourage deaf people to voice their needs, attitudes and opinions in the belief that they should be allowed a say in the provisions designed for them. Free publications list by request.

Sefton Association for the Deaf (SAD)

Queens Dr, West Derby, Liverpool, Merseyside L13 0DJ; Tel 0151 228 0888; Fax 0151 228 4872
Chair K. Wilson
Promotes the relief of deaf people and the hearing impaired. Provides social activities; visit the sick, aged and infirm; gives financial and material help to those in need; and stimulates public interest in the welfare of the deaf.

Sense West

The National Deafblind and Rubella Association, 9a Birkdale Ave, Selly Oak, Birmingham, West Midlands B29 6UB; Tel 0121 415 2720
Residential home for the elderly deaf, blind and hard of hearing from both inside and outside the county.

Sheffield Association in Aid of the Adult Deaf

c/o Voluntary Action Sheffield, 69 Division St, Sheffield, South Yorkshire S1 4GE; E-mail pat@vas.org.uk; Tel 0114 249 3360
Secretary   Pat Stabler
Provides modest financial support to the adult deaf in Sheffield within certain prescribed criteria.

Sheffield Club for the Hard of Hearing

Secretary   B. Smith
53 Hucklow Rd, Sheffield, South Yorkshire S5 6TB; Tel 0114 249 2995
Meet on Mondays from 1700; provides an opportunity for socialising with other people who are hard of hearing.

SPURS Club for Adult Deaf

St. Luke's Hall, St. Luke's St, Chelsea, London SW3; E-mail crgoulden@talk21.com
Contact   C.S. Goulden; Fax 020 8662 0525
Provides facilities and club activities for deaf adults; club hall in Chelsea, London SW3.

Sussex Deaf Association

Brighton Deaf Centre
Carlton Hill, Brighton, Brighton and Hove BN2 2GW; URL www.sda.deaf.co.uk; E-mail info@sussexdeaf.co.uk; Tel 01273 671899
Manager   P. Mitchell

Regional Office-Hastings
Hastings Deaf Centre, 28 Stockleigh Rd, Hastings, East Sussex TN38 0JP; E-mail sdahastings@freezone.co.uk
Aims to meet the welfare, social and spiritual needs of all deaf people in East and West Sussex. Sign language classes and church services weekly.

Regional Office-Worthing
Worthing Deaf Centre, Methold Hse, Worthing, West Sussex BN11 1NO; E-mail sda.worthing@freezone.co.uk

Tayside Association for the Deaf

36 Roseangle, Dundee DD1 4LY; E-mail assocdeafdundee@aol.com; Tel 01382 221124; Fax 01382 200025; Textphone 01382 227052
Provides a social work service, interpreting service and recreational facilities to deaf people in the area.

Torbay and District Deaf Society

Abbey Hall, Rock Rd (off Abbey Rd), Torquay, Torbay TQ2 5SP; Tel (Voice/Text Weds evenings only) 01803 290403; Fax 01803 215 918
Aims to provide a social, recreational and religious centre for the deaf and hard of hearing. All ages.

Young Sound Vision

Audiology Clinic, 17 Greek St, Stockport, Greater Manchester SK3 8AB; E-mail sensoryservice@stockport9.fsnet.co.uk; Tel 0161 474 3906
Chair   Angela Fawley
For hearing impaired and visually impaired children and their families.

Community Work and Development   25

ACRE (Action with Communities in Rural England)

Somerford Crt, Somerford Rd, Cirencester, Gloucestershire GL7 1TW; URL www.acre.org.uk; E-mail acre@acre.org.uk; Tel 01285 653477; Fax 01285 654537
Chief Executive   Sylvia Brown
Co-ordinator (Policy and Information)   Catherine Best
ACRE is the national association of rural community councils whose shared purpose is to improve the quality of life of local communities, particularly of disadvantaged people, in rural areas. Its aim is to promote the development of thriving, diverse and sustainable communities throughout England.

Association of Inner Wheel Clubs in Great Britain and Ireland

51 Warwick Sq, London SW1V 2AT; Tel 020 7834 4600
Secretary/Administrator   Anne Koh
To promote true friendship; to encourage the ideals of personal service; to foster international understanding. There are at present 998 clubs throughout Great Britain and Ireland.

BASSAC (British Association of Settlements and Social Action Centres)

Winchester Hse, 11 Cranmer Rd, London SW9 6EJ; URL www.bassac.org.uk; E-mail info@bassac.org.uk; Tel 020 7735 1075; Fax 020 7735 0840
Office Manager   J. Martyn
Local centres work to achieve social change in their neighbourhoods, through innovative or experimental projects, providing resources for local communities.

Business in the Community

Registered Charity Number 297716
137 Sheperdess Wlk, London N1 7RQ; URL www.bitc.org.uk; www.business-impact.org.uk; E-mail information@bitc.org.uk; Tel 0870 600 2482
Chair   David Varney
Business in the Community's mission is to inspire business, to increase the quality and extent of their contribution to social and economic regeneration, by making corporate social responsiblility an essential part of business excellence.

Calton Centre

121 Montgomery St, Edinburgh EH7 5EP; E-mail caltoncentre@talk21.com; Tel (Centre Office Calton Youth Ministry) 0131 661 5252; (Welfare) 0131 661 0678
Centre Manager (CYM)   Stanley Middleton
Welfare Co-ordinator (CWS)   Caroline Macpherson
Provides a caring ministry for people of all ages in the Calton community. Includes provision of a community centre; café; information and advice; youth clubs; groups for parents and toddlers, women, pensioners, disabled, housebound, homeless, AA, keep-fit; playgroup.

Carnegie United Kingdom Trust

Comely Park Hse, Dunfermline, Fife KY12 7EJ; URL www.carnegieuktrust.org.uk; Tel 01383 721445; Fax 01383 620682
Chief Executive   Charlie McConnell
Quinquennial Policy 2001–2006 includes village Initiatives – helping local communities to help themselves become more active villages by supporting local initiatives; village

halls- to widen the use of village halls as centres of services for the community; creativity and imagination – to enhance the capacity of creative and imaginative groups of people to benefit others; young people – to encourage active and constructive participation, particularly in public decision making and increase the role and responsibility of young people in education, health, the community or more widely.

Community Development Foundation

60 Highbury Gr, London N5 2AG; URL www.cdf.org.uk; E-mail admin@cdf.org.uk; Tel 020 7226 5375; Fax 020 7704 0313
Chief Executive   Alison West
Stengthens communities by ensuring the effective participation of people in determining the conditions which affect their lives. Contributes through local action projects, consultancies, training, conferences, information, publications and research.
Registered Charity Number 306130

Community Transport (National Office)

Office Suite D137, Dean Clough, Halifax, HX3 5AX; URL www.communitytransport.org; E-mail mseccombe@communitytransport.org; Tel 01422 364964
Chief Executive   Murray Seccombe
Projects in Birmingham, Coventry, Newcastle upon Tyne, Salford, Sandwell and Wolverhampton. Provides pre-used furniture for low-income individuals and families; provides furniture transport services including removals for low-income families and individuals; provides wheelchair-accessible mini-buses with or without drivers for loan to voluntary and other not-for-profit organisations; operates specialised transport services such as Mobility Shopping Services.

Deen City Farm

39 Windsor Ave, Merton Abbey, London SW19 2RR; URL www.deencityfarm.co.uk; E-mail deencity@deencityfarm.co.uk; Tel 020 8543 5300; Fax 020 8545 0142
Project Director   Ben Cheetham
Provides a range of community-based services for the south London region including play, youth facilities, education, riding and crafts.
Registered Charity Number 1008028

Free Form Arts Trust

Hothouse, London Fields, 274 Richmond Rd, London E8 3QW; Tel 020 7249 3394; Fax 020 7249 8499
Company Secretary   Barbara Wheeler-Early
Artistic Director   Martin Goodrich
Pioneering charity combining public art and architecture in urban regeneration. Involves communities through design and technical aid services; environmental improvement by design; community arts in education (school grounds); and produces artworks for the business environment. Provides work-based training programmes for NVQ Design level 3 for creative practitioners and runs building communities to support community involvement in housing regeneration.

Interchange Trust Ltd

WAC Performing Arts and Media, Interchange Studios, Hampstead Town, Hall Centre, 213 Haverstock Hill, London NW3 4QP; URL www.wac.co.uk; E-mail info@interchange.org.uk; Tel 020 7692 5888; Fax 020 7692 5889
Chief Executive   Dr Alan Tomkins
Community development organisation running projects and providing resources for other community groups to do the same. Resources for community groups, including

print, community arts, social services, and management training. Legal advisory service for charities and trusts and health promotion projects. Central London Conference and training facilities for hire.
Registered Charity Number 267043

Kaleidoscope Project

40–46 Cromwell Rd, Kingston upon Thames, Surrey KT2 6RE; E-mail kaleidoscope@cableinet.co.uk; Tel 020 8549 2681; Fax 020 8296 0510
Director   Rev Martin Blakebrough
A community project which provides specialist services for drug dependents, a programme for targeting young people at risk, and hostel accommodation and support for asylum seekers. Also social, recreational, educational and training amenities.

League of Welldoers

Lee Jones Centre, 119–133 Limekiln La, Liverpool, Merseyside L5 8SN; E-mail welldoers@lineone.net; Tel 0151 207 1984; Fax 0151 207 4445
Chief Executive   Ian Rankine
Serves people of all ages in the community of Merseyside.

National Playbus Association

2 Queen St, Bristol BS2 0JB; URL www.playbus.org.uk; E-mail playbus@playbus.org.uk; Tel 0117 977 5375; Fax 0117 972 1838
National body that supports and promotes mobile community resources through membership services including fieldwork visits and training.

Nucleus Legal Advice Centre

298 Old Brompton Rd, London; E-mail nucleus@dial.pipex.com; Tel 020 7373 4005; Fax 020 7835 1555
Independent voluntary organisation serving SW3, SW5, SW7, SW10, W3, W6 and W14. Provides free advice, assistance and representation at court and tribunals in social welfare law: general, debt housing, benefits, employment, immigration. Solicitor agency.

The Pilgrim Trust

Cowley Hse, 9 Little College St, London SW1P 3SH; URL www.thepilgrimtrust.org.uk; E-mail georgina@thepilgrimtrust.org.uk; Tel 020 7222 4723
Director   Georgina Nayler
The trust's interests in social welfare include alcohol/drug abuse, rehabilitaion of offenders, mental illness and young people leaving care; also art, learning and the preservation of the national heritage. Grants are given for capital projects and for project-related running costs. Application forms available from the trust's offices and from the website.

Rotary International in Great Britain and Ireland

Kinwarton Rd, Alcester, Warwickshire B49 6PB; URL www.rotary-ribi.org; E-mail secretary@ribi.org; Tel 01789 765411; Fax 01789 765570
Secretary   R.J. Freeman
Serves community locally, nationally and internationally.

Shape

356 Holloway Rd, London N7 6PA; Tel 020 7619 6160; Fax 020 7619 6162
Chief Executive   Steve Mannix
Shape opens up access to the arts, enabling greater participation by disabled and older people. It runs arts workshops, projects and events in a variety of settings;

NVQ, Certificate and Diploma arts management courses, short training courses and placements for disabled people and STAN a network of young disabled artists. There is a national Deaf Arts Programme and Ticket Scheme with reduced price tickets and volunteer drivers for disabled and older people.
Registered Charity Number 279184.

Toc H

Central Services, The Stable Block, The Firs, High St, Whitchurch, Aylesbury, Buckinghamshire HP22 4JU; URL www.toch.org.uk; E-mail info@toch.org.uk; Tel 01296 642020; (Freephone) 0800 018 2139; Fax 01296 640022
National Chair Di Claxton
Director Rev Geoffrey, Smith
Toc H aims to create a more compassionate, harmonious society. Based on Christian principles, its work focuses on self-help and the local community. Nationally it offers a flexible, wide ranging package of localised activities and services including Friendship Circles, projects and events, the Toc H Families and People under Pressure scheme and low key, practical pieces of community service through its network of branches.
Registered Charity Number 211042

Disability

Acting Up

Unit 304, 203–213 Mare St, London E8 3QE; URL www.acting-up.org.uk; E-mail acting-up@geo2.poptel.org.uk; Tel 020 8533 3344; Fax 020 8533 5511
Director John Ladle
Acting Up is a project of Matchbox Theatre Trust, a registered charity, and was established in 1987. Acting Up develops and disseminates information and training (multimedia profiling) about the needs and potential of people with communication difficulties.
Acting Up is committed to working in ways that are person-centred and service user-led. Using recent advances and availability of digital technology, Acting Up has developed new ways of supporting people who use a range of community services to have greater control over the process of planning their lives and the support they need.

Agenda 21 Architects

Chartered Architects and Interior Designers, 2–4 Sebastian St, London EC1V 0HE; URL agenda21architects.com; E-mail info@agenda21architects.com; Tel 020 7687 6001; Fax 020 7687 6002
Specialist in designing for people with disabilities. Private dwellings; schools; nursing homes; day care centres and special category projects. Personal service guaranteed.

Association to Aid the Sexual and Personal Relationships of People with a Disability (SPOD)

286 Camden Rd, London N7 0BJ; URL www.spod-uk.org; E-mail spoduk@aol.com; Tel 020 7607 8851
Director Simon Parritt
Provides an information service and counselling for disabled people, their partners and carers in sexual difficulty. Information for workers among the disabled; education and training on the sexual aspects of disability. Call for information sheets.

Association of Disabled Professionals

BCM ADP, London WC1N 3XX; URL www.adp.org.uk; E-mail assdisprof@aol.com; Tel 01204 431638; Fax 01204 431638

Chair Jane Hunt
Administration and Development Officer Kath Sutherland
Improves the education, training and employment opportunities of disabled people.

Association for Spina Bifida and Hydrocephalus (ASBAH)

ASBAH Hse, 42 Park Rd, Peterborough PE1 2UQ; URL www.asbah.org; E-mail postmaster@asbah.org; Tel 01733 555988
Executive Director A. Russell
Provides information and support to anyone with spina bifida and/or hydrocephalus, their parents and all involved in their care.

EASTERN REGIONAL OFFICE

ASBAH Hse, 42 Pk Rd, Peterborough PR1 2UQ; Tel 01733 555988
Regional Manager M. Malcolm

NORTHERN REGIONAL OFFICE

ASBAH Hse, North Bagley La, Farsley, Pudsey, West Yorkshire LS28 5LY; Tel 0113 255 6767
Regional Manager J. Pheasant

REGIONAL OFFICE (SOUTH EAST)

209 Crescent Rd, Barnet, London EN4 8SB; Tel 020 8441 9967
Regional Manager J. Francis

NORTHERN IRELAND REGION

Graham Hse, Knockbracken Healthcare Pk, Saintfield Pk, Belfast BT8 8BH; Tel 028 9079 8878
Regional Manager M. Young

WALES REGION

ASBAH yng Nghymru – ASBAH in Wales, 4 Llys y Fedwen, Parc Menai, Bangor, Gwynedd LL57 4BL; Tel 01248 671345
Regional Manager E. Ifan

Barrowmore

Great Barrow, Chester, Cheshire CH3 7JA; Tel 01829 740391; Fax 01829 740237
Manager (Supported Employment) Tom Jackson
Chief Executive Eric Lees
Barrowmore is a charity providing high quality care, accommodation, training and employment for people with special needs and physical disabilities.

British Computer Society Disability Group

West Hanningfield Rd, Gt Baddon, Chelmsford, Essex CM2 8HN; URL www.bcs.org.uk/siggroup/sglb.htm; Tel 01245 242950

British Society for Music Therapy

61 Church Hill Rd, East Barnet, Hertfordshire EN4 8SY; URL www.bsmt.org; E-mail info@bsmt.org; Tel 020 8441 6226; Fax 020 8441 4118
Chair Claire Flower, BMus(Hons), DipMTh (GSMD/York)
Promotes music therapy in the treatment and rehabilitation of children and adults suffering from emotional, physical or mental handicaps. Publishes a journal and bulletin, holds conferences, workshops and meetings. Sells books and videos. Sends information booklet to all enquiries.
Registered Charity Number 260837

British Wheelchair Sports Foundation

Guttmann Rd, Stoke Mandeville, Buckinghamshire
HP21 9PP; URL www.britishwheelchairsports.org;
E-mail enquiries@britishwheelchairsports.org; Tel 01296
395995; Fax 01296 424171
Chief Executive Martin McElhatton
Registered charity and the governing body of wheelchair
sport for men, women and children paralysed by injury to
the spinal cord and those with related disabilities. The
charity aims to enrich the lives of people in a wheelchair
through sport.

The Cedar Foundation

(formerly the NICOD)
Malcolm Sinclair Hse, 31 Ulsterville Ave, Belfast BT9 7AS;
URL www.cedar-foundation.org;
E-mail info@cedar-foundation.org; Tel 028 9066 6188;
Fax 028 9068 2400
Director Stephen Mathews
The Cedar Foundation is a voluntary organisation working
in partnership with people with physical disabilty
throughout Northern Ireland to develop services that
promote choice, opportunity independence and equality.
The Cedar Foundation promotes choice by offering a
variety of residential units, catering for moderate to severe
disability, ambulant individuals to wheelchair users, and
by offering a variety of training for employment
programmes.

Centre for Accessible Environments (Architectural Advice and Information)

see Chapter 14

Conquest Art – Enriching the Lives of Physically Disabled People

Conquest Art Centre, Cox La Day Centre, Cox La, West
Ewell, Epsom, Surrey KT19 9PL; Tel 020 8397 6157;
Fax 020 8397 6157
Secretary Lena Poppe
Conquest Art runs art classes for physically disabled
people. Exhibitions are held and talks given on request. A
magazine is published three times a year. This is also
available on tape for the visually impaired. Volunteer class
leaders and helpers always required. Training days are held
for occupational therapists, care personnel, potential class
leaders and helpers.

Continence Foundation

Unit 307, Hatton Square Gold, 16–16a Baldwin Gdns,
London EC1N 7RJ;
URL www.continence-foundation.org.uk;
E-mail continence.foundation@dial.pipex.com; Tel 020
7404 6875; (Helpline (Mon–Fri 0930–1400)) 0845 345
0165; Fax 020 7404 6876
Director David Pollock
Publicity Officer Ian Holland
Office Manager Carol Paul
Charity offering advice, education and information on
urinary and faecal incontinence.

Crossroads Association

10 Regent Pl, Rugby, Warwickshire CV21 2PN;
URL www.crossroads.org.uk;
E-mail communications@crossroads.org.uk; Tel 01788
573653; Fax 01788 565498
Chief Executive A. Roberts
Provides breaks for carers through the provision of a paid,
trained carer support to replace the carer, on a regular
basis. There are over 200 schemes operating in England and
Wales.

Deafblind UK

Founded in 1928.
100 Bridge St, Peterborough PE1 1DY;
URL www.deafblind.org.uk; Tel (Voice and Minicom)
01733 358100; Fax 01733 358356
Chief Executive Jackie Hicks
Provides information, advice, practical help, counselling,
support and encouragement to deafblind people. Brings
them together through holidays, rallies, regional activities,
quarterly magazine and weekly newspaper. Organises
training, rehabilitation programmes and respite care at
National Training and Rehabilitation centre in Peterborough.
National network of regional development officers.

Deafblind Scotland

21 Alexandra Ave, Lenzie, Glasgow G66 5BG;
URL www.deafblindscotland.org.uk;
E-mail info@deafblindscotland.org.uk; Tel (Voice and
Minicom) 0141 777 6111; Fax 0141 775 3311
Chief Executive Drena O'Malley

Derbyshire Coalition for Inclusive Living (DCIL)

Park Rd, Ripley, Derbyshire DE5 3EF;
URL www.dcll.org.uk; E-mail info@dcll.org.uk;
Tel 01773 740246; Fax 01773 570185; Minicom 01773
748452
Director Rob Jackson
Members are determined to stamp out discrimination and
exclusion for all disabled people. They provide a
comprehensive range of information and support services,
demanded and designed by disabled people, to take
control of their own lives.

DIAL UK – Disablement, information and Advice Lines

see Chapter 14

Disability Action, Northern Ireland

Portside Business Pk, 189 Airport Rd West, Belfast
BT3 9ED; E-mail hq@disabilityaction.org; Tel 028 9029
7880; Fax 028 9029 7881
Rights-based development agency working to ensure that
people with disabilities attain their full rights as citizens.
Disability Action is a charity with over 170 member groups
covering every aspect of disability – physical, mental,
sensory and hidden.

Disability Alliance

Universal Hse, 88–94 Wentworth St, London E1 7SA;
URL www.disabilityalliance.org;
E-mail office.da@dial.pipex.com; Tel 020 7247 8776;
Fax 020 7247 8765
A federation of over 400 organisations, campaigning to
break the link between poverty and disability. Disability
Alliance publishes The Disability Rights Handbook
annually, a guide to benefits and services for all people
with disabilities and provides advice service by phone on
020 7247 8763, Mon and Wed 1400–1600. Training courses
in a variety of social security benefits subjects are provided
during the year.
Disability Alliance is committed to breaking the link
between poverty and disability by providing information
to disabled people about their entitlements and
campaigning for improvements to the social security
system and for increases in disability benefits so that they
better reflect the real costs of disability. Disability Alliance
has 400 paid member organisations.

Disability Information Service Surrey (DISS)

Harrowlands, Harrowlands Pk, Dorking, Surrey RH4 2RA;
URL www.diss.org.uk; Tel (Administration) 01306
742282; (Enquiry) 01306 875156; Fax 01306 741740

Manager   Hazel Plastow
DISS is a free, confidential and independent information service covering all aspects of disability, to people with disabilities, their carers and service providers, particularly those within Surrey. Supplies DISSBASE a database of national disability service providers with optional add-on facility for local data entry.

Disability Law Service

39–45 Cavell St, London E1 2BP; E-mail advice@dls.org.uk; Tel 020 7791 9800; Fax 020 7791 9802; Minicom 020 7791 9801
Free and confidential advice service for disabled people and their families, carers and enablers. Areas covered include benefits, community care, discrimination, education, employment, consumer and contract, and other issues relating to disability.

Disability Sport England (DSE)

Unit 4G, 784–788 High Rd, Tottenham, London N17 0DA; URL www.disabilitysport.org.uk; Tel 020 8801 4466; Fax 020 8801 6644
DSE aims to provide, develop and co-ordinate opportunities in sport and recreation for people with disabilities in partnership with relevant agencies.
Registered Charity Number 297035

Disability Wales/Anabledd Cymru

Wernddu Crt, Caerphilly Business Pk, Van Rd, Caerphilly CF83 3ED; E-mail info@dwac.demon.co.uk
The national association of disability groups working to promote the rights, inclusion, equality and support of all disabled people in Wales.

Disabled Living Centres Council

Redbank Hse, 4 St. Chad's St, Cheetham, Manchester M8 8QA; URL www.dlcc.org.uk; E-mail dlcc@dlcc.org.uk; Tel 0161 834 1044; Fax 0161 839 0802; Textphone 0161 839 0885
Chair   Sue Butterworth
Office Manager   Graham Foster
The Disabled Living Centres Council leads a network of 50 disabled living centres in the UK. It actively promotes the concept and the establishment of DLCs providing information and support.

Dovetail Enterprises (1993) Ltd

Dunsinane Ave, Dundee DD2 3QN; URL www.dovetailenterprises.co.uk; E-mail sales@dovetailenterprises.co.uk; Tel 01382 810099; Fax 01382 817272
Manager (Finance)   Peter Castle
The training and employment of the blind and partially sighted and severely disabled.

Edinburgh University Settlement

Student Centre, Bristol Sq, Edinburgh EH8 9AL; URL www.ed.ac.uk eus; E-mail finance@eusett.sagehost.co.uk; Tel 0131 650 6313; Fax 0131 650 2569
Director   Nicholas A. Flavin
Undertakes projects with many groups including the physically disabled, mentally ill and handicapped, and the long-term unemployed. The Settlement is a care agency supported by a variety of public authority funding bodies, the University of Edinburgh and independent fund-raising.

emPOWER

c/o Limbless Association, Roehampton La, London SW15 5PR; URL www.empowernet.org; E-mail enquiries@empowernet.org; Tel 020 8355 2341; Fax 020 8788 3444
The charities consortium of users of disability equipment. emPOWER campaigns for a 'national look' based on individual needs.

Employment Opportunities for People with Disabilities

123 Minories, London EC3N 1NT; URL www.opportunities.org.uk; E-mail eopps.ho@care4free.net; Tel 020 7481 2727; Fax 020 7481 9797
Director (Operations)   Andrew Mills
The leading UK charity working directly with people with a wide range of disabilities to help them find employment. Employment Opportunities seeks to persuade employers to positively recognise ability and potential. They have a national network of regional centres offering practical help with training and advice on job searches, CVs, application forms and interviews. Many 'Employment Opportunities' staff have personal experience of disability in employment. Where possible they work closely with employers, PACTS and DEAs and their services are provided free of charge to clients and employers.

Enham

Enham Alamein, Andover, Hampshire SP11 6JS; URL www.enham.org.uk; E-mail learning@enham.co.uk; Tel 01264 345800; Fax 01264 333638
Customer Adviser   Val Hayes
Enham offers people with disablties the opportunity to make real choices in life. Access to worthwhile employment, decent accomodation, high-quality care, relevant training and a fulfilling social life are all fundamental to anyone taking their place in life. At Enham, their Choices for Learning programmes open up opportunities for employment and a fuller life-style. Choices for Living options provide short and long term solutions for all accommodation needs. Choices for Work give real-work opportunities for real life. Business Ability offers support for disabled people who want to become self-employed through setting up their own businesses.

Foundation for Assistive Technology (FAST)

12 City Forum, 250 City Road, London EC1V 8AF; URL www.fastuk.org; E-mail info@fastuk.org; Tel 020 7253 3303
Administrator   Keren Down
FAST is a national charity working with users of assistive technology to maximise their independence. We bring together people who use assistive technology, researchers, developers, manufacturers and service providers to build effective partnerships. To join the User Forum, look on the website under 'User Forum'.
As well as supporting user involvement in research and development in assistive technologies, FAST collates information on projects, organisations and events within the assistive technology community and disseminates the information on their website.

Gardening for Disabled Trust

Frittenden Hse, Frittenden, Cranbrook, Kent TN17 2DG; Fax 01580 852120
Chair   F. Seton
Helps disabled people to garden by providing advice and grants for special equipment, tools and garden adaptation.
Registered Charity Number 255066

Glencraft, Royal Aberdeen Workshops for the Blind and Disabled

132 Wellington Rd, Tullos Ind Est, Aberdeen AB12 3LQ;
   E-mail info@glencraft.co.uk; Tel 01224 873366; Fax 01224 894659
General Manager Ian. W. Logan
Voluntary society for the employment of blind and disabled people engaged in the manufacture of upholstery, bedding and furniture.

Great Britain Wheelchair Basketball Association

The Woodlands, Brook End, Keysoe, Bedfordshire
   MK44 2HR; E-mail g.perry@gbwba.org.uk; Tel 01234 708741
Manager (National Development) Gordon Perry
To promote and govern the game of wheelchair basketball in the UK. To organise and run national teams and the National League Programme.

Greater London Action on Disability (GLAD)

336 Brixton Rd, London SW9 7AA; URL www.glad.org.uk;
   E-mail info@glad.org.uk; Tel 020 7346 5800; Fax 020 7346 8844; Minicom 020 7326 4554
Director Reg McLaughlin
Information and support for disabled Londoners. Has a network of disability associations in the boroughs; publishes a monthly newsletter, various reports and information leaflets. Provides disability equality training.

Halliwick Association of Swimming Therapy

c/o ADKC Centre, Whitstable Hse, Silchester Rd, London
   W10 6SB; Tel 020 8968 7609; Fax 020 8968 7609
Hon Secretary E. Dilley
Provides recreational and competitive swimming to all types of disabled people of all ages. Halliwick instruction courses, lecturing, video hire/sale, book Swimming for People with Disabilities £9.99 + £1.00 postage.

The Home Farm Trust (HFT)

see Chapter 14

Homeworkers, Guild of Disabled

16 Fountain St, Nailsworth, Gloucestershire GL6 0BL;
   E-mail office@godh.fsnet.co.uk; Tel 01453 835623
Free market for products of disabled homeworkers.

IMPACT Foundation

151 Western Rd, Haywards Heath, West Sussex
   RH16 3LH; URL www.impact.org.uk;
   E-mail impact@impact.org.uk; Tel 01444 457080;
   Fax 01444 457877
Chief Executive Claire Hicks
Britain's link with international action against avoidable disability. Information; co-ordination, liaison; medical treatment; overseas aid and service.

Independent Living Resource Centre

Disability North, The Dene Centre, Newcastle upon Tyne,
   Tyne and Wear NE3 1PH;
   URL www.disabilitynorth.org.uk;
   E-mail reception@disabilitynorth.org.uk; Tel 0191 213 0910; 0191 284 0480
Comprehensive exhibition of aids for disabled people. Practical information and demonstration facilities, courses and seminars.

Invalids-at-Home Trust

Bamford Cottage, South Hill Ave, Harrow, Greater London
   HA1 3PA; Tel 020 8864 3818
Executive Officer Mary Rose
One-off financial assistance to help people who are long-term sick or disabled to remain in their own homes.

John Grooms

50 Scrutton St, London EC2A 4XQ;
   URL www.johngrooms.org.uk;
   E-mail charity@johngrooms.org.uk; Tel 020 7452 2000;
   Fax 020 7452 2001
Executive Director Rev M. Shaw
Provides residential care homes, nursing homes and independence training units that offer long-term and short-term care. The philosophy is that disabled people are people first. Independence is encouraged at all levels. A home care agency is also available in some areas. John Grooms also operates Grooms Holidays, offering its own accessible hotels and self-catering accommodation. Employment training opportunities are offered at FAITH plant centre in London. A brain injury rehabilitation unit opened in 1998 in Stowmarket, Suffolk. John Grooms Housing Association is the largest specialist builder of wheelchair-accessible housing in the UK.

League of the Helping Hand

Little Finches, Wheatsheaf Rd, Henfield, West Sussex
   BN5 9AT; E-mail secretary@lhh.org.uk; Tel 01253 493551
Secretary Moira Parrott
Aims to help and alleviate individual cases of suffering in mind and body who find themselves in financial difficulties through serious physical or mental illness; referrals via professionals only.

Let's Face It

14 Fallowfield, Yateley, Hampshire GU46 6LW;
   URL www.letsfaceit.force9.co.uk;
   E-mail chrisletsfaceit@aol.com; Tel 01252 879630;
   Fax 01252 872633; (London Office Tel/Fax) 020 8952 4990
Chief Executive Christine E. Piff
Personal Assistant Julia Wallace
Provides support for sufferers of facial cancer and disfigurement and links together those with similar disabilities.

Limbless Association

Rehabilitation Centre, Roehampton La, London SW15 5PR;
   URL www.limbless-association.org;
   E-mail chris@limbless-association.org; Tel 020 8788 1777;
   Fax 020 8788 3444
Information and advice; casework; visiting by volunteers; quarterly magazine; monitoring of equipment and services.

Listening Books

Registered Charity Number 264221.
12 Lant St, London SE1 1QH;
   URL www.listening-books.org.uk;
   E-mail info@listening-books.org.uk
Membership Officer;
   E-mail membership@listening-books.org.uk; Tel 020 7407 9417; Fax 020 7403 1377
President The Baroness Warnock, DBE
Director Bill Dee
Listening Books provides a postal audio book library service to anyone with an illness or disability that makes it impossible or difficult to hold a book, turn pages, or read in the usual way. Audio books for both pleasure and learning are available.
Patron
HRH The Duchess of Gloucester, GCVO

Liverpool Association of Disabled People

c/o Lime Crt Centre, Upper Baker St, Liverpool,
Merseyside L6 1NB; URL www.ladp.org.uk;
E-mail ladisabled@freenetname.co.uk; Tel 0151 263 8366;
Fax 0151 263 1855; Textphone 0151 260 3187
Manager   E. Evans
Campaigning organisation. Advice given on access, equal
opportunities and welfare rights.

Liverpool Disabled Living Centre

101–103 Kempston St, Liverpool, Merseyside L3 8HE;
Tel 0151 298 2055; Fax 0151 298 2952
Permanent display of equipment for disabled people.
Assessment and information services. Regular open days.
Visits by appointment.

Living Options (formerly The Crypt Foundation)

Kimbridge Hse, Kimbridge Rd, East Wittering, Chichester,
West Sussex PO20 8PE; URL www.livingoptions.org.uk;
E-mail livingoptions@hotmail.com; Tel 01243 671865;
Fax 01243 671865
Chair   Val Fethney
National Secretary   Sue Liversedge
Living Options provides opportunities for young people
(18 plus) to live in the community in small group homes
and experience independence.
Registered Charity Number 299206

MENCAP – Royal Society for Mentally Handicapped Children and Adults

see Chapter 14

Mouth and Foot Painting Artists

9 Inverness Pl, London W2 3JF; Tel 020 7229 4491; Fax 020
7229 7052
Those who paint with a brush in the mouth or feet and who
are seriously interested in art as a living should apply in
writing, giving details of disability and training.

National Association of Swimming Clubs for the Handicapped

The Willows, Mayles La, Wickham, Hampshire PO17 5ND;
Tel 01329 833689
Administrator   Rosemary O'Leary
Recognises the benefits of swimming for disabled people
and encourages, promotes and develops swimming
amongst the handicapped. Produces a free register of
swimming clubs and organised swimming sessions for
handicapped people.

New Trinity Centre

7a Loaning Rd, Edinburgh EH7 6JE;
URL www.capability-scotland.org.uk;
E-mail ntc@cabablility-scotland.org.uk; Tel 0131 661
1212; Fax 0131 661 8643
Day centre and special needs unit.

The Papworth Trust

Papworth Everard, Cambridge, Cambridgeshire CB3 8RG;
URL www.papworth.org.uk;
E-mail info@papworth.org.uk; Tel 01480 830341;
Fax 01480 830781
Chief Executive   Gordon Lister
Rehabilitation, training, employment, care and housing for
adults with physical or learning disabilities.

Personal and Medical Claims Service

13 Freda Ave, Gedling, Nottinghamshire NG4 4FY;
E-mail lesley@pmcs.org.uk; Tel 0115 987 8470; Fax 0115
987 2088

Case management and litigation service for solicitors.
Assessment and fully costed reports for compensation
claims and negotiating care facilities for the very severely
physically and mentally handicapped. Experience of
litigation following road traffic accidents, industrial
accidents and medical negligence. Free advice service for
clients and others seeking specialist solicitors and expert
witness in catastrophic injury cases.

Phab

see Chapter 14

Portland College for People with Disabilities

Nottingham Rd, Mansfield, Nottinghamshire NG18 4TJ;
URL www.portland.org.uk; Tel 01623 499111; Fax 01623
499134
Principal   M.E.A. Syms, OBE, FIMgt, MIFM
Foundation unit for remedial education and severely
handicapped; continuing education in the Further
Education unit; vocational courses; business studies,
technical studies and horticulture.
Registered Charity Number 214339

Possum Controls Ltd

8 Farmbrough Cl, Stocklake, Park Ind Est, Aylesbury,
Buckinghamshire HP20 1DQ; URL www.possum.co.uk;
E-mail sales@possum.co.uk; Tel 01296 461000; Fax 01296
461001
Possum Controls are specialists in home automation and
electronic assistive technology. A total solution is ensured
for people with a need to gain independence and easily
control their security, communication, comfort and
entertainment accessories.

Queen Elizabeth's Foundation for Disabled People

Leatherhead Crt, Woodlands Rd, Leatherhead, Surrey
KT22 0BN; URL www.qefd.org; E-mail info@qefd.org;
Tel 01372 841100
Chief Executive Officer and Secretary   Cynthia Robinson
National charity supporting physically disabled people,
from age 16 upwards. Aims to provide physical and
emotional support and information to enable individuals to
make informed choices, and works to encourage the
achievement of optimum independence. Eight units
provide: information services, day care, residential care,
rehabilitation for the head-injured, a sheltered workshop, a
training college and mobility centre.

QED 2000 Ltd

1 Prince Alfred St, Gosport, Hampshire PO12 1QH;
URL www.qedltd.com; E-mail sales@qedltd.com;
Tel 0870 787 8850; Fax 0870 787 8860
Managing Director   Richard Bullock
Communication aids, computer keyboard emulators,
speech synthesis, switches, page turners.

REMAP (Scotland) (Technical Aids for the Disabled)

Maulside Lodge, Beith, North Ayrshire KA15 1JJ;
E-mail golderjohn@hotmail.com; Tel 01294 832566;
Fax 01294 834162
National Organiser   John Golder
14 panels designing aids for disabled people where no
suitable aid is commercially available.

Remploy Ltd

Stonecourt, Siskin Dr, Coventry, West Midlands CV3 4FJ;
URL www.remploy.co.uk
Leading provider of employment opportunities for
disabled people.

Riding for the Disabled Association

Lavinia Norfolk Hse, Avenue R, Stoneleigh Deer Pk, Kenilworth, Warwickshire CV8 2LY; URL www.riding-for-disabled.org.uk; E-mail rdahq@riding-for-disabled.org.uk; Tel 024 7669 6510; Fax 024 7669 6532

Aims to provide the opportunity of riding to disabled people who might benefit in their general health and well-being. Over 600 groups throughout England, Wales, Scotland and Northern Ireland.
Registered Charity Number 244108

Royal Association for Disability and Rehabilitation (RADAR)

12 City Forum, 250 City Rd, London EC1V 8AF; URL www.radar.org.uk; E-mail radar@radar.org.uk; Tel 020 7250 3222; Fax 020 7250 0212; Minicom 020 7250 4119

Chief Executive Kate Nash

Provides information and advice on all aspects of physical disability, and campaigns to enable disabled people to take their rightful place in society.

Royal Society for Home Relief to Incurables, Edinburgh

Secretaries and Treasurers, Scott-Moncrieff, 17 Melville St, Edinburgh EH3 7PH; Tel 0131 473 3500; Fax 0131 473 3535

The society gives assistance to persons (normally under retirement age at the time of application) throughout Scotland who are no longer able to work on account of having an incurable illness.

Scottish Spina Bifida Association

190 Queensferry Rd, Edinburgh EH4 2BW; URL www.ssba.org.uk; E-mail mail@ssba.org.uk; Tel 0131 332 0743; Fax 0131 343 3651

Chief Executive A.H.D. Wynd

Information, family support service, group/family holidays, sports activities, independence training, young adults housing project. Local branches throughout Scotland.

Scottish Disability Sport (SDS)

Fife Sports Institute, 1 Viewfield Rd, Glenrothes, Fife KY6 2RB; E-mail ssadsds@aol.com; Tel 01592 415700; Fax 01592 415710

Chair Richard Brickley, MBE

Administrator Norma Buchanan

National governing body of sport for people with disabilities in Scotland with a nationwide structure of branches.

The Sequal Trust

3 Ploughmans Corner, Wharf Rd, Ellesmere, Shropshire SY12 0EJ; URL www.the-sequal-trust.org.uk; E-mail thesequeltrust@freeuk.com; Tel 01691 624222; Fax 01691 624222

Shaftesbury Society

16 Kingston Rd, London SW19 1JZ; URL www.shaftesburysoc.org.uk

Shaftesbury Education

Shaftesbury exists to enable people in great need to achieve security, self-worth and significance and through this to show Christian care in action. We provide care and education services to people with learning and/or physical disabilities, and support for people who are disadvantaged and/or on a low income. We run three non-maintained special schools for children in Bromley, Poole and Malmesbury, two of which also offer further education

facilities. Two specialist colleges of further education in Wellingborough and Bromley offer a wide range of courses for students with physical disabilities. Both are working with local colleges to offer students mainstream courses where possible.

The Snowdon Award Scheme

22 City Business Centre, 6 Brighton Rd, Horsham, West Sussex RH13 5BB; URL www.snowdonawardscheme.org.uk; E-mail info@snowdonawardscheme.org.uk; Tel 01403 211252; Fax 01403 271553

Bursaries for physically-disabled young people (17–25) who are in or about to enter into further or higher education or training. Awards are made for extra help with translators, computers, carers, wheelchairs or equipment related to their disability. Applications are considered from mature students if funds allow. Each bursary will be for a period of one or two years and will not normally exceed £2000 a year in value. The applications must be in by 31 May. Late applications may be considered if funds are available.

Spinal Injuries Association

76 St. James's La, London N10 3DF; E-mail sia@spinal.co.uk; Tel 020 8444 2121; (Freephone helpline) 0800 980 0501; Fax 020 8444 3761

Executive Director Paul Smith

National organisation of spinal cord injured (SCI) people. Membership open to all SCI individuals, families, friends and interested organisations. Services include: Information, peer support and publications. Subscription rates on application.

Spinal Injuries Scotland

Festival Business Centre, 150 Brand St, Glasgow G51 1DH; E-mail info@sisonline.org; Tel 0141 314 0056; (Support line) 0141 314 0057; Fax 0141 314 0057

Assists people with spinal cord injuries to return to an active life in the community. Sports, information and welfare services. Works to improve conditions for wheelchair users.

Thrive

The Geoffrey Udall Centre, Beech Hill, Reading RG7 2AT; URL www.carryongardening.org.uk; E-mail info@thrive.org.uk; Tel 0118 988 5688; Fax 0118 988 5677

Thrive promotes the use of gardening and horticulture for training and employment, therapy and health. It runs its own garden projects and supports a network of social and therapeutic horticulture projects across the UK. Thrive also gives advice, particularly to older and disabled people on easier ways to garden. The majority of Thrive's work is with professionals working in social care.

Welsh Paraplegic and Tetraplegic Association

Rookwood Hospital, Llandaff, Cardiff CF5 2YN; Tel 029 2056 6281

Secretary Janet Bridgeman

Welfare and sport for paraplegics and tetraplegics.

West Sussex Association for Disabled People

9a South Pallant, Chichester, West Sussex PO19 1SU; URL www.wsad.org.uk; E-mail info@wsad.org.uk; Tel 01243 774088; Fax 01243 533061

Director Roland Higgins

Information and advice, free quarterly newsletter, website information annual holiday, equipment fund, loans, grants and radar toilet keys. Local groups provide home-visiting, outings social activities transport and support.

Education

see Chapter 14

Environment

Arkleton Trust

Enstone, Oxford, Oxfordshire OX7 4HH;
URL www.enstoneuk.demon.co.uk/arkleton
Charitable trust which studies new approaches to rural
development. Aims to promote dialogue between
politicians, administrators and practitioners at all levels on
the problems of Europe and the developing world.

Centre for Alternative Technology

Machynlleth, Powys SY20 9AZ; URL www.cat.org.uk;
Tel 01654 705950; Fax 01654 702782

NEA

St. Andrew's Hse, 90–92 Pilgrim St, Newcastle upon Tyne,
Tyne and Wear NE1 6SG; URL www.nea.org.uk/;
E-mail info@nea.org.uk; Tel 0191 261 5677; Fax 0191 261
6496
Information Officer/Library Manager   Susan Clark
NEA develops and promotes energy efficiency services to
tackle the heating and insultation problems of low-income
households. Working with a variety of partners, NEA aims
to alleviate fuel poverty and campaigns for greater
investment in energy efficiency to help those who are poor
or vulnerable.

Newcastle Energy Centre

Scottish Life Hse, Block C, Newcastle upon Tyne, Tyne and
Wear NE2 1BZ; E-mail terry.dunn@newcastle.gov.uk;
Tel 0191 281 1303
Advice and information on energy matters; how to reduce
heating costs; increase comfort levels, combat dampness
and condensation, and meet fuel bills. Links with local
draught-proofing and insulation projects. Publications list
available.

Noise Abatement Society

Organisation was founded in 1959 by John Connell OBE,
FIEnvSc, MIPR.
PO Box 518, Eynsford, Dartford, Kent DA4 0LL;
URL www.noisenet.org; E-mail nas@noisenet.org;
Tel 01903 775578; Fax 01322 860381
Technical enquiries
Martec Environmental Consultants, Gerrard Place,
Skelmersdale, Lancashire, WN8 9SU; Tel: 01695 725121;
Fax: 01695 50219; E-mail: noise@globalnet.co.uk or
martecenvironmental@compuserve.com
Promotion of control and abatement of pollution of the
environment resulting from noise and the relief of distress
and ill health caused by noise. Technical assistance from
Martec Environmental Consultants.
Members
500 (local authorities, companies etc.)

Town and Country Planning Association

17 Carlton House Terr, London SW1Y 5AS;
URL www.tcpa.org.uk; Tel 020 7930 8903; Fax 020 7930
3280
Director   Gideon Amos, MA, RIBA
Registered charity making independent comment on
important planning and environmental matters.
Conferences, seminars, study tours, periodicals.
Registered Charity Number 214348

Family Welfare

see Chapter 13

Forces

see Armed Forces and Seafarers

Gypsies

see Chapter 15

Health Organisations

Health Care/Hospitals/Nursing

Association of General Practitioner Community Hospitals (AGPCH)

see the Community Hospitals Association

British Health Care Association

24a Main St, Garforth, Leeds, West Yorkshire LS25 1AA;
URL www.bhca.org.uk; E-mail cbell@bhca.org.uk;
Tel 0113 232 0903; Fax 0113 232 0904
Chief Executive   Carolyn Bell
National body of schemes providing cash benefits
defraying health charges for NHS or private treatment.

The Community Hospitals Association

Meadow Brow, Broadway Rd, Ilminster, Somerset
TA19 9RG; URL www.commhosp.org;
E-mail commhosp@gxn.co.uk; Tel 01460 55951;
Fax 01460 53207
President   Dr A.J.M. Cavenagh
To encourage the improvement and extension of services
provided by community hospitals and to positively
support community hospitals through periods of change.
To collate and disseminate information on all aspects of
work and promote audit and research.

Council for Music in Hospitals

74 Queens Rd, Hersham, Surrey KT12 5LW;
E-mail info@music-in-hospitals.org.uk; Tel 01932 252809;
01932 252811; Fax 01932 252966
Scottish Office
10 Forth St, Edinburgh EH1 3LD;
E-mail info@musicinhospitalsscotland.org.uk; Tel 0131
556 5848; Fax 0131 556 0225
Director   A. Frazer
Aims to improve the quality of the lives of people in care in
hospitals, hospices and nursing homes for people of all
ages, through the medium of live concerts given by
carefully selected professional musicians.

Forester Health

Forester Hse, Cromwell Ave, Bromley, Kent BR2 9BF;
URL www.foresterhealth.co.uk;
E-mail forester.health@foresters.co.uk; Tel 020 8628 3636;
Fax 020 8628 3535
Manager (Customer Services)   Yasmin Fraser
Managing Director   Euan Allison
Providing a unique range of cost-effective cash plans to
help reduce absenteeism and attract, retain and motivate
employees.

Health Libraries Group of the Library Association

Imperial College Charing Cross Campus, The Reynolds Bldg, St. Dunstan's Rd, London W6 8RP; URL www.la-hq.org.uk/groups/hlg.hlg.html; E-mail s.howard@lc.ac.uk; Tel 020 7594 0749; Fax 020 7594 0851
Hon Secretary Susan Howard

Hospice Information

34–44 Britannia St, London WC1X 9JG; URL www.hospiceinformation.info; E-mail info@hospiceinformation.info; Tel 0870 903 3903; Fax 020 7278 1021
Hospice Information publishes a directory of hospice services which provides details of hospices, home care teams and hospital support teams in the UK and the Republic of Ireland. For copies of the directory or details of local services, write or telephone.

Hospital Saturday Fund

24 Upper Ground, London SE1 9PD; E-mail sales@hsf.co.uk; Tel 020 7928 6662; Fax 020 7928 0446
Not-for-profit health care cash plan providing cash grants for members in hospital and towards the cost of a wide range of ancillary medical services. Associated charitable trust makes donations to hospitals, hospices, medically associated charities and individuals in need.

HSA

Hambleden Hse, Andover, Hampshire SP10 1LQ; Tel 08702 425454; Fax 01264 333650; Minicom 01264 353186
Chairman Major General Brian Pennicott, CVO
Non-profit-making association. For small weekly payments HSA provides a wide range of cash benefits covering hospital, optical and dental benefits, physiotherapy, consultation fees, chiropody and many other benefits.

International Hospital Federation (IHF)

46–48 Grosvenor Gdns, London SW1W 0EB; URL www.hospitalmanagement.net; E-mail 101662.1262@compuserve.com; Tel 020 7881 9922; Fax 020 7881 9223
Director-General Prof Per Gummar Svensson
The International Hospital Federation (IHF) organises: an International Hospital Congress held every two years; a pan-regional conference held every two years; a field study course; a senior managers' course in conjunction with the University of Birmingham for senior hospital and health service managers from developing countries.
The IHF provides fellowships to scholars from Asia and Africa to study the provision of healthcare facilities in different settings.
Main publications: World Hospitals and Health Services, the official Federation journal; Hospitals International, a quarterly newsletter; Hospital Management International, a year book and the new World Health year book.

King's Fund

11–13 Cavendish Sq, London W1G 0AN; URL www.kingsfund.org.uk; Tel 020 7307 2400; Fax 020 7307 2801
Chief Executive Rabbi Julia Neuberger
The King's Fund is an independent charity which works to improve health and social care through research, development and education. It has particular interests in services for older people and mental health.

North London Hospice

47 Woodside Ave, North Finchley, London N12 8TF; URL www.northlondonhospice.co.uk; E-mail nlh@northlondonhospice.co.uk; Tel 020 8343 8841; Fax 020 8343 7672

Chief Executive Douglas Bennett
Provides a hospice community specialist palliative care service, in-patient (20 beds) day care and bereavement service throughout the London boroughs of Barnet, Enfield and Haringey. As a registered charity, services are free to all who need them.

Nuffield House

1–4 The Crescent, Surbiton, Surrey KT6 4BN; URL www.nuffieldhospitals.org.uk; Tel 020 8390 1200; Fax 020 8339 7525
Chief Executive D.T. Ervine
Independent hospital group with 43 hospitals nationwide. A charity treating over 900 000 patients each year.

Nurses' Welfare Service

Victoria Chambers, 16–18 Strutton Ground, London SW1P 2HP; E-mail info@nurseswelfareservice.co.uk; Tel 020 7222 1563; 020 7222 1564; Fax 020 7799 1467
Chief Executive D. Morgan
Offers advice, support and occasionally counselling to nurses, midwives and health visitors in danger of losing their right to practise, or who are seeking restoration to the register.

Royal National Pension Fund for Nurses

Burdett Hse, 15 Buckingham St, London WC2N 6ED; Tel 020 7839 6785
General Manager D.W. Davies, BSc(Econ), FIA
Mutual life assurance company for members and spouses of the nursing and other health care professions; Nurses' Memorial to King Edward VII, Reigate, Surrey; residential home for retired nurses of modest means; Junius S. Morgan Benevolent Fund for Nurses; financial help for sick and elderly.

Scottish National Blood Transfusion Association

2 Otterburn Pk, Edinburgh EH14 1JX; Tel 0131 443 7636
Secretary and Treasurer William Mack
Safeguards the voluntary aspects of blood donation, and provides links between individual blood donors and the Blood Transfusion Service.

St. Joseph's Hospice Association

Jospice International, Ince Rd, Thornton, Liverpool, Merseyside L23 4UE; URL www.jospice.org.uk; E-mail keithcawdron@jospice.org.uk; Tel 0151 924 3812; Fax 0151 932 6020
General Manager Keith Cawdron
The running of hospices which care for the chronic and terminally sick both in England (Thornton and Ormskirk) and overseas.

Yoga for Health Foundation

Ickwell Bury, Biggleswade, Bedfordshire SG18 9EF; URL www.yogaforhealthfoundation.co.uk; E-mail admin@yogaforhealthfoundation.co.uk; Tel 01767 627271
PA to Director Caroline Himlin
Promotes the practice and philosophy of yoga as both a preventive and remedial health process.

Specific Health Problems

Cancer

Action Cancer

1 Marlborough Pk, Belfast BT9 6XS; URL www.actioncancer.org; E-mail info@actioncancer.org; Tel 028 9080 3344; Fax 028 9080 3356

Chief Executive   Robin McRoberts
Patron   James Nesbitt
Patron   Mary Peters, CBE
Patron   Lindy Burton-Edelstyn
Patron   Mike Nesbitt
Patron   Lynda Bryans
Chair   Stephen Kirk, FRCS
Patron   William Odling-Smee, FRCS

Action Cancer is a Northern Ireland organisation providing: health promotion in community and workplace settings, full time early detection clinics for women concerned about breast and cervical cancer, a men's health clinic and advice service, a mobile information and detection service for rural areas and workplaces, information, counselling and support for cancer patients and their families, funding for research carried out in Northern Ireland.

The charity has a range of information leaflets for use by patients, their families and carers.

The charity also promotes cancer prevention through schools programmes and awareness campaigns.

Breast Cancer Care

Kiln Hse, 210 New Kings Rd, London SW6 4NZ;
URL www.breastcancercare.org.uk;
E-mail info@breastcancercare.org.uk;
Tel (Administration) 020 7384 2984; (Helpline) 0808 800 6000; Fax 020 7384 3387; Textphone (For Deaf Calls) 0808 800 6001

Chief Executive   Christine Fogg

Breast Cancer Care is a national organisation offering support and information to those affected by breast cancer. Their free, confidential services are delivered by healthcare professionals and trained volunteers. Services include a national helpline, publications and practical and emotional support on a one to one or group basis.

Scotland

46 Gordon St, Glasgow G1 3PU; Tel 0141 221 2244; Fax 0141 221 9499

Breast Cancer Support Group (Reach for Recovery)

c/o The Breast Unit, Western General Hospital, Crewe Rd, Edinburgh EH4 2XU; Tel 0131 441 5942

Self-help group offering support to women who have had, or are about to have, breast surgery, or any treatment for breast cancer, and to their partners, families and friends. Small library of books and tapes available.

CancerBACUP

3 Bath Pl, Rivington St, London EC2A 3JR;
URL www.cancerbacup.org.uk;
E-mail info@cancerbacup.org; Tel (Cancer Information Service) 0808 8001234; (London) 020 7696 9003; Fax 020 7969 9002

National charity providing information and support for people with cancer, their families and friends. Also provides services for health professionals. Team of specialist cancer nurses respond to telephone and written enquiries on all aspects of cancer. Booklets and factsheets on specific cancers, treatments and guides on living with cancer. Interactive website available. Interpreting service available.

Cancer Care Society

11 The Cornmarket, Romsey, Hampshire SO51 8GB;
URL www.cancercaresociety.org;
E-mail info@cancercaresociety.org; Tel 01794 830300; Fax 01794 518133

Chief Executive   Stephen Hanvey
Chair   Paul McCloskey

Cancer Laryngectomee Trust

PO Box 618, Halifax, West Yorkshire HX3 8WX;
E-mail carole.stainton@btopenworld.com; Tel 01422 205522; Fax 01422 205522

Trustee   Carole Stainton

UK network of welfare representatives.

Cancerlink

Macmillan Cancer Relief, 89 Albert Embankment, London SE1 7UQ; URL www.cancerlink.org;
E-mail cancerlink@cancerlink.org.uk; Tel (Freephone Support Link) 0808 808 0000; (General Queries) 020 7840 7840; Fax 020 7840 7841

Cancerlink helps people affected by cancer to help each other and works to strengthen the network of support based on sharing experiences of cancer. The Freephone Support Link Service and website helps people living with cancer, carers and family members to find out about practical and emotional support services on offer locally and nationally. Cancerlink can also provide anyone affected by cancer in the UK with free publications concerning practical and emotional aspects of living with cancer.

Institute for Complementary Medicine

PO Box 194, London SE16 7QZ;
URL www.icmedicine.co.uk;
E-mail info@icmedicine.co.uk; Tel 020 7237 5165; Fax 020 7237 5175

Can supply names of registered practitioners and courses of all kinds of complementary medicine. Also has contact with support groups. Please send sae with two loose 1st class stamps for information, stating area of interest.

Irish Cancer Society

5 Northumberland Rd, Dublin 4, Republic of Ireland;
URL www.irishcancer.ie;
E-mail reception@irishcancer.ie; Cancer Information; E-mail helpline@irishcancer.ie; Tel 353 1 231 0500; (Helpline: Mon–Fri, 0900–1630) 1800 200 700; Fax 353 1 231 0555

Chair   Tom Finlay

The Irish Cancer Society is the national charity for cancer care and the largest voluntary funder of cancer research in Ireland. People concerned about cancer can talk to one of the seven support groups. Other services include homecare and night nurses who specialise in providing cancer care in people's own homes throughout Ireland. Cancer Liaison Nurses are available in the major cancer treatment hospitals to give emotional and practical support to patients from diagnosis and throughout treatment. A special fund for patients in need provides limited assistance in relieving immediate financial pressures.

Leukaemia CARE

2 Shrubbery Ave, Worcester, Worcestershire WR1 1QH;
URL www.leukaemiacare.org.uk;
E-mail info@leukaemiacare.org.uk; Tel (Care line) 0800 169 6680; (Office) 01905 330003; Fax 01905 330090

Director (Operations)   Mr M. Stowell

Free to the sufferers, their carers and families of leukaemia and other allied blood disorders.

Leukaemia CARE provides vital care and support. Their work extends to the welfare of families and carers as well as that of sufferers themselves by providing a level of care and support to those in need. They are a family focused charity. The charity receives no government funding and relies entirely on voluntary donations.

Macmillan Cancer Relief

89 Albert Embankment, London SE1 7UQ;
URL www.macmillan.org.uk;
E-mail cancerline@macmillan.org.uk; Tel 020 7840 7840;
Fax 020 7840 7841
Macmillan Cancer Relief helps people who are living with cancer through the provision of immediate practical and emotional support. Specialist services include Macmillan nurses and doctors, cancer centres, a range of cancer information and direct financial help. The Macmillan CancerLine provides information and emotional support. Textphone available.

Marie Curie Cancer Care

Registered charity no. 207994

Head Office
89 Albert Embankment, London SE1 7TP;
URL www.mariecurie.org.uk;
E-mail info@mariecurie.org.uk; Tel 020 7599 7777;
Fax 020 7599 7788

Scottish Office
29a Albany St, Edinburgh EH1 3QN;
URL www.mariecurie.org.uk;
E-mail info@mariecurie.org.uk; Tel 0131 456 3700
Chief Executive Thomas Hughes-Hallett
Marie Curie Cancer Care provides high quality nursing, totally free, to give terminally ill people the choice of dying at home supported by their families.
Marie Curie Nurses care for around half of all cancer patients who die at home. They work through the day or night, usually for eight or nine hours at a time to care for the patient and allow the family to get some well-earned rest.

The Neuroblastoma Society

41 Towncourt Cres, Petts Wood, Kent BR5 1PH; Tel 01689 873338; Fax 01689 873338
Secretary Ann Ward
Information and advice by telephone or letter for patients and their families. Provides contact where possible with others who have experienced the illness in the family, for mutual support.

New Approaches to Cancer

PO Box 194, Chertsey, Surrey KT16 0WJ;
URL www.anac.org.uk; E-mail help@anac.org.uk;
Tel 0800 389 2662
Acts as a focal point for people concerned with the holistic approach to cancer, and offers a referral system throughout the country and in certain countries overseas.

Oesophageal Patients' Association

22 Vulcan Hse, Vulcan Rd, Solihull, West Midlands B91 2JY;
URL www.opa.org.uk; E-mail opa@ukgateway.net;
Tel 0121 704 9860; Fax 0121 704 9860
Manager (Patient Support) Lynne Watson
Leaflets, telephone advice and support, before and during treatment.
Registered Charity Number 1062461

Quest Cancer Research

Unit E3 Seedbed Business Centre, Coldharbour Rd,
Pinnacles East, Harlow, Essex CM19 5AT;
URL www.questcancer.org;
E-mail questcancer@btinternet.com; Tel 01279 792233;
Fax 01279 793340
Chief Executive Jacqueline Taylor
Develops routine testing so that the first signs of cancer can be detected and treated before a tumour develops. No animals are used in the research.
Registered Charity Number 284526

Sargent Cancer Care for Children

Griffin Hse, 161 Hammersmith Rd, London W6 8SG;
URL www.sargent.org; E-mail care@sargent.org; Tel 020 8752 2800; Fax 020 8752 2806
Provides professional help and practical care to children (under 21 years of age) diagnosed with cancer and to their families. Supports the family at home and in the hospital from the day of diagnosis. Gives financial assistance to families in need. Provides short therapeutic holidays for these young people and their families.

Tak Tent

Cancer support organisation
Flat 5, 30 Shelley Crt, Gartnavel Complex, Glasgow
G12 0YN; E-mail tak.tent@care4free.net; Tel 0141 211 0122; Fax 0141 211 0010
Gives emotional support, counselling and information on cancers and treatments. Has support groups throughout Scotland, plus a one-to-one counselling service at centre by appointment. Youth project helps those 16–25 year olds affected by cancer.

Tenovus Cancer Information Centre

Velindre Hospital, Velindre Rd, Whitechapel, Cardiff
CF14 2TL; URL www.tenovus.com;
E-mail tcic@tenovus.com; Tel 029 2019 6100; (Freephone) 0808 808 1010; Fax 029 2019 6105
Head (Social Work/Welfare Rights) Sue Hall
Practical and emotional support for cancer patients and families. Grants. Resource library of videos, leaflets, posters, fact sheets and books on cancer, with particular emphasis on prevention and treatment.

The Ulster Cancer Foundation

40–42 Eglantine Ave, Belfast BT9 6DX;
URL www.ulstercancer.co.uk;
E-mail ruthcampbell@ulstercancer.org; Tel 028 9066 3281; (Helpline (0900–1700 Mon-Fri)) 0800 7833339
The Ulster Cancer Foundation is involved in many aspects of cancer, from prevention to patient support. Operates an information helpline for patients, relatives and health professionals and is staffed by experienced cancer nurses. Counselling can be arranged by appointment. Rehabilitation support services include: breast cancer support and mastectomy fitting service and headwear for patients with hair loss following chemotherapy; laryngectomy group; lymphoma support; prostate cancer support groups; ovarian support group; smoking cessation groups.

Other

Action Against Allergy (AAA)

PO Box 278, Twickenham, Greater London TW1 4QQ;
URL www.actionagainstallergy.co.uk;
E-mail aaa@actionagainstallergy.co.uk; Tel 020 8892 2711
Executive Director Patricia Schooling
Chair Amelia Nathan Hill
Provides information to those made ill through allergies or suffering allergy-related illness; promotes research into the causes of allergic illness and encourages wider resources of diagnosis and treatment through the NHS.

Arthritic Association

1 Upperton Gdns, Eastbourne, East Sussex BN21 2AA;
URL www.arthriticassociation.org.uk;
E-mail info@arthriticassociation.org.uk; Tel 01323 416550; Fax 01323 639793
President G.J. Keen
Treating arthritis naturally offers a home treatment for the relief of arthritis which includes dietary guidance together with homoeopathic and herbal preparations.

Arthritis Care

18 Stephenson Way, London NW1 2HD;
URL www.arthritiscare.org.uk;
E-mail helpline@arthritiscare.org.uk; Tel 020 7380 6500;
(For 16–26 year olds) 020 808 2000 (Freephone Helpline)
0808 800 4050; Fax 020 7380 6505
Works with and for all people with arthritis. Over 500
branches throughout the UK. Campaigning, self-
management courses, information, support, hotels.
Magazine six times a year and a range of useful
booklets.

Ataxia UK

10 Winchester Hse, Kennington Pk, Cranmer Rd, London
SW9 6EJ; URL www.ataxia.org.uk;
E-mail enquiries@ataxia.org.uk; Tel 020 7582 1444;
(Helpline) 020 7820 3900; Fax 020 7582 9444
Database Administrator   Sue Laycock
Supports people affected by Friedreich's, cerebellar and
other ataxias. Helps people with ataxia, their carers,
families and friends, to live with the condition. Information
through leaflets, magazines, reports and website;
information and support helpline; branches, self-help
groups, meetings; personal contacts; welfare grants. Also
supports world-class medical and scientific research into
causes and potential treatments. Information about these
under-diagnosed conditions is available for healthcare and
social service professionals.

Backcare

16 Elmtree Rd, Teddington, Greater London TW11 8ST;
URL www.backcare.org.uk;
E-mail info@backcare.org.uk; Tel 020 8977 5474; Fax 020
8943 5318
Chief Executive   Nia Taylor
Helps people manage and prevent back pain by providing
advice, promoting self-help, encouraging debate and
funding scientific research into better back care.

British Colostomy Association

15 Station Rd, Reading RG1 1LG; E-mail sue@bcass.org.uk;
Tel 0118 939 1537; Fax 0118 956 9095; Minicom 0800 328
4257
Director (Operations)   Margaret Reid
National charity. Provides a free advisory and visiting
service to all colostomy people.

British Epilepsy Association

New Anstey Hse, Gate Way Dr, Yeadon, Leeds, West
Yorkshire LS19 7XY; URL www.epilepsy.org.uk
Freepost LS0995, Leeds, West Yorkshire LS19 7YY
Epilepsy Action is the leading representative organisation
for epilepsy in the UK, with over 22 000 members. Epilepsy
Action serves over 2000 people each month through its
Advice and Information Centre, with many more people
offered support by Epilepsy Action volunteers and
branches throughout the country. The organisation's
award-winning website receives over 30 000 visitors a
month. Epilepsy Action provides the UK's only Freephone
Epilepsy Helpline on 0808 800 5050, available Mon–Fri
0900–1630 (1600 on Fridays).

British Kidney Patient Association

Bordon, Hampshire GU35 9JZ
President   E.D. Ward, OBE
Dedicated to the benefit and welfare of kidney patients
throughout the United Kingdom. Financial relief is given to
patients and close relatives where the financial need has
come about through the patient's renal illness. The BKPA
runs a holiday dialysis centre at Portelet Bay in Jersey. 'The
Kidney Question', an information pack, is available to
schools free of charge. Postage costs £5.75.

The British Polio Fellowship

Eagle Office Centre, The Runway, South Ruislip, Greater
London HA4 6SE; URL www.britishpolio.org;
E-mail info@britishpolio.org; Tel 020 8842 1898; Fax 020
8842 0555
National Welfare Officer   Dorothy Nattrass
Provides welfare services and financial help for all persons
disabled by polio and resident in the UK and Eire.

British Skin Foundation

19 Fitzroy Sq, London W1T 6EH; E-mail bsf@bad.org.uk;
Tel 020 7383 0266; Fax 020 7388 5263
Aims to provide funds for research into all skin disorders.

British Tay-Sachs Foundation

Jewish Care, Stuart Young Hse, 221 Golders Green Rd,
London NW11 9DQ; Tel 020 8922 2222; Fax 020 8922
2585; Mobile(Enquiries) 07980 611119
Manager (Specialist Services)   Jess Clare
Screening, education and awareness raising on the disease.
Fund raising; carrier testing; support for families; genetic
counselling. Free leaflets available.

Brittle Bone Society

30 Guthrie St, Dundee DD1 5BS; URL www.brittlebone.org;
E-mail bbs@brittlebone.org; Tel 01382 204446; (Helpline)
08000 282459; Fax 01383 206771
Promotes research into osteogenesis imperfecta and
provides support, advice and encouragement to patients
and relatives living with brittle bones.

Capability Scotland

Westlands, Rashielee Ave, Erskine, Renfrewshire PA8 7AE;
Tel 0141 812 6111
Manager   Gail McEwan
Residential accommodation for adults with a physical
disability.

Coeliac Society of Ireland

Carmichael Hse, 4 North Brunswick St, Dublin 7, Republic
of Ireland; Tel 353 1 872 1471; Fax 353 1 873 5737
Honorary Secretary   Marian Quinn
Helps coeliacs with problems relating to their condition.
Issues food list, cookery book, diet sheets and restaurant
leaflets.

Coeliac UK

PO Box 220, High Wycombe, Buckinghamshire HP11 2HY;
URL www.coeliac.co.uk; E-mail admin@coeliac.co.uk;
Tel 01494 437278; Fax 01494 474349
Chief Executive   Andrew Ladds
To support the health, welfare and rights of coeliacs, and
those with dermatitis herpetiformis (DH); to support other
medically diagnosed patients whose health and quality of
life can be improved by following the dietary regime beneficial to coeliacs; to provide easily accessible written, verbal
and electronic advice, information and resources to these
individuals and groups; to educate the public and those in
appropriate sectors of health, government, commerce and
industry on the conditions and the issues; to promote and
commission research into the causes, alleviation, treatment,
care and cure of the coeliac and DH conditions.

Cystic Fibrosis Trust

11 London Rd, Bromley, Kent BR1 1BY;
URL www.cftrust.org.uk;
E-mail enquiries@cftrust.org.uk; Tel 020 8464 7211;
Fax 020 8313 0472
Chief Executive   Rosie Barnes
Research; help, support and advice to people with cystic
fibrosis and their families.

David Lewis Centre

Mill La, Warford, Alderley Edge, Cheshire SK9 7UD;
URL www.davidlewis.org.uk;
E-mail enquiries@davidlewis.org.uk; Tel 01565 640000;
Fax 01565 640100
Chief Executive J. Bisset
An independent charity for the residential assessment,
treatment and rehabilitation of people, including
schoolchildren, suffering from epilepsy, and for the
promotion of the welfare of all people with epilepsy.

The Devon and Cornwall Autistic Community Trust (Spectrum)

Sterling Crt, Truro Hill, Penryn, Cornwall TR10 8DB;
E-mail mail@spectrum.eu.com; Tel 01326 371000;
Fax 01326 371099
CEO M. Simpson
To provide a full range of quality services for people with a
diagnosis of Asperger syndrome or autism, including
residential care, day services, family support, respite care,
information, education and training, etc. A non-profit-
making company limited by guarantee, and a registered
charity.

Diabetes UK

10 Parkway, London NW1 7AA;
URL www.diabetes.org.uk; E-mail info@diabetes.org.uk;
Tel 020 7424 1000; (Careline) 020 7424 1030; Fax 020 7424
1001
Chief Executive Benet Middleton
Provides comprehensive educational services and
information on living with diabetes, and supports research
into diabetes.

Digestive Disorders Foundation (Formerly The British Digestive Foundation)

3 St. Andrews Pl, Regents Pk, London NW1 4LB;
URL www.digestivedisorders.org.uk;
E-mail ddf@digestivedisorders.org.uk; Tel 020 7486 0341
Supports research into disorders of the digestive system
and produces 24 leaflets for sufferers on common digestive
disorders.

Disfigurement Guidance Centre/Laserfair

PO Box 7, Cupar, Fife KY15 4PF;
URL www.skinlaserdirectory.org.uk or www.dgc.org.uk;
Tel 01337 870281; Fax (24 hour fax line) 01334 839105; (24
hour fax line) 01337 870310
The UK centre for the disfigured, their families, and those
who care for them. Free impartial and confidential
information, advice, support and practical help to patients,
their relatives, teachers and employers through postal,
personal, family and telephone services. Covers all aspects
of disfigurement and appearance: conditions, problems and
treatment developments. Insurance/compensation advice.
Individual and family network. Initiates and supports
research into neglected skin and family problems.
Educational projects for primary schools. Disfigurement
workshops and seminars for lay and professional groups.
Sae with all enquiries Laserfair Campaign – Appeal to
encourage laser treatment within the NHS. Many
publications include Skin Camouflage Cosmetic Handbook
and International Skinlaser Directory (free of charge to GPs
in the UK). Sae for publications list.

DEBRA

Debra Hse, 13 Wellington Bus Pk, Dukes Ride, Crowthorne,
Berkshire RG45 6LS; URL www.debra-international.org;
E-mail debra@debra.org.uk; Tel 01344 771961; Fax 01344
762661
Director J. Dart

Promotes research into the cause, treatment and cure of all
forms of epidermolysis bullosa (EB). Support services
nationwide to families affected by EB including specialist
nurse advisers and social care managers.

Eating Disorders Association

1st Fl, Wensum Hse, 103 Prince of Wales Rd, Norwich,
Norfolk NR1 1DW; Tel (Helpline (Mon–Fri 0900–1830))
01603 621414; (Youth Helpline (18 years and under,
Mon–Fri 1600–1800)) 01603 765050
Help and understanding around anorexia and bulimia.
Services include: telephone helplines; a national network of
self-help groups; information about eating disorders;
members' newsletters; lists of treatment available in each
county; training courses; professional journal; service
specifications.
Recorded message (approximately eight minutes) about
anorexia and bulimia nervosa: 0906 302 0012 50p per
minute all day.

Eating Disorders, The Maisner Centre for

PO Box 464, Hove, East Sussex BN3 2BN;
URL www.eating-disorder.tripod.com;
E-mail maisnercentre@btinternet.com; Tel 01273 729818
Principal Paulette Maisner
One-to-one counselling and postal courses for sufferers of
bulimia and compulsive eating problems.

Ectodermal Dysplasia Society

108 Charlton La, Cheltenham, Gloucestershire GL53 9EA;
URL www.ectodermaldysplasia.org;
E-mail diana@ectodermaldysplasia.org; Tel 01242 261332
Contact D. Perry
Provides information and moral support to parents and
sufferers of ectodermal dysplasia through correspondence
and a quarterly newsletter.

Epilepsy Scotland

48 Govan Rd, Glasgow G51 1JL;
URL www.epilepsyscotland.org.uk;
E-mail enquiries@epilepsyscotland.org.uk; Tel 0141 427
4911; (Helpline) 0808 800 2200; Fax 0141 419 1709
Manager (PR and Government Relations) Allana M Parker
EAS works to enable people with epilepsy to maximise
their choices in life. It lobbies for better services to meet
local needs and campaigns against the stigma of epilepsy
by raising public awareness. EAS provides relevant
literature and information on epilepsy. There is an interactive website and a helpline that offers advice to people
with epilepsy and their families. EAS provides training
courses in epilepsy management. It runs a community
support service for adults with community support needs.
There is a network of support groups and branches.

Haemophilia Society

Chesterfield Hse, 385 Euston Rd, London NW1 3AU;
URL www.haemophilia.org.uk;
E-mail info@haemophilia.org.uk; Tel 020 7380 0600;
(Helpline) 0800 018 6068; Fax 020 7387 8220
Chief Executive Karin Pappenheim
Provides advice, support and assistance to people with
haemophilia and related bleeding disorders and their
families. Makes grants to assist cases of need.

Headway – the brain injury association Ltd

4 King Edward Crt, King Edward St, Nottingham
NG1 1EW; URL www.headway.org.uk;
E-mail enquiries@headway.org.uk; Tel 0115 924 0800;
Fax 0115 958 4446
Chief Executive Peter McCabe
Aims to promote understanding of all aspects of brain

injury and to provide information, support and services to people with a brain injury, their families and carers through numerous support groups and centres across the UK and by the distribution of information.

The Horder Centre for Arthritis

St. John's Rd, Crowborough, East Sussex TN6 1XP;
URL www.hordercentre.co.uk;
E-mail arthritis@hordercentre.co.uk; Tel 01892 665577;
Fax 01892 662142
Customer Services Officer   Lesley Taylor
The Horder Centre admits patients principally for the further management of their arthritis, rehabilitation and joint replacement surgery.

Huntington's Disease Association

108 Battersea High St, London SW11 3HP;
E-mail info@hda.org.uk; Tel 020 7223 7000; Fax 020 7223 9489
Chair   Sue Watkin
National charity concerned and specialised in all aspects of this hereditary condition. Provides a network of regional care advisers.

ia: The Ileostomy and Internal Pouch Support Group

Peverill Hse, 1–5 Mill Rd, Ballyclare, County Antrim BT39 9DR; URL www.ileostomypouch.demon.uk;
E-mail info@the-ia.org.uk; Tel 0800 018 6724
National Secretary   Anne Demick
60 support groups throughout the country where volunteer members help other people to return to full and active lives following ileostomy surgery. Also quarterly journal for members.

ISSUE (The National Fertility Association)

114 Lichfield St, Walsall, West Midlands WS1 1SZ;
URL www.issue.co.uk; E-mail webmaster@issue.co.uk;
Tel 01922 722888; Fax 01922 640070

Let's Face It

72 Victoria Ave, Westgate on Sea, Kent CT8 8BH;
URL www.letsfaceit.force9.co.uk;
E-mail chrisletsfaceit@aol.com; Tel 01843 833724;
Fax 01843 835695
A contact point for people of any age coping with facial disfigurement. Provides a link for people with similar experiences. Telephone and letter contact; meetings for self-help or social contact.

Lupus UK

St. James Hse, Eastern Rd, Romford, Essex RM1 3NH;
URL www.lupusuk.com; Tel 01708 731251; Fax 01708 731252
Aims to provide means of communication between lupus sufferers through organising support groups, education programme for patients, medical profession and general public. Raises funds for research and welfare.

The ME Association

4 Top Angel, Buckingham Ind Pk, Buckingham, Buckinghamshire MK18 1TH;
URL www.meassociation.org.uk;
E-mail enquiries@meassociation.org.uk; Tel (Office hours Mon–Fri 1000–1230; 1330–1600) 08707 443011

Meningitis Trust

Fern Hse, Bath Rd, Stroud, Gloucestershire GL5 3TJ;
URL www.meningitis-trust.org.uk

Worldwide charity leading the fight against meningitis / meningococcal disease by: funding research into vaccines and treatment; offering a wide range of support for people affected by meningitis including 24 hour nurse-led helpline, financial grants, counselling; home visiting programme; produces an extensive range of information material to make people aware of the disease.

Mid-Sussex Body Positive

The Diva Cntre, 194 Three Bridges Rd, Crawley, West Sussex RH10 1LR; URL www.msbp.org.uk;
E-mail s.cleeve@btconnect.com; Tel 01293 552111;
Fax 01293 413617
For people infected and affected by HIV and AIDS.

Migraine Action Association (Previously British Migraine Association)

Unit 6, Oakley Hay Lodge Bus Pk, Great Folds Rd, Corby, Northamptonshire NN18 9AS;
URL www.migraine.org.uk;
E-mail info@migraine.org.uk; Tel 01536 461333;
Fax 01536 461444
Chair   M. Ayres
Information service for sufferers and support for migraine research. Membership £8.50 per year.

Motor Neurone Disease Association

PO Box 246, Northampton, Northamptonshire NN1 2PR;
E-mail helpline@mndassociation.org; Tel 01604 250505;
(National helpline) 08457 626262
Chief Executive   G. Levvy
The Motor Neurone Disease (MND) Association aims to ensure that people affected by MND can secure the care and support they need, and funds research into the disease. Services include a national telephone helpline, a range of literature on all aspects of living with MND, free loan of specialist equipment, a network of regional care advisers, support groups and limited financial support to people with the disease.

Multiple Sclerosis Resource Centre Ltd (MSRC)

7 Peartree Business Centre, Peartree Rd, Stanway, Colchester, Essex CO3 0JN; URL www.msrc.co.uk;
E-mail info@msrc.co.uk; Tel 01206 505444; Fax 01206 505449
Chief Executive   Lawrence Wood
Provides disease management, information, advice and other information services, wide range of books and booklets / leaflets and advice lines on 0800 783 0518.
Publishes New Pathways magazine.

Multiple Sclerosis Society

MS National Centre, 372 Edgeware Rd, London NW2 6ND ; URL www.mssociety.org.uk;
E-mail info@mssociety.org.uk; Tel 020 8438 0700;
(Helpline) 0808 800 8000
360 branches in the UK offering self-help groups for advice and support; provision of information; research; provision for welfare of people with MS, their families / friends; carers and professionals. Publications available.

Muscular Dystrophy Campaign

7–11 Prescott Pl, London SW4 6BS; URL www.muscular-dystrophy.org; E-mail info@muscular-dystrophy.org;
Tel 020 7720 8055; Fax 020 7498 0670
Executive Director   Christine Cryne
The Muscular Dystrophy Campaign is the national charity which invests in research to find treatments and cures for people who are affected by any of the conditions known as

muscular dystrophy or by a related neuromuscular disorder. These conditions are largely characterised by gradual wasting and weakening of muscle tissue. They affect both adults and children and lead to varying degrees of disability. The charity provides support in the form of expert medical care at Muscle Centres; information; advice; a team of family care officers; and financial assistance with essential equipment. The charity relies on voluntary donations to fund its work.

National Ankylosing Spondylitis Society (NASS)

PO Box 179, Mayfield, East Sussex TN20 6ZL;
URL www.nass.co.uk; E-mail nass@nass.co.uk; Tel 01435 873527; Fax 01435 873027
Director Fergus J. Rogers
Aims to educate sufferers through newsletters and other publications and annual symposium. Forms branch organisations for group physiotherapy and fund raising. Videofilm and audio cassette tape of home exercises.

National Association for Colitis and Crohn's Disease (NACC)

4 Beaumont Hse, Sutton Rd, St. Albans, Hertfordshire AL1 5HH; URL www.nacc.org.uk; E-mail nacc@nacc.org.uk; Tel 01727 830038; Fax 01727 862550
Chair B. Brown
Secretary to Director W. Childs
Provides general information about inflammatory bowel disease to members. Promotes research. Newsletter. 70 area groups in the UK.

National Association of Laryngectomee Clubs

Ground Fl, 6 Rickett St, Fulham, London SW6 1RU; Tel 020 7381 9993; Fax 020 7381 0025
General Secretary V. Reed
Encourages the formation of new clubs and collects, co-ordinates and disseminates information relevant to the rehabilitation of the laryngectomee.

National Association for the Relief of Paget's Disease (NARPD)

323 Manchester Rd, Walkden, Worsley, Manchester M28 3HH; URL www.paget.org.uk;
E-mail director@paget.org.uk; Tel 0161 799 4646; Fax 0161 799 6511
Director Marilyn McCallum
Provides information and support to suffers about the condition and its treatment. Has a UK-wide network of sufferers, some of whom have organised groups for self-help, raising awareness and fundraising. Funds research.

National Eczema Society

Hill Hse, Highgate Hill, London N19 5NA;
URL www.eczema.org; Tel (Helpline) 0870 241 3604
The National Eczema Society provides support and practical information to people with eczema and their carers. It produces a range of publications including a members' information pack and a quarterly journal, as well as practical guides for professionals. For further information please send an sae to the address above.

The National Society for Epilepsy (NSE)

Chesham La, Chalfont St. Peter, Buckinghamshire SL9 0RJ;
URL www.epilepsynse.org.uk; www.e-epilepsy.org.uk
The National Society for Epilepsy (NSE) is the largest medical epilepsy charity in the UK, specialising in residential care, rehabilitation and resettlement, assessment and research, in addition to offering a comprehensive range of information and training services.
Residential care for people with complex epilepsy is

currently provided in 15 individual care homes on a single site at Chalfont St. Peter, South Buckinghamshire. Increasing emphasis is placed on rehabilitation and resettlement programmes, including supported living and supported housing.
A state-of-the-art epilepsy assessment centre opened in January 2002. In addition to reviews of diagnosis and treatment, the centre provides facilities for assessment of individual's abilities for independent living. A unique feature is the direct link into the NSE's existing MRI unit which opened in 1996.
Training programmes are tailored to suit specific requirements of any audience and can be delivered on and off-site. Information services include a national helpline (01494 601400), an information website at www.epilepsynse.org.uk, a website for professional audiences at www.e-epilepsy.org.uk and a community-based Epilepsy Information Network.
The NSE works in close collaboration with the National Hospital for Neurology and Neurosurgery and the Institute of Neurology in London.

National Kidney Federation

6 Stanley St, Worksop, Nottinghamshire S81 7HX;
URL www.kidney.org.uk; E-mail nkf@kidney.org.uk; Tel (Helpline) 0845 601 0209
Chief Executive Timothy F. Statham, OBE
Aims to promote the welfare of sufferers of kidney disease or renal failure.

National Kidney Research Fund (NKRF)

Registered Office, Kings Chambers, Priestgate, Peterborough PE1 1FG; URL www.nkrf.org.uk; E-mail enquiries@nkrf.org.uk; Tel 01733 704650; Fax 01733 704699
Chair Prof Charles Pusey, MSc, FRCP
Raises money to support research into all aspects of kidney disease by awarding grants to carefully screened applicants in the UK as well as funding fellowships, studentships, purchasing equipment and funding patient care and welfare. Registered Charity Number 252892

The National Society for Phenylketonuria (UK) Ltd

PO Box 26642, London N14 4ZF; URL www.nspku.org;
E-mail info@nspku.org; Tel 0845 603 9136
Administrator Lucy Welch
Chair Sara Bartlett
Voluntary organisation to promote the medical, social and educational welfare of people with phenylketonuria and their families.

Asbestos Department, Occupational and Environmental Diseases Association (OEDA)

Mitre Hse, 66 Abbey Rd, Bush Hill Pk, Enfield, Greater London EN1 2QH; URL www.oeda.demon.co.uk; Tel 020 8360 8490
Member of Management Committee Nancy Tait, MBE, HonDUniv

Parkinson's Disease Society of the United Kingdom

215 Vauxhall Bridge Rd, London SW1V 1EJ;
URL www.parkinsons.org.uk;
E-mail enquiries@parkinsons.org.uk; Tel 020 7931 8080; (Helpline (Mon–Fri 0900–1600)) 0808 800 0303; Fax 020 7233 9908
Sponsors medical research and provides welfare activities, counselling literature, education and a large local branch network.
Registered Charity Number 258197

Primary Immunodeficiency Association (PIA)

Alliance Hse, 12 Caxton St, London SW1H 0QS;
URL www.pia.org.uk; E-mail info@pia.org.uk; Tel 020
7976 7640; Fax 020 7976 7641
Membership Officer Vicky Lugris
The PIA was established in 1989 and exists to promote the
interests of people with any of the (more than 80) primary
immunodeficiencies (genetic disorders of the immune
system) identified by WHO. Advice and support available
along with specific help on state benefits.

Psoriasis Association

7 Milton St, Northampton, Northamptonshire NN2 7JG;
E-mail mail@psoriasis.demon.co.uk; Tel 01604 711129;
Fax 01604 792894
Chief Executive Gladys Edwards
Provides help and information and promotes and funds
research into the basic causes of psoriasis.

Raynaud's and Scleroderma Association

112 Crewe Rd, Alsager, Cheshire ST7 2JA;
URL www.raynauds.org.uk;
E-mail webmaster@raynauds.demon.co.uk; Tel 01270
872776; Fax 01270 883556
Director Anne H. Mawdsley, MBE
Aims to make contact with sufferers to offer help, comfort
and support, and raise funds for research. Publishes a
quarterly newsletter giving information and aids available
to alleviate the condition.

The Restricted Growth Association

PO Box 4744, Dorchester, Dorset DT2 9FA;
URL www.rgaonline.org.uk; E-mail rga1@talk21.com;
Tel 01308 898445
President Dr Charles Pocock, MBE
Vice president Martin Nelson
Aims to provide information and support to improve the
quality of life for persons of restricted growth; encourages
and supports the complete integration of people of
restricted growth within the wider community; provides
information and support to help lessen the fear and distress
of families when a child with restricted growth is
diagnosed; promotes wider public awareness for increased
understanding of restricted growth; promotes research into
matters related to restricted growth.
Publications
Free publication list available on request.
Registered Charity Number 261647

Scoliosis Association (UK)

2 Ivebury Crt, 323–327 Latimer Rd, London W10 6RA;
URL www.sauk.org.uk; E-mail sauk@sauk.org.uk;
Tel 020 8964 5343; (Helpline) 020 8964 1166; Fax 020 8964
5343
Chair Dr Stephanie Clark
Contact between adults and parents of children undergoing
treatment. Information provided on all aspects of scoliosis;
twice yearly newsletter.

Sickle Cell Society

54 Station Rd, Harlesden, London NW10 4UA;
URL www.sicklecellsociety.org;
E-mail info@sicklecellsociety.org; Tel 020 8961 7795;
Fax 020 8961 8346
Chair Linserd Miller
Director Dr Asa'ah Nkohkwo
Provides information, advice, support and financial
assistance to individuals and families living with sickle cell
disorders.
Education, training and information for health
professionals, teachers and the general public on medical,
social and psychological aspects of sickle cell disorder.

Campaigns for more research and better services for
sufferers.
Registered Charity Number 1046631

The Society for Mucopolysaccharide Diseases (MPS)

46 Woodside Rd, Amersham, Buckinghamshire HP6 6AJ;
URL www.mpssociety.co.uk;
E-mail mps@mpssociety.co.uk; Tel 01494 434156;
Fax 01494 434252
Director Christine Lavery
To act as a support group for those affected by MPS and
related diseases, their families and carers; to bring about
more public awareness of MPS and related diseases; to
raise funds in order to further research.

Steroid Aid Group

PO Box 220, London E17 3JR
Self-help group to exchange information and advice
between people suffering from the side effects of steroid
treatment, their relations and friends. Seeks information
about and stimulates further research into steroids and the
illness treated with them. Not anabolic steriods. Send an A5
SAE for information.

The Stroke Association

240 City Rd, London EC1V 2PR; URL www.stroke.org.uk;
E-mail stroke@stroke.org.uk; Tel 020 7566 0300;
(Helpline) 0845 303 3100; Fax 020 7490 2686
Director of Service Dr Ben Jabuni
The UK's leading stroke charity solely concerned with
fighting stroke and helping stroke sufferers and their families.
Stroke is the third biggest killer and most serious disabler in
the UK. Activities include dysphasia support service for
speech-impared patients; stroke family support service for all
stroke families; countrywide network of information and
education service; leaflets; publications; welfare grants.

Thalidomide Society

19 Central Ave, Pinner, Greater London HA5 5BT;
E-mail info@thalsoc.demon.co.uk; Tel 020 8868 5309;
Fax 020 8868 5309
Co-ordinator V.J. Kerr
A national charity founded with the aim of supporting
people with thalidomide-related and similar disabilities to
overcome their special difficulties.
The organisation is user-led and provides assistance and
advice enabling its members to meet, exchange
information, share experiences and tackle the practical and
emotional problems which they encounter on a daily basis.
Thalidomide caused a unique range of disabilities and peer
support is critical to the majority of those affected.
The society also provides information, advice and support
to the families of children with similar disabilities and to
professional workers in the statutory and voluntary sectors.

Tuberous Sclerosis Association

Po Box 9644, Bromsgrove, Worcestershire B61 0FP;
URL www.tuberous-sclerosis.org;
E-mail support@tuberous-sclerosis.org; Tel 01527 871898
Head (Support Services) Janet Medcalf
Self-help group providing information about TS and
associated problems and supporting research. Wide range
of fact sheets for parents and professionals; encourages
parents to keep in touch with each other and to keep up-to-
date with knowledge about TS through newsletters and
meetings, including the AGM and an annual Family
Weekend Meeting. International Medical Symposium every
three years. Operates a Benevolent Fund. Employs TS
specialist advisers to counsel and advise families. Supports
clinics in Leeds, Bath, Cambridge, Edinburgh, Northern
Ireland and London.

UK Thalassaemia Society

19 The Broadway, Southgate Circus, London N14 6PH;
URL www.ukts.org; E-mail office@ukts.org; Tel 020 8882
0011
Co-ordinator Mr Costas Paul
Offers counselling to sufferers and patients. Educates
people on the problems of thalassaemia and raises funds
for research.

Urostomy Association

Central Office, 18 Foxglove Avenue, Uttoxeter,
Staffordshire ST14 8UN; URL www.uagbi.org;
E-mail ua@centraloffice.fsnet.co.uk; Tel 0870 770 7931;
Fax 0870 770 7932
National Secretary Mrs H. Pixley

Other Health Organisations

Action Research

Vincent Hse, Horsham, West Sussex RH12 2DP;
URL www.actionresearch.org.uk;
E-mail info@actionresearch.org.uk; Tel 01403 210406
Chief Executive Simon Moore
A charity dedicated to preventing and treating disease and
disability by funding vital medical research.

British Association for Dramatherapy

41 Broomhouse La, London SW6 3DP; Tel 020 7371 0160;
Fax 020 7371 0160
Administrator Gillian W. Eckley

British Organ Donor Society (BODY)

Balsham, Cambridge, Cambridgeshire CB1 6DL;
URL www.argonet.co.uk/body;
E-mail body@argonet.co.uk; Tel 01223 893636
Chair John Evans, PhD, BSc
Acts as a support group for donors, recipients and waiting
recipients' families, promotes organ donation and
transplantation, increases public awareness.

The MedicAlert Foundation

1 Bridge Wharf, 156 Caledonian Rd, London N1 9UU;
URL www.medicalert.org.uk;
E-mail info@medicalert.org.uk; Tel 0800 581420; 020 7833
3034; Fax 020 7278 0647
Provides 24-hour emergency identification for people
suffering from hidden medical conditions, e.g. epilepsy,
asthma, diabetes, allergies.

Patients' Association

PO Box 935, Harrow, Greater London HA1 8YJ;
URL www.patients-association.com;
E-mail mailbox@patients-association.com;
Tel (Administration) 020 8423 9111; (Helpline) 0845 608
4455; Fax 020 8423 9119
Chief Executive Mike Stone
The Patients' Association represents the views and
interests of patients to government, professional bodies
and the media. It advises individual patients on their
rights, access to health services, self-help groups and
complaints procedures via a patient helpline. The
associaton publishes the 'Health Address Book' of self-
help groups, a quarterly magazine – 'Patients' Voices',
and the following booklets: Access to Your Medical
Records, How to Make a Complaint and You and Your
Doctor.

PSS

18 Seel St, Liverpool, Merseyside L1 4BE;
URL www.pss.org.uk; E-mail information@pss.org.uk;
Tel 0151 702 5555; Fax 0151 702 5566
Chief Executive Robin Currie, BA, MA, CQSW, MBA
Providing innovative health and social services in the UK.

Sue Ryder Care

PO Box 5044, Ashby de la Zouch, Leicestershire LE65 1ZP;
URL www.suerydercare.org; Tel 01332 694811; Fax 01332
865050
The 17 care centres in Britain care for patients/residents
with many different disabilities and diseases. Each care
centre specialises to meet the needs of the local community.
This includes services for people with cancer and HIV
related illnesses, Parkinson's disease, motor neurone
disease, multiple sclerosis, Huntington's disease, people
with acquired brain injury, and care of the elderly.
Services include long-term care, respite care, specialist
palliative care, rehabilitation, day care and domiciliary
care.
A new purpose-built facility is nearing completion in
Aberdeen, and will provide services for people with
neurological diseases.

Housing and Homelessness

Advisory Service for Squatters

2 St. Pauls Rd, London N1 2QN;
URL www.squat.freeserve.co.uk;
E-mail advice@squat.freeserve.co.uk; Tel 0845 644 5814;
(1400–1800 Mon–Fri) 020 7359 8814; Fax 020 7359 5185
Advice and information service for squatters, homeless
people and anyone in housing difficulties. Publishes
squatters' handbook £1.57 including postage.

Central and Cecil

Cecil Hse, 266 Waterloo Rd, London SE1 8RQ;
URL www.ccht.org.uk; Tel 020 7922 5300; Fax 020 7922
5301
Chief Exective D. McLaughlin, MBA, MCIH
Central and Cecil has hostels for homeless women, move-
on accommodation, residential care homes for older
people, sheltered housing for older people, flats for people
with mental health problems and general needs family
accomodation. Central and Cecil works in ten London
boroughs.

Centrepoint

Neil Hse, 7 Whitechapel Rd, London E1 1DU;
URL www.centrepoint.org.uk; Tel 020 7426 5300
Chief Executive Anthony Lawton
Centrepoint runs emergency shelters, hostels, foyers and
flats in Greater London and each year helps around 1000
newly homeless young people with accommodation and
advice and assists them with finding training
opportunities, a job and a permanent place to live.

Connection at St. Martin's

12 Adelaide St, London WC2N 4HW;
URL www.connection-at-stmartins.org.uk; Tel 020 7766
5555
Chief Executive Colin Glover
Practical facilities, advice, hostel referrals and support
services for homeless people of all ages in central London.
Services are provided from two day centres (one for young
people 16–25, the other for older homeless people 26+), and
a night centre. Please call for details and opening times.

Drug and Alcohol Rehabilitation Treatment

58 Cromwell Rd, Hove, Brighton and Hove BN3 3ES;
Tel 01273 823762; Fax 01273 823749
Arch Hse, 8 York Ave, Hove, Brighton and Hove BN3 1PH;
Tel 01273 321284
Registered Care Manager Jim Horton

English Churches Housing Group

Sutherland Hse, 70–78 West Hendon Broadway, London
NW9 7BT; Tel 020 8203 9233; Fax 020 8203 0092
Chief Executive Peter Walters
English Churches Housing Group is one of the country's
largest housing associations, providing homes for over 26
000 people through a range of affordable general needs,
sheltered and supported housing services.

Field Lane Foundation

16 Vine Hill, London EC1R 5EA;
E-mail info@fieldlane.org.uk; Tel 020 7837 0412; Fax 020
7278 4312
Chief Executive J.T. Lamb, CQSW, DMS
In London and South East England Field Lane provides
residential and nursing homes for elderly people and
people with physical or learning disabilities; flats for
independent elderly people; a drop-in centre for homeless
families.

Great Chapel Street Medical Centre

13 Great Chapel St, London W1F 8Fl;
URL business.virgin.net/gcs.medical/index.htm;
E-mail gcs.medical@virgin.net; Tel 020 7437 9360;
Fax 020 7734 1475
Practice Manager R. Bolus

Great Chapel Street Sick Bay
117 Sutherland Ave, London W9 2QJ;
URL www.wythamhall.co.uk;
E-mail enquiries@wythamhall.co.uk; Tel 020 7289 1978;
Fax 020 7266 1518
Provides general medical, psychiatric, nursing, chiropody,
and social work services and in-patient care to homeless
people and to people not registered with a doctor in
London.

Habinteg Housing Association Ltd

1 Pemberton Row, Fetter La, London EC4A 3PQ;
URL www.habinteg.org.uk;
E-mail info@habinteg.org.uk; Tel 020 7822 8700; Fax 020
7822 8701
Provides universal housing design and services including
25% of its 2000 units to full wheelchair standard and the
rest for general needs to mobility or lifetime Homes
standard. 60 estates throughout England with on-site or
visiting community assistants providing support.

Homeless Link

1st Fl, 10–13 Rushworth St, London SE1 0RB ;
URL www.homeless.org.uk;
E-mail info@homelesslink.org.uk; Tel 020 7960 3010
Homeless Link is the membership organisation
supporting and representing more than 700 agencies
working with homeless people across England and Wales.
Together, the member agencies deliver a wide range of
services to meet the needs of homeless people. The main
objectives are to provide homelessness agencies with a
single strong voice to influence policy and public opinion
on issues affecting homeless people and to enable the
sharing of good practice, ensuring that appropriate
quality services are delivered to homeless people at local,
regional and national level.

Homeless UK

c/o Alliance Hse, 12 Caxton St, London SW1H 0QS; Tel 020
7799 2404; Fax 020 7976 7248
Chair B. Domeroy
Second tier organisation for organisations working with
homeless people.

The Housing Corporation

Maple Hse, 149 Tottenham Crt Rd, London W1T 7BN;
URL www.housingcorp.gov.uk;
E-mail enquiries@housingcorp.gsx.gov.uk; Tel 020 7393
2000; Fax 020 7393 2111
Chair The Rt Hon Baroness Dean of Thornton-le-Fylde
Responsible for regulating housing associations and
investing public funds in high-quality homes for rent and
sale.

Hyde Housing Association Ltd

Leegate Hse, Burnt Ash Rd, Lee Grn, London SE12 8RR;
Tel 020 8297 1500; Fax 020 8297 3800
Chair D.N.G. Small
Chief Executive C. Adams
The Hyde Group provides housing management services
in London and the South East for over 30 000 properties.
The accommodation is varied, ranging from individual
houses and flats, to bedspaces in shared units, student
accommodation, sheltered and care homes for older people.

KeyChange Charity

5 St. George's Mews, 43 Westminster Bridge Rd, London
SE1 7JB; E-mail keychange@keychange.org.uk; Tel 020
7633 0533; Fax 020 7928 1872
Chief Executive D. Shafik
National Christian charity offering residential care for frail
elderly people and supported accommodation to young
homeless people. Nine projects. Three new projects in
development.

Margaret Blackwood Housing Association

77 Craigmount Brae, Edinburgh EH12 8XF;
URL www.mbha.org.uk; E-mail info@mbha.org.uk;
Tel 0131 317 7227; Fax 0131 317 7294
Chief Executive Peter Mountford-Smith
Provides a wide range of supported accommodation,
sheltered housing and independent houses in most parts of
mainland Scotland for disabled people and their families.

Metropolitan Housing Trust

Metropolitan Hse, Crescent La, London SW4 9RS; Tel 020
7501 2300; Fax 020 7501 2307
Federation of voluntary organisation in Lambeth,
Lewisham, Southwark who work with or whose work
relates to single homeless people.

National Housing Federation

175 Gray's Inn Rd, London WC1X 8UP;
URL www.housing.org.uk; E-mail info@housing.org.uk;
Tel 020 7278 6571; Fax 020 7833 8323
Chief Executive Jim Coulter
Promotional, representative and advisory organisation for
affiliated independent social landlords, dealing with central
and local government at all levels.

ST. ANNE'S SHELTER AND HOUSING ACTION

6 St. Mark's Ave, Leeds, West Yorkshire LS2 9BN;
URL www.st-annes.org.uk; Tel 0113 243 5151; Fax 0113
245 1526
Chief Executive W. Kilgallon
Director (Care Services) D.E. Jordan

Director (Finance) J.A. Micklethwaite
Director (Housing) D.A. Lerigo
A registered social Landlord and social care organisation providing a wide range of housing and support services for people with special needs. Services provided for single homeless people; people with learning disabilities; mental health problems; alcohol-related problems. Services provided across Yorkshire and in the North East.

St. Mungo Community Housing Association

Atlantic Hse, 1–3 Rockley Rd, London W14 0DJ; Tel 020 8740 9968; Fax 020 8600 3079
Chief Executive C. Fraser
Provides a unique range of services to single homeless adults covering supported housing, as well as non-resident specialists (alcohol and mental) and programmes outreach; resettlement; employment.

Shelter (The National Campaign for Homeless People)

88 Old St, London EC1V 9HU; URL www.shelter.org.uk; E-mail info@shelter.org.uk; Tel 020 7505 4699; (24 hour helpline) 0808 800 4444; Fax 020 7505 2169
Director Adam Simpson
Campaigns on behalf of homeless and badly housed people and gives assistance through housing aid centres and supported projects and free phone national 24-hour telephone helpline, Shelterline 0800 800 4444.
Includes SHAC (The London Housing Aid Centre).
Registered Charity Number 263710

The Simon Community

PO Box 1187, London NW5 4HW; E-mail thesimoncommunity@yahoo.com; Tel 020 7485 6639; Fax 020 7482 6305
Operates daily outreach work and residential projects run primarily by voluntary workers. Offers full room and board.

Stonham Housing Association Ltd

Octavia Hse, 235–241 Union St, London SE1 0LR; URL www.stonham.org.uk; Tel 020 7401 2020; Fax 020 7633 9901
Chief Executive Clare Tickell
National special needs housing association offering care and support to single homeless people, women and children escaping domestic violence, people with mental health problems, young people leaving care and ex-offenders.

William Sutton Trust

Sutton Crt, Tring, Hertfordshire HP23 5BB; Tel 01442 891100; Fax 01442 828433
Chief Executive Mike Morris
The trust has provided over 15 000 rented homes in over 40 local authorities throughout England. It builds and manages affordable quality homes for those people in housing need and works with its partners to build thriving communities.

Human Rights and Civil Liberties

A.T.D. Fourth World

48 Addington Sq, London SE5 7LB; URL www.atd-uk.org; E-mail atd@atd-uk.org; Tel 020 7703 3231; Fax 020 7703 3231
Contact Matt Davies
Brings people from all walks of life together in partnership with the most disadvantaged families to support the efforts of the poorest in overcoming poverty and taking an active role in the community; to develop a constructive public awareness of poverty; to encourage a fuller representation of the poorest families in all spheres of society.

British Institute of Human Rights

King's College London, 75-79 York Rd, London SE1 7AW; URL www.bihr.org; E-mail admin@bihr.org; Tel 020 7401 2712; Fax 020 7401 2675
Chair Hon S.M. Baring, OBE, JP
Co-Director Sarah Cooke
Co-Director Candy Whittome
Research and education in the human rights field. Promotes education and holds conferences, seminars, lectures, public meetings etc.

Church Action on Poverty (CAP)

Central Bldgs, Oldham St, Manchester M1 1JT; URL www.church-poverty.org.uk; E-mail info@church-poverty.org.uk; Tel 0161 236 9321; Fax 0161 237 5359
Chair A. Forbes
A growing membership organisation, aiming to mobilise the churches and to press for action to combat increasing poverty in the UK.

Citizen's Income Trust (CIT)

P.O Box 26586, London SE3 7WY; URL www.citizensincome.org; E-mail info@citizensincome.org; Tel 020 8305 1222; Fax 020 8305 1802
Director Dr Malcolm Tory
CIT researches the feasibility of citizens' income schemes.

Fawcett Society

5th Fl, 45 Beech St, London EC2Y 8AD; URL www.gn.apc.org/fawcett; E-mail fawcett@gn.apc.org; Tel 020 7628 4441; Fax 020 7628 2865
President Dorothy Wedderburn, MA, DLit
Director Mary-Ann Stephenson
Campaigns for gender equality. Details including membership available.

Free Representation Unit (FRU)

4th Fl, Peer Hse, 8–14 Verulam St, London WC1X 8LZ; URL www.fru.org.uk; E-mail christial.michell@lineone.net; Tel 020 7831 0692
Free representation for hearings before tribunals where legal aid is not available, including industrial, social security and immigration tribunals and criminal injuries compensation board. Referrals from agencies only.
Registered Charity Number 295952

The Hilden Charitable Fund

34 North End Rd, London W14 0SH; E-mail hildencharity@hotmail.com; Tel 020 7603 1525
Secretary R. Hedley
The trustees' main interests are: homelessness (particularly amongst the young); minorities and race relations; penal affairs; developing world countries. Grants are not made to individuals.
Registered Charity Number 232591

Index on Censorship/Writers and Scholars Educational Trust

33 Islington High St, London N1 9LH; URL www.indexoncensorship.org; E-mail contact@indexoncensorship.org; Tel 020 7278 2313; Fax 020 7278 1878

Editor and Chief Executive   Ursula Owen
Records censorship, especially of writers, journalists, publishers and scholars. Politically impartial.

Interights, The International Centre for the Legal Protection of Human Rights

Lancaster Hse, 33 Islington High St, London N1 9LH; URL www.interights.org; E-mail ir@interights.org; Tel 020 7278 3230; Fax 020 7278 4334
Executive Director   Leanne MacMillan
Advises individuals, lawyers and organisations on international and comparative human rights law; provides legal representation before international human rights tribunals; publishes a quarterly Bulletin and a Commonwealth Human Rights Law Digest; limits its work in Western Europe to casework of strategic importance concentrating on Africa, Central and Eastern Europe, South Asia and the Caribbean.

Liberty (National Council for Civil Liberties)

21 Tabard St, London SE1 4LA;
URL www.liberty-human-rights.org.uk;
E-mail info@liberty-human-rights.org.uk; Tel 020 7403 3888; Fax 020 7407 5354
Director   John Wadham
Chair   John Lyons
Legal services, campaigning and membership organisation for the protection and extension of human rights and civil liberties in the UK.

Josephine Butler Society

c/o 60 Rotherwick Rd, London NW11 7DB; Tel 020 8455 1664
Hon Secretary   J. Watts
A pressure group which promotes education relating to prostitution and contemporary forms of sexual slavery. Within basic principles of social justice, equality of all citizens before the law, and a single moral standard for men and women, the society aims to prevent any form of exploitation of prostitution by third parties; but it is not a 'rescue' organisation.

The Refugee Council

Bondway Hse, 3 Bondway, London SW8 1SJ;
URL www.refugeecouncil.org.uk; Tel 020 7820 3000; Fax 020 7582 9929
Chief Executive   N. Hardwick
Gives practical help to asylum seekers and refugees in the UK, and campaigns for their rights in the UK and abroad.

Scottish Human Rights Centre (SHRC)

146 Holland St, Glasgow G2 4NG;
URL www.scottishhumanrightscentre.org.uk;
E-mail info@scottishhumanrightscentre.org.uk; Tel 0141 332 5960; Fax 0141 332 5309
SHRC aims to promote human rights in Scotland through public education and advice, scrutiny of legislation, research and monitoring the application of international human rights treaties in Scotland. Advice and information are available by telephone, post, fax and email. The advice line is open Mon–Fri 1400–1700.

The Voluntary Euthanasia Society

13 Prince of Wales Terr, Kensington, London W8 5PG; URL www.ves.org.uk; E-mail info@ves.org.uk; Tel 020 7937 7770; Fax 020 7376 2648
Director   Deborah Annetts
VES is a national membership organisation which campaigns to make it legal for a competent adult who is suffering unbearably from an incurable illness to be able to choose to die with medical assistance at a time of their choosing. They also distribute living wills. Cost £15.

War on Want (Campaign against World Poverty)

Fenner Brockway Hse, 37–39 Great Guildford St, London SE1 0ES; URL www.waronwant.org; E-mail mailroom@waronwant.org; Tel 020 7620 1111; Fax 020 7261 9291
Executive Director   A. Royal
Links practical support for developing world projects with radical campaign in the UK to increase understanding of causes of poverty.

International and Overseas

Oxfam Development Education

274 Banbury Rd, Oxford, Oxfordshire OX2 7DZ;
URL www.oxfam.org.uk/coolplanet;
E-mail education@oxfam.org.uk; Tel 01865 311311
Relief and development agency working in any part of the world regardless of race, sex, religion or politics. Uses voluntary help in Oxfam shops and offices throughout Great Britain. Development Education Programme works in the UK, lobbying to ensure young people are taught about global issues. Also provides resources for teachers.

Population Concern

Studio 325, Highgate Studios, 53–79 Highgate Rd, London NW5 1TL; URL www.populationconcern.org.uk; E-mail info@populationconcern.org.uk; Tel 0870 770 2476; Fax 020 7267 6788
Chief Executive   Ros Davies
Population Concern works for the improvement of the quality of life world-wide by advancing the right of all people to exercise free and informed reproductive health choice and to have access to confidential sexual and reproductive health services, including family planning. They promote the right of women and young people to an education which enhances their economic and social standing. In the UK they aim to improve the understanding of how reproductive choice, rights and responsibilities contribute to population stabilisation and the advancement of human development by alleviating poverty, distress, loss of healthy life and environmental degradation. Registered Charity Number 1001698

Maternity and Motherhood

see Chapter 13

Mental Health

Alzheimer Scotland – Action on Dementia

22 Drumsheugh Gdns, Edinburgh EH3 7RN;
URL www.alzscot.org; E-mail alzheimer@alzscot.org; Tel 0131 243 1453; (24 hour Dementia Helpline) 0808 808 3000; Fax 0131 243 1450
Chief Executive   Jim Jackson
Convener   Alan Jacques
Training Officer   Jennifer Marlborough
Manager (Information)   Kate Fearnley
Provides information and services for people with dementia and the people who look after them and compaigns to improve public policy.

Alzheimer's Society

Gordon Hse, 10 Greencoat Pl, London SW1P 1PH;
URL www.alzheimers.org.uk;
E-mail info@alzheimers.org.uk; Tel 020 7306 0606;
(Helpline (0830–1830 Mon–Fri)) 0845 300 0336; Fax 020
7306 0808
Chair Dr Nick Carey
The Alzheimer's Society is a leading care and research
charity for people with Alzheimer's disease and other
forms of dementia, their families and carers. It is a
national membership organisation and works through
nearly 300 branches and support groups. The society has
expertise in information and education for carers and
professionals. It provides helplines and support for carers,
runs quality day and home care, funds medical and
scientific research and gives financial help to families in
need. It campaigns for improved health and social
services and greater public understanding of all aspects
of dementia.

Community Housing and Therapy

Bishop Creighton Hse, 378 Lillie Rd, London SW6 7PH;
URL www.cht.org.uk; E-mail co@cht.org.uk; Tel 020
7381 5888; Fax 020 7610 0608
Chief Executive John Gale
CHT runs therapeutic communities for the mentally ill.
Many of the people referred suffer from schizophrenia,
depression, anxiety, an obsessive compulsive disorder or an
eating disorder. Others come with substance misuse or
homelessness. They provide individual and group
psychotherapy and practical skills learning, including
education and re-training for work. Psychiatrists, social
workers, other professionals or family members may make
a referral. CHT also runs workshops and training courses
including a diploma in group therapy, accredited by
Middlesex University.

Crossways Community

8 Culverden Park Rd, Tunbridge Wells, Kent TN4 9QX;
E-mail admin@crosswayscommunity.freeserve co.uk;
Tel 01892 529321
Manager Martin Granger
A Christian residential home for 16 adults and a hostel for
18 adults providing a varied and flexible programme to
meet the needs of individual residents with mental health
difficulties.

Dementia Care Trust

Kingsley Hse, Greenbank Rd, Bristol BS5 6HE;
URL www.dct.org.uk; E-mail info@dct.org.uk; Tel 0117
952 5325; Fax 0117 951 8213
Resource Manager Debby Coombs
Dementia Care Trust provides support for the carers of
people with dementia, and associated conditions, by means
of caring at home, day care and counselling in Bristol,
North Somerset, South Gloucester, South Bristol and
Gloucestershire.

Depression Alliance

35 Westminster Bridge Rd, London SE1 7JB;
URL www.depressionalliance.org;
E-mail information@depressionalliance.org; Tel 020
7633 0557; Fax 020 7633 0559; Answerphone 020 7633
9929
Depression Alliance is the leading UK charity for people
with depression. Works to relieve and to prevent this
treatable condition by providing information, support and
understanding to those who are affected by it. Campaigns
to raise awareness amongst the general public about the
realities of depression.

Depressives Anonymous, Fellowship of

Box FDA, Self Help Nottingham, Ormiston Hse, 32–36
Pelham St, Nottingham NG1 2EG;
URL www.depressivesanon.co.uk;
E-mail fdainfo@aol.com; Tel (Information Line) 0870 774
4320 (Available 365 days a year with answerphone);
Fax 0870 774 4319
Information Line Pat Eyers
Hon Secretary Jocelyn Luxon
Self-help organisation for people with depression and those
who care for them. Members receive six newsletters a year,
can join penfriend or phonefriend schemes, and can be put
in touch with independent local self-help groups.
Information Line is available to anyone, answered
personally for at least four hours a day, with messages taken
at other times including weekends and bank holidays.
Annual Income
£12 000

Manic Depression Fellowship

Castle Works, 21 St. George's Rd, London SE1 6ES;
E-mail mdf@mdf.org.uk; Tel 020 7793 2600; Fax 020 7793
2639
Chief Executive Michelle Rowett
The Manic Depression Fellowship is a national user led
organisation which works to enable people affected by
manic depression to take control of their lives. Services
include: network of self help groups for people with manic
depression, their relatives and friends, a quarterly journal
Pendulum, publications, research papers, Self Management
training programme, employment advice, travel insurance
scheme, 24 hr Legal Advice Line, life assurance scheme,
STEADY, the young person's self management programme.
The Fellowship aims to educate the public and
professionals about manic depression and campaigns for
greater research into methods of treatment.

MACA (Mental After Care Association)

1st Fl, Lincoln Hse, 296–302 High Holborn, London
WC1V 7JH; URL www.maca.org.uk;
E-mail maca@maca.org.uk; Tel 020 7061 3400
Chief Executive Gil Hitchon
Provides a wide range of services in the community,
hospitals and prisons for people with mental health needs
and their carers including: advocacy; assertive outreach;
community support; employment training; helplines/
information; respite for carers, social clubs; schemes for
people in contact with the criminal justice system,
supported accommodation including 24 hour care.
Registered to offer NVQs in Promoting Independence.

The Matthew Trust

PO Box 604, London SW6 3AG; URL www.matthewtrust.org;
E-mail matthewtrust@ukonline.co.uk; Tel 020 7736 5976;
Fax 020 7731 6961
Director Annabel Thompson
National mental health trust (registered charity) for the
mentally disordered. Associated with special hospitals,
RSUs and the mentally ill in prisons, in the community as
well as for victims of aggression; grant making trust for
those who have exhausted all other avenues of funding, i.e.
'last stop' agency. Celebrating its 27th anniversary.

MIND

see Chapter 14

National Phobics Society

Zion Community Resource Centre, 339 Stretford Rd,
Hulme, Manchester M15 4ZY;
URL www.phobics-society.org.uk;
E-mail nationalphobic@btconnect.com; Tel 0870 7700
456; Fax 0161 227 9862

Director Glenmoure Kingsley-Nunes
Aims for the relief and rehabilitation of persons
suffering from all anxiety disorders. Sae with any
enquiries.

Rethink severe mental illness

30 Tabernacle St, London EC2A 4DD;
URL www.rethink.org; E-mail info@rethink.org; Tel 020
7330 9100; Fax 020 7330 9102
Registered Office, 28 Castle St, Kingston upon Thames,
Surrey KT1 1SS; Tel 0845 456 0455; Fax 020 8547
3862
Rethink – Northern Ireland, 'Wyndhurst', Knockbracken
Healthcare Pk, Saintfield Rd, Belfast BT8 8BH;
E-mail info.nireland@rethink.org; Tel 028 9040 2323;
Fax 028 9040 1616
Director L. Cuddy
Rethink severe mental illness provides a wide range of
community services for people with severe mental illness,
including residential care, employment and training,
supported housing, respite care, domiciliary support, day
services with emphasis upon out-of-hours opening and
advocacy. In addition, Rethink severe mental illness
provides a number of carer support and education services.

Northern Ireland Association for Mental Health

Beacon Hse, 80 University St, Belfast BT7 1HE; Tel 028 9032
8474
Chief Executive Alan C. Ferguson, OBE
Day care and residential care throughout Northern Ireland
for people with mental health problems; user initiatives,
mental health promotion, training and counselling services
also provided.

Philadelphia Association Therapeutic Communities

Registered Charity Number 242475
4 Marty's Yard, 17 Hampstead High St, London NW3 1QW;
URL www.philadelphia-association.co.uk;
E-mail paoffice@globalnet.co.uk; Tel 020 7794 2652;
Fax 020 7794 2652
The Philadelphia Association's low-cost community
households in London are places in which individuals
suffering mental disturbance or unhappiness of all
descriptions are able to explore the origins and
consequences of their situation.

Psychiatric Rehabilitation Association

Bayford Mews, Bayford St, London E8 3SF;
URL www.cityhack.dircon.co.uk;
E-mail ppra528898@aol.com; Tel 020 8985 3570; Fax 020
8986 1334
Director John Wilder, OBE
Deputy Director M. Manni, BSc, DCH-DipC
Provides rehabilitation programmes using day centres,
industrial units, PRA studios, art courses, evening centres,
residential care, research and a variety of teaching aids are
available for other organisations. Also provides training for
overseas groups. Video of PRA programmes on
application. Counselling service also available.

SANE

London Office, 1st Fl, Cityside Hse, 40 Alder St, London
E1 1EE; URL www.sane.org.uk;
E-mail london@sane.org.uk; Tel 020 7375 1002;
(SANELINE) 0845 767 8000; Fax 020 7375 2162
Bristol Office
Units 1 and 2, The Greenway Centre, Doncaster Rd,
Southmead, Bristol BS10 5PY; Tel 0117 950 2140; Fax 0117
950 2150

Macclesfield Office
1 Queen Victoria St, Macclesfield, SK11 6LD; Tel 01625
429050; Fax 01625 424975

Schizophrenia Association of Great Britain

International Schizophrenia Centre, Bryn Hyfryd, The Cres,
Bangor, Gwynedd LL57 2AG; URL www.sagb.co.uk;
E-mail info@sagb.co.uk; Tel 01248 354048; Fax 01248
353659
Honorary Secretary G. Hemmings
Provides an information service for patients and their
families through its newsletter. Individual queries are
answered by telephone or letter. Carries out research into
the biological causes of schizophrenia in its own Institute of
Biological Psychiatry. Volunteers are always needed to take
part in the research. Please telephone or write to Mrs
Hemmings as above for information. Free information pack
including nutritional advice, available on request.

Scottish Association for Mental Health

Cumbrae Hse, 15 Carlton Crt, Glasgow G5 9JP;
URL www.samh.org.uk;
E-mail enquire@samh.org.uk; Tel 0141 568 7000;
Fax 0141 568 7001
Chief Executive S. Barcus
Information on mental health and illness. Campaigns,
supported accommodation, employment projects, policy
development, including benefits and legal advice

Scottish Huntington's Association

Thistle Hse, 61 Main Rd, Johnstone, Renfrewshire PA5 9BA;
E-mail sha-admin@hdscotland.org; Tel 01505 322245;
Fax 01505 382980
Contact Ann Carruthers
Charity in Scotland providing care, support and
information to sufferers of Huntington's disease and their
families.

SHARE Community Ltd

64 Altenburg Gdns, London SW11 1JL;
URL www.sharecommunity.org.uk;
E-mail sharecommunity@talk21.com; Tel 020 7924 2949;
Fax 020 7350 1625
General Manager Peter Jablanski
A training and rehabilitation centre based on the principles
of self-help, whose aims are to help mentally and
physically disabled people, to promote their integration
into the working world.

Tulip Mental Health Group

38–46 Station Rd, London N22 7TX;
URL www.tulip.org.uk; E-mail mkabir@tulip.org.uk;
Tel 020 8889 6921; Fax 020 8365 7343
Executive Director Mr Masudul Kabir

United Response

see Chapter 14

Westminster Association for Mental Health (affiliated to MIND)

526 Harrow Rd, London W9 3QF;
URL www.westminstermind.org.uk;
E-mail admin@westminstermind.org.uk; Tel 020 8969
2434; Fax 020 8960 6788
Director Margaret Kesterton
Voluntary organisation. Manages supported housing, a
home support service, two work projects, a drop-in centre
and a counselling service.
Registered Charity Number 292708

Prisons, Offenders and Victims

Apex Trust

St. Alphage Hse, Wingate Annexe, 2 Fore St, London
EC2Y 5DA; URL www.apextrust.com;
E-mail jobcheck@apextrust.com; Tel (Helpline) 0870 608
4567; Fax 020 7638 5977
Apex Trust aims to improve the employment prospects of
(ex)offenders by providing services, training and advice
directly to those persons and to the voluntary and statutory
agencies working with them. In addition, the trust works
with employers to promote the appropriate employment of
(ex)offenders and break down the barriers to their
employment.

The Howard League for Penal Reform (incorporating the Howard Centre for Penology)

1 Ardleigh Rd, London N1 4HS;
URL www.howardleague.org.uk;
E-mail howardleague@ukonline.co.uk; Tel 020 7249
7373; Fax 020 7249 7788
Director Frances Crook
An independent membership organisation concerned with
education, research and campaigning on all aspects of
criminal justice.

The Langley House Trust

PO Box 181, Witney, Oxfordshire OX28 6WD;
URL www.langleyhousetrust.org;
E-mail info@langleyhousetrust.org
Promotions Officer Cathy Hill
Ex-prisoner rehabilitation and resettlement, registered
social landlord. Services based on Christian beliefs and
values whilst being open to men and women of any or no
faith.

Nacro

169 Clapham Rd, London SW9 0PU;
URL www.nacro.org.uk;
E-mail communications@nacro.org.uk; Tel 020 7582
6500; Fax 020 7735 4666
Nacro, the crime reduction charity, runs resettlement,
housing, learning and skills, youth and community
projects. We work with key agencies to develop effective
and inclusive strategies to reduce crime and resettle
offenders.

Nacro Cymru

35 Heathfield, Swansea SA1 6EJ;
E-mail info@nacrocym.demon.co.uk; Tel 01792 450870;
Fax 01792 450871
Communications Officer Richard Jones
Supports the care and resettlement of offenders and the
prevention of crime through services for offenders and
those most at risk of offending, and training and
consultancy work on youth justice, community safety and
the Crime and Disorder Act.

Northern Ireland Association for the Care and Resettlement of Offenders (NIACRO)

169 Ormeau Rd, Belfast BT7 1SQ;
E-mail niacro@niacro.org; Tel 028 9032 0157; Fax 028
9023 4084
Manager (Information Services) Tony Martin
Employment, training, youth and advisory services for
disadvantaged individuals, families and groups affected by
the criminal justice system.

Prison Reform Trust

2nd Fl, 15 Northburgh St, London EC1V 0JR;
URL www.prisonreformtrust.org.uk;
E-mail prt@prisonreformtrust.org.uk; Tel 020 7251 5070;
Fax 020 7251 5076
Director Juliet Lyon
Aims to encourage community interest in penal
establishments and build public support for penal reform.
Conducts research, information and prisoners' rights work.
Publishes quarterly magazine Prison Report. Full
publications list available.

Prisoners Abroad

89–93 Fonthill Rd, London N4 3JH;
URL www.prisonersabroad.org.uk;
E-mail info@prisonersabroad.org.uk; Tel 020 7561 6820;
Fax 020 7561 6821
Director Pauline A. Crowe
Support for British nationals in prison outside the UK, and
their families. Information, financial and practical
assistance. Resettlement service for released prisoners
returning to the UK. All services free of charge. Registered
Charity no. 1093710.

Prison Advice and Care Trust (PACT)

Family Support Services, 254 Caledonian Rd, Islington,
London N1 0NG; E-mail familysupport@pact.uk.net;
Tel (Admin) 020 7278 3981; (Freephone helpline) 0800
085 3021; Fax 020 7278 8765
Manager Pauline Hoare
Supports and assists prisoners' families and friends in any
way possible. Short-term living or overnight
accommodation, drop-in centre.

SOVA

Chichester Hse, 37 Brixton Rd, London SW9 6DZ;
URL www.sova.org.uk; E-mail mail@sova.org.uk;
Tel 020 7793 0404; Fax 020 7735 4410
Chief Executive G. Henson
Works nationally alongside the prison, probation and social
services to recruit members of the community as
volunteers. Trains and deploys volunteers to projects
supporting and befriending offenders, ex-offenders and
members of their families and to specialist schemes
working with juvenile offenders.

Victim Support (National Association of Victim Support Schemes)

National Office, Cranmer Hse, 39 Brixton Rd, London
SW9 6DZ; URL www.victimsupport.org;
E-mail contact@victimsupport.org.uk;
Tel (Administration) 020 7735 9166; (Helpline) 0845 303
0900; Fax 020 7582 5712
Chief Executive Dame Helen Reeves, DBE
Trained volunteers in branches and the Witness Service
throughout England, Wales and Northern Ireland provide
practical and emotional support to victims, witnesses, their
friends and families.

Training

The Caspari Foundation for Educational Therapy and Therapeutic Teaching

Successor to the Forum for the Advancement of
Educational Therapy and Therapeutic Teaching (FAETT).
Therapeutic work with individuals and groups of children.
Caspari Hse, Noel Rd, London N1 8HQ;
URL www.caspari.org.uk;
E-mail administrator@casparihouse.fsnet.co.uk; Tel 020
7704 1977

Training in educational therapy and in therapeutic teaching combines teaching with therapeutic exploration of the emotional factors which often underlie specific learning difficulties. There are various ongoing part-time courses run by the foundation including a four year part-time MA course validated by Middlesex University. Educational therapy sessions are offered to individual and groups of children.

Directory of Social Change

24 Stephenson Way, London NW1 2DP;
URL www.dsc.org.uk; E-mail info@dsc.org.uk; Tel 020 7391 4800
Director   D. Allcock Tyler
Publishers of Schools Funding Guide and many other directories of grant-making trusts. Also publishes The Educational Grants Directory and the report School Fundraising in England. Runs training courses.

Fairbridge

207 Waterloo Rd, London SE1 8XD;
URL www.fairbridge.org.uk;
E-mail info@fairbridge.org.uk; Tel 020 7928 1704; Fax 020 7928 6016
Director   Nigel Haynes
Fairbridge is a leading youth charity supporting 13–25 year olds in 13 of the most disadvantaged areas in the country. The young people they work with are outside education, training and employment. The aim of the programme is to develop motivation, confidence and personal, social and life skills using a wide range of challenging activities: from abseiling to business projects. For many, involvement with Fairbridge is the first step to reconnection with mainstream opportunities.

Federation of Community Work Training Groups

4th Fl, Furnival Hse, 48 Furnival Gate, Sheffield, South Yorkshire S1 4QP; URL www.fcdl.org.uk;
E-mail info@fcdl.org.uk; Tel 0114 273 9391; Fax 0114 276 2377
Co-ordinator (Support Services)   Emma Bennett
Promotion and development of opportunities for community work, training and learning, based upon participatory processes and anti-discriminatory practice. Operates both at a local and regional level and at a national level to promote community work; learning and developing arrangements for community work training and qualification.

Finchale Training College

Durham, County Durham DH1 5RX
Principal   Dr D. Etheridge
Provides residential training to equip disabled people and people with special needs for open employment. Registered charity and accredited training manager under the government's work-based training for adults.

Lifeskills

PO Box 311, Guernsey GY1 3TD; URL www.lifeskills.gg;
E-mail info@lifeskills.gg; Tel 08700 779246; Fax 08700 787377
Director   Kerstin Sharpe
Suppliers of therapeutic training cassettes and books in anxiety management and social skills.

Unemployment

Elephant Jobs Ltd

Aylesbury Learning Centre, Wendover, Thurlow St, London SE17 2UU; URL www.elephantjobs.org.uk;
E-mail info@elephantjobs.org.uk; Tel 020 7014141; Fax 020 7703 7927
Managing Director   Andy Burton
Charitable organisation working in the field of unemployment.

Low Pay Unit

9 Arkwright Rd, London NW3 6AB;
URL www.lowpayunit.org.uk;
E-mail bharti.patel@lowpayunit.org.uk; Tel 020 7435 4268; (Helpline) 020 7431 7385; Fax 020 7431 9614
Independent organisation drawing attention to the extent of low pay, its nature, causes and remedies. Providing advice to low paid workers on rights at work and social security.

Young People

see Chapter 13

Index

A

AA *see* Automobile Association Ltd
AAA *see* Action Against Allergy
ABAPSTAS *see* Association of Blind and Partially Sighted Teachers and Students
ABAYOMI—
    Counselling and Resource Centre 801
    and Hammersmith Crisis Centre 693
Abbeyfield Society, The 846
Aberdeen—
    Children's Reporters 89
    City—
        Children's Panels 87
        Citizens Advice 752
        Council 457
    College 912
    Consumer Advice 775
    and District, Samaritans 784
    and North East Deaf Society 957
    Prisons 33
    Workshops for the Blind and Disabled 966
Aberdeenshire—
    Children's Panels 87
    Children's Reporters 89
    Citizens Advice 752
    Council 455
    Prisons 33
Aberlour Child Care Trust 651
Aberystwyth—
    Citizens Advice Office 736
    Samaritans 784
Abstracts on Hygiene and Communicable Diseases 941
Abuse Centre, Sexual 794
Abuse and Neglect, British Association for Prevention of Child 647
ACA *see* Association for Continence Advice
ACAD *see* Advice and Counselling on Alcohol and Drugs
ACAPS *see* Alcohol Counselling and Prevention Services
Acas 103
Accept Services (Alcohol Community Centre) 786
Access by Design 933
Accidents, Royal Society for the Prevention of 922
ACRE (Action with Communities in Rural England) 807, 961
ACT *see* Aid for Children with Tracheostomies
Acting, Up 963
Action—
    Against Allergy (AAA) 972
    for Blind People 853, 954
    Cancer 970
    with Communities in Rural England (ACRE) 807, 961
    Medical Research 917
    on—
        Dementia 981
        Disability, Greater London 966

        Poverty, Church 980
        Smoking and Health (ASH) 786
            Scotland 787
    Research 978
    for Sick Children 687
Acupuncture Council, British 880
Addaction 786, 790
Addenbrooke's NHS Trust 528
Addiction—
    Moray Council on 790
    Society for Study of 792
Addiction Research Unit 917
ADFAM 786
Adlerian Society 891
Administrators, Institute of 882
Adolescence, Journal of 930
Adolescent Mental Health 929
Adoption—
    Agencies 639
    and Fostering 801, 929
        British Association 696, 801
    Societies 649
    UK 696, 801
ADSS *see* Association of Directors of Social Services
Adult—
    Basic Skills Strategy Unit 14
    Colleges 913
    Deaf, Sheffield 961
    Learning Group 14
    Protection, Journal of 940
Adur, Arun and Worthing Primary Care Trust 582
Advanced Nursing, Journal of 935
Advice—
    Centres, Independent 758
    and Counselling 735
    on Alcohol and Drugs (ACAD) 787
adviceUK 758
Advisory Officers for Special Educational Needs, National Association 882
Advisory Service for Squatters 978
Advocate, The 928, 933
AFASIC 687, 957
Affiliated Services 775
AFTA Thought Training Consultants Limited 891
After Adoption 647
After Care Association, Mental Health 893, 982
Age Concern—
    England 839
    Institute of Gerontology 846
    Northern Ireland 846
    Scotland 846
    Wales 845
AgeCare Aberdeen 846
Ageing—
    and the Elderly 927
    Selected Bibliographies 928
    and Society 927

987

B

D

I

J

M

N

O

S

T

Y

Index to Advertisers